D1288882

e=2
e=1
e=½

CME PROJECT

Precalculus

TEACHER'S EDITION

PEARSON

Boston, Massachusetts
Chandler, Arizona
Glenview, Illinois
Shoreview, Minnesota
Upper Saddle River, New Jersey

Education Development Center, Inc.
Center for Mathematics Education
Newton, Massachusetts

Acknowledgments appear on page T811, which constitutes an extension of this copyright page.

PEARSON

13-digit ISBN 978-0-13-350024-0
10-digit ISBN 0-13-350024-1

1 2 3 4 5 6 7 8 9 10 12 11 10 09 08

Precalculus
Teacher's Edition Contents

Student Edition With Teacher Notes

The Center for Mathematics Education Project was developed at Education Development Center, Inc. (EDC) within the Center for Mathematics Education (CME), with partial support from the National Science Foundation.

Education Development Center, Inc.
Center for Mathematics Education
Newton, Massachusetts

This material is based upon work supported by the National Science Foundation under Grant No. ESI-0242476, Grant No. MDR-9252952, and Grant No. ESI-9617369. Any opinions, findings, and conclusions or recommendations expressed in this material are those of the author(s) and do not necessarily reflect the views of the National Science Foundation.

CME Project Development Team

Lead Developer: Al Cuoco

Core Development Team: Anna Baccaglini-Frank, Jean Benson, Nancy Antonellis D'Amato, Daniel Erman, Brian Harvey, Wayne Harvey, Bowen Kerins, Doreen Kilday, Ryota Matsuura, Stephen Maurer, Sarah Sword, Audrey Ting, and Kevin Waterman

Others who contributed include Steve Benson, Paul D'Amato, Robert Devaney, Andrew Golay, Paul Goldenberg, Jane Gorman, C. Jud Hill, Eric Karnowski, Helen Lebowitz, Joseph Leverich, Melanie Palma, Mark Saul, Nina Shteingold, and Brett Thomas.

Acknowledgments appear on page 810, which constitutes an extension of this copyright page.

PEARSON

13-digit ISBN 978-0-13-350020-2
10-digit ISBN 0-13-350020-9

1 2 3 4 5 6 7 8 9 10 12 11 10 09 08

CME PROJECT

Introduction to the CME Project

The CME Project, developed by EDC's Center for Mathematics Education, is a new NSF-funded high school program, organized around the familiar courses of algebra 1, geometry, algebra 2, and precalculus. The CME Project provides teachers and schools with a third alternative to the choice between traditional texts driven by basic skill development and more progressive texts that have unfamiliar organizations. This program gives teachers the option of a problem-based, student-centered program, organized around the mathematical themes with which teachers and parents are familiar. Furthermore, the tremendous success of NSF-funded middle school programs has left a need for a high school program with similar rigor and pedagogy. The CME Project fills this need.

The goal of the CME Project is to help students acquire a deep understanding of mathematics. Therefore, the mathematics here is rigorous. We took great care to create lesson plans that, while challenging, will capture and engage students of all abilities and improve their mathematical achievement.

The Program's Approach

The organization of the CME Project provides students the time and focus they need to develop fundamental mathematical ways of thinking. Its primary goal is to develop in students robust mathematical proficiency.

- The program employs innovative instructional methods, developed over decades of classroom experience and informed by research, that help students master mathematical topics.
- One of the core tenets of the CME Project is to focus on developing students' Habits of Mind, or ways in which students approach and solve mathematical challenges.
- The program builds on lessons learned from high-performing countries: develop an idea thoroughly and then revisit it only to deepen it; organize ideas in a way that is faithful to how they are organized in mathematics; and reduce clutter and extraneous topics.
- It also employs the best American models that call for grappling with ideas and problems as preparation for instruction, moving from concrete problems to abstractions and general theories, and situating mathematics in engaging contexts.
- The CME Project is a comprehensive curriculum that meets the dual goals of mathematical rigor and accessibility for a broad range of students.

About CME

EDC's Center for Mathematics Education, led by mathematician and teacher **Al Cuoco**, brings together an eclectic staff of mathematicians, teachers, cognitive scientists, education researchers, curriculum developers, specialists in educational technology, and teacher educators, internationally known for leadership across the entire range of K–16 mathematics education. We aim to help students and teachers in this country experience the thrill of solving problems and building theories, understand the history of ideas behind the evolution of mathematical disciplines, and appreciate the standards of rigor that are central to mathematical culture.

Contributors to the CME Project

National Advisory Board The National Advisory Board met early in the project, providing critical feedback on the instructional design and the overall organization. Members include

Richard Askey, University of Wisconsin
Edward Barbeau, University of Toronto
Hyman Bass, University of Michigan
Carol Findell, Boston University
Arthur Heinricher, Worcester Polytechnic Institute
Roger Howe, Yale University
Barbara Janson, Janson Associates
Kenneth Levasseur, University of Massachusetts, Lowell
James Madden, Louisiana State University, Baton Rouge
Jacqueline Miller, Education Development Center
James Newton, University of Maryland
Robert Segall, Greater Hartford Academy of Mathematics and Science
Glenn Stevens, Boston University
Herbert Wilf, University of Pennsylvania
Hung-Hsi Wu, University of California, Berkeley

Core Mathematical Consultants **Dick Askey**, **Ed Barbeau**, and **Roger Howe** have been involved in an even more substantial way, reviewing chapters and providing detailed and critical advice on every aspect of the program. Dick and Roger spent many hours reading and criticizing drafts, brainstorming with the writing team, and offering advice on everything from the logical organization to the actual numbers used in problems. We can't thank them enough.

Teacher Advisory Board The Teacher Advisory Board for the CME Project was essential in helping us create an effective format for our lessons that embodies the philosophy and goals of the program. Their debates about pedagogical issues and how to develop mathematical topics helped to shape the distinguishing features of the curriculum so that our lessons work effectively in the classroom. The advisory board includes

Jayne Abbas, Richard Coffey, Charles Garabedian, Dennis Geller, Eileen Herlihy, Doreen Kilday, Gayle Masse, Hugh McLaughlin, Nancy McLaughlin, Allen Olsen, Kimberly Osborne, Brian Shoemaker, and **Benjamin Sinwell**

Field-Test Teachers Our field-test teachers gave us the benefit of their classroom experience by teaching from our draft lessons and giving us extensive, critical feedback that shaped the drafts into realistic, teachable lessons. They shared their concerns, questions, challenges, and successes and kept us focused on the real world. Some of them even welcomed us into their classrooms as co-teachers to give us the direct experience with students that we needed to hone our lessons. Working with these expert professionals has been one of the most gratifying parts of the development—they are "highly qualified" in the most profound sense.

California **Barney Martinez**, Jefferson High School, Daly City; **Calvin Baylon** and **Jaime Lao**, Bell Junior High School, San Diego; **Colorado** **Rocky Cundiff**, Ignacio High School, Ignacio; **Illinois** **Jeremy Kahan**, **Tammy Nguyen**, and **Stephanie Pederson**, Ida Crown Jewish Academy, Chicago; **Massachusetts** **Carol Martignette, Chris Martino,** and **Kent Werst**, Arlington High School, Arlington; **Larry Davidson**, Boston University Academy, Boston; **Joe Bishop** and **Carol Rosen**, Lawrence High School, Lawrence; **Maureen Mulryan**, Lowell High School, Lowell; **Felisa Honeyman**, Newton South High School, Newton Centre; **Jim Barnes** and **Carol Haney**, Revere High School, Revere; **New Hampshire** **Jayne Abbas** and **Terin Voisine,** Cawley Middle School, Hooksett; **New Mexico** **Mary Andrews**, Las Cruces High School, Las Cruces; **Ohio** **James Stallworth**, Hughes Center, Cincinnati; **Texas** **Arnell Crayton**, Bellaire High School, Bellaire; **Utah** **Troy Jones**, Waterford School, Sandy; **Washington** **Dale Erz**, **Kathy Greer**, **Karena Hanscom**, and **John Henry**, Port Angeles High School, Port Angeles; **Wisconsin** **Annette Roskam**, Rice Lake High School, Rice Lake.

Special thanks go to our colleagues at Pearson, most notably Elizabeth Lehnertz, Joe Will, and Stewart Wood. The program benefits from their expertise in every way, from the actual mathematics to the design of the printed page.

This Pacing Guide is provided to help you customize your course.

It accounts for 100 standard class periods for the lessons. If you allow five days for every three lessons, you should have adequate time for summative assessment.

A Daily Planner precedes each chapter and gives you lesson-by-lesson suggestions for that chapter.

Chapter 1 *Analyzing Trigonometric Functions*			**13 Days**
DAY	**LESSON**	**DAY**	**LESSON**
1	1.1 Getting Started	**8**	1.8 Graphing Periodic Functions
2	1.2 Trigonometry With Radians	**9**	1.9 Inverse Trigonometric Functions
3	1.3 Graphing Cosine and Sine Functions	**10**	1.10 Reciprocal Trigonometric Functions
4	1.4 Solving Cosine and Sine Equations	**11**	1.11 Getting Started
5	1.5 Analyzing Graphs	**12**	1.12 Sinusoidal Functions
6	1.6 Getting Started	**13**	1.13 Applying Trigonometric Functions
7	1.7 The Tangent Function		

Chapter 2 *Complex Numbers and Trigonometry*			**12 Days**
DAY	**LESSON**	**DAY**	**LESSON**
1	2.1 Getting Started	**7**	2.7 Proving Identities
2	2.2 The Complex Plane	**8**	2.8 Getting Started
3	2.3 Another Form for Complex Numbers	**9**	2.9 Powers of Complex Numbers
4	2.4 The Multiplication Law	**10**	2.10 Roots of Unity
5	2.5 Getting Started	**11**	2.11 Geometry of Roots of Unity
6	2.6 Building Formulas and Identities	**12**	2.12 Arithmetic With Roots of Unity

Chapter 3 *Analysis of Functions*			**14 Days**
1	3.1 Getting Started	**8**	3.8 Revisiting Secants and Tangents
2	3.2 Continuity of Polynomial Functions	**9**	3.9 Case Study: $y = \frac{ax + b}{cx + d}$
3	3.3 Graphs and Secant Lines	**10**	3.10 Getting Started
4	3.4 Polynomials in Powers of $x - a$	**11**	3.11 Compound Interest; the Number e
5	3.5 Secants and Tangents	**12**	3.12 Another Way to Find e
6	3.6 Getting Started	**13**	3.13 The Natural Logarithm Function
7	3.7 Graphing Rational Functions	**14**	3.14 Analysis of $f(x) = e^x$ and $g(x) = \ln x$

Chapter 4 *Combinatorics*			**11 Days**
DAY	**LESSON**	**DAY**	**LESSON**
1	4.1 Getting Started	**7**	4.7 Combinations
2	4.2 Are They Different or the Same?	**8**	4.8 Putting It Together
3	4.3 Strategies for Counting	**9**	4.9 Getting Started
4	4.4 Counting All Functions	**10**	4.10 Revisiting the Binomial Theorem
5	4.5 Getting Started	**11**	4.11 Connections
6	4.6 Permutations		

Chapter 5 *Functions and Tables*			**14 Days**
DAY	**LESSON**	**DAY**	**LESSON**
1	5.1 Getting Started	**8**	5.8 The Pascal Connection
2	5.2 Two Ways to Define a Function	**9**	5.9 Newton's Difference Formula
3	5.3 Multistep Recursive Definitions	**10**	5.10 Sums of Powers
4	5.4 Mathematical Induction	**11**	5.11 Getting Started
5	5.5 Ways to Think About Induction	**12**	5.12 Recurrences
6	5.6 Getting Started	**13**	5.13 $f(n) = Af(n - 1) + Bf(n - 2)$
7	5.7 Properties of Difference Tables	**14**	5.14 $f(n) = Af(n - 1) + B$

Chapter 6 *Analytic Geometry*			**13 Days**
DAY	**LESSON**	**DAY**	**LESSON**
1	6.1 Getting Started	**8**	6.8 Conics Anywhere
2	6.2 Equations as Point-Testers	**9**	6.9 They Are All the Same
3	6.3 Coordinates and Proof	**10**	6.10 Getting Started
4	6.4 The Power of a Point	**11**	6.11 Ordered Pairs, Points, and Vectors
5	6.5 Getting Started	**12**	6.12 Vector Equations of Lines
6	6.6 Slicing Cones	**13**	6.13 Affine Combinations and Geometry
7	6.7 Conics at the Origin		

Chapter 7 *Probability and Statistics*			**13 Days**
DAY	**LESSON**	**DAY**	**LESSON**
1	7.1 Getting Started	**8**	7.8 Adding Variances
2	7.2 Probability and Pascal's Triangle	**9**	7.9 Repeated Experiments
3	7.3 Polynomial Powers	**10**	7.10 Bernoulli Trials
4	7.4 Expected Value	**11**	7.11 Getting Started
5	7.5 Lotteries	**12**	7.12 The Central Limit Theorem
6	7.6 Getting Started	**13**	7.13 The Normal Distribution
7	7.7 Variance and Standard Deviation		

Chapter 8 *Ideas of Calculus*			**10 Days**
DAY	**LESSON**	**DAY**	**LESSON**
1	8.1 Getting Started	**6**	8.6 Fermat's Big Idea
2	8.2 Areas of Blobs	**7**	8.7 Getting Started
3	8.3 Finding the Area Under $y = x^2$	**8**	8.8 The Area Under $y = \frac{1}{x}$
4	8.4 Getting Started	**9**	8.9 Properties of the Function $\mathcal{L}$
5	8.5 Cavalieri's Approach	**10**	8.10 The Area Under $f(x) = e^x$

1 Analyzing Trigonometric Functions

2 Complex Numbers and Trigonometry

3 Analysis of Functions

Combinatorics

5 Functions and Tables

6 Analytic Geometry

7 Probability and Statistics

8 Ideas of Calculus

CME Project Student Handbook

What Makes CME Different

Welcome to the CME Project! The goal of this program is to help you develop a deep understanding of mathematics. Throughout this book, you will engage in many different activities to help you develop that deep understanding. Some of these instructional activities may be different from ones you are used to. Below is an overview of some of these elements and why they are an important part of the CME Project.

The Habits of Mind Experience

Mathematical Habits of Mind are the foundation for serious questioning, solid thinking, good problem solving, and critical analysis. These Habits of Mind are what will help you become a mathematical thinker. Throughout the CME Project, you will focus on developing and refining these Habits of Mind.

Developing Habits of Mind

Develop thinking skills. This feature provides you with various methods and approaches to solving problems.

You will develop, use, and revisit specific Habits of Mind throughout the course. These include

- **Process** (how you work through problems)
- **Visualization** (how you "picture" problems)
- **Representation** (what you write down)
- **Patterns** (what you find)
- **Relationships** (what you find or use)

Developing good habits will help you as problems become more complicated.

Habits of Mind

Think. These special margin notes highlight key thinking skills and prompt you to apply your developing Habits of Mind.

You can find Developing Habits of Mind **on pages** 19, 20, 21, 46, 70, 94, 101, 110, 112, 134, 145, 148, 175, 222, 250, 279, 286, 297, 298, 300, 346, 348, 382, 389, 428, 446, 452, 454, 460, 469, 478, 480, 486, 487, 492, 494, 504, 544, 545, 548, 551, 557, 565, 577, 593, 610, 619, 647, 659, 687, 692

Minds in Action

Discussion of mathematical ideas is an effective method of learning. The Minds in Action feature exposes you to ways of communicating about mathematics.

Join Sasha, Tony, Derman, and others as they think, calculate, predict, and discuss their way towards understanding.

Minds in Action prologue

Sasha, Tony, and Derman have just skimmed through their CME Project Precalculus *book.*

Sasha Did you notice the student dialogs throughout the book?

Derman Sure did!

Tony They talk and think just the way we do.

Sasha I know! And they even make mistakes sometimes, the way we do.

Tony But I like how they help each other to learn from those mistakes. I bet they use the Habits of Mind I saw all over the book, too.

Sasha That's great! They should help a lot.

Exploring Mathematics

Throughout the CME Project, you will engage in activities that extend your learning and allow you to explore the concepts you learn in greater depth. Two of these activities are In-Class Experiments and Chapter Projects.

In-Class Experiment

In-Class Experiments allow you to explore new concepts and apply the Habits of Mind.

You will explore math as mathematicians do. You start with a question and develop answers through experimentation.

You can find In-Class Experiments on pages 8, 24, 34, 50, 132, 170, 180, 197, 254, 352, 364, 376, 414, 468, 493, 504, 541, 554, 575, 582, 591, 638

Chapter Projects

Chapter Projects allow you to apply your Habits of Mind to the content of the chapter. These projects cover many different topics and allow you to explore and engage in greater depth.

Chapter Projects
Using Mathematical Habits

Here is a list of the Chapter Projects and page numbers.

Using Your CME Book

To help you make the most of your CME experience, we are providing the following overview of the organization of your book.

Focusing Your Learning

In *Precalculus*, there are 8 chapters, with each chapter devoted to a mathematical concept. With only 8 chapters, your class will be able to focus on these core concepts and develop a deep understanding of them.

Within each chapter, you will explore a series of Investigations. Each Investigation focuses on an important aspect of the mathematical concept for that chapter.

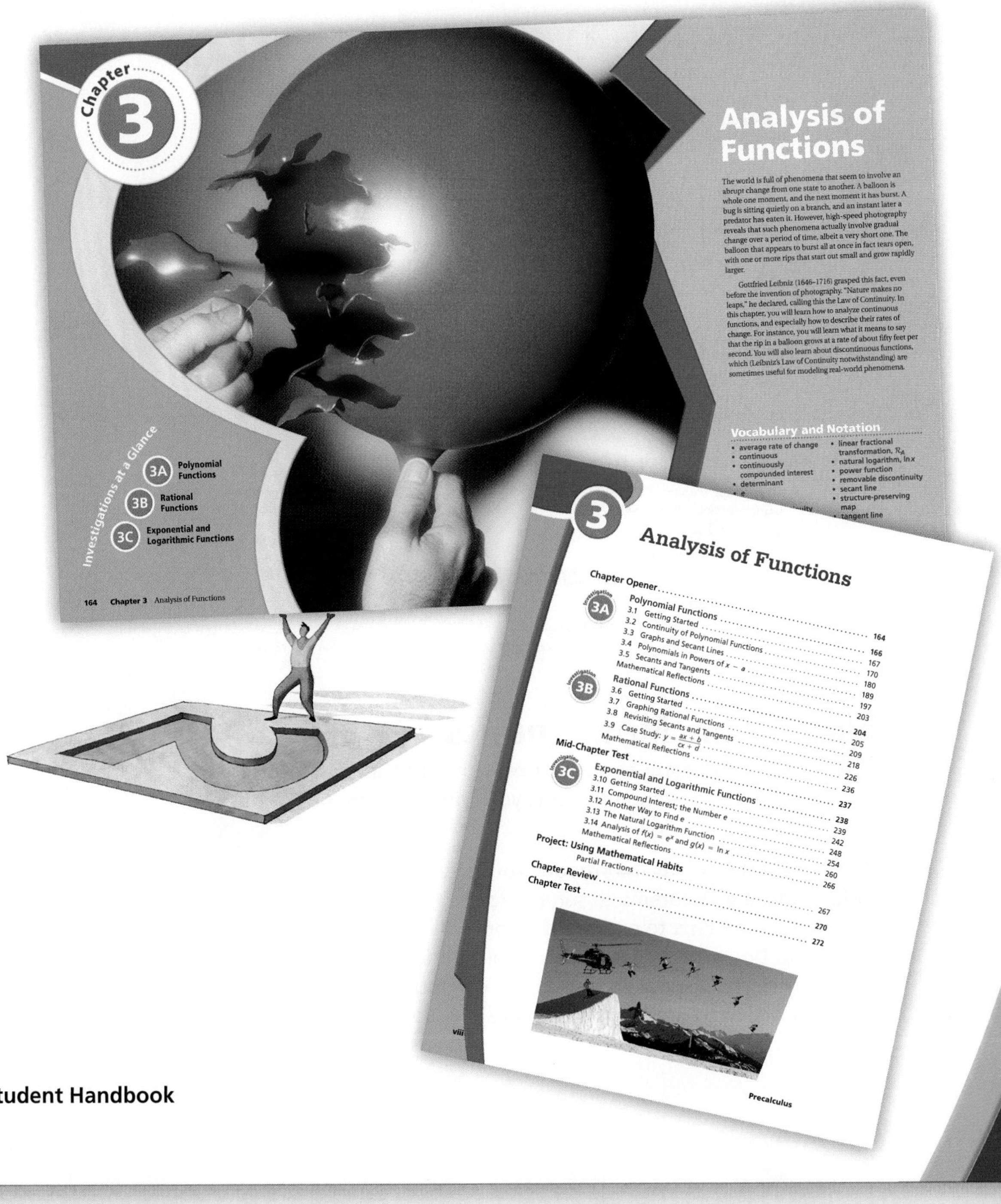

Chapter 3

Analysis of Functions

The world is full of phenomena that seem to involve an abrupt change from one state to another. A balloon is whole one moment, and the next moment it has burst. A bug is sitting quietly on a branch, and an instant later a predator has eaten it. However, high-speed photography reveals that such phenomena actually involve gradual change over a period of time, albeit a very short one. The balloon that appears to burst all at once in fact tears open, with one or more rips that start out small and grow rapidly larger.

Gottfried Leibniz (1646–1716) grasped this fact, even before the invention of photography. "Nature makes no leaps," he declared, calling this the Law of Continuity. In this chapter, you will learn how to analyze continuous functions, and especially how to describe their rates of change. For instance, you will learn what it means to say that the rip in a balloon grows at a rate of about fifty feet per second. You will also learn about discontinuous functions, which (Leibniz's Law of Continuity notwithstanding) are sometimes useful for modeling real-world phenomena.

Investigations at a Glance

- 3A Polynomial Functions
- 3B Rational Functions
- 3C Exponential and Logarithmic Functions

Vocabulary and Notation

- average rate of change
- continuous
- continuously compounded interest
- determinant
- e
- linear fractional transformation, $\mathcal{R}_A$
- natural logarithm, ln x
- power function
- removable discontinuity
- secant line
- structure-preserving map
- tangent line

164 Chapter 3 Analysis of Functions

3

Analysis of Functions

viii Precalculus

The CME Investigation

The goal of each mathematical Investigation is for you to formalize your understanding of the mathematics being taught. There are some common instructional features in each Investigation.

Getting Started

You will launch into each Investigation with a Getting Started lesson that activates prior knowledge and explores new ideas. This lesson provides you the opportunity to grapple with ideas and problems. The goal of these lessons is for you to explore—not all your questions will be answered in these lessons.

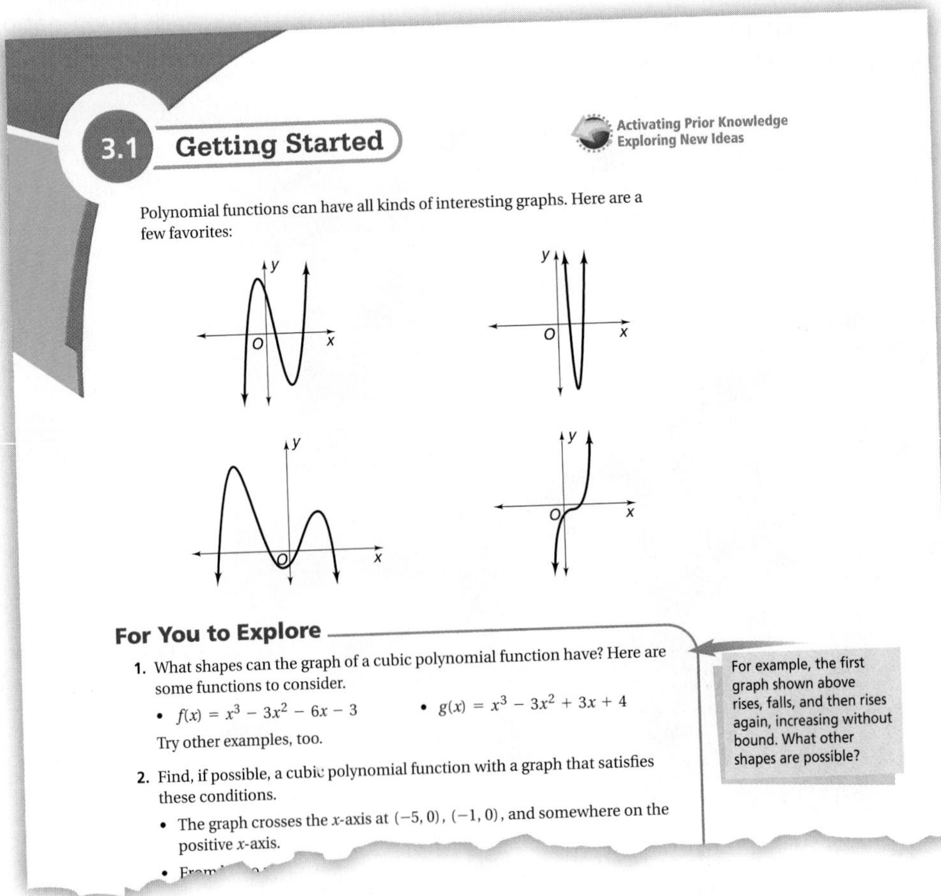

3.1 Getting Started

Activating Prior Knowledge
Exploring New Ideas

Polynomial functions can have all kinds of interesting graphs. Here are a few favorites:

For You to Explore

1. What shapes can the graph of a cubic polynomial function have? Here are some functions to consider.
   - $f(x) = x^3 - 3x^2 - 6x - 3$
   - $g(x) = x^3 - 3x^2 + 3x + 4$

   Try other examples, too.
2. Find, if possible, a cubic polynomial function with a graph that satisfies these conditions.
   - The graph crosses the x-axis at $(-5, 0)$, $(-1, 0)$, and somewhere on the positive x-axis.

For example, the first graph shown above rises, falls, and then rises again, increasing without bound. What other shapes are possible?

Learning the Mathematics

You will engage in, learn, and practice the mathematics in a variety of ways. The types of learning elements you will find throughout this course include

- **Worked-Out Examples** that model how to solve problems
- **Definitions and Theorems** to summarize key concepts
- **In-Class Experiments** to explore the concepts
- **For You to Do** assignments to check your understanding
- **For Discussion** questions to encourage communication
- **Minds in Action** to model mathematical discussion

Communicating the Mathematics

Minds in Action

Student dialogs

By featuring dialogs between characters, the CME Project exposes you to a way of communicating about mathematics. These dialogs will then become a real part of your classroom!

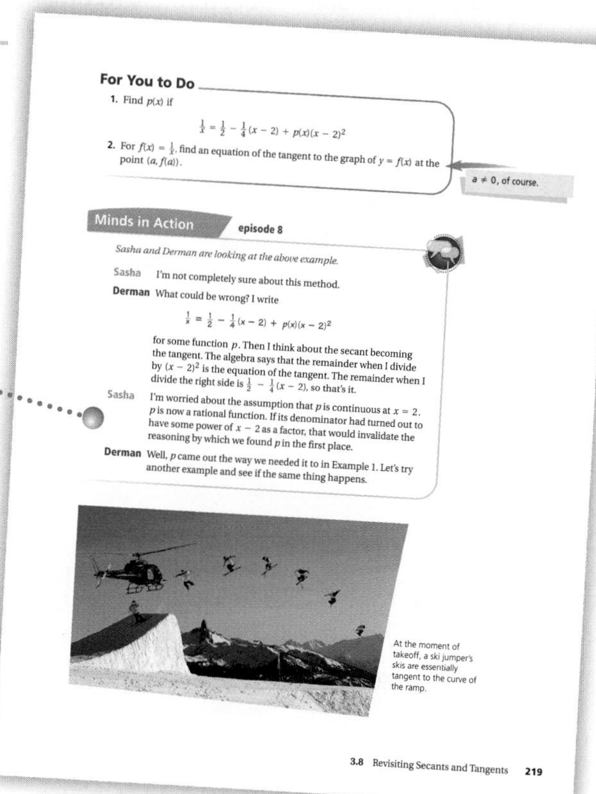

For You to Do

1. Find $p(x)$ if

$$\frac{1}{x} = \frac{1}{2} - \frac{1}{4}(x-2) + p(x)(x-2)^2$$

2. For $f(x) = \frac{1}{x}$, find an equation of the tangent to the graph of $y = f(x)$ at the point $(a, f(a))$.

$a \neq 0$, of course.

Minds in Action **episode 8**

Sasha and Derman are looking at the above example.

Sasha I'm not completely sure about this method.

Derman What could be wrong? I write

$$\frac{1}{x} = \frac{1}{2} - \frac{1}{4}(x-2) + p(x)(x-2)^2$$

for some function p. Then I think about the secant becoming the tangent. The algebra says that the remainder when I divide by $(x-2)^2$ is the equation of the tangent. The remainder when I divide the right side is $\frac{1}{2} - \frac{1}{4}(x-2)$, so that's it.

Sasha I'm worried about the assumption that p is continuous at $x = 2$. p is now a rational function. If its denominator had turned out to have some power of $x - 2$ as a factor, that would invalidate the reasoning by which we found p in the first place.

Derman Well, p came out the way we needed it to in Example 1. Let's try another example and see if the same thing happens.

At the moment of takeoff, a ski jumper's skis are essentially tangent to the curve of the ramp.

3.8 Revisiting Secants and Tangents 219

Reflecting on the Mathematics

At the end of each Investigation, Mathematical Reflections give you an opportunity to put ideas together. This feature allows you to demonstrate your understanding of the Investigation and reflect on what you learn.

Practice

The CME Project views extensive practice as a critical component of a mathematics curriculum. You will have daily opportunities to practice what you learn.

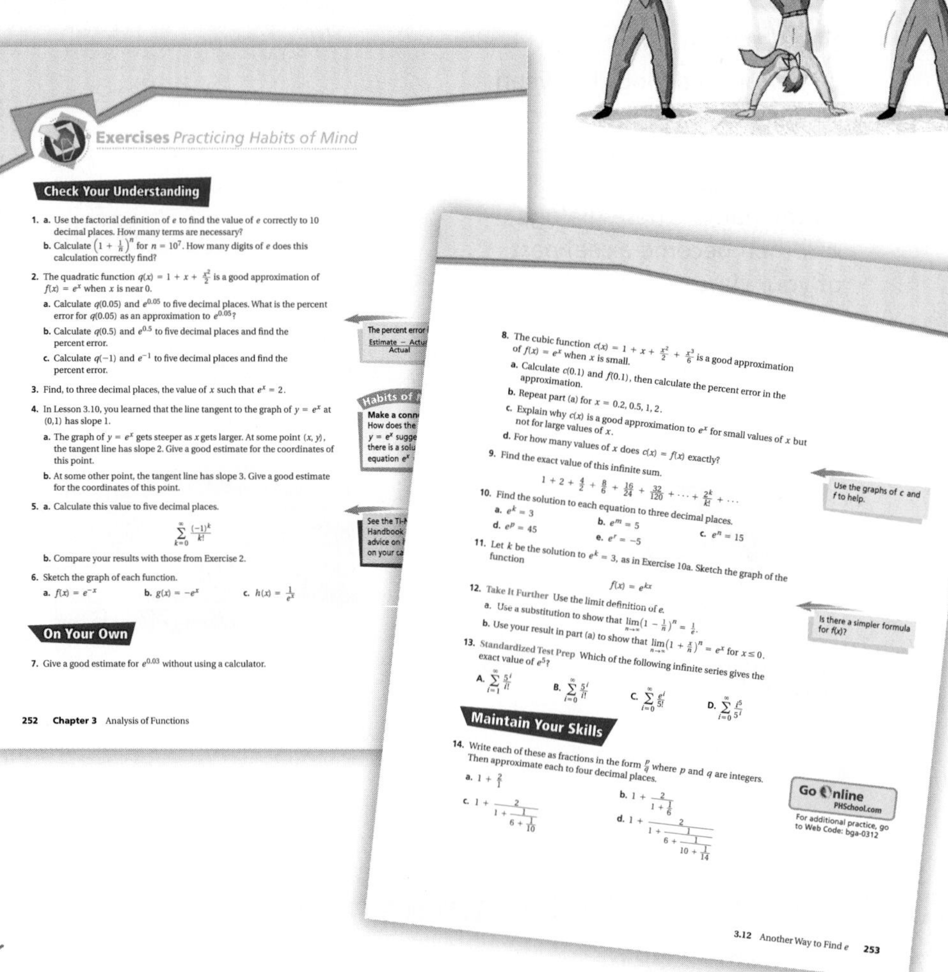

Exercises *Practicing Habits of Mind*

Check Your Understanding

1. a. Use the factorial definition of e to find the value of e correctly to 10 decimal places. How many terms are necessary?
   b. Calculate $\left(1 + \frac{1}{n}\right)^n$ for $n = 10^7$. How many digits of e does this calculation correctly find?
2. The quadratic function $q(x) = 1 + x + \frac{x^2}{2}$ is a good approximation of $f(x) = e^x$ when x is near 0.
   a. Calculate $q(0.05)$ and $e^{0.05}$ to five decimal places. What is the percent error for $q(0.05)$ as an approximation to $e^{0.05}$?
   b. Calculate $q(0.5)$ and $e^{0.5}$ to five decimal places and find the percent error.
   c. Calculate $q(-1)$ and e^{-1} to five decimal places and find the percent error.
3. Find, to three decimal places, the value of x such that $e^x = 2$.
4. In Lesson 3.10, you learned that the line tangent to the graph of $y = e^x$ at (0,1) has slope 1.
   a. The graph of $y = e^x$ gets steeper as x gets larger. At some point (x, y), the tangent line has slope 2. Give a good estimate for the coordinates of this point.
   b. At some other point, the tangent line has slope 3. Give a good estimate for the coordinates of this point.
5. a. Calculate this value to five decimal places.
$$\sum_{k=0}^{\infty} \frac{(-1)^k}{k!}$$
   b. Compare your results with those from Exercise 2.
6. Sketch the graph of each function.
   a. $f(x) = e^{-x}$ b. $g(x) = -e^x$ c. $h(x) = \frac{1}{e^x}$

On Your Own

7. Give a good estimate for $e^{0.03}$ without using a calculator.

252 Chapter 3 Analysis of Functions

8. The cubic function $c(x) = 1 + x + \frac{x^2}{2} + \frac{x^3}{6}$ is a good approximation of $f(x) = e^x$ when x is small.
   a. Calculate $c(0.1)$ and $f(0.1)$, then calculate the percent error in the approximation.
   b. Repeat part (a) for $x = 0.2, 0.5, 1, 2$.
   c. Explain why $c(x)$ is a good approximation to e^x for small values of x but not for large values of x.
   d. For how many values of x does $c(x) = f(x)$ exactly?
9. Find the exact value of this infinite sum.
$$1 + 2 + \frac{4}{2} + \frac{8}{6} + \frac{16}{24} + \frac{32}{120} + \cdots + \frac{2^k}{k!} + \cdots$$

Use the graphs of c and f to help.

10. Find the solution to each equation to three decimal places.
   a. $e^k = 3$ b. $e^m = 5$ c. $e^n = 15$
   d. $e^p = 45$ e. $e^r = -5$
11. Let k be the solution to $e^k = 3$, as in Exercise 10a. Sketch the graph of the function
$$f(x) = e^{kx}$$
12. **Take It Further** Use the limit definition of e.
   a. Use a substitution to show that $\lim_{n \to \infty}\left(1 - \frac{1}{n}\right)^n = \frac{1}{e}$.
   b. Use your result in part (a) to show that $\lim_{n \to \infty}\left(1 + \frac{x}{n}\right)^n = e^x$ for $x \leq 0$.

Is there a simpler formula for $f(x)$?

13. **Standardized Test Prep** Which of the following infinite series gives the exact value of e^5?
   A. $\sum_{i=1}^{\infty} \frac{5^i}{i!}$ B. $\sum_{i=0}^{\infty} \frac{5^i}{i!}$ C. $\sum_{i=0}^{\infty} \frac{e^i}{5!}$ D. $\sum_{i=0}^{\infty} \frac{i^5}{5^i}$

Maintain Your Skills

14. Write each of these as fractions in the form $\frac{p}{q}$ where p and q are integers. Then approximate each to four decimal places.
   a. $1 + \frac{2}{1}$
   b. $1 + \cfrac{2}{1 + \frac{1}{6}}$
   c. $1 + \cfrac{2}{1 + \cfrac{1}{6 + \frac{1}{10}}}$
   d. $1 + \cfrac{2}{1 + \cfrac{1}{6 + \cfrac{1}{10 + \frac{1}{14}}}}$

Go Online PHSchool.com
For additional practice, go to Web Code: bga-0312

3.12 Another Way to Find e 253

Check Your Understanding

Assess your readiness for independent practice by working through these problems in class.

On Your Own

Practice and continue developing the mathematical understanding you learn in each lesson.

Maintain Your Skills

Review and reinforce skills from previous lessons.

Also Available

An additional Practice Workbook is available separately.

Go Online

Throughout this book you will find links to the Prentice Hall Web site. Use the Web Codes provided with each link to gain direct access to online material. Here's how to Go Online.

1. **Go to PHSchool.com.**
2. **Enter the Web Code.**
3. **Click Go!**

Check out the TI-Nspire™ Technology Handbook on p. 704 for examples of how you can use handheld technology with your math learning!

Go Online Lesson Web Codes

Additional Practice Web Codes: For every lesson, (except Getting Started lessons) there is additional practice online. Access this additional practice using the Web Code format at the right.

Additional Practice
Web Code format: bga-0203
02 = Chapter 2 03 = Lesson 3

Go Online Chapter Web Codes

Chapter	Vocabulary Review	Mid-Chapter Test	Chapter Test
1	bgj-0151	bga-0152	bga-0153
2	bgj-0251	bga-0252	bga-0253
3	bgj-0351	bga-0352	bga-0353
4	bgj-0451	bga-0452	bga-0453
5	bgj-0551	bga-0552	bga-0553
6	bgj-0651	bga-0652	bga-0653
7	bgj-0751	bga-0752	bga-0753
8	bgj-0851	bga-0852	bga-0853

Go Online Additional Web Codes

Math Background

Use **Web Code:** bge-8031 to find additional historical background information. See page 414. Use **Web Code:** bge-9031 to find additional background information related to the mathematics at hand. See page 10.

Chapter 1 Analyzing Trigonometric Functions

This course begins with Trigonometry, the topic with which most Algebra 2 courses end. Chapter 1 extends the student understanding of trigonometry. Students start to think about the trigonometric functions more abstractly.

They learn that radian measure is more than just an alternative to degree measure. Radians allow a true mapping of the trigonometric functions from $\mathbb{R} \rightarrow \mathbb{R}$. Having this mapping makes analyzing the functions (taking derivatives, for example) much simpler.

Students study the graphs of the trigonometric functions, and the relationships between them.

They see that it is necessary to define a limiting domain in order to make each periodic function one-to-one and find the inverse.

They apply the graphs to solve periodic motion problems.

Chapter Overview

INVESTIGATION 1A, *The Cosine and Sine Functions,* introduces radian measure, reviews the cosine and sine functions, develops an understanding of periodic function, and has students begin solving simple equations involving cosine and sine.

INVESTIGATION 1B, *Other Trigonometric Functions,* introduces the tangent, secant, cosecant, and cotangent functions and discusses the inverses of the cosine, sine, and tangent functions.

INVESTIGATION 1C, *Sinusoidal Functions and Their Graphs,* discusses the common features of the graphs of trigonometric functions and has students model periodic behavior with these functions.

For more information on the investigations, see

- Chapter Road Map, pp. 2–3
- Investigation Road Maps, pp. 4, 30, 56

PROJECT The Project near the end of the chapter is optional. You can assign the project at any time during the chapter depending on how often and how long you feel students should work on it.

Pacing Suggestions and Materials

Investigation 1A *The Cosine and Sine Functions*

DAY	LESSON	HOMEWORK
1	1.1 Getting Started Core: 1, 2, 3, 6 Optional: 4, 5; Extension: 7	Core: 8, 11, 12, 13, 15 Optional: 9, 10, 14
2	1.2 Trigonometry With Radians Core: 2, 3, 5, 6 Optional: 1, 4; Extension: 7	Core: 8, 11, 12, 15, 16, 17 Optional: 9, 10, 13; Extension: 14
3	1.3 Graphing Cosine and Sine Functions Core: 1, 3, 4, 6 Optional: 2, 5	Core: 7, 9, 10, 12, 14 Optional: 8, 11, 15, 16; Extension:13
4	1.4 Solving Cosine and Sine Equations Core: 1, 2, 5 Optional: 3, 4, 6; Extension: 7, 8	Core: 9, 10, 12, 13, 15, 17 Optional: 11, 14a, 18, 19; Extension:14b, 16
5	1.5 Analyzing Graphs Core: 1, 3, 4 Optional: 2, 5a; Extension: 5b	Core: 6, 9, 10, 11, 13, 14 Optional: 7, 8; Extension: 12

Investigation 1B *Other Trigonometric Functions*

DAY	LESSON	HOMEWORK
1	1.6 Getting Started Core: 1, 2, 3 Optional: 4; Extension: 5	Core: 6, 7, 8, 10, 11 Optional: 9a; Extension: 9b
2	1.7 The Tangent Function Core: 1, 3 Optional: 2, 4, 5, 6	Core: 7, 8, 10, 13 Optional: 9, 11, 12, 14, 15
3	1.8 Graphing Periodic Functions Core: 1, 3a–b, 4, 5 Optional: 2; Extension: 3c	Core: 6, 7, 9, 10, 12, 13 Optional: 8; Extension: 11
4	1.9 Inverse Trigonometric Functions Core: 1, 2, 5 Optional: 3, 4, 6	Core: 7, 9a–c, 10, 13, 14 Optional: 8, 11, 12; Extension: 9d
5	1.10 Reciprocal Trigonometric Functions Core: 1, 4, 5 Optional: 2, 6, 7; Extension: 3	Core: 8, 9, 10, 11, 12, 14 Optional: 15, 16; Extension: 13

NOTES	MATERIALS
	• graph paper • graphing calculators • Blackline Masters MC1, BM1.1
	• geometry software • graph paper • graphing calculators • Blackline Masters MC1, MC2
	• graph paper • graphing calculators • Blackline Masters MC1, MC3
	• graph paper • graphing calculators • Blackline Masters MC1, MC5
	• geometry software • graph paper • graphing calculators • Blackline Masters MC2, MC3

NOTES	MATERIALS
	• graph paper • graphing calculators • Blackline Master MC4
	• geometry software • graph paper • graphing calculators • Blackline Masters MC1, MC2, MC5, MC6, BM1.7
	• geometry software • graph paper • graphing calculators • Blackline Masters MC1, MC3, MC4
	• graph paper • graphing calculators • Blackline Masters MC4, BM1.9A, BM1.9B
	• geometry software • graph paper • graphing calculators • Blackline Masters MC1, MC4, MC5, MC6, BM1.7

Mathematics Background

RADIANS This chapter defines radians as the length of arcs on the unit circle. It makes a strong distinction between radians and degrees to help students visualize radians, and not see them as "just another way to measure angles." While the chapter covers the ability to convert from degrees to radians, it frames this conversion as the relationship between a central angle and the arc it subtends.

Students revisit a context they saw in CME Project *Algebra 2* in which they visualize an observer standing at the origin of a coordinate plane and facing in the direction of its positive x-axis. This observer watches another person who begins walking along the unit circle, which is a circle of radius 1 centered at the origin, in a counterclockwise direction, starting at the point (1, 0). As the walker moves about the circle, the length of the walker's trip is recorded. The distance the walker travels is related to the coordinates of the walker's position on the unit circle. The walker can walk any distance, positive or negative (by traveling counterclockwise or clockwise), but every stopping point is immediately related to a specific right triangle—the triangle created by dropping a perpendicular to the x-axis from the walker's position.

Students see that for any distance the walker travels, they can find the coordinates of the walker's position, and that for any stopping point of the walker, they can give several candidates for the distance the walker traveled. For example, if the walker walks $\frac{5\pi}{3}$ units, the right triangle associated with this angle forms a 60 angle with the x-axis, so the horizontal distance from the origin to the walker's position is $\frac{1}{2}$ and the vertical distance from the origin to the walker's position is $\frac{\sqrt{3}}{2}$. Since the walker is in Quadrant IV, the x coordinate of the walker's location is positive, and the y-coordinate is negative. When the walker has traveled $\frac{5\pi}{3}$ units, the walker must be at the point $\left(\frac{1}{2}, -\frac{\sqrt{3}}{2}\right)$. However, if the walker's position is known to be $\left(\frac{1}{2}, -\frac{\sqrt{3}}{2}\right)$, then students understand that the walker may have walked any number of complete circle laps of 2π units and then walked a further $\frac{5\pi}{3}$ units. It is also possible that the walker moved in a clockwise direction, which would make the distance he traveled negative. In other words, for the position $\left(\frac{1}{2}, -\frac{\sqrt{3}}{2}\right)$, any distance of the form $\frac{5\pi}{3} + 2\pi n$ units with n any integer, could be the distance the walker traveled.

continued on p. 2c

continued from p. 2b

Once students understand this connection, they define the sine and cosine functions for any arc length to be the coordinates of the unit circle that correspond to the walker's stopping point. Students see that this definition gives the same values for angles measured in degrees. They continue to observe how the unit circle can demonstrate each of the six trigonometric functions: cosine, sine, tangent, secant, cosecant, and cotangent.

This process of choosing a new definition strategically so that critical properties still hold, lets students in on the reasons why mathematicians in the past made the choices they did. Instead of presenting students with a new definition of the trigonometric functions in a new domain, the chapter invites them to make sense of the choice of the definition by relating it to their previous work.

One of the driving motivators for using radians is that radians make trigonometric functions into genuine functions of a real-valued variable that will be necessary for some more advanced work in trigonometry, including calculus and Fourier analysis.

INVERSE TRIGONOMETRIC FUNCTIONS Students review the idea of inverses of functions in order to define the inverse trigonometric functions. They see that, since trigonometric functions are periodic, they cannot, by definition, be one-to-one, so they cannot define an inverse across their natural domain.

By limiting the domain of the functions strategically, they can make the functions one-to-one and thus define an inverse. They then apply that singular answer that the inverse function generates to express the entire set of possible solutions to equations involving trigonometric functions.

DAILY PLANNER DAILY PLANNER DAILY PL

Pacing Suggestions and Materials

Investigation 1C *Sinusoidal Functions and Their Graphs*		
DAY	**LESSON**	**HOMEWORK**
1	1.11 Getting Started Core: 1, 2, 3, 6 Optional: 4, 5; Extension: 7	Core: 8, 9, 10, 11 Optional: 12, 13, 14
2	1.12 Sinusoidal Functions Core: 1, 5 Optional: 2, 4, 6, 7; Extension: 3	Core: 8, 9, 12, 13, 15 Optional: 10, 11, 14, 16
3	1.13 Applying Trigonometric Functions Core: 1, 2, 4, 5, 6, 7 Optional: 3, 8a–b; Extension: 8c	Core: 9, 17 Optional: 10, 11, 12, 13, 14, 15, 18, 19 Extension: 16

	NOTES	MATERIALS
		• graphing calculators • Blackline Masters MC4, MC7, BM1.11
		• CAS (recommended) • graphing calculators • Blackline Masters MC4, MC7, BM1.12
		• graphing calculators • Blackline Master 1.13

REPRESENTATIONS Students review the graphs of the trigonometric functions using radians rather than degrees as the input to the trigonometric function. These graphs give new insights about the properties of the functions. Students can clearly see the periodic nature of the functions. They may have already made sense of this by realizing that as the walker continues around and around the unit circle, the walker's position will pass over a particular set of coordinates once on each circuit. For example, there are two occasions on each trip around the circle where the walker's position has a y-coordinate equal to $-\frac{1}{2}$. But there are more than two solutions to the equation $\sin x = -\frac{1}{2}$. When students look at the graph of the sine function, they can see that the line $y = -\frac{1}{2}$ has an infinite number of intersections with the graph of sine. By working back and forth between the graph of the function and its relationship to the coordinates of points on the unit circle, students make connections and increase their understanding of the behavior of this function.

Students begin to analyze the graphs of sine, cosine, and tangent by examining the slope of the graphs at particular points. Through experimentation with secant lines on the curves, they build tables of values that show estimates for the slope at each point. The relationship between sine and cosine (that the first derivative of the sine function is the cosine) is fairly evident from the table of the secant slopes of the sine function. This analysis is a preview of the work students will do in Chapter 3.

Developing Students' Mathematical Habits

EXPERIMENTATION Throughout the first two investigations, students work with constructions to visualize the various trigonometric functions. In the exercises throughout the earlier lessons, students answer questions about what that they observe. Later in the chapter, they answer questions about what they know mathematically. Chapter 1 enforces the notion of learning by experimenting and making conjectures. Then, as students fully understand the concepts, they prove theorems that they may have already conjectured.

ENCAPSULATION The most important habit that students develop in this investigation is encapsulation. Encapsulation is the ability to recognize regularity in a process and to extract the steps of that process to build an algorithm. In particular, students will recognize that a function like $A \sin(ax + b) + B$ is simply a transformation of $\sin x$. They developed this habit in Chapter 3 of CME Project *Algebra 1*, in which they transformed the basic graphs. They continued developing this habit in Chapter 6 of CME Project *Algebra 2*, which provided more work with transformations of basic graphs.

Chapter
1
Investigations at a Glance
1A The Cosine and Sine Functions
1B Other Trigonometric Functions
1C Sinusoidal Functions and Their Graphs

Chapter Road Map

INVESTIGATION 1A, *The Cosine and Sine Functions,* introduces radian measure. The lessons are careful not to equate degree and radian measurement (such as one would equate inch and centimeter measurement); radian measure is the length of an arc of the unit circle. 1 radian, then, is an arc of the unit circle with length 1 unit. Students work on the customary problems of converting between degrees and radians, but the goal is to enforce the concept that a radian is a distance measurement, not another way to measure angles. Students then review the graphs of the cosine and sine functions, and develop an understanding of a periodic function. Finally, they begin to solve equations that involve cosine and sine.

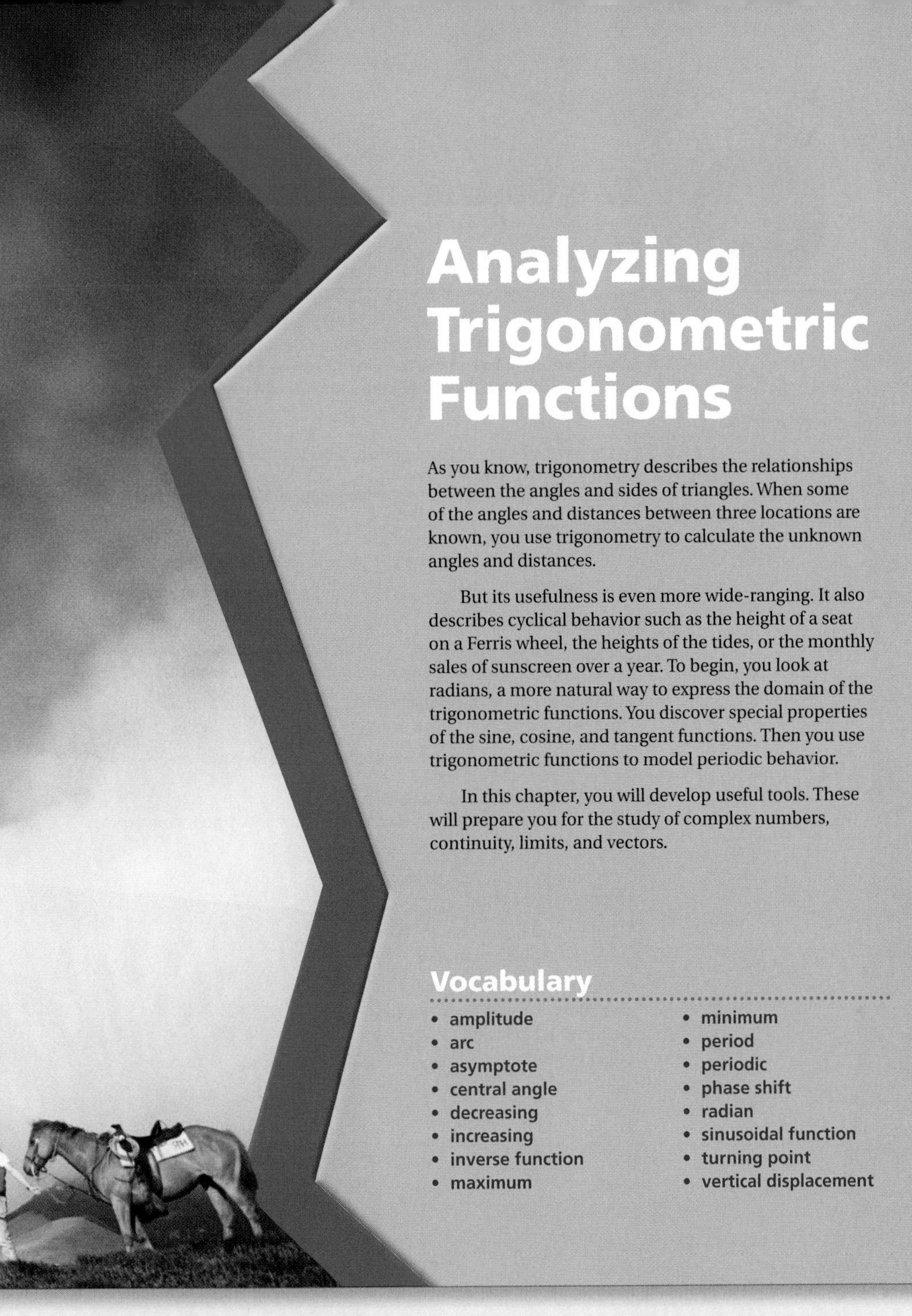

Analyzing Trigonometric Functions

As you know, trigonometry describes the relationships between the angles and sides of triangles. When some of the angles and distances between three locations are known, you use trigonometry to calculate the unknown angles and distances.

But its usefulness is even more wide-ranging. It also describes cyclical behavior such as the height of a seat on a Ferris wheel, the heights of the tides, or the monthly sales of sunscreen over a year. To begin, you look at radians, a more natural way to express the domain of the trigonometric functions. You discover special properties of the sine, cosine, and tangent functions. Then you use trigonometric functions to model periodic behavior.

In this chapter, you will develop useful tools. These will prepare you for the study of complex numbers, continuity, limits, and vectors.

Vocabulary

- amplitude
- arc
- asymptote
- central angle
- decreasing
- increasing
- inverse function
- maximum
- minimum
- period
- periodic
- phase shift
- radian
- sinusoidal function
- turning point
- vertical displacement

INVESTIGATION 1B, *Other Trigonometric Functions,* has students round out the list of trigonometric functions by learning the tangent and the three reciprocal functions, secant, cosecant, and cotangent. Students review the graphs of these functions, see how they can demonstrate each function on the unit circle, and work with some basic identities. They also review the definitions of one-to-one functions and inverse function. They learn to restrict the domain of cosine, sine, and tangent in order to define the inverses of these functions.

INVESTIGATION 1C, *Sinusoidal Functions and Their Graphs,* emphasizes the idea that trigonometric functions are "functions as usual"—once students are familiar with the graphs of the functions defined by $f(x) = \sin x$ and $f(x) = \cos x$, the sinusoidal functions emerge from the same transformations that students used beginning in CME Project *Algebra 1*. The lessons de-emphasize the memorization of formulas plucked from coefficients—instead, they motivate amplitude and phase shift with concrete examples.

Chapter Vocabulary and Notation

The following list gives the key vocabulary and notation used in the chapter. Selected new vocabulary and notation items are shown in boldface on the student page.

- amplitude, p. 62
- arc, p. 7
- asymptote, p. 38
- central angle, p. 7
- decreasing, p. 26
- increasing, p. 26
- inverse function, p. 43
- maximum, p. 27
- minimum, p. 27
- period, p. 15
- periodic, p. 15
- phase shift, p. 64
- Pythagorean identity, p. 20
- radian, p. 9
- secant line, p. 24
- sinusoidal function, p. 60
- turning point, p. 27
- vertical displacement, p. 62

Chapter Technology

CME Project *Precalculus* assumes that each student has access to a graphing calculator. It also recommends access to a computer algebra system (CAS) and to geometry software.

Support for the use of technology is available in the TI-Nspire™ Technology Handbook. See p. 704. The margin notes highlighted in purple in the Student Edition direct students to the handbook.

A list of technology used with important concepts in this chapter appears below. Students will need access to the functionality listed to develop complete understanding of these topics.

Computer Algebra System

LESSON 1.12 Solve a trigonometric equation, p. 66.

Geometry Software

LESSON 1.2 Compare angle measure, arc length, and coordinates on a unit circle, p. 8.

LESSON 1.5 Analyze the graph of the sine function, p. 24.

LESSON 1.7 Model the tangent function, p. 34.

LESSON 1.10 Model the secant function, p. 50.

Graphing Calculator

LESSON 1.4 Find values of the inverse sine and cosine functions, pp. 18–20 and pp. 22–23.

LESSON 1.9 Find values of the inverse trigonometric functions, pp. 47–48.

LESSON 1.13 Find the maximum change in a function, p. 74.

Investigation Overview

In this investigation, students learn how to calculate cosine and sine using radian measure. The investigation is careful not to equate degree and radian measurement in the way that one would equate inch and centimeter measurement. Radian measure is the length of an arc of the unit circle. One radian is an arc of the unit circle with a length of 1 unit. When students convert between degrees and radians in this investigation, the goal is to enforce the concept that a radian is a distance measurement. Radians are not just another way to measure angles.

Students review the graphs of the cosine and sine functions. They develop an understanding of a periodic function. Finally, they begin to solve equations that involve cosine and sine.

You may wish to assign Questions 1–3 for students to think and write about during the investigation.

Learning Goals

- Understand the relationship between degree and radian measure as the length of an arc on the unit circle subtended by a central angle.
- Relate the motion of an object around a circle to the graphs of the cosine and sine functions.
- Solve equations that involve cosine and sine (such as $3 \cos x + 2 = 1$).
- Estimate the slope of the graphs of the cosine and sine functions at a given point.

Habits and Skills

- Calculate cosine and sine using radians directly without converting to degrees.
- Visualize periodic functions, and identify their periods.
- Understand how to "undo" cosine or sine to solve equations.
- Compare the cosine and sine functions through their relation to the unit circle and through their graphs.

The Cosine and Sine Functions

In *The Cosine and Sine Functions,* you will learn how to measure in radians. You will learn how to think of cosine and sine as functions of radian measure. You will solve equations involving these trigonometric functions.

By the end of this investigation, you will be able to answer questions like these.

1. Where are the turning points of the cosine and sine functions?
2. What is a radian?
3. How can you use a graph of $y = \sin x$ to estimate solutions to the equation $\sin x = -0.6$?

You will learn how to

- understand the relationship between degree and radian measure as the length of an arc on the unit circle subtended by a central angle
- relate the motion of an object around a circle to the graphs of the cosine and sine functions
- solve equations that involve cosine and sine (such as $3 \cos x + 2 = 1$)

You will develop these habits and skills:

- Calculate cosine and sine using radians directly without converting to degrees.
- Visualize periodic functions, and identify their period.
- Understand how to "undo" cosine or sine to solve equations.
- Compare the cosine and sine functions through their relation to the unit circle and through their graphs.

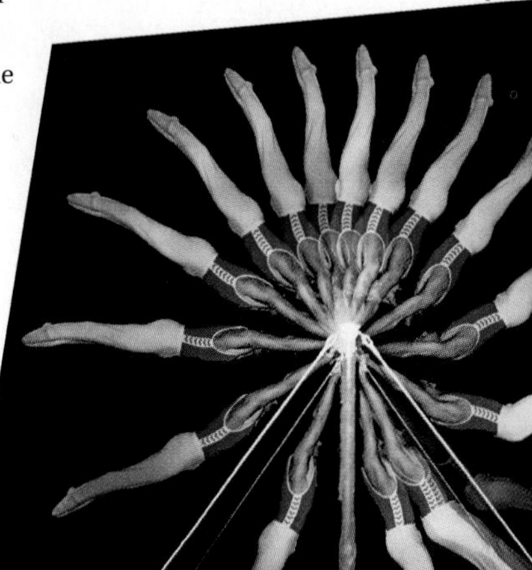

The gymnast traces a circle as he rotates about a fixed point.

Investigation Road Map

LESSON 1.1, *Getting Started,* reacquaints students with the unit circle definition of the cosine and sine functions.

LESSON 1.2, *Trigonometry With Radians,* defines radian measure, and de-emphasizes degree measure.

LESSON 1.3, *Graphing Cosine and Sine Functions,* steps students through the development of the graph of the sine function and defines periodic function and period.

LESSON 1.4, *Solving Cosine and Sine Equations,* has students solve simple equations that involve the cosine and sine functions.

LESSON 1.5, *Analyzing Graphs,* has students take a closer look at the graphs of the cosine and sine functions.

1.1 Getting Started

Olivia watches Paul walk around a circle. The circle's radius is 1 meter. Olivia stands at the center, and Paul begins walking counterclockwise. Consider a coordinate grid, with Olivia standing at the origin and Paul starting at the point $(1, 0)$.

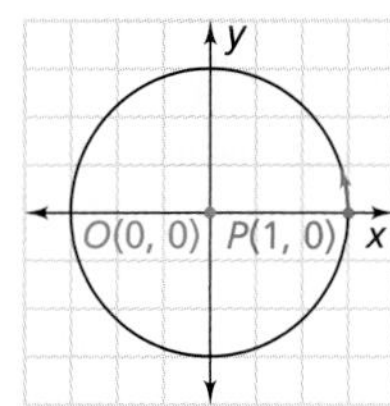

Remember...

The equation of the unit circle is $x^2 + y^2 = 1$.

As Paul walks an increasing distance around the circle, he passes through many points. The questions in this Getting Started ask about Paul's location after he has walked a specific distance.

For You to Explore

1. How far will Paul walk before returning to the point $(1, 0)$?
2. Draw the unit circle and plot the point where Paul will be after walking each distance.
   a. exactly π meters
   b. exactly $\frac{\pi}{2}$ meters
   c. exactly 3π meters
   d. exactly 3 meters
3. At some point, Paul has walked exactly $\frac{9\pi}{4}$ meters.
   a. What quadrant is Paul in after this much walking?
   b. Draw a unit circle and plot the point where Paul is after walking $\frac{9\pi}{4}$ meters.
   c. Find two other distances Paul could have walked around the circle to end up at this same point.
4. At some point, Paul has walked exactly $\frac{\pi}{3}$ meters. Find the exact coordinates of Paul's location.
5. **Write About It** At some point, Paul has walked exactly $\frac{\pi}{4}$ meters. Explain why his x- and y-coordinates must be equal at this point.
6. a. Find the exact coordinates of Paul's location after he walks $\frac{\pi}{4}$ meters.
   b. Find the exact coordinates of Paul's location after he walks $\frac{5\pi}{4}$ meters.
7. **Take It Further** Paul runs 100 meters along the circle. What quadrant is he in at the end of this 100-meter run?

Habits of Mind

Recognize symmetry. Is there any symmetry to Paul's location?

Remember...

Exact here means no decimals, just exact fractions or radicals.

Answers

For You to Explore

1. 2π m (≈ 6.28 m)
2. See back of book.
3. a. Quadrant I
   b. See back of book.
   c. Answers may vary. Sample: $\frac{17\pi}{4}$ m, $\frac{25\pi}{4}$ m
4. $\left(\frac{1}{2}, \frac{\sqrt{3}}{2}\right)$
5. Answers may vary. Sample: The arc of the unit circle from (1, 0) to (0, 1) has length $\frac{\pi}{2}$ m. When he has walked just $\frac{\pi}{4}$ m, he is at the point that bisects this arc. This point will lie on the line with equation $y = x$.
6. a. $\left(\frac{\sqrt{2}}{2}, \frac{\sqrt{2}}{2}\right)$ b. $\left(-\frac{\sqrt{2}}{2}, -\frac{\sqrt{2}}{2}\right)$
7. Quadrant IV

Lesson Overview

GOAL

- Warm up to the ideas of the investigation.

Students begin this investigation reviewing an experiment they may have seen in CME Project *Algebra 2*. In this experiment, Olivia watches Paul walk around a circle counter-clockwise. Students begin to equate the distance Paul walks with his location on their "map." Their work previews the idea of radian measure, and one way that radian measure is useful.

As always in a Getting Started lesson, there is no need to formalize any ideas today. Students revisit these concepts throughout the investigation. The lessons that follow define or otherwise formalize these ideas. These exercises are self-paced explorations for the students to review previously learned concepts or gain experience with these concepts for the first time.

FOR YOU TO EXPLORE
- Core: 1, 2, 3, 6
- Optional: 4, 5
- Extension: 7

MATERIALS
- graph paper
- graphing calculators
- Blackline Masters MC1, BM1.1

HOMEWORK
- Core: 8, 11,12, 13, 15
- Optional: 9, 10, 14

Launch

Begin the lesson by briefly reviewing the picture on page 5 that shows Paul and Olivia's setup. Then let students get started on the For You to Explore problems.

Explore

The problems in this Getting Started lesson provide students with raw experience that is used throughout the investigation. They start to build functions that equate the distance around a unit circle with coordinates of the stopping point. This process helps define the cosine and sine functions on the unit circle. The students generate a model to understand radians and build the graph of $y = \sin x$. They start to think about solving equations with the sine and cosine functions.

You may wish to provide copies of Blackline Master MC1 for students to use.

For You to Explore

ERROR PREVENTION Make sure students only have Paul walking counter-clockwise.

continued on p. 6

continued from p. 5

PROBLEM 3 prompts students to think about the periodic nature of the cosine and sine functions.

PROBLEM 4 Use the last part as a tester to see whether students can recognize and apply a 30–60–90 triangle to the situation.

PROBLEM 7 The goal is to have students work through this problem without thinking about degree measurements. Most students will first convert every radian measure to degrees, perform the calculations, and then convert back. By the end of this investigation, students should be starting to work in radians directly.

Wrap Up

Before assigning homework, allow students some time to discuss and summarize their findings. In particular have them discuss their strategy for finding the quadrant in Problem 7.

Exercises

HOMEWORK
- Core: 8, 11,12, 13, 15
- Optional: 9, 10, 14

On Your Own

EXERCISE 10 Check students' answers here for their understanding of the relationship between radian measure and angle measure. The goal is for students to differentiate between angle measure and radian measure while still seeing how they relate.

EXERCISE 11 gives evidence that the sine and cosine functions are periodic.

Maintain Your Skills

EXERCISE 15 shows students the radian equivalent for the basic angles that they should already know. It also provides data that can be used in the next lesson. You may wish to provide copies of Blackline Master BM1.1 for students to fill in the table. The table entries are essential information for the remainder of the chapter.

Exercises *Practicing Habits of Mind*

On Your Own

8. How far will Paul walk when he first reaches the point $(0, -1)$?

9. Write About It What is the importance of π in measuring the distance Paul has walked? In other words, why are so many of the questions about multiples of π and not integers?

10. Write About It Olivia, standing at $O(0, 0)$, says that Paul's $\frac{\pi}{2}$ behaves like $90°$. Explain Olivia's observation.

11. As Paul continues to walk, he will reach $(0, -1)$ again.

a. Give another distance Paul could walk to reach $(0, -1)$.

b. Describe a method you could use to generate a large number of these distances.

12. a. Draw the unit circle and plot the point where Paul will be after walking exactly $\frac{7\pi}{6}$ meters.

b. Find the exact coordinates of Paul's location after he walks $\frac{7\pi}{6}$ meters.

13. As Paul walks around the circle, is there ever a time when his y-coordinate is *exactly* $\frac{2}{3}$? If so, how many times will this happen each time Paul goes around the circle? If not, how do you know it can never happen?

14. As Paul walks around the circle, his x- and y-coordinates reach maximum and minimum values. What are these maximum and minimum values, and at what walking distances do they occur?

Maintain Your Skills

15. Copy and complete this table, giving the coordinates of Paul's location after walking each distance. Look for patterns to help make your work easier.

Distance	Coordinates
0	(1, 0)
$\frac{\pi}{4}$	$\left(\frac{\sqrt{2}}{2}, \frac{\sqrt{2}}{2}\right)$
$\frac{\pi}{2}$	■
$\frac{3\pi}{4}$	■
π	(−1, 0)
$\frac{5\pi}{4}$	■
$\frac{3\pi}{2}$	■
$\frac{7\pi}{4}$	■
2π	■
$\frac{9\pi}{4}$	■
$\frac{5\pi}{2}$	■

Answers

Exercises

8. $\frac{3\pi}{2}$ m ($\approx$4.71 m)

9. The distance around the unit circle in this situation is 2π m.

10. When Paul walks a distance of $\frac{\pi}{2}$ m, he has walked $\frac{1}{4}$ of the way around the circle. The degree measure of an arc that is $\frac{1}{4}$ of a circle is 90°.

11. a. Answers may vary. Sample: $\frac{7\pi}{2}$ m($\approx$11.00 m)

b. Start with $\frac{3\pi}{2}$ and add 2π repeatedly.

12. a. See back of book.

b. $\left(-\frac{\sqrt{3}}{2}, -\frac{1}{2}\right)$

13. Yes; two times

14. 1 and −1; maximum value of the x-coordinates occurs at 0 m and 2π m, minimum value occurs at π m, maximum value of the y-coordinates occurs at $\frac{\pi}{2}$ m, minimum value occurs at $\frac{3\pi}{2}$ m.

15. See back of book.

1.2 Trigonometry With Radians

In Lesson 1.1, Paul walked around a unit circle, and you found the coordinates of his stopping point. You may remember that the coordinates of any point on the unit circle are $(\cos\theta, \sin\theta)$, where θ is the measure of the angle between the positive x-axis and a ray drawn from the origin through the point.

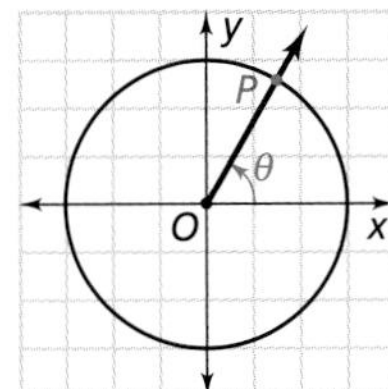

Remember...

A central angle for a circle is an angle that has its vertex at the center of the circle.

An arc is a set of points of a circle that lie in the interior of a particular central angle.

Since the origin is the center of the circle, the angle whose measure is θ is a **central angle.** The part of the circle that is between the two sides of the angle is an **arc.**

There is a direct correspondence between the length of an arc on the unit circle and the measure of the central angle that defines the arc.

Example 1

Problem For an arc length of $\frac{\pi}{3}$, what is the measure of the corresponding central angle?

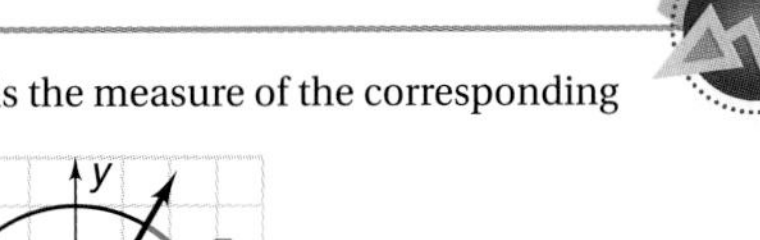

Solution The circumference of the unit circle is 2π. So the arc with length $\frac{\pi}{3}$ would be $\frac{1}{6}$ of the entire circle (since $\frac{\pi}{3} \cdot 6 = 2\pi$). The central angle is $\frac{\theta}{360°}$ of the full circle. Thus,

$$\frac{1}{6} = \frac{\theta}{360°}$$

so $\theta = 60°$.

Lesson Overview

GOALS

- Understand the relationship between degree and radian measure as the length of an arc on the unit circle subtended by a central angle.
- Relate the motion of an object around a circle to the graphs of the cosine and sine functions.

This lesson formally introduces radian measure, a topic that was previewed in Lesson 1.1. A key idea in this investigation is that radian measure is a distance measurement. One radian is an arc on the unit circle of length 1 or, equivalently, an arc on a circle the same length as the radius of the circle.

It is true that there is a direct correspondence between the central angle that defines an arc and the length of that arc. However, it is important to maintain the distinction between the two measures. Students should see that radian measure is not simply another way to measure angles.

The students build a sketch in this lesson that they expand when they develop the graph of $y = \sin x$ in the next lesson.

CHECK YOUR UNDERSTANDING

- Core: 2, 3, 5, 6
- Optional: 1, 4
- Extension: 7

MATERIALS

- geometry software
- graph paper
- graphing calculators
- Blackline Masters MC1, MC2

HOMEWORK

- Core: 8, 11, 12, 15, 16, 17
- Optional: 9, 10, 13
- Extension: 14

VOCABULARY

- arc
- central angle
- radian

Launch

Review Exercises 10 and 15 from Lesson 1.1. The answer in Exercise 15 shows a relationship between radian measure and familiar values of cosine and sine. Students should already be familiar with a similar correspondence between angle measure and these values.

Explore

You may wish to use Blackline Master MC1 to provide students with unit circles to use throughout the lesson.

In-Class Experiment

For the In-Class Experiment, you may wish to have students work in pairs. The goal is to have students gain experience that will help them understand a key concept or formula.

Making this model helps students get accustomed to using geometry software as a tool for learning. In the next lesson, students use this model to see how to build the basic sine graph.

For You to Do

1. How long is the arc that corresponds to a 135° central angle?

In-Class Experiment

In this experiment, you will build a model using your graphing calculator or geometry software. You will compare distance traveled around a circle, the corresponding central angle, and the coordinates of the stopping point.

Follow these steps to build your sketch:

Step 1 Construct a circle of radius of 1 unit on a coordinate grid.

Step 2 Add a point at $(1, 0)$. Label it A.

Step 3 Construct another point on the circle. Label it B.

Step 4 Have the software display the coordinates of point B.

Step 5 Have the software display the length of $\overset{\frown}{AB}$ (counterclockwise).

Step 6 Have the software display the degree measure of $\angle AOB$.

Drag point B around the circle, and compare the angle measure to the arc length.

See the TI-Nspire™ Handbook on p. 704 on how to make this sketch. Some geometry software will calculate actual length in inches or centimeters, not in relative units.

For You to Do

2. What is the maximum y-coordinate? For what arc length does it occur?
3. What arc length corresponds to 90°?
4. What angle corresponds to an arc length of $\frac{7\pi}{4}$?

In general, if R is the arc length, and D is the degree measure of the corresponding angle, then

$$\frac{R}{2\pi} = \frac{D}{360^\circ}$$

For You to Do

Find the measure of the angle (in degrees) for each of the following arc lengths.

5. $\frac{\pi}{4}$
6. $\frac{4\pi}{3}$
7. 4

Answers

For You to Do

1. $\frac{3\pi}{4}$

In-Class Experiment

Check students' sketches. The value of $m\angle AOB$ is $\left(\frac{180 \text{ length of } \overset{\frown}{AB}}{\pi}\right)^\circ$.

For You to Do

2. 1; $\frac{\pi}{2}$
3. $\frac{\pi}{2}$
4. 315°

For You to Do

5. 45°
6. 240°
7. $\frac{720^\circ}{\pi}$

At this point, you have defined the functions cosine and sine in terms of degrees. The input is the angle measure in degrees and the output is a real number. When you set the calculator in **radian** mode, it gives you the cosine and sine as a function of the length of an arc along the circle, rather than of the central angle.

Why think of a different way to define the trig functions? With this new definition, you can think of both input and output as lengths or distances—the same type of measurement. You input the arc distance from $(1, 0)$ of a point on a unit circle. The cosine function outputs the distance of that point from the y-axis. The sine function outputs the distance from the x-axis.

Think of a radian as an arc of length 1 unit. So π radians would correspond to a central angle of 180°.

See the TI-Nspire Handbook on p. 704 for details on how to put your calculator in radian mode.

Example 2

Problem Find $\cos\frac{\pi}{3}$ and $\sin\frac{\pi}{3}$.

Solution In the previous example, you saw that an arc of $\frac{\pi}{3}$ on the unit circle corresponds to a 60° angle. You might remember cos 60° and sin 60°, since 60° is one of the angles from a 30–60–90 right triangle. So

$$\cos\frac{\pi}{3} = \cos 60^\circ = \frac{1}{2}, \text{ and}$$

$$\sin\frac{\pi}{3} = \sin 60^\circ = \frac{\sqrt{3}}{2}$$

Since your experience now is mostly with degree measure, you may naturally try to convert any radian measure to degrees to find the sine and cosine. With practice, taking this extra step will be unnecessary. Your ultimate goal is to calculate cosine and sine directly from the arc length.

The cosine and sine functions look the same whether you are in degree or radian mode. The only way to be certain which mode is intended is to look at the argument: sin 30° is different from sin 30. When you see sin *x*, you can assume *x* is radians unless you are told otherwise.

As Paul walked around the circle, you may have noticed a correspondence between the distance he walked (the length of an arc if he walked less than once around the circle) and the coordinates of his stopping point. Using radian mode on your calculator, you can calculate the coordinates of his stopping point directly from the distance he actually traveled, without converting to degrees.

For You to Do

Find the exact coordinates of Paul's stopping point after walking each distance.

8. exactly π meters
9. exactly $\frac{\pi}{2}$ meters
10. exactly 3π meters
11. exactly $\frac{9\pi}{4}$ meters

Example 2

Spend time as needed going over Example 2. Make sure students understand the problem. As necessary, help them develop the detailed solution.

For You to Do

8. $(-1, 0)$

9. $(0, 1)$

10. $(-1, 0)$

11. $\left(\frac{\sqrt{2}}{2}, \frac{\sqrt{2}}{2}\right)$

Wrap Up

Have students begin work on the exercises. Be sure that students have enough time to complete the table in Exercise 3 during class.

Assessment Resources

Lesson Quiz 1.2

1. Find a point on the unit circle that has coordinates $\left(\cos\frac{3\pi}{4}, \sin\frac{3\pi}{4}\right)$.
2. An arc length on the unit circle has length $\frac{2\pi}{3}$. What is the measure of the corresponding central angle?
3. Suppose $\pi \le x \le \frac{3\pi}{2}$. Determine whether $\frac{\sin x}{\cos x}$ is positive or negative.
4. Which quadrant of the unit circle contains the value sin 3?

Exercises

HOMEWORK

- Core: 8, 11, 12, 15, 16, 17
- Optional: 9, 10, 13
- Extension: 14

Check Your Understanding

EXERCISE 2 If students need help, have them refer to Getting Started, or suggest that they draw a right triangle.

EXERCISE 3 is the most important exercise in this lesson. Be sure to spend a lot of time on this exercise in class. Remind students to use the unit circle to help them with the symmetry. The table contains enough information that it can be filled in using symmetry and quadrant angles. You may wish to provide copies of Blackline Master MC2 for students to fill in the table as they follow along. Point out that the table in Exercise 3 has three additional entries at the bottom that they should record on their own paper. Tell them that the worksheet will give them a handy reference for key values they will use throughout the chapter.

Exercises *Practicing Habits of Mind*

Check Your Understanding

1. Example 2 showed that $\cos\frac{\pi}{3} = \frac{1}{2}$ and $\sin\frac{\pi}{3} = \frac{\sqrt{3}}{2}$.
   a. The value of $\cos\frac{2\pi}{3}$ is negative, while $\sin\frac{2\pi}{3}$ is positive. What are these values?
   b. Find the values of $\cos\frac{4\pi}{3}$ and $\sin\frac{4\pi}{3}$.
   c. Find the values of $\cos\frac{5\pi}{3}$ and $\sin\frac{5\pi}{3}$.
   d. Find the values of $\cos\frac{6\pi}{3}$ and $\sin\frac{6\pi}{3}$.
2. Find the exact values of $\cos\frac{\pi}{4}$ and $\sin\frac{\pi}{4}$.
3. Copy and complete this table with exact values of cosine and sine. It may help to plot the point $(\cos x, \sin x)$ for each value of x.

x	$\cos x$	$\sin x$
0	■	■
$\frac{\pi}{6}$	$\frac{\sqrt{3}}{2}$	$\frac{1}{2}$
$\frac{\pi}{4}$	■	■
$\frac{\pi}{3}$	$\frac{1}{2}$	$\frac{\sqrt{3}}{2}$
$\frac{\pi}{2}$	■	■
$\frac{2\pi}{3}$	■	■
$\frac{3\pi}{4}$	$-\frac{\sqrt{2}}{2}$	$\frac{\sqrt{2}}{2}$
$\frac{5\pi}{6}$	■	■
π	■	■
$\frac{7\pi}{6}$	■	■
$\frac{5\pi}{4}$	■	$-\frac{\sqrt{2}}{2}$
$\frac{4\pi}{3}$	■	■
$\frac{3\pi}{2}$	0	-1
$\frac{5\pi}{3}$	■	■
$\frac{7\pi}{4}$	■	■
$\frac{11\pi}{6}$	$\frac{\sqrt{3}}{2}$	■
2π	■	■
$\frac{13\pi}{6}$	■	■
$\frac{9\pi}{4}$	■	■
$\frac{7\pi}{3}$	■	■

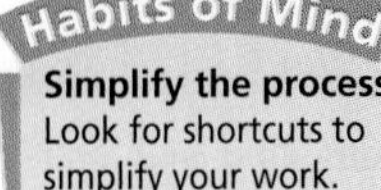

Simplify the process. Look for shortcuts to simplify your work.

For an overview of trigonometry, go to **Web Code:** bge-9031

Answers

Exercises

1. **a.** $\cos\frac{2\pi}{3} = -\frac{1}{2}$, $\sin\frac{2\pi}{3} = \frac{\sqrt{3}}{2}$
   b. $\cos\frac{4\pi}{3} = -\frac{1}{2}$, $\sin\frac{4\pi}{3} = -\frac{\sqrt{3}}{2}$
   c. $\cos\frac{5\pi}{3} = \frac{1}{2}$, $\sin\frac{5\pi}{3} = -\frac{\sqrt{3}}{2}$
   d. $\cos\frac{6\pi}{3} = 1$, $\sin\frac{6\pi}{3} = 0$
2. $\cos\frac{\pi}{4} = \sin\frac{\pi}{4} = \frac{\sqrt{2}}{2}$
3. See back of book.

4. For several different values of x, calculate the squares of $\cos x$ and of $\sin x$. How do the two values, $\cos^2 x$ and $\sin^2 x$, relate to each other?

5. a. Is there some number x that makes $\cos x = \frac{4}{5}$? Explain.
   b. If $\cos x = \frac{4}{5}$, what could $\sin x$ equal?

6. Which of the following values is greatest?
   A. sin 1 B. sin 2 C. sin 3 D. sin 4

7. **Take It Further**
   a. Is there an integer n such that $\sin n > 0.999$? Explain.
   b. Is there an integer n such that $\sin n = -1$? Explain.

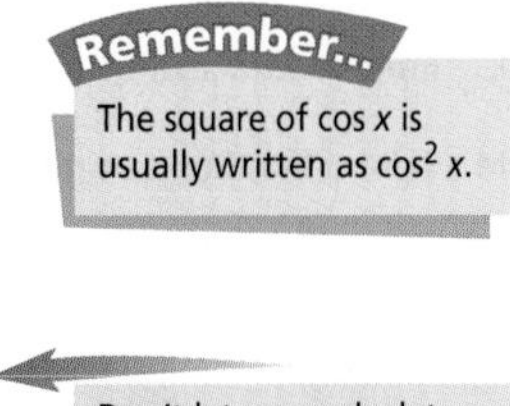

Remember...
The square of cos x is usually written as $\cos^2 x$.

Don't let your calculator have all the fun!

On Your Own

8. Locate the point on the unit circle with coordinates $\left(\cos \frac{\pi}{6}, \sin \frac{\pi}{6}\right)$.

9. Explain why $\sin \frac{\pi}{2} = 1$.

10. Simplify the sum $\cos \frac{\pi}{4} + \cos \frac{3\pi}{4} + \cos \frac{5\pi}{4} + \cos \frac{7\pi}{4}$.

11. Suppose $\frac{\pi}{2} < x < \pi$. State whether each of the following is positive or negative.
    a. $\sin x$ b. $\cos x$ c. $\frac{\sin x}{\cos x}$ d. $\cos^2 x + \sin^2 x$

12. **What's Wrong Here?** Walt can't decide whether sin 5 should be positive or negative.
    Walt says, "I drew a unit circle. Five radians is more than π, since π is just over 3. But 5 is less than 2π. Then 5 radians is somewhere around here:

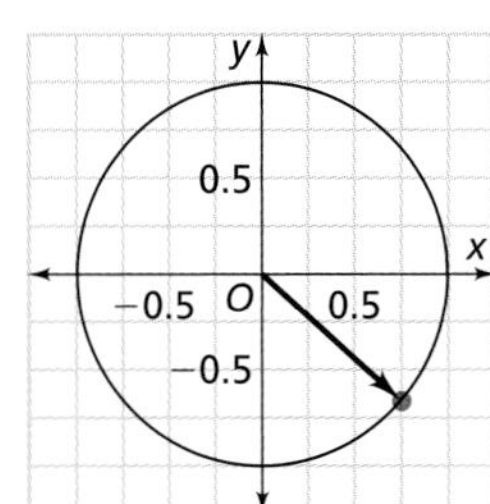

It looks like sin 5 should be negative, but the calculator says that the answer is about 0.087, positive."

Explain what happened. Is Walt right, or is the calculator right?

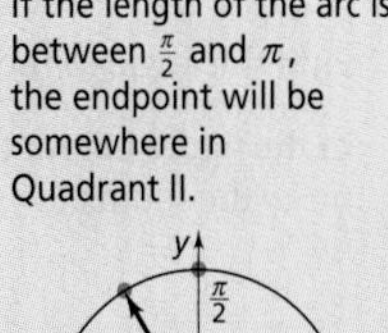

If the length of the arc is between $\frac{\pi}{2}$ and π, the endpoint will be somewhere in Quadrant II.

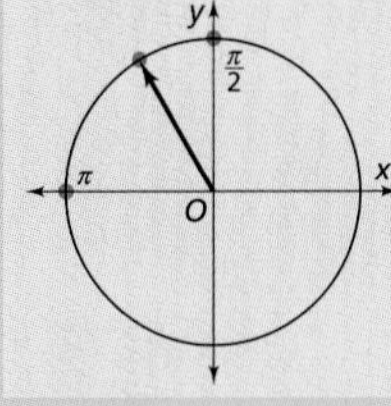

Go Online PHSchool.com

For additional practice, go to **Web Code: bga-0102**

4. $\cos^2 x + \sin^2 x = 1$

5. a. Yes; the vertical line through $\left(\frac{4}{5}, 0\right)$ intersects the unit circle in two points.
   b. $\pm\frac{3}{5}$

6. B

7. a. Yes; answers may vary. Sample: $\sin 33 \approx 0.999912$
   b. No; if $\sin x = -1$, then x must be a number of the form $\frac{3\pi}{2} + n(2\pi)$, where n is an integer.

8. $\left(\frac{\sqrt{3}}{2}, \frac{1}{2}\right)$

9. If you move from (1, 0) counterclockwise around the unit circle a distance of $\frac{\pi}{2}$ units, then you stop at (0, 1), or $\left(\cos\frac{\pi}{2}, \sin\frac{\pi}{2}\right)$. So $\sin\frac{\pi}{2} = 1$.

10. 0

11. a. positive b. negative
    c. negative d. positive

12. Walt is correct. The calculator was set for degree mode rather than radian mode.

EXERCISE 5 hints at the continuity of the cosine and sine functions.

EXERCISE 6 When students first start working with radians, they believe that radians must have π in them. This exercise reinforce the idea that radians are just numbers. All numbers, including integers, are acceptable for input. More importantly, they cannot assume that the question must be asking for sine or cosine of a degree measure since there is no π.

GOING FURTHER This exercise is fairly mechanical if done simply using the calculator. Encourage students to explain why the correct answer is B by estimating where 1, 2, 3, and 4 radians would fall on the unit circle.

On Your Own

EXERCISE 10 is an exercise where the calculator provides a simple answer. Students should explore why that answer is 0.

EXERCISE 12 highlights a common mistake students will make. Seeing Walt struggle with the difference between degree and radian mode reminds students to check the mode on their own calculator.

Additional Resources

PRINT RESOURCES
- Solution Manual
- Practice Workbook
- Assessment Resources
- Teaching Resources

TECHNOLOGY
- Interactive Textbook
- TeacherExpress CD-ROM
- ExamView CD-ROM
- PHSchool.com

Additional Practice

For Exercises 1–4, find the exact values. Do not use a calculator.

1. $\cos \frac{\pi}{6}$ and $\sin \frac{\pi}{6}$
2. $\cos \frac{5\pi}{6}$ and $\sin \frac{5\pi}{6}$
3. $\cos \frac{7\pi}{6}$ and $\sin \frac{7\pi}{6}$
4. $\cos \frac{11\pi}{6}$ and $\sin \frac{11\pi}{6}$

5. Which of the following values is the smallest?
   A. cos 2 **B.** cos 3
   C. cos 5 **D.** cos 6

For Exercises 6–9, suppose $\pi < x < \frac{3\pi}{2}$. State whether each is positive or negative.

6. $\sin x$
7. $\cos x$
8. $\frac{\sin x}{\cos x}$
9. $\cos^2 x + \sin^2 x$

10. On the unit circle, draw an angle so that the intercepted arc has length equal to three units. Find the angle to the nearest tenth of a degree.

For Exercises 11–14, find the exact values. Do not use a calculator.

11. $\cos\left(-\frac{\pi}{6}\right)$ and $\sin\left(-\frac{\pi}{6}\right)$
12. $\cos\left(-\frac{2\pi}{3}\right)$ and $\sin\left(-\frac{2\pi}{3}\right)$
13. $\cos\left(-\frac{\pi}{4}\right)$ and $\sin\left(-\frac{\pi}{4}\right)$
14. $\cos\left(-\frac{5\pi}{6}\right)$ and $\sin\left(-\frac{5\pi}{6}\right)$

15. James starts at (1, 0) and walks counterclockwise 19 radians along the unit circle. What quadrant is James in?

16. On the same axes, sketch these two graphs.
$$y = \cos x$$
$$y = 0.2$$
Use the graphs to estimate the two solutions to $\cos x = 0.2$ in the interval $0 \le x \le 2\pi$.

17. Sketch the graph of the equation on the interval $-2\pi \le x \le 2\pi$.
$$y = \cos\left(x + \frac{\pi}{2}\right)$$

Practice: For Lesson 1.2, assign Exercises 1–10.

13. Find the exact value of $\log_{10}\left(20 \sin \frac{5\pi}{6}\right)$.

14. **Take It Further** Simplify the sum $\cos \frac{2\pi}{5} + \cos \frac{4\pi}{5} + \cos \frac{6\pi}{5} + \cos \frac{8\pi}{5}$.

15. **Standardized Test Prep** Of the following four cosine values, which is the greatest?

A. cos 5.28 **B.** cos 6.28 **C.** cos 7.28 **D.** cos 8.28

Maintain Your Skills

16. In the figure below, the angle of the intercepted arc has length equal to the radius.

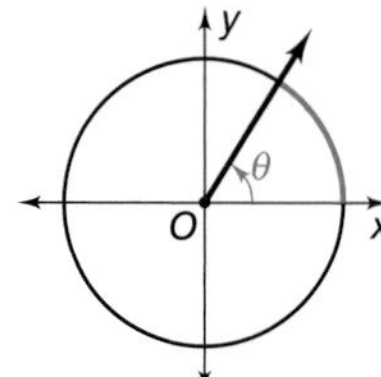

Find the angle to the nearest tenth of a degree.

17. In the figure below, the angle of the intercepted arc has length equal to twice the radius.

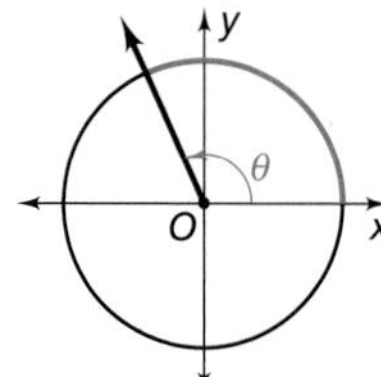

Find the measure of the angle to the nearest tenth of a degree.

Answers

13. 1

14. −1

15. B

16. 57.3°

17. 114.6°

1.3 Graphing Cosine and Sine Functions

After Paul has moved α meters around his circle of radius 1 meter, he reaches a certain point, (a, b). You can track how a and b change individually as Paul moves around the circle by making a graph.

The following diagram shows a series of arcs of the same unit circle. Each arc starts from the point $(1, 0)$, and ends at some stopping point (a, b). The arc is highlighted, along with the height of the stopping point. That height is, in fact, the same value as the y-coordinate of the stopping point, b. And b is equal to $\sin \alpha$.

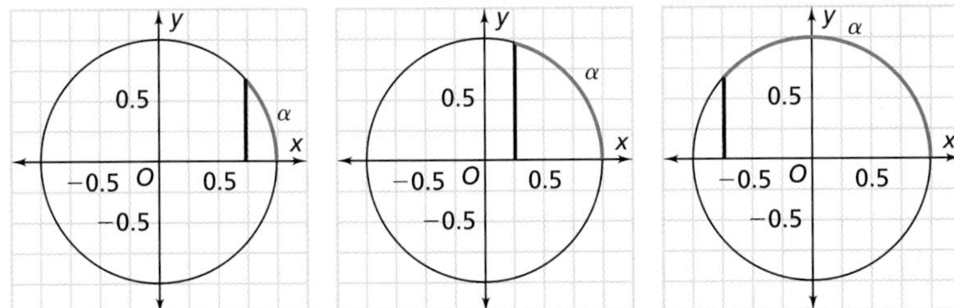

As the value of α, the arc length, increases from 0 to $\frac{\pi}{2}$, the y-coordinate, or $\sin \alpha$, increases from 0 to 1. Then, as the arc length increases from $\frac{\pi}{2}$ to π, the sine decreases from 1 to 0. The graph below shows the results for $0 \leq \alpha \leq \pi$.

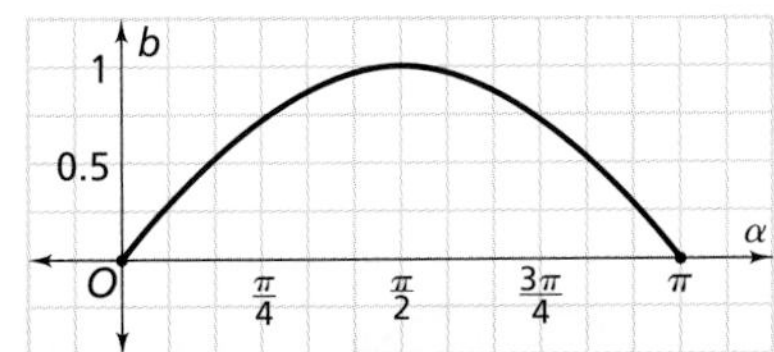

Temporal changes in the height of the sun follow a sine pattern as seen in this time-lapse photograph of the sun's daily cycle from the island of Loppa in Norway, north of the Arctic Circle.

Lesson Overview

GOAL

- Relate the motion of an object around a circle to the graphs of the cosine and sine functions.

In this lesson, students compare the unit circle experiment from the previous lesson with the graph of $y = \sin x$. After participating in this lesson, students should know the definition of periodic functions. They should also know the basic shape of the graphs of the cosine and sine functions.

CHECK YOUR UNDERSTANDING

- Core: 1, 3, 4, 6
- Optional: 2, 5

MATERIALS

- graph paper
- graphing calculators
- Blackline Masters MC1, MC3

HOMEWORK

- Core: 7, 9, 10, 12, 14
- Optional: 8, 11, 15, 16
- Extension: 13

VOCABULARY

- period
- periodic function

Launch

Review the model that students built in the previous lesson. Then suggest that students use that model to see how the sine curve is built.

Explore

You may want to use Blackline Master MC1 on an overhead to illustrate the presentation. Then transfer the coordinates you just found to Blackline Master MC3 to sketch the graph of the sine function. You may wish to provide copies of both Blackline Masters for students to use during the discussion.

For You to Do

PROBLEM 1 Have students practice the ideas just introduced by doing this problem.

To continue this graph, look at more arcs. As the arc length grows larger than π, the y-coordinate of the stopping point becomes negative.

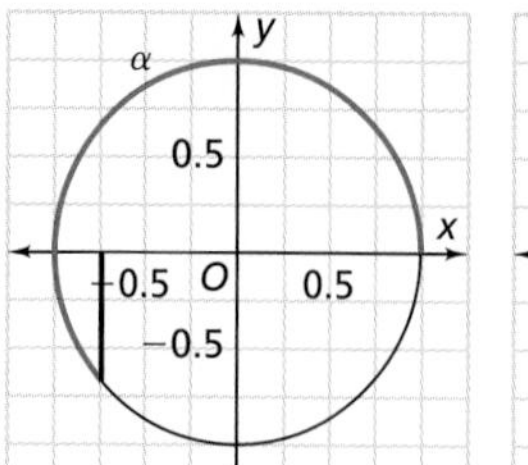

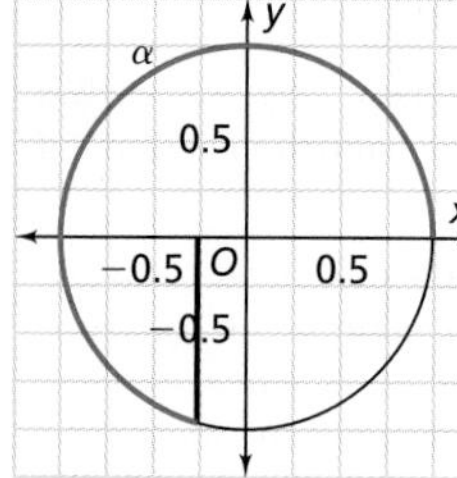

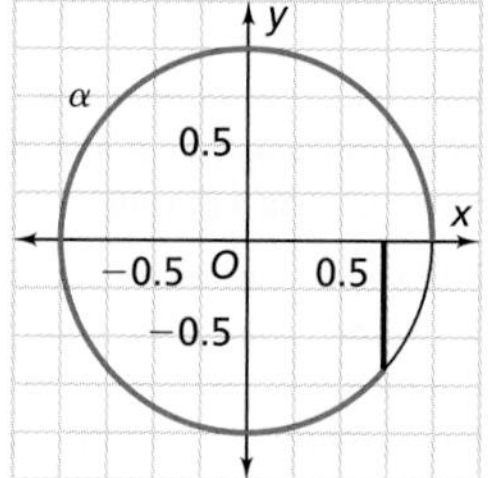

So the sine of arcs that are between π and 2π are all negative. The following graph shows a full rotation around the unit circle.

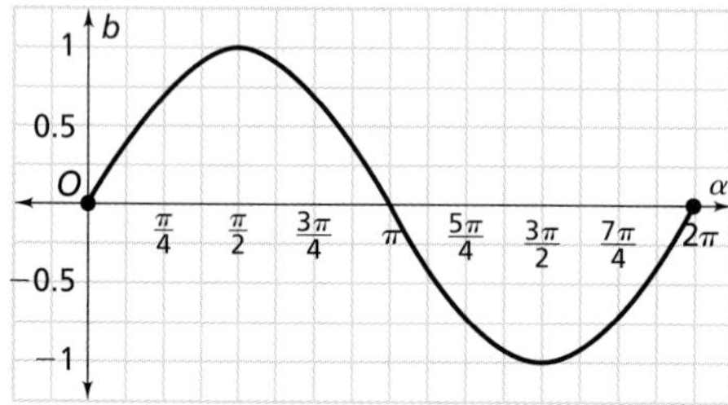

For You to Do

1. Find all numbers x such that $0 \leq x \leq 2\pi$ and $\sin x = 1$.

After Paul has walked 2π meters, he has returned to his starting point. If he continues walking, he ends up retracing his earlier steps. For instance, his stopping point is the same when he walks $\frac{\pi}{4}$ meters and when he walks $\frac{9\pi}{4}$ meters.

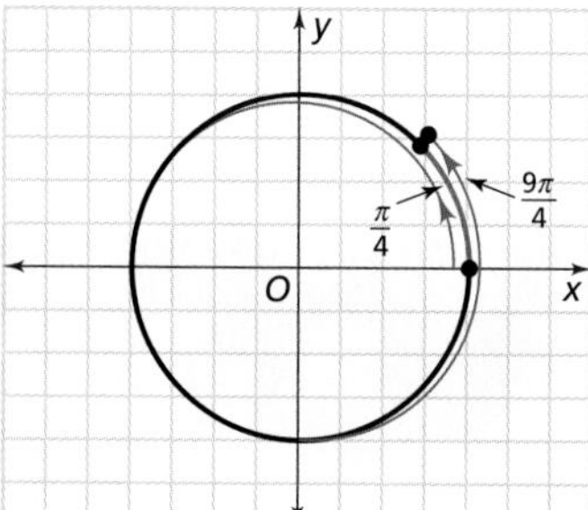

Answers

For You to Do

1. $x = \frac{\pi}{2}$

For You to Do

2. Find 4 values for x such that $\sin x = 1$. Write a general statement in terms of n, such that $\sin n\pi = 1$.

The values of n may or may not be integers.

You can generate the graph $a = \cos \alpha$ in a similar manner. As Paul walks from the point $(1, 0)$ to the point (a, b) on his circle, graph the distance he travels α on the horizontal axis and the value of a on the vertical axis. Below is the graph of $a = \cos \alpha$, for domain $0 \le \alpha \le 2\pi$.

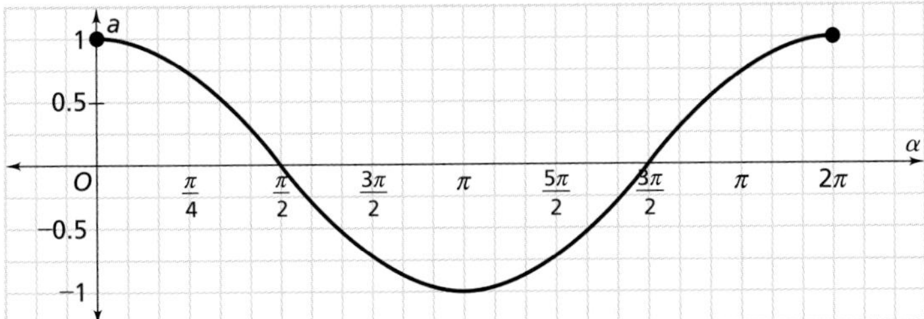

For Discussion

3. Apply the transformation $x \mapsto x + \frac{\pi}{2}$ to the graph of $y = \cos x$. How does this graph compare to the graph of $y = \sin x$?

You built the graphs for both the cosine and sine functions by observing Paul walking around a circle. Since he only walks around in circles, he will continue to move through the exact same set of points each lap around the circle.

When the outputs of a function, like cosine and sine, repeat in a regular pattern, the function is called periodic.

Definitions

A nonconstant function f is periodic if there exists a real number $p > 0$ such that, for all x, $f(x + p) = f(x)$.
The period of a periodic function is the smallest value p such that, for all x, $f(x + p) = f(x)$.

For You to Do

2. Answers may vary. Sample: $\frac{\pi}{2}$, $\frac{5\pi}{2}$, $\frac{9\pi}{2}$, and $\frac{13\pi}{2}$; if n can be written in the form $\frac{4k + 1}{2}$, where k is an integer, then $\sin n\pi = 1$.

For Discussion

3. The image graph coincides with the graph of $y = \sin x$.

For Discussion

PROBLEM 3 The translated cosine graph is the same as the sine graph. Students may recognize this effect from the identity $\sin x = \cos(90 - x)$, which they saw in the right triangle definitions of these functions (the side opposite an angle is adjacent to that angle's complement).

DEFINITION OF PERIODIC In Investigation 1C, students will see how to prove that a given value p is the smallest value.

Wrap Up

Have students begin work on the Check Your Understanding exercises.

Assessment Resources

Lesson Quiz 1.3

1. Paul starts at $(1, 0)$ and walks counterclockwise 48 radians along the unit circle. What quadrant is Paul in?

2. What should $\cos\left(-\frac{3\pi}{2}\right)$ and $\sin\left(-\frac{3\pi}{2}\right)$ equal?

3. a. On the unit circle how many solutions does $\sin x = 0.25$ have?
   b. Draw the unit circle indicating the location(s) where $\sin x = 0.25$.
   c. Sketch the graphs of $y = \sin x$ and $y = 0.25$ on the same axes. Use these graphs to estimate the solution(s) to $\sin x = 0.25$ in the interval $0 \le x \le 2\pi$.

4. a. Sketch the graph of $y = \cos\left(x - \frac{\pi}{2}\right)$ in the interval $0 \le x \le 2\pi$.
   b. What other function can be used to obtain the same graph?

Exercises

HOMEWORK
- Core: 7, 9, 10, 12, 14
- Optional: 8, 11, 15, 16
- Extension: 13

You may wish to provide copies of Blackline Masters MC1 and MC3 to help them with some of the exercises, particularly Exercises 3, 7, 10, and 11.

Check Your Understanding

EXERCISE 4 works towards expanding the domain of cosine and sine to include all real numbers.

On Your Own

EXERCISE 10 reviews the graphing method for solving equations. To solve an equation of the form $f(x) = g(x)$, graph the equations $y = f(x)$ and $y = g(x)$ on the same axes. Then find the point(s) where the two graphs intersect.

EXERCISE 11 reinforces the identity $\sin\left(x + \frac{\pi}{2}\right) = \cos x$.

EXERCISE 12 previews the idea of altering the period of the cosine and sine functions. Students will explore this concept in more detail in Investigation 1C.

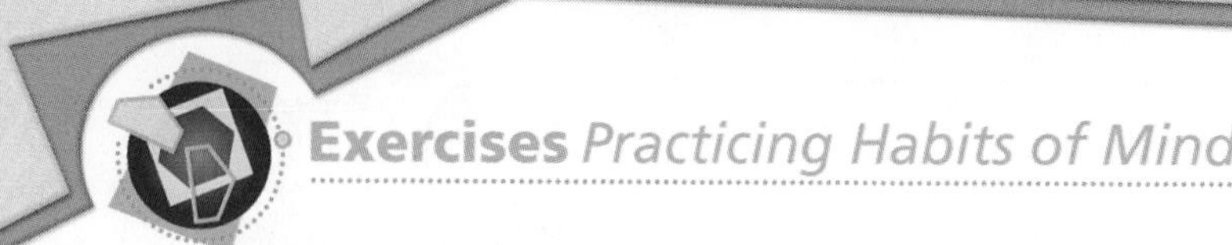

Exercises *Practicing Habits of Mind*

Check Your Understanding

1. Starting from standard position, an angle that intercepts an arc of length $\frac{4\pi}{3}$ ends in what quadrant?

   A. Quadrant I **B.** Quadrant II
   C. Quadrant III **D.** Quadrant IV

2. **a.** If $\cos x = 0.6$, what is $\cos^2 x$? What is $\sin^2 x$?
   b. Find both possible values of $\sin x$.
   c. On the unit circle, show the two possible locations where $\cos x = 0.6$.

3. On the same axes, sketch the graphs of these two equations.

$$y = \cos x$$
$$y = 0.6$$

   Use the graphs to estimate the two solutions to $\cos x = 0.6$ in the interval $0 \le x < 2\pi$.

4. You can extend the domain of the cosine and sine functions to include negative values.
   a. What should $\cos\left(-\frac{\pi}{2}\right)$ and $\sin\left(-\frac{\pi}{2}\right)$ equal?
   b. What should $\cos\left(-\frac{\pi}{3}\right)$ and $\sin\left(-\frac{\pi}{3}\right)$ equal?

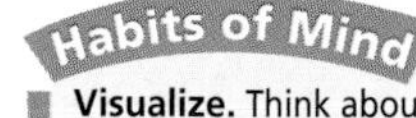

For negative values in the domain, think of Paul walking backward, or clockwise, around his circle.

5. Paul and his twin brother Saul follow the instructions from the Getting Started, except Paul moves counterclockwise and Saul moves clockwise. (Assume they walk at the same speed.)
   a. As Paul and Saul continue, what is the relationship between their x-coordinates?
   b. What is the relationship between Paul and Saul's y-coordinates?

6. Decide whether each statement is always true. Use what you have learned from Paul and Saul in Exercise 5.
   a. $\cos(-x) = -\cos x$ **b.** $\cos(-x) = \cos x$
   c. $\sin(-x) = -\sin x$ **d.** $\sin(-x) = \sin x$

On Your Own

7. Sketch accurate graphs of $y = \cos x$ and $y = \sin x$, where the domain of each is $-2\pi \le x \le 4\pi$.

Habits of Mind

Visualize. Think about Paul's walk. How many times around the circle would it be from -2π to 4π?

Answers

Exercises

1. A
2. **a.** 0.36; 0.64 **b.** ± 0.8
   c.

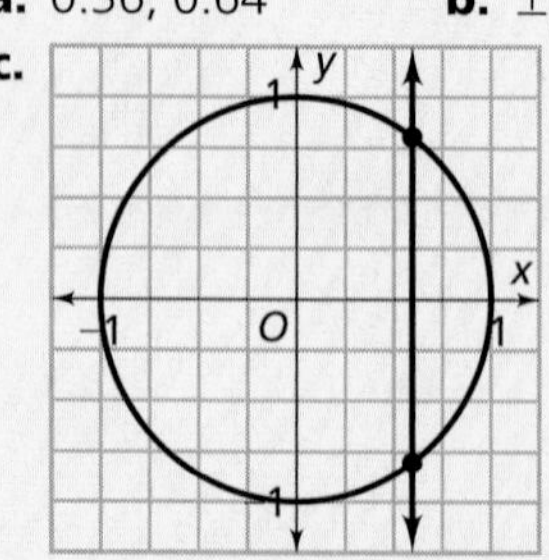

3. The solutions are approximately 0.9 and 5.4.

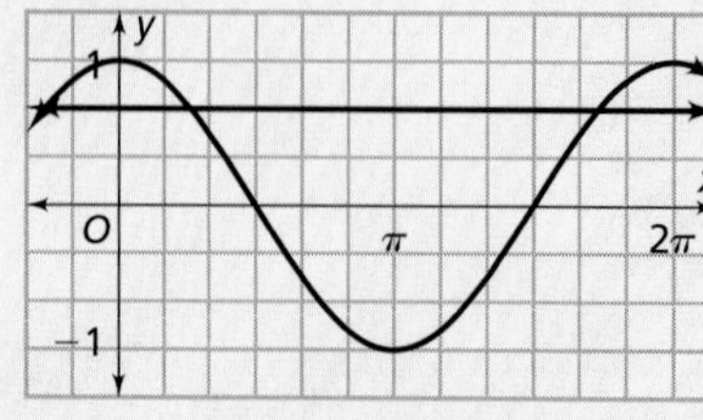

4. **a.** $\cos\left(-\frac{\pi}{2}\right) = 0$, $\sin\left(-\frac{\pi}{2}\right) = -1$
   b. $\cos\left(-\frac{\pi}{3}\right) = \frac{1}{2}$, $\sin\left(-\frac{\pi}{3}\right) = -\frac{\sqrt{3}}{2}$

5. **a.** They are equal.
   b. They are opposites.

6. **a.** not always **b.** always
   c. always **d.** not always

7.

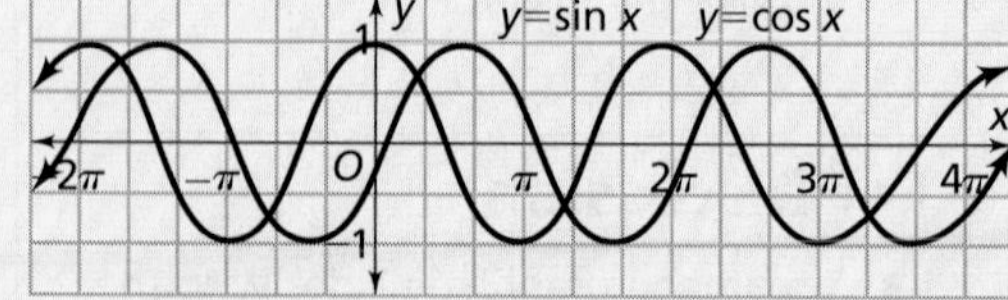

8. Paul starts at $(1, 0)$ and walks counterclockwise 24 radians along the unit circle. What quadrant is Paul in?

9. On the unit circle, show the two possible locations where $\sin x = 0.8$.

10. On the same axes, sketch these two graphs.

$$y = \sin x$$
$$y = 0.8$$

Use the graphs to estimate the two solutions to $\sin x = 0.8$ in the interval $0 \le x < 2\pi$.

11. Sketch the graph of the equation.

$$y = \sin\left(x + \frac{\pi}{2}\right)$$

12. Instead of graphing the arc length against the height, Olivia decides to make graphs of Paul's x- and y-coordinates against time (in seconds).

   a. Suppose Paul walks 1 meter per second. How would Olivia's graph compare to her graph of arc length against the height?

   b. Suppose Paul walks 2 meters per second. How would Olivia's graph compare to the graph from part (a)?

13. **Take It Further** Simplify the sum $\sin\frac{2\pi}{9} + \sin\frac{4\pi}{9} + \sin\frac{\pi}{3} + \cos\frac{\pi}{6} + \cos\frac{13\pi}{18} + \cos\frac{17\pi}{8}$

14. **Standardized Test Prep** Let x be the length of an arc on the unit circle in standard position. In which quadrants can the arc terminate if the product $(\cos x)(\sin x)$ is positive?

   A. I and II   **B.** I and III   **C.** I and IV   **D.** II and IV

Go Online PHSchool.com

For additional practice, go to **Web Code: bga-0103**

Maintain Your Skills

15. Find the corresponding radian measure for each of the following degree values.

   a. 30°   **b.** 150°   **c.** 210°   **d.** 330°   **e.** 390°

16. Find the corresponding measure in degrees for each of the following radian values.

   a. $\frac{\pi}{3}$ radians   **b.** $\frac{2\pi}{3}$ radians   **c.** $\frac{4\pi}{3}$ radians

   d. $\frac{5\pi}{3}$ radians   **e.** $\frac{7\pi}{3}$ radians

Remember...

The radian measure is the length of the arc on a unit circle cut by a central angle.

Additional Resources

PRINT RESOURCES

- Solution Manual
- Practice Workbook
- Assessment Resources
- Teaching Resources

TECHNOLOGY

- Interactive Textbook
- TeacherExpress CD-ROM
- ExamView CD-ROM
- PHSchool.com

Additional Practice

For Exercises 1–4, find the exact values. Do not use a calculator.

1. $\cos\frac{\pi}{6}$ and $\sin\frac{\pi}{6}$
2. $\cos\frac{5\pi}{6}$ and $\sin\frac{5\pi}{6}$
3. $\cos\frac{7\pi}{6}$ and $\sin\frac{7\pi}{6}$
4. $\cos\frac{11\pi}{6}$ and $\sin\frac{11\pi}{6}$

5. Which of the following values is the smallest?

   A. cos 2   **B.** cos 3   **C.** cos 5   **D.** cos 6

For Exercises 6–9, suppose $\pi < x < \frac{3\pi}{2}$. State whether each is positive or negative.

6. $\sin x$
7. $\cos x$
8. $\frac{\sin x}{\cos x}$
9. $\cos^2 x + \sin^2 x$

10. On the unit circle, draw an angle so that the intercepted arc has length equal to three units. Find the angle to the nearest tenth of a degree.

For Exercises 11–14, find the exact values. Do not use a calculator.

11. $\cos\left(-\frac{\pi}{6}\right)$ and $\sin\left(-\frac{\pi}{6}\right)$
12. $\cos\left(-\frac{2\pi}{3}\right)$ and $\sin\left(-\frac{2\pi}{3}\right)$
13. $\cos\left(-\frac{\pi}{4}\right)$ and $\sin\left(-\frac{\pi}{4}\right)$
14. $\cos\left(-\frac{5\pi}{6}\right)$ and $\sin\left(-\frac{5\pi}{6}\right)$

15. James starts at $(1, 0)$ and walks counterclockwise 19 radians along the unit circle. What quadrant is James in?

16. On the same axes, sketch these two graphs.

$$y = \cos x$$
$$y = 0.2$$

Use the graphs to estimate the two solutions to $\cos x = 0.2$ in the interval $0 \le x \le 2\pi$.

17. Sketch the graph of the equation on the interval $-2\pi \le x \le 2\pi$.

$$y = \cos\left(x + \frac{\pi}{2}\right)$$

Practice: For Lesson 1.3, assign Exercises 11–17.

8. Quadrant IV

9.

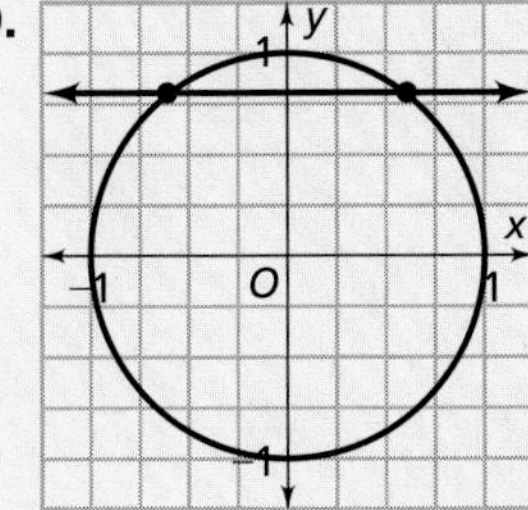

10. solutions: ≈0.9 and ≈2.2

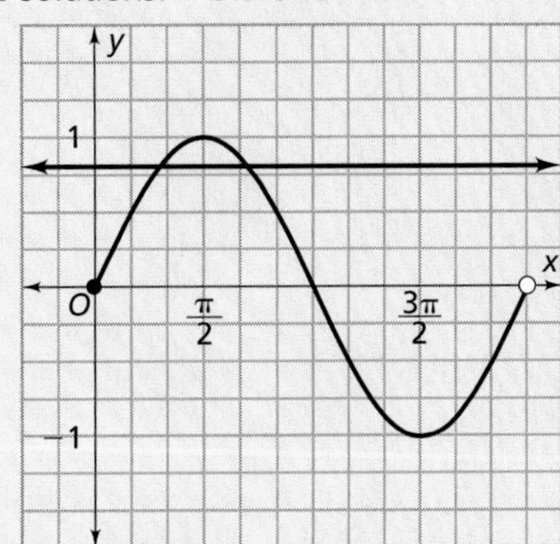

11.

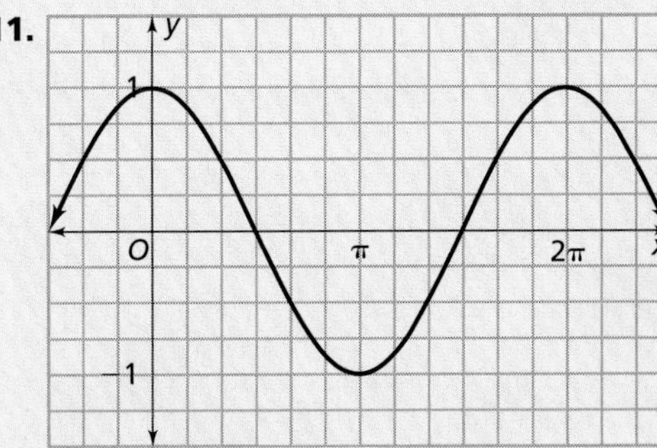

12. a. The graphs will be the same.

b. The period of the new graph will be half the period of the graph in part (a).

13. $\sqrt{3}$ **14.** B

15. a. $\frac{\pi}{6}$ **b.** $\frac{5\pi}{6}$ **c.** $\frac{7\pi}{6}$ **d.** $\frac{11\pi}{6}$ **e.** $\frac{13\pi}{6}$

16. a. 60°   **b.** 120°   **c.** 240°   **d.** 300°   **e.** 420°

Lesson Overview

GOAL

- Solve equations that involve cosine and sine.

In this lesson, students solve basic equations that include cosine or sine functions. The key idea is for students to solve these equations by "lumping" their work. First, replace a more complicated component of the equation with a simpler one. Then solve the simpler equation. Finally put back the component you replaced. Students should have seen this method in CME Project *Algebra 2.*

For cosine and sine functions, students see that there are usually two solutions within one period. They also see how to formulate an expression for all possible solutions.

CHECK YOUR UNDERSTANDING
- Core: 1, 2, 5
- Optional: 3, 4, 6
- Extension: 7, 8

MATERIALS
- graph paper
- graphing calculators
- Blackline Masters MC1, MC5

HOMEWORK
- Core: 9, 10, 12, 13, 15, 17
- Optional: 11, 14a, 18, 19
- Extension: 14b, 16

VOCABULARY
- Pythagorean identity

Launch

Review exercises 9 and 10 from Lesson 1.3. These exercises preview methods for solving equations with sine and cosine.

1.4 Solving Cosine and Sine Equations

To solve an equation involving a trigonometric function, you begin the same way you begin with an ordinary equation.

Minds in Action — episode 1

Tony and Sasha are trying to solve the equation $4 \sin x + 5 = 7$, *with x in radians.*

Tony I know we want to solve for x, but what do we do with $\sin x$?

Sasha Let's use the lumping-together technique from algebra.

Sasha goes to the board and covers up the $\sin x$ *with her hand.*

$$4 \text{ [hand] } + 5 = 7$$

Sasha See? It now looks like it's saying "4 times something plus 5 is 7." That sounds like a simple equation. So, if we let H stand for $\sin x$, we can write the equation as

$$4H + 5 = 7$$

Tony I know how to solve that ... $H = \frac{1}{2}$.

Sasha Right. And remember, H was just an alias for $\sin x$. So just replace H with $\sin x$ to get the new equation $\sin x = \frac{1}{2}$.

Tony And I know how to solve that, too. You just use the $\sin^{-1}$ function and get about 0.52.

Tony typed $\sin^{-1}(0.5)$ into his calculator. His calculator was in radian mode.

Sasha We can find the exact answer. Remember, $\frac{1}{2}$ is one of the ratios from a 30–60–90 triangle: $\sin 30^\circ = \frac{1}{2}$.

Tony And 30° corresponds to $\frac{\pi}{6}$ radians, and $\frac{\pi}{6}$ is about 0.52, the number I got before. So that's it, we're done!

Sasha Well, um, no. Look at this:

Sasha draws on the board.

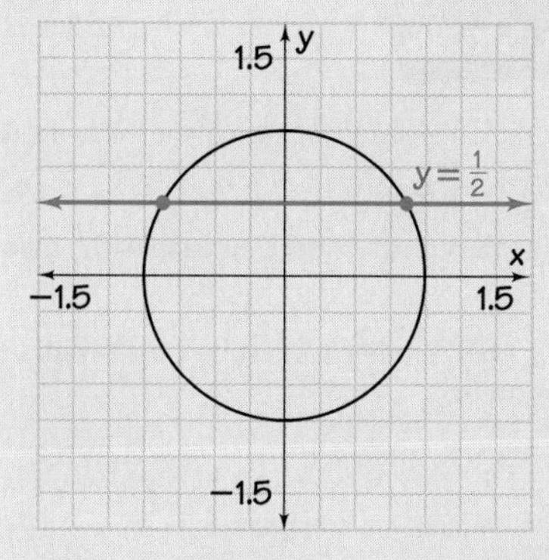

Sasha See? Sine is the y-coordinate, and there are *two* points on the unit circle whose y-coordinate is $\frac{1}{2}$.

Tony The point in the first quadrant is the solution we already got, $\frac{\pi}{6}$.

Sasha And the other solution is in the second quadrant. It's $\pi - \frac{\pi}{6} = \frac{5\pi}{6}$, which is about 2.62.

Tony Okay, so there are two answers. I wonder why the calculator only gave me one. Anyway, is that all?

Sasha That's all we'd find on the unit circle. So we can say at least that that's all between 0 and 2π.

By the end of this chapter, you will see why the calculator only gave Tony one answer.

For You to Do

1. Solve $-8 \cos x + 5 = 11$ for x between 0 and 2π radians.

Developing Habits of Mind

Extend the process. The unit circle makes it clear how many solutions there are between 0 and 2π. But if you lift that restriction, you will find infinitely many solutions to Tony and Sasha's equation.

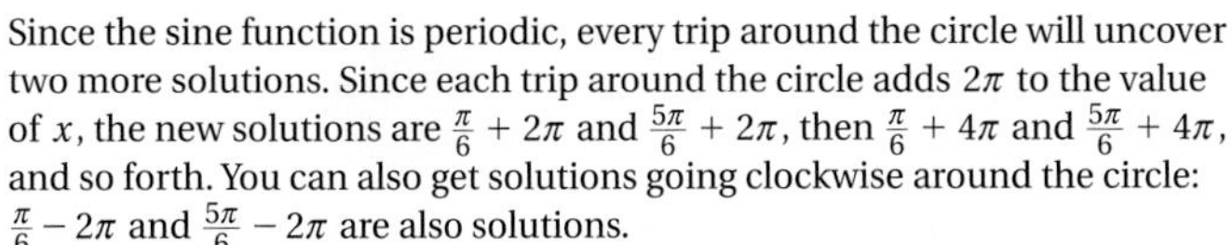

Since the sine function is periodic, every trip around the circle will uncover two more solutions. Since each trip around the circle adds 2π to the value of x, the new solutions are $\frac{\pi}{6} + 2\pi$ and $\frac{5\pi}{6} + 2\pi$, then $\frac{\pi}{6} + 4\pi$ and $\frac{5\pi}{6} + 4\pi$, and so forth. You can also get solutions going clockwise around the circle: $\frac{\pi}{6} - 2\pi$ and $\frac{5\pi}{6} - 2\pi$ are also solutions.

In the end, there are infinitely many solutions. They are of the form $\frac{\pi}{6} + 2\pi n$ and $\frac{5\pi}{6} + 2\pi n$ for all integer values of n.

For Discussion

2. Plot the equations $y = \sin x$ and $y = \frac{1}{2}$ on the same axes. How can you use your graphs to show all the solutions to $\sin x = \frac{1}{2}$?

Your may not actually *see* every solution, but your graph definitely suggests all the solutions.

Explore

You may wish to use Blackline Master MC1 on an overhead for much of the discussion.

For You to Do

PROBLEM 1 Make sure that students see that although their calculator gives them an answer, it does not give them all the answers. In Investigation 1B, students will look explicitly at the conventions calculators use for giving a single answer for inverse trigonometric functions. For now, it is sufficient to note that the sine of a radian measure in Quadrants I or II is positive and one in Quadrants III or IV is negative. The cosine of a radian measure in Quadrants I or IV is positive and one in Quadrants II or III is negative

Developing Habits of Mind

Have students connect the habits of mind in Developing Habits of Mind with the ways they have used their minds in prior mathematics work and/or in life outside the classroom. In this case, you might have them consider how a bus schedule gives a process over a given cycle but it really provides information for multiple cycles.

For Discussion

PROBLEM 2 Every place the graphs intersect shows a solution to the equation. Those intersections follow a regular pattern. The two points on one period of the graph repeat every 2π units to both the right and the left of the given period.

Answers

For You to Do

1. ≈ 2.42 and ≈ 3.86

For Discussion

2. The solutions in the interval from 0 to 2π are $\frac{\pi}{6}$ and $\frac{5\pi}{6}$. The other solutions can be found by adding to them numbers of the form $2\pi n$, where n is an integer.

Developing Habits of Mind

Have students connect the habits of mind in Developing Habits of Mind with the ways they have used their minds in prior mathematics work and/or in life outside the classroom. In this case, you might have them consider their strategy for doing a jigsaw puzzle.

Example

Spend time as needed going over the example. Make sure students understand the problem. As necessary, help them develop the detailed solution.

Developing Habits of Mind

Simplify complicated problems. Use the lumping idea that Sasha used to solve trigonometric equations that look like ordinary algebraic equations. For example, the equation

$$10 \sin^2 x - 3 \sin x = 4$$

is a quadratic equation in $\sin x$. That is, if you let $H = \sin x$, the equation becomes

$$10H^2 - 3H = 4$$

You can solve this equation like any other quadratic. When you find two values for H, replace H by $\sin x$ and then solve for x.

For You to Do

3. Solve the equation for all x, where $0 \le x < 2\pi$.

$$10 \sin^2 x - 3 \sin x = 4$$

Some trigonometry problems are not explicit equations, but ask you to relate cosine and sine for the same angle.

Example

Problem If $\sin \alpha = 0.4$, find all possible values of $\cos \alpha$.

Solution It might help to start with a picture. The figure below shows the two possible points where $\sin \alpha = 0.4$. So the possible values for $\cos \alpha$ will be the x-coordinates of those two points, which seem to be about ± 0.9.

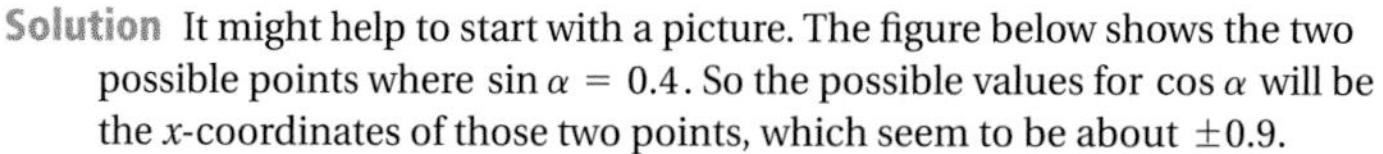

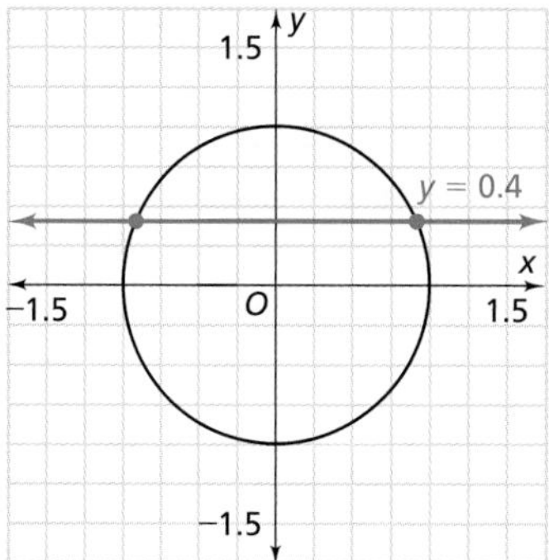

But how do you find the exact answers? You may recall the Pythagorean identity

$$\cos^2 \alpha + \sin^2 \alpha = 1$$

Answers

For You to Do

3. $\sin^{-1}\left(\frac{4}{5}\right) \approx 0.93$,
$\pi - \sin^{-1}\left(\frac{4}{5}\right) \approx 2.21$,
$\frac{7\pi}{6} \approx 3.67$, and
$\frac{11\pi}{6} \approx 5.76$

You can use this identity to find the exact answers. Since $\sin x = 0.4$, you have

$$\cos^2 x + (0.4)^2 = 1$$
$$\cos^2 x + 0.16 = 1$$
$$\cos^2 x = 0.84$$
$$\cos x = \pm\sqrt{0.84} = \pm\frac{\sqrt{21}}{5}$$

And $\frac{\sqrt{21}}{5} \approx 0.917$, which is close to the estimate from the graph.

For You to Do

4. If $3 \cos x + 4 = 2$, find all possible values of $\sin x$.

Developing Habits of Mind

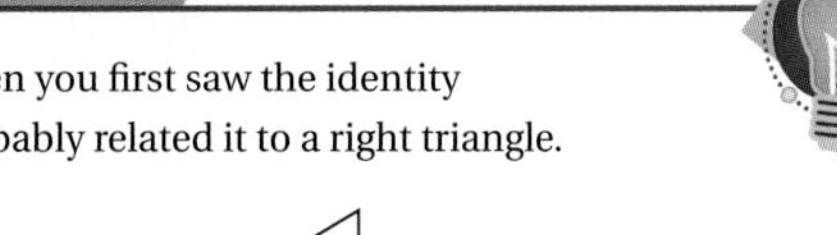

Look for relationships. When you first saw the identity $\cos^2 \theta + \sin^2 \theta = 1$, you probably related it to a right triangle.

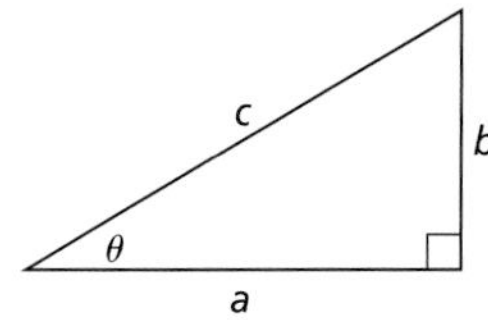

By the Pythagorean Theorem, you know that $a^2 + b^2 = c^2$. You can divide through by c^2 to get

$$\left(\frac{a}{c}\right)^2 + \left(\frac{b}{c}\right)^2 = 1$$

If θ is the angle opposite the side a, then $\cos \theta = \frac{a}{c}$ and $\sin \theta = \frac{b}{c}$. Substitution gives you the identity.

Another way to see the identity is to think about the unit circle. An equation for the unit circle is $x^2 + y^2 = 1$. But remember that any point on the circle is $(\cos \theta, \sin \theta)$. Substitute $\cos \theta$ for x and $\sin \theta$ for y and, you get the identity again.

For You to Do

PROBLEM 4 Have students practice the ideas just introduced by doing this problem.

Developing Habits of Mind

You may want to use Blackline Master MC5 on an overhead to illustrate the discussion.

Wrap Up

Give students time to work on the core Check Your Understanding exercises. Review them as a class.

Assessment Resources

Lesson Quiz 1.4

1. Find all the solutions to the equation $8 \sin x - 3 = 0$.
2. If $\cos \theta = \frac{5}{7}$, find the two possible values of $\sin \theta$.
3. Find all the solutions to the equation $2 \cos x - 8 = 0$.
4. a. What is the relationship between sin 35° and sin 145°?
   b. What is the relationship between cos 35° and cos 145°?

For You to Do

4. $\pm\frac{\sqrt{5}}{3}$

Exercises

HOMEWORK
- Core: 9, 10, 12, 13, 15, 17
- Optional: 11, 14a, 18, 19
- Extension: 14b, 16

Check Your Understanding

EXERCISE 6 The simplest solutions preview some ideas of period. Other acceptable solutions, especially for parts (d) and (e) include quadratic and cubic equations.

On Your Own

EXERCISE 10 previews the identities $\sin(-x) = -\sin x$ and $\cos(-x) = \cos x$.

Maintain Your Skills

EXERCISE 19 provides a good opportunity to discuss the close relationship between the solutions to $\sin x = k$ and $\cos x = k$. Students explore this relationship further in upcoming investigations as part of the co-function relationship $\cos x = \sin\left(\frac{\pi}{2} - x\right)$.

Exercises *Practicing Habits of Mind*

Check Your Understanding

1. If $0 \le x < 2\pi$, find the two possible values of x such that $\sin x = -\frac{1}{2}$.

2. Find all possible values of x so that $\sin x = -\frac{1}{2}$.

3. Suppose x is the length of an arc intercepted by an angle in Quadrant III and $\cos x = -0.65$. Find $\sin x$ to four decimal places.

4. If θ is degree measure, and $\sin\theta = \sin 50^\circ$, what are all possible values of θ?

5. If x is the length of an arc intercepted by an angle in Quadrant I, and $\sin x = 0.62$, find $\frac{\sin x}{\cos x}$ to two decimal places.

6. Let $0 \le x < 2\pi$. Find a trigonometric equation in x with the given number of solutions.

a. one solution **b.** two solutions **c.** 0 solutions

d. four solutions **e.** six solutions

7. Take It Further Find all solutions to this system of equations, if $0 \le \theta \le \pi$ and $0 \le \alpha \le \pi$.

$$4\sin\theta + \cos\alpha = 3$$
$$2\sin\theta + 4\cos\alpha = 5$$

8. Take It Further Suppose $\sin x = 2\cos x - 1$.
Find the two possible values of $\sin x$ if $0 \le x \le 2\pi$.

On Your Own

9. Find all solutions to the equation.

$$3\sin x + 4 = 0$$

10. a. Show, using a unit circle, that $\sin 20^\circ = \sin 160^\circ$.
b. What is the relationship between $\cos 20^\circ$ and $\cos 160^\circ$?

11. If θ is a degree measure, and $\cos\theta = \cos 50^\circ$, what are all possible values of θ?

12. If $\cos x = \frac{1}{3}$, find both possible values of $\sin x$.

13. If $\cos x = \frac{1}{3}$, find the two possible values of x between 0 and 2π.

Answers

Exercises

1. $\frac{7\pi}{6}$ and $\frac{11\pi}{6}$

2. all numbers of the forms $\frac{7\pi}{6} + 2\pi n$ and $\frac{11\pi}{6} + 2\pi n$, where n is an integer

3. -0.7599

4. all measures of the forms $50^\circ + 360^\circ n$ and $130^\circ + 360^\circ n$, where n is an integer

5. 0.79

6. a–e. Answers may vary. Samples are given.

a. $\sin x = 1$ **b.** $\sin x = \frac{1}{2}$

c. $\cos x = 2$ **d.** $\sin 2x = \frac{1}{2}$

e. $\sin 3x = \frac{1}{2}$

7. $\alpha = 0, \theta = \frac{\pi}{6}$ or $\alpha = 0, \theta = \frac{5\pi}{6}$

8. -1 and $\frac{3}{5}$

9. no solutions

10. a.

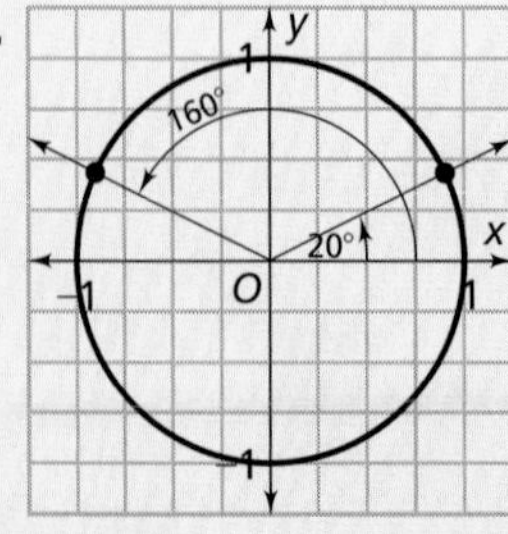

b. $\cos 160^\circ = -\cos 20^\circ$

11. $50^\circ + 360^\circ n$ and $310^\circ + 360^\circ n$, where n is an integer

12. $\pm\frac{2\sqrt{2}}{3}$

13. $x \approx 1.231$ and $x \approx 5.052$

14. The value of $\sin 56.3^\circ = 0.832$ to three decimal places.

   a. Find all possible angle measures θ, in degrees, for which $\sin\theta = 0.832$.

   b. **Take It Further** Find all possible angle measures θ, in degrees, for which $\cos\theta = 0.832$.

15. Find all solutions if $0 \le x < 2\pi$.

$$2\cos^2 x = \cos x$$

16. **Take It Further** Find all solutions.

$$\cos^2 x + \sin x = 1.$$

17. **Standardized Test Prep** If $\cos x = \frac{5}{13}$, which of the following could be the value of $\sin x$?

   A. $\frac{5}{12}$ B. $\frac{5}{13}$ C. $\frac{12}{13}$ D. $\frac{13}{5}$

Maintain Your Skills

18. Solve each equation if $0 \le x < 2\pi$.

   a. $\sin x = \frac{1}{2}$
   b. $\sin x = \frac{2}{3}$
   c. $\sin x = \frac{5}{3}$
   d. $5\sin x = 4$
   e. $3\sin x + 2 = 0$
   f. $3\sin x - 5 = 0$
   g. $(3\sin x + 2)(3\sin x - 5) = 0$

19. Solve each equation if $0 \le x < 2\pi$.

   a. $\cos x = \frac{1}{2}$
   b. $\cos x = \frac{2}{3}$
   c. $\cos x = \frac{5}{3}$
   d. $5\cos x = 4$
   e. $3\cos x + 2 = 0$
   f. $3\cos x - 5 = 0$
   g. $(3\cos x + 2)(3\cos x - 5) = 0$

The surface of the water intersects the circular paddlewheel in two places. A cross-section view would look similar to the graph of the Example on page 20.

For additional practice, go to Web Code: bga-0104

Additional Resources

PRINT RESOURCES
- Solution Manual
- Practice Workbook
- Assessment Resources
- Teaching Resources

TECHNOLOGY
- Interactive Textbook
- TeacherExpress CD-ROM
- ExamView CD-ROM
- PHSchool.com

Additional Practice

1. If $0 \le x < 2\pi$, find the two possible values of x such that $\cos x = -\frac{1}{2}$.

2. If θ is degree measure, and $\sin\theta = \sin 20^\circ$, what are all the possible values of θ?

In Exercises 3–6, let $0 \le x \le 2\pi$. Find all solutions to each equation.

3. $2\sin x + 5 = 0$
4. $3\sin x - 3 = 0$
5. $4\cos x - 2 = 0$
6. $2\cos x - \sqrt{3} = 0$

7. If $\cos x = \frac{1}{5}$, find both possible values of $\sin x$.

8. If $\cos x = \frac{1}{5}$, find the two possible values of x between 0 and 2π.

9. The value of $\sin 42.7^\circ = 0.678$ to three decimal places.
   a. Find all possible angles θ, in degrees, for which $\sin\theta = 0.678$.
   b. Find all possible angles θ, in degrees, for which $\cos\theta = 0.678$.

10. What are the maximum and minimum values of the slope of the graph of $y = \cos x$, and where does each occur?

11. a. For what values of x, where $-2\pi \le x \le 2\pi$, is the function $f(x) = \sin x$ maximum?
    b. For what values of x, where $-2\pi \le x \le 2\pi$, is the function $f(x) = \sin x$ minimum?

12. a. Sketch the graph of $y = 3\sin x + 2$ on the interval $0 \le x \le 2\pi$.
    b. Find the minimum and maximum.
    c. What input(s) are turning points?

13. a. Sketch the graph of $y = 4\cos x - 3$ on the interval $0 \le x \le 2\pi$.
    b. Find the minimum and maximum.
    c. What input(s) are turning points?

Practice: For Lesson 1.4, assign Exercises 1–9.

14. a. $\theta \approx 56.3^\circ + 360^\circ n$ and $\theta \approx 123.7^\circ + 360^\circ n$, where n is an integer

b. $\theta \approx 33.7^\circ + 360^\circ n$ and $\theta \approx 326.7^\circ + 360^\circ n$, where n is an integer

15. $\frac{\pi}{3}, \frac{\pi}{2}, \frac{3\pi}{2}, \frac{5\pi}{3}$

16. πn and $\frac{\pi}{2} + 2\pi n$, where n is an integer

17. C

18. a. $\frac{\pi}{6}$ and $\frac{5\pi}{6}$

b. $\sin^{-1}\left(\frac{2}{3}\right) \approx 0.7297$ and $\pi - \sin^{-1}\left(\frac{2}{3}\right) \approx 2.4119$

c. no solutions

d. $\sin^{-1}\left(\frac{4}{5}\right) \approx 0.9273$ and $\pi - \sin^{-1}\left(\frac{4}{5}\right) \approx 2.2143$

e. $\pi - \sin^{-1}\left(-\frac{2}{3}\right) \approx 3.8713$ and $2\pi + \sin^{-1}\left(-\frac{2}{3}\right) \approx 5.5535$

f. no solutions

g. $\pi - \sin^{-1}\left(-\frac{2}{3}\right) \approx 3.8713$ and $2\pi + \sin^{-1}\left(-\frac{2}{3}\right) \approx 5.5535$

19. a. $\frac{\pi}{3}$ and $\frac{5\pi}{3}$

b. $\cos^{-1}\left(\frac{2}{3}\right) \approx 0.8411$ and $2\pi - \cos^{-1}\left(\frac{2}{3}\right) \approx 5.4421$

c. no solutions

d. $\cos^{-1}\left(\frac{4}{5}\right) \approx 0.6435$ and $2\pi - \cos^{-1}\left(\frac{4}{5}\right) \approx 5.6397$

e. $\cos^{-1}\left(-\frac{2}{3}\right) \approx 2.3005$ and $2\pi - \cos^{-1}\left(-\frac{2}{3}\right) \approx 3.9827$

f. no solutions

g. $\cos^{-1}\left(-\frac{2}{3}\right) \approx 2.3005$ and $2\pi - \cos^{-1}\left(-\frac{2}{3}\right) \approx 3.9827$

Lesson Overview

GOAL

- Estimate the slope of the graphs of the cosine and sine functions at a given point.

In this lesson, students experiment with the slope of a secant line through two points on the graph of $\sin x$. They explore the limit of that slope as one of the points converges upon the other. Students examine the fact that if $f(x) = \sin x$, then $f'(x) = \cos x$.

CHECK YOUR UNDERSTANDING
- Core: 1, 3, 4
- Optional: 2, 5a
- Extension: 5b

MATERIALS
- geometry software
- graph paper
- graphing calculators
- Blackline Masters MC2, MC3

HOMEWORK
- Core: 6, 9, 10, 11, 13, 14
- Optional: 7, 8
- Extension: 12

VOCABULARY
- decreasing
- increasing
- secant line
- turning point

Launch

Have students dive right into the construction in the In-Class Experiment.

Explore

In-Class Experiment

In this experiment, students approximate the slope of a line tangent to a curve at a point. Formally, the definition of a line tangent to the function f at point x is the line through point x with slope $f'(x)$.

You may want to use Blackline Master MC3 on an overhead to demonstrate some parts of this activity.

This lesson, and this experiment, informally develops this relationship without specifically identifying the derivative.

This experiment and the For You to Do problem that follows will take at least 20 minutes, but it is worth it!

1.5 Analyzing Graphs

When you draw the graphs of linear functions, an important property of the graph is the slope of the line. And the most important property of a line is that it has constant slope: pick any two points on the line and calculate the slope between them, and you will always get the same value.

Only lines have constant slope. But you can think about slope for non-linear functions: you can pick any two points on the graph of any function and calculate the slope between them. But those two points can be anywhere on the graph, so the only information you will get is that comparing several calculations of these slopes can tell you that a function is not linear.

To analyze a graph, it is most useful to think of the slope of a curve at a single point. But how do you calculate slope if you are only considering one point?

In-Class Experiment

In this experiment, you will use your graphing calculator or geometry software to analyze the graph of $y = \sin x$.

Make a figure following these steps.

Step 1 Draw the graph of $y = \sin x$.

Step 2 Put two points on the graph. Label them A and B. Test to make sure the points are on your graph by dragging them around. You should not be able to move them off of your graph.

Step 3 Construct the line through points A and B.

Step 4 Measure the slope of $\overleftrightarrow{AB}$.

See the TI-Nspire Handbook on p. 704 for details on how to make this construction.

A line that contains two points of a graph is called a secant line.

Keep point A constant—that will be the point you are analyzing. Move point B slowly toward A, observing the slope. Your goal is to estimate the slope of the line when the two points are as close as the software allows you to make them. In some cases, you may get the two points to coincide, making the line and slope disappear. If that happens, move point B off until the line reappears, and record that slope value as your estimate.

For You to Do

1. Copy and complete the following table by estimating the slope at each value of x to three decimal places. You can use the symmetry of the graph of $f(x) = \sin x$ to help make this task less daunting.

x	$\sin x$	Slope
0	0	■
$\frac{\pi}{6}$	$\frac{1}{2}$	■
$\frac{\pi}{4}$	■	■
$\frac{\pi}{3}$	$\frac{\sqrt{3}}{2}$	■
$\frac{\pi}{2}$	1	■
$\frac{2\pi}{3}$	■	■
$\frac{3\pi}{4}$	$\frac{\sqrt{2}}{2}$	■
$\frac{5\pi}{6}$	■	■
π	■	■
$\frac{7\pi}{6}$	■	■
$\frac{5\pi}{4}$	$-\frac{\sqrt{2}}{2}$	■
$\frac{4\pi}{3}$	■	■
$\frac{3\pi}{2}$	-1	■
$\frac{5\pi}{3}$	■	■
$\frac{7\pi}{4}$	■	■
$\frac{11\pi}{6}$	$-\frac{1}{2}$	■
2π	0	■

When analyzing the graph of $f(x) = \sin x$ or $g(x) = \cos x$, start with inputs like $x = \frac{\pi}{4}$ or $x = \frac{2\pi}{3}$.

As the experiment suggests, you can find the slope of a curve at a particular point A by finding the limit of the slope of a secant $\overleftrightarrow{AB}$, where B is also on the curve, as B gets close to A.

A formal definition requires some ideas of calculus that you will see in Chapter 3.

Answers

For You to Do

1. See back of book.

For You to Do

PROBLEM 1 Encourage students to use symmetry to speed up their work. They may also want to divide the tasks among a group. You may wish to provide copies of Blackline Master MC2 for students to fill in the table.

Wrap Up

Review the students' entries in the table. Then have them begin on the Check Your Understanding exercises.

Assessment Resources

Lesson Quiz 1.5

1. a. For what inputs is $\cos x$ decreasing on the interval $0 \le x \le 2\pi$?
   b. What is the slope of $y = \cos x$ at $x = \pi$?
   c. What is the slope of $y = \cos x$ at $x = \frac{\pi}{2}$?
2. a. Sketch the graph of $y = \sin(x + \pi)$ on $0 \le x \le 2\pi$.
   b. At what x values do the maximum and minimum occur?
   c. For what inputs is the function increasing?
3. Consider the function $y = 4 \sin x + 2$.
   a. What are the maximum and minimum values of this function?
   b. At what x values do the maximum and minimum occur?

Exercises

HOMEWORK
- Core: 6, 9, 10, 11, 13, 14
- Optional: 7, 8
- Extension: 12

Check Your Understanding

You may want to use Blackline Master MC3 on an overhead to illustrate several of the exercises. You may also wish to provide copies for students to use.

EXERCISE 1 previews the idea that if $f'(x) = 0$, then $f(x)$ is a local extrema (either maximum or minimum).

EXERCISE 3 is the most important exercise in this lesson.

EXERCISE 4 previews the first derivative of the sine function. Students will work more closely with this concept in Chapter 3.

EXERCISE 5 exploits the identity $\sin^2 x + \cos^2 x = 1$. Furthermore, students may notice that the graph of d looks like the basic graph of $\cos x$. The double-angle formula confirms this observation, $\cos^2 x - \sin^2 x = \cos 2x$.

EXERCISE 9 You may wish to provide copies of Blackline Master MC2 for students to fill in the table.

Exercises *Practicing Habits of Mind*

Check Your Understanding

1. When the graph of the sine function reaches a maximum or minimum value, what happens to the slope of its graph there?

2. What are the maximum and minimum values of the slope of the graph of $y = \sin x$, and where does each occur? Could you answer this question by looking at a graph of the sine function?

3. a. Zoom in on the graph of $y = \sin x$ near $x = 0$. What specific line does the graph begin to look like?

b. What is the slope of the graph of $\sin x$ at $x = 0$?

4. a. By plotting points, sketch the graph of function s, where $s(x)$ is the slope of $y = \sin x$ at input x.

b. What function most closely matches the values of s?

5. a. Sketch the graphs of the following two functions on the same axes.

$$d(x) = \cos^2 x - \sin^2 x$$
$$e(x) = \cos^4 x - \sin^4 x$$

b. Take It Further Explain how the functions d and e relate.

On Your Own

6. a. For what value of x, where $0 \le x < 2\pi$, is the function $f(x) = \cos x$ a maximum?

b. For what value of x, where $0 \le x < 2\pi$, is the function $f(x) = \cos x$ a minimum?

c. How do these values compare to the maximums and minimums of the sine function?

7. a. For what inputs is the sine function increasing?

b. For what inputs is the sine function decreasing?

c. For what inputs is the cosine function increasing?

A function f is **increasing** on an interval if, for any two values in the interval a and b, $a < b$ implies $f(a) < f(b)$.

A function f is **decreasing** on an interval if, for any two values in the interval a and b, $a < b$ implies $f(a) > f(b)$.

Answers

Exercises

1. The slope is 0.

2. The maximum slope is 1, and it occurs where $x = 2\pi n$ (n an integer). The minimum slope is -1, and it occurs where $x = (2n + 1)\pi$ (n an integer). You can estimate these maximum and minimum slopes by examining the graph of $y = \sin x$.

3. a. $y = x$

b. 1

4. a. The graph should look the same as the graph of $y = \cos x$.

b. the cosine function

5. a.

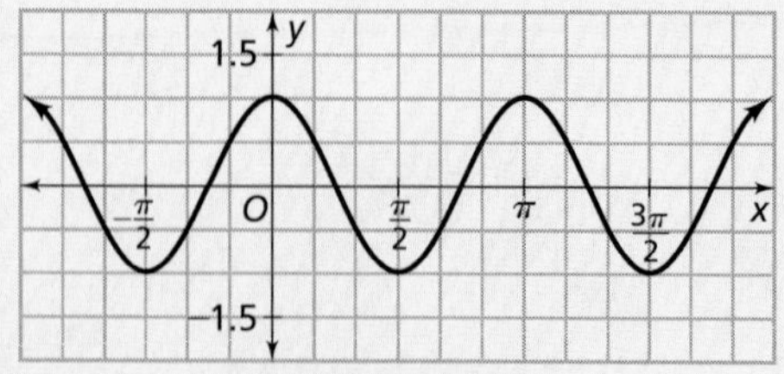

b. The functions have the same value for each value of x since $\cos^4 x - \sin^4 x = (\cos^2 x + \sin^2 x)(\cos^2 x - \sin^2 x) = \cos^2 x - \sin^2 x$.

6. a. $x = 0$ **b.** $x = \pi$

c. The values of x where the maximum and minimum of $y = \sin x$ occur are, respectively, $\frac{\pi}{2}$ units greater than those for $y = \cos x$.

7. a. in intervals of the form $\left[-\frac{\pi}{2} + 2\pi n, \frac{\pi}{2} + 2\pi n\right]$, where n is an integer

b. in intervals of the form $\left[\frac{\pi}{2} + 2\pi n, \frac{3\pi}{2} + 2\pi n\right]$, where n is an integer

c. in intervals of the form $[\pi + 2\pi n, 2\pi + 2\pi n]$, where n is an integer

8. A **turning point** for a function is an input x where the function changes from increasing to decreasing, or from decreasing to increasing.

Sometimes the phrase turning point refers instead to the actual coordinates $(x, f(x))$ of the point where this change occurs.

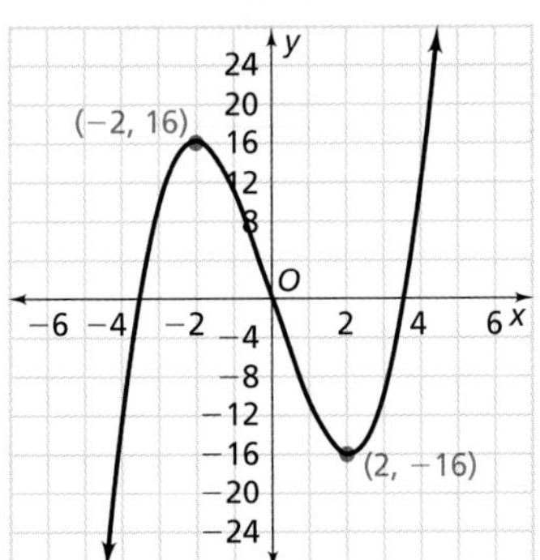

The turning points of $f(x) = x^3 - 12x$ are 2 and −2.

a. What inputs are turning points for the sine function?

b. What inputs are turning points for the cosine function?

9. Repeat the In-Class Experiment on page 24 and Problem 1 on page 25 for the function $g(x) = \cos x$. Then sketch the graph of the function r, where $r(x)$ is the slope of g at input x. What function matches the table for r?

10. Sketch the graphs of the two functions $a(x) = \cos^2 x$ and $b(x) = \sin^2 x$ on the same axes.

11. Without graphing, describe the shape of the graph of $c(x) = a(x) + b(x)$, where $a(x)$ and $b(x)$ are the functions in Exercise 10.

12. **Take it Further** Sketch a reasonably accurate graph of $k(x) = 2^{\sin x}$.

13. **Standardized Test Prep** Given $0 < a < b < 17$, which of the following is the maximum value of $a \sin x + b$?

A. $a + b$ **B.** $b - a$ **C.** $-(a + b)$ **D.** 17

Go Online PHSchool.com

For additional practice, go to **Web Code:** bga-0105

Maintain Your Skills

14. Sketch the graph of each equation on the interval $0 \le x \le 2\pi$ and find the maximum and minimum.

a. $y = 5 \sin x$
b. $y = 5 \sin x + 7$
c. $y = 5 \sin x - 7$
d. $y = 10 \sin x + 5$
e. $y = A \sin x + B$

The **maximum** of a graph is the highest value achieved on the vertical axis. The **minimum** of a graph is the lowest.

Additional Resources

PRINT RESOURCES
- Solution Manual
- Practice Workbook
- Assessment Resources
- Teaching Resources

TECHNOLOGY
- Interactive Textbook
- TeacherExpress CD-ROM
- ExamView CD-ROM
- PHSchool.com

Additional Practice

1. If $0 \le x < 2\pi$, find the two possible values of x such that $\cos x = -\frac{1}{2}$.

2. If θ is degree measure, and $\sin \theta = \sin 20°$, what are all the possible values of θ?

In Exercises 3–6, let $0 \le x \le 2\pi$. Find all solutions to each equation.

3. $2 \sin x + 5 = 0$
4. $3 \sin x - 3 = 0$
5. $4 \cos x - 2 = 0$
6. $2 \cos x - \sqrt{3} = 0$

7. If $\cos x = \frac{1}{5}$, find both possible values of $\sin x$.

8. If $\cos x = \frac{1}{5}$, find the two possible values of x between 0 and 2π.

9. The value of $\sin 42.7° = 0.678$ to three decimal places.
   a. Find all possible angles θ, in degrees, for which $\sin \theta = 0.678$.
   b. Find all possible angles θ, in degrees, for which $\cos \theta = 0.678$.

10. What are the maximum and minimum values of the slope of the graph of $y = \cos x$, and where does each occur?

11. a. For what values of x, where $-2\pi \le x \le 2\pi$, is the function $f(x) = \sin x$ maximum?
    b. For what values of x, where $-2\pi \le x \le 2\pi$, is the function $f(x) = \sin x$ minimum?

12. a. Sketch the graph of $y = 3 \sin x + 2$ on the interval $0 \le x \le 2\pi$.
    b. Find the minimum and maximum.
    c. What input(s) are turning points?

13. a. Sketch the graph of $y = 4 \cos x - 3$ on the interval $0 \le x \le 2\pi$.
    b. Find the minimum and maximum.
    c. What input(s) are turning points?

Practice: For Lesson 1.5, assign Exercises 10–13.

8. a. $x = \frac{\pi}{2} + \pi n$ (n an integer)
b. $x = \pi n$ (n an integer)

9. See back of book.

10.

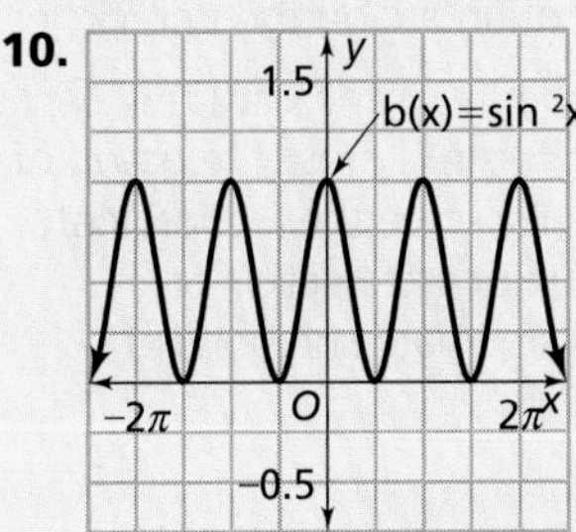

11. The graph of $c(x)$ is the same as the graph of $y = 1$.

12.

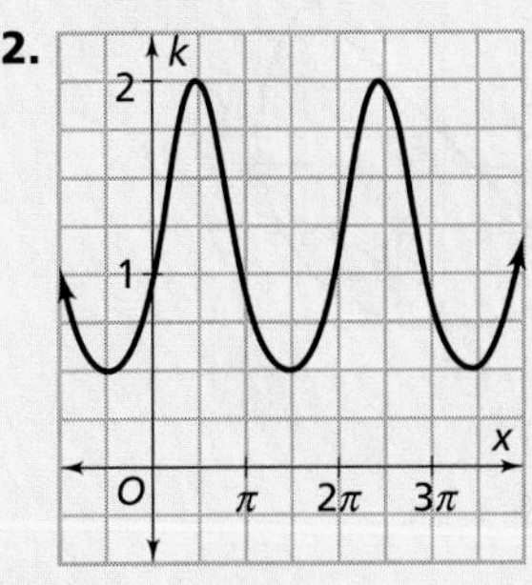

13. A

14. a. maximum = 5, minimum = −5

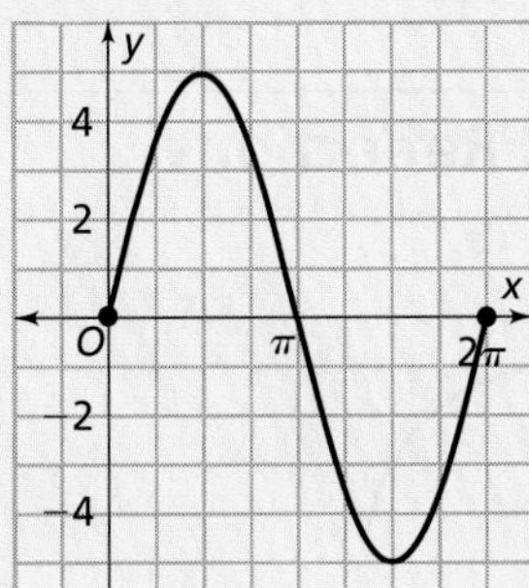

b–d. See back of book.
e. maximum = $|A| + B$, minimum = $-|A| + B$

Mathematical Reflections

EXERCISES 6–8 At the start of the Investigation, you may have assigned these as Questions 1–3 for students to think and write about.

In this investigation, you learned what radians are and how they relate to degrees. You graphed the cosine and sine functions. You solved equations involving these trigonometric functions. The following questions will help you summarize what you have learned.

1. a. What angle measure corresponds to $\frac{9\pi}{2}$ radians?
   b. For what value of x, where $0 \leq x < 2\pi$, will both $\cos x = \cos \frac{9\pi}{2}$ and $\sin x = \sin \frac{9\pi}{2}$?
2. a. On a unit circle, locate approximately the point with coordinates $(\cos 3, \sin 3)$.
   b. Estimate the values of $\cos 3$ and $\sin 3$.
   c. Use a calculator to find the values of $\cos 3$ and $\sin 3$ to four decimal places.
3. a. Using a unit circle, identify the places where cosine and sine are equal.
   b. Find all angle measures θ, where $0 \leq \theta < 2\pi$, such that $\cos \theta = \sin \theta$.
4. Using the graphs of cosine and sine on the interval $0 \leq x < 2\pi$, find all values of x such that $\cos x = \sin x$.
5. Find all solutions if $0 \leq x < 2\pi$.

   $$\sin x \cos x - 2 \sin x = \sin x$$
6. Where are the turning points of the cosine and sine functions?
7. What is a radian?
8. How can you use a graph of $y = \sin x$ to estimate solutions to the equation $\sin x = -0.6$?

Vocabulary

In this investigation, you learned these terms. Make sure you understand what each one means and how to use it.

- **arc**
- **central angle**
- **decreasing**
- **increasing**
- **period**
- **periodic function**
- **Pythagorean identity**
- **radian**
- **secant line**
- **turning point**

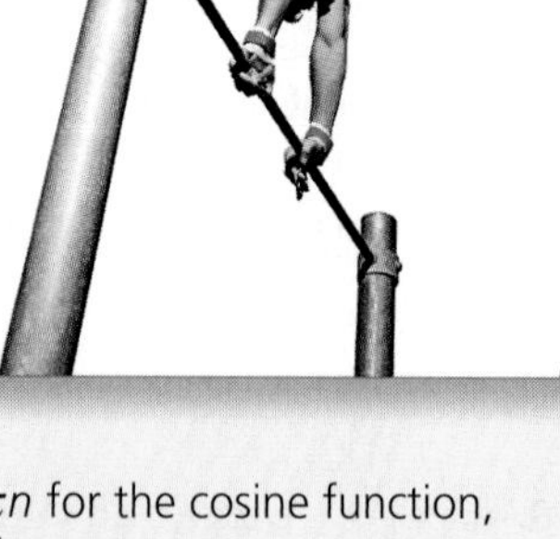

Many athletic activities involve circular motion.

Answers

Mathematical Reflections

1. a. 810° b. $\frac{\pi}{2}$
2. a.

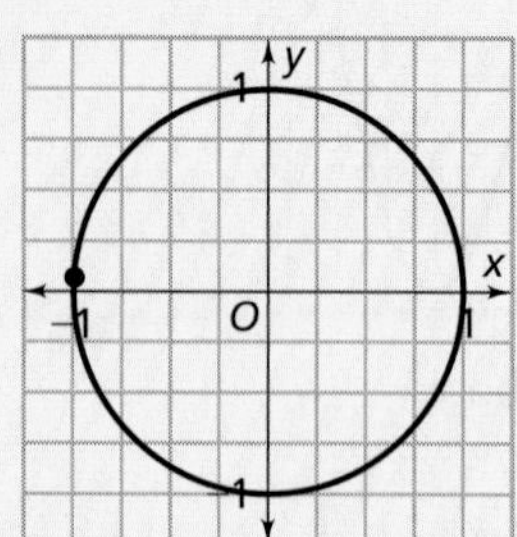

   b. Answers may vary. Sample: $\cos 3 \approx -0.9$, $\sin 3 \approx 0.1$
   c. $\cos 3 \approx -0.9900$, $\sin 3 \approx 0.1411$
3. a.

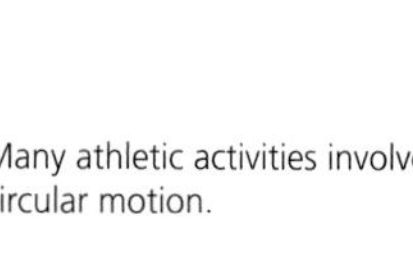

   b. $\frac{\pi}{4}$ and $\frac{5\pi}{4}$
4. See back of book.
5. 0 and π
6. at $x = \pi n$ for the cosine function, at $x = \frac{\pi}{2} + \pi n$ for the sine function, where n is an integer
7. the length of an arc on the unit circle
8. In the coordinate plane with the graph of $y = \sin x$, draw the graph of $y = -0.6$. Estimate the x-coordinates of the points of intersection to get the approximate solutions of $\sin x = -0.6$.

Mid-Chapter Test

Go Online PHSchool.com — For a mid-chapter test, go to Web Code: bga-0152

Multiple Choice

1. Simplify $\sin\frac{7\pi}{6}\cdot\sin\frac{5\pi}{6}-\cos\frac{7\pi}{6}\cdot\cos\frac{5\pi}{6}$.

   A. 1 B. $-\cos 2\pi$ C. $\sin\pi$ D. 2π

2. The graph below represents which of the following functions?

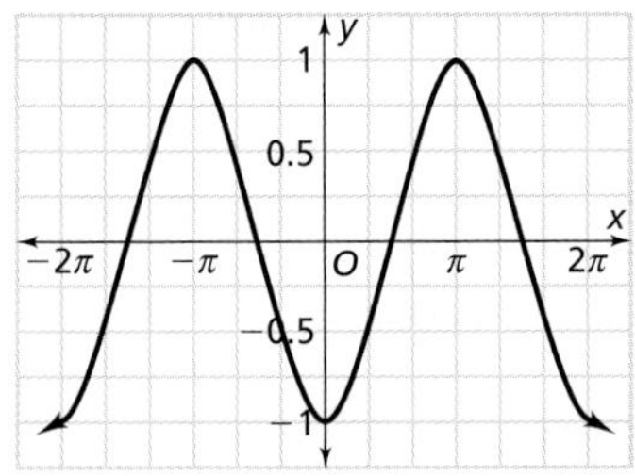

   A. $y=\sin x$ B. $y=\sin\left(x+\frac{\pi}{2}\right)$
   C. $y=\cos x$ D. $y=\sin\left(x-\frac{\pi}{2}\right)$

3. Which system of equations does the graph represent?

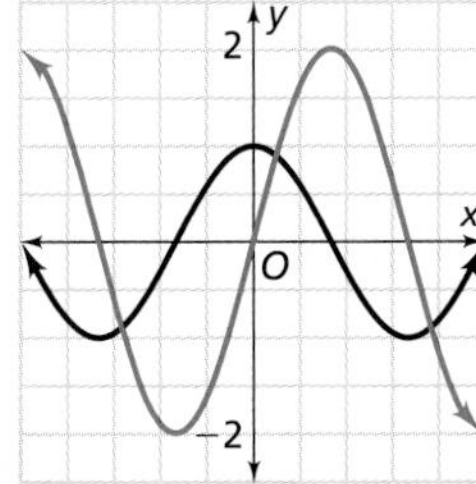

   A. $y=\sin x$, $y=\cos x$ B. $y=2\sin x$, $y=x$
   C. $y=2\sin x$, $y=\cos x$ D. $y=-\sin x$, $y=2\sin x$

4. Simplify $\sin\left(-\frac{\pi}{6}\right)$.

   A. $\sin\frac{\pi}{6}$ B. $-\cos\frac{\pi}{3}$ C. $\frac{1}{2}$ D. $\frac{\sqrt{3}}{2}$

5. Simplify $\cos 360^\circ+\frac{3}{2}\cos 0^\circ+\sqrt{2}\cos 45^\circ$.

   A. 0 B. $\frac{1}{2}$ C. $\frac{7}{2}$ D. -3

6. Which expression gives all possible solutions to the equation

$$\cos x=-\frac{1}{2}$$

   if k can represent any integer?

   A. $120^\circ+k360^\circ$ B. $\frac{2\pi}{3}+2k\pi$
   C. $120^\circ+k360^\circ$ and $240^\circ+k360^\circ$ D. $\frac{2\pi}{3}$ and $\frac{4\pi}{3}$

Open Response

7. For each radian value, find the corresponding degree measure.

   a. $\frac{\pi}{6}$ b. $\frac{5\pi}{3}$ c. 2π d. $\frac{7\pi}{6}$

8. Find the maximum and minimum values of the slope of the graph of $f(x)=\cos x$. Where does each occur?

9. Sketch the graph of $y=6\sin x+2$ on the interval $0\le x\le 2\pi$ and find the maximum and minimum.

10. Solve the equation $-\sin x=\frac{1}{2}$ on $-\frac{\pi}{2}\le x\le\frac{3\pi}{2}$.

11. If $0<x<\pi$, is $\sin x$ always positive or always negative? What about $\cos x$? Explain your reasoning.

12. What inputs are turning points for the function $f(x)=2\sin x$ on $-\pi\le x\le\pi$?

Challenge Problem

13. Find all solutions to $2\cos^2 x-5\cos x+2=0$.

Mid-Chapter Test

EXERCISE 1 The addition formulas lead to $-\cos\left(\frac{7}{6}\pi+\frac{5}{6}\pi\right)=-\cos 2\pi$.

Assessment Resources

Mid-Chapter Test page 1 of 3

Multiple Choice

1. Philippe runs in a counterclockwise direction around a circular track that has a radius of 15 meters. He starts from the point (0, 15).

   After running $\frac{7\pi}{2}$ radians along the track, at what point is Philippe?

   A. (0, −15) B. (−15, 0) C. (0, −1) D. (15, 0)

2. Simplify.

$$\cos\frac{3\pi}{2}-\sin\frac{\pi}{2}+\cos\pi-\sin\frac{3\pi}{2}+\cos 2\pi$$

   A. 1 B. 2
   C. −2 D. none of the above

3. Simplify $\sin\left(-\frac{\pi}{3}\right)$.

   A. $\sin\frac{\pi}{3}$ B. $\cos\frac{\pi}{3}$ C. $\frac{1}{2}$ D. $-\frac{\sqrt{3}}{2}$

4. The graph below represents which one of the following functions?

   A. $y=\cos\left(x-\frac{\pi}{2}\right)$ B. $y=\sin\left(x+\frac{\pi}{2}\right)$
   C. $y=\cos x+1$ D. $y=\sin\left(x-\frac{\pi}{2}\right)$

Also available: Form B

Mid-Chapter Test

1. B 2. D 3. B
4. C 5. C 6. C
7. a. 30° b. 300°
   c. 360° d. 210°
8. The maximum slope, 1, occurs when $x=\frac{3\pi}{2}+2\pi n$ (n an integer). The minimum slope, −1, occurs when $x=\frac{\pi}{2}+2\pi n$ (n an integer).
9. maximum = 8, minimum = −4

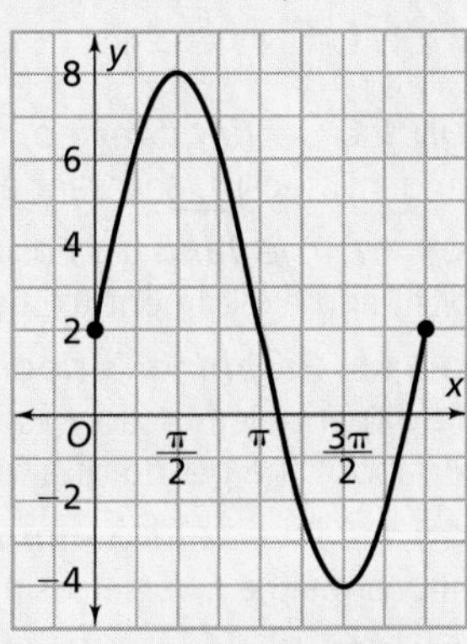

10. $-\frac{\pi}{6}$ and $\frac{7\pi}{6}$
11. The value of $\sin x$ is always positive for $0<x<\pi$ since on the unit circle, $(\cos x, \sin x)$ is a point above the x-axis. The value of $\cos x$ is positive for $0<x<\frac{\pi}{2}$, 0 for $x=\frac{\pi}{2}$, and negative for $\frac{\pi}{2}<x<\pi$. This is true because these three cases correspond to the situations in which, respectively, $(\cos x, \sin x)$ is to the right of, on, or to the left of the y-axis.
12. $-\frac{\pi}{2}$ and $\frac{\pi}{2}$
13. The solutions are the numbers $\frac{\pi}{3}+2\pi n$ and $\frac{5\pi}{3}+2\pi n$ (n an integer).

Investigation Overview

Investigation 1B introduces the tangent functions and the three reciprocal functions: secant, cosecant, and cotangent. Students review the graphs of these functions, learn about how each function can be demonstrated on the unit circle, and work with some basic identities. They also review the definitions of an inverse function and a one-to-one function. They learn how to restrict the domain of cosine, sine, and tangent in order to define their inverses.

You may wish to assign Questions 1–3 for students to think and write about during the investigation.

Learning Goals

- Understand several relationships between the tangent function and the unit circle.
- Sketch and describe the graph of the tangent function.
- Define an inverse of cosine, sine, and tangent.
- Recognize three other trigonometric functions: secant, cosecant, and cotangent.

Habits and Skills

- Use the unit circle to generate the graph of $y = \tan x$.
- Visualize geometrically the tangent and secant functions.
- Restrict the domain of a function to make it one-to-one.
- Solve equations and prove identities using trigonometric functions.

Other Trigonometric Functions

In *Other Trigonometric Functions*, you will study the tangent function and draw its graph. You will define the inverse cosine, sine, and tangent functions. You will also learn about the three other trigonometric functions: secant, cosecant, and cotangent.

By the end of this investigation, you will be able to answer questions like these.

1. How are the six trigonometric functions defined?
2. Why does the $\sin^{-1}$ function on a calculator only return results between $-\frac{\pi}{2}$ and $\frac{\pi}{2}$?
3. How many solutions are there to the equation $\cos x = 0.8$?

You will learn how to

- understand several relationships between the tangent function and the unit circle
- sketch and describe the graph of the tangent function
- define an inverse of cosine, sine, and tangent
- recognize three other trigonometric functions: secant, cosecant, and cotangent

You will develop these habits and skills:

- Use the unit circle to generate the graph of $y = \tan x$.
- Visualize geometrically the tangent and secant functions.
- Restrict the domain of a function to make it one-to-one.
- Solve equations and prove identities using trigonometric functions.

Since the column and its shadow form a right angle, you can use elementary trigonometry to calculate its height.

Investigation Road Map

LESSON 1.6, ***Getting Started,*** reviews the concept of inverse functions, and defines the tangent, secant, cosecant and cotangent functions.

LESSON 1.7, ***The Tangent Function,*** has students formally review the tangent function, and experiment to see how to describe the tangent using the unit circle.

LESSON 1.8, ***Graphing Periodic Functions,*** has students further explore the graphs of periodic functions, specifically tangent. They review asymptotes and think further about the period of a function.

LESSON 1.9, ***Inverse Trigonometric Functions,*** introduces students to formal definitions for the inverse cosine, sine, and tangent functions.

LESSON 1.10, ***Reciprocal Trigonometric Functions,*** reviews the three other common trigonometric functions: secant, cosecant and cotangent.

1.6 Getting Started

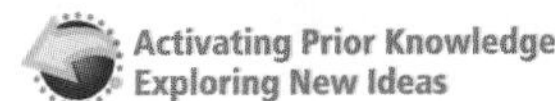

To start this investigation, you will have to work with definitions. You will have to recall how to relate the inverse of a function to the function. You will also have to work with definitions of some new functions.

For You to Explore

1. Two of these four functions are inverses of each other. Which two?

   I. $f(x) = 3x + 5$ **II.** $g(x) = 3x - 5$

   III. $h(x) = \frac{1}{3}x + 5$ **IV.** $k(x) = \frac{1}{3}(x + 5)$

   A. I and III

   B. I and IV

   C. II and III

   D. II and IV

2. On the same axes, sketch the graphs of the two functions f and g over the domain $-\pi \leq x \leq 2\pi$.

$$f(x) = \sin x$$
$$g(x) = \frac{1}{\sin x}$$

3. **Write About It** Consider the two functions in Problem 2. Is g the inverse of f? Justify your answer.

4. **a.** Sketch the graph of $h(x) = \cos x$ on the domain $-\pi \leq x \leq 2\pi$.

   b. Explain why $h(x)$ does not have an inverse function on this domain.

   c. Can $h(x)$ have an inverse function on some other domain? If so, give an example. If not, explain why not.

5. **Take It Further** Sketch and describe the graph of the equation

$$j(x) = \sin\frac{1}{x}$$

Make sure you leave enough room for the graph of g. You might want your y-axis to range from -10 to 10.

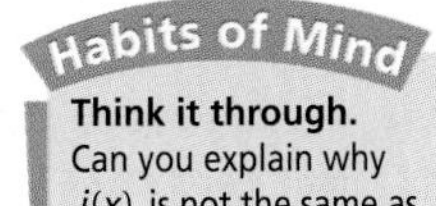

Think it through. Can you explain why $j(x)$ is not the same as $g(x) = \frac{1}{\sin x}$?

Answers

For You to Explore

1. $B(x)$ and $D(x)$
2. See back of book.
3. No; answers may vary. Sample: $f\left(g\left(\frac{\pi}{2}\right)\right) = \sin\left(\frac{1}{\sin\frac{\pi}{2}}\right) = \sin 1$. Since $\sin 1 \neq \frac{\pi}{2}$, f and g are not inverses of each other.
4. **a.** See back of book.

   b. Answers may vary. Sample: $h(x)$ is not one-to-one on the given domain.

   c. Yes; answers may vary. Sample: $[-\pi, 0]$, $[0, \pi]$, or $[\pi, 2\pi]$
5. See back of book.

Lesson Overview

GOAL

- Warm up to the ideas of the investigation.

As always in a Getting Started lesson, students should use these exercises to explore and gain experience in new topics. There is no need to formalize any ideas today—the lessons later in this investigation will formalize the key ideas.

Encourage students to work through these exercises without using their calculator. In particular, they should avoid using the graphing features of their calculator.

FOR YOU TO EXPLORE
- Core: 1, 2, 3
- Optional: 4
- Extension: 5

HOMEWORK
- Core: 6, 7, 8, 10, 11
- Optional: 9a
- Extension: 9b

MATERIALS
- graph paper
- graphing calculators
- Blackline Master MC4

Launch

You may wish to have students work in pairs.

Explore

For You to Explore

PROBLEM 1 For students who are struggling with the idea of inverse functions, describe them as functions that "undo" another function.

PROBLEM 2 Even with a range of $-10 \leq x \leq 10$, students may have a difficult time seeing exactly what is happening with the graph of $y = \frac{1}{\sin x}$. Have students take their time with this exercise. They may want to start by graphing the two functions on separate axes first. Then, once they see the nature of the graph of g, they can graph the two functions on the same axes. You may find using Blackline Master MC4 on an overhead useful.

PROBLEM 3 addresses the unfortunate conventions chosen to describe inverse functions. This convention contradicts the convention used for raising the trigonometric functions to a power.

When raising a trigonometric function to a power, the convention is to place the superscript between the function name and the argument. For example, the notation for squaring $\sin x$, $(\sin x)^2$ is $\sin^2 x$. The issue arises with the exponent of -1. The general convention is that $\sin^n x = (\sin x)^n$, but in fact, $\sin^{-1} x \neq (\sin x)^{-1}$. The first indicates the

continued on p. 32

continued from p. 31

inverse sine of a value x. In that case, the solution is the angle (or arc length) whose sine is x. The second notation indicates the reciprocal of sine x, $(\sin x)^{-1} = \csc x$.

ERROR PREVENTION Watch out for students misinterpreting the meaning of $\sin^{-1}x$, as they work through this investigation.

Wrap Up

Before assigning homework, allow students some time to discuss and summarize their findings.

Exercises

HOMEWORK

- Core: 6, 7, 8, 10, 11
- Optional: 9a
- Extension: 9b

On Your Own

EXERCISE 7 Encourage students to use the definitions to solve these exercises. Their calculators may have these functions available, even if they are not buttons on the keypad.

EXERCISE 8 Although students will get the same answer whether they are in degree or radian mode, watch for students who solve this problem using degrees. Since 1.22 does not have a degree symbol, the value of x is in radians.

EXERCISE 9 previews the identity $1 + \tan^2 x = \sec^2 x$.

Maintain Your Skills

EXERCISE 10 Students can save a lot of time if they use the definitions for this exercise. Each term cancels and leaves 1.

LEADING QUESTION What is the value of $PROD\left(\frac{\pi}{2}\right)$? (Answer: undefined)

EXERCISE 11 If you asked the follow-up question for Exercise 10, this exercise should be a breeze.

TEACHING TIP Use this exercise to check that students realize that they cannot cancel expressions from the numerator and denominator without first ensuring that the value of that term cannot be 0. By canceling without checking, they risk introducing numbers in the domain that should not be there.

Exercises Practicing Habits of Mind

On Your Own

In this investigation, you will be using the cosine and sine functions frequently, as well as these four other functions related to them:

$\tan x = \frac{\sin x}{\cos x}$ — **tangent** of x

$\sec x = \frac{1}{\cos x}$ — **secant** of x

$\csc x = \frac{1}{\sin x}$ — **cosecant** of x

$\cot x = \frac{\cos x}{\sin x}$ — **cotangent** of x

The names tangent and secant have geometric meanings, and you will see how those meanings apply to the unit circle later in this investigation.

6. Find the domain and range for the function.

$$g(x) = \csc x$$

Have you sketched the graph of g earlier?

7. Find each value.

a. $\sec \frac{\pi}{3}$ **b.** $\tan \frac{3\pi}{4}$

c. $\cot \frac{3\pi}{4}$ **d.** $\sec \frac{\pi}{4} \cdot \cos \frac{\pi}{4}$

8. a. Let $x = 1.22$. Which is greater, $\tan x$ or $\sec x$?

b. Let x be the length of an arc intercepted by any angle in Quadrant I. Which is greater, $\tan x$ or $\sec x$? Explain.

Habits of Mind

Make a connection. Think about how to calculate $\tan x$ and $\sec x$. How are they similar? How are they different?

9. a. For any value of x where both functions are defined, which is larger: $\tan^2 x$ or $\sec^2 x$?

b. Take It Further Justify, with proof, your answer.

Maintain Your Skills

10. Let $PROD(x)$ be the product of the six trigonometric functions.

$$PROD(x) = \cos x \cdot \sin x \cdot \tan x \cdot \sec x \cdot \csc x \cdot \cot x$$

For each x, calculate $PROD(x)$.

a. $x = \frac{\pi}{4}$ **b.** $x = \frac{\pi}{3}$ **c.** $x = 30^\circ$

d. $x = 0$ **e.** $x = 150^\circ$

11. Find the domain and range of the $PROD$ function given in Exercise 10.

Answers

Exercises

6. all real numbers x such that $x \neq \pi n$ (n an integer); $(-\infty, -1] \cup [1, \infty)$.

7. a. 2 **b.** -1 **c.** -1 **d.** 1

8. a. $\sec 1.22$

b. $\sec x$; by definition, $\tan x = \frac{\sin x}{\cos x}$ and $\sec x = \frac{1}{\cos x}$. For $0 < x < \frac{\pi}{2}$, $\frac{\sin x}{\cos x} < \frac{1}{\cos x}$ since $\sin x < 1$. Therefore $\tan x < \sec x$.

9. a. $\sec^2 x$

b. $1 + \tan^2 x = 1 + \frac{\sin^2 x}{\cos^2 x} = \frac{\cos^2 x + \sin^2 x}{\cos^2 x} = \frac{1}{\cos^2 x} = \sec^2 x$, so for all x where $\tan^2 x$ and $\sec^2 x$ are both defined, $\sec^2 x$ is 1 greater than $\tan^2 x$.

10. a. 1 **b.** 1 **c.** 1 **d.** The product is undefined. **e.** 1

11. all real numbers x such that $x = \frac{\pi}{2} \cdot n$ (n an integer); $\{1\}$.

1.7 The Tangent Function

You first learned the tangent function in geometry using a right triangle.

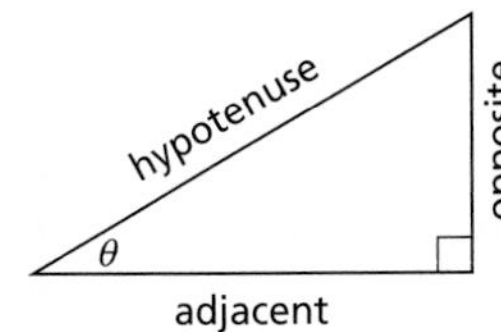

Using that, you defined $\tan \theta$ as

$$\tan \theta = \frac{\text{opposite}}{\text{adjacent}}$$

In Lesson 1.6, you defined tangent as

$$\tan \theta = \frac{\sin \theta}{\cos \theta}$$

For You to Do

1. Show how the two definitions will give the same results for $0° < \theta < 90°$.

By using the words *opposite* and *adjacent*, you are referring to sides of a right triangle. Therefore, the definition of tangent in a right triangle is limited to angle inputs from 0° to 90°.

Since $\cos x$ and $\sin x$ are just numbers, and you have definitions of them for any real value of x (with x in either degrees or radians), you can use the relationship $\tan x = \frac{\sin x}{\cos x}$ to extend the definition of tangent as well.

For Discussion

2. The cosine and sine functions have the same domain: all real numbers. What is the domain of the tangent function?

Remember...

The *natural domain* of a function f is the set of values x for which $f(x)$ is defined. When you are asked "What is the domain of f?" the real question is "What is the natural domain of f?"

For You to Do

1. For the given right triangle, $\sin\theta = \frac{\text{opposite}}{\text{hypotenuse}}$ and $\cos\theta = \frac{\text{adjacent}}{\text{hypotenuse}}$. Hence

$$\frac{\sin \theta}{\cos \theta} = \frac{\frac{\text{opposite}}{\text{hypotenuse}}}{\frac{\text{adjacent}}{\text{hypotenuse}}} = \frac{\text{opposite}}{\text{adjacent}} = \tan \theta.$$

For Discussion

2. all real numbers x such that $x \neq \frac{\pi}{2} + n\pi$ (n an integer)

Lesson Overview

GOAL

- Understand several relationships between the tangent function and the unit circle.

In this lesson, students review the definitions of the tangent function from the right triangle, and from the unit circle. Then they build a model for demonstrating tangent on a unit circle. The lesson focuses on the intersection of the line $x = 1$ and the line $\overleftrightarrow{OB}$, where O is the origin and B is the "stopping point" of the arc. They see another representation, as the slope of $\overleftrightarrow{OB}$, in the exercises. They also think about the period of the tangent function.

CHECK YOUR UNDERSTANDING
- Core: 1, 3
- Optional: 2, 4, 5, 6

MATERIALS
- geometry software
- graph paper
- graphing calculators
- Blackline Masters MC1, MC2, MC5, MC6, BM1.7

HOMEWORK
- Core: 7, 8, 10, 13
- Optional: 9, 11, 12, 14, 15

Launch

Start today's lesson with a review of tangent as defined using a right triangle. CME Project *Geometry* first introduced this definition and CME Project *Algebra 2* also presented it. Use Blackline Master MC5 on an overhead during the presentation. Then use Blackline Master MC6 as needed. As shown in the lesson, the tangent of an acute angle in a right triangle is the ratio of the length of the side opposite the angle and the length of the side adjacent to the angle. This definition only defines the tangent for acute angles. This lesson extends the definition to include all real numbers for which tangent is defined. The students are asked to determine restrictions on the domain.

Explore

For Discussion

PROBLEM 2 The function $\tan x$ is not defined where $\cos x = 0$. Since $\cos\left(\frac{\pi}{2} + n\pi\right) = 0$ for all integer values of n, the domain for $\tan x$ is all real numbers except $\frac{\pi}{2} + n\pi$ for all integer values of n.

In-Class Experiment

Use Blackline Master BM1.7 on an overhead as the class proceeds through the steps. The unit circle on Blackline Master MC5 may also be helpful.

The picture is easy to relate to when *B* is in the first quadrant. You might want to point out to your students that they can move *B* anywhere on the circle.

LEADING QUESTION What do you notice when *B* is in Quadrant II? (Answer: The cosine is negative so the tangent will be negative.)

TECHNOLOGY TIP Some geometry software uses actual measurements (such as cm or in.), so it will calculate length in those measurements, and not in the unit measurement of the axes. In order to display the correct unit lengths, you need to divide any lengths with units other than "units" by a unit length segment. You can build a segment from the origin to point *A* for this length.

Wrap Up

Wrap up today's lesson by reviewing the construction from the experiment as a class. Focus on what happens if *B* is the point (0, 1). Compare values for tangent when *B* is in Quadrants I and III (or II and IV). You may also want to review Exercise 1 as a class.

Assessment Resources

Lesson Quiz 1.7

1. Given the values $\sin\theta = 0.766$ and $\cos\theta = 0.643$, find $\tan\theta$.

2. a. Using what you know about cosine and sine, find $\tan x$ when $x = \frac{\pi}{2}$.
   b. Find $\tan x$ when $x = \frac{\pi}{4}$.

3. Given that $\frac{\pi}{2} \leq \theta \leq \pi$ and $\sin\theta = \frac{1}{2}$, find the exact value of $\tan\theta$.

You can also relate the tangent function to the unit circle.

In-Class Experiment

In this experiment, you will use your graphing calculator or geometry software to model the tangent function.

Follow these steps to build your sketch:

Step 1 Construct a circle of radius of 1 unit with center at the origin on a coordinate grid.

Step 2 Add a point at $(1, 0)$, and label it A.

Step 3 Construct the graph of the equation $x = 1$.

Step 4 Place another point on the circle. Label it B.

Step 5 Construct a line containing the origin $(0, 0)$ and point B.

Step 6 Construct the intersection between this line and the graph of the equation $x = 1$. Label that point T.

Step 7 Have the software display the y-coordinate of point T.

Step 8 Have the software display the length of $\widehat{AB}$.

Step 9 Have the software calculate the tangent of that arc length.

As you drag your point around the circle, compare the y-coordinate of point T to the value $\tan m\widehat{AB}$.

See the TI-Nspire Handbook on p. 704 for details on how to make this sketch on your calculator.

Your geometry software may not be able to graph equations like $x = 1$. In that case, you need to construct a line perpendicular to the x-axis through the point (1, 0).

For You to Do

3. In the experiment, how did the y-coordinate of T compare to the tangent calculation?
4. What happens when you drag B across $(0, 1)$? Explain.
5. What are the coordinates of B if the y-coordinate of T is equal to 2? Is there more than one answer? If so, how are the answers related?

As the experiment suggests, the y-coordinate of the point T is equal to the tangent of the arc measure $m\widehat{AB}$.

Answers

For You to Do

3. The *y*-coordinate of *T* is equal to the value of the tangent function.
4. The slope of $\overleftrightarrow{OB}$ changes from positive to negative.
5. About (0.4472, 0.8944) or about (−0.4472, −0.8944); yes; the *x*-coordinates are opposites, and the *y*-coordinates are opposites.

Exercises

1. a.

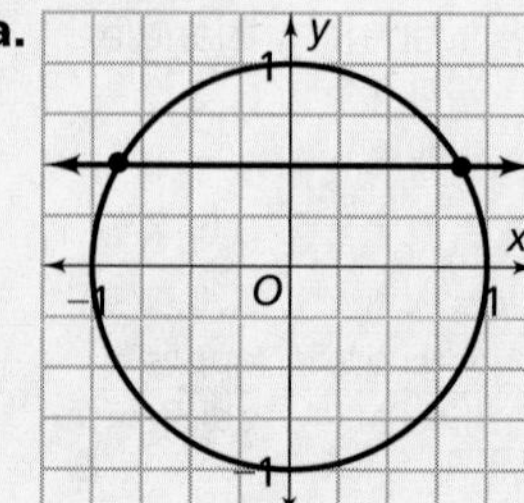

Exercises *Practicing Habits of Mind*

Check Your Understanding

1. With a unit circle, draw one line that indicates the two possible solutions to each equation in the interval $0 \le x < 2\pi$.

   a. $\sin x = 0.5$ **b.** $\sin x = -0.7$ **c.** $\cos x = 0.3$

   d. $\tan x = 2.5$ **e.** $\tan x = -0.4$

2. Suppose your calculator could compute only the sine function. Describe how you might calculate tan 0.38.

3. Describe how $\tan x$ relates to $\tan\left(\frac{\pi}{2} + x\right)$.

4. Write About It Suppose $\widehat{AB}$ is on the unit circle with A at $(1, 0)$. In which two quadrants can B be in if the tangent of $m\widehat{AB}$ negative? Justify your answer in at least two different ways.

5. Is it possible for $\tan x$ to be larger than 200? If so, find a number x such that $\tan x > 200$. If not, explain why not.

6. Answer the following to prove that $x < \tan x$ for $0 \le x < \frac{\pi}{2}$.

   a. Find $\tan\frac{\pi}{6}$, $\tan\frac{\pi}{4}$, and $\tan 1$. For these values, is it true that $x < \tan x$? Calculate $\tan x$ for three other values of x between 0 and $\frac{\pi}{2}$ to show that $x < \tan x$ for each value.

   b. The figure below shows a unit circle and the graph of the equation $x = 1$. α is the length of $\widehat{AB}$. Find the area of $\triangle OAT$ and sector OAB.

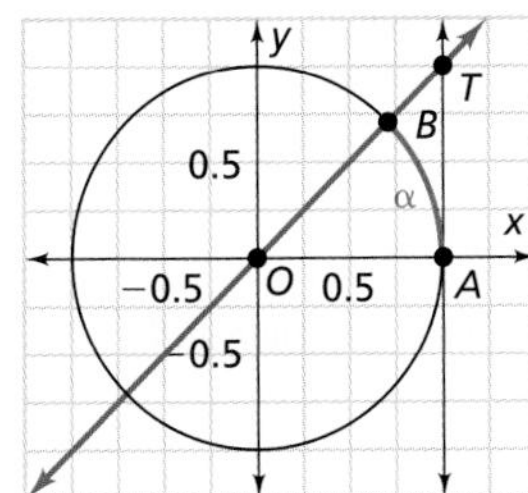
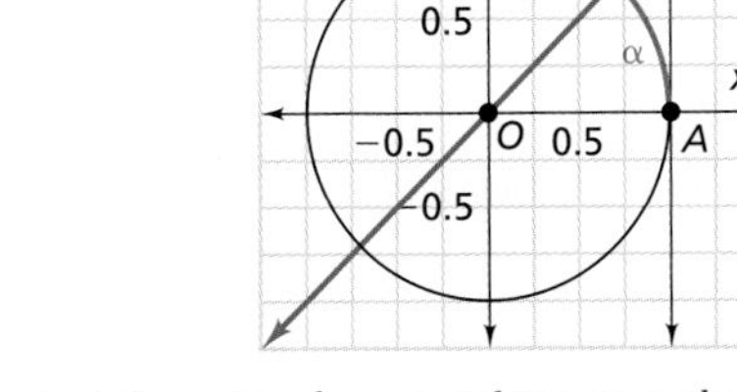

   c. Use the information from part (b) to prove that $x < \tan x$ for $0 \le x < \frac{\pi}{2}$.

Habits of Mind

Represent a function. Which representation of the tangent function is most helpful here?

Exercises

HOMEWORK
- Core: 7, 8, 10, 13
- Optional: 9, 11, 12, 14, 15

Check Your Understanding

EXERCISE 1 You may want to review the first part of this exercise together as a class. Remind students to draw the unit circle. You may wish to provide copies of Blackline Master MC1 for students to use. Then if they draw the line $x = 0.5$, it will intersect the circle in 2 places. Those two places show the two endpoints of arcs whose lengths are the values of x.

For the last two parts involving tangent, direct students toward their construction.

EXERCISE 3 If you have time, and students are struggling with this exercise, you may want to have students add a second line to their construction to compare the tangents of the two angles. Because most measurements will be in decimals, suggest that students try to make one tangent value an integer.

EXERCISE 5 Since both cosine and sine have ranges restricted to between −1 and 1, students assume the same is true for tangent. This exercise challenges that assumption.

EXERCISE 6 This exercise shows an important process that mathematicians go through to prove a conjecture. First they gather and analyze the evidence. Then, when possible, they draw a picture that represents the situation. You may wish to provide copies of Blackline Master MC1 for students to use. Next, they assemble their ideas. Finally, they work out a proof. By now, students should understand that the process of writing the proof of a conjecture rarely happens in the order of the proof.

1. b.

c.

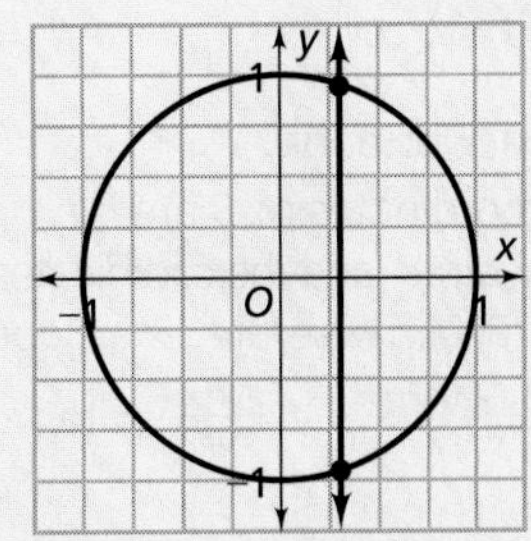

d–e. See back of book.

2–6. See back of book.

On Your Own

EXERCISE 7 You may wish to provide copies of Blackline Master MC2 for students to use to fill in most of the table. They will need to add the last two entries to the worksheet.

EXERCISE 8 represents tangent as the slope of a line on which the terminating ray of the angle lies.

EXERCISE 9 reminds students that for any angle $\sin\theta = \cos(90 - \theta)$. There's no need to spend time on a proof here.

On Your Own

7. Use what you know about cosine and sine to copy and complete this table for $f(x) = \tan x$. Look for shortcuts to simplify your work.

x	$\tan x$
0	■
$\frac{\pi}{6}$	$\frac{\sqrt{3}}{3}$
$\frac{\pi}{4}$	■
$\frac{\pi}{3}$	■
$\frac{\pi}{2}$	■
$\frac{2\pi}{3}$	■
$\frac{3\pi}{4}$	-1
$\frac{5\pi}{6}$	■
π	■
$\frac{7\pi}{6}$	■
$\frac{5\pi}{4}$	■
$\frac{4\pi}{3}$	$\sqrt{3}$
$\frac{3\pi}{2}$	undefined
$\frac{5\pi}{3}$	■
$\frac{7\pi}{4}$	■
$\frac{11\pi}{6}$	■
2π	0
$\frac{13\pi}{6}$	■
$\frac{9\pi}{4}$	■

8. **Write About It** Explain why $\tan\alpha$ is equal to the slope from the origin (0, 0) to a point on the unit circle at distance α.

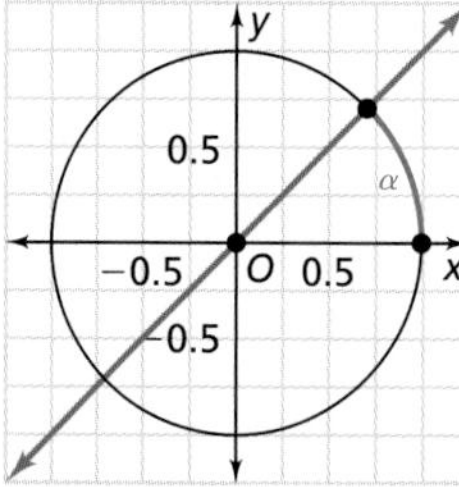

Answers

7. See back of book.
8. The coordinates of B are $(\cos x, \sin x)$, and the coordinates of O are (0, 0). Therefore, the slope of $\overleftrightarrow{OB}$ is $\frac{\sin x - 0}{\cos x - 0} = \frac{\sin x}{\cos x} = \tan x$.

9. **a.** Both are equal to $\frac{1}{2}$.
   b. Both are about 0.99255.
   c. Both are equal to 1.
   d. Both are about 0.34202.
   e. Both are equal to -1.

10. $\tan\left(\frac{\pi}{2} - x\right) = \frac{\sin\left(\frac{\pi}{2} - x\right)}{\cos\left(\frac{\pi}{2} - x\right)} = \frac{\cos x}{\sin x} = \cot x$; $\tan\left(\frac{\pi}{2} - x\right)$ and $\tan x$ are reciprocals for all values of x for which both are defined.

9. For each angle θ in degrees, calculate $\sin\theta$ and $\cos(90° - \theta)$.

a. $\theta = 30°$ **b.** $\theta = 83°$ **c.** $\theta = 90°$ **d.** $\theta = 160°$ **e.** $\theta = -90°$

10. Here are two relationships for cosine and sine.

$$\sin\left(\frac{\pi}{2} - x\right) = \cos x$$

$$\cos\left(\frac{\pi}{2} - x\right) = \sin x$$

What can you say about $\tan\left(\frac{\pi}{2} - x\right)$? How do $\tan\left(\frac{\pi}{2} - x\right)$ and $\tan x$ compare?

11. What is the relationship between $\tan(\pi - x)$ and $\tan x$?

12. What is the relationship between $\tan(\pi + x)$ and $\tan x$?

13. **Standardized Test Prep** Suppose that the walk on the unit circle from the point $(1, 0)$ to point B has length α. Which of the following gives the slope of OB?

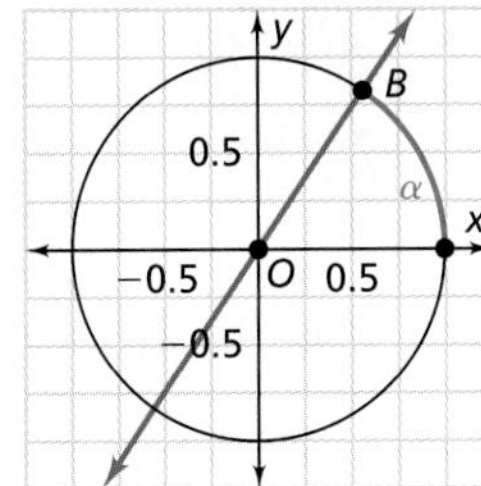

A. $\sin\alpha$ **B.** $\cos\alpha$ **C.** $\tan\alpha$ **D.** $\cot\alpha$

Maintain Your Skills

14. Let $f(x) = 5\sin x + 7$.

a. What is the maximum possible value of $f(x)$? Find two values of x that produce this maximum.

b. What is the minimum possible value of $f(x)$? Find two values of x that produce this minimum.

c. How many solutions are there to the equation $5\sin x + 7 = 0$?

15. For each function, find the maximum and minimum value.

a. $g(x) = 10\sin x + 7$ **b.** $h(x) = 20\sin x + 7$

c. $j(x) = 20\sin x + 34$ **d.** $k(x) = A\sin x + B$

For additional practice, go to Web Code: bga-0107

Additional Resources

PRINT RESOURCES
- Solution Manual
- Practice Workbook
- Assessment Resources
- Teaching Resources

TECHNOLOGY
- Interactive Textbook
- TeacherExpress CD-ROM
- ExamView CD-ROM
- PHSchool.com

Additional Practice

For Exercises 1–4, find $\tan\theta$ using the given information and $0 \le \theta < \frac{\pi}{2}$.

1. $\cos\theta = 0.156$ and $\sin\theta = 0.988$
2. $\cos\theta = 0.961$ and $\sin\theta = 0.276$
3. $\sin\theta = 0.454$
4. $\cos\theta = 0.848$

5. If $\tan\theta = 1.111$ and $\cos\theta = 0.669$, find $\sin\theta$.

6. If $\tan\theta = 2.145$ and $\sin\theta = 0.906$, find $\cos\theta$.

7. The figure at the right shows a unit circle and the graph of the equation $y = \frac{3}{2}x$. θ is the measure of the angle formed between the x-axis and the graph of $y = \frac{3}{2}x$. Use this information to find the following.

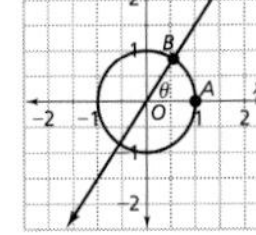

a. $\tan\theta$
b. $\sin\theta$
c. $\cos\theta$
d. the degree measure of angle θ

8. The period of the tangent function is π.
a. What is the period of $f(x) = \tan 3x$?
b. What is the period of $g(x) = \tan\left(\frac{x}{4}\right)$?

9. Suppose g is a periodic function with period 5, and $g(2) = 14$. Which of the following must also be true?
A. $g(24) = 5$
B. $g(5) = 14$
C. $g(7) = 5$
D. $g(17) = 14$

10. Consider the function $f(x) = \frac{1}{\cos x} = \sec x$.
a. Sketch the graph of f on the interval $-2\pi \le x \le 2\pi$.
b. Is f a periodic function? If so, what is its period? If not, explain why.

Practice: For Lesson 1.7, assign Exercises 1–7.

11. $\tan(\pi - x) = -\tan x$

12. $\tan(\pi + x) = \tan x$

13. C

14. a. 12; answers may vary. Sample: $\frac{\pi}{2}$ and $\frac{5\pi}{2}$

b. 2; answers may vary. Sample: $\frac{3\pi}{2}$ and $\frac{7\pi}{2}$

c. There are no solutions.

15. a. maximum = 17, maximum = −3

b. maximum = 27, maximum = −13

c. maximum = 54, maximum = 14

d. maximum = $|A| + B$, minimum = $-|A| + B$

Lesson Overview

GOALS

- Understand several relationships between the tangent function and the unit circle.
- Sketch and describe the graph of the tangent function.

In Lesson 1.7, students built a model for visualizing the tangent function with the unit circle. In this lesson, they expand on that model to build the graph of the tangent function. They solidify their ideas of the period of the tangent function, and review the concept of asymptotes.

CHECK YOUR UNDERSTANDING
- Core: 1, 3a–b, 4, 5
- Optional: 2
- Extension: 3c

MATERIALS
- geometry software
- graph paper
- graphing calculators
- Blackline Masters MC1, MC3, MC4

HOMEWORK
- Core: 6, 7, 9, 10, 12, 13
- Optional: 8
- Extension: 11

VOCABULARY
- asymptote

Launch

Begin the lesson by reviewing the model built in Lesson 1.7.

Explore

You may wish to have students work in groups of 3 to estimate the tangent of 3 points on the unit circle in each quadrant. Students should graph their estimates as a function of radian measure and compare their graphs to the graphs in the text. Use Blackline Masters MC1 and MC3 on an overhead throughout the presentation as needed.

1.8 Graphing Periodic Functions

In the last lesson, you built a model for seeing the tangent function in relation to the unit circle. As you move your point a distance α around the unit circle, the line connecting the origin and your point intersects the graph of the equation $x = 1$ at the point $(1, b)$. You can track how b changes as the point moves around the circle by making a graph.

The following diagram shows a series of arcs of the same unit circle. Each arc starts from the point $A(1, 0)$, and ends at some stopping point B. Draw the line containing the origin O and the point B which intersects the graph of the equation $x = 1$ at point T. You can calculate the y-coordinate of the point T as $\tan \alpha$.

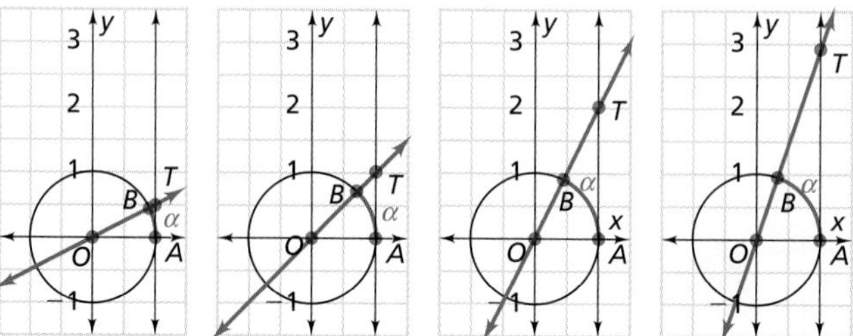

As the value of the arc length α increases from 0 to $\frac{\pi}{2}$, the y-coordinate of T, or $\tan \alpha$, also increases. As B approaches $(0, 1)$ and α approaches $\frac{\pi}{2}$, the y-coordinate of T grows greater and greater.

When B is at $(0, 1)$, $\overleftrightarrow{OB}$ is parallel to the graph of the equation $x = 1$, so there is no intersection point T. The graph shows that the values of the tangent function increase without bound as α approaches $\frac{\pi}{2}$.

An **asymptote** is a line that the graph of a function approaches, but does not intersect. The dotted vertical line in this graph is an asymptote.

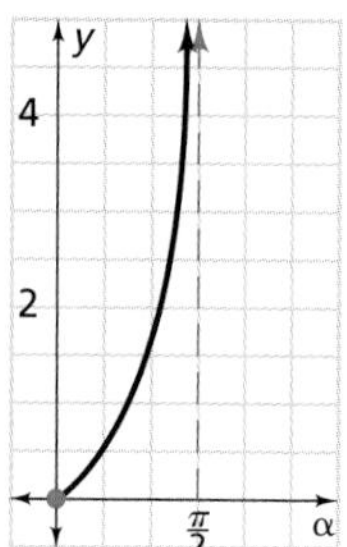

To continue this graph, look at more arcs. When B is in Quadrant II, $\overleftrightarrow{OB}$ intersects the graph of the equation $x = 1$ in Quadrant IV, so the y-coordinate of T is negative.

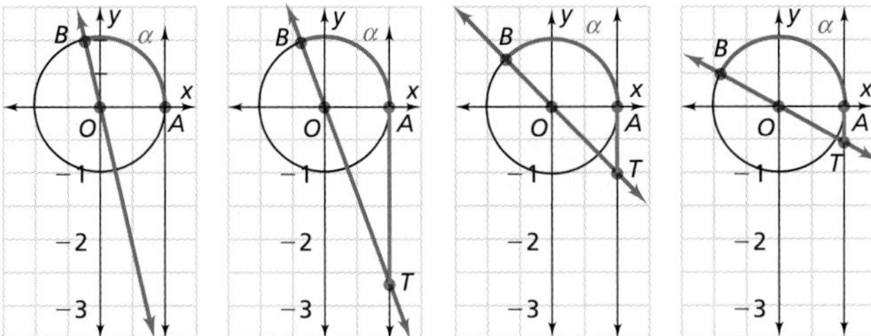

If α is a little less than $\frac{\pi}{2}$, the outputs of the tangent function are large positive numbers. If α is a little more than $\frac{\pi}{2}$, then the outputs of the tangent function are large negative numbers. As α increases from $\frac{\pi}{2}$ to π, the outputs of the tangent function are negative, but increase toward 0.

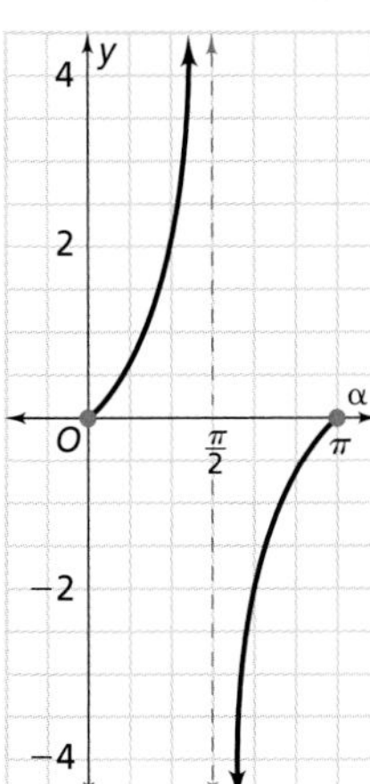

For You to Do

PROBLEMS 1–3 Have students practice the ideas just introduced by doing these problems.

Wrap Up

Before assigning homework, allow students some time to discuss and summarize their findings.

Assessment Resources

Lesson Quiz 1.8

1. **a.** What is the period of $\tan(x + 3\pi)$?
   b. How does $\tan(x + 3\pi)$ relate to $\tan x$?
2. **a.** What is the period of $\sin 2x$?
   b. What is the period of $\sin \frac{1}{3}x$?
3. If h is a periodic function with period 20 and $h(2) = 4$, what is $h(42)$?
4. Is the function $y = \cos^2 x$ periodic? If so, what is the period?

What happens next? As point B moves into Quadrant III, notice what happens to T. It follows the same path as it did when B was in Quadrant I.

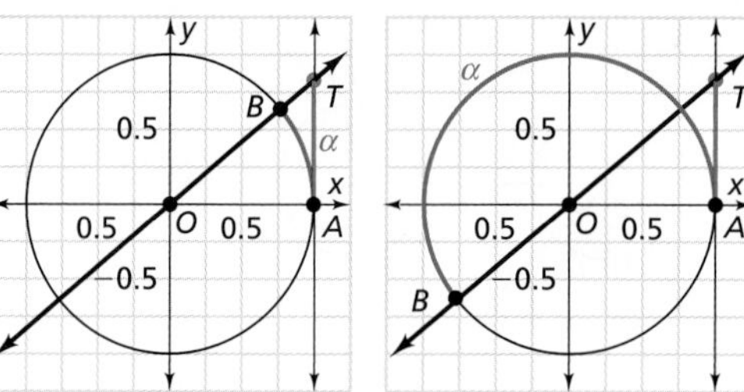

Notice that T is in the same position in both pictures, but B is at opposite ends of a diameter. So $\tan\alpha$ is equal for two different values on the unit circle.

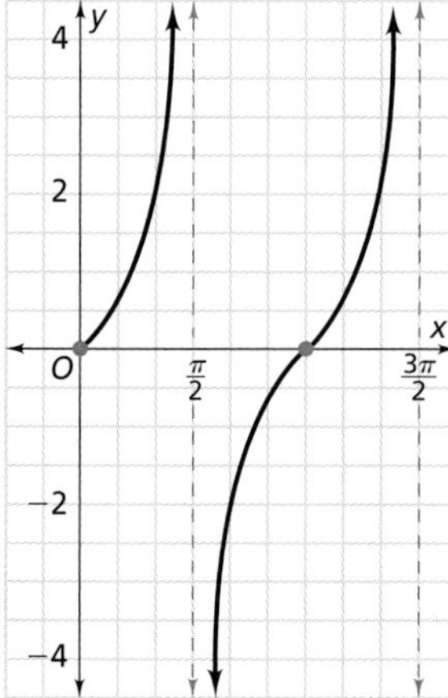

For You to Do

1. Find all numbers x such that $0 \le x \le 2\pi$ and $\tan x = 1$.
2. What is the period of the tangent function?
3. Find all real numbers x such that $\tan x = 1$.

Remember...

The period of a periodic function is the least value p such that, for all x, $f(x + p) = f(x)$.

Answers

For You to Do

1. $\frac{\pi}{4}$ and $\frac{5\pi}{4}$
2. π
3. real numbers of the form $\frac{\pi}{4} + \pi n$ (n an integer)

Exercises

1. **a.** $\frac{\pi}{2}$ **b.** 2π
2. **a.** about 1.249
   b. Infinitely many; approximately, real numbers of the form $1.249 + \pi n$ (n an integer)
3. **a.**

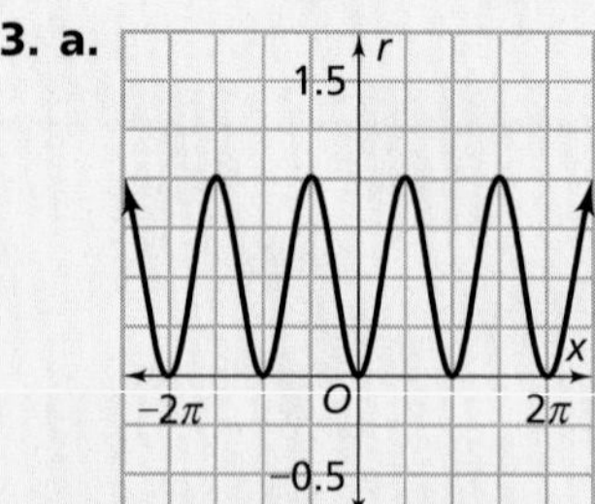

   b. π

   c. Since $\sin(\pi + x) = -\sin x$, it follows that $\sin^2(\pi + x) = (-\sin x)^2 = \sin^2 x$. Hence the period of $r(x)$ is not greater than π. Since the zeros of $r(x)$ are all of the form πn (n an integer), the period of $r(x)$ is not less than π. Therefore, the period of $r(x)$ is equal to π.

Exercises *Practicing Habits of Mind*

Check Your Understanding

1. The period of the tangent function is π.
   a. What is the period of $g(x) = \tan 2x$?
   b. What is the period of $h(x) = \tan \frac{x}{2}$?

2. a. Use the graph of $y = \tan x$ to find the least value of x such that $x > 0$ and $\tan x = 3$.
   b. How many solutions are there to the equation $\tan x = 3$? What are they?

3. a. Sketch the graph of $r(x) = \sin^2 x$.
   b. Find the period of r.
   c. **Take It Further** Prove, using properties of the sine function, that this is the correct period for r.

4. Consider the function $t(x) = \sin x + x$.
   a. Sketch a graph of this function on the interval $-2\pi \le x \le 2\pi$.
   b. Is t a periodic function? Justify your answer.

5. a. Find the period of $n(x) = \sin \frac{x}{2}$.
   b. **Write About It** For a real number $B > 0$, describe how the period of $p(x) = \sin Bx$ relates to the value of B. Include examples when $B > 1$ and when $B < 1$.

On Your Own

6. This lesson showed that this statement is true for every value of x.

$$\tan(x + \pi) = \tan x$$

How does $\tan(x + 2\pi)$ relate to $\tan x$?

7. Suppose f is a periodic function with period 10, and $f(3) = 13$. Which of the following must also be true?

A. $f(10) = 13$ B. $f(13) = 3$
C. $f(-13) = 13$ D. $f(83) = 13$

Exercises

HOMEWORK
- Core: 6, 7, 9, 10, 12, 13
- Optional: 8
- Extension: 11

Check Your Understanding

You may wish to provide copies of Blackline Masters MC3 and MC4 for students to use.

EXERCISE 1 Students will formally work with finding the period of trigonometric functions in Investigation 1C. In this exercise, they simply observe how the period changes. They determine the period by looking at the graph. Encourage them to conjecture how the period changes with respect to the coefficient of x inside the function.

EXERCISE 5 Students should use their work on Exercise 1 to help answer part (b).

On Your Own

EXERCISES 6–12 Students do not necessarily need a graphing calculator for these exercises, but they might find one helpful.

5. a. 4π

b. For $B > 0$, the period of $\sin Bx$ is $\frac{2\pi}{B}$. For example, the period of $\sin 2x$ is π, and the period of $\sin \frac{1}{2}x$ is 4π.

6. $\tan(x + 2\pi) = \tan x$

7. D

4. a.

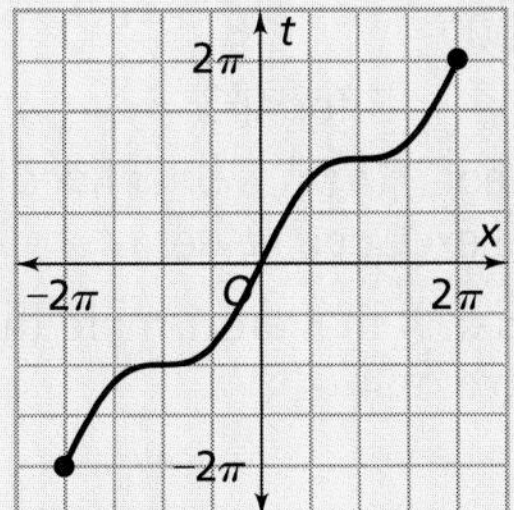

b. No; if $x > 1$, then $t(x) > \sin x + 1 \ge 0$. This means the value $t(0) = 0$ is not repeated for $x > 1$, although it would have to be repeated for $t(x)$ to be periodic.

EXERCISE 8 previews the double angle formula for cosine.

EXERCISE 11 previews the way the equation of a trigonometric function relates to its period. Students experiment and conjecture about functions whose graphs contain a maximum value at the same point. Students will work more formally with this relationship in Investigation 1C.

Maintain Your Skills

EXERCISE 13 Investigation 1C presents a formal process for identifying the period and amplitude of a trigonometric function. For this exercise, students should answer each question by looking at the graphs.

Additional Resources

PRINT RESOURCES
- Solution Manual
- Practice Workbook
- Assessment Resources
- Teaching Resources

TECHNOLOGY
- Interactive Textbook
- TeacherExpress CD-ROM
- ExamView CD-ROM
- PHSchool.com

Additional Practice

For Exercises 1–4, find $\tan\theta$ using the given information and $0 \le \theta < \frac{\pi}{2}$.

1. $\cos\theta = 0.156$ and $\sin\theta = 0.988$
2. $\cos\theta = 0.961$ and $\sin\theta = 0.276$
3. $\sin\theta = 0.454$
4. $\cos\theta = 0.848$

5. If $\tan\theta = 1.111$ and $\cos\theta = 0.669$, find $\sin\theta$.

6. If $\tan\theta = 2.145$ and $\sin\theta = 0.906$, find $\cos\theta$.

7. The figure at the right shows a unit circle and the graph of the equation $y = \frac{3}{2}x$. θ is the measure of the angle formed between the x-axis and the graph of $y = \frac{3}{2}x$. Use this information to find the following.
   - a. $\tan\theta$
   - b. $\sin\theta$
   - c. $\cos\theta$
   - d. the degree measure of angle θ

8. The period of the tangent function is π.
   - a. What is the period of $f(x) = \tan 3x$?
   - b. What is the period of $g(x) = \tan\left(\frac{x}{4}\right)$?

9. Suppose g is a periodic function with period 5, and $g(2) = 14$. Which of the following must also be true?
   - A. $g(24) = 5$
   - B. $g(5) = 14$
   - C. $g(7) = 5$
   - D. $g(17) = 14$

10. Consider the function $f(x) = \frac{1}{\cos x} = \sec x$.
    - a. Sketch the graph of f on the interval $-2\pi \le x \le 2\pi$.
    - b. Is f a periodic function? If so, what is its period? If not, explain why.

Practice: For Lesson 1.8, assign Exercises 8–10.

8. Sketch the graphs of $g(x) = \cos 2x$ and $s(x) = \cos^2 x - \sin^2 x$ on the same axes. How do the graphs of g and s compare?

9. Problem 2 on page 31 asked you to graph
$$g(x) = \frac{1}{\sin x} = \csc x$$
Is g a periodic function? If so, what is its period? If not, explain why.

The notation "csc" is short for "cosecant."

10. In Lesson 1.10, you will learn more about three additional trigonometric functions: secant (sec), cosecant (csc), and cotangent (cot). The definitions are as follows.
$$\sec x = \frac{1}{\cos x},\ \csc x = \frac{1}{\sin x},\ \text{and } \cot x = \frac{\cos x}{\sin x}$$
For this exercise, consider the function given by the following rule.
$$h(x) = \sin x \cdot \csc x + \cos x \cdot \sec x + \tan x \cdot \cot x$$
    - a. Use a calculator. Find the value of $h(0.5)$ to three decimal places.
    - b. Find $h(1)$ to three decimal places.
    - c. Describe the overall behavior of h.

11. **Take It Further** Let n be a positive integer. For what values of n does the function $z(x) = \sin nx$ have a maximum at the point $\left(\frac{\pi}{2}, 1\right)$?

12. **Standardized Test Prep** Which of the following is the period of $f(x) = \tan ax$?
    - A. a
    - B. $\frac{2\pi}{a}$
    - C. $2a\pi$
    - D. $\frac{\pi}{a}$

Maintain Your Skills

13. Find the period of each function.
    - a. $f(x) = 5\sin x + 7$
    - b. $g(x) = 3\cos x - 10$
    - c. $h(x) = 2\tan x + 1$
    - d. $j(x) = 4\sin 2x - 3$
    - e. $k(x) = 6\cos 5x + 14$
    - f. $m(x) = A\sin ax + B$

Go Online PHSchool.com

For additional practice, go to **Web Code:** bga-0108

Answers

8.

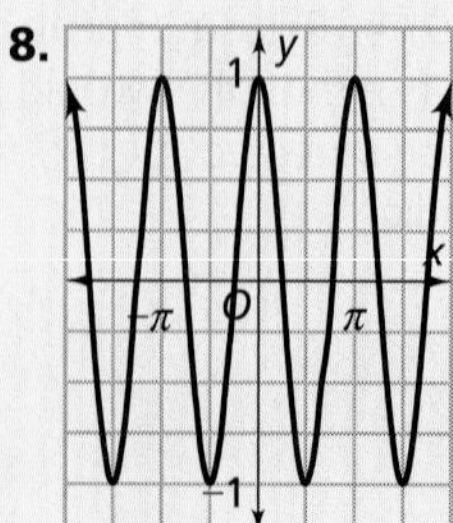

The graphs are the same.

9. Yes; 2π

10. a. 3.000 b. 3.000
    c. $h(x) = 3$ for all $x \ne \frac{\pi}{2} \cdot n$ (n an integer); $h(x)$ is undefined at all the excluded values of x.

11. values of n that are 1 more than a multiple of 4

12. D

13. a. 2π b. 2π c. $\frac{\pi}{2}$ d. π e. $\frac{2\pi}{5}$
    f. $\frac{2\pi}{B}$ for $B \ne 0$, no period if $B = 0$

1.9 Inverse Trigonometric Functions

In Lesson 1.4, you learned how to solve equations that involve trigonometric functions. Tony found the solution by using the $\sin^{-1}$ function on his calculator, the inverse sine.

In algebra, you learned about inverse functions.

Definition

Suppose f is a one-to-one function with domain A and range B. The inverse function f^{-1} is a function with these properties.

- **f^{-1} has domain B and range A**
- **$f(f^{-1}(x)) = x$**

You later proved that $f^{-1}(f(x)) = f(f^{-1}(x)) = x$. An important part of this definition and the subsequent theorem is that a function f must be one-to-one in order for the inverse function f^{-1} to exist.

For Discussion

Recall that a function f is one-to-one if $f(a) = f(b)$ only when $a = b$.

1. Explain why a periodic function cannot be one-to-one.
2. Explain why a function that is not one-to-one cannot have an inverse function.

For instance, $f(x) = x^2$ is not one-to-one, because $f(2) = f(-2) = 4$, but $2 \neq -2$.

Since the cosine, sine, and tangent functions are periodic, they cannot be one-to-one. So how can you define inverse trigonometric functions?

Public transportation schedules are periodic. The period may be an hour, a day, or a week but the plane, train, bus, or ferry will eventually retrace its route.

For Discussion

1. If f is a periodic function, then there is a number $p > 0$ such that $f(x + p) = f(x)$ for all x in the domain of f. If a is a particular number in the domain of f, then f has the same value at $x = a$ and at $x = a + p$, which means that f is not one-to-one.
2. If f is not one-to-one, then there are numbers a and b in the domain of f such that $a \neq b$ and $f(a) = f(b)$. If f has an inverse function f^{-1}, then it follows that $f^{-1}(f(a)) = f^{-1}(f(b))$ and hence that $a = b$, contradicting the fact that $a \neq b$.

Lesson Overview

GOAL

- Define an inverse of cosine, sine, and tangent.

In this lesson, students review the concept of one-to-one functions and inverse functions. They see why periodic functions are never one-to-one. They work with restricting the domain of a periodic function so they can define an inverse.

CHECK YOUR UNDERSTANDING
- Core: 1, 2, 5
- Optional: 3, 4, 6

MATERIALS
- graph paper
- graphing calculators
- Blackline Masters MC4, BM1.9A, BM1.9B

HOMEWORK
- Core: 7, 9a–c, 10, 13, 14
- Optional: 8, 11, 12
- Extension: 9d

VOCABULARY
- inverse function

Launch

Remind students of Tony and Sasha's discussion from Lesson 1.4. Review the concept that while the $\cos^{-1}$ button gives them one answer, the equation $4\sin x + 5 = 7$ has infinitely many solutions.

Explore

DEFINITIONS Students should be familiar with the definitions for inverse functions and one-to-one functions. They used the terms in their work in Chapter 2 of CME Project *Algebra 2*.

For Discussion

PROBLEM 1 By definition, a periodic function is a function in which $f(x) = f(x + p)$ for some $p > 0$. If that function f is one-to-one, then $x = x + p$, so $p = 0$. But, $p > 0$, so there is a contradiction. Thus, a periodic function cannot be one-to-one.

PROBLEM 2 helps students understand why a function must be one-to-one in order to have an inverse function. At first, students may think that $f(x) = x^2$ has the inverse $\pm\sqrt{x}$. However, since one input gives more than one output, that inverse is not a function. Similarly, students may solve an equation such as $\sin x = 1$ and get multiple answers for x. The value of $\sin^{-1}x$ should only give one answer if $\sin^{-1}x$ is considered a function.

Minds in Action

This dialog fosters experimentation as students try to resolve apparent contradictions. Encourage your students to repeat Tony and Sasha's experiments with the $\sin^{-1}$ and $\cos^{-1}$ buttons. You may wish to use Blackline Master MC4 on an overhead or provide copies for your students to fill in as they follow along with Sasha and Tony.

Minds in Action **episode 2**

Tony and Sasha are trying to decide what $\tan^{-1}$ *means.*

Tony I'm lost. If the tangent function is periodic, then it can't be one-to-one, so it can't have an inverse. Then what does the $\tan^{-1}$ mean?

Sasha jabs at the keys on her calculator.

Sasha Look. I've calculated the inverse tangent of a bunch of numbers. The answers the calculator gives all fall in the range between about −1.57 and −1.57.

Tony That's a weird number. I wonder where it comes from. Wait a second. Let me check.

Tony hits a few keys on his calculator.

Yes. It looks like your numbers are all between $-\frac{\pi}{2}$ and $\frac{\pi}{2}$.

Sasha Of course, that makes sense. Look. If I draw only one cycle of the graph of $y = \tan x$, between $-\frac{\pi}{2}$ and $\frac{\pi}{2}$, it looks like this.

One *cycle* of the graph of a periodic function $f(x)$ results as x ranges over one fundamental period.

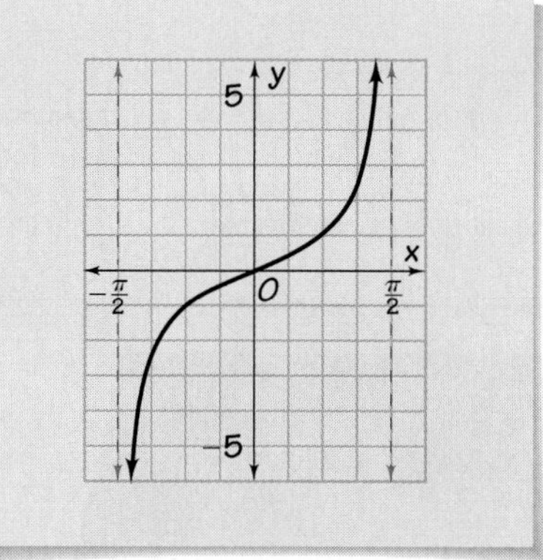

Now it looks one-to-one. Any horizontal line I draw will hit the graph in only one spot.

Tony So if we restrict the domain of tangent to include just the interval $-\frac{\pi}{2}$ to $\frac{\pi}{2}$, it's one-to-one, and the range is all real numbers.

Sasha And then the domain of the inverse tangent function would be all real numbers, and the range would be $-\frac{\pi}{2}$ to $\frac{\pi}{2}$.

Answers

For You to Do

3. 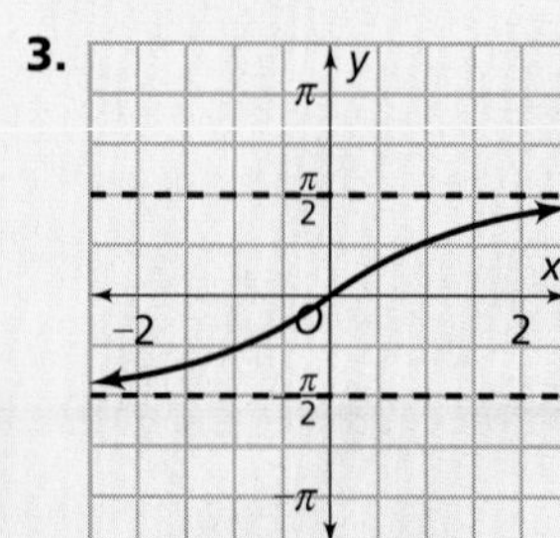

The graph of $y = \tan^{-1} x$ is the reflection image across $y = x$ of the graph of $y = \tan x$ when the domain of $y = \tan x$ is restricted to $\left(-\frac{\pi}{2}, \frac{\pi}{2}\right)$.

For You to Do

3. Sketch a graph of the equation $y = \tan^{-1} x$. How does it compare to the graph of $y = \tan x$ with domain $-\frac{\pi}{2} < x < \frac{\pi}{2}$?

Just as Tony and Sasha did for the tangent function, you can restrict the domains of the cosine and sine functions to make them one-to-one. The figure below shows the graph of one cycle of $y = \sin x$, for $-\pi \le x \le \pi$.

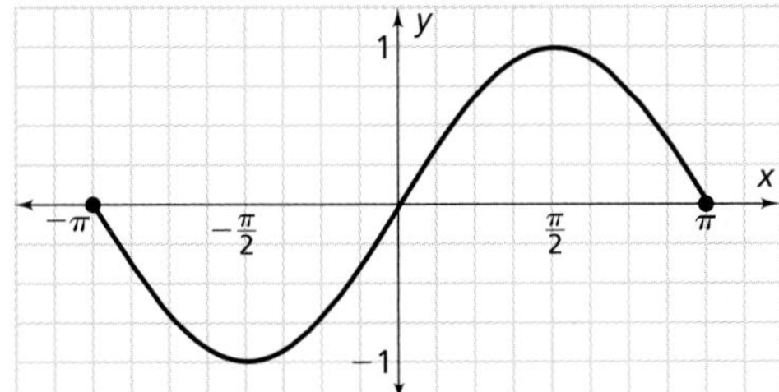

Notice that in most cases, if you draw a horizontal line, it will still hit the graph of $y = \sin x$ in two spots. If you restrict the domain to $-\frac{\pi}{2} \le x \le \frac{\pi}{2}$, any horizontal line will intersect the graph in at most one point.

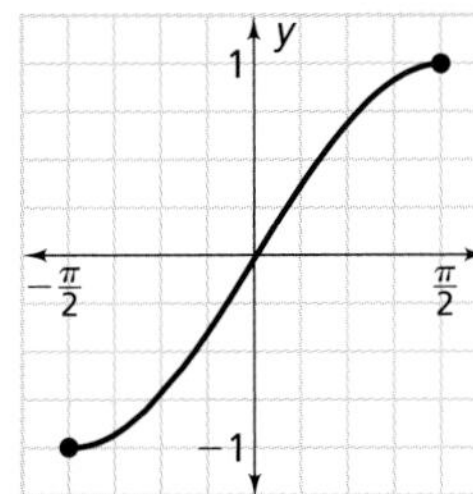

The domain for the inverse sine function is $-1 \le x \le 1$, and the range is $-\frac{\pi}{2} \le x \le \frac{\pi}{2}$. Its notation is $f(x) = \sin^{-1} x$.

For You to Do

4. Sketch a graph of the equation $y = \sin^{-1} x$.

For You to Do

4.

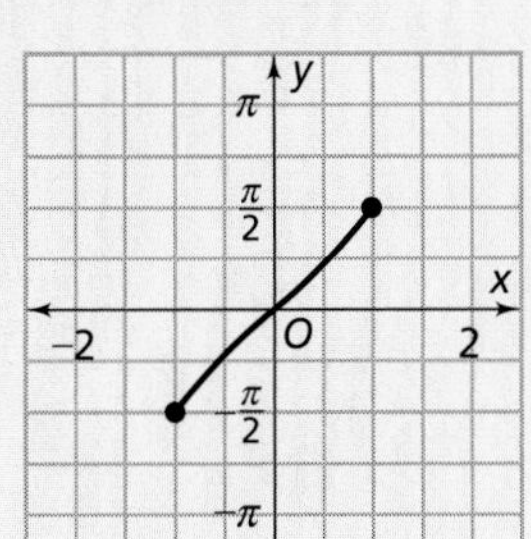

Use Blackline Master BM1.9A on an overhead to illustrate the discussion.

For You to Do

PROBLEM 4 Have students practice the ideas just introduced by doing this problem. Use Blackline Master BM1.9B on an overhead to help in sketching the graph.

Use Blackline Master BM1.9A on an overhead to illustrate the discussion.

For You to Do

PROBLEM 5 Use Blackline Master BM1.9B on an overhead to help in sketching the graph.

Developing Habits of Mind

Have students connect the habits of mind in Developing Habits of Mind with the ways they have used their minds in prior mathematics work and/or in life outside the classroom. In this case, you might want to have them discuss strategic choices players make when playing a sport such as baseball.

Wrap Up

Review the Developing Habits of Mind at the end of the lesson. Remind students that the ranges of the inverse sine, cosine, and tangent functions are different. Sine and tangent are similar, but tangent is an open-ended interval, while sine is closed.

Then have students start work on the exercises.

Assessment Resources

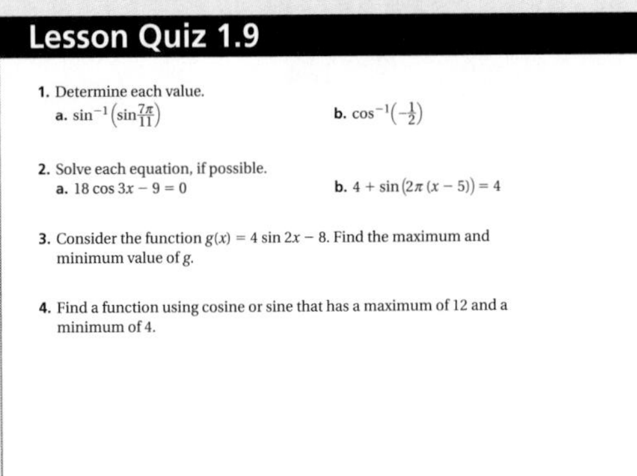
Lesson Quiz 1.9

1. Determine each value.
   a. $\sin^{-1}\left(\sin\frac{7\pi}{11}\right)$
   b. $\cos^{-1}\left(-\frac{1}{2}\right)$
2. Solve each equation, if possible.
   a. $18\cos 3x - 9 = 0$
   b. $4 + \sin(2\pi(x - 5)) = 4$
3. Consider the function $g(x) = 4\sin 2x - 8$. Find the maximum and minimum value of g.
4. Find a function using cosine or sine that has a maximum of 12 and a minimum of 4.

Restricting the cosine function to a domain between $-\frac{\pi}{2}$ and $\frac{\pi}{2}$ will not work as it did for the tangent and sine functions.

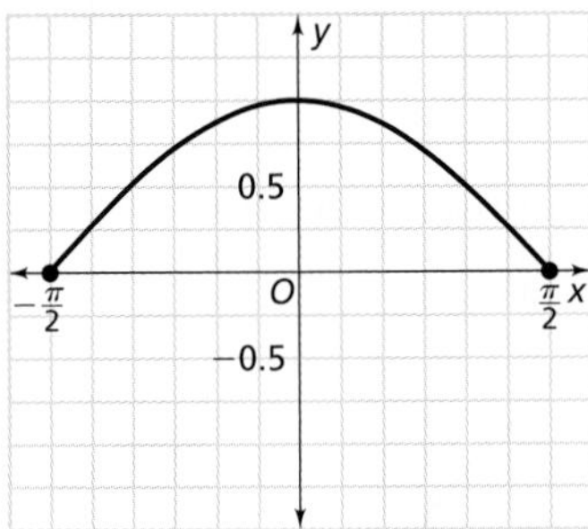

This portion of the cosine graph is not one-to-one, so you must use a different interval. One interval that makes the function one-to-one is $0 \leq x \leq \pi$.

The domain for the inverse cosine function is $-1 \leq x \leq 1$, and the range is $0 \leq y \leq \pi$. Its notation is $f(x) = \cos^{-1} x$.

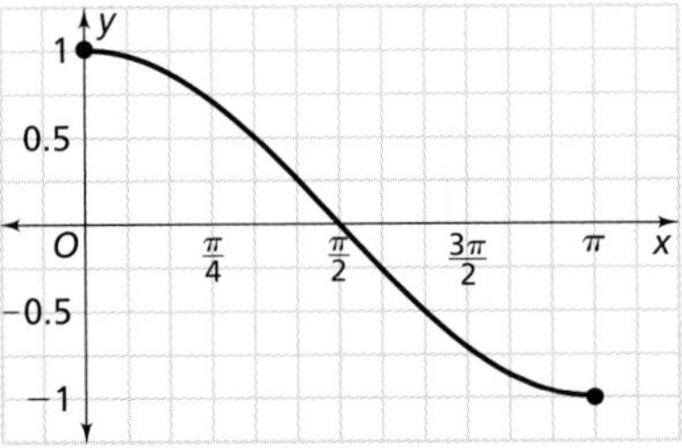

For You to Do

5. Sketch a graph of the equation $y = \cos^{-1} x$.

Developing Habits of Mind

Make strategic choices. Since the cosine, sine, and tangent functions are periodic, you could have chosen to restrict your domain in infinitely many ways. For example, the cosine function is also one-to-one on the interval $-\pi \leq x \leq 0$. So why are these particular intervals important?

The reason goes back to the unit circle, and even the right triangle. Each interval includes lengths of arcs intersected by angles that terminate in Quadrant I, the angles over which you first defined the functions. So it makes sense to include these angles in the restricted domains. The shape of its graph determines the rest of the interval for each function.

Answers

For You to Do

5.

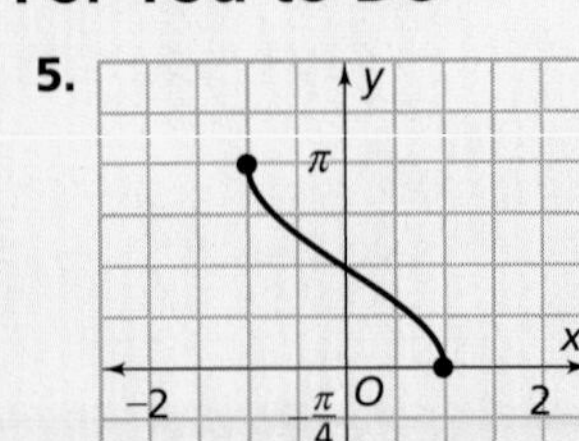

Exercises *Practicing Habits of Mind*

Check Your Understanding

1. Solve each equation, if possible.

a. $3 \sin x + 7 = 5$

b. $5 \cos x - 12 = 14$

c. $2 \tan x + 3 = -10$

d. $10 \cos(x + 3) - 7 = 13$

2. Consider the equation $\tan x = 0.75$.

a. Use a calculator. Find one solution for x to three decimal places.

b. Use the graph of the tangent function to show where more solutions lie.

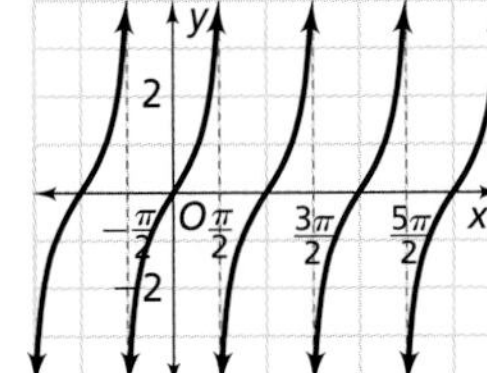

c. For $\tan x = 0.75$, find the least solution that is greater than your solution in part (a).

3. Consider the equation $\cos x = 0.8$.

a. Use a calculator. Find one solution for x to three decimal places.

b. Use the graph of the cosine function to show where more solutions lie.

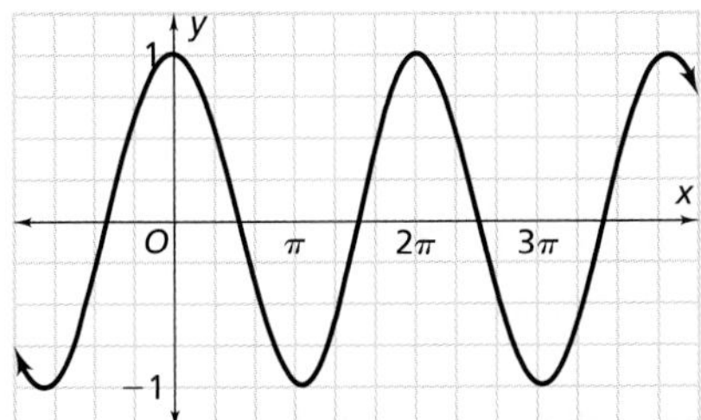

c. For $\cos x = 0.8$, find the least solution greater than your solution in part (a).

Exercises

HOMEWORK

- Core: 7, 9a–c, 10, 13, 14
- Optional: 8, 11, 12
- Extension: 9d

Exercises

1. a. all the numbers $-\sin^{-1}\left(\frac{2}{3}\right) + 2n\pi$ and $\sin^{-1}\left(\frac{2}{3}\right) + (2n + 1)\pi$ (n an integer)

b. no solutions

c. all the numbers $\tan^{-1}\left(-\frac{13}{2}\right) + n\pi$ (n an integer)

d. no solutions

2. a. Answers may vary. Sample: $\tan^{-1} 0.75 \approx 0.644$

b. at x-values that are $n\pi$ units (n an integer) from the solution in part (a)

c. for the solution in part (a): $\pi + \tan^{-1} 0.75 \approx 3.785$

3. a. Answers may vary. Sample: $\cos^{-1} 0.8 \approx 0.644$

b. the x-values $2n\pi \pm \cos^{-1} 0.8$

c. for the solution in part (a): $2\pi - \cos^{-1} 0.8 \approx 5.640$

Check Your Understanding

EXERCISE 5 Have students to do this exercise without a calculator. It may be helpful to use Blackline Master BM1.9A on an overhead.

ERROR PREVENTION Watch out for students who answer $\frac{11\pi}{6}$ on part (f), since $\frac{11\pi}{6}$ is not in the range of $f(x) = \cos^{-1}x$.

On Your Own

EXERCISE 8 The key point of this exercise is part (b). It reminds students that while all three functions are positive in Quadrant I, they have different signs in the other three quadrants.

EXERCISE 11 is a preview of the amplitude of the sine function. Students will formally learn how to find the amplitude in Investigation 1C.

EXERCISE 12 stretches students to think about both changing the amplitude of a trigonometric function as well as translating the function up or down.

4. Consider the equation $\sin x = 0.6$.

a. Use a calculator. Find one solution for x to three decimal places.

b. Use the graph of the sine function to show where more solutions lie.

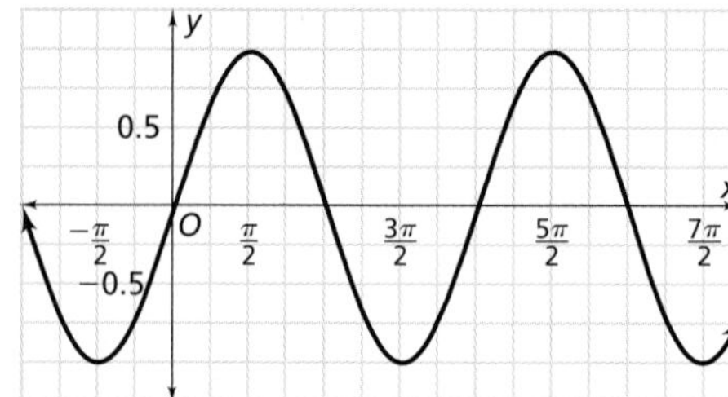

c. For $\sin x = 0.6$, find the least solution greater than the solution you found in part (a).

5. Determine each value.

a. $\sin^{-1}\frac{1}{2}$ **b.** $\cos^{-1}0$

c. $\tan^{-1}1$ **d.** $\cos^{-1}(\cos 120°)$

e. $\tan(\tan^{-1}2.14)$ **f.** $\cos^{-1}\left(\cos\frac{11\pi}{6}\right)$

Don't let your calculator have all the fun!

6. a. If x is the length of an arc intersected by an angle in Quadrant I and $\sin x = \frac{7}{25}$, find $\cos x$.

b. Determine the value of $\cos\left(\sin^{-1}\frac{7}{25}\right)$.

On Your Own

7. Solve each equation, if possible.

a. $6\sin 2x + 1 = -2$ **b.** $12\sin 2(x-3) + 8 = 22$

c. $3\sin\pi(x-5) + 4 = 7$ **d.** $36\cos\left(\frac{2\pi}{30}(x-3)\right) + 39 = 50$

8. Look back at Exercises 2–4. You should have gotten the same answer for part (a) of each exercise.

a. Draw a triangle that has one angle of measure corresponding to an arc of length $\tan^{-1}0.75$. Find integer lengths for each of the sides of the triangle that satisfy the three statements for $\tan^{-1}0.75$, $\sin^{-1}0.6$, and $\cos^{-1}0.8$. What special triangle is it?

b. **Write About It** Explain why the answer you got in part (a) from each exercise was the same, but the answer you got in part (c) was not.

Answers

4. a. Answers may vary. Sample: $\sin^{-1}0.6 \approx 0.644$

b. the x-values $\sin^{-1}0.6 + 2n\pi$ and $(2n+1)\pi - \sin^{-1}0.6$ (n an integer)

c. for the solutions in part (a): $\pi - \sin^{-1}0.6 \approx 2.498$

5. a. $\frac{\pi}{6}$ **b.** $\frac{\pi}{2}$ **c.** $\frac{\pi}{4}$

d. 120° **e.** 2.14 **f.** $\frac{\pi}{6}$

6. a. $\frac{24}{25}$ **b.** $\frac{24}{25}$

7. a. the numbers $\frac{7}{12}\pi + n\pi$ and $-\frac{1}{12}\pi + n\pi$ (n an integer)

b. no solutions

c. the numbers $\frac{11}{2} + 2n$ (n an integer)

d. the numbers $30n \pm \frac{15\cos^{-1}\frac{11}{36}}{\pi} + 3$ (n an integer)

8. a. Check students' diagrams. The triangle should have side lengths in the ratio 3:4:5.

b. Sine is positive in Quadrants I and II, cosine is positive in Quadrants I and IV, and tangent is positive in Quadrants I and III.

9. **a.** Find the value of $\sin^{-1}\frac{1}{2} + \cos^{-1}\frac{1}{2}$.

b. Find the value of $\sin^{-1}\frac{\sqrt{3}}{2} + \cos^{-1}\frac{\sqrt{3}}{2}$.

c. Find the value of $\sin^{-1}(-1) + \cos^{-1}(-1)$.

d. **Take It Further** Explain why the pattern in these three results occurs.

10. Is this statement true for every x?

$$\sin^{-1}(\sin x) = x$$

If so, explain why. If not, when is it true and when is it false?

11. Find the maximum and minimum values for each function.

a. $a(x) = 5 \sin x + 8$

b. $b(x) = 10 \sin x + 17$

c. $c(x) = 10 \sin x + 3$

d. $d(x) = 4 \sin x - 2$

12. **a.** Find a function using cosine or sine that has a maximum of 27, and a minimum of 11.

b. Find a function using cosine or sine that has a maximum of 75, and a minimum of 3.

c. Find a function using cosine or sine that has a maximum of 23, and a minimum of −15.

13. **Standardized Test Prep** Which of the following is true?

A. $\cos^{-1} x = \frac{1}{\cos x}$ **B.** $\cos^{-1} x = \sin x$

C. $\cos^{-1} x = \frac{1}{\sin x}$ **D.** $\cos(\cos^{-1} x) = x$

Maintain Your Skills

14. Find one solution to each equation.

a. $4 \cos x + 5 = 7$

b. $4 \cos 2x + 5 = 7$

c. $4 \cos \frac{x}{2} + 5 = 7$

d. $4 \cos \pi x + 5 = 7$

e. $4 \cos(\pi(x + 3)) + 5 = 7$

f. $4 \cos\left(\frac{2\pi}{10}(x - 3)\right) + 5 = 7$

Taking the output of f as the input for f^{-1} is like flipping a toggle switch twice. In the end, you are back where you started.

For additional practice, go to Web Code: bga-0109

Additional Resources

PRINT RESOURCES
- Solution Manual
- Practice Workbook
- Assessment Resources
- Teaching Resources

TECHNOLOGY
- Interactive Textbook
- TeacherExpress CD-ROM
- ExamView CD-ROM
- PHSchool.com

Additional Practice

For Exercises 1–4, determine each value.

1. $\sin^{-1}\left(-\frac{\sqrt{3}}{2}\right)$ **2.** $\cos\left(\cos^{-1}\left(\frac{4\pi}{5}\right)\right)$

3. $\tan^{-1}\sqrt{3}$ **4.** $\sin^{-1} 0$

For Exercises 5–8, solve each equation, if possible.

5. $5 \cos(x + 10) + 4 = 4$ **6.** $12 \sin(2x) - 2 = 4$

7. $-14 \cos(4\pi x) + 2 = 9$ **8.** $9 \sin(3x + 2) - 2 = 16$

For Exercises 9–10, find the maximum and minimum values for each function.

9. $f(x) = 4 \sin x + 8$ **10.** $g(x) = 2 \cos x - 12$

11. Find a function using cosine or sine that has a maximum of 17 and a minimum of −3.

For Exercises 12–15, find all solutions to each equation if $0 \le x \le 2\pi$.

12. $\sec x = 2$ **13.** $\csc x = \frac{2}{\sqrt{3}}$

14. $\cot x = 1$ **15.** $\csc x = -2$

16. Here is the graph of $f(x) = \csc x$ on the interval $-2\pi \le x \le 2\pi$.

a. Find the domain and range of f.

b. How many solutions does $\csc x = 0$ have? Explain.

c. How many solutions does $\csc x = 1$ have? What are they?

d. Explain why there is a horizontal gap in the graph between the graphs of the equations $y = -1$ and $y = 1$.

17. Show graphically that there are two solutions to the equation $\csc x = 3$ in the interval $0 \le x \le 2\pi$.

18. Show graphically that there are two solutions to the equation $\cot x = -2$ in the interval $0 \le x \le 2\pi$.

Practice: For Lesson 1.9, assign Exercises 1–11.

14. Answers may vary. Sample answers are given.

a. $\frac{\pi}{3}$ **b.** $\frac{\pi}{6}$ **c.** $\frac{2\pi}{3}$

d. $\frac{1}{3}$ **e.** $-\frac{8}{3}$ **f.** $-\frac{4}{3}$

9. **a.** $\frac{\pi}{2}$ **b.** $\frac{\pi}{2}$ **c.** $\frac{\pi}{2}$

d. The pattern stems from the fact that the sine of an angle is equal to the cosine of the complement of the angle.

10. The equation is not true for every x. This has to do with the use of a restricted domain for $y = \sin x$ in the definition of $\sin^{-1}x$. The given equation is true provided $-\frac{\pi}{2} \le x \le \frac{\pi}{2}$.

11. **a.** maximum = 13, minimum = 3

b. maximum = 27, minimum = 7

c. maximum = 13, minimum = −7

d. maximum = 2, minimum = −6

12. **a.** Answers may vary. Sample: $t(x) = 8 \sin x + 19$

b. Answers may vary. Sample: $u(x) = 36 \cos x + 39$

c. Answers may vary. Sample: $v(x) = 19 \sin x + 4$

13. D

Lesson Overview

GOAL

- Recognize three other trigonometric functions: secant, cosecant, and cotangent.

In this lesson, students are formally introduced to three additional trigonometry functions: secant, cosecant, and cotangent. They expand on the model they built in Lesson 1.7 to show how secant can be modeled on the unit circle. At the end of the lesson, they see the graphs of the three functions.

CHECK YOUR UNDERSTANDING

- Core: 1, 4, 5
- Optional: 2, 6, 7
- Extension: 3

MATERIALS

- geometry software
- graph paper
- graphing calculators
- Blackline Masters MC1, MC4, MC5, MC6, BM1.7

HOMEWORK

- Core: 8, 9, 10, 11, 12, 14
- Optional: 15, 16
- Extension: 13

Launch

Review the exercises from Lesson 1.6 and the tangent construction from Lesson 1.7.

Explore

Use Blackline Master MC5 or MC6 on an overhead for a quick review of the right triangle definitions of the trigonometric functions. Use MC1 to illustrate the discussion preceding the In-Class Experiment.

In-Class Experiment

For the In-Class Experiment, you may wish to have students work in pairs. The goal is to have students gain experience that will help them understand the meaning of the secant function. You may wish to use Blackline Master BM 1.7 here to review the steps used in the Lesson 1.7 In-Class Experiment.

1.10 Reciprocal Trigonometric Functions

Go Online PHSchool.com

For more information on trigonometric functions, go to **Web Code:** bge-9031

There are six possible ratios of side lengths of a right triangle. The three more common trig functions, cosine, sine, and tangent.

$$\cos\theta = \frac{\text{adjacent}}{\text{hypotenuse}} \quad \sin\theta = \frac{\text{opposite}}{\text{hypotenuse}} \quad \tan\theta = \frac{\text{opposite}}{\text{adjacent}}$$

The reciprocal of each of these ratios account for the other three.

$$\sec\theta = \frac{\text{hypotenuse}}{\text{adjacent}} \quad \csc\theta = \frac{\text{hypotenuse}}{\text{opposite}} \quad \cot\theta = \frac{\text{adjacent}}{\text{opposite}}$$

You can represent each of these functions on the unit circle as well. Recall in Lesson 1.7 you built a model for $\tan\alpha$. You can use that same model to find $\sec\alpha$.

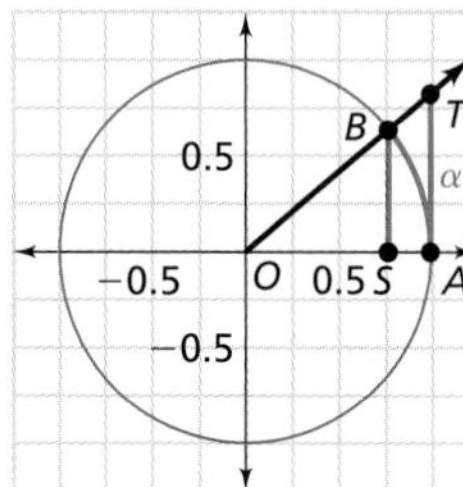

The measure of $\overset{\frown}{AB}$ is α. $\overline{OA}$ and $\overline{OB}$ are both radii. So they each have length 1. As you saw in Investigation 1A, $\cos\alpha = OS$ and $\sin\alpha = SB$. Earlier in this investigation, you saw that $\tan\alpha = AT$, and $\overline{AT}$ is on a line tangent to the unit circle at A.

Recall that a secant line is a line that intersects a curve in at least two points. Notice that $\overline{OT}$ is on a secant line through the center of the unit circle.

In-Class Experiment

Start with the sketch you made in the In-Class Experiment of Lesson 1.7. Follow these steps to add to your sketch.

Step 1 Label the origin as point O.

Step 2 Construct the line segment $\overline{OT}$.

Step 3 Have the software display the length of $\overline{OT}$.

Step 4 Have the software calculate the secant of the radian measure of $\overset{\frown}{AB}$.

As you drag point B around the circle, compare the length of segment $\overline{OT}$ to the value of the secant of the radian measure of $\overset{\frown}{AB}$.

If your software does not calculate $\sec x$ directly, have it calculate $\frac{1}{\cos x}$.

For You to Do

1. In the experiment, how did the length of $\overline{OT}$ compare to the secant calculation?
2. What happens to the two values when you drag B across $(0, 1)$? Explain.

For Discussion

3. Your sketch will display the length of $\overline{OT}$ as positive, since length is a measure of distance, which is always positive. The value of the secant function, however, can be negative. For arcs terminating in which quadrants will the secant of the arc be negative? Explain how your sketch shows where the secant is negative.

You can also define the secant, cosecant, and cotangent functions by their relationships to the cosine and sine functions.

$\sec x = \frac{1}{\cos x}$ $\quad\csc x = \frac{1}{\sin x}$ $\quad\cot x = \frac{\cos x}{\sin x}$

The following figures show the graphs of $y = \sec x$, $y = \csc x$ and $y = \cot x$.

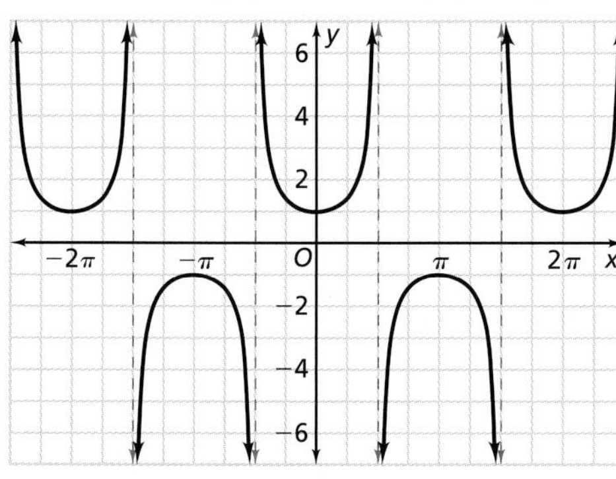

$y = \sec x$

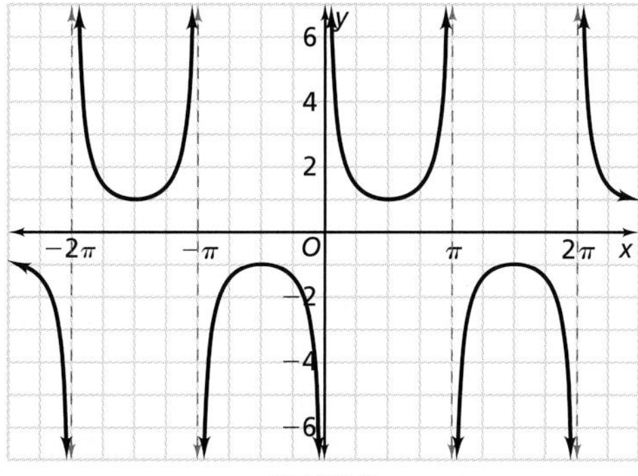

$y = \csc x$

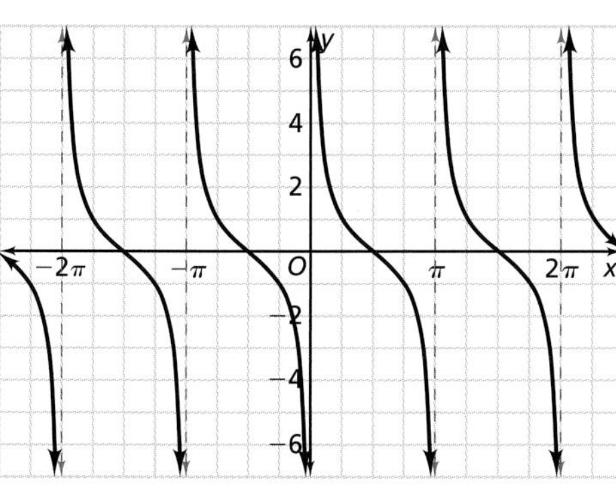

$y = \cot x$

For Discussion

PROBLEM 3 The secant will be negative for the same values of the point on the unit circle where cosine is negative. It is negative for points on the unit circle in Quadrants II and III. On the graph, think of the line $\overleftrightarrow{OB}$ as an axis, where the ray $\overrightarrow{OB}$ indicates the positive direction. When B is in Quadrants II or III, T is on the opposite side of O from B, so you can think of T as being in the negative direction.

Wrap Up

Review the graphs of $y = \sec x$, $y = \csc x$, and $y = \cot x$. Use Blackline Master MC4 to demonstrate how the sketches were made. Point out the asymptotes and discuss their location. Be sure that students see that they are located where the corresponding function equals 0. Then have students start work on the Check Your Understanding exercises.

Assessment Resources

Lesson Quiz 1.10

1. Find all solutions to each equation if $0 \le x \le 2\pi$.
   a. $\csc x = 1$
   b. $\cot^2 x = \frac{1}{3}$
2. The graph of $f(x) = \cot x$ on the interval $0 \le x \le 2\pi$ is pictured to the right.
   a. Explain why the graph has vertical asymptotes at $x = \pi$ and $x = 2\pi$.
   b. How many solutions does the equation $\cot x = 0$ have on the interval $0 \le x \le 2\pi$? Use the graph to explain your answer.
   c. What is the range of f?
3. Consider the function $g(x) = \sec^2 x + \csc^2 x$. Evaluate $g\left(\frac{\pi}{3}\right)$.

Answers

For You to Do

1. $\sec\alpha = OT$
2. For $\alpha < \frac{\pi}{2}$, $\sec\alpha$ is a large positive number and increasing as $\alpha \to \frac{\pi}{2}$; for $\alpha > \frac{\pi}{2}$, $\sec\alpha$ is a large negative number and increasing (in magnitude); and $\sec\frac{\pi}{2}$ is undefined. OT increases to $+\infty$, then decreases, but is always positive, as B crosses the y-axis.

For Discussion

3. Secant is negative in Quadrants II and III, where cosine is negative. That is, $\sec x$ will be negative for $\frac{\pi}{2} < x < \frac{3\pi}{2}$ and that section of the graph of $y = \sec x$ will lie below the x-axis.

Exercises

HOMEWORK
- Core: 8, 9, 10, 11, 12, 14
- Optional: 15, 16
- Extension: 13

Check Your Understanding

EXERICSE 3 Remind students that looking at the graphs is evidence, but not proof, that the two functions are equal.

EXERICSE 4 shows important identities. It also provides information as to why cosine, cosecant, and cotangent have the names that they do.

Exercises *Practicing Habits of Mind*

Check Your Understanding

1. Find all solutions to each equation if $0 \le x \le 2\pi$.

a. $\csc x = 2$

b. $\cot x = \sqrt{3}$

c. $\sec x = 0$

d. $\sec^2 x = 1$

Remember... Use radians unless the degree symbol is present.

2. Consider the functions f and g.

$$f(x) = \sec^2 x + \csc^2 x$$

$$g(x) = \sec^2 x \cdot \csc^2 x$$

For each value below, calculate $f(x)$ and $g(x)$.

a. $x = 30°$

b. $x = \frac{\pi}{4}$

c. $x = 60°$

d. $x = 120°$

e. $x = 2$

3. Take It Further Show that $f(x)$ and $g(x)$ from Exercise 2 are equal wherever they are defined.

4. The identity $\cos\theta = \sin(90° - \theta)$ is the *co-function identity*. Similar identities exist for the tangent and secant functions.

a. Give an example to show that $\cot\theta = \tan(90° - \theta)$ for a particular angle measure θ.

b. Give an example to show that $\csc\theta = \sec(90° - \theta)$ for a particular angle measure θ.

c. Show that $\cot\theta = \tan(90° - \theta)$ for any angle measure θ in the domain of the cotangent function.

d. Show that $\csc\theta = \sec(90° - \theta)$ for any angle measure θ in the domain of the cosecant function.

In fact, the *co* part of *cosine* is short for *complement*. Two angles are complementary if the measures add up to 90°.

Answers

Exercises

1. a. $\frac{\pi}{6}$ and $\frac{5\pi}{6}$ **b.** $\frac{\pi}{6}$ and $\frac{7\pi}{6}$

c. 0, π, and 2π **d.** 0, π, and 2π

2. a. $f(30°) = \frac{16}{3}$, $g(30°) = \frac{16}{3}$

b. $f\left(\frac{\pi}{4}\right) = 4$, $g\left(\frac{\pi}{4}\right) = 4$

c. $f(60°) = \frac{16}{3}$, $g(60°) = \frac{16}{3}$

d. $f(120°) = \frac{16}{3}$, $g(120°) = \frac{16}{3}$

e. $f(2) \approx 6.9838$, $g(2) \approx 6.9838$

3.
$$\begin{aligned} f(x) &= \sec^2 x + \csc^2 x \\ &= \frac{1}{\cos^2 x} + \frac{1}{\sin^2 x} \\ &= \frac{\sin^2 x + \cos^2 x}{(\cos^2 x)(\sin^2 x)} \\ &= \frac{1}{(\cos^2 x)(\sin^2 x)} \\ &= \sec^2 x \cdot \csc^2 x \\ &= g(x) \end{aligned}$$

4. a. Answers may vary. Sample: Use $\theta = 60°$.

b. Answers may vary. Sample: Use $\theta = 60°$.

c. Use the equations $\cos\theta = \sin(90° - \theta)$ and $\sin\theta = \cos(90° - \theta)$.

$\tan(90° - \theta) = \frac{\sin(90° - \theta)}{\cos(90° - \theta)} = \frac{\cos\theta}{\sin\theta} = \cot\theta$

d. $\sec(90° - \theta) = \frac{1}{\cos(90° - \theta)} = \frac{1}{\sin\theta} = \csc\theta$

5. Consider the following graph of the unit circle and the tangent at $(1, 0)$.

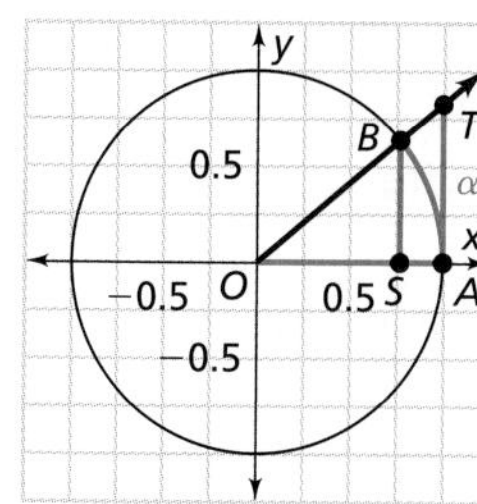

a. Explain why $\triangle OSB \sim \triangle OAT$.

b. Use similar triangles to show that the length of $\overline{OT}$ is $\sec \alpha$.

6. Consider the following geometric series.

$$1 + \sin^2 x + \sin^4 x + \sin^6 x + \cdots$$

As long as $|\sin x| < 1$, this series converges to a specific sum. Which is it?

A. $\cos^2 x$ B. $\tan^2 x$

C. $\cot^2 x$ D. $\sec^2 x$

Recall from algebra, if the first term of an infinite geometric series is a and the common ratio is r with $|r| < 1$, the sum is $\frac{a}{1-r}$.

7. Consider the following geometric series.

$$\sin^2 x + \sin^4 x + \sin^6 x + \sin^8 x + \cdots$$

Assuming $|\sin x| < 1$, which of these is the sum of this series?

A. $\cos^2 x$ B. $\tan^2 x$

C. $\cot^2 x$ D. $\sec^2 x$

On Your Own

8. Here is the graph of $f(x) = \sec x$ on the interval $-\pi \le x \le 2\pi$.

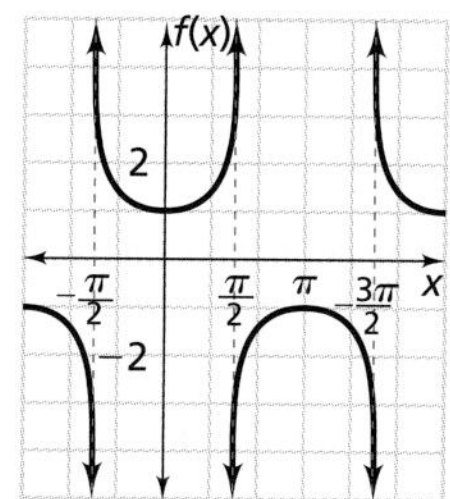

a. Find the domain and range of f.

b. Explain why there is a horizontal gap in the graph between the graphs of the equations $y = -1$ and $y = 1$.

EXERCISE 5 Most students will remember the CPCTC Theorem from Geometry that states that corresponding parts of congruent triangles are congruent. However, some may have forgotten the CPSTP Theorem that states that corresponding parts of similar triangles are proportional.

On Your Own, p. 54

EXERCISE 13 previews the first derivative of the tangent function.

5. a. $\triangle OSB$ and $\triangle OAT$ are right triangles that share the acute angle with vertex O. Hence the acute angles $\angle OBS$ and $\angle OTA$ are congruent. If the angles of one triangle are congruent to those of another triangle, then the triangles are similar. So $\triangle OSB \sim \triangle OAT$.

b. By definition, $\sec\alpha = \sec\angle TOS = \frac{\text{hypotenuse}}{\text{adjacent}}$. So $\sec\alpha = \frac{OT}{1} = OT$.

6. D

7. B

8. a. domain $= \{x \mid x \neq (2n+1)\frac{\pi}{2}$ (n an integer)$\}$, range $= \{x \mid x \le -1 \text{ or } x \ge 1\}$

b. $\sec x = \frac{1}{\cos x}$ and the range of values of $\cos x$ is $[-1, 1]$.

Additional Resources

PRINT RESOURCES
- Solution Manual
- Practice Workbook
- Assessment Resources
- Teaching Resources

TECHNOLOGY
- Interactive Textbook
- TeacherExpress CD-ROM
- ExamView CD-ROM
- PHSchool.com

Additional Practice

For Exercises 1–4, determine each value.

1. $\sin^{-1}\left(-\frac{\sqrt{3}}{2}\right)$
2. $\cos\left(\cos^{-1}\left(\frac{4\pi}{5}\right)\right)$
3. $\tan^{-1}\sqrt{3}$
4. $\sin^{-1} 0$

For Exercises 5–8, solve each equation, if possible.

5. $5 \cos(x + 10) + 4 = 4$
6. $12 \sin(2x) - 2 = 4$
7. $-14 \cos(4\pi x) + 2 = 9$
8. $9 \sin(3x + 2) - 2 = 16$

For Exercises 9–10, find the maximum and minimum values for each function.

9. $f(x) = 4 \sin x + 8$
10. $g(x) = 2 \cos x - 12$

11. Find a function using cosine or sine that has a maximum of 17 and a minimum of −3.

For Exercises 12–15, find all solutions to each equation if $0 \le x \le 2\pi$.

12. $\sec x = 2$
13. $\csc x = \frac{2}{\sqrt{3}}$
14. $\cot x = 1$
15. $\csc x = -2$

16. Here is the graph of $f(x) = \csc x$ on the interval $-2\pi \le x \le 2\pi$.
   a. Find the domain and range of f.
   b. How many solutions does $\csc x = 0$ have? Explain.
   c. How many solutions does $\csc x = 1$ have? What are they?
   d. Explain why there is a horizontal gap in the graph between the graphs of the equations $y = -1$ and $y = 1$.

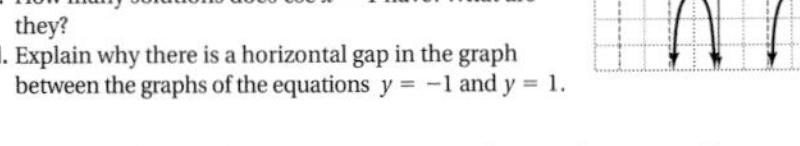

17. Show graphically that there are two solutions to the equation $\csc x = 3$ in the interval $0 \le x \le 2\pi$.

18. Show graphically that there are two solutions to the equation $\cot x = -2$ in the interval $0 \le x \le 2\pi$.

Practice: For Lesson 1.10, assign Exercises 12–18.

9. Show graphically that there are two solutions to the equation

$$\sec x = -2$$

in the interval $0 \le x \le 2\pi$.

10. Use the results from Exercises 6 and 7 to show the following.

$$1 + \tan^2 x = \sec^2 x$$

11. The Pythagorean identity $\cos^2 x + \sin^2 x = 1$ leads to two other major identities.

a. If you divide through each term of $\cos^2 x + \sin^2 x = 1$ by $\cos^2 x$, you will get the following equation.

$$\frac{\cos^2 x}{\cos^2 x} + \frac{\sin^2 x}{\cos^2 x} = \frac{1}{\cos^2 x}$$

You can simplify each of these terms. What do you get after simplifying?

b. Construct a second identity by dividing through by $\sin^2 x$.

12. Use the picture from Exercise 5 to show the following identity.

$$1 + \tan^2 \alpha = \sec^2 \alpha$$

13. **Take It Further** In Investigation 1A, you looked at the slope of lines tangent to the graph of $y = \sin x$. Those slopes approximated the outputs of the function $f(x) = \cos x$. You can apply the same process to $f(x) = \tan x$. Find a function that matches the slopes you find.

14. **Standardized Test Prep** Which of the following is false?

A. $\sin x \cdot \csc x = 1$ for all x in the domain of the cosecant function.

B. $\cos x \cdot \sec x = 1$ for all x in the domain of the secant function.

C. $\tan x \cdot \cot x = 1$ for all x in the domain of both the tangent and cotangent functions.

D. $\cot x = \frac{\sin x}{\cos x}$ for all x in the domain of the cosine function.

Maintain Your Skills

15. Each of these equations has $x = 30°$ as a solution. Find the other solution in the interval $0 \le x \le 360°$.

a. $2 \sin x = 1$ **b.** $2 \cos x = \sqrt{3}$ **c.** $3 \tan x = \sqrt{3}$
d. $\csc x = 2$ **e.** $\sqrt{3} \sec x = 2$ **f.** $\sqrt{3} \cot x = 3$

16. Calculate each of these to three decimal places.

a. $\sin 40°$ **b.** $\sin(180° - 40°)$ **c.** $\cos 40°$
d. $\cos(360° - 40°)$ **e.** $\tan 40°$ **f.** $\tan(180° + 40°)$

Go Online PHSchool.com

For additional practice, go to Web Code: bga-0110

Answers

9. Note that if you graph $y = -2$ on the same axes as in Exercise 8, there are two points of intersection for x in the interval $[0, 2\pi]$.

10. $\sec^2 x = 1 + \sin^2 x + \sin^4 x + \sin^6 x + \ldots$
$= 1 + (\sin^2 x + \sin^4 x + \sin^6 x + \ldots)$
$= 1 + \tan^2 x$

11. a. $1 + \tan^2 x = \sec^2 x$
b. $1 + \cot^2 x = \csc^2 x$

12. $\triangle OAT$ is a right triangle, so $OA^2 + AT^2 = OT^2$. But $OA = 1$, $AT = \tan \alpha$, and $OT = \sec \alpha$. So $1 + \tan^2 \alpha = \sec^2 \alpha$.

13. $y = \sec^2 x$ **14.** D

15. a. 150° **b.** 330° **c.** 210°
d. 150° **e.** 330° **f.** 210°

16. a. 0.643 **b.** 0.643 **c.** 0.766
d. 0.766 **e.** 0.839 **f.** 0.839

In this investigation, you learned the relationship between the tangent function and lines tangent to the unit circle. You defined inverse cosine, sine, and tangent functions by restricting domains. You graphed all six trigonometric functions, including secant, cosecant, and cotangent. The following questions will help you summarize what you have learned.

1. Suppose $\tan x = 2.4$. Find the two possible exact values of $\sec x$.
2. Let $A = (1, 0)$, and let $\widehat{AB}$ be an arc on the unit circle with length α. What is the slope of the line $\overleftrightarrow{OB}$, where O is the origin, in terms of α?
3. Solve the equation $7 \csc 5x - 8 = 6$.
4. Each of these equations has $x = \frac{\pi}{3}$ as a solution. Find the other solution in the interval $0 \leq x \leq 2\pi$.
   a. $2 \cos x = 1$ **b.** $\tan x = \sqrt{3}$ **c.** $\sqrt{3} \csc x = 2$ **d.** $3 \cot x = \sqrt{3}$
5. The figure at the right shows the unit circle with three triangles, $\triangle OSB$, $\triangle OAT$, and $\triangle OPQ$. Point A is at $(1, 0)$ and $\overleftrightarrow{AT}$ is perpendicular to the x-axis. Point P is at $(0, 1)$ and $\overleftrightarrow{PQ}$ is perpendicular to the y-axis. B and T are both on $\overleftrightarrow{OQ}$. You have already seen how $\triangle OSB$ lets you find cosine and sine of α, and how $\triangle OAT$ lets you find tangent and secant of α.

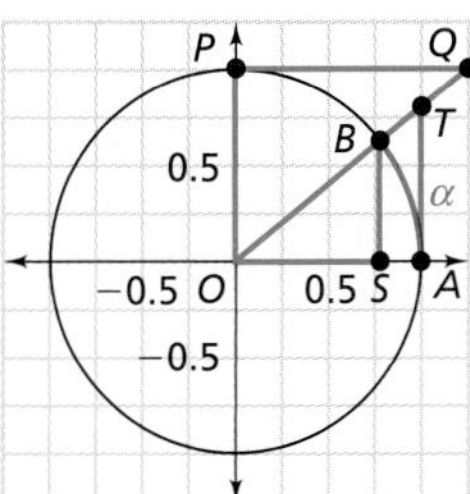

   a. Show that $\triangle OPQ \sim \triangle TAO$.
   b. Use similar triangles to show that the length of $\overline{OQ}$ is equal to $\csc \alpha$ and that the length of $\overline{PQ}$ is equal to $\cot \alpha$.
6. How are the six trigonometric functions defined?
7. Why does the $\sin^{-1}$ function on a calculator in degree mode return only results between −90 and 90 degrees?
8. Solve the equation $\cos x = 0.8$ for x. How many solutions are there?

Vocabulary

In this investigation, you learned these terms. Make sure you understand what each one means and how to use it.

- **asymptote**
- **inverse function**

Mathematical Reflections

EXERCISES 6–8 At the start of the investigation, you may have assigned these as Questions 1–3 for students to think and write about.

Mathematical Reflections

1. ± 2.6 **2.** $\tan \alpha$

3. $\frac{\pi}{30} + \frac{2\pi}{5}n$ and $\frac{\pi}{6} + \frac{2\pi}{5}n$ (n an integer)

4. a. $\frac{5\pi}{3}$ **b.** $\frac{4\pi}{3}$ **c.** $\frac{2\pi}{3}$ **d.** $\frac{4\pi}{3}$

5. a. Since alternate interior angles formed by two parallel lines and a transversal are congruent, $\angle BOA \cong \angle PQO$. The angles of $\triangle OPQ$ and $\triangle TAO$ that have vertices at P and A, respectively, are right angles. Therefore $\triangle OPQ \sim \triangle TAO$ by AA Similarity.

b. $\triangle TAO \sim \triangle BSO$ since these are right triangles with a common acute angle. So $\triangle OPQ \sim \triangle BSO$, and thus $\frac{QP}{OP} = \frac{OS}{BS}$. But $OP = 1$, $OS = \cos \alpha$, and $BS = \sin \alpha$. It follows that $\frac{QP}{1} = \frac{\cos\alpha}{\sin\alpha}$, or $QP = \cot \alpha$. Since $\triangle OPQ \sim \triangle BSO$, it also follows that $\frac{OQ}{OP} = \frac{BO}{BS}$ and hence that $\frac{OQ}{1} = \frac{1}{\sin\alpha}$. Therefore $OQ = \csc \alpha$.

6. Let A be the point with coordinates (1, 0), and let $\widehat{AB}$ be an arc of length α on the unit circle. Then $\cos \alpha$ is the x-coordinate of B and $\sin \alpha$ is the y-coordinate of B. Define $\tan \alpha$ to be $\frac{\sin\alpha}{\cos\alpha}$, where $\alpha \neq (2n + 1)\frac{\pi}{2}$ (n an integer). The other three functions are defined as follows:

$\csc \alpha = \frac{1}{\sin\alpha}$ ($\alpha \neq n\pi$, where n is an integer)

$\sec \alpha = \frac{1}{\cos\alpha}$ ($\alpha \neq (2n + 1)\frac{\pi}{2}$, where n is an integer)

$\cot\alpha = \frac{\cos\alpha}{\sin\alpha}$ ($\alpha \neq n\pi$, where n is an integer).

7. The domain of the sine function is restricted in order to define an inverse relation that will also be a function. The domain is restricted to [−90°, 90°] (or, alternatively, to $\left[-\frac{\pi}{2}, \frac{\pi}{2}\right]$).

8. $\pm\cos^{-1}\left(\frac{4}{5}\right) + 2\pi n$ (n an integer); infinitely many

Investigation Overview

This investigation emphasizes the idea that trigonometric functions are "functions as usual." Once students are familiar with the graphs of the functions defined by $f(x) = \sin x$ and $f(x) = \cos x$, the sinusoidal functions emerge from the same transformations that students used in Chapter 6 of CME Project *Algebra 2*.

De-emphasize memorization. Do not have students memorize a lot of coefficients. Instead, motivate amplitude and phase shift with concrete examples.

In the second lesson, it is important that students understand that trigonometry models two kinds of situations. In both cases, the feature being modeled has a repeating cycle.

In one case, the geometry of the situation has a repeating cycle. For instance the height of a seat on a Ferris wheel has a cycle that is sinusoidal because the seat moves around the wheel.

In the other case, the measurement of a quantity as a function of time or some other quantity is periodic. For instance, the height of the tide over time is periodic.

You may wish to assign Questions 1–3 for students to think and write about during the investigation.

Learning Goals

- Make sense of sinusoidal functions in the context of previous experience.
- Understand the geometry of sinusoidal functions.
- Model with sinusoidal functions.

Habits and Skills

- See that the graph of $y = A\sin(ax + b) + B$ is simply a transformation of the graph of $y = \sin x$.

Sinusoidal Functions and Their Graphs

In *Sinusoidal Functions and Their Graphs*, you will graph translations and dilations of the cosine and sine functions. You will learn how to relate the graphs to the parameters in the sinusoidal forms $A\cos(ax + b) + B$ and $A\sin(ax + b) + B$. You will relate these functions to everyday periodic behavior.

By the end of this investigation, you will be able to answer questions like these.

1. Given the maximum and minimum values of a cosine or sine function, how do you find the amplitude and vertical displacement?
2. How can you make a sinusoidal function that has a specific period?
3. How can you use sinusoidal functions to model periodic phenomena?

You will learn how to

- make sense of sinusoidal functions in the context of previous experience
- understand the geometry of sinusoidal functions
- model with sinusoidal functions

You will develop these habits and skills:

- See the graph of $y = A\sin(ax + b) + B$ is simply a transformation of the basic graph of $y = \sin x$.

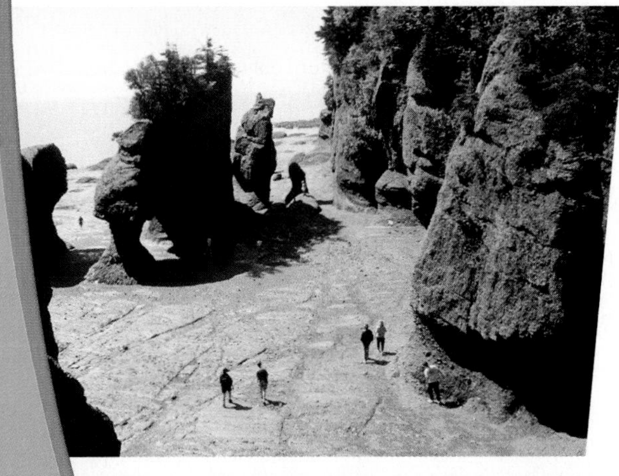

The minimum value of a sinusoidal curve that models the height of the tide represents the height of low tide.

Investigation Road Map

LESSON 1.11, *Getting Started,* introduces sinusoidal functions.

LESSON 1.12, *Sinusoidal Functions,* uses a concrete example to introduce new vocabulary words that describe the characteristics of a graph of a sinusoidal function.

LESSON 1.13, *Applying Trigonometric Functions,* gives students opportunities to build and interpret models with sinusoidal functions.

1.11 Getting Started

As you work though these problems, make sure to write down any conjectures you have about trigonometric functions and their graphs.

For You to Explore

1. Suppose $f(x) = \sin x$. For each function below, sketch its graph and the graph of $y = f(x)$ on the interval $-\pi \le x \le 2\pi$. Describe how the two graphs relate to each other.

   a. $f(2x) = \sin 2x$ b. $f(3x) = \sin 3x$
   c. $f(4x) = \sin 4x$ d. $f(10x) = \sin 10x$

See the TI-Nspire Handbook on p. 704 for ideas about how to graph each function.

2. Let $f(x) = \sin x$ as in Problem 1. For each function below, sketch its graph and the graph of $y = f(x)$ on the interval $-\pi \le x \le 2\pi$. Describe how the two graphs relate to each other.

   a. $2f(x) = 2 \sin x$ b. $5f(x) = 5 \sin x$
   c. $\frac{1}{3}f(x) = \frac{1}{3} \sin x$ d. $-3f(x) = -3 \sin x$

3. Let $g(x) = \cos x$. Sketch the graph of $g(x)$ on the interval $-\pi \le x \le 2\pi$ along with the graph of each of these functions. Describe how the two graphs relate to each other.

   a. $g(x) + 1 = \cos x + 1$ b. $g(x) - 2 = \cos x - 2$
   c. $g(x + 1) = \cos(x + 1)$ d. $g(x - 2) = \cos(x - 2)$

Note the change in order of operations. Add 1, then take the cosine of the result. As usual, use radians unless the degree symbol is present.

4. Sketch the graph of each function.

   a. $A(x) = 3\cos x$ b. $B(x) = 3\cos x - 2$
   c. $C(x) = 3\cos(x - 2)$ d. $D(x) = 2\sin(x + 1) + 2$

5. Find two functions that have graphs that pass through the point $\left(\frac{\pi}{2}, 4\right)$.

6. The function $f(x) = \sin x$ has period 2π. Find a function in the form $h(x) = \sin ax$ with the following period.

   a. period π b. period $\frac{\pi}{2}$
   c. period 4π d. period 2
   e. period 1 f. period 17

Remember...

The *period* of a periodic function is the least positive number p so that $f(x + p) = f(x)$ always. On a graph, it is where the function begins to repeat itself.

7. **Take It Further** Determine the number of intersections of the graphs of the following two equations.

$$y = \sin x$$
$$y = \frac{x}{10}$$

Answers

For You to Explore

1–4. See back of book.

5. Answers may vary. Sample: $y = 4 \sin x$, $y = 4$

6. a. $h(x) = \sin 2x$
b. $h(x) = \sin 4x$
c. $h(x) = \sin \frac{x}{2}$
d. $h(x) = \sin \pi x$
e. $h(x) = \sin 2\pi x$
f. $h(x) = \sin \frac{2}{17}\pi x$

7. 7 points of intersection

Lesson Overview

GOAL

- Warm up to the ideas of the investigation.

This lesson introduces sinusoidal functions. As always in a Getting Started, there is no need to formalize these ideas today. Students will meet all of the ideas again throughout the investigation.

FOR YOU TO EXPLORE
- Core: 1, 2, 3, 6
- Optional: 4, 5
- Extension: 7

MATERIALS
- graphing calculators
- Blackline Masters MC4, MC7, BM1.11

HOMEWORK
- Core: 8, 9, 10, 11
- Optional: 12, 13, 14

Launch

You may wish to have students work in pairs or small groups.

Explore

For You to Explore

Use Blackline Master MC4 on an overhead to provide students help in sketching the graphs. The Blackline Master shows only part of the interval the students will graph.

PROBLEM 1 is a good spot to remind students they can model $f(2x)$ and other functions on a graphing calculator. If they define $f(x)$, students can type the exact expression $f(2x)$.

PROBLEM 5 Not all the solutions students find will be trigonometric functions, but if you discuss this problem, look for at least one or two trigonometric functions that do this.

Wrap Up

Before assigning homework, allow students some time to discuss and summarize their findings in Problems 1 and 2.

Exercises

HOMEWORK
- Core: 8, 9, 10, 11
- Optional: 12, 13, 14

On Your Own

EXERCISES 9–12 Use Blackline Master MC7 to prepare an accurate sketch of the graph before class.

Exercises *Practicing Habits of Mind*

On Your Own

8. Find a solution to this equation.

$$6\cos(\pi(x-1)) + 2 = 5$$

Exercises 9 through 12 refer to the graph and function below.

$$H(t) = 36\cos\left(\frac{2\pi}{60}t\right) + 39$$

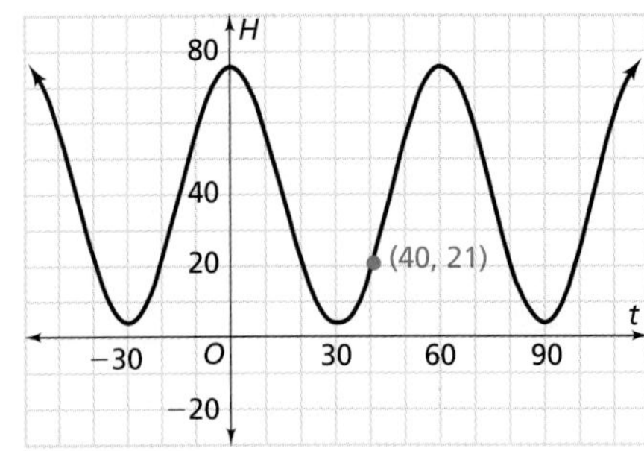

9. Use the graph of H to answer these questions.

a. What is the maximum possible output of H?

b. What is the minimum possible output of H?

c. What is the period of H?

10. a. What appears to be the average value of H?

b. How far is it from the average value of H to the maximum?

c. How far is it from the average value of H to the minimum?

11. According to the graph, $H(40) = 21$.

a. Using the symmetry of the graph, find the one positive value of $t < 40$ with $H(t) = 21$.

b. Use the period of this function to find the next two values of t with $H(t) = 21$.

Answers

Exercises

8. Answers may vary. Sample: $\frac{4}{3}$

9. a. 75 **b.** 3 **c.** 60

10. a. 39 **b.** 36 **c.** 36

11. a. 20

b. The next two positive solutions are 40 and 80.

12. a. Find a value of t, that makes $H(t) = 55$. In other words, find a solution to the equation

$$55 = 36 \cos\left(\frac{2\pi}{60}t\right) + 39$$

Round your answer to two decimal places.

b. Find the next two larger values of t with $H(t) = 55$.

13. Determine the number of intersections of the graphs of these two equations.

$$y = \tan x$$
$$y = \frac{x}{10}$$

Draw a picture. Try sketching the graphs.

Maintain Your Skills

14. Copy and complete this table. Each column is a new instance of the variables D and A.

$D + A$	■	■	23	46	100	75	−10	x
D	7	−5	10	20	■	■	■	■
A	3	7	■	■	■	■	■	■
$D - A$	■	■	■	■	40	3	−32	y

Sinusoidal patterns are common in the natural world.

12. a. Answers may vary. Sample: 10.60
b. based on the answer for part (a): 49.40 and 70.60

13. infinitely many points of intersection

14.

$D + A$	10	2	23	46	100	75	−10	x
D	7	−5	10	20	70	39	−21	$\frac{x+y}{2}$
A	3	7	13	26	30	36	11	$\frac{x-y}{2}$
$D - A$	4	−12	−3	−6	40	3	−32	y

Maintain Your Skills

EXERCISE 14 Point out that the column in the table with $D + A = 75$ and $D - A = 3$ corresponds to the equation, $H(t) = 36\cos(\text{anything}) + 39$, in On Your Own for the case that gave a maximum value of 75 and a minimum of 3. You may wish to provide students with copies of BM1.11 to fill in the table.

Lesson Overview

GOALS

- Make sense of sinusoidal functions in the context of previous experience.
- Understand the geometry of sinusoidal functions.

This lesson uses a concrete example to introduce the following terminology that describes the characteristics of the graph of a sinusoidal function:

- vertical displacement
- amplitude
- period (revisited from Investigation 1A)
- phase shift

CHECK YOUR UNDERSTANDING
- Core: 1, 5
- Optional: 2, 4, 6, 7
- Extension: 3

MATERIALS
- CAS (recommended)
- graphing calculators
- Blackline Masters MC4, MC7, BM1.12

HOMEWORK
- Core: 8, 9, 12, 13, 15
- Optional: 10, 11, 14, 16

VOCABULARY
- amplitude
- phase shift
- sinusoidal function
- vertical displacement

Launch

Open this lesson by asking students to describe what they think the graph of $H(x) = 36\cos\left(2x - \frac{\pi}{3}\right) + 39$ will look like.

Use Blackline Master BM1.12 on an overhead throughout the presentation to summarize the results after each definition.

1.12 Sinusoidal Functions

Unlike polynomials, trigonometric functions are periodic. For example, cosine and sine are periodic with period 2π. For any real number x

$$\cos(x + 2\pi) = \cos x \quad \text{and} \quad \sin(x + 2\pi) = \sin x$$

Because they are periodic, you can use them to model many periodic phenomena like the height of a rider as a Ferris wheel turns or the heights of the tides in the ocean as the day progresses. Actually, you can not model physical situations well directly simply by using cosine and sine. You need a wider class of functions that you could call *sinusoidal.*

Habits of Mind

Recognize periodicity. This is a direct consequence of the definition of cosine and sine and the way you extended the definition from acute angles to any angle and then from angles to radians. Look back at the definitions in Investigation 1A.

Definition

A sinusoidal function is a function that is defined by a formula of the form

$$f(x) = A\cos(ax + b) + B \text{ or } f(x) = A\sin(ax + b) + B$$

where A, B, a, and b are real numbers.

As you will see in this investigation, if you model a function with one of these formulas, you can also model the function with the other formula.

Look at an example.

Example

Problem Let

$$H(x) = 36\cos\left(2x - \frac{\pi}{3}\right) + 39$$

a. Sketch the graph of the equation $y = H(x)$.

b. What appears to be the average value of H?

c. How far is it from the average value of H to the maximum?

d. How far is it from the average value of H to the minimum?

e. What is the period of H?

Solution

a. Use Derman's replacing-the-axis method from CME Project *Algebra 2.* First, rewrite the equation

$$y = 36\cos\left(2x - \frac{\pi}{3}\right) + 39$$

as

$$\frac{y - 39}{36} = \cos\left(2x - \frac{\pi}{3}\right)$$

Then let

$$M = 2x - \frac{\pi}{3} \text{ and } N = \frac{y - 39}{36}$$

Upon making these substitutions, you have

$$N = \cos M$$

Its graph appears below.

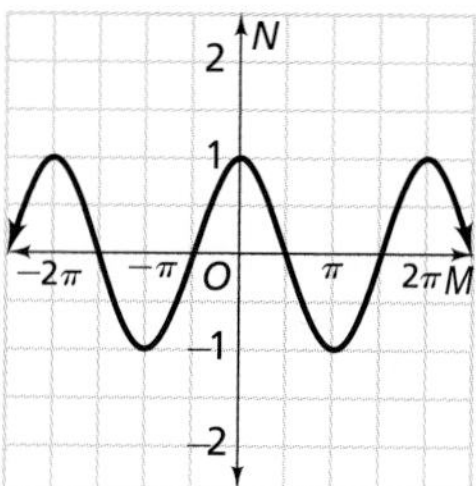

Since

$$M = 2x - \frac{\pi}{3}$$

$$= 2\left(x - \frac{\pi}{6}\right)$$

you have

$$x = \frac{M}{2} + \frac{\pi}{6}$$

And below is a pair of number lines depicting the relationship between M and x.

-2π	$-\pi$	0	π	2π	M
$-\frac{5\pi}{6}$	$-\frac{2\pi}{6}$	$\frac{\pi}{6}$	$\frac{4\pi}{6}$	$\frac{7\pi}{6}$	x

Likewise, $N = \frac{y - 39}{36}$ implies

$$y = 36N + 39$$

which gives the following pair of number lines relating N and y.

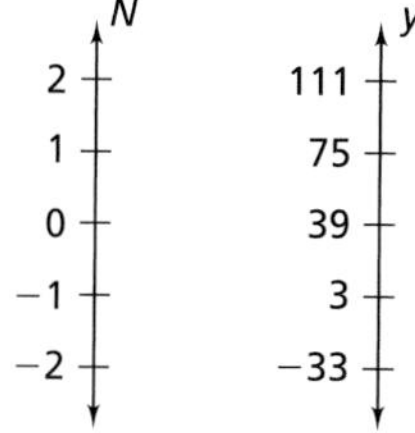

Finally, take the graph of $N = \cos M$ and

- replace the M-axis with the x-axis.
- replace the N-axis with the y-axis.

Explore

Example

Spend time as needed going over this Example. Make sure students understand the problem. As necessary, help them develop the detailed solution.

Use Blackline Master MC7 to sketch the graph on an overhead.

The resulting graph appears below.

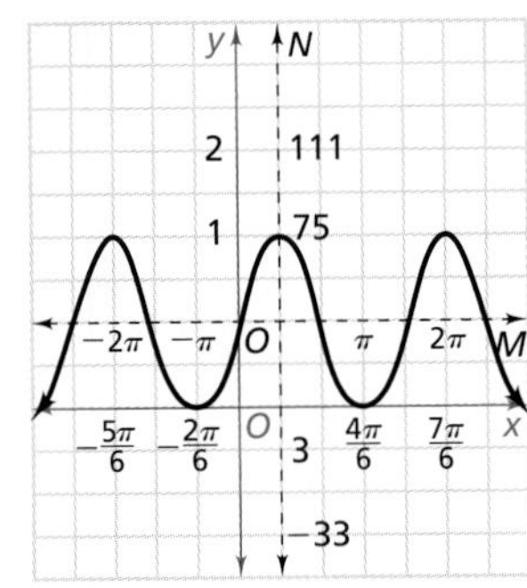

b. The horizontal dotted line, which is the graph of the equation $y = 39$, tells you that the average value of H is 39.

c. The maximum value of H occurs when $\cos M = 1$. The maximum is

$$36 \cdot 1 + 39 = 75$$

Thus, the distance from the average value to the maximum is

$$75 - 39 = 36$$

d. The minimum value of H occurs where $\cos M = -1$.
The minimum is 3. Thus, the distance from the average value to the minimum is

$$39 - 3 = 36$$

You could also use the graph of H to see the values of the maximum and minimum.

Note that the average value is equidistant to the maximum and the minimum.

e. Pick the point $\left(\frac{\pi}{6}, 75\right)$ as a reference point. The graph of $y = H(x)$ starts to repeat itself at $\left(\frac{7\pi}{6}, 75\right)$. Thus, the period of H is

$$\frac{7\pi}{6} - \frac{\pi}{6} = \pi$$

Remember...

You can find the period by looking for where the graph begins to repeat itself.

The following definitions introduce some new terms that describe the characteristics of the graph of a sinusoidal function.

Definitions

Let *f* be a sinusoidal function.

The vertical displacement of *f* is its average value. More precisely, it is the average of the maximum and the minimum values of *f*.

The amplitude of *f* is the distance from its average value to the maximum or the minimum value.

Note that the amplitude is always positive.

For You to Do

1. Find the amplitude and the vertical displacement of
$$H(x) = 36\cos\left(2x - \frac{\pi}{3}\right) + 39$$
2. Find the amplitude and the vertical displacement of
$$g(x) = 5\sin 2x - 7$$
3. Find the amplitude and the vertical displacement of
$$f(x) = A\cos(ax + b) + B$$

The amplitude and the vertical displacement of
$$f(x) = A\cos(ax + b) + B \text{ or } f(x) = A\sin(ax + b) + B$$
describe how the graph of f relates to the graph of $N = \sin M$. More specifically, they describe how you transform the graph of $N = \sin M$ vertically to obtain the graph of $y = f(x)$. The next two concepts deal with how you transform the graph of $N = \sin M$ horizontally to obtain the graph of a sinusoidal function.

Minds in Action episode 3

Derman and Tony are working on Exercise 6 on page 57.

Derman Okay, we need a function $h(x) = \sin ax$ with period π.

Tony Well, $f(x) = \sin x$ has period 2π and the graph of $y = f(2x)$ is the same as the graph of $y = f(x)$, except it's shrunk horizontally by the factor $\frac{1}{2}$.

Derman So the period of $f(2x) = \sin 2x$ is half of 2π, which is π.

Tony Right. How about a function $h(x) = \sin ax$ with period 2?

Derman We'd want it to shrink by the factor of, I think, 1 over π?

Tony That looks good. I guess it would be $f(\pi x) = \sin \pi x$.

Derman Fine, but what about this period 17? That seems tougher.

Tony It is. But I think you can use the one with period 2. So we could scale it by $\frac{1}{\pi}$ then adjust the coefficient to become 17.

Derman What?

Tony Instead of scaling by $\frac{1}{\pi}$, we could scale by $\frac{17}{2\pi}$.
$$f\left(\frac{2\pi}{17}x\right) = \sin\frac{2\pi}{17}x$$

Derman I put that in the calculator and it worked great! I bet we could do this for any period P by replacing the 17.

Answers

For You to Do

1. amplitude = 36, vertical displacement = 39
2. amplitude = 5, vertical displacement = −7
3. amplitude = $|A|$, vertical displacement = B

For You to Do

PROBLEMS 1–3 Have students practice the ideas just introduced by doing these problems.

Minds in Action

You may wish to assign students Minds in Action roles and present the conversation to the class. This is more effective if you assign the roles one class day prior to the "performance." Urge the students to "get into" their parts by using their own words instead of memorizing lines.

For Discussion

PROBLEMS 4–6 Use the For Discussion problems to elicit conversation about the key ideas that immediately precede this section.

Use Blackline Master MC4 to help illustrate the discussion of the phase shift.

Tony Yes. I think that works. We want to scale the graph of $y = f(x)$ horizontally by a factor of $\frac{P}{2\pi}$. So the function would be

$$f\left(\frac{2\pi}{P}x\right) = \sin\frac{2\pi}{P}x$$

Derman And that has period P.

For Discussion

4. In terms of a, find the period of the sinusoidal function

$$f(x) = \sin ax$$

5. Find the period of the sinusoidal function

$$f(x) = A\sin(ax + b) + B$$

6. Find a sinusoidal function with period 3.

Finally, compare the graphs of

$$y = \cos x \text{ and } y = \cos\left(x - \frac{\pi}{6}\right)$$

which appears below.

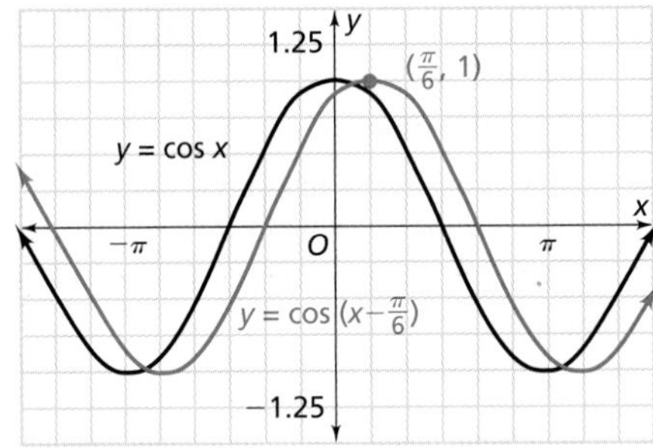

To obtain the graph of $y = \cos\left(x - \frac{\pi}{6}\right)$, shift the graph of $y = \cos x$ to the right by $\frac{\pi}{6}$ units. Thus, the function $y = \cos\left(x - \frac{\pi}{6}\right)$ has a phase shift of $\frac{\pi}{6}$. Here is the precise definition.

Phase shift is positive because you shifted the graph of $y = \cos x$ to the right.

Definition

Let

$$f(x) = A\cos(ax + b) + B \text{ or } f(x) = A\sin(ax + b) + B$$

be a sinusoidal function. The phase shift of f is the amount of horizontal translation required to obtain the graph of $y = f(x)$ from the graph of

$$y = A\cos ax \text{ or } y = A\sin ax$$

Answers

For Discussion

4. $\frac{2\pi}{a}$
5. $\frac{2\pi}{a}$
6. Answers may vary. Sample: $y = \sin\frac{2\pi}{3}x$

For You to Do

7. Consider again the function

$$H(x) = 36\cos\left(2x - \frac{\pi}{3}\right) + 39$$

What is its phase shift? Explain your reasoning.

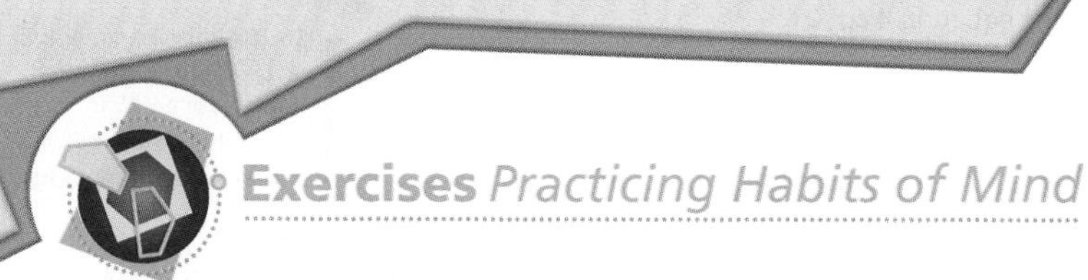

Check Your Understanding

1. Here is the graph of a sinusoidal function f.

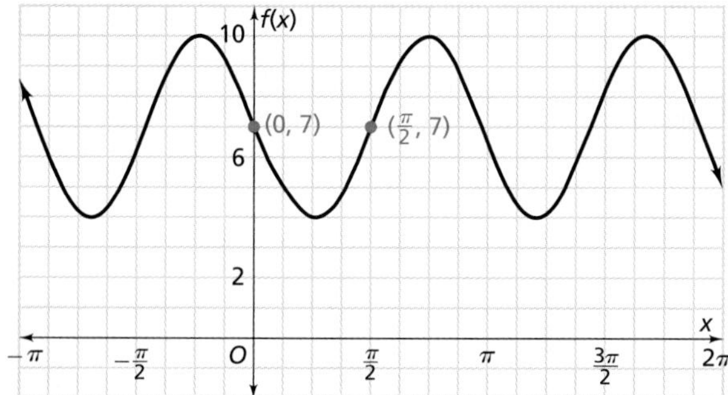

a. Find the amplitude and vertical displacement of f.

b. Find the period of f.

c. If you write f as a cosine, find a value for the phase shift. (There is more than one possible answer.)

d. Write f in the form

$$f(x) = A\cos(ax + b) + B$$

that could generate this graph.

Some of the values of A, B, a, and b might be negative.

2. Find a function in the form

$$f(x) = A\sin(ax + b) + B$$

that generates the graph in Exercise 1.

For You to Do

7. $\frac{\pi}{6}$; $H(x) = 36\cos\left(2\left(x - \frac{\pi}{6}\right)\right) + 39$

Exercises

1. a. amplitude = 3, vertical displacement = 7

b. π

c. Answers may vary. Sample: $\frac{\pi}{2}$

d. Answers may vary. Sample: $f(x) = -3\cos 2\left(x - \frac{\pi}{4}\right) + 7$

2. $f(x) = -3\sin 2x + 7$

Wrap Up

To end this day, go over Exercise 5 as a class.

Assessment Resources

Lesson Quiz 1.12

1. Here is the graph of a sinusoidal function.

a. Find the amplitude and vertical displacement of this function.

b. Find the period of this function.

c. Does this function have a phase shift? Explain.

d. Write a function $f(x) = A\cos(ax + b) + B$ that could generate this graph.

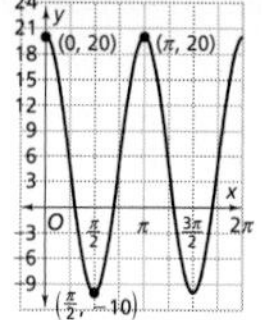

2. Consider the function $h(x) = 32\sin\left(\frac{\pi}{8}(x - 78)\right) + 21$.

a. What is the amplitude of this function?

b. What is the vertical displacement of h?

c. What is the period of h?

d. What is the phase shift of h?

Exercises

HOMEWORK

- Core: 8, 9, 12, 13, 15
- Optional: 10, 11, 14, 16

3. **Take It Further** It is possible to write a function that generates the graph in Exercise 1 with no phase shift. How?

4. **a.** Find one solution to the equation $4\cos 2x + 3 = 5$.
   b. Sketch the graph of $y = 4\cos 2x + 3$. Show how you could use this graph to locate solutions to the equation $4\cos 2x + 3 = 5$.
   c. Find all solutions to the equation $4\cos 2x + 3 = 5$.

See TI-Nspire Handbook on p. 704 for ideas about how to use a CAS to solve equations like this.

5. Consider the function

$$g(x) = 13\sin(4x - \pi) + 10$$

   a. Show that $\left(\frac{\pi}{4}, 10\right)$ must be on the graph of g.
   b. Find the amplitude and vertical displacement of g.
   c. Find the maximum and minimum of g.
   d. Find the period of g.
   e. Sketch the graph of $y = g(x)$.

6. **a.** Sketch the graph of $h(x) = \cos^2 x$.
   b. Assume this function is sinusoidal. Find its amplitude, vertical displacement, and period.

You will probably have to enter this as $(\cos x)^2$ on the calculator.

7. The graph of $h(x) = \cos^2 x$ appears sinusoidal. Use your results from Exercise 6 to write another expression for $\cos^2 x$ in the form $A\cos ax + B$.

On Your Own

8. Here is the graph of a sinusoidal function.

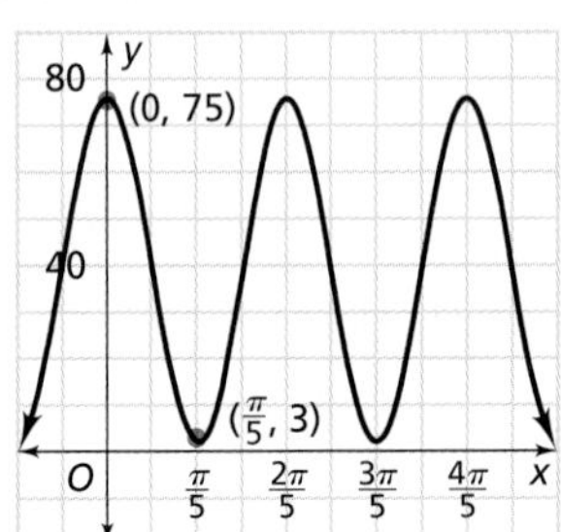

   a. Find the amplitude and vertical displacement of this function.
   b. Find the period of this function.
   c. Explain why you can write this function as a cosine with no phase shift.
   d. Write a function in the form $f(x) = A\cos ax + B$ that could generate this graph.

Answers

3. $f(x) = -3\sin 2x + 7$

4. a. Answers may vary. Sample: $\frac{\pi}{6}$

b.

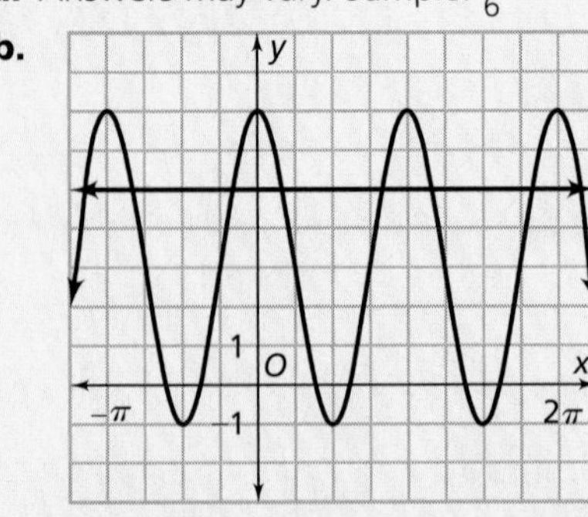

Find the x-coordinates of the points of intersection of the graphs.

c. $\frac{\pi}{6} + n\pi$ and $\frac{5\pi}{6} + n\pi$ (n an integer)

5. a. $g(x) = 13\sin\left(4 \cdot \frac{\pi}{4} - \pi\right) + 10$
$= 13\sin 0 + 10 = 10$

b. amplitude = 13, vertical displacement = 10

c. maximum = 23, minimum = −3

d. $\frac{\pi}{2}$

e.

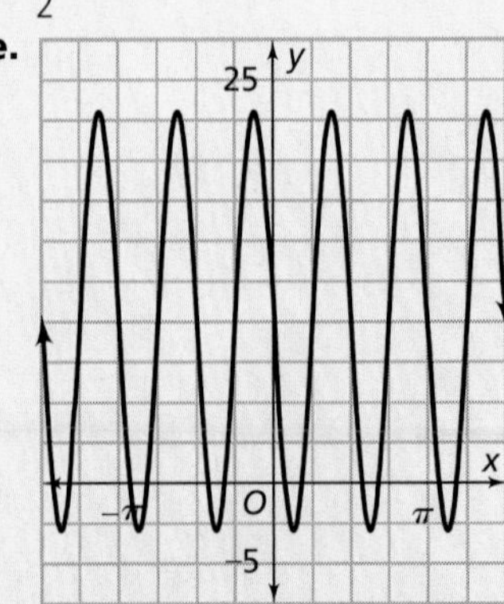

6. a.

h
1
x
$-\pi$
O
2π

b. amplitude $= \frac{1}{2}$, vertical displacement $= \frac{1}{2}$, period $= \pi$

9. **a.** Show that for all numbers x, $\sin\left(x + \frac{\pi}{2}\right) = \cos x$

b. Graph the equations $y = \sin\left(x + \frac{\pi}{2}\right)$ and $y = \cos x$ on the same axes.

10. Here is the graph of $g(x) = \cos x \sin x$, the product of the cosine and sine functions.

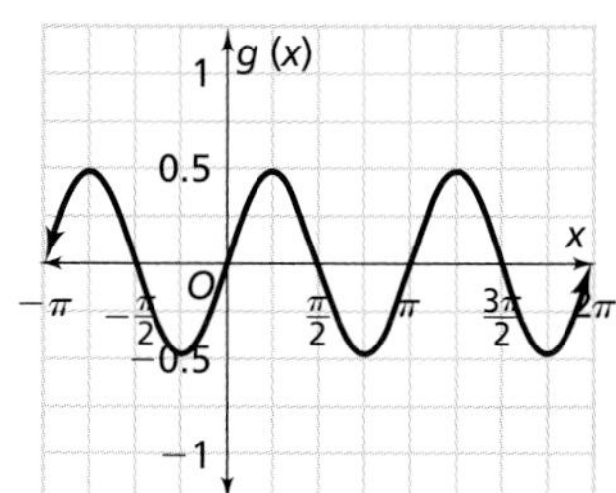

Assume that g is sinusoidal. Find its amplitude, vertical displacement, and period.

11. The graph of $g(x) = \cos x \sin x$ appears sinusoidal. Use your results from Exercise 10 to write another expression for $\cos x \sin x$ in the form

$$\cos x \sin x = A \sin ax + B$$

12. What is the period of the sinusoidal function $f(x) = A \sin(ax + b) + B$?

13. Consider the function

$$h(x) = 20 \cos\left(\frac{2\pi}{7}(x - 4)\right) + 26$$

Evaluate each of these.

a. $h(4)$ **b.** $h(11)$ **c.** $h(18)$ **d.** $h(-3)$

e. Function h is periodic. What is its period?

14. Write an equation for a sinusoidal function with period 5.

15. **Standardized Test Prep** Which of the following represents the average value of the function $f(x) = A\cos(B(x - C)) + D$?

A. A **B.** B **C.** C **D.** D

Go Online
PHSchool.com

For additional practice, go to **Web Code:** bga-0112

Maintain Your Skills

16. Write an equation for a sinusoidal function with each given period.

a. π **b.** 4π

c. 10π **d.** $n\pi$, $n \neq 0$

Additional Resources

PRINT RESOURCES
- Solution Manual
- Practice Workbook
- Assessment Resources
- Teaching Resources

TECHNOLOGY
- Interactive Textbook
- TeacherExpress CD-ROM
- ExamView CD-ROM
- PHSchool.com

Additional Practice

1. Here is the graph of a sinusoidal function:
   a. Find the amplitude and vertical displacement of this function.
   b. Find the period of this function.
   c. Write a function in the form $f(x) = A \sin ax + B$ that could generate this graph.

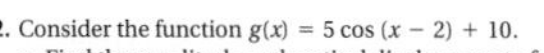

2. Consider the function $g(x) = 5\cos(x - 2) + 10$.
   a. Find the amplitude and vertical displacement of g.
   b. Find the maximum and minimum of g.
   c. Find the period of g.
   d. Sketch the graph of $y = g(x)$ on the interval $0 \leq x \leq 2\pi$.

3. **a.** Find one solution to the equation $6 \sin 2x + 5 = 8$.
   b. Sketch the graph of $y = 6 \sin 2x + 5$. Show how you could use this graph to locate solutions to the equation $6 \sin 2x + 5 = 8$.
   c. Find all solutions to the equation $6 \sin 2x + 5 = 8$.

4. **a.** Show that for all numbers x, $\cos\left(\frac{\pi}{2} + x\right) = -\sin x$.
   b. Graph the equations $y = \cos\left(\frac{\pi}{2} + x\right)$ and $y = -\sin x$ on the same axes.

5. Consider the function

$$f(x) = 18 \sin\left(\frac{2\pi}{9}(x - 6)\right) + 24$$

Evaluate each of these.
a. $f(6)$ **b.** $f(15)$
c. $f(24)$ **d.** $f(33)$
e. Function f is periodic. What is its period?

Practice: For Lesson 1.12, assign Exercises 1–5.

7. $\frac{1}{2}\cos 2x + \frac{1}{2}$

8. **a.** amplitude $= 36$, vertical displacement $= 39$

   b. $\frac{2\pi}{5}$

   c. The function has a maximum for $x = 0$.

   d. $f(x) = 36 \cos 5x + 39$

9. **a.** $\sin\left(x + \frac{\pi}{2}\right) = \cos\left(\frac{\pi}{2} - \left(x + \frac{\pi}{2}\right)\right) = \cos(-x) = \cos x$

   b.

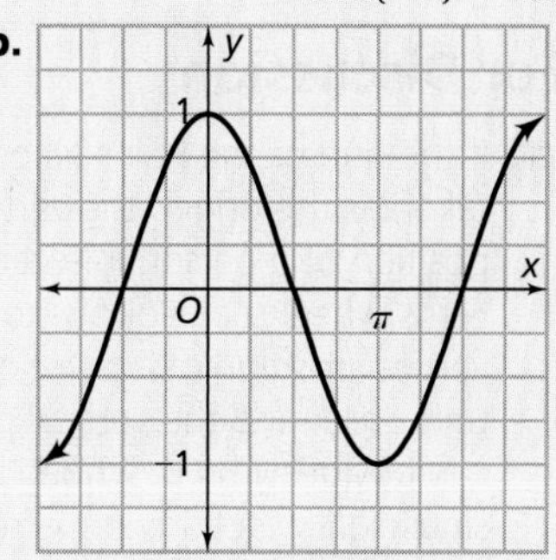

10. amplitude $= \frac{1}{2}$, vertical displacement $= 0$, period $= \pi$

11. $\frac{1}{2}\sin 2x$

12. $\frac{2\pi}{|a|}$

13. **a.** 46 **b.** 46 **c.** 46 **d.** 46 **e.** 7

14. Answers may vary. Sample: $f(x) = \sin\frac{2\pi}{5}x$

15. D

16. Answers may vary. Equations of the forms given below will work for any constants A ($A \neq 0$), B, and D.

   a. $f(x) = A\sin\left(2x + B\right) + D$

   b. $f(x) = A\sin\left(\frac{1}{2}x + B\right) + D$

   c. $f(x) = A\sin\left(\frac{1}{5}x + B\right) + D$

   d. $f(x) = A\sin\left(\frac{2}{n}x + B\right) + D$ $(n \neq 0)$

Lesson Overview

GOAL

- Model with sinusoidal functions.

This lesson gives students equations of a sinusoidal function $f(x)$ and asks them to find the vertical displacement, the amplitude, the period, and the phase shift. It also gives them graphs of sinusoidal functions and asks them to find equations for the graphs.

Students also see two kinds of models. The trigonometric model comes right from the geometry of the situation—the ferris wheel, for example. Here you know that the height is sinusoidal because moving around the wheel is like moving around the unit circle. The second model is inferred by the periodic nature of the situation and by empirical measurements—the tides (or population growth), for example.

CHECK YOUR UNDERSTANDING

- Core: 1, 2, 4, 5, 6, 7
- Optional: 3, 8a–b
- Extension: 8c

MATERIALS

- graphing calculators
- Blackline Master BM1.13

HOMEWORK

- Core: 9, 17
- Optional: 10, 11, 12, 13, 14, 15, 18, 19
- Extension: 16

Launch

Begin this lesson with the discussion of Ferris wheels at the start of the lesson.

Explore

For Discussion

PROBLEM 1 You define the cosine and sine functions using the coordinates (x, y) of a point as it moves around the unit circle. Moving around the Ferris wheel is like moving around the unit circle. Thus, the person's height, which may be thought of as her y-coordinate, can be modeled by a sinusoidal function.

1.13 Applying Trigonometric Functions

In this lesson, you will study some applications of sinusoidal functions. Sinusoidal functions model many phenomena in the world, such as the Ferris wheel, the heights of tides, and lengths of days over the course of a year.

For Discussion

1. Suppose $f(t)$ describes the height of a person on a Ferris wheel after some time t. Based on what you know about how cosine and sine functions are defined using the unit circle, explain why $f(t)$ must be a sinusoidal function.

Remember Paul and Saul from Investigation 1A? Well, their younger brother Gaul also walks around a circle, but a much larger one with a radius of 36 feet. Gaul starts at the point $(36, 0)$ and walks counterclockwise. He takes only 60 seconds to travel one lap around the circle.

The center of the circle is at the origin.

Example 1

Problem

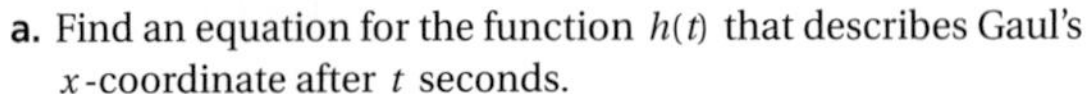

a. Find an equation for the function $h(t)$ that describes Gaul's x-coordinate after t seconds.

b. Suppose instead that the center of the circle is at the point $(39, 0)$. Find an equation for $h(t)$ and sketch its graph.

Solution

a. Since Gaul's circle is the unit circle scaled by a factor of 36, the definition of the cosine function implies

$$h(t) = 36 \cos(at)$$

for some parameter a. You saw in the last lesson that

$$a = \frac{2\pi}{P}$$

where P is the period of h. Since it takes Gaul 60 seconds to make one revolution, you have $P = 60$. Therefore, $a = \frac{2\pi}{60}$ and you have

$$h(t) = 36 \cos\left(\frac{2\pi}{60} t\right)$$

Given a real number t, locate the point on the unit circle that is at an angle t radians (measured counter-clockwise from the positive x-axis). By definition, this point has coordinates $(\cos t, \sin t)$.

Answers

For Discussion

1. If the hub of the Ferris wheel is taken as the origin, the vertical position of a person in a cab of the Ferris wheel is analogous to the vertical position of a point on the unit circle, and the vertical position can obviously be described by a sinusoidal function. In the real world, the hub of the Ferris wheel is above ground level, you need to take a vertical displacement into account.

b. If you were to locate the center of the circle at (39, 0). Gaul's x-coordinate simply increases by 39 units at every point on his path. Therefore, you have

$$h(t) = 36 \cos\left(\frac{2\pi}{60} t\right) + 39$$

Its graph appears below.

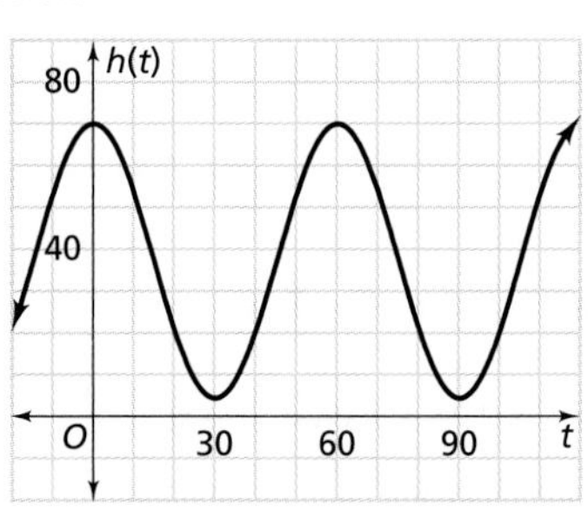

What happens to his y-coordinates?

Now consider a Ferris wheel with the following specifications.

- It makes a full revolution every 60 seconds.
- Its maximum height is 75 feet.
- Its minimum height is 3 feet.

Then the center of the Ferris wheel must be at the average of the maximum and the minimum heights.

$$\frac{1}{2}(75 + 3) = 39$$

or 39 feet. The radius of the wheel must be the difference of the maximum height and the average value.

$$75 - 39 = 36$$

Or $39 - 3 = 36$ feet.

or 36 feet. Let $H(t)$ denote the height of a person on this Ferris wheel t seconds after he or she is at the highest point of the wheel.

For Discussion

2. Explain why

$$H(t) = 36 \cos\left(\frac{2\pi}{60} t\right) + 39$$

In other words, explain why $H(t)$ equals the function describing Gaul's x-coordinate when his circle has center at (39, 0).

For Discussion

2. The situation here is much like the situation when you found $h(t)$, except this time the circle is translated up instead of to the right.

Use Blackline Master BM1.13 on an overhead to record the Ferris wheel information. The resulting function $H(t)$ is used in For Discussion and Developing Habits of Mind.

For Discussion

PROBLEM 2 By rotating Gaul's circle with radius 36 feet and center at (39, 0) about the origin by 90° counter-clockwise, you will obtain a circle whose center is at the point (0, 39), which corresponds to the fact that the center of the ferris wheel is at 39 feet. Moreover, what was originally Gaul's x-coordinate is now his y-coordinate, which corresponds to the person's height on the ferris wheel. And on the rotated picture, Gaul starts walking at the point (0, 75), corresponding to the fact that you start counting time when the person is at the peak of the wheel.

Developing Habits of Mind

Have students connect the habits of mind in Developing Habits of Mind with the ways they have used their minds in prior mathematics work and/or in life outside the classroom. In this case you might want to have them think about a current issue in your community. Discuss how knowing the issue from more than one point of view gives you a better understanding of the issue.

For You to Do

PROBLEM 3 Have students practice the ideas just introduced by doing this problem.

Developing Habits of Mind

Think about it another way. You took a rather rigorous approach to finding an equation for $H(t)$, starting from the unit circle definition of the cosine function. In practice, you often skip these steps and conclude that the height of a person on a Ferris wheel must be sinusoidal because moving around the wheel is like moving around the unit circle.

So, you could write

$$H(t) = A\cos(at + b) + B$$

and proceed to find the parameters A, B, a, and b. From the analysis of the Ferris wheel, you can deduce the following

- The amplitude of $H(t)$ equals the radius of the wheel, and thus $A = 36$.
- The vertical displacement of $H(t)$ is the height of the center of the wheel. Therefore $B = 39$.
- The period of $H(t)$ is 60 and so $a = \frac{2\pi}{60}$.
- $H(t)$ assumes its maximum value when $t = 0$. And since you are modeling $H(t)$ using a cosine function, which also assumes its maximum value at $t = 0$, there is no need for horizontal translation. Thus, the phase shift is zero and so $b = 0$.

Therefore, conclude that

$$H(t) = 36\cos\left(\frac{2\pi}{60}t\right) + 39$$

Note that although you could have chosen a sine wave instead, there would be a phase shift involved. Knowing the behavior of the function can help you decide whether to choose a cosine or sine form.

The model comes directly from the geometry of the situation. Here, the person riding the Ferris wheel is moving around a circle, so the definition of cosine and sine dictate that their height over time should be modeled by a sinusoidal function.

Remember...

Circular behavior is often the underlying cause of a sinusoidal function.

You could have also written $H(t) = A\sin(at + b) + B$.

Recall that $t = 0$ when the person is at the peak of the wheel.

For You to Do

3. Consider again the Ferris wheel from the discussion above, but this time, suppose you model it with a sine function—in other words, write

$$H(t) = A\sin(at + b) + B.$$

Find the values of the parameters A, B, a, and b.

Answers

For You to Do

3. $A = 36, B = 39, a = -\frac{2\pi}{60}, b = \frac{\pi}{2}$

You can model many phenomena occurring in nature with sinusoidal functions. For example, consider the example of the tide, the periodic rise and fall of the sea level caused by the gravitational pull of the moon. Observations show that when you graph the height of the tide as a function of time, the resulting graph is approximately a sinusoidal curve.

Example 2

Problem Suppose you have the following information about the height of the tide in a particular region.

- The maximum height (i.e., a high tide) of 10 feet occurred at 8 A.M.
- The minimum height (i.e., a low tide) measured 6 feet.
- On average, high tides occur about every 12.4 hours (i.e., 12 hours and 24 minutes).

Assuming that the height of the tide is a sinusoidal function, find the equation for $H(t)$, the height of the tide t hours after midnight.

Solution Since you are assuming that H is a sinusoidal function, write

$$H(t) = A\cos(at + b) + B$$

and proceed to find the parameters A, B, a, and b.

The average height of the tide is

$$\frac{1}{2}(10 + 6) = 8$$

or 8 feet, and thus the vertical displacement of H is $B = 8$. Moreover, the amplitude of H is

$$10 - 8 = 2$$

That is, $A = 2$. Since H has period $P = 12.4$, you have

$$a = \frac{2\pi}{12.4}$$

Now consider the function

$$f(t) = 2\cos\left(\frac{2\pi}{12.4}t\right) + 8$$

The period of the tide depends mostly on the earth's rotation and the moon's orbit around the earth. If the moon never moved, the period of the tide would be 12 hours, but the moon moves in its orbit a little over that time. Note that it is an underlying circular motion that is responsible for the sinusoidal tide.

Or $8 - 6 = 2$.

Example 2

Spend time as needed going over Example 2. Make sure students understand the problem. As necessary, help them develop the detailed solution.

For Discussion

PROBLEM 4 Use the For Discussion problem to elicit conversation about the key ideas that immediately precede this section.

Wrap Up

To end this day, you might go over Exercise 1 in the Check Your Understanding section.

Assessment Resources

Lesson Quiz 1.13

1. The center of a Ferris wheel is 25 feet above the ground and its highest point is 45 feet above the ground. The Ferris wheel takes 1.25 minutes (1 minute 15 seconds) to make a complete revolution.
   a. What is the minimum height above the ground that the Ferris wheel reaches?
   b. What is the radius of the Ferris wheel?
   c. Write a function $H(t)$ that represents the height of a person of the Ferris wheel t minutes after reaching the highest point of the wheel.
   d. Sketch the graph of this function for two periods.

whose graph appears below.

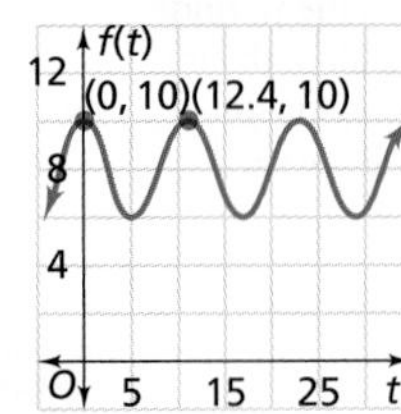

To obtain the graph of H, you need to shift the graph of f to the right by 8 units, reflecting the fact that the high tide occurs at 8 A.M. In other words, H has a phase shift of 8 and thus

$$H(t) = 2\cos\left(\frac{2\pi}{12.4}(t - 8)\right) + 8.$$

Here is the graph of $y = H(t)$.

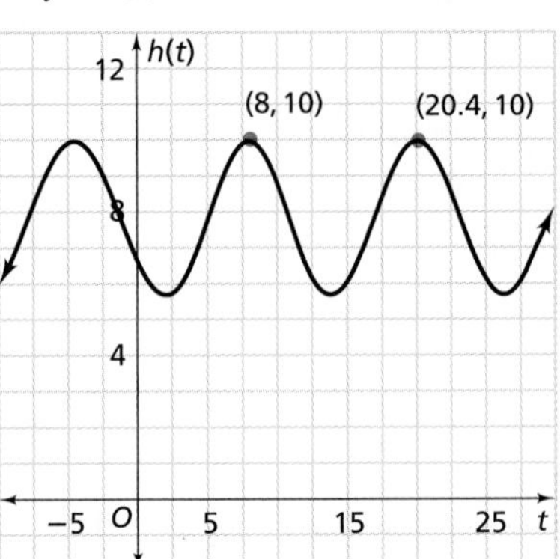

So, $b = -\frac{16\pi}{12.4}$.

For Discussion

4. Explain why, in the above example, you can also obtain the graph of H by translating the graph of f to the left by 4.4 units. What would be the corresponding phase shift and equation for H? And how does this equation relate to the equation

$$H(t) = 2\cos\left(\frac{2\pi}{12.4}(t - 8)\right) + 8$$

that you obtained in the above example?

Answers

For Discussion

4. The period of $H(t)$ is 12.4; −4.4; the graph is shifted 12.4 units to the left.

Exercises *Practicing Habits of Mind*

Check Your Understanding

1. The first ever Ferris wheel had a radius of 125 feet, and a maximum height of 264 feet.

This Ferris wheel made a full revolution every 9 minutes. Write a rule for $H(t)$, the height of a person on this wheel t minutes after they are at the peak of the wheel.

2. Sketch an accurate graph of H from Exercise 1 on the domain $-9 \le t \le 9$.

3. **a.** Find, to the nearest second, the elapsed time for a person on the Ferris wheel in Exercise 1 to go from the top of the wheel to a height of exactly 200 feet.
   b. Use the graph of H from Exercise 2 to locate, approximately, the second time that person will be at a height of exactly 200 feet.
   c. Use the symmetry of the graph of H to give an answer to part(b) that is accurate to the nearest second.

4. On average, high tides occur about every 12 hours and 24 minutes. Suppose a high tide occurred at 8 A.M. this morning.
   a. What time would you predict for the next high tide, and the one after that?
   b. What time would you predict for the next low tide? the next low tide after that?
   c. Sketch, approximately, the graph of the tide's height for 30 hours, starting at 8 A.M. today.

Remember, you will need the amplitude, period, phase shift, and vertical displacement. One of them is zero, probably not the period!

What equation do you need to solve here? How can backtracking help?

Exercises

HOMEWORK
- Core: 9, 17
- Optional: 10, 11, 12, 13, 14, 15, 18, 19
- Extension: 16

Check Your Understanding

EXERCISE 3

Judge for yourself whether an answer in decimal minutes is acceptable.

ERROR PREVENTION Watch out for students using a graphing calculator's intersection tool, rather than backtracking, to solve the first part of this exercise.

Exercises

1. $H(t) = 125 \cos \frac{2\pi}{9}t + 139$
2.

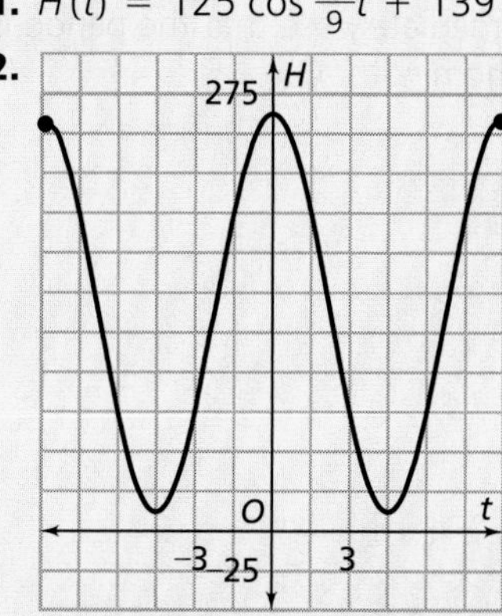

3. **a.** 1 min 31 s
   b. about $7\frac{1}{2}$ min
   c. 7 min 29 s
4. **a.** 8:24 P.M.; 8:48 A.M. (next day)
   b. 2:12 p.m; 2:36 a.m (next day)
   c. The numbers on the x-axis represent minutes.

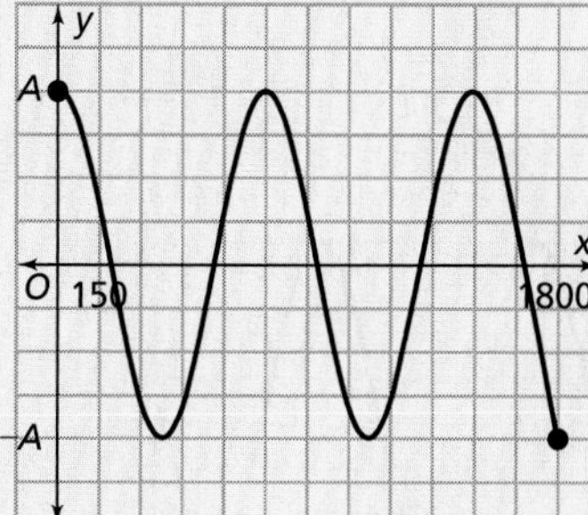

On Your Own

EXERCISE 10 previews the form $s(x) = A\sin 2\pi ft$ used when the frequency of a wave is known. For this form, the period is $\frac{1}{f}$.

5. A reporting station records a high tide of 9 feet at 8 A.M., then a low tide of 2 feet at about 2:12 P.M. Assuming the height of the tide is a sinusoidal function with period 12.4 hours, find an equation for $H(t)$, the height of the tide t hours after midnight.

6. Sketch the graph of the function you found in Exercise 5.

7. Use the equation you found in Exercise 5 to answer these questions.
   a. What is the predicted tide height at noon? at midnight?
   b. What is the height of the tide at 11:06 A.M.?
   c. Find another time when the tide is the same as it is at 11:06 A.M.
   d. Find a time, to the nearest minute, when the tide is 6 feet high.

8. Consider the Ferris wheel on page 69. The wheel has a radius of 36 feet. You travel around it once per 60 seconds.
   a. Find your speed as you move around the Ferris wheel, in feet per second. Drawing a picture of the situation may help.
   b. How fast are you traveling in miles per hour?
   c. **Take It Further** Consider the graph of H, vertical height on this Ferris wheel. At what times t is $H(t)$ changing the fastest? Use a graphing calculator to determine the maximum change in H as a slope, in feet per second.

On Your Own

9. Sketch the graph of this function over two periods.

$$f(x) = 20\cos\left(\frac{2\pi}{7}(x - 4)\right) + 26$$

10. Which of these is the period of $g(t) = 5\sin 100\pi t + 3$?

    A. $\frac{1}{100}$ B. $\frac{1}{50}$ C. 50 D. 100

11. **Write About It** The equation for the Ferris wheel on page 69 is

$$H(t) = 36\cos\left(\frac{2\pi}{60}t\right) + 39$$

You can simplify the fraction $\frac{2\pi}{60}$ to $\frac{\pi}{30}$. Why does it make sense not to simplify this fraction?

Answers

5. $H(t) = 3.5\cos\frac{2\pi}{12.4}(t - 8) + 5.5$

6. 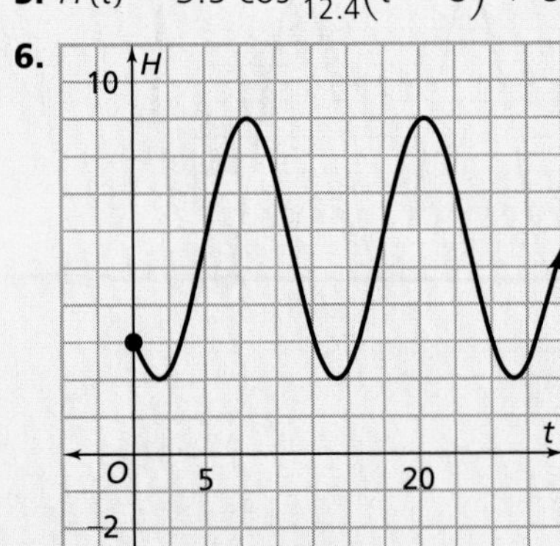

7. a. about 4 ft; about 4.6 ft
   b. about 5.5 ft
   c. Answers may vary. Sample: about 11:30 p.m
   d. Answers may vary. Sample: about 10:49 a.m

8. a. about 3.77 ft/s
   b. about 2.57 mph
   c. The first two times are $t = 15$ s and $t = 45$ s.

9. 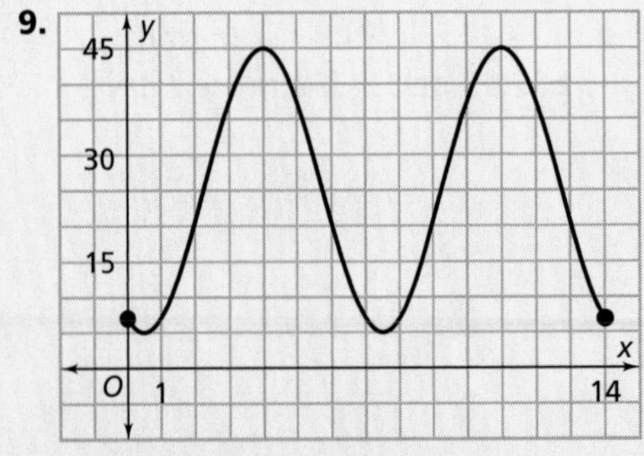

10. B

11. Since the numerator of $\frac{2\pi}{60}$ is 2π, you can immediately see that the period is the denominator 60.

12. Suppose you get on at the bottom of the Ferris wheel described on page 69. Then you start keeping track of time immediately as it moves.

a. Copy and complete this table for your height on the wheel after t seconds.

Assume the Ferris wheel moves at its full speed immediately. Its period is still 60 seconds.

Time t (seconds)	Height $H(t)$ (feet)
0	3
15	■
30	■
45	■
60	■
75	■
90	■

b. Sketch the graph of height against time for this situation.

c. Write an equation for $H(t)$, the height after t seconds, for this situation.

There is more than one possible answer here.

13. Would you move faster if you sat on the Ferris wheel from page 69 or the Ferris wheel from Exercise 1? One completes its rotation more quickly but is smaller in radius.

14. Tide tables report the times and depths of high tides, and the times and depths of low tides. For example, here is part of a tide from Salem, Massachusetts, dated September 19, 2006.

10:14 A.M.	8.14 feet	High Tide
4:05 P.M.	1.27 feet	Low Tide
10:24 P.M.	8.97 feet	High Tide

These tables do not report the tide heights in between. However, there is a guideline called the Rule of Twelfths that you can use to predict the tide each hour (for six hours) between a high and low tide:

Divide the amount the tide changes from high to low (or from low to high) into 12 equal parts. The first hour's gain (or loss) is 1 part (or, $\frac{1}{12}$ of the total change), the second hour is 2 parts, then 3, 3, 2, and 1.

a. Show that the predicted tide at 11:14 A.M. should be about 7.57 feet.

b. Find the predicted tide for 2:14 P.M. using the Rule of Twelfths.

c. Find the predicted tide for 6:05 P.M.

d. Draw a plot that includes the predicted tides from 10:14 A.M. to 10:24 P.M.

15. **Write About It** Describe how the Rule of Twelfths is related to sinusoidal behavior. Why does the rule group the equal parts the way it does?

12. a.

Time t (seconds)	Height $H(t)$
0	3
15	39
30	75
45	39
60	3
75	39
90	75

b.

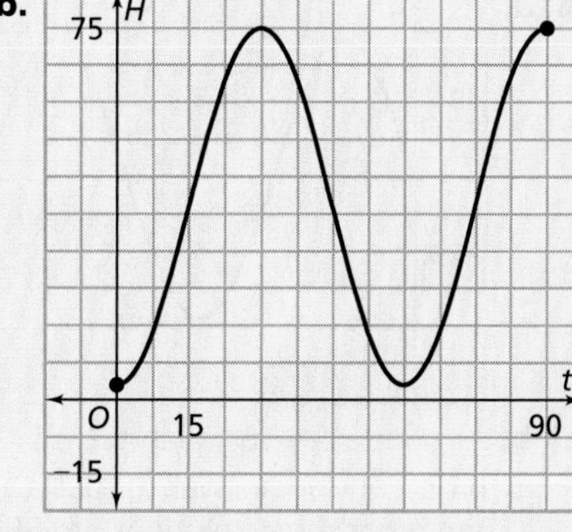

c. $H(t) = 36\cos\left(\pi\left(\frac{t}{30} - 1\right)\right) + 39$

13. the Ferris wheel with radius 36 ft

14. a. $8.14 - \left(\frac{8.14 - 1.27}{12}\right) \approx 7.57$ ft

b. about 2.99 ft

c. about 3.20 ft

d.

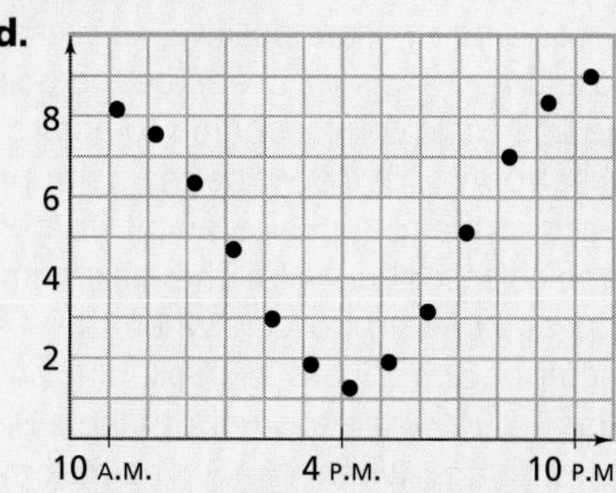

15. The Rule of Twelfths roughly mimics the relative decreases of the cosine function from a maximum point to the succeeding minimum point when you divide the corresponding interval on the horizontal axis into 6 equal parts.

EXERCISE 16 Suggest that students use a graphing calculator to help them judge the behavior of $f(x)$.

Additional Resources

PRINT RESOURCES
- Solution Manual
- Practice Workbook
- Assessment Resources
- Teaching Resources

TECHNOLOGY
- Interactive Textbook
- TeacherExpress CD-ROM
- ExamView CD-ROM
- PHSchool.com

Additional Practice

1. Consider the function $f(x) = 15 \sin(82\pi(t - \pi)) + \frac{3}{2}$.
   a. What is the period of f?
   b. What is the amplitude of f?
   c. What is the phase shift of f?

2. Consider a Ferris wheel with a maximum height of 70 feet and a minimum height of 10 feet. It takes the Ferris wheel 40 seconds to make a full revolution.
   a. Find the height of the center and the radius of the Ferris wheel.
   b. Write a function $H(t)$ that describes the height of a person on the Ferris wheel t seconds after he or she passes the highest point of the wheel.
   c. Sketch the graph of $y = H(t)$.

3. Suppose you have the following information about the height of the tide in Newport, Rhode Island. The maximum height (high tide) of 15 feet occurred at 9:00 A.M. The minimum height (low tide) measured 3 feet. High tide occurs approximately every 12.6 hours (12 hours and 36 minutes).
   a. Assuming that the height of the tide is a sinusoidal function, find an equation $H(t)$ that gives the height of the tide t hours after 6:00 A.M.
   b. What is the height of the tide at noon?
   c. What is the height of the tide at 8:00 P.M.?
   d. Sketch the graph of $y = H(t)$.

4. Sketch the graph of this function over two periods.
$$f(x) = 18 \sin\left(\frac{2\pi}{5}(x - 7)\right) + 4$$

5. Consider the function $g(x) = 6 \cos 48\pi x + 7$.
   a. What is the period of g?
   b. What is the amplitude of g?
   c. What is the phase shift of g?

Practice: For Lesson 1.13, assign Exercises 1–5.

16. **Take It Further** The function $f(x) = \cos x + \sin x$ is sinusoidal.
   a. Using the unit circle, show that the maximum possible value of f is $\sqrt{2}$. For what x does the maximum occur?
   b. Show that the minimum possible value of f is $-\sqrt{2}$. Find where it occurs.
   c. Write an equation for f based on amplitude and phase shift.

Go Online PHSchool.com
For additional practice, go to Web Code: bga-0113

17. **Standardized Test Prep** A Ferris wheel has a radius of 20 feet. The center is 35 feet above the ground and the wheel is rotating counterclockwise at a rate of 1 revolution every π minutes. Which of the following is a function giving the height of a rider in feet at time t minutes if the rider passes location S (35 feet above the ground) at time $t = 0$?
   A. $35 \sin\left(2\left(t - \frac{\pi}{2}\right)\right) + 20$
   B. $20 \sin 2t + 35$
   C. $2 \sin 20t + 35$
   D. $20 \sin (t - 35) + 2$

Maintain Your Skills

18. Consider the function
$$H(t) = 36 \cos\left(\frac{2\pi}{60}(t - 15)\right) + 39$$
   a. Sketch a graph of H on the interval $0 \le t \le 120$.
   b. Find a value of t for which $H(t) = 21$.
   c. Use the graph of H to find the three other values of t between 0 and 120 that make $H(t) = 21$.

How might it help to draw a line on top of the graph of H?

19. Find all the values of t between 0 and 120 that are solutions to the equation
$$36 \cos\left(\frac{2\pi}{60}(t - 5)\right) + 39 = 12$$
to two decimal places.

Answers

16. a. The function will have a maximum when both cos x and sin x are positive, so you can suppose that $0 < x < \frac{\pi}{2}$. Let P be the point on the unit circle corresponding to an arc of length x from (1, 0). Let M be the point on the x-axis at the foot of a segment from P perpendicular to the x-axis. The maximum value of $\cos x + \sin x$ occurs when the perimeter of $\triangle PMO$ has its maximum value, and this occurs when this right triangle is isosceles, that is, when $x = \frac{\pi}{4}$. The maximum is $\frac{\sqrt{2}}{2} + \frac{\sqrt{2}}{2}$, or $\sqrt{2}$.

b. The symmetry of the situation shows that the minimum is $-\sqrt{2}$ and that it occurs when $x = \frac{5\pi}{4}$.

c. Answers may vary. Sample: $f(x) = \sqrt{2} \sin\left(x + \frac{\pi}{4}\right)$

17. B

18. a.

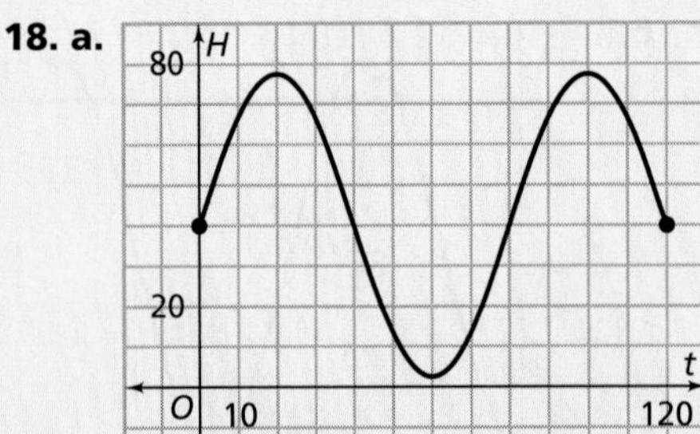

b. Answers may vary. Sample: 35

c. Based on the answer for part (b), the other three solutions are 55, 95, and 115.

19. 38.10, 51.90, 98.10, and 111.90

In this investigation, you studied graphs, properties, and applications of sinusoidal functions. The following questions will help you summarize what you have learned.

1. Suppose a Ferris wheel has a radius of 78 feet and a minimum height of 10 feet. It makes a full revolution every 6 minutes. Let $H(t)$ denote the height of a person on this wheel t minutes after they are at the highest point of the wheel.
   a. Sketch the graph of H on the domain $-6 \le t \le 6$.
   b. Find an equation for $H(t)$.
2. Find the amplitude, vertical displacement, period, and phase shift of the sinusoidal function $f(x) = 21\cos\left(\frac{2\pi}{3}(x-5)\right) - 14$.
3. Sketch the graph of the function $f(x) = 10\sin\left(\frac{4\pi}{5}(x+2)\right) + 3$ over two periods.
4. Find, to two decimal places, a solution to the equation $8 = 10\sin\left(\frac{4\pi}{5}(x+2)\right) + 3$.
5. Suppose $f(x) = \sin x$. For each function below, sketch the graph and the graph of $y = f(x)$ on the interval $-\pi \le x \le 2\pi$. Describe how the two graphs relate.
   a. $f(2x) = \sin 2x$ b. $2f(x) = 2\sin x$ c. $f(x) + 1 = \sin x + 1$
6. Given the maximum and minimum values of a cosine or sine function, how do you find the amplitude and vertical displacement?
7. How can you make a sinusoidal function that has a specific period?
8. How can you use sinusoidal functions to model periodic phenomena?

Vocabulary

In this investigation, you learned these terms. Make sure you understand what each one means and how to use it.

- **amplitude**
- **phase shift**
- **sinusoidal function**
- **vertical displacement**

The differences in high and low tidal levels can often be dramatic.

Mathematical Reflections

EXERCISES 6–8 At the start of the investigation, you may have assigned these as Questions 1–3 for students to think and write about.

Mathematical Reflections

1. a.

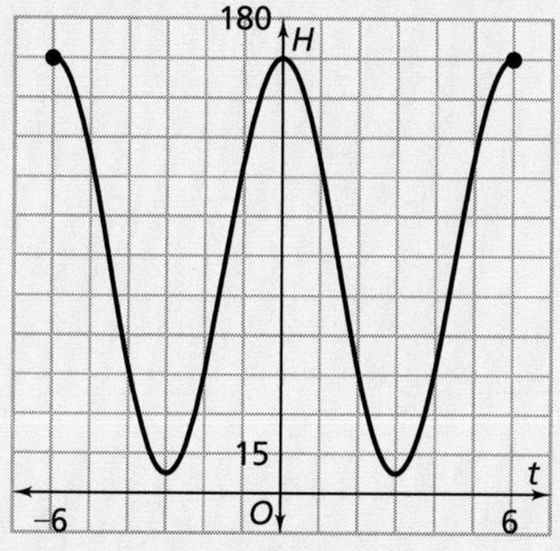

b. $H(t) = 78\cos\left(\frac{2\pi}{6}t\right) + 88$

2. amplitude = 21, vertical displacement = −14, period = 3, phase shift = 5

3.

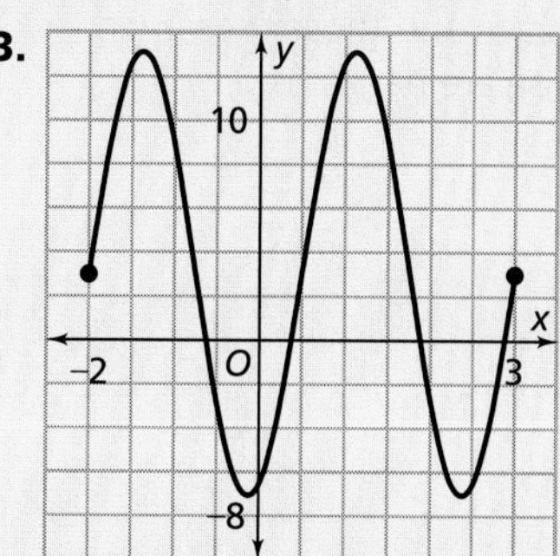

4. Answers may vary. Sample: $-\frac{43}{24}$

5. See back of book.

6. amplitude $= \frac{\text{maximum} - \text{minimum}}{2}$, vertical displacement = maximum − amplitude

7. Answers may vary. Sample: If you want the period to be P, you can use $f(x) = \sin\frac{2\pi}{P}x$ or $g(x) = \cos\frac{2\pi}{P}x$.

8. Answers may vary. Sample: Use information about the situation to determine maximum and minimum values, period, vertical displacement, and phase shift. Calculate the amplitude, then use appropriate values for A, B, a, and b in $y = A\sin(ax+b) + B$ or $y = A\cos(ax+b) + B$ to get a function that will have these maximum and minimum values, period, and so on.

Project

Throughout the chapter, students may work on the Chapter Project, *"Trigonometry" of the Unit Square.*

This project has students explore how one might define a "trigonometry" on the unit square.

Have students review the unit circle exploration at the beginning of the chapter. You can also have students build a construction of this square trigonometry.

After students have completed the project, ask a couple of students to present their explanations of the exercises to the class.

Project: Using Mathematical Habits

"Trigonometry" of the Unit Square

The unit circle was the basis for the work in this chapter. You can measure cosine and sine by looking at the coordinates of someone walking α units counterclockwise around the unit circle.

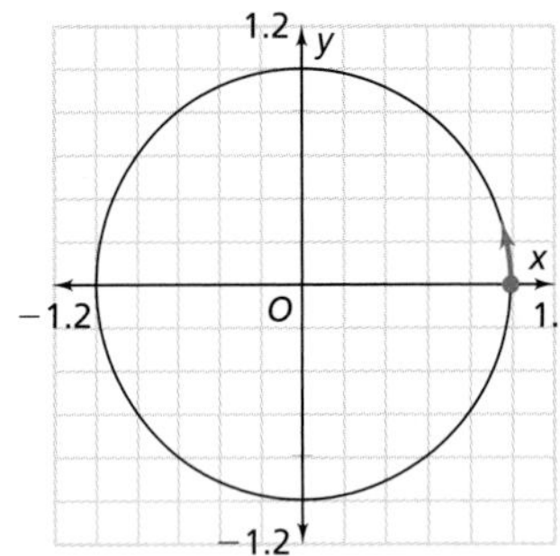

What would happen if everything stayed the same, but you replaced the circle by a square with side length 2?

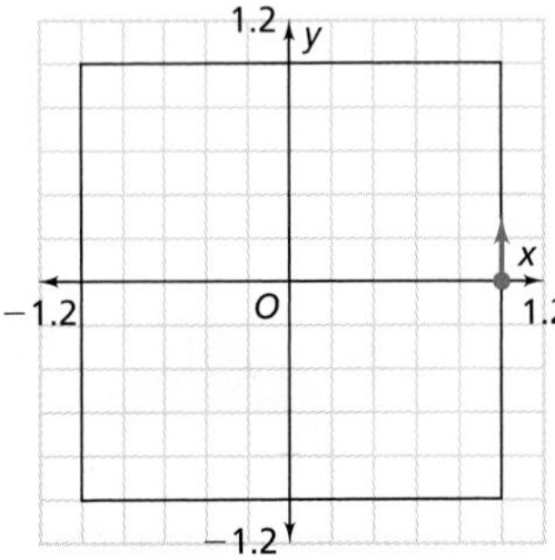

1. Paul walks 2π units around the unit circle. How far does he walk when he goes completely around the square once?

2. Copy and complete this table. Give the coordinates of Paul's location after walking each distance around a square with side length 2.

Distance	Coordinates
0	(1, 0)
$\frac{1}{2}$	$\left(1, \frac{1}{2}\right)$
1	■
$1\frac{1}{2}$	■
2	(0, 1)
3	■
4	■
5	■
6	■
7	■
8	■
9	■
10	■

3. After walking around the square for 3 units, Paul is at the point $(-1, 1)$. If he continues walking, how far has he walked once he reaches these coordinates again? Find a rule that generates all the answers to this question.

Answers

Project

1. 8 units

2.

Distance	Coordinates
0	(1,0)
$\frac{1}{2}$	$(1,\frac{1}{2})$
1	(1,1)
$1\frac{1}{2}$	$(\frac{1}{2},1)$
2	(0,1)
3	(−1,1)
4	(−1,0)
5	(−1,−1)
6	(0,−1)
7	(1,−1)
8	(1,0)
9	(1,1)
10	(0,1)

3. He has walked another 8 units; $3 + 8n$ units (n an integer), assuming distances measured counterclockwise are positive and those measured clockwise are negative

4. Determine where an exhausted Paul would be after walking 739 units on the square.

On the unit circle, define the sine function by using the distance walked as the input, and the y-coordinate as the output.

For the unit square, let $SSIN(t)$ be the y-coordinate on the square after walking distance t. Let $SCOS(t)$ be the x-coordinate on the square after walking distance t.

5. Find each value.

a. $SSIN(5)$	b. $SSIN(21)$
c. $SSIN(3.6)$	d. $SCOS(3.6)$
e. $SCOS(0)$	f. $SCOS(2) + SCOS(6)$
g. $SCOS(3) + SCOS(7)$	

6. Two examples above suggest that $SCOS(t) + SCOS(t + 4) = 0$. Is this true for all values of t? What is the corresponding identity for the unit circle?

7. Sketch a graph of the $SSIN$ function on the domain $0 \le t \le 16$. Consider the proper range before laying out the axes of your sketch.

8. On the same axes used for the $SSIN$ function, sketch the $SCOS$ function on the domain $0 \le t \le 16$.

9. Here are some questions for further study.
   - On the unit circle, $\cos^2 t + \sin^2 t = 1$ for all values of t. Is there any relationship like this on the unit square? What does the graph of $f(t) = SCOS^2(t) + SSIN^2(t)$ look like?
   - What would cosine and sine look like for someone walking around a different polygon with center (0, 0) and one vertex at (1, 0)? Consider an equilateral triangle, a regular hexagon, a rectangle, and other shapes.
   - What does the graph of the tangent function $STAN$ look like for the unit square? Here, define the tangent in any of the ways used for the circle. Will each option for the definition of tangent give the same result?
   - What do the graphs of the reciprocal trigonometric functions look like for the unit square?
   - Is it possible to model the $SSIN$ and $SCOS$ functions on a graphing calculator?

Let the square base of the Transamerica Pyramid be the unit square. If you walked around the base, how far would you walk?

4. $(-1, 1)$

5. a. -1 **b.** -1
c. 0.4 **d.** -1
e. 1 **f.** 0
g. 0

6. yes; $\cos x + \cos(x + \pi) = 0$.

7.

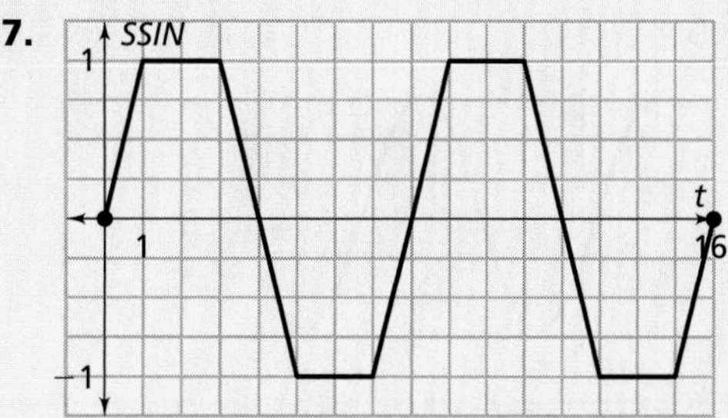

8.

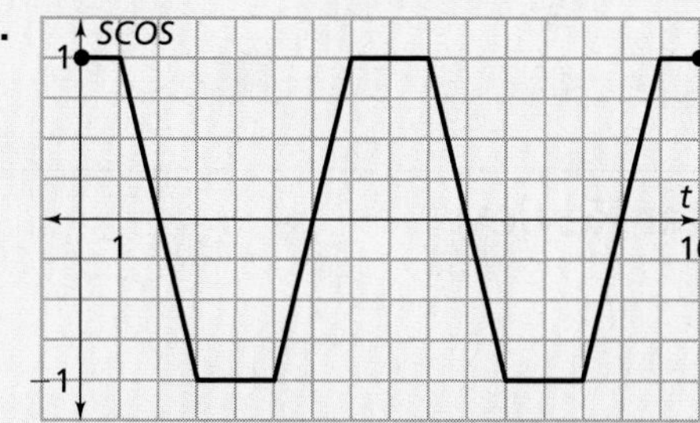

9. See students' work.

Review

For vocabulary review, go to **Web Code:** bgj-0151

In **Investigation 1A,** you learned how to ...

- understand the relationship between degree and radian measure as the length of an arc on the unit circle subtended by a central angle.
- relate the motion of an object around a circle to the graphs of the cosine, sine, and tangent functions.
- solve equations that involve cosine and sine (such as $3 \cos x + 2 = 1$).

The following questions will help you check your understanding.

1. Draw the unit circle. A toy car is driving along this circle in the clockwise direction, starting from the point $(0, -1)$. After exactly $\frac{\pi}{2}$ meters, the car will be at which point?

A. $(1, 0)$ **B.** $(-1, 0)$

C. $(0, 1)$ **D.** $(0, -1)$

2. Evaluate the expression below.

$$\sin 30° + \cos \pi - 3 \cos 60°$$

3. How many radians corresponds to an angle with degree measure 160°?

A. $\frac{8\pi}{9}$ **B.** $\frac{3\pi}{4}$

C. 3π **D.** $\frac{5\pi}{6}$

4. Solve the following system of equations if $0 \le x \le \frac{\pi}{2}$.

$$y = 4 \sin x + 1$$
$$y = 3$$

In **Investigation 1B,** you learned how to ...

- understand several relationships between the tangent function and the unit circle.
- sketch and describe the graph of the tangent function.
- define an inverse of cosine, sine, and tangent.
- recognize three other trigonometric functions: secant, cosecant, and cotangent.

The following questions will help you check your understanding.

5. Solve the following equation.

$$\sin x - \sqrt{3} \cos x = 0$$

6. Solve the following equation.

$$2 \cot x = \frac{\cos x}{1 - \cos^2 x}$$

7. What is the period of $f(x) = \tan \frac{x}{2}$?

A. π **B.** 2π **C.** $\frac{\pi}{2}$ **D.** $\frac{1}{2}$

In **Investigation 1C,** you learned how to ...

- make sense of sinusoidal functions in the context of real-world applications.
- understand the geometry of sinusoidal functions.
- model with sinusoidal functions.

The following questions will help you check your understanding.

8. Give two examples of sinusoidal functions that have period $\frac{\pi}{4}$.

9. Sketch the graph of the function.

$$S(x) = 3 \cos (x + 2) + 1$$

Answers

Chapter Review

1. B

2. -2

3. A

4. $\frac{\pi}{6}$

5. $\frac{\pi}{3} + n\pi$ (n an integer)

6. $\frac{1}{2}\pi + n\pi, \frac{1}{6}\pi + 2n\pi, \frac{5}{6}\pi + 2n\pi$ (n an integer)

7. B

8. Answers may vary. Sample: $f(x) = \sin 8x, g(x) = \frac{1}{2} \cos 8x + 1$

9.

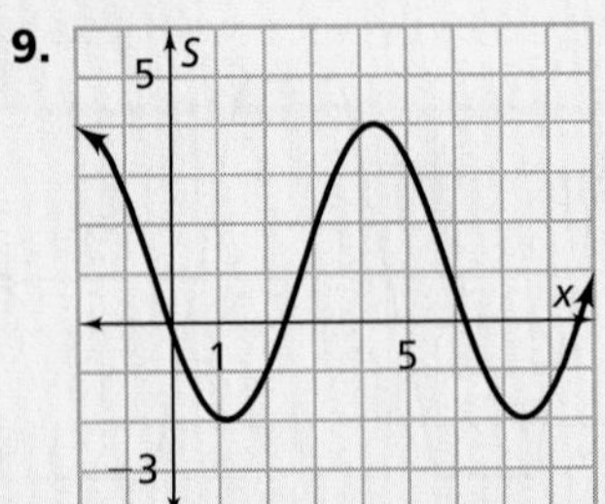

Test

Go Online PHSchool.com — For a chapter test, go to **Web Code:** bga-0153

[Mul]tiple Choice

1. What is the value of the following expression?

$$\sin\frac{\pi}{2} + 2\sin\pi - 3\sin\frac{3\pi}{2}$$

A. 4 **B.** −2 **C.** −3 **D.** 3

2. Which of the following radian measures corresponds to 90°?

A. π **B.** $\frac{\pi}{4}$ **C.** $\frac{\pi}{2}$ **D.** $\frac{3\pi}{2}$

3. Which function has the graph below?

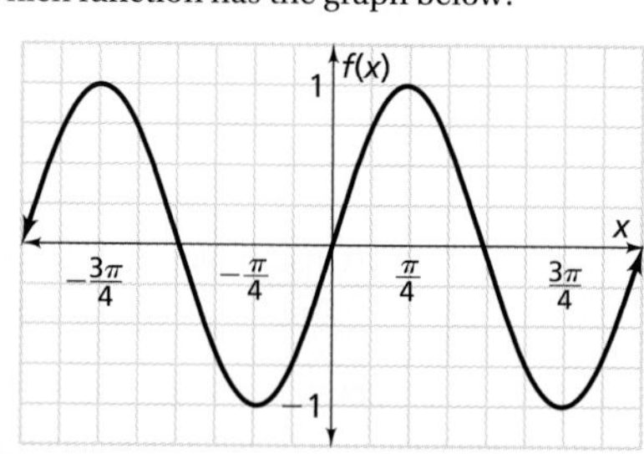

A. $f(x) = \sin x$ **B.** $f(x) = 2\sin x$
C. $f(x) = 2\cos x$ **D.** $f(x) = \sin 2x$

4. Which is equal to $\sin\left(\cos^{-1}\frac{1}{2}\right)$?

A. $\frac{\sqrt{3}}{2}$ **B.** $\frac{1}{2}$
C. $\frac{\sqrt{3}}{2}$ or $-\frac{\sqrt{3}}{2}$ **D.** $-\frac{1}{2}$

5. What is the period of the function below?

$$h(t) = \cos 3t$$

A. π **B.** 3π **C.** $\frac{1}{3}$ **D.** $\frac{2\pi}{3}$

6. What is the value of the following expression, where α is some real number?

$$\sin(\alpha + \pi) \cdot \sin\left(\frac{\pi}{2} - \alpha\right) + \cos\left(\frac{\pi}{2} - \alpha\right) \cdot \cos\alpha$$

A. 0 **B.** 2
C. $2\sin\alpha \cdot \cos\alpha$ **D.** $2(\sin\alpha + \cos\alpha)$

Open Response

7. Answer the following questions. Explaining your reasoning.
   a. For what values of α is $\sin\alpha > 1$?
   b. For what values of α is $\cos\alpha < -1$?

8. Evaluate the expression below, where a and b are real numbers.

$$a^2\cos 2\pi - 2ab\cos\pi + b^2\sin\frac{\pi}{2}$$

9. Solve the following equation.

$$4\cos^2 x - 1 = 0$$

10. Solve the equation below on $0 \le x \le \pi$.

$$3\tan\left(\frac{x}{2} - \frac{\pi}{3}\right) + \sqrt{3} = 0$$

11. The sea level at a given point on the coast changes sinusoidally as a function of the time t. The following function gives the height x (in meters) of the water.

$$x = 6 + 5\sin\frac{1}{6}\pi(t - 2)$$

   a. What is the maximum height of the water. What is its minimum height?
   b. If you start measuring the height at 10 A.M., at what time does the high tide occur?
   c. How many hours are there between successive high tides?

12. Solve the following equation.

$$\cot x = \tan x$$

Challenge Problem

13. Find all the solutions of the following equation.

$$\sqrt{3}\sin x - \cos x = 1$$

Test

Assessment Resources

Chapter Test Form A **Page 1 of 2**

Multiple Choice

1. What is the value of the following expression?

$$\cos\frac{\pi}{2} + 2\sin\pi - 3\cos\pi$$

A. 5 B. 0 C. 3 D. 6

2. Which of the following radian measures corresponds to 180°?

A. π B. $\frac{\pi}{4}$ C. 2π D. $\frac{3\pi}{2}$

3. Which function has the graph below?

A. $f(x) = \cos x$ B. $f(x) = 2\sin 3x$
C. $f(x) = 2\cos 2x$ D. $f(x) = \cos 3x$

4. What is $\cos\left(\sin^{-1}\left(\frac{1}{2}\right)\right)$?

A. $\frac{\sqrt{3}}{2}$ B. $\frac{1}{2}$ C. $\frac{\sqrt{3}}{2}$ or $-\frac{\sqrt{3}}{2}$ D. $-\frac{1}{2}$

5. What is the period of the function below?

$$h(t) = 3\sin 3t + 5$$

A. π B. $\frac{2\pi}{3}$ C. 3π D. $\frac{5}{3}$

6. What is the value of the following expression, where α is some real number?

$$2\cos(\alpha + \pi)\sin\alpha + \sin\left(\frac{\pi}{2} - \alpha\right)\cos\alpha + \sin^2(\alpha - \pi)$$

A. 0 B. $(\sin\alpha - \cos\alpha)^2$
C. $2\sin\alpha\cos\alpha$ D. 2

Also available: Form B

Chapter Test

1. A
2. C
3. D
4. A
5. D
6. A
7. a. There are no values of α such that $\sin\alpha > 1$, since no point on the unit circle has a y-coordinate greater than 1.
   b. There are no values of α such that $\cos\alpha < -1$, since no point on the unit circle has an x-coordinate less than −1.
8. $a^2 + 2ab + b^2$, or $(a + b)^2$
9. $\frac{1}{3}\pi + 2n\pi, \frac{5}{3}\pi + 2n\pi, \frac{2}{3}\pi + 2n\pi$, and $\frac{4}{3}\pi + 2n\pi$ (n an integer)
10. $\frac{\pi}{3}$
11. a. 11 m; 1 m
   b. Assuming that 10 a.m corresponds to $t = 0$, at 1 pm
   c. 4 hours
12. $\frac{\pi}{4} + n \cdot \frac{\pi}{2}$ (n an integer)
13. $\frac{1}{3}\pi + 2n\pi$ and $(2n + 1)\pi$ (n an integer)

Chapter 2 Complex Numbers and Trigonometry

In this chapter, students leverage the study of trigonometry from Chapter 1 and re-examine arithmetic and properties of complex numbers. They use trigonometric properties to write complex numbers in polar form, they use arithmetic of complex numbers to derive the Angle-Sum Formulas for cosine and sine, and they examine unit-length complex numbers (points on the unit circle) to understand the connection between algebra, geometry, and analysis.

Chapter Overview

INVESTIGATION 2A, *Graphing Complex Numbers,* has students explore polar form as a way to represent complex numbers.

INVESTIGATION 2B, *Trigonometric Identities,* has students explore ways to build and prove trigonometric formulas and identities.

INVESTIGATION 2C, *De Moivre's Theorem,* has students study the roots of unity.

For more information on the Investigations, see

- Chapter Road Map, pp. 82–83
- Investigation Road Maps, pp. 84, 106, 124

PROJECT The Project near the end of the chapter is optional. You can assign the Project at any time during the chapter depending on how often and how long you feel students should work on it.

DAILY PLANNER DAILY PLANNER DAILY PL

Pacing Suggestions and Materials

Investigation 2A *Graphing Complex Numbers*

DAY	LESSON	HOMEWORK
1	2.1 Getting Started Core: 1, 2, 3, 5 Optional: 4, 6, 7	Core: 8, 9, 10, 14 Optional: 11, 12, 13
2	2.2 The Complex Plane Core: 1, 2, 3, 5 Optional: 4	Core: 6, 7, 9, 11, 13, 16 Optional: 8, 10, 12, 14, 15, 17
3	2.3 Another Form for Complex Numbers Core: 1, 2, 4, 5, 7 Optional: 3, 6	Core: 8, 9, 10, 11, 14 Optional: 12, 13, 15
4	2.4 The Multiplication Law Core: 1, 2, 3, 4 Optional: 5, 6	Core: 7, 9a, 11, 12, 14 Optional: 8, 10, 15; Extension: 9b, 13, 16

Investigation 2B *Trigonometric Identities*

DAY	LESSON	HOMEWORK
1	2.5 Getting Started Core: 2, 3, 6, 8, 9 Optional: 1, 4, 5, 7; Extension: 10	Core: 11, 12, 13, 14, 17, 22 Optional: 15, 16, 18, 19, 20, 21a–d, 23 Extension: 21e
2	2.6 Building Formulas and Identities Core: 1, 2, 3, 6 Optional: 4, 5; Extension: 7	Core: 8, 9a–e, 11, 13, 17, 18 Optional: 10, 12, 14, 15; Extension: 9f, 16
3	2.7 Proving Identities Core: 1, 2, 5 Optional: 3, 4	Core: 6, 8, 9, 10, 12 Optional: 7, 13; Extension: 11

NOTES	MATERIALS
	• CAS (recommended) • graph paper • graphing calculators • Blackline Master 2.1
	• CAS (recommended) • graph paper • graphing calculators • Blackline Master MC10
	• CAS (recommended) • graph paper • graphing calculators • Blackline Masters MC1, MC10, 2.3
	• CAS (recommended) • graph paper • graphing calculators • Blackline Masters MC1, MC7, MC10, 2.4

NOTES	MATERIALS
	• graphing calculators • Blackline Master MC3
	• graphing calculators • Blackline Master 2.6
	• graphing calculators • Blackline Master MC3

Mathematics Background

COMPLEX NUMBERS THROUGH TRIGONOMETRY You can think of complex numbers as polynomials in i, where i is the number whose square is -1. Therefore you can perform calculations with complex numbers just like you would perform calculations with polynomials, but with a final simplification step in which the powers of i are replaced by their simplest value. (For example, $i^2 = -1$, $i^3 = -i$, $i^4 = 1$, and so on.) However, you can also think about complex numbers in a geometric sense as locations in the complex plane.

In this view of complex numbers, you can describe each location in the plane with two numbers. For example, you can reach the location of a complex number $z = a + bi$ in the plane by traveling a units from the origin horizontally (which is the orientation of the real axis) and then b units vertically (in the direction of the imaginary axis). So where is the trigonometry? Well, you can describe the location of this complex number as a distance and an angle, or the magnitude and argument of the complex number. Standing at the origin and facing in the positive direction of the real axis, turn counterclockwise through the angle measured by the argument and then walk, in that direction, the distance measured by the magnitude. Trigonometry defines the relationship between these two methods for locating a complex number in the complex plane. If $z = a + bi$, then $\theta = \tan^{-1}\left(\frac{b}{a}\right)$, chosen in the appropriate quadrants, is the argument and $\sqrt{a^2 + b^2}$ is the magnitude. If a complex number has magnitude r and argument θ, then you can write it as $z = r(\cos\theta + i\sin\theta)$. Students use this relationship to prove identities in trigonometry through calculations in complex numbers.

TRIGONOMETRY THROUGH COMPLEX NUMBERS In many courses, students prove the identities for the cosine and sine of the sum of two angles using some fairly complicated geometric arguments. In fact, in Chapter 8 of CME Project *Algebra 2*, students prove these Angle-Sum Formulas in two different ways—through rotated triangles and by using coordinate geometry. However, in this chapter, they prove these identities in a new way. The technique they use will allow them to generate and prove many other trigonometric identities very elegantly and efficiently.

The CME Project chooses a different way to develop the multiplication of complex numbers. Many courses develop the Multiplication Law for complex numbers by using the Angle-Sum Formulas from trigonometry. However, in Chapter 2 of CME Project *Algebra 2*, students use only plane geometry and similar triangles to show that the argument of the product of two complex numbers is the sum of the arguments of the factors.

continued on p. 82c

continued from p. 82b

That means that it is now possible to turn around and use complex number multiplication to prove the Angle-Sum Formulas without writing a circular argument.

DE MOIVRE'S THEOREM This theorem, which provides a very simple way to calculate powers of complex numbers, was the central tool used by Johann Carl Friedrich Gauss (1777–1855) to make connections between regular polygons and the complex plane. He used this idea to show that the regular 17-gon is constructible with a straightedge and a compass. It was one of his own favorite results in a lifetime of mathematical and scientific results. He even wanted to have a regular 17-gon inscribed on his tombstone. In Investigation C, students learn how to find roots of equations involving complex numbers using De Moivre's Theorem.

Another topic that your students can investigate with these powerful tools is roots of unity, which are the roots of equations of the form $x^n - 1 = 0$. Not only can students find these roots, but they can use their CAS to perform calculations with them in an interesting way. When students first begin to work with complex numbers, they originally think of them as "polynomials in *i*." They treat *i* as a variable, and then at the end of the calculation, they include an extra step in which powers of *i* are rewritten as i, -1, $-i$, or 1. This is followed by a final simplification. Similarly, when calculating with roots of unity, students treat the root as a variable, calculate as though they were dealing with a polynomial in this variable, and then add in a final simplification step. For example, if ζ is a root of the equation $x^5 - 1 = 0$, a fifth root of unity, then you can calculate any ζ, even with a CAS, as though ζ were a simple variable like x. Then you can further simplify the powers of ζ, because $\zeta^5 = 1$, $\zeta^6 = \zeta$, $\zeta^7 = \zeta^2$, and so on. The polynomial remainder function in a CAS facilitates a nice implementation of this method. This kind of calculation is described in greater detail in the optional Lesson 2.12 on calculating with roots of unity.

Pacing Suggestions and Materials

Investigation 2C *De Moivre's Theorem*

DAY	LESSON	HOMEWORK
1	2.8 Getting Started Core: 1, 2, 3, 4, 6 Optional: 5, 7, 8	Core: 9, 10, 11 Optional: 12, 13, 14, 15, 16, 17
2	2.9 Powers of Complex Numbers Core: 1, 2, 3, 4 Optional: 5	Core: 7, 8, 9, 11, 14, 15, 16 Optional: 6, 10, 12, 13, 17
3	2.10 Roots of Unity Core: 1, 2, 3, 4, 5 Optional: 6, 7; Extension: 8	Core: 9, 10, 11, 12, 14, 15, 19 Optional: 13, 18, 20; Extension: 16, 17
4	2.11 Geometry of Roots of Unity Core: 3, 4, 5, 6, 7a Optional: 1, 2; Extension: 7b–c, 8	Core: 10, 11, 12, 13, 16 Optional: 9, 14, 17, 18, 19; Extension: 15
5	2.12 Arithmetic With Roots of Unity Core: 1, 2, 3, 6, 7 Optional: 4, 5	Core: 9, 10, 11, 12, 15, 17, 18, 23 Optional: 13, 14, 16, 19, 24 Extension: 8, 20, 21, 22, 25

NOTES	MATERIALS
	• CAS (recommended) • graph paper • graphing calculators • Blackline Masters MC1, MC10, 2.8
	• CAS (recommended) • graph paper • graphing calculators • Blackline Masters MC1, MC10
	• CAS (recommended) • graph paper • graphing calculators • Blackline Masters MC1, MC10, 2.10
	• CAS (recommended) • graph paper • graphing calculators • Blackline Masters MC1, MC10
This lesson is optional.	• CAS • Blackline Master 2.12

Developing Students' Mathematical Habits

VISUALIZATION Students use the complex plane as a way to visualize the complex numbers and calculations with complex numbers geometrically.

LOGICAL REASONING Students make the connection between calculations with complex numbers and calculations with trigonometric functions. They learn to generate and prove trigonometric identities with this technique.

EXTENSION Students view the process of calculating with roots of unity as an extension of calculating with polynomials. Since roots of unity have similar behavior, students can use a CAS to help with the calculations. There is just one extra simplification step at the end of the process.

Chapter Road Map

INVESTIGATION 2A, *Graphing Complex Numbers,* explores polar form as a way to represent complex numbers. The exercises lead up to the Multiplication Law for complex numbers, $(r_1 \text{ cis } \theta_1)(r_2 \text{ cis } \theta_2) = (r_1r_2) \text{ cis } (\theta_1 + \theta_2)$, which highlights the connection between complex numbers and transformational geometry—a vector can be dilated and rotated by performing a single multiplication.

INVESTIGATION 2B, *Trigonometric Identities,* explores ways to build and prove trigonometric formulas and identities. Students learn that by using complex number arithmetic, they can easily prove trigonometric facts that are quite difficult to show strictly using algebra and geometry of the real plane.

Complex Numbers and Trigonometry

What do complex numbers have to do with trigonometry? As it turns out, a whole lot!

In your earlier courses, you may have thought about how trigonometry could be used to rewrite complex numbers. In this chapter, you will first learn how to plot complex numbers on the complex plane. Next, you will discover how to transform any complex number $a + bi$ to a new polar form. Then, using the powerful techniques of complex number calculation, you will generate and prove complicated trigonometric identities.

Scientists and engineers use complex numbers to model electrical circuits and water flow, to process digital signals, and to study nuclear phenomena. But artists use these same numbers to animate fractal domains in virtual reality scenarios, to visualize stunning works of art, and to compose audacious new soundscapes.

Vocabulary and Notation

- argument, arg(z)
- polar coordinates
- complex numbers
- conjugate, $\bar{z}$
- cyclotomy
- discriminant
- identically equal
- identity
- magnitude, $|z|$
- modulus
- norm, $N(z)$
- polar coordinates
- polar form for complex numbers
- rectangular coordinates
- rectangular form for complex numbers
- roots of unity

INVESTIGATION 2C, *De Moivre's Theorem,* introduces the roots of unity. Students study the connections between algebra, geometry, and analysis. By using trigonometric functions to represent complex numbers, students use analytic methods to solve algebraic problems (and vice versa). In connecting the roots of $x^n - 1 = 0$ and the regular n-gon, students use the power of algebra to solve geometric problems and, in turn, use geometric methods to gain algebraic insights. When students perform calculations with *cyclotomic integers* (complex numbers that are linear combinations of nth roots of unity with integer coefficients), they see how algebraic systems can be modeled with polynomials and computer algebra systems.

Chapter Vocabulary and Notation

The following list gives key vocabulary and notation used in the chapter. Selected new vocabulary and notation items are shown in boldface on the student page.

- absolute value of a complex number, p. 88
- algebraic numbers, p. 146
- argument, p. 89
- complex numbers, p. 145
- conjugate, $\bar{z}$, p. 85
- identically equal, p. 107
- identity, p. 107
- magnitude, $|z|$, p. 87
- modulus, p. 87
- norm, $N(z)$, p. 88
- polar coordinates, p. 92
- polar form for complex numbers, p. 93
- primitive nth root of unity, p. 150
- rectangular coordinates, p. 92
- rectangular form for complex numbers, p. 93
- roots of unity, p. 134
- $\psi_n(x)$ (polynomial whose roots are precisely the primitive nth roots of unity), p. 152

Chapter Technology

CME Project *Precalculus* assumes that each student has access to a graphing calculator. It also recommends access to a computer algebra system (CAS) and to geometry software.

Support for the use of technology is available in the TI-Nspire™ Technology Handbook. See p. 704.

A list of technology used with important concepts in this chapter appears below. Students will need access to the functionality listed to develop complete understanding of these topics.

Computer Algebra System

LESSON 2.12 Expand a sum of products of polynomials, p. 148.

LESSON 2.12 Find the remainder in polynomial division, p. 149.

LESSON 2.12 Factor polynomials over $\mathbb{Z}$, $\mathbb{R}$, and $\mathbb{C}$, p. 151.

Graphing Calculator

LESSON 2.2 Approximate the argument of a complex number, p. 89.

LESSON 2.7 Compare the graphs of trigonometric functions, p. 117.

LESSON 2.8 Approximate complex solutions to polynomial equations, p. 127.

LESSON 2.11 Define a sequence of polynomial functions, p. 144.

Investigation Overview

In this investigation, students explore a new way to represent complex numbers: using polar form. (Students looked briefly at polar form in CME Project *Algebra 2*.) The exercises throughout this investigation lead up to the following theorem.

$$(r_1 \text{ cis } \theta_1)(r_2 \text{ cis } \theta_2) = (r_1 r_2) \text{ cis } (\theta_1 + \theta_2)$$

This theorem highlights the connection between complex numbers and transformational geometry: you can dilate and rotate a vector by performing one multiplication. For example, if you multiply the complex number z by 3 cis 60°, then you dilate z by a factor of 3 and rotate it 60° counterclockwise.

In the next investigation, students apply this theorem to develop new ways to generate the Angle-Sum Formulas for cosine and sine.

You may wish to assign Questions 1–3 for students to think and write about during the investigation.

Learning Goals

- Represent complex numbers using both rectangular coordinates and polar coordinates.
- Determine the magnitude and argument of any complex number.
- Decide when it is best to use either rectangular or polar coordinates to represent complex numbers.

Habits and Skills

- Graph complex numbers in the complex plane.
- Use geometry to explain arithmetic facts of complex numbers.
- Multiply two complex numbers of the form $r\ (\cos \theta + i \sin \theta)$.

Graphing Complex Numbers

In *Graphing Complex Numbers*, you will view complex numbers as points in a plane. You will learn two coordinate representations for each complex number.

By the end of this investigation, you will be able to answer questions like these.

1. How can you write a complex number using trigonometry?
2. What are the magnitude and argument of a complex number, and how do you find them?
3. How do you use geometry to calculate $(1 - i\sqrt{3}) \cdot (-3\sqrt{3} + 3i)$?

You will learn how to

- represent complex numbers using both rectangular coordinates and polar coordinates
- determine the magnitude and argument of any complex number
- decide when it is best to use either rectangular or polar coordinates to represent complex numbers

You will develop these habits and skills:

- Graph complex numbers in the complex plane.
- Use geometry to explain arithmetic facts of complex numbers.
- Multiply two complex numbers of the form $r(\cos \theta + i \sin \theta)$.

The famous Mandelbrot set exists in the complex plane as the graph of a complex quadratic polynomial. Its (literally) infinite self-similar features include structures referred to as hooks and antennas, islands and valleys, and seahorses and satellites. You may be able to identify some of these in this detail.

Investigation Road Map

LESSON 2.1, *Getting Started,* reviews complex number arithmetic and other simple properties of complex numbers. It also explores representing complex multiplication by rotation.

LESSON 2.2, *The Complex Plane,* reviews the absolute value and the argument of complex numbers, which provide the basis for introducing polar coordinates, as well as geometric ways to represent complex multiplication.

LESSON 2.3, *Another Form for Complex Numbers,* introduces the polar form for complex numbers, which opens up many more connections, especially between complex number arithmetic and geometry.

LESSON 2.4, *The Multiplication Law,* formalizes a fact that is key to working through the rest of the chapter, $(r_1 \text{ cis } \theta_1)(r_2 \text{ cis } \theta_2) = (r_1 r_2) \text{ cis } (\theta_1 + \theta_2)$.

2.1 Getting Started

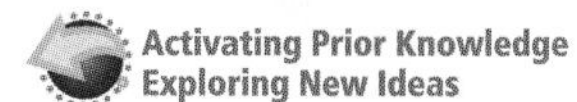

In an earlier algebra course, you learned about the complex numbers. A complex number is a number that is written in the form $x + yi$, where x and y are real numbers, and i is the imaginary unit, a number that has a square of -1. These Getting Started problems will give you an opportunity to refresh your memory about the arithmetic of complex numbers ($\mathbb{C}$).

For You to Explore

For Problems 1 and 2, calculate each expression. Write each result in the form $x + yi$ with real numbers x and y.

1. **a.** $(3 + i) + (2 + i)$ **b.** $(3 + i) - (2 + i)$
   c. $(3 + i)(2 + i)$ **d.** $(3 + i)^2$
   e. $(3 + i)^2 \cdot (2 + i)^2$ **f.** $(3 + i)^4 \cdot (2 + i)^4$

> The results from part (c) can help you answer parts (e) and (f).

2. **a.** $(3 + 5i) + (3 - 5i)$ **b.** $(3 + 5i)(3 - 5i)$
   c. $(-7 + 2i) + (-7 - 2i)$ **d.** $(-7 + 2i)(-7 - 2i)$
   e. $(12 + 5i) + (12 - 5i)$ **f.** $(12 + 5i)(12 - 5i)$
3. Let $z = x + yi$. The complex number $\overline{z} = x - yi$ is the **conjugate** of z.
   a. What is the conjugate of $12 + 5i$?
   b. What is the conjugate of $12 - 5i$?
   c. If $z = x + yi$, show that $z + \overline{z} = 2x$.
   d. If $z = x + yi$, show that the product $z\overline{z} = x^2 + y^2$.

> The real part stays the same. The imaginary part switches its sign. The conjugate of $z = 3 + 5i$ is $\overline{z} = 3 - 5i$.

4. For each point A, find the coordinates of the point A' by rotating A 90° counterclockwise about the origin.
   a. $A = (1, 0)$ **b.** $A = (0, -1)$
   c. $A = (3, 5)$ **d.** $A = (6, -1)$
5. Multiply each complex number z by i.
   a. $z = 1$ **b.** $z = -i$ **c.** $z = 3 + 5i$ **d.** $z = 6 - i$
6. Let $z = x + yi$.
   a. Calculate z^2.
   b. What is the real part of z^2?
   c. What is the imaginary part of z^2?
7. Show that the following equation is true for all x and y.

$$(x^2 - y^2)^2 + (2xy)^2 = (x^2 + y^2)^2$$

Answers

For You to Explore

1. **a.** $5 + 2i$ **b.** 1
   c. $5 + 5i$ **d.** $8 + 6i$
   e. $50i$ **f.** -2500
2. **a.** 6 **b.** 34
   c. -14 **d.** 53
   e. 24 **f.** 169
3. **a.** $12 - 5i$ **b.** $12 + 5i$
   c. $z + \overline{z} = (x + yi) + (x - yi) = 2x$
   d. $z\overline{z} = (x + yi)(x - yi) = x^2 - (yi)^2 = x^2 - (-y)^2 = x^2 + y^2$
4. **a.** $(0, 1)$ **b.** $(1, 0)$
   c. $(-5, 3)$ **d.** $(1, 6)$
5. **a.** i **b.** 1
   c. $-5 + 3i$ **d.** $1 + 6i$
6. **a.** $(x^2 - y^2) + (2xy)i$
   b. $x^2 - y^2$
   c. $2xy$
7. See back of book.

Lesson Overview

GOAL

- Warm up to the ideas of the investigation.

In this lesson, students review complex number arithmetic and other simple properties of complex numbers by working through the exercises. In some of the exercises, they explore how to represent complex multiplication with rotation.

As always in a Getting Started, there is no need to formalize these ideas today. Students meet all of the ideas again throughout the investigation.

FOR YOU TO EXPLORE
- Core: 1, 2, 3, 5
- Optional: 4, 6, 7

MATERIALS
- CAS (recommended)
- graph paper
- graphing calculators
- Blackline Master 2.1

HOMEWORK
- Core: 8, 9, 10, 14
- Optional: 11, 12, 13

VOCABULARY
- conjugate, $\overline{z}$

Launch

Depending on your class, you may want to illustrate the rules for complex arithmetic with a few examples before the students attempt the exercises.

Explore

For You to Explore

PROBLEM 5 The goal is for students to connect rotation and multiplication. Later in this investigation, students learn that multiplying a complex number by i rotates it 90 degrees counterclockwise in the complex plane.

PROBLEM 6 Eventually students connect the real part of a complex number with cosine, and the imaginary part of a complex number with sine. Here, the real part $x^2 - y^2$ relates to the rule $\cos 2\theta = \cos^2 \theta - \sin^2 \theta$, while the imaginary part $2xy$ relates to the rule $\sin 2\theta = 2 \cos \theta \sin \theta$.

PROBLEM 7 Point out to students that they just recently encountered the expressions $x^2 - y^2$ and $2xy$. The purpose of this problem is to show that results for complex numbers are meaningful for working with real numbers.

Wrap Up

Review the For You to Explore section, especially Problems 1–3.

Before assigning homework, allow students some time to discuss and summarize their findings.

Exercises

HOMEWORK
- Core: 8, 9, 10, 14
- Optional: 11, 12, 13

On Your Own

EXERCISE 10 Students could also use the result $z\bar{z} = x^2 + y^2$ from earlier. They should recognize the connection between the products and the segment length. Students learn that the magnitude of a complex number is its distance from the origin when drawn in the complex plane.

EXERCISE 11 You may want to provide copies of Blackline Master 2.1 for your students to use on this exercise. The Pythagorean triples represented here are 5–12–13, 3–4–5, 8–6–10, 7–24–25, 15–8–17, and 21–10–29. Not all students will recognize these, but hopefully they will notice 3–4–5 and 5–12–13.

Exercises Practicing Habits of Mind

On Your Own

8. Define $f(x) = x^2 - 2x + 2$.

a. Show that $f(x) = (x - 1)^2 + 1$.

b. Explain why the graph of f does not have any x intercepts.

c. Show that $f(1 + i) = 0$.

d. Find one other nonreal number for which $f(x) = 0$.

9. Find the exact length of each line segment with the given endpoints.

a. (0, 0) and (4, 1) **b.** (0, 0) and (2, 1) **c.** (0, 0) and (7, 6) **d.** (0, 0) and (3, 4)

e. (0, 0) and (6, 8) **f.** (0, 0) and $(1, \sqrt{3})$ **g.** (0, 0) and (x, y)

10. Compute each of these products.

a. $(4 + i)(4 - i)$ **b.** $(2 + i)(2 - i)$ **c.** $(7 + 6i)(7 - 6i)$

d. $(3 + 4i)(3 - 4i)$ **e.** $(6 + 8i)(6 - 8i)$ **f.** $(1 + i\sqrt{3})(1 - i\sqrt{3})$

11. a. Let $x = 3$ and $y = 2$ in the equation from Problem 7. Calculate the values of $x^2 - y^2$, $2xy$, and $x^2 + y^2$.

b. Copy and complete the table at the right.

x	y	$x^2 - y^2$	$2xy$	$x^2 + y^2$
3	2	■	■	■
2	1	■	■	■
3	1	■	■	■
4	3	■	■	■
4	1	■	■	■
5	2	■	■	■

12. a. Sketch the graph of $f(x) = \cos^2 x - \sin^2 x$.

b. Find the amplitude and period of f.

c. Sketch the graph of $g(x) = \cos 2x$ on the same axes.

d. Compare the graphs of f and g.

13. a. If $z = x + yi$, find the real part of z^3.

b. Sketch the graph of $h(x) = \cos^3 x - 3\cos x \sin^2 x$.

c. Sketch the graph of $j(x) = \cos 3x$ on the same axes.

d. Compare the graphs of h and j.

Maintain Your Skills

14. Expand each of these expressions.

a. $(a + b)(a - b)$ **b.** $(a + b\sqrt{2})(a - b\sqrt{2})$ **c.** $(a + b\sqrt{3})(a - b\sqrt{3})$

d. $(a + b\sqrt{c})(a - b\sqrt{c})$ **e.** $(x + yi)(x - yi)$

Answers

Exercises

8. a. $(x - 1)^2 + 1 = x^2 - 2x + 1 + 1 = x^2 - 2x + 2$

b. For all real numbers x, $(x - 1)^2 \geq 0$. Hence $f(x) = (x - 1)^2 + 1$ is always positive.

c. $f(1 + i) = (1 + i - 1)^2 + 1 = i^2 + 1 = 0$

d. $1 - i$

9. a. $\sqrt{17}$ **b.** $\sqrt{5}$
c. $\sqrt{85}$ **d.** 5
e. 10 **f.** 2
g. $\sqrt{x^2 + y^2}$

10. a. 17 **b.** 5
c. 85 **d.** 25
e. 100 **f.** 4

11–13. See back of book.

14. a. $a^2 - b^2$
b. $a^2 - 2b^2$
c. $a^2 - 3b^2$
d. $a^2 - cb^2$
e. $x^2 + y^2$

2.2 The Complex Plane

Any complex number is made up of two parts, the real part, and the imaginary part. Two complex numbers are equal if and only if their real and imaginary parts are equal. In 1806, Jean-Robert Argand, a Parisian, published his ideas about a geometric representation of complex numbers. He used the x-axis to represent the real part, and the y-axis to represent the imaginary part.

Another name for the complex plane is the *Argand plane.* Gauss and Caspar Wessel described the complex plane in much the same way around the same time.

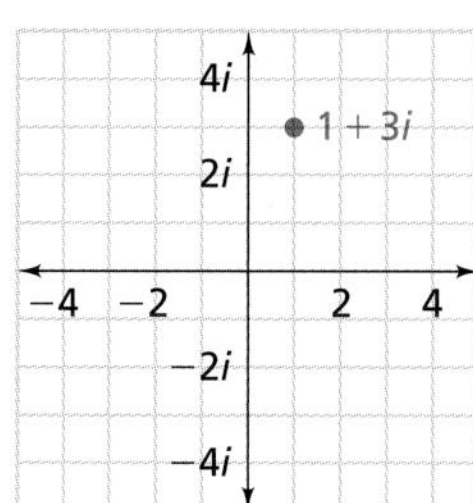

In the complex plane, the horizontal axis is the real axis, and the vertical axis is the imaginary axis.

For a review of complex numbers, go to **Web Code:** bge-9031

For You to Do

1. Identify the complex number represented by each point.

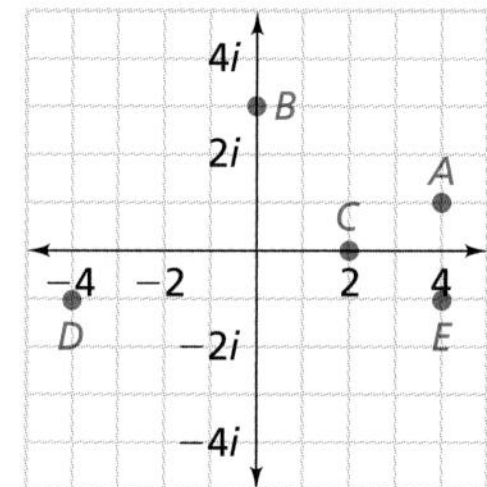

2. Which two of the five points are conjugates of one another?

In an earlier algebra course, you saw that the absolute value of a number x is its distance from 0 on the number line. In the same way, the absolute value $|z|$ of a complex number is also the distance from 0 on the complex plane.

Definition

The magnitude of a complex number z, denoted by $|z|$, is the distance between the complex number and 0 in the complex plane.

Some older texts call the magnitude of a complex number the *modulus*.

For You to Do

1. **A.** $4 + i$
   B. $0 + 3i$
   C. $2 + 0i$
   D. $-4 - i$
   E. $4 - i$
2. A and E

Lesson Overview

GOAL

- Determine the magnitude and argument of any complex number.

In this lesson, students review two key properties of complex numbers: absolute value and argument. These two properties provide the basis for introducing polar coordinates, as well as geometric ways to represent complex multiplication.

Throughout the text, "absolute value" and "magnitude" are used interchangeably, as are "argument" and "direction."

CHECK YOUR UNDERSTANDING
- Core: 1, 2, 3, 5
- Optional: 4

MATERIALS
- CAS (recommended)
- graph paper
- graphing calculators
- Blackline Master MC10

HOMEWORK
- Core: 6, 7, 9, 11, 13, 16
- Optional: 8, 10, 12, 14, 15, 17

VOCABULARY
- absolute value of a complex number
- argument
- magnitude, $|z|$
- modulus
- norm, $N(z)$

Launch

Review Exercise 9 from Lesson 2.1. It provides a basis for students to calculate the absolute value of a complex number.

Explore

You may want to use Blackline Master MC10 on an overhead. Prepare several points before class and have the students identify the complex numbers. Then plot several other examples. Demonstrate the geometric relationship of conjugate pairs. Use examples to demonstrate the geometric meanings of the magnitude and argument of complex numbers. You may wish to provide copies for students to use during the lesson or while working the exercises.

If $z = x + yi$, $|z|$ is the length of the line segment connecting 0 and $x + yi$ in the complex plane, or (0, 0) and (x, y) in the coordinate plane.

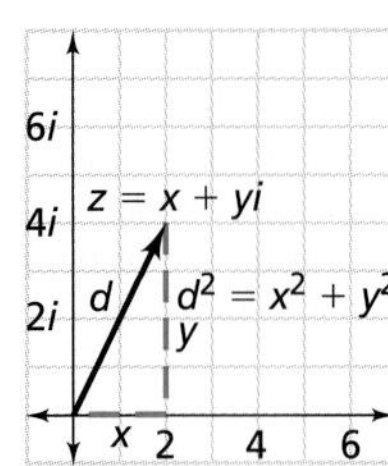

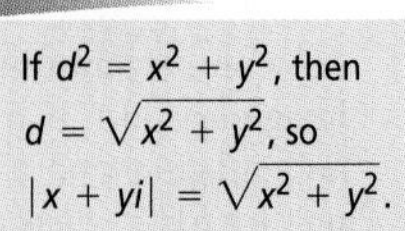

If $d^2 = x^2 + y^2$, then $d = \sqrt{x^2 + y^2}$, so $|x + yi| = \sqrt{x^2 + y^2}$.

For You to Do

3. Find $|-2 + 7i|$.

4. Find a complex number in Quadrant IV with magnitude 13.

See TI-Nspire™ Handbook on p. 704 for advice on calculating magnitude.

You may recall another attribute of a complex number, the *norm*.

Definition

The norm of a complex number z, written $N(z)$, is the product of the complex number and its conjugate, $z\bar{z}$.

The norm and absolute value of a complex number are similar, as the following theorem suggests.

Theorem 2.1

The absolute value of a complex number is equal to the square root of its norm.

$$|z| = \sqrt{N(z)}$$

For You to Do

5. Prove Theorem 2.1.

You can think of a real number x as having a size $|x|$, and a positive or negative sign. The absolute value denotes the magnitude of x, and the sign is the direction from 0. So the number 3 is 3 units in the positive direction from 0, and -3 is 3 units in the negative direction from 0.

The complex plane gives a convenient way to think of the direction of a complex number.

Answers

For You to Do

3. $\sqrt{53}$

4. Answers may vary. Sample: $5 - 12i$

For You to Do

5. Let $z = x + yi$ (x and y real numbers). Then $|z| = |x + yi| = \sqrt{x^2 + y^2}$. But $N(z) = (x + yi)(x - yi) = x^2 + y^2$. So $|z| = \sqrt{N(z)}$.

Definition

The argument of a complex number z, written arg(z), is the measure of the angle in standard position with z on the terminal side.

The argument arg (z) of a complex number is also its direction.

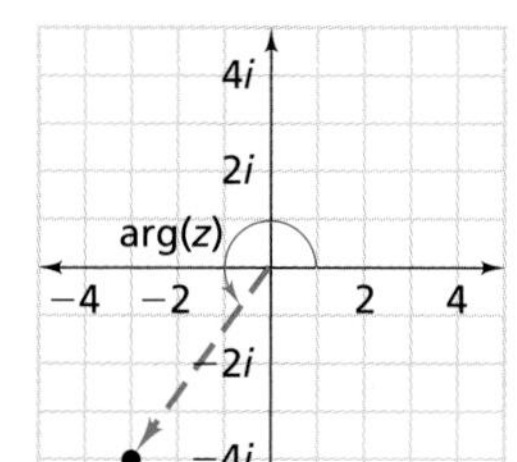

A good way to think of a complex number and its attributes is to think of it as a vector. Instead of a ray as described in this definition, you could think of the vector ***z***.

The value arg(z) is expressed in either degrees or radians. To find the argument, you need to use trigonometry.

Example

Problem Find the magnitude and argument of $-2 + 3i$.

Solution The figure below shows $-2 + 3i$ graphed in the complex plane.

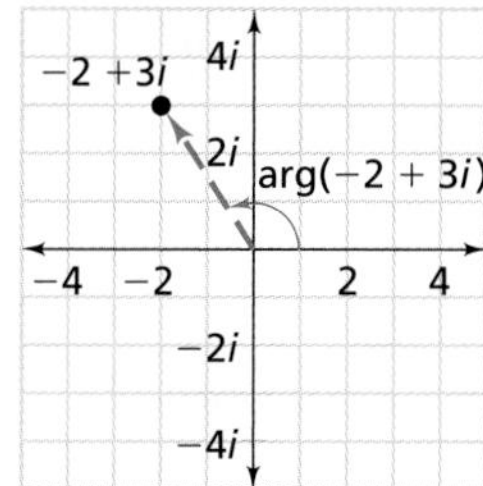

Use the formula $|x + yi| = \sqrt{x^2 + y^2}$ to find the magnitude.

$$|-2 + 3i| = \sqrt{(-2)^2 + (3)^2} = \sqrt{4 + 9} = \sqrt{13}$$

In Chapter 1, you saw that the slope of a line through the origin was equal to the tangent of the angle from the positive x-axis to the line. The slope of the line through the origin and the complex number z is $\frac{3 - 0}{(-2) - 0} = -\frac{3}{2}$. You can find the argument by using inverse trigonometric functions. However, you might need to adjust the result from a calculator to find an angle in the correct quadrant.

Your calculator will say that $\tan^{-1}\left(-\frac{3}{2}\right) \approx -0.9828$, which corresponds to an angle in the fourth quadrant. $-2 + 3i$ is in the second quadrant, so

$$\arg(z) \approx \pi - 0.9828 \approx 2.1588$$

Example

Spend time as needed going over this completed example. Make sure students understand the problem. As necessary, help them develop the detailed solution.

For You to Do

PROBLEM 6 asks for degrees since it may be easier for students to see that all of the angles have the same reference angle, $\arg(4 + 3i)$. Have students compare their answers and see if they can make this connection. Their graphs should also help.

Wrap Up

To end this day, you might go over Exercises 3 and 5. It is also valuable to see what students notice about the geometric transformations that result as i is taken to various powers in Exercise 5.

Assessment Resources

Lesson Quiz 2.2

1. Find the exact magnitude and argument of each complex number.
   a. $4 + 3i$ b. $-5 + 2i$
2. Suppose a complex number z is multiplied by four. How do $\arg(z)$ and $\arg(4z)$ compare? How do $|z|$ and $|4z|$ compare?
3. For each complex number, find the exact magnitude and approximate the direction to two decimal places.
   a. $(-2 + 3i)^3$ b. $(-6 + 2i)^4$

Exercises

HOMEWORK
- Core: 6, 7, 9, 11, 13, 16
- Optional: 8, 10, 12, 14, 15, 17

Check Your Understanding

EXERCISE 1 Assign this exercise along with the one that immediately follows. Discuss the similarity of the results.

EXERCISE 2 Make the connection explicit by pointing out that the magnitude calculated for $x + yi$ in Exercise 1 was $\sqrt{x^2 + y^2}$. Here, the result of the multiplication $(x + yi)(x - yi)$ is $x^2 + y^2$.

You will revisit this in the next lesson on magnitude and direction, since one potential definition of magnitude is $\sqrt{z\bar{z}}$.

EXERCISE 3 reinforces the idea that multiplying by i causes a 90° rotation in the complex plane.

EXERCISE 4 Some students will note that these numbers are "halfway" through the quadrant and should therefore be at 45° increments. However, it does not work for 30°, 60°, and 90°. Again, try to stress the notion of related angles here.

For You to Do

6. Graph and label each of these complex numbers in the same complex plane. For each number, find its magnitude and argument (in degrees between 0° and 360°).
   a. $4 + 3i$ b. $4 - 3i$ c. $-4 + 3i$ d. $-4 - 3i$

Exercises *Practicing Habits of Mind*

Check Your Understanding

Unless otherwise specified, write the argument using radians.

1. For each complex number, find its exact magnitude.
   a. $4 + i$ b. $2 + i$ c. $3 - 2i$ d. $6 + 5i$
2. Compute each product. Compare the result to the magnitudes found in Exercise 1.
   a. $(4 + i)(4 - i)$ b. $(2 + i)(2 - i)$
   c. $(3 - 2i)(3 + 2i)$ d. $(6 + 5i)(6 - 5i)$
3. For each complex number z, graph z and $i \cdot z$ as vectors in the same complex plane. Estimate $\arg(z)$ and $\arg(iz)$.
   a. $z = 3 + 2i$ b. $z = -1 + 4i$
   c. $z = -1 - 3i$ d. $z = 2 - 3i$
4. Find the exact magnitude and argument of each complex number.
   a. $2 + 2i$ b. $2 - 2i$ c. $-2 + 2i$ d. $-2 - 2i$
5. Let z be a complex number. For each of the expressions below, describe how its magnitude and argument compare to $|z|$ and $\arg(z)$.
   a. iz b. i^2z c. $(-i)z$ d. $2z$ e. $\frac{1}{z}$

For additional practice, go to Web Code: bga-0202

On Your Own

6. Suppose you triple a complex number z. How do $|3z|$ and $\arg(3z)$ compare to $|z|$ and $\arg(z)$?

Answers

For You to Do

6. See back of book.

Exercises

1. a. $\sqrt{17}$ b. $\sqrt{5}$
   c. $\sqrt{13}$ d. $\sqrt{61}$
2. a. 17 b. 5 c. 13 d. 61
   Each product is the square of the corresponding answer in Exercise 1.
3. See back of book.
4. a. magnitude $= 2\sqrt{2}$, argument $= \frac{\pi}{4}$
   b. magnitude $= 2\sqrt{2}$, argument $= \frac{7\pi}{4}$
   c. magnitude $= 2\sqrt{2}$, argument $= \frac{3\pi}{4}$
   d. magnitude $= 2\sqrt{2}$, argument $= \frac{5\pi}{4}$
5. See back of book.
6. $|3z| = 3|z|$ and $\arg(3z) = \arg(z)$

7. **Write About It** Suppose you multiply a complex number z by a real number c. How do $|cz|$ and $\arg(cz)$ compare to $|z|$ and $\arg(z)$?

> There may be several cases to consider, since c can be any real number.

8. Let $z = x + yi$, where x and y are positive real numbers.
   a. Graph what z and $\overline{z}$ might look like in the same complex plane.
   b. Graph $z + \overline{z}$.
   c. Show that the four complex numbers 0, z, $\overline{z}$, and $z + \overline{z}$ are the vertices of a parallelogram when plotted in the complex plane.

9. Let $z = \cos t + i \sin t$.
   a. Calculate z^2.
   b. What is the imaginary part of z^2?

10. Find the vertices of a square in the complex plane.

11. Find the four solutions to the equation $x^4 - 16 = 0$. Plot them in the complex plane.

> Two of the solutions are real numbers, and two are not.

12. For each complex number, find the exact magnitude. Also, approximate to two decimal places the argument in degrees.
    a. $(3 + 2i)^0$
    b. $(3 + 2i)^1$
    c. $(3 + 2i)^2$
    d. $(3 + 2i)^3$
    e. $(3 + 2i)^4$

13. For each complex number, find the exact magnitude.
    a. $(1 + i)^2$
    b. $(2 + i)^2$
    c. $(3 + i)^2$
    d. $(7 + i)^2$
    e. $(2 + 3i)^2$
    f. Find a complex number $x + yi$ with a magnitude of 29, where $x \neq 0$ and $y \neq 0$.

14. Find the magnitude and argument of each solution to each equation.
    a. $x^2 - 1 = 0$
    b. $x^3 - 1 = 0$
    c. $x^4 - 1 = 0$

15. Establish the identity $(ac - bd)^2 + (bc + ad)^2 = (a^2 + b^2)(c^2 + d^2)$.

16. **Standardized Test Prep** Which of the following is the product of $-1 + i$ and its complex conjugate?

    A. 0   B. −1.1   C. −0.9   D. 2

Maintain Your Skills

17. Let $\omega = \frac{1 + i\sqrt{3}}{2}$. Plot each of the following in the same complex plane.
    a. ω
    b. ω^2
    c. ω^3
    d. ω^4
    e. ω^5
    f. ω^6
    g. ω^7
    h. ω^{12}

> ω is the Greek letter *omega*.

7. $|cz| = |c||z|$; if $cz \neq 0$, then $\arg(cz) = \arg(z)$. If $c < 0$ then $\arg(cz) = \arg(z) + \pi$.

8. See back of book.

9. a. $(\cos^2 t - \sin^2 t) + (2 \sin t \cos t)i$

b. $2 \sin t \cos t$

10. Answers may vary. Sample: $1 + i$, $1 - i$, $-1 + i$, $-1 - i$

11. See back of book.

12. a. magnitude = 1, direction = 0°

b. magnitude = $\sqrt{13}$, direction ≈ 33.69°

c. magnitude = 13, direction ≈ 67.38°

d. magnitude = $13\sqrt{13}$, direction ≈ 101.07°

e. magnitude = 169, direction ≈ 134.76°

13. a. 2 **b.** 5 **c.** 10

d. 50 **e.** 13

f. Answers may vary. Sample: $21 + 20i$

14–15. See back of book.

16. D

17. See back of book.

On Your Own

EXERCISE 12 provides experience with powers of complex numbers. Once students learn to write complex numbers in the form $r(\cos \theta + i \sin \theta)$, they will be able to use De Moivre's Theorem to more easily calculate the powers.

EXERCISE 13 In general, this method with $(m + ni)^2$ leads to the formula for generating Pythagorean triples you used in Lesson 2.1 Exercise 11:

$(m^2 - n^2, 2mn, m^2 + n^2)$ is a Pythagorean triple

Here, $(m + ni)^2 = (m^2 - n^2) + (2mn)i$, and the magnitude is $m^2 + n^2$.

EXERCISE 15 provides one way to prove that the magnitude of a product equals the product of the magnitudes. See Developing Habits of Mind on page 101.

Maintain Your Skills

EXERCISE 17 Students may use either points or vectors to plot each expression, since the exercise is not specific.

Additional Resources

PRINT RESOURCES
- Solution Manual
- Practice Workbook
- Assessment Resources
- Teaching Resources

TECHNOLOGY
- Interactive Textbook
- TeacherExpress CD-ROM
- ExamView CD-ROM
- PHSchool.com

Additional Practice

1. Find the exact magnitude and argument of each complex number.
   a. $4 + 6i$
   b. $-3 + 5i$
   c. $-2 - 6i$
   d. $5 - i$

2. Let $z = -2 + 5i$. Find the exact magnitude and argument of each complex number.
   a. z
   b. iz
   c. z^2
   d. $i^2 z$

3. Find the four solutions to the equation $x^4 - 81 = 0$. Plot them in the complex plane.

4. For each complex number find the exact magnitude.
   a. $(2 - 2i)^2$
   b. $(1 + 3i)^3$

5. Let z and w be complex numbers, with $|z| = 2$, $\arg(z) = \frac{\pi}{4}$, $|w| = 2\sqrt{5}$, and $\arg(w) = 150°$.
   a. Write z in $a + bi$ form.
   b. Write w in $a + bi$ form.

6. Find the magnitude and argument of each complex number.
   a. $8 \text{ cis } 135°$
   b. $3\sqrt{2} \text{ cis } \frac{\pi}{6}$

7. Suppose $z = 8 \text{ cis } 150°$ and $w = 6 \text{ cis } 300°$. Find the following.
   a. z^2
   b. zw
   c. $|zw|$
   d. $|w^2|$

8. Consider the complex numbers $z = \text{cis } \frac{3\pi}{2}$ and $w = 3 + 2i$.
   a. Find the argument of z and the argument of w.
   b. Calculate zw and find the argument of zw.
   c. Describe the effect in the complex plane of multiplying a complex number by z.

Practice: For Lesson 2.2, assign Exercises 1–4.

Lesson Overview

GOAL

- Represent complex numbers using both rectangular coordinates and polar coordinates.

This lesson briefly introduces polar notation for points, then moves on to polar notation for complex numbers. The notation $r(\cos\theta + i\sin\theta)$, or r cis θ, provides much more than just another way to view complex numbers. It opens up many more connections, especially between complex number arithmetic and geometry.

CHECK YOUR UNDERSTANDING
- Core: 1, 2, 4, 5, 7
- Optional: 3, 6

MATERIALS
- CAS (recommended)
- graph paper
- graphing calculators
- Blackline Masters MC1, MC10, 2.3

HOMEWORK
- Core: 8, 9, 10, 11, 14
- Optional: 12, 13, 15

VOCABULARY
- polar coordinates
- polar form for complex numbers
- rectangular coordinates
- rectangular form for complex numbers

Launch

To launch today's lesson, start by graphing a point on the board, such as (3, 4). Ask students how they would direct a person standing at the origin to walk toward the point. There are two common methods.

- Move 3 units to the right, then 4 units up.
- Rotate approximately 53° counterclockwise until you face the point, then walk 5 units to the point.

The first method is an example of using rectangular coordinates, and the second method is an example of using polar coordinates.

You can summarize this discussion by reviewing the Facts and Notation section.

Explore

For Discussion

PROBLEMS 1 AND 2 The statement is always true in this direction: If $P_1 = (r_1, \theta_1)$ and $P_2 = (r_2, \theta_2)$,

$$r_1 = r_2 \text{ and } \theta_1 = \theta_2 \Rightarrow P_1 = P_2$$

The statement is not always true in the other direction, since θ can be any real number, so for any integer value of k, $\theta + 2\pi k$ represents the same angle as θ. Moreover, the point (r, θ) is the same point as $(-r, \theta + \pi)$.

When using polar coordinates for points, both r and θ typically range over all real numbers. However, when using r cis θ for complex numbers, r is typically restricted to non-negative real numbers, and θ is typically restricted to $[0, 2\pi)$.

2.3 Another Form for Complex Numbers

Coordinates are a perfectly good way to describe a point in the plane. The two numbers x and y identify a unique location. You start at the origin. You count $|x|$ units left or right (depending on the sign of x). Then you count $|y|$ units up or down (depending on the sign of y).

Suppose you are walking from the origin to the point (x, y). Regardless of how you define your axes, you could move x units in some direction, then turn 90° clockwise or counterclockwise before moving y units. The key idea is that your second movement would be perpendicular to the first.

But think, for instance, how you would actually move from one point to another. Suppose you were in an open field. You would likely walk in a straight line directly from one point to the other. You would first turn in the proper direction, then walk the proper distance.

This idea, and your work in the previous lesson, suggest another way to identify points in the plane. To get from the origin to the point (x, y), instead of walking two separate distances, you can move just one distance, providing you are heading in the right direction. So if you have two numbers, a direction (given by an angle measurement) and a distance, you can find your point.

Is it easier for you to desribe this fan in terms of polar coordinates or rectangular coordinates?

Facts and Notation

You can locate a point P in the plane in two ways.

Rectangular coordinates: (x, y) denotes distances along two axes that are perpendicular.

Polar coordinates: (r, θ) denotes a direction (an angle θ counterclockwise from the positive real axis) and distance r.

For Discussion

Let P_1 and P_2 be two points in the plane. If $P_1 = (x_1, y_1)$ and $P_2 = (x_2, y_2)$, it is a true statement that

$$P_1 = P_2 \Leftrightarrow x_1 = x_2 \text{ and } y_1 = y_2$$

Can you make the same statement about polar coordinates? Decide if the following statement is true: if $P_1 = (r_1, \theta_1)$ and $P_2 = (r_2, \theta_2)$

$$P_1 = P_2 \Leftrightarrow r_1 = r_2 \text{ and } \theta_1 = \theta_2$$

Consider these questions.

1. Is the statement true for either direction $\Leftrightarrow$?
2. If either implication is not always true, modify the statement to make both implications always true.

Answers

For Discussion

1. $(r_1 = r_2 \text{ and } \theta_1 = \theta_2) \Rightarrow P_1 = P_2$ is always true.
2. The statement $P_1 = P_2 \Rightarrow (r_1 = r_2$ and $\theta_1 = \theta_2)$ is not always true, but it will always be true if you change "$\theta_1 = \theta_2$" to "$\theta_1 - \theta_2 = 2n\pi$ for some integer n."

Complex numbers of the form $x + yi$ correspond directly to rectangular coordinates of the point (x, y). You can find a complex number if you are given polar coordinates (r, θ).

Example

Problem Let $|z| = 1$ and $\arg(z) = \frac{\pi}{6}$. Write z in the form $x + yi$.

Solution From the argument, z is in the first quadrant.

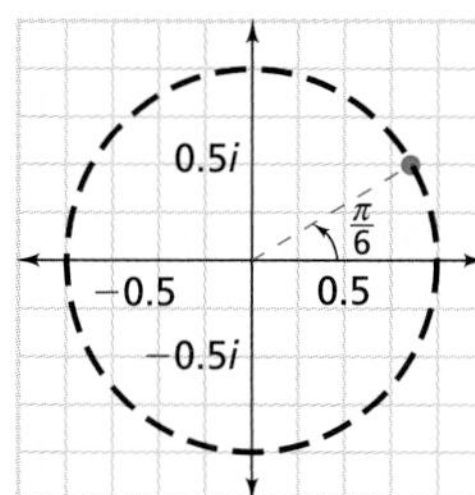

Since $|z| = 1$, z is on the unit circle. So x cos $\frac{\pi}{6} = \frac{\sqrt{3}}{2}$ and y is $\sin\frac{\pi}{6} = \frac{1}{2}$. Thus, you can write $z = \cos\frac{\pi}{6} + i\sin\frac{\pi}{6} = \frac{\sqrt{3}}{2} + \frac{1}{2}i$.

For You to Do

For each absolute value and argument, write z in the form $x + yi$.

3. $|z| = 2$ and $\arg(z) = \frac{\pi}{6}$.
4. $|z| = 4$ and $\arg(z) = 135°$.

Just as you can express a point in the coordinate plane in two ways, you can express a complex number in two ways.

Rectangular Form: $x + yi$, where x and y are real numbers.

Polar Form: $r(\cos\theta + i\sin\theta)$, where r is a nonnegative real number and θ is a measurement in either degrees or radians.

Facts and Notation

To identify the complex number $\cos\theta + i\sin\theta$, you can use the abbreviation cis θ.

Notice that the convention is to write "$i\sin\frac{\pi}{6}$." If you wrote "$\sin\frac{\pi}{6}i$" to match the "*yi*," it would be unclear whether you mean $\sin\left(\frac{\pi}{6}i\right)$ or $\left(\sin\frac{\pi}{6}\right)i$. Of course, parentheses make the intent clear, but the convention is to avoid parentheses whenever possible.

By convention, r is not negative. You could express a complex number using $r < 0$, but if r is nonnegative, it will be equal to the magnitude of the complex number.

For You to Do

3. $2\cos\frac{\pi}{6} + 2i\sin\frac{\pi}{6}$, or $\sqrt{3} + i$
4. $4\cos 135° + 4i\sin 135°$, or $2\sqrt{2} + 2\sqrt{2}i$

Example

You may wish to use Blackline Master MC1 on an overhead to illustrate the solution.

For You to Do

PROBLEM 3

$$z = 2\left(\cos\frac{\pi}{6} + i\sin\frac{\pi}{6}\right) = 2\left(\frac{\sqrt{3}}{2} + i\frac{1}{2}\right) = \sqrt{3} + i$$

PROBLEM 4

$$z = 4(\cos 135° + i\sin 135°)$$
$$= 4\left(-\frac{\sqrt{2}}{2} + i\frac{\sqrt{2}}{2}\right) = -2\sqrt{2} + 2\sqrt{2}i$$

Wrap Up

As students work through the Check Your Understanding exercises, review the following key idea.

For any complex number z,

$$z = |z| \text{ cis}(\arg(z))$$

Make sure that students understand the correct argument. In Chapter 1, students saw that their calculator will return a base angle in the range $\left(-\frac{\pi}{2}, \frac{\pi}{2}\right)$ when calculating $\tan^{-1}$ of a number. They need to make sure the measurement they use is in the correct quadrant.

You may want to use Blackline Master 2.3 on an overhead to summarize the key items in the lesson.

Assessment Resources

Lesson Quiz 2.3

1. Consider the complex numbers $z = 2$ cis $70°$ and $w = 4$ cis $130°$. Find $|zw|$ and arg (zw).

2. Consider the complex number $z = 2$ cis $\frac{2\pi}{3}$.
   a. Write z in the form $x + yi$ where x and y are real numbers.
   b. Calculate z^2.
   c. What is the relationship between arg (z) and arg (z^2)?

3. For the pair of complex numbers, find the magnitude and direction of z and w. Then find the magnitude and direction of the product zw.
   a. $z = 5 + i$ and $w = -4 - i$
   b. $z = 5i$ and $w = \frac{3 - 2i}{5}$

Exercises

HOMEWORK
- Core: 8, 9, 10, 11, 14
- Optional: 12, 13, 15

You can make handouts from Blackline Master MC5 for students to use while working on the exercises.

Check Your Understanding

EXERCISE 2 provides students with more evidence of the Multiplication Law and De Moivre's Theorem. You do not need to develop these concepts here, since the students will work explicitly with these theorems in Lesson 2.4 and in Investigation 2C.

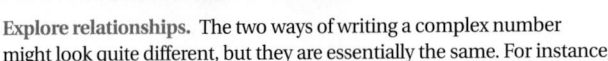

Developing Habits of Mind

Explore relationships. The two ways of writing a complex number might look quite different, but they are essentially the same. For instance,

$$1 + i\sqrt{3} = 2 \operatorname{cis} \frac{\pi}{3}$$

is a true statement. To see why, look at the right side.

$$\begin{aligned} 2 \operatorname{cis} \frac{\pi}{3} &= 2\left(\cos \frac{\pi}{3} + i \sin \frac{\pi}{3}\right) \\ &= 2\left(\frac{1}{2} + i\frac{\sqrt{3}}{2}\right) \\ &= 1 + i\sqrt{3} \end{aligned}$$

Either way you write it, you can see that the complex number has a real part and an imaginary part.

In general, you can write a complex number of the form $r \operatorname{cis} \theta$ as $x + yi$ by realizing that

$$x = r\cos\theta, \text{ and}$$
$$y = r\sin\theta$$

Also, if $z = r\operatorname{cis}\theta$, then you know that

$$|z| = r, \text{ and}$$
$$\arg(z) = \theta$$

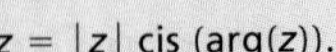

So, for any complex number z, you can say $z = |z| \operatorname{cis} (\arg(z))$.

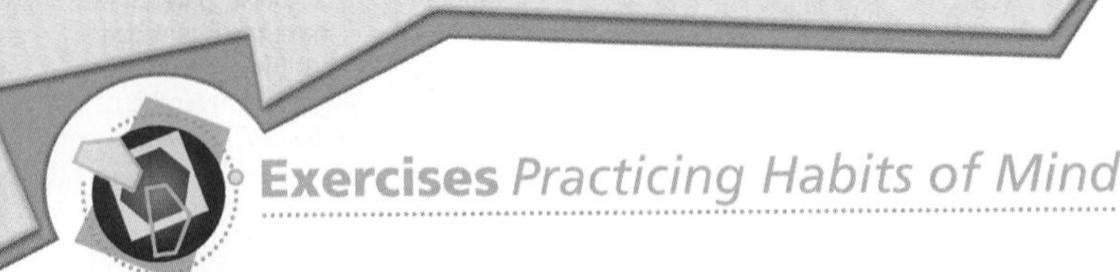

Exercises Practicing Habits of Mind

Check Your Understanding

1. Find the magnitude and argument of each complex number.
   a. $z = 5 \operatorname{cis} 60°$
   b. $w = \frac{1}{5} \operatorname{cis} 300°$
2. Consider the complex numbers z and w from Exercise 1.
   a. Find the magnitude and argument of z^2.
   b. Find the magnitude and argument of z^3.
   c. Find the magnitude and argument of zw.

Answers

Exercises

1. a. magnitude = 5, argument = 60°
   b. magnitude = $\frac{1}{5}$, argument = 300°
2. a. magnitude = 25, argument = 120°
   b. magnitude = 125, argument = 180°
   c. magnitude = 1, argument = 0° (or 360°)

3. a.

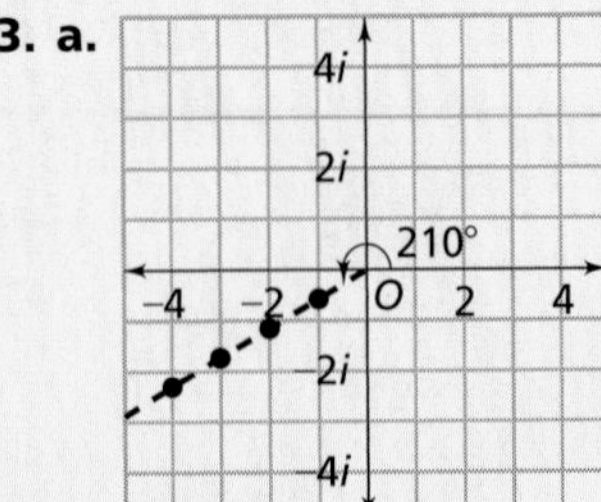

b.

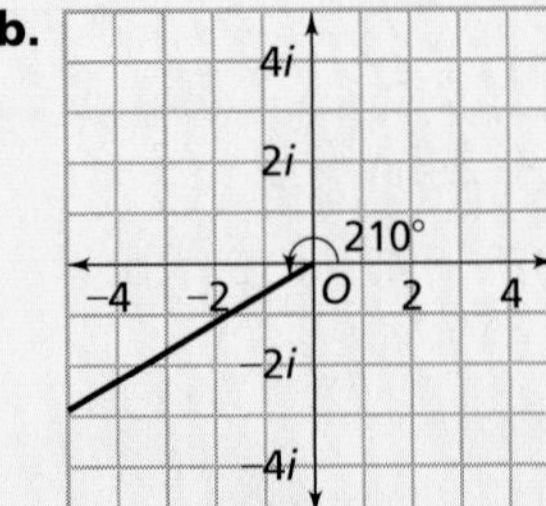

c. $-5\sqrt{3} - 5i$

4. a. $4 \cos \frac{2\pi}{3} + 4i \sin \frac{2\pi}{3}$
   b. $-2 + 2i\sqrt{3}$

3. a. In the complex plane, plot (as points) four different numbers with argument 210°.

   b. Plot the set of all points with argument 210°.

   c. What complex number has magnitude 10 and argument 210°?

4. Suppose q is a complex number with $|q| = 4$ and $\arg(q) = \frac{2\pi}{3}$.

   a. Write q using trigonometric functions.

   b. Write q without using trigonometric functions.

5. Let a and b be complex numbers, with $|a| = 5$, $\arg(a) = 60°$, $|b| = 3$, and $\arg(b) = 30°$.

   a. Write a and b in any form.

   b. Calculate the product ab. Find its magnitude and argument.

6. Suppose $z = 3 \text{ cis } \theta$ for some value of θ.

   a. Pick seven different values of θ. For each, plot z as a point in the complex plane.

   b. **Write About It** What does the graph of all possible such points look like? Explain.

7. a. Show that, for any value of θ, $|\text{cis } \theta| = 1$.

   b. Show that, for any value of r and θ, $|r \text{ cis } \theta| = |r|$.

On Your Own

8. Find the magnitude and argument of each complex number.

   a. $5\sqrt{3} - 5i$

   b. $10 \text{ cis } 330°$

   c. $4\sqrt{2} \text{ cis } \frac{5\pi}{4}$

   d. $-4 - 4i$

9. Consider the complex number $z = \text{cis } \frac{\pi}{2}$.

   a. Calculate z^2.

   b. Describe the effect in the complex plane of multiplying a complex number by z.

10. Suppose $z = 5 \text{ cis } 160°$ and $w = 2 \text{ cis } 110°$. Find $|zw|$ and $\arg(zw)$.

11. Complex number w has magnitude 1 and argument α. Complex number z has magnitude 1 and argument β.

    a. Write expressions for z and w.

    b. Write an expression for the product zw in the form $x + yi$, where x and y are in the set $\mathbb{R}$.

EXERCISES 3 AND 6 You may wish to provide copies of Blackline Master MC10 to your students for these exercises.

EXERCISE 7 Students may be skeptical of the fact that $|z| \cdot |w| = |zw|$. They proved this fact for real numbers in Algebra 1, and it is also true for complex numbers.

You do not need to convince them of this fact at this point. On Your Own Exercises 12 and 13 provide some additional examples.

On Your Own

EXERCISE 10 Encourage students to make some conjectures about the fact that $|zw| = |z||w|$ and $\arg(zw) = \arg(z) + \arg(w)$ (plus or minus 360°). This exercise allows them to test their conjectures or to gather some additional evidence.

5. a. Answers may vary. Samples:
$a = 5 \text{ cis } 60°$ or $a = \frac{5}{2} + \frac{5\sqrt{3}}{2}i$,
$b = 3 \text{ cis } 30°$ or $b = \frac{3\sqrt{3}}{2} + \frac{3}{2}i$

b. $15i$; magnitude $= 15$, argument $= 90°$

6. a. Check students' work. The values of θ will vary, but for each value of θ that is selected, the number z should be on the ray that has endpoint O and makes an angle of measure θ with the positive x-axis, and z should be 3 units from O.

b. The circle with center O and radius 3; $|z| = 3$ since $z = 3 \text{ cis } \theta$. Since there are no restrictions on θ, all points 3 units from O are included.

7. a. $|\text{cis } \theta| = |\cos \theta + i \sin \theta| = \sqrt{\cos^2 \theta + \sin^2 \theta} = 1$

b. $|r \text{ cis } \theta| = |r| \cdot |\text{cis } \theta| = |r| \cdot 1 = |r|$

8. a. magnitude $= 10$, argument $= 330°$

b. magnitude $= 10$, argument $= 330°$

c. magnitude $= 4\sqrt{2}$, argument $= \frac{5\pi}{4}$

d. magnitude $= 4\sqrt{2}$, argument $= \frac{5\pi}{4}$

9. a. -1

b. The result is the image you get if you rotate z around the origin by 90° (that is, $\frac{\pi}{2}$ radians).

10. $|zw| = 10$, $\arg(zw) = 270°$

11. a. $w = \text{cis } \alpha$ (or $\cos \alpha + i \sin \alpha$), $z = \text{cis } \beta$ (or $\cos \beta + i \sin \beta$)

b. $(\cos \alpha \cos \beta - \sin \alpha \sin \beta) + (\cos \alpha \sin \beta + \sin \alpha \cos \beta)i$

EXERCISE 12 and the one that follows previews the upcoming lesson on general complex multiplication (and De Moivre's Theorem).

EXERCISE 13 Students prove this fact in the next investigation, so expect only top students to provide a proof at this time.

Maintain Your Skills

EXERCISE 15 Not all students will recognize the pattern here, that each magnitude doubles and each direction is exactly 30° larger. There is no need to force this upon students, as they will learn the Multiplication Law in the next lesson. This is another chance for students to discover the Multiplication Law before you introduce it.

Additional Resources

PRINT RESOURCES
- Solution Manual
- Practice Workbook
- Assessment Resources
- Teaching Resources

TECHNOLOGY
- Interactive Textbook
- TeacherExpress CD-ROM
- ExamView CD-ROM
- PHSchool.com

Additional Practice

1. Find the exact magnitude and argument of each complex number.
   a. $4 + 6i$
   b. $-3 + 5i$
   c. $-2 - 6i$
   d. $5 - i$

2. Let $z = -2 + 5i$. Find the exact magnitude and argument of each complex number.
   a. z
   b. iz
   c. z^2
   d. i^2z

3. Find the four solutions to the equation $x^4 - 81 = 0$. Plot them in the complex plane.

4. For each complex number find the exact magnitude.
   a. $(2 - 2i)^2$
   b. $(1 + 3i)^3$

5. Let z and w be complex numbers, with $|z| = 2$, $\arg(z) = \frac{\pi}{4}$, $|w| = 2\sqrt{5}$, and $\arg(w) = 150°$.
   a. Write z in $a + bi$ form.
   b. Write w in $a + bi$ form.

6. Find the magnitude and argument of each complex number.
   a. $8 \text{ cis } 135°$
   b. $3\sqrt{2} \text{ cis } \frac{\pi}{6}$

7. Suppose $z = 8 \text{ cis } 150°$ and $w = 6 \text{ cis } 300°$. Find the following.
   a. z^2
   b. zw
   c. $|zw|$
   d. $|w^2|$

8. Consider the complex numbers $z = \text{cis } \frac{3\pi}{2}$ and $w = 3 + 2i$.
   a. Find the argument of z and the argument of w.
   b. Calculate zw and find the argument of zw.
   c. Describe the effect in the complex plane of multiplying a complex number by z.

Practice: For Lesson 2.3, assign Exercises 5–8.

12. For each pair of complex numbers, find the magnitude and direction of z and w. Then find the magnitude and direction of the product zw.
    a. $z = 2 + i$ and $w = 3 + i$
    b. $z = 2 + i$ and $w = 3 + 2i$
    c. $z = 5i$ and $w = 3i$
    d. $z = 2 + i$ and $w = \frac{2 - i}{5}$

13. a. Based on the results in Exercise 12, describe a relationship between $|z|$, $|w|$, and $|zw|$.
    b. Describe a relationship between $\arg(z)$, $\arg(w)$, and $\arg(zw)$.
    c. Let $z = x + yi$ and $w = c + di$. Show that the relationship you found between $|z|$, $|w|$, and $|zw|$ holds for any choice of z and w.

Remember...

$|z|$ is the magnitude of the complex number z.

14. **Standardized Test Prep** In polar coordinates, which of the following is the same as $(1, \frac{\pi}{3})$?
    A. $\left(-1, \frac{4\pi}{3}\right)$
    B. $\left(1, \frac{4\pi}{3}\right)$
    C. $\left(-1, \frac{\pi}{3}\right)$
    D. $\left(\frac{\pi}{3}, 1\right)$

Go Online
PHSchool.com

For additional practice, go to Web Code: bga-0203

Maintain Your Skills

15. The complex number $z = \sqrt{3} + i$ has magnitude 2 and direction $\frac{\pi}{6}$ (or 30°). For each complex number w listed below, find its magnitude and argument. Then find the magnitude and argument of zw.
    a. $w = 1 + i\sqrt{3}$
    b. $w = 5i$
    c. $w = 10$
    d. $w = 1 + i$
    e. $w = -2 + i$

Answers

12. a. $|z| = \sqrt{5}$, $\arg(z) \approx 26.565°$; $|w| = \sqrt{10}$, $\arg(w) \approx 18.435°$; $|zw| = 5\sqrt{2}$, $\arg(zw) = 45°$

b. $|z| = \sqrt{5}$, $\arg(z) \approx 26.565°$; $|w| = \sqrt{13}$, $\arg(w) \approx 33.690°$; $|zw| = \sqrt{65}$, $\arg(zw) \approx 60.255°$

c. $|z| = 5$, $\arg(z) = 90°$; $|w| = 3$, $\arg(w) = 90°$; $|zw| = 15$, $\arg(zw) = 180°$

d. $|z| = \sqrt{5}$, $\arg(z) \approx 26.565°$; $|w| = \frac{\sqrt{5}}{5}$, $\arg(w) \approx 333.435°$; $|zw| = 1$, $\arg(zw) = 0°$

13. a. $|z| \cdot |w| = |zw|$

b. $\arg(zw) = \arg(z) + \arg(w)$ or $\arg(zw) = \arg(z) + \arg(w) - 360°$

c. See back of book.

14. A

15. a–e. See back of book.

2.4 The Multiplication Law

There are two ways to represent a complex number graphically, as a point and as a vector (a directed distance). Both methods are useful, just as it is useful on the number line to present numbers as both points and arrows.

Throughout this lesson, the representation of complex numbers will alternate between points and vectors. What is most important is that you become comfortable with both representations and that you develop a knack for when to "think point" and when to "think vector."

- Thinking of complex numbers as points allows you to apply all the machinery of geometry to questions about complex numbers. This representation helps you do some very algebraic jobs, including equation solving.
- Thinking of complex numbers as vectors allows you to picture operations like adding two vectors or multiplying by i. Using vectors also allows you to think about the relative size of complex numbers, since a vector has a length.

Throughout this investigation, you have worked on arithmetic of complex numbers. You may have found the following ways of representing complex arithmetic geometrically.

- You can add two complex numbers by completing a parallelogram. The first two sides are vectors that represent the two numbers.

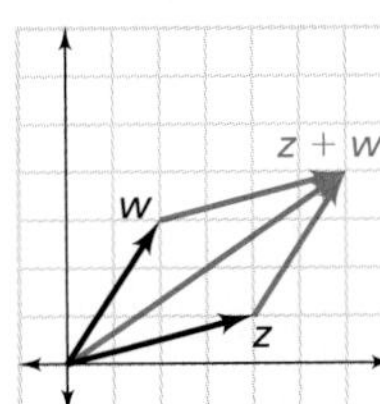

- You can multiply a complex number and a real number k by stretching the vector for the complex number by a factor of k.

If $k > 0$, the head of the vector is k times as far from the origin in the same direction. If $k < 0$, the head of the vector is $|k|$ times as far from the origin in the opposite direction.

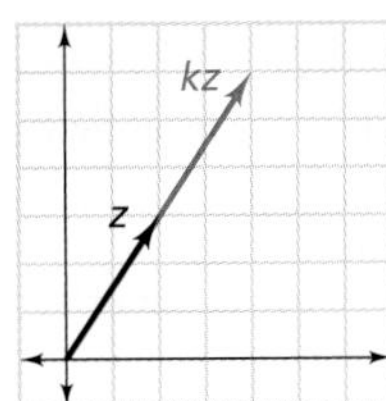

- You can multiply a complex number by i by rotating the vector for the complex number 90 degrees counterclockwise.

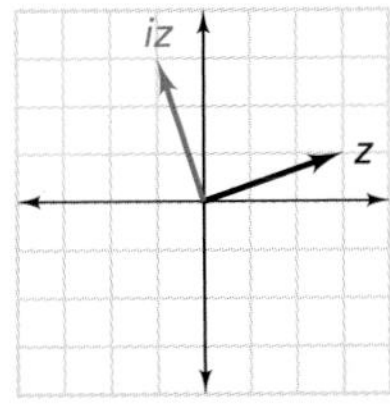

Lesson Overview

GOAL

- Decide when it is best to use either rectangular or polar coordinates to represent complex numbers.

With an understanding of polar form for complex numbers, students can find a quicker way to multiply two complex numbers. The basic thrust of this lesson is the following:

$$(r_1 \text{ cis } \theta_1)(r_2 \text{ cis } \theta_2) = (r_1 r_2) \text{ cis } (\theta_1 + \theta_2)$$

In the next investigation students will explore how this simple statement provides new ways to envision the geometry of complex numbers and to remember basic formulas for trigonometric functions.

CHECK YOUR UNDERSTANDING
- Core: 1, 2, 3, 4
- Optional: 5, 6

MATERIALS
- CAS (recommended)
- graph paper
- graphing calculators
- Blackline Masters MC1, MC7, MC10, 2.4

HOMEWORK
- Core: 7, 9a, 11, 12, 14
- Optional: 8, 10, 15
- Extension: 9b, 13, 16

Launch

Review Exercise 13 from the previous lesson. The students will gain some insight into today's lesson from the relationship they described in part (a).

Explore

Example

You may want to use Blackline Master 2.4 to demonstrate each step of this example.

You can also represent the multiplication of two complex numbers geometrically.

Example

Problem Let $z = 3 + 2i$ and $w = 4 + i$. Describe how to find the product zw geometrically.

Solution You already know how to multiply two complex numbers.

$$\begin{aligned}(3 + 2i)(4 + i) &= 3(4 + i) + 2i(4 + i)\\ &= (12 + 3i) + (-2 + 8i)\\ &= (12 - 2) + (3 + 8)i\\ &= 10 + 11i\end{aligned}$$

Just graphing the three vectors does not help much.

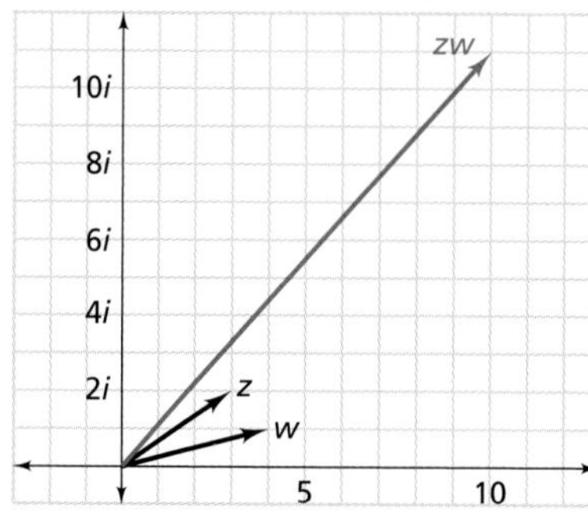

To see the geometry of the multiplication, you need to add a few more lines. Take a look at the first step in the calculation above.

$$(3 + 2i)(4 + i) = 3(4 + i) + 2i(4 + i)$$

On the right side, you have two arithmetic expressions that you know how to represent geometrically.

- $3(4 + i)$ is the product of a real number and a complex number. To show the product geometrically, you stretch the vector $4 + i$ by a factor of 3.

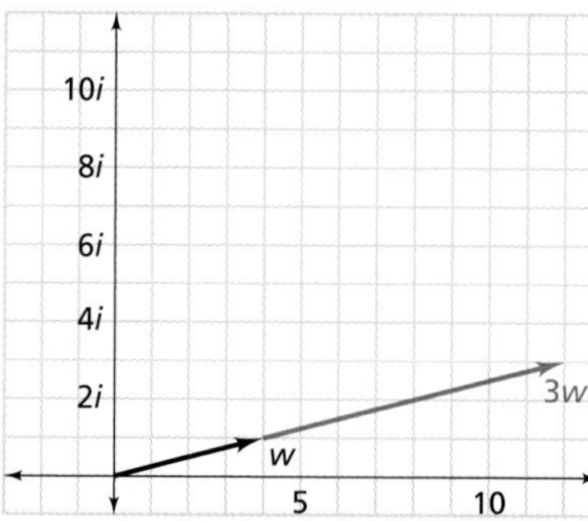

- $2i(4 + i)$ involves two steps. First, you can show the product $i(4 + i)$ by rotating $4 + i$ by 90 degrees counterclockwise.

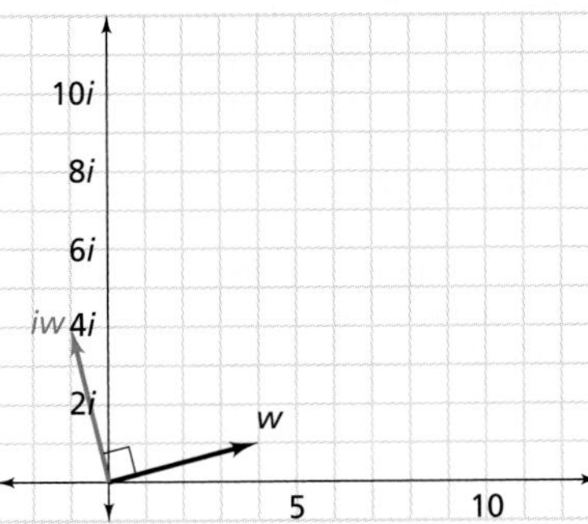

You can show the product of that resulting vector, $-1 + 4i$, and 2 by stretching the vector by a factor of 2.

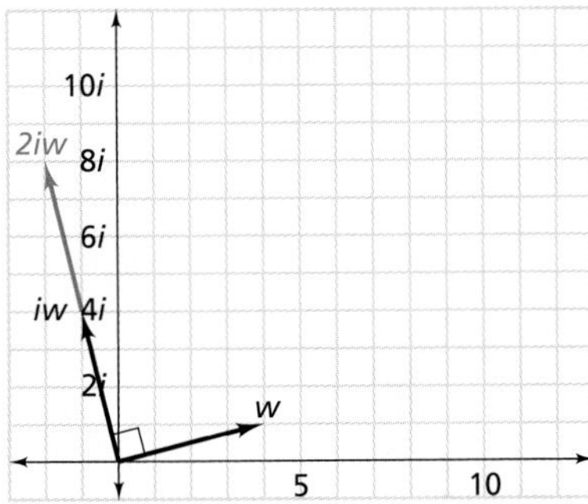

- Finally, add the two vectors by completing the parallelogram.

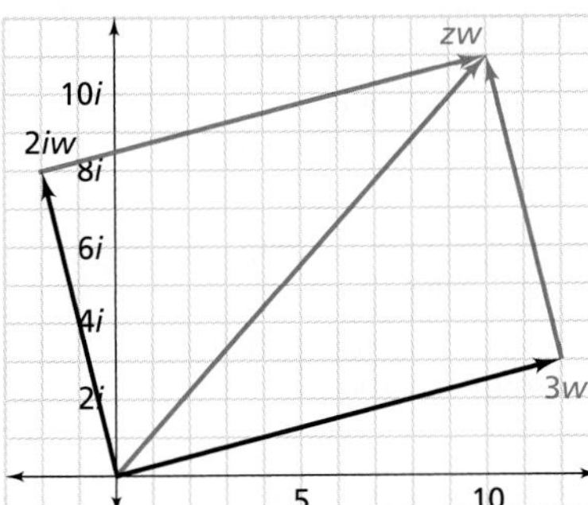

The parallelogram is actually a rectangle, because of the right angle.

The Example shows how to construct the product. But you may find it more difficult to follow the construction steps when finding the product of complex numbers written in cis notation, like $5 \text{ cis } \frac{\pi}{6}$ and $2 \text{ cis } \frac{\pi}{2}$.

To multiply complex numbers written this way, you can use certain properties of absolute value and argument, some of which you may have picked up in the exercises throughout this investigation. Your results from those exercises suggest the following theorem about the magnitude and argument of products.

Theorem 2.2 The Multiplication Law

Given complex numbers $z = a \operatorname{cis} \alpha$ and $w = b \operatorname{cis} \beta$,

$$zw = (a \operatorname{cis} \alpha)(b \operatorname{cis} \beta) = ab \operatorname{cis}(\alpha + \beta)$$

In other words,

- $|zw| = |z| \cdot |w|$
- $\arg(zw) = \arg(z) + \arg(w)$.

You can use $z = 3 + 2i$ and $w = 4 + i$ from the Example to demonstrate both parts of the theorem. Consider this figure.

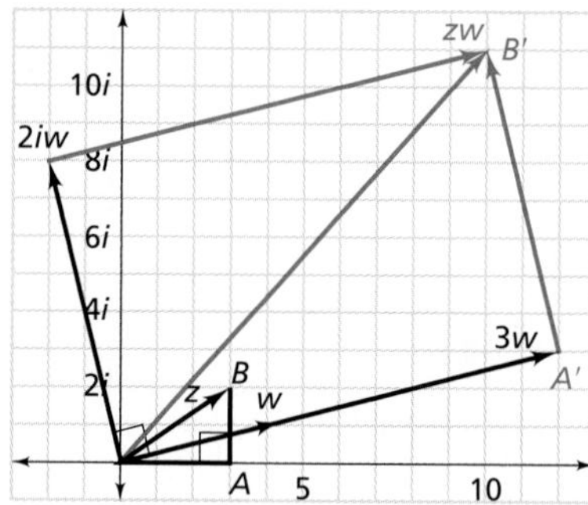

The smaller triangle is made from dropping a perpendicular from B to the real axis. The larger triangle is made from the construction from the examples. The two triangles are similar.

- Both are right triangles: the smaller because you made it by dropping a perpendicular, the larger because the angle at A' is part of a rectangle.
- Two pairs of sides are proportional: since $z = 3 + 2i$, you know that $OA = 3$ and $AB = 2$, so $\frac{OA}{AB} = \frac{3}{2}$. For the corresponding sides on the larger triangle, you have

$$OA' = |3(4 + i)| = |12 + 3i| = \sqrt{12^2 + 3^2} = \sqrt{144 + 9}$$
$$= \sqrt{153} = 3\sqrt{17}$$

and

$$A'B' = \sqrt{(10 - 12)^2 + (11 - 3)^2} = \sqrt{(-2)^2 + 8^2} = \sqrt{4 + 64}$$
$$= \sqrt{68} = 2\sqrt{17}$$

Thus

$$\frac{OA'}{A'B'} = \frac{3\sqrt{17}}{2\sqrt{17}} = \frac{3}{2}$$

Since the ratios are the same, the two pairs of sides are proportional.

Thus, by the SAS Theorem for similar triangles, the two triangles are similar. Now that you know the two triangles are similar, you can show both parts of the theorem.

- Corresponding sides in similar triangles are proportional. Every side in the larger triangle is $\sqrt{17}$ times as long as every side in the smaller triangle, and $\sqrt{17} = |w|$.
  The length of the hypotenuse of the smaller triangle is $|z| = \sqrt{3^2 + 2^2} = \sqrt{13}$. Thus, the length of the hypotenuse of the larger triangle is $\sqrt{13} \cdot \sqrt{17} = |zw|$. Thus, $|z| \cdot |w| = |zw|$.
- Corresponding angles in similar triangles are congruent. Thus, $\angle AOB \cong \angle A'OB'$. By definition, $\arg(z) = m\angle AOB$, $\arg(w) = m\angle AOA'$, and $\arg(zw) = m\angle AOB'$. Notice, though, that

$$\begin{aligned}\arg(zw) &= m\angle AOB' \\ &= m\angle AOA' + m\angle A'OB' \\ &= m\angle AOA' + m\angle AOB \\ &= \arg(z) + \arg(w)\end{aligned}$$

You can double check:

$$\begin{aligned}|zw| &= \sqrt{10^2 + 11^2} \\ &= \sqrt{100 + 121} \\ &= \sqrt{221} \\ &= \sqrt{13} \cdot \sqrt{17}\end{aligned}$$

For Discussion

1. Using algebra, prove for any two complex numbers $z = a + bi$ and $w = c + di$ that

$$|z| \cdot |w| = |zw|$$

Developing Habits of Mind

Visualize. Another way to envision what is happening with the geometry of complex multiplication is to look at what happens to z. You rotate it by $\arg(w)$, and then dilate it by $|w|$.

So, to multiply any complex number by $1 + i$, rotate it 45°, (since $45° = \arg(1 + i)$). Then scale by $\sqrt{2}$ (since $\sqrt{2} = |1 + i|$). To multiply by i, rotate it 90° and scale by 1.

It might help to think of the transformation of z by seeing how it transforms as part of the triangle AOB.

For You to Do

2. Describe multiplication of z by each of these numbers in terms of the rotation and scaling of z.

a. $\sqrt{3} + i$ b. $-i$ c. -1

For Discussion

PROBLEM 1 The product of $a + bi$ and $c + di$ is $(ac - bd) + (bc + ad)i$. So, the magnitude of the product is

$$\sqrt{(ac - bd)^2 + (bc + ad)^2}$$

The product of the magnitudes is

$$\sqrt{a^2 + b^2} \cdot \sqrt{c^2 + d^2}$$

The numbers under the square roots are not negative, so rewrite as

$$\sqrt{(a^2 + b^2)(c^2 + d^2)}$$

The result follows from Exercise 15 on page 91.

Another method for proving this statement algebraically uses the fact that the magnitude equals $\sqrt{z\overline{z}}$ where $\overline{z}$ is the conjugate of z. Then

$$\begin{aligned}|zw| &= \sqrt{zw\overline{zw}} \\ &= \sqrt{zw\overline{z}\,\overline{w}} \\ &= \sqrt{z\overline{z}w\overline{w}} \\ &= \sqrt{z\overline{z}}\sqrt{w\overline{w}} = |z||w|\end{aligned}$$

Wrap Up

Review Exercise 3. The idea that there are three numbers z such that $z^3 = 27 \text{ cis } 120°$ is important for Investigation 2C.

Assessment Resources

Lesson Quiz 2.4

1. Suppose z and w are complex numbers with $|z| = 2$ and $|w| = 4$. Find each magnitude.
   a. $|zw|$ b. $|\overline{w}|$
   c. $|z^2|$ d. $|2w|$

2. The graph on the right shows two complex numbers z and w drawn in the complex plane. Estimate the magnitude and argument of zw.

3. Consider the complex numbers $z = -8 - 6i$ and $w = 2 - 7i$.
   a. Plot z and w as vectors in the complex plane.
   b. In what quadrant is zw? Explain how you know.

Answers

For Discussion

1. See the answer for Exercise 13(c) of Lesson 2.3.

For You to Do

2. a. Multiplying by $\sqrt{3} + i$ rotates z by $\frac{\pi}{6}$ and multiplies its magnitude by 2.
   b. Multiplying by $-i$ rotates z by $\frac{3\pi}{2}$ but does not change its magnitude.
   c. Multiplying by -1 rotates z by π but does not change its magnitude.

Exercises

HOMEWORK
- Core: 7, 9a, 11, 12, 14
- Optional: 8, 10, 15
- Extension: 9b, 13, 16

You can make handouts of Blackline Masters MC7 and MC10 for students to use while working the exercises.

Check Your Understanding

EXERCISE 1 If students have trouble with this exercise, ask them to first try an example with two distinct complex numbers.

EXERCISE 2 Students should be able to articulate the pattern, as long as they correctly answered Exercise 1. You use this property in the lesson on roots of unity.

EXERCISE 3 Many students will answer that only part (b) is true, not recognizing the possibility of multiple solutions. This is important to the understanding of roots of unity, but is not central in this lesson. You can liken this to the fact that $x^2 = 9$ has two solutions, but only the positive solution is usually thought of as $\sqrt{9}$.

EXERCISE 4 Check that students are not trying to write z and w in $x + yi$ form, and that they are using the multiplication properties correctly.

EXERCISE 5 A student would also be correct in stating that the argument can be greater than 360°.

Exercises *Practicing Habits of Mind*

Check Your Understanding

1. Suppose $z = 3 \text{ cis } 120°$.

a. Find the magnitude and argument of z^2.

b. Explain why $z^3 = 27$.

2. **Write About It** If you know the magnitude and argument of z, describe (in words) how to find the magnitude and argument of z^2, z^3, and in general, z^n.

3. Suppose the complex number z^3 has magnnitude 27 and argument 120°. Decide whether each statement about z could be true. Explain.

a. z has magnitude 9 and argument 40°.

b. z has magnitude 3 and argument 40°.

c. z has magnitude 3 and argument 120°.

d. z has magnitude 3 and argument 160°.

4. Here are two complex numbers z and w drawn in the complex plane. Estimate the magnitude and argument of zw.

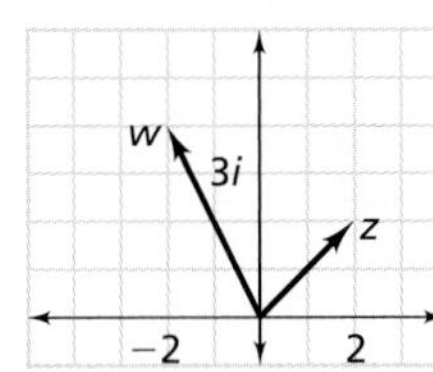

5. **Write About It** Two complex numbers have arguments that add up to more than 360°. Describe how to find the magnitude and argument of their product.

6. For each z, plot the first few powers of z (that is, $z^0, z^1, z^2, \dots$). If you take higher powers of z, describe and explain the pattern you see.

a. $z = i$

b. $z = -i$

c. $z = 1 + i$

d. $z = 1 - i$

e. $z = 2 + i$

f. $z = 2 - i$

Answers

Exercises

1. a. $|z^2| = 9$, $\arg(z^2) = 240°$

b. Answers may vary. Sample: $z^3 = 3^3 \text{ cis } 3(120°) = 27(\cos 360° + i \sin 360°) = 27(1 + i \cdot 0) = 27$

2. To find $|z^2|$, square $|z|$; to find $\arg(z^2)$, multiply $\arg(z)$ by 2. To find $|z^3|$, cube $|z|$; to find $\arg(z^3)$, multiply $\arg(z)$ by 3. In general, if n is a non-negative integer, to find $|z^n|$, raise $|z|$ to the nth power; to find $\arg(z^n)$, multiply $\arg(z)$ by n.

3. a. false

b. true; $3^3 = 27$ and $3 \cdot 40° = 120°$

c. false

d. true; $3^3 = 27$ and $3 \cdot 160° = 480°$ and $480° - 360° = 120°$

4. Answers may vary. Sample: $|zw| \approx 13$, $\arg(zw) \approx 160°$

5. To find the magnitude of the product, multiply the magnitudes of the two numbers. To find the argument of the product, use the sum modulo 360° of the arguments of the numbers.

6. See back of book.

7. a. yes **b.** no **c.** yes **d.** yes **e.** yes **f.** no

8. a.

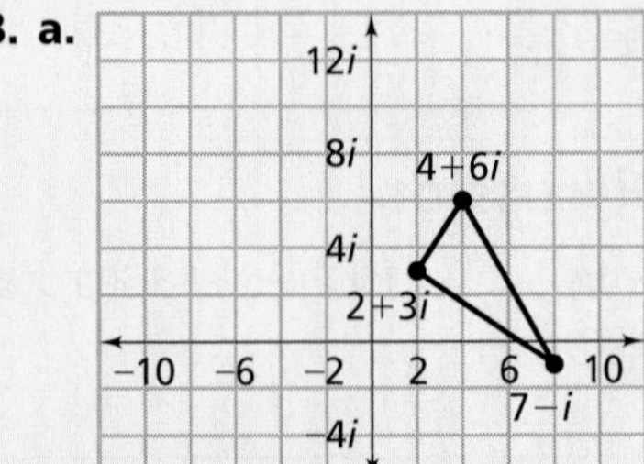

On Your Own

7. Suppose z and w are complex numbers with magnitude 1. For each complex number, decide whether it must also have magnitude 1.

   a. zw
   b. $z + w$
   c. $\overline{w}$
   d. $\frac{1}{z}$
   e. z^2
   f. $2z$

8. a. In the complex plane, plot the triangle with vertices $2 + 3i$, $4 + 6i$, and $7 - i$.

   b. Plot the triangle that results if you multiply each vertex by i.

   c. Plot the triangle that results if you multiply each vertex by $1 + i$.

9. The product of two complex numbers is $10i$. Neither is a real number.

   a. Find one possible pair of numbers that works.

   b. **Take It Further** Given any nonzero complex number z, explain how to find w so that $zw = 10i$.

10. Here are two complex numbers z and w drawn in the complex plane. Estimate the magnitude and argument of zw.

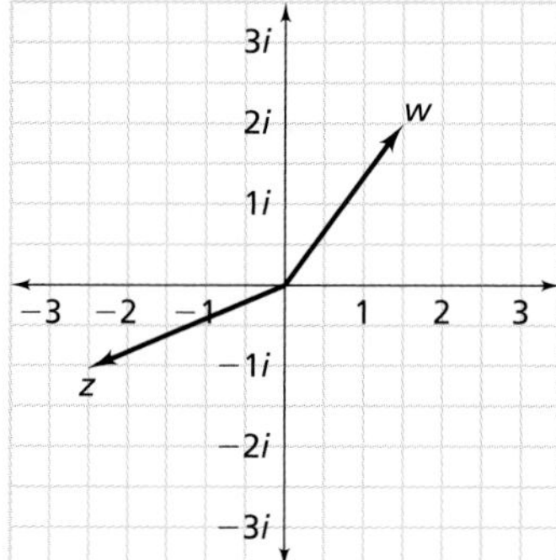

11. Consider the complex numbers $z = 3 - 2i$ and $w = 1 + 3i$.

    a. Plot z and w as vectors. Determine the magnitude and argument of each.

    b. In what quadrant is zw? Explain how you know.

    c. Find the magnitude and argument of zw.

EXERCISE 6 There is no need to assign all parts of this exercise. However, you should assign at least one conjugate pair. Easily the most important pair is the powers of i and $-i$. You can give students copies of Blackline Master MC1 to help them with this exercise.

On Your Own

EXERCISE 10 Again, check that students are using the multiplication properties from the lesson and not writing z and w in $x + yi$ form.

b.

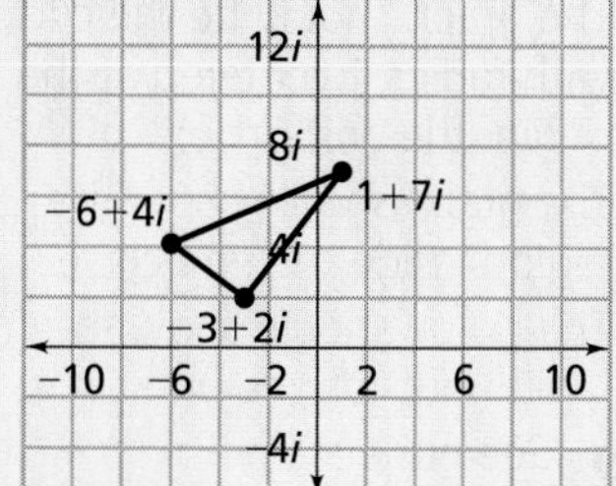

c.

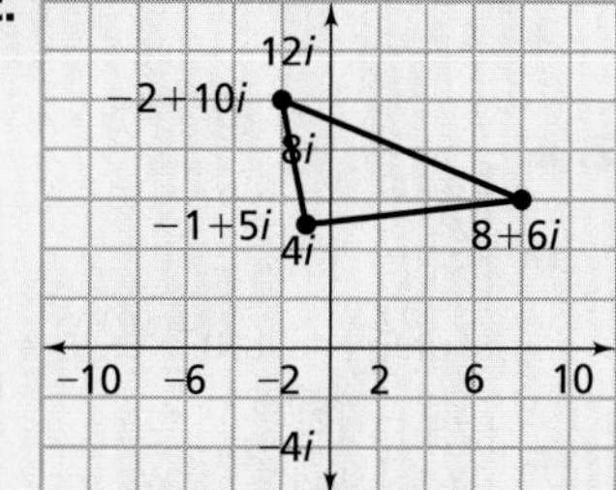

9. a. Answers may vary. Sample: $1 + i$ and $5 + 5i$

b. Answers may vary. Sample: Write the fraction $\frac{10i}{z}$ in the form $x + yi$. (To do this, it may be necessary to multiply numerator and denominator by $\overline{z}$.)

10. Answers may vary. Sample: $|zw| \approx 7$, $\arg(zw) \approx 250°$

11. a.

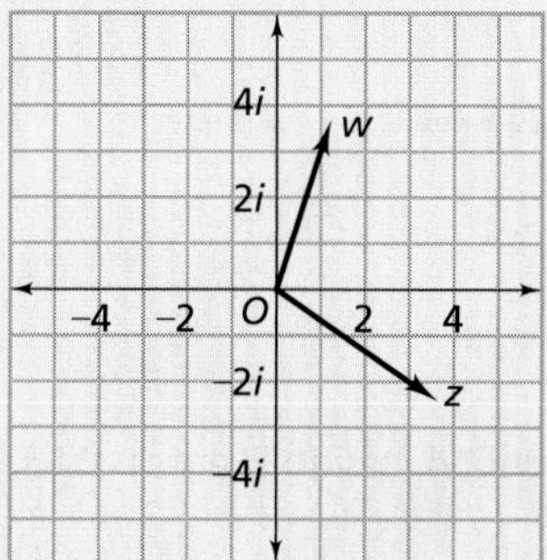

$|z| = \sqrt{13}$, $\arg(z) \approx 326.3°$;
$|w| = \sqrt{10}$, $\arg(w) \approx 71.6°$

b. Quadrant I; $\arg(zw)$ is the sum of $\arg(z)$ and $\arg(w)$, or about 398°. Since $398° - 360° = 38°$, the vector for zw will be in Quadrant I.

c. $|zw| = \sqrt{130}$, $\arg(z) \approx 37.9°$

EXERCISE 12 Not every student will notice the relationship. In the end, this is not a critical relationship but is tied to the fact that $\frac{z}{w} = z \cdot \frac{1}{w}$.

EXERCISE 13 These graphs become progressively more difficult. This exercise relates to our model of graphs as point-testers. Any value of z that makes the equation or inequality true corresponds to a point on the graph.

Maintain Your Skills

EXERCISE 16 Assign this exercise only if working with a top group. The arithmetic is quite challenging unless students see the pattern quickly.

Additional Resources

PRINT RESOURCES
- Solution Manual
- Practice Workbook
- Assessment Resources
- Teaching Resources

TECHNOLOGY
- Interactive Textbook
- TeacherExpress CD-ROM
- ExamView CD-ROM
- PHSchool.com

Additional Practice

1. Here are two complex numbers z and w drawn in the plane. Estimate the magnitude and argument of zw.

2. Consider the complex number $z = 2 + 2i$. Find the following.
   a. $|z|$
   b. $|z^2|$
   c. $|z^3|$
   d. $|z^4|$
   e. Write an expression that would give you $|z^n|$.

3. a. In the complex plane, plot the triangle with vertices $2 - 2i$, $-4 + 5i$, and $7 + 4i$.
   b. Plot the triangle that results if you multiply each vertex by $-i$.
   c. Plot the triangle that results if you multiply each vertex by $1 - i$.

4. Consider the complex numbers $z = -5 + 2i$ and $w = 2 - 6i$.
   a. Plot z and w as vectors. Determine the magnitude and argument of each.
   b. In what quadrant is zw? Explain how you know.
   c. Find the magnitude of zw.
   d. Find the argument of zw.

5. Consider the complex numbers $z = 6 + 3i$ and $w = 2 - i$.
   a. Write $\frac{z}{w}$ as $a + bi$ where a and b are real numbers.
   b. Find the magnitude of $\frac{z}{w}$.
   c. Find the argument of $\frac{z}{w}$.

6. Plot the set of all complex numbers that satisfy each equation. Make a new graph for each part.
   a. $|z| = 4$
   b. $|z| > 2$
   c. $|z| \leq 2$
   d. $z^3 = z$

Practice: For Lesson 2.4, assign Exercises 1–6.

12. This lesson explains how to find the magnitude and argument of the product of two complex numbers, but what about the quotient? Consider the complex numbers $z = 4 + 2i$ and $w = 3 + i$.

    a. Write $\frac{z}{w}$ as $a + bi$ where a and b are real numbers.

    b. Find the magnitude and argument of $\frac{z}{w}$.

    c. Find a relationship between the magnitudes of z, w, and $\frac{z}{w}$. Also find a relationship between their arguments.

13. **Take It Further** Plot the set of all complex numbers that satisfy each equation. Make a new graph for each part.

    a. $|z| = 3$ **b.** $|z| = 1$ **c.** $|z| < 1$ **d.** $|z| > 1$
    e. $|z| = \left|\frac{1}{z}\right|$ **f.** $z^2 = z$ **g.** $|z|^2 = |z|$

14. **Standardized Test Prep** Which of the following is equivalent to multiplying a complex number z by the number i?

    A. reflection of z over the x-axis
    B. reflection of z over the y-axis
    C. rotation 90° counterclockwise
    D. rotation 90° clockwise

For additional practice, go to Web Code: bga-0204

Maintain Your Skills

15. Simplify each expression. Write the result in the form $x + yi$ where x and y are real numbers.

    a. $1 + i + i^2$
    b. $1 + i + i^2 + i^3$
    c. $1 + i + i^2 + i^3 + i^4$
    d. $1 + i + i^2 + i^3 + i^4 + i^5$
    e. $1 + i + i^2 + i^3 + i^4 + i^5 + i^6$
    f. $1 + i + i^2 + i^3 + i^4 + i^5 + i^6 + i^7 + \cdots + i^{67}$

16. **Take It Further** Let $\omega = \frac{-1 + i\sqrt{3}}{2}$.

    Simplify each expression. Write the result in the form $x + yi$ where x and y are real numbers.

    a. $1 + \omega + \omega^2$
    b. $1 + \omega + \omega^2 + \omega^3$
    c. $1 + \omega + \omega^2 + \omega^3 + \omega^4$
    d. $1 + \omega + \omega^2 + \omega^3 + \omega^4 + \omega^5$
    e. $1 + \omega + \omega^2 + \omega^3 + \omega^4 + \omega^5 + \omega^6$
    f. $1 + \omega + \omega^2 + \omega^3 + \omega^4 + \omega^5 + \omega^6 + \omega^7 + \cdots + \omega^{67}$

Answers

12. a. $\frac{7}{5} + \frac{1}{5}i$

b. $\left|\frac{z}{w}\right| = \sqrt{2}$,
$\arg\left(\frac{z}{w}\right) = \tan^{-1}\left(\frac{1}{7}\right) \approx 8.13°$

c. $\left|\frac{z}{w}\right| = \frac{|z|}{|w|}$; $\arg\left(\frac{z}{w}\right) = \arg(z) - \arg(w)$

13. a. The graph should be the circle with radius 3 centered at the origin.

b. The graph should be the circle with radius 1 centered at the origin (the unit circle).

c. The graph should show the region inside the unit circle.

d. The graph should show the region outside the unit circle.

e–g. See back of book.

14. C

15. a. i **b.** 0 **c.** 1
d. $1 + i$ **e.** i **f.** 0

16. See back of book.

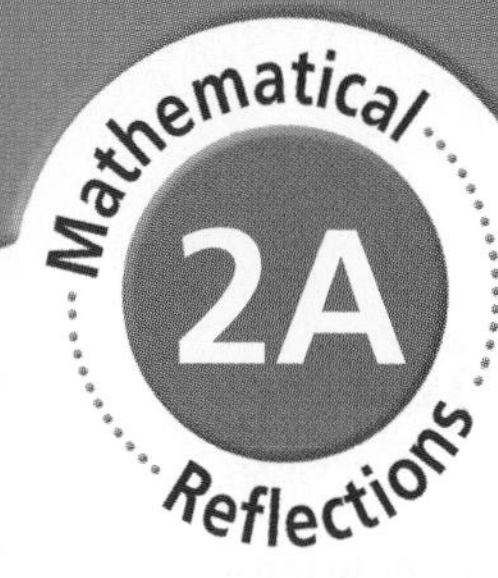

In this investigation, you described complex numbers as points in a plane using both rectangular and polar coordinates. You learned geometric interpretations of addition and multiplication of complex numbers. The following questions will help you summarize what you have learned.

1. Describe the effect of multiplying a complex number by $2i$ in terms of scaling and rotation.
2. Graph all complex numbers having magnitude 2.
3. Name three complex numbers that have argument 120°.
4. If z is any complex number, show that $z\overline{z} = |z|^2$.
5. Use the result from Exercise 4 to show that $\frac{1}{z} = \frac{\overline{z}}{|z^2|}$ for any nonzero complex number z.
6. How can you write a complex number using trigonometry?
7. What are the magnitude and argument of a complex number, and how do you find them?
8. How do you use geometry to calculate $(1 - i\sqrt{3}) \cdot (-3\sqrt{3} + 3i)$?

Vocabulary and Notation

In this investigation, you learned these terms. Make sure you understand what each one means and how to use it.

- **argument, arg(z)**
- **cis(θ)**
- **conjugate, $\overline{z}$**
- **magnitude, $|z|$**
- **norm, $N(z)$**
- **polar coordinates**
- **polar form for complex numbers**
- **rectangular coordinates**
- **rectangular form for complex numbers**

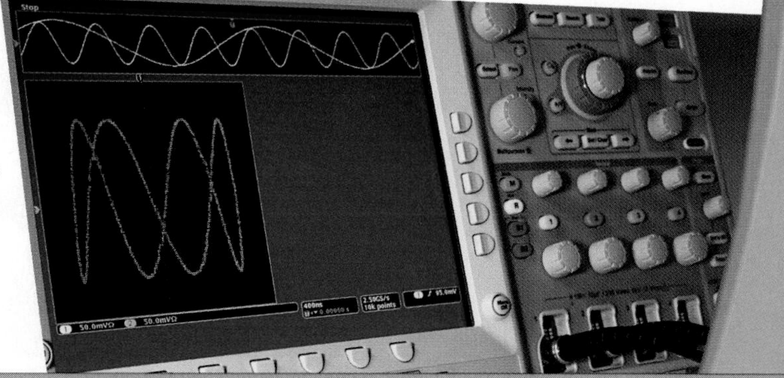

Lissajous figures are the graphs of equations containing cosine and sine functions. You can best observe their lively display on an oscilloscope.

Mathematical Reflections

EXERCISES 6–8 At the start of the investigation, you may have assigned these as Questions 1–3 for students to think and write about.

Mathematical Reflections

1. Multiplying z by $2i$ rotates z by 90° counterclockwise around the origin and scales it by a factor of 2.
2. The graph should show the circle with radius 2 centered at the origin.
3. Answers may vary. Sample: $-\frac{1}{2} + \frac{\sqrt{3}}{2}i$, $-1 + \sqrt{3}i$, and $-\frac{3}{2} + \frac{3\sqrt{3}}{2}i$
4. If $z = a + bi$, then $z\overline{z} = (a + bi)(a - bi) = a^2 + b^2 = |z|^2$.
5. Answers may vary. Sample: $\frac{\overline{z}}{|z^2|} = \frac{\overline{z}}{|z|^2} = \frac{\overline{z}}{z\overline{z}} = \frac{1}{z}$
6. If z is a complex number ($z \neq 0$), $|z| = r$, and $\arg(z) = \theta$, then $z = r\cos\theta + ir\sin\theta$.
7. If $z = a + bi$, then the magnitude of z is $\sqrt{a^2 + b^2}$. The argument of z is the measure of the angle formed by the positive x-axis and a ray that rotates from the position of the positive x-axis counterclockwise until it passes through the point for z.
8. $12i$

Investigation Overview

In this investigation, students explore ways to build and prove trigonometric formulas and identities. Students study the algebraic manipulation of trigonometric equations to build skills for two main purposes.

- Reduce complex trigonometric expressions to simpler ones.
- Evaluate trigonometric expressions containing unknown quantities by transforming them into expressions with known quantities.

Along the way, students exercise their algebraic skills and learn an important concept: they can treat a function (in this case, a trigonometric function) in exactly the same way that they would treat a variable, using the same basic rules of algebra. The inherent definitions of the functions yield further possibilities for substitution or other manipulation.

Moreover, students learn that by using complex arithmetic, they can easily prove trigonometric facts that are quite difficult to prove using only algebra and geometry of the real plane.

You may wish to assign Questions 1–3 for students to think and write about during the investigation.

Learning Goals

- Test trigonometric equations to predict whether they are identities.
- Show the basic addition rules for cosine and sine using the Multiplication Law for complex numbers.
- Use Pythagorean identities and algebra to prove that a trigonometric equation is an identity.

Habits and Skills

- Manipulate trigonometric expressions.
- Determine useful test cases and techniques to identify identities.
- Use basic rules to generate more complicated rules.

Trigonometric Identities

In *Trigonometric Identities*, you will use complex arithmetic to prove basic trigonometric identities. You will learn techniques to validate other identities.

By the end of this investigation, you will be able to answer questions like these.

1. How can you test to see if an equation might be an identity?
2. How can you use complex numbers to find formulas for $\cos 2x$ and $\sin 2x$?
3. How can you use identities to prove other identities?

You will learn how to

- test trigonometric equations to predict whether they are identities
- show the basic addition rules for cosine and sine using the Multiplication Law for complex numbers
- use Pythagorean identities and algebra to prove that a trigonometric equation is an identity

You will develop these habits and skills:

- Manipulate trigonometric expressions.
- Determine useful test cases and techniques to identify identities.
- Use basic rules to generate more complicated rules.

Much like these multicolored plastic toy bricks, you assemble theorems using mathematical objects. If you don't put the pieces together correctly, the resulting structure may fall apart.

Investigation Road Map

LESSON 2.5, *Getting Started,* explores the ideas of trigonometric identities by having students gather evidence (by testing numbers or comparing graphs) to decide whether an identity is true or false.

LESSON 2.6, *Building Formulas and Identities,* explores ways to build trigonometric formulas and identities using complex arithmetic and the Multiplication Law. Students build the formulas for the sum of cosines, sines, and tangents and also several multiple angle formulas. Students also look at a variety of ways to create their own identities using the Multiplication Law.

LESSON 2.7, *Proving Identities,* focuses on the algebraic proof of identities. Students develop a formal chain of reasoning to show how one expression can be transformed (using the basic rules of algebra and proved formulas and theorems). Students also see that they can prove identities using other identities that they have already proven.

2.5 Getting Started

Activating Prior Knowledge
Exploring New Ideas

Two expressions are **identically equal** if you can transform one to the other using the basic rules of algebra, and any other proven identities or theorems. An **identity** is any equation that equates two identically equal expressions.

To prove an identity, you have to show that the equation is true for all values of the variable for which both expressions are defined. Even before you prove an identity, however, you should convince yourself that the equation is indeed likely an identity.

Here are two ways to gather evidence that an equation is an identity.

Try some numbers: The fastest way to prove an equation is not an identity is to provide a counterexample. Treat each side of the equation as a separate function. Choose several numbers to plug into each of the functions.

- If the outputs are different, you know the equation is not an identity.
- If the outputs are the same, you have some evidence that the expressions are identically equal.

Compare graphs: Graph each side of the equation as a separate function. If the two graphs look identical, you have good evidence that the equation may be an identity.

The basic rules of algebra include the commutative, associative, and distributive properties, along with the additive and multiplicative inverses and identities.

For You to Explore

1. For which values of x is the following equation true?

$$\sec^2 x + \csc^2 x = \sec^2 x \cdot \csc^2 x$$

A. $x = \frac{3\pi}{4}$ B. $x = 115°$

C. $x = \frac{2\pi}{7}$ D. all of the above

2. Find the pairs of expressions that are identically equal.

$\cos^4 x - \sin^4 x$	$\cot^2 x$	$\sin^3 x + \sin x \cos^2 x$
$\sin(-x)$	$\cot x$	$\sec^2 x$
$1 + \tan^2 x$	$-\sin x$	$(\csc x + 1)(\csc x - 1)$
$\cos^2 x - \sin^2 x$	$\frac{\csc x}{\sec x}$	$\sin x$

3. Is this statement true? If so, explain why. If not, what changes to the statement will make it an identity? (Your answer should not be of the trivial form $A = A$.)

$$\frac{\cos x + 1}{\sin x} = \frac{\sin x}{\cos x - 1}$$

4. Sketch and describe the graph of $f(x) = \cos^3 x + \cos x \sin^2 x$.

5. Define the function $g(n) = n^2 + n + 41$ for whole-number values of n.
 a. Calculate $g(0)$ through $g(5)$, $g(10)$, and $g(20)$.
 b. The values of $g(0)$ through $g(5)$ are prime. Do you think $g(n)$ will be prime for all values of n? Explain your answer.

Answers

For You to Explore

1. D
2. $\sin(-x) = -\sin x$
 $\cos^4 x - \sin^4 x = \cos^2 x - \sin^2 x$
 $\cos^3 x + \sin x \cos^2 x = \sin x$
 $1 + \tan^2 x = \sec^2 x$
 $\frac{\csc x}{\sec x} = \cot x$
 $(\csc x + 1)(\csc x - 1) = \cot^2 x$
3. No; $\frac{\cos x + 1}{\sin x} = -\frac{\sin x}{\cos x - 1}$
4. See back of book.
5. a. $g(0) = 41, g(1) = 43,$ $g(2) = 47, g(3) = 53,$ $g(4) = 61, g(5) = 71,$ $g(10) = 151, g(20) = 461$
 b. No; answers may vary. Sample: $g(41) = 41 \cdot 43$ and $41 \cdot 43$ is not prime.

Lesson Overview

GOAL

- Warm up to the ideas of the investigation.

In this lesson, students begin exploring the ideas of trigonometric identities. At this point, do not expect them to formally prove identities. Instead, they should be looking for evidence as to whether an identity is true or false, by testing numbers or by comparing graphs. In the later lessons, they will work toward proving them formally using algebra.

FOR YOU TO EXPLORE
- Core: 2, 3, 6, 8, 9
- Optional: 1, 4, 5, 7
- Extension: 10

MATERIALS
- graphing calculators
- Blackline Master MC3

HOMEWORK
- Core: 11, 12, 13, 14, 17, 22
- Optional: 15, 16, 18, 19, 20, 21a–d, 23
- Extension: 21e

VOCABULARY
- identically equal
- identity

Launch

Review the definitions of identity and identically equal. In many cases, it is equivalent to say that an equation is an identity if it is true for all possible values of a variable (where each expression is defined). However, this definition of identity proves limiting as students study more advanced mathematics. For that reason, the definition here is one that leads students to the best way to prove identities. Two expressions are identically equal if you can transform one to the other using the basic rules of algebra and any other proven identities or theorems.

Explore

For You to Explore

PROBLEM 2 Spend the majority of discussion time on this exercise, looking at methods students use to pair up the expressions. Expect some students to test values, others to look at graphs, and others to look at algebraic means of simplification. This investigation covers all of these methods.

PROBLEM 5 gives students a sense that there is more to identities than testing values. The behavior of this function continues for a very long time (from $n = 0$ to 40), but cannot continue forever. You might see the same result if you are testing to see whether an equation is an identity. One, two, five, or forty matches does not prove it must always be true.

PROBLEM 6 You may wish to use Blackline Master MC3 on an overhead as you solve this problem in class. Some students may notice that you can modify the statement to be $2 \sin x \cos x = \sin 2x$. Acknowledge the identity, but note that they do not yet have the proper foundation to prove it. This proof will come in the next lesson.

PROBLEM 9 Students prove that this is an identity in Lesson 2.7 using the rules for $\cos(a - b)$ and $\sin(a + b)$. They can also prove the statement using the co-function identity $\sin\left(\frac{\pi}{2} - x\right) = \cos x$.

Wrap Up

Review core exercises with the students. Before assigning homework, allow students some time to discuss and summarize their findings.

Exercises

HOMEWORK

- Core: 11, 12, 13, 14, 17, 22
- Optional: 15, 16, 18, 19, 20, 21a–d, 23
- Extension: 21e

On Your Own

EXERCISE 11 If you discuss this exercise, point out the relationship to Exercise 1. Its result helps the simplification if the product is multiplied out instead of converting to tangent and cotangent.

6. a. Sketch the graphs of $f(x) = \sin x \cos x$ and $g(x) = \sin 2x$ on the same axes.

b. Is the equation $\sin x \cos x = \sin 2x$ an identity? Explain your answer.

7. One of these two equations is an identity, and the other is not.

$$(\tan x \sin x)^2 = (\tan x + \sin x)(\tan x - \sin x)$$
$$\sin^2 x + \cos^2 x \csc x = \csc x$$

a. Pick a value for x and test it in each equation.

b. Which equation is the identity?

8. What's Wrong Here? Candace thinks the equation $\cos 13x = \cos x$ is an identity.

Candace says, "I decided to test some values. I tried 0 and it worked, I tried $\frac{\pi}{6}$ and it worked, I tried $\frac{\pi}{2}$ and it worked. I even tried $\frac{7\pi}{6}$, and *that* worked! So, I'm convinced, it's an identity."

Help Candace see why this equation is not an identity.

9. a. On the same axes, sketch the graphs of $f(x) = \sin\left(x + \frac{\pi}{3}\right)$ and $g(x) = \cos\left(x - \frac{\pi}{6}\right)$. How do the two graphs compare?

b. Must the equation

$$\sin\left(x + \frac{\pi}{3}\right) = \cos\left(x - \frac{\pi}{6}\right)$$

be an identity, according to these graphs?

10. Take It Further Candace found several values of x that make $\cos 13x = \cos x$. Find the total number of values of x with $0 \le x < 2\pi$ that make $\cos 13x = \cos x$.

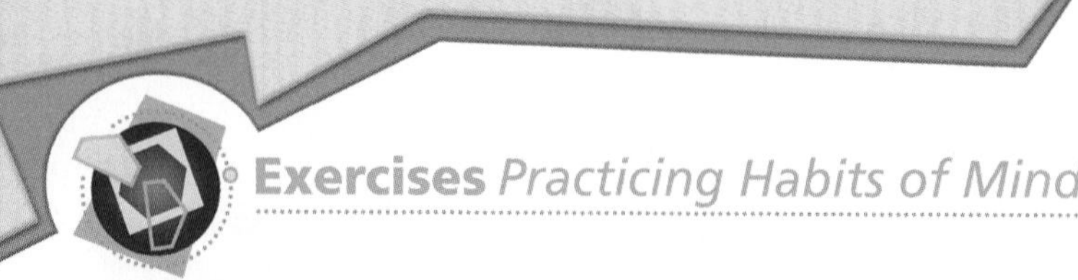

Exercises *Practicing Habits of Mind*

On Your Own

11. Simplify the following product.

$$(\csc^2 x - 1)(\sec^2 x - 1)$$

A. $\sin x$ **B.** $\tan^2 x$ **C.** $\sec^4 x$ **D.** 1

12. a. Sketch graphs of $f(x) = \sin x$ and $g(x) = \cos x$ on $-2\pi \le x \le 2\pi$.

b. Use the graph of f to demonstrate that $\sin(-x) = -\sin x$.

c. Use the graph of g to demonstrate an identity involving $\cos(-x)$.

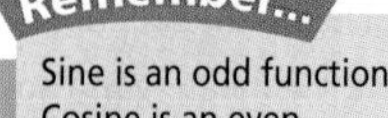

Remember...

Sine is an odd function. Cosine is an even function.

Answers

6. a.

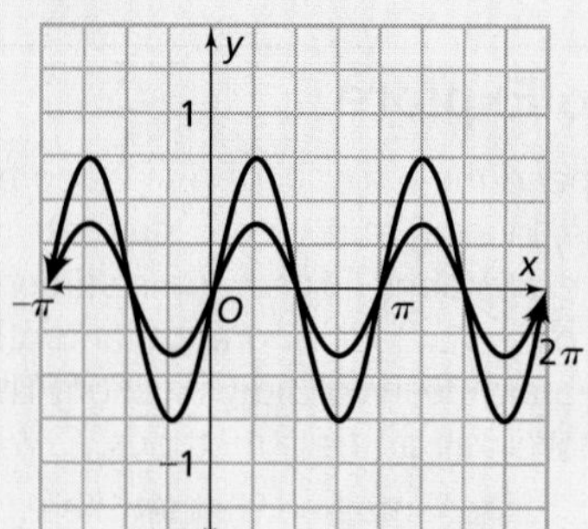

b. No; the graphs of $f(x)$ and $g(x)$ are not the same.

7. a. Answers may vary. Sample: $x = \frac{\pi}{4}$ makes the first equation true but not the second equation.

b. $(\tan x \sin x)^2 = (\tan x + \sin x)(\tan x - \sin x)$

8. The values of x that Candace used are of the form $\frac{1}{6}\pi n$ (n an integer), and these values will always make the equation true. However, the equation is not true for $x = \frac{\pi}{4}$.

9. a.

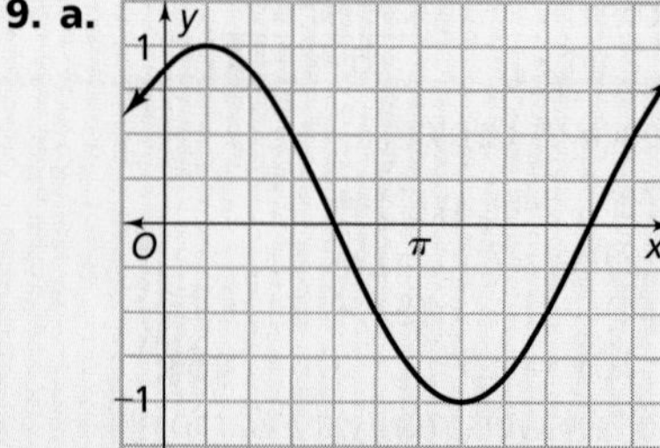

b. yes

10. 24 values

Exercises

11. D

12. a.

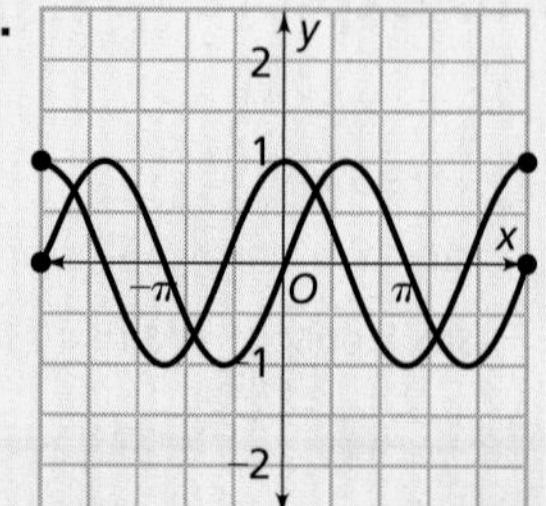

b. The graph is symmetric with respect to the origin.

13. Find the pairs of expressions that are identically equal.

$\sin^4 x - \cos^4 x$	$\tan^2 x$	$-\cos^3 x - \cos x \sin^2 x$
$\cos(-x)$	$\tan x$	$\csc^2 x$
$1 + \cot^2 x$	$\cos x$	$(\sec x + 1)(\sec x - 1)$
$\sin^2 x - \cos^2 x$	$\frac{\sec x}{\csc x}$	$-\cos x$

14. Calculate the product $(\operatorname{cis} x)\left(\operatorname{cis} \frac{\pi}{4}\right)$ to show that

$$\sin\left(x + \frac{\pi}{4}\right) = \frac{\sqrt{2}}{2}(\sin x + \cos x)$$

15. Write this expression as a single trigonometric function of x.

$$\frac{\tan x}{(\sec x + 1)(\sec x - 1)}$$

16. One of these equations is an identity, and the other is not. Determine which equation is the identity by testing values for the variables.

$$\sin(x + y) + \sin(x - y) = 2 \sin x \sin y$$
$$\cos(x + y) + \cos(x - y) = 2 \cos x \cos y$$

17. Show that these three expressions are all equivalent.

$$\cos^2 x - \sin^2 x$$
$$2\cos^2 x - 1$$
$$1 - 2\sin^2 x$$

Remember...

Two expressions are *equivalent* if you can get from one expression to the other using the basic rules of algebra.

18. Find all values of x on the interval $0 \le x < 2\pi$ with $\cos^2 x - \sin^2 x = \frac{1}{2}$.

19. Find all values of x on the interval $0 \le x < 2\pi$ with $\cos^2 x - \sin^2 x = \sin x$.

20. Determine whether or not the equation, $\cos 5x = 2 \cos x \cos 4x - \cos 3x$, is an identity. Explain your answer.

Do not try to prove it, just decide whether or not you think it is an identity.

Maintain Your Skills

21. In Exercise 1, you may have found that $\sec^2 x + \csc^2 x = \sec^2 x \cdot \csc^2 x$. It is quite rare for two numbers to have the same sum and product.
    a. If $\sec^2 x = 3$, what is $\csc^2 x$?
    b. If $\sec^2 x = 4$, what is $\csc^2 x$?
    c. If $\sec^2 x = 11$, what is $\csc^2 x$?
    d. If $\sec^2 x = A$, find a formula for $\csc^2 x$ in terms of A.
    e. **Take It Further** What is the smallest possible value of $\sec^2 x + \csc^2 x$? Explain your answer.

22. Simplify $\sin\frac{\pi}{7} + \sin\frac{2\pi}{7} + \sin\frac{3\pi}{7} + \sin\frac{-\pi}{7} + \sin\frac{-2\pi}{7} + \sin\frac{-3\pi}{7}$.

23. Simplify $\cos\frac{\pi}{2} + \cos\frac{\pi}{3} + \cos\frac{\pi}{4} + \cos\frac{-\pi}{4} + \cos\frac{-\pi}{3} + \cos\frac{-\pi}{2}$.

EXERCISE 12 It is important that students are comfortable with the identities for $\cos(-x)$ and $\sin(-x)$ in this investigation, since they will use them often in working with the expansion of $\cos(a - b)$ and $\sin(a - b)$.

EXERCISE 16 Students prove the identity $\cos(x + y) + \cos(x - y) = 2 \cos x \cos y$ in the next lesson.

EXERCISE 18 Students should use either of the transformations of $\cos^2 x - \sin^2 x = 2\cos^2 x - 1$ for this exercise.

EXERCISE 19 Only the transformation to $1 - 2\sin^2 x$ works here. Some students will substitute $1 - \sin^2 x$ for $\cos^2 x$, but point out that by doing so they are repeating the steps from Exercise 17.

Maintain Your Skills

EXERCISE 22 is a quick reminder that $\sin(-x) = -\sin x$.

EXERCISE 23 This time the sum does not cancel out nicely, but students can simplify their work by recalling $\cos(-x) = \cos x$.

c. Since the graph is symmetric with respect to the y-axis, $\cos(-x) = \cos x$.

13. $\cos(-x) = \cos x$, $\frac{\sec x}{\csc x} = \tan x$, $\sin^4 x - \cos^4 x = \sin^2 x - \cos^2 x$, $-\cos^3 x - \cos x \sin^2 x = -\cos x$, $1 + \cot^2 x = \csc^2 x$, $(\sec x + 1)(\sec^2 x - 1) = \tan^2 x$

14. $\operatorname{cis}\left(x + \frac{\pi}{4}\right) = (\operatorname{cis} x)\left(\operatorname{cis} \frac{\pi}{4}\right)$, so $\cos\left(x + \frac{\pi}{4}\right) + i \sin\left(x + \frac{\pi}{4}\right) = (\cos x + i \sin x)\left(\cos\frac{\pi}{4} + i \sin\frac{\pi}{4}\right)$. The imaginary part of the expression on the left is $\sin\left(x + \frac{\pi}{4}\right)$, and it must equal the imaginary part of the product on the right, which is $\sin x \cos\frac{\pi}{4} + \cos x \sin\frac{\pi}{4}$, or $\frac{\sqrt{2}}{2}(\sin x + \cos x)$.

15. $\cot x$

16. The first equation is not true for $x = \frac{\pi}{2}$, $y = \frac{\pi}{2}$. So the identity must be the second equation.

17. Since $\cos^2 x + \sin^2 x = 1$, we have $\cos^2 x - \sin^2 x = \cos^2 x - (1 - \cos^2 x) = 2\cos^2 x - 1$

Also, $\cos^2 x - \sin^2 x = (1 - \sin^2 x) - \sin^2 x = 1 - 2\sin^2 x$. Hence the three expressions are equivalent.

18. $\frac{\pi}{6}, \frac{5\pi}{6}, \frac{7\pi}{6}, \frac{11\pi}{6}$

19. $\frac{\pi}{6}, \frac{5\pi}{6}, \frac{3\pi}{2}$

20. The graph of $y = \cos 5x$ seems to be the same as the graph of $y = 2 \cos x \cos 4x - \cos 3x$, so the given equation appears to be an identity.

21. a. $\frac{3}{2}$ **b.** $\frac{4}{3}$ **c.** $\frac{11}{10}$ **d.** $\frac{A}{A - 1}$
e. From the graph of $y = \sec^2 x + \csc^2 x$, the minimum value appears to be 4.

22. 0

23. $1 + \sqrt{2}$

Lesson Overview

GOAL

- Show the basic addition rules for cosine and sine using the Multiplication Law for complex numbers.

In this lesson, students explore ways to build trigonometric formulas and identities using complex arithmetic and the Multiplication Law. They build the formulas for the sum of cosines, sines, and tangents, and also several multiple angle formulas. They also look at a variety of ways to write their own identities using the Multiplication Law.

CHECK YOUR UNDERSTANDING
- Core: 1, 2, 3, 6
- Optional: 4, 5
- Extension: 7

MATERIALS
- graphing calculators
- Blackline Master 2.6

HOMEWORK
- Core: 8, 9a–e, 11, 13, 17, 18
- Optional: 10, 12, 14, 15
- Extension: 9f, 16

Launch

Review exercises from the previous lesson. In particular, the work from Exercise 14 leads directly to the main topic of the lesson.

Explore

You may want to use Blackline Master 2.6 during your presentation.

2.6 Building Formulas and Identities

Recall Theorem 2.2, the Multiplication Law for complex numbers. If $z = r_1 \operatorname{cis} \alpha$ and $w = r_2 \operatorname{cis} \beta$, then

$$zw = (r_1 \operatorname{cis} \alpha)(r_2 \operatorname{cis} \beta) = r_1 r_2 \operatorname{cis} (\alpha + \beta)$$

If both z and w are on the unit circle, then $r_1 = r_2 = 1$ and you get a simpler expression.

$$zw = (\operatorname{cis} \alpha)(\operatorname{cis} \beta) = \operatorname{cis} (\alpha + \beta)$$

In fact, the product of any two complex numbers on the unit circle will also be on the unit circle.

These facts about complex numbers will help you find many important trigonometric relationships, which involve real numbers only.

Jacques Hadamard (1865–1963) said, "The shortest path between two truths in the real domain passes through the complex domain."

Developing Habits of Mind

Simplify complicated problems. There are two ways to go about building and proving identities for trigonometric functions.

- Cosine and sine are real-valued functions. They take a real input (like π) and they give you a real output (like $\sin \pi = 0$). You can study their relationships entirely in the real numbers without ever thinking about complex numbers at all. But when you try to prove many of these relationships with real numbers, you end up with long, tedious calculations—not exactly elegant mathematics.
- As you have seen in this chapter, you can use cosine and sine to describe coordinates of complex numbers on the unit circle. This relationship lets you use the properties of complex numbers to prove relationships involving cosine and sine. You can write a proof that could be 15 lines long using real numbers alone in only 1 or 2 lines using complex numbers.

You can build many identities involving cosines and sines with mathematical elegance by using complex numbers. You may want to try proving some of these identities with real numbers just to appreciate how nice it is to work with the complex numbers.

Cosine and sine are still real-valued functions. They take a real input (the argument of the complex number) and give real outputs (the *x*- and *y*-coordinates of the complex number).

Example

Problem Write a formula for $\cos\left(x + \frac{\pi}{3}\right)$.

Solution From the Multiplication Law, you know that

$$\text{cis}\left(x + \frac{\pi}{3}\right) = (\text{cis}\,x)\left(\text{cis}\,\frac{\pi}{3}\right)$$

From there, expand the cis notation.

$$\begin{aligned}(\text{cis}\,x)\left(\text{cis}\,\frac{\pi}{3}\right) &= (\cos x + i\sin x)\left(\cos\frac{\pi}{3} + i\sin\frac{\pi}{3}\right)\\ &= (\cos x + i\sin x)\left(\frac{1}{2} + \frac{\sqrt{3}}{2}i\right)\\ &= \left(\frac{1}{2}\cos x - \frac{\sqrt{3}}{2}\sin x\right) + i\left(\frac{1}{2}\sin x + \frac{\sqrt{3}}{2}\cos x\right)\end{aligned}$$

Since

$$\cos\left(x + \frac{\pi}{3}\right) + i\sin\left(x + \frac{\pi}{3}\right) = \left(\frac{1}{2}\cos x - \frac{\sqrt{3}}{2}\sin x\right) + i\left(\frac{1}{2}\sin x + \frac{\sqrt{3}}{2}\cos x\right)$$

then the real parts are equal, so

$$\cos\left(x + \frac{\pi}{3}\right) = \frac{1}{2}\cos x - \frac{\sqrt{3}}{2}\sin x$$

Likewise, the imaginary parts are also equal, so

$$\sin\left(x + \frac{\pi}{3}\right) = \frac{1}{2}\sin x + \frac{\sqrt{3}}{2}\cos x$$

For You to Do

1. Use the Multiplication Law to write a formula for $\sin(x + \pi)$.

The Multiplication Law makes it easy to prove two of the most useful trigonometric identities.

Theorem 2.3 The Angle-Sum Formulas

The following two equations are true for all values of α and β.

$$\cos(\alpha + \beta) = \cos\alpha\cos\beta - \sin\alpha\sin\beta$$
$$\sin(\alpha + \beta) = \sin\alpha\cos\beta + \cos\alpha\sin\beta$$

Go Online PHSchool.com

For practice with angle-sum identities, go to Web Code: bge-9031

Proof

$$\begin{aligned}\text{cis}(\alpha + \beta) &= (\text{cis}\,\alpha)(\text{cis}\,\beta)\\ &= (\cos\alpha + i\sin\alpha)(\cos\beta + i\sin\beta)\\ &= (\cos\alpha\cos\beta + i^2\sin\alpha\sin\beta) + (i\sin\alpha\cos\beta + i\cos\alpha\sin\beta)\\ &= (\cos\alpha\cos\beta - \sin\alpha\sin\beta) + i(\sin\alpha\cos\beta + \cos\alpha\sin\beta)\end{aligned}$$

Example

Spend time as needed going over this completed example. Make sure students understand the problem. As necessary, help them develop the detailed solution.

For You to Do

PROBLEM 1 Have students practice for the ideas just introduced by doing this problem.

Answers

For You to Do

1. $\sin(x + \pi) = -\sin x$

For Discussion

PROBLEM 3 The real component of the square of the complex number $\cos x + i \sin x$ is $\cos 2x$, which is $\cos^2 x - \sin^2 x$ by the result in part (a).

The imaginary component of the square of the complex number $\cos x + i \sin x$ is $\sin 2x$, which is $2 \sin x \cos x$ by the result in part (a).

Recall that $a + bi = c + di \Leftrightarrow a = c$ and $b = d$. So if

$$\cos(\alpha + \beta) + i\sin(\alpha + \beta) = (\cos\alpha\cos\beta - \sin\alpha\sin\beta) + i(\sin\alpha\cos\beta + \cos\alpha\sin\beta)$$

then

$$\cos(\alpha + \beta) = \cos\alpha\cos\beta - \sin\alpha\sin\beta$$

and

$$\sin(\alpha + \beta) = \sin\alpha\cos\beta + \cos\alpha\sin\beta$$

The Angle-Sum Formulas lead directly to four more identities.

Corollary 2.3.1 The Angle-Difference Formulas

The following two equations are true for all values of α and β.

$$\cos(\alpha - \beta) = \cos\alpha\cos\beta + \sin\alpha\sin\beta$$
$$\sin(\alpha - \beta) = \sin\alpha\cos\beta - \cos\alpha\sin\beta$$

For You to Do

2. Prove the Angle-Difference Formulas.

Use the relationship $\alpha - \beta = \alpha + (-\beta)$.

Corollary 2.3.2 The Double-Angle Formulas

The following two equations are true for all values of θ.

$$\cos 2\theta = \cos^2\theta - \sin^2\theta$$
$$\sin 2\theta = 2\sin\theta\cos\theta$$

For Discussion

3. **a.** If $z = \cos\theta + i\sin\theta$, show that

$$z^2 = (\cos^2\theta - \sin^2\theta) + (2\sin\theta\cos\theta)i$$

b. Explain how the result from part (a) leads to the Double-Angle Formulas.

Developing Habits of Mind

Prove a special case. Remember that corollaries are typically statements that follow directly from a previous theorem. In this case, the formulas for $\cos(\alpha - \beta)$, $\sin(\alpha - \beta)$, $\cos(2\theta)$, and $\sin(2\theta)$ all follow directly from the Angle-Sum Formulas for cosine and sine. You do not really have to memorize six formulas. You can quickly derive the Angle-Difference Formulas and the Double-Angle Formulas from the Angle-Sum Formulas.

Answers

For You to Do

2. Use the Angle-Sum Formulas, $\cos(-x) = \cos x$, and $\sin(-x) = -\sin x$.

$\cos(\alpha - \beta) = \cos(\alpha + (-\beta))$
$= \cos\alpha\cos(-\beta) - \sin\alpha\sin(-\beta)$
$= \cos\alpha\cos\beta + \sin\alpha\sin\beta$

$\sin(\alpha - \beta) = \sin(\alpha + (-\beta))$
$= \sin\alpha\cos(-\beta) + \cos\alpha\sin(-\beta)$
$= \sin\alpha\cos\beta - \cos\alpha\sin\beta$

For Discussion

3. **a.** $z^2 = (\cos\theta + i\sin\theta)^2$
$= \cos^2\theta + 2i\cos\theta\sin\theta + i^2\sin^2$
$= (\cos^2\theta - \sin^2\theta) + (2\sin\theta\cos$

b. $z = \operatorname{cis}\theta$, so $z^2 = (\operatorname{cis}\theta)(\operatorname{cis}\theta) = \operatorname{cis} 2\theta = \cos 2\theta + (\sin 2\theta)i$
To get the Double-Angle Formulas, equate the real and imaginary parts of $\cos 2\theta + (\sin 2\theta)i$ to those of the product from part (a).

In fact, you do not even need to memorize the Angle-Sum Formulas! The fact that

$$(\cos\alpha + i\sin\alpha)(\cos\beta + i\sin\beta) = \cos(\alpha + \beta) + i\sin(\alpha + \beta)$$

means you can always perform the arithmetic on the left side to rebuild the Angle-Sum Formulas. So here, you get six formulas for the price of one.

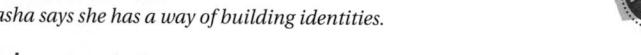

Minds in Action episode 4

Sasha says she has a way of building identities.

Sasha I can build an identity starting with anything I want if I make an expression equal to 0.

Derman What? How can you make something zero?

Sasha I multiply what I start with by zero, then the product is zero.

Derman But if you multiply by zero, there won't be any expression to see! It'll just say "0".

Sasha I will show you what I mean. Start with cosecant of x and multiply it by something equal to zero.

$$(\csc x)(\cos^2 x + \sin^2 x - 1) = 0$$

That's an identity. The left side is always zero, right?

Derman Well yeah, since $\cos^2 x + \sin^2 x = 1$.

Sasha Now expand the left side.

$$\csc x \cos^2 x + \sin x - \csc x = 0$$

That's still an identity. If I know an equation is always true, I can use the basic rules to make new equations that are also always true. I can add $\csc x$ to each side to get another identity.

$$\csc x \cos^2 x + \sin x = \csc x$$

Derman Clever. Maybe they used your idea when writing this book.

For You to Do

4. Show how you can build the identity

$$2\cos x - 2\sec x + \sec^2 x = 1 + \tan^2 x - 2\sin x \tan x$$

by starting from the identity

$$(2\cos x - 1)(1 + \tan^2 x - \sec^2 x) = 0$$

For You to Do

4. $(2\cos x - 1)(1 + \tan^2 x - \sec^2 x)$ equals 0 because the second factor is equal to 0. Expand the expression and set the result equal to 0 to obtain $2\cos x + 2\cos x \tan^2 x - 2\sec x + \sec^2 x - \tan^2 x - 1 = 0$. This last equation leads immediately to the given identity.

For You to Do

PROBLEM 4 You can use Sasha's identity-building method to write any number of identities for your students to prove. The focus in this chapter is on reducing complicated trigonometric expressions to simpler ones, providing a way to perform fewer calculations to get the same result.

Wrap Up

Review the addition formulas for cosine and sine, and go over Exercise 6 (which is referred to in the homework).

Assessment Resources

Lesson Quiz 2.6

1. a. Find two "nice" complex numbers that have a product with argument 195°.
   b. Use the complex numbers to find the exact values for cos 195° and sin 195°.

2. Use the Angle-Difference Formula to determine an identity for

$$\sin(A + B) - \sin(A - B)$$

3. a. Calculate this product:

$$\left(\frac{8}{10} + \frac{6}{10}i\right)\left(\frac{8}{17} + \frac{15}{17}i\right)$$

   b. If α and β are in Quadrant I and $\cos\alpha = \frac{8}{10}$ and $\sin\beta = \frac{15}{17}$, find the value of $\sin(\alpha + \beta)$.

Exercises

HOMEWORK
- Core: 8, 9a–e, 11, 13, 17, 18
- Optional: 10, 12, 14, 15
- Extension: 9f, 16

Check Your Understanding

EXERCISE 7 The solutions show how to use the Multiplication Law for complex numbers, but students could also use the sum formulas directly.

On Your Own

EXERCISE 11 These formulas are important for this chapter's Project.

EXERCISE 12 encourages students to use previous identities to prove new ones.

EXERCISE 15 Students may not realize that they need to replace $\cos^2 A$ and $\cos^2 B$ with $1 - \sin^2 A$ and $1 - \sin^2 B$, respectively.

Maintain Your Skills

EXERCISE 18 This rule is actually a direct consequence of the rule $\cos(A + B) + \cos(A - B) = \cos A \cos B$, with the particular value $A = 60°$. For this value, $2 \cos A \cos B$ becomes simply $\cos B$, leading to the remarkable property in the table. The same property applies to 300°, of course, since $\cos 300°$ also equals $\frac{1}{2}$.

Exercises *Practicing Habits of Mind*

Check Your Understanding

1. Find formulas for $\cos 3x$ and $\sin 3x$ in terms of $\cos x$ and $\sin x$.
2. a. Find two "nice" complex numbers that have a product with argument 75°.
   b. Use the complex numbers you found in part(a) to get exact values for $\cos 75°$ and $\sin 75°$.
   c. Find the value of $2 \sin 75° \cos 75°$.

> **Remember...**
> Arguments add, so you need to find two complex numbers with "nice" arguments that add to 75°.

3. a. Evaluate the product.

$$\left(\frac{3}{5} + \frac{4}{5}i\right)\left(\frac{12}{13} + \frac{5}{13}i\right)$$

   b. If α and β are in Quadrant I and $\cos \alpha = \frac{3}{5}$ and $\sin \beta = \frac{5}{13}$, find the value of $\sin(\alpha + \beta)$.
4. a. Show that this equation is an identity by using the Angle-Sum and Angle-Difference Formulas on the left side.

$$\cos(\alpha + \beta) + \cos(\alpha - \beta) = 2 \cos \alpha \cos \beta$$

   b. Determine a similar identity for $\sin(\alpha + \beta) + \sin(\alpha - \beta)$.
5. **Write About It** Use Sasha's method in episode 4 to write your own identity.
6. Write a formula for $\tan(\alpha + \beta)$ that includes only $\tan\alpha$ and $\tan\beta$.
7. **Take It Further** Determine formulas for $\cos(\alpha + \beta + \gamma)$ and $\sin(\alpha + \beta + \gamma)$. ($\gamma$ is the Greek letter *gamma*.)

On Your Own

8. a. Find the magnitude and argument of the complex number $\frac{\sqrt{2}}{2} + \frac{\sqrt{2}}{2}i$.
   b. Evaluate the product $(\cos x + i \sin x)\left(\frac{\sqrt{2}}{2} + \frac{\sqrt{2}}{2}i\right)$.
   c. Write a rule for $\cos\left(x + \frac{\pi}{4}\right)$ and for $\sin\left(x + \frac{\pi}{4}\right)$.

> **Go Online** PHSchool.com
> For additional practice, go to Web Code: bga-0206

9. Use the Angle-Sum and Angle-Difference Formulas for cosine and sine to prove each of these identities.
   a. $\cos(x + \pi) = -\cos x$
   b. $\sin\left(\frac{\pi}{2} - x\right) = \cos x$
   c. $\cos\left(x + \frac{\pi}{2}\right) = -\sin x$
   d. $\cos(x + 2\pi) = \cos x$
   e. $\tan\left(x + \frac{\pi}{2}\right) = -\frac{1}{\tan x}$
   f. **Take It Further** Prove $\tan\left(x + \frac{\pi}{4}\right) = \frac{\cos x + \sin x}{\cos x - \sin x}$.

Answers

Exercises

1. Answers may vary. Sample:
   $\cos 3x = \cos^3 x - 3 \sin^2 x \cos x$,
   $\sin 3x = 3 \sin x \cos^2 x - \sin^3 x$
2. a. Answers may vary. Sample: $\frac{\sqrt{2}}{2} + \frac{\sqrt{2}}{2}i$ and $\frac{\sqrt{3}}{2} + \frac{1}{2}i$
   b. $\cos 75° = \frac{\sqrt{6} - \sqrt{2}}{4}$, $\sin 75° = \frac{\sqrt{6} + \sqrt{2}}{4}$
   c. $\frac{1}{2}$
3. a. $\frac{16}{65} + \frac{63}{65}i$ b. $\frac{63}{65}$
4. a. $\cos(\alpha + \beta) + \cos(\alpha - \beta)$
   $= \cos \alpha \cos \beta - \sin \alpha \sin \beta + \cos \alpha \cos(-\beta) - \sin \alpha \sin(-\beta)$
   $= \cos \alpha \cos \beta - \sin \alpha \sin \beta + \cos \alpha \cos \beta + \sin \alpha \sin \beta$
   $= 2 \cos \alpha \cos \beta$
   b. $\sin(\alpha + \beta) + \sin(\alpha - \beta) = 2 \sin \alpha \cos \beta$
5. Check students' work.
6. $\tan(\alpha + \beta) = \frac{\tan \alpha + \tan \beta}{1 - \tan \alpha \tan \beta}$
7. $\cos(\alpha + \beta + \gamma) = \cos\alpha \cos\beta \cos\gamma - \cos\alpha \sin\beta \sin\gamma - \sin\alpha \cos\beta \sin\gamma - \sin\alpha \sin\beta \cos\gamma$
   $\sin(\alpha + \beta + \gamma) = \cos\alpha \cos\beta \sin\gamma + \cos\alpha \sin\beta \cos\gamma + \sin\alpha \cos\beta \cos\gamma - \sin\alpha \sin\beta \cos\gamma$
8. a. magnitude $= 1$, argument $= \frac{\pi}{4}$
   b. $\left((\cos x)\frac{\sqrt{2}}{2} - (\sin x)\frac{\sqrt{2}}{2}\right) + \left((\cos x)\frac{\sqrt{2}}{2} + (\sin x)\frac{\sqrt{2}}{2}\right)i$
   c. $\cos\left(x + \frac{\pi}{4}\right) = \frac{\sqrt{2}}{2}\cos x - \frac{\sqrt{2}}{2}\sin x$
   $\sin\left(x + \frac{\pi}{4}\right) = \frac{\sqrt{2}}{2}\sin x + \frac{\sqrt{2}}{2}\cos x$

10. **a.** What do you get if you use the Angle-Difference Formula to expand the expression $\cos(x - x)$?

    b. What is the value of $\cos(x - x)$?

11. **a.** Write a formula for $\tan 2x$ in terms of $\tan x$.

    b. Write a formula for $\tan 3x$ in terms of $\tan x$.

12. Is this equation an identity? Justify your answer.

$$\cos 5x + \cos 3x = 2\cos x \cos 4x$$

13. **a.** Calculate this product: $\left(\frac{2}{3} + \frac{\sqrt{5}}{3}i\right)\left(\frac{3}{4} + \frac{\sqrt{7}}{4}i\right)$

    b. If α and β are in Quadrant I and $\cos\alpha = \frac{3}{5}$ and $\sin\beta = \frac{5}{13}$, find the value of $\cos(\alpha + \beta)$.

14. Verify the Angle-Difference Formulas by expanding this complex number multiplication.

$$(\cos\alpha + i\sin\alpha)(\cos(-\beta) + i\sin(-\beta))$$

15. Show that this equation is an identity.

$$\sin(\alpha + \beta)\sin(\alpha - \beta) = \sin^2\alpha - \sin^2\beta$$

16. **Take it Further** The Angle-Sum Formulas for cosine and sine show that, in general,

$$\cos(\alpha + \beta) \neq \cos\alpha + \cos\beta$$

Are the two expressions ever equal? Explain.

17. **Standardized Test Prep** Which of the following is equal to $\cos\left(x - \frac{\pi}{2}\right)$?

    A. $\sin x$ **B.** $-\sin x$ **C.** $\cos^2 x - \sin^2 x$ **D.** $\cos\left(x + \frac{\pi}{2}\right)$

Use facts you know. First express $\tan 2x$ and $\tan 3x$ in terms of cosine and sine.

Cosine is an even function, and sine is an odd function.

Maintain Your Skills

18. Suppose θ is the measure of an angle in Quadrant I.

    a. If $\cos\theta = \cos 40^\circ + \cos 80^\circ$, find θ.

    b. If $\cos\theta = \cos 50^\circ + \cos 70^\circ$, find θ.

    c. If $\cos\theta = \cos 55^\circ + \cos 65^\circ$, find θ.

    d. If $\cos\theta = \cos 57^\circ + \cos 63^\circ$, find θ.

    e. Write a general rule suggested by the pattern above.

    f. Use the identities from this lesson to prove your rule.

Additional Resources

PRINT RESOURCES
- Solution Manual
- Practice Workbook
- Assessment Resources
- Teaching Resources

TECHNOLOGY
- Interactive Textbook
- TeacherExpress CD-ROM
- ExamView CD-ROM
- PHSchool.com

Additional Practice

1. **a.** Find two "nice" complex numbers that have a product with argument 105°.
   b. Use the complex numbers you found in part (a) to get exact values for $\cos 105^\circ$ and $\sin 105^\circ$.
   c. Find the value of $2\sin 105^\circ \cos 105^\circ$.

2. Find the magnitude and argument of the complex number $-\frac{\sqrt{3}}{2} - \frac{1}{2}i$.

3. **a.** Evaluate the product.
$$\left(\frac{4}{5} + \frac{3}{5}i\right)\left(\frac{24}{25} + \frac{7}{25}i\right)$$
   b. If α and β are in Quadrant I and $\cos\alpha = \frac{3}{5}$ and $\sin\beta = \frac{5}{13}$, find the value of $\cos(\alpha + \beta)$.

4. Use the Angle-Sum and Angle-Difference Formulas for cosine and sine to prove each of these identities.
   a. $\cos\left(x + \frac{3\pi}{2}\right) = \sin x$ **b.** $\cos(x - \pi) = -\cos x$
   c. $\tan(x + \pi) = \tan x$ **d.** $\sin(\pi - x) = \sin x$
   e. $\sin\left(2x + \frac{\pi}{2}\right) = \cos^2 x - \sin^2 x$

5. Use the Angle-Sum Formula for cosine and sine to find the exact value of the following.
   a. $\cos 150^\circ$ **b.** $\sin 135^\circ$
   c. $\cos(-75^\circ)$ **d.** $\sin(-105^\circ)$

6. **a.** What do you get if you use the Angle-Difference Formula to expand the expression $\sin(x - x)$?
   b. What is the value of $\sin(x - x)$?

Practice: For Lesson 2.6, assign Exercises 1–6.

9. a. $\cos(x + \pi) = \cos x \cos\pi - \sin x \sin\pi = -\cos x$

b. $\sin\left(\frac{\pi}{2} - x\right) = \sin\frac{\pi}{2}\cos x - \cos\frac{\pi}{2}\sin x = \cos x$

c. $\cos\left(x + \frac{\pi}{2}\right) = \cos x \cos\frac{\pi}{2} - \sin x \sin\frac{\pi}{2} = -\sin x$

d. $\cos(x + 2\pi) = \cos x \cos 2\pi - \sin x \sin 2\pi = \cos x$

e–f. See back of book.

10. a. $\cos x \cos x + \sin x \sin x = \cos^2 x + \sin^2 x = 1$

b. 1

11. a. $\tan 2x = \dfrac{2\tan x}{1 - \tan^2 x}$

b. $\tan 3x = \dfrac{3\tan x - \tan^3 x}{1 - 3\tan^2 x}$

12. Yes; use the identity in Ex. 4(a), and let $A = 4x$ and $B = x$.

13. a. $\dfrac{6 - \sqrt{35}}{12} + \dfrac{2\sqrt{7} + 3\sqrt{5}}{12}i$

b. $\dfrac{6 - \sqrt{35}}{12}$

14–15. See back of book.

16. Yes; answers may vary. Sample: Obviously $\cos(A + B) = \cos A + \cos B$ is never true if $B = 0$, since in that case the equation becomes $\cos A = \cos A + \cos 0$, or $\cos A = \cos A + 1$. But if $B = 1$, then the graphs of $y = \cos(x + 1)$ and $y = \cos x + \cos 1$ intersect, and so $\cos(x + 1) = \cos x + \cos 1$ has solutions, which means there are values of A and B such that $\cos(A + B) = \cos A + \cos B$. There is no immediately obvious rule that tells, in general, what pairs of values of A and B will work.

17. A

18. a. 20° **b.** 10° **c.** 5° **d.** 3°

e. $\cos k = \cos(60^\circ - k) + \cos(60^\circ + k)$

f. $\cos(60^\circ - k) + \cos(60^\circ + k)$
$= \cos 60^\circ \cos k + \sin 60^\circ \sin k + \cos 60^\circ \cos k - \sin 60^\circ \sin k$
$= 2\cos 60^\circ \cos k$
$= \cos k$

Lesson Overview

GOALS

- Test trigonometric equations to predict whether they are identities.
- Use Pythagorean identities and algebra to prove that a trigonometric equation is an identity.

This lesson focuses on the algebraic proof of identities. Students develop a formal chain of reasoning to show how to transform an expression, using the basic rules of algebra and proved formulas and theorems. They also see that they can prove identities using other identities that they proved previously.

Emphasize that each step of these proofs is reversible. It is less important that students write out a formal step-by-step process to convert one side to the other. Students can work on both sides, manipulating each in turn, provided each step is valid. For instance, you cannot square both sides of an equation.

CHECK YOUR UNDERSTANDING
- Core: 1, 2, 5
- Optional: 3, 4

MATERIALS
- graphing calculators
- Blackline Master MC3

HOMEWORK
- Core: 6, 8, 9, 10, 12
- Optional: 7, 13
- Extension: 11

Launch

Review the Pythagorean Identity ($\cos^2 x + \sin^2 x = 1$).

Explore

Example 1

Use Blackline Master MC3 on an overhead to demonstrate the identity. One idea is to graph and label the functions on two separate masters—use two different colors—then superimpose one over the other to show they coincide at all values of the domain.

2.7 Proving Identities

In Chapter 1, you proved geometrically one of the key trigonometric identities, the Pythagorean identity.

$$\cos^2 x + \sin^2 x = 1$$

Two identities that follow directly from the one above are

$$1 + \tan^2 x = \sec^2 x \quad \text{and} \quad \cot^2 x + 1 = \csc^2 x$$

> You proved both of these identities in Chapter 1 as well. How do they relate to $\cos^2 x + \sin^2 x = 1$?

These two identities differ slightly from the first one since there are values of x where their expressions are not defined. But it is true that the two sides are equal wherever the expressions are defined.

One way to build these identities is to start with a known identity and then transform it using the basic rules of algebra. But how would you proceed if you wanted to consider

$$\csc x \cos^2 x + \sin x = \csc x$$

as a possible identity? A first step is to gather evidence to decide whether the equation might indeed be an identity. Lesson 2.5 suggested two ways to gather such evidence:

- substituting some values for x, and
- comparing graphs.

Example 1

Problem Determine whether $\cos\left(\frac{\pi}{2} - x\right) = \sin x$ is an identity.

Solution Gather some evidence.

> Start by picking numbers for x that make the calculations easy. But be careful. Some expressions are equal for the "easy" numbers, but equal elsewhere.

- Try some values of x

a. Let $x = 0$.

$$\cos\left(\frac{\pi}{2} - 0\right) = \cos\frac{\pi}{2} = 0$$

$$\sin 0 = 0$$

The equation is true when $x = 0$.

b. Let $x = \frac{\pi}{2}$.

$$\cos\left(\frac{\pi}{2} - \frac{\pi}{2}\right) = \cos 0 = 1$$

$$\sin\frac{\pi}{2} = 1$$

The equation is true when $x = \frac{\pi}{2}$.

c. Let $x = \pi$.

$$\cos\left(\frac{\pi}{2} - \pi\right) = \cos\left(-\frac{\pi}{2}\right) = 0$$

$$\sin\pi = 0$$

The equation is true when $x = \pi$.

These results support the idea that the equation is an identity.

- Graph $y = \cos\left(\frac{\pi}{2} - x\right)$ and $y = \sin x$.

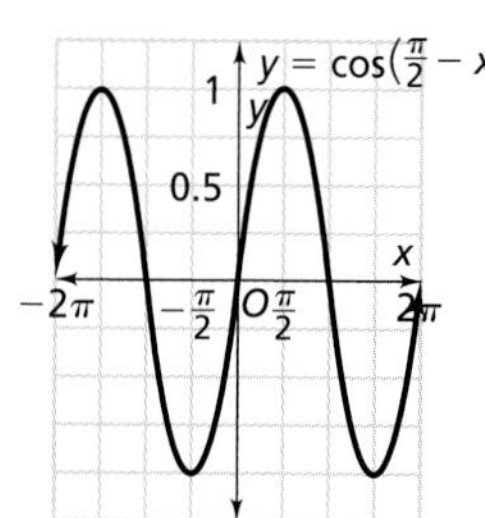

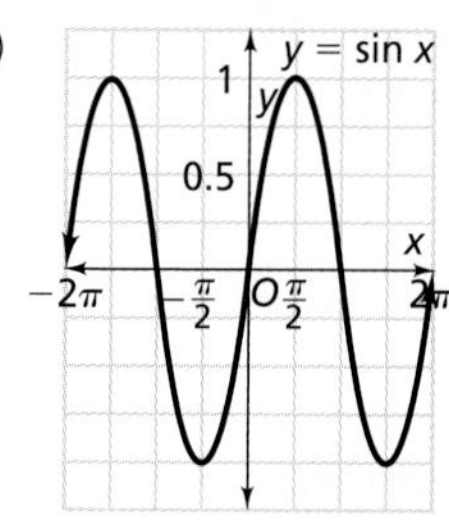

Always have the graphs of cosine and sine handy.

Both graphs look identical. If you graph them on the same axes on your calculator, they look like just one graph. So it is a good bet that the equation is an identity.

Keep in mind that evidence is not proof. Just because the two sides agree on lots of inputs and their graphs look the same, you cannot conclude that you have an identity. This first step can help you decide to try to prove the identity. But it does not constitute a proof.

One way to prove an identity is to use the basic rules of algebra, along with any other theorems you know, to transform one side of the equation into the other.

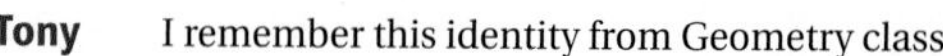

Minds in Action episode 5

Tony and Derman are working to prove that $\cos\left(\frac{\pi}{2} - x\right) = \sin x$ *is an identity.*

Tony I remember this identity from Geometry class.

Derman Of course, then we were only talking angles in triangles, and we worked with degrees.

Tony Yeah, it was $\cos(90° - \theta) = \sin \theta$. The sine of an angle is equal to the cosine of its complement.

Derman Right, because the leg opposite one angle is the leg adjacent to the other one. But θ has values between 0° and 90°, and we want to prove the identity for any value of x.

Tony Well, we can use the Angle-Difference Formulas, right?

Derman Great idea.

After all, the *co* in *cosine* stands for *complement*.

Minds in Action

You may wish to assign students Minds in Action roles and present the conversation to the class. This is more effective if you assign the roles one class day prior to the "performance." Urge the students to "get into" their parts by using their own words instead of memorizing lines.

For You to Do

PROBLEM 1 Have students practice for the ideas just introduced by doing this problem.

Tony writes on his paper.

$$\cos(A - B) = \cos A \cos B + \sin A \sin B$$
$$\cos\left(\frac{\pi}{2} - x\right) = \cos\frac{\pi}{2}\cos x + \sin\frac{\pi}{2}\sin x$$
$$= 0 \cdot \cos x + 1 \cdot \sin x$$
$$= \sin x$$

Tony And there it is!

For You to Do

1. Prove that the following equation is an identity.

$$\sin\left(x + \frac{\pi}{3}\right) = \cos\left(x - \frac{\pi}{6}\right)$$

You graphed the left and right sides of this identity in Exercise 9 of Lesson 2.5.

The idea of proving identities is to show that two expressions are identically equal. In other words, you can transform one expression to the other using

- the basic rules of algebra (the commutative, associative, and distributive properties, the additive and multiplicative identities, and additive and multiplicative inverses)
- substitution
- proven theorems

In the Minds in Action above, Tony started with one side of the identity, and showed each step he took to end up with the other side of the identity.

For some identities, like $\csc x \cos^2 x + \sin x = \csc x$, the steps may not be as apparent as in Tony's example. To prove this identity, treat it like an equation.

There are three types of equations: those with one solution, no solution, or those with all real numbers as a solution. Equations with all real numbers as a solution are identities. They are always true no matter the value of the variable.

You saw in Chapter 1 that you can solve trigonometric equations much as you do any other equations. In fact, if you try to solve a trigonometric equation and the resulting statement is always true, then the original equation is an identity.

You may find it easier to prove some trigonometric identities by trying to solve them as you would any equation, looking for an equation that you know is true. Make sure that each step you take is reversible.

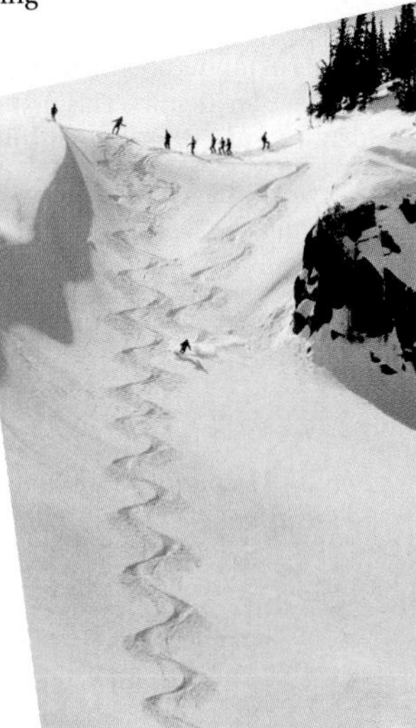

There are many routes from Point A to Point B. Some are shorter while others are more scenic. Proving an identity is similar. The important thing is arriving at the goal.

Answers

For You to Do

1. $\sin\left(x + \frac{\pi}{3}\right) = \sin x \cos\frac{\pi}{3} + \cos x \sin\frac{\pi}{3} = \frac{1}{2}\sin x + \frac{\sqrt{3}}{2}\cos x$ and $\cos\left(x - \frac{\pi}{6}\right) = \cos x \cos\frac{\pi}{6} + \sin x \sin\frac{\pi}{6} = \frac{\sqrt{3}}{2}\cos x + \frac{1}{2}\sin x$, so by the transitive property of equality, $\sin\left(x + \frac{\pi}{3}\right) = \cos\left(x - \frac{\pi}{6}\right)$.

Example 2

Problem Prove that $\csc x \cos^2 x + \sin x = \csc x$ is an identity.

Solution One way to prove an identity is to minimize the number of different functions shown. Here, each term has $\sin x$ in it.

$$\frac{1}{\sin x}(1 - \sin^2 x) + \sin x = \frac{1}{\sin x}$$
$$\frac{1 - \sin^2 x}{\sin x} + \frac{\sin^2 x}{\sin x} = \frac{1}{\sin x}$$
$$\frac{(1 - \sin^2 x) + \sin^2 x}{\sin x} = \frac{1}{\sin x}$$
$$\frac{1}{\sin x} = \frac{1}{\sin x} \checkmark$$

You may have recognized this identity. Sasha built it in Lesson 2.6. So another way to prove the identity is to reverse Sasha's steps. To show $\csc x \cos^2 x + \sin x = \csc x$, show $\csc x \cos^2 x + \sin x - \csc x = 0$.

You could make some progress by factoring out $\csc x$ from the expression on the left side, but the second term does not have a factor of $\csc x$. But notice that, since $\csc x = \frac{1}{\sin x}$, then $\csc x \sin x = 1$, so you can multiply the second term, $\sin x$, by $\sin x \csc x$.

$$\csc x \cos^2 x + \sin x - \csc x = 0$$
$$\csc x \cos^2 x + \sin x \sin x \csc x - \csc x = 0$$
$$\csc x \cos^2 x + \sin^2 x \csc x - \csc x = 0$$
$$\csc x(\cos^2 x + \sin^2 x - 1) = 0$$
$$\csc x \cdot 0 = 0$$
$$0 = 0 \checkmark$$

In each method, your steps are reversible, so you are done. Notice that the two methods are quite similar. In fact, you could combine ideas from both methods to write a very simple formal proof.

$$\begin{aligned}\csc x \cos^2 x + \sin x &= \csc x \cos^2 x + \sin^2 x \csc x && (\text{since } \sin x \csc x = 1)\\ &= \csc x(\cos^2 x + \sin^2 x) && (\text{by factoring out } \csc x)\\ &= \csc x \checkmark && (\text{since } \cos^2 x + \sin^2 x = 1)\end{aligned}$$

For You to Do

2. Prove that the following equation is an identity.

$$\frac{\sin^2 y}{1 - \cos y} - 1 = \cos y$$

For You to Do

2. $\frac{\sin^2 y}{1 - \cos y} - 1 = \frac{1 - \cos^2 y}{1 - \cos y} - 1$
$= \frac{(1 + \cos y)(1 - \cos y)}{1 - \cos y} - 1$
$= 1 + \cos y - 1 = \cos y$

For You to Do

PROBLEM 2 This identity suggests one that is used in calculus. By definition, the derivative of a function f is

$$f'(x) = \lim_{h \to 0} \frac{f(x + h) - f(x)}{h}$$

So, for the sine function,

$$\frac{d}{dx}\sin x = \lim_{h \to 0} \frac{\sin(x + h) - \sin x}{h}$$

Use the Angle-Sum Formula for sine to get

$$\begin{aligned}\frac{d}{dx}\sin x &= \lim_{h \to 0} \frac{\sin x \cos h + \sin h \cos x - \sin x}{h}\\ &= \left(\lim_{h \to 0}\left(\frac{\cos h - 1}{h}\right)\right)\sin x\\ &\quad + \left(\lim_{h \to 0}\left(\frac{\sin}{h}\right)\right)\cos x\end{aligned}$$

Since $\lim_{h \to 0} \frac{\sin h}{h} = 1$ and $\lim_{h \to 0} \frac{\cos h - 1}{h} = 0$, then

$$\frac{d}{dx}\sin x = 0 \cdot \sin x + 1 \cdot \cos x = \cos x$$

Wrap Up

Before having your students begin today's Check Your Understanding exercises, state your expectations on the formality of their proofs. You may want to use the last For You to Do section to demonstrate how you want your students to write up a proof.

Assessment Resources

Lesson Quiz 2.7

1. Prove this identity.

$$\frac{\cos x}{1 + \sin x} = \sec x - \tan x$$

2. Show that this expression is equal to zero.

$$(\cos x)(\tan x + \sin x \cot x) - (\sin x + \cos^2 x)$$

3. One of these two equations is an identity. Find and prove the identity.

$$\frac{\sec^2 x - 1}{\sin x} = \frac{\sin x}{1 - \sin^2 x}$$
$$\frac{\sec^2 x - 1}{\sin x} = \frac{\cos x}{1 - \sin^2 x}$$

4. Use the Angle-Sum Formula to prove this identity.

$$\cos 3x = \cos^3 x - 3\sin^2 x \cos x$$

Exercises

HOMEWORK

- Core: 6, 8, 9, 10, 12
- Optional: 7, 13
- Extension: 11

Check Your Understanding

EXERCISE 2 You might also ask students to take the equation that is not an identity and transform it into an identity. (Answer: $\cos 2x + 1 = 2\cos^2 x$)

Exercises *Practicing Habits of Mind*

Check Your Understanding

1. Prove each of these identities.

a. $\tan^2 x \sin^2 x = \tan^2 x - \sin^2 x$ **b.** $\dfrac{\cos x}{1 - \sin x} = \dfrac{1 + \sin x}{\cos x}$

c. $\cot^2 x \cos^2 x = \cot^2 x - \cos^2 x$ **d.** $\dfrac{\sin x}{1 - \cos x} = \dfrac{1 + \cos x}{\sin x}$

2. Only one of these two equations is an identity. Find and prove the identity.

$$\cos 2x + 1 = \frac{1}{2}\cos^2 x$$

$$\sin 2x + 1 = (\cos x + \sin x)^2$$

Use the identity from Exercise 4a in Lesson 2.6.

3. Prove this identity.

$$\cos 5x = 2\cos x \cos 4x - \cos 3x$$

4. Show that, for any integer $n > 1$,

$$\cos((n + 1)x) = 2\cos x \cos nx - \cos((n - 1)x)$$

Exercise 3 showed a specific case of this identity, with $n = 4$. Perhaps you could use the same method to prove this identity?

5. a. Show that this expression is equal to zero.

$$(\sec x \sin x)^2 - (\sec x + 1)(\sec x - 1)$$

b. Explain how to use the results from part (a) to justify this identity.

$$(\sec x \sin x)^2 = (\sec x + 1)(\sec x - 1)$$

On Your Own

6. a. Show that you can use the result in Exercise 4 to get a formula for $\cos 2x$.

$$\cos 2x = 2\cos^2 x - 1$$

b. Use the result in Exercise 4 to find a formula for $\cos 3x$.

7. One of these two equations is an identity. Find and prove the identity.

$$\tan^2 x - \cos^2 x = (\sec x - \sin x)^2$$

$$\tan^2 x - \sin^2 x = (\sec x - \cos x)^2$$

Answers

Exercises

1. a.
$$\begin{aligned}\tan^2 x - \sin^2 x &= \frac{\sin^2 x}{\cos^2 x} - \sin^2 x\\ &= \left(\frac{1}{\cos^2 x} - 1\right)\sin^2 x\\ &= \left(\frac{1 - \cos^2 x}{\cos^2 x}\right)\sin^2 x\\ &= \frac{\sin^2 x}{\cos^2 x}\cdot \sin^2 x\\ &= \tan^2 x \sin^2 x\end{aligned}$$

b.
$$\begin{aligned}\frac{\cos x}{1 - \sin x} &= \frac{\cos x}{1 - \sin x}\cdot\frac{1 + \sin x}{1 + \sin x}\\ &= \frac{\cos x(1 + \sin x)}{1 - \sin^2 x}\\ &= \frac{\cos x(1 + \sin x)}{\cos^2 x}\\ &= \frac{1 + \sin x}{\cos x}\end{aligned}$$

c–d. See back of book.

2. The second equation is an identity. $(\cos x + \sin x)^2 = \cos^2 x + 2\cos x \sin x + \sin^2 x = 2\cos x \sin x + 1 = \sin 2x + 1$

3. Since $\cos(\alpha + \beta) + \cos(\alpha - \beta) = 2\cos\alpha\cos\beta$ is an identity, $\cos 5x + \cos 3x = 2\cos 4x \cos x$. Hence $\cos 5x = 2\cos x \cos 4x - \cos 3x$.

4. This identity follows directly from the identity $\cos(\alpha + \beta) + \cos(\alpha - \beta) = 2\cos\alpha\cos\beta$ if you let $\alpha = (n + 1)x$ and $\beta = (n - 1)x$.

5–6. See back of book.

7. The second equation is an identity.

$$\begin{aligned}\tan^2 x - \sin^2 x &= \frac{\sin^2 x}{\cos^2 x} - \frac{\sin^2 x \cos^2 x}{\cos^2 x}\\ &= \frac{\sin^2 x(1 - \cos^2 x)}{\cos^2 x}\\ &= \left(\frac{\sin^2 x}{\cos x}\right)^2\\ &= \left(\frac{1 - \cos^2 x}{\cos x}\right)^2\\ &= \left(\frac{1}{\cos x} - \cos x\right)^2\\ &= (\sec x - \cos x)^2\end{aligned}$$

8. Provide explicit steps to transform the expression

$\frac{1 - \tan x}{\sec x} + \frac{\sec x}{\tan x}$ into $\frac{1 + \tan x}{\sec x \tan x}$

9. Peter has an idea for proving the identity

$$\frac{\sec x + 1}{\tan x} = \frac{\tan x}{\sec x - 1}$$

Peter says, "The right side of the identity has $\sec x - 1$ in the denominator. Maybe I should try to get $\sec x - 1$ in the denominator of the left side, too. I can do this by multiplying both the numerator and denominator of the left side by $\sec x - 1$, since that's the same thing as multiplying by 1."

a. Prove the identity using Peter's idea.

b. Use Peter's method to prove this identity.

$$\frac{\cot x}{\csc x - 1} = \frac{\csc x + 1}{\cot x}$$

10. Show that each of these equations is an identity.

a. $\sin 2x = \frac{2 \tan x}{1 + \tan^2 x}$ b. $\cos 2x = \frac{1 - \tan^2 x}{1 + \tan^2 x}$

c. $\tan 2x = \frac{2 \tan x}{1 - \tan^2 x}$

It might help to rewrite $1 + \tan^2 x$ using an identity.

11. **Take It Further** Prove each of these identities.

a. $\cos^6 x + \sin^6 x = 3 \cos^4 x - 3 \cos^2 x + 1$

b. $\frac{1 + \cos x}{\sin x} = \frac{1 + \cos x + \sin x}{1 - \cos x + \sin x}$

12. **Standardized Test Prep** Which of the following equations is a trigonometric identity?

A. $\cos x + \sin x = 1$ B. $\sin x = \sin(-x)$

C. $\cos x = \cos(-x)$ D. $\sin^{-1} x = x$

Go Online PHSchool.com

For additional practice, go to Web Code: bga-0207

Maintain Your Skills

13. Consider the identities from Exercise 10.

a. Let $\tan x = \frac{1}{2}$. Calculate the exact values of $\sin 2x$, $\cos 2x$, and $\tan 2x$.

b. Let $\tan x = \frac{2}{3}$. Calculate $\sin 2x$, $\cos 2x$, and $\tan 2x$.

c. Let $\tan x = \frac{1}{4}$. Calculate $\sin 2x$, $\cos 2x$, and $\tan 2x$.

d. Let $\tan x = \frac{3}{4}$. Calculate $\sin 2x$, $\cos 2x$, and $\tan 2x$.

e. Let $\tan x = \frac{m}{n}$. Calculate $\sin 2x$, $\cos 2x$, and $\tan 2x$ in terms of m and n.

Additional Resources

PRINT RESOURCES
- Solution Manual
- Practice Workbook
- Assessment Resources
- Teaching Resources

TECHNOLOGY
- Interactive Textbook
- TeacherExpress CD-ROM
- ExamView CD-ROM
- PHSchool.com

Additional Practice

1. Prove each of these identities.

a. $\tan x + \cot x = \csc x \sec x$ b. $\frac{1}{\sec x - 1} + \frac{1}{\sec x + 1} = 2 \cot x \csc x$

c. $\frac{\cos^2 x - 1}{\cos x} = -\tan x \sin x$ d. $\frac{\sec x + 1}{\tan x} = \frac{\sin x}{1 - \cos x}$

2. Only one of these two equations is an identity. Find and prove the identity.

$$\sin^2 x - \cos^2 x = 1 - 2\cos^2 x$$
$$\tan^2 x - \sin^2 x = 2\tan^2 x \sin^2 x$$

3. Use the Angle-Sum Formula to prove the following identity.

$$\sin 3x = 3 \sin x \cos^2 x - \sin^3 x$$

4. a. Show that this expression is equal to zero.

$$\tan x \sin x - (1 + \sec x)(1 - \cos x)$$

b. Explain how to use the results from part (a) to justify this identity.

$$\tan x \sin x = (1 + \sec x)(1 - \cos x)$$

5. Only one of these two equations is an identity. Find and prove the identity.

$$\frac{\tan^2 x}{\sec x + 1} = \frac{1 - \sin x}{\cos x}$$
$$\frac{\tan^2 x}{\sec x + 1} = \frac{1 - \cos x}{\cos x}$$

6. Provide explicit steps to transform the expression

$\frac{1}{1 + \sin x} + \frac{1}{1 - \sin x}$ into $2 \sec^2 x$

7. Show that each of these equations is an identity.

a. $\sin 4x = 2 \sin 2x \cos 2x$ b. $2 \csc 2x = \csc x \sec x$

Practice: For Lesson 2.7, assign Exercises 1–7.

8. $$\frac{1 - \tan x}{\sec x} + \frac{\sec x}{\tan x} = \frac{\tan x - \tan^2 x + \sec^2 x}{\sec x \tan x} = \frac{\tan x - \tan^2 x + (1 + \tan^2 x)}{\sec x \tan x} = \frac{1 + \tan x}{\sec x \tan x}$$

9. a. $$\frac{\sec x + 1}{\tan x} = \frac{\sec x + 1}{\tan x} \cdot \frac{\sec x - 1}{\sec x - 1} = \frac{\sec^2 x - 1}{\tan x(\sec x - 1)} = \frac{\tan^2 x}{\tan x(\sec x - 1)} = \frac{\tan x}{\sec x - 1}$$

b. $$\frac{\csc x + 1}{\cot x} = \frac{\csc x + 1}{\cot x} \cdot \frac{\csc x - 1}{\csc x - 1} = \frac{\csc^2 x - 1}{\cot x(\csc x - 1)} = \frac{\cot^2 x}{\cot x(\csc x - 1)} = \frac{\cot x}{\csc x - 1}$$

10. a–b. See back of book.

c. From Exercise 6 of Lesson 2.6, $\tan(\alpha + \beta) = \frac{\tan \alpha + \tan \beta}{1 - \tan \alpha \tan \beta}$. Let $\alpha = x$ and $\beta = x$. This immediately gives $\tan 2x = \frac{2 \tan x}{1 - \tan^2 x}$.

11. a. Factor $(\cos^2 x)^3 + (\sin^2 x)^3$ as the sum of two cubes to get $(\cos^2 x + \sin^2 x) \cdot (\cos^4 x - \cos^2 x \sin^2 x + \sin^4 x)$. In this latter expression, replace $\cos^2 x + \sin^2 x$ with 1, and in the second factor, replace $\sin^2 x$ with $1 - \cos^2 x$ and $\sin^4 x$ with $(1 - \cos^2 x)^2$. Simplify the result to obtain $3\cos^4 x - 3\cos^2 x + 1$.

b. See back of book.

12. C

13. a. $\sin(2x) = \frac{4}{5}$, $\cos(2x) = \frac{3}{5}$, $\tan(2x) = \frac{4}{3}$

b. $\sin(2x) = \frac{12}{13}$, $\cos(2x) = \frac{5}{13}$, $\tan(2x) = \frac{12}{5}$

c. $\sin(2x) = \frac{8}{17}$, $\cos(2x) = \frac{15}{17}$, $\tan(2x) = \frac{8}{15}$

d. $\sin(2x) = \frac{24}{25}$, $\cos(2x) = \frac{7}{25}$, $\tan(2x) = \frac{24}{7}$

e. $\sin(2x) = \frac{2mn}{m^2 + n^2}$, $\cos(2x) = \frac{n^2 - m^2}{m^2 + n^2}$, $\tan(2x) = \frac{2mn}{n^2 - m^2}$

Mathematical Reflections

EXERCISES 6–8 At the start of the investigation, you may have assigned these as Questions 1–3 for students to think and write about.

In this investigation, you used the Multiplication Law to prove the Angle-Sum Formulas. You used known identities to prove new trigonometric identities. The following questions will help you summarize what you have learned.

1. For which values of x is the following equation true?
$$\cos x - \cos^3 x = \cos x \sin^2 x$$
A. $x = \frac{\pi}{3}$ **B.** $x = \frac{4\pi}{3}$
C. $x = \pi$ **D.** all of the above

2. Find the pairs of expressions that are identically equal.

$\csc^2 x$	$\cos x + \tan x \cdot \sin x$
$(1 + \sin x)(1 - \sin x)$	$\cos^2 x$
$1 + \cos^2 x \cdot \csc^2 x$	$\sec x$

3. **a.** Find the magnitude and argument of the complex number $\frac{1}{2} + \frac{\sqrt{3}}{2}i$.
b. Multiply out the product $(\cos x + i \sin x)\left(\frac{1}{2} + \frac{\sqrt{3}}{2}i\right)$.
c. Write a rule for $\cos\left(x + \frac{\pi}{3}\right)$ and another for $\sin\left(x + \frac{\pi}{3}\right)$.

4. Prove each of these identities.
a. $\sin(x + \pi) = -\sin x$ **b.** $\cos\left(\frac{\pi}{2} - x\right) = \sin x$
c. $\cos(2\pi - x) = \cos x$ **d.** $\sin(2\pi - x) = -\sin x$

5. One of these two equations is an identity and the other is not. Find and prove the identity.
$(\cos x - \sin x)^2 = \cos 2x$ $\quad (\cos x + \sin x)(\cos x - \sin x) = \cos 2x$

6. How can you test to see if an equation might be an identity?

7. How can you use complex numbers to find formulas for $\cos 2x$ and $\sin 2x$?

8. How can you use identities to prove other identities?

Vocabulary and Notation

In this investigation, you learned these terms. Make sure you understand what each one means and how to use it.

- **identically equal**
- **identity**

Beginning with the same set of materials, you might construct a car while your friend may build a house. Each is a personal expression. Just as two figures built with the same pieces can look quite dissimilar, two sides of a mathematical identity can look very different.

Answers

Mathematical Reflections

1. D

2. $\csc^2 x$ and $1 + \cos^2 x \cdot \csc^2 x$, $\cos x + \tan x \cdot \sin x$ and $\sec x$, $(1 + \sin x)(1 - \sin x)$ and $\cos^2 x$

3. a. magnitude $= 1$, argument $= \frac{\pi}{3}$

b. $\left(\frac{1}{2}\cos x - \frac{\sqrt{3}}{2}\sin x\right) + \left(\frac{\sqrt{3}}{2}\cos x + \frac{1}{2}\sin x\right)i$

c. $\cos\left(x + \frac{\pi}{3}\right) = \frac{1}{2}\cos x - \frac{\sqrt{3}}{2}\sin x$, $\sin\left(x + \frac{\pi}{3}\right) = \frac{\sqrt{3}}{2}\cos x + \frac{1}{2}\sin x$

4. a. $\sin(x + \pi) = \sin x \cos \pi + \cos x \sin \pi = -\sin x$

b. $\cos\left(\frac{\pi}{2} - x\right) = \cos\frac{\pi}{2}\cos x + \sin\frac{\pi}{2}\sin x = \sin x$

c. $\cos(2\pi - x) = \cos 2\pi \cos x + \sin 2\pi \sin x = \cos x$

d. $\sin(2\pi - x) = \sin 2\pi \cos x - \cos 2\pi \sin x = -\sin x$

5. $(\cos x + \sin x)(\cos x - \sin x) = \cos^2 x - \sin^2 x = 1 - \sin^2 x - \sin^2 x = 1 - 2\sin^2 x = \cos 2x$

6. One approach is to replace the variables with several specific values to see whether you get a true equation each time. For equations with just one variable, another approach is to use the expressions on the two sides of the equation to get two graphs. If the graphs appear to be the same, then the equation may be an identity.

7–8. See back of book.

Mid-Chapter Test

For a mid-chapter test, go to Web Code: bga-0252

Multiple Choice

1. Find $|4 - 2i|$.
   A. 2 B. $2\sqrt{5}$
   C. $2\sqrt{2}$ D. 6
2. Let $|z| = 2$ and $\arg(z) = \frac{3\pi}{2}$. Write z without using trigonometric functions.
   A. $-1 + i\sqrt{3}$ B. $\sqrt{3} + i$
   C. $-2i$ D. 2
3. If $z = -2 + i$, then find arg(z) to two decimal places (in radians).
   A. -0.46 B. 2.68
   C. 3.61 D. 153.43
4. If the magnitude of z is 4 and the magnitude of w is 9, find the magnitude of zw.
   A. 5 B. 6
   C. 13 D. 36
5. Simplify $\sin(x + \pi)$.
   A. $\sin x$ B. $\cos x$
   C. $-\sin x$ D. $-\cos x$

Open Response

6. Let z and w have the following values.
   $$z = 3 - 4i$$
   $$w = 2 + 2i$$
   a. In the complex plane, graph and label z, w, and zw.
   b. Copy and complete the table.

	a + bi	Magnitude	Direction (in radians)
z	3 − 4i	■	■
w	2 + 2i	■	■
zw	■	■	■

   c. Write w in polar form.

7. Let z and w be complex numbers, with $|z| = 2$, $\arg(z) = 80°$, $|w| = 4$, and $\arg(w) = 200°$.
   a. Find zw
   b. Find z^2
   c. Find w^4
   d. Write z in rectangular form.
8. One of these two equations is an identity, and the other is not. Determine which equation is the identity by finding a value for x that makes one of the equations false.
   $$\sin x(1 - \cos x) = \sin x - \frac{1}{2}\sin 2x$$
   $$\frac{(1 - \sin x)^2}{\cos x} = \tan x$$
9. Use the Angle-Sum Formulas to find each of the following.
   a. $\cos(x + 45°)$ b. $\sin(\pi - x)$
   c. $\cos\left(x - \frac{5\pi}{6}\right)$ d. $\sin\left(x + \frac{5\pi}{3}\right)$
10. Prove the identity.
   $$\cos x - \cos^3 x = \tan^2 x \cdot \cos^3 x$$
11. Use geometry to calculate the product.
   $$(1 - i\sqrt{3})(-3\sqrt{3} + 3i)$$

Mid-Chapter Test

Assessment Resources

Mid-Chapter Test page 1 of 2

Multiple Choice

1. Find $|-3 - 4i|$.
   A. 1 B. 5 C. 7 D. 12
2. Write $4 \text{ cis } \frac{\pi}{2}$ in rectangular form.
   A. 4 B. $4i$ C. $-2i$ D. $2i$
3. If $z = 3 + 2i$, find arg (z) in radians.
   A. 0.588 B. 0.983 C. 33.7 D. 56.3
4. If the magnitude of z is 5 and the magnitude of w is 6, find the magnitude of zw.
   A. 5 B. 6 C. 11 D. 30
5. Simplify $\cos(x - \pi)$.
   A. $\sin x$ B. $\cos x$ C. $-\sin x$ D. $-\cos x$

Open Response

6. $z = 1 - i$
   $w = 3i$
   a. In the complex plane, graph and label z, w, and zw.
   b. Complete the table.

	a + bi	Magnitude	Direction (in radians)
z	1 − i		
w	3i		
zw			

   c. Write w in polar form.

Also available: Form B

Mid-Chapter Test

1. B 2. C 3. B
4. D 5. C
6. a–b. See back of book.
   c. $2\sqrt{2} \text{ cis } \frac{\pi}{4}$
7. a. 8 cis 280°
   b. 4 cis 160°
   c. 256 cis 800°, or 256 cis 80°
   d. $2 \cos 80° + (2 \sin 80°)i \approx 0.347 + 1.970i$
8. Answers may vary. Sample: Let $x = \frac{\pi}{6}$. Both sides of the first equation are equal to $\frac{1}{2} - \frac{\sqrt{3}}{4}$. For the second equation, the left side is equal to $\frac{\sqrt{3}}{6}$, but the right side is equal to $\frac{\sqrt{3}}{3}$. So the first equation is the identity.
9. a. $\frac{\sqrt{2}}{2}\cos x - \frac{\sqrt{2}}{2}\sin x$
   b. $\sin x$
   c. $-\frac{\sqrt{3}}{2}\cos x + \frac{1}{2}\sin x$
   d. $\frac{1}{2}\sin x - \frac{\sqrt{3}}{2}\cos x$
10. Transform both sides of the equation.
   $\cos x - \cos^3 x = \cos x(1 - \cos^2 x) = \cos x \sin^2 x$ and $\tan^2 x \cdot \cos^3 x = \frac{\sin^2 x}{\cos^2 x} \cdot \cos^3 x = \cos x \sin^2 x$.
   Since both sides of the given equation are equal to $\cos x \sin^2 x$, the equation is an identity.
11. $12i$

Investigation Overview

The system of complex numbers encompasses the three major areas of high school mathematics: algebra, geometry, and analysis. The study of roots of unity is especially well suited for demonstrating the connections between these three disciplines.

- By using trigonometric functions to represent complex numbers, you can employ analytic methods to solve algebraic problems and vice versa. You can use De Moivre's Theorem to find the nth power of any complex number via trigonometry, and the resulting algebra produces the multiple angle formulas for cosine and sine.
- Gauss first exploited the connection between roots of $x^n - 1 = 0$ and the regular n-gon. You can use this connection in two ways: to apply the power of algebra to solve geometric problems, and to use geometric methods to gain algebraic insights. For example, Gauss used this connection to characterize the regular polygons that you can construct with a straightedge and a compass. In this chapter, students use Gauss' methods to analyze the pentagon and the 17-gon.
- Arithmetic with *cyclotomic* integers (complex numbers that are linear combinations of nth roots of unity with integer coefficients) demonstrates once again that you can model algebraic systems with polynomials and computer algebra systems.

You may wish to assign Questions 1–3 for students to think and write about during the investigation.

Learning Goals

- Calculate powers of complex numbers using De Moivre's Theorem.
- Understand the geometry of roots of unity, and the connection to roots of equations of the form $x^n - 1 = 0$.
- Find exact algebraic expressions for certain trigonometric values.

Habits and Skills

- Calculate with complex numbers.
- Visualize complex numbers and their arithmetic.

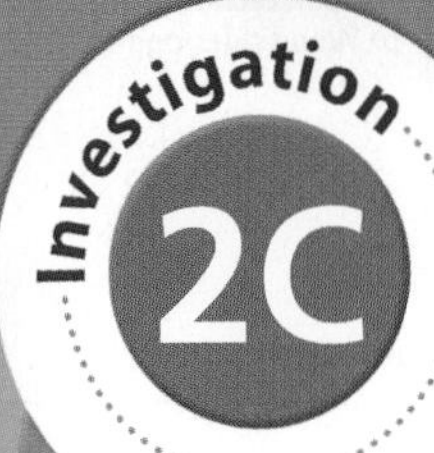

De Moivre's Theorem

Complex numbers are rooted in algebra, but once mathematicians like Gauss and Argand had the insight to represent complex numbers geometrically, the floodgates opened. Complex numbers permeated every part of mathematics. One of the most striking applications of complex numbers is to geometry. You have already seen how beautifully the addition and multiplication of complex numbers work on the complex plane, but that is just the beginning.

In *De Moivre's Theorem,* you will peek at one of the deepest connections between geometry and algebra. It is the connection between the roots of certain equations (equations of the form $x^n - 1 = 0$, where n is a positive integer) and regular polygons. This connection is sometimes called cyclotomy ("circle division") because regular polygons divide a circle into congruent pieces.

By the end of this investigation, you will be able to answer questions like these.

1. How do you use De Moivre's Theorem to write a rule for $\cos 3x$?
2. How can you connect roots of unity to regular polygons?
3. For what values of $\cos x$ does $\cos 3x = 0$?

You will learn how to

- calculate powers of complex numbers using De Moivre's Theorem
- understand the geometry of roots of unity, and the connection to roots of equations of the form $x^n - 1 = 0$
- find exact algebraic expressions for certain trigonometric values

You will develop these habits and skills:

- Calculate with complex numbers.
- Visualize complex numbers and their arithmetic.

The design of this skylight reflects the connection between the 18 roots of unity and a regular 18-gon.

Investigation Road Map

LESSON 2.8, *Getting Started,* begins with the Factor Game. The remainder of the exercises provide experience with the graphs of the solutions to equations of the form $x^n - 1 = 0$ and the sums of series of trigonometric functions.

LESSON 2.9, *Powers of Complex Numbers,* extends the Multiplication Law from the previous investigation. Students find multiple angle formulas and roots of unity.

LESSON 2.10, *Roots of Unity,* begins with the Polynomial Factor Game, so students see that $x^m - 1$ is a factor of $x^n - 1$ if and only if m is a factor of n. Students go on to look at the geometry of those roots.

LESSON 2.11, *Geometry of Roots of Unity,* shows that for any $n > 3$, the graph of the nth roots of unity form the vertices of a regular n-gon.

LESSON 2.12, *Arithmetic With Roots of Unity,* is optional.

2.8 Getting Started

There are n complex numbers that satisfy the equation $x^n - 1 = 0$. Each is known as an **nth root of unity.** To work with roots of unity, you will have to know how to find powers of complex numbers. The following problems will help you get started.

For You to Explore

1. Play the Factor Game! It is a game for two players.

   The board is all the integers from 1 to 30.

1	2	3	4	5
6	7	8	9	10
11	12	13	14	15
16	17	18	19	20
21	22	23	24	25
26	27	28	29	30

   Here are the rules.

   - Player 1 picks any available number on the board.
   - Player 2 identifies all the remaining proper factors of that number.
   - If there are no proper factors remaining on the board, Player 1 loses a turn and no points are scored.
   - Remove from the board all numbers used in a turn.

   In successive rounds, players alternate between picking the number and finding the factors.

   Scoring.

   - Player 1 scores points equal to the value of the number picked.
   - For each proper factor identified, Player 2 scores points equal to the value of that factor.
   - If there are no factors remaining on the board, Player 1 scores 0.
   - **Bonus Points**. If Player 1 finds a factor that Player 2 missed, Player 1 scores points equal to the value of that factor.

   a. Play the game a few times.

   b. Describe some of the strategies a player could use in this game.

2. Find the 4 complex numbers that are solutions to the equation $x^4 - 1 = 0$. Plot them as points in the complex plane.

For example, the proper factors of 18 are 1, 2, 3, 6, and 9.

If the first pick is 18, that player earns 18 points while the opponent earns $1 + 2 + 3 + 6 + 9 =$ 21 points. Not a great first pick!

Answers

For You to Explore

1. a. No answer required.

b. Answers may vary. Sample: Pick large numbers with the fewest factors. Picking a perfect square gives a higher total to the player than to the opponent.

2. 1, −1, i, and $-i$ are the solutions.

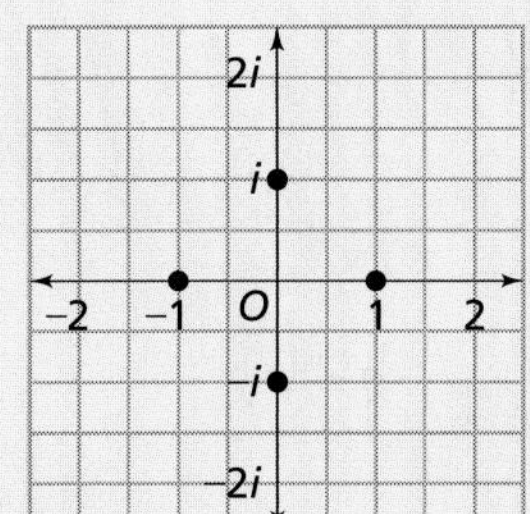

Lesson Overview

GOAL

- Warm up to the ideas of the investigation.

This lesson begins with the Factor Game that students may have played in junior high or middle school. Later, in Lesson 2.10, students extend this game to the Polynomial Factor Game, where they see that the set of polynomials as an algebraic system is similar in structure to the integers.

The remaining problems provide experience with the graphs of the solutions to equations of the form $x^n - 1 = 0$ and with the sums of series of trigonometric functions. As always in a Getting Started lesson, there is no need to formalize these ideas today. Students encounter all of the ideas again throughout the investigation.

FOR YOU TO EXPLORE
- Core: 1, 2, 3, 4, 6
- Optional: 5, 7, 8

MATERIALS
- CAS (recommended)
- graph paper
- graphing calculators
- Blackline Masters MC1, MC10, 2.8

HOMEWORK
- Core: 9, 10, 11
- Optional: 12, 13, 14, 15, 16, 17

Launch

Explain the rules of the Factor Game. You might want to ask students if they have seen the game before. You can play the game as a class, in groups, or in pairs.

Explore

For You to Explore

PROBLEM 1 Students revisit this game using polynomials later in the chapter. Blackline Master 2.8 reproduces the game board and rules. Use it on an overhead and let the students play the game as you shade in the integers used.

PROBLEM 3 Use Blackline Master MC1 or MC10 to show the geometric relationship between several of the complex numbers and their powers.

PROBLEM 5 Check students' progress on this problem. They may not have properly learned sigma notation previously, so this is a good problem to cover with the whole class. Direct students to the Maintain Your Skills exercise later, which provides more practice on summations.

Wrap Up

Debrief the Factor Game, and ask students to summarize their strategies. You might also want to review Problems 2–4.

Exercises

HOMEWORK
- Core: 9, 10, 11
- Optional: 12, 13, 14, 15, 16, 17

You may want to give students copies of Blackline Master MC1 or MC10 to use while they work on the exercises.

3. Plot the first 10 powers of each complex number as points in the complex plane, starting with $z^0 = 1$.

a. $z = i$ b. $z = \frac{1}{2} + \frac{\sqrt{3}}{2}i$ c. $z = \frac{3}{5} + \frac{4}{5}i$

d. $z = \text{cis } 36°$ e. $z = 1 + i$ f. $z = \frac{1}{2} \text{ cis } \frac{\pi}{4}$

4. Describe the picture you get when you plot the powers of a complex number z (starting with z^0) given each condition.

a. $|z| = 1$ b. $|z| > 1$ c. $|z| < 1$

5. Calculate the sum

$$\sum_{k=0}^{3} \cos \frac{2\pi k}{4}$$

6. Find the 3 complex numbers that are solutions to the equation $x^3 - 1 = 0$. Plot them as points in the complex plane.

7. Calculate the sum

$$\sum_{k=0}^{2} \sin \frac{2\pi k}{3}$$

8. Calculate the sum

$$\sum_{k=1}^{6} \cos \frac{2\pi k}{7}$$

Remember...

You can use summation notation to describe the sum of terms. The general form is

$$\sum_{k=0}^{n} a_k = a_0 + a_1 + a_2 + \cdots + a_n$$

where k is the index variable, 0 is the starting value, and n is the final value.

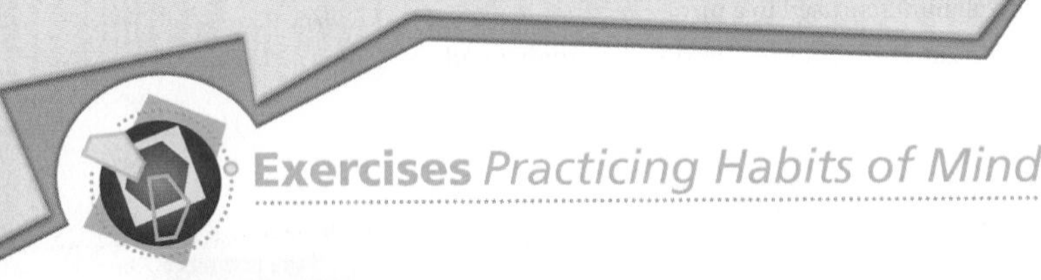

On Your Own

9. For $z = \text{cis } 72°$, find each of the following.

a. $\arg(z^2)$ b. $\arg(z^3)$ c. $\arg(z^4)$

d. $\arg(z^5)$ e. $\arg(z^{10})$ f. $\arg(z^n)$

Answers

3. a.

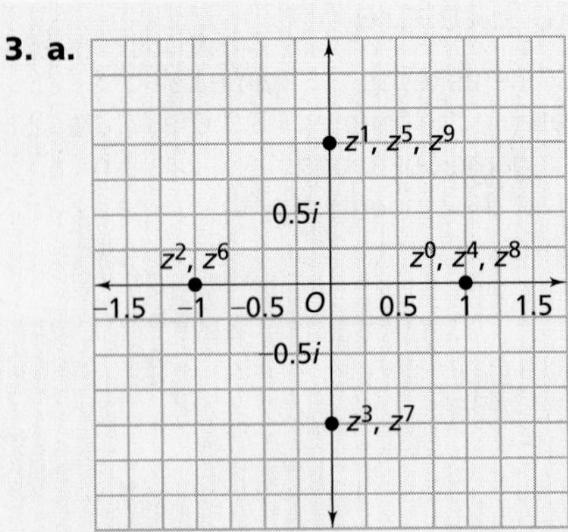

b–f. See back of book.

4. a. The powers lie on the unit circle.
b. The powers spiral out away from the origin.
c. The powers spiral in toward the origin.

5. 0

6. $1, -\frac{1}{2} \pm \frac{\sqrt{3}}{2}i$

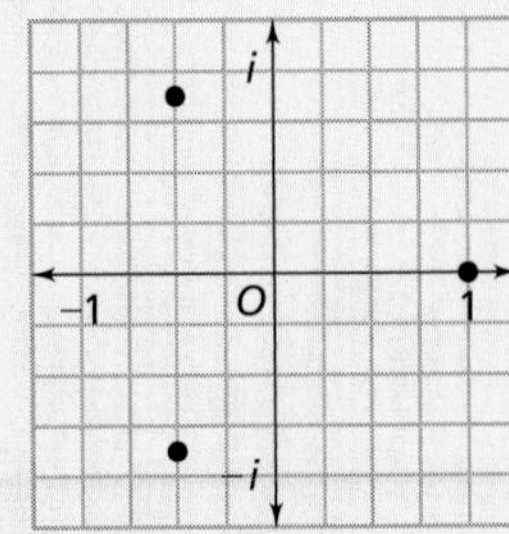

7. 0

8. −1

9. a. 144° **b.** 216° **c.** 288°
d. 0° **e.** 0°
f. $(72n)°$ (mod 360°)

10. For each expression, write an equivalent expression that includes only $\cos x$ and $\sin x$.

a. $\cos(x + 90°)$

b. $\cos(x + x)$

c. Write $\cos 4x$ in terms of powers of $\cos x$ and $\sin x$.

d. Write $\cos 4x$ in terms of powers of $\cos x$ only.

The identity $\sin 2x = 2 \sin x \cos x$ might be helpful here.

11. The factorization of $x^6 - 1$ over $\mathbb{Z}$ is

$$x^6 - 1 = (x - 1)(x + 1)(x^2 - x + 1)(x^2 + x + 1)$$

a. Is $x^2 - 1$ a factor of $x^6 - 1$? Explain.

b. Is $x^3 - 1$ a factor of $x^6 - 1$? Explain.

c. Is $x^4 - 1$ a factor of $x^6 - 1$? Explain.

12. Find the two solutions to the equation $x^2 - 8x + 15 = 0$. Then find their sum and product.

13. Find the two solutions to the equation $x^2 - 8x + 17 = 0$. Then find their sum and product.

14. Find the five complex numbers that are solutions to the equation $x^5 - 1 = 0$. Approximate any decimal answers to four decimal places.

See TI-Nspire Handbook on p. 704 for an example of how to solve using your calculator.

15. Plot the five complex numbers from Exercise 14 as points in the same complex plane. Compare the results to your results for Problems 2 and 6.

16. **a.** Approximate the value of $\cos 72°$ to four decimal places.

b. Approximate the value of $\cos \frac{4\pi}{5}$ to four decimal places.

c. Approximate the value of $\cos \frac{6\pi}{5}$ to four decimal places.

Maintain Your Skills

17. Calculate each sum.

a. $\sum_{k=0}^{3} \sin \frac{2\pi k}{4}$

b. $\sum_{k=0}^{5} \sin \frac{2\pi k}{6}$

c. $\sum_{k=0}^{5} \cos \frac{2\pi k}{6}$

d. $\sum_{k=0}^{7} \sin (45k)°$

e. $\sum_{k=0}^{7} \cos \frac{2\pi k}{8}$

On Your Own

EXERCISE 11 starts students thinking about the factors of polynomials of the form $x^n - 1$, preparing them for the Polynomial Factor Game.

EXERCISE 12 Later in this investigation, students look at sum and product as an explanation of why the roots of unity are placed how they are; it can explain the summation results in the Check Your Understanding exercises for this lesson, too.

EXERCISE 16 is a follow-up question to Exercise 14. Students may not recognize the connection between these two exercises yet. They should at least notice that they are getting the same answers.

Maintain Your Skills

EXERCISE 17 Note that your students' calculators may be able to evaluate these sums directly, so you might ask students to calculate all the intermediate answers.

10. a. $-\sin x$

b. $\cos^2 x - \sin^2 x$

c. Answers may vary. Sample: $\cos^4 x + \sin^4 x - 6 \sin^2 x \cos^2 x$

d. $8 \cos^4 x - 8 \cos^2 x + 1$

11. a. Yes; $x^2 - 1 = (x - 1)(x + 1)$, and both $x - 1$ and $x + 1$ are in the factorization of $x^6 - 1$.

b. Yes; $x^3 - 1$ has the factors $x - 1$ and $x^2 + x + 1$, both of which are in the factorization of $x^6 - 1$.

c. No; $x^2 + 1$ is a factor of $x^4 - 1$, but it is not in the factorization of $x^6 - 1$.

12. 3 and 5, sum = 8, product = 15

13. $4 + i$ and $4 - i$; sum = 8, product = 17

14. 1, $0.3090 \pm 0.9511i$, $-0.8090 \pm 0.5878i$

15.

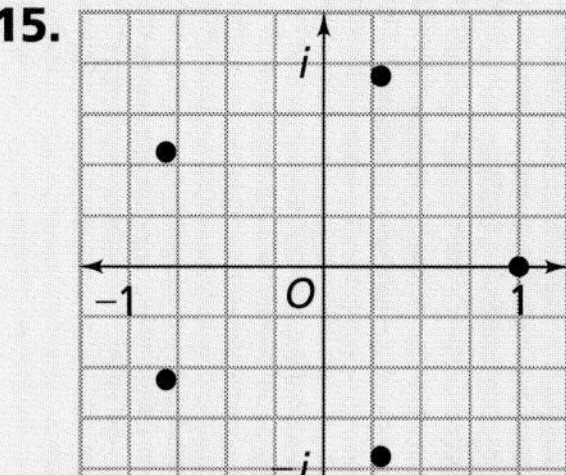

As in Ex. 2 and 6, the points appear to be the vertices of a regular polygon with vertices on the unit circle.

16. a. 0.3090

b. −0.8090

c. −0.8090

17. a. 0

b. 0

c. 0

d. 0

e. 0

Lesson Overview

GOAL

- Calculate powers of complex numbers using De Moivre's Theorem.

Students extend the Multiplication Law of complex numbers from the previous investigation to include powers of complex numbers. They apply these new theorems to finding multiple angle formulas (such as sin 3x), and they use the theorems when exploring roots of unity.

CHECK YOUR UNDERSTANDING

- Core: 1, 2, 3, 4
- Optional: 5

MATERIALS

- CAS (recommended)
- graph paper
- graphing calculators
- Blackline Master MC1, MC10

HOMEWORK

- Core: 7, 8, 9, 11, 14, 15, 16
- Optional: 6, 10, 12, 13, 17

Launch

Review Exercises 9 and 14 from Lesson 2.8.

Explore

For Discussion

Use the For Discussion problem to elicit conversation about the key ideas that immediately precede this section.

2.9 Powers of Complex Numbers

In Lesson 2.4, you proved a theorem for the multiplication of complex numbers. A direct consequence to Theorem 2.2 lets you find a simpler way to take powers of complex numbers.

For Discussion

In Exercise 9 of Lesson 2.8, you looked at powers of $z = \text{cis } 72°$. One pattern you may have noticed is that the argument of each successive power was 72° greater than the argument of the argument of the previous one.

1. Use Theorem 2.2 to explain why $\arg(z^n) = n(\arg(z))$ for any $n \in \mathbb{Z}^+$.

"For any $n \in \mathbb{Z}^+$" means "for any number n contained in the positive integers."

When $|z| = 1$, you can use the statement above to determine exactly where z^n is in the complex plane. Since $|z| = 1$, $|z^n| = 1$, too. So,

$$z^n = \text{cis } \theta$$

Now the only question is, what is θ? The result stated in the discussion above suggests that $\theta = n(\arg(z))$. Theorem 2.4, first published by Abraham de Moivre (1667–1754), summarizes these ideas.

Theorem 2.4 ***De Moivre's Theorem***

For all real θ, $(\text{cis } \theta)^n = \text{cis } n\theta$.

The argument outlined above should help you see why De Moivre's Theorem is true, but is not a solid proof.

You can use these ideas here to make a proof by induction.

Proof The proof is a repeated application of Theorem 2.2. As a first step, Theorem 2.2 states that

$$(\text{cis } \theta)(\text{cis } \alpha) = \text{cis } (\theta + \alpha)$$

So,

$$\begin{aligned}(\text{cis } \theta)^2 &= (\text{cis } \theta)(\text{cis } \theta)\\ &= \text{cis } (\theta + \theta)\\ &= \text{cis } 2\theta\end{aligned}$$

Similarly,

$$\begin{aligned}(\text{cis } \theta)^2 &= (\text{cis } \theta)(\text{cis } \theta)^2\\ &= (\text{cis } \theta)(\text{cis } 2\theta)\\ &= \text{cis } (\theta + 2\theta)\\ &= \text{cis } 3\theta\end{aligned}$$

If you keep doing this for n steps, you have

$$\begin{aligned}(\text{cis } \theta)^n &= (\text{cis } \theta)(\text{cis } \theta)^{n-1}\\ &= (\text{cis } \theta)(\text{cis } (n-1)\,\theta)\\ &= \text{cis } (\theta + (n-1)\,\theta)\\ &= \text{cis } n\theta\end{aligned}$$

In Chapter 4, you will formalize and streamline this "Keep up the good work" style of proof.

Answers

For Discussion

1. If $z = r \text{ cis } \theta$, then $z^n = (r \text{ cis } \theta)^n = r^n(\text{cis } \theta)^n = r^n \text{ cis}(n\theta)$. But $\theta = \arg(z)$ and $n\theta = \arg(z^n)$.

De Moivre's Theorem as stated here applies only to complex numbers that fall on the unit circle. But you can generalize the theorem to include any complex number.

Corollary 2.4.1

For all real θ, $(r \operatorname{cis}\theta)^n = r^n \operatorname{cis} n\theta$.

For You to Do

2. Prove Corollary 2.4.1.

You can use De Moivre's Theorem and Corollary 2.4.1 to solve equations that involve complex numbers.

Example

Problem Find all three solutions to the equation $x^3 = 8i$.

Solution To solve this equation, first write $8i$ in "$r \operatorname{cis}\theta$" format. Since $i = \operatorname{cis}\frac{\pi}{2}$, $8i = 8 \operatorname{cis}\frac{\pi}{2}$.

Now, suppose $x = a \operatorname{cis}\alpha$. Then you have $(a \operatorname{cis}\alpha)^3 = 8 \operatorname{cis}\frac{\pi}{2}$. By Corollary 2.4.1, $a^3 \operatorname{cis} 3\alpha = 8 \operatorname{cis}\frac{\pi}{2}$.

From there, you can say that $a^3 = 8$, so $a = 2$ since a must be a real number.

Also, you have $3\alpha = \frac{\pi}{2}$. So $\alpha = \frac{\pi}{6}$.

But recall that when you are solving for radians, you also have to consider $3\alpha = \frac{\pi}{2} + 2\pi k$ for integer values of k.

$$3\alpha = \frac{\pi}{2} + 2\pi k$$

$$\alpha = \frac{\pi}{6} + \frac{2\pi}{3}k$$

For $k = 0, 1$, and 2, you get $\alpha = \frac{\pi}{6}, \frac{5\pi}{6}$, and $\frac{3\pi}{2}$, respectively. Any other value for k gives an α value that differs from one of these three by a multiple of 2π. Since $\operatorname{cis}(\alpha + 2\pi) = \operatorname{cis}\alpha$, the three solutions of the equation are $x = 2 \operatorname{cis}\frac{\pi}{6}$, $x = 2 \operatorname{cis}\frac{5\pi}{6}$, and $x = 2 \operatorname{cis}\frac{3\pi}{2}$.

In fact, in addition to $a = 2$, there are two other possible solutions to $a^3 = 8$. They are both complex numbers: $2 \operatorname{cis}\frac{2\pi}{3}$ and $2 \operatorname{cis}\frac{4\pi}{3}$.

For You to Do

3. Find all four solutions to the equation $x^4 = -16$.

For You to Do

2. $(r \operatorname{cis}\theta)^n = r^n(\operatorname{cis}\theta)^n = r^n \operatorname{cis}(n\theta)$

3. $2 \operatorname{cis}\frac{\pi}{4}, 2 \operatorname{cis}\frac{3\pi}{4}, 2 \operatorname{cis}\frac{5\pi}{4}, 2 \operatorname{cis}\frac{7\pi}{4}$

For You to Do

PROBLEM 3 The key step in this problem is to write -16 as $16 \operatorname{cis}\pi$. There may be other ways to solve the problem, but in general, it is easier to keep the r positive when working in $r \operatorname{cis}\theta$ form.

Students may also question how you can go directly from $r^4 = 16$ to $r = 2$ and not consider $r = -2$. In fact, there are 4 solutions to $r^4 = 16$ alone: ± 2 and $\pm 2i$.

You may want to have your students work through all of the combinations of possible values of r with the possible values of θ. They will see that each time, the set of answers is duplicated, so they could choose any of the solutions for $x^4 = -16$ and get the correct answer.

Wrap Up

To reinforce the geometry of multiplication of complex numbers, review the For You to Do section where students found the solutions to $x^4 = -16$. For each solution of x, you can plot x^2, x^3, and x^4 to show the pattern.

Assessment Resources

Lesson Quiz 2.9

1. Given each z, find $|z^5|$ and $\arg(z^5)$.
   a. $\frac{1}{2} + \frac{\sqrt{3}}{2}i$
   b. $z = 3 \operatorname{cis} 135°$
2. Show that $z = \operatorname{cis}\left(\frac{4\pi}{7}\right)$ is a solution to $x^7 - 1 = 0$.
3. Find the three solutions to the equation $x^3 + 4x^2 - 15x - 60 = 0$. Then find their sum and product.

Exercises

HOMEWORK
- Core: 7, 8, 9, 11, 14, 15, 16
- Optional: 6, 10, 12, 13, 17

Check Your Understanding

EXERCISE 5 provides one key to why the roots of unity work the way they do.

On Your Own

EXERCISE 6 reminds students that for a polynomial of degree n,

- the sum of the roots of an equation is the coefficient of the x^{n-1} term
- if n is even, the product of the roots is equal to the constant term
- if n is odd, the product of the roots is equal to the opposite of the constant term

EXERCISE 7 is similar to an exercise in Investigation 2B. It is here for review, if necessary.

EXERCISE 8 Hopefully students will follow up on the previous exercise and expand $(x + yi)^5$ or $(\cos\theta + i\sin\theta)^5$, then write out the real part.

Maintain Your Skills

EXERCISE 17 You might want to point out that the terms in part (c) are the same as the terms from part (b), but in a different order.

Exercises *Practicing Habits of Mind*

Check Your Understanding

1. Let z be a complex number where $|z| = 3$ and $\arg(z) = \frac{\pi}{3}$. Find the magnitude and argument of each of the following expressions.

a. z^2 **b.** z^3 **c.** z^5
d. $10z$ **e.** z^0 **f.** z^{-1}

2. Suppose $z = 3 \text{ cis } \frac{\pi}{3}$ as in Exercise 1. If $a^2 = z$, what possible value(s) can a have?

3. Given each z, find $|z^3|$ and $\arg(z^3)$.

a. $z = 4$ **b.** $z = 4 \text{ cis } 120°$
c. $|z| = 2$ and $\arg(z) = \frac{\pi}{6}$ **d.** $z = -2i$

4. In the Example, you found three solutions to the equation $x^3 = 8i$. Find their sum and product.

5. Suppose a is a solution to the equation $x^{11} = 1$.

a. Show that a^2 is also a solution to this equation.

b. Show that if k is any integer, then a^k is also a solution to this equation.

On Your Own

6. Find the three solutions to the equation $x^3 + 2x^2 - 80x - 160 = 0$. Then find their sum and product.

One way to find the solutions is to look at the graph of $f(x) = x^3 + 2x^2 - 80x - 160$. What points on the graph correspond to solutions to the equation?

7. Expand $(\cos\theta + i\sin\theta)^2$. Use the result to generate rules for $\cos 2\theta$ and $\sin 2\theta$.

8. Find a formula for $\cos 5x$ in terms of $\cos x$ and $\sin x$.

9. Describe how to use De Moivre's Theorem to prove this fact about powers of -1.

For integer n, $(-1)^n = -1$ if n is odd and $(-1)^n = 1$ if n is even.

10. **Write About It** Describe how to use De Moivre's Theorem to figure out whether a power of i equals i, $-i$, 1, or -1.

What are $|i|$ and $\arg(i)$?

11. Given the equation $x^5 - 1 = 0$, one possible solution is $x = 1$.

a. Show that $x = \text{cis } \frac{2\pi}{5}$ is also a solution to the equation $x^5 - 1 = 0$.

b. Find all five solutions to $x^5 - 1 = 0$.

Answers

Exercises

1. a. $|z^2| = 9$, $\arg(z^2) = \frac{2\pi}{3}$
b. $|z^3| = 27$, $\arg(z^3) = \pi$
c. $|z^5| = 243$, $\arg(z^5) = \frac{5\pi}{3}$
d. $|10z| = 30$, $\arg(10z) = \frac{\pi}{3}$
e. $|z^0| = 1$, $\arg(z^0) = 0$
f. $|z^{-1}| = \frac{1}{3}$, $\arg(z^{-1}) = \frac{5\pi}{3}$

2. $\sqrt{3} \text{ cis } \frac{\pi}{6}$, $\sqrt{3} \text{ cis } \frac{7\pi}{6}$

3. a. $|z^3| = 64$, $\arg(z^3) = 0$
b. $|z^3| = 64$, $\arg(z^3) = 0°$
c. $|z^3| = 8$, $\arg(z^3) = \frac{\pi}{2}$
d. $|z^3| = 8$, $\arg(z^3) = \frac{\pi}{2}$

4. sum $= 0$, product $= 8i$

5. a. a^2 is a solution of $x^{11} = 1$ if and only if $(a^2)^{11} = 1$. Since $(a^2)^{11} = (a^{11})^2 = 1^2 = 1$, a^2 is a solution.
b. The proof is the same as in part (a), but with 2 replaced by k.

6. Solutions are -2 and $\pm 4\sqrt{5}$; their sum is -2, their product is 160.

7. $(\cos^2\theta - \sin^2\theta) + (2\sin\theta\cos\theta)i$,
$\cos 2\theta = \cos^2\theta - \sin^2\theta$,
$\sin 2\theta = 2\sin\theta\cos\theta$

8. See back of book.

9. Use $-1 = \text{cis } \pi$ and $1 = \text{cis } 0$. By De Moivre's Theorem, $(\text{cis } \pi)^n = \text{cis } \pi n$. If n is even, then $n = 2k$ for some integer k. Thus $\pi n = \pi(2k) = 2\pi k$, which is equivalent to 0 modulo 2π. So if n is even, $(\text{cis } \pi)^n = \text{cis } 0 = 1$. If n is odd, then $n = 2k + 1$ for some integer k. Thus $\pi n = \pi(2k + 1) = \pi + 2\pi k$. As above, $2\pi k$ is equivalent to 0 modulo 2π, so $\pi + 2\pi k$ is equivalent to π modulo 2π. So if n is odd, $(\text{cis } \pi)^n = \text{cis } \pi = -1$.

12. **a.** Sketch the graph of $f(x) = 4\cos^3 x - 3\cos x$ on $0 \le x < 2\pi$.

b. Suppose $g(x) = \cos 3x$. Show that $f = g$.

13. **a.** Suppose $\cos 3x = 0$. What are the three possible values of $\cos x$?

b. Find all angles on $0 \le x < 2\pi$ with $\cos 3x = 0$.

14. Find the exact value of $\cos \frac{\pi}{12}$.

15. **Standardized Test Prep** Which of the following is a solution to the equation $x^2 = i$?

A. $\text{cis}\left(\frac{\pi}{6}\right)$ **B.** $\text{cis}\left(\frac{\pi}{4}\right)$ **C.** $\text{cis}\left(\frac{\pi}{3}\right)$ **D.** $\text{cis}\left(\frac{\pi}{2}\right)$

Maintain Your Skills

Go Online PHSchool.com

For additional practice, go to Web Code: bga-0209

16. Solve each equation. Write the complete set of solutions in the form cis θ.

a. $x^2 - 1 = 0$ **b.** $x^3 - 1 = 0$ **c.** $x^4 - 1 = 0$

d. $x^5 - 1 = 0$ **e.** $x^6 - 1 = 0$ **f.** $x^7 - 1 = 0$

17. Approximate each sum to four decimal places.

a. $\sum_{k=0}^{6} \sin \frac{2\pi k}{7}$ **b.** $\sum_{k=0}^{6} \cos \frac{2\pi k}{7}$ **c.** $\sum_{k=0}^{6} \cos \frac{4\pi k}{7}$

d. $\sum_{k=0}^{8} \sin \frac{2\pi k}{9}$ **e.** $\sum_{k=0}^{8} \cos (40k)^\circ$ **f.** $\sum_{k=0}^{10} \cos \frac{2\pi k}{12}$

Historical Perspective

Mathematicians now recognize Abraham de Moivre (1667–1754) as a genius, but this was not always the case. Despite de Moivre's mathematical talent, he did not enjoy the fame he deserved during his lifetime.

When he was 18, de Moivre moved to England because of civil and religious unrest in France. Although he had studied mathematics extensively in France, he was unable to get a job in an English university due to his status as a foreigner.

For most of his life, de Moivre's main source of income was tutoring mathematics. In his later years, he earned money by solving math puzzles in local coffee shops. He is remembered for predicting the day of his own death. He noticed he was sleeping 15 minutes longer each night and calculated he would die on the day he slept 24 hours. He was correct!

Additional Resources

PRINT RESOURCES
- Solution Manual
- Practice Workbook
- Assessment Resources
- Teaching Resources

TECHNOLOGY
- Interactive Textbook
- TeacherExpress CD-ROM
- ExamView CD-ROM
- PHSchool.com

Additional Practice

1. Given each z, find $|z^4|$ and $\arg(z^4)$.
   a. $z = 2i$ **b.** $z = 3 \text{ cis } 30^\circ$
   c. $|z| = 4$ and $\arg(z) = \frac{\pi}{4}$ **d.** $z = 1 + \sqrt{3}i$
2. Find three solutions to the equation $2x^3 - 4x^2 - 51x + 102 = 0$. Then find their sum and product.
3. Given the equation $x^7 - 1 = 0$, one solution is $x = 1$.
   a. Show that $x = \text{cis} \frac{2\pi}{7}$ is also a solution to the equation $x^7 - 1 = 0$.
   b. Find all seven solutions to $x^7 - 1 = 0$.
4. Use what you found in Exercise 3 and plot all seven solutions to $x^7 - 1 = 0$ on the complex plane.
5. Suppose $z = \text{cis } 145^\circ$. Can z be a root of unity? If so, find the smallest n such that z is an nth root of unity. If not, explain why z can never be a root of unity.
6. **a.** Plot all 4 of the solutions to the equation $x^4 - 1 = 0$ on the complex plane.
   b. Show that these 4 solutions are also solutions to $x^8 - 1 = 0$.
   c. Are the four solutions to $x^4 - 1 = 0$ also solutions to $x^7 - 1 = 0$? Explain.
   d. Find a value for n, with $n \neq 4$, such that every fourth root of unity is also an nth root of unity.
7. Find the smallest positive integer n such that $w = -\frac{\sqrt{2}}{2} + \frac{\sqrt{2}}{2}i$ is an nth root of unity.

Practice: For Lesson 2.9, assign Exercises 1–3.

10. $i = \text{cis} \frac{\pi}{2}$, so by De Moivre's Theorem, $i^n = \left(\text{cis} \frac{\pi}{2}\right)^n = \text{cis} \frac{\pi}{2}n$. For $n = 1, 2, 3$, and 4, $\text{cis} \frac{\pi}{2}n$ has the values $i, -1, -i$, and 1, respectively. These will repeat again and again since angles of measure $\frac{\pi}{2}n + 2\pi$ are coterminal with the angle of measure $\frac{\pi}{2}n$.

11. a. $\left(\text{cis} \frac{2\pi}{5}\right)^5 = \text{cis}\left(5 \cdot \frac{2\pi}{5}\right) = \text{cis } 2\pi = \text{cis } 0 = 1$

b. $\text{cis } 0, \text{cis} \frac{2\pi}{5}, \text{cis} \frac{4\pi}{5}, \text{cis} \frac{6\pi}{5}$, and $\text{cis} \frac{8\pi}{5}$

12. a. See back of book.

b. $\cos 3x + i \sin 3x = \text{cis } 3x$ and $\text{cis } 3x = (\text{cis } x)^3 = (\cos x + i \sin x)^3 = \cos^3 x - 3 \cos x \sin^2 x + (3 \cos^2 x \sin x - \sin^3 x)i$. Therefore $\cos 3x = \cos^3 x - 3 \cos x \sin^2 x$. Replace $\sin^2 x$ with $1 - \cos^2 x$ in this last equation. When you expand and simplify, you get $\cos 3x = 4 \cos^3 x - 3 \cos x$.

13. a. $0, \frac{\sqrt{3}}{2}, -\frac{\sqrt{3}}{2}$

b. $\frac{\pi}{6}, \frac{\pi}{2}, \frac{5\pi}{6}, \frac{7\pi}{6}, \frac{3\pi}{2}, \frac{11\pi}{6}$

14. $\frac{\sqrt{2} + \sqrt{6}}{4}$

15. B

16. a. cis 0 and cis π

b. $\text{cis } 0, \text{cis} \frac{2\pi}{3}, \text{cis} \frac{4\pi}{3}$

c. $\text{cis } 0, \text{cis} \frac{\pi}{2}, \text{cis } \pi, \text{cis} \frac{3\pi}{2}$

d. $\text{cis } 0, \text{cis} \frac{2\pi}{5}, \text{cis} \frac{4\pi}{5}, \text{cis} \frac{6\pi}{5}, \text{cis} \frac{8\pi}{5}$

e. $\text{cis } 0, \text{cis} \frac{\pi}{3}, \text{cis} \frac{2\pi}{3}, \text{cis } \pi, \text{cis} \frac{4\pi}{3}, \text{cis} \frac{5\pi}{3}$

f. $\text{cis } 0, \text{cis} \frac{2\pi}{7}, \text{cis} \frac{4\pi}{7}, \text{cis} \frac{6\pi}{7}, \text{cis} \frac{8\pi}{7}, \text{cis} \frac{10\pi}{7}, \text{cis} \frac{12\pi}{7}$

17. a. 0 **b.** 0

c. 0 **d.** 0

e. 0 **f.** −0.8660

Lesson Overview

GOAL

- Understand the geometry of roots of unity, and the connection to roots of equations of the form $x^n - 1 = 0$.

Students start this lesson by playing the Polynomial Factor Game, an extension of the earlier Factor Game. The point of the game is to see that $x^m - 1$ is a factor of $x^n - 1$ if and only if m is a factor of n.

Students then go on to look at the geometry of those roots, in that the roots form vertices of regular polygons. They can use the geometry to show the fact above, since, for example, all vertices of an equilateral triangle where one vertex is at (1, 0) are vertices of a regular hexagon where one vertex is at (1, 0).

CHECK YOUR UNDERSTANDING
- Core: 1, 2, 3, 4, 5
- Optional: 6, 7
- Extension: 8

MATERIALS
- CAS (recommended)
- graph paper
- graphing calculators
- Blackline Masters MC1, MC10, 2.10

HOMEWORK
- Core: 9, 10, 11, 12, 14, 15, 19
- Optional: 13, 18, 20
- Extension: 16, 17

VOCABULARY
- roots of unity

Launch

Jump right into explaining the rules of the Polynomial Factor Game, and have students start playing.

Explore

In-Class Experiment

Blackline Master 2.10 reproduces the game board and rules. Use it on an overhead and let the students play the game as you shade in the polynomials used.

2.10 Roots of Unity

In Lesson 2.8, you played the Factor Game. Now, it is time to play the Polynomial Factor Game!

In-Class Experiment

The Polynomial Factor Game. This game is also for two players. The rules are similar to those of the Factor Game. Decide who goes first.

- Player 1 picks any available polynomial on the board.
- Player 2 identifies all polynomials on the board that are factors of that polynomial.
- If there are no factors of that polynomial remaining on the board, Player 1 loses a turn and no points are scored.
- All polynomials used in a turn are removed from the board.

For each successive round, players alternate between picking the polynomial and finding the factors.

Scoring.

- Player 1 scores points equal to the degree of the polynomial picked.
- For each factor identified, Player 2 scores points equal to the degree of that factor.
- **Bonus Points.** If Player 1 finds a factor that Player 2 missed, Player 1 scores points equal to the degree of that factor.

For example, $x - 1$ is a factor of $x^2 - 1$. So if the first pick was $x^2 - 1$, that player earns 2 points while the other player earns 1.

The board is polynomials of the form $x^n - 1$ for all integer values from 1 to a set maximum. 20 is a good maximum for this game.

For a longer game, you could use 30 as you did in the Factor Game.

$x - 1$	$x^2 - 1$	$x^3 - 1$	$x^4 - 1$	$x^5 - 1$
$x^6 - 1$	$x^7 - 1$	$x^8 - 1$	$x^9 - 1$	$x^{10} - 1$
$x^{11} - 1$	$x^{12} - 1$	$x^{13} - 1$	$x^{14} - 1$	$x^{15} - 1$
$x^{16} - 1$	$x^{17} - 1$	$x^{18} - 1$	$x^{19} - 1$	$x^{20} - 1$

Play the game a few times.

1. Describe some of the strategies a player could use in this game.
2. Compare strategies in this game with those from the Factor Game you played in Lesson 2.8.

Answers

In-Class Experiment

1. No answer required.
2. No answer required.

In an earlier algebra course, you learned an important theorem regarding factors of polynomials.

***Theorem 2.5** The Factor Theorem*

Suppose $f(x)$ is a polynomial. Then $x - a$ is a factor of $f(x)$ if and only if the number a is a root of the equation $f(x) = 0$.

One strategy for finding factors in the Polynomial Factor Game is to find polynomials that have the same roots as the polynomial that the other player picked. That is, $x^n - 1$ is a factor of $x^m - 1$ if and only if every root of $x^n - 1 = 0$ is also a root of $x^m - 1 = 0$.

But what are the roots of those polynomials? You can use De Moivre's Theorem to find them. You can use geometry to get a visual idea of where those roots lie on the complex plane.

For You to Do

3. Find and plot the three roots of the equation $x^3 - 1 = 0$.
4. Find and plot the six roots of the equation $x^6 - 1 = 0$.

For Discussion

5. Explain how the results from Problems 3 and 4 show that $x^3 - 1$ is a factor of $x^6 - 1$.

For You to Do

PROBLEMS 3 AND 4 There are two ways to solve these problems: using basic factoring techniques, or using De Moivre's Theorem. At this point, students should feel comfortable using De Moivre's Theorem to find the solutions, but you may also want to review how to solve by factoring:

$$x^6 - 1 = (x^3 + 1)(x^3 - 1)$$
$$= (x + 1)(x^2 - x + 1)(x - 1)(x^2 + x + 1)$$

You need to remember the basic rules for factoring $x^n + 1$ and $x^n - 1$ to factor out the $x + 1$ and $x - 1$. You can then use the quadratic formula to find the other four roots.

For Discussion

PROBLEM 5 The roots of $x^3 - 1$ form an equilateral triangle. The roots of $x^6 - 1$ form a regular hexagon. The vertices of the triangle are also every second vertex of the hexagon.

The figure shows that the three roots of $x^3 - 1 = 0$ are also roots of $x^6 - 1 = 0$. Thus, $x^3 - 1$ must be a factor of $x^6 - 1$.

For You to Do

3.

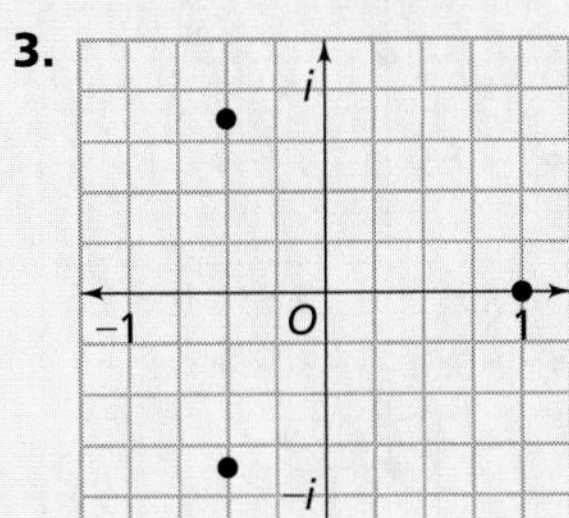

4.

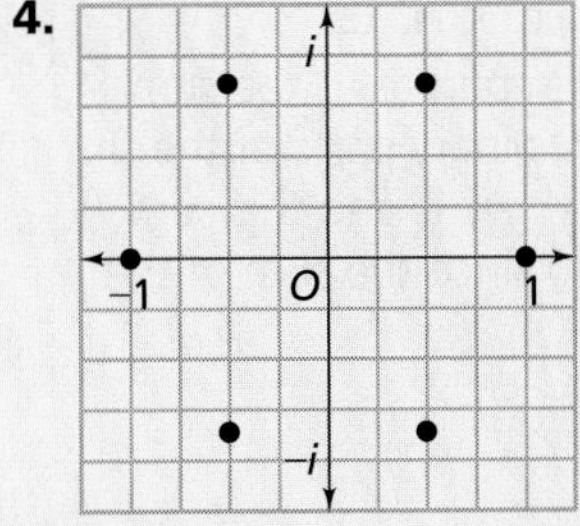

For Discussion

5. All three roots of $x^3 - 1 = 0$ are also roots of $x^6 - 1 = 0$.

Wrap Up

Review the meaning of roots of unity as students work on the Check Your Understanding exercises. Ask them to think of how many real *roots* there are to the equation $x^2 - 1 = 0$ or any equation $x^{2n} - 1 = 0$, where n is a positive integer. Then have them answer the same question for $x^{2n-1} - 1 = 0$ where n is a positive integer. The geometry and symmetry of the roots illustrate the fact that even powers have two real roots and odd powers have one real root.

Assessment Resources

Lesson Quiz 2.10

1. Plot all nine solutions to the equation $x^9 - 1 = 0$ on the complex plane.
2. a. Plot the four solutions to the equation $x^4 - 1 = 0$ on the complex plane.
   b. Are these four solutions also solutions to the equation $x^9 - 1 = 0$?
3. Suppose $z = \text{cis } 282°$. Can z be a root of unity? If so, find the smallest n so that z is an nth root of unity. If not, explain why z can never be a root of unity.

Developing Habits of Mind

Find another way. As you saw in Lesson 2.9, you can use De Moivre's Theorem to find the roots of an equation. There is a more direct way to find all of the roots to equations of the form $x^n - 1 = 0$.

For instance, in Exercise 5 from Lesson 2.9, you supposed a was a solution of $x^{11} - 1 = 0$, and showed that a^2 was also a solution.

This fact can help you find all of the solutions to $x^{11} - 1 = 0$.

- One solution is $x = 1$, since $1^{11} = 1$.
- $x^{11} - 1 = 0 \Rightarrow x^{11} = 1$. You can find a second solution by letting $x = r \text{ cis } \theta$. Since $1 = \text{cis } 2\pi$ you have

$$(r \text{ cis } \theta)^{11} = 1 \text{ cis } 2\pi$$
$$r^{11} \text{ cis } 11\theta = 1 \text{ cis } 2\pi$$
$$r^{11} = 1 \quad \text{and} \quad 11\theta = 2\pi$$
$$r = 1 \quad \text{and} \quad \theta = \frac{2\pi}{11}$$

  So cis $\frac{2\pi}{11}$ is also a solution.
- You know that if a is a solution, then a^2 is also a solution. Therefore $(\text{cis } \frac{2\pi}{11})^2$ is a solution. By De Moivre's Theorem,

$$\left(\text{cis } \frac{2\pi}{11}\right)^2 = \text{cis}\left(2 \cdot \frac{2\pi}{11}\right) = \text{cis } \frac{4\pi}{11}$$

- In fact, any power of a is a solution because

$$(a^k)^{11} = (a^{11})^k = 1^k = 1$$

  So, if $a = \text{cis } \frac{2\pi}{11}$, then all of the following are solutions to $x^{11} - 1 = 0$.

$$1, a, a^2, a^3, a^4, a^5, a^6, a^7, a^8, a^9, a^{10}, a^{11}, a^{12}, a^{13}, \ldots$$

  It looks like there are too many solutions. There should only be eleven. But if you plot all these on the complex plane, they repeat. For example, $a^{11} = 1$, $a^{12} = a$, $a^{13} = a^2$, and so on. There are, in fact, only eleven solutions. They are $1, a, a^2, a^3, a^4, a^5, a^6, a^7, a^8, a^9$, and a^{10}.

  By De Moivre's Theorem, $a^k = \text{cis } \frac{2k\pi}{11}$, since $a = \text{cis } \frac{2\pi}{11}$. Thus, the complete solution set is

$$\left\{1, \text{cis } \frac{2\pi}{11}, \text{cis } \frac{4\pi}{11}, \text{cis } \frac{6\pi}{11}, \text{cis } \frac{8\pi}{11}, \text{cis } \frac{10\pi}{11}, \text{cis } \frac{12\pi}{11}, \text{cis } \frac{14\pi}{11}, \text{cis } \frac{16\pi}{11}, \text{cis } \frac{18\pi}{11}, \text{cis } \frac{20\pi}{11}\right\}$$

Habits of Mind

Draw a diagram. As you work through these roots, plot each one on the complex plane.

Remember...

$A \Rightarrow B$ means "A implies B": if A is true then B is true.

The solutions to $x^n = 1$ are called roots of unity, so named since solving the equation involves taking a root of 1.

- A square root of unity is a root of the equation $x^2 - 1 = 0$.
- A cube root of unity is a root of the equation $x^3 - 1 = 0$.
- In general, an nth root of unity is a root of the equation $x^n - 1 = 0$.

So, 1 is considered "unity." And in $\mathbb{C}$, there are 2 second roots of unity, 3 third roots of unity, 4 fourth roots of unity, and in general, n nth roots of unity.

Answers

Exercises

1. a. The solution in Quadrant I should be labeled ω, ω^6, the solution in Quadrant II should be labeled ω^2, the solution in Quadrant III should be labeled ω^3, ω^{13}, the solution in Quadrant IV should be labeled ω^4, and the solution on the positive part of the real axis should be labeled ω^5.

b. 1

2. a. 0 **b.** 0

c. The sum in part (b) is the sum of the imaginary parts of the six roots of $x^6 = 1$, and this sum must be 0 since the sum of the roots is 0.

3.

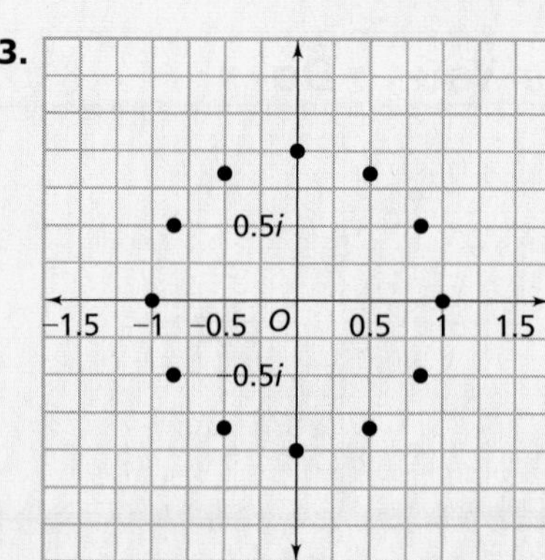

Exercises Practicing Habits of Mind

Check Your Understanding

1. Let ω be the fifth root of unity marked in this diagram.

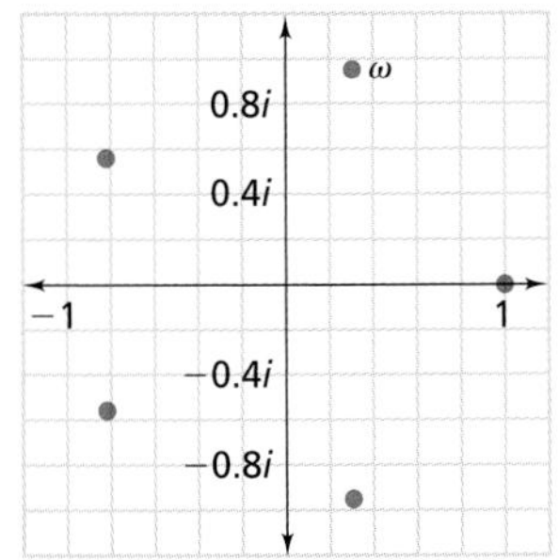

a. Copy the diagram. Label $\omega^2, \omega^3, \omega^4, \omega^5, \omega^6$, and ω^{13}.

b. The product of all five fifth roots of unity is $1 \cdot \omega \cdot \omega^2 \cdot \omega^3 \cdot \omega^4$. Simplify this product as much as possible.

2. a. Calculate the sum of the sixth roots of unity.

b. Evaluate the sum.

$$\sum_{k=0}^{5} \sin \frac{2\pi k}{6}$$

c. How are the results from parts (a) and (b) related?

3. Plot all 12 solutions to the equation $x^{12} - 1 = 0$ on the complex plane.

4. a. Plot all 6 solutions to the equation $x^6 - 1 = 0$ on the complex plane.

b. Show that these 6 solutions are also solutions to the equation $x^{12} - 1 = 0$

c. Show that $x^6 - 1$ is a factor of $x^{12} - 1$.

Your work in Exercise 3 may be helpful here.

5. The fifth roots of unity appear in the diagram for Exercise 1. Find a value of n, with $n \neq 5$, such that every fifth root of unity is also an nth root of unity.

6. Find the smallest positive integer n such that $w = \frac{1}{2} - \frac{\sqrt{3}}{2}i$ is an nth root of unity.

7. Suppose $z = \text{cis } 310°$. Can z be a root of unity? If so, find the smallest n such that z is an nth root of unity. If not, explain why z can never be a root of unity.

Exercises

HOMEWORK

- Core: 9, 10, 11, 12, 14, 15, 19
- Optional: 13, 18, 20
- Extension: 16, 17

You may want to give students copies of Blackline Master MC1 or MC10 to use while they work on the exercises.

Check Your Understanding

EXERCISE 7 Some students may notice that $gcd(310, 360) = 10$, and $\frac{360}{10} = 36$. The solution notes that any integer degree value can be a root of unity. In fact, any *rational* degree value can be a root of unity. The proof explores areas of number theory, and may be too advanced for most classes, but you might find the discussion worthwhile.

5. Every multiple of 5 greater than 5 will work.

6. 6

7. Yes; $n = 36$

4. a.

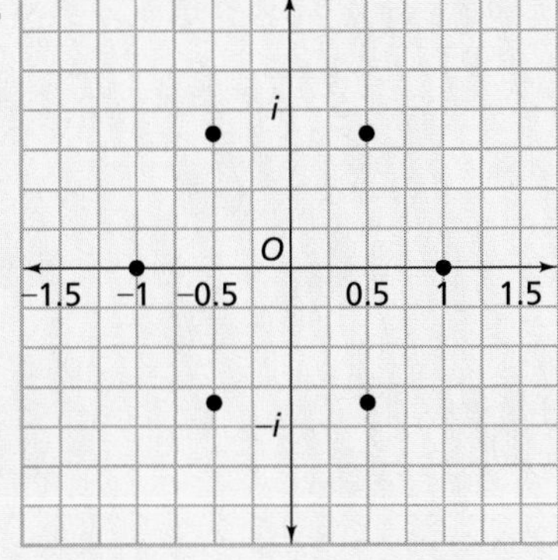

b. The plot in part (a) is part of the plot from Exercise 3, so this illustrates graphically that the solutions of $x^6 - 1 = 0$ are solutions of $x^{12} - 1 = 0$. Algebraically, the solutions of $x^6 - 1 = 0$ are the numbers $\text{cis } \frac{2\pi}{6}k$ where k goes from 0 to 5. The solutions of $x^{12} - 1 = 0$ are the numbers $\text{cis } \frac{2\pi}{6}n$ where n goes from 0 to 11.

c. This result follows immediately from part (b).

On Your Own

EXERCISE 10 It is not necessary for students to prove the fact from part (c) at this point. The proof is not that complicated, should you want to review it.

If n is odd, then

$$\prod_{k=0}^{n-1} \text{cis } \frac{2\pi k}{n} = \text{cis } 0 \cdot \text{cis } \frac{2\pi}{n} \cdot \text{cis } \frac{4\pi}{n} \cdots$$
$$\cdot \text{ cis } \frac{2\pi \cdot \left(\frac{n-1}{2}\right)}{n} \cdot \text{cis } \frac{2\pi \cdot \left(\frac{n}{2}+1\right)}{n} \cdots$$
$$\cdot \text{ cis } \frac{2\pi \cdot (n-2)}{n} \cdot \text{cis } \frac{2\pi \cdot (n-1)}{n}$$
$$= \text{cis } 0 \cdot \left(\text{cis } \frac{2\pi}{n} \cdot \text{cis } \frac{2\pi \cdot (n-1)}{n}\right)$$
$$\cdot \left(\text{cis } \frac{4\pi}{n} \cdot \text{cis } \frac{2\pi \cdot (n-2)}{n}\right) \cdots$$
$$\cdot \left(\text{cis } \frac{2\pi \cdot \left(\frac{n-1}{2}\right)}{n} \cdot \text{cis } \frac{2\pi \cdot \left(\frac{n+1}{2}\right)}{n}\right)$$
$$= \text{cis } 0 \cdot \left(\text{cis}\left(\frac{2\pi}{n} + \frac{2\pi \cdot (n-1)}{n}\right)\right)$$
$$\cdot \left(\text{cis}\left(\frac{4\pi}{n} + \frac{2\pi \cdot (n-2)}{n}\right)\right) \cdots$$
$$\cdot \left(\text{cis}\left(\frac{2\pi \cdot \left(\frac{n-1}{2}\right)}{n} + \frac{2\pi \cdot \left(\frac{n+1}{2}\right)}{n}\right)\right)$$
$$= \text{cis } 0 \cdot \text{cis } 2\pi \cdot \text{cis } 2\pi \cdots \text{cis } 2\pi$$
$$= 1 \cdot 1 \cdot 1 \cdots 1$$
$$= 1$$

8. **Take It Further** Suppose z is a fifth root of unity and w is a third root of unity, as pictured.

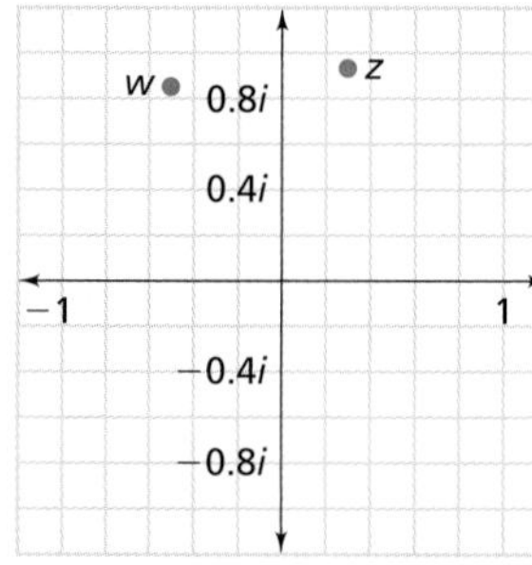

a. Find a root of unity x that lies between z and w on the unit circle.

b. Find a root of unity y that lies between z and x.

c. Given any two distinct roots of unity (of any order), can you always find another root of unity between them?

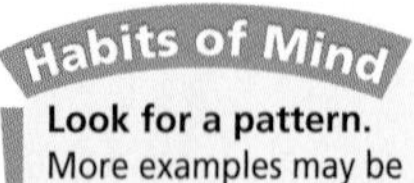

The answer might be a sixth root of unity, or seventh, or eighth. . . .

On Your Own

9. On the same axes, plot all the fifth roots of unity. Also, plot all the eighth roots of unity. Show how plotting these roots explains why $x^5 - 1$ is not a factor of $x^8 - 1$.

10. a. Find the product of all the sixth roots of unity.

b. Find the product of all the seventh roots of unity.

c. What are all possible values of the product of all the nth roots of unity? For what n do each of these results occur?

Habits of Mind

Look for a pattern. More examples may be helpful.

11. Describe how you can use the roots of $x^6 - 1 = 0$ to find the solutions to these equations.

a. $x^6 - 64 = 0$ b. $x^6 + 64 = 0$

Answers

8. a. Answers may vary. Sample: i

b. Answers may vary. Sample: cis $\frac{4\pi}{9}$

c. yes

9.

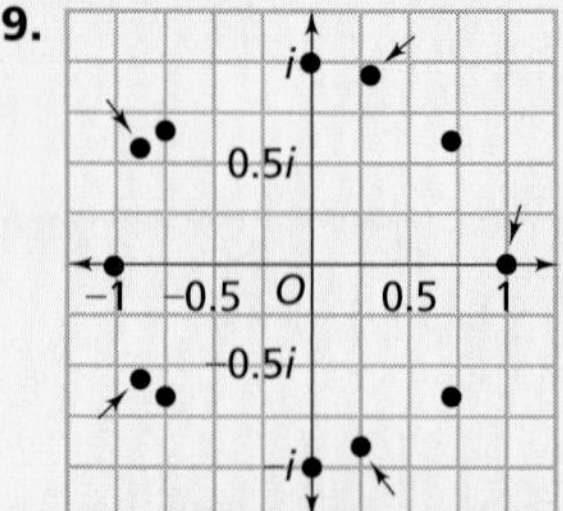

The arrows show the 5th roots of unity. The number 1 is the only number that is both a 5th root and an 8th root of unity.

10. a. −1 **b.** 1

c. −1 (when n is even) and 1 (when n is odd)

11. a. To find the roots of $x^6 - 64 = 0$ (that is, the roots of $x^6 - 2^6 = 0$), multiply the roots of $x^6 - 1 = 0$ by 2.

b. Multiply the roots of $x^6 - 1 = 0$ by $2i$.

12. a. Calculate the sum of the eighth roots of unity.

b. Find the value of

$$\sum_{k=0}^{7} \cos\frac{2\pi k}{8}$$

c. How are the results from parts (a) and (b) related?

13. Complex number z is a ninth root of unity. Find all possible values for the magnitude and argument of z.

14. **Write About It** Roots of unity must lie on the unit circle. That is, they must be complex numbers with magnitude 1. Is every complex number with magnitude 1 a root of unity? Explain.

15. Suppose z is an nth root of unity.

a. Show that $\frac{1}{z} = \overline{z}$.

b. Show that $\overline{z}$ is also an nth root of unity.

16. **Take It Further** Consider the sixth roots of unity as labeled in this diagram.

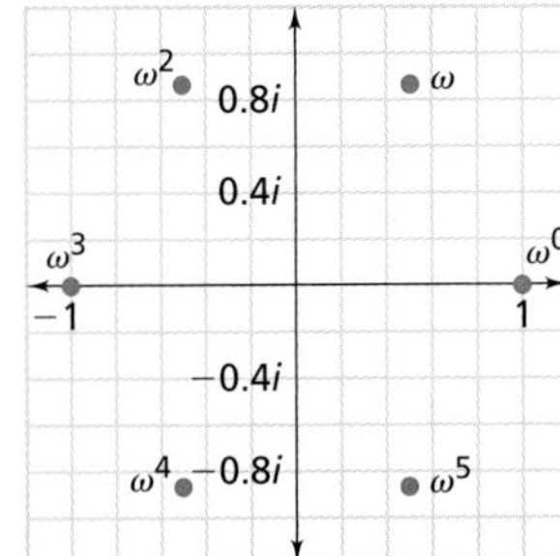

The product of all these roots is -1, but the product of the first three roots is 1.

$$\omega \cdot \omega^2 \cdot \omega^3 = \omega^6 = 1$$

a. Find another situation where the product of the first k nth roots of unity is 1, with k less than $n - 1$.

b. For what values of n will this situation occur? In other words, for what n is there a k such that the product of the first k nth roots of unity is 1 (with $k < n - 1$)?

If n is even, then

$$\begin{aligned}
\prod_{k=0}^{n-1} \text{cis}\,\frac{2\pi k}{n} &= \text{cis}\,0 \cdot \text{cis}\,\frac{2\pi}{n} \cdot \text{cis}\,\frac{4\pi}{n} \cdots \\
&\quad \cdot \text{cis}\,\frac{2\pi \cdot \left(\frac{n}{2} - 1\right)}{n} \cdot \text{cis}\,\frac{2\pi \cdot \frac{n}{2}}{n} \cdot \\
&\quad \cdot \text{cis}\,\frac{2\pi \cdot \left(\frac{n}{2} + 1\right)}{n} \cdots \\
&\quad \cdot \text{cis}\,\frac{2\pi \cdot (n-2)}{n} \cdot \text{cis}\,\frac{2\pi \cdot (n-1)}{n} \\
&= \text{cis}\,0 \cdot \left(\text{cis}\,\frac{2\pi}{n} \cdot \text{cis}\,\frac{2\pi \cdot (n-1)}{n}\right) \\
&\quad \cdot \left(\text{cis}\,\frac{4\pi}{n} \cdot \text{cis}\,\frac{2\pi \cdot (n-2)}{n}\right) \cdots \\
&\quad \cdot \left(\text{cis}\,\frac{2\pi \cdot \left(\frac{n}{2} - 1\right)}{n} \right.\\
&\quad \left.\cdot \text{cis}\,\frac{2\pi \cdot \left(\frac{n}{2} + 1\right)}{n}\right) \cdot \text{cis}\,\frac{2\pi \cdot \frac{n}{2}}{n} \\
&= \text{cis}\,0 \cdot \left(\text{cis}\left(\frac{2\pi}{n} + \frac{2\pi \cdot (n-1)}{n}\right)\right) \\
&\quad \cdot \left(\text{cis}\left(\frac{4\pi}{n} + \frac{2\pi \cdot (n-2)}{n}\right)\right) \cdots \\
&\quad \cdot \left(\text{cis}\left(\frac{2\pi \cdot \left(\frac{n}{2} - 1\right)}{n} + \right.\right. \\
&\quad \left.\left.\frac{2\pi \cdot \left(\frac{n}{2} + 1\right)}{n}\right)\right) \cdots \\
&\quad \cdot \text{cis}\,\frac{2\pi \cdot \frac{n}{2}}{n} \\
&= \text{cis}\,0 \cdot \text{cis}\,2\pi \cdot \text{cis}\,2\pi \cdots \text{cis}\,2\pi \cdot \text{cis}\,\pi \\
&= 1 \cdot 1 \cdot 1 \cdots 1 \cdot -1 \\
&= -1
\end{aligned}$$

16. a. The first four 10th roots of unity will work. If $\omega = \text{cis}\left(\frac{2\pi}{10} \cdot 1\right)$, then $\omega \cdot \omega^2 \cdot \omega^3 \cdot \omega^4 = 1$.

b. Suppose $k > 2$. Let n denote the number $\frac{k(k+1)}{2}$. The product of the first k nth roots of unity is 1.

12. a. 0 **b.** 0

c. The terms added in part (b) are the same as those that are added to get the real part of the sum in part (a).

13. The magnitude is 1, and the arguments are the values $\frac{2\pi k}{9}$ for $k = 0, 1, \ldots, 8$.

14. If n is rational, then cis $2\pi n$ is a root of unity. If n is real but not rational, then cis $2\pi n$ is not a root of unity.

15. a. Suppose $z = x + yi$ and that z is a root of unity. Then $\frac{1}{z} = \frac{1}{x + yi} = \frac{x - yi}{x^2 + y^2}$. But $x^2 + y^2 = 1$ since z is a root of unity. So $\frac{1}{z} = x - yi = \overline{z}$.

b. By part (a), if z is an nth root of unity, then $\frac{1}{z} = \overline{z}$. Therefore $\overline{z}^n = \left(\frac{1}{z}\right)^n = \frac{1}{z^n} = \frac{1}{1} = 1$. Thus $\overline{z}$ is a root of unity.

EXERCISE 18 This function (of the power) is called Euler's phi function, and measures the number of values in $\{1, 2, 3, \dots, n-1\}$ that are relatively prime to n; that is, they share no common factor with n. The phi function is very prominent in number theory.

Maintain Your Skills

EXERCISE 20 Each sum is nearly a complete set of the roots of unity, so students will answer these questions more easily by figuring out what roots are missing. In particular, part (d) appears in the next lesson in relation to the vertices of a regular pentagon.

Additional Resources

PRINT RESOURCES

- Solution Manual
- Practice Workbook
- Assessment Resources
- Teaching Resources

TECHNOLOGY

- Interactive Textbook
- TeacherExpress CD-ROM
- ExamView CD-ROM
- PHSchool.com

Additional Practice

1. Given each z, find $|z^4|$ and $\arg(z^4)$.
   a. $z = 2i$
   b. $z = 3 \text{ cis } 30°$
   c. $|z| = 4$ and $\arg(z) = \frac{\pi}{4}$
   d. $z = 1 + \sqrt{3}i$

2. Find three solutions to the equation $2x^3 - 4x^2 - 51x + 102 = 0$. Then find their sum and product.

3. Given the equation $x^7 - 1 = 0$, one solution is $x = 1$.
   a. Show that $x = \text{cis } \frac{2\pi}{7}$ is also a solution to the equation $x^7 - 1 = 0$.
   b. Find all seven solutions to $x^7 - 1 = 0$.

4. Use what you found in Exercise 3 and plot all seven solutions to $x^7 - 1 = 0$ on the complex plane.

5. Suppose $z = \text{cis } 145°$. Can z be a root of unity? If so, find the smallest n such that z is an nth root of unity. If not, explain why z can never be a root of unity.

6. a. Plot all 4 of the solutions to the equation $x^4 - 1 = 0$ on the complex plane.
   b. Show that these 4 solutions are also solutions to $x^8 - 1 = 0$.
   c. Are the four solutions to $x^4 - 1 = 0$ also solutions to $x^7 - 1 = 0$? Explain.
   d. Find a value for n, with $n \neq 4$, such that every fourth root of unity is also an nth root of unity.

7. Find the smallest positive integer n such that $w = -\frac{\sqrt{2}}{2} + \frac{\sqrt{2}}{2}i$ is an nth root of unity.

Practice: For Lesson 2.10, assign Exercises 4–7.

17. **Take It Further** Suppose that a is an nth root of unity, and n is odd.

a. Prove that one of the roots of $x^2 - a = 0$ is an nth root of unity.

b. Why is this false when n is even?

18. Some roots of unity are repeats. For example, the cube roots of unity (solutions to $x^3 - 1 = 0$) are also sixth roots of unity (solutions to $x^6 - 1 = 0$). And $x = 1$ is always an nth root of unity, for any n. But some roots of unity are "new" for that power. For example, i and $-i$ are solutions to $x^4 - 1 = 0$, but not $x^3 - 1 = 0$, $x^2 - 1 = 0$, or $x^1 - 1 = 0$.

a. Copy and complete this table with the number of new roots of unity for each equation. It may help to think of the solutions in terms of their argument.

Equation	# New Roots
$x - 1 = 0$	1
$x^2 - 1 = 0$	1
$x^3 - 1 = 0$	2
$x^4 - 1 = 0$	2
$x^5 - 1 = 0$	■
$x^6 - 1 = 0$	■
$x^7 - 1 = 0$	■
$x^8 - 1 = 0$	■
$x^9 - 1 = 0$	■
$x^{10} - 1 = 0$	■

b. Describe any relationships you notice in the table. State a rule for the number of new roots of unity in terms of n.

19. **Standardized Test Prep** Which of the following is a factor of $x^5 - 1$?

A. $x^4 + x^3 + x^2 + x + 1$ **B.** $x - 5$

C. $x + 1$ **D.** $x^4 - 1$

For additional practice, go to **Web Code:** bga-0210

Maintain Your Skills

20. Evaluate each sum based on what you know about roots of unity.

a. $\sum_{k=0}^{2} \sin \frac{2\pi k}{4}$ **b.** $\sum_{k=0}^{4} \cos \frac{2\pi k}{6}$ **c.** $\sum_{k=0}^{4} \sin \frac{2\pi k}{6}$ **d.** $\sum_{k=1}^{4} \cos \frac{2\pi k}{5}$

Answers

17. a. See back of book.

b. In the proof for part (a), if n is even and k is odd, then neither $\text{cis } \frac{\pi k}{n}$ nor $\text{cis } \frac{\pi(n+k)}{n}$ $\left(= \cos \frac{\pi(n+k)}{n} + i \sin \frac{\pi(n+k)}{n}\right)$ is an nth root of unity, since the numerator of each fraction is an odd-numbered rather than an even-numbered multiple of π.

18. a. See back of book.

b. Answers may vary. Sample: If n is prime, then the number of new roots is $n - 1$. If $n \geq 2$, then the number of new roots is the number of elements of $\{1, 2, \dots, n-1\}$ that have no common factor with n other than 1.

19. A

20. a. 1 **b.** $-\frac{1}{2}$ **c.** $\frac{\sqrt{3}}{2}$ **d.** -1

2.11 Geometry of Roots of Unity

Your work in previous lessons revealed interesting geometric patterns generated by powers of complex numbers. For instance, suppose $z = \text{cis}\,\frac{2\pi}{3}$. If you plot z^0, z^1, and z^2, you get the following picture.

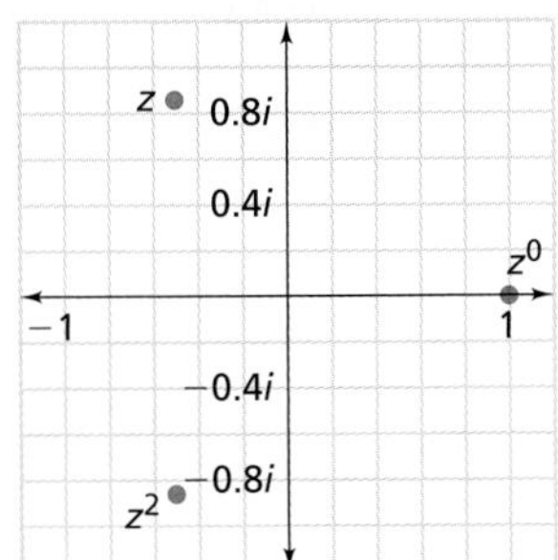

You may recognize these numbers. They are the third roots of unity.

For You to Do

1. Prove that the three roots of $x^3 - 1 = 0$ form the vertices of an equilateral triangle.

The roots of $x^3 - 1 = 0$ and the equilateral triangle they form exemplify the remarkable connection between the algebra of $\mathbb{C}$ and the geometry of regular polygons. The following theorem generalizes this fact. It also summarizes much of the work so far in this investigation.

Theorem 2.6

If n is a positive integer, the roots of the equation

$$x^n - 1 = 0$$

are

$$1, z, z^2, z^3, \ldots, z^{n-1}$$

where

$$z = \text{cis}\,\frac{2\pi}{n}$$

If $n \geq 3$, these roots lie on the vertices of a regular n-gon inscribed in the unit circle in the complex plane.

One vertex of this polygon is at 1.

For You to Do

1. The points A_0, A_1, and A_2 corresponding to $\text{cis}\,\frac{2\pi k}{3}$ for $k = 0, 1$, and 2 divide the unit circle into three congruent arcs, each of length $\frac{2\pi}{3}$. Therefore, the chords $\overline{A_0A_1}$, $\overline{A_1A_2}$, and $\overline{A_2A_0}$ are congruent, and this implies that $\triangle A_0A_1A_2$ is equilateral.

Lesson Overview

GOAL

- Find exact algebraic expressions for certain trigonometric values.

Although hinted at throughout the investigation, this lesson solidifies the fact that for any positive integer $n > 0$, the graph of the nth roots of unity form the vertices of a regular n-gon. Students start to examine the geometry, and they see that they can use these facts to write exact values for $\cos\frac{2\pi}{5}$ and $\sin\frac{2\pi}{5}$.

CHECK YOUR UNDERSTANDING

- Core: 3, 4, 5, 6, 7a
- Optional: 1, 2
- Extension: 7b-c, 8

MATERIALS

- CAS (recommended)
- graph paper
- graphing calculators
- Blackline Masters MC1, MC10

HOMEWORK

- Core: 10, 11, 12, 13, 16
- Optional: 9, 14, 17, 18, 19
- Extension: 15

Launch

Review Exercises 8, 9, and 16 from Lesson 2.10.

Explore

You may wish to use Blackline Master MC10 on an overhead during the lesson.

Wrap Up

Review the Check Your Understanding exercises and show that you can express the cosine and sine of $\frac{2\pi}{5}$ exactly.

Assessment Resources

Lesson Quiz 2.11

1. Suppose $w = \text{cis } 15°$. The powers of w form the vertices of a regular polygon in the complex plane. What is the smallest number of sides this polygon can have?

2. a. The plot of powers from 0 to 20 of $z = \text{cis } 16°$ do not form a regular polygon. Explain why.
   b. Will the powers of z ever come back to 1? If so, how many times around the unit circle will it take? If not, why not?

3. Let $z = \text{cis } \frac{2\pi}{3}$, where z is a third root of unity.
   a. Show that $(1 + z)^2 = z$.
   b. Show that $(1 + z - z^2)^3 = (1 - z + z^2)^3$.

For You to Do

2. Prove Theorem 2.6.

You can use the theorem in two ways. If you know a simple form for the vertices of a regular n-gon in the complex plane, you can solve the equation $x^n - 1 = 0$. Conversely, if you can solve the equation, you have a simple form for the vertices of the polygon in the complex plane.

In the case $n = 5$, Theorem 2.6 says that the roots of $x^5 - 1 = 0$ are

$$1, z, z^2, z^3, z^4$$

where

$$z = \text{cis } \frac{2\pi}{5}$$

These roots lie on the vertices of a regular pentagon inscribed in the unit circle on the complex plane.

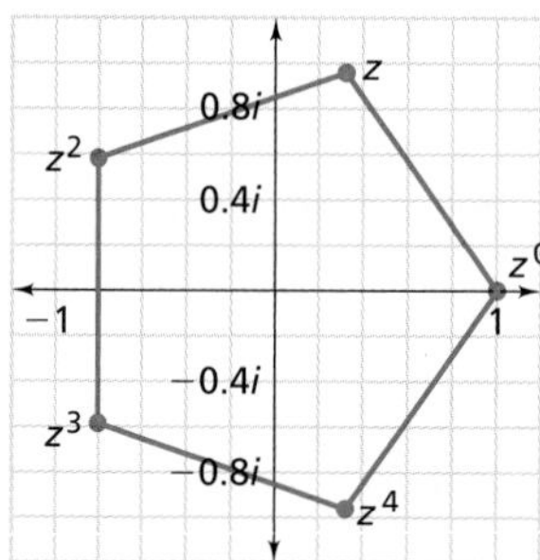

Carl Friedrich Gauss (1777–1855) was one of the greatest mathematicians of all time. He was so proud of his regular 17-sided polygon construction that he wanted it to appear on his tombstone!

Suppose you wanted exact expressions for these five roots that do not involve trigonometric functions. That is, can you express $\cos \frac{2\pi}{5}$ and $\sin \frac{2\pi}{5}$ in an algebraic form?

Earlier, you broke down angles into sums of special angles in order to use the Angle-Sum Formulas. This helped you find algebraic values of cosine and sine. For instance:

$$\cos \frac{5\pi}{12} = \cos\left(\frac{\pi}{6} + \frac{\pi}{4}\right)$$

Answers

For You to Do

2. The points $A_0, A_1, \ldots, A_{n-1}$ that correspond to $\text{cis}\left(\frac{2\pi}{n} \cdot k\right)$ for $k = 0, 1, \ldots, n - 1$ divide the unit circle into n congruent arcs of length $\frac{2\pi}{n}$. Therefore, the chords $\overline{A_0A_1}, \overline{A_1A_2}, \ldots, \overline{A_{n-1}A_0}$ are congruent. Since the angles of the polygon $A_0A_1A_2 \ldots A_{n-1}$ intercept congruent arcs, they are congruent. Therefore, the polygon is a regular polygon.

Unfortunately, there are no convenient angles that sum to $\frac{2\pi}{5}$. But Gauss invented a method using the algebra of this problem—he focused on the roots of the equation $x^5 - 1 = 0$. Gauss started by finding as many relationships as possible among the roots. Such relationships can often be inspired by looking at the roots as vertices of a regular pentagon.

Gauss applied the method to higher degrees. He handled the degree 17 case when he was 19 years old!

In the exercises, you will work through his method for finding the roots of $x^5 - 1 = 0$ written in the form $a + bi$, where a and b are exact, algebraic expressions.

Exercises *Practicing Habits of Mind*

Check Your Understanding

1. Suppose $w = \text{cis } 20°$. The powers of w form the vertices of a regular polygon in the complex plane. What is the smallest number of sides that this polygon can have?

2. The graph below shows the plot of the powers (from 0 to 20) of $z = \text{cis } 17°$.

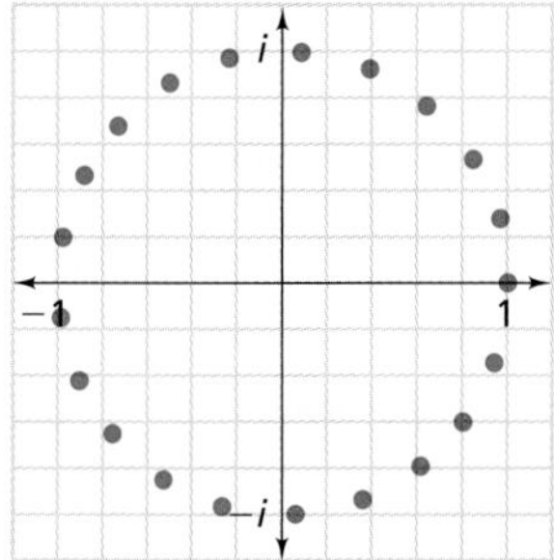

a. Why are these powers of z not vertices of a regular polygon?

b. Will the powers of z ever come back to 1? If so, how many times around the unit circle will it take? If not, why not?

c. Describe all the values of θ for which the powers of $z = \text{cis } \theta$ are vertices of a regular polygon.

z^{21} does not quite make it all the way around. z^{22} would be back in the first quadrant.

Exercises

HOMEWORK

- Core: 10, 11, 12, 13, 16
- Optional: 9, 14, 17, 18, 19
- Extension: 15

You may want to give students copies of Blackline Master MC1 or MC10 to use while they work on the exercises.

Exercises

1. 18

2. a. $z^{21} = \text{cis } 357°$

b. Yes; 360 times

c. all rational values of θ

For Exercises 3–7, let $z = \text{cis}\,\frac{2\pi}{5}$, one of the roots of $x^5 - 1 = 0$.

3. **a.** Show that $z^4 = \text{cis}\left(-\frac{2\pi}{5}\right)$.

b. Show that $z + z^4 = 2\cos\frac{2\pi}{5}$.

4. **a.** Factor the expression $x^5 - 1$ into two terms.

b. Show that $z^4 + z^3 + z^2 + z = -1$.

5. Let $a = z + z^4$ and $b = z^2 + z^3$.

a. Explain why a is a positive real number, and b is a negative real number.

b. Show that $a + b = -1$ using the result from Exercise 4b.

c. Write the product ab in terms of z.

d. Show that $ab = -1$.

6. In Exercise 5 you showed that a and b are two numbers that have a sum of -1 and a product of -1. Find exact values for a and b, given that a is positive and b is negative.

7. In Exercise 3, you found that $z + z^4 = 2\cos\frac{2\pi}{5}$.

a. Find an exact expression for $\cos\frac{2\pi}{5}$ that does not use trigonometric functions.

b. **Take It Further** Find an exact expression for $\sin\frac{2\pi}{5}$.

c. **Take It Further** Write algebraic expressions for each of the roots of $x^5 - 1 = 0$ that do not involve cosine and sine.

8. **Take It Further** Let $\phi = \frac{1+\sqrt{5}}{2}$. Show that the polynomial $x^5 - 1$ factors over $\mathbb{R}$ as

$$x^5 - 1 = (x - 1)(x^2 + \phi x + 1)\left(x^2 - \tfrac{1}{\phi}x + 1\right)$$

Remember...

z is the fifth root of unity in Quadrant I.

Remember...

The number $\phi = \frac{1+\sqrt{5}}{2}$ is the *golden ratio*. (ϕ is the Greek letter *phi*, pronounced "fie" or "fee.")

Answers

3. a. $z^4 = \left(\text{cis}\,\frac{2\pi}{5}\right)^4 = \text{cis}\,\frac{8\pi}{5} = \text{cis}\left(-\frac{2\pi}{5}\right)$

b. Use the result from part (a). $z + z^4 = \text{cis}\,\frac{2\pi}{5} + \text{cis}\left(-\frac{2\pi}{5}\right) = 2\cos\frac{2\pi}{5}$

4. a. $(x - 1)(x^4 + x^3 + x^2 + x + 1)$

b. z is a root of $(z - 1)(z^4 + z^3 + z^2 + z + 1) = 0$, and since $z \neq 1$, the value of $z^4 + z^3 + z^2 + z + 1$ must be 0. It follows that $z^4 + z^3 + z^2 + z = -1$.

5. a. From Exercise 3(b), we know that $z + z^4$ is positive, since $2\cos\frac{2\pi}{5}$ is positive. (We know this is so because $0 < \frac{2\pi}{5} < \frac{\pi}{2}$.) By Exercise 4(b), $z^2 + z^3 = -1 - (z + z^4)$, and subtracting a positive number from -1 results in a negative number.

b. This result follows immediately from Exercise 4(b).

c. $z^3 + z^4 + z^6 + z^7$, or $z + z^2 + z^3 + z^4$ (since $z^6 = z$ and $z^7 = z^2$)

d. $ab = -1$ follows directly from part (c) and Exercise 4(b).

6. $a = \frac{-1+\sqrt{5}}{2}$, $b = -\frac{1+\sqrt{5}}{2}$

7. See back of book.

8. $x^5 - 1 = (x - 1)(x^4 + x^3 + x^2 + x + 1)$, so the given factorization is correct if $x^4 + x^3 + x^2 + x + 1$ equals $(x^2 + \phi x + 1)\left(x^2 - \frac{1}{\phi}x + 1\right)$. Expand this last expression and collect like terms to obtain $x^4 + \left(\phi - \frac{1}{\phi}\right)x^3 + x^2 + \left(\phi - \frac{1}{\phi}\right)x + 1$. Use $\phi = \frac{1+\sqrt{5}}{2}$ to show that $\phi - \frac{1}{\phi} = 1$. It follows that $x^4 + x^3 + x^2 + x + 1 = (x^2 + \phi x + 1)\left(x^2 - \frac{1}{\phi}x + 1\right)$.

On Your Own

9. Let $w = \text{cis}\,12°$. The powers of w form the vertices of a regular polygon in the complex plane. How many sides does this polygon have?

Exercises 10–13 refer to this isosceles triangle, with each base angle measuring 72°.

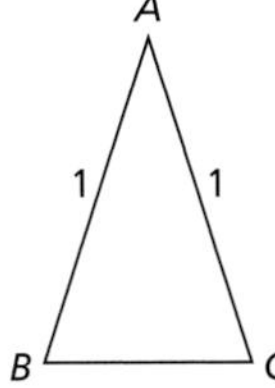

The congruent sides of the triangle have length 1.

10. Show that the third side length is $q = 2\cos 72°$.

11. Draw $\overline{BD}$ bisecting angle ABC.

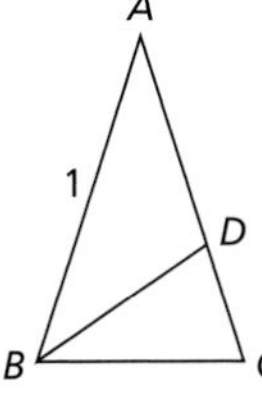

Show that triangle ABC is similar to triangle BCD.

Go Online PHSchool.com

For additional practice, go to **Web Code:** bga-0211

12. Use the result from Exercise 11 to show the following.

a. $CD = q^2$ **b.** $CD = 1 - q$

13. a. Use the results from Exercise 12 to find the exact value of q without using trigonometric functions.

b. In Exercise 10 you found that $q = 2\cos 72°$. Find the exact value of $\cos 72°$.

14. Find the exact value of $\cos 144°$.

15. **Take It Further** Prove the following statement.

In a regular pentagon, any diagonal drawn is exactly ϕ times as long as a side of the pentagon, where ϕ is the golden ratio $\frac{1 + \sqrt{5}}{2}$.

16. **Standardized Test Prep** The powers of $\text{cis}\left(\frac{3\pi}{7}\right)$ form the vertices of a regular polygon. How many sides does the polygon have?

A. 3 **B.** 7 **C.** 14 **D.** 21

9. 30 sides

10. Let $\overline{AM}$ be the altitude to the base $\overline{BC}$ of isosceles $\triangle ABC$. Right triangle trigonometry tells you that $\cos \angle B = \cos 72° = \frac{BM}{1} = BM$. Likewise, $CM = \cos 72°$.

11. $m\angle A = 36°$ and $m\angle CBD = 36°$ (since $\overline{BD}$ bisects $\angle ABC$). $\angle C$ is common to $\triangle ABC$ and $\triangle BCD$, Therefore, these triangles are similar by AA Similarity.

12. a. $\frac{AB}{BC} = \frac{BC}{CD}$, so $\frac{1}{q} = \frac{q}{CD}$. Hence $CD = q^2$.

b. Since $m\angle ABD = 36°$, $\triangle DAB$ is isosceles (because $\angle DAB \cong \angle DBA$). So $AD = BD$. Also, since $\triangle BDC$ is isosceles (because $\triangle ABC \sim \triangle BCD$), $BD = BC$. Thus $AD = BC$. Given that $AC = 1$ and $BC = q$, it follows that $DC = AC - BC = 1 - q$.

13. a. $\frac{\sqrt{5}-1}{2}$ (the positive root of $q^2 = 1 - q$)

b. $\frac{\sqrt{5}-1}{4}$

14. $-\frac{\sqrt{5}+1}{4}$

15. Consider vertex A of pentagon $ABCDE$. Draw the two diagonals $\overline{AC}$ and $\overline{AD}$ from this vertex. $\triangle ACD$ is an isosceles triangle with base angles 72°, so $\triangle ACD$ is similar to the triangle from Exercise 10. In that triangle, the length of the longer side is 1, and the length of the shorter side is $2\cos 72° = 2 \cdot \left(-\frac{1}{4} + \frac{\sqrt{5}}{4}\right) = \frac{-1+\sqrt{5}}{2}$. So

$$\frac{AC}{CD} = \frac{2}{-1+\sqrt{5}} = \frac{2(1+\sqrt{5})}{(-1+\sqrt{5})(1+\sqrt{5})} = \frac{2(1+\sqrt{5})}{4} = \phi$$

Therefore $AC = CD \cdot \phi$.

16. C

Maintain Your Skills

EXERCISE 17 Students may do this exercise by finding the angle directly, and that is fine. This exercise sets up Exercise 19.

EXERCISE 18 reminds students one last time about the connection between complex numbers and cosine and sine. Students should recall that $z = \cos\theta + i\sin\theta$ (since $|z| = 1$).

EXERCISE 19 helps introduce the Chebyshev polynomials, which is the topic of the Project in Chapter 3. Students may have trouble with the notation, which is why the exercise asks them to first verify $P(2, x)$ and $P(3, x)$. The last part of the exercise points out to students that these polynomials work with the cosine of multiple angles, since it gives the same answers as in Exercise 17. Assign and review this exercise before asking students to work on the Project.

Additional Resources

PRINT RESOURCES	TECHNOLOGY
• Solution Manual	• Interactive Textbook
• Practice Workbook	• TeacherExpress CD-ROM
• Assessment Resources	• ExamView CD-ROM
• Teaching Resources	• PHSchool.com

Additional Practice

1. Suppose $z = \text{cis } 10°$. The powers of z form the vertices of a regular polygon in the complex plane. What is the smallest number of sides that this polygon can have?

2. The graph at the right shows the plot of the powers (from 0 to 5) of $z = \text{cis } 71°$.
   a. Why are these powers of z not vertices of a regular polygon?
   b. Will the powers of z ever come back to 1? If so, how many times around the unit circle will it take? If not, why not?

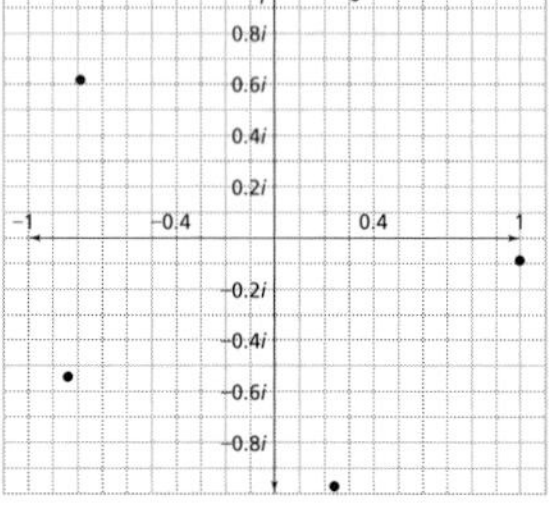

3. Consider the complex number $z = \text{cis } \frac{2\pi}{9}$, one of the roots of $x^9 - 1 = 0$.
   a. Show that $z^8 = \text{cis}\left(-\frac{2\pi}{9}\right)$.
   b. Show that $z + z^8 = 2\cos\left(\frac{2\pi}{9}\right)$.

4. The isosceles triangle ABC has base angles measuring 41°. The congruent sides of the triangle have length 2. Show that the third side length is $4\cos 41°$.

5. Suppose that $\alpha = \text{cis } \frac{2\pi}{7}$. Evaluate each sum.
   a. 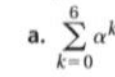 $\sum_{k=0}^{6} \alpha^k$
   b. $\alpha^3 + \alpha^4$

6. Suppose $z = \text{cis } \frac{2\pi}{6}$. Find the value of $(z - z^2 - z^3 + z^4)^2$.

7. Suppose $z = \text{cis } \frac{2\pi}{11}$.
   a. Find the value of $z + z^4 + z^7 + z^{10}$.
   b. Find the value of $z^2 + z^5 + z^6 + z^9$.

Practice: For Lesson 2.11, assign Exercises 1–4.

Maintain Your Skills

17. Let $\cos\theta = 0.8$. Find the exact value of each of the following.

a. $\cos 2\theta$

b. $\cos 3\theta$

c. $\cos 4\theta$

d. $\cos 5\theta$

18. Let $z = 0.8 + 0.6i$. Calculate each of these powers of z.

a. z^2

b. z^3

c. z^4

d. z^5

19. Let $P(n, x)$ be a sequence of polynomial functions defined as follows.

$$P(n, x) = \begin{cases} 1 & \text{if } n = 0 \\ x & \text{if } n = 1 \\ 2x \cdot P(n-1, x) - P(n-2, x) & \text{if } n > 1 \end{cases}$$

a. Show that $P(0, x) = 1$ and $P(1, x) = x$.

b. Show that $P(2, x) = 2x^2 - 1$.

c. Show that $P(3, x) = 4x^3 - 3x$.

d. Find $P(4, x)$ and $P(5, x)$.

e. Let $x = 0.8$. Find $P(2, x)$, $P(3, x)$, $P(4, x)$, and $P(5, x)$.

See TI-Nspire Handbook on p. 704 for help in defining this function on your calculator.

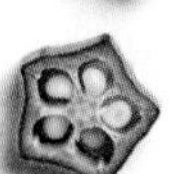

Compare these slices of okra to the figure on p. 140. If you pay attention to detail, you will find that symmetrical patterns are common in the natural world.

Answers

17. a. 0.28
b. −0.352
c. −0.8432
d. −0.99712

18. a. $0.28 + 0.96i$
b. $-0.352 + 0.936i$
c. $-0.8432 + 0.5376i$
d. $-0.99712 - 0.07584i$

19. a. The first two parts of the definition of $P(n, x)$ tell you that $P(0, x) = 1$ and $P(1, x) = x$.

b. $P(2, x) = 2x \cdot P(1, x) - P(0, x) = 2x^2 - 1$

c. $P(3, x) = 2x \cdot P(2, x) - P(1, x) = 2x \cdot (2x^2 - 1) - x = 4x^3 - 3x$

d. $P(4, x) = 8x^4 - 8x^2 + 1$ and $P(5, x) = 16x^5 - 20x^3 + 5x$

e. $P(2, 0.8) = 0.28$, $P(3, 0.8) = -0.352$, $P(4, 0.8) = -0.8432$, $P(5, 0.8) = -0.99712$

2.12 Arithmetic With Roots of Unity

When you perform arithmetic with complex numbers, you likely treat expressions like $3 + 5i$ as "polynomials in i." You calculate with them using the basic rules of algebra. Then, you use one more simplification rule: you replace i^2 by -1. For example, you can reduce expressions like $3 + 2i + 4i^2 - i^3$ to something of the form $x + yi$ where x and y are real numbers.

For You to Do

1. Write $3 + 2i + 4i^2 - i^3$ in the form $x + yi$, where x and y are real numbers.

In fact, you can define the set of complex numbers by thinking of them as polynomials in i.

Definition

The set of complex numbers $\mathbb{C}$ consists of all expressions in the form $a + bi$ where:

- **a and b are real numbers**
- **$i^2 = -1$**
- **Perform addition and multiplication as if $a + bi$ were a polynomial in i, using the new rule $i^2 = -1$.**

Developing Habits of Mind

Recognize a similar process. When working on any new algebraic system, you often experiment with calculations by following the rules and practicing with examples. Eventually, the calculations begin to feel familiar, ultimately behaving like something you already know.

Working with complex numbers, they start to feel like polynomials with additional simplification rules. In fact, many algebraic systems work this way. In this lesson, you will look at examples where the new objects are expressions that involve roots of unity.

In Exercise 7 from Lesson 2.11, you found the exact value for $\cos\frac{2\pi}{5}$ by looking at the fifth roots of unity (roots of $x^5 - 1 = 0$). First, you grouped the nonreal roots into pairs, then you built a quadratic equation with one solution, $2\cos\frac{2\pi}{5}$. Following a similar technique, you can find exact values for cosines of other numbers using roots of unity. The equations will not be quadratic, but they will be polynomials.

For You to Do

1. $-1 + 3i$

Lesson Overview

GOAL

- Apply roots of unity.

This is an optional lesson in which students explore calculations with roots of unity.

CHECK YOUR UNDERSTANDING

- Core: 1, 2, 3, 6, 7
- Optional: 4, 5

MATERIALS

- CAS
- Blackline Master 2.12

HOMEWORK

- Core: 9, 10, 11, 12, 15, 17, 18, 23
- Optional: 13, 14, 16, 19, 24
- Extension: 8, 20, 21, 22, 25

VOCABULARY

- algebraic numbers
- complex numbers
- primitive nth root of unity
- $\psi_n(x)$ (polynomial whose roots are precisely the primitive nth roots of unity)

Launch

Start the lesson with the first For You to Do problem.

Explore

For You to Do

PROBLEM 1 You might introduce the idea that you can use polynomial division to divide $3 + 2x + 4x^2 - x^3$ by $x^2 + 1$.

$3 + 2x + 4x^2 - x^3 = (x^2 + 1)(4 - x) + (-1 + 3x)$

Replace x with i on both sides.

For You to Do

PROBEM 2 You may wish to use Blackline Master 2.12 to illustrate the geometric properties of the seven roots of unity. Students will have an easier time following the algebraic results if they recognize the symmetry of ζ and ζ^6, ζ^2 and ζ^5, and ζ^3 and ζ^4.

Consider $\cos \frac{2\pi}{7}$. Does it satisfy an equation with real coefficients? You know from the last lesson that the regular 7-gon is lurking in the background. In fact, here are the roots of $x^7 - 1 = 0$ in the complex plane.

Maybe it even satisfies an equation with rational coefficients. Such numbers are called *algebraic numbers*.

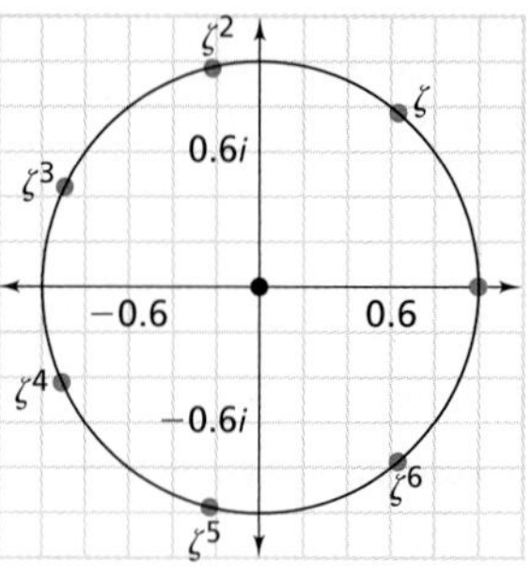

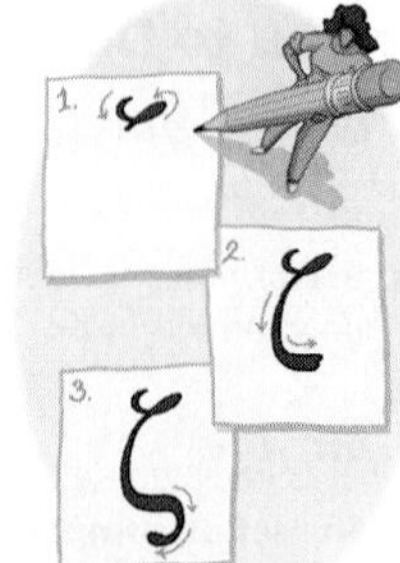

Recall Exercises 3–7 of Lesson 2.11. You know that $\zeta + \zeta^6 = 2\cos\frac{2\pi}{7}$. If you find an algebraic expression for $\zeta + \zeta^6$, you can find an algebraic expression for $\cos\frac{2\pi}{7}$. (ζ is the Greek letter *zeta*.)

There are two other pairs of seventh roots of unity that add to real numbers.

For You to Do

2. Show that

$$\zeta^2 + \zeta^5 = 2\cos\frac{4\pi}{7}$$

$$\zeta^3 + \zeta^4 = 2\cos\frac{6\pi}{7}$$

Habits of Mind

Develop your understanding. Recognize that you can evaluate trigonometric functions as sums of roots of unity and know which sums produce real results. Each pair here is a number plus its conjugate. Use the geometry of the *n*-gon to help with this.

You now have three pairs of roots that add to real numbers.

$$\alpha = \zeta + \zeta^6 = 2\cos\frac{2\pi}{7}$$

$$\beta = \zeta^2 + \zeta^5 = 2\cos\frac{4\pi}{7}$$

$$\gamma = \zeta^3 + \zeta^4 = 2\cos\frac{6\pi}{7}$$

You can find a polynomial with roots α, β, and γ. Those roots satisfy this cubic equation.

$$(x-\alpha)(x-\beta)(x-\gamma) = x^3 - (\alpha+\beta+\gamma)x^2 + (\alpha\beta+\alpha\gamma+\beta\gamma)x - \alpha\beta\gamma = 0 \quad (1)$$

But are the coefficients real?

Answers

For You to Do

2. $\zeta^2 + \zeta^5 = \text{cis}\,\frac{4\pi}{7} + \text{cis}\,\frac{10\pi}{7}$

$= \text{cis}\,\frac{4\pi}{7} + \text{cis}\left(-\frac{4\pi}{7}\right)$

$= \text{cis}\,\frac{4\pi}{7} + \overline{\text{cis}\,\frac{4\pi}{7}}$

$= 2\cos\frac{4\pi}{7}$

$\zeta^3 + \zeta^4 = \text{cis}\,\frac{6\pi}{7} + \text{cis}\,\frac{8\pi}{7}$

$= \text{cis}\,\frac{6\pi}{7} + \text{cis}\left(-\frac{6\pi}{7}\right)$

$= \text{cis}\,\frac{6\pi}{7} + \overline{\text{cis}\,\frac{6\pi}{7}}$

$= 2\cos\frac{6\pi}{7}$

Example

Problem

a. Find the value of $\alpha + \beta + \gamma$.

b. Find the value of $\alpha\beta + \alpha\gamma + \beta\gamma$.

Solution

a. To find $\alpha + \beta + \gamma$, replace the three real numbers by their definitions to get

$$\alpha + \beta + \gamma = (\zeta + \zeta^6) + (\zeta^2 + \zeta^5) + (\zeta^3 + \zeta^4)$$

This sum includes six of the seven vertices of the 7-gon—all except for the "anchor point" 1. You worked through this sum, approximating each of the terms, using your calculator in Problem 8 of Lesson 2.8. You can also figure out the sum exactly. Try it before continuing.

You know that ζ is a root of $x^7 - 1 = 0$. The factorization

$$x^7 - 1 = (x - 1)(x^6 + x^5 + x^4 + x^3 + x^2 + 1)$$

means that ζ is a root of one of the factors on the right-hand side. But it is not a root of the first factor (why?), so it must be true that

$$\zeta^6 + \zeta^5 + \zeta^4 + \zeta^3 + \zeta^2 + \zeta + 1 = 0 \qquad (2)$$

From this identity, you can say that

$$\zeta^6 + \zeta^5 + \zeta^4 + \zeta^3 + \zeta^2 + \zeta = -1$$

But the left-hand side is just $\alpha + \beta + \gamma$, so

$$\alpha + \beta + \gamma = -1$$

b. To find $\alpha\beta + \alpha\gamma + \beta\gamma$, again replace each of the numbers by its definition.

$$\alpha\beta + \alpha\gamma + \beta\gamma = (\zeta + \zeta^6)(\zeta^2 + \zeta^5) + (\zeta + \zeta^6)(\zeta^3 + \zeta^4) + (\zeta^2 + \zeta^5)(\zeta^3 + \zeta^4)$$

Expand each product of binomials to get

$$\zeta^3 + \zeta^4 + 2\zeta^5 + 2\zeta^6 + 2\zeta^8 + 2\zeta^9 + \zeta^{10} + \zeta^{11}$$

Finally, replace ζ^7 by 1 and simplify to get

$$2\zeta + 2\zeta^2 + 2\zeta^3 + 2\zeta^4 + 2\zeta^5 + 2\zeta^6 = 2(\zeta + \zeta^2 + \zeta^3 + \zeta^4 + \zeta^5 + \zeta^6)$$

From above, you know that $\zeta + \zeta^2 + \zeta^3 + \zeta^4 + \zeta^5 + \zeta^6 = -1$, so the value of $\alpha\beta + \alpha\gamma + \beta\gamma$ is -2.

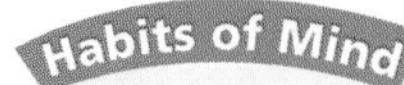

Make connections. To calculate expressions with ζ, treat them like polynomials in ζ and use the basic rules of algebra. Then, as a last step, reduce higher powers of ζ by using the relation $\zeta^7 = 1$.

For You to Do

3. Show that $\alpha\beta\gamma = 1$.

Example

Spend time as needed going over this completed example. Make sure students understand the problem. As necessary, help them develop the detailed solution.

For You to Do

3. Replace α, β, and γ by the expressions that define them. Then expand and simplify.

$$\begin{aligned}\alpha\beta\gamma &= (\zeta + \zeta^6)(\zeta^2 + \zeta^5)(\zeta^3 + \zeta^4) \\ &= \zeta^{15} + \zeta^{14} + \zeta^{12} + \zeta^{11} \\ &\quad + \zeta^{10} + \zeta^9 + \zeta^7 + \zeta^6 \\ &= \zeta + 1 + \zeta^5 + \zeta^4 + \zeta^3 \\ &\quad + \zeta^2 + 1 + \zeta^6 \\ &= 2 + (\zeta + \zeta^2 + \zeta^3 + \zeta^4 \\ &\quad + \zeta^5 + \zeta^6) \\ &= 2 + (-1) \\ &= 1\end{aligned}$$

Developing Habits of Mind

Have students connect the habits of mind with the ways they have used their minds in prior mathematics work and/or in life outside the classroom.

So, the three coefficients are, in fact, real:

$$\alpha + \beta + \gamma = -1,$$
$$\alpha\beta + \alpha\gamma + \beta\gamma = -2, \quad \text{and}$$
$$\alpha\beta\gamma = 1$$

Thus, the three real numbers $2 \cos \frac{2\pi}{7}$, $2 \cos \frac{4\pi}{7}$, and $2 \cos \frac{6\pi}{7}$ are roots of the nice cubic equation (going back to equation (1))

$$x^3 + x^2 - 2x - 1 = 0 \qquad (3)$$

From here, you could try to find an exact value of $\cos \frac{2\pi}{7}$ like you did for $\cos \frac{2\pi}{5}$. Just solve the above equation.

For the pentagon in Lesson 2.11, the resulting equation was quadratic, and the quadratic formula helps you solve quadratics easily. To solve equation (3), you need a "cubic formula." In the project for this chapter, you will derive Cardano's Formula, a formula for finding roots of cubic equations. Unfortunately, the cubic formula is not very useful for numerical calculations—the resulting solutions involve cube roots of complex numbers.

You will apply Cardano's Formula to this equation in the project for this chapter.

For You to Do

4. Find approximate solutions to equation (3). Verify that these approximations agree with the value of $2 \cos \frac{2\pi}{7}$, $2 \cos \frac{4\pi}{7}$, and $2 \cos \frac{6\pi}{7}$.

Developing Habits of Mind

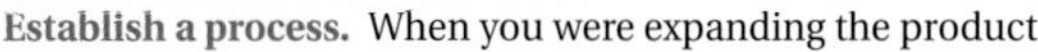

Establish a process. When you were expanding the product

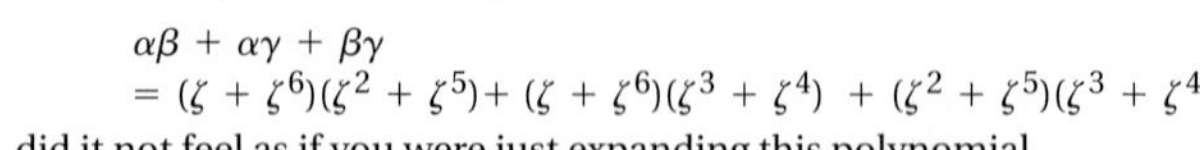

$$\begin{aligned} &\alpha\beta + \alpha\gamma + \beta\gamma \\ &= (\zeta + \zeta^6)(\zeta^2 + \zeta^5) + (\zeta + \zeta^6)(\zeta^3 + \zeta^4) + (\zeta^2 + \zeta^5)(\zeta^3 + \zeta^4) \end{aligned}$$

did it not feel as if you were just expanding this polynomial

$$(x + x^6)(x^2 + x^5) + (x + x^6)(x^3 + x^4) + (x^2 + x^5)(x^3 + x^4)$$

to find its normal form?

You could have just entered the above expression in your CAS getting

$$x^3 + x^4 + 2x^5 + 2x^6 + 2x^8 + 2x^9 + x^{10} + x^{11}$$

replacing x by ζ in the result. Then you replaced high powers of ζ (powers 8, 9, 10, and 11) by lower ones, using the relation $\zeta^7 = 1$.

But there is an even better idea here. Suppose you take the above polynomial and divide it by $x^7 - 1$. You get:

$$\begin{aligned} &x^3 + x^4 + 2x^5 + 2x^6 + 2x^8 + 2x^9 + x^{10} + x^{11} \\ &\quad = (x^7 - 1)(2x + 2x^2 + x^3 + x^4) + 2x + 2x^2 + 2x^3 + 2x^4 + 2x^5 + 2x^6 \end{aligned}$$

Answers

For You to Do

4. Approximate roots of the polynomial equation are 1.2470, −0.4450, and −1.8019. Approximate values of $2 \cos \frac{2\pi}{7}$, $2 \cos \frac{4\pi}{7}$, and $2 \cos \frac{6\pi}{7}$ are 1.2470, −0.4450, and −1.8019, respectively.

Now replace x by ζ on both sides. Since $\zeta^7 - 1 = 0$, you get

$$\begin{aligned}
&\zeta^3 + \zeta^4 + 2\zeta^5 + 2\zeta^6 + 2\zeta^8 + 2\zeta^9 + \zeta^{10} + \zeta^{11} \\
&= (\zeta^7 - 1)(2\zeta + 2\zeta^2 + \zeta^3 + \zeta^4) + 2\zeta + 2\zeta^2 + 2\zeta^3 + 2\zeta^4 + 2\zeta^5 + 2\zeta^6 \\
&= 2\zeta + 2\zeta^2 + 2\zeta^3 + 2\zeta^4 + 2\zeta^5 + 2\zeta^6
\end{aligned}$$

From here, proceed as before.

If you think about it, this process amounts to

- divide the expression

$$x^3 + x^4 + 2x^5 + 2x^6 + 2x^8 + 2x^9 + x^{10} + x^{11}$$

  by $x^7 - 1$,
- take the remainder,
- replace x by ζ in this remainder, and
- simplify the result.

Most CAS systems allow you to get the remainder directly with a built in function.

See TI-Nspire Handbook on p. 704 for more about finding the remainder in polynomial division with a CAS.

For Discussion

5. Use a CAS. Find the remainder when you divide
$(x^3 + x^4)(x^2 + x^5) + (x^3 + x^4)(x^1 + x^6) + (x^2 + x^5)(x + x^6)$
by $x^6 + x^5 + x^4 + x^3 + x^2 + x + 1$.
Interpret the reuslt in the context of this lesson.

Exercises *Practicing Habits of Mind*

Check Your Understanding

1. For each of the following values of ζ, find the sum

$$\sum_{k=0}^{6} \zeta^{5k}$$

a. $\zeta = \text{cis}\,\frac{2\pi}{7}$ **b.** $\zeta = \text{cis}\,\frac{2\pi}{5}$ **c.** $\zeta = \text{cis}\,\frac{2\pi}{10}$

For Discussion

5. When $x = \zeta$, the value of the polynomial remainder is -2.

Exercises

1. a. 0
b. 7
c. 1

For Discussion

PROBLEM 5
$(x^3 + x^4)(x^2 + x^5) + (x^3 + x^4)(x + x^6) + (x^2 + x^5)(x + x^6) = (x^6 + x^5 + x^4 + x^3 + x^2 + x + 1) \cdot (\text{something}) - 2$

Since ζ is also a root of $x^6 + x^5 + x^4 + x^3 + x^2 + x + 1 = 0$, replacing x with ζ on both sides shows that

$$(\zeta^3 + \zeta^4)(\zeta^2 + \zeta^5) + (\zeta^3 + \zeta^4)(\zeta + \zeta^6) + (\zeta^2 + \zeta^5)(\zeta + \zeta^6) = -2$$

Wrap Up

As time allows, let students work on the core Check Your Understanding exercises. You may want to go over some of the solutions in class.

Assessment Resources

Lesson Quiz 2.12

1. Suppose that $\alpha = \text{cis}\,\frac{2\pi}{8}$. Evaluate each sum.

a. $\sum_{k=0}^{7} \alpha^k$ **b.** $1 + \alpha^4$

2. Suppose $z = \text{cis}\,\frac{2\pi}{9}$.

a. Find the value of $1 + z^3 + z^6$.

b. Find the value of
$\cos\frac{2\pi}{9} + \cos\frac{4\pi}{9} + \cos\frac{6\pi}{9} + \cos\frac{8\pi}{9} + \cos\frac{10}{9} + \cos\frac{12\pi}{9} + \cos\frac{14\pi}{9} + \cos\frac{16\pi}{9}$

3. Find all the primitive 6th roots of unity.

Exercises

HOMEWORK
- Core: 9, 10, 11, 12, 15, 17, 18, 23
- Optional: 13, 14, 16, 19, 24
- Extension: 8, 20, 21, 22, 25

Check Your Understanding

EXERCISE 1 Of course, students can evaluate these sums directly on a calculator that has a complex number package. Encourage them to only use the calculator to check their results.

EXERCISE 2 Students could reduce each formal sum modulo the minimal polynomial for α, which is $1 - x + x^2$.

EXERCISE 6 The reciprocal of a root of unity is also its conjugate.

EXERCISE 7 In general, the first primitive nth root of unity is $\zeta = \text{cis}\,\frac{2\pi}{n}$, and the others are the powers ζ^k where k is relatively prime to (shares no common factor with) n. See Exercises 12–14.

On Your Own

EXERCISE 9 The sum that is being squared and the sum in Exercise 6 are examples of *Gauss sums*. If p is prime, and $\zeta = \text{cis}\,\frac{2\pi}{p}$, the corresponding Gauss sum is

$$\sum_{k=1}^{p-1} \left(\frac{k}{p}\right)\zeta^k$$

where $\left(\frac{k}{p}\right)$ is the *Legendre symbol* (1 if k differs from a perfect square by a multiple of p and -1 otherwise). Gauss showed that this sum always evaluated to $\pm i^{\frac{p-1}{2}}\sqrt{p}$. Gauss conjectured in 1801 that the "$\pm$" was always "$+$," but he was not able to prove it for 4 years (during which time, by his own account, it was always on his mind) until 1805, when he writes in his diary that "as lightning strikes was the puzzle solved." The proof, as you can imagine, is not easy.

2. Suppose $\alpha = \text{cis}\,\frac{2\pi}{6}$. Evaluate each sum.

a. $\sum_{k=0}^{5} \alpha^k$ **b.** $1 + \alpha^3$ **c.** $\alpha^2 + \alpha^4$

3. Suppose $\alpha = \text{cis}\,\frac{2\pi}{5}$. Define a function f on nonnegative integers by

$$f(n) = \sum_{k=0}^{4} \alpha^{kn}$$

Tabulate f and find a simpler way to define it.

4. Suppose $z = \text{cis}\,\frac{2\pi}{5}$.

a. Find $\sum_{k=0}^{4} z^k$ **b.** Find $\prod_{k=0}^{4} z^k$ **c.** Find $\prod_{k=1}^{4}(1 - z^k)$

The Greek letter $\prod$ (pi) means to form a product. The following product ranges from $k = 0$ to 4:
$\prod_{k=0}^{4} z^k = z^0 \cdot z^1 \cdot z^2 \cdot z^3 \cdot z^4$

5. Suppose $z = \text{cis}\,\frac{2\pi}{5}$. Find the value of

$$(z - z^2 - z^3 + z^4)^2$$

6. Suppose $z = \text{cis}\,\frac{2\pi}{12}$.

a. Find the value of $z + z^5 + z^7 + z^{11}$.

b. Find the value of

$$\cos\frac{\pi}{6} + \cos\frac{5\pi}{6} + \cos\frac{7\pi}{6} + \cos\frac{11\pi}{6}$$

7. a. A *primitive* n*th root of unity* is a solution to $x^n - 1 = 0$ that is not a solution of any equation $x^m - 1 = 0$ where $m < n$. Find all the primitive 12th roots of unity. Graph the corresponding 12-gon on the complex plane.

b. Factor $x^{12} - 1$ into irreducible polynomials over $\mathbb{Z}$. Let $\zeta = \text{cis}\,\frac{2\pi}{12}$. Label each vertex of the 12-gon in two ways

- as a power of ζ
- with the factor of $x^{12} - 1$ that it makes zero when you substitute it for x.

On Your Own

8. Take It Further Suppose $\alpha = \text{cis}\,\frac{2\pi}{6}$. Define a function f on nonnegative integers by

$$f(n) = \sum_{k=0}^{5} \alpha^{kn}$$

Tabulate f and find a simpler way to define it.

Answers

2. a. 0 **b.** 0 **c.** -1

3. $f(n) = 5$ if n is a multiple of 5, otherwise $f(n) = 0$

4. a. 0 **b.** 1 **c.** 5

5. 5

6. a. 0 **b.** 0

7. a. $\text{cis}\left(\frac{2\pi}{12}\cdot 1\right)$, $\text{cis}\left(\frac{2\pi}{12}\cdot 5\right)$, $\text{cis}\left(\frac{2\pi}{12}\cdot 7\right)$, $\text{cis}\left(\frac{2\pi}{12}\cdot 11\right)$

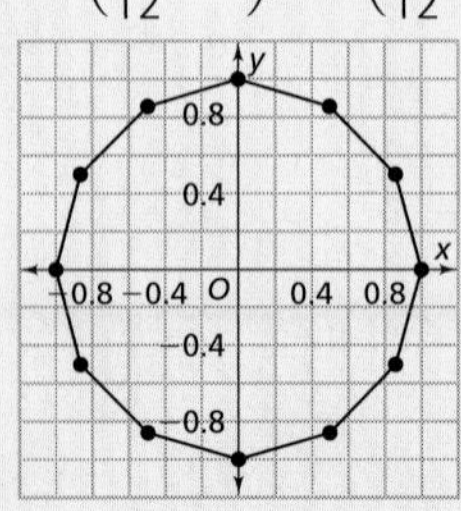

b. $x^{12} - 1 = (x - 1)(x + 1)\cdot(x^2 + 1)(x^2 + x + 1)\cdot(x^2 - x + 1)(x^4 - x^2 + 1)$

The table shows which powers of ζ make which factors equal to 0.

Factor	Powers of ζ
$x - 1$	ζ^0
$x + 1$	ζ^6
$x^2 + 1$	ζ^3, ζ^9
$x^2 + x + 1$	ζ^4, ζ^8
$x^2 - x + 1$	ζ^2, ζ^{10}
$x^4 - x^2 + 1$	$\zeta, \zeta^5, \zeta^7, \zeta^{11}$

8. For nonnegative integers n, $f(n) = 6$ if n is a multiple of 6, otherwise $f(n) = 0$.

9. Suppose $z = \text{cis}\,\frac{2\pi}{7}$. Find the value of

$$(z + z^2 - z^3 + z^4 - z^5 - z^6)^2$$

10. Suppose $z = \text{cis}\,\frac{2\pi}{11}$. Let

$$\alpha_1 = z + z^3 + z^4 + z^5 + z^9 \quad \text{and}$$
$$\alpha_2 = z^2 + z^6 + z^7 + z^8 + z^{10}$$

Find a quadratic equation satisfied by α_1 and α_2.

11. Factor $x^5 - 1$ over each of the following sets.

a. over $\mathbb{Z}$ **b.** over $\mathbb{R}$ **c.** over $\mathbb{C}$

See TI-Nspire Handbook on p. 704 to learn how to use your CAS to factor over $\mathbb{Z}$, $\mathbb{R}$, and $\mathbb{C}$.

12. Suppose that $\zeta = \text{cis}\,\frac{2\pi}{n}$. Show that ζ is a primitive nth root of unity.

13. Suppose that $\zeta = \text{cis}\,\frac{2\pi}{n}$. Show that if $\zeta^t = 1$ for some integer t, then n is a factor of t.

14. Suppose that $\zeta = \text{cis}\,\frac{2\pi}{n}$. Show that if $z = \zeta^r$ for some integer r that has no common factor with n, then z is a primitive nth root of unity.

15. **a.** Find all the primitive ninth roots of unity. Graph the corresponding 9-gon on the complex plane.

b. Factor $x^9 - 1$ into irreducible polynomials over $\mathbb{Z}$.
Let $\zeta = \text{cis}\,\frac{2\pi}{9}$. Label each vertex of the 9-gon in two ways
- as a power of ζ
- with the factor of $x^9 - 1$ that it makes zero when you substitute it for x.

16. Show that if z is an nth root of unity that is not primitive, $z^q = 1$ for some factor q of n.

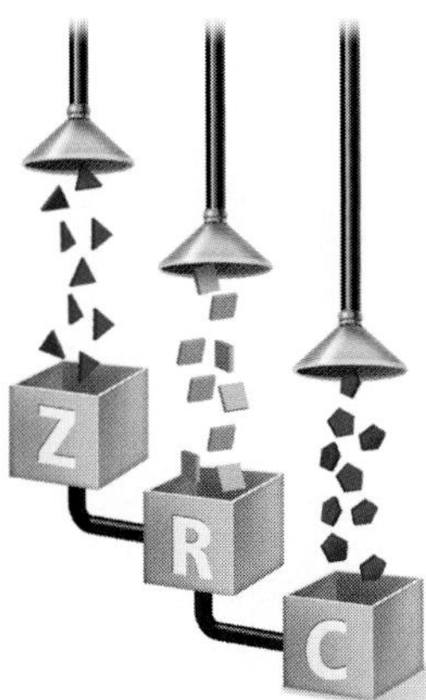

EXERCISE 11 There is a general criterion, called *Eisenstein's criterion*, that implies that, if p is a prime number,

$$\frac{x^p - 1}{x - 1} = x^{p-1} + x^{p-2} + \cdots + x + 1$$

is irreducible over $\mathbb{Z}$. You can find the proof of Eisenstein's criterion and its application to this problem in almost any text on higher algebra.

EXERCISE 15 Note that the primitive 9th roots are the powers ζ^k where k is relatively prime to 9. So, z is one of these numbers, say $z = \zeta^k = \text{cis}\,\frac{k(2\pi)}{n}$. From Exercise 14, if k has no common factor with n, z is a primitive nth root of unity. Suppose k has a common factor with n—say $n = jq$ and $k = js$ for some integers r, s, and j.

Then

$$\begin{aligned} z &= \text{cis}\,\frac{k(2\pi)}{n} \\ &= \text{cis}\,\frac{js(2\pi)}{jq} \\ &= \text{cis}\,\frac{s(2\pi)}{q} \end{aligned}$$

But the last number is a qth root of unity (why?). And since $n = jq$, q is a factor of n.

9. -7

10. $x^2 + x + 3 = 0$

11. **a.** $(x - 1)(x^4 + x^3 + x^2 + x + 1)$

b. $(x - 1)\left(x^2 - \frac{-1 + \sqrt{5}}{2}x + 1\right) \cdot \left(x^2 + \frac{1 + \sqrt{5}}{2}x + 1\right)$

c. $(x - 1)(x - \zeta)(x - \zeta^2) \cdot (x - \zeta^3)(x - \zeta^4)$, where $\zeta = \text{cis}\,\frac{2\pi}{5} = \frac{-1 + \sqrt{5}}{4} + \frac{\sqrt{10 + 2\sqrt{5}}}{4}i$

12. If k is a positive integer, the first ζ^k that is equal to 1 is ζ^n.

13. Assume $\zeta^t = 1$. Let $t = nq + r$, where $0 \le r < n$ (so that r is the whole number remainder obtained when t is divided by n). Since $\zeta = \text{cis}\,\frac{2\pi}{n}$, $\zeta^t = \zeta^{nq+r} = (\zeta^n)^q \cdot \zeta^r = 1 \cdot \zeta^r = \zeta^r$. If $r \neq 0$, then ζ is not a primitive nth root of unity. This would contradict the result in Exercise 12. So $r = 0$, which means that t is a multiple of n.

14. Suppose $\zeta = \text{cis}\,\frac{2\pi}{n}$ and consider ζ^r, where r is an integer relatively prime to n. All powers of ζ are nth roots of unity, so $\zeta^{rm} = 1$ for some positive integer m. By Exercise 13, n is a divisor of rm. Since r and n are relatively prime, n is a divisor of m. Hence m cannot be less than n.

15. **a.** If $\zeta = \text{cis}\,\frac{2\pi}{9}$, then the primitive 9th roots of unity are $\zeta, \zeta^2, \zeta^4, \zeta^5, \zeta^7$, and ζ^8.

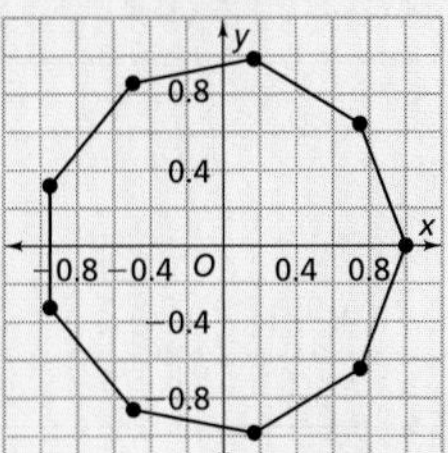

b. See back of book.

16. This result follows directly from Exercise 14 and the definition of a primitive nth root of unity.

EXERCISE 19 In general, $x^n - 1$ factors as the product of all the $\psi_m(x)$ where m runs over the factors of n. This gives a way of computing $\psi_n(x)$ recursively (how?). It turns out that each $\psi_m(x)$ has integer coefficients and is irreducible over $\mathbb{Z}$, but the proof is not easy.

EXERCISE 22 These are the calculations that Gauss used when he was 17 years old to show that you can construct a regular 17-gon with a straightedge and a compass. In the CME Project *Geometry* course, students learn to construct lengths that they can obtain from a unit length using the operations

$$+, -, \times, \div, \text{ and } \sqrt{\ }$$

One such length is r_0. The genius of Gauss' method lies in how he constructed the various sums—his choice of roots of unity for P_0 and so on. Gauss called these the "periods" of the cyclotomic equation, and they are formed through the use of some subtle results in number theory, also pioneered by Gauss.

Maintain Your Skills

EXERCISE 25 The function ϕ defined on positive integers by

$\phi(n) =$ The number of positive integers between 1 and n that have no common factor with n

is known as *Euler's ϕ function.*

17. The polynomial that has the primitive nth roots of unity as solutions is usually denoted by $\psi_n(x)$. (ψ is the Greek letter *psi.*) Show that

$$\psi_1(x) = x - 1$$
$$\psi_2(x) = x + 1$$
$$\psi_3(x) = x^2 + x + 1$$
$$\psi_4(x) = x^2 + 1$$

18. Find $\psi_m(x)$ for $m = 5, 6, 7, 8, 9, 10, 11$, and 12.

m	$\psi_m(x)$
5	$x^4 + x^3 + x^2 + x + 1$
6	■
7	■
8	■
9	■
10	■
11	■
12	■

19. Show that $x^{12} - 1$ factors as

$$x^{12} - 1 = \psi_1(x)\psi_2(x)\psi_3(x)\psi_4(x)\psi_6(x)\psi_{12}(x)$$

Take It Further In Exercises 20–22, $\zeta = \text{cis}\,\frac{2\pi}{17}$.

- Let $P_0 = \zeta + \zeta^9 + \zeta^{13} + \zeta^{15} + \zeta^{16} + \zeta^8 + \zeta^4 + \zeta^2$ and
  $P_1 = \zeta^3 + \zeta^{10} + \zeta^5 + \zeta^{11} + \zeta^{14} + \zeta^7 + \zeta^{12} + \zeta^6$
- Let $Q_0 = \zeta + \zeta^{13} + \zeta^{16} + \zeta^4$,
  $Q_1 = \zeta^3 + \zeta^5 + \zeta^{14} + \zeta^{12}$,
  $Q_2 = \zeta^9 + \zeta^{15} + \zeta^8 + \zeta^2$, and
  $Q_3 = \zeta^{10} + \zeta^{11} + \zeta^7 + \zeta^6$
- And let $r_0 = \zeta + \zeta^{16}$,
  $r_1 = \zeta^3 + \zeta^{14}$,
  $r_2 = \zeta^9 + \zeta^8$,
  $r_3 = \zeta^{10} + \zeta^7$,
  $r_4 = \zeta^{13} + \zeta^4$,
  $r_5 = \zeta^5 + \zeta^{12}$,
  $r_6 = \zeta^{15} + \zeta^2$, and
  $r_7 = \zeta^{11} + \zeta^6$

Answers

17. $\psi_1(x) = x - \text{cis}\,\frac{2\pi}{1} = x - 1$

$\psi_2(x) = x - \text{cis}\,\frac{2\pi}{2} = x + 1$

$\psi_3(x) = \left(x - \text{cis}\,\frac{2\pi}{3}\right)\left(x - \text{cis}\,\frac{4\pi}{3}\right) = x^2 + x + 1$

$\psi_4(x) = \left(x - \text{cis}\,\frac{2\pi}{4}\right)\left(x - \text{cis}\,\frac{6\pi}{4}\right) = x^2 + 1$

18.

m	$\psi_m(x)$
5	$x^4+x^3+x^2+x+1$
6	x^2-x+1
7	$x^6+x^5+x^4+x^3+x^2+x+1$
8	x^4+1
9	x^6+x^3+1
10	$x^4-x^3+x^2-x+1$
11	$x^{10}+x^9+x^8+x^7+x^6+x^5+x^4+x^3+x^2+x+1$
12	x^4-x^2+1

19. Replace each of the ψ_ks on the right side of the equation with the appropriate polynomial. When you multiply, you get $x^{12} - 1$.

20. In the expression for P_0, for each power of ζ there is a power of ζ that is symmetric to it with respect to the real axis. In the sum, the imaginary parts of the symmetric pairs are opposites and have a sum of 0. Hence the sum for P_0 is real. Similar statements apply to P_1, to all of the Q_ks, and to all of the r_ks.

21. a. See back of book.

b. The definitions of P_0, Q_0, and Q_2 show at once that $Q_0 + Q_2 = P_0$. To find Q_0Q_2, use the definitions of Q_0 and Q_2 to obtain the following: $Q_0Q_2 = \zeta^{31} + \zeta^{28} + \zeta^{24} + \zeta^{22} + \zeta^{21} + \zeta^{19} + \zeta^{18} + \zeta^{16} + \zeta^{15} + \zeta^{13} + \zeta^{12} + \zeta^{10} + \zeta^9 + \zeta^6 + \zeta^3 = \sum_{k=1}^{16} \zeta^k = -1$

Use a calculator to verify that $Q_0 > Q_2$. Then solve the system consisting of

20. Show that each of the P's, Q's, and r's are real numbers.

21. a. Show that

$$P_0 + P_1 = -1 \quad \text{and}$$
$$P_0 P_1 = -4$$

Find P_0 and P_1.

b. Show that

$$Q_0 + Q_2 = P_0 \quad \text{and}$$
$$Q_0 Q_2 = -1$$

Find Q_0 and Q_2.

c. Show that

$$Q_1 + Q_3 = P_1 \quad \text{and}$$
$$Q_1 Q_3 = -1$$

Find Q_1 and Q_3.

22. a. Show that

$$r_0 + r_4 = Q_0 \quad \text{and}$$
$$r_0 r_4 = -1$$

Find r_0 and r_4.

b. Find an exact formula for $\cos \frac{2\pi}{17}$, using only square roots and the four operations of arithmetic.

23. **Standardized Test Prep** Which of the following is the sum of the fourth roots of -1?

A. 0 **B.** -1 **C.** $-\frac{\sqrt{2}}{2}$ **D.** $-\frac{\sqrt{3}}{2}$

Go Online PHSchool.com

For additional practice, go to **Web Code:** bga-0212

Maintain Your Skills

24. Find all primitive nth roots of unity if

a. $n = 3$ **b.** $n = 4$ **c.** $n = 5$ **d.** $n = 7$

e. $n = 10$ **f.** $n = 11$ **g.** $n = 24$

25. **Take It Further** In terms of n, how many primitive nth roots of unity are there?

Additional Resources

PRINT RESOURCES
- Solution Manual
- Practice Workbook
- Assessment Resources
- Teaching Resources

TECHNOLOGY
- Interactive Textbook
- TeacherExpress CD-ROM
- ExamView CD-ROM
- PHSchool.com

Additional Practice

1. Suppose $z = \text{cis } 10°$. The powers of z form the vertices of a regular polygon in the complex plane. What is the smallest number of sides that this polygon can have?

2. The graph at the right shows the plot of the powers (from 0 to 5) of $z = \text{cis } 71°$.
   a. Why are these powers of z not vertices of a regular polygon?
   b. Will the powers of z ever come back to 1? If so, how many times around the unit circle will it take? If not, why not?

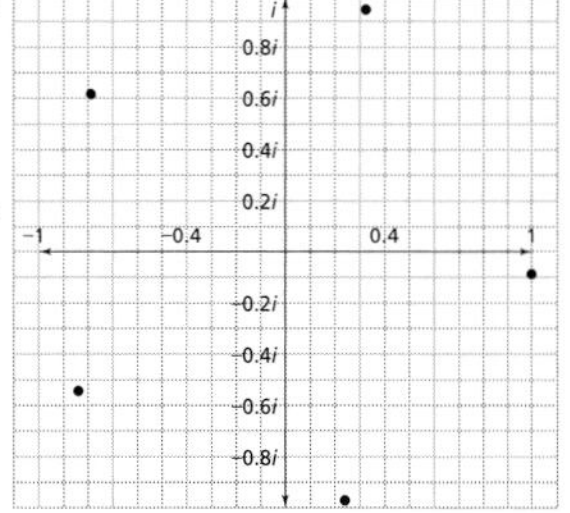

3. Consider the complex number $z = \text{cis } \frac{2\pi}{9}$, one of the roots of $x^9 - 1 = 0$.
   a. Show that $z^8 = \text{cis}\left(-\frac{2\pi}{9}\right)$.
   b. Show that $z + z^8 = 2\cos\left(\frac{2\pi}{9}\right)$.

4. The isosceles triangle ABC has base angles measuring 41°. The congruent sides of the triangle have length 2. Show that the third side length is $4 \cos 41°$.

5. Suppose that $\alpha = \text{cis } \frac{2\pi}{7}$. Evaluate each sum.
   a. 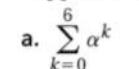 $\sum_{k=0}^{6} \alpha^k$
   b. $\alpha^3 + \alpha^4$

6. Suppose $z = \text{cis } \frac{2\pi}{6}$. Find the value of $(z - z^2 - z^3 + z^4)^2$.

7. Suppose $z = \text{cis } \frac{2\pi}{11}$.
   a. Find the value of $z + z^4 + z^7 + z^{10}$.
   b. Find the value of $z^2 + z^5 + z^6 + z^9$.

Practice: For Lesson 2.12, assign Exercises 5–7.

$Q_0 + Q_2 = \frac{-1 + \sqrt{17}}{2}$ and $Q_0 Q_2 = -1$ to obtain

$$Q_0 = \frac{-1 + \sqrt{17} - \sqrt{2(17 - \sqrt{17})}}{4},$$

$$Q_2 = \frac{-1 + \sqrt{17} - \sqrt{2(17 - \sqrt{17})}}{4}$$

c. The proof that $Q_1 + Q_3 = P_1$ and $Q_1 Q_3 = -1$ is similar to the proof in part (b). To find Q_1 and Q_3, first use a calculator to verify that $Q_1 > Q_3$. Then use this fact with the solutions of the system of equations $Q_1 + Q_3 = \frac{-1 - \sqrt{17}}{2}$ and $Q_1 Q_3 = -1$ to obtain

$$Q_1 = \frac{-1 - \sqrt{17} + \sqrt{2(17 + \sqrt{17})}}{4},$$

$$Q_3 = \frac{-1 - \sqrt{17} + \sqrt{2(17 + \sqrt{17})}}{4}.$$

22. See back of book.

23. A

24. a. $\text{cis } \frac{2\pi k}{3}$ for $k = 1$ and 2

b. $\text{cis } \frac{2\pi k}{4}$ for $k = 1$ and 3

c. $\text{cis } \frac{2\pi k}{5}$ for $k = 1, 2, 3$ and 4

d. $\text{cis } \frac{2\pi k}{7}$ for $k = 1, 2, 3, 4, 5$, and 6

e. $\text{cis } \frac{2\pi k}{10}$ for $k = 1, 3, 7$ and 9

f. $\text{cis } \frac{2\pi k}{11}$ for k an integer from 1 to 10

g. $\text{cis } \frac{2\pi k}{24}$ for $k = 1, 5, 7, 11, 13, 17, 19$, and 23

25. the number of whole numbers from 1 to $n - 1$ that are relatively prime to n

Mathematical Reflections

EXERCISES 6–8 At the start of the investigation, you may have assigned these as Questions 1–3 for students to think and write about.

In this investigation, you learned De Moivre's Theorem for calculating powers of complex numbers. You saw how this connected to roots of unity and regular polygons in the complex plane. The following questions will help you summarize what you have learned.

1. Find all the roots of each equation.
   a. $x^6 - 1 = 0$ **b.** $x^8 = 1$ **c.** $x^8 = 256$
2. Find the exact value of the following.
   a. $\cos \frac{\pi}{12}$ **b.** $\cos \frac{\pi}{8}$
   c. Take It Further $\cos \frac{3\pi}{8}$
3. Find the exact value of the following sums.
   a. $\sum_{k=0}^{6} \sin \frac{2\pi k}{7}$ **b.** $\sum_{k=1}^{6} \cos \frac{2\pi k}{7}$ **c.** $\sum_{k=0}^{6} \cos \frac{(7-4k)\pi}{14}$
4. Suppose $\zeta = \text{cis } \frac{2\pi}{12}$.
   a. Plot the distinct powers of ζ on the complex plane. Label each power with the polynomial of least degree over $\mathbb{Z}$ for which it is a zero.
   b. Find the value of
   $$(1-\zeta)(1-\zeta^5)(1-\zeta^7)(1-\zeta^{11})$$
5. Suppose $\zeta = \text{cis } \frac{2\pi}{5}$.
   a. Plot the distinct powers of ζ on the complex plane.
   b. Find a quadratic equation with $\zeta + \frac{1}{\zeta}$ as a root.
   c. Take It Further Find the length of a side of the polygon which has the powers of ζ as vertices.
6. How do you use De Moivre's Theorem to write a rule for $\cos 3x$?
7. How can you connect roots of unity to regular polygons?
8. For what values of $\cos x$ does $\cos 3x = 0$?

Vocabulary and Notation

In this investigation, you learned these terms. Make sure you understand what each one means and how to use it.

- **algebraic numbers**
- **complex numbers**
- **primitive *n*th root of unity**
- **roots of unity**

Symmetry about the center is a familiar and attractive design element in architecture.

Answers

Mathematical Reflections

1. a. $\frac{1}{2} \pm \frac{\sqrt{3}}{2}i, -\frac{1}{2} \pm \frac{\sqrt{3}}{2}i, \pm 1$

b. $\frac{\sqrt{2}}{2} \pm \frac{\sqrt{2}}{2}i, -\frac{\sqrt{2}}{2} \pm \frac{\sqrt{2}}{2}i, \pm i, \pm 1$

c. $-2 \pm i\sqrt{2}, 2 \pm i\sqrt{2}, \pm 2i, \pm 2$

2. a. $\frac{\sqrt{2}+\sqrt{6}}{4}$ **b.** $\frac{\sqrt{2+\sqrt{2}}}{2}$

c. $\frac{\sqrt{2-\sqrt{2}}}{2}$

3. a. 0 **b.** −1 **c.** 0

4. a.

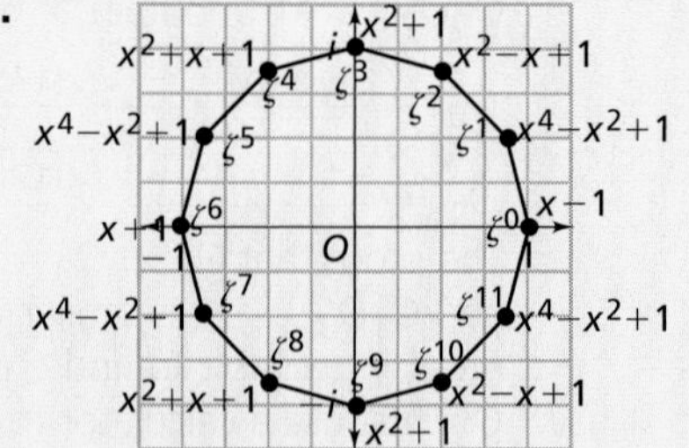

b. 1

Project: Using Mathematical Habits

Cardano's Method

Square roots of negative numbers emerged in the first half of the sixteenth century. Many people were interested in finding a formula that would let them solve cubic equations. Girolamo Cardano (1501–1575), Rafael Bombelli (1526–1572), and others developed an algorithm for solving cubic equations. But when they applied the method to cubics that have real roots, like $x^3 - 15x - 4 = 0$, they sometimes ended up with expressions that involved square roots of negative numbers.

Cardano, Bombelli, and their contemporaries realized that the equation $x^3 - 15x - 4 = 0$ has the same form as the identity

$$(r + s)^3 - 3rs(r + s) - (r^3 + s^3) = 0$$

if you look at it like this.

$$(r \quad s)^3 - 3rs(r \quad s) - (r^3 + s^3) = 0$$
$$x^3 \quad - 15 \quad x \quad - \quad 4 \quad = 0$$

So, if you can find r and s such that

$$3rs = 15 \quad \text{and} \quad r^3 + s^3 = 4$$

you could let $x = r + s$ and you would have a root. If $3rs = 15$, then $rs = 5$. Cube rs to get $r^3s^3 = 125$. Now you know the sum and product of the cubes of r and s.

$$r^3s^3 = 125 \quad \text{and} \quad r^3 + s^3 = 4$$

You now have a sum and product relationship. From this, you can say that r^3 and s^3 are the roots of the quadratic equation

$$y^2 - 4y + 125 = 0$$

which are $2 + 11i$ and $2 - 11i$. So

$$r^3 = 2 + 11i \quad \text{and} \quad s^3 = 2 - 11i$$

It is not clear how the 16th century mathematicians found values for r and s—de Moivre lived over a century later. It is likely that they just started cubing expressions until they found the correct answer. But you can use de Moivre's Theorem to solve the equations directly. First, write $2 + 11i$ in polar form

$$2 + 11i = |2 + 11i| \operatorname{cis}(\arg(2 + 11i))$$

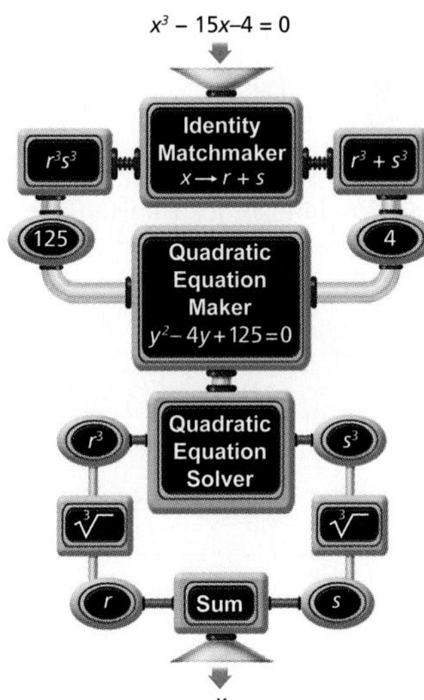

5. a.

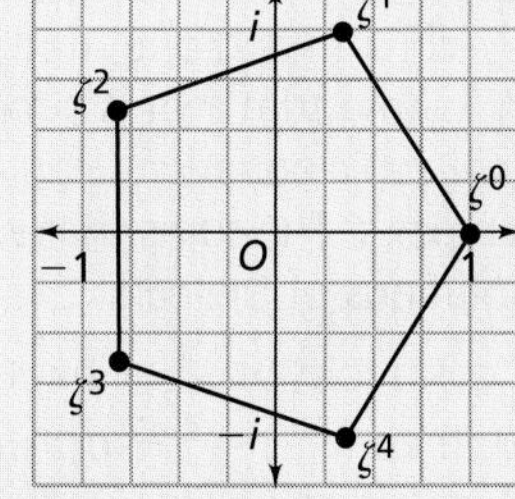

b. $x^2 + x - 1 = 0$

c. $\dfrac{\sqrt{10 - 2\sqrt{5}}}{2}$

6. Expand $(\cos x + i \sin x)^3$ and use the real part of the result as the expression for $\cos 3x$.

7. The graphs of the nth roots of unity for $n > 2$ are the vertices of a regular n-gon centered at the origin of the complex plane.

8. $-\dfrac{\sqrt{3}}{2}, 0, \dfrac{\sqrt{3}}{2}$

Project

In this Project, students trace the path Cardano (and his contemporaries) followed to develop a formula for determining roots of a general cubic. They will see how complex numbers crop up in their development, even for polynomials with real roots.

As always with a Project, there are several options. You can do this as a class, working on some or all of the questions together or assigning them as group or individual homework. You can also decide not to cover the Project in class, but allow interested students to prepare individual or group reports. In this particular Project, most of what is necessary to understand Cardano's Method is here, and students will have to read the mathematics, figure it out, and write up the results in their own words, making the proof their own.

Now

$$|2 + 11i| = \sqrt{125} = (\sqrt{5})^3 \text{ and}$$

$$\arg(2 + 11i) = \tan^{-1}\frac{11}{2}$$

So, if $r^3 = 2 + 11i$, you can say that

$$|r|^3 = (\sqrt{5})^3 \text{ and}$$

$$3\arg(r) = \tan^{-1}\frac{11}{2}$$

Since z has to be a nonnegative real number, you can say $r = \sqrt{5}$. To find $\arg(r) = \theta$, use a calculator to find that if $\alpha = \tan^{-1}\frac{11}{2}$, then

$$\tan\frac{\alpha}{3} = 0.5$$

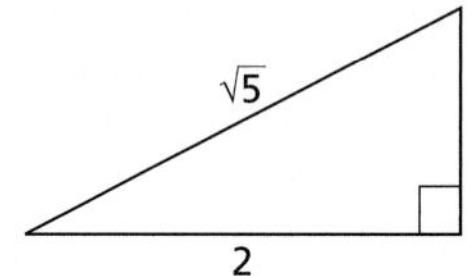

In Exercise 1, you will verify that this answer is exact. So,

$$\begin{aligned} r &= \sqrt{5}(\cos\theta + i\sin\theta) \\ &= \sqrt{5}\left(\cos\frac{\alpha}{3} + i\sin\frac{\alpha}{3}\right) \\ &= \sqrt{5}\left(\cos\left(\tan^{-1}\frac{1}{2}\right) + i\sin\left(\tan^{-1}\frac{1}{2}\right)\right) \\ &= \sqrt{5}\left(\frac{2}{\sqrt{5}} + i\frac{1}{\sqrt{5}}\right) = 2 + i \end{aligned}$$

So $r = 2 + i$. You can follow the same process to find that $s = 2 - i$. Notice that $r + s = 4$ and 4 is a root of the equation $x^3 - 15x - 4 = 0$.

What about the other roots? Of course, you could just divide $x^3 - 15x - 4$ by $x - 4$, get a quadratic, and solve it. But the goal of the project (and Cardano's original goal) is to find a general method for finding all three roots of any cubic.

Go back to the equations

$$r^3 = 2 + 11i \quad \text{and} \quad s^3 = 2 - 11i$$

There are three roots to each equation. You have found one for each:

$$\alpha = 2 + i \quad \text{for the first equation, and}$$

$$\beta = 2 - i \quad \text{for the second}$$

But, from Investigation 2C, you have seen that if $\omega = \frac{-1 + i\sqrt{3}}{2}$, then ω and ω^2 are cube roots of unity so their cubes are each 1. In other words, the three roots of $r^3 = 2 + 11i$ are

$$\alpha, \ \omega\alpha, \text{ and } \omega^2\alpha$$

And the three roots of $s^3 = 2 - 11i$ are

$$\beta, \ \omega\beta, \text{ and } \omega^2\beta$$

You now have nine choices for the roots of the original equation, corresponding to the possible values for r and s.

r	s
$2+i$	$2-i$
$\omega(2+i) = \frac{-2-\sqrt{3}}{2} + \left(\frac{2\sqrt{3}-1}{2}\right)i$	$\omega(2-i) = \frac{-2+\sqrt{3}}{2} + \left(\frac{2\sqrt{3}+1}{2}\right)i$
$\omega^2(2+i) = \frac{-2+\sqrt{3}}{2} + \left(\frac{-2\sqrt{3}-1}{2}\right)i$	$\omega^2(2-i) = \frac{-2-\sqrt{3}}{2} + \left(\frac{-2\sqrt{3}+1}{2}\right)i$

Answers

Project

1. $r = 2 + i$ and $s = 2 - i$; $r = \omega(2 + i)$ and $s = \omega^2(2 - i)$; $r = \omega^2(2 + i)$ and $s = \omega(2 - i)$

2. $\tan 3x = \frac{3\tan x - \tan^3 x}{1 - 3\tan^2 x} = \frac{3\left(\frac{1}{2}\right) - \left(\frac{1}{2}\right)^3}{1 - 3\left(\frac{1}{2}\right)^2} = \frac{\frac{3}{2} - \frac{1}{8}}{1 - \frac{3}{4}} = \frac{12 - 1}{8 - 6} = \frac{11}{2}$

3. Substitute each number in the equation and do the arithmetic to verify that you get a true result each time.

4. $3, -\frac{3}{2} \pm \frac{\sqrt{3}}{2}i$

5. Step 1 Write the equation in the form $(r + s)^3 - 3rs(r + s) - (r^3 + s^3) = 0$.

Step 2 Write a system consisting of the equations $r^3s^3 = -\frac{p^3}{27}$ and $r^3 + s^3 = -q$.

Step 3 Write a quadratic equation of the form $y^2 + by + c = 0$ that has $-q$ as the sum of its roots and $-\frac{p^3}{27}$ as the product of its roots.

Step 4 Solve the equation from Step 3 to get values for r^3 and s^3.

Step 5 Make a two-column table with the three possible values of r in the r-column and the three possible values of s in the s-column.

Step 6 Look for pairs of values, one from the r-column and one from the s-column, with a sum that is a root of the original cubic equation. Find all three such pairs. The sums that work are the solutions of the cubic.

6. a. If $r + s$ is a root of $x^3 + px + q = 0$, then $(r + s)^3 + p(r + s) + q = 0$. This last equation gives $(r + s)^3 + 3rs(r + s) = -q - p(r + s)$. So $r^3 + s^3 = -q$ and $3rs = -p$. From $3rs = -p$, it follows that $r^3s^3 = -\frac{p^3}{27}$.

But there are only three values of $r + s$ that work in the original cubic.

1. Find the three combinations from the nine possibilities for $r + s$ that satisfy

$$x^3 - 15x - 4 = 0$$

2. Using the formula for tan 3x, show that if $\tan x = \frac{1}{2}$, then $\tan 3x = \frac{11}{2}$.

It may seem that you now have a general method of solving a cubic of the form

$$x^3 + px + q = 0$$

You will generalize the algorithm used for $x^3 - 15x - 4 = 0$ in the remaining exercises for this project. But this is a special kind of cubic—monic with no x^2 term. What about cubics like

$$x^3 + x^2 - 2x - 1 = 0$$

or even

$$8x^3 + 4x^2 - 4x - 1 = 0$$

In CME Project *Algebra 2,* you saw that you can transform any cubic, using affine transformations, to a monic cubic with no x^2 term. So, if you can solve $x^3 + px + q = 0$, you can solve any cubic.

3. Show that the roots of $x^3 - 15x - 4 = 0$ are $4, -2 + \sqrt{3}$, and $-2 - \sqrt{3}$.
4. Solve $x^3 - 6x - 9 = 0$
   a. By any method you like
   b. By Cardano's method
5. Describe Cardano's method for solving a cubic of the form

$$x^3 + px + q = 0$$

as an algorithm

6. Consider a cubic of the form

$$x^3 + px + q = 0$$

   a. Show that if you represent a root as a sum $r + s$, then

$$r^3 + s^3 = -q$$

and

$$rs = -\frac{p}{3}$$

so

$$r^3s^3 = -\frac{p^3}{27}$$

   b. Show that

$$r^3 = \frac{-q + \sqrt{q^2 + 4\frac{p^3}{27}}}{2}$$

and

$$s^3 = \frac{-q - \sqrt{q^2 + 4\frac{p^3}{27}}}{2}.$$

   c. Explain how you can use the expressions in part (b) to find the roots of the equation.

Cardano's Formula is often stated as a theorem.

Theorem 2.7 Cardano's Formula

The roots of $x^3 + px + q = 0$ are

$$\sqrt[3]{\frac{-q + \sqrt{\frac{27q^2 + 4p^3}{27}}}{2}} + \sqrt[3]{\frac{-q - \sqrt{\frac{27q^2 + 4p^3}{27}}}{2}}$$

7. Explain how you can use the above formula to produce three roots.

7. From Exercise 5, it follows that $\sqrt[3]{\frac{-q + \sqrt{\frac{27q^2 + 4p^3}{27}}}{2}} + \sqrt[3]{\frac{-q - \sqrt{\frac{27q^2 + 4p^3}{27}}}{2}}$ is one root. Another root will be $\left(\frac{-1 + i\sqrt{3}}{2}\right)\sqrt[3]{\frac{-q + \sqrt{\frac{27q^2 + 4p^3}{27}}}{2}} + \left(\frac{-1 + i\sqrt{3}}{2}\right)\sqrt[3]{\frac{-q - \sqrt{\frac{27q^2 + 4p^3}{27}}}{2}}$. The third root will be $\left(\frac{-1 - i\sqrt{3}}{2}\right)\sqrt[3]{\frac{-q + \sqrt{\frac{27q^2 + 4p^3}{27}}}{2}} + \left(\frac{-1 + i\sqrt{3}}{2}\right)\sqrt[3]{\frac{-q - \sqrt{\frac{27q^2 + 4p^3}{27}}}{2}}$.

b. The quadratic equation that has $r^3 + s^3$ as the sum of its roots and r^3s^3 as the product of its roots is $y^2 - (r^3 + s^3)y + r^3s^3 = 0$. Using the result from part (a), this equation becomes $y^2 + qy - \frac{p^3}{27} = 0$. Use the quadratic formula to solve this equation. The roots are the values of r^3 and s^3; that is, $r^3 = \frac{-q + \sqrt{q^2 + \frac{4p^3}{27}}}{2}$ and $s^3 = \frac{-q - \sqrt{q^2 + \frac{4p^3}{27}}}{2}$.

c. Use the specific values of p and q (from the original cubic equation) to obtain values for r^3 and s^3 using the expressions found in part (b). Make a table with an r-column and an s-column, and in the respective columns, list the three possible values of r and the three possible values of s. Identify the sums $r + s$, , each involving a value from the r-column and a value from the s-column, that will make the original cubic true. There will be three such sums, and they are the roots of the original cubic equation.

Wrap Up

If you have done this Project in class, you may want to assign some of the exercises as homework, or ask students to write a description of Cardano's Method in their own words. If only some students have worked on the Project, you may want to give them an opportunity to present their work to the class.

8. When solving

$$x^3 + px + q = 0$$

with Cardano's method, you are led to a "reduced quadratic" that has roots r^3 and s^3.

$$x^2 + qx - \frac{p^3}{27} = 0$$

a. Show that if the discriminant of this equation is D then

$$27D = 27q^2 + 4p^3$$

b. If $27q^2 + 4p^3 > 0$, show that the cubic has one real root and two complex roots.

c. If $27q^2 + 4p^3 = 0$, show that the cubic has two real roots.

d. If $27q^2 + 4p^3 < 0$, show that the cubic has three distinct real roots.

9. a. Use scaling and translating to transform the cubic

$$8x^3 + 36x^2 + 52x + 24$$

into a monic cubic with no x^2-term.

b. Find the zeros of the cubic you found in part a.

c. Solve $8x^3 + 36x^2 + 52x + 24 = 0$.

10. In Lesson 2.12, you saw that

$$2\cos\frac{2\pi}{7},\ 2\cos\frac{4\pi}{7},\text{ and } 2\cos\frac{6\pi}{7}$$

are roots of the cubic equation

$$x^3 + x^2 - 2x - 1 = 0$$

a. Transform this equation so that it has the form

$$x^3 + px + q = 0$$

b. Find the roots of the equation in part (a) in terms of

$$r = \frac{\sqrt{7}}{3}\operatorname{cis}\left(\frac{1}{3}\tan^{-1}3\sqrt{3}\right)$$

11. a. Take It Further Suppose that α, β, and γ are three numbers that have a sum of 0. Show that

$$((\alpha-\beta)(\alpha-\gamma)(\beta-\gamma))^2 + 4(\alpha\beta+\alpha\gamma+\beta\gamma)^3 + 27(\alpha\beta\gamma)^2 = 0$$

b. Suppose that α, β, and γ are roots of

$$x^3 + px + q = 0$$

Show that

$$-((\alpha-\beta)(\alpha-\gamma)(\beta-\gamma))^2 = 27q^2 + 4p^3$$

($27q^2 + 4p^3$ is the **discriminant** of the cubic. It is 0 if and only if the cubic has a double root. Compare with Exercise 8.)

Answers

8. See back of book.

9. a. Replace x with $\frac{N-3}{2}$. The polynomial $8x^3 + 36x^2 + 52x + 24$ becomes $N^3 - N$.

b. 0, 1, −1

c. The solutions are $-\frac{3}{2}$, −1, and −2.

10. a. Replace x with $N - \frac{1}{3}$. The polynomial equation $x^3 + x^2 - 2x - 1 = 0$ becomes $N^3 - \frac{7}{3}N - \frac{7}{27} = 0$.

b. For $r = \frac{\sqrt{7}}{3}\operatorname{cis}\left(\frac{1}{3}\tan^{-1}3\sqrt{3}\right)$, $s = \bar{r}$, and $\omega = \operatorname{cis}\frac{2\pi}{3}$, the roots of $N^3 - \frac{7}{3}N - \frac{7}{27} = 0$ are $r + s$, $r\omega + s\omega^2$, and $r\omega^2 + s\omega$.

11. a. Since $\alpha + \beta + \gamma = 0$, it follows that $\gamma = -\alpha - \beta$. Replace γ with $-\alpha - \beta$ in the expression on the left side of the equation that is to be proved. Expand and simplify. The result is 0.

b. If α, β, and γ are the roots of $x^3 + px + q = 0$, then

$x^3 + px + q$
$= (x-\alpha)(x-\beta)(x-\gamma)$
$= x^3 - \alpha x^2 - \beta x^2 - \gamma x^2 + \alpha\beta x + \alpha\gamma x + \beta\gamma x - \alpha\beta\gamma$
$= x^3 - (\alpha+\beta+\gamma)x^2 + (\alpha\beta+\alpha\gamma+\beta\gamma)x - \alpha\beta\gamma$

The coefficient of x^2 is 0, and hence $\alpha + \beta + \gamma = 0$, Also, $p = \alpha\beta + \alpha\gamma + \beta\gamma$ and $q = -\alpha\beta\gamma$. Substitute into part (a) to obtain the following.

$((\alpha-\beta)(\alpha-\gamma)(\beta-\gamma))^2 + 4(\alpha\beta+\alpha\gamma+\beta\gamma)^3 + 27(\alpha\beta\gamma)^2 = 0$
$((\alpha-\beta)(\alpha-\gamma)(\beta-\gamma))^2 + 4(p)^3 + 27(-q)^2 = 0$
$4p^3 + 27q^2 = -((\alpha-\beta)(\alpha-\gamma)(\beta-\gamma))^2$

Chapter 2 Review

Go Online PHSchool.com

For vocabulary review, go to Web Code: bgj-0251

In **Investigation 2A,** you learned to

- represent complex numbers using both rectangular coordinates and trigonometry.
- determine the magnitude and argument of any complex number.
- decide when it is best to use rectangular or polar coordinates to represent complex numbers.

The following questions will help you check your understanding.

1. a. Represent $-3 + 3i$ in polar form.

b. Represent $2 \text{ cis } \frac{5\pi}{3}$ in rectangular form.

2. Find the magnitude and argument of each complex number z.

a. $z = 1 - \sqrt{3}i$

b. $z = 4$

c. $z = -2i$

d. $z = -1 - 3i$

e. $z = 5 \text{ cis } \frac{\pi}{6}$

f. $z = 2 \text{ cis } 35°$

3. Let z and w have the following values.

$$z = 2 - 2i$$
$$w = -4i$$

a. Find zw.

b. Copy and complete the following table.

	Magnitude	Argument
z	■	■
w	■	■
zw	■	■
z^2	■	■
w^3	■	■

c. Find the magnitude of z^5.

d. Find the argument of w^6

In **Investigation 2B,** you learned to

- test trigonometric equations to predict whether they are identities.
- show the Angle-Sum Formulas for cosine and sine using the Multiplication Law for complex numbers.
- use Pythagorean identities and algebra to prove a trigonometric equation is an identity.

The following questions will help you check your understanding.

4. One of these two equations is an identity. The other is not.

$$1 - \cos^2 x \cdot \sin x = \sin^3 x$$
$$\tan^2 x - \sin^2 x \cdot \tan^2 x = \sin^2 x$$

a. Pick a value of x and test it in each equation.

b. Which equation is the identity?

5. a. Write a formula for $\cos\left(x + \frac{3\pi}{4}\right)$ using

$$\text{cis}\left(x + \frac{3\pi}{4}\right) = (\text{cis } x)\left(\text{cis } \frac{3\pi}{4}\right)$$

b. Write a formula for $\cos\left(x + \frac{3\pi}{4}\right)$ using an addition formula.

6. Prove that each of the following equations is an identity.

a. $\frac{2}{\sec^2 x} = \cos 2x + 1$

b. $\tan x - \sin^2 x \tan x = \frac{1}{2} \sin 2x$

Chapter Review

1. a. $3\sqrt{2} \text{ cis } \frac{3\pi}{4}$

b. $1 - i\sqrt{3}$

2. a. $|z| = 2$, $\arg(z) = \frac{5\pi}{3}$

b. $|z| = 4$, $\arg(z) = 0$

c. $|z| = 2$, $\arg(z) = \frac{3\pi}{2}$

d. $|z| = \sqrt{10}$, $\arg(z) = \frac{3\pi}{2} - \tan^{-1}\frac{1}{3} \approx 4.39$

e. $|z| = 5$, $\arg(z) = \frac{\pi}{6}$

f. $|z| = 2$, $\arg(z) = 35°$

3. a. $-8 - 8i$

b.

C	$\lvert C \rvert$	arg C
z	$2\sqrt{2}$	$\frac{7\pi}{4}$
w	4	$\frac{3\pi}{2}$
zw	$8\sqrt{2}$	$\frac{5\pi}{4}$
z^2	8	$\frac{3\pi}{2}$
w^3	64	$\frac{\pi}{2}$

c. $128\sqrt{2}$

d. π

4. a. Answers may vary. Sample: Let $x = \frac{\pi}{6}$. The first equation gives $\frac{5}{8} = \frac{1}{8}$, which is false. The second equation gives $\frac{1}{4} = \frac{1}{4}$, which is true.

b. the second equation

5. a. See back of book.

b. Use the formula for $\cos(x + y)$.

$$\cos\left(x + \frac{3\pi}{4}\right) = \cos x \cos \frac{3\pi}{4} - \sin x \sin \frac{3\pi}{4}$$
$$= -\frac{\sqrt{2}}{2} \cos x - \frac{\sqrt{2}}{2} \sin x$$

So $\cos\left(x + \frac{3\pi}{4}\right) = -\frac{\sqrt{2}}{2} \cos x - \frac{\sqrt{2}}{2} \sin x$.

6. a.

$$\cos 2x + 1 = 2\cos^2 x - 1 + 1$$
$$= 2\cos^2 x = \frac{2}{\sec^2 x}$$

b.

$$\tan x - \sin^2 x \tan x = \tan x (1 - \sin^2 x)$$
$$= \tan x \cos^2 x$$
$$= \sin x \cos x$$
$$= \frac{1}{2}(2 \sin x \cos x)$$
$$= \frac{1}{2} \sin 2x$$

In **Investigation 2C,** you learned to

- calculate powers of complex numbers using De Moivre's Theorem.
- understand the geometry of roots of unity, and the connection to roots of equations of the form $x^n - 1 = 0$.
- find exact algebraic expressions for certain trigonometric values.

The following questions will help you check your understanding.

7. Let z and w have the following values.

$$z = 2 \text{ cis } 40^\circ$$
$$w = -2 + 2i$$

Find each of the following.

a. z^2

b. z^{10}

c. w^2

d. w^4

8. a. Find all the roots of

$$x^9 - 1 = 0$$

b. Graph the roots of $x^9 - 1 = 0$ on the complex plane.

c. Find the exact value of

$$\sum_{k=0}^{8} \sin \frac{2\pi k}{9}$$

9. Find the exact value of $\sin \frac{5\pi}{12}$.

Answers

7. a. $4 \cos 80^\circ + 4i \sin 80^\circ$

b. $1024 \cos 40^\circ + 1024\, i \sin 40^\circ$

c. $-8i$

d. -64

8. a. $\text{cis } \frac{2\pi k}{9}$ for k a whole number from 0 to 8

b.

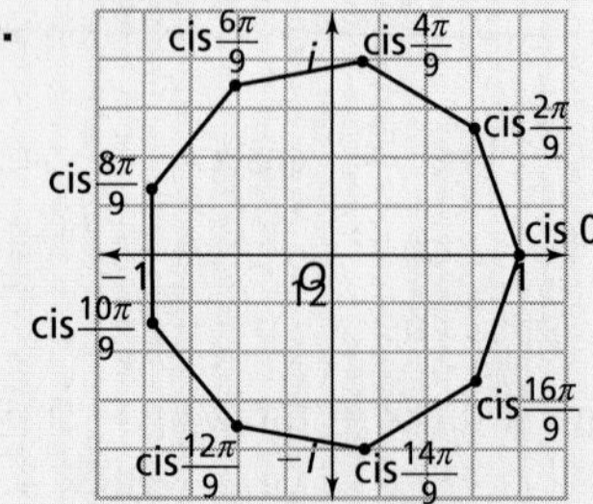

c. 0

9. $\frac{\sqrt{\sqrt{3} + 2}}{2}$, or $\frac{\sqrt{2} + \sqrt{6}}{4}$

Chapter 2

Test

Go Online PHSchool.com

For a chapter test, go to Web Code: bga-0253

Multiple Choice

1. Find $2 \text{ cis } \frac{3\pi}{4}$ in rectangular form.

   A. $-1 + i$ B. $-\sqrt{2} + i\sqrt{2}$

   C. $\sqrt{2} - i\sqrt{2}$ D. $\frac{\sqrt{2}}{2} - \frac{\sqrt{2}}{2}i$

2. Let z and w have the following values.

$$z = 3 \text{ cis } \frac{\pi}{6}$$

$$w = 5 \text{ cis } \frac{2\pi}{3}$$

   Find $\arg(zw)$.

   A. 8 B. 15 C. $\frac{5\pi}{6}$ D. $\frac{\pi}{9}$

3. Which of the following are identically equal to $\cos 2x$?

   I. $2\cos^2 - 1$

   II. $2 \sin x \cos x$

   III. $\cos^2 x + \sin^2 x$

   A. I only B. I and II

   C. II only D. I, II, and III

4. Let z be a complex number where $|z| = 4$ and $\arg(z) = \frac{\pi}{6}$. What is the magnitude of z^3?

   A. $\frac{\pi}{2}$ B. $\frac{\pi}{18}$ C. 12 D. 64

5. Evaluate the sum.

$$\sum_{k=0}^{4} \sin \frac{2k\pi}{5}$$

   A. -1 B. 0 C. 1 D. 2π

Open Response

6. Let z and w have the following values.

$$z = -2 - 2i$$

$$w = 2\sqrt{3} + 2i$$

   Copy and complete the following table.

	Magnitude	Argument
z	■	■
w	■	■
zw	■	■
z^2	■	■
w^3	■	■

7. Use the Angle-Sum Formulas to find each of the following.

   a. $\cos\left(x + \frac{\pi}{6}\right)$ b. $\sin(x - 2\pi)$

   c. $\cos\left(x - \frac{\pi}{2}\right)$ d. $\sin\left(x + \frac{3\pi}{2}\right)$

8. Prove the identity.

$$\tan x + \cot x = \sec x \cdot \csc x$$

9. Find $|z^4|$ and $\arg(z^4)$.

   a. $z = 3$ b. $z = 3 \text{ cis } 50°$

   c. $z = -5i$ d. $z = \sqrt{3} - i$

10. a. Find all the roots of $x^5 - 1 = 0$.

    b. Graph the roots of $x^5 - 1 = 0$ on the complex plane.

11. How can complex numbers be used to find formulas for $\cos 2x$ and $\sin 2x$?

Test

Assessment Resources

Chapter Test Form A page 1 of 2

Multiple Choice

1. Find $-5 + 5i$ in polar form.

   A. $5\sqrt{2} \text{ cis } \frac{\pi}{4}$ B. $5 \text{ cis } \frac{3\pi}{4}$ C. $5\sqrt{2} \text{ cis } \frac{3\pi}{4}$ D. $\sqrt{10} \text{ cis } \frac{3\pi}{4}$

2. $$z = 6 \text{ cis } \frac{5\pi}{6}$$

$$w = 3 \text{ cis } \frac{\pi}{3}$$

   Find $\arg(zw)$.

   A. 9 B. 18 C. $\frac{5\pi}{18}$ D. $\frac{7\pi}{6}$

3. Which of the following are identically equal to $\sin 2x$?

   I. $2\cos^2 x - 1$

   II. $2 \sin x \cos x$

   III. $\cos^2 x - \sin^2 x$

   A. I only B. II only C. I and II D. I, II, and III

4. Let z be a complex number such that $|z| = 5$ and $\arg(z) = \frac{\pi}{4}$. What is the magnitude of z^2?

   A. 10 B. 25 C. $\frac{\pi}{2}$ D. $\frac{\pi}{8}$

5. Evaluate the sum.

$$\sum_{k=0}^{3} \sin \frac{2k\pi}{4}$$

   A. -1 B. 0 C. 1 D. 2π

Open Response

6. $$z = -1 + i$$

$$w = \sqrt{3} + i$$

   Complete the table.

	Magnitude	Argument
z		
w		
zw		
z^4		
w^5		

Also Available: Form B

Test

1. B 2. C 3. A

4. D 5. B

6.

C	|C|	arg C
z	$2\sqrt{2}$	$\frac{5\pi}{4}$
w	4	$\frac{\pi}{6}$
zw	$8\sqrt{2}$	$\frac{17\pi}{12}$
z^2	8	$\frac{\pi}{2}$
w^3	64	$\frac{\pi}{2}$

7. a. $\frac{\sqrt{3}}{2}\cos x - \frac{1}{2}\sin x$ b. $\sin x$

   c. $\sin x$ d. $-\cos x$

8. $$\tan x + \cot x = \frac{\sin x}{\cos x} + \frac{\cos x}{\sin x}$$

$$= \frac{\sin^2 x + \cos^2 x}{\cos x \sin x} = \frac{1}{\cos x \sin x}$$

$$= \sec x \cdot \csc x$$

9. a. $|z^4| = 81$, $\arg(z^4) = 0$

   b. $|z^4| = 81$, $\arg(z^4) = \frac{10\pi}{9}$

   c. $|z^4| = 625$, $\arg(z^4) = 0$

   d. $|z^4| = 16$, $\arg(z^4) = \frac{4\pi}{3}$

10. a. all the numbers $\text{cis } \frac{2\pi k}{5}$ for whole numbers k from 0 to 4

    b.

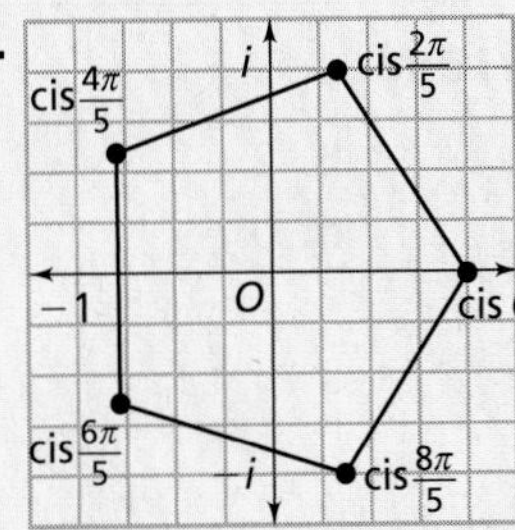

11. Square $\cos x + i \sin x$ to obtain $(\cos^2 x - \sin^2 x) + (2 \sin x \cos x)i$. Then $\cos 2x$ is the real part of the product, and $\sin 2x$ is the imaginary part.

Cumulative Review

Assessment Resources

Quarter Test page 1

Multiple Choice

1. Simplify the expression $\cos\frac{4\pi}{3}\cdot\sin\frac{2\pi}{3}-\sin\frac{11\pi}{6}\cdot\cos\frac{5\pi}{6}$.
   A. $-\frac{\sqrt{3}}{2}$ B. 0 C. 1 D. $\frac{\sqrt{3}}{2}$

2. Solve $4\cos^2 x-3=0$ on the interval $0\le x<2\pi$.
   A. $\frac{\pi}{3}, \frac{5\pi}{3}$ B. $\frac{\pi}{6}, \frac{11\pi}{6}$
   C. $\frac{\pi}{6}, \frac{5\pi}{6}, \frac{7\pi}{6}, \frac{11\pi}{6}$ D. $\frac{\pi}{3}, \frac{2\pi}{3}, \frac{4\pi}{3}, \frac{5\pi}{3}$

3. Let x be an arc on the unit circle. If $\cos x>0$ and $\sin x<0$, in which quadrant must x lie?
   A. I B. II C. III D. IV

4. If $z=3\text{ cis }74°$ and $w=2\text{ cis }47°$, find zw.
   A. 6 cis 121° B. 5 cis 121° C. $\frac{3}{2}$ cis 27° D. 6 cis 3478°

5. Simplify $\cos\left(x+\frac{\pi}{2}\right)$.
   A. $-\cos x$ B. $\cos x$ C. $\sin x$ D. $-\sin x$

6. If $z=-3+5i$, find arg (z) in radians.
   A. −1.03 B. 1.03 C. 2.11 D. 5.25

7. Simplify $|-7+3i|$.
   A. −4 B. $\sqrt{58}$ C. 10 D. $2\sqrt{10}$

Open Response

8. Simplify $\cos\left(-\frac{\pi}{6}\right)+\cos\frac{\pi}{6}$.

9. For each degree measure, find the corresponding radians measure.
   a. 144° b. 210° c. 270° d. 315°

10. Solve the equation $4\sin x-3=0$ on the interval $0\le x<2\pi$. Round your answer(s) to four decimal places.

Cumulative Review

1. Find the value of each expression.
   a. $\tan\left(\cos^{-1}\frac{\sqrt{3}}{2}+\sin^{-1}\frac{1}{2}\right)$
   b. $\cos 0+3\sin 150°-\cos\frac{\pi}{3}$
   c. $|-7+i|$
   d. $\sum_{k=0}^{7}\cos\frac{2\pi k}{8}$

2. Find the solutions to each equation for $0\le x<2\pi$.
   a. $2\sin x+1=0$
   b. $\tan\left(2x+\frac{\pi}{6}\right)+\sqrt{3}=0$
   c. $2\cos^2 x-\cos x=0$

3. Simplify the expression below.

$$\cos(\tan^{-1}0)-\sin\left(\cos^{-1}\frac{\sqrt{3}}{2}\right)+\tan\left(\sin^{-1}\frac{\sqrt{2}}{2}\right)$$

4. Find the degree measure that correspond to each of the following.
   a. $\frac{7\pi}{4}$ radians
   b. $\frac{3\pi}{2}$ radians

5. Find the period of each function.
   a. $f(t)=\sin(4t)$
   b. $h(t)=\cos\left(\frac{t}{2}\right)$

6. The temperature in an experimental chamber changes periodically as a function of time. The temperature, h, in degrees Celsius, is given by

$$h=25+8\sin\left(\pi\left(\frac{t+1}{3}\right)\right)$$

where t is the number of hours after the experiment begins.
   a. What is temperature when the experiment begins?
   b. What is maximum temperature during the experiment?
   c. What is minimum temperature during the experiment?

7. Evaluate the expression below, where a and b are real numbers.

$$a^2\sin\left(-\frac{\pi}{6}\right)+2ab\cos\frac{3\pi}{2}+b^2\sin\frac{3\pi}{4}\cos\frac{5\pi}{4}$$

8. Copy and complete the table.

	Amplitude	Minimum	Maximum
$f(x)=3\sin 2x$	■	■	■
$g(x)=-\sin x+1$	■	■	■

9. Solve the equation below for $0\le x<2\pi$.

$$\tan^3 x-3\tan x=0$$

10. Sketch the graph of $y=-2\sin x+1$ on $0\le x\le 2\pi$.

Answers

Cumulative Review

1. a. $\sqrt{3}$ b. 2
   c. $5\sqrt{2}$ d. 0
2. a. $\frac{7\pi}{6}, \frac{11\pi}{6}$
   b. $\frac{\pi}{4}, \frac{3\pi}{4}, \frac{5\pi}{4}, \frac{7\pi}{4}$
   c. $\frac{\pi}{3}, \frac{\pi}{2}, \frac{3\pi}{2}, \frac{5\pi}{3}$
3. $\frac{3}{2}$
4. a. 315° b. 270°
5. a. $\frac{\pi}{2}$ b. 4π
6. a. 32°C b. 33°C c. 17°C
7. $-\frac{1}{2}a^2-\frac{1}{2}b^2$

8.

	Amplitude	Minimum	Maximum
3 sin 2x	3	−3	3
− sin x + 1	1	0	2

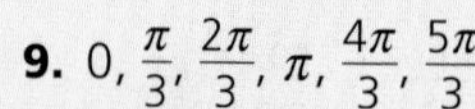

9. $0, \frac{\pi}{3}, \frac{2\pi}{3}, \pi, \frac{4\pi}{3}, \frac{5\pi}{3}$

10.

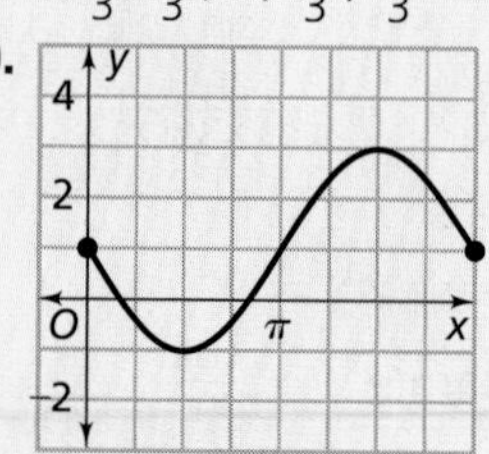

11. $\frac{\pi}{4}, \frac{5\pi}{4}$

12. a. $\frac{\sqrt{2}}{4}-\frac{\sqrt{6}}{4}$ b. $-\sqrt{3}$
    c. 1
13. a. $\frac{\sqrt{2}}{2}\sin x+\frac{\sqrt{2}}{2}\cos x$
    b. $-\frac{1}{2}\cos x-\frac{\sqrt{3}}{2}\sin x$
    c. $-\sin x$
    d. $\frac{\sqrt{3}}{2}\cos x+\frac{1}{2}\sin x$

11. Where do the graphs of $y = \sin x$ and $y = \cos x$ intersect for $0 \leq x < 2\pi$?

12. Find the value of each expression.

a. $\cos \frac{7\pi}{12}$

b. $\tan\left(\sin^{-1}\left(-\frac{\sqrt{3}}{2}\right)\right)$

c. $\left(\frac{\sqrt{2}}{2} + \frac{\sqrt{2}}{2}i\right)^{80}$

13. Use the Angle-Sum and Angle-Difference formulas to simplify each expression.

a. $\sin\left(x + \frac{\pi}{4}\right)$

b. $\cos\left(x + \frac{2\pi}{3}\right)$

c. $\sin\left(x - \pi\right)$

d. $\cos\left(x - \frac{\pi}{6}\right)$

14. a. Find all the roots of $x^6 - 1 = 0$.

b. Graph the roots of $x^6 - 1 = 0$ on the complex plane.

15. For $z = -1 + i\sqrt{3}$ and $w = 3 - 3i$, copy and complete the table.

Number	Magnitude	Argument
z	■	■
w	■	■
zw	■	■
z^4	■	■
w^2	■	■

16. Let $\omega = \frac{\sqrt{2}}{2} + \frac{i\sqrt{2}}{2}$. Simplify the expression below.

$$1 + \omega + \omega^2 + \omega^3 + \omega^4$$

17. Find the magnitude and argument (in radians) of each complex number. Approximate your answer to two decimal places.

a. $z = 5 - 5i$

b. $z = 7 \text{ cis}\left(\frac{2\pi}{3}\right)$

c. $z = -2\sqrt{3} + 2i$

d. $z = 3 - i$

18. Prove the identity $\frac{1}{1 + \tan x} = \frac{\cot x}{1 + \cot x}$.

19. Suppose $\sin\theta = \frac{15}{17}$ and $\cos\theta = -\frac{8}{17}$. Find the value of each expression.

a. $\tan\theta$

b. $\cos 2\theta$

c. $\sin 2\theta$

d. $\tan 2\theta$

20. Let $z = 2 - 2i\sqrt{3}$ and $w = -\sqrt{3} + i$. Graph and label z, w, and zw on the complex plane.

Quarter Test page 2

11. Use the addition formulas for the cosine and sine functions to simplify each of the following.

a. $\sin(x + \pi)$

b. $\cos(270° - x)$

c. $\sin(x - 135°)$

d. $\cos\left(x + \frac{2\pi}{3}\right)$

12. Prove the identity.

$$1 - \sin^2 x = \frac{1}{1 + \tan^2 x}$$

13. If $z = 2 \text{ cis } \frac{3\pi}{4}$, find each of the following. Write your answers in rectangular form.

a. z^2

b. z^3

c. z^4

Challenge Problem

14. Suppose $z = 2 \text{ cis } \frac{\pi}{6}$ and $zw = -7i$.

a. Explain a method for finding w.

b. Use your method to find w.

c. Check your work by finding the product zw.

14. a. $\text{cis } 0$, $\text{cis } \frac{\pi}{3}$, $\text{cis } \frac{2\pi}{3}$, $\text{cis } \pi$, $\text{cis } \frac{4\pi}{3}$, $\text{cis } \frac{5\pi}{3}$

b.

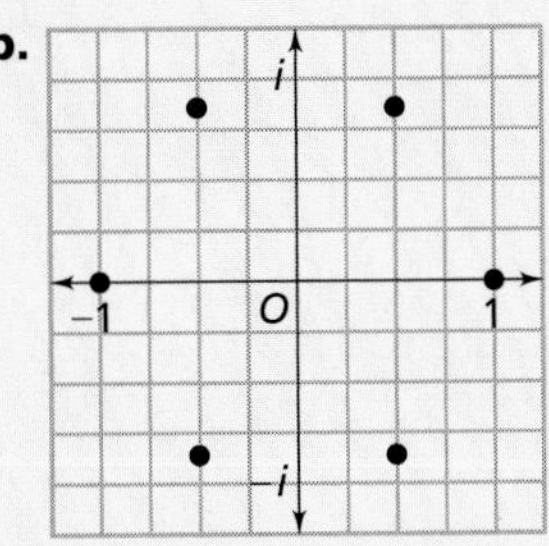

15.

	Magnitude	Argument
z	2	$\frac{2\pi}{3}$
w	$3\sqrt{2}$	$\frac{7\pi}{4}$
zw	$6\sqrt{2}$	$\frac{5\pi}{12}$
z^4	16	$\frac{2\pi}{3}$
w^2	18	$\frac{3\pi}{2}$

16. $(1 + \sqrt{2})i$

17. a. 7.07, 5.50 **b.** 7, 2.09 **c.** 4, 2.62 **d.** 3.16, 5.96

18. Answers will vary. Sample:

$$\frac{1}{1 + \tan x} = \frac{\cot x}{1 + \cot x}$$

$$\frac{1}{1 + \frac{\sin x}{\cos x}} = \frac{\frac{\cos x}{\sin x}}{1 + \frac{\cos x}{\sin x}}$$

$$\frac{1}{\frac{\cos x}{\cos x} + \frac{\sin x}{\cos x}} = \frac{\frac{\cos x}{\sin x}}{\frac{\sin x}{\sin x} + \frac{\cos x}{\sin x}}$$

$$\frac{\cos x}{\cos x + \sin x} = \frac{\frac{\cos x}{\sin x} \cdot \sin x}{\left(\frac{\cos x}{\sin x} + \frac{\sin x}{\sin x}\right) \cdot \sin x}$$

$$\frac{\cos x}{\cos x + \sin x} = \frac{\cos x}{\cos x + \sin x}$$

19. a. $-\frac{15}{8}$ **b.** $-\frac{161}{289}$ **c.** $-\frac{240}{289}$ **d.** $\frac{240}{161}$

20. See back of book.

Chapter 3
Analysis of Functions

In this chapter, students begin to analyze graphs by thinking about continuity and the slope of a line tangent to a graph at a point. Along the way, they review and practice sketching the basic graphs. They also review and practice factoring and algebraic calculation, as they convert functions into different forms for different purposes. They even practice polynomial long division as they learn to write the Taylor expansion for a function around a point. However, to students, the review and practice are incidental, because they are grappling with new questions. Although they calculate limits informally for the most part, they gain experience that helps prepare them for the more formal limit proofs of calculus. Also, their growing informal understanding of the meaning of the slope of a non-linear graph prepares them for their study of derivatives.

Chapter Overview

INVESTIGATION 3A, *Polynomial Functions,* has students analyze the graphs of many different polynomial functions and develop a general description of the properties of these functions.

INVESTIGATION 3B, *Rational Functions,* has students analyze the graphs of rational functions and develop a general description of the properties of these functions.

INVESTIGATION 3C, *Exponential and Logarithmic Functions,* has students analyze the graphs of exponential and logarithm functions and develop a general description of the properties of these functions.

For more information on the Investigations, see

- Chapter Road Map, pp.164–165
- Investigation Road Maps, pp. 166, 204, 238

PROJECT The Project near the end of the chapter is optional. You can assign the Project at any time during the chapter depending on how often and how long you feel students should work on it.

Pacing Suggestions and Materials

Investigation 3A *Polynomial Functions*

DAY	LESSON	HOMEWORK
1	3.1 Getting Started Core: 1, 2, 3, 4, 5, 6 Optional: 7	Core: 8, 9, 10, 11 Optional: 12, 13
2	3.2 Continuity of Polynomial Functions Core: 1, 2, 4, 5 Optional: 3, 6; Extension: 7	Core: 8, 9, 10, 11, 14, 15, 18, 19, 22 Optional: 12, 13, 16, 20, 23; Extension: 17, 2
3	3.3 Graphs and Secant Lines Core: 1, 2, 3, 4, 5, 8, 9 Optional: 6, 10; Extension: 7	Core: 11, 13, 15, 16, 18, 20 Optional: 12, 19, 21a–d, 22; Extension: 14, 1
4	3.4 Polynomials in Powers of $x - a$ Core: 1, 3, 4, 5 Optional: 2	Core: 6, 7, 10, 11, 12, 16, 17 Optional: 8, 9, 13, 15; Extension: 14
5	3.5 Secants and Tangents Core: 1, 2, 3, 4, 5 Optional: 6, 7	Core: 8, 9, 10, 11, 13 Optional: 14; Extension: 12

Investigation 3B *Rational Functions*

DAY	LESSON	HOMEWORK
1	3.6 Getting Started Core: 1, 2, 3, 4, 5, 6 Optional: 7, 8a–b; Extension: 8c	Core: 9, 10, 12, 13, 14 Optional: 11, 15, 16
2	3.7 Graphing Rational Functions Core: 1, 2, 3, 4, 6, 8 Optional: 5, 7; Extension: 9	Core: 10, 11, 12, 14, 15, 16, 17, 18 Optional: 13, 19, 20, 21, 22
3	3.8 Revisiting Secants and Tangents Core: 1, 3, 4, 6, 7 Optional: 2, 5	Core: 8, 9, 10, 11, 12, 14 Optional: 15, 16, 17; Extension: 13
4	3.9 Case Study: $y = \frac{ax + b}{cx + d}$ Core: 1, 2, 3, 4, 5 Optional: 6, 7	Core: 8, 9, 11, 12, 15 Optional: 10, 13, 16, 17; Extension: 14

NOTES	MATERIALS
	• graph paper • graphing calculators • Blackline Masters MC7, MC8
	• graph paper • graphing calculators • Blackline Masters MC7, MC8, 3.2
	• geometry software • graph paper • graphing calculators • Blackline Masters MC7, MC8, MC11, 3.3
	• CAS (recommended) • graph paper • graphing calculators • Blackline Masters MC7, 3.4A, 3.4B
	• CAS (recommended) • geometry software • graph paper • graphing calculators • Blackline Master 3.5

NOTES	MATERIALS
	• graph paper • graphing calculators • Blackline Masters MC7, MC8, 3.6A, 3.6B
	• CAS (recommended) • graph paper • graphing calculators • Blackline Masters MC7, MC8
	• CAS (recommended) • graph paper • graphing calculators • Blackline Masters MC7, 3.8
This optional lesson requires some knowledge of matrices and matrix operations.	• CAS (recommended) • graph paper • graphing calculators • Blackline Masters MC7, MC8

Mathematics Background

FUNCTIONS AS ALGEBRAIC OBJECTS Throughout the CME Project curriculum, students develop a flexible understanding of functions, and approach the idea that functions are not just input-output machines. Functions are also algebraic objects in their own right, and you can compute with functions in much the same way you compute with numbers. One valuable strategy is to define a function using technology, and then use that definition in further calculations. Students use this idea when they transform functions. Once they define $f(x)$ on their calculators, they can simply graph it, and also graph $3f(x)$ or $f(3x)$. Then students dig in to the reasons for the behavior they see.

Similarly, students know how to use technology to calculate with functions they define. Certainly they can add, subtract, multiply, or divide functions and draw conclusions about the results, but students also compose functions and analyze the algebraic structure of functions under the operation of composition. They deepen their understanding of functions as objects with which to compute, as well as rules describing a series of computations.

Experience in computing with functions helps students form an understanding of functions that allows them to make sense of the calculations they see in this chapter, such as

$$\lim_{x \to \infty} \frac{f(x + a) - f(x)}{(x + a) - x}$$

SLOPE OF THE TANGENT TO A GRAPH One way for students to develop their understanding of the slope of the tangent to a graph at a point is by first thinking about average speed. If you start out at a particular place at time 0, and in 2 hours you are 100 miles away, then your average speed is 50 miles per hour. If you look at a graph that plots distance as a function of time for this trip, the two points you know, (0, 0) and (2, 100), are two points on that graph. The average speed is the slope of the line between those two points. In other words, average speed is the slope of the secant line for the function.

However, the instantaneous speed, which is the reading on the speedometer of the car at any moment, is something different. By looking at a distance-time graph, students see that the car is going fastest when the curve is moving upward steeply. It is slowing down when the curve is less steep. If the graph is horizontal for a while, the car has stopped. To calculate the instantaneous speed of the car by looking at the graph, students see that if they choose two points that are very close together to define the secant line, they get a much better estimate of the instantaneous speed. And in fact, the slope of the tangent to the graph at a fixed point is the limit of the slope of the secant as the second point approaches the fixed point along the graph.

continued on p. 164c

continued from p.164b

In this chapter, students use this idea to find the slope of the tangent to the graph of many different kinds of functions.

EXPERIENCE BEFORE FORMALIZATION A hallmark of the CME Project is the notion of *experience before formalization*. You see this at work in the Getting Started lessons that begin each investigation. Students have a chance to look at the kinds of questions they will answer in the investigation, and to gain experience in the material they will study. Students often develop informal solution techniques and conjectures that they can evaluate as the work continues.

This chapter is another instance of experience before formalization. Students gain informal experience with limits and derivatives that will serve them well when they continue on to a formal study of calculus. Later in Chapter 8, they gain similar informal experience with integration as they learn techniques for calculating the area of irregular shapes, such as the area between the graph of a function and the x-axis.

Pacing Suggestions and Materials

Investigation 3C *Exponential and Logarithmic Functions*

DAY	LESSON	HOMEWORK
1	3.10 Getting Started Core: 1, 2, 3, 4, 5, 6 Optional: none	Core: 7, 8, 9, 10 Optional: 11, 12
2	3.11 Compound Interest; the Number e Core: 1, 2, 3, 4, 5, 6 Optional: 7, 8	Core: 9, 10, 13, 14, 15, 16, 17, 18 Optional: 11, 12
3	3.12 Another Way to Find e Core: 1, 2, 3, 5, 6 Optional: 4	Core: 7, 8, 9, 10, 11, 13 Optional: 14; Extension: 12
4	3.13 The Natural Logarithm Function Core: 2, 3, 4, 5, 6a–c Optional: 1, 7; Extension: 6d	Core: 8, 9, 10, 12, 13, 14 Optional: 11a; Extension: 11b
5	3.14 Analysis of $f(x) = e^x$ and $g(x) = \ln x$ Core: 1, 2, 3, 4, 5, 6, 7 Optional: none	Core: 8, 9, 10, 11, 12, 13, 16 Optional: 14, 17; Extension: 15

	NOTES	MATERIALS
		• graph paper • graphing calculators • Blackline Masters MC7, 3.10
		• CAS (recommended) • graph paper • graphing calculators • Blackline Master MC7
		• graph paper • graphing calculators • Blackline Master MC7
		• CAS (recommended) • graph paper • graphing calculators • Blackline Master 3.13
		• graph paper • graphing calculators

Developing Students' Mathematical Habits

REASONING BY CONTINUITY Students look at the graph of a function and choose two points on that graph. They visualize a line through those two points—a secant line. As one of the points remains fixed, students think of the other point as moving along the graph toward the fixed point. When the two points coincide, the secant line becomes a tangent line to the function at a point. The slope of this tangent is the limit of the slopes of the secant lines as the moving point approaches the fixed point.

VISUALIZATION Students learn to relate the graph of a function to the slope of its tangent at any point and use that information to analyze the graph. For example, students look at the graph of $y = \frac{1}{x}$ and see that it is increasing everywhere except at $x = 0$, where it has an asymptote. Then, when they calculate the slope of the tangent to this graph at any point $\left(a, \frac{1}{a}\right)$ as $\frac{1}{a^2}$, they confirm that this expression is, in fact, positive everywhere the function is defined.

GENERALIZATION After finding equations for the tangent to the graph of various polynomial functions and rational functions, students generalize the process and find an equation for the slope of the tangent to the graph of an exponential or logarithm function, even though they have no formal way to calculate the limits involved.

Chapter
3
Investigations at a Glance
3A Polynomial Functions
3B Rational Functions
3C Exponential and Logarithmic Functions

Chapter Road Map

INVESTIGATION 3A, *Polynomial Functions,* explores the graphs of many different polynomial functions and develops a general description of the properties of these functions. Students develop both a formal and an informal understanding of what continuity means. Through key theorems, students draw conclusions about the possible number of roots for a polynomial function of given degree. Students calculate the slope of the line tangent to the graph of polynomial functions at a point by finding the limit of the secant slope as one of the two points that determines the secant line approaches the other. Students also use iterated long division, the method of undetermined coefficients, and technology to write the Taylor expansion for various polynomial functions about a point, and use this expansion to find the equation for the tangent to a polynomial graph at a point.

Analysis of Functions

The world is full of phenomena that seem to involve an abrupt change from one state to another. A balloon is whole one moment, and the next moment it has burst. A bug is sitting quietly on a branch, and an instant later a predator has eaten it. However, high-speed photography reveals that such phenomena actually involve gradual change over a period of time, albeit a very short one. The balloon that appears to burst all at once in fact tears open, with one or more rips that start out small and grow rapidly larger.

Gottfried Leibniz (1646–1716) grasped this fact, even before the invention of photography. "Nature makes no leaps," he declared, calling this the Law of Continuity. In this chapter, you will learn how to analyze continuous functions, and especially how to describe their rates of change. For instance, you will learn what it means to say that the rip in a balloon grows at a rate of about fifty feet per second. You will also learn about discontinuous functions, which (Leibniz's Law of Continuity notwithstanding) are sometimes useful for modeling real-world phenomena.

Vocabulary and Notation

- **average rate of change**
- **continuous**
- **continuously compounded interest**
- **determinant**
- ***e***
- **hole**
- **infinite discontinuity**
- **instantaneous speed**
- **linear fractional transformation, $\mathcal{R}_A$**
- **natural logarithm, $\ln x$**
- **power function**
- **removable discontinuity**
- **secant line**
- **structure-preserving map**
- **tangent line**

INVESTIGATION 3B, *Rational Functions,* explores the graphs of rational functions. These graphs are continuous for points where the function is defined, so students can find equations for the slope of the line tangent to a rational function graph at a point. In an optional lesson, students analyze all functions of the form $y = \frac{ax + b}{cx + d}$ as transformations of the graph $y = \frac{1}{x}$ using polynomial long division and 2-by-2 matrices.

INVESTIGATION 3C, *Exponential and Logarithmic Functions,* continues the analysis to exponential and logarithmic functions. First, *e* is defined through an analysis of compound interest. Students see that as interest is compounded more and more frequently, the yield of the account is greater, but there seems to be a limit to how much it can grow. This leads to the definition of continuously compounded interest and the limit definition of *e*. Students also learn a factorial definition for *e* and show that the two definitions are equivalent. The lesson introduces the function $y = \ln x$ and shows it to be the inverse of $y = e^x$. Then students analyze the functions $y = e^x$ and $y = \ln x$ by finding the equation for the line tangent to the graph at a point.

Chapter Vocabulary and Notation

The following list gives key vocabulary and notation used in the chapter. Selected new vocabulary and notation items are shown in boldface on the student page.

- average rate of change, p. 180
- continuous, p. 171
- continuously compounded interest, p. 243
- determinant, p. 227
- e, p. 243
- hole, p. 211
- infinite discontinuity, p. 211
- instantaneous speed, p. 197
- linear fractional transformation, $\mathcal{R}_A$, p. 227
- natural logarithm, $\ln x$, p. 255
- power function, p. 174
- rational function, p. 205
- reciprocal function, p. 206
- removable discontinuity, p. 211
- secant line, p. 180
- structure-preserving map, p. 228
- tangent line, p. 198
- Taylor expansion, p. 190

Chapter Technology

CME Project *Precalculus* assumes that each student has access to a graphing calculator. It also recommends access to a computer algebra system (CAS) and to geometry software.

Support for the use of technology is available in the TI-Nspire™ Technology Handbook. See p. 704.

A list of technology used with important concepts in this chapter appears below. Students will need access to the functionality listed to develop complete understanding of these topics.

Computer Algebra System

LESSON 3.4 Find the Taylor expansion of a function, p. 193.

LESSON 3.5 Find the remainder in polynomial division, p. 199.

LESSON 3.11 Approximate $\lim_{n \to \infty} P\left(1 + \frac{r}{n}\right)^{nt}$, p. 244.

LESSON 3.11 Evaluate a binomial coefficient, p. 247.

Function-Modeling Language

LESSON 3.1 Model a function definition, p. 168.

LESSON 3.2 Model and graph a function, p. 171.

Geometry Software

LESSON 3.3 Construct a secant line and examine its slope, p. 185.

LESSON 3.5 Construct a tangent line, p. 197.

Graphing Calculator

LESSON 3.3 Sketch a secant line and find its equation, p. 181.

LESSON 3.11 Find *e*, p. 243.

LESSON 3.12 Evaluate an infinite series, p. 252.

LESSON 3.13 Evaluate natural logarithms, p. 254.

Investigation Overview

In this investigation, students work toward understanding the tangent to a polynomial curve at a point, and learn how to find an equation for one. They begin by characterizing polynomial graphs and thinking about continuity, zeros, and the sign of the function value. Although it is beyond the scope of the course to prove the Change of Sign Theorem and the Intermediate Value Theorem, students use these ideas to further explore polynomial functions and their graphs. Then they look at secant lines, which intersect the graph of a polynomial function in two or more points. They explore what happens as one of the two points approaches the other and see that there is a particular tangent line at any point on the curve. Of course, the slope of this tangent to the curve at a point is the derivative, but students do not find derivatives yet. However, they develop an informal understanding that will provide an excellent background for derivatives and what it means to find the derivative in different contexts. Then students learn to write the Taylor expansion for a polynomial function around a point. They use that work, along with connections to polynomial long division, to develop new ways to find the equation of the tangent to a polynomial curve at a point.

You may wish to assign Questions 1–3 for students to think and write about during the investigation.

Learning Goals

- State the Change of Sign Theorem and the Intermediate Value Theorem for Polynomials and use them to analyze the graphs of polynomial functions.
- Find the equation of a line secant to a polynomial function and the average rate of change of a function between two points.
- Write the Taylor expansion for a Polynomial function about a point.
- Find the equation of the tangent to a polynomial curve at a point.

Habits and Skills

- Visualize the graph of a polynomial function from its factored form.
- Use the continuity of a polynomial function to draw conclusions about the function's behavior at extreme values or about lines tangent to the graph of the function.
- Connect quotients in polynomial long division to Taylor expansions and to equations of tangent lines.

Polynomial Functions

In *Polynomial Functions*, you will study the graphs of polynomial functions from various viewpoints. For each graph, you will learn the connection between the rates of change of the function and the graph's secant and tangent lines.

By the end of this investigation, you will be able to answer questions like these.

1. How can you graph a polynomial function given its factored form?
2. How can you determine a polynomial's behavior at very large or very small inputs?
3. How can you use long division to find equations of secant or tangent lines to the graph of a polynomial function?

You will learn how to

- state the Change of Sign Theorem and the Intermediate Value Theorem for Polynomials, and to use them to analyze the graphs of polynomial functions
- find the equation of a line secant to a polynomial function and the average rate of change of a function between two points
- write the Taylor expansion for a polynomial function about a point
- find the equation of the tangent to a polynomial curve at a point

You will develop these habits and skills:

- Visualize the graph of a polynomial function from its factored form.
- Use the continuity of a polynomial function to draw conclusions about the function's behavior at extreme values or about lines tangent to the graph of the function.
- Relate quotients in polynomial long division to Taylor expansions and to equations of tangent lines.

A polynomial function can describe the height, over time, of a falling object.

Investigation Road Map

LESSON 3.1, *Getting Started,* looks closely at the graphs of polynomial functions. Students think about zeroes, signs, and behavior at extreme values.

LESSON 3.2, *Continuity of Polynomial Functions,* introduces continuity, the Change of Sign Theorem, and the Intermediate Value Theorem for Polynomials.

LESSON 3.3, *Graphs and Secant Lines,* explores secant lines intersecting a polynomial function at two points A and B. Students look at the secant line as point B approaches point A and make connections to polynomial long division.

LESSON 3.4, *Polynomials in Powers of $x - a$,* finds a Taylor expansion of a polynomial using polynomial long division, algebraic simplification, and CAS.

LESSON 3.5, *Secants and Tangents,* connects what students learned in the investigation to the equation of the line tangent to a polynomial curve at a point.

3.1 Getting Started

Polynomial functions can have all kinds of interesting graphs. Here are a few favorites:

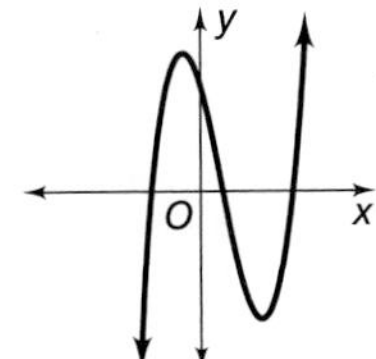

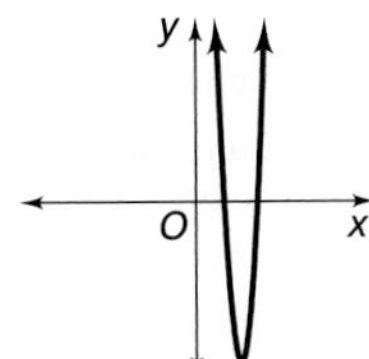

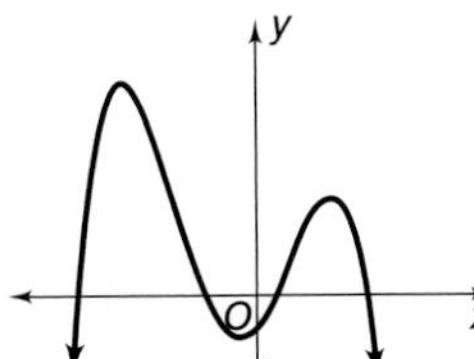

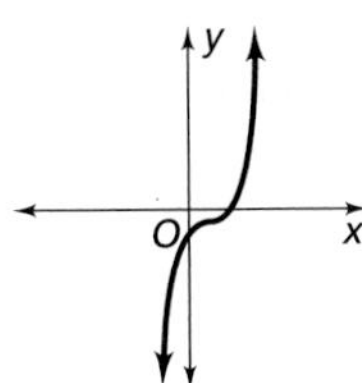

For You to Explore

1. What shapes can the graph of a cubic polynomial function have? Here are some functions to consider.
   - $f(x) = x^3 - 3x^2 - 6x - 3$
   - $g(x) = x^3 - 3x^2 + 3x + 4$

   Try other examples, too.

For example, the first graph shown above rises, falls, and then rises again, increasing without bound. What other shapes are possible?

2. Find, if possible, a cubic polynomial function with a graph that satisfies these conditions.
   - The graph crosses the x-axis at $(-5, 0)$, $(-1, 0)$, and somewhere on the positive x-axis.
   - From left to right, the graph rises, falls, and rises.
   - The graph crosses the y-axis at $(0, -7)$.

   Explain your work.

3. Find, if possible, a cubic polynomial function with a graph that satisfies these conditions.
   - The graph crosses the line with equation $y = 3$ at $(-5, 3)$, $(-1, 3)$, and somewhere with a positive x-coordinate.
   - From left to right, the graph rises, falls, and rises.
   - The graph crosses the y-axis at $(0, -4)$.

   Explain your work.

Answers

For You to Explore

1. There are four possible shapes. From left to right:
   - the graph rises, falls, then rises, increasing without bound.
   - the graph rises, turns, then continues to rise, increasing without bound.
   - the graph falls, rises, then falls, decreasing without bound.
   - the graph falls, turns, and then continues to fall, decreasing without bound.
2. See back of book.
3. Answers may vary. Sample: $g(x) = \frac{7}{10}x^3 + \frac{14}{5}x^2 - \frac{49}{10}x - 4$. Suppose $(2, 3)$ is the third point chosen on the line $y = 3$. A function that works is $g(x) = f(x) + 3$, where $f(x)$ is the function found in Problem 2. The graph of $g(x)$ is $f(x)$ shifted up 3 units.

Lesson Overview

GOAL

- Warm up to the ideas of the investigation.

This Getting Started lesson asks students to describe and characterize the graphs of cubic functions, by relating the factored form of the equation to the shape of its graph. Students pay special attention to the sign of the function and to its zeros. You will encourage them to think about using particular forms of an equation for special purposes, such as predicting the behavior of the graph for large negative and positive values, evaluating the function at a particular point, or finding its zeros. They also begin some informal work to understand the meaning of continuity through limits. Students are exposed to many ideas in this lesson that are formally developed as the investigation continues. Do not expect students to master this material today. They are simply gaining experience that helps motivate their future work.

FOR YOU TO EXPLORE
- Core: 1, 2, 3, 4, 5, 6
- Optional: 7

MATERIALS
- graph paper
- graphing calculators
- Blackline Masters MC7, MC8

HOMEWORK
- Core: 8, 9, 10, 11
- Optional: 12, 13

Launch

Have students start right in on the problems. You may want to give students some guidance about the critical information they must include with the sketch of a graph. For example, you might require students to label any x- or y-intercepts on graphs that they sketch. The material here also reviews the Factor Theorem, which states that if $f(a) = 0$ for a polynomial function $f(x)$, then $(x - a)$ is a factor of the polynomial.

Explore

For You to Explore

As students work, listen for key points that you want to bring up in your end-of-class discussion. Problem 4 is particularly critical, because it asks students to think about the different purposes for different forms of a polynomial equation. Although students may not know how to write a particular special form (such as the one in Expression 4), they can determine that the forms are equivalent and figure out how each form is useful.

You may wish to provide copies of Blackline Masters MC7 and MC8 for students to sketch graphs of polynomial functions.

continued on p. 168

continued from p. 167

PROBLEM 1 A side note in the text gives a brief description of the shape of a graph, but you may want to make this more explicit. For example, you might ask students to tell you the sign of the function for any value of x, identify its zeros, and state whether it is increasing or decreasing. You may or may not require students to determine the maximum and minimum values in each interval. If you do not require it, they can just say something like, "The function is positive between $x = 0$ and $x = 3$, and as you move from left to right in that interval, it increases and then decreases." Students might also want to distinguish between graphs that have three zeros and graphs that only have one zero.

PROBLEM 2 reveals how much students remember about the Factor Theorem and whether you need an in-class review. Most students remember they can use the points where a polynomial function crosses the x-axis to determine factors of the polynomial.

PROBLEM 3 gives students information about where this function crosses the line $y = 3$ rather than the x-axis (which has equation $y = 0$). Some of your students may approach this directly using the points $(-5, 3)$ and $(-1, 3)$. Other students may see this problem as a translation of the graph from Problem 2, and modify their answer from that problem to solve this one.

PROBLEM 4 During this investigation, students learn how to use long division to find expressions such as Expression 2 and Expression 4. These are the Taylor expansions for f about 3 and -3 respectively. Such expressions are handy for finding the equation of the tangent to the curve at a point.

TECHNOLOGY TIP Students can also find these Taylor expansions using the taylor function on the TI-Nspire.

PROBLEM 5 When graphing a function based on its factored form, students likely are comfortable locating the x-intercepts but may not know an effective way to complete a sketch without substituting a lot of values. If you like, you can direct their focus to the sign of the function values, or let them develop their own techniques. They formalize this process as the investigation continues. Some of your students may notice the relationship between these graphs. The two roots to the right of -3 are both approaching 2.

PROBLEM 6 This course takes an informal approach to limits, but students come close to the classic epsilon-delta proofs. As x approaches some value a, the limit for a function is equal to b as long as you can show that there is a value of x near a such that $f(x)$ is within some small distance of b.

4. Here are some expressions that define a function f.

Expression 1: $f(x) = (x - 1)(x - 6)(x - 7)$

Expression 2: $f(x) = 24 - 2(x - 3) - 5(x - 3)^2 + (x - 3)^3$

Expression 3: $f(x) = x^3 - 14x^2 + 55x - 42$

Expression 4: $f(x) = -360 + 166(x + 3) - 23(x + 3)^2 + (x + 3)^3$

Expression 5: $f(x) = x^3\left(1 - \frac{14}{x} + \frac{55}{x^2} - \frac{42}{x^3}\right)$

a. Show that definitions 1–4 are equivalent and that definition 5 is equivalent to the others except at $x = 0$.

b. Which form is best for finding the zeros of f? What are the zeros of f?

c. Which form is best for finding $f(-3)$? What is $f(-3)$?

d. Which form is best for deciding how $f(x)$ behaves if x is a large positive number? If x is a large negative number (such as -1000)?

e. Which form is best for estimating the outputs of f for very small inputs? Estimate (without a calculator) the value of $f(0.00001)$. Explain your estimate.

f. Sketch the graph of $y = f(x)$.

Try adding a statement for the case $x = 0$ to make the last definition fully equivalent to the others. Could you model this two-part definition in your function-modeling language (FML)?

5. Sketch the graph of each function.

a. $f(x) = (x + 3)(x - 1)(x - 3)$

b. $h(x) = (x + 3)(x - 1.5)(x - 2.5)$

c. $k(x) = (x + 3)(x - 1.99)(x - 2.01)$

d. $g(x) = (x + 3)(x - 2)^2$

Habits of Mind

Make connections. The idea in Problem 5 is for you to connect what is happening with the equations to what is happening with the graphs. Use your calculator to check your sketches, but try to imagine the graphs before you use the technology.

6. Let f be the function from Problem 4. How close do you have to make a to 5 in order to be sure that the following conditions are met?

a. $|f(a) - f(5)| < 0.1$?

b. $|f(a) - f(5)| < 0.01$?

c. $|f(a) - f(5)| < 0.001$?

d. $|f(a) - f(5)| < 0.0001$?

7. The graph of the function h is at the right.

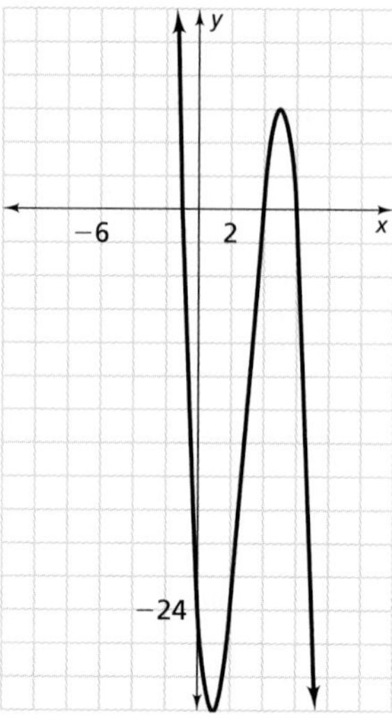

Which of these could be an equation for $h(x)$?

A. $h(x) = (x + 4)(x + 1)(x - 6)$

B. $h(x) = -(x + 4)(x + 1)(x - 6)$

C. $h(x) = (x + 1)(x - 4)(x - 6)$

D. $h(x) = -(x + 1)(x - 4)(x - 6)$

Answers

4. a. Each expression has the same normal form: $x^3 - 14x^2 + 55x - 42$. To make the expressions equivalent for all real numbers, define $f(0) = -42$ for Expression 5.

b. Expression 1; 1, 6, 7

c. Expression 4; $f(-3) = -360$

d. Expression 5; Expression 5

e. Expression 3; -42; because the other terms of $f(x)$ are close to zero.

f. See back of book.

5. See back of book.

6. a. $|a - 5| < 0.00999$

b. $|a - 5| < 0.000999$

c. $|a - 5| < 0.0000999$

d. $|a - 5| < 0.00000999$

7. D

Exercises *Practicing Habits of Mind*

On Your Own

8. Find, if possible, a cubic polynomial function with a graph that satisfies these conditions:

- The graph crosses the x-axis at $(-9, 0)$, $(-5, 0)$, and somewhere on the positive x-axis.
- From left to right, the graph falls, rises, and falls.
- The graph passes through the point $(-4, -5)$.

Explain your work.

9. Sketch the graph of a function that could not possibly be a polynomial function. Explain why it could not be the graph of a polynomial.

10. Write About It Make your own polynomial function graph gallery.

- Sketch or generate 10 particularly interesting polynomial function graphs.
- Give the polynomial function for each graph.
- Describe what you find interesting about each graph.

Make believe you are preparing a guided tour in an art museum, except the pictures are graphs of polynomial functions.

11. Draw sketches of each of these functions. A calculator should not be necessary.

a. $f_1(x) = (x - 2)(x - 4)(x - 7)$ **b.** $f_2(x) = (x - 2)(x - 4)(x - 5)$

c. $f_3(x) = (x - 2)(x - 4)(x - 4.5)$ **d.** $f_4(x) = (x - 2)(x - 4)(x - 4.1)$

e. $f_5(x) = (x - 2)(x - 4)^2$

Do not worry about being very accurate. Is $f_1(0)$ positive or negative?

12. Suppose $f(x) = 3x^3 - 14x^2 + 15x + 9$. Find numbers A, B, C, and D if another way to write $f(x)$ is

$$f(x) = A(x - 2)^3 + B(x - 2)^2 + C(x - 2) + D$$

Maintain Your Skills

13. Sketch the graph of each of these functions.

a. $f(x) = (x - 3)^2$ **b.** $g(x) = (x + 4)^2$

c. $h(x) = -(x + 2)^2$ **d.** $j(x) = (x - 5)^3$

e. $k(x) = -(x - 5)^3$ **f.** $m(x) = x^4$

Exercises

8. Not possible. For the graph to meet the first and third conditions, it would have to change directions more than just twice, as described in the second condition.

9. See back of book.

10. Answers may vary, but should include functions of varying degrees, which exhibit typical properties and shapes. Samples:

- $f(x) = (x - 2)^2$
- $f(x) = -x^2 + 2$
- $f(x) = x^3 + 1$
- $f(x) = -(x + 1)^3$
- $f(x) = x^3 - x + 1$
- $f(x) = x^4 - 3$
- $f(x) = -x^4 + x$
- $f(x) = x^4 - 3x^2 + 1$
- $f(x) = x^8$
- $f(x) = x^9$

11. See back of book.

12. $A = 3, B = 4, C = -5, D = 7$

13. See back of book.

Wrap Up

As you go over the For You to Explore problems, ask students to explain any techniques they developed to analyze the sign of a function or to write a function with given characteristics. You might also ask students to state conjectures they have about cubic equations. Possible conjectures include the number of zeros and the behavior of the graph for large positive and negative values of x.

Exercises

HOMEWORK

- Core: 8, 9, 10, 11
- Optional: 12, 13

You can make copies of Blackline Masters MC7 and MC8 for students to sketch functions.

On Your Own

EXERCISE 8 A key to this exercise is the fact that you know the function has three zeros, and as a cubic polynomial it cannot have more than three. Without another zero, the graph of the function cannot cross the x-axis, so it cannot have a negative y-value between -5 and its intercept on the positive x-axis.

EXERCISE 9 The solution given for this exercise suggests that a sudden jagged turn is not possible for a polynomial graph, but students might not focus on the smoothness of the curve. Other types of non-polynomial curves include curves with discontinuities.

ERROR PREVENTION Be sure students do not suggest graphs such as $x^2 + y^2 = 1$ that are not functions.

EXERCISE 10 gives students an opportunity to look at a selection of polynomial graphs and to make conjectures about the graphs of polynomial functions. Some students may notice that all of the graphs are smooth curves.

EXERCISE 11 Note that the graphs of f_4 and f_5 are almost identical; f_4 barely dips into the negative between 4 and 4.1. Overall, a core concept in this investigation is that behavior as two points move closer together is a good approximation for behavior as the two points coincide. This is one underpinning of calculus that students explore throughout the chapter.

EXERCISE 12 Another method is to multiply the expression in A, B, C, and D and write the result in normal form. Then students can set the coefficients from both forms equal to each other and solve the equations to find A, B, C, and D.

Maintain Your Skills

EXERCISE 13 Students need to know these general graph shapes in this investigation, so this is a good question for in-class review.

Lesson Overview

GOAL

- State the Change of Sign Theorem and the Intermediate Value Theorem for Polynomials and use them to analyze the graphs of polynomial functions.

In this lesson, students come to an informal understanding of limits and continuity. Their definition of continuity prepares them for the epsilon-delta proofs in calculus. Students also see examples of graphs that are not continuous, and develop a visual understanding of this important property. This lesson introduces two key theorems—the Change of Sign Theorem and the Intermediate Value Theorem. Students analyze the implications of these theorems on power functions, which are polynomial functions with only one term. They see how, as x gets extremely large or extremely small, power functions can approximate all polynomial functions.

CHECK YOUR UNDERSTANDING
- Core: 1, 2, 4, 5
- Optional: 3, 6
- Extension: 7

MATERIALS
- graph paper
- graphing calculators
- Blackline Masters MC7, MC8, 3.2

HOMEWORK
- Core: 8, 9, 10, 11, 14, 15, 18, 19, 22
- Optional: 12, 13, 16, 20, 23
- Extension: 17, 21

VOCABULARY
- continuous
- power function

Launch

Begin today's lesson with the In-Class Experiment. Make sure that students can solve problems like this efficiently with their calculators. If some students are still substituting numbers, pair them with a classmate who is more comfortable with the solve operation so they can see how to use it. Reiterate the point of this process—how close must x be to 5 so that $f(x)$ is within a certain distance of $f(5)$?

If students do not see why this is even a question of interest, you may want to show them the graph of a discontinuous function, such as the greatest integer function. (Each y-value is equal to the greatest integer that is less than x.)

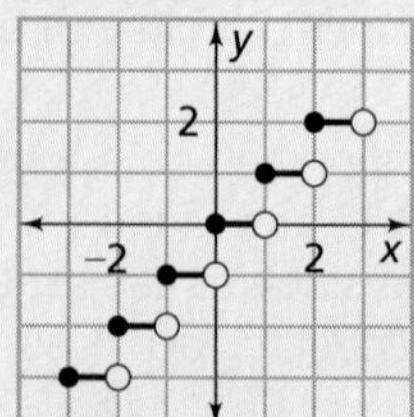

Here, $f(1) = 1$ but if $x = 0.99999$, within 0.00001 of 1, $f(x) = 0$. If you are approaching 1 from the left, you cannot get any closer to $f(1)$.

3.2 Continuity of Polynomial Functions

Graphs of polynomial functions have no breaks in them. This means that domain values that are close to each other will always have range values that are close to each other.

In-Class Experiment

Suppose $f(x) = x^3 - 2x^2 + 7$, so that $f(5) = 82$. How close must x be to 5 to meet the following conditions?

1. $|f(x) - f(5)| < 0.1$
2. $|f(x) - f(5)| < 0.01$
3. $|f(x) - f(5)| < 0.001$
4. $|f(x) - f(5)| < 10^{-6}$

In the In-Class Experiment, you saw that you could make $f(x)$ as close as you wanted to $f(5)$ by making x close enough to 5. How does the graph of $y = f(x)$ reflect this fact?

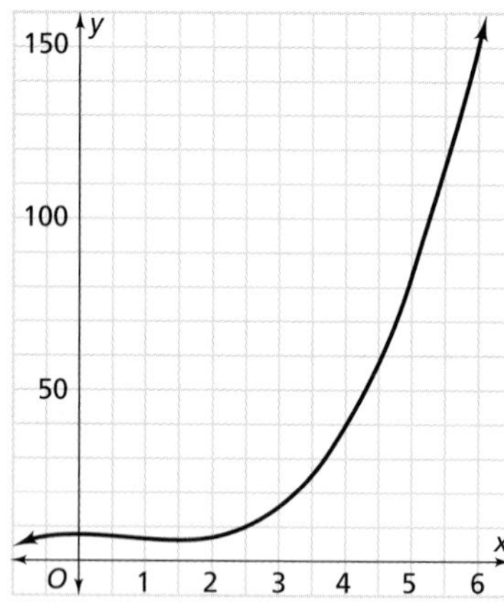

For Discussion

5. Using the graph of $y = f(x)$, explain why you can make $f(x)$ arbitrarily close to $f(5)$ by making x close enough to 5.

Answers

In-Class Experiment

1. x must be within 0.001817 of 5.
2. x must be within 0.0001817 of 5.
3. x must be within 0.00001817 of 5.
4. x must be within 0.00000001817 of 5.

For Discussion

5. For a continuous function, you can draw the graph without lifting your pen. That means that if a point $(a, f(a))$ is on the graph of the function, as x gets close to a, $f(x)$ must be getting close to $f(a)$.

Definition

A function f is continuous at an input a if you can make $f(x)$ as close as you want to $f(a)$ by making x close enough to a.

You will learn a more precise definition when you take calculus.

You have seen that $f(x) = x^3 - 2x^2 + 7$ is continuous at $a = 5$. In fact, there was nothing special about the input 5. The function f is continuous at every real number. In this case, you say that f is continuous on $\mathbb{R}$, or simply that f is continuous.

To understand continuous functions, it helps to study functions that are not continuous. Consider a function f with the graph shown below.

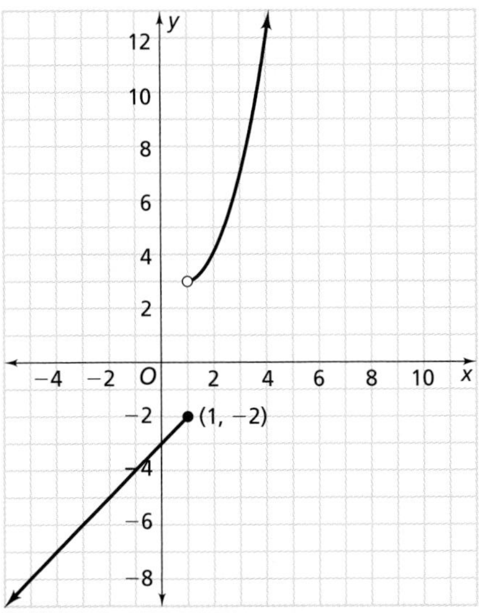

Habits of Mind

Represent a function. Model f in your FML and graph it.

The graph shows that $f(1) = -2$. However, the graph also shows that the values

$$f(1.01), f(1.001), f(1.0001), f(1.00001), \ldots$$

approach 3. In other words, no matter how close you bring x to 1 (with $x > 1$), the distance between $f(x)$ and $f(1)$ will never be less than 5. Thus, f is not continuous at $x = 1$.

On the other hand, the values

$$f(0.99), f(0.999), f(0.9999), f(0.99999), \ldots$$

Explore

In-Class Experiment

PROBLEMS 1–4 Conclude that you can make $f(x)$ as close as you want to $f(5)$ by making x close to 5.

For Discussion

PROBLEM 5 For a continuous function, you can draw the graph without lifting your pen. That means that if a point $(a, f(a))$ is on the graph of the function, as x gets close to a, $f(x)$ approaches $f(a)$. Again, this is a good time to show students a discontinuous function, such as a step function or the function $f(x) = \frac{1}{x}$. For the greatest integer function, you can see that as x approaches any integer a from the left, $f(x)$ is consistently equal to $f(a) - 1$. It is not approaching $f(a)$ at all. For the function $f(x) = \frac{1}{x}$, $f(0)$ does not exist, and you can see why. As you approach 0 from the left, $f(x)$ decreases without bound. As you approach from the right, $f(x)$ increases without bound. There is no way for the graph to "join up." You have to lift your pen and draw the curve in two pieces.

You may want to use Blackline Master 3.2 on an overhead. Locate 5 on the x-axis and $f(5) = 82$ on the y-axis. Show the students how the distance $|x - 5|$ is related to the distance $|f(x) - f(5)|$, so that one gets smaller as the other does. Then sketch an alteration to the curve to create a jump discontinuity at $x = 5$, and note how the relationship between $|x - 5|$ and $|f(x) - 82|$ changes.

DEFINITION Here is a somewhat more formal definition of continuity.

f is continuous at a if (1) f is defined at a and near a (that is, on an interval containing a and not having a as either endpoint), and (2) for any positive number ε, no matter how small, there is another positive number δ such that $f(x)$ lies within ε units of $f(a)$ whenever x lies within δ units of a. This is commonly called an "epsilon-delta" definition of continuity.

For You to Do

PROBLEMS 6 AND 7 You may wish to provide copies of Blackline Masters MC7 and MC8 for students to sketch graphs of continuous and non-continuous functions.

PROBLEM 7 Look for examples of types of discontinuous graphs that you have not yet covered, such as graphs with point discontinuities or asymptotes, and have students share these graphs with the class. You are not requiring students to define the functions here, but just to sketch their graphs.

GOING FURTHER You may wish to encourage students to define the functions for their graphs as well.

do approach -2. So you can make $f(x)$ as close as you want to $f(1)$ by making x close enough to 1 with the added restriction that $x < 1$. But to say that f is continuous at 1, you must be able to make $f(x)$ close to $f(1)$ from both sides of $x = 1$. In other words, you need to show it for $x > 1$ and $x < 1$.

You could say, however, that f is continuous at 1 from the left.

For You to Do

6. Name and sketch the graphs of three functions that are continuous.

7. Sketch the graphs of two functions that are not continuous.

Roughly speaking, a function is continuous if its graph has no breaks. You could trace the entire curve without picking up your pencil. Your experience tells you that polynomial functions are continuous.

Minds in Action episode 6

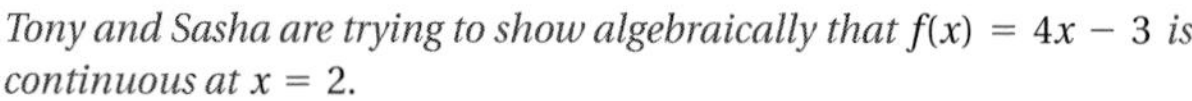

Tony and Sasha are trying to show algebraically that $f(x) = 4x - 3$ is continuous at $x = 2$.

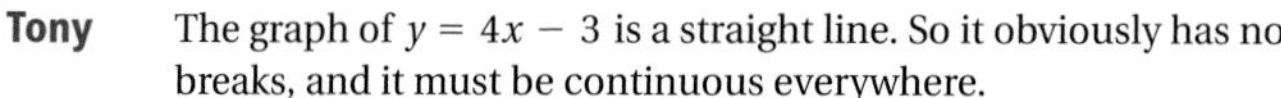

Tony The graph of $y = 4x - 3$ is a straight line. So it obviously has no breaks, and it must be continuous everywhere.

Sasha True, but we're suppose to show this algebraically—so no graphs allowed.

Tony Okay, then let's go back to the definition. We need to show that we can make $f(x)$ as close as we want to $f(2)$ by making x close enough to 2.

Sasha Well, $f(2) = 5$. And let's say we want to make $f(x)$ be within 0.01 of $f(2)$.

Tony So we want,

$$|f(x) - f(2)| < 0.01$$

Sasha Looks good. We can substitute for $f(x)$ and $f(2)$, too. So we have

$$|(4x - 3) - 5| < 0.01$$

or, simplifying a bit,

$$|4x - 8| < 0.01$$
$$4 \cdot |x - 2| < 0.01$$
$$|x - 2| < 0.0025$$

So if x is within 0.0025 of 2, then we're guaranteed that $f(x)$ is within 0.01 of $f(2)$.

Answers

For You to Do

6–7. See back of book.

Tony But what if we have to make $f(x)$ within 0.001 of $f(2)$? Do we have to go through this all over again?

Sasha No, you don't need to do any extra work. There was nothing special about the value 0.01 in the above calculation. So if we have to make $f(x)$ within any distance d from $f(2)$, just replace 0.01 with d and go through the same steps!

For You to Do

8. Explain what Sasha meant by saying there was nothing special about the value 0.01. Let d be any positive number. How close must x be to $a = 2$ to ensure that $f(x)$ is no more than a distance d away from $f(2)$?

A nice result of the fact that polynomial functions are continuous is that their graphs cannot get from one side of a horizontal line (such as the x-axis) to the other without crossing that line.

Theorem 3.1 The Change of Sign Theorem

Suppose f is a polynomial function and there are two numbers a and b such that $f(a) < 0$ and $f(b) > 0$. Then $f(c) = 0$ for some number c between a and b.

This theorem is easy to believe but not so easy to prove. You will see its proof when you take calculus. The theorem is actually true for all continuous functions, not just polynomial functions.

The Change of Sign Theorem says that if a polynomial changes sign between inputs a and b, it must equal zero for some input between a and b. The number that makes it zero is a root of the equation $f(x) = 0$. The theorem says nothing about how to find the root. It just says the root exists somewhere between a and b.

A more general result, which also follows from the continuity of polynomials, is the following theorem.

Theorem 3.2 The Intermediate Value Theorem for Polynomials

Suppose f is a polynomial function and a and b are two numbers such that $f(a) < f(b)$. Then for any number c between $f(a)$ and $f(b)$, there is at least one number d between a and b such that $f(d) = c$.

For You to Do

8. She meant that by letting the distance be a variable in the inequality, the inequality would represent all cases; $|x - 2| < \frac{d}{4}$

For Discussion

PROBLEM 11 If the power function has odd degree, it starts and ends with different signs. Of course, to talk about "starting" and "ending" for a function with the real numbers as its domain is very informal intuitive language. What you are really saying is that for very large negative numbers the function has one sign, while for very large positive numbers the function has a different sign. There is not a "start" or an "end" to a polynomial graph.

For You to Do

PROBLEM 12 Remind students that if they encounter any polynomial graphs that have different properties than those in their graph gallery, they should add the new graphs to their collection. The idea is for students to have a comprehensive picture of what sorts of graphs are possible for polynomial functions so they can draw on their experience with many kinds of functions to make conjectures about polynomial graphs in general.

Wrap Up

You might ask students to follow up on the Developing Habits of Mind section on page 175 by giving an example (if possible) of a function that is positive for large negative values of x and negative for large positive values of x. This helps them see how the sign of the coefficient of the largest degree term affects the graph of a polynomial function.

Go over the core Check Your Understanding exercises as time allows. If students found the In-Class Experiment very straightforward, you may not even want to assign Exercise 4. However if they had trouble with the experiment, this is an important exercise to assign and go over. Exercise 7 is a nice summary of the properties of cubic functions, so you may want to spend some time on it.

Assessment Resources

Lesson Quiz 3.2

1. Find a polynomial function f with $f(2) = f(-6) = 0$ and $f(0) = 15$.
2. Suppose g is a degree four polynomial in the form $g(x) = -x^4 + \cdots$
   a. What can you say about $g(x)$ as x takes on large positive values?
   b. What can you say about $g(x)$ as x takes on large negative values?
   c. Sketch an example of what the graph of g could be.
3. Suppose f and g are two quadratic polynomials.
   a. Must there be a real number x, that makes $f(x) = 0$? Explain.
   b. Let h be the polynomial defined as $h = f \cdot g$. Must there be a real number x for which $h(x) = 0$? Explain.

For Discussion

9. Show that Theorem 3.1 implies Theorem 3.2.
10. Show that Theorem 3.2 implies Theorem 3.1.

Have you noticed that some polynomials have real roots while others do not? How can you tell which ones do and which ones do not? The Change of Sign Theorem tells you that if the graph starts out on one side of the x-axis and ends up on the other, there must be a real root.

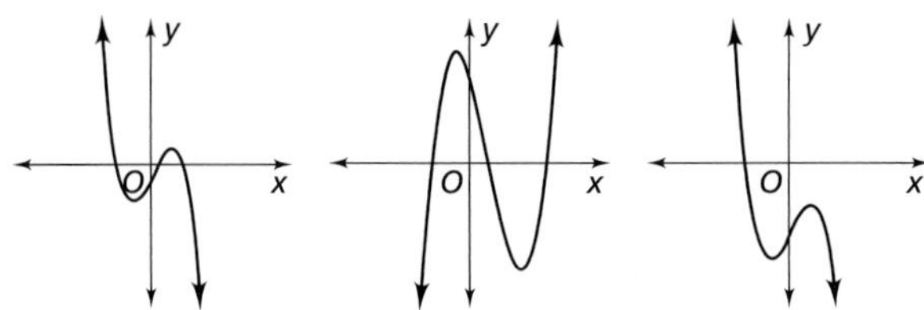

Also, the graph of a polynomial can start and end positive, or start and end negative, and still cross the x-axis.

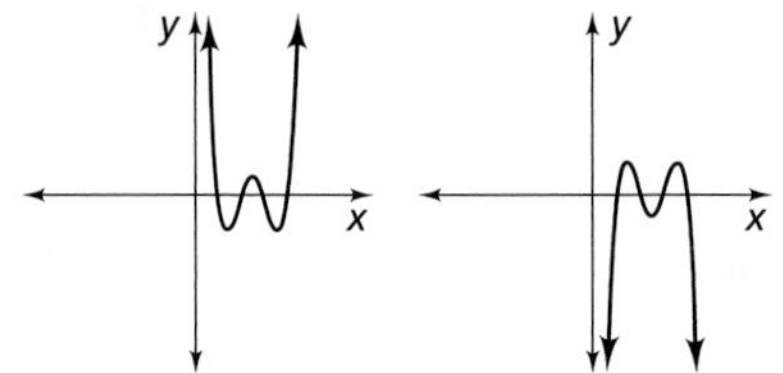

But it does not have to cross.

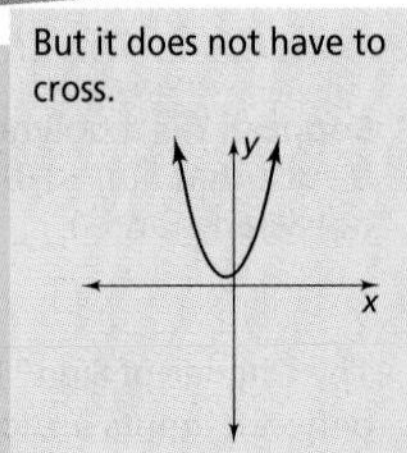

For Discussion

11. Polynomial functions with only one term, like $f(x) = 4x^3$ or $g(x) = -5x^8$, are called **power functions.** Which power functions have graphs that start on one side of the x-axis and end on the other?

For You to Do

12. Look at your polynomial function graph gallery (see Exercise 10 of Lesson 3.1). State a conjecture about how you can tell if a polynomial changes sign by looking at its degree. Give evidence to support your conjecture, even if you do not completely prove it.

Answers

For Discussion

9. If you translate the graph of $f(x)$ by $-c$, then you can use the Change of Sign Theorem on the translated graph to prove the Intermediate Value Theorem. You know that $f(a) < c < f(b)$, so if $y = g(x)$ is the image after translation c units down, then $g(a) < 0$ and $g(b) > 0$, and you can use the Change of Sign Theorem to find d so that $g(d) = 0$. Then, on the graph of $f(x)$, you know that $f(d) = c$.
10. Consider the Intermediate Value Theorem with $c = 0$. Since $f(a) < c < f(b)$, then $f(a) < 0$ and $f(b) > 0$ and there is a change of sign. The Intermediate Value Theorem also says that there exists a d between a and b so that $f(d) = 0$.
11. power functions with odd degree

Developing Habits of Mind

Make strategic choices. Since they only have one term, power functions can be easier to analyze than other polynomial functions. For instance, it is clear that the function $f(x) = x^3$ increases quite quickly as x increases. But consider the polynomial

$$g(x) = x^3 - 14x^2 - 55x - 42$$

Is it equally clear what happens to the function g as x increases?

For $x \neq 0$, you can rewrite $g(x)$ like this:

$$g(x) = x^3\left(1 - \frac{14}{x} - \frac{55}{x^2} - \frac{42}{x^3}\right)$$

As $|x|$ gets large, $\frac{14}{x}$, $\frac{55}{x^2}$, and $\frac{42}{x^3}$ all get closer and closer to 0, so the values inside the parentheses get closer to 1. So when $|x|$ is large,

- $g(x) \approx x^3 =$ a large positive number, when $x > 0$.
- $g(x) \approx x^3 =$ a large negative number, when $x < 0$.

In other words, the graph of g starts out negative and ends positive, just as the graph of f does.

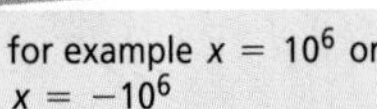

for example $x = 10^6$ or $x = -10^6$

Exercises *Practicing Habits of Mind*

Check Your Understanding

1. Was there ever a time in your life when your weight in pounds was exactly equal to your height in inches? Justify your answer.

2. Consider $a(x) = 2(x - 5)(x + 3)(x - 1) = 2x^3 - 6x^2 - 26x + 30$. Give estimates for each of these values.

   a. $a(5)$ b. $a(5.001)$ c. $a(0)$
   d. $a(0.001)$ e. $a(1000)$ f. $a(0.999)$
   g. $a(-1000)$

An answer like "it's a really big negative number" is fine here.

3. a. Find a polynomial function g with $g(3) = g(-7) = 0$.
   b. Find a polynomial function h with $h(5) = h(-3) = 0$ and $h(0) = 10$.
   c. Find a polynomial function j with $j(5) = j(-3) = 2$ and $j(0) = 12$.

For You to Do

12. If a polynomial function has odd degree, it must change sign at some point. Non-real complex roots come in conjugate pairs, so an odd degree polynomial cannot have all non-real roots, because it must have the same number of roots as its degree.

Exercises

1. At birth, height in inches is larger; later in life, weight in pounds is larger. Since both change continuously, there must be at least one intersection.

2. **a.** 0
b. a very small positive number
c. 30
d. approximately 30
e–g. See back of book.

3. See back of book.

Exercises

HOMEWORK

- Core: 8, 9, 10, 11, 14, 15, 18, 19, 22
- Optional: 12, 13, 16, 20, 23
- Extension: 17, 21

You can make copies of Blackline Masters MC7 and MC8 for students to sketch functions.

Check Your Understanding

EXERCISE 1 Some of your students may not have thought about heights and weights of newborn babies, and may not know reasonable numbers. It is critical that they realize that at birth, height in inches is larger than weight in pounds. They are likely to know that their own weight in pounds is larger than their height in inches, though. Since both change continuously, there is at least one intersection.

You use a similar argument in a later lesson as to why an odd-degree polynomial *must* have at least one real root.

EXERCISE 2 This exercise looks at some of the implications of the continuity of polynomial functions. You may want to ask students not to use their calculators on this one. They can use simple integer substitutions, capitalize on the factored form of the function, and think about the general shape of the graph to answer all of these questions.

EXERCISE 3 This exercise gives students another chance to review the Factor Theorem. It adds a little twist by giving *y*-intercepts as well as *x*-intercepts, but students can use a constant factor to get the *y*-intercept they want without increasing the degree of the function they write.

EXERCISE 5 If students approach this exercise by experimenting with graphs and looking for intersections within the graphing window, they may think that it is possible to have a cubic function and a linear function that do not intersect. Remind them to use the capability in their calculator to locate intersections. This may lead them to develop a more algebraic and less experiential argument, but you may have to guide them to that way of thinking.

EXERCISE 7 Encourage students to use their polynomial graph galleries to look for counterexamples. In parts (b) and (c), some students may conclude that since the product or square has even degree, it need not have any real roots. However, you cannot write all degree-six polynomials as the product of two cubic polynomials. These are not general degree-six polynomials, and in both cases the function must have at least one real root.

4. Suppose $f(x) = 3x + 2$. How close must x be to 5 to meet the following conditions?

a. $|f(x) - f(5)| < 0.1$

b. $|f(x) - f(5)| < 0.01$

c. $|f(x) - f(5)| < 0.001$

d. $|f(x) - f(5)| < 10^{-6}$

5. Suppose g is a cubic polynomial and ℓ is any line in the plane. What are the maximum and minimum numbers of intersections that ℓ can have with the graph of g? Explain.

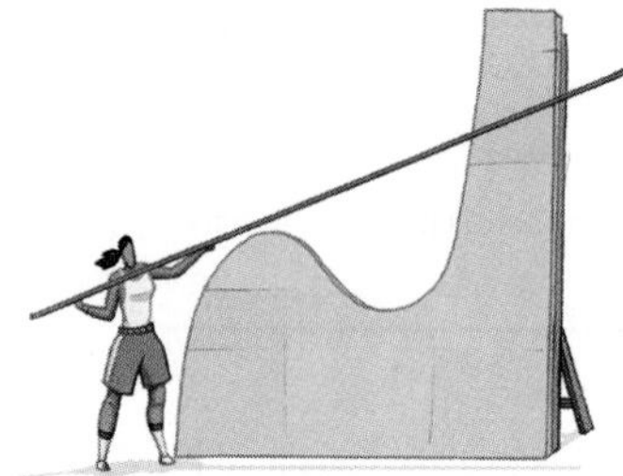

6. What shape can the graph of a fourth degree polynomial function have? Here are some functions to try:

- $f(x) = x^4 - 3x^3 - 2x^2 + 2x + 4$
- $g(x) = x^4 - 3x^3 - 2x^2 - 3x + 6$
- $t(x) = x^4 + 2$

7. Take It Further Let f and g be arbitrary cubic polynomial functions.

a. Must there be three real numbers x that make $f(x) = 0$? Explain.

b. Let h be the polynomial defined as $h = f \cdot g$ (the product). Must there be a real number x for which $h(x) = 0$? Explain.

c. Let j be the polynomial defined as $j = f^2$ (the square of function f). Must there be a real number x for which $j(x) = 0$? Explain.

d. Let k be the polynomial defined as $k = f + g$. Must there be a real number x for which $k(x) = 0$? Explain.

e. Let m be the polynomial defined as $m = f \circ g$. Must there be a real number x for which $m(x) = 0$? Explain.

Answers

4. a. x must be within 0.033 of 5.

b. x must be within 0.0033 of 5.

c. x must be within 0.00033 of 5.

d. x must be within $0.00000033 = 3.3 \cdot 10^{-7}$ of 5.

5. The maximum number of intersections is 3 and the minimum number of intersections is 1. It is easy to see that if the cubic has the right shape, a straight line can intersect the curve up to three times; but more than that is impossible. Therefore, the maximum number of intersections is 3. It is obviously possible to draw a line that intersects the graph only once, and since g is a polynomial of odd degree, it is impossible to draw a straight line that will not intersect that graph of g at all. Therefore, the minimum number of intersections is 1.

6. See back of book.

7. a. No. For example, $f(x) = x^3$ has only one real zero.

b. Yes. Since f has at least one real zero, $f \cdot g$ will have at least one real zero.

c. Yes. Every zero of f is also a zero of f^2. Since f has at least one real zero, so does f^2.

d. No. For example, $f(x) = x^3 + x^2$ and $g(x) = -x^3 + 4$ each have real zeros, but $k(x) = f(x) + g(x) = x^2 + 4$ does not.

e. Yes. The composition of two cubic functions is a polynomial function of degree 9, and it must have at least one real zero.

On Your Own

8. Toby drives exactly 200 miles from San Jose to Morro Bay, CA. The trip takes exactly four hours. Show that at some point in the trip, Toby's speedometer indicates a speed of exactly 50 miles per hour.

9. Consider $b(x) = (x - 2)(x + 5)(x - 3) = x^3 - 19x + 30$. Give estimates for each of these values.

   a. $b(-5)$ b. $b(-5.001)$ c. $b(0)$
   d. $b(0.001)$ e. $b(-0.001)$ f. $b(1000)$
   g. $b(-1000)$

An answer like "it's a little bit more than 10" is fine. Try to give quick answers without use of paper or calculator.

10. **Write About It** Use the Change of Sign Theorem to explain why the Odd-Degree Root Theorem is true.

Theorem 3.3 The Odd-Degree Root Theorem

A polynomial function of odd degree has at least one real root.

11. Suppose $f(x) = x^2$. How close must x be to 5 to meet the following conditions?

   a. $|f(x) - f(5)| < 0.6$ b. $|f(x) - f(5)| < 0.06$
   c. $|f(x) - f(5)| < 0.006$ d. $|f(x) - f(5)| < 6 \cdot 10^{-6}$

12. Find, if possible, a fourth degree polynomial function the graph of which satisfies these conditions:
   - The graph crosses the x-axis at $(-5, 0)$, $(-1, 0)$, and intersects it somewhere on the positive x-axis.
   - From left to right, the graph rises, falls, rises, and falls.
   - The graph crosses the y-axis at $(0, -7)$.

   Explain your work.

13. Suppose h is a degree four polynomial and ℓ is any line in the plane.
   a. What are the maximum and minimum numbers of intersections that ℓ can have with the graph of h?
   b. Can ℓ ever intersect the graph at an odd number of points? Explain.

14. Suppose g is a monic cubic polynomial.
   a. What can you say about $g(x)$ as x takes on large positive values?
   b. What can you say about $g(x)$ as x takes on large negative values?
   c. Sketch an example of what the graph of g could be.

For additional practice, go to Web Code: bga-0302

On Your Own

EXERCISE 9 is similar to Exercise 2 in the Check Your Understanding exercises. Assign it to give students a chance to review the implications of continuity in polynomial functions.

EXERCISE 10 At the end of today's lesson, you can use the Developing Habits of Mind section on page 175 to explain why every polynomial function behaves like a power function at extremely large positive and negative values of x. Students can prove this result by approximating general polynomial functions by a power function if they wish.

EXERCISE 11 is another chance to make sure students understand and can apply the definition of continuity given in this lesson.

EXERCISE 13 Contrast this exercise with Exercise 5. Just as a cubic polynomial must have at least one real root, it must intersect any line in the plane at least once. And, just as a fourth-degree polynomial may not have any real roots, it may not have any intersections with some lines in the plane.

EXERCISE 14 points out a key result of this lesson. The highest degree term in a polynomial function determines its behavior for very large positive and negative values of x.

8. Tony's average speed was $\frac{200}{4} = 50$ miles per hour. By the Intermediate Value Theorem, if there is a time, t_1 when he is going more than 50 mph and a time t_2 where he is traveling less than 50 mph, there must be a time t_3 between t_1 and t_2 when he is going exactly 50 mph.

9. a. 0
b. a little less than 0
c. 30
d. a little less than 30
e. a little more than 30
f. a very large positive number
g. a very large negative number

10. See back of book.

11. a. x must be within 0.059 of 5.
b. x must be within 0.0059 of 5.
c. x must be within 0.0006 of 5.
d. x must be within $6 \cdot 10^{-7}$ of 5.

12. If the fourth degree polynomial rises, falls, rises, and falls and crosses the x-axis at $(-5, 0)$, $(-1, 0)$, and intersects it somewhere on the positive x-axis, it could be of the form $f(x) = A(x + 5)(x + 1)(x - b)^2$ where $A < 0$ and $b > 0$. Choose some positive value for b, say $b = 1$. Then

$$f(x) = A(x + 5)(x + 1)(x - 1)^2 = A(x^4 + 4x^3 - 6x^2 - 4x + 5)$$

To find A, use the fact that $f(0) = -7$:

$$f(0) = A(5) = -7 \Rightarrow A = -\tfrac{7}{5}$$

A polynomial that satisfies the conditions is

$$f(x) = -\tfrac{7}{5}(x^4 + 4x^3 - 6x^2 - 4x + 5) = -\tfrac{7}{5}x^4 - \tfrac{28}{5}x^3 + \tfrac{42}{5}x^2 + \tfrac{28}{5}x - 7$$

13–14. See back of book.

EXERCISE 15 It is important to emphasize the conditions for any theorem.

ERROR PREVENTION Make sure students know that the Change of Sign Theorem and the Intermediate Value Theorem only hold for continuous functions, and that the Odd Degree Root Theorem only holds for polynomial functions.

EXERCISE 16 Once you consider the idea of a double real root (where the graph is tangent to the x-axis at the point but does not cross it) then it is possible to see that 0, 1, 2, 3, and 4 real roots are all possible for degree-four polynomials.

EXERCISE 18 is another exercise where students may wish to use (or to add to) their polynomial graph galleries.

EXERCISE 19 In fact, as long as there are an odd number of zeros between a and b, there are as many as you like. If the function is below the x-axis at a and above it at b, then it must cross at least once. However, if it crosses an even number of times, it ends up on the same side of the x-axis it started on. An even number of crossings is not possible when a change of sign occurs.

EXERCISE 20 Students see that as they decrease the value of c, they translate the graph downward. By using a straightedge held horizontally to represent the position of the x-axis in relation to the graph and moving it down the graph of the function, students can see that it intersects the function once for any horizontal line above the "bumpy" part, then for a moment it is tangent to the first bump and there are two intersections. Then there are three intersections until the moment when the horizontal line is tangent to the second bump. At this moment, there are two intersections. Then, as the horizontal line continues down below the "bumpy" part, there is only one intersection again.

15. **What's Wrong Here** Derman thinks there is a problem with the Odd-Degree Root Theorem.

> Derman says, "What about $\frac{1}{x}$? I can write that as x^{-1}, which has an odd exponent. And $\frac{1}{x}$ is positive if x is positive, and it's negative when x is negative, but you'll never find a number that makes $\frac{1}{x}$ equal zero."

Why can you not apply the reasoning in this lesson to a function like $f(x) = \frac{1}{x}$?

Explore the possibilities. A degree-4 polynomial has four roots in the complex numbers (some may show up more than once in the factorization into linear factors).

16. **a.** What are the maximum and minimum number of real roots that a degree-4 polynomial can have? Illustrate with graphs.

b. Can a fourth degree polynomial have exactly two real roots? Explain.

17. **Take It Further** Let $g(x) = x^3 - 3$. Show that g changes sign. Is there any rational number x such that $g(x) = 0$?

18. Is there a polynomial that fits each description? If so, find one. If not, explain why none exists.

a. even degree, no real roots
b. odd degree, one real root
c. odd degree, three real roots
d. odd degree, two real roots
e. fourth degree, exactly three real roots

19. Supose that f is a polynomial function such that $f(a)$ and $f(b)$ have opposite sign for some numbers a and b. Can there be more than one value c between a and b with $f(c) = 0$? Give examples to support what you say.

20. Let $g_c(x) = x^3 - 7x^2 + 14x + c$. Find, if possible, a value of c such that $g_c(x) = 0$ has

a. exactly one real solution
b. exactly two real solutions
c. exactly three real solutions
d. no real solutions

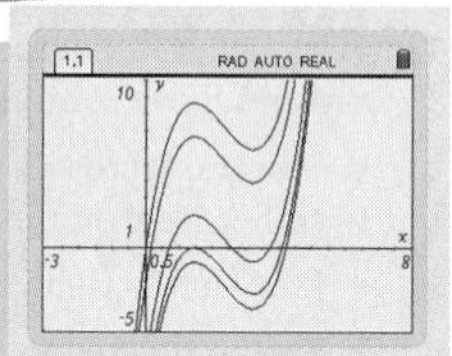

21. **Take It Further** Pick any two points on the graph of $g(x) = x^3 - x$. The coordinates will be

$$(a, g(a)) \text{ and } (b, g(b))$$

a. Write an expression for the slope of the line connecting these two points as a polynomial in a and b.

b. Let $a = 2$ and $b = 2.01$. Calculate the slope using the new expression.

c. Suppose a and b are very close together. Write a new expression, using only one variable, that would do a good job of approximating the slope of the line connecting these points.

If a and b are very close to each other, you can approximate the value of the expression by assuming $a = b$.

Answers

15. Polynomials have positive exponents only. So $\frac{1}{x}$ is not a polynomial and the Odd Degree Root Theorem does not apply.

16. See back of book.

17. If $x = 2$, $g(2) = 5$ and if $x = 1$, $g(1) = -2$. So g changes sign between 1 and 2; no

18. Answers may vary.

a. Yes; Sample: $f(x) = x^4 + 1$.

b. Yes; Sample: $f(x) = x^3 + 8$.

c. Yes; Sample:
$f(x) = (x - 1)(x - 2)(x - 3)$
$= x^3 - 6x^2 + 11x - 6$

d. Yes; Sample:
$f(x) = (x - 1)(x - 2)^2$
$= x^3 - 5x^2 + 8x - 4$

e. Yes; Sample:
$f(x) = (x - 2)(x + 2)(x - 3)^2$
$= x^4 - 6x^3 + 5x^2 + 24x - 36$

22. Standardized Test Prep Which of the following functions is continuous?

A. $f(x) = -\sin\left(-\frac{x}{999}\right)$ **B.** $f(x) = \tan \frac{x}{16}$

C. $f(x) = \sec \frac{x}{16}$ **D.** $f(x) = \frac{\sin 16x}{x}$

Maintain Your Skills

If you divide $x^4 - 5x^3 + 3x - 1$ by $x - 3$, the quotient is $x^3 - 2x^2 - 6x - 15$ and the remainder is -46.

$$\begin{array}{r|l} & x^3 - 2x^2 - 6x - 15 \\ \hline x - 3 & x^4 - 5x^3 \qquad + 3x - 1 \\ & x^4 - 3x^3 \\ \hline & -2x^3 \qquad + 3x - 1 \\ & -2x^3 + 6x^2 \\ \hline & -6x^2 + 3x - 1 \\ & -6x^2 + 18x \\ \hline & -15x - 1 \\ & -15x + 45 \\ \hline & -46 \end{array}$$

In short,

$$x^4 - 5x^3 + 3x - 1 = (x - 3)(x^3 - 2x^2 - 6x - 15) - 46$$

23. a. Find a number c such that

$$x^3 - 2x^2 - 6x - 15 = (x - 3)(x^2 + x - 3) + c$$

b. Find a number d such that

$$x^2 + x - 3 = (x - 3)(x + 4) + d$$

c. Find numbers A, B, C, D, and E such that

$$x^4 - 5x^3 + 3x - 1 = A + B(x - 3) + C(x - 3)^2 + D(x - 3)^3 + E(x - 3)^4$$

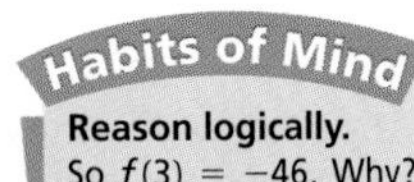

Reason logically. So $f(3) = -46$. Why?

To finish the pattern, note that $x + 4 = (x - 3) \cdot 1 + 7$.

19. Yes; Sample: let $g(x) = x^3 - 4x + 1$. If $a = -3$, then $g(-3) = -14$ and if $b = 3$, $g(3) = 16$, but $g(x) = 0$ three times between $a = -3$ and $b = 3$. $g(x) = 0$ between $x = -3$ and $x = -2$, between $x = 0$ and $x = 1$ and between $x = 1$ and $x = 2$.

20. a. Answers may vary. Sample: $c = 0$.

b. $c \approx -5.8$ or -8.6

c. Answers may vary. Sample: $c = -7$.

d. not possible

21. a. $a^2 + ab + b^2 - 1$

b. 11.0601

c. $3a^2 - 1$

22. A

23. a. $c = -24$

b. $d = 9$

c. $A = -46$, $B = -24$, $C = 9$, $D = 7$, $E = 1$

Maintain Your Skills

EXERCISE 23 Students can do part (c) by using the information above or they can do other equivalent things, such as: If

$$x^4 - 5x^3 + 3x - 1 = A + B(x - 3) + C(x - 3)^2 + D(x - 3)^3 + E(x - 3)^4$$

let $x = 3$ to find $A = -46$. Add 46 to both sides, to find that

$$x^4 - 5x^3 + 3x + 45 = B(x - 3) + C(x - 3)^2 + D(x - 3)^3 + E(x - 3)^4$$

Since $x - 3$ is a factor of the right side, it is also a factor of the left side. Use the CAS to find the other factor—it is $x^3 - 2x^2 - 6x - 15$, so

$$(x - 3)(x^3 - 2x^2 - 6x - 15) = B(x - 3) + C(x - 3)^2 + D(x - 3)^3 + E(x - 3)^4$$

Divide both sides by $x - 3$ and repeat the process.

Additional Resources

PRINT RESOURCES
- Solution Manual
- Practice Workbook
- Assessment Resources
- Teaching Resources

TECHNOLOGY
- Interactive Textbook
- TeacherExpress CD-ROM
- ExamView CD-ROM
- PHSchool.com

Additional Practice

1. Consider $g(x) = (x - 3)(x + 6)(x - 4) = x^3 - x^2 - 30x + 72$. Give estimates for each of these values.

a. $g(-6)$ **b.** $g(0)$
c. $g(-6.001)$ **d.** $g(1000)$

2. Find, if possible, a cubic polynomial function the graph of which satisfies these conditions:
- The graph crosses the x-axis at $(2, 0)$, $(7, 0)$, and intersects it somewhere on the negative x-axis.
- From left to right the graph rises, falls, and then rises again. The graph crosses the y-axis at $(0, 4)$.

3. Suppose that f is a cubic polynomial and ℓ is any line in the plane. What are the maximum and minimum numbers of intersections that ℓ can have with the graph of f?

4. Let $f(x) = 2x^3 + 4x - 3$.

a. Find the equation of the secant through the points $(1, f(1))$ and $(2, f(2))$.

b. Calculate, in terms of b, the equation of the secant between the points $(1, f(1))$ and $(b, f(b))$.

c. Using what you found in part (b), what happens to the slope of the secant as $(b, f(b))$ gets closer to $(1, f(1))$?

5. Consider a line secant to the graph of $y = x^3$, through $(2, 8)$ and a point very close to $(2, 8)$.

a. Approximate the slope of this line.

b. Write an equation for a line that has the slope you found in part (a) and passes through $(2, 8)$.

6. The graph at the right shows the distance-time graphs of two people skating around an ice rink.

a. Who is skating faster, person A or person B?

b. When does person A overtake person B?

c. At what speed is each person skating?

d. Write an equation for person A's graph.

e. Write an equation for person B's graph.

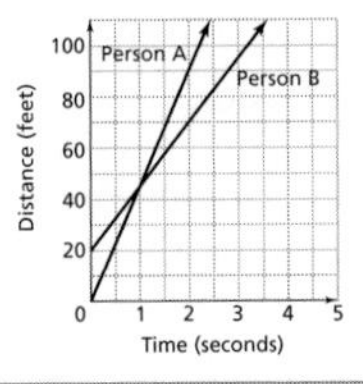

Practice: For Lesson 3.2, assign Exercises 1–3.

Lesson Overview

GOAL

- Find the equation of a line secant to a polynomial function and the average rate of change of a function between two points.

In order to prepare students for formal derivatives in calculus, you want them to understand the idea of the slope of a curve at a point. This lesson begins that process by looking at secant lines. These lines intersect the graph of a function in two (or more) points. By using the coordinates of these two points, $(a, f(a))$ and $(b, f(b))$, you can write the equation of the secant line. You can interpret the slope of this secant line as the average rate of change for the function over the interval from a to b.

Ask students to reason by continuity—visualize what happens to the secant line as one of the two intersection points is held fixed while the other moves along the graph of the function, approaching the fixed point. When the two points coincide, the line in question is tangent to the curve at the fixed point and its slope is the rate of change for the function at that point. You formalize this concept later in the investigation. Right now, you are just getting students started.

CHECK YOUR UNDERSTANDING

- Core: 1, 2, 3, 4, 5, 8, 9
- Optional: 6, 10
- Extension: 7

MATERIALS

- geometry software
- graph paper
- graphing calculators
- Blackline Masters MC7, MC8, MC11, 3.3

HOMEWORK

- Core: 11, 13, 15, 16, 18, 20
- Optional: 12, 19, 21a–d, 22
- Extension: 14, 17, 21e

VOCABULARY

- average rate of change
- secant line

Launch

Begin today's lesson with the In-Class Experiment. The graph of the distance Jerry walks as a function of time is a piecewise linear function. Finding the slope of the piece of the line at any point is really a review of techniques from Algebra 1, but it prepares students to think about the slope of a curve at a point. Do not spend a lot of time here unless your students need a review of slope.

Explore

In-Class Experiment

You may want to use Blackline Master MC11 on an overhead. Start by sketching the curve of Jerry's progress as shown in Problem 1, and explain to the students how to obtain average speed over a time interval. Then sketch variations of the curve to

3.3 Graphs and Secant Lines

At any moment of time, you are moving at a certain speed (which could be 0). Over an interval of time, your average speed is the distance you cover divided by the time you take to do it.

In-Class Experiment

1. Below is a graph that shows how far Jerry has walked in 40 seconds. Determine his average speed between $t = 10$ and $t = 30$.

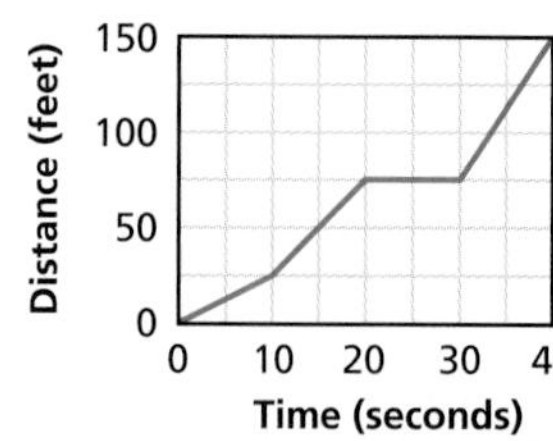

Recall that the average rate of change on a distance-time graph between two events A and B (points on the graph) is the slope $m(A, B)$ between these two points. For example, in the In-Class Experiment, the two points are $A = (10, 25)$ and $B = (30, 75)$, which give the slope

$$m(A, B) = \frac{75 - 25}{30 - 10} = \frac{5}{2}.$$

Thus, Jerry walks with an average speed of $\frac{5}{2}$ feet per second between $t = 10$ and $t = 30$.

More generally, let f be any function and let A and B be points on the graph of $y = f(x)$. The slope $m(A, B)$ is the **average rate of change** of $f(x)$ with respect to x between A and B. The line through A and B is so important that it deserves a special name.

Make a connection. This use of the word *secant* is the same as in plane geometry, except that there the curve is generally a circle.

Definition

Let f be a function and suppose A and B are distinct points on the graph of $y = f(x)$. The line passing through A and B is called a secant to the graph of $y = f(x)$. Its slope is the average rate of change of $f(x)$ with respect to x between A and B.

Answers

In-Class Experiment

1. 2.5 ft/s

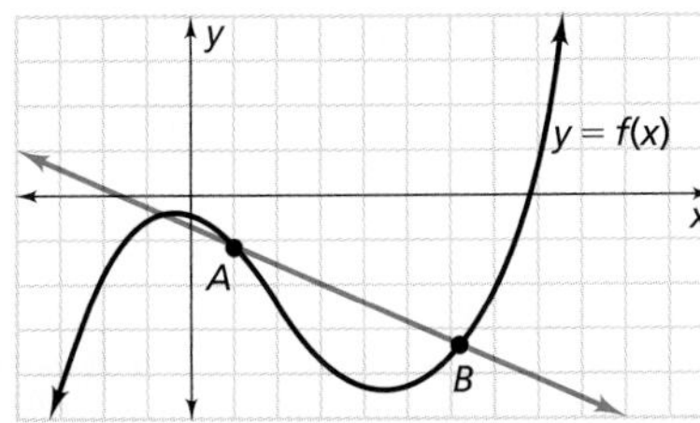

The secant to the graph between A and B

Here are three methods for finding or approximating the equations of secants to graphs of polynomial functions.

Method 1: Use Your Calculator

Some calculators can find the equation of the line through any two points on the xy-plane. If you choose your two points to be on the graph of some function, it will then find the equation of the secant to the graph between these points.

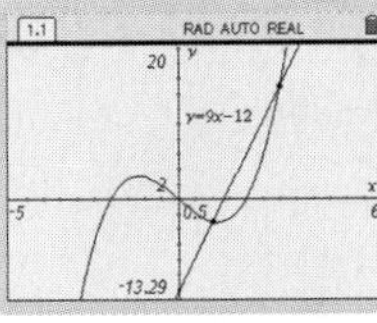

See the TI-Nspire™ Handbook on p. 704 for details about how to set up this sketch.

Method 2: Use the Definition of Slope

If $(a, f(a))$ and $(b, f(b))$ are points on the graph of $y = f(x)$, then the slope of the secant between them is

$$\frac{f(b) - f(a)}{b - a}$$

From here you can find the equation.

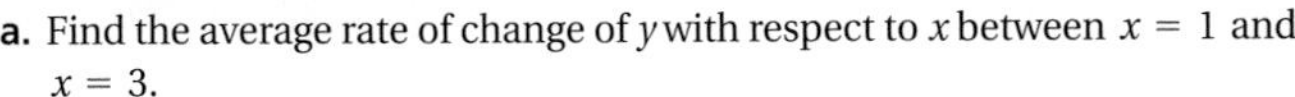

Example 1

Problem Suppose $f(x) = x^3 - 4x$.

a. Find the average rate of change of y with respect to x between $x = 1$ and $x = 3$.

b. Find the equation of the secant between $(1, f(1))$ and $(3, f(3))$.

c. Find all intersections of the graph of $y = f(x)$ and the secant you found in part (b).

Solution

a. To find the average rate of change, find the slope between the points $(1, f(1))$ and $(3, f(3))$.

$$\frac{f(3) - f(1)}{3 - 1} = \frac{15 - (-3)}{3 - 1} = 9$$

illustrate different average speeds over the same time interval.

PROBLEM 1 From $t = 10$ to $t = 20$, Jerry's speed is the slope of the line segment on the graph, or $\frac{75 - 25}{20 - 10} = 5$ feet per second. From $t = 20$ to $t = 30$, his speed is $\frac{75 - 75}{30 - 20} = 0$ feet per second. That means that over the entire 20 second interval, his average speed is $\frac{5(10) + 0(10)}{20} = \frac{5}{2} = 2.5$ feet per second.

You could also find the average speed over the entire interval in one step by finding the slope between the points (10, 25) and (30, 75).

b. The secant has slope 9. To find its equation, take the base point to be either $A = (1, f(1)) = (1, -3)$ or $B = (3, f(3)) = (3, 15)$.

Suppose you pick A. Then an equation of the secant is

$$\frac{y-(-3)}{x-1} = 9 \quad \text{or} \quad 9x - y = 12$$

Compare this with the answer you get when you use a calculator to find the equation of the secant.

c. Shown below are the graphs of $y = f(x)$ and $9x - y = 12$.

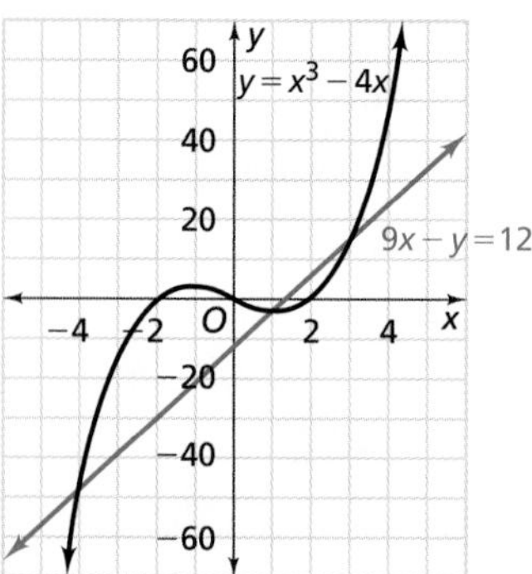

The graphs intersect at three points. You already know two of them, namely $A = (1, -3)$ and $B = (3, 15)$. To find the third, solve $9x - y = 12$ for y and set y equal to $f(x)$. Thus,

$$x^3 - 4x = 9x - 12$$

or equivalently,

$$x^3 - 13x + 12 = 0$$

Since 1 is a root of this equation, $x - 1$ is one of the factors of the cubic polynomial on the left side. Long division and factoring gives

$$\begin{aligned} x^3 - 13x + 12 &= (x-1)(x^2 + x - 12) \\ &= (x-1)(x-3)(x+4) \end{aligned}$$

So the three roots are 1, 3, and -4. The third intersection point is $C = (-4, -48)$.

Method 3: Use the Remainder Theorem

The Remainder Theorem says that if a is any real number,

$$f(x) = (x - a)q(x) + f(a)$$

where you can find $q(x)$ and $f(a)$ by long division. You can rewrite the equation as

$$\frac{f(x) - f(a)}{x - a} = q(x)$$

This is an identity, so it is true when $x = b$.

$$\frac{f(b) - f(a)}{b - a} = q(b)$$

So $q(b)$ is the slope of the secant between $(a, f(a))$ and $(b, f(b))$. From here you can find the equation.

For a review of the Remainder Theorem, go to **Web Code:** bge-9031

Example 2

Problem Suppose $f(x) = x^3 - 4x$ again. Using the Remainder Theorem method, find the equation of the secant between $(1, f(1))$ and $(3, f(3))$.

Solution Long division gives

$$\begin{array}{r|l} & x^2 + x - 3 \\ \hline x - 1 & x^3 \qquad - 4x \\ & x^3 - x^2 \\ \hline & x^2 - 4x \\ & x^2 - x \\ \hline & -3x \\ & -3x + 3 \\ \hline & -3 \end{array}$$

Write this as

$$f(x) = (x - 1)(x^2 + x - 3) - 3 = (x - 1)(x^2 + x - 3) + f(1)$$

and then as

$$\frac{f(x) - f(1)}{x - 1} = x^2 + x - 3$$

Now substitute $x = 3$ to find the slope of the secant,

$$\frac{f(3) - f(1)}{3 - 1} = 3^2 + 3 - 3 = 9$$

and proceed as in part (b) of Example 1.

This approach may not seem like a time saver, but it is more general than the calculator- and definition-based methods. You can use $x^2 + x - 3$ to find the slope of the secant between $(1, f(1))$ and any point $(b, f(b))$ on the graph.

Wrap Up

Expect students to have difficulty seeing the point of using long division to find the slope of a secant line through two known points. Encourage them to try it out as a mental exercise, or show how they can use the long division result to find the slope of any secant line that includes the base point. For example, when the base point is $(3, 15)$, the slope of the secant line through $(3, 15)$ and $(1, -3)$ is 9. However, they can also calculate the slope of the secant through $(3, 15)$ and $(100, f(100))$ as $(100)^2 + 3(100) + 5 = 10{,}305$ without ever finding $f(100)$. This still may not motivate them, but in the exercises, students find the slope for a series of secant lines with the same base point. This may help them see the usefulness of this calculation.

Assessment Resources

Lesson Quiz 3.3

1. Consider $f(x) = x^3 - 4x^2 + 5x - 4$. One point on the graph is $(0, -4)$.
   a. Set up a sketch that contains the graph of f and two points on the graph: $(0, -4)$ and an arbitrary point $(b, f(b))$.
   b. Draw the secant line between these two points and find its slope in terms of b.
   c. As b moves closer to 0, what happens to the slope of the secant line?

2. Consider $f(x) = 3x^2 - 5x + 2$. When $a = 1$ and $b = 2$, find the y-intercept of the secant line containing $(a, f(a))$ and $(b, f(b))$.

3. a. Using secants, approximate the slope of the line tangent to the graph of $y = x^2 + x$ at the point $(2, 6)$.
   b. Find the equation of the line tangent to the graph of $y = x^2 + x$ at the point $(2, 6)$.

For You to Do

Let $f(x) = x^3 - 4x$.

2. By long division, you found that

$$f(x) = (x - 1)(x^2 + x - 3) - 3$$

Using this equation, explain why $f(1) = -3$.

3. Note that

$$f(x) + 3 = (x - 1)(x^2 + x - 3)$$

Since $x - 1$ is a factor of the right side, it must be a factor of the left side, which equals $x^3 - 4x + 3$. Find the other factor.

4. Find the slope of the secant through $(1, f(x))$ and $(3, f(x))$ again, but use $(3, f(3))$ as the base point. In other words, start by dividing $x^3 - 4x$ by $x - 3$ to obtain the quotient $q(x)$. Then write

$$f(x) = (x - 3)q(x) + f(3)$$

Try long division.

Later in this chapter, you will see another way to use long division to find equations of secants. If $f(x) = (x - a)(x - b)q(x) + r(x)$, then $r(x)$ is linear and agrees with f at $x = a$ and $x = b$.

Exercises *Practicing Habits of Mind*

Check Your Understanding

1. Consider $f(x) = x^2$.
   a. Let $a = 2$ and $b = 5$. Find the average rate of change of $f(x)$ between $x = a$ and $x = b$.
   b. Let $a = -3$ and $b = 11$. Find the equation of the secant line through $(a, f(a))$ and $(b, f(b))$.
   c. Write m as a polynomial in a and b using the equation

$$m = \frac{f(b) - f(a)}{b - a}$$

Answers

For You to Do

2. If $f(x) = (x - 1)(x^2 + x - 3) - 3$, then when $x = 1$, the first term will be zero and $f(1) = -3$.
3. $x^2 + x - 3$
4. 9

Exercises

1. a. 7
   b. $8x - y = -33$
   c. $m = a + b$

2. Let $f(x) = x^3 - 2x + 1$.

   a. Find the equation of the secant through the points $(2, f(2))$ and $(2.01, f(2.01))$.

   b. Calculate, in terms of b, the equation of the secant between the points $(2, f(2))$ and $(b, f(b))$.

   c. Use geometry software to draw the graph of f. Plot the point $A(2, f(2))$. Place a moveable point B on the graph of f. Move B closer to A. What happens to the slope between A and B?

See the TI-Nspire Handbook on p. 704 for details on how set up this sketch.

3. Consider $f(x) = x^3 - 2x + 1$.

   a. Use geometry software to draw the graph of f. Plot the point $A(1, f(1))$. Place a moveable point B on the graph of f.

   b. Construct the secant line through A and B. Find the equation of this line.

   c. Let b be the x-coordinate of B. Write $m(A, B)$ as a polynomial in b, using the formula
   $$m(A, B) = \frac{f(b) - f(1)}{b - 1}$$

   d. Move B closer to A. What happens to the slope of the secant line?

You denote the *limiting value* of the slope as b approaches 1 in Exercise 3d by
$$\lim_{b \to 1} \frac{f(b) - 0}{b - 1}$$
Where does the 0 come from?

4. Consider $f(x) = x^3 - 7x^2 + 3x - 2$.

   a. Use geometry software to draw the graph of f. Plot the point $A(0, f(0))$. Place a moveable point B on the graph of f.

   b. Construct the secant line through A and B. Find the equation of this line.

   c. Let b be the x-coordinate of B. Write $m(A, B)$ as a polynomial in b, using the formula
   $$m(A, B) = \frac{f(b) - f(0)}{b - 0}$$

   d. Move B closer to A. What happens to the slope of the secant line?

5. Let $f(x) = 3x^2 + 5x - 7$. Find an expression in terms of a and b for the slope of the secant connecting $(a, f(a))$ and $(b, f(b))$.

6. Consider $f(x) = x^2$.

   a. Let $a = 2$ and $b = 5$. Find the y-intercept of the secant line connecting $(a, f(a))$ and $(b, f(b))$.

   b. Repeat for part (a) $a = -3$ and $b = 11$.

   c. Find and prove a general result based on parts (a) and (b).

7. **Take It Further** Show algebraically that the slope of any secant line on the graph of $y = x^3$ must be positive.

2. **a.** $\frac{y-5}{x-2} = 10.0601$ or $10.0601x - y = 15.1202$

   b. $\frac{y-5}{x-2} = b^2 + 2b + 2$ or $(b^2 + 2b + 2)x - y = 2b^2 + 4b - 1$

   c. See back of book.

3. **a–b.** See back of book.

   c. $m = b^2 + b - 1$

   d. As b gets closer to 1, the slope gets closer to $1^2 + 1 - 1 = 1$.

4. **a–d.** See back of book.

5. $m = 3a + 3b + 5$

6. **a.** $(0, -10)$

   b. $(0, 33)$

   c. $(0, -ab)$

7. The slope is $a^2 + ab + b^2 = (a - b)^2 + 3ab = (a + b)^2 - ab$. Either the second or third expression must always be positive unless $a = b = 0$, which cannot happen since $a \neq b$.

Exercises

HOMEWORK

- Core: 11, 13, 15, 16, 18, 20
- Optional: 12, 19, 21a–d, 22
- Extension: 14, 17, 21e

You can make copies of Blackline Masters MC7 and MC8 for students to sketch function graphs and secant lines.

Check Your Understanding

EXERCISE 1 Part (c) is really the point of this exercise, but it is easier for students to do if they use their calculations in parts (a) and (b) as a model for the process.

EXERCISE 2 relates to the next lesson on local behavior. As the two points come closer together, the slope of the secant line connecting the points comes closer to approximating the tangent line. Students explore these limiting behaviors as a precursor to calculus. The next two exercises involve this same process, asking students to visualize the effect on the slope of the secant line of moving its intersection at a general point on the curve closer and closer along the curve to the base point.

EXERCISE 5 Now that students have seen several general expressions for the slope of a secant line to a polynomial curve, they may have noticed that the final expression for the slope is defined even when the two points of intersection for the secant coincide. The slope of a line through a single point is not determined, but these expressions hint that there is a well-defined slope for a polynomial curve at a point. As the investigation continues, you formalize this intuition through the use of limits.

EXERCISE 6 Some students may regard this as an important result that they should memorize. You may want to emphasize that the point of this exercise is really to practice calculating slopes of secant lines, especially using variable coordinates for one or both points of intersection.

EXERCISES 8–10 are a review of work that students did in Algebra 1. They are meant to emphasize that the slope in a time and distance graph indicates the speed, that the slope of a line is constant, and that steeper slopes indicate faster speeds. Students also gain practice in finding the intersection between the graphs of two lines.

You can use Blackline Master MC11 on an overhead to sketch the graphs showing John's and Pete's progress, or you can hand out printed copies for students to do their own sketches.

On Your Own

EXERCISES 11 AND 12 Sketching the graphs in these first two exercises is a review. Encourage students to look for patterns and to use graphs they have already drawn to help them draw the graphs that follow.

EXERCISE 13 In this exercise and the two that follow, students work on finding equations of secant lines when one of the two points of intersection between the secant and the graph is held fixed and the other is moving toward the fixed point. You further formalize this visualization using limits in upcoming lessons, but for now, students look for patterns and think about the process as they practice these calculations.

8. John leaves home at 8:00 A.M. riding his mountain bike. He pedals at a constant rate of 15 ft/s.

a. How far has John ridden at 8:10 A.M.?

b. How far has John ridden at 8:20 A.M.?

c. How far has John ridden at 8:45 A.M.?

d. Write an expression for how far John has ridden t minutes after 8:00 A.M.

9. Pete, John's older brother, leaves 10 minutes after John, heading down the same trail. He rides at 20 ft/s.

a. How far has Pete ridden at 8:10 A.M.? Has Pete caught John?

b. How far has Pete ridden at 8:20 A.M.? Has Pete caught John?

c. How far has Pete ridden at 8:45 A.M.? Has Pete caught John?

d. Write an expression for how far Pete has ridden at t minutes after 8:00 A.M.

e. How can you find the exact time Pete caught John?

10. Demitri and Yakov are running on a track. The figure at the right shows their distance-time graphs.

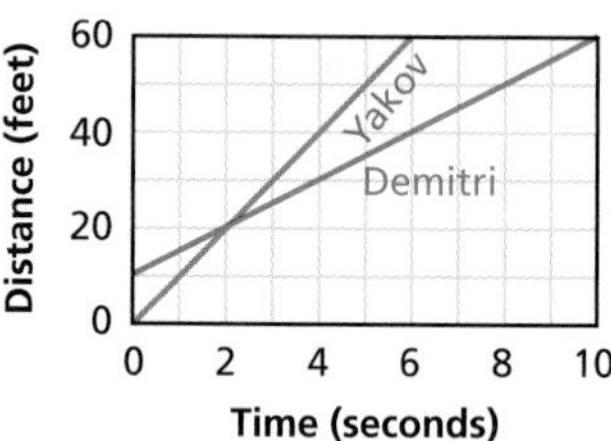

a. Who is running faster, Demitri or Yakov?

b. When does Yakov overtake Demitri?

c. At what distance does Yakov overtake Demitri?

d. What is each runner's speed?

e. Write an equation for Yakov's graph.

f. Write an equation for Demitri's graph.

g. Write and solve an equation for which the solution is the time at which Yakov overtakes Demitri.

A speed of 20 feet per second is equivalent to about 13.6 miles per hour.

Answers

8. a. 9000 ft or approx. 1.7 mi
b. 18,000 ft or approx. 3.4 mi
c. 40,500 ft or approx. 7.7 mi
d. $900t$ ft

9. a. 0 ft; Pete has not caught John yet
b. 12,000 ft, or about $2\frac{1}{4}$ mi; Pete has not caught John yet
c. 42,000 ft, or about 8 mi; Pete has passed John
d. $1200(t - 10)$, where $t \geq 10$
e. Solve $900t = 1200(t - 10)$.

10. a. Yakov
b. 2 s
c. 20 ft
d. Yakov: 10 ft/s; Demitri: 5 ft/s
e. $y = 10x$
f. $y = 5x + 10$
g. $10x = 5x + 10$

11. a.

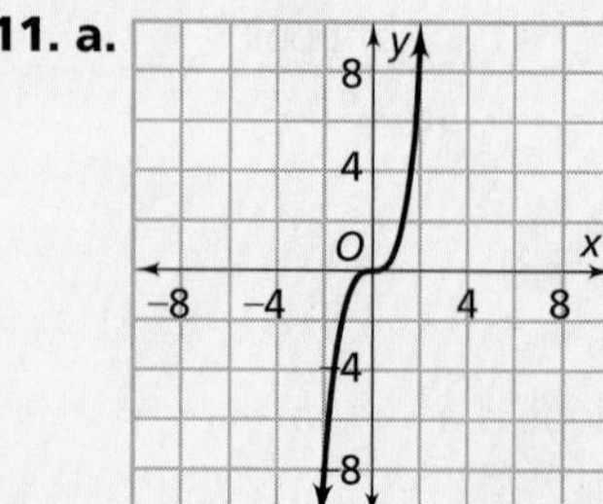

b.

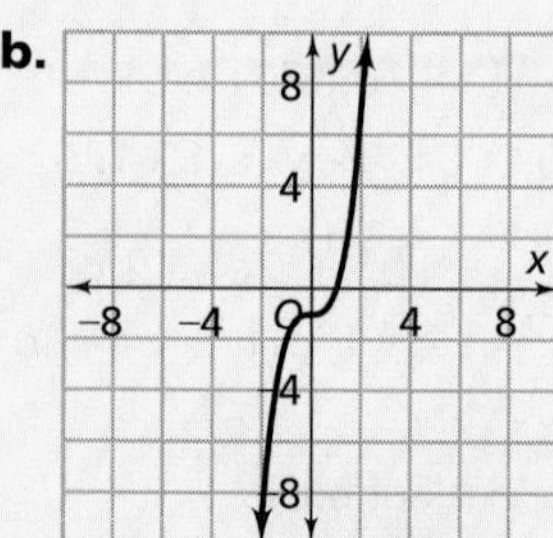

c–d. See back of book.

On Your Own

11. Sketch each graph.

a. $y = x^3$

b. $y = x^3 - 1$

c. $y = (x + 4)^3$

d. $y = (x + 4)^3 - 1$

12. Sketch the graph of each polynomial function.

a. $a(x) = (x - 5)^3$

b. $b(x) = (x - 5)^3(x + 2)$

c. $c(x) = x^3 - 4x$

d. $d(x) = (x - 4.9)(x - 5)(x - 5.1)$

e. $e(x) = (x + 3)^{100}$

Think it through. Try sketching the graphs first, without a calculator.

13. The graph of $g(x) = x^3 - x$ passes through the point $(2, 6)$.

a. Use geometry software to draw the graph of f. Plot the point $A(2, f(2))$. Place a moveable point B on the graph of f.

b. Let b be the x-coordinate of B. The slope of the line through A and B is

$$m(A, B) = \frac{f(b) - f(2)}{b - 2}$$

Describe what happens to this slope as you move B closer to A.

14. Take It Further Consider a line secant to the graph of $y = x^2$, through $(3, 9)$ and a point very close to $(3, 9)$.

a. Approximate the slope of this line.

b. Write an equation for a line that has the slope you found in part (a) and passes through $(3, 9)$.

15. The graph of $f(x) = x^3 - 3x$ passes through the point $(-1, 2)$.

a. Use geometry software to draw the graph of f. Plot the point $A(-1, f(-1))$. Place a moveable point B on the graph of f.

b. Construct the secant line through A and B. Find the equation of this line.

c. Let b be the x-coordinate of B. Write $m(A, B)$ as a polynomial in b, using the formula

$$m(A, B) = \frac{f(b) - f(-1)}{b - (-1)}$$

d. Move B closer to A. What happens to the slope of the secant line?

For additional practice, go to Web Code: bga-0303

EXERCISE 16 Most students use the shape of the graph to determine if the function is increasing.

GOING FURTHER If some of your students are ready to think about this question in terms of the slope of the tangent to the curve, encourage them to try finding the slope of a general secant line, between two points $(x, x^3 - 3x)$ and $(a, a^3 - 3a)$ and thinking about the limit of that slope as x approaches a. If they are able to get that far, and find that the slope of the tangent at any point is $3x^2 - 3$, then they can see that that slope is positive for $x < -1$ and $x > 1$, negative for $-1 < x < 1$, and equal to zero at $x = 1, -1$. Do not expect all of your students to attempt this calculation yet.

EXERCISE 17 Again, some interested students may want to think about what happens to this slope when p approaches q. The slope is then $2Aq + B$, which is the slope of the tangent to the parabola at q.

EXERCISE 18 In this exercise and in the one that follows, the equation of the first function in each part is written in a special form that makes it particularly easy to see where the two functions intersect. In part (b) of both exercises, the line does not just intersect the curve at the intersection point—it is tangent to the curve there. As the investigation continues, students develop the skill of writing equations in special forms in order to easily see the equation of the tangent line at a particular point.

12. a.

b.

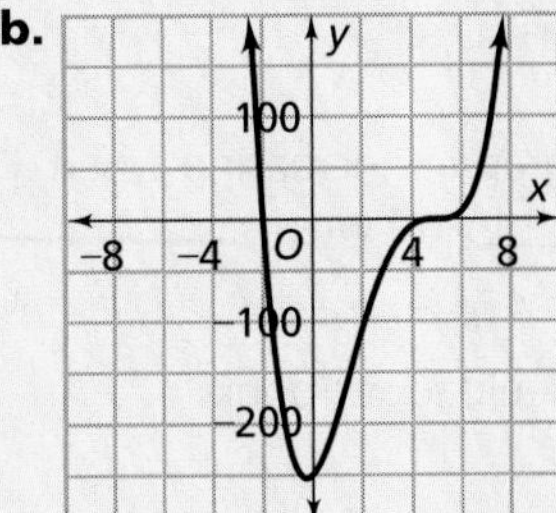

c–e. See back of book.

13. a.

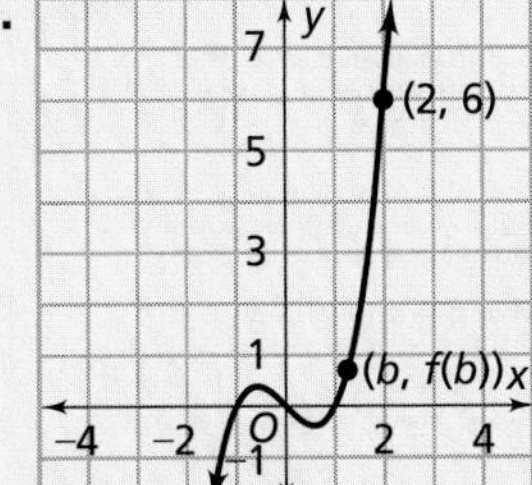

b. The slope gets closer to 11.

14. a. $m \approx 6$

b. $6x - y = 9$

15. a–b. See back of book.

c. $m = b^2 - b - 2$

d. The slope gets closer to 0.

Maintain Your Skills

EXERCISE 21 These are the Mahler polynomials, which are a focus in Chapter 4. For now, this is just an exercise on writing the form of a polynomial when the roots are known. Not many students see how they can find the last part from the earlier parts using $f = 7a + 10b + 20c + 52d$ and the earlier polynomials.

EXERCISE 22 Some students might define a function like this on their CAS to find the secant slopes near x more efficiently:

$$g(x) = \frac{f(x + .000001) - f(x)}{.000001}$$

While completing the table, many students notice that the entries for the slopes of the secants near x seem to match a linear function, $g(x) = 2x - 4$. This function is the derivative of f.

You may want to use Blackline Master 3.3 on an overhead and fill in the entries as students calculate each value.

Additional Resources

PRINT RESOURCES
- Solution Manual
- Practice Workbook
- Assessment Resources
- Teaching Resources

TECHNOLOGY
- Interactive Textbook
- TeacherExpress CD-ROM
- ExamView CD-ROM
- PHSchool.com

Additional Practice

1. Consider $g(x) = (x - 3)(x + 6)(x - 4) = x^3 - x^2 - 30x + 72$. Give estimates for each of these values.
   a. $g(-6)$
   b. $g(0)$
   c. $g(-6.001)$
   d. $g(1000)$

2. Find, if possible, a cubic polynomial function the graph of which satisfies these conditions:
   - The graph crosses the x-axis at (2, 0), (7, 0), and intersects it somewhere on the negative x-axis.
   - From left to right the graph rises, falls, and then rises again. The graph crosses the y-axis at (0, 4).

3. Suppose that f is a cubic polynomial and ℓ is any line in the plane. What are the maximum and minimum numbers of intersections that ℓ can have with the graph of f?

4. Let $f(x) = 2x^3 + 4x - 3$.
   a. Find the equation of the secant through the points $(1, f(1))$ and $(2, f(2))$.
   b. Calculate, in terms of b, the equation of the secant between the points $(1, f(1))$ and $(b, f(b))$.
   c. Using what you found in part (b), what happens to the slope of the secant as $(b, f(b))$ gets closer to $(1, f(1))$?

5. Consider a line secant to the graph of $y = x^3$, through (2, 8) and a point very close to (2, 8).
   a. Approximate the slope of this line.
   b. Write an equation for a line that has the slope you found in part (a) and passes through (2, 8).

6. The graph at the right shows the distance-time graphs of two people skating around an ice rink.
   a. Who is skating faster, person A or person B?
   b. When does person A overtake person B?
   c. At what speed is each person skating?
   d. Write an equation for person A's graph.
   e. Write an equation for person B's graph.

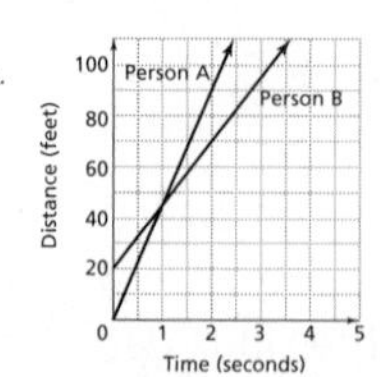

Practice: For Lesson 3.3, assign Exercises 4–6.

16. Use graphs and your work from Exercise 15 to determine when $f(x) = x^3 - 3x$ is increasing.

17. **Take It Further** Let $g(x) = Ax^2 + Bx + C$. What is the slope of the secant line between $(p, g(p))$ and $(q, g(q))$?

> **Remember...**
> The slope equals the change in y divided by the change in x. You can also look back at Exercise 5 for an example using specific values of A, B, and C.

18. On the same axes, sketch the graph of each equation. Where do the graphs intersect?

a. $y = x + (4x + 1)$ and $y = 4x + 1$

b. $y = x^2 + (4x + 1)$ and $y = 4x + 1$

19. On the same axes, sketch the graph of each equation. Where do the graphs intersect?

a. $y = (x - 5) + (2x - 6)$ and $y = 2x - 6$

b. $y = (x - 5)^2 + (2x - 6)$ and $y = 2x - 6$

20. **Standardized Test Prep** What is the average rate of change of $f(x) = \frac{3}{x^2}$ as x goes from 1 to 3?

A. $-\frac{1}{3}$ **B.** $-\frac{3}{2}$ **C.** $-\frac{3}{4}$ **D.** $-\frac{4}{3}$

Maintain Your Skills

21. Find a polynomial function that satisfies the conditions.

a. $a(0) = 0$ and $a(1) = 1$

b. $b(0) = b(1) = 0$ and $b(2) = 1$

c. $c(0) = c(1) = c(2) = 0$ and $c(3) = 1$

d. $d(0) = d(1) = d(2) = d(3) = 0$ and $d(4) = 1$

e. **Take It Further** $f(0) - 0, f(1) = 7, f(2) = 10, f(3) = 20$, and $f(4) = 52$

22. Copy and complete this table for $f(x) = x^2 - 4x + 1$.

x	$f(x)$	Slope of secant through $(x, f(x))$ and a point near it
−1	6	■
0	■	■
1	−2	■
2	■	0
3	■	■

> "Near $(x, f(x))$" might mean that the x-value for the point is "within 0.01 of x."

Answers

16. The graph is increasing when $x < -1$ and when $x > 1$.

17. $m = A(p + q) + B$

18–19. See back of book.

20. D

21. a. $a(x) = x$

b. $b(x) = \frac{1}{2}x(x - 1)$

c. $c(x) = \frac{1}{6}x(x - 1)(x - 2)$

d. $d(x) = \frac{1}{24}x(x - 1)(x - 2)(x - 3)$

e. $f(x) = \frac{x^4}{6} + \frac{5x^3}{6} - \frac{17x^2}{3} + \frac{35x}{3}$

22.

x	$f(x)$	Slope of secant through $(x, f(x))$ and a point near it
−1	6	−6
0	1	−4
1	−2	−2
2	−3	0
3	−2	2

3.4 Polynomials in Powers of $x - a$

You have a lot of experience writing expressions in different forms. Now you will learn how to write a polynomial in a form that will help you find the rate at which it is changing.

For You to Do

1. Show that

$$2(x-3)^3 + 5(x-3)^2 - 7(x-3) + 14 = 2x^3 - 13x^2 + 17x + 26$$

Given a polynomial written in powers of $x - 3$, you can rewrite it as a polynomial in x, expanding it by hand or by using your calculator. The goal in this lesson, however, is to start with a polynomial in x such as

$$f(x) = 2x^3 - 13x^2 + 17x + 26$$

and rewrite it as a polynomial in powers of $x - 3$ or, in general, $x - a$.

There are at least three different methods for doing this.

Example

Problem Write $f(x) = x^4 - 5x^3 + 3x - 1$ as a polynomial in $x - 3$.

Solution Here is the first method.

Method 1: Iterated Long Division

Start with the calculation in the Maintain Your Skills section on page 179.

$$\begin{array}{r|l} & x^3 - 2x^2 - 6x - 15 \\ x-3 & x^4 - 5x^3 \qquad + 3x - 1 \\ & x^4 - 3x^3 \\ \hline & -2x^3 \qquad + 3x - 1 \\ & -2x^3 + 6x^2 \\ \hline & -6x^2 + 3x - 1 \\ & -6x^2 + 18x \\ \hline & -15x - 1 \\ & -15x + 45 \\ \hline & -46 \end{array}$$

This says that

$$f(x) = -46 + (x-3)\underbrace{(x^3 - 2x^2 - 6x - 15)}_{q_1(x)}$$

Let $x = 3$ to find that $f(3) = -46$.

Lesson Overview

GOAL

- Write the Taylor expansion for a polynomial function about a point.

This lesson introduces the Taylor expansion for a function f about a point. Students will study this special form for the equation of a function in calculus. Right now, students see the advantage of using this form when determining not just the value of the function at a point, but also the behavior of the graph of this function near this point. Students learn two methods for producing the Taylor expansion by hand and see how to use their CAS to find the expansion. In the exercises, students begin to see some of the applications of the Taylor expansion and to experiment with finding remainders after long division.

CHECK YOUR UNDERSTANDING
- Core: 1, 3, 4, 5
- Optional: 2

MATERIALS
- CAS (recommended)
- graph paper
- graphing calculators
- Blackline Masters MC7, 3.4A, 3.4B

HOMEWORK
- Core: 6, 7, 10, 11, 12, 16, 17
- Optional: 8, 9, 13, 15
- Extension: 14

VOCABULARY
- Taylor expansion

Launch

Begin today's lesson with the For You to Do problem on page 189. You have several choices with this problem. You may want students to do this independently with or without using a CAS. You might also choose to work the problem as a class, either by hand or with technology. Depending on your students, if you are doing this problem by hand you may want to review the binomial theorem to aid in the expansion of the polynomial in $x - 3$. You might also choose to skip this problem for time considerations or because it provides more review than your students require.

For You to Do

1. $2(x-3)^3 + 5(x-3)^2 - 7(x-3) + 14 = 2(x^3 - 9x^2 + 27x - 27) + 5(x^2 - 6x + 9) - 7x + 21 + 14 = 2x^3 - 18x^2 + 54x - 54 + 5x^2 - 30x + 45 - 7x + 21 + 14 = 2x^3 - 13x^2 + 17x + 26$

Now work with the quotient $q_1(x) = x^3 - 2x^2 - 6x - 15$.

$$\begin{array}{r|l} & x^2 + x - 3 \\ x - 3 & x^3 - 2x^2 - 6x - 15 \\ & \underline{x^3 - 3x^2} \\ & \quad x^2 - 6x - 15 \\ & \quad \underline{x^2 - 3x} \\ & \quad\quad -3x - 15 \\ & \quad\quad \underline{-3x + 9} \\ & \quad\quad\quad -24 \end{array}$$

This says that

$$q_1(x) = -24 + (x - 3)\underbrace{(x^2 + x - 3)}_{q_2(x)}$$

Now work with the quotient $q_2(x) = x^2 + x - 3$.

$$\begin{array}{r|l} & x + 4 \\ x - 3 & x^2 + x - 3 \\ & \underline{x^2 - 3x} \\ & \quad 4x - 3 \\ & \quad \underline{4x - 12} \\ & \quad\quad 9 \end{array}$$

This says that

$$q_2(x) = 9 + (x - 3)\underbrace{(x + 4)}_{q_3(x)}$$

Now work with the quotient $q_3(x) = x + 4$.

$$\begin{array}{r|l} & 1 \\ x - 3 & x + 4 \\ & \underline{x - 3} \\ & \quad 7 \end{array}$$

This says that

$$q_3(x) = 7 + (x - 3)(\underbrace{1}_{q_4(x)})$$

Now put it all together.

$$\begin{aligned} f(x) &= -46 + (x - 3)\underbrace{(x^3 - 2x^2 - 6x - 15)}_{q_1(x)} \\ &= -46 + (x - 3)(-24 + (x - 3)(x^2 + x - 3)) \\ &= -46 - 24(x - 3) + (x - 3)^2\underbrace{(x^2 + x - 3)}_{q_2(x)} \\ &= -46 - 24(x - 3) + (x - 3)^2(9 + (x - 3)(x + 4)) \\ &= -46 - 24(x - 3) + 9(x - 3)^2 + (x - 3)^3\underbrace{(x + 4)}_{q_3(x)} \\ &= -46 - 24(x - 3) + 9(x - 3)^2 + (x - 3)^3(7 + (x - 3)) \\ &= -46 - 24(x - 3) + 9(x - 3)^2 + 7(x - 3)^3 + (x - 3)^4 \end{aligned}$$

The expression of $f(x)$ in terms of powers of $x - 3$ is the **Taylor expansion** for f about 3. The tools of calculus make it possible to write Taylor expansions for non-polynomial functions, as well.

For Discussion

Some older math books describe an elegant shorthand for doing polynomial division. Follow the instructions to find $(x^4 - 5x^3 + 3x - 1) \div (x - 3)$.

For a divisor $x - a$, put a in the L-shaped bracket on the left. After the bracket, write the coefficients of the dividend polynomial in descending order of degree. Leave a space, draw a line, and bring down the leading coefficient.

Put in a zero if there is no term with a particular degree.

3	1	−5	0	3	−1
	1				

Multiply the number you just wrote under the line by the number in the bracket. Put the product under the next coefficient, and add down.

3	1	−5	0	3	−1
		3			
	1	−2			

Repeat the previous step until you reach the end.

3	1	−5	0	3	−1
		3	−6	−18	−45
	1	−2	−6	−15	(−46)

Now you have completed the first division. Look back at your long division result on page 190. You can read off the coefficients of the quotient and remainder from this shorthand. You can do repeated divisions to get the complete Taylor expansion.

3	1	−5	0	3	−1
		3	−6	−18	−45
	1	−2	−6	−15	(−46)
		3	3	−9	
	1	1	−3	(−24)	
		3	12		
	1	4	(9)		
		3			
	(1)	(7)			

This gives you $(x - 3)^4 + 7(x - 3)^3 + 9(x - 3)^2 - 24(x - 3) - 46$.

2. Use this algorithm to expand $2x^3 + 5x^2 + x - 1$ as a polynomial in $x - 2$.

3. **Take It Further** Why does this algorithm work?

Answers

For Discussion

2. $2(x - 2)^3 + 17(x - 2)^2 + 45(x - 2) + 37$

3. The algorithm makes repeated use of the Remainder Theorem and the Distributive Property of Multiplication over Addition.

Explore

For Discussion

This For Discussion section is optional. If you want to cover synthetic division with your students, then you may want to spend some time on this demonstration of the method. For students who use the algorithm, it is valuable to ask them to take the algorithm apart and figure out why it works.

You may wish to use Blackline Master 3.4A on an overhead to illustrate the solution process.

PROBLEM 2 The shorthand notation would look like:

2	2	5	1	−1
		4	18	38
	2	9	19	(37)
		4	26	
	2	13	(45)	
		4		
	(2)	(17)		

So the expansion is

$2(x - 2)^3 + 17(x - 2)^2 + 45(x - 2) + 37$.

PROBLEM 3 In the first step of the algorithm, you see that $(x^4 - 5x^3 + 3x - 1) \div (x - 3)$ gives quotient $x^3 - 2x^2 - 6x - 15$ with a remainder of -46. One way to see why this algorithm works is to look back at expansion boxes for multiplication. This figure shows $x^3 - 2x^2 - 6x - 15$ multiplied by $x - 3$.

	x^3	$-2x^2$	$-6x$	-15
x	x^4	$-2x^3$	$-6x^2$	$-15x$
-3	$-3x^3$	$6x^2$	$18x$	45

You can see the coefficients from the third row of the shorthand notation in the top row of expansion boxes. This row of boxes represents the terms of the product that result from multiplying x by $x^3 - 2x^2 - 6x - 15$. The second row in the shorthand notation matches the bottom row from the expansion boxes, so these are the terms that result from multiplying -3 by $x^3 - 2x^2 - 6x - 15$. But of course, you do not know the quotient $x^3 - 2x^2 - 6x - 15$ when you begin dividing, so the key here is to figure out how the quotient results.

When you bring down the leading coefficient, you are just acknowledging that when you divide a polynomial with leading term bx^n by a binomial of the form $x - a$, the first term in the quotient is bx^{n-1}. The leading term in a product is the result of multiplying the two highest degree terms from the factors, so you know the highest degree in the unknown factor (the quotient).

continued on p. 192

continued from p. 191

Think about multiplying your quotient by the divisor to get the polynomial into which you are dividing. That highest degree term from the quotient that you just found also contributes to the next-highest degree term in the product. It has been multiplied by x, so it also must get multiplied by $-a$. That is where the step of multiplying by the number in the bracket and putting the product under the coefficient of next-highest degree comes in. But since it is a in the bracket, your product has the opposite sign from the term you would get if you multiplied by $-a$. That means that when you add down, you are subtracting the contribution to the next-highest degree coefficient. What is left is the term of next-highest degree in the quotient.

To go back to the example, bringing down the leading coefficient means that you know the first term in the coefficient is x^3. This term, when multiplied by $x - 3$ gives x^4 and $-3x^3$. x^4 is the leading term in the product. The second term in the product is $-3x^3$ plus the product of degree-two term in the quotient and x. You know that their sum is $-5x^3$. So if you add the opposite of $-3x^3$ and $-5x^3$, the result is $-2x^3$. This means that the degree-two term in the quotient is $-2x^2$.

In each step of the algorithm, you are subtracting the contribution from the higher-degree term to figure out the next-lowest-degree term. Since the quotient has to have degree one less, the final number under the line is the remainder after division by $x - 3$.

Here is a second method for writing a polynomial in powers of $x - 3$.

Method 2: Undetermined Coefficients

Suppose

$$f(x) = x^4 - 5x^3 + 3x - 1 = A + B(x-3) + C(x-3)^2 + D(x-3)^3 + E(x-3)^4 \quad (1)$$

Why do you only need to go up to $(x - 3)^4$?

You need to find A, B, C, D, and E.

- Substitute $x = 3$ into (1) to find that $A = f(3) = -46$. Subtract -46 from each side of (1) to get

$$x^4 - 5x^3 + 3x + 45 = B(x-3) + C(x-3)^2 + D(x-3)^3 + E(x-3)^4 \quad (2)$$

The right side of (2) has $x - 3$ as a factor, and the left side does, too. You can check this by noting that

$$3^4 - 5 \cdot 3^3 + 3 \cdot 3 + 45 = 0$$

That is, $x = 3$ is a zero of the left side of (2). The left side of (2) factors as

$$(x-3)(x^3 - 2x^2 - 6x - 15)$$

- So you can write (2) as

$$(x-3)(x^3 - 2x^2 - 6x - 15) = B(x-3) + C(x-3)^2 + D(x-3)^3 + E(x-3)^4$$

Divide each side by $x - 3$ to get

$$x^3 - 2x^2 - 6x - 15 = B + C(x-3) + D(x-3)^2 + E(x-3)^3 \quad (3)$$

Since the left and right sides are equal for $x \neq 3$, they must be equal for $x = 3$, as well.

What property of polynomials justifies this statement?

- Substitute $x = 3$ into (3) to find that $B = -24$. Subtract -24 from each side of (3) to get

$$x^3 - 2x^2 - 6x + 9 = C(x-3) + D(x-3)^2 + E(x-3)^3 \quad (4)$$

The right side of (4) has $x - 3$ as a factor, and thus so does the left side. Again, note that $x = 3$ is a zero of the left side, which factors as

$$(x-3)(x^2 + x - 3)$$

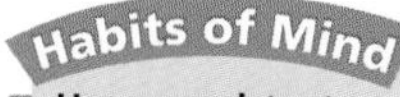

Use a consistent process. Get into the rhythm of the calculations.

- So (4) becomes

$$(x-3)(x^2 + x - 3) = C(x-3) + D(x-3)^2 + E(x-3)^3$$

Divide by $x - 3$ to get

$$x^2 + x - 3 = C + D(x-3) + E(x-3)^2 \quad (5)$$

Again, the equation holds both for $x \neq 3$ and for $x = 3$.

- Substitute $x = 3$ into (5) to find that $C = 9$. Subtract 9 from each side of (5) to get

$$x^2 + x - 12 = D(x-3) + E(x-3)^2 \quad (6)$$

The right side of (6) has $x - 3$ as a factor, and so does the left side. Note that $x = 3$ is a zero of the left side, which factors as

$$(x-3)(x+4)$$

- So write (6) as $(x-3)(x+4) = D(x-3) + E(x-3)^2$.

Divide by $x - 3$ to get

$$x + 4 = D + E(x - 3) \qquad (7)$$

- Finally, substitute $x = 3$ into (7) to find $D = 7$, and then $E = 1$.

Here is a third method for writing a polynomial in powers of $x - 3$.

Method 3: Use Your CAS

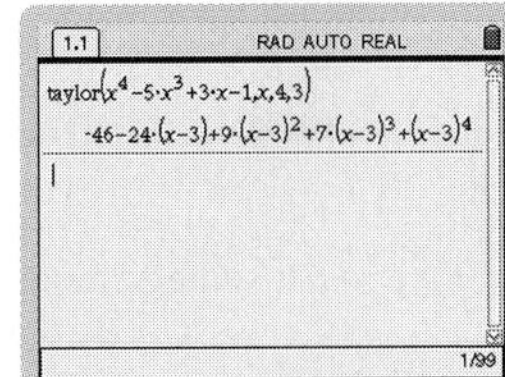

Your CAS has a built-in function that carries out the calculations you have been doing by hand. It allows you to expand a polynomial in terms of powers of $x - a$ for any number a. The function has different names in different systems, but they all work basically the same way.

This says, "Give me the expansion of $x^4 = 5x^3 + 3x - 1$. The variable is x, give me terms up to degree is 4, and I want it in terms of $x - 3$."

taylor ($x^4 - 5x^3 + 3x - 1$,	x,	4,	3)
↓	↓	↓	↓
polynomial	variable	degree	in terms of $(x - 3)$

See the TI-Nspire Handbook on p. 704 for more information about the taylor function.

For You to Do

4. Using whatever method you prefer, write

$$f(x) = 2x^3 + 5x^2 + x + 3$$

as a polynomial in $x - 1$.

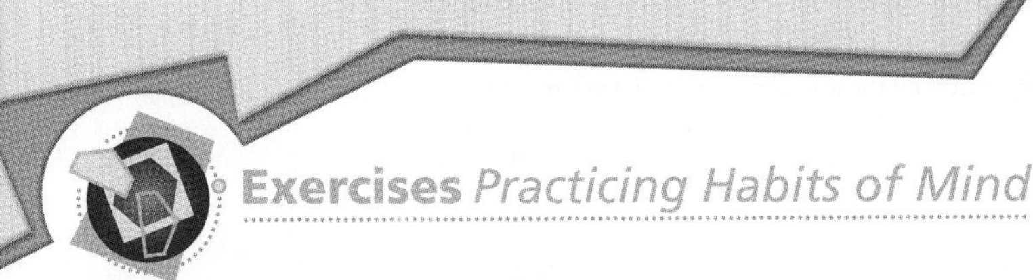

Check Your Understanding

1. Suppose that $f(x) = 2x^3 + 5x^2 + x - 1$ and $g(x) = x^2 + 2x - 3$. Expand the following in powers of $x - 3$.

   a. $f(x)$ b. $g(x)$ c. $f(x) + g(x)$

   d. $4f(x)$ e. $4f(x) - g(x)$

Answers

For You to Do

4. $2(x - 1)^3 + (x - 1)^2 - 3(x - 1) + 1$

Exercises

1. a. $101 + 85(x - 3) + 23(x - 3)^2 + 2(x - 3)^3$

   b. $12 + 8(x - 3) + (x - 3)^2$

   c. $113 + 93(x - 3) + 24(x - 3)^2 + 2(x - 3)^3$

   d. $404 + 340(x - 3) + 92(x - 3)^2 + 8(x - 3)^3$

   e. $392 + 332(x - 3) + 91(x - 3)^2 + 8(x - 3)^3$

Wrap Up

If your students do not have access to a CAS with a function for finding the Taylor expansion for a polynomial, assign exercises very lightly in this lesson. When students do these calculations by hand, it is a lot of work! If students are able to use a CAS, though, it should not take too long to go through the lesson. You have plenty of time to go through the core Check Your Understanding exercises with students.

Make sure that students notice the key results in Exercise 1—the expansion of a sum is equal to the sum of the expansions, and the expansion of a constant a times a function is equal to a times the expansion of the function. If you assign Exercise 2, students can also see that the expansion of a product is equal to the product of the expansions. Note that none of these results have been *proven*; that is beyond the scope of this course.

Assessment Resources

Lesson Quiz 3.4

1. Suppose that $f(x) = 3x^3 - 2x^2 + 5x - 8$ and $g(x) = 4x^2 - 7x + 12$. Expand the following in powers of $x - 3$.
   a. $f(x)$
   b. $g(x)$
   c. $2g(x)$
   d. $f(x) - g(x)$

Exercises

HOMEWORK

- Core: 6, 7, 10, 11, 12, 16, 17
- Optional: 8, 9, 13, 15
- Extension: 14

You can make a handout from Blackline Master 3.4A for students to use while working on the exercises.

Check Your Understanding

EXERCISE 1 Students should notice that the expansion of the sum $f(x) + g(x)$ is equal to the sum of the expansions of $f(x)$ and $g(x)$, and that the expansion of $4f(x)$ is equal to 4 times the expansion of $f(x)$. Similarly, the expansion of $4f(x) - g(x)$ is equal to 4 times the expansion of $f(x)$ minus the expansion of $g(x)$.

EXERCISE 2 Again, students should see that the expansion of the sum is the sum of the expansions, and that the expansion of 3 times a function is equal to 3 times the expansion of the function. In part (e), students can also see that the expansion of the product of two functions is equal to the product of their expansions.

EXERCISE 3 A general expansion such as the one in this exercise is useful if you are asked to find expansions for the same function around several different points.

EXERCISES 4 AND 5 Exercise 4, along with what students have learned in Exercises 1 and 2 about Taylor expansions of linear combinations of functions, sets up Exercise 5. In Exercise 5, Sasha uses the linear combinations of the expansions of the powers of x to quickly find the expansion of a polynomial.

On Your Own

EXERCISE 6 As in Exercises 1 and 2 from the Check Your Understanding section, students should notice that the expansion of $3f(x) - 2g(x)$ is equal to 3 times the expansion of $f(x)$ minus 2 times the expansion of $g(x)$, and that the expansion of the square of $f(x)$ is equal to the square of the expansion of $f(x)$.

EXERCISE 7 prepares students to tackle the even more general expansion in the next exercise. Some students might find it challenging to keep track of all the variables in a calculation like this, so it is helpful to take an intermediate step.

2. Suppose that $f(x) = 2x^3 + 5x^2 + x - 1$ and $g(x) = x^2 + 2x - 3$. Expand the following in powers of $x - 2$.

a. $f(x)$ **b.** $g(x)$

c. $f(x) + g(x)$ **d.** $3f(x)$

e. $f(x) \cdot g(x)$

3. Suppose that $g(x) = x^2 + 2x - 3$ and a is some number. Expand $g(x)$ in powers of $x - a$ as

$$g(x) = A + B(x - a) + C(x - a)^2$$

where A, B, and C are expressions in a.

4. Expand each polynomial in powers of $x - 3$.

a. x^3 **b.** x^2 **c.** x **d.** 1

Sasha is thinking about Exercise 4.

Sasha I see an easy way to get the expansion for $f(x) = 2x^3 + 5x^2 + x - 1$ from Exercise 1 in powers of $x - 3$.

Tony How?

Sasha I use what we got from Exercise 4.

First, we know the expansion for x^3. Since $f(x)$ starts out with $2x^3$, I multiply all the coefficients in the expansion for x^3 by 2.

Next, we know the expansion for x^2. Since $f(x)$ has a $5x^2$ term, I multiply all the coefficients in the expansion for x^2 by 5.

Tony And you multiply the expansion of x by 1 and the expansion of 1 by -1, right?

Where did Tony get the 1 and -1?

Sasha Right, and then I add all these expressions together, making believe that the variable is $x - 3$. This will work for any cubic—I just need to know the expansions about 3 for the powers of x.

Tony Nice, but how do we know it works?

Sasha There's only one way to find out.

5. Write About It Does Sasha's method work for $f(x) = 2x^3 + 5x^2 + x - 1$? Does it work for any cubic polynomial? Justify your answers.

On Your Own

6. Suppose that $f(x) = 2x^3 + 5x^2 + x - 1$ and $g(x) = x^2 + 2x - 3$. Expand the following in powers of $x - 5$.

a. $f(x)$ **b.** $g(x)$ **c.** $3f(x) - 2g(x)$ **d.** $f(x) \cdot f(x)$

Answers

2. a. $37 + 45(x - 2) + 17(x - 2)^2 + 2(x - 2)^3$
b. $5 + 6(x - 2) + (x - 2)^2$
c. $42 + 51(x - 2) + 18(x - 2)^2 + 2(x - 2)^3$
d. $111 + 135(x - 2) + 51(x - 2)^2 + 6(x - 2)^3$
e. $185 + 447(x - 2) + 392(x - 2)^2 + 157(x - 2)^3 + 29(x - 2)^4 + 2(x - 2)^5$

3. $a^2 + 2a - 3 + (2a + 2)(x - a) + (x - a)^2$

4. a. $27 + 27(x - 3) + 9(x - 3)^2 + (x - 3)^3$
b. $9 + 6(x - 3) + (x - 3)^2$
c. $3 + (x - 3)$
d. $1 + 0(x - 3)$

5. Yes, it works for $f(x) = 2x^3 + 5x^2 + x - 1$. It will work for any cubic.

6. a. $379 + 201(x - 5) + 35(x - 5)^2 + 2(x - 5)^3$
b. $32 + 12(x - 5) + (x - 5)^2$
c. $1073 + 579(x - 5) + 103(x - 5)^2 + 6(x - 5)^3$
d. See back of book.

7. Suppose that $g(x) = rx^2 + sx + t$. Expand $g(x)$ in powers of $x - 3$

$$g(x) = A + B(x - 3) + C(x - 3)^2$$

where, A, B, and C are in terms of r, s, and t.

8. Suppose that $g(x) = rx^2 + sx + t$ and a is a number. Expand $g(x)$ in powers of $x - a$ as

$$g(x) = A + B(x - a) + C(x - a)^2$$

where, A, B, and C are in terms of r, s, t, and a.

9. Until now, you have been dividing polynomials by a linear term. But the divisor can have any degree.

a. Find the missing numbers in this long division.

$$\begin{array}{r} x + \_\_ \\ x^2 - 7x + 10 \overline{)\,x^3 - 4x^2 - 10x + 31} \\ \underline{x^3 - 7x^2 + \_\_x \quad\quad} \\ 3x^2 + \_\_x + 31 \\ \underline{\_\_x^2 + \_\_x + \_\_} \\ \_\_x + \_\_ \end{array}$$

b. How can you tell when the long division is complete?

c. Write the result as

$$x^3 - 4x^2 - 10x + 31 = (x^2 - 7x + 10)q(x) + r(x)$$

where q and r are polynomials in x.

10. Find the remainder when you divide $x^3 - 4x^2 - 10x + 31$ by

a. x **b.** x^2 **c.** x^3

11. *Derman is still reviewing his notes.*

Derman I really like the way you can write $f(x)$ in powers of $x + 3$.

$$f(x) = x^3 - 14x^2 + 55x - 42$$
$$= -360 + 166(x + 3) - 23(x + 3)^2 + (x + 3)^3$$

Tony Why?

Derman It lets me find the remainders when I divide $f(x)$ by any power of $x + 3$.

Tony Derman, sometimes you can be so deep.

Use Derman's idea to find the remainder when you divide $f(x)$ by

a. $x + 3$ **b.** $(x + 3)^2$ **c.** $(x + 3)^3$ **d.** $(x + 3)^8$

7. $9r + 3s + t + (6r + s)(x - 3) + r(x - 3)^2$

8. $a^2r + as + t + (2ar + s)(x - a) + r(x - a)^2$

9. a.

$$\begin{array}{r} x + 3 \\ x^2 - 7x + 10 \overline{)\,x^3 - 4x^2 - 10x + 31} \\ \underline{x^3 - 7x^2 + 10x \quad\quad} \\ 3x^2 + -20x + 31 \\ \underline{3x^2 + -21x + 30} \\ 1x + 1 \end{array}$$

b. The division ends when the degree of the remainder is less than the degree of the divisor.

c. $x^3 - 4x^2 - 10x + 31 = (x^2 - 7x + 10)(x + 3) + x + 1$

10. a. 31
b. $-10x + 31$
c. $-4x^2 - 10x + 31$

11. a. -360
b. $-360 + 166(x + 3)$
c. $-360 + 166(x + 3) - 23(x + 3)^2$
d. $-360 + 166(x + 3) - 23(x + 3)^2 + (x + 3)^3$ or $x^3 - 14x^2 + 55x - 42$

EXERCISE 8 This expression is the Taylor expansion of a general quadratic about a general point, so you can use it to find the Taylor expansion of any quadratic about any point. If your students are working without technology, you could give them this formula to use if you like. However, do not expect them to memorize it, as it is not a tool they need often.

EXERCISE 9 Depending on your state and district standards, you might not need to cover long division by non-linear divisors. You can skip this exercise without having trouble later. However, it is nice for students to see that polynomial long division can work with divisors that are non-linear, and by working through examples such as this one, they may come to have a deeper understanding of both polynomial long division and traditional long division. Also, in the next lesson, students learn a technique for finding the equation of the tangent to the graph of a function at a point that involves dividing a polynomial by a quadratic. If you want your students to do this by hand, spend a little time on this exercise. Discuss the differences between dividing by a quadratic and dividing by a linear polynomial.

EXERCISE 10 Students should notice that the remainders are just the terms of the original polynomial that have smaller degree than the divisor. This realization leads to Derman's work in Exercise 11 and illuminates one of the uses of Taylor expansions. With the Taylor expansion of a polynomial about the point $x = a$, students can easily list the remainder after division by powers of $(x - a)$.

EXERCISE 12 uses the results of Exercise 6. It also applies the ideas developed in Exercises 10 and 11. Assign Exercises 6, 10, and 11 if you plan to assign Exercise 12.

You can use Blackline Master 3.4B on an overhead and fill in the entries as students supply them, or you can hand out printed copies for students to record their work.

EXERCISE 13 Your students should recognize the binomial coefficients as they crop up in these expansions. If they follow the directions in the side note, they see that the expansion for x is $1 + 1(x-1)$, and for 1, the expansion is just 1. These two additional expansions, placed on top of the Pascal's triangle they have written with the coefficients of the other expansions, complete the pointy top of the triangle.

EXERCISE 14 can help students see why they got the results they did for Exercise 13, because they use the binomial theorem directly to write the expansions.

EXERCISE 15 Students can see that the Taylor expansions of different degrees are actually approximations of the function at the point of expansion. For example, the Taylor expansion of f of degree 2 that students find in part (b) is a quadratic curve that closely approximates the cubic around $x = 2$. If you look at the four graphs in a window that shows $0 \le x \le 4$ and $-30 \le y \le 0$, you can see the four graphs coming together in that region.

Maintain Your Skills

EXERCISE 17 If students look at the two graphs near $x = 3$, which is the point of expansion, they see that the line they are graphing is the tangent to the curve at $x = 3$. Whenever you divide a cubic function by a quadratic, the remainder is linear (or constant), so they should expect all the remainders in this exercise to be linear equations. As they saw in Exercise 15, the Taylor polynomials of various degrees closely approximate the function near the point of expansion. So the Taylor expansion is another way to find the equation of the tangent to a curve at a point.

You can make copies of Blackline Master MC7 for students to sketch each pair of function graphs.

Additional Resources

PRINT RESOURCES
- Solution Manual
- Practice Workbook
- Assessment Resources
- Teaching Resources

TECHNOLOGY
- Interactive Textbook
- TeacherExpress CD-ROM
- ExamView CD-ROM
- PHSchool.com

Additional Practice

1. Suppose that $f(x) = x^3 - 3x^2 + 5x + 7$ and $g(x) = x^2 + 6x + 17$. Expand the following in powers of $x - 1$.
   a. $f(x)$ b. $g(x)$
   c. $3f(x)$ d. $f(x) + g(x)$

2. Suppose that $f(x) = x^3 - 3x^2 + 5x + 7$ and $g(x) = x^2 + 6x + 17$. Expand the following in powers of $x - 2$.
   a. $f(x)$ b. $g(x)$
   c. $4g(x)$ d. $f(x) + g(x)$

3. Suppose $g(x) = x^2 + 6x + 17$ and a is some number. Expand $g(x)$ in powers of $x - a$ as
$$g(x) = A + B(x - a) + C(x - a)^2$$
where A, B, and C are expressions in a.

4. Consider $h(x) = x^3 - 4x^2 + 5x + 3$. Write an equation for the line tangent to the graph of h at (2, 5).

5. Find the equation of the line tangent to the graph of each polynomial when $x = 1$.
   a. $f(x) = x^2 + 2x$ b. $f(x) = x^3 + 3x + 7$
   c. $f(x) = 2x^4 + 3x^2 - 5x$ d. $f(x) = x^6 - 4x$

6. Copy and complete the table for $f(x) = x^3 + 4x^2 - 6x + 2$.

x	$f(x)$	Slope of the tangent at $(x, f(x))$
−1		
0		
1		
2		
3		
4		
10		
100		

Practice: For Lesson 3.4, assign Exercises 1–3.

12. In Exercise 6, you expanded combinations of $f(x) = 2x^3 + 5x^2 + x - 1$ and $g(x) = x^2 + 2x - 3$ in powers of $x - 5$. That should make filling in this table a snap. Copy and complete the table.

	Remainder when divided by					
	$x - 5$	$(x - 5)^2$	$(x - 5)^3$	$(x - 5)^4$	$(x - 5)^5$	$(x - 5)^6$
$f(x)$	■	■	■	■	■	■
$g(x)$	■	■	■	■	■	■
$3f(x) - 2g(x)$	■	■	■	■	■	■
$f(x) \cdot f(x)$	■	■	■	■	■	■

13. Write each polynomial in the form $A + B(x - 1) + C(x)(x - 1)^2$ where $C(x)$ is a polynomial in x.
   a. x^2 b. x^3 c. x^4 d. x^5 e. x^6
   f. x^n (where n is a positive integer)

While you are at it, you might as well expand 1 and x, too.

14. **Take It Further** Use the identity $x^n = ((x - 1) + 1)^n$ and the Binomial Theorem to write each polynomial in powers of $x - 1$.
   a. x^2 b. x^3 c. x^5 d. x^n (n a positive integer)

15. Suppose $f(x) = x^3 - 5x^2 - 2x + 1$. Graph each of the following.
   a. f b. $x \mapsto \text{taylor}(f(x), x, 1, 2)$
   c. $x \mapsto \text{taylor}(f(x), x, 2, 2)$ d. $x \mapsto \text{taylor}(f(x), x, 3, 2)$

The taylor function on your CAS might look a bit different.

16. **Standardized Test Prep** What is the remainder when you divide $P(x) = 3x^5 - 5x^4 + 2x^3 - 4x^2 + x - 1$ by $x - 1$?
   A. 2 B. −3 C. 4 D. −4

Maintain Your Skills

17. For each polynomial $f(x)$,
   - Find the remainder $r(x)$ when you divide $f(x)$ by $(x - 3)^2$.
   - Sketch the graphs of f and r on the same axes.

   a. $f(x) = x^3 - 5x + 6$ b. $f(x) = (x - 1)(x - 5)$
   c. $f(x) = x^3$ d. $f(x) = x^3 + 3x^2 - 2x + 1$
   e. $f(x) = (x - 1)^3$ f. $f(x) = (x - 3)^3$

For additional practice, go to Web Code: bga-0304

Answers

12. See back of book.

13. a. $1 + 2(x - 1) + (x - 1)^2$
   b. $1 + 3(x - 1) + (x + 2)(x - 1)^2$
   c. $1 + 4(x - 1) + (x^2 + 2x + 3)(x - 1)^2$
   d. $1 + 5(x - 1) + (x^3 + 2x^2 + 3x + 4)(x - 1)^2$
   e. $1 + 6(x - 1) + (x^4 + 2x^3 + 3x^2 + 4x + 5)(x - 1)^2$
   f. $1 + n(x - 1) + (x - 1)^2 \sum_{k=1}^{n-1} (k \cdot x^{n-k-1})$ for positive integer n.

14–15. See back of book.

16. D

17. See back of book.

3.5 Secants and Tangents

You know how to find the average rate of change between two points in time. This lesson will help you find the rate of change at a particular instant in time.

In-Class Experiment

Let $d = t^2$ denote the distance d (in feet) that Jerry has walked in t seconds. The graph of this function is shown below.

1. Determine his average speed between $t = 1$ and $t = 2$.
2. Determine his average speed between $t = 1$ and $t = 1.1$.
3. Determine his average speed between $t = 1$ and $t = 1.01$.
4. Determine his instantaneous speed at $t = 1$.

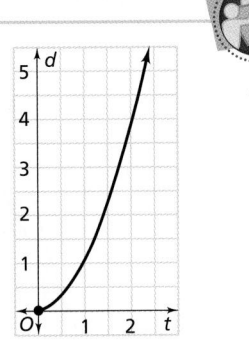

This function does not make sense as a model when t is large, but it is plausible if t is small.

To find Jerry's **instantaneous speed** at $t = 1$, you need to find the slope of the tangent to the graph of $d = t^2$ at the point (1, 1).

For You to Do

5. Use geometry software to make a sketch with the graph of $y = x^2$ and a movable point (a, a^2) on the graph. Construct the tangent to the curve at the point (a, a^2).
6. Copy the table below. Move the point along the graph and record the slope of the corresponding tangents in your table.

See the TI-Nspire Handbook on p. 704 for details on how to draw tangent lines.

x	$y = x^2$	Slope of the tangent at (x, x^2)
−1	■	■
0	■	■
1	■	■
2	■	■
3	■	■
4	■	■
10	■	■
100	■	■

In-Class Experiment

1. 3 ft/s
2. 2.1 ft/s
3. 2.01 ft/s
4. 2 ft/s

For You to Do

5. Check students' work.
6. See back of book.

Lesson Overview

GOAL

- Find the equation of the tangent to a polynomial curve at a point.

This lesson formalizes the relationship between secant lines and tangent lines. Students learn several techniques for finding the equation of the tangent line to the graph of a function at a point, including long division, using the polyremainder function on a CAS, or using the Taylor expansion for the function. Students get an opportunity to do the calculations by hand and with technology.

CHECK YOUR UNDERSTANDING
- Core: 1, 2, 3, 4, 5
- Optional: 6, 7

MATERIALS
- CAS (recommended)
- geometry software
- graph paper
- graphing calculators
- Blackline Master 3.5

HOMEWORK
- Core: 8, 9, 10, 11, 13
- Optional: 14
- Extension: 12

VOCABULARY
- instantaneous speed
- tangent line

Launch

Begin today's lesson with the In-Class Experiment. Students find average speed for several intervals on a distance and time graph. In effect, they are finding the slope of several secant lines, which are related to each other. Each includes the fixed point (1, 1), and another point which is closer and closer to the fixed point each time. In the final question of the experiment, students are asked to compute the instantaneous speed for the first time.

Explore

In-Class Experiment

PROBLEM 4 There are several ways to answer this question. Some students substitute a number that is *very* close to 1 in the equation, to get something like $\frac{1.000002000001-1}{1.000001-1} = 2.000001$. Then they might conclude that the answer is 2. Other students might approach the question with a more formal algebraic argument:

$$\lim_{b\to 0} \frac{(1+b)^2 - 1}{(1+b) - 1} = \lim_{b\to 0} \frac{2b + b^2}{b} = \lim_{b\to 0} 2 + b = 2$$

Still other students might use the Taylor expansion of the function about 1 and the results of the previous lesson to find the tangent line.

continued on p. 198

continued from p. 197

PROBLEM 6 You may want to use Blackline Master 3.5 on an overhead and fill in the entries as students find each value, or you can hand out printed copies for students to record their results.

Given a function f and a point $A = (a, f(a))$ on the graph of $y = f(x)$, you can think of the **tangent line** at A as the secant between A and itself.

More precisely, recall Exercise 2 from Lesson 3.3, where you let $f(x) = x^3 - 2x + 1$ and used geometry software to sketch the graph of f, the base point $A = (2, f(2))$ on the graph, and a movable point $B = (b, f(b))$ on the graph.

As B moves closer to A, the secant through A and B approaches the tangent at A. The slope of the tangent at A is the "limiting value" of the slope of the secant as b approaches 2. The usual way to write this is

$$\lim_{b \to 2} \frac{f(b) - f(2)}{b - 2}$$

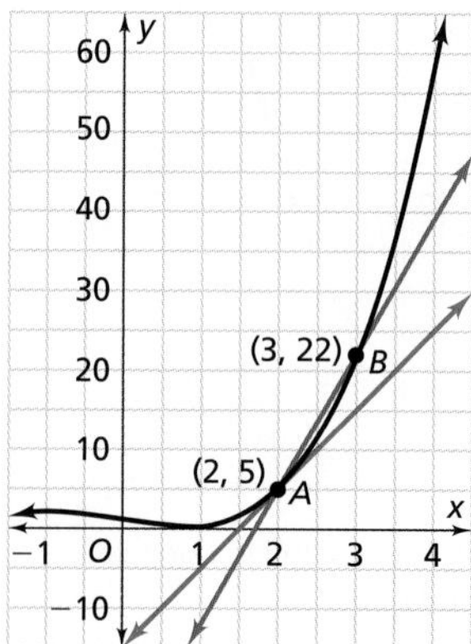

Computing the Tangent

To find the equation of a tangent line algebraically, go back to secants for a moment. Let $f(x) = x^3 - 2x + 1$. Divide $f(x)$ by $(x - 2)(x - 3) = x^2 - 5x + 6$. Using long division, you get

$$\begin{array}{r|l} & x + 5 \\ \hline x^2 - 5x + 6 & x^3 \qquad - 2x + 1 \\ & \underline{x^3 - 5x^2 + 6x} \\ & 5x^2 - 8x + 1 \\ & \underline{5x^2 - 25x + 30} \\ & 17x - 29 \end{array}$$

so you have

$$f(x) = x^3 - 2x + 1 = (x - 2)(x - 3)q(x) + r(x)$$

where $q(x) = x + 5$ and $r(x) = 17x - 29$. Substituting $x = 2$ shows that $f(2) = r(2)$. Likewise, $f(3) = r(3)$. In other words, r is a linear function that agrees with f at $x = 2$ and $x = 3$. So the graph of $y = r(x)$ must be the secant to the graph of $y = f(x)$ through the points $(2, f(2))$ and $(3, f(3))$.

Here is the generalization.

Theorem 3.4

Let $f(x)$ be a polynomial and $a, b \in \mathbb{R}$. Write

$$f(x) = (x - a)(x - b)q(x) + r(x)$$

where $r(x)$ is a linear function. Then the graph of $y = r(x)$ is the secant to the graph of $y = f(x)$ through $(a, f(a))$ and $(b, f(b))$.

In the above theorem, all you are really interested in is the remainder $r(x)$. In other words, you do not need to know what $q(x)$ is. A CAS can find this remainder easily and quickly.

See the TI-Nspire Handbook on p. 704 for details on how to use the polyremainder function to find the remainder $r(x)$ when you divide one polynomial by another.

How about the tangent? Let $f(x) = x^3 - 2x + 1$ again. Suppose you want to find the tangent to its graph at $A = (2, f(2))$. Consider a movable point $B = (b, f(b))$ on the graph. The secant between A and B is given by the remainder when you divide $f(x)$ by $(x - 2)(x - b)$. As point B approaches point A, the corresponding division by $(x - 2)(x - b)$ becomes division by $(x - 2)^2$.

This type of argument works because polynomial functions are continuous.

The following theorem summarizes this result.

Theorem 3.5

Let $f(x)$ be a polynomial and $a \in \mathbb{R}$. Write

$$f(x) = (x - a)^2q(x) + r(x)$$

where $r(x)$ is a linear function. Then the graph of $y = r(x)$ is the tangent to the graph of $y = f(x)$ at $(a, f(a))$.

Example 1

Problem Suppose $f(x) = x^3 - 2x + 1$. Find the equation of the tangent to the graph of $y = f(x)$ at the point $(2, 5)$.

Solution By Theorem 3.5, the equation of the tangent is the linear function $r(x)$ where

$$f(x) = (x - 2)^2q(x) + r(x)$$

In other words, $r(x)$ is the remainder when you divide $f(x)$ by $(x - 2)^2 = x^2 - 4x + 4$. A CAS shows that

$$r(x) = 10x - 15$$

Example 1

Spend time as needed going over this completed example. Make sure students understand the problem. As necessary, help them develop the detailed solution.

Wrap Up

Encourage students to graph at least some of the functions and their tangents to get a clearer idea of what the tangent to a curve at a point looks like. They can also use the graphs to check their work and gain confidence in these calculations. As time allows, go over the core Check Your Understanding exercises. Try to show a variety of solution methods, so that each student can find a method they understand and can use.

Assessment Resources

Lesson Quiz 3.5

1. Consider $g(x) = x^3 + 3x^2 - 4x + 2$. Find the slope of the tangent at the point $(x, f(x))$ for each value of x.
   a. $x = 0$
   b. $x = -1$
   c. $x = 2$
   d. $x = 10$

2. Consider $f(x) = 5x^2 - 8x - 10$.
   a. Find the equation of the line tangent to the graph of f at $(-1, 3)$.
   b. Find the equation of the line tangent to the graph of f at $(0, -10)$.

3. Consider $g(x) = x^8$.
   a. Find, in terms of b, the slope of the line tangent to g at $(b, f(b))$.
   b. Find, in terms of b, the equation of the line tangent to g at $(b, f(b))$.

So far, you have seen two ways to find the remainder $r(x)$:

- Using long division.
- Using a CAS.

The following technique uses methods from Lesson 3.4.

Example 2

Problem Let $f(x) = 2x^2 + 3x + 1$. Find the equation of the tangent to the graph of $y = f(x)$ at the point $(3, f(3))$.

Solution First, write $f(x)$ in powers of $x - 3$.

$$f(x) = 2x^2 + 3x + 1 = m + n(x - 3) + p(x)(x - 3)^2 \qquad (1)$$

You can read off the remainder when you divide $f(x)$ by $(x - 3)^2$—it is $m + n(x - 3)$.

See Exercise 11 from Lesson 3.4.

With $r(x) = m + n(x - 3)$, the graph of $r(x)$ is the desired tangent. So you need to solve for m and n. Substitute $x = 3$ in (1) to get

$$m = f(3) = 2 \cdot 3^2 + 3 \cdot 3 + 1 = 28$$

So

$$2x^2 + 3x + 1 = 28 + n(x - 3) + p(x)(x - 3)^2 \qquad (2)$$

Subtracting 28 from both sides of (2) gives

$$2x^2 + 3x - 27 = n(x - 3) + p(x)(x - 3)^2$$

The right side says that $x - 3$ is a factor of the left side. This makes factoring the left side easy:

$$(x - 3)(2x + 9) = n(x - 3) + p(x)(x - 3)^2$$

Dividing by $x - 3$ gives

$$2x + 9 = n + p(x)(x - 3) \qquad (3)$$

Substituting $x = 3$ into (3) gives $n = 15$. So the equation of the tangent is

$$r(x) = 28 + 15(x - 3) = 15x - 17.$$

For You to Do

7. Let $f(x) = 2x^2 + 3x + 1$ again. Using the method in Example 2, find the equation of the tangent to the graph of $y = f(x)$ at the point $(a, f(a))$. (Your equation will be in terms of a.)

Habits of Mind

You can also use a CAS to solve this, but do not let the calculator have all the fun.

Answers

For You to Do

7. $r(x) = (4a + 3)x - 2a^2 + 1$

Exercises *Practicing Habits of Mind*

Check Your Understanding

1. Find the equation of the line tangent to the graph of $y = x^2$ at the point $(5, 25)$.
2. Consider $f(x) = x^3 - 7x^2 + 3x - 2$. Write an equation for the line tangent to the graph of f at $(0, -2)$.
3. Generalize the result in Exercise 1 by finding the equation of the line tangent to the graph of $y = x^2$ at the point (a, a^2).
4. Copy and complete this table for $f(x) = x^2 + 1$.

x	$f(x)$	Slope of tangent at $(x, f(x))$
−1	■	■
0	■	■
1	■	■
2	■	■
3	■	■
4	■	■
10	■	■
100	■	■

5. Copy and complete this table for $f(x) = x^2 + x$.

x	$f(x)$	Slope of tangent at $(x, f(x))$
−1	■	■
0	■	■
1	■	■
2	■	■
3	■	■
4	■	■
10	■	■
100	■	■

6. Find the equation of the line tangent to the graph of each polynomial at $(1, 1)$.
   a. $f(x) = x^2$
   b. $f(x) = x^3$
   c. $f(x) = x^4$
   d. $f(x) = x^5$
   e. $f(x) = x^6$
   f. $f(x) = x$
7. Find, in terms of n, a formula for the equation of the tangent to the graph of $y = x^n$ (where n is a positive integer) at $(1, 1)$.

Exercises

HOMEWORK

- Core: 8, 9, 10, 11, 13
- Optional: 14
- Extension: 12

Check Your Understanding

EXERCISE 1 Make clear to students the methods you want them to use. For a fairly simple exercise like this one, you can show several methods.

EXERCISE 3 If students have trouble with both x and a as variables, you might suggest that they go back to their work on Exercise 1 and do this new calculation in parallel with the old one.

EXERCISES 4 AND 5 You can use Blackline Master 3.5 as an overhead and fill in the entries as students find each value, or you can hand out printed copies for students to write on.

EXERCISE 4 By looking at a table of the slopes, students can see that the slope for any value x is equal to $2x$. This is the derivative of x^2, but for your students, it is enough that they see that the slope of the tangent line is a function of x.

EXERCISE 5 Here the slope of the tangent is equal to $2x + 1$.

EXERCISE 6f For some of your students, the task of finding a tangent to the graph of a line is straightforward. It may bother them that the equation of the graph of the tangent line is the same as the equation of the graph of the polynomial. If they are thinking geometrically, they may state that it is not a tangent line at all, since it has more than one intersection. However, from a calculus perspective, the tangent to a graph at a point is the line that contains the point and has the same slope as the slope of the graph.

Exercises

1. $y = 10x - 25$
2. $y = 3x - 2$
3. $y = 2ax - a^2$

4–5. See back of book.

6. a. $y = 2x - 1$
   b. $y = 3x - 2$
   c. $y = 4x - 3$
   d. $y = 5x - 4$
   e. $y = 6x - 5$
   f. $y = x$
7. $y = n(x - 1) + 1$

On Your Own

EXERCISE 9 If students choose to solve the general problem and find the equation for the tangent line through a point $(a, f(a))$, they will not be surprised to see that the slope of the tangent line at x is $3x^2$.

You can hand out Blackline Master 3.5 for students to fill in the table.

EXERCISE 10 Students use the patterns they see in this exercise to solve Exercise 11 (and further extend the pattern in Exercise 12), so assign this exercise if you plan to assign either Exercise 11 or 12.

EXERCISE 11 previews one of the first derivatives students learn to find in calculus—the derivative with respect to x of x^n is nx^{n-1}.

EXERCISE 12 Students see that the formula they found in Exercise 11 still works even when x is raised to a non-integer power.

Maintain Your Skills

EXERCISE 14 By the end of this exercise, students should not try to carry out the division, but will hopefully substitute inputs into the function instead.

Additional Resources

PRINT RESOURCES
- Solution Manual
- Practice Workbook
- Assessment Resources
- Teaching Resources

TECHNOLOGY
- Interactive Textbook
- TeacherExpress CD-ROM
- ExamView CD-ROM
- PHSchool.com

Additional Practice

1. Suppose that $f(x) = x^3 - 3x^2 + 5x + 7$ and $g(x) = x^2 + 6x + 17$. Expand the following in powers of $x - 1$.
   a. $f(x)$ b. $g(x)$
   c. $3f(x)$ d. $f(x) + g(x)$

2. Suppose that $f(x) = x^3 - 3x^2 + 5x + 7$ and $g(x) = x^2 + 6x + 17$. Expand the following in powers of $x - 2$.
   a. $f(x)$ b. $g(x)$
   c. $4g(x)$ d. $f(x) + g(x)$

3. Suppose $g(x) = x^2 + 6x + 17$ and a is some number. Expand $g(x)$ in powers of $x - a$ as
$$g(x) = A + B(x - a) + C(x - a)^2$$
where A, B, and C are expressions in a.

4. Consider $h(x) = x^3 - 4x^2 + 5x + 3$. Write an equation for the line tangent to the graph of h at $(2, 5)$.

5. Find the equation of the line tangent to the graph of each polynomial when $x = 1$.
   a. $f(x) = x^2 + 2x$ b. $f(x) = x^3 + 3x + 7$
   c. $f(x) = 2x^4 + 3x^2 - 5x$ d. $f(x) = x^6 - 4x$

6. Copy and complete the table for $f(x) = x^3 + 4x^2 - 6x + 2$.

x	$f(x)$	Slope of the tangent at $(x, f(x))$
−1		
0		
1		
2		
3		
4		
10		
100		

Practice: For Lesson 3.5, assign Exercises 4–6.

On Your Own

8. Find the slope and equation of the line tangent to the graph of $f(x) = x^3 - x$ at the point $(-1, 2)$.

9. Copy and complete this table for $f(x) = x^3$.

x	$f(x)$	Slope of tangent at $(x, f(x))$
−1	■	■
0	■	■
1	■	■
2	■	■
3	■	■
4	■	■
10	■	■
100	■	■

10. Find, in terms of a, the equation of the line tangent to the graph of each polynomial at $(a, f(a))$.
    a. $f(x) = x^2$ b. $f(x) = x^3$ c. $f(x) = x^4$
    d. $f(x) = x^5$ e. $f(x) = x^6$ f. $f(x) = x$

11. Find, in terms of n and a, a formula for the equation of the tangent to the graph of $f(x) = x^n$ (where n is a positive integer) at $(a, f(a))$.

12. **Take It Further** Find the equation of the line tangent to the graph of $y = \sqrt{x}$ at $(1, 1)$.

13. **Standardized Test Prep** If a function f has a well-defined slope over its entire domain, which of the following expressions gives the slope of $f(x)$ at $x = 0$?

    A. $\lim\limits_{x \to a} \frac{f(a) - f(0)}{x - a}$ B. $\lim\limits_{a \to b} \frac{f(b) - f(a)}{b - a}$ C. $\lim\limits_{b \to 0} \frac{f(b) - f(0)}{b}$ D. $\lim\limits_{x \to 0} \frac{f(a) - f(0)}{x}$

Maintain Your Skills

14. Find the remainder when you divide $f(x) = x^3 - 2x + 1$ by each of these linear factors.
    a. $(x + 1)$ b. x c. $(x - 1)$ d. $(x - 2)$
    e. $(x - 3)$ f. $(x - 4)$ g. $(x - 10)$ h. $(x - 100)$

Go Online
PHSchool.com
For additional practice, go to **Web Code:** bga-0305

Answers

8. 2; $y = 2x + 2$

9. See back of book.

10. a. $y = 2ax - a^2$
    b. $y = 3a^2x - 2a^3$
    c. $y = 4a^3x - 3a^4$
    d. $y = 5a^4x - 4a^5$
    e. $y = 6a^5x - 5a^6$
    f. $y = x$

11. $y = na^{n-1}x - (n - 1)a^n$

12. $\frac{y - 1}{x - 1} = \frac{1}{2}$ or $y = \frac{1}{2}x + \frac{1}{2}$

13. C

14. a. $f(-1) = 2$ b. $f(0) = 1$
    c. $f(1) = 0$ d. $f(2) = 5$
    e. $f(3) = 22$ f. $f(4) = 57$
    g. $f(10) = 981$
    h. $f(100) = 999{,}801$

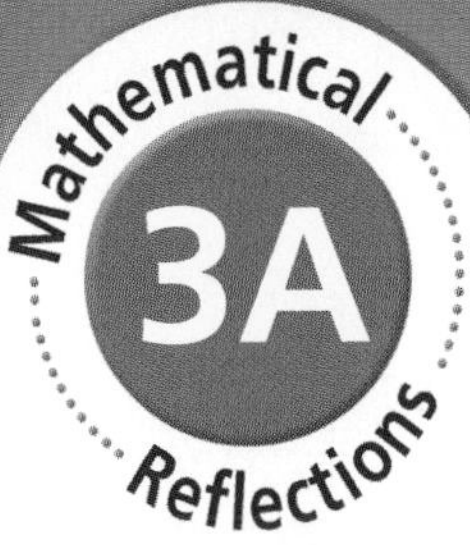

In this investigation, you found slopes of lines secant or tangent to the graph of a polynomial function. You learned that these slopes represent, respectively, average and instantaneous rates of change of the function. The following questions will help you summarize what you have learned.

1. Here are three expressions that each define the function f.

   Expression 1: $f(x) = x^4 - 5x^3 - x^2 + 17x + 12$

   Expression 2: $f(x) = (x + 1)^2(x - 3)(x - 4)$

   Expression 3: $f(x) = (x - 1)^4 - (x - 1)^3 - 10(x - 1)^2 + 4(x - 1) + 24$

   a. Which expression would be the most useful for sketching the graph of the function? Choose an expression, use it to sketch the graph of the function, and explain how the form of the expression was helpful.

   b. Which expression is the most useful for finding the equation of the line tangent to the graph at the point (1, 24)? Choose an expression, use it to find the equation of the tangent, and explain how the form of the expression was helpful.

2. For each of the following numbers, sketch the graph of a third-degree polynomial which has the indicated number of x-intercepts, or explain why such a graph does not exist.

   a. 0 **b.** 1 **c.** 2 **d.** 3 **e.** 4

3. Let $f(x) = x^3 + 8x^2 + 5x - 50$.

   a. Expand the function $f(x)$ in powers of $x + 4$.

   b. Use your expansion to find the equation of the tangent to the graph of $f(x)$ at the point $(-4, f(-4))$.

4. How can you graph a polynomial function given its factored form?

5. How can you determine a polynomial's behavior at very large or very small inputs?

6. How can you use long division to find equations of secant or tangent lines to the graph of a polynomial function?

Vocabulary

In this investigation, you learned these terms. Make sure you understand what each one means and how to use it.

- **average rate of change**
- **continuous**
- **instantaneous speed**
- **power function**
- **secant line**
- **tangent line**
- **Taylor expansion**

Mathematical Reflections

1–4. See back of book.

5. The highest-degree term of the polynomial will govern the behavior of its graph for very large positive or negative inputs. For very small inputs, the value will be close to the y-intercept.

6. To find the slope of a secant line between the points $(a, f(a))$ and $(b, f(b))$, you can use long division to evaluate $\frac{f(b) - f(a)}{b - a}$. Then, to find the slope of the tangent line, you can take the limit of that expression as b approaches a. You could also use repeated division by a factor $(x - a)$ to create the Taylor expansion of the polynomial around $x = a$. Then you can read off the remainder after division by $(x - a)^2$, which gives the equation of the tangent to the graph of the polynomial at $x = a$. You could also just use long division by $(x - a)^2$, and the remainder after this division is the equation of the tangent.

Mathematical Reflections

EXERCISES 4–6 At the start of the investigation, you may have assigned these as Questions 1–3 for students to think and write about.

Investigation Overview

Students analyze rational functions, adapting many of the techniques they developed in Investigation 3A. They learn to sketch the graph of a rational function and identify its asymptotes and holes. They learn to find limits as x approaches an asymptote or as it goes to ∞ or $-\infty$. Students also work through finding the equations of secants and tangents to rational functions. In an optional lesson, they examine the connections between linear transformations of the graph of $y = \frac{1}{x}$ and matrix multiplication.

You may wish to assign Questions 1–3 for students to think and write about during the investigation.

Learning Goals

- Sketch the graph of a rational function, including asymptotes and holes.
- Evaluate limits of rational expressions.
- Find the equation of the tangent to the graph of a rational function at a point.
- Use matrices to write linear fractional transformations of the function $f(x) = \frac{1}{x}$.

Habits and Skills

- Visualize different types of discontinuities, relating equations and their graphs.
- Reason logically to find limits at infinity.
- Extend the methods of Investigation 3A to find the equation of the tangent to the graph of a rational function.

Rational Functions

In *Rational Functions*, you will graph functions $f(x)$ that are quotients of polynomials. You will have to pay particular attention to values of x for which the denominator polynomial has value 0.

By the end of this investigation, you will be able to answer questions like these.

1. What happens to $f(x) = \frac{3x^2 + 2x - 1}{5x^2 - 3x + 10}$ as x gets larger and larger?
2. Why do the graphs of $g(x) = \frac{x^2 - 15}{x - 4}$ and $h(x) = \frac{x^2 - 16}{x - 4}$ look so different from each other?
3. How can you find tangent lines to rational functions?

You will learn how to

- sketch the graph of a rational function, including asymptotes and holes
- evaluate limits of rational expressions
- find the equation of the tangent to the graph of a rational function at a point

You will develop these habits and skills:

- Visualize different types of discontinuities, relating equations and their graphs.
- Reason logically to find limits at infinity.
- Extend the methods of Investigation 3A to find the equation of the tangent to the graph of a rational function.

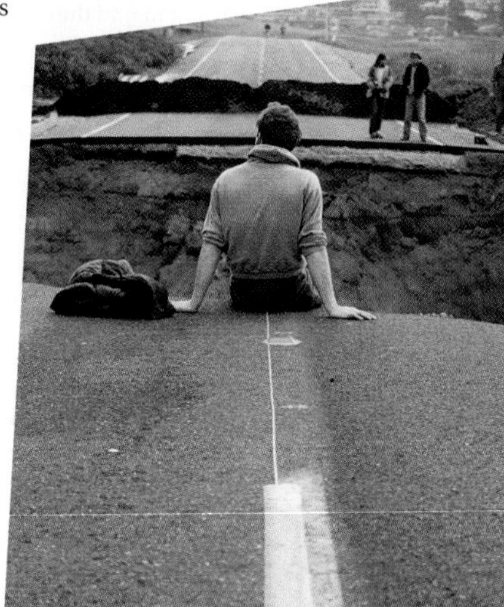

Holes and vertical asymptotes represent discontinuities in the graph of a rational function.

Investigation Road Map

LESSON 3.6, *Getting Started,* looks closely at the graphs of rational functions. Students develop a rational function graph gallery and begin to think about the behavior of rational functions at key locations.

LESSON 3.7, *Graphing Rational Functions*, has students distinguish between graphs with asymptotes and graphs with holes. Students develop limit techniques to find equations of horizontal asymptotes for the graphs of rational functions.

LESSON 3.8, *Revisiting Secants and Tangents*, extends the methods from Investigation 3A to allow students to find the equations of secants and tangent lines for rational functions.

LESSON 3.9, *Case Study: $y = \frac{ax + b}{cx + d}$*, examines linear transformations of the graph of $y = \frac{1}{x}$ both as rational function transformations and as matrix transformations.

3.6 Getting Started

Activating Prior Knowledge
Exploring New Ideas

In CME Project *Algebra 2*, you learned to calculate with rational expressions, expressions of the form $\frac{p}{q}$ where p and q are polynomials. The emphasis there was on the formal algebraic properties of these expressions. In this investigation, you will study **rational functions.** A rational function is a function of the form $x \mapsto \frac{p(x)}{q(x)}$, where p and q are polynomial functions of x. Rational functions have all kinds of interesting graphs. Here are some examples.

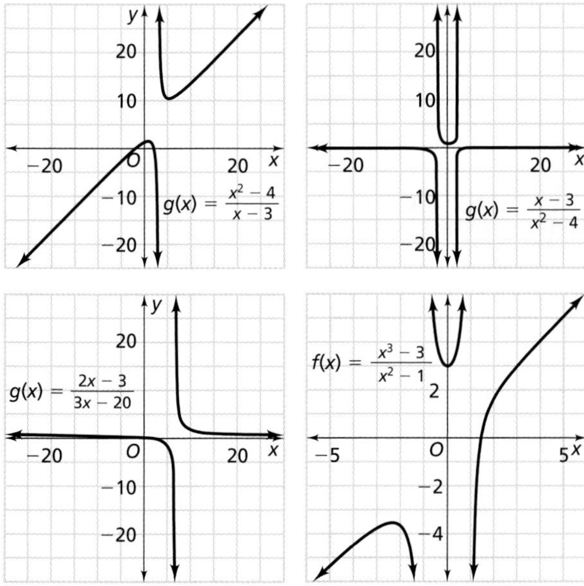

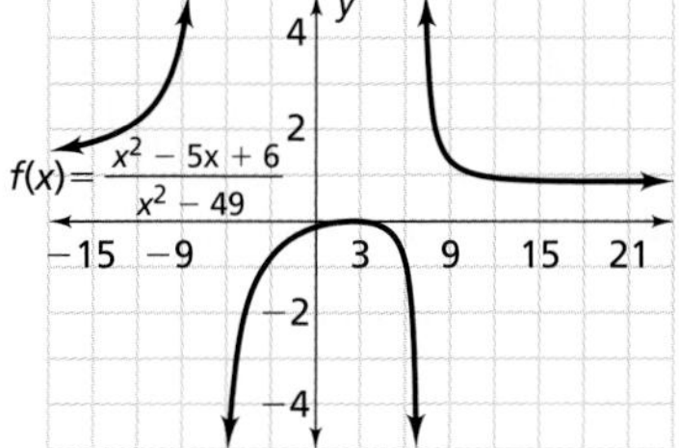

Lesson Overview

GOAL

- Warm up to the ideas of the investigation.

Students develop a general understanding of the possible shapes for the graph of a rational function. They experiment with drawing the graphs of reciprocals of other functions, and with finding graphs that have certain characteristics. They also begin to think about the behavior of rational functions for very large positive and negative values of *x*.

FOR YOU TO EXPLORE

- Core: 1, 2, 3, 4, 5, 6
- Optional: 7, 8a–b
- Extension: 8c

MATERIALS

- graph paper
- graphing calculators
- Blackline Masters MC7, MC8, 3.6A, 3.6B

HOMEWORK

- Core: 9, 10, 12, 13, 14
- Optional: 11, 15, 16

VOCABULARY

- rational function
- reciprocal function

Launch

Have students start right in with the problems. At the beginning of class point out Problem 6, in which students make a gallery of rational function graphs. That way students can begin to collect graphs as they are working on the other problems.

Explore

As students are working, note any conjectures that they make for later discussion. Possible conjectures include, "If the denominator of the function is zero, you get an asymptote," and "When you draw the graph of a reciprocal function, the *y*-values of the reciprocal are positive and negative in the same places that the *y*-values of the original function are positive and negative."

For You to Explore

You can make copies of Blackline Masters MC7 and MC8 for students to sketch graphs of functions.

PROBLEM 1 asks the questions that students should ask themselves in solving Problem 2, and directs their attention to zeros of the original function, behavior of the original function for large positive and negative values, and the relationship between the value of the original function and its reciprocal.

PROBLEM 2 At this point, students do not necessarily have an equation to associate with this graph. Since this looks like a parabola with zeros at $x = 1$ and $x = 7$, they might deduce that it is the graph of $y = x^2 - 8x + 7$. In any case, they should decide what happens to $g(x)$ when $f(x) = 0$, and show that they understand the relationship between the signs of the functions and their values.

PROBLEM 3 The function in part (a) is the function students graphed in Problem 2.

PROBLEM 4 asks students to distinguish between discontinuities that result in asymptotes and those that result in a hole. You formalize this distinction in the next lesson.

PROBLEM 5 Without a lot of experience with rational functions, students may have to hunt around for a while to find functions that meet these conditions. Encourage them to share techniques such as thinking about reciprocal functions, or translating a known graph.

For You to Explore

1. Suppose f and g are functions with the property that $g(x) = \frac{1}{f(x)}$ for any x in the domain of both functions.

   Functions *f* and *g* are called **reciprocal functions.** They are not inverse functions.

   a. Give an example of two functions f and g that are reciprocal functions.
   b. Suppose $f(a) = 3$. What is the value of $g(a)$?
   c. If $f(b)$ is very large, what can you say about $g(b)$?
   d. If $f(c) = 0$, what can you say about $g(c)$?
   e. If $f(5) = k$ and $g(5) = k$, what are the possible values of k?

2. Suppose f and g are functions with $g(x) = \frac{1}{f(x)}$ for any x in the domain of both functions. Here is the graph of f:

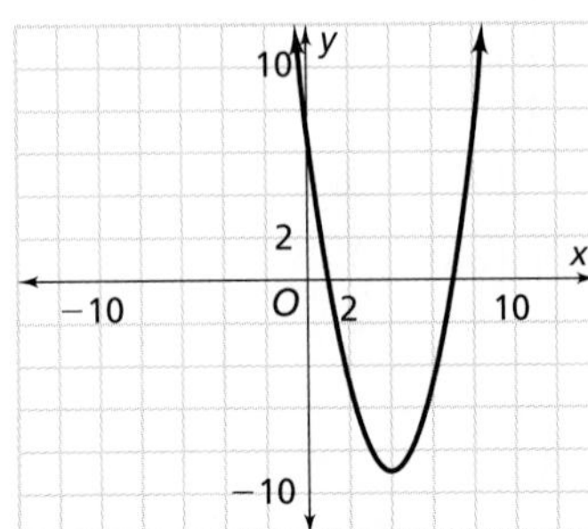

   Copy the graph and, on the same axes, sketch the graph of g.

3. a. Find the domain of $g(x) = \frac{1}{x^2 - 8x + 7}$.
   b. Sketch the graph of $f(x) = x^2 - 8x + 12$.
   c. Use the graph of $f(x) = x^2 - 8x + 12$ to sketch the graph of $g(x) = \frac{1}{x^2 - 8x + 12}$.
   d. Find the domain of $g(x) = \frac{1}{x^2 - 8x + 12}$.

4. Let

$$f(x) = \frac{x - 2}{x^2 - 9} \quad \text{and} \quad g(x) = \frac{x - 3}{x^2 - 9}$$

   a. Find the domain of each function.
   b. Describe the behavior of the graphs of f and g near $x = 3$.

5. Find, if possible, a rational function f that satisfies each condition.
   - $f(3) = f(5) = 0$.
   - The function f is undefined at 3 and 5.
   - As x gets larger, $f(x)$ approaches 0.
   - As x gets larger, $f(x)$ approaches 3.

Answers

For You to Explore

1. a. Answers may vary. Sample: $f = \tan x$ and $g = \cot x$. Then

$$f(x) = \frac{\sin x}{\cos x} = \frac{1}{\frac{\cos x}{\sin x}} = \frac{1}{g(x)}$$

   b. $\frac{1}{3}$
   c. $g(b)$ must be "very small."
   d. $g(c)$ is undefined.
   e. $k = 1$ or $k = -1$

2. See back of book.
3. a. $\{x | x \neq 1, 7\}$
   b–c. See back of book.
   d. $\{x | x \neq 2, 6\}$
4. a. Both functions have the same domain, $\{x | x \neq -3, 3\}$.
   b. See back of book.
5. a–d. See back of book.

6. Write About It Make your own rational function graph gallery.
   - Sketch or generate 10 particularly interesting rational function graphs.
   - Give the rational function for each graph.
   - Describe what you find interesting about each graph.

7. a. Make an accurate sketch of
$$h(x) = \frac{|x|}{x}$$
   b. What can you say about $\lim_{x\to 0} h(x)$?

$\lim_{x\to 0} h(x)$ means the limit of $h(x)$ as x approaches 0.

8. Consider $j(x) = x + \frac{1}{x}$.
   a. Give estimates for $j(100)$ and $j(0.01)$.
   b. What positive value of x makes $j(x)$ as small as possible?
   c. Take It Further Show algebraically that if $x > 0$, then $j(x) \geq 2$.

Exercises *Practicing Habits of Mind*

On Your Own

9. If $f(x) = \frac{x+3}{2x-1}$ and $g(x) = \frac{x+1}{x-1}$, find all values of a such that $f(a) = g(a) - \frac{4}{3}$.

10. Find, if possible, a rational function f that satisfies each condition.
   a. $f(3) = 0$ and f has no other zeros.
   b. The domain of f is all real numbers except for 5, and f has no zeros.
   c. The domain of f is all real numbers except for 5, and $f(3) = 0$.
   d. As x gets larger, the graph of f gets closer and closer to the graph of $y = x$.

6. Answers may vary. Samples:

a. $f(x) = \frac{1}{x-2}$

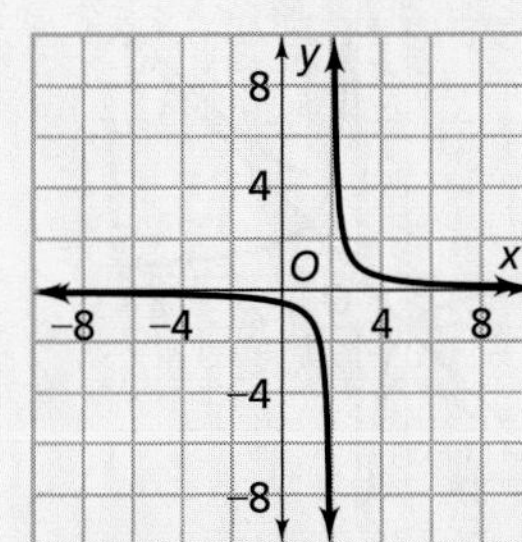

b–j. See back of book.

7–8. See back of book.

Exercises

9. $x = -\frac{1}{5}$ or $x = 2$

10. a. Answers may vary. Sample: $f(x) = \frac{x-3}{x^2}$

b. Answers may vary. Sample: $f(x) = \frac{1}{x-5}$

c. Answers may vary. Sample: $f(x) = \frac{x-3}{x-5}$

d. Answers may vary. Sample: $f(x) = \frac{x^2-5x+1}{x-5}$

PROBLEM 7 Sometimes students are able to accept the idea of a graph with a hole in it, but are not able to accept that the limit exists. When you try to evaluate this function, you get $\frac{0}{0}$, which is especially puzzling. Students are even more perplexed when they see that some functions with widely differing limits all evaluate to $\frac{0}{0}$. Encourage students to look at graphs as well as equations when computing limits, and their intuition should improve.

PROBLEM 8 Precalculus students often use the technique of substituting a very large value for x when finding the limit as x approaches ∞. In most cases, this technique results in a good approximation of the answer. However, you need to emphasize that this technique does not prove the value of a limit, and students should only use it as a check.

Wrap Up

Have students share graphs from their rational function galleries. Look for types of graphs that they have omitted, such as a graph of $y = \frac{x^2-1}{x-1}$, which is the same as the graph of $y = x + 1$, but with a hole at $x = 1$. Since the problems include graphs with more than one vertical asymptote, students should include examples like this in their galleries. Discuss any conjectures that you have collected.

Exercises

HOMEWORK
- Core: 9, 10, 12, 13, 14
- Optional: 11, 15, 16

On Your Own

EXERCISE 9 Since both of the solutions are in the domain of both functions, this method works.

ERROR PREVENTION You may want to make sure that students realize that if they multiply both sides of an equation by an expression in x, that operation includes the assumption that the expression is not equal to zero. That is why it is always a good idea to make sure that the solutions you get make sense in the original equation.

EXERCISE 10 Students may need to experiment a bit before they hit on a graph with the right characteristics. The more graphs of rational functions they see, the more they can add to their mental picture of the graph of a rational function.

EXERCISE 11 Think about your students' familiarity with trigonometric functions when deciding whether to assign this exercise. It is a nice example of a graph with infinitely many asymptotes, though.

You may want to use Blackline Master 3.6A as an overhead and sketch part of the answer, then ask students to fill in the rest on their own copies.

EXERCISE 12 The distinction between a rational *function* and a rational *expression* is an important one. Even though you can simplify the expression, the functions are not identical due to their different domains.

This exercise also serves as an opportunity for students to develop their own understanding of a "hole" in a graph. This is a good exercise for discussion, where you might eventually write $k(x) = x + 2, x \neq 3$.

You may want to use Blackline Master 3.6B on an overhead and fill in the entries as students calculate each value.

EXERCISES 14–16 You can make copies of Blackline Masters MC7 and MC8 for students to sketch graphs of functions.

EXERCISE 14 Students can get at the sketch of $f_3(x) = x + \frac{1}{x}$ by looking at the graphs of $f_1(x) = x$ and $f_2(x) = \frac{1}{x}$, and doing some thought experiments. For example, as x approaches zero from the right, the values of $\frac{1}{x}$ are get very large. They are so large that the value of x has little effect on the value of f_3. So for positive numbers close to zero, f_3 looks like f_2. Similarly, for very large positive values of x, f_1 overshadows the effect of f_2, and f_3 looks like f_1.

Maintain Your Skills

EXERCISE 15 Most of these functions are meant to remind students about the rules for translating graphs, but they also provide practice with the shape of $y = \frac{1}{x^2}$. If you discuss this question, make sure you address the last part and why this is not just the graph of the horizontal line $y = 1$.

11. Here is the graph of $f(x) = \sin x$. Use it to sketch the graph of $g(x) = \csc x$.

$\csc x = \frac{1}{\sin x}$ whenever $\sin x \neq 0$.

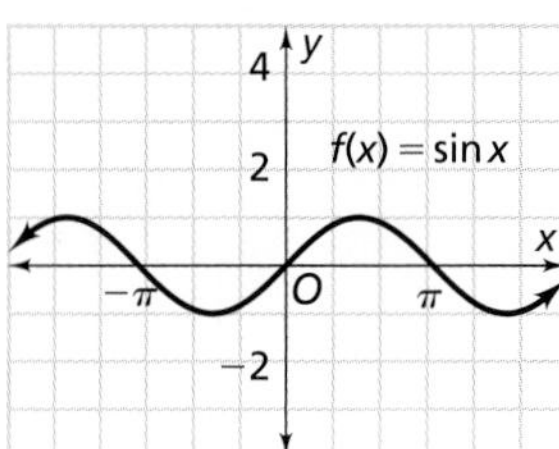

12. Let $k(x) = \frac{x^2 - x - 6}{x - 3}$.

a. Copy and complete this table for $k(x)$.

x	$k(x)$
0	2
1	■
2	■
3	■
4	■

b. Use factoring to simplify the expression $\frac{x^2 - x - 6}{x - 3}$. Assume that $x \neq 3$.

c. Explain why k is not the same function as $m(x) = x + 2$.

d. Write About It In what way does the graph of k look different from the graph of m?

13. Find a rational function k that is identical to $m(x) = x - 1$, except that k is undefined when $x = 4$.

14. Sketch the graphs of these three functions on the same axes.

$$f_1(x) = x$$
$$f_2(x) = \frac{1}{x}$$
$$f_3(x) = x + \frac{1}{x}$$

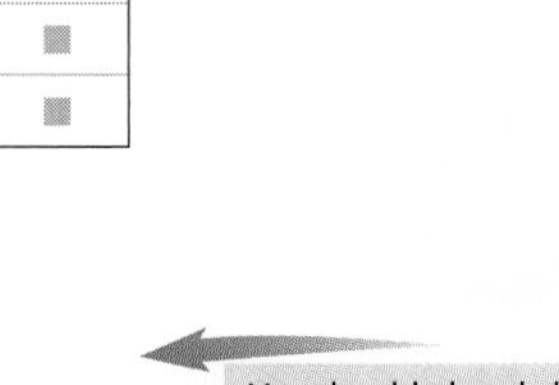
You should already be able to graph f_1 and f_2 without a calculator. Try graphing f_3 without a calculator, too.

Maintain Your Skills

15. Sketch the graph of each function.

a. $f(x) = \frac{1}{x}$ **b.** $f(x) = \frac{1}{x + 3}$ **c.** $f(x) = \frac{1}{x + 3} + 5$

d. $f(x) = \frac{1}{x^2}$ **e.** $f(x) = \frac{1}{(x - 4)^2}$ **f.** $f(x) = \frac{(x - 3)(x + 5)}{(x - 3)(x + 5)}$

16. Sketch the graph of each function.

a. $f(x) = \frac{1}{x}$ **b.** $f(x) = \frac{1}{x - 4}$ **c.** $f(x) = \frac{1}{2x - 4}$

d. $f(x) = \frac{x}{2x - 4}$ **e.** $f(x) = \frac{x - 3}{2x - 4}$ **f.** $f(x) = \frac{x - 3}{2x - 4} + 5$

Answers

11. See back of book.

12. a. See back of book.

b. $x + 2$

c. $k(x)$ is *not* the same function as $m(x) = x + 2$, because the domain of $m(x)$ is $\mathcal{R}$, while the domain of $k(x)$ is $\{x \mid x \neq 3\}$.

d. The graph of k looks different from the graph of m in that it is "missing" the point (3, 5).

13. Answers may vary. Sample:

$$k(x) = \frac{x^2 - 5x + 4}{x - 4}$$

14.

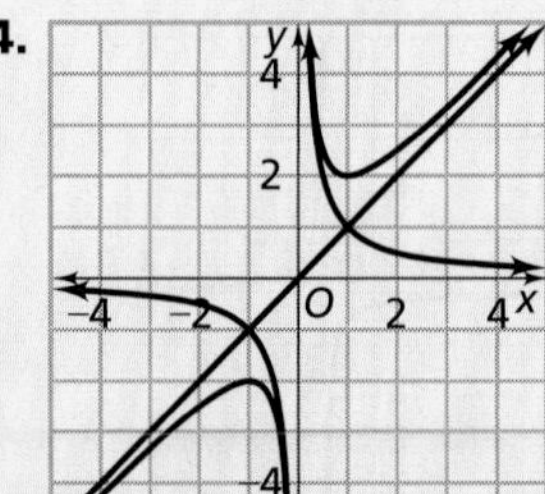

15–16. See back of book.

3.7 Graphing Rational Functions

Subtle differences in functions can make their graphs look very different.

Consider the rational functions f and g from Problem 4 in Lesson 3.6:

$$f(x) = \frac{x-2}{x^2-9} \quad \text{and} \quad g(x) = \frac{x-3}{x^2-9}$$

Both have denominator $x^2 - 9 = (x+3)(x-3)$, so they are both undefined at $x = 3$. Their graphs, however, look very different. The graph of f has a vertical asymptote at $x = 3$, while the graph of g looks practically flat at $x = 3$. Why the difference?

Of course, they are also undefined at $x = -3$.

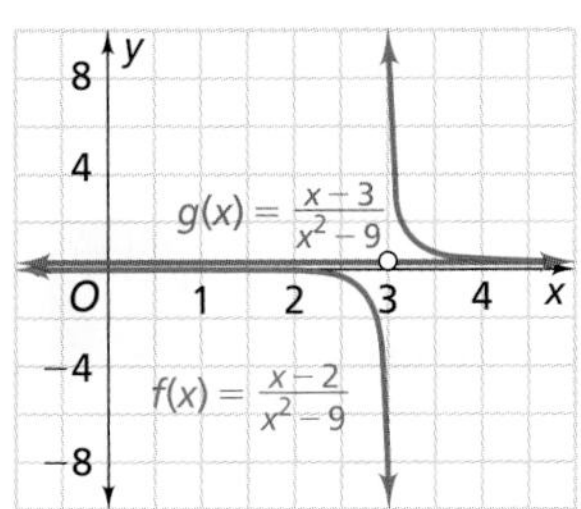

Start with f. Since $f(x) = \frac{x-2}{x^2-9}$, you can write it as

$$f(x) = m(x) \cdot \frac{1}{x-3}$$

where $m(x) = \frac{x-2}{x+3}$. Thus,

$$m(3) = \frac{3-2}{3+3} = \frac{1}{6}$$

So near $x = 3$, f behaves like the function

$$x \mapsto \frac{1}{6} \cdot \frac{1}{x-3}$$

the graph of which has a vertical asymptote at $x = 3$.

Remember...

A vertical asymptote is a line that the graph of a function approaches, but does not intersect.

Now consider $g(x) = \frac{x-3}{x^2-9}$. For any $a \neq 3$,

$$g(a) = \frac{a-3}{(a+3)(a-3)} = \frac{1}{a+3}$$

Since $a - 3 \neq 0$, you can cancel the term $a - 3$ from the numerator and denominator. So,

$$g(x) = \begin{cases} \frac{1}{x+3} & \text{if } x \neq 3 \\ \text{undefined} & \text{if } x = 3 \end{cases}$$

Lesson Overview

GOALS

- Sketch the graph of a rational function, including asymptotes and holes.
- Evaluate limits of rational expressions.

In this lesson, students begin to analyze the graphs of rational functions. First, they distinguish between two types of discontinuities that occur in rational functions—infinite discontinuities which result in vertical asymptotes and removable discontinuities that result in holes. Students also learn a technique for finding horizontal asymptotes in the graphs of rational functions. They divide the numerator and denominator of the function by the largest power of x in the expression. Then they look at the limit as x approaches 0 of this new expression to determine its behavior for very large and very small values of x. They also use polynomial long division to find the equation of an asymptote that is not horizontal.

CHECK YOUR UNDERSTANDING

- Core: 1, 2, 3, 4, 6, 8
- Optional: 5, 7
- Extension: 9

MATERIALS

- CAS (recommended)
- graph paper
- graphing calculators
- Blackline Masters MC7, MC8

HOMEWORK

- Core: 10, 11, 12, 14, 15, 16, 17, 18
- Optional: 13, 19, 20, 21, 22

VOCABULARY

- hole
- infinite discontinuity
- removable discontinuity

Launch

Review Problem 4 from Lesson 3.6. Make sure that students can identify a hole in a graph even when using their graphing calculators. (See the TI-Nspire Technology Handbook p. 704 in the student edition for help with this.) Ask students to give their own informal ways of determining whether a discontinuity in the graph of a rational function is a vertical asymptote or a hole. As you continue with the lesson, return to these descriptions and formalize them.

Explore

Example 1

Spend time as needed going over this completed example. Make sure students understand the problem. As necessary, help them develop the detailed solution.

The graph of g looks just like the graph of $y = \frac{1}{x+3}$, except with a *hole* at $x = 3$.

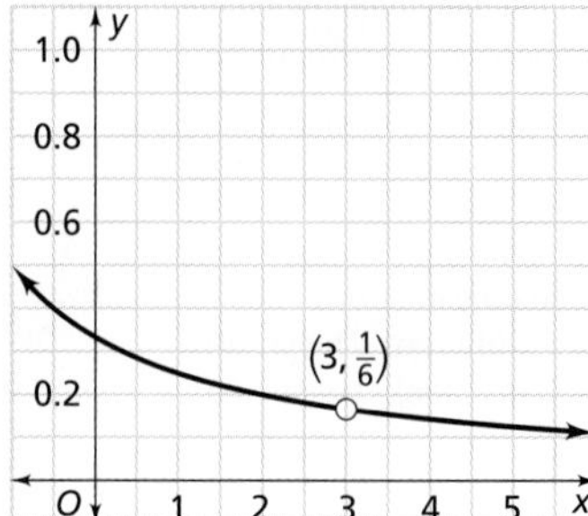

Example 1

Problem For each function below, describe the behavior of its graph near $x = 3$.

a. $f(x) = \dfrac{(x-3)^2}{(x-3)^6}$

b. $g(x) = \dfrac{(x-3)^6}{(x-3)^2}$

Solution

a. For any $a \neq 3$,

$$f(a) = \frac{(a-3)^2}{(a-3)^6} = \frac{1}{(a-3)^4}$$

Again, you can cancel here because $a - 3 \neq 0$.

Thus, as functions, the maps

$$x \mapsto f(x) \quad \text{and} \quad x \mapsto \frac{1}{(x-3)^4}$$

are equal because neither is defined at $x = 3$ and they agree on all $x \neq 3$. Their graphs are the same and so the graph of f has a vertical asymptote at $x = 3$.

b. For any $a \neq 3$,

$$g(a) = \frac{(a-3)^6}{(a-3)^2} = (a-3)^4.$$

Thus, the graph of g looks just like the graph of $y = (x-3)^4$, except with a hole at $x = 3$.

The previous example leads to the following definition and theorem.

Definitions

Let $h(x) = \frac{f(x)}{g(x)}$ be a rational function such that

- $f(x) = (x - a)^m \cdot p(x)$
- $g(x) = (x - a)^n \cdot q(x)$

where $p(a), q(a) \neq 0$.

1. h has an **infinite discontinuity** at $x = a$ if $n > m \geq 0$.
2. h has a **removable discontinuity** at $x = a$ if $m \geq n > 0$.

f and *g* are polynomials.

Functions can also have jump discontinuities or discontinuities like $x \mapsto \sin \frac{1}{x}$ at 0, but these do not happen with rational functions.

Theorem 3.6

Let h be a rational function.

1. If h has an infinite discontinuity at $x = a$, then the graph of h has $x = a$ as a vertical asymptote.
2. If h has a removable discontinuity at $x = a$, then the graph of h has a **hole** at $x = a$.

Minds in Action episode 7

Sasha and Tony have been discussing the function f from the start of this lesson.

Tony Well, what's next?

Sasha We know that the graph of $f(x) = \frac{x-2}{x^2-9}$ has vertical asymptotes at $x = 3$ and $x = -3$, but I wonder if it has a horizontal asymptote.

Tony I was looking ahead at Exercise 13 in this lesson. How about dividing every term by the highest degree?

Sasha What do you mean?

Tony Here, like this:

$$f(x) = \frac{x-2}{x^2-9} \cdot \frac{\frac{1}{x^2}}{\frac{1}{x^2}} = \frac{\frac{1}{x} - \frac{2}{x^2}}{1 - \frac{9}{x^2}}.$$

Sasha Wait, what if $x = 0$?

Tony Then this new expression for f doesn't work. But I'm using it to figure out what happens when x is really big.

Minds in Action

You may wish to assign students Minds in Action roles and present the conversation to the class. This is more effective if you assign the roles one class day prior to the "performance." Urge the students to "get into" their parts by using their own words instead of memorizing lines.

BACKGROUND FOR TEACHER Infinite discontinuities are also called *poles* or *essential singularities*. Removable discontinuities are also called *removable singularities*.

For You to Do

PROBLEMS 1 AND 2 Have students practice for the ideas just introduced by doing these problems.

Sasha Got it. And when x is big, the terms $\frac{1}{x}$, $\frac{2}{x^2}$, and $\frac{9}{x^2}$ are close to zero, and only the 1 is left.

Tony Exactly! So if x is really big, we get

$$f(x) \approx \frac{0}{1}$$

And that means the horizontal asymptote is $y = 0$.

For You to Do

1. Use Tony's method to find the horizontal asymptote of the graph of each function.

   a. $g(x) = \frac{x - 3}{x^2 - 9}$ **b.** $h(x) = \frac{9x^3 + 5x + 1}{4x^3 - 7}$

2. Explain how Tony's method offers an explanation for why the same method works when x is a large positive or negative number.

Remember...

A large negative number is something like -1 million. Here, *large* refers to absolute value.

Consider $f(x) = \frac{x-2}{x^2-9}$ again. Sasha and Tony showed that $f(x) \approx 0$ if x is a big number. In other words, you can make $f(x)$ as close to 0 as you want by making x large enough. To express this fact, write

$$\lim_{x \to \infty} f(x) = 0$$

You will see a more precise definition when you take a course in calculus.

As another example, you saw in the For You to Do above that

$$\lim_{x \to \infty} \frac{9x^3 + 5x + 1}{4x^3 - 7} = \frac{9}{4}$$

In fact, this limit is the same even if x becomes a large negative number. You express this fact by writing

$$\lim_{x \to -\infty} \frac{9x^3 + 5x + 1}{4x^3 - 7} = \frac{9}{4}$$

Theorem 3.7

Let $h(x) = \frac{f(x)}{g(x)}$ be a rational function with deg $f = m$ and deg $g = n$.

1. **If $m < n$, then $\lim_{x \to \infty} h(x) = 0$.**
2. **If $m = n$, then $\lim_{x \to \infty} h(x)$ is the ratio of the leading coefficients of f and g.**

   Moreover, the graph of h has a horizontal asymptote with equation $y = L$ where $L = \lim_{x \to \infty} h(x)$.

deg f means the degree of the polynomial f.

You may be wondering what happens when deg $f >$ deg g. Take a look at the following example.

Answers

For You to Do

1. **a.** $y = 0$

   b. $y = \frac{9}{4}$

2. If x approaches either ∞ or $-\infty$, any fraction of the form $\frac{a}{x^n}$ with a constant and n a positive integer must approach 0. If n is odd and x approaches $-\infty$, the value of $\frac{a}{x^n}$ will be negative as it approaches 0. When x approaches ∞, however, the value of $\frac{a}{x^n}$ will be positive as it approaches 0. The sign of these values does not change the fact that both expressions approach 0. If n is even, both terms would be positive and approach 0.

Example 2

Problem Let

$$h(x) = \frac{x^3 - 4x}{x - 1}$$

Describe the behavior of h for large values of x.

Solution Using long division as shown in Method 3 from Lesson 3.3, you have

$$x^3 - 4x = (x - 1)(x^2 + x - 3) - 3$$

so that

$$h(x) = q(x) + \frac{-3}{x - 1}$$

where $q(x) = x^2 + x - 3$. Thus you can make $h(x)$ as large as you want by making x large enough. In other words,

$$\lim_{x \to \infty} h(x) = \infty$$

This limit statement says that as x increases without bound, so does $h(x)$.

Furthermore,

$$\lim_{x \to \infty}(h(x) - q(x)) = \lim_{x \to \infty} \frac{-3}{x - 1} = 0$$

so that the outputs of h become arbitrarily close to the outputs of q for large positive and negative values of x. Thus, the graph of h has a nonhorizontal asymptote, namely the graph of the polynomial q.

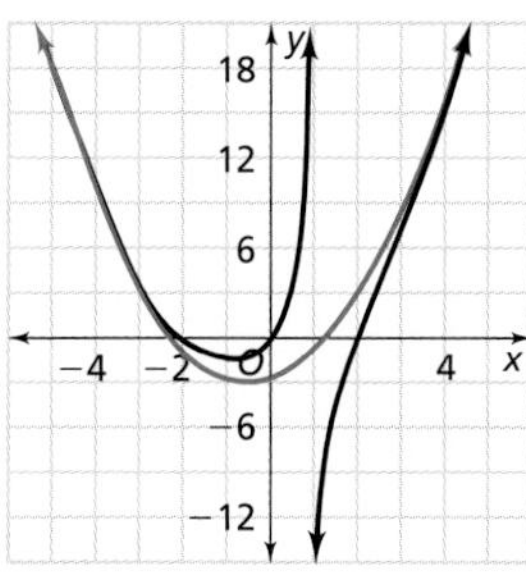

For You to Do

Let

$$k(x) = \frac{x^2 + x - 1}{3 - x}$$

3. Find $\lim_{k \to \infty} k(x)$.
4. Find all asymptotes of the graph of k.

Example 2

LEADING QUESTION What happens to $q(x)$ and $\frac{-3}{x - 1}$ as x gets large? (Answer: $q(x)$ gets very large and $\frac{-3}{x - 1}$ gets very small.)

For You to Do

PROBLEM 4 If students are doing polynomial long division of $\frac{x^2 + x - 1}{3 - x}$ to find the non-horizontal asymptote by hand, you might suggest that they write the divisor as $-x + 3$ (which is the normal form of $3 - x$) in their work. This makes it easier to do the division correctly.

Wrap Up

You may want to take some time to make a distinction between limits as x approaches ∞ or $-\infty$ and limits where x approaches a point of discontinuity. Take a function with a hole, such as $f(x) = \frac{x - 2}{x^3 - 4x}$. Have students find all of its asymptotes, and then find the limit of the function as x approaches 2. (This limit is $\frac{1}{8}$.) Tony's technique of dividing the numerator and denominator of a rational function by x to its largest degree is only helpful when finding limits as x approaches ∞ or $-\infty$.

Go through the core Check Your Understanding exercises as time permits. You may want to spend more time on Exercises 3 and 4. In Exercise 3, students use the techniques of the lesson to sketch the graph of a rational function. In Exercise 4, they reverse the process and use the properties of the graph to determine a function whose graph has those properties.

Assessment Resources

Lesson Quiz 3.7

1. Consider $g(x) = \frac{2x^2 - 5x + 3}{x^2 + 5x - 6}$.
   a. The graph of g has a horizontal asymptote. What is its equation?
   b. The graph of g has a vertical asymptote. What is its equation?
   c. The graph of g has a hole at what point?
2. Calculate each limit.
   a. $\lim_{x \to \infty} \frac{2x + 5}{3x + 12}$
   b. $\lim_{x \to \infty} \frac{x^2 + 4x - 11}{5x + 2}$
3. Find the domain of the function $f(x) = \frac{x + 3}{x^2 - 9}$.

For You to Do

3. $-\infty$

4. $x = 3, y = -x - 4$

Exercises

HOMEWORK
- Core: 10, 11, 12, 14, 15, 16, 17, 18
- Optional: 13, 19, 20, 21, 22

You can make copies of Blackline Masters MC7 and MC8 for students to sketch graphs of functions.

Check Your Understanding

EXERCISE 1 Students should notice that there are two rational functions represented in this exercise, and that they are reciprocals of one another.

EXERCISE 2 The most important parts to this exercise are the last two, where students should recognize that the answer is not as simple as the ratio of highest degree terms in the numerator and denominator. Students learn that the limit is this fraction when the highest degrees of both numerator and denominator are the same, is infinite (either positive or negative) if the numerator has larger degree, or is 0 if the denominator has larger degree.

EXERCISE 3 Students may find it difficult to find a hole in the graph if they are expecting to spot it in the image produced by their graphing calculators. Remind them that even though a hole does not "show," it can still exist. They need to look at the function with its numerator and denominator in factored form to spot the hole.

EXERCISE 4 "Undoing" a process is a really nice way to reinforce it. By thinking of equations for graphs with the given characteristics, students develop a deeper understanding of how to look for the characteristics when all they have is the equation.

Theorem 3.8

Let $h(x) = \frac{f(x)}{g(x)}$ be a rational function with deg $f >$ deg g. Then $\lim_{x\to\infty} h(x) = \infty$ or $-\infty$. Moreover, if you write

$$\frac{f(x)}{g(x)} = q(x) + \frac{r(x)}{g(x)}$$

where q and r are polynomials with deg $r <$ deg g, then the graph of q is a nonhorizontal asymptote of the graph of h.

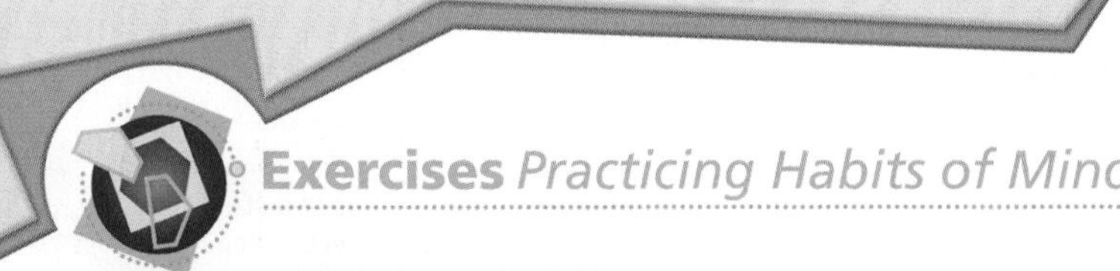

Exercises *Practicing Habits of Mind*

Check Your Understanding

1. Calculate each limit.

 a. $\lim_{x\to\infty} \frac{x-4}{x^2-4}$ b. $\lim_{x\to\infty} \frac{x^2-4}{x-4}$ c. $\lim_{x\to-\infty} \frac{x-4}{x^2-4}$ d. $\lim_{x\to-\infty} \frac{x^2-4}{x-4}$

2. Calculate each limit.

 a. $\lim_{x\to\infty} \frac{3x^2-1}{5x^2+3}$ b. $\lim_{x\to\infty} \frac{10x^3-7}{3x^3+5}$ c. $\lim_{x\to-\infty} \frac{10+5x^4}{2x^4-2}$

 d. $\lim_{x\to-\infty} \frac{7x-6x^5}{3x^5-17x}$ e. $\lim_{x\to\infty} \frac{10x^3-5}{4x^2+3x}$ f. $\lim_{x\to\infty} \frac{x^2+1}{3x^3-10}$

3. Consider $f(x) = \frac{x^2-3x-4}{x^2-2x-8}$.

 a. The graph of f has a horizontal asymptote. What is its equation?

 b. The graph of f has a vertical asymptote. What is its equation?

 c. The graph of f has a hole at what point?

4. Let f be a rational function.

 a. Give an example of a function f the graph of which has a horizontal asymptote with equation $y = 4$.

 b. Give an example of a function f that is undefined at $x = 2$ and $x = 5$.

 c. Give an example of a function f the graph of which has $x = -3$ as a vertical asymptote and has a hole at $x = 2$.

 d. Give an example of a function f with $f(2) = 0$, $f(1)$ undefined, and a graph with no horizontal asymptote.

Answers

Exercises

1. a. 0 **b.** ∞ **c.** 0 **d.** $-\infty$

2. a. $\frac{3}{5}$ **b.** $\frac{10}{3}$ **c.** $\frac{5}{2}$ **d.** -2

e. ∞ **f.** 0

3. a. $y = 1$

b. $x = -2$

c. $\left(4, \frac{5}{6}\right)$

4. a. Answers may vary. Sample: $f(x) = \frac{4x}{x-5}$

b. Answers may vary. Sample: $f(x) = \frac{x}{(x-2)(x-5)}$

c. Answers may vary. Sample: $f(x) = \frac{x-2}{(x-2)(x+3)}$

d. Answers may vary. Sample: $f(x) = \frac{x(x-2)}{x-1}$

5. $K = \frac{1}{6}$

6. a. $f(10) = 10.1$, $f(100) = 100.01$

b. The graph approaches the line $y = x$.

c. $f(0.1) = 10.1$, $f(0.01) = 100.01$

d. The graph of $f(x)$ as x approaches zero goes to ∞; the function has a vertical asymptote $x = 0$.

e.

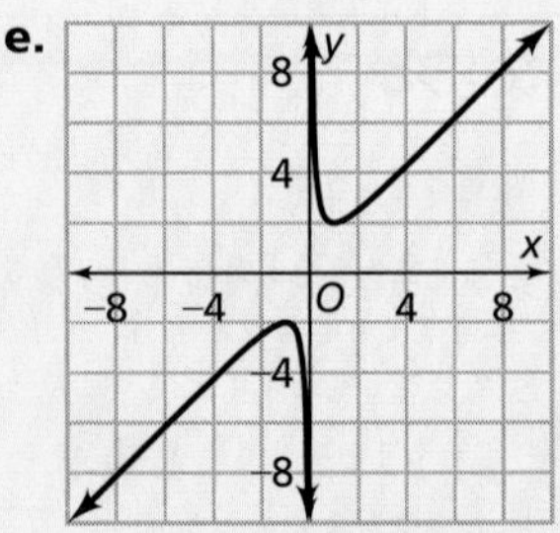

7. D

5. The function $h(x) = \frac{x-3}{x^2-9}$ has a removable discontinuity at $x = 3$. Define function j as

$$j(x) = \begin{cases} h(x) & \text{if } x \neq 3 \\ K & \text{if } x = 3 \end{cases}$$

What value of K would make $j(x)$ continuous at $x = 3$?

What value of K would "plug" the hole left by h at $x = 3$?

6. Consider the function $f(x) = \frac{x^2+1}{x}$.

a. Calculate $f(10)$ and $f(100)$.

b. What does the graph of $f(x)$ look like as x gets large?

c. Calculate $f(0.1)$ and $f(0.01)$.

d. What does the graph of $f(x)$ look like as x approaches zero?

e. Sketch the graph of f.

7. The graph of $y = \frac{x^3+1}{x^2-x^4+1}$ looks like which of these when $x > 4$?

A. $y = x$ **B.** $y = -x$ **C.** $y = \frac{1}{x}$ **D.** $y = -\frac{1}{x}$

8. **a.** Sketch the graphs of $f(x) = (x-1)(x+3)$ and $g(x) = \frac{1}{(x-1)(x+3)}$ on the same axes.

b. Find the exact values of all x such that $f(x) = g(x)$.

9. **Take It Further** Let $d(x)$ be defined for nonnegative real numbers as the decimal part of x. For example, $d(10.63)$ is 0.63, and $d(\pi)$ starts out 0.14159… .

a. Let $x = \frac{7}{4}$. Calculate $d(x)$, $d(2x)$, $d(3x)$, and $d(4x)$.

b. Sketch a graph of d on $0 \leq x \leq 10$.

c. Sketch a graph of $r(x) = \frac{1}{d(x)}$ on $0 \leq x \leq 10$. Describe the domain and range of r.

On Your Own

10. Consider $g(x) = \frac{2x^2-5x+2}{x^2+x-6}$.

a. The graph of g has a horizontal asymptote. What is its equation?

b. The graph of g has a vertical asymptote. What is its equation?

c. The graph of g has a hole at what point?

11. What is the domain of

a. $x \mapsto \frac{x-4}{x^2-4}$?

b. $x \mapsto \frac{x-2}{x^2-4}$?

EXERCISE 6 One technique for calculating limits is to substitute a value for x that is close to the value it is approaching. Even as students' ideas of limits become more formal, this strategy can provide a reassuring check.

EXERCISE 7 is a little tricky in that the denominator is not in normal form. This is a common twist in problems on standardized tests, and this exercise may help remind students to be wary and look closely.

EXERCISE 8 When solving for the intersections of the two graphs, students may not immediately think of capitalizing on the factored form of the equation and further factoring it as the difference of two squares. If you want students to find the intersection points by hand, you may need to give them a hint about this strategy.

EXERCISE 9 These graphs require some imagination on the part of your students, as they are very different from the graphs they have experienced so far. Even graphing $y = d(x)$ is pretty complex if students have not seen any kind of a "step" function.

ERROR PREVENTION You may want to remind them that a function has only one value for any given x if they are showing a point at $(z, 1)$ for z integers. Their graphs should have an open circle at that point, because the point on the graph of the function is $(z, 0)$.

8. a.

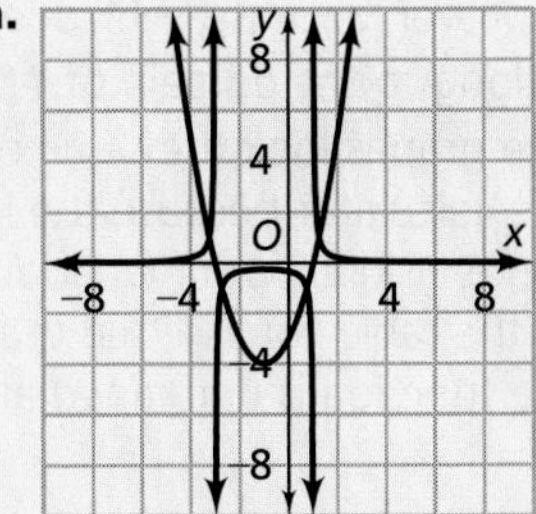

b. $-1+\sqrt{3}$; $-1-\sqrt{3}$; $-1+\sqrt{5}$; $-1-\sqrt{5}$

9. a. $d(x) = 0.75$; $d(2x) = 0.5$; $d(3x) = 0.25$; $d(4x) = 0$

b.

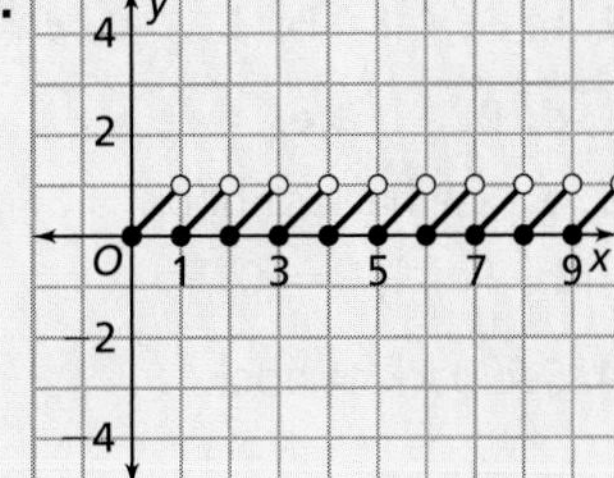

c.

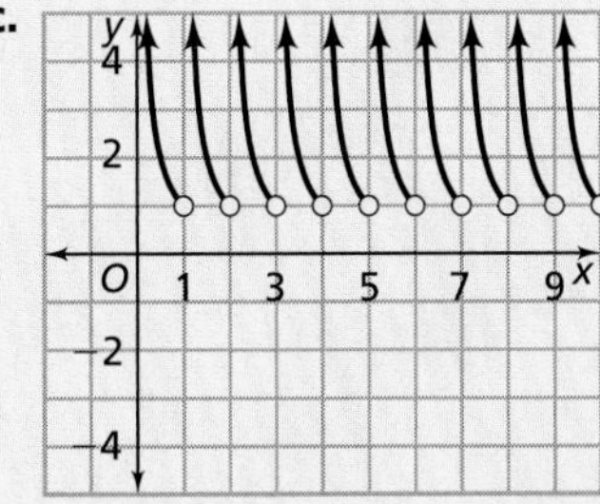

The domain of $r(x)$ is the set of all positive real numbers that are not integers. Its range is the positive real numbers.

10. a. $y = 2$ **b.** $x = -3$ **c.** $\left(2, \frac{3}{5}\right)$

11. a. $\{x \mid x \neq -2, 2\}$

b. $\{x \mid x \neq -2, 2\}$

On Your Own

EXERCISE 13 demonstrates a nice technique for finding limits of functions that are not as straightforward as polynomial or rational functions.

BACKGROUND FOR TEACHER You *bound* the function for which you want to find the limit by two functions that you know about. In this case, since $\sin x$ oscillates back and forth between -1 and 1, you can bound the function $\frac{\sin x}{x}$ by $\frac{1}{x}$ and $-\frac{1}{x}$. These two functions act as a fence to hold in the function $\frac{\sin x}{x}$. Since they both approach 0 as x approaches ∞, the fence closes in and forces the oscillating function to also approach 0.

EXERCISE 14 When students list the characteristics of graphs that have a horizontal asymptote, they solidify their own understanding of when this occurs. Instead of just following a rote procedure, they understand when it is appropriate to look for a horizontal asymptote, and have a better understanding of non-horizontal asymptotes.

EXERCISE 16 You should focus any discussion of this exercise on how you can use the graphs of f and g to generate the graph of $f + g$, the sum of the functions. This exercise is referenced in the next lesson as an example of working with partial fractions.

EXERCISE 17 This is the first example of using a partial fraction decomposition; more examples follow in the next lesson.

12. Calculate each limit.

a. $\lim\limits_{x\to\infty} \dfrac{1 + \frac{1}{x}}{2 + \frac{1}{x}}$ **b.** $\lim\limits_{x\to\infty} \dfrac{x+1}{2x+1}$ **c.** $\lim\limits_{x\to\infty} \dfrac{\frac{3}{x} - \frac{4}{x^2}}{1 - \frac{5}{x} + \frac{6}{x^2}}$

d. $\lim\limits_{x\to\infty} \dfrac{3x-4}{x^2-5x+6}$ **e.** $\lim\limits_{x\to\infty} \dfrac{x^2-5x+6}{3x-4}$

13. a. Sketch the graphs of these three functions on the same axes with $x \geq 0$.

$$f_1(x) = \frac{1}{x},\ f_2(x) = \frac{\sin x}{x},\ f_3(x) = -\frac{1}{x}$$

b. Use the graphs to find the value of $\lim\limits_{x\to\infty} \frac{\sin x}{x}$.

14. Write About It Describe how you can determine the horizontal asymptote, if any, of a given rational function. Include in your explanation an example of a rational function with a horizontal asymptote $y = 0$, one with a horizontal asymptote $y = c$ (where c is a nonzero real number), and one with no horizontal asymptote at all.

15. The graphs of these two functions look identical on a graphing calculator.

$$f(x) = \frac{x+11}{x^2+14x+33}$$

$$g(x) = \frac{1}{x+3}$$

a. Explain why they are not the same function.

b. Explain why their graphs look identical on the calculator.

16. a. Show that this equation is an identity.

$$\frac{1}{x+2} - \frac{1}{x+3} = \frac{1}{x^2+5x+6}$$

b. Without using a calculator, sketch the graphs of $f(x) = \frac{1}{x+2}$ and $g(x) = -\frac{1}{x+3}$ on the same axes.

c. Use the graphs of f and g to make a rough sketch of $h(x) = \frac{1}{x^2+5x+6}$. Check your work using a graphing calculator.

17. a. Find constants A and B that make this equation true.

$$\frac{x+9}{x^2-2x-3} = \frac{A}{x+1} + \frac{B}{x-3}$$

b. For the values of A and B you found, sketch the graphs of $f(x) = \frac{A}{x+1}$ and $g(x) = \frac{B}{x-3}$ on the same axes.

c. Use the graphs of f and g to make a rough sketch of $h(x) = \frac{x+9}{x^2-2x-3}$. Check your work using a graphing calculator.

Answers

12. a. $\frac{1}{2}$ **b.** $\frac{1}{2}$ **c.** 0

d. 0 **e.** ∞

13. a. See back of book.

b. $\lim\limits_{x\to\infty} \frac{\sin x}{x} = 0$

14. See back of book.

15. a. $f(x) = \frac{x+11}{(x+11)(x+3)}$ so for all $x \neq 11$ $f(x) = g(x)$. These two functions are not the same, however, because -11 does not belong to the domain of $f(x)$.

b. The graphs look the same on the calculator because the hole is not visible, but if you look at the table you will see that the function is undefined at $x = -11$.

16. See back of book.

17. a. $A = -2$ $B = 3$

b–c. See back of book.

18. Standardized Test Prep Let $P(x) = \dfrac{x^5}{36x^4 - 13x^2 + 1}$. If h is the number of horizontal asymptotes and v is the number of vertical asymptotes of the graph of P, what is the value of the product hv?

A. 0 **B.** 2 **C.** 4 **D.** 8

Go Online PHSchool.com

For additional practice, go to Web Code: bga-0307

Maintain Your Skills

19. Sketch the graph of each function.

a. $a(x) = \dfrac{x - 2}{x - 3}$ **b.** $b(x) = \dfrac{2x - 5}{x - 3}$

c. $c(x) = \dfrac{3x - 8}{x - 3}$ **d.** $d(x) = \dfrac{4x - 11}{x - 3}$

20. For each equation, find the value of a that makes the equation true.

a. $\dfrac{2x - 5}{x - 3} = a + \dfrac{1}{x - 3}$

b. $\dfrac{3x - 8}{x - 3} = a + \dfrac{1}{x - 3}$

c. $\dfrac{4x - 11}{x - 3} = a + \dfrac{1}{x - 3}$

21. Find each value of K so the function has no removable discontinuity.

What value of K plugs the hole in the graph?

a. $f(x) = \begin{cases} \dfrac{x}{x^2 - 3x} & \text{if } x \neq 0 \\ K & \text{if } x = 0 \end{cases}$

b. $g(x) = \begin{cases} \dfrac{x^3 - 6x^2 + 11x - 6}{x - 2} & \text{if } x \neq 2 \\ K & \text{if } x = 2 \end{cases}$

c. $h(x) = \begin{cases} \dfrac{(x + 1)(x - 4)}{(x - 4)(x + 10)} & \text{if } x \neq 4 \\ K & \text{if } x = 4 \end{cases}$

d. $j(x) = \begin{cases} \dfrac{(x + 2)^2(x - 3)}{x^2 - 3x - 10} & \text{if } x \neq -2 \\ K & \text{if } x = -2 \end{cases}$

22. Sketch the graph of each function.

a. $a(x) = \dfrac{x - 3}{(x + 1)^2}$ **b.** $b(x) = \dfrac{x^2 - 4}{x^2 - 1}$

c. $c(x) = \dfrac{x^2 - 6x + 5}{x^2 - 6x + 8}$ **d.** $d(x) = \dfrac{(x - 1)^2}{(x + 2)^2}$

e. $e(x) = \dfrac{(x - 1)^2}{(x + 2)^3}$

18. A

19. See back of book.

20. a. 2
b. 3
c. 4

21. a. $-\frac{1}{3}$
b. -1
c. $\frac{5}{14}$
d. 0

22. a.

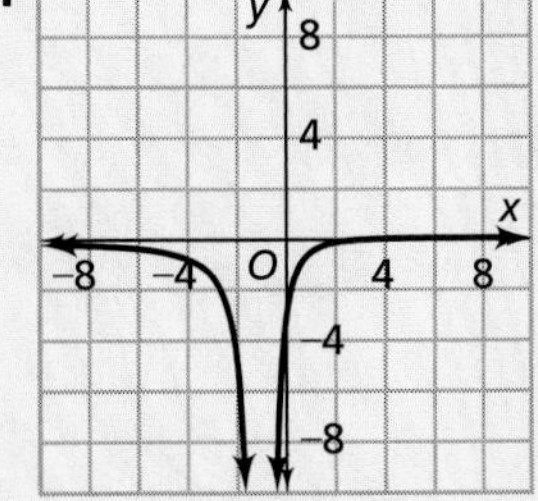

b–e. See back of book.

Maintain Your Skills

EXERCISE 19 In this exercise, students see a relationship in the graphs of the rational functions they are being asked to graph, but may not see the reason for this relationship. It appears that the graphs in parts (b), (c), and (d) are images of the graph in part (a) after a vertical translation. In Exercise 20, students see why this makes sense algebraically.

EXERCISE 21 For students to make an accurate sketch of a function with a removable discontinuity, they need to know not only the input value that leads to the discontinuity, but the value that the function would take on at that point. Then they know the limit as x approaches the discontinuity and can place an open circle correctly at the point of discontinuity in the graph.

EXERCISE 22 does more than provide practice in graphing rational functions. It also encourages students to analyze the effect of factors raised to powers in either the numerator or denominator of the function.

Additional Resources

PRINT RESOURCES
- Solution Manual
- Practice Workbook
- Assessment Resources
- Teaching Resources

TECHNOLOGY
- Interactive Textbook
- TeacherExpress CD-ROM
- ExamView CD-ROM
- PHSchool.com

Additional Practice

1. Consider the function $f(x) = \dfrac{x^2 + 5}{x}$.
a. Calculate $f(10)$ and $f(100)$.
b. What does the graph of f look like as x gets large?
c. Calculate $f(0.1)$ and $f(0.01)$.
d. What does the graph of f look like as x approaches zero?
e. Sketch the graph of f.

2. Consider $f(x) = \dfrac{2x^2 + x - 6}{x^2 - 5x - 14}$.
a. The graph of f has a horizontal asymptote. What is its equation?
b. The graph of f has a vertical asymptote. What is its equation?
c. The graph of f has a hole at what point?

3. Find the domain of each function.
a. $h(x) = \dfrac{x + 3}{x^2 - 9}$ **b.** $g(x) = \dfrac{x^2 + 5x + 6}{x^2 - 9}$

4. Calculate each limit.
a. $\lim\limits_{x \to \infty} \dfrac{2 + \frac{1}{x}}{3 + \frac{1}{x}}$ **b.** $\lim\limits_{x \to \infty} \dfrac{x^2 + 1}{2x^2 + 2}$
c. $\lim\limits_{x \to \infty} \dfrac{5x - 3}{2x^2 - x + 2}$ **d.** $\lim\limits_{x \to \infty} \dfrac{x^3 + 2x^2}{x + 1}$

5. a. Sketch the graphs of $f(x) = (x - 2)(x + 5)$ and $g(x) = \dfrac{1}{(x - 2)(x + 5)}$ on the same axes.
b. Find the exact values of all x such that $f(x) = g(x)$.

6. The graphs of these two functions look identical on a calculator.

$$f(x) = \frac{x + 10}{x^2 + 6x - 40}$$

$$g(x) = \frac{1}{x - 4}$$

a. Explain why they are not the same function.
b. Explain why their graphs look identical on the calculator.

Practice: For Lesson 3.7, assign Exercises 1–6.

Lesson Overview

GOAL

- Find the equation of the tangent to the graph of a rational function at a point.

In this lesson, students look back at the methods they developed in Investigation 3A for finding the equation of a secant line through two points on the graph of a polynomial function and the equation of the tangent to the graph at a point. Theorems 3.4 and 3.5 summarize these results, but the proofs of those theorems rely on continuity. Since rational functions are not continuous everywhere, students need to see if they can justify for rational functions the methods they used to find equations for secants and tangents of polynomial functions. The key idea is that rational functions are not continuous everywhere, but they are continuous in pieces.

CHECK YOUR UNDERSTANDING
- Core: 1, 3, 4, 6, 7
- Optional: 2, 5

MATERIALS
- CAS (recommended)
- graph paper
- graphing calculators
- Blackline Masters MC7, 3.8

HOMEWORK
- Core: 8, 9, 10, 11, 12, 14
- Optional: 15, 16, 17
- Extension: 13

Launch

Begin today's lesson with the following problem, which is a review of results from Investigation 3A.

Let $f(x) = x^3 - 2x + 1$.

1. Find a linear function $r(x)$ such that
$$f(x) = (x - 2)(x - 3)q(x) + r(x)$$
for some polynomial $q(x)$.
2. Explain why the graph of r is the secant to the graph of f between the points $(2, f(2))$ and $(3, f(3))$.

The solution follows:

1. Students can use their calculator or divide by hand to find that $x^3 - 2x + 1 = (x - 2)(x - 3)(x + 5) + 17x - 29$. This gives $r(x) = 17x - 29$.
2. At the points $(2, f(2))$ and $(3, f(3))$, the first term in the new expression for the function is equal to zero. That means that the value of the function at both of those points is $17x - 29$, so the equation of the line through those two points is $y = 17x - 29$.

You may also want to look back at Theorems 3.4 and 3.5 from Lesson 3.5. Remind students that the proofs use the fact that the function f is

3.8 Revisiting Secants and Tangents

In Lesson 3.5, you saw two theorems (Theorem 3.4 and Theorem 3.5) that provided a method for finding the equations of secants and tangents to graphs of polynomial functions. In this lesson, you will see that the same method works even if f is a rational function.

Of course, you can talk about the tangent at $(a, f(a))$ only if f is continuous at $x = a$.

Example 1

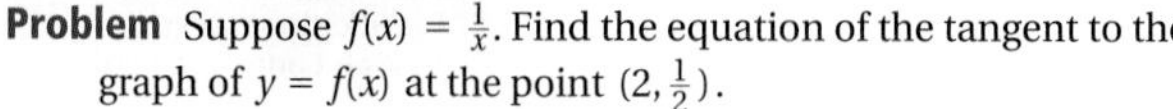

Problem Suppose $f(x) = \frac{1}{x}$. Find the equation of the tangent to the graph of $y = f(x)$ at the point $(2, \frac{1}{2})$.

Solution First, assume you can write $f(x)$ in powers of $x - 2$ up to $(x - 2)^2$ using the method of undetermined coefficients.

$$f(x) = \frac{1}{x} = m + n(x - 2) + p(x)(x - 2)^2 \qquad (1)$$

Then the polynomial method indicates that the equation of the line tangent to the graph of $f(x)$ at $(2, f(2))$ is $y = m + n(x - 2)$.

Substitute $x = 2$ in (1) to get

$$m = f(2) = \frac{1}{2}$$

$$\frac{1}{x} = \frac{1}{2} + n(x - 2) + p(x)(x - 2)^2 \qquad (2)$$

Subtract $\frac{1}{2}$ from each side of (2)

$$\frac{1}{x} - \frac{1}{2} = n(x - 2) + p(x)(x - 2)^2$$

Rewrite this as

$$\frac{-(x - 2)}{2x} = n(x - 2) + p(x)(x - 2)^2$$

Divide by $x - 2$ to get

$$\frac{-1}{2x} = n + p(x)(x - 2) \qquad (3)$$

Now suppose p is defined and continuous at $x = 2$. Since the left and right sides of (3) are equal for $x \neq 2$, they must be equal for $x = 2$, as well. Substitute $x = 2$ in (3) to get $n = -\frac{1}{4}$.

$$\frac{1}{x} = \frac{1}{2} - \frac{1}{4}(x - 2) + p(x)(x - 2)^2$$

for some function $p(x)$. This means that the equation of the tangent at $x = 2$ is

$$r(x) = m + n(x - 2) = \frac{1}{2} - \frac{1}{4}(x - 2)$$

For You to Do

1. Find $p(x)$ if

$$\frac{1}{x} = \frac{1}{2} - \frac{1}{4}(x - 2) + p(x)(x - 2)^2$$

2. For $f(x) = \frac{1}{x}$, find an equation of the tangent to the graph of $y = f(x)$ at the point $(a, f(a))$.

$a \neq 0$, of course.

Minds in Action — episode 8

Sasha and Derman are looking at the above example.

Sasha I'm not completely sure about this method.

Derman What could be wrong? I write

$$\frac{1}{x} = \frac{1}{2} - \frac{1}{4}(x - 2) + p(x)(x - 2)^2$$

for some function p. Then I think about the secant becoming the tangent. The algebra says that the remainder when I divide by $(x - 2)^2$ is the equation of the tangent. The remainder when I divide the right side is $\frac{1}{2} - \frac{1}{4}(x - 2)$, so that's it.

Sasha I'm worried about the assumption that p is continuous at $x = 2$. p is now a rational function. If its denominator had turned out to have some power of $x - 2$ as a factor, that would invalidate the reasoning by which we found p in the first place.

Derman Well, p came out the way we needed it to in Example 1. Let's try another example and see if the same thing happens.

At the moment of takeoff, a ski jumper's skis are essentially tangent to the curve of the ramp.

continuous. As stated, the two theorems apply only to polynomial functions. Ask students to think about the kinds of problems that could result from using these theorems on a rational function. You might sketch a case showing a line through two points on the graph of a rational function that are on either side of a horizontal asymptote. Is it possible to find the equation of the tangent to the curve at one of those two points by finding the limit as the other point approaches it? Not with the discontinuity in the way! Advise your students to proceed with caution and to think about the consequences of the discontinuities present in rational functions.

A detail that you may notice, but that will not concern your students, is that this lesson implies that as long as a rational function is continuous at a point, it is possible to find the equation of the tangent to its graph at that point. In other words, continuity implies differentiability. This is not true in general, but it is true for rational functions.

The absolute value function is an example of a function that is continuous everywhere, but where the slope of the tangent to the function is not defined everywhere. The absolute value function is continuous—you can draw its V-shape without lifting your pen—but the slope of the tangent to the graph at the point $(0, 0)$ is not defined. If you look at secant lines where a point on the left branch of the graph approaches $(0, 0)$, you might conclude that the slope of the tangent is -1. If you look at secant lines where a point on the right branch of the graph approaches $(0, 0)$, you would conclude that the slope of the tangent is 1. Because these limits are not the same, the derivative (the slope of the tangent to the curve) does not exist at $x = 0$ for the absolute value function.

Answers

For You to Do

1. $p(x) = \frac{1}{4x}$

2. $r(x) = \frac{1}{a} - \frac{1}{a^2}(x - a)$.

Example 2

Problem Let

$$f(x) = \frac{x + 2}{2x^2 + 3x + 1}.$$

Find an equation of the tangent to the graph of $y = f(x)$ at the point $(3, f(3))$.

Solution

Write f in powers of $x - 3$.

$$f(x) = \frac{x + 2}{2x^2 + 3x + 1} = m + n(x - 3) + p(x)(x - 3)^2 \qquad (4)$$

If $r(x) = m + n(x - 3)$, then the graph of r will be the tangent.
So you need to solve for m and n. Substitute $x = 3$ in (4) and you get

$$m = f(3) = \frac{5}{28}$$

So,

$$\frac{x + 2}{2x^2 + 3x + 1} = \frac{5}{28} + n(x - 3) + p(x)(x - 3)^2 \qquad (5)$$

Subtract $\frac{5}{28}$ from each side of (5).

$$\frac{x + 2}{2x^2 + 3x + 1} - \frac{5}{28} = n(x - 3) + p(x)(x - 3)^2$$

Rewrite this as

$$\frac{-10x^2 + 13x + 51}{28(2x^2 + 3x + 1)} = n(x - 3) + p(x)(x - 3)^2$$

The right side of this equation implies that its left side has a factor of $x - 3$.
Use this fact to factor the numerator of the left side.

$$\frac{-(x - 3)(10x + 17)}{28(2x^2 + 3x + 1)} = n(x - 3) + p(x)(x - 3)^2$$

Divide each side by $x - 3$.

$$\frac{-(10x + 17)}{28(2x^2 + 3x + 1)} = n + p(x)(x - 3) \qquad (6)$$

Substitute $x = 3$ into (6) to get $n = -\frac{47}{28^2}$. The equation of the tangent at $x = 3$ is

$$r(x) = \frac{5}{28} - \frac{47}{28^2}(x - 3)$$

For You to Do

3. Find $p(x)$ if

$$\frac{x+2}{2x^2+3x+1} = \frac{5}{28} - \frac{47}{28^2}(x-3) + p(x)(x-3)^2$$

4. Let

$$f(x) = \frac{2x+5}{x+3}$$

Find an equation of the tangent to the graph of $y = f(x)$ at the point $(1, f(1))$.

Minds in Action episode 9

Tony, Sasha, and Derman are talking some more about the mysterious $p(x)$.

Derman Look, in both cases we've tried, $p(x)$ had almost the same denominator as the original function.

Tony In fact, it was a perfect square times the denominator of the original.

Sasha It looks too good to be true. But two examples don't make a theorem.

Tony Here's what I think. Suppose the rational function you start with is defined at a number, say 2, and you make believe that $p(x)$ is also defined and continuous at 2. If you plow ahead and find $p(x)$ by first finding m and then n and then solving for $p(x)$, you'll see in the end that $p(x)$ is continuous at 2. I bet it's true.

Sasha Here's what worries me. Take the $\frac{1}{x}$ example. We figured out that

$$\frac{1}{x} = \frac{1}{2} - \frac{1}{4}(x-2) + \frac{1}{4x}(x-2)^2$$

If I wanted to, I could write

$$\frac{1}{x} = 3 - 17(x-2) + p(x)(x-2)^2$$

and solve for a different $p(x)$. And I bet that one would not be continuous at 2.

Tony Right, but I'm finding m and n in by a special method—our method of undetermined coefficients. Replace x by 2, find m, divide by $x - 2$, and so on.

Derman Try another?

Tony Or do it in general, once and for all.

Sasha I feel some algebra coming on.

The $\frac{1}{4x}$ comes from Problem 1 on page 219.

Answers

For You to Do

3. $p(x) = \dfrac{94x + 143}{784(2x^2 + 3x + 1)}$

4. $r(x) = \frac{7}{4} + \frac{1}{16}(x - 1)$

Explore

For You to Do

PROBLEM 3 Even when students use a CAS for this first calculation, they can get answers in many different forms and may find it challenging to compare answers. As a consequence, you may want to do this together as a class so that students feel confident they know what to do. You may not want to spend the time to do this calculation if your students do not have access to technology, but you can go through the process with them. Basically, you just want to use the rules of algebra to isolate (and solve for) $p(x)$, so subtract the equation for the tangent line from the expression that defines the function and then divide the result by $(x - 3)^2$.

PROBLEM 4 Here is a fully worked out solution:

$$\frac{2x+5}{x+3} = m + n(x-1) + p(x)(x-1)^2$$

Substitute $x = 1$: $m = f(1) = \frac{2(1)+5}{(1)+3} = \frac{7}{4}$.

$$\frac{2x+5}{x+3} = \frac{7}{4} + n(x-1) + p(x)\cdot(x-1)^2$$

$$\frac{2x+5}{x+3} - \frac{7}{4} = n(x-1) + p(x)(x-1)^2$$

$$\frac{8x+20-7x-21}{4(x+3)} = n(x-1) + p(x)(x-1)^2$$

$$\frac{x-1}{4(x+3)} = n(x-1) + p(x)(x-1)^2$$

Divide each side by $x - 1$.

$$\frac{1}{4(x+3)} = n + p(x)(x-1)$$

Substitute $x = 1$.

$$\frac{1}{4(1+3)} = n + p(1)(1-1)$$

$$\frac{1}{16} = n$$

For Discussion

PROBLEM 5 is rather technical. When students study Taylor series in calculus, they learn that $p(x)$ has a power series representation in $x - r$ of the form $p(x) = \sum_{n=0}^{\infty} p_n(x - r)^n$, so it is defined at $x = r$. But you can establish the theorem with algebra. If time is short, think about just making the theorem an assumption or assigning the proof as an extra project.

Wrap Up

Depending on time and on your students, you may want to spend some time discussing the argument for Theorem 3.9. This limits the time you can give students to work on the Check Your Understanding exercises, but if your students have shown that they understand how to use the method of undetermined coefficients, then they are ready for the homework exercises without further practice in class. If your students had difficulty with the process, you might choose instead to ask them to accept Theorem 3.9 without proof, and spend more time on the exercises. With the Developing Habits of Mind section at the end of the lesson, they can use their calculators to check their work when they are on their own. You may even be comfortable enough with their use of this technology that you do not require them to do the process by hand.

Assessment Resources

Lesson Quiz 3.8

1. Let
$$g(x) = \frac{4x - 10}{x^2 + 5x + 6}$$
Find an equation of the tangent to the graph of g at $x = 1$.

2. Let $f(x) = \frac{1}{x^3}$. Find an equation of the tangent to the graph of f at the point $(a, f(a))$.

3. Find A and B such that
$$\frac{3x - 10}{x^2 - 7x + 12} = \frac{A}{x - 3} + \frac{B}{x - 4}$$

Theorem 3.9

Suppose that f is a rational function for which the denominator is not zero at $x = r$. Suppose also that you use the method of undetermined coefficients to write

$$f(x) = m + n(x - r) + p(x)(x - r)^2$$

finding first the number m and then the number n. Then p is a rational function that is defined at $x = r$.

Remember...

The Method of Undetermined Coefficients: Replace x by r, find m, subtract m from both sides, divide by $x - r$, find n, subtract n from both sides, divide by $x - r$.... When finding m and n, assume that $p(x)$ is defined and continuous at $x = r$. In the end, your assumption will be correct.

For Discussion

5. Develop a proof or a plausible argument for Theorem 3.9.

Developing Habits of Mind

Use a different process to get the same result. The Taylor expansion command in your CAS works with rational functions as well. It produces results that agree with the method of undetermined coefficients. For example, to find m and n such that

$$\frac{1}{x} = m + n(x - 2) + p(x)(x - 2)^2$$

tell the system to expand $\frac{1}{x}$ about $x = 2$ up to terms of degree 1.

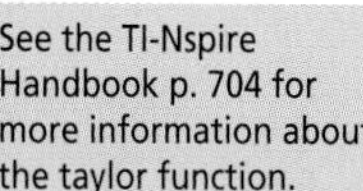

See the TI-Nspire Handbook p. 704 for more information about the taylor function.

Answers

For Discussion

5. If $r(x)$ is not defined at $x = r$, then $f(x)$ is not defined at $x = r$, which would imply that the denominator of $f(x)$ is zero at $x = r$. If $p(x)$ has a factor of $x - r$ in the denominator, then it is not defined at $x = r$, which implies $f(x)$ is not defined at $x = r$.

Exercises *Practicing Habits of Mind*

Check Your Understanding

1. Let $g(x) = -\frac{1}{x}$. Find an equation of the tangent to the graph of g at the point $(2, g(2))$.

2. In Example 1 on page 218, you saw that the tangent to the graph of $f(x) = \frac{1}{x}$ at $(2, f(2))$ has the equation

$$y = \frac{1}{2} - \frac{1}{4}(x - 2)$$

How does this compare to the tangent of g you found in Exercise 1? Explain your answer.

3. Let $h(x) = \frac{1}{x^2}$. Find an equation of the tangent to the graph of $y = h(x)$ at the point $(a, h(a))$.

4. Copy and complete this table by finding the slope of the tangent to the graphs of $f(x) = \frac{1}{x}$ and $h(x) = \frac{1}{x^2}$ at each value of x. Explain the results using the graphs of f and h.

x	Slope of tangent to f	Slope of tangent to h
$\frac{1}{10}$	■	■
$\frac{1}{4}$	■	■
$\frac{1}{2}$	■	■
1	■	■
2	$-\frac{1}{4}$	$-\frac{1}{4}$
4	■	■
10	■	■

5. Let

$$h(x) = \frac{2x - 3}{x^2 + 4x + 5}$$

Find an equation of the tangent to the graph of h at $x = -2$.

6. Find A and B so that

$$\frac{4x - 26}{x^2 - 7x + 10} = \frac{A}{x - 2} + \frac{B}{x - 5}$$

Exercises

1. $y = -\frac{1}{2} + \frac{1}{4}(x - 2)$

2. Since $f(x) = \frac{1}{x}$ and $g(x) = -\frac{1}{x}$ are reflections of each other over the x-axis, their tangents at $x = 2$ will also be reflections of each other over the x-axis.

3. $y = \frac{1}{a^2} + \frac{-2}{a^3}(x - a)$

4. See back of book.

5. $y = 2(x + 2) - 7$

6. $A = 6, B = -2$

Exercises

HOMEWORK

- Core: 8, 9, 10, 11, 12, 14
- Optional: 15, 16, 17
- Extension: 13

Check Your Understanding

EXERCISE 2 Some students compare the graphs algebraically, rather than geometrically. They say, "The constant and the coefficient of the $x - 2$ term have opposite signs." Encourage these students to look at the graphs of the two original functions and of the two tangent lines.

EXERCISE 3 You may want to take time to look at this exercise and analyze what it reveals about the slope of the tangent to the curve for various values of x. Since the slope of the tangent to the graph at $(a, h(a))$ is $\frac{-2}{a^3}$, the curve has positive slope when x is negative and negative slope when x is positive. Looking at the graph of $f(x) = \frac{1}{x^2}$, students can see that it is increasing for negative x and decreasing for positive x.

EXERCISE 4 Students should use the equations they found for the tangent line to each curve at the general point $(a, f(a))$ or $(a, h(a))$ to fill in this table.

You can hand out Blackline Master 3.8 for students to fill in the table.

EXERCISE 6 is an example of a partial fraction decomposition. This type of computation will help students who continue their studies in calculus, as it is part of a technique for integrating rational functions. Students use this result in Exercise 7. If you plan to assign it, you should assign this one.

On Your Own

EXERCISE 7 The concept here is that these slopes are additive.

GOING FURTHER If students are interested in this, you might ask them to do similar exercises to show that slopes are additive and multiplicative. This underlies the calculus idea that if $h(x) = f(x) + g(x)$, then $h'(x) = f'(x) + g'(x)$.

You can make copies of Blackline Master MC7 for students to sketch graphs of functions.

EXERCISE 8 Now that students have had some experience finding the slope of the tangent to a curve for different functions, they should make the connection between the slope of the tangent and whether the function is increasing, decreasing, or even equal to 0. If you do not see evidence of this connection, you may want to use a ruler as your "tangent line" and follow along a graph of a general function talking about the slope of the tangent at various points. You can also use a roller-coaster analogy as you travel along a function graph, asking whether the car is going up, going down, or is level.

EXERCISE 9 Encourage students to look at the graph of the original function and to think about whether their answer makes sense. They can do this by graphing the tangent line with the function, or by looking at the function when $x = 3$ and seeing if the curve is decreasing there and whether the tangent line at that point has a positive y-intercept.

EXERCISE 10 Students should start by finding a general equation for the tangent line for the function g. Some students may already accept that slopes are additive, and would expect the slope for g to be one more than the slope for f. However, they have not proven this result in this course and students have only seen one example so far in Exercise 7. Encourage students to check it here by finding the general equation for the tangent to the graph of g.

You can hand out Blackline Master 3.8 for students to fill in the table.

7. Let $f(x) = \frac{A}{x-2}$ and $g(x) = \frac{B}{x-5}$ where A and B are the values you found in Exercise 6.

a. Graph f. Find the slope of the line tangent to f at $x = 4$.

b. Graph g. Find the slope of the line tangent to g at $x = 4$.

c. Graph $h(x) = \frac{4x - 26}{x^2 - 7x + 10}$. Find the slope of the line tangent to h at $x = 4$.

On Your Own

8. **Write About It** The function $f(x) = \frac{1}{x}$ is "decreasing everywhere." What does this mean? Give other examples of functions that are increasing everywhere, functions that are decreasing everywhere, and functions that are neither.

9. Let

$$g(x) = \frac{2x + 7}{5x - 2}$$

Find an equation of the tangent to the graph of g at $(3, g(3))$.

10. Copy and complete this table with the slope of the tangent to $f(x) = \frac{1}{x}$ and $g(x) = x + \frac{1}{x}$ at each value of x. Explain your answer.

x	Slope of tangent to f	Slope of tangent to g
-2	■	■
-1	■	■
$-\frac{1}{2}$	■	■
0	undefined	undefined
$\frac{1}{2}$	■	■
1	■	■
2	■	■
3	■	■

Answers

7. a. $-\frac{3}{2}$;

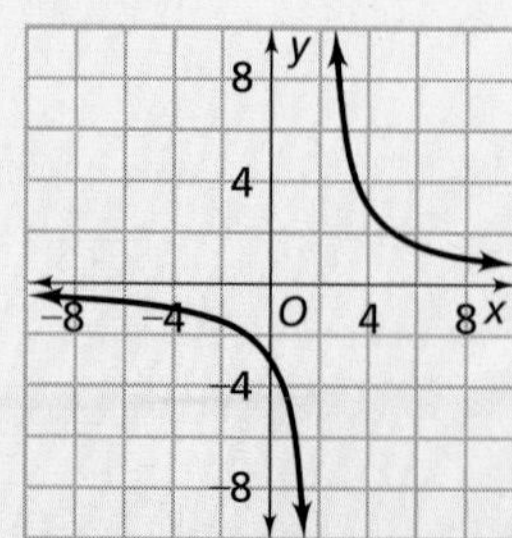

b–c. See back of book.

8. Answers may vary. Sample: $f(x)$ is decreasing everywhere if it has a negative slope everywhere. $g(x) = x$ is increasing everywhere, $h(x) = -x$ is decreasing everywhere, and $k(x) = x^2$ is neither.

9. $y = 1 - \frac{3}{13}(x - 3)$

10. See back of book.

11. Consider the function $j(x) = \frac{1}{x^2 + 1}$.

a. Find the slope of the tangent to j at $x = 2$.

b. Find the slope of the tangent to j at $x = -2$.

c. How are the answers in (a) and (b) related? Explain.

12. Let

$$f(x) = \frac{ax + b}{cx + d}$$

Find an equation of the tangent to the graph of f at $x = 0$.

Assume $d \neq 0$.

13. **Take It Further** Let $f(x) = \frac{ax + b}{cx + d}$ again, with $d \neq 0$. Write f as a power series

$$f(x) = \alpha_0 + \alpha_1 x + \alpha_2 x^2 + \alpha_3 x^3 + \alpha_4 x^4 + \cdots$$

You saw in Exercise 12 that

$$\alpha_0 = \frac{b}{d} \text{ and } \alpha_1 = \frac{ad - bc}{d^2}$$

Find α_n for $n \geq 2$.

It might help to use a letter such as Δ to replace the constant value of $ad - bc$. If you do this, you can get simpler expressions, like $\alpha_1 = \frac{\Delta}{d^2}$.

14. **Standardized Test Prep** What is the slope of the tangent to the graph of $f(x) = \frac{4}{x}$ at $(3, f(3))$?

A. $-\frac{9}{4}$ B. $-\frac{4}{9}$ C. $-\frac{4}{3}$ D. $-\frac{3}{4}$

Maintain Your Skills

15. Sketch the graphs of all four functions on the same axes. A graphing calculator may be helpful.

a. $a(x) = 1 + x$

b. $b(x) = 1 + x + \frac{x^2}{2}$

c. $c(x) = 1 + x + \frac{x^2}{2} + \frac{x^3}{6}$

d. $d(x) = 1 + x + \frac{x^2}{2!} + \frac{x^3}{3!} + \frac{x^4}{4!}$

16. For each of functions in Exercise 15, find the slope of the tangent line through the point $(0, 1)$.

17. a. Write out the first six lines of Pascal's Triangle.

b. What is the value of $\binom{7}{3}$?

Go Online PHSchool.com

For additional practice, go to **Web Code: bga-0308**

11. a. $-\frac{4}{25}$

b. $\frac{4}{25}$

c. The answers to parts (a) and (b) are opposites because $j(x)$ is symmetric across the y-axis.

12. $y = \frac{b}{d} + \frac{ad - bc}{d^2}x$

13. $\alpha_n = (-1)^{n+1} \cdot \frac{(ad - bc) \cdot c^{n-1}}{d^{n+1}}$

14. B

15. a–d. See back of book.

16. a. 1 **b.** 1 **c.** 1 **d.** 1

17. a.

1
1 1
1 2 1
1 3 3 1
1 4 6 4 1
1 5 10 10 5 1

b. 35

EXERCISE 11 Some students may not think to use the symmetry present in the graph of j to draw conclusions about the slope of the tangent to the graph at different points. Hopefully they notice how the symmetry impacts the slope, guaranteeing that points which are reflection images of each other after reflection over the y-axis have slopes of the same magnitude but opposite sign.

EXERCISE 12 Students who attempt this calculation by hand and find it challenging because of the large number of unknowns might benefit from working step by step in parallel to one of their own more-specific calculations or with the example on page 220.

Maintain Your Skills

EXERCISE 15 You may recognize these functions as the Taylor series approximations for the function e^x, where e is the base of the natural logarithm. However students should zoom in on the sequence of graphs around the point (0, 1) and see that the graphs are very close together in that region.

You can make copies of Blackline Master MC7 for students to sketch graphs of functions.

Additional Resources

PRINT RESOURCES
- Solution Manual
- Practice Workbook
- Assessment Resources
- Teaching Resources

TECHNOLOGY
- Interactive Textbook
- TeacherExpress CD-ROM
- ExamView CD-ROM
- PHSchool.com

Additional Practice

1. Find A and B so that

$$\frac{23x - 89}{x^2 - 8x + 15} = \frac{A}{x - 3} + \frac{B}{x - 5}$$

2. Let $f(x) = \frac{A}{x - 3}$ and $g(x) = \frac{B}{x - 5}$ where A and B are the values you found in Exercise 1.

a. Graph f. Find the slope of the line tangent to f at $x = 1$.

b. Graph g. Find the slope of the line tangent to g at $x = 1$.

c. Graph $h(x) = \frac{23x - 89}{x^2 - 8x + 15}$. Find the slope of the line tangent to h at $x = 1$.

3. Consider the function $h(x) = \frac{2}{x^2 + 3}$.

a. Find the slope of the tangent to h at $x = 1$.

b. Find the slope of the tangent to h at $x = -1$.

c. How are the answers in (a) and (b) related? Explain.

4. Suppose

$$A = \begin{pmatrix} 2 & 1 \\ -5 & -3 \end{pmatrix} \text{ and } B = \begin{pmatrix} -4 & 3 \\ 2 & -1 \end{pmatrix}$$

a. Sketch the graphs of $y = \mathcal{R}_A(x)$ and $y = \mathcal{R}_B(x)$.

b. Find a matrix C such that $\mathcal{R}_A \circ \mathcal{R}_C = \mathcal{R}_B$.

c. Find a matrix D such that $\mathcal{R}_D \circ \mathcal{R}_A = \mathcal{R}_B$.

5. Suppose

$$A = \begin{pmatrix} 2 & 4 \\ 1 & 3 \end{pmatrix} \text{ and } B = \begin{pmatrix} 0 & 1 \\ 1 & 0 \end{pmatrix}$$

a. Sketch the graphs of $y = \mathcal{R}_A(x)$ and $y = \mathcal{R}_B(x)$.

b. Find a translation T_g and an affine transformation $\mathcal{A}_{(e,f)}$ so that $\mathcal{R}_A = T_g \circ \mathcal{R}_B \circ \mathcal{A}_{(e,f)}$.

c. Explain in words how to transform the graph of $y = \mathcal{R}_B(x)$ into the graph of $y = \mathcal{R}_A(x)$.

Practice: For Lesson 3.8, assign Exercises 1–3.

Lesson Overview

GOAL

- Use matrices to write linear fractional transformations of the function $f(x) = \frac{1}{x}$.

Students should be familiar with matrix multiplication and finding determinants and inverses of matrices for this optional lesson. This matrix material was covered in Chapter 4 of CME Project *Algebra 2*. Depending on your students' background in linear algebra, you may want to skip this lesson. It focuses on transformations of graphs through matrix multiplication, and classifies graphs of the form $\frac{ax + b}{cx + d}$ as transformations of the graph of $\frac{1}{x}$ where possible.

CHECK YOUR UNDERSTANDING
- Core: 1, 2, 3, 4, 5
- Optional: 6, 7

MATERIALS
- CAS (recommended)
- graph paper
- graphing calculators
- Blackline Masters MC7, MC8

HOMEWORK
- Core: 8, 9, 11, 12, 15
- Optional: 10, 13, 16, 17
- Extension: 14

VOCABULARY
- determinant
- linear fractional transformation
- structure-preserving map

Launch

Begin today's lesson with the For You to Do section on page 226. Have students think about how the graphs are related through geometric transformations and to describe a transformation that would map the first graph onto the second.

Explore

For You to Do

PROBLEMS 1 AND 2 You may wish to use Blackline Masters MC7 and MC8 on overheads to sketch graphs of functions.

3.9 Case Study: $y = \frac{ax+b}{cx+d}$

There is a connection between the graph of $f(x) = \frac{1}{x}$ and an entire family of rational functions that have a particular form.

For You to Do

Sketch the graph of each function.

1. $f(x) = \frac{1}{x}$

2. $g(x) = \frac{3x + 1}{5x - 10}$

You have probably noticed in For You to Do that the graphs of

$$f(x) = \frac{1}{x} \text{ and } g(x) = \frac{3x + 1}{5x - 10}$$

look similar. Here are the graphs of a few more functions having the same form.

$m(x) = \frac{2x + 1}{7x - 10}$

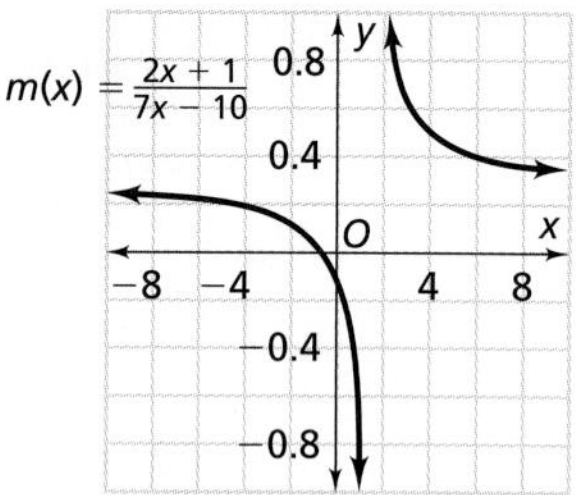

$n(x) = \frac{-x + 5}{2x - 1}$

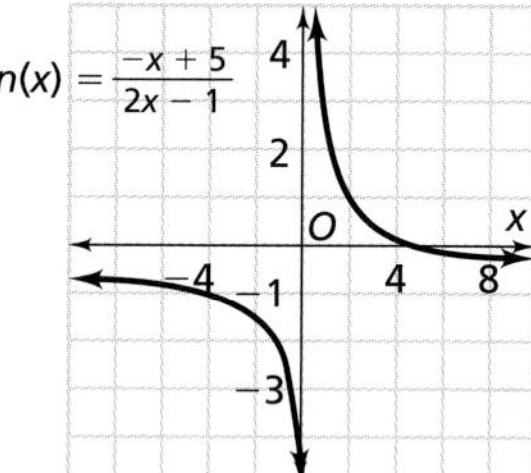

$p(x) = \frac{4x - 1}{3x - 2}$

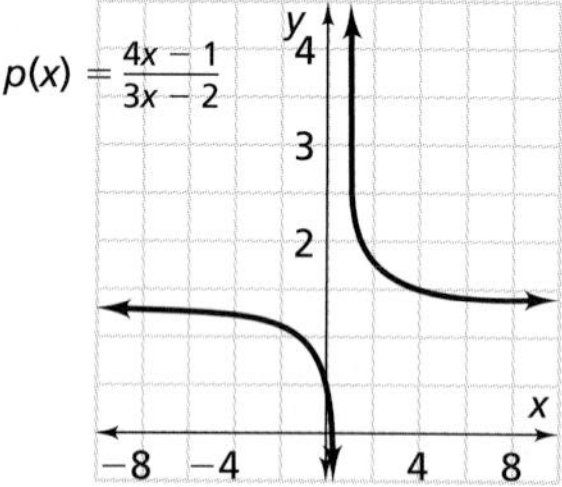

$q(x) = \frac{4x - 1}{3x + 2}$

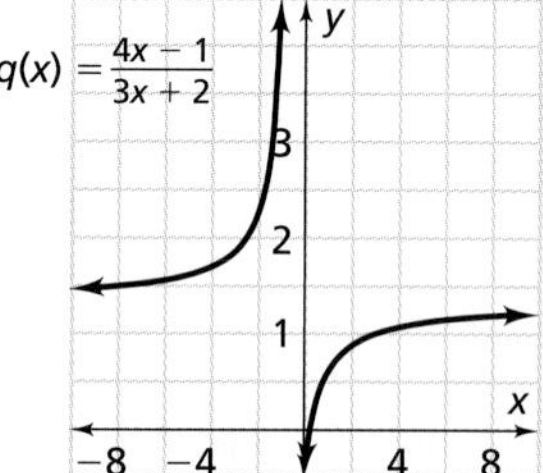

Each graph has the same general shape as the graph of $y = \frac{1}{x}$. You can transform one graph into the other through some combination of translation, scaling, and reflection. Starting with the following definition and notation, you will explore the relationship between the graphs of $y = \frac{1}{x}$ and $y = \frac{ax + b}{cx + d}$.

Answers

For You to Do

1.

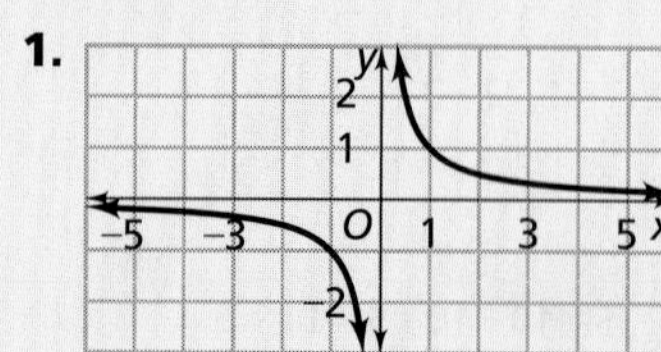

2.

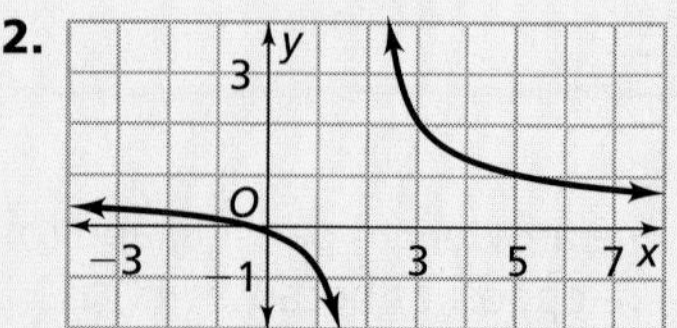

Definition

Let

$$A = \begin{pmatrix} a & b \\ c & d \end{pmatrix}$$

be a 2 × 2 matrix with real entries. The **linear fractional transformation** associated with A is the rational function

$$\mathcal{R}_A(x) = \frac{ax + b}{cx + d}$$

Facts and Notation

- Assume $c \neq 0$. Otherwise, $\mathcal{R}_A$ would be just a linear function.
- Recall that the **determinant** of A is $\det A = ad - bc$. In general, you may assume that $\det A \neq 0$.

You will see in the exercises what happens when $\det A = 0$.

For You to Do

For each matrix A below, find all the asymptotes of the graph of $y = \mathcal{R}_A(x)$.

3. $A = \begin{pmatrix} 1 & 2 \\ 3 & 4 \end{pmatrix}$

4. $A = \begin{pmatrix} 0 & 5 \\ 2 & 3 \end{pmatrix}$

5. $A = \begin{pmatrix} a & b \\ c & d \end{pmatrix}$

Rational functions with linear numerators and denominators typically have a "skateboard ramp" shape.

For You to Do

3. Vertical asymptote at $x = -\frac{4}{3}$, horizontal asymptote at $y = \frac{1}{3}$

4. Vertical asymptote at $x = -\frac{3}{2}$, horizontal asymptote at $y = 0$

5. Assume $c \neq 0$, then there is a vertical asymptote at $x = -\frac{d}{c}$, horizontal asymptote at $y = \frac{a}{c}$. If $c = 0$, there are no asymptotes—this is a linear function.

For You to Do

PROBLEM 5 For this problem, it makes sense to assume that $c \neq 0$, but students should state this assumption. If $c = 0$, this is a linear function and has no asymptotes.

For You to Do

PROBLEM 6 You may need to review the process of matrix multiplication here with a few numerical examples. Show intermediate steps in detail to help students keep track of the terms. For example:

$$\begin{pmatrix} 1 & 2 \\ 3 & 4 \end{pmatrix}\begin{pmatrix} 5 & 6 \\ 7 & 8 \end{pmatrix} = \begin{pmatrix} 1(5) + 2(7) & 1(6) + 2(8) \\ 3(5) + 4(7) & 3(6) + 4(8) \end{pmatrix}$$

$$= \begin{pmatrix} 19 & 22 \\ 43 & 50 \end{pmatrix}$$

TECHNOLOGY TIP You can review how to do matrix calculations with available technology, depending on how you intend students to use technology with this lesson.

Answers

For You to Do

6. $AB = \begin{pmatrix} a & b \\ c & d \end{pmatrix}\begin{pmatrix} \alpha & \beta \\ \gamma & \delta \end{pmatrix}$

$$= \begin{pmatrix} a\alpha + b\gamma & a\beta + b\delta \\ c\alpha + d\gamma & c\beta + d\delta \end{pmatrix}$$

So $R_{AB}(x) = \dfrac{(a\alpha + b\gamma)x + a\beta + b\delta}{(c\alpha + d\gamma)x + c\beta + d\delta}$

The following theorem explains why matrices can represent linear fractional transformations.

Theorem 3.10

Suppose A and B are 2×2 matrices with real coefficients. Then

$$\mathcal{R}_A \circ \mathcal{R}_B = \mathcal{R}_{AB}$$

Suppose

$$A = \begin{pmatrix} a & b \\ c & d \end{pmatrix} \text{ and } B = \begin{pmatrix} \alpha & \beta \\ \gamma & \delta \end{pmatrix}$$

δ is the lower-case Greek letter delta.

To start the proof of Theorem 3.10, compute $\mathcal{R}_A \circ \mathcal{R}_B$.

$$\begin{aligned}(\mathcal{R}_A \circ \mathcal{R}_B)(x) &= \mathcal{R}_A(\mathcal{R}_B(x)) \\ &= \mathcal{R}_A\left(\frac{\alpha x + \beta}{\gamma x + \delta}\right) \\ &= \frac{a\left(\frac{\alpha x + \beta}{\gamma x + \delta}\right) + b}{c\left(\frac{\alpha x + \beta}{\gamma x + \delta}\right) + d} \\ &= \frac{a(\alpha x + \beta) + b(\gamma x + \delta)}{c(\alpha x + \beta) + d(\gamma x + \delta)} \\ &= \frac{(a\alpha + b\gamma)x + (a\beta + b\delta)}{(c\alpha + d\gamma)x + (c\beta + d\delta)}\end{aligned}$$

For You to Do

6. Complete the proof of Theorem 3.10 by computing $\mathcal{R}_{AB}$ to obtain the same expression as you just found for $\mathcal{R}_A \circ \mathcal{R}_B$.

Theorem 3.10 says that the mapping

$$A \mapsto \mathcal{R}_A$$

from the set of 2×2 matrices to the set of linear fractional transformations is **structure preserving.** In other words, after

- multiplying matrices A and B to get AB
- composing functions $\mathcal{R}_A$ and $\mathcal{R}_B$ to get $\mathcal{R}_A \circ \mathcal{R}_B$

the product AB still maps to the composition $\mathcal{R}_A \circ \mathcal{R}_B$ because

$$AB \mapsto \mathcal{R}_{AB} = \mathcal{R}_A \circ \mathcal{R}_B.$$

For Discussion

Discuss the following facts, using the structure-preserving nature of the map $A \mapsto \mathcal{R}_A$.

7. The multiplicative identity matrix

$$I = \begin{pmatrix} 1 & 0 \\ 0 & 1 \end{pmatrix}$$

maps to the identity function

$$\mathcal{R}_I(x) = x$$

8. The inverse matrix A^{-1} maps to the inverse function $(\mathcal{R}_A)^{-1}$. In other words,

$$(\mathcal{R}_A)^{-1} = \mathcal{R}_{A^{-1}}$$

If A is an invertible matrix, then $\det A \neq 0$.

For You to Do

9. For each matrix A below, write down the corresponding function $\mathcal{R}_A$.

a. $A = \begin{pmatrix} 1 & 2 \\ 3 & 4 \end{pmatrix}$

b. $A = \begin{pmatrix} 2 & 4 \\ 6 & 8 \end{pmatrix}$

c. $A = \begin{pmatrix} -3 & -6 \\ -9 & -12 \end{pmatrix}$

d. $A = \begin{pmatrix} a & 2a \\ 3a & 4a \end{pmatrix}$

10. Explain why

$$\mathcal{R}_{kA} = \mathcal{R}_A$$

for any nonzero real number k.

11. Is the map

$$A \mapsto \mathcal{R}_A$$

one-to-one? Explain.

You can take two approaches to examine the relationship between the graphs of $y = \frac{1}{x}$ and $y = \frac{ax+b}{cx+d}$. One involves the algebra of rational expressions. The other involves the algebra of 2×2 matrices.

For Discussion

PROBLEM 7 This fact makes sense if you use the definition to write out $\mathcal{R}_I$. You get $\frac{1(x) + 0}{0(x) + 1} = \frac{x}{1} = x$, which is the identity mapping.

For You to Do

9. a. $\mathcal{R}_A(x) = \frac{x + 2}{3x + 4}$

b. $\mathcal{R}_A(x) = \frac{2x + 4}{6x + 8}$

c. $\mathcal{R}_A(x) = \frac{-3x - 6}{-9x - 12}$

d. $\mathcal{R}_A(x) = \frac{ax + 2a}{3ax + 4a}$

10. In $\mathcal{R}_{kA}$, you can factor k out of the numerator and the denominator of the corresponding function, and it will cancel out, leaving you with the function that corresponds to $\mathcal{R}_A$.

11. No; all matrices of the form kA with $k \neq 0$ map to R_A.

For Discussion

7. If $I = \begin{pmatrix} 1 & 0 \\ 0 & 1 \end{pmatrix}$, then

$$\mathcal{R}_I(x) = \frac{1 \cdot x + 0}{0 \cdot x + 1} = x.$$

8. Assume that $(\mathcal{R}_A)^{-1} = \mathcal{R}_B$ for some matrix B. From Theorem 3.10,

$$(\mathcal{R}_A) \circ (\mathcal{R}_A)^{-1} = (\mathcal{R}_A) \circ (\mathcal{R}_B) = \mathcal{R}_{AB}$$

This means that $AB = I$. You can also do the composition the other way and show that $BA = I$. The only way this can happen is if $B = A^{-1}$.

For You to Do

PROBLEM 12 Remind students that horizontal transformations involve replacing x with an expression in x. Replacing x with ex scales a graph horizontally by a factor of $\frac{1}{e}$. Replacing x with $x + f$ translates a graph to the left f units.

ERROR PREVENTION Students often get mixed up when performing two or more transformations in succession. Replacing x with ex and then replacing x with $x + f$ (a scaling followed by a translation) turns $y = \frac{1}{x}$ into $y = \frac{1}{e(x + f)}$. By contrast, replacing x with $x + f$ and then replacing x with ex (a translation followed by a scaling) turns $y = \frac{1}{x}$ into $y = \frac{1}{e(x + f)}$.

Using Rational Expressions

Let

$$g(x) = \frac{3x + 1}{5x - 10}$$

as in the For You to Do section at the start of this lesson. Long division gives

$$\begin{array}{r} \frac{3}{5} \\ 5x - 10 \overline{)3x + 1} \\ \underline{3x - 6} \\ 7 \end{array}$$

so that

$$3x + 1 = 7 + \tfrac{3}{5}(5x - 10)$$

Dividing each side by $5x - 10$ gives

$$\frac{3x + 1}{5x - 10} = \frac{7}{5x - 10} + \frac{3}{5} = \frac{1}{\frac{5}{7}(x - 2)} + \frac{3}{5}$$

Using what you have learned about transformations, you can conclude that the graph of $y = g(x)$ looks just like the graph of $y = \frac{1}{x}$, except it is

- scaled horizontally by a factor of $\frac{7}{5}$
- translated 2 units to the right
- translated $\frac{3}{5}$ units up

For You to Do

12. Using long division, show that for $\Delta = ad - bc \neq 0$,

$$\frac{ax + b}{cx + d} = \frac{1}{ex + f} + g$$

where

$$e = -\frac{c^2}{\Delta}$$

$$f = -\frac{cd}{\Delta}$$

$$g = \frac{a}{c}$$

Conclude that the graph of $y = \frac{ax + b}{cx + d}$ is the same as the graph of $y = \frac{1}{x}$ after a scaling and translation in x and a translation in y.

The skateboarder and ramp have been scaled horizontally by a factor of $-\frac{2}{3}$.

Answers

For You to Do

12. When you do the long division, you get a quotient of $\frac{a}{c}$ and a remainder of $\frac{-\Delta}{c}$. This means that you can write

$$\frac{ax + b}{cx + d} = \frac{a}{c} + \frac{\frac{-\Delta}{c}}{cx + d}$$

Rearrange the two addends on the right and divide top and bottom of the fraction by $-\Delta$, and you get

$$\frac{ax + b}{cx + d} = \frac{1}{\frac{-c^2}{\Delta}x - \frac{cd}{\Delta}} + \frac{a}{c}$$

This gives you the expression you want.

Using Matrices

First, recall affine transformations from CME Project *Algebra 2*.

$$\mathcal{A}_{(a,b)}(x) = ax + b$$

It follows that

$$\mathcal{A}_{(a,b)} = \mathcal{R}_A \text{ where } A = \begin{pmatrix} a & b \\ 0 & 1 \end{pmatrix}$$

Thus, you can think of linear fractional transformations as a generalization of affine transformations.

Here, make an exception and let $c = 0$.

For ease of notation, let

$$J = \begin{pmatrix} 0 & 1 \\ 1 & 0 \end{pmatrix}$$

and note that

$$\mathcal{R}_J(x) = \frac{0 \cdot x + 1}{1 \cdot x + 0} = \frac{1}{x}$$

Let

$$A = \begin{pmatrix} a & b \\ c & d \end{pmatrix}$$

and consider

$$\mathcal{R}_A(x) = \frac{ax + b}{cx + d}$$

You have already seen that you can write

$$\frac{ax + b}{cx + d} = \frac{1}{ex + f} + g$$

for some e, f, and g. Furthermore,

$$\begin{aligned} \frac{1}{ex + f} + g &= \frac{1}{\mathcal{A}_{(e,f)}(x)} + g \\ &= \mathcal{R}_J(\mathcal{A}_{(e,f)}(x)) + g \\ &= T_g(\mathcal{R}_J(\mathcal{A}_{(e,f)}(x))) \end{aligned}$$

Recall that T_g denotes the translation map $x \to x + g$.

So,

$$\mathcal{R}_A = T_g \circ \mathcal{R}_J \circ \mathcal{A}_{(e,f)}$$

which corresponds to the matrix equation

$$\begin{pmatrix} a & b \\ c & d \end{pmatrix} = \begin{pmatrix} 1 & g \\ 0 & 1 \end{pmatrix} \begin{pmatrix} 0 & 1 \\ 1 & 0 \end{pmatrix} \begin{pmatrix} e & f \\ 0 & 1 \end{pmatrix}$$

Wrap Up

As time allows, go over the core Check Your Understanding exercises. In terms of reinforcing the properties of rational graphs, you may want to emphasize Exercises 1 through 3.

Assessment Resources

Lesson Quiz 3.9

1. Let $f(x) = \frac{5x - 2}{4x + 3}$.
   a. Find the equations of the vertical and horizontal asymptotes of the graph of f.
   b. Find all intercepts of the graph of f.
   c. Use the information about asymptotes and intercepts to sketch the graph of f.

2. Suppose
$$A = \begin{pmatrix} -2 & 1 \\ -5 & 3 \end{pmatrix} \text{ and } B = \begin{pmatrix} 3 & -4 \\ -1 & 1 \end{pmatrix}$$
   a. Sketch the graphs of $y = \mathcal{R}_A(x)$ and $y = \mathcal{R}_B(x)$.
   b. Find a matrix C so that $\mathcal{R}_A \circ \mathcal{R}_C = \mathcal{R}_B$.
   c. Find a matrix D so that $\mathcal{R}_D \circ \mathcal{R}_A = \mathcal{R}_B$.

3. Suppose
$$A = \begin{pmatrix} 3 & 4 \\ 2 & 1 \end{pmatrix} \text{ and } B = \begin{pmatrix} 0 & 1 \\ 1 & 0 \end{pmatrix}$$
   a. Sketch the graphs of $y = \mathcal{R}_A(x)$ and $y = \mathcal{R}_B(x)$.
   b. Find a translation T_g and an affine transformation $M_{(e,f)}$ so that
$$\mathcal{R}_A = T_g \circ \mathcal{R}_B \circ M_{(e,f)}$$
   c. Explain in words how to transform the graph of $y = \mathcal{R}_B(x)$ into the graph of $y = \mathcal{R}_A(x)$.

Well, not quite. The matrices determine the functions only up to a scale factor, so the equation is really

$$k\begin{pmatrix} a & b \\ c & d \end{pmatrix} = \begin{pmatrix} 1 & g \\ 0 & 1 \end{pmatrix}\begin{pmatrix} 0 & 1 \\ 1 & 0 \end{pmatrix}\begin{pmatrix} e & f \\ 0 & 1 \end{pmatrix} = \begin{pmatrix} eg & fg + 1 \\ e & f \end{pmatrix}$$

This gives four equations

$$ka = eg$$
$$kb = fg + 1$$
$$kc = e$$
$$kd = f$$

with four unknowns e, f, g, and k. Solving this system, either by hand or calculator, you get

$$e = -\frac{c^2}{\Delta}$$
$$f = -\frac{cd}{\Delta}$$
$$g = \frac{a}{c}$$
$$k = -\frac{c}{\Delta}$$

where $\Delta = \det A = ad - bc$.

For You to Do

Consider the following matrices.

$$M = \begin{pmatrix} 2 & 1 \\ 7 & -10 \end{pmatrix}$$
$$N = \begin{pmatrix} -1 & 5 \\ 2 & -1 \end{pmatrix}$$
$$P = \begin{pmatrix} 4 & -1 \\ 3 & -2 \end{pmatrix}$$
$$Q = \begin{pmatrix} 4 & -1 \\ 3 & 2 \end{pmatrix}$$

13. Find the determinant of each matrix.

14. Consider the functions $\mathcal{R}_M$, $\mathcal{R}_N$, $\mathcal{R}_P$, and $\mathcal{R}_Q$. You have seen how to obtain the graphs of these functions by transforming the graph of $y = \frac{1}{x}$. Which of these transformations involve a reflection? Why? Explain your answer.

Have you seen these graphs before?

Answers

For You to Do

13. $\det M = -27$; $\det N = -9$; $\det P = -5$; $\det Q = 11$

14. $\mathcal{R}_Q$; the value of e is negative.

Exercises

1. a. $x = -\frac{7}{2}$; $y = \frac{3}{2}$

b. $x = -\frac{5}{3}$; $y = \frac{5}{7}$

c.

2. a.

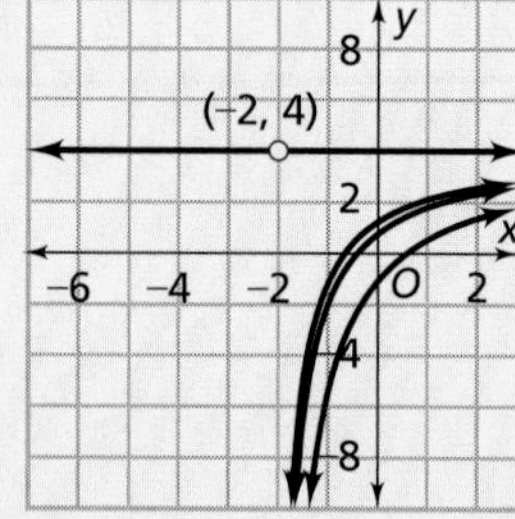

b. $D = 8$

c. $\lim_{x \to \infty} b(x) = 4$

Exercises *Practicing Habits of Mind*

Check Your Understanding

1. Let $a(x) = \frac{3x + 5}{2x + 7}$.
   a. Find the equations of the vertical and horizontal asymptotes of the graph of a.
   b. Find all intercepts of the graph of a.
   c. Use the information about asymptotes and intercepts to sketch the graph of a.

Check your sketch using a graphing calculator.

2. Let $b(x) = \frac{4x + D}{x + 2}$.
   a. Sketch the graph of b for several choices of D.
   b. What value of D produces a hole in the graph of b?
   c. Calculate $\lim_{x\to\infty} b(x)$.
3. Let $c(x) = \frac{Ax + B}{Cx + D}$, with $C \neq 0$.
   a. In terms of A, B, C, and D, describe when the graph of c will have a vertical asymptote and when it will have a hole.
   b. Calculate $\lim_{x\to\infty} c(x)$ and explain its meaning in terms of the graph of c.

Habits of Mind

Look for relationships. You might try some specific cases first, then work your way up to a general fact.

4. **Write About It** Make your own linear fractional transformation function graph gallery. That is, assemble a gallery of graphs of functions of the form $f(x) = \mathcal{R}_A(x)$ for various matrices A.
   - Sketch or generate 10 particularly interesting graphs. Try to include every possible behavior.
   - Give the rational function for each graph.
   - Describe what you find interesting about each graph.
5. Suppose
$$A = \begin{pmatrix} 3 & 5 \\ 10 & 3 \end{pmatrix} \text{ and } B = \begin{pmatrix} 1 & 3 \\ 4 & -2 \end{pmatrix}$$
   a. Sketch the graphs of $y = \mathcal{R}_A(x)$ and $y = \mathcal{R}_B(x)$.
   b. Find a matrix C so that $\mathcal{R}_A \circ \mathcal{R}_C = \mathcal{R}_B$.
   c. Find a matrix D so that $\mathcal{R}_D \circ \mathcal{R}_A = \mathcal{R}_B$.

Exercises

HOMEWORK
- Core: 8, 9, 11, 12, 15
- Optional: 10, 13, 16, 17
- Extension: 14

You can make copies of Blackline Masters MC7 and MC8 for students to sketch graphs of functions.

Check Your Understanding

EXERCISE 2 Students should realize that this graph has a hole when the numerator is a multiple of the denominator. The various graphs do not help them make this determination—instead they need to think about the definition of a removable discontinuity. This same realization is important for Exercise 3.

EXERCISE 3 In this exercise, students should assume that $C \neq 0$, because otherwise, this is a linear function.

EXERCISE 4 Give examples of every possible behavior, including affine transformations, different sign limits at infinity, and so on. You cannot find 10 different behaviors. That is the point—except for lines, they are "all the same."

3. a. The graph has a vertical asymptote $x = -\frac{D}{C}$ if $AD \neq BC$; it has a hole if $AD = BC$.

b. $\lim_{x\to\infty} c(x) =$

$$\lim_{x\to\infty}\left(\frac{A}{C} + \frac{B - \frac{AD}{C}}{Cx + D}\right) = \frac{A}{C};$$

the graph has a horizontal asymptote: $y = \frac{A}{C}$.

4. Answers may vary. Samples:

$A = \begin{pmatrix} 0 & 1 \\ 1 & 0 \end{pmatrix}$; $A = \begin{pmatrix} 0 & -1 \\ 1 & 0 \end{pmatrix}$;
$A = \begin{pmatrix} 0 & 1 \\ 1 & -2 \end{pmatrix}$; $A = \begin{pmatrix} 1 & 0 \\ 1 & -2 \end{pmatrix}$;
$A = \begin{pmatrix} 1 & -1 \\ 1 & 3 \end{pmatrix}$; $A = \begin{pmatrix} 2 & 1 \\ 1 & 3 \end{pmatrix}$;
$A = \begin{pmatrix} 2 & 1 \\ 3 & -1 \end{pmatrix}$

5. a.

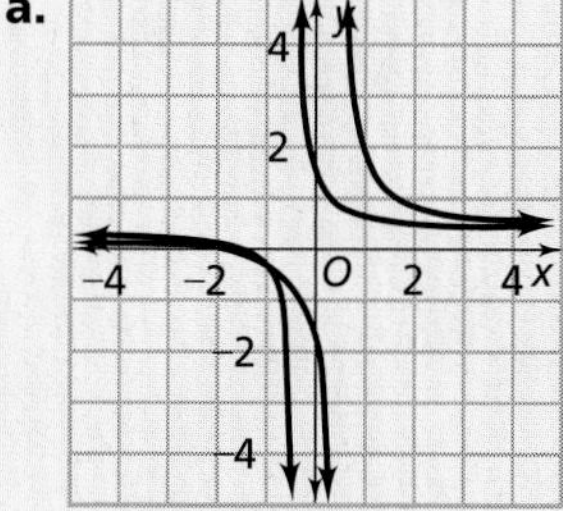

b. $C = \begin{pmatrix} \frac{17}{41} & -\frac{19}{41} \\ -\frac{2}{41} & \frac{36}{41} \end{pmatrix}$

c. $D = \begin{pmatrix} \frac{21}{41} & -\frac{4}{41} \\ -\frac{32}{41} & \frac{26}{41} \end{pmatrix}$

EXERCISE 6 In this exercise, students become confident that every graph of the form $\frac{ax+b}{cx+d}$ where $c \neq 0$ is a transformation of the graph of $y = \frac{1}{x}$.

On Your Own

EXERCISE 8 To find the requested matrices in parts (b) and (c), students solve a matrix equation. To do this, they need to find the inverse of matrix A and multiply both sides of their matrix equation by it, on the appropriate side.

ERROR PREVENTION Depending on your students' memory of linear algebra, you may need to remind them that matrix multiplication is not commutative and that left multiplication and right multiplication have different results in general.

EXERCISE 10 ties into later exercises, starting with Exercise 12. Remind students of the rule for the sum of an infinite geometric series, $\frac{1}{1-r} = 1 + r + r^2 + \cdots$. The later exercises look at plotting successive polynomials on the right side against the rational function on the left, and the polynomials become increasingly accurate on $-1 < x < 1$.

EXERCISE 11 This graph is a nice counterexample for many assumptions students may begin to make about rational functions in general after concentrating heavily on functions of the form $\frac{ax+b}{cx+d}$, and puts them back into the mode of thinking about general rational functions.

6. Suppose

$$A = \begin{pmatrix} 3 & 5 \\ 10 & 3 \end{pmatrix} \text{ and } B = \begin{pmatrix} 0 & 1 \\ 1 & 0 \end{pmatrix}$$

a. Sketch the graphs of $y = \mathcal{R}_A(x)$ and $y = \mathcal{R}_B(x)$.

b. Find a translation T_g and an affine transformation $\mathcal{A}_{(e,f)}$ such that

$$\mathcal{R}_A = T_g \circ \mathcal{R}_B \circ \mathcal{A}_{(e,f)}$$

c. Explain in words how to transform the graph of $y = \mathcal{R}_B(x)$ into the graph of $y = \mathcal{R}_A(x)$.

Habits of Mind

Recall what you know. The graph of $y = \mathcal{R}_B(x)$ is very familiar to you.

7. Let

$$A = \begin{pmatrix} a & b \\ c & d \end{pmatrix}$$

Find conditions on a, b, c, and d so that $\mathcal{R}_A$ will have a fixed point. In other words, find a real number x such that $\mathcal{R}_A(x) = x$.

On Your Own

8. Suppose

$$A = \begin{pmatrix} 2 & 5 \\ 3 & 7 \end{pmatrix} \text{ and } B = \begin{pmatrix} 2 & -3 \\ 4 & -2 \end{pmatrix}$$

a. Sketch the graphs of $y = \mathcal{R}_A(x)$ and $y = \mathcal{R}_B(x)$.

b. Find a matrix C such that $\mathcal{R}_A \circ \mathcal{R}_C = \mathcal{R}_B$.

c. Find a matrix D such that $\mathcal{R}_D \circ \mathcal{R}_A = \mathcal{R}_B$.

9. Suppose

$$A = \begin{pmatrix} 2 & 5 \\ 3 & 7 \end{pmatrix} \text{ and } B = \begin{pmatrix} 0 & 1 \\ 1 & 0 \end{pmatrix}$$

a. Sketch the graphs of $y = \mathcal{R}_A(x)$ and $y = \mathcal{R}_B(x)$.

b. Find a translation T_g and an affine transformation $\mathcal{A}_{(e,f)}$ so that

$$\mathcal{R}_A = T_g \circ \mathcal{R}_B \circ \mathcal{A}_{(e,f)}$$

c. Explain in words how to transform the graph of $y = \mathcal{R}_B(x)$ into the graph of $y = \mathcal{R}_A(x)$.

10. Find the value of

$$1 + \frac{1}{3} + \frac{1}{9} + \frac{1}{27} + \cdots = \sum_{k=0}^{\infty} \frac{1}{3^k}$$

11. Why does the graph of $f(x) = \frac{1}{x^2+1}$ not have any vertical asymptotes?

Answers

6. a.

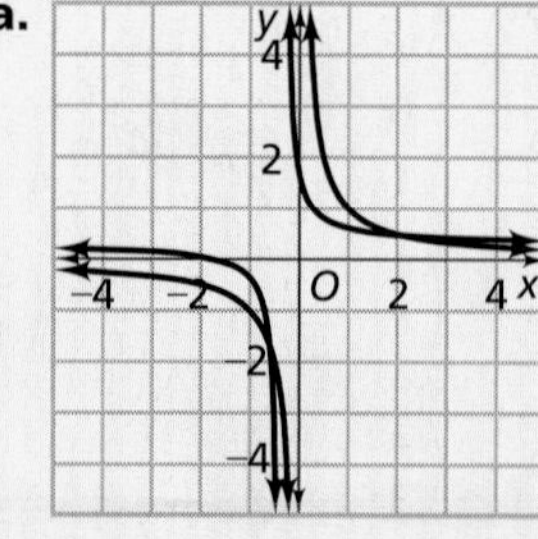

b. $T_g = T_{\frac{3}{10}}$ and $\mathcal{A}_{(e,f)} = \mathcal{A}_{\left(\frac{100}{41}, \frac{30}{41}\right)}$

c. Scale horizontally by a factor of $\frac{41}{100}$, then translate $\frac{3}{10}$ units left and $\frac{3}{10}$ units up.

7. There will be a fixed point if $(d - a)^2 + 4bc \geq 0$.

8–9. See back of book.

10. $\frac{3}{2}$

11. See back of book.

12. Sketch the graph of this function.

$$f(x) = \frac{1}{1-x}$$

13. a. Sketch the graph of $f(x) = \frac{1}{1-x}$ and $g(x) = 1 + x$ on the same axes. In your graph, let $-2 \le x \le 2$, and $0 \le y \le 5$.
    b. Make a table of the outputs of f and g for the inputs $x = 0.1, 0.2, 0.5, 0.8$.
    c. Sketch the graph of f and $h(x) = 1 + x + x^2$ on the same axes.
    d. Make a table of the outputs of f and h for the inputs $x = 0.1, 0.2, 0.5, 0.8$.
    e. Sketch the graph of f and $j(x) = 1 + x + x^2 + x^3 + x^4 + x^5$ on the same axes.
    f. Make a table of the outputs of f and j for the inputs $x = 0.1, 0.2, 0.5, 0.8, 1.1$.

14. **Take It Further** Consider the function $f(x) = x + \frac{A}{x}$, with $A > 0$.
    a. In terms of A, what value of x generates the least possible output $f(x)$?
    b. Prove your result from part (a).

15. **Standardized Test Prep** Consider the linear fractional transformation $\mathcal{R}_A(x)$ associated with the matrix $A = \begin{pmatrix} -2 & 3 \\ 1 & 1 \end{pmatrix}$. Which of these is an asymptote of the graph of the rational function?

    A. $x = -\frac{1}{2}$ B. $x = -\frac{2}{3}$ C. $x = -\frac{1}{3}$ D. $x = -1$

Maintain Your Skills

16. For each matrix A, write $\mathcal{R}_A(x) - \mathcal{R}_A(r)$ in the form

$$(x - r)Q(x)$$

where $Q(x)$ is a rational expression in x and r.

a. $A = \begin{pmatrix} 2 & 5 \\ 3 & 7 \end{pmatrix}$ b. $A = \begin{pmatrix} -2 & 5 \\ 5 & 7 \end{pmatrix}$

c. $A = \begin{pmatrix} -\pi & 5 \\ 5 & 7 \end{pmatrix}$ d. $A = \begin{pmatrix} a & b \\ c & d \end{pmatrix}$

17. Calculate each sum.

a. $\sum_{k=0}^{5} 2^k = 2^0 + 2^1 + 2^2 + 2^3 + 2^4 + 2^5$ b. $\sum_{k=0}^{5} 3^k$

c. $\sum_{k=0}^{5} \left(\frac{1}{2}\right)^k$ d. $\sum_{k=0}^{\infty} \left(\frac{1}{2}\right)^k$

e. $\sum_{k=0}^{5} \left(\frac{1}{4}\right)^k$ f. $\sum_{k=0}^{\infty} \left(\frac{1}{4}\right)^k$

Go Online PHSchool.com

For additional practice, go to Web Code: bga-0309

$Q(x)$ will be in terms of a, b, c, and d.

12–14. See back of book

15. D

16. a. $(x - r)\left(\frac{-1}{(3x + 7)(3r + 7)}\right)$

b. $(x - r)\left(\frac{-39}{(5x + 7)(5r + 7)}\right)$

c. $(x - r)\left(\frac{-7\pi - 25}{(5x + 7)(5r + 7)}\right)$

d. $(x - r)\left(\frac{ad - bc}{(cx + d)(cr + d)}\right)$

17. a. 63 **b.** 364

c. $\frac{63}{32}$ **d.** 2

e. $\frac{1365}{1024}$ **f.** $\frac{4}{3}$

EXERCISE 13 The functions that students are graphing are the Taylor series expansions for f around 0, so that as the degree of the expansion increases, the Taylor series approximates the function f more and more closely near 0. Notice that this is the sum of the geometric series with ratio x and first term 1.

Maintain Your Skills

EXERCISE 17 Note that students with a CAS can evaluate these directly, so consider asking students to show and explain their work. The intent here is to remind students of the identity

$$1 + r + r^2 + \cdots + r^{n-1} = \frac{1 - r^n}{1 - r}$$

with the special case that if $|r| < 1$ the infinite sum is $\frac{1}{1 - r}$.

Additional Resources

PRINT RESOURCES
- Solution Manual
- Practice Workbook
- Assessment Resources
- Teaching Resources

TECHNOLOGY
- Interactive Textbook
- TeacherExpress CD-ROM
- ExamView CD-ROM
- PHSchool.com

Additional Practice

1. Find A and B so that

$$\frac{23x - 89}{x^2 - 8x + 15} = \frac{A}{x - 3} + \frac{B}{x - 5}$$

2. Let $f(x) = \frac{A}{x - 3}$ and $g(x) = \frac{B}{x - 5}$ where A and B are the values you found in Exercise 1.
   a. Graph f. Find the slope of the line tangent to f at $x = 1$.
   b. Graph g. Find the slope of the line tangent to g at $x = 1$.
   c. Graph $h(x) = \frac{23x - 89}{x^2 - 8x + 15}$. Find the slope of the line tangent to h at $x = 1$.

3. Consider the function $h(x) = \frac{2}{x^2 + 3}$.
   a. Find the slope of the tangent to h at $x = 1$.
   b. Find the slope of the tangent to h at $x = -1$.
   c. How are the answers in (a) and (b) related? Explain.

4. Suppose

$$A = \begin{pmatrix} 2 & 1 \\ -5 & -3 \end{pmatrix} \text{ and } B = \begin{pmatrix} -4 & 3 \\ 2 & -1 \end{pmatrix}$$

   a. Sketch the graphs of $y = \mathcal{R}_A(x)$ and $y = \mathcal{R}_B(x)$.
   b. Find a matrix C such that $\mathcal{R}_A \circ \mathcal{R}_C = \mathcal{R}_B$.
   c. Find a matrix D such that $\mathcal{R}_D \circ \mathcal{R}_A = \mathcal{R}_B$.

5. Suppose

$$A = \begin{pmatrix} 2 & 4 \\ 1 & 3 \end{pmatrix} \text{ and } B = \begin{pmatrix} 0 & 1 \\ 1 & 0 \end{pmatrix}$$

   a. Sketch the graphs of $y = \mathcal{R}_A(x)$ and $y = \mathcal{R}_B(x)$.
   b. Find a translation T_g and an affine transformation $\mathcal{A}_{(e,f)}$ so that $\mathcal{R}_A = T_g \circ \mathcal{R}_B \circ \mathcal{A}_{(e,f)}$.
   c. Explain in words how to transform the graph of $y = \mathcal{R}_B(x)$ into the graph of $y = \mathcal{R}_A(x)$.

Practice: For Lesson 3.9, assign Exercises 4–5.

Mathematical Reflections

EXERCISES 6–8 At the start of the investigation, you may have assigned these as Questions 1–3 for students to think and write about.

In this investigation, you learned about removable continuities and infinite discontinuities. You learned the effects of these discontinuities on graphs of functions. You graphed rational functions using their horizontal and vertical asymptotes. You also found equations of lines tangent to these graphs. The following questions will help you summarize what you have learned.

1. **a.** Give an example of a rational function the graph of which has a hole at $x = 3$. Sketch its graph.
   b. Give an example of a rational function the graph of which has a vertical asymptote at $x = 3$. Sketch its graph.
2. **a.** Give an example of a rational function the graph of which has a horizontal asymptote at $y = 0$. Sketch its graph.
   b. Give an example of a rational function the graph of which has a horizontal asymptote at $y = 2$. Sketch its graph.
3. Let $f(x) = \frac{3x^2 + 10x + 8}{x - 3}$.
   a. Find all x- and y-intercepts of the graph of f.
   b. Find all asymptotes of the graph of f.
   c. Sketch the graph of f.
4. Find an equation for the tangent to the graph of $g(x) = \frac{4x + 1}{x - 3}$ at $(0, g(0))$.
5. Let $h(x) = \frac{x - 1}{x}$.
   a. Find an equation for the tangent to the graph of h at $(a, h(a))$ for $a \neq 0$.
   b. Use your answer to part (a) to find all values of x where the function h is increasing. Explain your answer.
6. What happens to $f(x) = \frac{3x^2 + 2x - 1}{5x^2 - 3x + 10}$ as x gets larger and larger?
7. Why do the graphs of $g(x) = \frac{x^2 - 15}{x - 4}$ and $h(x) = \frac{x^2 - 16}{x - 4}$ look so different from each other?
8. How can you find tangent lines to rational functions?

Vocabulary and Notation

In this investigation, you learned these terms. Make sure you understand what each one means and how to use it.

- **determinant**
- **hole**
- **infinite discontinuity**
- **linear fractional transformation, $\mathcal{R}_A$**
- **removable discontinuity**
- **structure-preserving map**

Answers

Mathematical Reflections

1–2. See back of book.

3. a. The x-intercepts are $\left(-\frac{4}{3}, 0\right)$ and $(-2, 0)$. The y-intercept is $\left(0, -\frac{8}{3}\right)$.

b. This graph has a vertical asymptote at $x = 3$ and a non-horizontal asymptote at $y = 3x + 19$.

c. See back of book.

4. $y = -\frac{13}{9}x - \frac{1}{3}$

5. a. $y = \frac{1}{a^2}(x - a) + \frac{a - 1}{a}$

b. The slope of the tangent to the curve at the point $(a, h(a))$ is $\frac{1}{a^2}$ with $a \neq 0$. Since this slope is always positive, this function is always increasing where its value is defined.

6. $f(x)$ approaches $\frac{3}{5}$.

7. The graph of $h(x) = \frac{x^2 - 16}{x - 4}$ is the graph of the line $y = x + 4$ with a hole at $(4, 8)$. Its discontinuity at $x = 4$ is a removable discontinuity. The graph of $g(x) = \frac{x^2 - 15}{x - 4}$, on the other hand, has a vertical asymptote at $x = 4$.

8. You can use the method of undetermined coefficients, just as you did for polynomial functions. Start with $f(x) = m + n(x - a) + p(x)(x - a)^2$. Substitute $x = a$ to get $m = f(a)$. Then subtract $f(a)$ from both sides of the equation and simplify the left side. You will find it has a factor of $x - a$, as does the right side. Factor that out, and substitute $x = a$ into the resulting expression to find m. You are essentially finding the limit as x approaches a of $\frac{f(x) - f(a)}{x - a} = m$. Then $y = m(x - a) + n$ is an equation for the tangent.

Mid-Chapter Test

For a mid-chapter test, go to Web Code: bga-0352

Multiple Choice

1. Which of the following is not true of the graph of $f(x) = 2x^3 - 6x^2 - 12x + 16$?
   A. From left to right, the graph rises, falls, and rises.
   B. The graph crosses the positive x-axis at 1 and 4.
   C. The graph crosses the negative x-axis twice.
   D. The graph crosses the y-axis at (0, 16).

2. Which of the following functions is continuous?
   A. Number of children enrolled in a particular school as a function of time
   B. Outdoor temperature as a function of time
   C. Cost of postage as a function of the weight of the letter
   D. Average number of soft drinks sold at a ballpark as a function of outdoor temperature

3. Calculate the average rate of change of $h(x) = x^3 - 9x$ with respect to x as x goes from 2 to 4.
   A. -19 **B.** $\frac{19}{3}$ **C.** 9 **D.** 19

4. Find the remainder when you divide $2x^4 - 7x^3 - 8x^2 + 14x + 8$ by x^3.
   A. $2x^4 - 7 - 8x^2 + 14x + 8$
   B. $2x - 7$
   C. $2x - 7 - \frac{8}{x} + \frac{14}{x^2} + \frac{8}{x^3}$
   D. $-8x^2 + 14x + 8$

5. Which function has tangent line $y = 2x - 1$ at (1, 1)?
   A. $a(x) = x$ **B.** $b(x) = x^2$
   C. $c(x) = x^3$ **D.** $d(x) = x^4$

Open Response

6. Suppose that $f(x) = -(x - 3)(x + 2)(x + 5)$.
   a. Where does the graph cross the x-axis?
   b. Find $f(0)$.
   c. Sketch the graph of f.

7. Consider $g(x) = x^3 - 13x - 12 = (x - 4)(x + 1)(x + 3)$. Give estimates for each of these values.
   a. $g(4)$ **b.** $g(4.001)$ **c.** $g(0)$
   d. $g(0.001)$ **e.** $g(1000)$

8. A water balloon dropped from a window will fall a distance of $s = 16t^2$ feet during the first t seconds. Find the average velocity of the balloon during the first 4 seconds of falling.

9. Expand $f(x) = x^3 - 14x^2 + 55x - 42$ in powers of $x - 4$.

10. Copy and complete this table for $f(x) = x^2 - 2x + 5$.

x	$f(x)$	Slope of the tangent at $(x, f(x))$
-1	■	■
0	■	■
1	■	■
2	■	■
3	■	■
4	■	■
10	■	■
100	■	■

Mid-Chapter Test

Assessment Resources

Mid-Chapter Test page 1 of 2

Multiple Choice

1. Which of the following conditions is not true of the graph of $f(x) = 2x^3 + 6x^2 - 26x - 30$?
   A. From left to right, the graph rises, falls, and rises.
   B. The graph crosses the positive x-axis at 1 and 3.
   C. The graph crosses the negative x-axis twice.
   D. The graph crosses the y-axis at (0, −30).

2. Which of the following functions is continuous?
   A. Height of a growing tree as a function of time
   B. A town's population as a function of time
   C. Number of mile markers passed as a function of distance
   D. Number of items that can be purchased, as a function of cash on hand

3. Calculate the average rate of change of $f(x) = 2x^3 - 5x$ with respect to x as x goes from −3 to 2.
   A. 6 **B.** 45 **C.** −39 **D.** 9

4. Find the remainder when you divide $x^4 - 3x^3 + 5x - 1$ by x^2.
   A. $x^3 - 3x$
   B. $x^3 - 3x + 5x - 1$
   C. $5x - 1$
   D. $\frac{5}{x} - \frac{1}{x^2}$

5. Which function has tangent line $y = 3x + 2$ at (−1, −1)?
   A. $f(x) = x$
   B. $f(x) = -x^2$
   C. $f(x) = x^3$
   D. $f(x) = -x^4$

Open Response

6. Suppose that $f(x) = -(x - 4)(x + 1)(x + 7)$.
   A. Where does the graph cross the x-axis?
   B. Find $f(0)$.
   C. Graph $f(x)$.

Also available: Form B

Mid-Chapter Test

1. C
2. B
3. D
4. D
5. B
6. **a.** (−5, 0), (−2, 0), (3, 0)
   b. 30
   c.

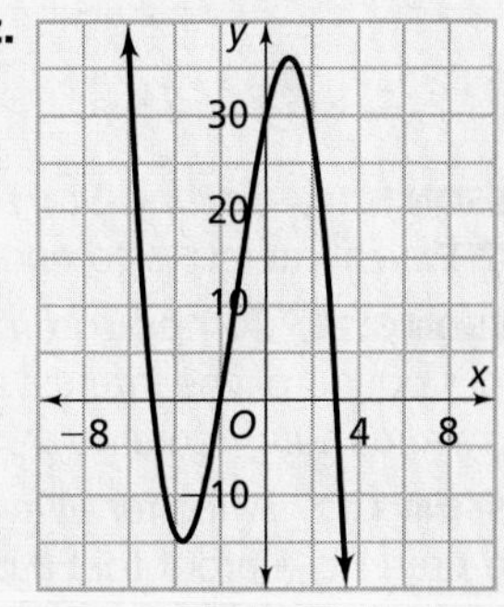

7. **a.** 0 **b.** 0 **c.** −12
   d. −12 **e.** 1,000,000,000
8. 64 feet per second
9. $f(x) = (x - 4)^3 - 2(x - 4)^2 - 9(x - 4) + 18$
10.

x	$f(x)$	Slope of the tangent at $(x, f(x))$
−1	8	−4
0	5	−2
1	4	0
2	5	2
3	8	4
4	13	6
10	85	18
100	9805	198

Investigation Overview

In this investigation, students analyze the graphs of exponential and logarithm functions in the same way that they analyzed the graphs of polynomial and rational functions. They find an equation of the tangent to the graphs of exponential and logarithm functions for different bases, and realize that there is some base for which the slope of the tangent to the graph is equal to 1 at $x = 0$. Students learn that this special base is e. They also develop an understanding of e by working with interest compounded more and more often until, at the limit, it is compounded continuously. They investigate the ln button on their calculators and see that this function is the inverse of e^x. They use this relationship to solve equations involving e and ln. Students then find the slopes of the tangent to the graphs of $y = e^x$ and $y = \ln x$ to further understand these two functions.

You may wish to assign Questions 1–3 for students to think and write about during the investigation.

Learning Goals

- State and use the limit definitions of e and e^x.
- State and use the factorial definitions of e and e^x.
- Use the inverse relationship between e^x and ln x to solve equations.
- Find an equation for the tangent to the graph of $y = e^x$ or $y = \ln x$ at a point.

Habits and Skills

- Develop a definition of continuously compounded interest.
- Visualize relationships between the graphs of $f(x) = e^x$ and $g(x) = \ln x$ and the slopes of the tangents to these graphs.
- Use functional equations to recognize the ln function as a logarithm.

Exponential and Logarithmic Functions

In earlier math courses you learned to use the constant π. In *Exponential and Logarithmic Functions*, you will learn about another important constant, *e*. You will see how it naturally appears in a variety of settings.

By the end of this investigation, you will be able to answer questions like these.

1. What happens when interest is compounded more and more frequently?
2. What are some reasons to introduce the number e?
3. How can you relate any exponential or logarithmic function to $f(x) = e^x$ and $g(x) = \ln x$?

You will learn how to

- state and use the limit and factorial definitions of e and e^x
- use the inverse relationship between e^x and $\ln x$ to solve equations
- find an equation for the line tangent to the graph of $y = e^x$ or $y = \ln x$ at a point

You will develop these habits and skills:

- Develop a definition of continuously compounded interest.
- Visualize relationships between the graphs of $f(x) = e^x$ and $g(x) = \ln x$ and the slopes of the tangents to these graphs.
- Use functional equations to recognize the ln function as a logarithm.

The same street in Shanghai, before and after several decades of essentially exponential growth.

Investigation Road Map

LESSON 3.10, *Getting Started,* explores the relationship between the frequency with which interest is compounded and the yearly yield for an account.

LESSON 3.11, *Compound Interest; the Number e,* formally defines e as the upper bound of the interest earned on an account as the interest is compounded more and more frequently.

LESSON 3.12, *Another Way to Find e,* gives students a factorial definition for e and presents a proof that e is irrational.

LESSON 3.13, *The Natural Logarithm Function,* has students conclude that the base of the ln function is e and that ln x and e^x are inverse functions.

LESSON 3.14, *Analysis of $f(x) = e^x$ and $g(x) = \ln x$,* asks students to find and analyze equations for tangent lines to the functions e^x and ln x at a point.

3.10 Getting Started

A bank could compound interest every year, half year, quarter year, month, week, day, hour, or second, or over even smaller intervals. The limiting action is to compound interest continuously. For each compounding plan, a wise consumer should know how the interest grows.

For You to Explore

1. A representative of Seventh Fifth Bank offered Danielle an incredible investment, a 100% APR savings account, but only for one year. Danielle went for the offer right away, giving them all the money she had, $100.

   As she left the bank, Danielle realized she forgot to ask how often the interest was compounded. Determine, to the nearest penny, how much money Danielle will have after a year if interest is compounded on each of the following schedules.

   a. annually (once per year)
   b. semi-annually (twice per year)
   c. quarterly (four times per year)
   d. monthly (12 times per year)

As much as Danielle would like to get 100% interest every time the bank calculates it, the interest is broken up over the year. With semi-annual compounding, Danielle would earn 50% each period. With quarterly compounding, she earns 25% per quarter.

2. Danielle, still thinking about her incredible offer, says, "Maybe they'll compound every day, or every minute, or every second! Then I'll really be raking it in."

   a. Is this true? How much money could Danielle have after a year if interest were compounded more frequently?
   b. If interest is compounded n times during the year, write a formula for the amount of money Danielle will have at the end of the year (in terms of n).

3. Sketch the graph of $f(x) = 2^x$.

   a. Draw a secant line connecting $(0, f(0))$ and $(2, f(2))$. Calculate its slope.
   b. Draw a secant line connecting $(0, f(0))$ and $(0.5, f(0.5))$. Calculate its slope to two decimal places.
   c. Give a good estimate for the slope of the tangent line to the graph of f at $x = 0$.

Check your results. Set up a sketch using your geometry software, similar to the sketch described in the first For You to Do section in Lesson 3.5.

4. Sketch the graph of $g(x) = 4^x$.

   a. Draw a secant line connecting $(0, g(0))$ and $(0.25, g(0.25))$. Calculate its slope to two decimal places.
   b. Give a good estimate for the slope of the tangent line to the graph of g at $x = 0$.

Answers

For You to Explore

1. a. $200 b. $225
   c. $244.14 d. $261.30
2. a. no; $271.83.
   b. $a(n) = 100\left(1 + \frac{1}{n}\right)^n$
3. a–b. See back of book.
   c. Since the slope is positive and less than 0.828, a good estimate might be 0.7.
4. a.

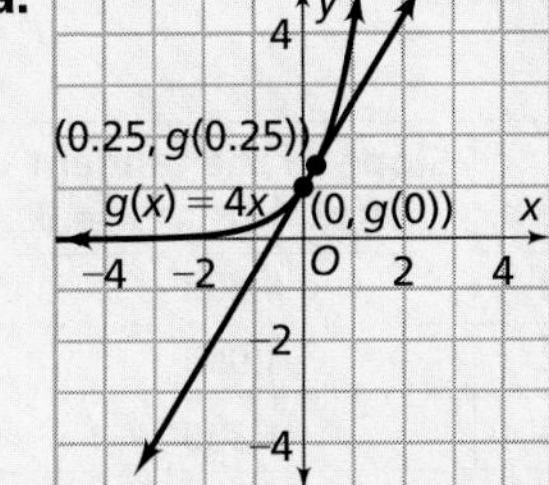

The slope of the secant is $\frac{1.4142 - 1}{0.25} \approx 1.66$.

   b. Since the slope is positive and a little less than 1.66, a good estimate might be 1.5.

Lesson Overview

GOAL

- Warm up to the ideas of the investigation.

Some of the problems in this lesson look at how the yield of a savings account with compound interest varies with the number of times the interest is compounded over the course of a year. In the next lesson, students see that there is a limit to the yield of such an account, when interest is compounded continuously, leading to a definition of the mathematical constant e. Other problems ask students to find equations for the tangent to exponential and logarithm graphs, which they have not done previously. As the investigation continues, introducing the functions e^x and $\ln x$, students find equations for the tangents to these graphs as well. As always in a Getting Started lesson, do not worry about formalizing the concepts today. Just let the students explore and get a preview for what is coming up in future lessons.

FOR YOU TO EXPLORE
- Core: 1, 2, 3, 4, 5, 6
- Optional: none

MATERIALS
- graph paper
- graphing calculators
- Blackline Masters MC7, 3.10

HOMEWORK
- Core: 7, 8, 9, 10
- Optional: 11, 12

Launch

Have the students jump right in to the For You to Explore problems. Problems 1 and 2 preview the compound interest work in Lesson 3.11. You might discuss how to calculate interest to give students a foothold. Problems 3 through 6 ask students to find equations for tangent lines to the graphs of exponential curves. Students do not have a formal method for finding the slope of one of these graphs, but encourage them to visualize the process where one point of a secant line approaches a fixed point, with the tangent line as the limit of that process. The students' goal is to find a way to get an accurate estimate of the equation of the tangent line by using their calculators.

Explore

As students are working, make sure that they are able to come up with equations to compute the interest in Problems 1 and 2. As they continue with the rest of the problems, evaluate their memory of exponential functions as well as their understanding of the process of finding the slope of a tangent to the graph of a function at a point.

For You to Explore, p. 239

You may wish to use Blackline Master MC7 on an overhead to sketch graphs of functions.

PROBLEM 1 In this first problem, students notice that as the interest is compounded more and more frequently, Danielle receives more and more money. They may also notice that the relationship is not linear. You do not earn 12 times as much interest if you compound 12 times as often. In Problem 2, students look at really frequent compounding and see that there is a limit to how much interest Danielle earns.

PROBLEM 2 Some students may decide to solve part (b) of this problem before they finish Problem 1. This function is closely related to the function that students analyzed in CME Project *Algebra 2* for computing the balance on a loan, but since this is interest that Danielle earns rather than a loan she is paying out, it is a little different.

PROBLEM 3 There are several ways to tackle this problem. Students may develop a function such as $m(x) = \frac{2^x - 1}{x}$, and plug in numbers very close to zero to estimate the slope of the tangent to this graph at $x = 0$. (You can get a really good estimate this way. The slope is approximately 69314718056...)

Some students may try to use the method of undetermined coefficients, but will get stuck. The method starts out fine. If $s^x = m + nx + p(x)x^2$, then at $x = 0, m = 1$. But then there is no way to factor an x out of $2^x - 1$, so the method fails.

Some students may try taylor(2^x, x, 2, 0) as they did for polynomials and rational functions. They get an answer, but the coefficients are just mysterious numbers. These numbers are demystified later in the investigation.

PROBLEM 4 Some, but not all, students notice the connection that the slopes for $g(x)$ are twice as large as those of $f(x)$. This is due to the fact that $4^x = (2^2)^x = 2^{2x}$ so the graph of g is a horizontal axis dilation of the graph of f by a factor of $\frac{1}{2}$. One goal of the investigation is for students to see that any function of the form $f(x) = b^x$ with $b > 1$ is a horizontal axis dilation of any other function of the same form.

PROBLEM 5 Students do not have a formal way to calculate these limits, so they can simply calculate the slope of a secant line using a point very close to the fixed point at (0, 1) to approximate the slope of the tangent.

You may want to use Blackline Master 3.10 on an overhead and fill in the entries as students find each slope.

5. Copy and complete this table giving the approximate slope of the tangent line at $x = 0$ for each function in the form $f(x) = b^x$.

Base b	Slope of tangent to $f(x) = b^x$ at $x = 0$
2	■
3	■
4	■
5	1.609
8	■
10	■

6. By continuity, there must be some base b where the slope of the tangent line to the graph of $f(x) = b^x$ at $x = 0$ is exactly 1.

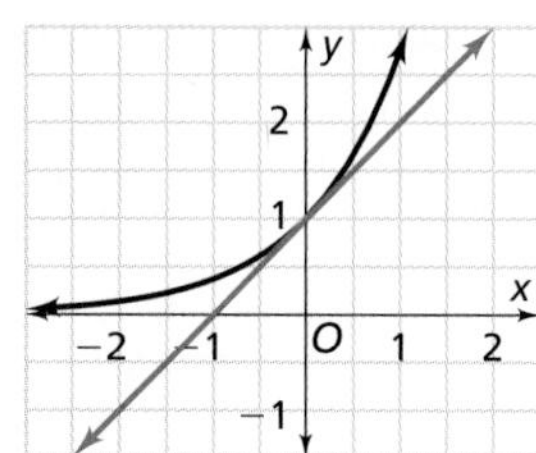

Give a good estimate for this base b.

Exercises *Practicing Habits of Mind*

On Your Own

7. Sketch the graph of $f(x) = \log_2 x$.

a. Draw a secant line connecting $(1, f(1))$ and $(2, f(2))$. Calculate its slope.

b. Draw a secant line connecting $(1, f(1))$ and $(1.2, f(1.2))$. Calculate its slope to two decimal places.

c. Give a good estimate for the slope of the line tangent to the graph of f at $x = 1$.

Answers

5.

Base b	Slope of the tangent to $f(x) = b^x$ at $x = 0$
2	0.693
3	1.099
4	1.386
5	1.609
8	2.079
10	2.303

6. A good estimate is $b = 2.72$.

Exercises

7. a.

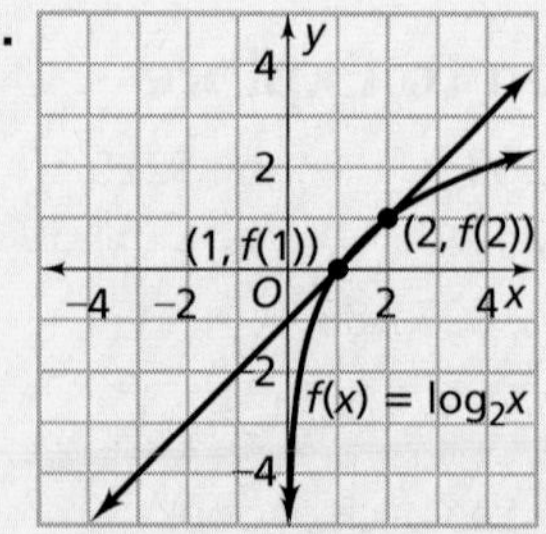

The slope of the secant is 1.

b–c. See back of book.

8. Sketch the graph of $g(x) = \log_4 x$.

a. Draw a secant line connecting $(1, g(1))$ and $(2, g(2))$. Calculate its slope.

b. Give a good estimate for the slope of the line tangent to the graph of g at $x = 1$.

9. Copy and complete this table giving the approximate slope of the tangent line at $x = 1$ for each function in the form $f(x) = \log_b x$.

Base b	Slope of tangent to $f(x) = \log_b x$ at $x = 1$
2	■
3	■
4	■
5	0.621
8	■
10	■

10. By continuity, there must be some base b where the slope of the tangent line to the graph of $f(x) = \log_b x$ at $x = 1$ is exactly 1.

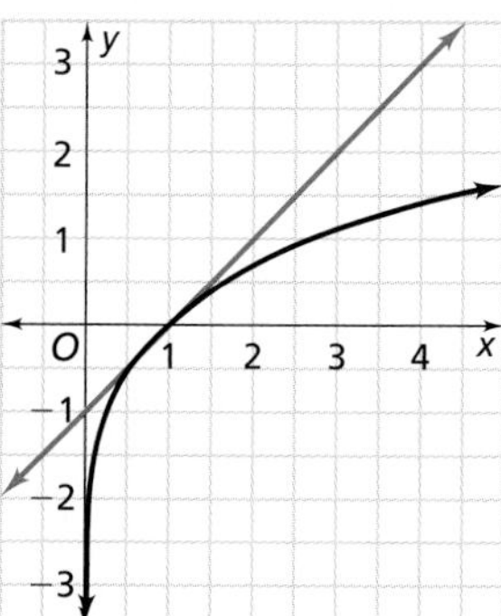

Give a good estimate for this base b.

Maintain Your Skills

11. Use the Binomial Theorem to expand each expression.

a. $\left(1 + \frac{x}{2}\right)^2$ b. $\left(1 + \frac{x}{3}\right)^3$ c. $\left(1 + \frac{x}{4}\right)^4$

12. Let $f(x, n) = \left(1 + \frac{x}{n}\right)^n$ for any real x and positive integer n. Calculate each of the following.

a. $f(1, n)$ for $n = 1, 2, 3, 4, 10, 100, 10000$

b. $f(2, n)$ for $n = 1, 2, 3, 4, 10, 100, 10000$

c. $f(0.05, n)$ for $n = 1, 4, 12, 365, 10000$

8. a.

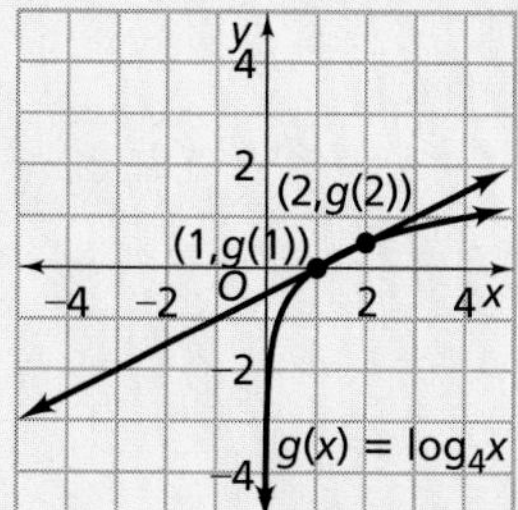

The slope of the secant is 0.5.

b. Since the slope is positive and a little more than 0.5, a good estimate might be 0.7.

9.

Base b	Slope of tangent to $f(x) = \log_b x$ at $x = 1$
2	1.443
3	0.910
4	0.721
5	0.621
8	0.481
10	0.434

10–12. See back of book.

Wrap Up

Depending on your class, you may want to take time to do a brief review of logarithm functions to prepare students for their homework. Some calculators only have the ability to calculate logarithms with base 10 and natural logarithms (base e). If your students are using such calculators, give them this formula to evaluate logarithms with other bases:

$$\log_b x = \frac{\log x}{\log b}$$

You do not have to discuss the derivation of this formula now. Just give it to students as a tool if they happen to have calculators that cannot evaluate logarithms with any base.

You may also want to go over Problems 1 and 2 to prepare students for tomorrow's lesson.

Exercises

HOMEWORK
- Core: 7, 8, 9, 10
- Optional: 11, 12

On Your Own

EXERCISE 7 As with Problems 3 through 6 in the For You to Explore section, students can use different techniques to estimate the slope, but they will get stuck if they use the method of undetermined coefficients. The taylor function gives an answer, and using a point very close to the fixed point also gives an answer. A more accurate estimate is 1.442695.

EXERCISE 8 By using a taylor function or a point much closer to (1, 0), students could get an estimate like 0.7213475.

EXERCISE 9 Many students want to reduce calculations by setting up a function that allows them to vary the base of the logarithm. Enterprising students can even set up an equation for their calculator to solve.

You can make copies of Blackline Master 3.10 for students to write on.

Maintain Your Skills

EXERCISE 12 The actual limit as n approaches infinity of $f(1, n)$ is e, of $f(2, n)$ is e^2, and of $f(0.05, n)$ is $e^{0.05}$, so in general, the limit as n approaches infinity of $f(x, n)$ is e^x. Of course, your students do not know this yet, but if they are able to realize that the limit in part (b) is approximately the square of the limit in part (a), they might check to see that the limit in part (c) is equal to the limit in part (a) raised to the 0.05 power.

Lesson Overview

GOAL

- State and use the limit definitions of e and e^x.

Students look back at Problems 1 and 2 from the Getting Started lesson and synthesize the result—as you increase the number of times your interest is compounded, you end up with more money, but there is an upper bound to how much interest you can earn. This leads to a formal definition of e using limits, and the meaning of continuously compounded interest. In the problems, students continue to examine compound interest for different compounding periods and contrast it with continuous compounding. They also use the limit definition to rewrite expressions involving appropriate limits in terms of e.

CHECK YOUR UNDERSTANDING
- Core: 1, 2, 3, 4, 5, 6
- Optional: 7, 8

MATERIALS
- CAS (recommended)
- graph paper
- graphing calculators
- Blackline Master MC7

HOMEWORK
- Core: 9, 10, 13, 14, 15, 16, 17, 18
- Optional: 11, 12

VOCABULARY
- continuously compounded interest
- e

Launch

Begin today's lesson by looking back at Problems 1 and 2 from the Getting Started lesson. Ask students whether compounding more often results in more money. They should answer that compounding more often is a better deal, but that it seems that there is a limit to how much interest you can actually earn.

3.11 Compound Interest; the Number e

In Problems 1 and 2 from Lesson 3.10, you helped Danielle figure out how much money she would make on her \$100 investment in a savings account with 100% APR, compounded at different intervals. You can write a function that takes the period as the input and outputs the balance at the end of the year.

Let $F(n)$ denote the amount of money Danielle would have after a year if interest were compounded n times during the year. Then

$$F(n) = 100\left(1 + \frac{1}{n}\right)^n$$

You can evaluate $F(n)$ for large values of n, rounded to six decimal places:

$$F(100) = 270.481383$$
$$F(1000) = 271.692393$$
$$F(10^4) = 271.814593$$
$$F(10^5) = 271.826824$$
$$F(10^6) = 271.828047$$
$$F(10^7) = 271.828169$$

It seems that F keeps growing as n grows, which makes sense. After all, the more compounding of the interest there is, the more money Danielle earns. But for large values of n, the rate of growth of F slows down considerably. For example, it seems unlikely that $F(n)$ will ever surpass 300, no matter how large n is.

The key point here is that

$$f(n) = \left(1 + \frac{1}{n}\right)^n$$

Assume $n > 0$.

is an increasing function, but it also has an upper bound. In fact, the graph of f seems to have a horizontal asymptote at $y \approx 2.7183$.

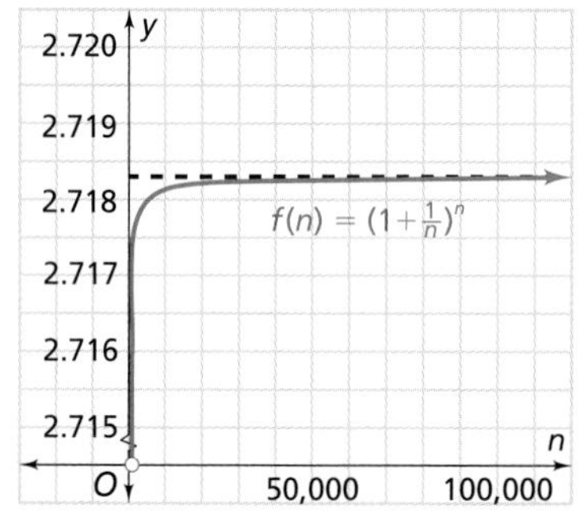

In the context of investing money, the function $f(n)$ only makes sense for positive integers n. But you can certainly evaluate $f(n)$ at all real $n > 0$.

Historically, many people felt (as Danielle did) that more frequent compounding could lead to unbounded interest. But in the late 17th century, mathematician Jacob Bernoulli showed that there was an upper limit on the amount of money that you can earn. His proof introduced a new mathematical constant.

Definition

The number e is, by definition,

$$e = \lim_{n \to \infty}\left(1 + \frac{1}{n}\right)^n$$

The value of *e* is approximately $e \approx 2.71828\ldots$

See the TI-Nspire Handbook on p. 704 for information about how to find *e* on your calculator.

Continuously compounded interest is computed by taking the limit as the frequency of compounding increases. In Danielle's case, this amounts to

$$\begin{aligned}\lim_{n \to \infty} F(n) &= \lim_{n \to \infty} 100\left(1 + \frac{1}{n}\right)^n \\ &= 100 \cdot e \\ &\approx 271.828\end{aligned}$$

So, rounded to the nearest penny, Danielle would have \$271.83 after a year if the interest were compounded continuously.

Example 1

Problem Suppose David invests \$100 at 12% APR. If the interest is compounded quarterly, how much money will he have after five years?

Solution The 12% APR means David earns 3% per quarter. Since there are 20 quarters in five years, you can calculate

$$100(1.03)^{20} \approx 180.61$$

to show that David will have \$180.61 at the end of five years.

$3 = 12 \div 4$
$20 = 4 \cdot 5$

Explore

Example 1

You may want to suggest that students set up a function on their calculators to calculate compound interest under general conditions. A possible function is

$$b(a, r, n, t) = A \cdot \left(1 + \frac{r}{n}\right)^{nt}$$

In this function, *b* is the balance in the account after *t* years, *A* is the initial amount in the account, *r* is the annual interest rate, and *n* is the number of times interest is compounded in a year.

Example 2

TECHNOLOGY TIP If you use the CAS function described for the previous example, you can estimate the yield from continuously compounded interest by substituting a very large number for n, or more directly by using the limit capability in your calculator. Similarly, you can approximate $\lim_{n \to \infty} \left(1 + \frac{1}{n}\right)^n$ by evaluating $b(1, 1, 100000000, 1)$. You get approximately 2.71828181487, which you may recognize as an approximation for e. This is fortunate, because the limit you are computing is the defined value for e.

Another side note also asks students to compare quarterly compounding to continuous compounding. Continuous is better, but not by much.

Wrap Up

To finish today's lesson, have students work on the core Check Your Understanding exercises. If students use the general balance function described above, these exercises are fairly straightforward, but Exercise 6 asks students to apply the definition of e to rewrite some limit expressions. This is a much less familiar task, so you should probably focus on it in your end-of-class discussion. If time allows, you might choose to go over optional Exercises 7 and 8.

Assessment Resources

Lesson Quiz 3.11

1. You invest \$250 in a savings account earning 5.5% APR for two years. Find the balance to the nearest penny if interest is compounded at the following frequencies.
   a. quarterly
   b. monthly
   c. weekly
   d. hourly

2. Jamie invests \$5000 in a savings account that earns 7% APR compounded continuously.
   a. How much money will Jamie have after 3 years?
   b. How long will it take for Jamie's money to double?
   c. How long will it take for Jamie's account to be worth exactly \$8000?

Now suppose you invest P dollars at interest rate r, compounded n times per year. Let $B(t)$ denote your balance at the end of t years. Then

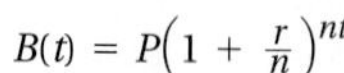

$$B(t) = P\left(1 + \frac{r}{n}\right)^{nt}$$

- The interest rate in each compounding period is $\frac{r}{n}$.
- There are nt compounding periods in t years.

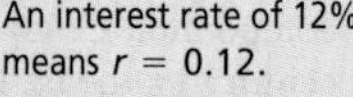

An interest rate of 12% means $r = 0.12$.

Example 2

Problem Suppose David invests \$100 at 12% APR, but this time the interest is compounded continuously. How much money will he have after five years?

Solution Let n be the number of times the interest gets compounded per year so that:

- the interest rate in each compounding period is $\frac{0.12}{n}$.
- there are $5n$ compound periods in five years.

Thus after five years, David will have $100\left(1 + \frac{0.12}{n}\right)^{5n}$ dollars.

As n grows larger and larger, you get

$$\lim_{n \to \infty} 100\left(1 + \frac{0.12}{n}\right)^{5n} \approx 182.212$$

So David has approximately \$182.21.

See the TI-Nspire Handbook on p. 704 to use your CAS to approximate $\lim_{n \to \infty} 100\left(1 + \frac{0.12}{n}\right)^{5n}$.

Exercises *Practicing Habits of Mind*

Check Your Understanding

1. Suppose Danielle could invest \$100 with Seventh Fifth Bank at 100% APR for more than just a year.
   a. What would her balance be at the end of two years if compounding were annual? At the end of three years? At the end of t years?
   b. What would her balance be at the end of two years if compounding were quarterly? At the end of three years? At the end of t years?
   c. In terms of the number e, what would her balance be at the end of three years of continuous compounding? Find this value to the nearest cent.

Go Online PHSchool.com

For more information on compound interest and e, go to **Web Code:** bge-9031

2. Jamie says that 100% APR is totally unrealistic. "I've never seen any savings account with more than 5% or 6% interest. So could we please look at something more realistic?"
   a. If Jamie invests \$100 at 6% APR, compounded annually, how much money will she have at the end of one year? At the end of two years? At the end of t years?
   b. If the 6% APR is compounded twice per year, how much money will she have at the end of one year? At the end of two years? At the end of t years?
   c. **Write About It** Danielle says that after three years of monthly compounding at 6% APR, Jamie will have $100(1.005)^{36}$ dollars in the account. Describe in detail where the values 100, 1.005, and 36 come from.
3. Jamie invests P dollars at 5% APR, compounded n times per year for t years. Find a formula for the balance of this account at the end of t years in terms of P, n, and t.
4. Jamie invests \$100 at 5% APR and is looking at what happens as interest is compounded more and more often. To the nearest penny, find the balance of Jamie's account after one year if interest is compounded on each of the following schedules.
   a. quarterly
   b. monthly
   c. daily
   d. hourly
5. Jamie invests \$100 at 5% APR, compounded continuously to earn the maximum interest. Find Jamie's balance, to the nearest penny, after each of the following time periods.
   a. 5 years
   b. 10 years
   c. 20 years
   d. 40 years
6. For each of the values found in Exercise 5, rewrite the result in terms of e.

Answers

Exercises

1. a. \$400; \$800; $100(2)^t$
b. \$596.05; \$1455.19; $100(2.441406)^t$
c. \$2008.55
2. a. \$106.00; \$112.36; $100(1.06)^t$
b. \$106.09; \$112.55; $100(1.0609)^t$
c. The 100 is the amount Jamie invested. The 1.005 is $1 + \frac{0.06}{12}$, 0.06 is the interest rate expressed as a decimal, 12 is the number of times it is compounded in a year (monthly). $36 = 12 \cdot 3$ is (number of times compounded in a year)(number of years).
3. $B = P\left(1 + \frac{0.05}{n}\right)^{nt}$
4. a. \$105.09 **b.** \$105.12
c. \$105.13 **d.** \$105.13
5. a. \$128.40 **b.** \$164.87
c. \$271.83 **d.** \$738.91
6. a. $47.237e$ **b.** $60.653e$
c. $100e$ **d.** $271.828e$

Exercises

HOMEWORK
- Core: 9, 10, 13, 14, 15, 16, 17, 18
- Optional: 11, 12

Check Your Understanding

EXERCISE 2 Moving to a more realistic interest rate means that the effect of the compound interest is less dramatic and the values are not as easy to compute, but most students are ready for this change. Part (c) of this exercise is especially critical if your students are working with a balance function that you developed as a class. Make sure that they understand each piece of the function so that they could, if necessary, recreate it in the future.

EXERCISE 3 If you and your students have already programmed a balance function into your calculators, you may want to skip this exercise entirely. If not, this is the point at which many students would think to do this for themselves. If you leave the balance function to individual choice and readiness, you may want to check students' functions at some point.

EXERCISE 5 The following exercise depends on the results of this one, so if you want to assign Exercise 6, also assign Exercise 5.

EXERCISE 6 Understanding the limit definition for e is a hurdle for some students, so you may want to spend some class time discussing this exercise. Exercise 8 produces a formula for continuously compounded interest, but here students are still (likely) answering these questions by evaluating a balance function with a large number of compounding periods per year as a way to approximate the limit. Students write things out with limit notation to reinforce the thinking behind what is going on.

EXERCISE 7 There are many assumptions about limits buried beneath the surface here. For example, implicit in the argument is the fact that

$$\lim_{K\to\infty}\left(1+\frac{1}{K}\right)^{Kx} = \left(\lim_{K\to\infty}\left(1+\frac{1}{K}\right)^{K}\right)^{x}$$

This is true, but it requires a proof, usually made explicit in calculus when discussing the properties of limits for continuous functions—"the limit of the product is the product of the limits," for example. You might want to mention that some of the fine points of this argument are left for a later course.

Also, if your students did Exercise 12 in Lesson 3.10, they might want to look back at it now. In that exercise, they found limits of this form. Now they can see the connection to the function e^x that was embedded in the exercise.

EXERCISE 8 If time allows, this exercise gives students a nice opportunity to apply the limit definition for e^x.

On Your Own

EXERCISE 9 Most students are probably surprised to find e here. Assign this exercise as homework then use it to pick up the start of the next lesson.

EXERCISES 12–15 present different ways to compare two situations—one with interest compounded annually and the other with a different interest rate compounded continuously. Students could answer this first question by choosing some amount of money and a term and comparing yields for both situations. Exercise 13 asks them to look at the graphs, which is another way of comparing yields. They see which graph has larger y-values. Exercise 14 invites them to compare the slope of the tangent to each graph at a point, so they are comparing the rate of increase for each function. Finally, in Exercise 15, students use the rules of algebra to convert the form of g so they can make a direct comparison.

You can make copies of Blackline Master MC7 for students to sketch the pair of function graphs.

7. This exercise is a proof of the fact that for $x > 0$,

$$\lim_{n\to\infty}\left(1+\frac{x}{n}\right)^{n} = e^{x}$$

using the limit definition of e.

a. If $\frac{1}{K} = \frac{x}{n}$, write n in terms of x and K.

b. Rewrite the expression

$$\left(1+\frac{x}{n}\right)^{n}$$

by making the substitution $\frac{1}{K} = \frac{x}{n}$.

c. Explain why the equation is true.

$$\lim_{n\to\infty}\left(1+\frac{x}{n}\right)^{n} = \lim_{K\to\infty}\left(1+\frac{1}{K}\right)^{Kx}$$

As n grows, what happens to K?

d. Show that

$$\lim_{K\to\infty}\left(1+\frac{1}{K}\right)^{Kx} = e^{x}$$

using the limit definition of e.

8. You have already seen that if you invest P dollars at an APR of r, compounded n times per year, your balance at the end of t years is

$$B(t) = P\left(1+\frac{r}{n}\right)^{nt}$$

Consider the limit of the expression on the right as n gets larger and larger. Show that

$$\lim_{n\to\infty} P\left(1+\frac{r}{n}\right)^{nt} = Pe^{rt}$$

On Your Own

9. Find the value of $\sum_{k=0}^{\infty}\frac{1}{k!}$ to five decimal places.

10. Suppose Danielle was able to invest \$1000 instead of \$100 in her Seventh Fifth Bank account.

a. What would be the effect on her balance at the end of the year?

b. What is the maximum amount of money Danielle could have at the end of a year, investing \$1000 this way?

Remember... Danielle's investment was \$100 at 100% APR.

Answers

7. a.
$$\frac{1}{K} = \frac{x}{n}$$
$$n\cdot\frac{1}{K} = n\cdot\frac{x}{n}$$
$$\frac{n}{K} = x$$
$$n = Kx$$

b. $\left(1+\frac{x}{n}\right)^{n} = \left(1+\frac{1}{K}\right)^{Kx}$

c. The two limits are the same because as $n\to\infty$, $K\to\infty$.

d.
$$\lim_{K\to\infty}\left(1+\frac{1}{K}\right)^{Kx}$$
$$= \lim_{K\to\infty}\left(\left(1+\frac{1}{K}\right)^{K}\right)^{x}$$
$$= \left(\lim_{K\to\infty}\left(1+\frac{1}{K}\right)^{K}\right)^{x}$$
$$= e^{x}$$

8.
$$\lim_{n\to\infty} P\left(1+\frac{r}{n}\right)^{nt}$$
$$= P\left(\lim_{n\to\infty}\left(1+\frac{r}{n}\right)^{n}\right)^{t}$$
$$= P(e^{r})^{t} = Pe^{rt}$$

9. $\sum_{k=0}^{\infty}\frac{1}{k!} = e \approx 2.71828$

11. Jamie puts $1000 in a savings account that earns 6% APR, compounded continuously.
    a. How much money will Jamie have after 3 years? After 5 years? After t years?
    b. How long will it take for Jamie's account balance to double?
    c. How long will it take for Jamie's account to be worth $4000?

12. Which would be a better investment—an account at 6% APR compounded annually, or an account at 5.5% APR compounded continuously?

13. Sketch the graphs of these two functions on the same axes.

$$f(t) = 1.06^t,\ g(t) = e^{0.055t}$$

14. The graph of $g(t) = e^{0.055t}$ passes through the point (0, 1). Find the slope of the line tangent to the graph of g at this point. Round your answer to three decimal places.

15. Rewrite $g(t)$ from Exercise 13 in the form $g(t) = b^t$ with base b accurate to four decimal places.

16. **Standardized Test Prep** Jo and Eddie each deposited $100 in a bank account paying 4% (APR) interest. Jo's bank compounds interest quarterly, while Eddie's bank compounds it continuously. What is the difference between the two account balances after one year?

    A. $0.02 B. $0.20 C. $2.00 D. $20.00

Try putting the same amount of money into each account for the same time period. What does $e^{0.055}$ have to do with this exercise?

For additional practice, go to **Web Code**: bga-0311

Maintain Your Skills

17. Write the first four terms of the expansion of each expression (starting with $1 + x + \cdots$).

    a. $\left(1 + \frac{x}{3}\right)^3$ b. $\left(1 + \frac{x}{5}\right)^5$

    c. $\left(1 + \frac{x}{10}\right)^{10}$ d. $\left(1 + \frac{x}{n}\right)^n$

18. Find each limit.

    a. $\lim\limits_{n\to\infty} \frac{\binom{n}{1}}{n}$ b. $\lim\limits_{n\to\infty} \frac{\binom{n}{2}}{n^2}$ c. $\lim\limits_{n\to\infty} \frac{\binom{n}{3}}{n^3}$

    d. $\lim\limits_{n\to\infty} \frac{\binom{n}{4}}{n^4}$ e. $\lim\limits_{n\to\infty} \frac{\binom{n}{5}}{n^5}$

You can use most CAS software to evaluate the binomial coefficient $\binom{n}{2}$ as $nCr(n, 2)$.

10. a. Her balance is $2000; it is multiplied by a factor of 10.
b. $2718.28

11. a. $1197.22; $1349.86; $1000 \cdot e^{0.06 \cdot t}$ dollars
b. 11.55 years
c. 23.1 years

12. 6% APR compounded annually

13. See back of book.

14. $m = 0.055$

15. 1.0565^t

16. A

17. a. $1 + x + \frac{x^2}{3} + \frac{x^3}{27}$
b. $1 + x + \frac{2x^2}{5} + \frac{2x^3}{25}$
c–d. See back of book.

18. See back of book.

Maintain Your Skills

EXERCISE 17 In part (d), students write out the terms in the series for e^x. Writing out the terms of the expansions for parts (a)–(c) helps them see how to do part (d). They recall how to use the binomial theorem to write these expansions and are ready to try the general case.

EXERCISE 18 The results here are used in the next lesson to show the equivalence of the rules

$$e^x = \lim_{n\to\infty}\left(1 + \frac{x}{n}\right)^n = 1 + x + \frac{x^2}{2} + \frac{x^3}{6} + \cdots$$

You might need to suggest that students write out each expression as a rational function, using the factorial definition for the binomial coefficients if students do not think of it themselves.

Additional Resources

PRINT RESOURCES
- Solution Manual
- Practice Workbook
- Assessment Resources
- Teaching Resources

TECHNOLOGY
- Interactive Textbook
- TeacherExpress CD-ROM
- ExamView CD-ROM
- PHSchool.com

Additional Practice

1. Robyn invests $1200 at 6% APR and is looking at what happens as interest is compounded more and more often. Find to the nearest penny the balance of Robyn's account at the end of one year if interest is compounded on each of the following schedules.
   a. biannually b. monthly
   c. weekly d. daily

2. You put $2000 into a savings account that earns 5% APR compounded continuously.
   a. How much money will you have after 2 years? After 5 years? After t years?
   b. How long will it take for your account balance to double?
   c. How long will it take for your account to be worth $3000?

3. Which would be a better investment—an account at 7% APR compounded monthly, or an account at 6.5% APR compounded continuously?

4. The cubic function $c(x) = 1 + x + \frac{x^2}{2} + \frac{x^3}{6}$ is a good approximation of $f(x) = e^x$ when x is near 0.
   a. Calculate $c(0.03)$ and $e^{0.03}$. What is the percent error for $c(0.03)$ as an approximation to $e^{0.03}$?
   b. Repeat part (a) for $x = 0.04, 0.8, 1.1$.

5. Find the exact value of the infinite sum

$$1 + 3 + \frac{9}{2} + \frac{27}{6} + \frac{81}{24} + \frac{243}{120} + \cdots + \frac{3^k}{k!} + \cdots$$

6. Find the solution to each equation to four decimal places.
   a. $e^k = 4$ b. $e^m = 8$
   c. $e^n = 12$ d. $e^p = 16$

7. Consider the function $f(x) = 2e^{-x}$.
   a. Sketch the graph of f.
   b. Find the slope of the tangent line at the point (0, 2)
   c. Give a good estimate for the coordinates of the point where the tangent line has slope -3.
   d. Give a good estimate for the coordinates of the point where the tangent line has slope -4.

Practice: For Lesson 3.11, assign Exercises 1–3.

Lesson Overview

GOAL

- State and use the factorial definitions of e and e^x.

This lesson presents a different definition for e that uses factorials. This definition is previewed in some of the exercises in Lesson 3.11. Students prove that the two definitions they have for e are equivalent, and see that this new factorial definition converges quickly to give a good approximation for e. There is also a proof in the lesson that e is irrational. In the problems, students consider the error in different approximations for e and begin to see the value of this new definition.

CHECK YOUR UNDERSTANDING
- Core:1, 2, 3, 5, 6
- Optional: 4

MATERIALS
- graph paper
- graphing calculators
- Blackline Master MC7

HOMEWORK
- Core: 7, 8, 9, 10, 11, 13
- Optional: 14
- Extension: 12

Launch

Begin today's lesson by looking back at Exercises 9, 16, and 17 from Lesson 3.11. Each of these exercises is related in some way to the mathematical constant e. See what students observed in their own work, and go through the solutions with your class. These exercises hint that there is another way to define e. See if your students have anticipated the new factorial definition of e that is formalized in this lesson.

Explore

LEMMA 3.11 In the algebraic calculations that lead to the proof of Lemma 3.11, students see the value of using a particular form of an expression for a particular purpose. Whenever you attempt to calculate limits approaching infinity, writing rational expressions of the form $\frac{a}{n^b}$ gets you closer to your answer. Terms of this form go to zero and simplify the calculation of the limit. Another way to think about this calculation is to say that

$$\frac{n(n-1)(n-2)(n-3)(n-4)}{5!n^5}$$

is of the form

$$\frac{n^5 + \text{some lower-degree terms}}{5! \cdot n^5}$$

This is a less formal, but useful argument for some students.

3.12 Another Way to Find *e*

In Lesson 3.11, you saw the following definition for the number e.

$$e = \lim_{n\to\infty}\left(1 + \frac{1}{n}\right)^n \qquad (1)$$

Using this definition, you proved that

$$e^x = \lim_{n\to\infty}\left(1 + \frac{x}{n}\right)^n \qquad (2)$$

Actually, you proved this for $x > 0$ only. But (2) holds for all real x. See Exercise 12.

Equations (1) and (2) are the limit definitions of e and e^x, respectively. You can, however, define e and e^x another way, using the *factorial definition.* These alternatives are equivalent to the limit definitions.

A Useful Lemma

Recall Exercise 18 from Lesson 3.11. In it, you saw that

$$\lim_{x\to\infty}\frac{\binom{n}{5}}{n^5} = \lim_{x\to\infty}\frac{n(n-1)(n-2)(n-3)(n-4)}{5!n^5}$$
$$= \frac{1}{5!}\lim_{n\to\infty}\left(\frac{n}{n}\cdot\frac{n-1}{n}\cdot\frac{n-2}{n}\cdot\frac{n-3}{n}\cdot\frac{n-4}{n}\right)$$
$$= \frac{1}{5!}\lim_{n\to\infty}\left(1\cdot\left(1-\frac{1}{n}\right)\left(1-\frac{2}{n}\right)\left(1-\frac{3}{n}\right)\left(1-\frac{4}{n}\right)\right)$$

As $n\to\infty$, the terms $\frac{1}{n}$, $\frac{2}{n}$, $\frac{3}{n}$, and $\frac{4}{n}$ all go to zero, and thus

$$\lim_{x\to\infty}\frac{\binom{n}{5}}{n^5} = \frac{1}{5!}$$

You can generalize this result to state the following lemma.

Lemma 3.11

Let $k \geq 0$ be an integer. Then

$$\lim_{x\to\infty}\frac{\binom{n}{k}}{n^k} = \frac{1}{k!}$$

It even works for $k = 0$. Remember that $0! = 1$.

Factorial Definitions of e and e^x

Let

$$f(n) = \sum_{k=0}^{n}\frac{1}{k!} = 1 + \frac{1}{1!} + \frac{1}{2!} + \frac{1}{3!} + \cdots + \frac{1}{n!}$$

Compute $f(n)$ for some values of n, rounded to five decimal places.

$$\begin{aligned} f(1) &= 2 \\ f(5) &= 2.71667 \\ f(6) &= 2.71806 \\ f(7) &= 2.71825 \\ f(8) &= 2.71828 \\ f(100) &= 2.71828 \end{aligned}$$

Recall Exercise 9 from Lesson 3.11.

It appears that

$$\lim_{n\to\infty} f(n) = e$$

and the series seems to converge to e rather quickly.

To confirm this conclusion, start by expanding

$$\left(1 + \frac{1}{n}\right)^n$$

using the Binomial Theorem.

$$\left(1 + \frac{1}{n}\right)^n = 1 + n\left(\frac{1}{n}\right) + \binom{n}{2}\left(\frac{1}{n}\right)^2 + \binom{n}{3}\left(\frac{1}{n}\right)^3 + \cdots \qquad (3)$$

$$+ \binom{n}{2}\left(\frac{1}{n}\right)^k + \cdots + \binom{n}{n}\left(\frac{1}{n}\right)^n$$

A typical term on the right side of (3) has the form

$$\binom{n}{k}\left(\frac{1}{n}\right)^k = \frac{\binom{n}{k}}{n^k}$$

Using the lemma above,

$$\lim_{n\to\infty} \binom{n}{k}\left(\frac{1}{n}\right)^k = \lim_{n\to\infty} \frac{\binom{n}{k}}{n^k} = \frac{1}{k!}$$

Now let n get large in equation (3). The left side, by the limit definition, approaches e. And the right side looks like this:

$$1 + \frac{1}{1!} + \frac{1}{2!} + \frac{1}{3!} + \cdots + \frac{1}{k!} + \cdots$$

"Letting n get large" here is actually a tricky issue involving calculus. But you should get the general gist of what is going on.

You can now state the following theorem.

Theorem 3.12

$$\lim_{n\to\infty}\left(1 + \frac{1}{n}\right)^n = 1 + \frac{1}{1!} + \frac{1}{2!} + \frac{1}{3!} + \cdots = \sum_{k=0}^{\infty} \frac{1}{k!}$$

THEOREM 3.12 Students who completed Exercise 17 from Lesson 3.11 have already written out an expansion of $\left(1 + \frac{1}{n}\right)^n$ using the binomial theorem, so you may prove this theorem fairly quickly.

$$\begin{aligned} e^x &= \lim_{n\to\infty}\left(1 + \frac{x}{n}\right)^n \\ &= \lim_{n\to\infty}\left(1 + n\frac{x}{n} + \binom{n}{2}\left(\frac{x}{n}\right)^2 + \cdots + \right. \\ &\qquad \left. \binom{n}{k}\left(\frac{x}{n}\right)^k + \cdots + \left(\frac{x}{n}\right)^n\right) \end{aligned}$$

A typical term in this expansion is

$$\binom{n}{k}\left(\frac{x}{n}\right)^k$$

or

$$x^k\binom{n}{k}n^k$$

By Lemma 3.11, this typical term is equal to

$$x^k k!$$

You can conclude that

$$e^x = \sum_{k=0}^{\infty} \frac{x^k}{k!}$$

Developing Habits of Mind

Some students have difficulty proving by contradiction. If they lose track of what the assumption is and where it is applied, they can take statements in the proof out of context. For example, a student might see the equation $k!e = \frac{k!}{q} \cdot p$ in the text and cite it as proof that e is rational. One technique that you can use when doing a proof by contradiction in class is to use a different color pen or chalk when you are "under the assumption." Then, anything written in that special color is considered "suspect" until the argument is resolved or hits a contradiction.

Theorem 3.12 states that the following definition of e is equivalent to the limit definition.

Definition

The factorial definition of e is

$$e = 1 + \frac{1}{1!} + \frac{1}{2!} + \frac{1}{3!} + \cdots = \sum_{k=0}^{\infty} \frac{1}{k!}$$

For You to Do

1. Using the limit definition of e^x,

$$e^x = \lim_{n \to \infty} \left(1 + \frac{x}{n}\right)^n$$

derive the factorial definition of e^x:

$$e^x = 1 + x + \frac{x^2}{2!} + \frac{x^3}{3!} + \cdots = \sum_{k=0}^{\infty} \frac{x^k}{k!}$$

Expand $\left(1 + \frac{x}{n}\right)^n$ using the Binomial Theorem, and let n get large.

Using the factorial definition, you can approximate e^x accurately with polynomials. For example, consider the cubic polynomial

$$c(x) = 1 + x + \frac{x^2}{2!} + \frac{x^3}{3!}$$

The graphs of $y = e^x$ and $y = c(x)$ are shown below.

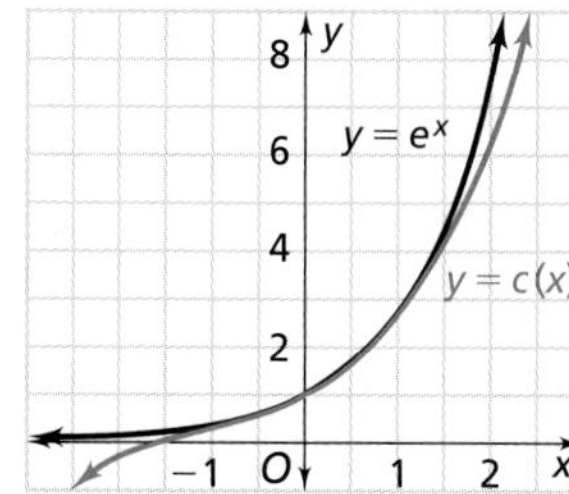

Notice how the two graphs almost agree when $-1 \leq x \leq 1$.

Developing Habits of Mind

Make strategic choices. Why is it useful to have different equivalent definitions of e and e^x based on factorials, when there are already ones using limits? It is useful because you can pick and choose the definition that is most convenient a given context.

Answers

For You to Do

1. $e^x = \lim_{n \to \infty} \left(1 + \frac{x}{n}\right)^n$

$$= \lim_{n \to \infty} \left(1 + n\frac{x}{n} + \binom{n}{2}\left(\frac{x}{n}\right)^2 + \cdots + \binom{n}{k}\left(\frac{x}{n}\right)^k + \cdots + \left(\frac{x}{n}\right)^n\right)$$

A typical term in this expansion is $\binom{n}{k}\left(\frac{x}{n}\right)^k = x^k \frac{\binom{n}{k}}{n^k} = \frac{x^k}{k!}$.

You can conclude that $e^x = \sum_{k=0}^{\infty} \frac{x^k}{k!}$.

For example, here is a proof that the number e is irrational, using its factorial definition. By the factorial definition of e,

$$e = 1 + \frac{1}{1!} + \frac{1}{2!} + \frac{1}{3!} + \cdots + \frac{1}{k!} + \frac{1}{(k+1)!} + \frac{1}{(k+2)!} + \cdots \qquad (4)$$

Suppose e is a rational number and write $e = \frac{p}{q}$ for some integers p and q, with $q > 0$. Choose a positive integer k such that $k > q$. Therefore,

We will come up with a contradiction.

$$k! = k(k-1)(k-2)\cdots q(q-1)(q-2)\cdots 3 \cdot 2 \cdot 1$$

and thus $\frac{k!}{q}$ is an integer. Multiply each side of (4) by $k!$ to get

$$k!e = k!\left(1 + \frac{1}{1!} + \frac{1}{2!} + \frac{1}{3!} + \cdots + \frac{1}{k!}\right) + k!\left(\frac{1}{(k+1)!} + \frac{1}{(k+2)!} + \cdots\right) \quad (5)$$

The left side of (5) equals

$$k!e = \frac{k!}{q} \cdot p$$

which is an integer. On the right side of (5), the term

$$k!\left(1 + \frac{1}{1!} + \frac{1}{2!} + \frac{1}{3!} + \cdots + \frac{1}{k!}\right)$$

is an integer because $m!$ is a divisor of $k!$ for all m such that $0 \le m \le k$. Hence the remaining term on the right side of (5), namely

$$k!\left(\frac{1}{(k+1)!} + \frac{1}{(k+2)!} + \cdots\right)$$

must also be an integer. But

$$\begin{aligned}
k!\left(\frac{1}{(k+1)!} + \frac{1}{(k+2)!} + \cdots\right) &= \frac{1}{k+1} + \frac{1}{(k+2)(k+1)} + \\
&\quad \frac{1}{(k+3)(k+2)(k+1)} + \cdots \\
&< \frac{1}{k+1} + \frac{1}{(k+1)^2} + \frac{1}{(k+1)^3} + \\
&\quad \frac{1}{(k+1)^4} + \cdots \\
&= \frac{1}{k+1}\left(1 + \frac{1}{k+1} + \frac{1}{(k+1)^2} + \right. \\
&\quad \left. \frac{1}{(k+1)^3} + \frac{1}{(k+1)^4} + \cdots\right) \\
&= \frac{1}{k+1}\left(\frac{1}{1 - \frac{1}{k+1}}\right) \\
&= \frac{1}{k} \\
&< 1
\end{aligned}$$

Replace each term in the sum by something greater.

Remember...

$\sum_{i=0}^{\infty} r^i = \frac{1}{1-r}$ when $|r| < 1$. Here, $r = \frac{1}{k+1}$.

Therefore

$$k!\left(\frac{1}{(k+1)!} + \frac{1}{(k+2)!} + \cdots\right)$$

is a positive integer which is strictly less than 1, a contradiction. And thus, e must be irrational.

Wrap Up

This lesson does not really contain much new material, so you should have time for students to work on the Check Your Understanding exercises and become accustomed to the new definition for e. Many of the exercises focus on calculating error and noticing how quickly this new definition converges. Students often are surprised to see how well a degree two or three polynomial can approximate e^x for some values of x.

Assessment Resources

Lesson Quiz 3.12

1. Give a good approximation for $e^{0.2}$ without using a calculator.

2. The cubic function $c(x) = 1 + x + \frac{x^2}{2} + \frac{x^3}{6}$ is a good approximation of $f(x) = e^x$ when x is small.
   a. Calculate $c(0.25)$ and $f(0.25)$ to five decimal places, then calculate the percent error in the approximation.
   b. Calculate $c(2.3)$ and $f(2.3)$ to five decimal places, then calculate the percent error in the approximation.
   c. Which value of x has less percent error when using c to approximate $f(x) = e^x$?

3. Find the solution to each equation to three decimal places.
   a. $e^k = 8$
   b. $e^n = 12$

Exercises

HOMEWORK
- Core: 7, 8, 9, 10, 11, 13
- Optional: 14
- Extension: 12

Check Your Understanding

EXERCISE 3 This exercise assumes that students do not know about the ln function, but some of them may just find ln 2. Other students may not even think about using logarithms at all, but just try different values of x to find the one that gives e^x closest to 2. That is also fine at this stage of the game.

EXERCISE 4 This exercise previews work that students do in Lesson 3.14 to find an expression for the slope of the tangent to the graph of e^x for any value of x.

GOING FURTHER If students connect their solution to $e^x = 2$ to their solution for the value of x which has a slope of 2, they may make the conjecture that the slope of the tangent to the graph of e^x at a point (a, e^a) is equal to e^a.

EXERCISE 5 In part (c) of Exercise 2, students calculated e^{-1} to five decimal places, and that answer agrees with their answer for part (a) here. The fact that the two answers agree should lead students who have not already thought of it to look at this sum and compare it to the factorial definition for e^x.

EXERCISE 6 Hopefully, students see that parts (a) and (c) have the same graph because of the Laws of Exponents, and that this graph is the image of the graph of e^x after a reflection over the y-axis. Once students start thinking about transformations, they should expect that the graph in part (b) is the image of the graph of e^x after a reflection over the x-axis.

You can make copies of Blackline Master MC7 for students to sketch the function graphs.

On Your Own

EXERCISE 8 You may want to discuss what is meant by "large enough" in this exercise. When you graph the two functions together, you can see where they start to diverge. You could also graph a new function equal to the difference of these two functions and see where its graph diverges from the x-axis. In real-world situations there is often some tolerance level for error, so if you can accept any value that is within, say, 1% of the exact value, then you may have a different response to this question.

Exercises *Practicing Habits of Mind*

Check Your Understanding

1. a. Use the factorial definition of e to find the value of e correctly to 10 decimal places. How many terms are necessary?

b. Calculate $\left(1 + \frac{1}{n}\right)^n$ for $n = 10^7$. How many digits of e does this calculation correctly find?

2. The quadratic function $q(x) = 1 + x + \frac{x^2}{2}$ is a good approximation of $f(x) = e^x$ when x is near 0.

a. Calculate $q(0.05)$ and $e^{0.05}$ to five decimal places. What is the percent error for $q(0.05)$ as an approximation to $e^{0.05}$?

b. Calculate $q(0.5)$ and $e^{0.5}$ to five decimal places and find the percent error.

c. Calculate $q(-1)$ and e^{-1} to five decimal places and find the percent error.

> The percent error is $\frac{\text{Estimate} - \text{Actual}}{\text{Actual}} \cdot 100$

3. Find, to three decimal places, the value of x such that $e^x = 2$.

> **Habits of Mind**
> **Make a connection.** How does the graph of $y = e^x$ suggest that there is a solution to the equation $e^x = 2$?

4. In Lesson 3.10, you learned that the line tangent to the graph of $y = e^x$ at (0,1) has slope 1.

a. The graph of $y = e^x$ gets steeper as x gets larger. At some point (x, y), the tangent line has slope 2. Give a good estimate for the coordinates of this point.

b. At some other point, the tangent line has slope 3. Give a good estimate for the coordinates of this point.

5. a. Calculate this value to five decimal places.

$$\sum_{k=0}^{\infty} \frac{(-1)^k}{k!}$$

b. Compare your results with those from Exercise 2.

> See the TI-Nspire Handbook on p. 704 for advice on how to do this on your calculator.

6. Sketch the graph of each function.

a. $f(x) = e^{-x}$ **b.** $g(x) = -e^x$ **c.** $h(x) = \frac{1}{e^x}$

On Your Own

7. Give a good estimate for $e^{0.03}$ without using a calculator.

Answers

Exercises

1. a. 2.7182818285; 14 terms

b. 2.71828169255; 6

2. a. $q(0.05) = 1.05125$, $e^{0.05} = 1.05127$; -0.002%

b. $q(0.5) = 1.625$, $e^{0.05} = 1.64872$; -1.44%

c. $q(-1) = 0.5$, $e^{-1} = 0.36788$; 35.91%

3. 0.693

4. a. (0.693, 2) **b.** (1.099, 3)

5. a. 0.36788

b. The summation gives the same rule as e^x where $x = -1$. So it should equal e^{-1}, and it does.

6. See back of book.

7. 1.03045

8. The cubic function $c(x) = 1 + x + \frac{x^2}{2} + \frac{x^3}{6}$ is a good approximation of $f(x) = e^x$ when x is small.
   - a. Calculate $c(0.1)$ and $f(0.1)$, then calculate the percent error in the approximation.
   - b. Repeat part (a) for $x = 0.2, 0.5, 1, 2$.
   - c. Explain why $c(x)$ is a good approximation to e^x for small values of x but not for large values of x.
   - d. For how many values of x does $c(x) = f(x)$ exactly?

Use the graphs of c and f to help.

9. Find the exact value of this infinite sum.

$$1 + 2 + \frac{4}{2} + \frac{8}{6} + \frac{16}{24} + \frac{32}{120} + \cdots + \frac{2^k}{k!} + \cdots$$

10. Find the solution to each equation to three decimal places.
   - a. $e^k = 3$
   - b. $e^m = 5$
   - c. $e^n = 15$
   - d. $e^p = 45$
   - e. $e^r = -5$

11. Let k be the solution to $e^k = 3$, as in Exercise 10a. Sketch the graph of the function

$$f(x) = e^{kx}$$

Is there a simpler formula for $f(x)$?

12. **Take It Further** Use the limit definition of e.
   - a. Use a substitution to show that $\lim_{n\to\infty}\left(1 - \frac{1}{n}\right)^n = \frac{1}{e}$.
   - b. Use your result in part (a) to show that $\lim_{n\to\infty}\left(1 + \frac{x}{n}\right)^n = e^x$ for $x \le 0$.

13. **Standardized Test Prep** Which of the following infinite series gives the exact value of e^5?
   - A. $\sum_{i=1}^{\infty} \frac{5^i}{i!}$
   - B. $\sum_{i=0}^{\infty} \frac{5^i}{i!}$
   - C. $\sum_{i=0}^{\infty} \frac{e^i}{5!}$
   - D. $\sum_{i=0}^{\infty} \frac{i^5}{5^i}$

Maintain Your Skills

14. Write each of these as fractions in the form $\frac{p}{q}$ where p and q are integers. Then approximate each to four decimal places.
   - a. $1 + \frac{2}{1}$
   - b. $1 + \cfrac{2}{1 + \cfrac{1}{6}}$
   - c. $1 + \cfrac{2}{1 + \cfrac{1}{6 + \cfrac{1}{10}}}$
   - d. $1 + \cfrac{2}{1 + \cfrac{1}{6 + \cfrac{1}{10 + \cfrac{1}{14}}}}$

Go Online PHSchool.com

For additional practice, go to **Web Code**: bga-0312

8. a. $c(0.1) = 1.10516666667$, $f(0.1) = 1.10517091808$, -0.00038%

b. See back of book.

c. The graphs are very close together for small values of x. As x gets larger, the graphs are farther apart.

d. $x = 0$

9. e^2

10. a. $k \approx 1.09861$

b. $m \approx 1.60944$

c. $n \approx 2.70805$

d. $p \approx 3.80666$

e. no solution

11–12. See back of book.

13. B

14. a. 3

b. $\frac{19}{7} \approx 2.7143$

c. $\frac{193}{71} \approx 2.7183$

d. $\frac{2721}{1001} \approx 2.7183$

EXERCISE 10 As with Exercise 3, students do not have an established procedure for solving these equations. Students may use the ln function if they already know about it, or may use trial and error to arrive at estimates for the correct exponent. If you went over Exercise 3 in class, students likely will use the solution technique you demonstrated.

EXERCISE 11 This exercise may require a class review of the Laws of Exponents, or even just a need to say that these laws apply even if e is the base.

Maintain Your Skills

GOING FURTHER Interested students should do a Web search on "continued fraction" representations for e or π. Continued fractions are a rich historical topic.

Additional Resources

PRINT RESOURCES
- Solution Manual
- Practice Workbook
- Assessment Resources
- Teaching Resources

TECHNOLOGY
- Interactive Textbook
- TeacherExpress CD-ROM
- ExamView CD-ROM
- PHSchool.com

Addtional Practice

1. Robyn invests $1200 at 6% APR and is looking at what happens as interest is compounded more and more often. Find to the nearest penny the balance of Robyn's account at the end of one year if interest is compounded on each of the following schedules.
   - a. biannually
   - b. monthly
   - c. weekly
   - d. daily

2. You put $2000 into a savings account that earns 5% APR compounded continuously.
   - a. How much money will you have after 2 years? After 5 years? After t years?
   - b. How long will it take for your account balance to double?
   - c. How long will it take for your account to be worth $3000?

3. Which would be a better investment—an account at 7% APR compounded monthly, or an account at 6.5% APR compounded continuously?

4. The cubic function $c(x) = 1 + x + \frac{x^2}{2} + \frac{x^3}{6}$ is a good approximation of $f(x) = e^x$ when x is near 0.
   - a. Calculate $c(0.03)$ and $e^{0.03}$. What is the percent error for $c(0.03)$ as an approximation to $e^{0.03}$?
   - b. Repeat part (a) for $x = 0.04, 0.8, 1.1$.

5. Find the exact value of the infinite sum

$$1 + 3 + \frac{9}{2} + \frac{27}{6} + \frac{81}{24} + \frac{243}{120} + \cdots + \frac{3^k}{k!} + \cdots$$

6. Find the solution to each equation to four decimal places.
   - a. $e^k = 4$
   - b. $e^m = 8$
   - c. $e^n = 12$
   - d. $e^p = 16$

7. Consider the function $f(x) = 2e^{-x}$.
   - a. Sketch the graph of f.
   - b. Find the slope of the tangent line at the point (0, 2)
   - c. Give a good estimate for the coordinates of the point where the tangent line has slope −3.
   - d. Give a good estimate for the coordinates of the point where the tangent line has slope −4.

Practice: For Lesson 3.12, assign Exercises 4–7.

Lesson Overview

GOAL

- Use the inverse relationship between e^x and $\ln x$ to solve equations.

Rather than just tell students that the ln function is the inverse of e^x; which is a conjecture that many students may already have made based on the position of the ln function key on their calculators, this lesson asks them to think of the ln function as a mystery. They tabulate it and use relationships that are visible in the table to see that this function has the same functional equations as logarithms have. They conclude that it is a type of logarithm. So, what is its base? Students use the properties of logarithms to calculate its base and they recognize the resulting number as e. They look at the graphs of ln and of e^x and recognize these as inverse functions. Finally, students experiment with using this inverse relationship to solve equations.

CHECK YOUR UNDERSTANDING
- Core: 2, 3, 4, 5, 6a–c
- Optional: 1, 7
- Extension: 6d

MATERIALS
- CAS (recommended)
- graph paper
- graphing calculators
- Blackline Master 3.13

HOMEWORK
- Core: 8, 9, 10, 12, 13, 14
- Optional: 11a
- Extension: 11b

VOCABULARY
- natural logarithm, $\ln x$

Launch

Begin today's lesson with the In-Class Experiment on page 254. You may want to briefly review functional equations before you ask students to tabulate the ln function and look for functional equations that it satisfies. You might give an example of a functional equation such as $f(a) + f(b) = f(a + b)$, and ask students to give you some functions that satisfy it (linear functions) and others that do not.

Explore

In-Class Experiment

You may want to use Blackline Master 3.13 on an overhead and fill in the entries as students find each function value.

PROBLEM 5 From the table, students should know that x is between 2 and 3, and probably closer to 3. They can substitute different values for x until they get close, or use the equation solution capability of their calculator to solve the equation $\ln x = 1$ for x. In any case, $x \approx 2.7183$, which may lead them to conjecture that $\ln e = 1$. They might even type this in to their calculators to check.

3.13 The Natural Logarithm Function

In this In-Class Experiment, you will investigate a function on your calculator called "ln." One way to investigate a function is to tabulate it and to see if there are any familiar "functional equations" lurking in the background.

In-Class Experiment

1. Use your calculator to find the output of the ln function for each integer input from 0 to 10. Record each output to five decimal places.
2. Calculate the value of $\ln 2 + \ln 3$ to four decimal places.
3. Calculate the value of $3 \ln 2$ to four decimal places.
4. Find and describe some rules that appear to be true for the ln function.
5. Find x, to four decimal places, if $\ln x = 1$.
6. Draw the graph of $y = \ln x$.

x	$\ln x$
0	■
1	■
2	■
3	■
4	■
5	■
6	■
7	■
8	■
9	■
10	■

It is only by convention that $\ln x$, like $\sin x$, is normally written without parentheses. On a calculator, parentheses are usually required.

Your table in the In-Class Experiment should show that

- $\ln 2 + \ln 3 = \ln 6$
- $\ln 2 + \ln 5 = \ln 10$
- $\ln 3 + \ln 3 = \ln 9$

And if you extend the table, you can also see that

- $\ln 3 + \ln 4 = \ln 12$
- $\ln 5 + \ln 7 = \ln 35$
- $\ln 6 + \ln 9 = \ln 54$

and so on. In other words, for $M, N > 0$, the function $g(x) = \ln x$ seems to satisfy the functional equation

$$\ln(MN) = \ln M + \ln N$$

But this is precisely the Fundamental Law of Logarithms.

A functional equation is an equation satisfied by a function.

Answers

In-Class Experiment

1. See back of book.
2. 1.7917
3. 2.0794
4. Answers may vary. Sample:
$\ln a + \ln b = \ln(ab)$,
$\ln a - \ln b = \ln\left(\frac{a}{b}\right)$,
$\ln (a^k) = k \ln a$
5. 2.7183
6.

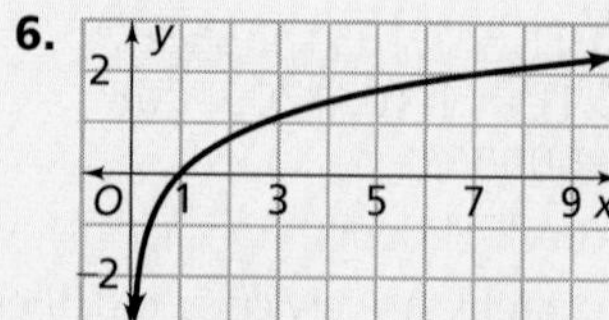

For You to Do

Use your table of data from the In-Class Experiment to verify that the ln function has the following properties.

7. $\ln \frac{M}{N} = \ln M - \ln N$

8. $\ln M^p = p \ln M$

Recall that these are the corollaries to the Fundamental Law of Logarithms.

Why does the function ln behave like a logarithm? Because it is a logarithm! In other words,

$$\ln x = \log_b x$$

for some base $b > 0$. What, then, is the base?

- From the definition of the logarithm, you know that the output of $\log_b M$ is the exponent k such that $b^k = M$, that is

$$b^k = M \iff \log_b M = k \qquad (1)$$

- $\log_b$ is a one-to-one function.
- It follows from equation (1) that if $\log_b x = 1$, then $x = b$, the base of the logarithm.
- In the In-Class Experiment, you found that $\ln e$ seems to be 1. If that were so, the base of ln would be e.

And in fact, the ln function built into your calculator is just the logarithm to the base e.

Definition

The **natural logarithm** function ln is the logarithm to base e:

$$\ln x = \log_e x$$

Why "natural" logarithm? You will see why in the next lesson. For an alternative approach to ln, see Chapter 8 of this book.

For You to Do

9. Copy and complete the following table.

x	e^x
0	■
0.69315	■
1.09861	■
1.38629	■
1.60944	■
1.79176	■
1.94591	■
2.07944	■
2.19722	■
2.30259	■

For You to Do

PROBLEM 8 At this point you might want to ask students why it makes sense that $\ln 0$ is undefined, and $\ln 1 = 0$. The multiplication rule is a good one to use to justify the first of these facts, and the power rule can justify the second.

PROBLEM 9 By now, students should catch on to the idea that the functions $\ln x$ and e^x are inverses of each other. If not, ask them why they think the authors of the book chose the numbers in the left-hand column of this table.

For You to Do

7. Answers may vary. Sample:
$\ln 10 - \ln 5 = \ln 2$,
$\ln 8 - \ln 4 = \ln 2$,
$\ln 6 - \ln 2 = \ln 3$

8. Answers may vary. Sample:
$2 \ln 3 = \ln 9$, $2 \ln 2 = \ln 4$,
$3 \ln 2 = \ln 8$

9.

x	e^x
0	1
0.693147	2
1.09861	3
1.38629	4
1.60944	5
1.79176	6
1.94591	7
2.07944	8
2.19722	9
2.30259	10

Wrap Up

Discuss the key Check Your Understanding Exercises 4, 5, and 6, because they explore the process of writing any logarithm in terms of the natural logarithm function and solving equations involving e and ln.

Assessment Resources

Lesson Quiz 3.13

1. Simplify each of the following.
   a. $\ln e^7$
   b. $\ln \frac{1}{e^3}$
   c. $e^{\ln 6}$
   d. $2 \ln e^2$
2. Find x to three decimal places.
   a. $3^x = 135$
   b. $4 \cdot 7^x = 241$
3. A savings account earns 4.5% APR. How many years will it take for the savings account to double in value?

From the two tables of data you have generated so far in this lesson,

- $e^{0.69315} = 2$ and $\ln 2 = 0.69315$
- $e^{1.09861} = 3$ and $\ln 3 = 1.09861$
- $e^{1.38629} = 4$ and $\ln 4 = 1.38629$

Note: These are approximate values.

and so on. And in general,

$$e^a = b \iff \ln b = a \qquad (2)$$

Statement (2) is another way of saying that the functions $x \mapsto e^x$ and $x \mapsto \ln x$ are inverses of each other. This should come as no surprise, since the logarithmic function

$$x \mapsto \log_b x$$

is the inverse of the exponential function

$$x \mapsto b^x$$

In this case, $b = e$.

For You to Do

10. Sketch the graphs of $x \mapsto e^x$ and $x \mapsto \ln x$ on the same axes.

11. Find the domain and range of each function. Do your results make sense? Explain.

12. How are the two graphs related?

13. Why is the ln function undefined for $x \le 0$?

Example

Problem Solve the equation

$$e^{x^2} = 27$$

Solution Apply the ln function to each side and use a corollary to the Law of Logarithms to proceed.

$$\begin{aligned} \ln e^{x^2} &= \ln 27 & \\ x^2 \ln e &= \ln 27 & \ln M^p = p \ln M \\ x^2 &= \ln 27 & \ln e = 1 \\ x^2 &\approx 3.29584 & \\ x &\approx \pm 1.81544 & \end{aligned}$$

Answers

For You to Do

10.

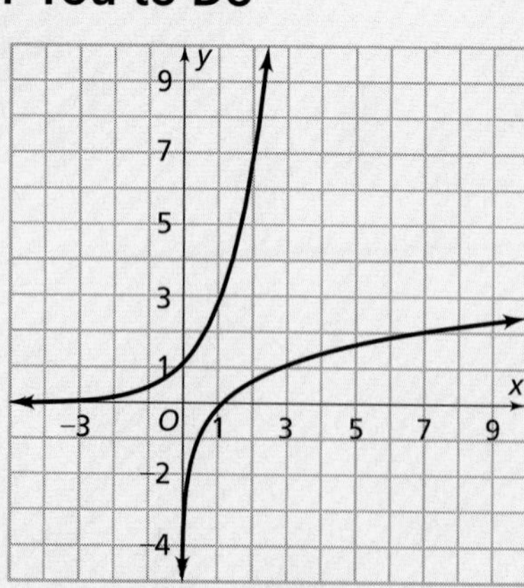

11. The domain of $y = e^x$ is all real numbers, and its range is all positive real numbers. The domain of $y = \ln x$ is all positive real numbers and its range is all real numbers. Since the two functions are inverses of each other, the domain of one is the range of the other, and vice versa.

12. The graphs are reflections of each other over the line with equation $y = x$.

13. If $\ln x = y$, then $e^y = x$. e is a positive number, and there is no power that you can raise it to that will give you a negative result.

Exercises *Practicing Habits of Mind*

Check Your Understanding

1. Using only the table from the In-Class Experiment, find the value of $\ln 1024$ to three decimal places.

2. Use the fact that $\ln M^p = p \ln M$.
   a. Find values for p and M if $\ln 81 = p \ln M$.
   b. Write $\ln \sqrt[3]{2}$ as a multiple of $\ln 2$.
   c. Write $\ln \frac{1}{25}$ as a multiple of $\ln 5$.

Indeed, for any number $b > 0$, $\log_b M^p = p \log_b M$.

3. Simplify each of the following.
   a. $\ln e^2$
   b. $\ln e^{10}$
   c. $\ln \frac{1}{e}$
   d. $e^{\ln 5}$

4. In Lesson 3.12, you found a number k such that $e^k = 3$.
   a. If you use a CAS to solve the equation $e^k = 3$, what answer do you get?
   b. What number m is the solution to $e^m = 5$?
   c. Show that this statement is true for any real number x.

$$e^{x \ln 2} = 2^x$$

5. Show that you can write any exponential function $f(x) = a^x$, where $a > 0$ is real, in the form

$$f(x) = e^{kx}$$

for some real number k.

6. Logarithms are useful in solving equations that involve exponents.
   a. If $2^x = 7$, show that $x \ln 2 = \ln 7$. Then find x to three decimal places.
   b. Find z to three decimal places if $5^z = 123$.
   c. Use logarithms to find the one solution to $2 \cdot 6^x = 0.1$.
   d. **Take It Further** In terms of the parameters a, b, c, and d, find the solution to

$$a \cdot b^x = c \cdot d^x$$

Exercises

HOMEWORK
- Core: 8, 9, 10, 12, 13, 14
- Optional: 11a
- Extension: 11b

Check Your Understanding

EXERCISE 1 expects students to recognize 1024 as a power of 2, but if students are stuck, you can just suggest that they factor 1024.

EXERCISE 3 Students could just type each of these expressions into their calculators, but they might get a greater benefit if you ask them to try this using only the table of values for ln and any applicable properties of e^x and $\ln x$. If they do use calculators, they should look back at the results and see that they make sense from this other perspective.

EXERCISE 4 gives some specific instances that help students reach the more general conclusion in Exercise 5.

EXERCISE 6 helps students work out a process for solving equations involving exponents by exploiting the properties of e^x and $\ln x$.

Exercises

1. 6.931
2. a. $p = 4$ and $M = 3$
   b. $\frac{1}{3} \ln 2$
   c. $-2 \ln 5$
3. a. 2
   b. 10
   c. -1
   d. 5
4. a. $\ln 3$ b. $m = \ln 5$
   c. $e^{x \ln 2} = e^{\ln 2^x} = 2^x$
5. $a^x = e^{\ln a^x} = e^{x \ln a} = e^{kx}$ where $k = \ln a$.
6. a. $x \approx 2.807$
   b. $z \approx 2.990$
   c. $x \approx -1.672$
   d. $x = \frac{\ln c - \ln a}{\ln b - \ln d} = \frac{\ln \frac{c}{a}}{\ln \frac{b}{d}}$

EXERCISE 7 Many students are still developing a clear understanding of what it means for two functions to be inverses of each other. This exercise points out that if f and g are inverses and the point (a, b) is on the graph of f, the point (b, a) is on the graph of g.

On Your Own

EXERCISE 8 Students could type these expressions into their calculators to evaluate them, but as with Exercise 3, they get a greater benefit if they just use their table of values for $\ln x$ and the properties of $\ln x$ and e^x.

EXERCISES 9–11 investigate doubling time, which is a common measure in the banking industry for evaluating an interest deal. Before hand calculators were common, it was really important for people to have simple rules they could use to evaluate complicated functions involving exponents. Even today, it is nice to have a way to approximate such functions.

7. You have seen that $e^a = b$ if and only if $\ln b = a$. Here are the graphs of $y = e^x$ and $y = \ln x$ on the same axes.

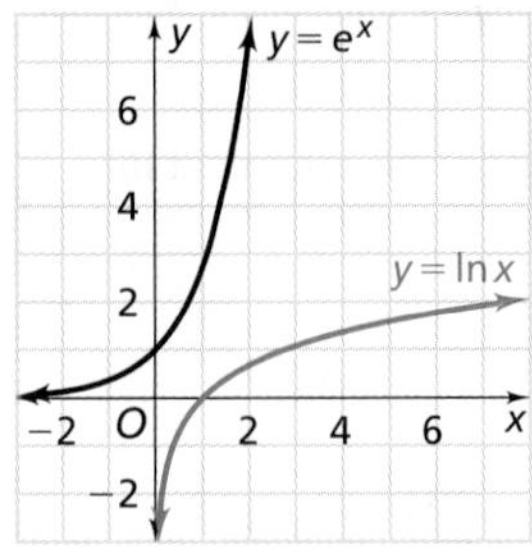

a. Exactly one point on the graph of $y = \ln x$ has x-coordinate 3. What are the coordinates of this point?

b. Exactly one point on the graph of $y = e^x$ has y-coordinate 3. What are the coordinates of this point?

c. Exactly one point on the graph of $y = e^x$ has x-coordinate 2. What are the coordinates of this point?

d. Exactly one point on the graph of $y = \ln x$ has y-coordinate 2. What are the coordinates of this point?

e. If the point $(g, 4)$ is on the graph of $y = \ln x$, find g.

f. If the point $(p, 4)$ is on the graph of $y = e^x$, find p.

On Your Own

8. Calculate each of the following to three decimal places, if possible.

a. $\ln 3$ b. $\ln 5$ c. $\ln 15$

d. $\ln 45$ e. $\ln \frac{5}{3}$ f. $\ln(-5)$

9. Jamie invests \$100 at 6% APR, compounded continuously. After t years her account balance is

$$B = 100e^{0.06t}$$

a. How much money will Jamie have in this account after 5 years? After 10 years? After 20 years?

b. How long will it take for Jamie's account to grow to exactly \$200?

c. How long will it take for Jamie's account to grow to exactly \$400?

d. Solve the equation $B = 100e^{0.06t}$ for t. Use the result to determine how long it will take for Jamie's account to grow to \$1000.

Answers

7. a. $(3, \ln 3)$ **b.** $(\ln 3, 3)$
c. $(2, e^2)$ **d.** $(e^2, 2)$
e. $g = e^4$ **f.** $p = \ln 4$

8. a. 1.099 **b.** 1.609 **c.** 2.708
d. 3.807 **e.** 0.511
f. undefined

9. a. \$134.99; \$182.21; \$332.01
b. $\frac{\ln 2}{0.06}$ years or about 11.55 years
c. $\frac{\ln 4}{0.06}$ years or about 23.10 years
d. $t = \frac{\ln \frac{B}{100}}{0.06}$; 38.38 years

10. For each interest rate, compounded continuously, determine how long (in years) it will take for a savings account to double in value.

a. 2% APR b. 3% APR c. 4% APR
d. 5% APR e. 8% APR f. p% APR

11. Many financial advisors use the Rule of 72 to estimate the doubling time of an account. To find the number of years it takes to double an investment's value, divide 72 by the percent interest rate.

If the interest rate is 6%, divide by 6.

a. How does the Rule of 72 compare to the results of Exercise 10?

b. **Take It Further** Ryo jokes that it should have been called the "Rule of ln 2." Why?

12. **Standardized Test Prep** On the day Aaron was born, his parents deposited \$24,000 into an account paying 8% (APR) interest compounded continuously. How old will Aaron be, to the nearest month, when the account balance is \$100,000?

A. 17 years, 1 month B. 17 years, 10 months
C. 18 years, 3 months D. 18 years, 6 months

Maintain Your Skills

13. Find the slope of the line segment connecting each pair of points.

a. (3, 5) and (4, 8) b. (5, 3) and (8, 4)
c. (2, 1) and (10, 2) d. (1, 2) and (2, 10)
e. (0, 4) and (a, b) f. (4, 0) and (b, a)

14. For parts (a) through (f), find a good estimate for the slope of the line tangent to the graph of $y = \ln x$ at each value of x.

a. $x = 1$ b. $x = 2$ c. $x = 3$
d. $x = 10$ e. $x = \frac{1}{2}$ f. $x = \frac{1}{3}$

g. What relationship does the slope of the tangent have to x?

Go Online PHSchool.com

For additional practice, go to Web Code: bga-0313

Maintain Your Skills

EXERCISE 13 The next lesson explores why the slopes of tangents to $y = e^x$ and $y = \ln x$ are reciprocals. Use this exercise as a reference.

EXERCISE 14 The next lesson begins with a review of this exercise. You can either assign it as part of the homework, or do it in class to launch tomorrow's lesson.

Additional Resources

PRINT RESOURCES
- Solution Manual
- Practice Workbook
- Assessment Resources
- Teaching Resources

TECHNOLOGY
- Interactive Textbook
- TeacherExpress CD-ROM
- ExamView CD-ROM
- PHSchool.com

Additional Practice

1. Use logarithms to solve the following equations for x to three decimal places.
a. $3^x = 10$ b. $4^x = 102$
c. $5 \cdot 3^x = 0.2$ d. $2 \cdot 7^x = 52$

2. Calculate each of the following to three decimal places.
a. $\ln 4$ b. $\ln 9$
c. $\ln \frac{3}{4}$ d. $\ln 51$

3. You invest \$500 at 5% APR, compound continuously. After t years your account balance is
$$B = 500e^{0.05t}$$
a. How much money will you have in this account after 3 years? After 9 years? After 12 years?
b. How long will it take for your account to grow to exactly \$800?
c. How long will it take for your account to double?

4. Find the slope of the line tangent to the point at $x = 1$ for each of the following functions.
a. $f(x) = 3e^x$ b. $h(x) = e^{4x}$
c. $g(x) = 4 \ln x$ d. $j(x) = \ln 5x$

5. Consider the function $f(x) = e^{x \ln 3}$.
a. Rewrite f without using logarithms.
b. What is the slope of the tangent to the graph of f at the point (2, 9)? Write your answer in terms of a logarithm.
c. What is the slope of the tangent to the graph of $h(x) = 4^x$ at the point (2, 16)? Write your answer in terms of logarithms.

6. a. At what point does the graph of $f(x) = e^x$ have a tangent line of slope 6?
b. What is the y-intercept of this tangent line? Is it positive or negative?

Practice: For Lesson 3.13, assign Exercises 1–3.

10. a. 34.7 years
b. 23.1 years
c. 17.3 years
d. 13.9 years
e. 8.7 years
f. $\frac{\ln 2}{0.01p}$ years

11. a. It is a good approximation.
b. The actual calculation involves dividing ln 2 by the interest rate expressed as a decimal.

12. B

13. a. 3 **b.** $\frac{1}{3}$ **c.** $\frac{1}{8}$
d. 8 **e.** $\frac{b-4}{a}$ **f.** $\frac{a}{b-4}$

14. a. 1 **b.** $\frac{1}{2}$ **c.** $\frac{1}{3}$
d. $\frac{1}{10}$ **e.** 2 **f.** 3
g. The slope seems to be equal to $\frac{1}{x}$.

Lesson Overview

GOAL

- Find an equation for the tangent to the graph of $y = e^x$ or $y = \ln x$ at a point.

In Exercise 13 of Lesson 3.13, students approximated the slope of the tangent to the graph of $y = \ln x$ at several points, and conjectured that the slope of the tangent at a point $(a, \ln a)$ is $\frac{1}{a}$. In this lesson, they use the result of that exercise as a working conjecture along with the fact that the functions $y = \ln x$ and $y = e^x$ are inverses, to draw a conclusion about the slope of the tangent to the graph of $y = e^x$. In the exercises, they continue this work and find the slope of the tangent to the graph of functions of the form $y = b^x$ and $y = \log_b x$.

CHECK YOUR UNDERSTANDING
- Core: 1, 2, 3, 4, 5, 6, 7
- Optional: none

MATERIALS
- graph paper
- graphing calculators

HOMEWORK
- Core: 8, 9, 10, 11, 12, 13, 16
- Optional: 14, 17
- Extension: 15

Launch

Begin today's lesson by going over Exercise 13 from Lesson 3.13. Since students did not have a formal way to find the slope of the tangent to the graph of $y = \ln x$ using limits, you may want to have them share their approximation techniques as well as their conclusions. To prove that the slope of the tangent to the graph of $y = \ln x$ at a point $(a, \ln a)$ is equal to $\frac{1}{a}$ would require techniques from calculus, but you and your students can use this result as a working conjecture.

3.14 Analysis of $f(x) = e^x$ and $g(x) = \ln x$

In Exercise 14 from Lesson 3.13, you looked at the slopes of several tangents to the graph of $y = \ln x$. From your results, you might have made a conjecture that describes an interesting property of the ln function. That property is detailed in the following theorem.

Theorem 3.13

The tangent to the graph of $y = \ln x$ at the point $(a, \ln a)$ has slope $\frac{1}{a}$.

The proof of this theorem requires results from calculus. For now, you can assume it is true.

Is there a similar theorem to be found regarding tangents to $y = e^x$? You could repeat the experiment and try to find a pattern. But you can use the fact that $f(x) = e^x$ and $g(x) = \ln x$ are inverses of each other to determine a statement about tangents to f.

The figure below shows the graphs of f and g with the point $P = (2, \ln 2)$ on the graph of g and the corresponding point $Q = (\ln 2, 2)$ on the graph of f. The figure also shows the tangent to f at P, and the tangent to g at Q.

From Theorem 3.13, you know that the line tangent to g at P has slope $\frac{1}{2}$. But what is the slope of the line tangent to f at Q? From the figure, it looks as though the two tangent lines are also reflections of each other over $y = x$. The next problems help you prove this.

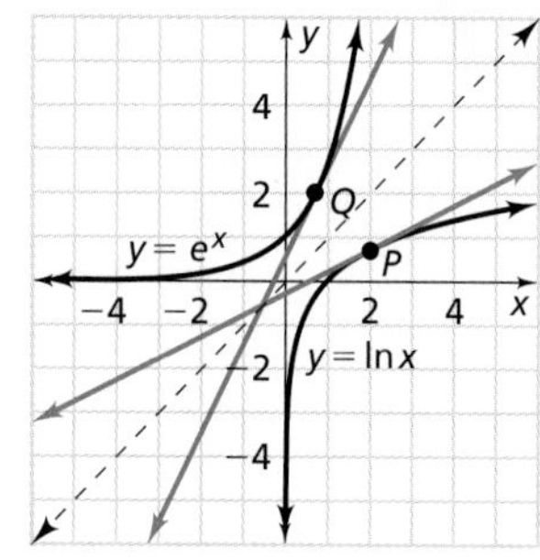

Remember...

If f and g are inverse functions, the graph of f is the reflection of the graph of g across the line $y = x$. A point (a, b) is on the graph of f if and only if (b, a) is on the graph of g.

For You to Do

Suppose h and j are inverse functions.

1. Let $R = (a, b)$ and $R' = (c, d)$ be a pair of points on the graph of h, and $S = (b, a)$ and $S' = (d, c)$ the corresponding points on the graph of j. Show that the slope of the secant between R and R' is the reciprocal of the slope of the secant between S and S'.
2. Explain why Problem 1 implies that the slope of the tangent at R is the reciprocal of the slope of the tangent at S.

If you let R' approach R, what happens to S'?

Answers

For You to Do

1. The slope between the points R and R' is $\frac{d-b}{c-a}$. The slope between the points S and S' is $\frac{c-a}{d-b}$. These two slopes are reciprocals, because their product is 1. (Remember, for both of these slopes to be defined, you have to assume that $a \neq c$ and $b \neq d$.)
2. When you find the slope of the tangent to the graph of a function, you are taking the limit of the slopes of the secant lines you get as R' approaches R (and on the inverse function the corresponding point S' approaches S). The reciprocal relationship between the secant slopes holds all throughout the process as the points get closer and closer together, so it will also be true of the limit.

Since the slope of the line tangent to g at P is $\frac{1}{2}$, by Problem 2, the slope of the line tangent to f at Q is its reciprocal. Therefore, the line tangent to the graph of $f(x) = e^x$ at $Q = (\ln 2, 2)$ has slope 2. From this result, you can state the following theorem.

If you cannot see the pattern, think about a point on f such as $(4, e^4)$. What would the slope of the tangent at this point be? The corresponding point on the graph of g would be $(e^4, 4)$, which is $(e^4, \ln e^4)$. The slope of the tangent at that point would be $\frac{1}{e^4}$.

Theorem 3.14

The tangent to the graph of $y = e^x$ at the point (a, e^a) has slope e^a.

For You to Do

3. Prove Theorem 3.14.

Once you know how to find the slopes of these tangent lines, you can find their equations.

Example

Problem

a. Find the equation $y = j(x)$ of the tangent to the graph of $g(x) = \ln x$ at $(3, \ln 3)$.

b. Find the equation $y = k(x)$ of the tangent to the graph of $f(x) = e^x$ at $(\ln 3, 3)$.

c. Verify that j and k are inverses of each other.

Solution

a. From Theorem 3.13, the slope of the tangent is $\frac{1}{3}$. Since the line passes through the point $(3, \ln 3)$, an equation for the line is

$$\frac{1}{3} = \frac{y - \ln 3}{x - 3}$$

and

$$j(x) = \frac{1}{3}(x - 3) + \ln 3$$

b. From Theorem 3.14, the slope of the tangent is 3. The line passes through the point $(\ln 3, 3)$, so its equation is

$$3 = \frac{y - 3}{x - \ln 3}$$

and

$$k(x) = 3(x - \ln 3) + 3$$

For You to Do

3. Start with a point (a, e^a) on the graph of $y = e^x$. This point corresponds to the point (e^a, a) on the graph of $y = \ln x$. By our assumption, the slope of the tangent to the graph of $y = \ln x$ at a point is equal to the reciprocal of its x-value, which means that the slope of the tangent to the graph of $y = \ln x$ at the point (e^a, a) is $\frac{1}{e^a}$. $y = e^x$ and $y = \ln x$ are inverses, so the slopes of the tangents to their graphs at corresponding points are reciprocals. That means that the slope of the tangent to the graph of $y = e^x$ at the point (a, e^a) is the reciprocal of $\frac{1}{e^a}$, which is e^a.

Explore

For You to Do

PROBLEM 3 You may find that some students want to include a proof that the point (e^a, a) is on the graph of $y = \ln x$ in their proof of this theorem. It is certainly not mathematically necessary to do so, but if it is still an open question for a student, then encourage them to show their thinking. Eventually students are asked to write more "elegant" proofs, but in high school students are basically trying to convince *themselves* that something is true. If they do not feel that they "know" something is true yet, they really ought to cite the theorem again. Worry more about students who make assumptions they cannot justify than about students who prove things more than once.

For You to Do

PROBLEM 4 It is possible that some of your students are uncomfortable with the notation in this question and are happier to see the coordinates of the point written as $\left(\frac{1}{2}, e^{\frac{1}{2}}\right)$. Some students are just confused by the notation until you ask to what power e is being raised.

Wrap Up

If your students do not have enough time to do all of the Check Your Understanding exercises in this set, you might choose to go through Exercises 1 through 4 in class, and assign Exercises 5 through 7 as part of their homework. The process in Exercises 5 through 7 is parallel to the process in the first three exercises, so students can do them independently using the first three exercises as an example. You can assign Exercise 4 as homework as well if your students work confidently with logarithms. However, if they needed significant in-class logarithm review, they may need your guidance on this brief proof.

Assessment Resources

Lesson Quiz 3.14

1. Determine the slope of the tangent line at any point (x, y) for the following functions.
   a. $f(x) = 4e^x$
   b. $g(x) = e^{3x}$

2. You can write the function $h(x) = e^{x \ln 4}$ as $h(x) = 4^x$.
   a. What is the slope of the line tangent to the graph of h at the point (0,1)?
   b. What is the slope of the line tangent to the graph of h at the point (2, 16)? Write your answer in terms of a logarithm.

3. You can write the function $m(x) = \frac{\ln x}{\ln 5}$ as $m(x) = \log_5 x$.
   a. What is the slope of the line tangent to the graph of m at the point (1, 0)?
   b. What is the slope of the line tangent to the graph of m at the point (25, 2)? Write your answer in terms of a logarithm.

Exercises

HOMEWORK

- Core: 8, 9, 10, 11, 12, 13, 16
- Optional: 14, 17
- Extension: 15

c. You can verify that j and k are inverses by showing that $j(k(x)) = k(j(x)) = x$.

$$\begin{aligned} j(k(x)) &= \tfrac{1}{3}(k(x) - 3) + \ln 3 \\ &= \tfrac{1}{3}([3(x - \ln 3) + 3] - 3) + \ln 3 \\ &= \tfrac{1}{3}(3(x - \ln 3)) + \ln 3 \\ &= (x - \ln 3) + \ln 3 \\ &= x \end{aligned}$$

Likewise, $k(j(x)) = x$. Consequently, the graphs of j and k are reflections of each other across the line $y = x$.

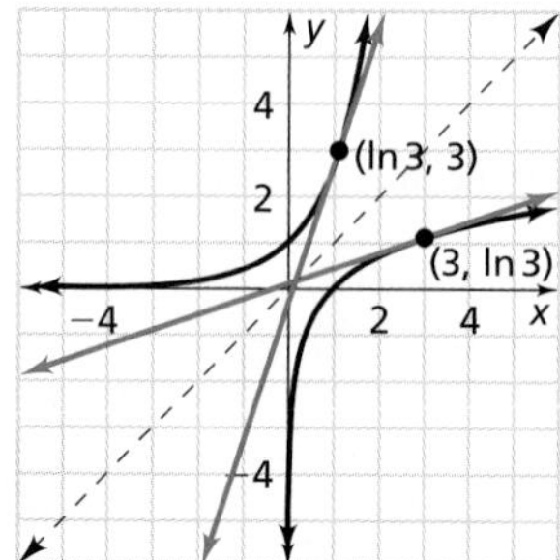

For You to Do

4. Find the equation of the line tangent to $f(x) = e^x$ at the point $\left(\frac{1}{2}, \sqrt{e}\right)$.

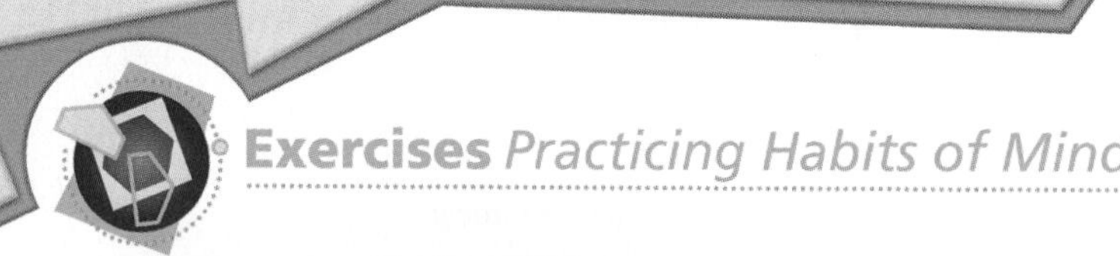

Check Your Understanding

1. In this lesson you learned that $f(x) = e^x$ has an interesting property: the slope of its tangent line at any point (x, y) is the same as the y-coordinate of that point. What can you say about the slopes of the following functions?
   a. $h(x) = 3e^x$
   b. $j(x) = e^{2x}$
   c. $k(x) = e^{5x}$
   d. $m(x) = e^{x \ln 2}$

Answers

For You to Do

4. $y = \sqrt{e}\left(x + \frac{1}{2}\right)$

Exercises

1. a. The slope of the tangent at any point is equal to the y-value of that point.
   b. The slope of the tangent at any point is equal to the y-value of that point times 2.
   c. The slope of the tangent at any point is equal to the y-value of that point times 5.
   d. The slope of the tangent at any point is equal to the y-value of that point times ln 2.

2. Exercise 4 of Lesson 3.13 asked you to show that $e^{x \ln 2} = 2^x$ for any x. Exercise 1 of this lesson asked about the function $m(x) = e^{x \ln 2}$. You can also write this function as $m(x) = 2^x$.
   - a. What is the slope of the tangent to the graph of $m(x) = 2^x$ at the point $(0, 1)$?
   - b. What is the slope of the tangent to the graph of m at the point $(2, 4)$? Write your answer in terms of a logarithm.
   - c. What is the slope of the tangent to the graph of $p(x) = 5^x$ at the point $(1, 5)$? Write your answer in terms of a logarithm. Verify by using a graphing calculator.

The ability to express these slopes using the logarithm to base e is a main reason to introduce the number e and the natural logarithm function. It is also one reason why $x \mapsto \ln x$ is called the *natural* logarithm. The functions $x \mapsto e^x$ and ln play a key role throughout calculus.

3. Look back at the table from Problem 5 of Lesson 3.10.
   - a. The output for base 5 is 1.609. What expression could you use to find this number directly?
   - b. Give a reason why the output for base 8 is three times the output for base 2.
   - c. What base would make the slope of the tangent exactly 1?
   - d. What base would make the slope of the tangent equal to zero?

4. Below is a three-step proof that

$$\log_2 x = \frac{\ln x}{\ln 2}$$

Justify each step.
   - a. If $\log_2 x = y$, then $2^y = x$.
   - b. If $2^y = x$, then $y \ln 2 = \ln x$.
   - c. $\log_2 x = \frac{\ln x}{\ln 2}$

5. In this lesson you learned that $g(x) = \ln x$ has an interesting property: the slope of its tangent line at any point (x, y) is the reciprocal of the x-coordinate of that point. What can you say about the slopes of the following functions?
   - a. $h(x) = 3 \ln x$
   - b. $j(x) = \ln 2x$
   - c. $k(x) = \frac{\ln x}{5}$
   - d. $m(x) = \frac{\ln x}{\ln 2}$

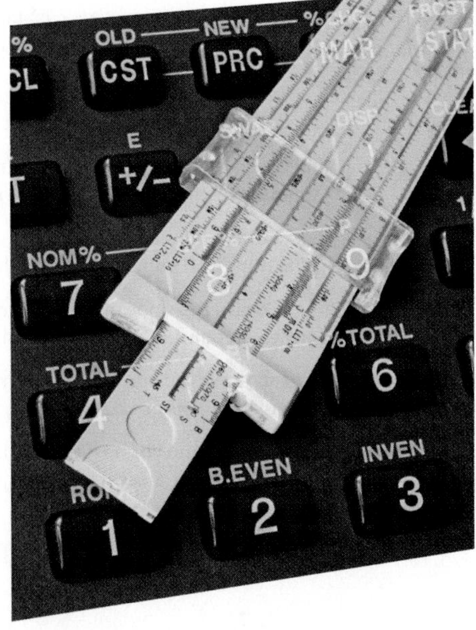

A slide rule uses logarithmic scales to perform multiplication and division by the addition and subtraction of lengths.

2. a. ln 2
   b. ln 16
   c. See back of book.
3. a. $5^0 \ln 5 = \ln 5$
   b. $\ln 8 = \ln 2^3 = 3 \ln 2$
   c. e
   d. 1
4. a. This is the definition of logarithm.
   b. $2^y = x \Rightarrow \ln 2^y = \ln x \Rightarrow y \ln 2 = \ln x$
   c. Divide both sides by ln 2 to get $y = \frac{\ln x}{\ln 2}$. Since $\log_2 x = y$, $\log_2 x = y = \frac{\ln x}{\ln 2}$.
5. a. The slope is 3 times the reciprocal of the x-value.
   b. The slope is the reciprocal of the x-value.
   c. The slope is the reciprocal of the x-value times $\frac{1}{5}$.
   d. The slope is the reciprocal of the x-value times $\frac{1}{\ln 2}$.

Check Your Understanding

EXERCISES 1–3 These exercises help students use their general result (the slope of the tangent to the graph of $y = e^x$ at a point is e^x) to find the slope of the tangent to the graph of e^{ax} at a point. Since you can write b^x as $e^{x \ln b}$ for any $b > 0$, you can find the slope of the tangent to the graph of exponential functions. Students see how these results match their experience in the Getting Started lesson.

Of course, your students are not thinking in terms of derivatives yet, but this nice property of the function $y = e^x$, that its derivative is equal to e^x, is at the root of the importance of e^x as an exponential function. It is one reason it gets its own button on most scientific calculators.

EXERCISE 4 Most students are not as experienced with the laws of logarithms as they are with the laws of exponents, so it is worth it to justify this result. A parallel exercise for the exponential function asks students to show $2^x = e^{x \ln 2}$. Here is one justification:

$$e^{x \ln 2} = (e^{\ln 2})^x \quad \text{Law of Exponents: } b^{mn} = (b^m)^n$$
$$= 2^x \quad e^x \text{ and } \ln x \text{ are inverses}$$

EXERCISES 5–7 These exercises help students use their general result (the slope of the tangent to the graph of $y = \ln x$ at a point is $\frac{1}{x}$) to find the slope of the tangent to the graph of $\ln(ax)$ at a point. Since you can write $\log_b x$ as $\frac{\ln x}{\ln b}$ for any $b > 0$, you can find the slope of the tangent to the graph of logarithm functions. Students see how these results match their experience in the Getting Started lesson.

On Your Own

EXERCISE 9 One way to solve this exercise involves finding a general equation for a tangent line to the graph of $y = e^x$ for any point (a, e^a), and this is the solution given in the solution manual. You could also solve it by thinking of a general equation for a line passing through the origin, $y = kx$, and realizing that $k = e^a$ for some a. The point of tangency (a, e^a) is on this line, so $e^a = (e^a)(a)$, which tells you that $a = 1$.

EXERCISE 10 Students should look back to their results in Exercise 1 to see how the coefficients in an exponential equation with e as the base impact the slope of the tangent to the graph of the function.

EXERCISE 11 For this exercise, students should look back to their results in Exercise 5 to see how the coefficients in an equation involving the ln function impact the slope of the tangent to the graph of the function.

EXERCISES 12 AND 13 Students have a way to find the slope of the tangent to any exponential function that has e as its base, and a way to convert an exponential expression with any base into an expression in e. In Exercise 12 they put those pieces together to write a rule that finds the slope of the tangent to the graph of any exponential function. Exercise 13 goes through the same process for logarithms, using the general rule for the slope of the tangent to the graph of any natural logarithm function and conversion from logarithms of any base to natural logarithms to write a general rule for finding the tangent to the graph of any logarithm function.

6. Exercise 4 asked you to show that $\log_2 x = \frac{\ln x}{\ln 2}$ for $x > 0$. Exercise 5 asked about the function $m(x) = \frac{\ln x}{\ln 2}$, which you can also write as $m(x) = \log_2 x$.

a. What is the slope of the tangent to the graph of $m(x) = \log_2 x$ at the point $(1, 0)$?

b. What is the slope of the tangent to the graph of m at the point $(4, 2)$? Write your answer in terms of a logarithm.

c. What is the slope of the tangent to the graph of $p(x) = \log_5 x$ at the point $(5, 1)$? Write your answer in terms of a logarithm. Verify your answer using a graphing calculator.

7. Look back at the table from Exercise 9 of Lesson 3.10.

a. The output given for base 5 is 0.621. What expression could you use to find this number directly?

Of what significance is the reciprocal of 0.621?

b. Give a reason why the output for base 8 is one-third of the output for base 2.

c. What base would make the slope of the tangent exactly 1?

d. What base would make the slope of the tangent equal to zero?

On Your Own

8. a. At what point does the graph of $f(x) = e^x$ have a tangent line of slope 8?

b. What is the y-intercept of this tangent line? Is it positive or negative?

9. Exactly one line tangent to the graph of $f(x) = e^x$ passes through the origin. What is its equation? At what point is it tangent to the graph of f?

10. Find a rule that can give the slope of the line tangent to the graph of $p(x) = Ae^{bx}$ at any given point $(x, p(x))$ on the graph.

This rule generalizes some of the results from Exercise 1.

11. Find a rule that can give the slope of the line tangent to the graph of $q(x) = A \ln Bx$ at any given point $(x, q(x))$ on the graph.

12. Find a rule that can give the slope of the line tangent to the graph of $r(x) = b^x$ at any given point $(x, r(x))$ on the graph.

13. Find a rule that can give the slope of the line tangent to the graph of $s(x) = \log_b x$ at any given point $(x, s(x))$ on the graph.

14. **Write About It** Compare and contrast the results from Exercises 2 and 6 from this lesson. Why are the answers similar, and in what ways do they differ?

Answers

6. a. $\frac{1}{1 \cdot \ln 2} \approx 1.443$

b. $\frac{1}{4 \ln 2} \approx 0.361$

c. $\frac{1}{5 \ln 5} \approx 0.124$

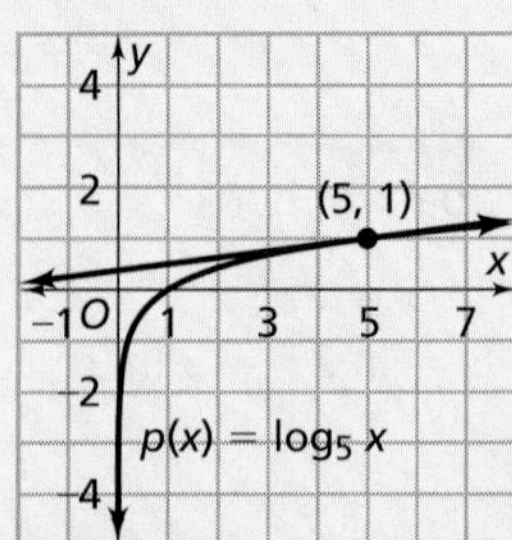

7. a. $\frac{1}{\ln 5} \approx 0.621$

b. The output for base 8 will be $\frac{1}{\ln 8} = \frac{1}{\ln 2^3} = \frac{1}{3 \ln 2} = \frac{1}{3}\left(\frac{1}{\ln 2}\right)$ and $\frac{1}{\ln 2}$ is the output for base 2.

15. **Take It Further** Using the rules from Exercises 10 and 11, show that if a line tangent to $p(x) = Ae^{bx}$ at (c, d) has slope m, then the line tangent to the inverse function $p^{-1}(x)$ at (d, c) has slope $\frac{1}{m}$.

16. **Standardized Test Prep** Which of the following is an equation of the line tangent to the graph of $f(x) = 5^x$ at $(c, 5^c)$?

A. $y = 5^c(x - c) + 5^c$ **B.** $y = (\ln c)(x - c) + 5^c$

C. $y = 5^c(x - c) + \ln c$ **D.** $y = 5^c(\ln 5)(x - c) + 5^c$

Maintain Your Skills

17. For each recursively defined function, find a closed-form definition that is equivalent for all nonnegative integers n.

a. $a(n) = \begin{cases} 1 & \text{if } n = 0 \\ 2a(n-1) & \text{if } n > 0 \end{cases}$

b. $b(n) = \begin{cases} 0 & \text{if } n = 0 \\ b(n-1) + 2n + 4 & \text{if } n > 0 \end{cases}$

c. $c(n) = \begin{cases} 0 & \text{if } n = 0 \\ c(n-1) + n & \text{if } n > 0 \end{cases}$

d. $d(n) = \begin{cases} 1 & \text{if } n = 0 \\ 5 & \text{if } n = 1 \\ 7d(n-1) - 10d(n-2) & \text{if } n > 1 \end{cases}$

e. $f(n) = \begin{cases} 2 & \text{if } n = 0 \\ 7 & \text{if } n = 1 \\ 7f(n-1) - 10f(n-2) & \text{if } n > 1 \end{cases}$

Go Online PHSchool.com

For additional practice, go to **Web Code:** bga-0313

Historical Perspective

Leonhard Euler (1707–1783) was one of the greatest mathematicians of all time. He was an extraordinary algebraist—he loved to calculate with expressions, series, and functions. He was the person who first derived the identity

$$e^x = \sum_{k=0}^{\infty} \frac{x^k}{k!}$$

Euler established hundreds of identities like this, and he found connections among many of them.

Go Online PHSchool.com

For a proof, in the style of Euler, that the graph of $y = e^x$ has slope e^a at $x = a$, go to **Web Code:** bge-8031

c. e

d. The slope of the tangent will never be zero.

8. a. $(\ln 8, 8)$

b. $-8 \ln 8 + 8 \approx -8.636$; negative

9. $y = ex$; $(1, e)$

10. slope $= Abe^{bx} = b \cdot p(x)$

11. slope $= \frac{A}{x}$

12. slope $= b^x \cdot \ln b$

13. slope $= \frac{1}{x \ln b}$

14. They both involve $\ln b$.

15. Start with the rule $p(x) = Ae^{bx}$, slope at (d, c) is bc. The inverse function is $p^{-1}(x) = \frac{1}{b} \ln\left(\frac{x}{A}\right)$, and the slope at (c, d) is $\frac{1}{bc}$. They are reciprocals.

16. D

17. a. $a(n) = 2^n$

b. $b(n) = n(n + 5)$

c. $c(n) = \frac{n^2 + n}{2}$

d. $d(n) = 5^n$

e. $f(n) = 2^n + 5^n$

Maintain Your Skills

EXERCISE 17 Of course, this exercise is a review of a critical skill that students have learned, but there is also a deeper connection for a couple of the functions. In a recursive definition of a function which also has a closed form polynomial definition, as in parts (b) and (c), the expression that is added to the previous term in the recursion is the slope of a secant line between two points one unit apart.

Additional Resources

PRINT RESOURCES
- Solution Manual
- Practice Workbook
- Assessment Resources
- Teaching Resources

TECHNOLOGY
- Interactive Textbook
- TeacherExpress CD-ROM
- ExamView CD-ROM
- PHSchool.com

Additional Practice

1. Use logarithms to solve the following equations for x to three decimal places.

a. $3^x = 10$ **b.** $4^x = 102$

c. $5 \cdot 3^x = 0.2$ **d.** $2 \cdot 7^x = 52$

2. Calculate each of the following to three decimal places.

a. $\ln 4$ **b.** $\ln 9$

c. $\ln \frac{3}{4}$ **d.** $\ln 51$

3. You invest \$500 at 5% APR, compound continuously. After t years your account balance is

$$B = 500e^{0.05t}$$

a. How much money will you have in this account after 3 years? After 9 years? After 12 years?

b. How long will it take for your account to grow to exactly \$800?

c. How long will it take for your account to double?

4. Find the slope of the line tangent to the point at $x = 1$ for each of the following functions.

a. $f(x) = 3e^x$ **b.** $h(x) = e^{4x}$

c. $g(x) = 4 \ln x$ **d.** $j(x) = \ln 5x$

5. Consider the function $f(x) = e^{x \ln 3}$.

a. Rewrite f without using logarithms.

b. What is the slope of the tangent to the graph of f at the point $(2, 9)$? Write your answer in terms of a logarithm.

c. What is the slope of the tangent to the graph of $h(x) = 4^x$ at the point $(2, 16)$? Write your answer in terms of logarithms.

6. a. At what point does the graph of $f(x) = e^x$ have a tangent line of slope 6?

b. What is the y-intercept of this tangent line? Is it positive or negative?

Practice: For Lesson 3.14, assign Exercises 4–6.

Mathematical Reflections

EXERCISES 6–8 At the start of the investigation, you may have assigned these as Questions 1–3 for students to think and write about.

In this investigation, you saw how the constant e arises, and you found different ways of computing it. You studied the natural logarithm (base e) function and its inverse, $f(x) = e^x$. You used the ln function to solve exponential equations. The following questions will help you summarize what you have learned.

1. Adam has had \$500 invested at 6% interest, compounded quarterly for 5 years. He was telling Jamie about his account, and Jamie said. "If you'd invested that money at my bank, where they compound continuously, you would have made more money." How much more would Adam have made in 5 years at the same rate of interest?
2. **a.** Approximate e using the first five terms of its factorial definition.
   b. What is the percent error in your estimate from part (a)?
   c. How large must n be for the expression $\left(1 + \frac{1}{n}\right)^n$ to give just as good an approximation?
3. If you put \$5000 into an account paying 7% interest compounded continuously, when will the value of the account reach \$8000?
4. Find an equation for the tangent to the graph of $y = 3 \ln x$ at the point $(2, 3 \ln 2)$.
5. Rewrite the function $g(x) = 5^x$ in terms of e. Find an equation for the tangent to the graph of g at the point $(2, 25)$.
6. What happens when interest is compounded more and more frequently?
7. What are some reasons to introduce the number e?
8. How can you relate any exponential or logarithmic function to $f(x) = e^x$ and $g(x) = \ln x$?

Vocabulary and Notation

In this investigation, you learned these terms. Make sure you understand what each one means and how to use it.

- **continuously compounded interest**
- ***e***
- **natural logarithm, ln *x***

Answers

Mathematical Reflections

1. \$1.50
2. **a.** 2.708333
   b. 0.365997%
   c. $n = 136$
3. a little more than 6.7 years
4. $y = \frac{3}{2}x - 3(1 - \ln 2)$
5. $g(x) = e^{x \cdot \ln 5}$; $y = (25 \ln 5)x + 25 - 50 \ln 5$
6. See back of book.
7. Answers may vary. Key reasons include noticing the upper bound for interest compounded more and more frequently, or perhaps looking for a function where the slope of the tangent to the graph of the function at any point is equal to the y-value of the function.
8. Any exponential function $h(x) = b^x$, for $b > 0$ can be rewritten as $h(x) = e^{x \ln b}$. Any logarithm function $j(x) = log_b(x)$ for $b > 0$ can be rewritten as $j(x) = \frac{\ln x}{\ln b}$.

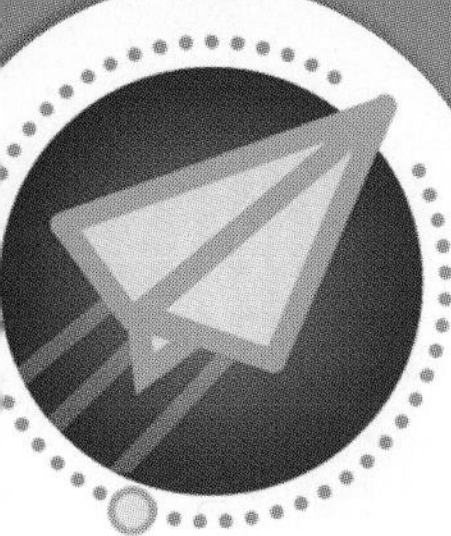

Project: Using Mathematical Habits

Partial Fractions

Consider the rational function

$$f(x) = \frac{1}{x^2 + 5x + 6}$$

and suppose you want to find the sum

$$\sum_{k=1}^{10} f(k) = \sum_{k=1}^{10} \frac{1}{k^2 + 5k + 6}$$

One way to do this is to compute the values

$$f(1) = \frac{1}{12}$$

$$f(2) = \frac{1}{20}$$

$$f(3) = \frac{1}{30}$$

$$\vdots$$

$$f(10) = \frac{1}{156}$$

and then add them up. But here is a more efficient approach. Note that

$$\frac{1}{x^2 + 5x + 6} = \frac{1}{x + 2} - \frac{1}{x + 3}$$

so that

$$\sum_{k=1}^{10} \frac{1}{k^2 + 5k + 6} = \sum_{k=1}^{10} \frac{1}{k + 2} - \frac{1}{k + 3} \qquad (1)$$

Now, the right side of (1) is the series

$$\underbrace{\left(\frac{1}{3} - \frac{1}{4}\right)}_{k=1} + \underbrace{\left(\frac{1}{4} - \frac{1}{5}\right)}_{k=2} + \underbrace{\left(\frac{1}{5} - \frac{1}{6}\right)}_{k=3} + \cdots + \underbrace{\left(\frac{1}{11} - \frac{1}{12}\right)}_{k=9} + \underbrace{\left(\frac{1}{12} - \frac{1}{13}\right)}_{k=10}$$

But notice how every term except for the first $\left(\frac{1}{3}\right)$ and the last $\left(-\frac{1}{13}\right)$ cancel with an adjacent term. Thus, you get

$$\sum_{k=1}^{10} \frac{1}{k + 2} - \frac{1}{k + 3} = \frac{1}{3} - \frac{1}{13} = \frac{10}{39}$$

This canceling of adjacent terms is sometimes called "telescoping."

Writing a rational function such as $f(x)$ as a sum of simpler rational functions is a process known as *partial fraction decomposition*. (In this case, the simpler rational functions are $\frac{1}{x + 2}$ and $-\frac{1}{x + 3}$.) In this project, you will study how to decompose a rational function into partial fractions and how partial fraction decomposition can help you in computing various sums (as you have already seen) and in graphing.

1. Use partial fractions to quickly calculate this sum.

$$\sum_{k=0}^{20} \frac{1}{k^2 + 3k + 2}$$

2. Calculate this sum.

$$\sum_{k=0}^{\infty} \frac{1}{k^2 + 3k + 2}$$

3. Use telescoping to find this infinite sum.

$$\sum_{k=0}^{\infty} \frac{1}{k^2 + 7k + 12}$$

Project

1. $\frac{21}{22}$

2. 1

3. $\frac{1}{3}$

Project

Students see how to use the partial fraction decomposition of a rational function to evaluate sums and to graph rational functions. They also learn how to produce a partial fraction decomposition for certain rational functions. This project gives students significant practice with algebraic manipulation of rational functions, with visualizing the results of a calculation without doing the entire calculation, and with choosing and writing a special form of an expression for a special purpose.

There are many ways to deal with projects in the CME Project. You can assign it to the entire class and have them work individually, in pairs, or in groups to produce a write up. You can allow students to choose to do one or more projects over the course of the year, or can assign projects to students based on their knowledge, interest, and background. You can also use projects as optional assignments for extra credit.

This project is fairly accessible, but some students need help and advice if they get stuck. Clearly explain your expectations and the Project's deadlines, the amount of class time you plan to devote to the Project, and your availability.

EXERCISE 1 In general (that is, if you sum to the nth term),

$$\sum_{k=0}^{n} \frac{1}{k^2 + 3k + 2} = 1 - \frac{1}{n + 2}$$

Students need this result in the next exercise.

EXERCISE 3 At this point, students are performing partial fraction decomposition "by inspection." Starting with Exercise 6, they see a more systematic way of finding a partial fraction decomposition.

EXERCISE 6 It is always a good habit to check your result. With $A = 3$ and $B = -1$,

$$\frac{3}{x-2} - \frac{1}{x-5} = \frac{3(x-5)-(x-2)}{(x-2)(x-5)} = \frac{2x-13}{x^2-7x+10}$$

as desired.

EXERCISE 8 The key here, as you saw in this investigation, is that as *algebraic expressions*,

$$\frac{6x-30}{x^2-7x+10} \text{ and } \frac{6}{x-2}$$

are the same. But as *functions*, they are different because one is defined at $x = 5$ while the other is not.

EXERCISE 11 Of course, the above results agree with those in Exercise 9.

4. a. Show that this is an identity.

$$\frac{1}{k^2} - \frac{1}{(k+1)^2} = \frac{2k+1}{k^4+2k^3+k^2}$$

b. Use telescoping to find this sum.

$$\sum_{k=1}^{19} \frac{2k+1}{k^4+2k^3+k^2}$$

5. a. Write out the first five terms of this summation, without evaluating or simplifying anything.

$$\sum_{k=1}^{19} \frac{1}{k} - \frac{1}{k+2}$$

b. Use telescoping to find the entire sum.

6. You can break the function $f(x) = \frac{2x-13}{x^2-7x+10}$ into partial fractions as

$$f(x) = \frac{A}{x-2} + \frac{B}{x-5}$$

a. Write a system of two equations and two unknowns that you can solve for A and B.

b. Find A and B.

c. Sketch the graphs of $a(x) = \frac{A}{x-2}$ and $b(x) = \frac{B}{x-5}$ on the same axes.

d. Sketch the graph of f using the graphs of a and b.

7. a. Find values of A and B so that

$$\frac{A}{x-2} + \frac{B}{x-5} = \frac{4x+11}{x^2-7x+10}$$

b. Sketch the graph of $g(x) = \frac{4x+11}{x^2-7x+10}$.

8. a. Find values of A and B so that

$$\frac{A}{x-2} + \frac{B}{x-5} = \frac{6x-30}{x^2-7x+10}$$

b. Sketch the graph of $h(x) = \frac{6x-30}{x^2-7x+10}$. Relate the shape of the graph to your answer in part (a).

9. Find values of A and B so that

$$\frac{A}{x-2} + \frac{B}{x-5} = \frac{px+q}{x^2-7x+10}$$

Here, your answers will be in terms of p and q.

10. Suppose you want to find A and B so that

$$\frac{A}{x+5} + \frac{B}{x-2} = \frac{3x-16}{x^2+3x-10}$$

Multiplying each side by $x^2 + 3x - 10$ gives

$$A(x-2) + B(x+5) = 3x - 16 \qquad (2)$$

a. Substitute $x = -5$ into (2) and solve for A.

b. Substitute $x = 2$ into (2) and solve for B.

11. Repeat Exercise 9 using the method from Exercise 10.

Answers

4. a. $\frac{1}{k^2} - \frac{1}{(k+1)^2} = \frac{1}{k^2} - \frac{1}{k^2+2k+1} = \frac{(k^2+2k+1)-k^2}{k^2(k^2+2k+1)} = \frac{2k+1}{k^4+2k^3+k^2}$

b. $\frac{399}{400}$

5. a. $\left(\frac{1}{1}-\frac{1}{3}\right) + \left(\frac{1}{2}-\frac{1}{4}\right) + \left(\frac{1}{3}-\frac{1}{5}\right) + \left(\frac{1}{4}-\frac{1}{6}\right) + \left(\frac{1}{5}-\frac{1}{7}\right)$

b. $\frac{589}{420}$

6–8. See back of book.

9. $A = -\frac{1}{3}(2p+q)$, $B = -\frac{1}{3}(5p+q)$

10. a. $A = \frac{31}{7}$

b. $B = -\frac{10}{7}$

11. $A = -\frac{1}{3}(2p+q)$, $B = -\frac{1}{3}(5p+q)$

12. See back of book.

12. The method of partial fractions will not work when the numerator has degree greater than or equal to the degree of the denominator, but polynomial long division can help.

   a. Find the quotient and remainder when you divide $x^3 - 4x^2 - 9x + 17$ by $x^2 - 7x + 10$.

   b. Use a graphing calculator to sketch the graph of $f(x) = \frac{x^3 - 4x^2 - 9x + 17}{x^2 - 7x + 10}$.

   c. Find A, B, C, and D so that

$$\frac{x^3 - 4x^2 - 9x + 17}{x^2 - 7x + 10} = Ax + B + \frac{C}{x-2} + \frac{D}{x-5}$$

13. **Take It Further** Consider the function $k(x) = \frac{1}{x^2 - x - 1}$. The denominator does not factor over the integers, but it does factor over the reals.

   a. Find the two roots of the polynomial
$$x^2 - x - 1$$

   b. Find A and B so you can write $k(x)$ in the form
$$k(x) = \frac{A}{x - \phi} + \frac{B}{x - \phi'}$$
   Here, ϕ is the positive root and ϕ' is the negative root of the polynomial $x^2 - x - 1$.

   c. Let $p(n) = A \cdot (\phi)^n + B \cdot (\phi')^n$ using the values from this exercise. Tabulate $p(n)$ for integers $n = 0, 1, 2, \ldots, 10$.

14. Write the rational function
$$f(x) = \frac{3x^2 + x}{x^3 - 3x^2 + x - 3}$$
as a sum of two terms with integer numerators.

15. Write the rational function
$$f(x) = \frac{5x^2 - 13x - 22}{x^3 - 19x + 30}$$
as a sum of three terms with integer numerators.

16. Consider the rational function $f(x) = \frac{2x - 1}{x^2 - 4x + 4}$. The denominator factors as $(x - 2)^2$.

   a. Show that $f(x)$ cannot be written in the form
$$f(x) = \frac{A}{x-2} + \frac{B}{x-2}$$
   with A and B real numbers.

   b. Find C and D with
$$f(x) = \frac{C}{x-2} + \frac{D}{(x-2)^2}$$

17. Write each of the following rational expressions as a sum,
$$\frac{A}{x - r_1} + \frac{B}{x - r_2}$$
where A, B, r_1, and r_2 are real numbers (possibly negative).

   a. $\frac{7x - 8}{2x^2 - 5x + 2}$

   b. $\frac{14x - 16}{2x^2 - 5x + 2}$

   c. $\frac{70x - 80}{2x^2 - 5x + 2}$

   d. $\frac{7x + 31}{x^2 + 5x - 14}$

   e. $\frac{8x + 29}{x^2 + 5x - 14}$

   f. $\frac{9x + 27}{x^2 + 5x - 14}$

13. a. $x = \frac{1 \pm \sqrt{5}}{2}$

b. $A = \frac{1}{\sqrt{5}}, B = -\frac{1}{\sqrt{5}}$

c. See back of book.

14. $f(x) = \frac{1}{x^2 + 1} + \frac{3}{x - 3}$

15. $f(x) = \frac{4}{x-2} - \frac{2}{x-3} + \frac{3}{x+5}$

16. a. If it were possible, then there would be a real number C which made $\frac{C}{x-2} = \frac{2x-1}{(x-2)^2}$ true for all x in the domain of f. But then $C(x - 2) = 2x - 1$ would be true for all x other than $2\frac{1}{m}$ and there is no C for which this is the case.

b. $C = 2, D = 3$

17. a. $\frac{3}{2x-1} + \frac{2}{x-2}$

b. $\frac{6}{2x-1} + \frac{4}{x-2}$

c. $\frac{30}{2x-1} + \frac{20}{x-2}$

d. $\frac{5}{x-2} + \frac{2}{x+7}$

e. $\frac{5}{x-2} + \frac{3}{x+7}$

f. $\frac{5}{x-2} + \frac{4}{x+7}$

EXERCISE 13 Students revisit this particular situation when looking at the closed form of the Fibonacci numbers in Investigation 4C. Students who work this problem sometimes are amazed to find that $p(n)$ is the Fibonacci sequence.

EXERCISE 14 In general, the equation you use to find the partial fraction decomposition for a fraction with this denominator should have the form
$$\frac{ax + b}{x^2 + 1} + \frac{B}{x - 3} = \frac{3x^2 + x}{x^3 - 3x^2 + x - 3}$$
from which you get a system of three equations with three unknowns: a, b, and B. In this exercise, you are lucky in the sense that this system of three equations and two unknowns has a solution – but this is not always the case.

EXERCISE 16 Do a quick check.
$$\begin{aligned}\frac{C}{x-2} + \frac{D}{(x-2)^2} &= \frac{2}{x-2} + \frac{3}{(x-2)^2} \\ &= \frac{2(x-2) + 3}{(x-2)^2} \\ &= \frac{2x - 1}{(x-2)^2}\end{aligned}$$
as desired.

EXERCISE 17 If you take the rational function in part (d) and add $\frac{1}{x+7}$, you get
$$\begin{aligned}\frac{7x + 31}{x^2 + 5x - 14} + \frac{1}{x+7} &= \frac{7x + 31}{x^2 + 5x - 14} \\ &\quad + \frac{x - 2}{x^2 + 5x - 14} \\ &= \frac{8x + 29}{x^2 - 5x - 14},\end{aligned}$$
which is the rational function in part (e). And if you add $\frac{1}{x+7}$ again, you get the rational function in part (f).

Wrap Up

The solutions to the exploration exercises can serve as the write up for this project, or you can ask students to research partial fractions in addition to this work. If only some students worked on the Project, you can give them an opportunity to present their work to the class.

Answers

Chapter Review

1. a. Answers may vary. Sample:
$f(x) = \frac{3}{4}x^3 + 3x^2 - \frac{3}{4}x - 3$

b. Not possible. For the graph to meet the first two conditions, it must have a negative *y*-intercept.

2. a. -1

b. $y = -x - 2$

c. $(-1, -1)$, $(1, -3)$, $(-0.618, -1.382)$, $(1.618, -3.618)$

3. a. $f(x) = 4(x + 1)^3 - 11(x + 1)^2 + 7(x + 1) + 5$

b. $y = 7x + 12$

4. a. There are no *x*-intercepts. The *y*-intercept is $(0, -1)$. The vertical asymptote is $x = 1$. The horizontal asymptote is $y = 0$. There is a hole at $\left(-1, -\frac{1}{2}\right)$.

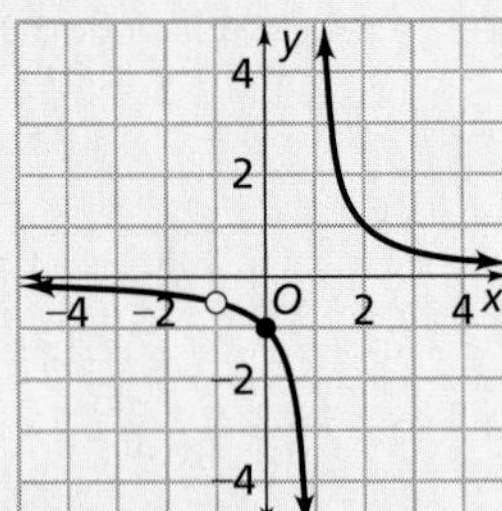

b. The *x*-intercept is (3, 0) and the *y*-intercept is $\left(0, \frac{1}{3}\right)$. The vertical asymptotes are $x = \pm\frac{3}{2}$. The horizontal asymptote is $y = 0$. There are no holes.

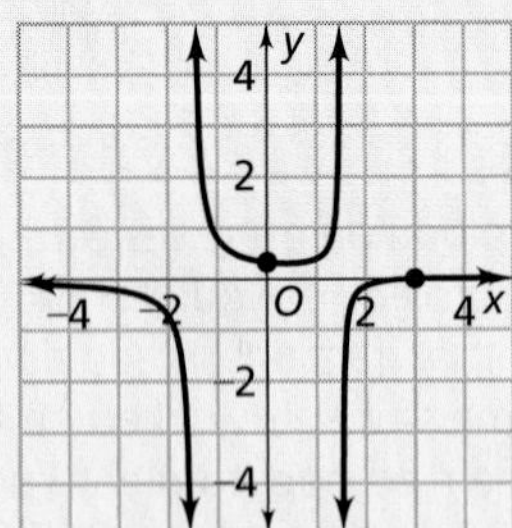

c. The *x*-intercept is (4, 0) and the *y*-intercept is $(0, -4)$. The vertical asymptote is $x = -\frac{1}{3}$. The horizontal asymptote is $y = -\frac{1}{3}$. There is a hole at $\left(-\frac{3}{2}, \frac{11}{7}\right)$.

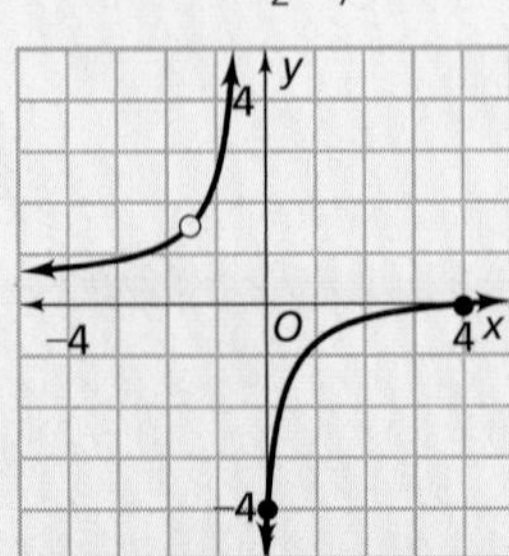

d. The *x*-intercepts are $(-3, 0)$ and $(-2, 0)$. The *y*-intercept is $(0, -6)$. The vertical asymptote is $x = 1$. The non-horizontal asymptote is $y = x + 6$. There are no holes.

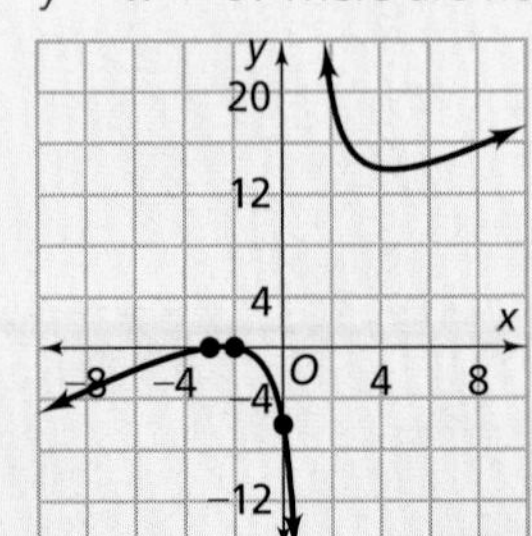

5. a. $\frac{3}{2}$

b. 0

c. ∞

Chapter 3

Review

Go Online PHSchool.com — For vocabulary review, go to Web Code: bgj-0351

In **Investigation 3A,** you learned to

- state the Change of Sign Theorem and the Intermediate Value Theorem for Polynomials, and to use them to analyze the graphs of polynomial functions
- find the equation of a line secant to a polynomial function and the average rate of change of a function between two points
- write the Taylor expansion for a polynomial function about a point
- find the equation of the tangent to a polynomial curve at a point

The following questions will help you check your understanding.

1. a. Find, if possible, a third-degree polynomial function f with a graph that satisfies the following conditions.
- The graph of f crosses the *x*-axis at $(-4, 0)$ and $(-1, 0)$, and intersects it somewhere on the positive *x*-axis.
- From left to right, the graph of f rises, falls, and rises.
- The graph of f crosses the *y*-axis at $(0, -3)$.

b. Can you find a polynomial that satisfies the first two conditions but crosses the *y*-axis at $(0, 3)$ instead of $(0, -3)$? Explain.

2. Suppose $f(x) = x^4 - x^3 - 2x^2 - 1$.

a. Find the average rate of change of *y* with respect to *x* as *x* goes from -1 to 1.

b. Find the equation of the secant line between $(-1, f(-1))$ and $(1, f(1))$.

c. Find all intersections of the graph of $y = f(x)$ and the secant you just found. Give coordinates to the nearest thousandth.

3. Suppose that $f(x) = 4x^3 + x^2 - 3x + 5$.

a. Expand $f(x)$ in powers of $x + 1$.

b. Find the equation of the line tangent to the graph of $f(x)$ at the point $(-1, 5)$.

In **Investigation 3B,** you learned to

- sketch the graph of a rational function, including asymptotes and holes
- evaluate limits of rational expressions
- find the equation of the tangent to the graph of a rational function at a point

The following questions will help you check your understanding.

4. For the graph of each rational function, find, if possible,
- the *x*- and *y*-intercepts
- the equation of each vertical asymptote
- the equation of each horizontal asymptote
- the coordinates of any holes

Then sketch the graph.

a. $f(x) = \frac{x + 1}{x^2 - 1}$

b. $g(x) = \frac{x - 3}{4x^2 - 9}$

c. $h(x) = \frac{2x^2 - 5x - 12}{6x^2 + 11x + 3}$

d. $j(x) = \frac{x^2 + 5x + 6}{x - 1}$

5. Find each limit.

a. $\lim_{x \to \infty} \frac{3x + 1}{2x + 3}$

b. $\lim_{x \to \infty} \frac{4x - 5}{3x^2 - x - 2}$

c. $\lim_{x \to \infty} \frac{x^2 - 2x + 1}{x - 2}$

6. Find an equation of the line tangent to the graph of $f(x) = \frac{x-3}{x^2+3x-4}$ at the point $(2, f(2))$.

In **Investigation 3C,** you learned to

- state and use the limit and factorial definitions of e and e^x
- use the inverse relationship between e^x and $\ln x$ to solve equations
- find the equation for the line tangent to the graph of $y = e^x$ or $y = \ln x$ at a point

The following questions will help you check your understanding.

7. a. Give an estimate of $e^{0.08}$ using the first four terms of the factorial definition of e^x.

   b. Give an estimate of $e^{0.08}$ by evaluating $\left(1 + \frac{0.08}{n}\right)^n$ for $n = 10$.

   c. Use your calculator to find $e^{0.08}$ to five decimal places.

8. Jane invests \$1000 at 5.5% APR, compounded continuously. After t years, her account balance is

$$B = 1000e^{0.055t}$$

   a. How much money will Jane have in this account after 5 years? After 10 years?

   b. How long will it take for Jane's account to grow to \$2000? \$10,000?

9. Let $f(x) = e^x$ and $g(x) = \ln x$.

   a. Find an equation of the line tangent to the graph of f at the point $(2, f(2))$.

   b. Find an equation of the line tangent to the graph of g at the point $(2, g(2))$.

   c. At what point does the graph of f have a tangent line of slope 3?

   d. At what point does the graph of g have a tangent line of slope $\frac{1}{3}$?

6. $y = -\frac{1}{6} + \frac{13(x-2)}{36}$

7. a. $e^{0.08} \approx 1.08329$

b. $e^{0.08} \approx 1.08294$

c. $e^{0.08} \approx 1.08329$

8. a. \$1316.53; \$1733.25

b. 12.063 years; 41.865 years

9. a. $y = e^2x - e^2$ or $y = 7.38906x - 7.38906$

b. $y = \frac{1}{2}x - 1 + \ln 2$ or $y = 0.5x - 0.306853$

c. $(\ln 3, 3)$ or $(1.09861, 3)$

d. $(3, \ln 3)$ or $(3, 1.09861)$

Test

Assessment Resources

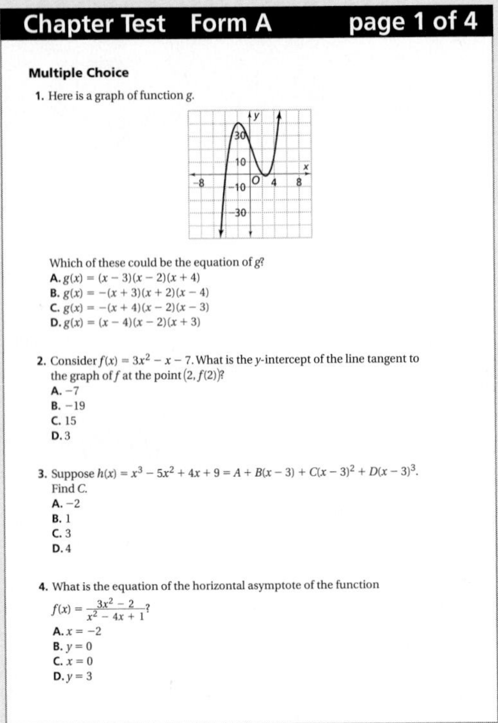

Chapter Test Form A page 1 of 4

Multiple Choice

1. Here is a graph of function g.

Which of these could be the equation of g?
A. $g(x) = (x - 3)(x - 2)(x + 4)$
B. $g(x) = -(x + 3)(x + 2)(x - 4)$
C. $g(x) = -(x + 4)(x - 2)(x - 3)$
D. $g(x) = (x - 4)(x - 2)(x + 3)$

2. Consider $f(x) = 3x^2 - x - 7$. What is the y-intercept of the line tangent to the graph of f at the point $(2, f(2))$?
A. −7
B. −19
C. 15
D. 3

3. Suppose $h(x) = x^3 - 5x^2 + 4x + 9 = A + B(x - 3) + C(x - 3)^2 + D(x - 3)^3$. Find C.
A. −2
B. 1
C. 3
D. 4

4. What is the equation of the horizontal asymptote of the function $f(x) = \frac{3x^2 - 2}{x^2 - 4x + 1}$?
A. $x = -2$
B. $y = 0$
C. $x = 0$
D. $y = 3$

Also available: Form B

Chapter 3 Test

For a chapter test, go to Web Code: bga-0353

Multiple Choice

1. Here is a graph of function g.

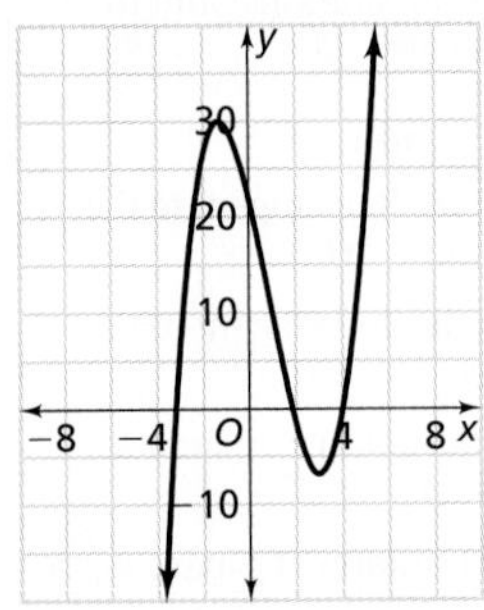

Which of these could be the equation of g?

A. $g(x) = (x + 4)(x + 2)(x - 3)$
B. $g(x) = -(x + 4)(x + 2)(x - 3)$
C. $g(x) = -(x - 4)(x - 2)(x + 3)$
D. $g(x) = (x - 4)(x - 2)(x + 3)$

2. Consider $f(x) = 2x^2 - 5x + 6$. What is the y-intercept of the line tangent to the graph of f at the point $(2, f(2))$?

A. −2 B. 2 C. 3 D. 4

3. Suppose $h(x) = x^3 - 4x^2 + 8x + 11 = A + B(x - 3) + C(x - 3)^2 + D(x - 3)^3$. Find C.

A. −13 B. −1 C. 5 D. 11

4. What is the equation of the horizontal asymptote of the function $f(x) = \frac{x - 1}{x^2 - x - 6}$?

A. $x = 0$ B. $y = 0$
C. $y = -2$ D. $x = 3$

5. Which of the following is an x-intercept of the function $f(x) = \frac{2x^2 - 2}{x^2 - 4}$?

A. −2 B. $\frac{1}{2}$ C. 1 D. 2

6. Let $h(x) = \frac{3x - 7}{x - 2}$. Find $\lim_{x \to \infty} h(x)$.

A. ∞ B. 3
C. 2 D. $-\infty$

7. Estimate the slope of the line tangent to the graph of $g(x) = 3^x$ at $x = 0$.

A. 0.2 B. 0.8
C. 1.1 D. 2.5

8. Calculate the total value after 6 years of an initial investment of $2250 that earns 7% interest compounded quarterly.

A. $3412.00 B. $3424.41
C. $3472.16 D. $3472.27

9. Which expression could be used to directly calculate $\log_5 18$?

A. $\ln 5 - \ln 18$
B. $\ln 18 - \ln 5$
C. $\frac{\ln 5}{\ln 18}$
D. $\frac{\ln 18}{\ln 5}$

10. Which statement about the graph of $f(x) = \ln x$ is false?

A. It is symmetric about the origin.
B. It is unbounded.
C. It has a vertical asymptote.
D. It is increasing on its domain.

Answers

Chapter Test

1. D
2. A
3. C
4. B
5. C
6. B
7. C
8. A
9. D
10. A

11. a.

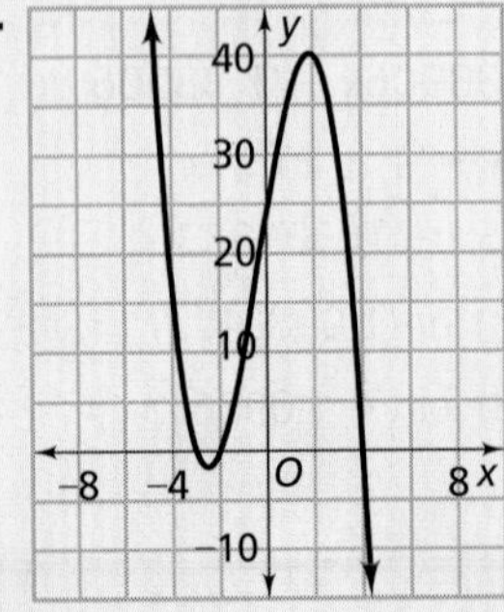

b. (−3, 0), (−2, 0), (4, 0), (0, 24)
c. −3
d. $y = -3x + 39$

12. a. $h(x) = (x - 1)^3 + 2$
b. $(x - 1)^2 + \frac{2}{x - 1}$
c. $x^2 - 2x + 1 + \frac{2}{x - 1}$
d. They are equal, so you can use expansion to divide a polynomial by a binomial.

13. a. 106 feet per second
b. 106 feet per second

Open Response

11. Consider $f(x) = -(x - 4)(x + 2)(x + 3)$.

a. Sketch the graph of f.

b. Identify all intercepts of the graph.

c. Find the average rate of change of y with respect to x as x goes from 1 to 3.

d. Write the equation of the secant between $(1, f(1))$ and $(3, f(3))$.

12. Suppose that $h(x) = x^3 - 3x^2 + 3x + 1$.

a. Expand $h(x)$ into powers of $x - 1$.

b. Divide the result by $x - 1$.

c. Simplify $\frac{h(x)}{x - 1}$.

d. What conclusion can you draw from your answers to parts (b) and (c)?

13. A toy rocket takes off straight up in the air from level ground. The rocket's distance (in feet) above the ground at time t (in seconds) is $f(t) = 170t - 16t^2$.

a. Find the average velocity during the first 4 seconds.

b. Find the instantaneous velocity at $t = 2$.

14. Let $p(x) = \frac{2x^3 - 3x^2 - 5x - 12}{x - 3}$.

a. Copy and complete this table for $p(x)$.

x	$p(x)$
0	■
1	■
2	■
3	■
4	■

b. Simplify the expression $\frac{2x^3 - 3x^2 - 5x - 12}{x - 3}$.

c. Let $q(x) = 2x^2 + 3x + 4$. Find $\lim_{x \to 3} p(x)$ and $\lim_{x \to 3} q(x)$.

d. Explain why the graph of p is not the same as q.

15. Find the limit.

a. $\lim_{x \to \infty} \frac{x + 2}{3x + 2}$ **b.** $\lim_{x \to \infty} \frac{\cos x}{x}$ **c.** $\lim_{x \to 3} \frac{\ln x}{\ln x^2}$

16. Let $f(x) = \frac{5x - 1}{x^2 - 2x - 15}$, $g(x) = \frac{A}{x + 3}$, and $h(x) = \frac{B}{x - 5}$, where A and B are constants.

a. Find A and B so that $f(x) = g(x) + h(x)$.

b. Find the slope of the line tangent to g at $x = 4$.

c. Find the slope of the line tangent to h at $x = 4$.

d. Find the slope of the line tangent to f at $x = 4$.

17. Copy and complete the table, using continuous compounding.

Initial Investment	APR	Time to Double	Amount in 15 years
\$12,500	9%	■	■
\$32,500	8%	■	■
\$9,500	■	4 years	■
\$16,800	■	6 years	■

18. Calculate each of the following. If necessary, round to three decimal places.

a. $e^{2 \ln 3}$ **b.** $\ln 2 + \ln 3$

c. $\log_2 3$ **d.** $\ln(-2)$

e. $\ln e^{2-3}$

19. Solve for x to three decimal places.

a. $e^x = 5$ **b.** $\ln x = 2$

20. At what point does the graph of $f(x) = \ln x$ have a tangent line of slope 5?

21. Find the polynomial function that has the following characteristics:

- Leading coefficient 2
- Degree 3
- Zeros -2, 1, and 4
- From left to right, its graph rises, falls, and rises.

Assessment Resources

Chapter Test Form A page 2 of 4

5. Which of the following is an x-intercept of the function $f(x) = \frac{2x^2 - 8}{x^2 - 9}$?
A. -3
B. -2
C. 4
D. 3

6. Let $h(x) = \frac{4x - 9}{2x + 1}$. Calculate $\lim_{x \to \infty} h(x)$.
A. 2
B. ∞
C. -9
D. $-\infty$

7. Estimate the slope of the line tangent to the graph of $f(x) = \log_3 x$ at $x = 0$.
A. -1
B. 0
C. 1
D. undefined

8. Calculate the total value after 5 years of an initial investment of \$2375 that earns 4% interest compounded monthly.
A. \$2899.87
B. \$2900.95
C. \$2901.13
D. \$2902.28

9. Which expression could be used to directly calculate $\log_4 21$?
A. $\frac{\ln 21}{\ln 4}$ B. $\frac{\ln 4}{\ln 21}$
C. $\ln 21 - \ln 4$ D. $\ln 4 - \ln 21$

10. Which statement about the graph of $f(x) = \ln x$ is correct?
A. It is symmetric about the origin.
B. It has a horizontal asymptote.
C. It has a vertical asymptote.
D. It is decreasing on its domain.

Also available: Form B

14. a.

x	$p(x)$
0	4
1	9
2	18
3	undefined
4	48

b. $2x^2 + 3x + 4$

c. $\lim_{x \to 3} p(x) = \lim_{x \to 3} q(x) = 31$

d. There is a hole in the graph of $p(x)$ at $x = 3$.

15. a. $\frac{1}{3}$

b. 0

c. $\frac{1}{2}$

16. a. $A = 2$, $B = 3$

b. about -0.04

c. about -3.00

d. about -3.04

17.

Initial Investment	APR	Time to Double	Amount in 15 years
\$12,500	9%	7.7 years	\$48,217.82
\$32,500	8%	8.66 years	\$107,903.80
\$9,500	17.33%	4 years	\$127,841.57
\$16,800	11.55%	6 years	\$95,000.19

18. a. 9 **b.** 1.792 **c.** 1.585

d. undefined **e.** -1

19. a. $x \approx 1.609$

b. $x \approx 7.389$

20. $\left(\frac{1}{5}, \ln \frac{1}{5}\right)$

21. $f(x) = 2x^3 - 6x^2 - 12x + 16$

Chapter 4 Combinatorics

Many consider combinatorics an art—the art of knowing when to apply the various techniques you know. There are only a few algorithms that you can apply uniformly to counting problems. For this reason, many students feel frustrated when tackling these problems.

In this chapter, students have plenty of opportunities to try unfamiliar problems, develop their own strategies, run into blind alleys, make mistakes, and correct those mistakes. Students begin with three problems, that they continue to approach throughout the chapter as they develop more strategies for solving them.

Early in the chapter, students learn the approach of identifying *isomorphic problems*, problems with similar mathematical structures. The focus changes from algorithms to the similarities among the problems.

Students are also introduced to simple and intuitive strategies for solving certain classes of problems. As the chapter progresses, they learn more formal notation for permutations and combinations, as well as more complicated problems.

The last investigation focuses on cementing ideas from the entire chapter. It is typical for students to know that Pascal's Triangle entries, combinations, and binomial coefficients are connected in a vague way, but they concretize the connection by answering questions from multiple perspectives.

Throughout the chapter, encourage students to try to solve problems in multiple ways. The more ways they can explain a problem, the easier it will be for them to tackle new problems.

Chapter Overview

INVESTIGATION 4A, *Learning to Count,* shows students fairly challenging combinatorial problems and three strategies for solving them.

INVESTIGATION 4B, *Permutations and Combinations,* formally introduces students to permutations and combinations.

INVESTIGATION 4C, *Making Connections,* has students revisit Pascal's triangle with the goal of making sense of connected ideas.

For more information on the Investigations, see

- Chapter Road Map, p. 274
- Investigation Road Maps, pp. 276, 294, 324

PROJECT The Project near the end of the chapter is optional. You can assign the Project at any time during the chapter depending on how often and how long you feel students should work on it.

DAILY PLANNER DAILY PLANNER DAILY PL

Pacing Suggestions and Materials

Investigation 4A *Learning to Count*

DAY	LESSON	HOMEWORK
1	4.1 Getting Started Core: 1, 2 Optional: none	Core: 3 Optional: 4
2	4.2 Are They Different or the Same? Core: 1, 2, 3, 4, 5, 7 Optional: 6	Core: 8, 9, 10, 13, 16, 17 Optional: 11, 12, 14; Extension: 15
3	4.3 Strategies for Counting Core: 1, 2, 3, 4, 6, 7, 9 Optional: 5, 8	Core: 10, 11, 12, 14, 16, 18, 19, 20, 21 Optional: 13, 15, 17, 22, 23
4	4.4 Counting All Functions Core: 1, 2, 3, 5 Optional: 4	Core: 6, 7, 9, 10 Optional: 8, 11, 12

Investigation 4B *Permutations and Combinations*

DAY	LESSON	HOMEWORK
1	4.5 Getting Started Core: 1, 2 Optional: none	Core: 3 Optional: 4
2	4.6 Permutations Core: 1, 2, 3, 4, 5, 6, 9, 10 Optional: 7, 8, 11	Core: 12, 13, 14, 15, 16, 17, 18, 21, 22, 23, Optional: 19, 20, 24, 26, 27
3	4.7 Combinations Core: 1, 2, 3, 4, 9, 10, 11, 15, 18 Optional: 5, 6, 7, 8, 12, 13, 14, 16, 17, 19, 20	Core: 21, 22, 23, 24, 27, 28, 32, 33, 34, 35, Optional: 25, 26, 29, 30, 31, 38, 40 Extension: 36, 37
4	4.8 Putting It Together Core: 1, 2, 4, 6 Optional: 3; Extension: 5	Core: 7, 8, 9, 10, 11, 12, 13, 14, 15, 16, 17, Optional: 20; Extension: 18

NOTES	MATERIALS
Let students focus on "strategies" rather than "answers" in this first lesson.	• graphing calculators • Blackline Masters 4.1A–B
	• graphing calculators • Blackline Master 4.2
Students should get lots of practice with these exercises.	• graphing calculators • Blackline Master 4.3
Since this is a short lesson, you may want to give students more time to work on the exercises from the previous lesson.	• graphing calculators • Blackline Master 4.4

NOTES	MATERIALS
Have students focus on *new* strategies for these exercises.	• graphing calculators • Blackline Masters 4.1A–B
You may want to take two days for this lesson.	• graphing calculators • Blackline Masters 4.6A–B
You may want to take two days for this lesson. There are many exercises for practice.	• graphing calculators • Blackline Masters MC12, 4.7A–B
While the lesson text is short, the heart of the lesson is in the exercises.	• graphing calculators • Blackline Master 4.7A

Mathematics Background

ISOMORPHIC PROBLEMS The words *isomorphic* and *isomorphism* have technical meanings in other branches of mathematics that are compatible with, but not exactly the same as, their use in this chapter. Here *isomorphic problems* is a phrase used to identify problems with similar mathematical structures. A favorite example of identifying isomorphic problems comes from this string of problems, taken from the end of Investigation 4B:

- In how many different ways can you write 20 as a sum of three counting numbers?
- In how many different ways can you put 20 quarters into three colored pockets (red, green, and blue) so that there is at least one coin in each pocket?
- There are 19 people and only 2 tickets to a concert. How many ways are there to choose which two people go to the concent?

At first glance, these problems do not look isomorphic to students, because two of the problems seem to be about 20 objects, and one seems to be about 19 objects. But all of these problems essentially involve choosing 2 objects from 19, and they all can be solved using the formula $\binom{19}{2}$. Understanding why all three of these problems are structurally similar helps students shake the uneasy feeling they sometimes have around solving combinatorial problems.

THE COUNTING PRINCIPLE In Lesson 4.3 of the first investigation, students develop multiple counting strategies for situations that can be counted in stages. The Counting Principle underlies these strategies. Students apply it indirectly in two counting strategies.

In the box method, students translate a problem into an isomorphic problem that amounts to filling in boxes with various objects. For example, to count the number of five-digit numbers that can be made from the digits {1, 2, 4}, imagine five boxes. In each box, you can put a 1, 2, or 4. In how many ways can you fill the boxes?

For the tree approach to this same problem, you start to construct (and imagine finishing) a tree:

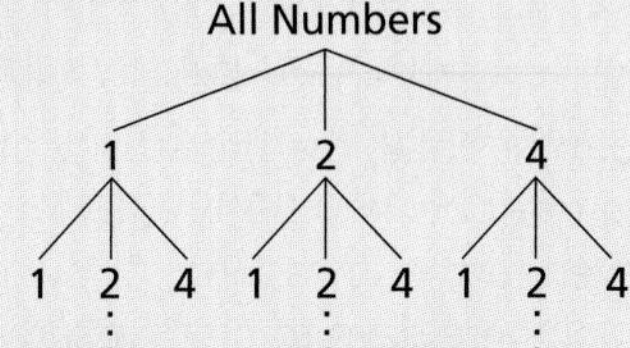

At each stage, each number points to three possibilities. This goes on for five generations. How many paths are there from top to bottom? Or, how many numbers are along the bottom row?

continued on p. 274c

continued from p. 274b

Students are also introduced to the approach of *solve a simpler problem*. This is more subtle, and in some ways, more abstract. It is closely aligned with recursive thinking in the sense that it requires one to

- peel off a stage and count the remaining stages (a simpler problem), and then
- multiply this result by the number of ways in the last stage

The number of possible outcomes for a situation consisting of n independent outcomes is the product $m_1 \cdot m_2 \cdot \ldots \cdot m_{n-1} \cdot m_n$. Here n is the number of stages. In order for this to apply, each element at any stage has to have the same number of extensions to the next stage. The Simplex Lock in the chapter project is an example of a counting problem that does *not* have this property.

In our example of five-digit numbers, you could reason that the number of five-digit numbers using only 1, 2, and 4 is three times the number of four-digit numbers using only 1, 2 and 4. The thinking involves imagining the list of four digit numbers already made and counting the number of ways (3) you can complete each to get a five-digit number.

Extensions and Connections

Consider the following question from Investigation 4A:

> In a kindergarten class, each student has four pictures: a square, a triangle, a circle, and a star. Each of the kids will make a design by gluing these four pictures in a line. There are 20 kids in the class. Can each child make a different design or will there have to be repeats? (Note: Each symbol can be used only once!)

There are 24 possibilities and 20 students, so each one might have made a different design. But there are other interesting problems here to explore.

First, try switching perspectives from just counting to determining the likelihood of having different designs:

> If the 20 students make their designs at random, what is the probability that all of them will make different designs? What is the probability that there is at least one duplicate?

The probability that they are all different is $\frac{24 \cdot 23 \cdot 22 \cdot \ldots \cdot 5}{24^{20}} \approx 0.0000064$. By subtracting this result from the total, the probability of at least one duplicate must be ≈ 0.9999936. You can extend this even further by asking, "How many students would there have to be to assure at least a 50% chance of at least one repeat if they make the designs at random? (The answer is 7.) (Also note the relationship to the birthday problem!)

DAILY PLANNER DAILY PLANNER DAILY PL

Pacing Suggestions and Materials

Investigation 4C *Making Connections*

DAY	LESSON	HOMEWORK
1	4.9 Getting Started Core: 1, 2, 3, 4, 5, 6, 7, 8, 9, 10 Optional: none	Core: 11, 12, 13, 14, 15, 17 Optional: 16
2	4.10 Revisiting the Binomial Theorem Core: 1, 2, 3, 4 Optional: 5	Core: 6, 7, 10 Optional: 8, 11; Extension: 9
3	4.11 Connections Core: 1, 2, 3, 4, 5, 6 Optional: 7, 8	Core: 9, 10, 11, 12, 14 Optional: 15; Extension: 13

NOTES	MATERIALS
	• graphing calculators • Blackline Masters 4.1B, 4.9
This lesson is short.	• CAS • graphing calculators • Blackline Master MC12
This lesson is short.	• graphing calculators • Blackline Master MC12

What if a match is a bad thing? That is, what if you want all different designs? That leads to another interesting extension:

> Suppose a whole school of kindergartners makes these designs and arranges them randomly along the hallways of the school. How many random designs would you expect them to put up to have each design on the wall at least once?

This is the famous *collector's problem*, usually stated as the isomorphic problem of finding the expected number of boxes of cereal a collector must buy to get one each of n prizes distributed at random with equal probability in the boxes.

This is a great problem to simulate with your students. Have them pick numbers from 1–24 at random and record how many trials they need in order to get each number once. You may want students to work in groups to get a good sampling of data. Then average the number of trials. Compare this with the expected value for the number of trials needed: $n\left(\frac{1}{1} + \frac{1}{2} + \frac{1}{3} + \cdots + \frac{1}{n}\right)$, where you are selecting at random from n equally likely things. In the case of 24 designs, this comes out to be slightly more than 90.

To prove this, ask yourself how long you expect to wait to get the kth new number as you run through your trials.

Another interesting problem arises when you consider what happens when you enlarge the class size:

> If more kids join the class, so that the total exceeds 24, then there must be repeats. Suppose there are m kindergartners in the school completing this activity. Explain why one design must be used by at least $m/24$ students, rounded up. Explain why one design must be used by no more than $m/24$ students, rounded down.

These questions are based on the *Dirichlet Box Principle*, which states that if you distribute m things (in this case, students) into n boxes (in this case, designs) some box must have at least m/n, rounded up, objects, and some box must have no more than m/n, rounded down, objects.

RESOURCES If you or your students want to pursue other counting methods, good sources are:

- *The Book of Numbers* by Conway and Guy. Copernicus Books (1997).
- *Concrete Mathematics* by Graham, Knuth, and Patashinik. Addison Wesley (1989).
- *The Mathematics of Chance: Counting without Counting* by Niven. Mathematical Association of America (1965).
- *Combinatorics: A Problem Oriented Approach* by Marcus. Mathematical Association of America (1998).

Developing Students' Mathematical Habits

SOLVING A SIMPLER PROBLEM The strategy of solving a simpler problem to solve counting problems is subtle and abstract. It is closely aligned with recursive thinking in the sense that it requires one to:

- peel off a stage and count the remaining stages (a simpler problem) and then
- multiply this result by the number of ways in the last stage.

IDENTIFYING AND CREATING ISOMORPHIC PROBLEMS By actively searching for isomorphic problems, students find ways to link new and unfamiliar problems to other problems they know how to solve.

COUNTING FUNCTIONS Students learn to solve counting problems by counting the number of functions from one finite set to another.

KNOWING *WHEN* TO USE PARTICULAR COUNTING STRATEGIES One big goal for students in this chapter is that they leave aside the common habit students sometimes have—when faced with a combinatorics problem—of wondering, "Is this a permutations problem or a combinations problem?" At the end of this chapter, students have a number of counting strategies at their disposal, and they will be in the habit of looking at the mathematical structure of a problem to determine what strategies make sense to use.

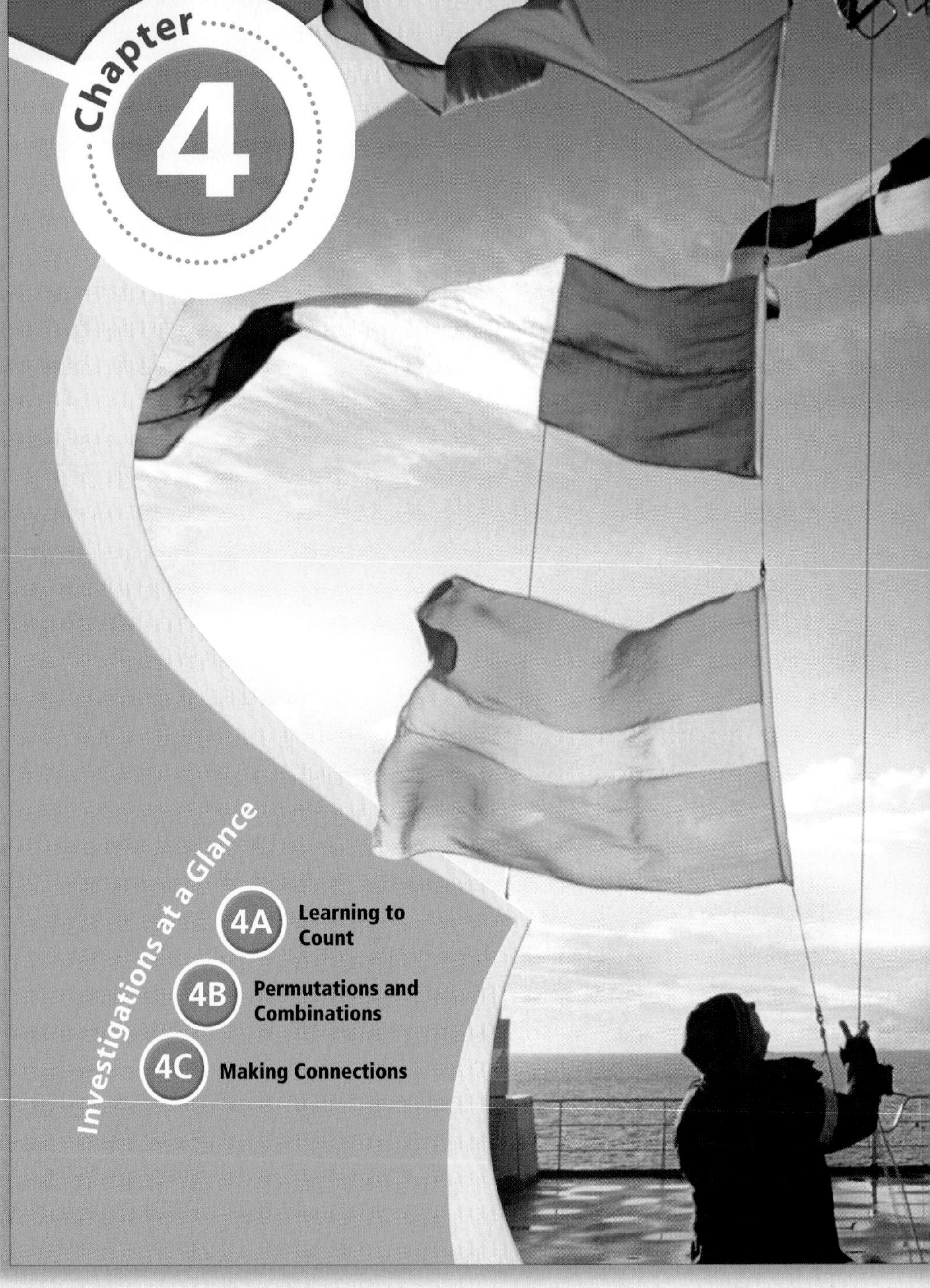

Chapter Road Map

INVESTIGATION 4A, ***Learning to Count,*** has students explore fairly challenging combinatorial problems before presenting them with formal strategies for solving these problems. At the end of the investigation, students see three strategies—the "box method," building tree diagrams, and "solving a smaller problem."

INVESTIGATION 4B, ***Permutations and Combinations,*** formally introduces permutations and combinations.

INVESTIGATION 4C, ***Making Connections,*** revisits Pascal's triangle with the goal of making sense of connected ideas.

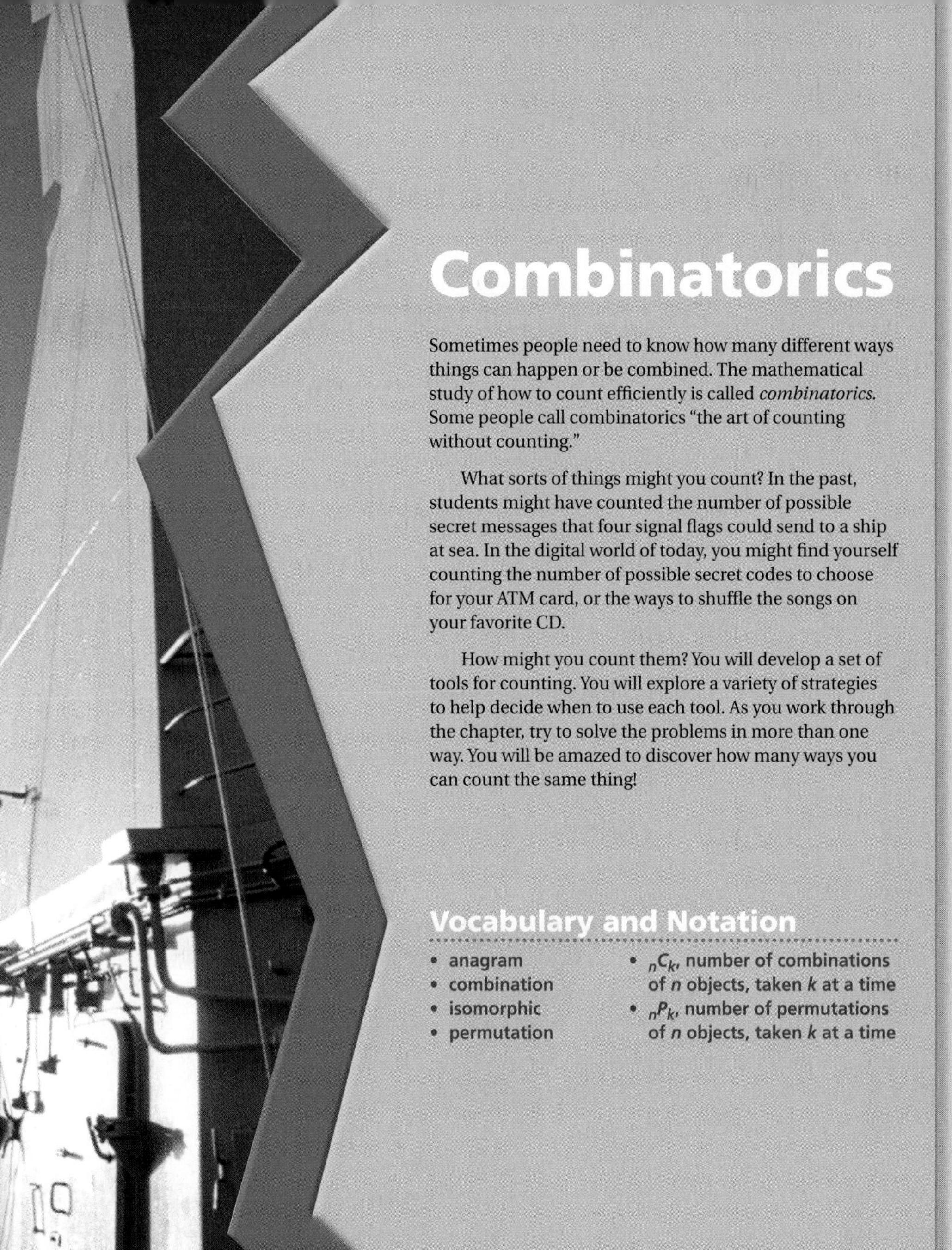

Combinatorics

Sometimes people need to know how many different ways things can happen or be combined. The mathematical study of how to count efficiently is called *combinatorics*. Some people call combinatorics "the art of counting without counting."

What sorts of things might you count? In the past, students might have counted the number of possible secret messages that four signal flags could send to a ship at sea. In the digital world of today, you might find yourself counting the number of possible secret codes to choose for your ATM card, or the ways to shuffle the songs on your favorite CD.

How might you count them? You will develop a set of tools for counting. You will explore a variety of strategies to help decide when to use each tool. As you work through the chapter, try to solve the problems in more than one way. You will be amazed to discover how many ways you can count the same thing!

Vocabulary and Notation

- **anagram**
- **combination**
- **isomorphic**
- **permutation**
- **$_nC_k$, number of combinations of n objects, taken k at a time**
- **$_nP_k$, number of permutations of n objects, taken k at a time**

Chapter Vocabulary and Notation

The following list gives key vocabulary and notation used in the chapter. Selected new vocabulary and notation items are shown in boldface on the student page.

- anagram, p. 300
- combination, p. 305
- isomorphic, p. 281
- permutation, p. 298
- $_nC_k$, number of combinations of n objects, taken k at a time, p. 306
- $_nP_k$, number of permutations of n objects, taken k at a time, p. 298

Chapter Technology

CME Project *Precalculus* assumes that each student has access to a graphing calculator. It also recommends access to a computer algebra system (CAS) and to geometry software.

Support for the use of technology is available in the TI-Nspire™ Technology Handbook. See p. 704.

A list of technology used with important concepts in this chapter appears below. Students will need access to the functionality listed to develop complete understanding of these topics.

Computer Algebra System

LESSON 4.10 Expand a binomial raised to a power, p. 329.

LESSON 4.10 Find the coefficient of a specific term in a binomial expansion, p. 330.

Geometry Software

CUMULATIVE REVIEW Sketch the graph of a function, p. 338.

Investigation Overview

The Getting Started lesson presents students with three prototypes of the problems answered by combinatorics. The problems posed are themes throughout the chapter; do not expect students to solve them immediately. The interest, learning, and *fun* come from working on these problems and seeing different approaches. The methods developed later in the chapter will give students much more machinery to use.

Combinatorics is a collection of mathematical methods that can be used to count the number of elements in a set without enumerating them. This investigation previews the types of problems that combinatorics seeks to answer. Part of the attraction of combinatorics for students is that the problems are completely comprehensible; students can read them, understand what the question is asking, and perhaps even formulate some strategies for working towards an answer. However, the actual process of arriving at a correct answer is a bit of a challenge.

The first part of the investigation emphasizes the importance of having a good counting strategy that includes every case once and only once. Then, in the second part of the investigation, students recognize that the similarities among the problems are due to similarities in their mathematical structure; that is, they are isomorphic problems.

The third and fourth lessons prepare students to begin the formal development of permutations and combinations. Students develop multiple counting strategies for situations that can be counted in stages. The Counting Principle underlies these strategies, although students are not formally introduced to it by name.

You may wish to assign Questions 1–3 for students to think and write about during the investigation.

Learning Goals

- Recognize the kinds of problems that you can solve using combinatorics.
- Develop your own strategies for systematic counting.

Habits and Skills

- Use efficient strategies for counting.
- Identify isomorphic problems.
- Apply counting strategies to functions defined on finite sets.

Learning to Count

In *Learning to Count,* you will learn some techniques to solve counting problems. You will learn that some problems that appear different actually have the same underlying mathematical structure.

By the end of this investigation, you will be able to answer questions like these.

1. How many five-digit numbers can you make using only the digits 1 and 2?
2. In a kindergarten class, each student has four pictures: a square, a triangle, a circle, and a star. Each of the kids will make a design by gluing these four pictures in a line. There are 20 kids in the class. Can each child make a different design or will there have to be repeats?
3. What does it mean for two problems to be isomorphic?

You will learn how to

- recognize the kinds of problems that you can solve using combinatorics
- develop your own strategies for systematic counting

You will develop these habits and skills:

- Use efficient strategies for counting.
- Identify isomorphic problems.
- Apply counting strategies to functions defined on finite sets.

What does a softball team's batting order have in common with the outcome in a race of 9 horses?

Investigation Road Map

LESSON 4.1, *Getting Started,* has students experiment with new (and fairly sophisticated) problems.

LESSON 4.2, *Are They Different or the Same?,* shows students multiple informal strategies for solving combinatorics problems and presents the idea of "isomorphic problems."

LESSON 4.3, *Strategies for Counting,* introduces students to slightly more formal strategies for problem solving, although the nature of the lesson remains experimental.

LESSON 4.4, *Counting All Functions,* has students learn the strategy of counting functions from one finite set to another as a way of solving combinatorics problems.

4.1 Getting Started

Throughout this chapter, you will see three problems several times: The Same Birthday, Trains, and Pascal's Paths. You will see them for the first time in this Getting Started lesson. Try to develop your own techniques for solving them. You might not solve them all today, but you will get plenty of chances to try them during this chapter as you learn more ways to "count without counting."

For You to Explore

1. **The Same Birthday**

   In Ms. Roskam's class of 25 students, two of them have the same birthday. The students are very surprised to discover this. Ms. Roskam tells them that it is actually a good bet that, in a group of 25 people chosen at random, at least two of them will share a birthday.

   Is Ms. Roskam right? Suppose you choose 25 people at random and put them in a classroom. What is the probability that at least two of them share a birthday? If you want to ensure that the probability is more than 50%, what is the number of people you must have in that classroom?

2. **Trains**

   You can use number rods to build "trains" that all share a common length. A "train of length 5" is a row of rods that has a combined length of 5.

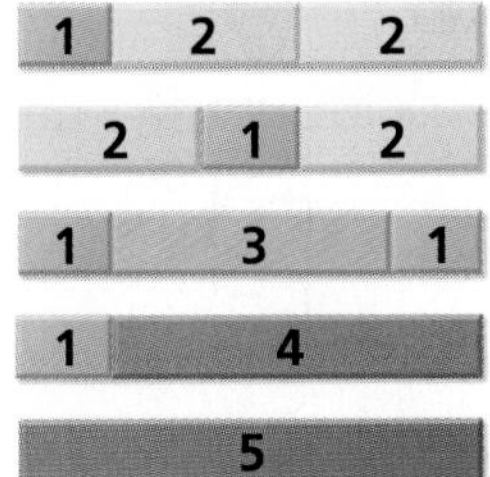

   Notice that the 1–2–2 train and the 2–1–2 train contain the same rods. If you use identical rods in different orders, you make different trains.

   How many distinct trains of length n can you make?

Within a train you can repeat a length, and trains can contain different numbers of rods.

Answers

For You to Explore

1. Yes; about 56.87%; 23
2. 2^{n-1}

Lesson Overview

GOAL

- Warm up to the ideas of the investigation.

This is the quintessential Getting Started lesson! Students really get to experience the mathematics before they see any development of the formal ideas. They may feel frustrated because they do not yet have tools to solve the exercises, but encourage them to try things out. The point here is for kids to muck about in the mathematics and to have fun with the problems.

FOR YOU TO EXPLORE
- Core: 1, 2
- Optional: none

MATERIALS
- graphing calculators
- Blackline Masters 4.1A–B

HOMEWORK
- Core: 3
- Optional: 4

Launch

Begin this lesson by asking students to read over the problems, and then begin working on them.

Explore

For You to Explore

Do not expect students to solve the problems at this time, although some might! For each problem, you might ask them to explain what the problem is about, develop some theories about how to go about solving it, and even hypothesize about the solution. Have them record any work they do, so that they can revisit these original solutions later, after they develop formal counting strategies. They can evaluate how accurate their original solutions were, and write revised solutions based on their new learning.

PROBLEM 1 When the class reads this problem, ask students what it means for the probability to be more than 50%. Check to see that they have some sense of how to calculate probability. If not, you may want to review basic probability before continuing with this chapter. They will see more probability problems in Chapter 7.

Students are often surprised by this problem, so one teacher developed an interesting simulation. At the beginning of each class period, she had each student in her class of 27 write down a number between 1 and 365. Then she asked each student to read his or her number to see if there was a match. She kept a record on a big calendar of matches and non-matches. More than half the days were matches.

Use Blackline Master 4.1A on an overhead to initially acquaint students with this example. It reoccurs often in the chapter.

PROBLEM 3 Students revisit this exercise several times in this chapter, and very few will find the correct solution now. Spend some time discussing it with Blackline Master 4.1B on an overhead. At first, just draw several paths, indicating which ones are correct and which are incorrect. Suggest the complexity of the problem but do not expect a solution; that will come much later. Do not give away the answer; just check that students are making progress to a correct solution.

Wrap Up

You might wrap this lesson up with a discussion of strategies the students tried. You could also let them know that they will see actual strategies for solving these problems in the upcoming chapter.

Exercises

HOMEWORK

- Core: 3
- Optional: 4

Exercises *Practicing Habits of Mind*

On Your Own

3. Pascal's Paths

Ms. Pascal likes to take a different route to work every day. She will quit her job the day she has to repeat a route she has already taken. The grid of streets below shows her home and her workplace. She only travels north and east and never backtracks. How many days will she work at this job?

Two trips are different if they are not the same everywhere. They might overlap on some segments though, like the two valid paths shown below.

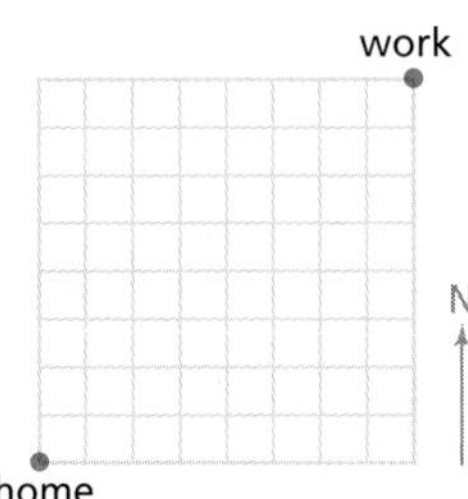

To understand the problem better, look at some possible paths on a grid of streets. Only two of the paths below are Pascal paths. The third path is not a Pascal path since Ms. Pascal never travels south or west.

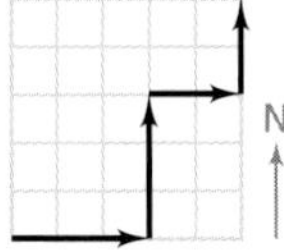

Here is a valid path.

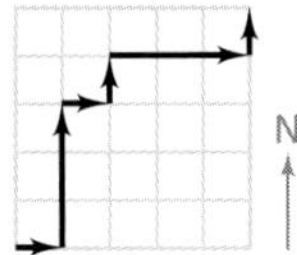

This is also valid.

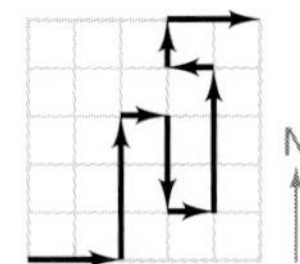

This is not a valid path.

Maintain Your Skills

4. Consider the following three games.

Game 1 Flip two coins. If you get exactly two heads, you win.

Game 2 Flip three coins. If you get exactly two heads, you win.

Game 3 Flip four coins. If you get exactly two heads, you win.

Which game gives you the greatest probability of winning?

Answers

Exercises

3. 12,830 days

4. games 2 and 3 (The probability of winning each is $\frac{3}{8}$.)

4.2 Are They Different or the Same?

In Getting Started, you got a sense for the kinds of objects that you might count in combinatorial problems. In this lesson, you will practice counting more objects. As you work through the problems, think about how you are counting as well as what you are counting.

For You to Do

1. How many three-digit numbers can you make using only the digits 1 and 2? (In each number you may use a digit more than once.)
2. In a kindergarten class, children are to color each of three different shapes either green or red. How many different colorings are possible?
3. A pizzeria has three choices of toppings: onions, mushrooms, and pepperoni. How many different kinds of pizza are possible?
4. Flip a coin three times. One of the possible outcomes is *tail-head-head*, another is *head-tail-head*. How many possible outcomes are there?

Some of these numbers are 111, 112, 221.

You may choose not to have any topping—this would be a plain pizza.

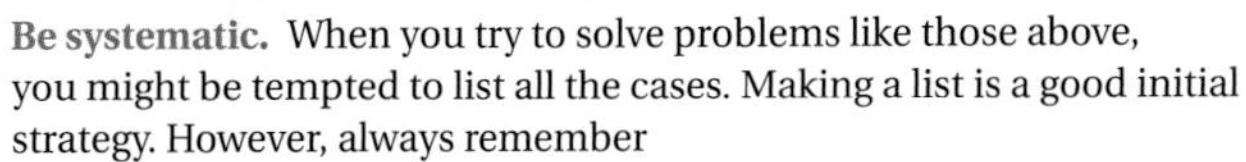

Developing Habits of Mind

Be systematic. When you try to solve problems like those above, you might be tempted to list all the cases. Making a list is a good initial strategy. However, always remember

- to count every case
- not to count any case more than once

To solve a counting problem, a good strategy is to use a system to list all the cases.

Minds in Action episode 10

Sasha and Tony are listing possible three-digit numbers while working on Problem 1 in For You to Do above.

Sasha I'm listing numbers with no 2's, and then numbers with one 2, and then numbers with two 2's. What are you doing?

Tony I'm listing numbers from least to greatest.

For You to Do

1. 8 numbers
2. 8 colorings
3. 8 kinds of pizza
4. 8 outcomes

Lesson Overview

GOALS

- Recognize the kinds of problems that you can solve using combinatorics.
- Develop your own strategies for systematic counting.

There are not many algorithms that can be applied uniformly to counting problems. For this reason, many students become frustrated when tackling these problems. This lesson introduces the notion of *isomorphic problems* to change the focus from the algorithms to the problems, or rather to the similarities between the problems. By actively searching for isomorphic problems, students find ways to link new and unfamiliar problems to other problems they know how to solve. Students revisit this concept throughout the chapter. (By the way, as noted in the introduction, the words *isomorphic* and *isomorphism* have technical meanings in other branches of mathematics that are compatible with, but not exactly the same as, our uses in this chapter.

CHECK YOUR UNDERSTANDING
- Core: 1, 2, 3, 4, 5, 7
- Optional: 6

MATERIALS
- graphing calculators
- Blackline Master 4.2

HOMEWORK
- Core: 8, 9, 10, 13, 16, 17
- Optional: 11, 12, 14
- Extension: 15

VOCABULARY
- isomorphic

Launch

Jump right into the first For You to Do section.

Explore

When introducing the term *isomorphic*, emphasize that it means the problems are the same *mathematically*. It is different than saying, "the same problem with different numbers"—a phrase students are probably more familiar with. Rather, it is more like saying, "a pair of seemingly different problems with the same answer, and the same method for finding the solution." This is really the meaning of "the same mathematical structure." It is not the mathematics of the problem, but the context and application of the mathematics, that change.

Problems 1–4 are presented graphically on Blackline Master 4.2. Use the master on an overhead as needed here and throughout the lesson as the problems return. The table of pizza toppings is expanded for use with Problems 9–12. Let students order pizzas, fill in the table, and use the entries for examples.

For You to Do, p. 279

PROBLEM 1 One way to solve this problem is to list each of the 8 possibilities. Of course, you might not know there are 8 possibilities until you have listed them.

111, 112, 121, 211, 122, 212, 221, 222

One way to construct the list is with a tree diagram:

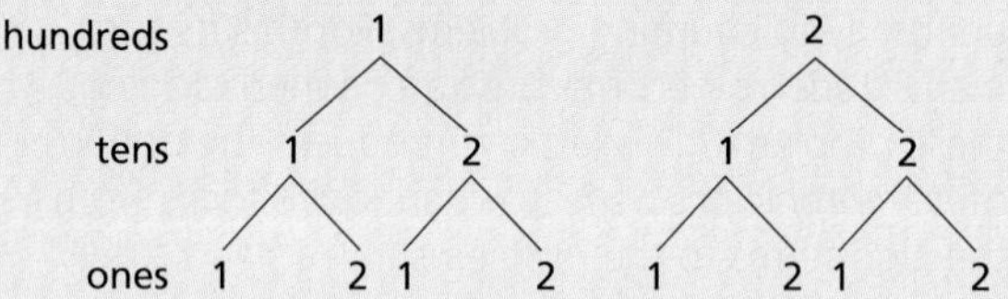

Using the tree diagram idea, imagine constructing the list. There are two choices (1 and 2) for the hundreds place. For each choice of the hundreds place, there are two choices (1 and 2) for the tens place, giving us $2 \cdot 2 = 4$ ways to fill in the tens *and* hundreds places. For each of these 4 possible ways, there are two choices for the ones place, so there are $2 \cdot 4 = 8$ total possibilities.

PROBLEM 2 You can either list out all 8 colorings or notice that there are two possibilities for each of the three shapes. The 8 colorings are:

Shape 1	Shape 2	Shape 3
red	red	red
red	red	green
red	green	red
green	red	red
green	red	green
red	green	green
green	green	red
green	green	green

PROBLEM 3 As in the previous problems, there are two choices for each of the three toppings. The 8 pizzas are:

onions	mushrooms	pepperoni
X	X	X
X	X	
X		X
	X	X
		X
	X	
X		

PROBLEM 4 On each of three tosses, there are two possibilities (a head or a tail). The 8 possible outcomes are:

HHH, HHT, HTH, THH, TTH, THT HTT, TTT

For You to Do

5. Make a list of possible three-digit numbers using Sasha's system.
6. Make a list of possible three-digit numbers using Tony's system.

For Discussion

7. For listing the possible cases in Problem 1, which method seems more convenient, Sasha's or Tony's? Explain your choice.
8. Did you use either of these methods when you solved the problem yourself? If not, what approach did you use and why?

What do Problems 1–4 have in common besides the answer?

Suppose you are done with Problem 1 and know exactly how many three-digit numbers are possible using only the digits 1 and 2. Now you are working on Problem 3. You are trying to list all possible pizzas by completing the following chart.

Pizza	Onions	Mushrooms	Pepperoni
First	X	X	
Second			
Third	X	X	X
⋮			

The first row is for pizza with onions and mushrooms. The second row is for plain cheese pizza.

For You to Do

9. What kind of pizza corresponds to the third row?

You could change the table a little by writing 1 if you want a certain topping on a pizza and 2 if you do not. Then, for the pizza with onions and mushrooms you write 112.

Pizza	Onions	Mushrooms	Pepperoni
First	1	1	2
⋮			

Answers

For You to Do

5. 111; 211, 121, 112; 221, 212, 122; 222
6. 111, 112, 121, 122, 211, 212, 221, 222

For Discussion

7. Check students' work.
8. Check students' work.

For You to Do

9. pizza with all three toppings

For You to Do

10. What number would you write for the second pizza? For the third pizza?

11. Does the pizza described by the number 211 have any mushrooms on it?

12. Which pizza corresponds to the number 121?

Each pizza corresponds to a three-digit number made of 1's and 2's. Also, any three-digit number made of 1's and 2's represents a type of pizza. Now you can see that the number of pizzas and the number of three-digit numbers made of 1's and 2's are the same. You do not have to solve both the pizza problem and the three-digit number problem. From a mathematical point of view, they are the same.

Definition

If two problems have the same mathematical structure then they are isomorphic.

Isomorphic is from Greek *iso-* meaning "same," and *morphe* meaning "shape." You use this word in mathematics to refer to structures that are essentially the same.

If two problems are isomorphic then you can solve them using the same calculation, formula, or equation.

In recognizing isomorphic problems, keep the following facts in mind.

- Context does not matter.

  These problems are isomorphic:

  Problem 1 In a class of 24 students there are 2 more girls than boys. How many girls are there in this class?

  Problem 2 Tim earned \$24 in two weeks. He earned \$2 more during the second week than during the first week. How much did Tim earn during the second week?

  Solution In Problem 1, let x be the number of girls in the class. In Problem 2 let x be the amount Tim earned during the second week. These problems yield the same equation with the same solution.

  Equation: $x + (x - 2) = 24$

  Solution: $x = 13$

  The contexts differ, but the mathematics is the same.

- Two problems can have the same answers without being isomorphic.

  These problems involve different sorts of operations and are not isomorphic:

  Problem Jane had four apples. She ate two apples. How many apples does she have now?

  Solution $4 - 2 = 2$ (Subtraction)

  Problem Jane had four apples. She shared them equally with John. How many apples does she have now?

  Solution $4 \div 2 = 2$ (Division)

For You to Do

10. 222; 111

11. yes

12. pizza with onions and pepperoni, no mushrooms

For Discussion

PROBLEM 7 Some students might find Tony's method more straightforward for this particular problem, especially if this is the way they thought about solving the problem initially.

Wrap Up

You might end this class with a discussion of the question, "Why bother finding isomorphic problems?" This is a good question to revisit at the end of the chapter, when students can find many different situations where you can solve an unfamiliar problem by finding a problem you understand that is isomorphic to it (or to part of it).

Assessment Resources

Lesson Quiz 4.2

1. Decide if the two given problems are isomorphic. Explain.
   a. • Jamie ran four miles on Monday and Tuesday and five miles on Friday and Saturday. How many total miles did she run during the week?
      • A rectangle has a base of five feet and a height of four feet. What is the perimeter of the rectangle?
   b. • A regular pentagon has side length 6 centimeters. What is the perimeter?
      • An equilateral triangle has side length 10 centimeters. What is the perimeter?

2. Find a pair of isomorphic problems that you can solve using the given calculation.
   a. $20 \cdot 3 + 10 = 70$
   b. $2 + 4 + 7 = 13$

3. How many four-digit numbers can you make with only 2's and 5's?

Exercises

HOMEWORK
- Core: 8, 9, 10, 13, 16, 17
- Optional: 11, 12, 14
- Extension: 15

- If two problems have different numbers they are not isomorphic (even though you may be able to use the same method to solve them both).

  These problems involve the same methods and operations but are not isomorphic:

  Problem There were 6 chickens in a cage. Two ran away. How many are still there?

  Solution $6 - 2 = 4$ (Subtraction)

  Problem There were 12 eggs in a box. Eight are broken. How many remain whole?

  Solution $12 - 8 = 4$ (Subtraction)

Exercises *Practicing Habits of Mind*

Check Your Understanding

For Exercises 1–4 decide if the two given problems are isomorphic. Explain.

1. • What is the area of a 3 meter-by-6 meter rectangle?
   • What is the perimeter of a 3 meter-by-6 meter rectangle?
2. • There are 230 pages in a book. Lisa read 45 pages yesterday and 99 pages today. How many pages does she still have to read?
   • Looking for ideas for his science project, Leo got 230 suggestions. Considering them, he found 45 too easy and 99 too difficult. How many more ideas does Leo have left to consider?
3. • Peter has twice as much money as Jack. The total is $18. How much money does each boy have?
   • Kim cuts an 18-inch long stick in two pieces. One piece is twice as long as the other. How long is each piece?
4. • Lila is organizing her 740 photos. Each of her picture albums holds 60 pictures. How many albums will she need to store all the photos?
   • What is the smallest integer n such that $60n \geq 740$?

Answers

Exercises

1. Not isomorphic; the area is found by using multiplication alone, but the perimeter is found by using addition at least once.
2. Isomorphic; both problems can be solved by using the same calculation of subtracting 45 and 99 from 230.
3. Isomorphic; both problems can be solved by solving the same equation, $x + 2x = 18$.
4. Isomorphic; both problems can be solved by using the same calculation of dividing 740 by 60 to find the smallest integer number.
5. Answers may vary. Samples are given.
   a. The Red Sox scored nine runs and the Yankees scored seven runs in the same game. How many more runs did the Red Sox score?
   b. Three friends divide a dozen cookies equally among them. How many cookies does each friend get?
6. Answers will vary. Samples are given.
   a. • Joe had $40 at the beginning of the day. He spent $3 on breakfast and $7 on lunch. How much money does he have left for dinner?
   • Paula had 40 baseball cards. She gave 3 to Jesse, and 7 to Kira. How many does she have left?

5. Make up a problem isomorphic to each of the following.

   a. My cat is nine years old. My dog is seven years old. How much older is my cat than my dog?

   b. Cut a 12-yard long ribbon into three equal pieces. How long is each one?

6. Find a pair of isomorphic problems that you can solve using the given calculation.

   a. $40 - (3 + 7) = 30$ b. $7 \cdot 8 = 56$

7. Explain why Problems 2, 3, and 4 on page 279 are isomorphic to Problem 1 on that same page.

On Your Own

8. Harriet used a *tree* to solve the three-digit problem in the For You to Do section at the beginning of this lesson. This is how she started:

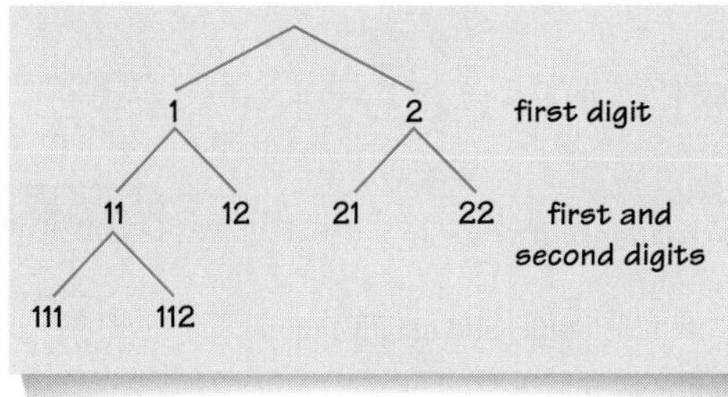

   a. Copy this tree and finish it.

   b. Does Harriet's strategy resemble either Tony's or Sasha's? If so, how?

9. How many four-digit numbers can you make with only 1's and 2's?

10. How many subsets does the set $\{A, B, C\}$ have? Count the empty set and the whole set, too.

Any group of elements from a set is a subset. Note that $\{A, B\}$ and $\{B, A\}$ are the same subset.

For Exercises 11 and 12, decide if the two given problems are isomorphic. Explain your answers.

11. • Each of seven friends has \$15. How much do they have altogether?
    • A rectangle has sides of lengths 7 inches and 15 inches. Find its area.

12. • What is $1 + 2 + 3 + \cdots + 8 + 9 + 10$?
    • On the first day of January, Jane learned one new word. Each day she learned one more word than she learned the day before. During the first ten days of January, how many words did she learn?

On Your Own

EXERCISE 8 is a very useful problem to discuss as a class. This method of listing possible numbers will be helpful for many students in later, more complex problems.

b. • If seven people go out to dinner and each contributes eight dollars toward the bill, what is the total contribution?
• Mr. Hill made cookies for the 8 students on the Math Team. He made enough so that each student could have exactly 7 cookies. How many cookies did he make?

7. The text explained how Problems 1 and 3 can be viewed as essentially the same.

In Problem 2, let 1 denote the color green and 2 denote the color red. Then let the ones digit denote the color of the circle, let the tens digit denote the color of the triangle, and finally let the hundreds digit denote the color of the square. In Problem 4, let 1 denote a head and 2 to denote a tail. Then let the hundreds digit denote the first toss, let the tens digit denote the second toss, and the ones digit denote the third toss.

8. a.

b. It resembles Tony's strategy because the final numbers are in order from least to greatest. This happens because Harriet always chooses to have the left branch add a 1. So, for any pair of branches, the number on the left branch is smaller than the number on the right branch.

9. 16 four-digit numbers

10. 8 subsets

11. Isomorphic; both problems yield the same equation ($7 \cdot 15 = x$) and same solution ($x = 105$).

12. Isomorphic; both problems yield the same equation ($1 + 2 + 3 + \cdots + 8 + 9 + 10 = x$) and same solution ($x = 55$).

Additional Resources

PRINT RESOURCES
- Solution Manual
- Practice Workbook
- Assessment Resources
- Teaching Resources

TECHNOLOGY
- Interactive Textbook
- TeacherExpress CD-ROM
- ExamView CD-ROM
- PHSchool.com

Additional Practice

1. Determine if the two given problems are isomorphic. Explain.
   a. • Jack spends $25 on a new pair of shoes and $15 on a new hat. How much money did he spend in total?
   • Peter invited 25 of his friends and 15 of his relatives to a party. How many people did he invite in total?
   b. • What is the area of a triangle with a base of ten inches and a height of six inches?
   • What is the perimeter of a triangle with a base of two inches and each leg three inches?

2. Make up a problem isomorphic to the following.
   Jack has 200 songs in a playlist on his MP3 player. He buys 20 more songs to add to the playlist. How many songs does he have in total?

3. Copy and complete the tree to the right. Determine how many three-letter combinations are possible by using the letters B and G.

B G first letter
BB BG first and second letter

4. How many subsets does the set $\{1, 2, 3\}$ have?

5. Determine if the following are isomorphic.
   • What is $2 + 4 + 6 + \cdots + 16 + 18 + 20$?
   • Jane is training for a marathon. Each Saturday she runs two more miles than the previous Saturday. On the first Saturday she runs 2 miles, and on the last she runs 20 miles. How many miles in total will she run on Saturdays while training?

6. Solve the problem and then make up a problem that is isomorphic to it.
   A farmer has three pastures: the first contains five cows, the second contains three horses, and the third contains six sheep. How many total hooves are there at the farm?

7. For each of the following, find an isomorphic problem that you can solve using the given calculation.
   a. $21 \div 7 = 3$ b. $2 + 5 + 7 = 14$
   c. $2(3) + 2(6) = 18$ d. $8 \cdot 4 = 32$

Practice: For Lesson 4.2, assign Exercises 1–7.

13. Solve the problem and then make up a problem isomorphic to it.

In each corner of a rectangular room there is a cat. Each cat has four kittens with her. How many paws are there in the room?

Draw a picture of this room.

14. Find a pair of isomorphic problems that you can solve using the given calculation.

a. $27 \div 9 = 3$ **b.** $6 + 7 + 8 = 21$

15. Take It Further In class, Paul noticed something when he was working out the solution to the three-digit problem in the For You to Do section at the beginning of this lesson. First, he systematically listed all the numbers.

Then, Paul discovered a pattern. He said, "All the numbers in each column add up to 12." If you list all four-digit numbers made of 1's and 2's, will each column sum still be 12? Can you extend this pattern to five-digit numbers? To n-digit numbers? How would the pattern change if you used the digits 1, 2, and 3?

1	1	1
1	1	2
1	2	1
1	2	2
2	1	1
2	1	2
2	2	1
2	2	2

Habits of Mind

Experiment. If you make all the four-digit numbers from 1's and 2's and line them up like this, will the sum of the numbers in any column be the same? What if you use the digits 1, 2, 3?

16. Standardized Test Prep Given the following two problems, which sentence describes the relationship between them?

Problem I Find the area of a triangle with base 3 units and height 4 units.

Problem II Find the area of a triangle with base 6 units and height 2 units.

A. Problems I and II are isomorphic and have the same answer.
B. Problems I and II have the same answer but are not isomorphic.
C. Problems I and II are isomorphic but do not have the same answer.
D. Problems I and II are neither isomorphic nor have the same answer.

For additional practice, go to **Web Code: bga-0402**

Maintain Your Skills

17. If you expand the product, how many terms are in the resulting sum?

a. $(a + b)(c + d)$
b. $(a + b)(c + d)(e + f)$
c. $(a + b)(c + d)(e + f)(g + h)$
d. $(a + b)(c + d)(e + f)\cdots(y + z)$ (13 factors in all)

Answers

13. 80; Answers may vary. Sample:

A car dealer sells cars that all have a spare tire in addition to the four regular tires. The dealer has 4 different models and each model is available in four different colors. If the dealer has 1 of each model in each color, how many tires in all does the dealer have?

14. See back of book.

15. No, each column for four-digit numbers sum is 24; each column sum for five-digit numbers is 48; each column sum for n-digit numbers is $3 \cdot 2^{n-1}$; for the digits 1, 2, and 3, each column sum for n-digit numbers is $(1 + 2 + 3) \cdot 3^{n-1}$ or $2 \cdot 3^n$.

16. B

17. a. 4 terms
b. 8 terms
c. 16 terms
d. $2^{13} = 8192$ terms

4.3 Strategies for Counting

In this lesson, you will see some strategies for counting. Students in a course just like this one developed these strategies.

For You to Do

1. How many five-digit numbers can you make using only 1's and 2's?

Minds in Action episode 11

Sasha and Tony were working on Problem 1.

Sasha In the last lesson, we found all the three-digit numbers we can make using only the digits 1 and 2. We can find all the four-digit numbers by attaching either 1 or 2 to the end of those. So there must be twice as many four-digit numbers as three-digit numbers. Then I can use the four-digit numbers to build the five-digit numbers in the same way.

Tony The first digit of a number can be either 1 or 2. This gives 2 cases. In each case, the second digit can also be 1 or 2. That would give $2 \cdot 2 = 4$ cases. Then I can consider the third digit, then the fourth, and then the fifth.

For You to Do

2. Solve Problem 1 using Sasha's method.
3. Solve Problem 1 using Tony's method.

For Discussion

Using either Sasha's or Tony's method (or both!), solve the following problems.

4. How many six-digit numbers can you make using only the digits 1 and 2?
5. How many n-digit numbers can you make using only 1's and 2's?

For You to Do

1. 32 numbers

For You to Do

2. $(8 \cdot 2) \cdot 2$ gives 32.
3. $2 \cdot 2 \cdot 2 \cdot 2 \cdot 2$ gives 32.

For Discussion

4. 64 numbers
5. 2^n numbers

Lesson Overview

GOALS

- Recognize the kinds of problems that you can solve using combinatorics.
- Develop your own strategies for systematic counting.

In this lesson, students develop multiple counting strategies for situations that can be counted in stages. The basic principle underlying these strategies is the Counting Principle:

> The number of possible outcomes for a situation consisting of n independent outcomes is the product $m_1 \cdot m_2 \cdot \ldots \cdot m_{n-1} \cdot m_n$. Here n is the number of stages. In order for this to apply, each element at any stage has to have the same number of extensions to the next stage.

Students are not formally introduced to the Counting Principle by name. Rather, they apply it indirectly in two counting strategies: the *box method* and the *tree approach*, as described in the introduction to this investigation.

The problems in this lesson build up to the introduction of permutations (in the next investigation) and the connection between factorials and counting. The last section introduces a final and even more abstract strategy: counting the functions that could map one set to another. This strategy provides another perspective for counting, and a nice connection to functions.

Note that although the main topic of this section is the Counting Principle, it is never fully stated as a strategy, although the big theorem of the lesson describes a specific formula that results from it. You may choose to provide your students with a stated version of the principle, but in general the strategies that rest upon it prove to be more useful in solving problems than the actual principle itself.

CHECK YOUR UNDERSTANDING

- Core: 1, 2, 3, 4, 6, 7, 9
- Optional: 5, 8

MATERIALS

- graphing calculators
- Blackline Master 4.3

HOMEWORK

- Core: 10, 11, 12, 14, 16, 18, 19, 20, 21
- Optional: 13, 15, 17, 22, 23

Launch

Jump into the first For You to Do section.

Explore

You might go over students' strategies for the first For You to Do problem before moving on to the subsequent dialog between Tony and Sasha.

For You to Do, p. 285

PROBLEM 1 One way to approach this problem is by using a tree. You can make the tree in order to see all the outcomes, but you already know from Lesson 4.2 that there are 8 three-digit numbers on the tree. To form the next row on the tree, add 2 branches to each number, to add a 1 or a 2 to the end of it. There are 16 four-digit numbers. Then to form the next row, add 2 branches to each of the numbers. This gives a total of 32 five-digit numbers.

You also could think of it this way: there are two choices each for the ones, tens, hundreds, and thousands place holders, so there are $2 \cdot 2 \cdot 2 \cdot 2 \cdot 2 = 32$ total possibilities.

PROBLEM 2 You may want to model Sasha's method with a tree. Since Sasha deduced that there would be twice as many 4-digit numbers as 3-digit numbers and there were 8 three-digit numbers, there must be $2 \cdot 8 = 16$ four-digit numbers. For the same reason, there are twice as many 5-digit numbers as there are 4-digit numbers. The number of 5-digit numbers is $16 \cdot 2 = 32$.

PROBLEM 3 Tony's recursive reasoning illustrates the *reducing it to a smaller problem* strategy. Since Tony deduced that there are 2 choices for each of the four digits, there must be $2 \cdot 2 \cdot 2 \cdot 2 \cdot 2 = 32$ five-digit numbers.

For Discussion, p. 285

You may want to limit discussion to the general form. If you have extra time, or if some students finish these quickly, you could also pose a variation. What if you could not repeat the digits? How would this affect the result? Could you still use Sasha's strategy? Could you use Tony's? How? You could continue this discussion to include a general formula for non-repeating digits, which incorporates the factorial function that students will see in the upcoming investigation.

PROBLEM 4 Using Sasha's method, there are twice as many 6-digit numbers as there are 5-digit numbers. The total number of 6-digit numbers is $32 \cdot 2 = 64$. Using Tony's method, there are 2 choices for each of the 6 digits, so there are $2^6 = 64$ such numbers.

PROBLEM 5 By Tony's method, each digit has 2 cases. For n-digits, multiply n-many 2's together (or just 2^n). By Sasha's method, there are twice as many n-digit numbers as there are $(n - 1)$-digit numbers.

Problems 6–9 are a little different from the ones you have seen before. For each new problem, think carefully about the set from which you are choosing your digits (or other objects). A counting strategy can help. The students who developed the following strategy called it "the box strategy."

For You to Do

6. Miss Rainbow has 20 hats, 30 dresses, and 10 pairs of shoes. She makes an outfit consisting of a hat, a dress, and a pair of shoes. How many outfits can she make?

Developing Habits of Mind

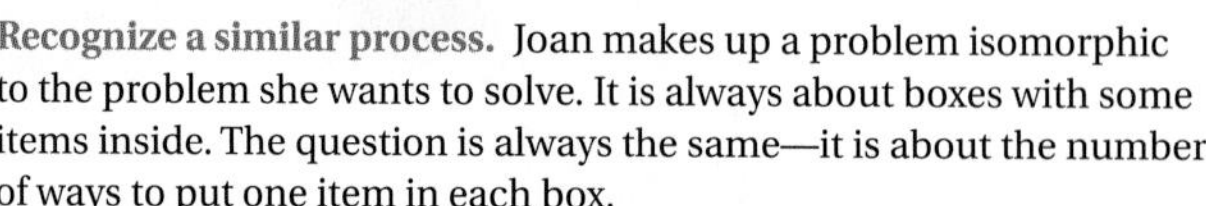

Recognize a similar process. Joan makes up a problem isomorphic to the problem she wants to solve. It is always about boxes with some items inside. The question is always the same—it is about the number of ways to put one item in each box.

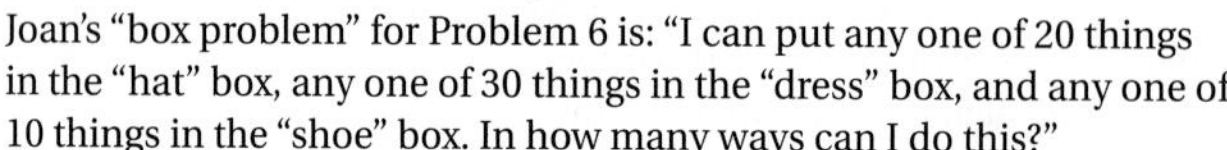

Joan's "box problem" for Problem 6 is: "I can put any one of 20 things in the "hat" box, any one of 30 things in the "dress" box, and any one of 10 things in the "shoe" box. In how many ways can I do this?"

For You to Do

Use Joan's method to solve the following.

7. A class has 10 boys and 12 girls. You want a committee with one boy and one girl. How many possible committees are there?

8. There are four grades in a school, and 200 students in each grade. You want a committee with one representative from each grade. How many different committees are possible?

9. Suppose you want to make three-digit ATM PINs from the numbers $\{1, 2, 3, 4, 5\}$. (Numbers can be used more than once.) How many codes are there?

Answers

For You to Do

6. 6000 outfits

For You to Do

7. 120 committees
8. 1,600,000,000 committees
9. 125 numbers

For Discussion

10. Use Problem 9 to illustrate the following theorem.

Theorem 4.1

It is possible to make m^n different strings of length n using m different symbols, if you can use a symbol more than once.

In a kindergarten class, each student has four pictures: a square, a triangle, a circle, and a star. Each of the kids will make a design by gluing these four pictures in a line. There are 20 kids in the class. Can each child make a different design or will there have to be repeats? (Note: This time unlike in Problem 9, each symbol can be used only once!)

These are two possible designs:

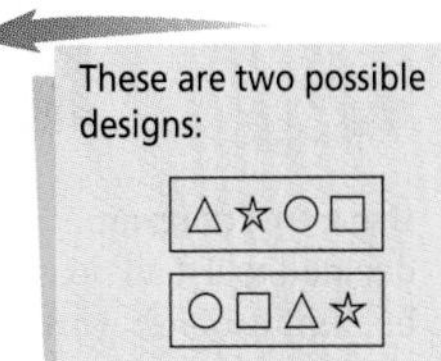

Consider three strategies for solving this problem.

Solve a simpler problem. There are four groups of designs:

- designs that start with a square (□ ? ? ?)
- designs that start with a star (☆ ? ? ?)
- designs that start with a triangle (△ ? ? ?)
- designs that start with a circle (○ ? ? ?)

Each group has the same number of designs (why?), so you can reduce the problem to a simpler one:

How many designs start with a square?

Then to find the total number of possible designs, multiply the result by 4.

You could have chosen to count designs of any other single group.

? ? ? ? = 4 · (□ ? ? ?)

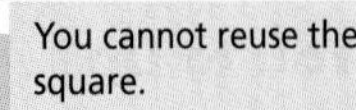

Now, each design that starts with a square falls into one of three groups:

- a square then a star (□☆ ? ?)
- a square then a triangle (□△ ? ?)
- a square then a circle (□○ ? ?)

You cannot reuse the square.

So, here is a new, even simpler problem:

How many designs start with a square followed by a star?

? ? ? ? = 4 · (□ ? ? ?) = 4 · 3 · (□☆ ? ?)

For Discussion

10. Since each PIN number is to consist of 3 digits and there are 5 digits to choose from, there are 5^3 possible PIN numbers.

For You to Do

PROBLEM 6 You might also ask students to compare this problem to the *n*-digit number problems they solved earlier.

Students seem to gravitate toward the box method for this problem. You may want to discuss *why* the box method works here. You can even extend this to a discussion of how all three methods—box, tree, and recursion—work here. You might want to make a complete enumeration for a similar but more manageable problem (for example: 2 hats, 3 dresses, and 4 pairs of shoes).

PROBLEM 7 Be sure that students use 2 boxes, one for the boy on the committee and one for the girl on the committee.

PROBLEM 8 Be sure that students use 4 boxes, one for each grade.

PROBLEM 9 Be sure that students use 3 boxes, one for each digit of the ATM PIN.

For You to Do

PROBLEM 11

Solve a simpler problem: As explained on the previous page, the number of different designs is 4 times the number of designs that start with a square. Similarly, since the second symbol can be any of 3 remaining symbols, the number of designs that start with a square is 3 times the number of designs that start with a square and a star. But there are only 2 designs that start with a square and a star: square-star-triangle-circle and square-star-circle-triangle. Therefore there are $4 \cdot 3 \cdot 2 = 24$ different designs in all.

Use the box strategy: A design has 4 boxes. The first box can be filled with any of the 4 shapes, the second box can be filled with any 3 of the remaining shapes, the third box can be filled with either of the 2 remaining shapes, and the fourth box can only have the last remaining shape. There are $4 \cdot 3 \cdot 2 \cdot 1 = 24$ possible designs.

You may want to use Blackline Master 4.3 on an overhead during the discussion of the different strategies for solving this problem.

Wrap Up

Wrap up this lesson with a discussion of the different strategies—solving a simpler problem, using the box strategy, and using a tree diagram—used to solve the kindergartners' four-pictures problem. You might ask students why the theorem does not apply to this problem. (Answer: They cannot use a design more than once.)

Assessment Resources

Lesson Quiz 4.3

1. If you have six different books, how many ways are there to line them up on a bookshelf?
2. In how many different ways can you arrange the letters in the word *world*?
3. a. A town follows the following criteria to assign seven-digit phone numbers.
   - The first digit cannot be 0, 1, or 2.
   - The second digit must be 4.
   - The last digit must be even.

   How many phone numbers are possible using these rules?

   b. If the town did not allow use of the digits 5 and 6, how many phone numbers would be possible?
4. How many four-digit numbers are possible using only odd numbers?

Use the box strategy. Think of making a design starting with four empty boxes. You fill them up, one at a time, with a picture shape. You can put any one of four shapes into the first box. For each of those choices, you can put any one of three shapes into the second box (so there are now $4 \cdot 3$ partially completed designs), and so on.

How many ways can you choose one shape to put into each box?

Use a tree diagram. Karen, who was trying to solve this problem, decided to list all possible designs. She arranged them in a tree. Below is the beginning of her work.

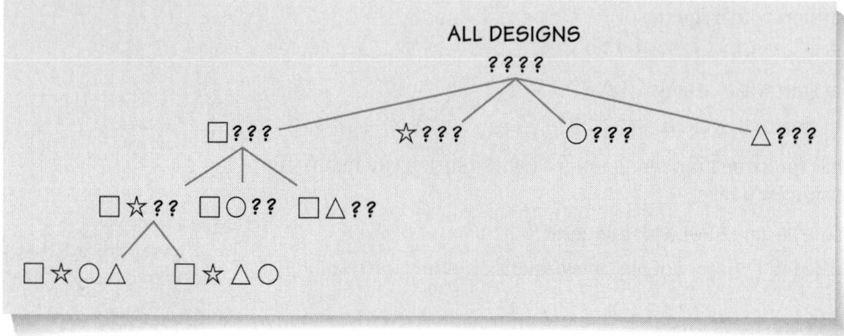

For You to Do

11. Pick one of the these three methods. Solve the problem about the kindergarten kids' designs using that method. Write up your solution in detail. Explain every step.

Answers

For You to Do

11. Check students' work.

Exercises *Practicing Habits of Mind*

Check Your Understanding

1. Let $f(n)$ be the number of possible n-digit numbers consisting of only 1's and 2's.
   a. Write a recursive rule for f.
   b. Write a closed rule for f.
2. How many four-digit numbers can you make using only the digits 1, 2, and 3?
3. **a.** How many five-digit numbers can you make using only the digits 1, 2, and 3?
   b. How many n-digit numbers can you make using only the digits 1, 2, and 3?
4. How many n-digit numbers can you make using digits from 1 to m? Assume you can invent new digits to stand for numbers greater than 9.
5. Mr. Flyer is going to travel to Europe. He wants to visit Paris, London, Bonn, and Rome, and stay three days in each city. He can visit these cities in different orders. In how many different ways can he plan this trip?
6. In how many different ways can you arrange the letters of the word *math*?
7. How many different batting orders are possible for the nine players of a baseball team?
8. How many ways are there to line up a set of five distinct objects in a single row?
9. How many ways are there to line up a set of n distinct objects in a single row?

Habits of Mind

Check extreme cases. You should convince yourself that the formula you have made is correct. A good habit is to check extreme cases. What if there is just one digit to use? What if the numbers are only one digit long?

A "batting order" is a list that shows the order in which the players will get to bat.

On Your Own

10. There are three towns in Wonderland: A, B, and C. There are six routes from A to B and three routes from B to C. No direct routes exist between A and C. How many ways are there to travel from A to C without backtracking?
11. How many four-digit numbers are there? (Hint: A number cannot start with zero.)

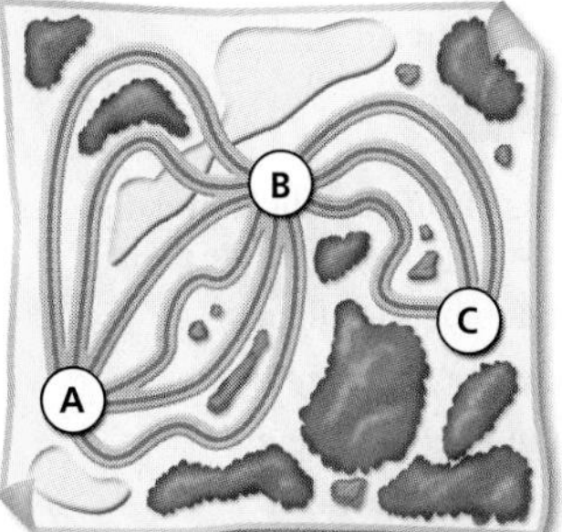

Habits of Mind

Use a different process. Another way to think about it: The largest 4-digit number is 9999. The smallest is 1000. How many numbers are between 1000 and 9999?

Exercises

HOMEWORK

- Core: 10, 11, 12, 14, 16, 18, 19, 20, 21
- Optional: 13, 15, 17, 22, 23

Check Your Understanding

EXERCISE 6 *Arrange* is a key word in combinatorics problems. Make sure students know what the word means, and in particular that it implies to order objects in a line.

Exercises

1. **a.** $f(n) = \begin{cases} 2 & \text{if } n = 1 \\ f(n-1) \cdot 2 & \text{if } n > 1 \end{cases}$
   b. $f(n) = 2^n$
2. 81 numbers
3. **a.** 243 numbers
   b. 3^n numbers
4. m^n
5. 24 ways
6. 24 ways
7. 362,880 batting orders
8. 120 ways
9. $n!$ ways
10. 18 ways
11. 9000 numbers

Additional Resources

PRINT RESOURCES
- Solution Manual
- Practice Workbook
- Assessment Resources
- Teaching Resources

TECHNOLOGY
- Interactive Textbook
- TeacherExpress CD-ROM
- ExamView CD-ROM
- PHSchool.com

Additional Practice

1. In how many ways can you arrange the letters of the word *nicely*?

2. How many three-digit numbers can you make that do not contain the digit 1 or 2? (*Hint:* A number cannot start with zero.)

3. How many five-digit numbers are possible if the digits cannot be odd or zero?

4. A bank's requirements for assigning a five-digit PIN are as follows:
   - The first and last digits cannot be 0 or 9.
   - The second digit cannot be 2.
   - There are no restrictions on the third or fourth digit.

   How many possible PINs are possible?

5. A state assigns license plates using six characters. The first two characters are letters from the alphabet, the next three characters are digits between 0 and 9, and the last character is one of the letters A, B, or C. How many different license plates are possible?

6. How many functions have the inputs from {1, 2, 3, 4} and outputs from {A, B}?

7. Suppose a unique language has an alphabet containing six letters. Each word in the language contains no more than five letters. At most how many words are in the language?

8. a. How many functions are there from a three-element set to a four-element set?
   b. How many of these functions are one-to-one?
   c. How many of these functions are not one-to-one?

9. a. Write an expression for the number of functions from the set {1, 2, 3, 4, . . ., 49, 50} to the set {1, 2, 3, . . ., 399, 400}.
   b. What is the numerical value of the expression?

10. How many one-to-one functions are there from a six-element set to a nine-element set?

Practice: For Lesson 4.3, assign Exercises 1–5.

12. A number is *cute* if it consists of only even digits. How many cute five-digit numbers are there?

13. How many four-digit multiples of five are there?

14. Before 1995, the rules for three-digit United States telephone area codes were as follows.
    - The first digit cannot be 0 or 1.
    - The second digit must be 0 or 1.
    - The third digit has no restriction.

    How many possible area codes did the United States have before 1995?

15. Believe it or not, the United States ran out of phone numbers and had to add more area codes. The area code rules changed to these:
    - The first digit cannot be 0 or 1.
    - The second digit has no restriction.
    - The third digit has no restriction.

    How many area codes were possible using these rules?

Go Online PHSchool.com

For additional practice, go to **Web Code:** bga-0403

16. Suppose the license plate for a car must have six characters. The first three characters are digits between 0 and 9. The remaining three characters are letters from the alphabet. How many different license plates are possible?

17. A car knocked over a stop sign, but then sped off. The only information that an eyewitness remembers is that the car's license plate contains two W's and one D, but not necessarily in this order. How many license plates must the police check?

For the description of possible license plates see Exercise 16.

18. **Standardized Test Prep** Janie has n different coats and n different scarves. Katie has $n + 1$ different coats and $n - 1$ different scarves. Which statement below is true?

    A. Janie has more ways to choose a coat and a scarf than Katie does.
    B. Katie has more ways to choose a coat and a scarf than Jamie does.
    C. Katie and Janie have the same number of choices.
    D. You cannot tell who has more choices without knowing what n is.

Maintain Your Skills

19. A number is *wild* if it consists of different digits and does not contain zero as a digit. How many wild two-digit numbers are there?
20. How many wild three-digit numbers are there?
21. How many wild six-digit numbers are there?
22. How many wild nine-digit numbers are there?
23. How many wild ten-digit numbers are there?

Do you think most mathematicians would recognize this definition?

Answers

12. 2500 numbers
13. 1800 numbers
14. 160 area codes
15. 800 area codes
16. 17,576,000 license plates
17. 3000 license plates
18. A
19. 72 numbers
20. 504 numbers
21. 60,480 numbers
22. 362,880 numbers
23. none

4.4 Counting All Functions

Another counting strategy is to translate your problem to one that counts the number of possible functions from one finite set to another.

Suppose you have a set of inputs $\{A, B, C\}$ and a set of outputs $\{1, 2, 3, 4\}$. Here is one function:

$$f(A) = 1$$
$$f(B) = 2$$
$$f(C) = 3$$

Here is another function: $f(A) = 1$, $f(B) = 1$, $f(C) = 1$

It is easy to define a function that has only three inputs. You just list the output for each input. If there are infinitely many inputs, you could not make such a list.

Here is a third function from $\{A, B, C\}$ to $\{1, 2, 3, 4\}$:

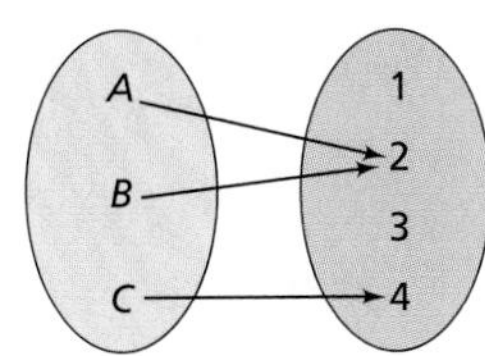

For You to Do

1. How many functions have inputs from the set $\{A, B, C\}$ and outputs from the set $\{1, 2, 3, 4\}$?

In other words, how many functions have domain $\{A, B, C\}$ and target $\{1, 2, 3, 4\}$?

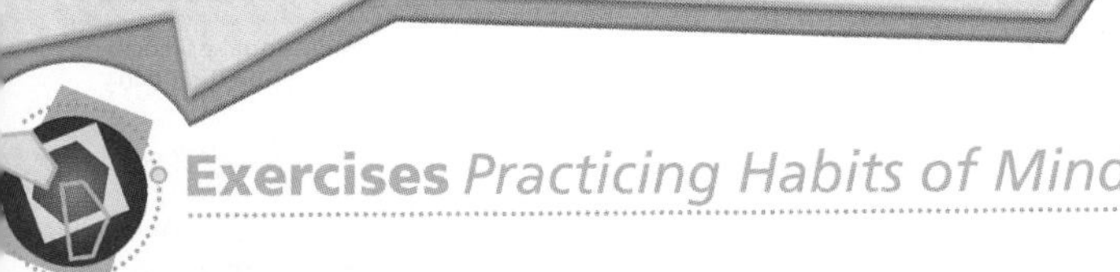

Exercises *Practicing Habits of Mind*

Check Your Understanding

1. How many functions have inputs from $\{A, B, C\}$ and outputs from {yes, no}?
2. Suppose the Martian alphabet consists of five letters. No word in the Martian language is more than four letters long. At most how many words can there be in such a language?

For You to Do

1. 64 functions

Exercises

1. 8 functions
2. 780 words

Lesson Overview

GOALS

- Recognize the kinds of problems that you can solve using combinatorics.
- Develop your own strategies for systematic counting.

This short lesson builds the strategy of translating combinatorics problems to problems that count functions from one finite set to another.

CHECK YOUR UNDERSTANDING
- Core: 1, 2, 3, 5
- Optional: 4

MATERIALS
- graphing calculators
- Blackline master 4.4

HOMEWORK
- Core: 6, 7, 9, 10
- Optional: 8, 11, 12

Launch

Start the students on the For You to Do problem. They may resist the idea of counting functions from one finite set to another, but have probably used informal versions of this method in previous lessons.

Explore

For You to Do

PROBLEM 1 One way to find the answer is to list out all of the functions. It is faster to notice that for each of the 3 inputs, there are 4 possible outputs. Since outputs can be repeated, there are $4 \cdot 4 \cdot 4 = 64$ different functions.

You may wish to use Blackline Master 4.4 on an overhead to illustrate some of the mappings.

Wrap Up

Go over the Check Your Understanding exercises.

Assessment Resources

Lesson Quiz 4.4

1. Suppose a unique language consists of seven letters. No word in the language is more than four letters long. At most how many words can there be in such a language?
2. Write an expression for the number of functions from the set {1, 2, 3, ... 98, 99} to the set {1, 2, 3, ..., 199, 200}.
3. a. How many functions are there from a six-element set to an eight-element set?
   b. How many of these functions are one-to-one?
   c. How many of these functions are not one-to-one?

Exercises

HOMEWORK
- Core: 6, 7, 9, 10
- Optional: 8, 11, 12

Check Your Understanding

EXERCISE 2 You may want to discuss the question, "Is the empty word a word?" Students may or may not decide that the empty word should be counted.

BACKGROUND FOR TEACHER In formal languages, the empty word is usually allowed, although it is usually not allowed in practice. It is not really useful for anything! If you do allow the empty word, there are $5^4 + 5^3 + 5^2 + 5^1 + 5^0 = 781$ words. The same alternatives hold for the general version of this problem.

Additional Resources

PRINT RESOURCES
- Solution Manual
- Practice Workbook
- Assessment Resources
- Teaching Resources

TECHNOLOGY
- Interactive Textbook
- TeacherExpress CD-ROM
- ExamView CD-ROM
- PHSchool.com

Additional Practice

1. In how many ways can you arrange the letters of the word *nicely*?

2. How many three-digit numbers can you make that do not contain the digit 1 or 2? (*Hint:* A number cannot start with zero.)

3. How many five-digit numbers are possible if the digits cannot be odd or zero?

4. A bank's requirements for assigning a five-digit PIN are as follows:
   - The first and last digits cannot be 0 or 9.
   - The second digit cannot be 2.
   - There are no restrictions on the third or fourth digit.

   How many possible PINs are possible?

5. A state assigns license plates using six characters. The first two characters are letters from the alphabet, the next three characters are digits between 0 and 9, and the last character is one of the letters A, B, or C. How many different license plates are possible?

6. How many functions have the inputs from {1, 2, 3, 4} and outputs from {A, B}?

7. Suppose a unique language has an alphabet containing six letters. Each word in the language contains no more than five letters. At most how many words are in the language?

8. **a.** How many functions are there from a three-element set to a four-element set?
   b. How many of these functions are one-to-one?
   c. How many of these functions are not one-to-one?

9. **a.** Write an expression for the number of functions from the set $\{1, 2, 3, 4, \ldots, 49, 50\}$ to the set $\{1, 2, 3, \ldots, 399, 400\}$.
   b. What is the numerical value of the expression?

10. How many one-to-one functions are there from a six-element set to a nine-element set?

Practice: For Lesson 4.4, assign Exercises 6–10.

3. Suppose there are k letters in the alphabet of a certain language. Suppose further that no word of this language has more than n letters. At most how many words can there be in this language?

4. Write an expression for the number of functions from the set $\{1, 2, 3, 4, \ldots, 25\}$ to the set $\{1, 2, 3, 4, \ldots, 365\}$.

What is the numerical value of your expression?

5. How many functions are there from a five-element set to an eight-element set?

On Your Own

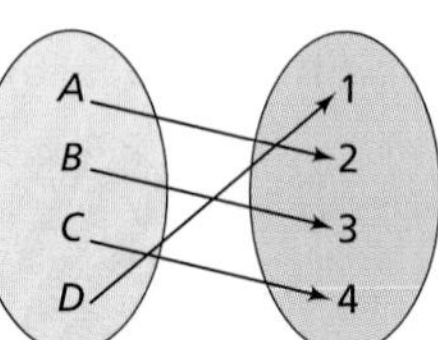

a one-to-one function

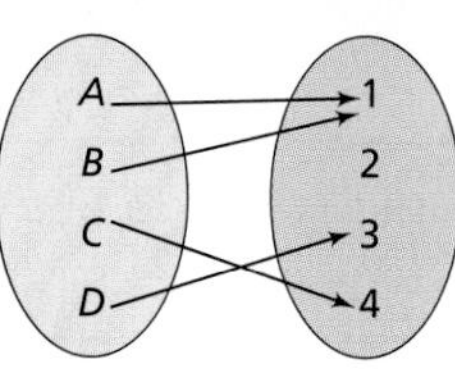

not a one-to-one function

In a one-to-one function, no two inputs have the same output.

6. a. How many functions are there from a two-element set to a three-element set?

b. How many of these functions are one-to-one?

c. How many of these functions are not one-to-one?

7. How many one-to-one functions are there from a five-element set to an eight-element set?

8. How many one-to-one functions are there from an eight-element set to a five-element set?

9. Write an expression for the number of one-to-one functions from the set $\{1, 2, 3, 4, \ldots, 25\}$ to the set $\{1, 2, 3, 4, \ldots, 365\}$.

What is the numerical value of the expression?

10. Standardized Test Prep Suppose there are exactly 81 functions from a four-element set to an n-element set. What is the value of n?

A. 2 **B.** 4 **C.** 3 **D.** 9

Go Online PHSchool.com

For additional practice, go to **Web Code: bga-0404**

Maintain Your Skills

11. How many wild four-digit numbers are cute?

12. How many cute five-digit numbers are wild?

Remember...

A number is *cute* if it consists of only even digits. A number is *wild* if it consists of different digits and does not have a zero.

Note: neither of these are official terms in mathematics. Inventing your own definitions can be fun as well as useful.

Answers

3. There are $k + k^2 + \cdots + k^n$ words (that is, n words if $k = 1$ and $\frac{k^{n+1} - k}{k - 1}$ words if $k > 1$).

4. $365^{25} \approx 1.14 \times 10^{64}$

5. 32,768 functions

6. a. 9 functions
b. 6 functions
c. 3 functions

7. 6720 functions

8. none

9. $\frac{365!}{340!} \approx 4.92 \times 10^{63}$

10. C

11. 24 numbers

12. none

In this investigation, you studied a variety of counting problems. Some of these appear different on the surface, but are really the same, or isomorphic. The following questions will help you summarize what you have learned.

1. How many n-digit numbers can you make using only the digits 1 through m? Assume you can invent new digits to stand for numbers greater than 9.
2. How many ways are there to line up a set of n distinct objects in a row?
3. Solve this problem and then make up a problem isomorphic to it. Matt is applying to four different colleges. Each application has a fee of \$75. How much will Matt have to pay in application fees?
4. Andrew noticed that many of the newer license plates have six characters. The first two characters and the last two characters are digits between 0 and 9. The middle two characters are letters from the alphabet. How many different license plates are there with this format?
5. How many one-to-one functions are there from a six-element set to a ten-element set?
6. How many five-digit numbers can you make using only the digits 1 and 2?
7. In a kindergarten class, each student has four pictures: a square, a triangle, a circle, and a star. Each of the kids will make a design by gluing these four pictures in a line. There are 20 kids in the class. Can each child make a different design or will there have to be repeats?
8. What does it mean for two problems to be isomorphic?

Vocabulary

In this investigation, you learned this term. Make sure you understand what it means and how to use it.

- **isomorphic**

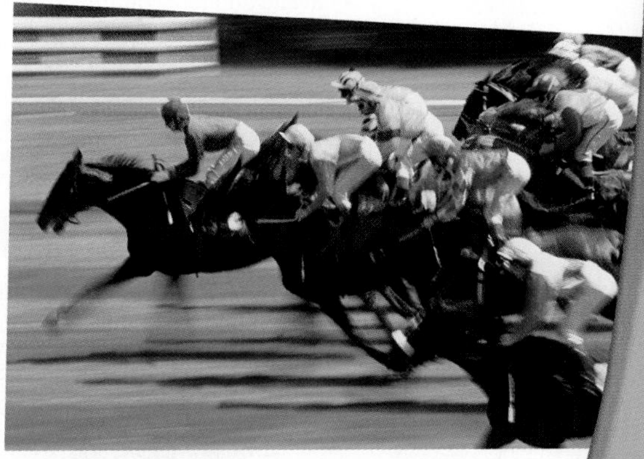

The number of possible batting orders for a softball team is the same as the number of possible outcomes in a race of 9 horses.

Mathematical Reflections

1. m^n numbers
2. $n!$ ways
3. \$300; Answers may vary. Sample: Gina drives 75 miles every week for her job. How many miles does she drive in 4 weeks?
4. 6,760,000 license plates
5. 151,200 functions
6. 32 numbers
7. Each child can make a different design.
8. Answers may vary. Ideal answers will have some version of, "they have similar mathematical structures," possibly with an example to illustrate what this means.

Mathematical Reflections

EXERCISES 6–8 At the start of the investigation, you may have assigned these as Questions 1–3 for students to think and write about.

Investigation Overview

This investigation utilizes the counting strategies from the last investigation to introduce two major counting strategies, permutations and combinations. Many of the problems in the last lesson were also permutations or arrangements of objects. However, the problems in the first part of this investigation differ in one main way; they do not have to be arrangements of ALL the objects. Students develop permutation formulas from the different counting strategies they know, and apply these formulas to counting problems.

Students also learn an indirect method for counting by counting the complement of the desired subset. This technique turns out to be very useful in solving the *Same Birthday* problem. Students have developed the appropriate counting tools to handle this problem, although the challenge for them lies in seeing how to apply what they know to this problem.

In Lesson 4.7 of the investigation, students see the final counting technique, *using combinations*. They develop techniques for counting combinations of cards and other objects by finding the number of ordered groupings and then dividing out by the different possible orderings, much as they did when counting anagrams with repeated letters. Students then use combinatorial proof to demonstrate the recursive formula for combinations, which leads directly to Pascal's Triangle.

Students develop the intuition they need to use the combinations formulas in conjunction with all the other techniques and formulas they know—the essence of counting. As they work on problems, encourage students to discuss solutions and try to solve problems using multiple methods. Also, they should try to find problems that are isomorphic to ones they already know how to solve. These habits will promote combinatorial thinking.

You may wish to assign Questions 1–3 for students to think and write about during the investigation.

Learning Goals

- Develop and use formulas for finding the number of permutations of *n* objects, taken *k* at a time.
- Find a formula for the number of combinations of *n* objects, taken *k* at a time.
- Find the number of anagrams for a word.

Habits and Skills

- Count the number of elements in a subset by counting the complement of the desired subset.
- Use appropriate counting tools and formulas.
- Relate different counting strategies to each other.

Investigation 4B

Permutations and Combinations

In *Permutations and Combinations*, you will learn more formal ways to approach counting problems. In particular, you will learn what permutations and combinations are, and how to count them.

By the end of this investigation, you will be able to answer questions like these.

1. In how many ways can you pick three objects, in order, from a set of six distinct objects?
2. How many three-digit numbers are there that have repeated digits?
3. How many five-student committees are possible in a class of 26 students?

You will learn how to

- develop and use formulas for finding the number of permutations of n objects, taken k at a time
- find a formula for the number of combinations of n objects, taken k at a time
- find the number of anagrams for a word

You will develop these habits and skills:

- Count the number of elements in a subset by counting the complement of the desired subset.
- Use appropriate counting tools and formulas.
- Relate different counting strategies to each other.

Jazz musicians often improvise by experimenting with the possible ways to choose combinations from the set of 12 notes in the diatonic scale.

Investigation Road Map

LESSON 4.5, *Getting Started,* shows students the same problems they saw in the first investigation, but gives students more tools to work on them. By the end of this investigation, students should be able to solve all of these problems.

LESSON 4.6, *Permutations,* introduces students to the formal notation and strategy of using permutations to solve counting problems. A featured type of problem is figuring out the number of anagrams of a given word.

LESSON 4.7, *Combinations,* uses the game of SET® to help students understand how to use combinations to solve counting problems.

LESSON 4.8, *Putting It Together,* has students return to the Getting Started problems with their new tools.

4.5 Getting Started

Now that you know some different strategies for counting, you are ready for another chance at those three problems from Lesson 4.1. See if you can make more progress now that you are getting better at the art of counting! If you solved all three problems in the last investigation, try to solve them again using a different method this time.

For You to Explore

1. **The Same Birthday**
   - **a.** In a random group of 25 people, what is the probability that at least two of them share a birthday? For the probability to be greater than 50%, how many people must there be in the group?
   - **b.** **Take It Further** In a random group of 25 people, what is the probability that exactly two of them share a birthday?

2. **Trains**

   You can use number rods to build "trains" that all share a common length. A "train of length 5" is a row of rods that have a combined length of 5.

   1 | 2 | 2
   2 | 1 | 2
   1 | 3 | 1
   1 | 4
   5

   Notice that the 1–2–2 train and the 2–1–2 train contain the same rods. If you use identical rods in different orders, this makes different trains.
   - **a.** How many trains of length n are possible?
   - **b.** Describe an algorithm that will generate all trains of length n.

Within a train you can repeat a length. Also, trains can contain different numbers of rods.

Lesson Overview

GOAL

- Warm up to the ideas of the investigation.

Again, this Getting Started lesson captures the essence of the Getting Started experience! Students have seen these exercises before, but now they can look at them with new eyes.

FOR YOU TO EXPLORE
- Core: 1, 2
- Optional: none

MATERIALS
- graphing calculators
- Blackline Masters 4.1A–B

HOMEWORK
- Core: 3
- Optional: 4

Launch

To launch this lesson, assign students to work on the For You to Explore problems.

Explore

For You to Explore

Students may object to seeing the same problems again! Encourage them to try to apply what they have learned so far to the problems. They still may not be able to solve all of them, but they should be able to make more progress than they made during the first investigation.

PROBLEM 2 Use Blackline Master 4.1A to illustrate the discussion of this problem.

Wrap Up

To wrap up this lesson, ask students for strategies they tried to solve the problems.

Answers

For You to Explore

1. **a.** about 56.87%; 23 people
   b. about 38%
2. **a.** 2^{n-1} trains
   b. Check students' work.

Exercises

HOMEWORK
- Core: 3
- Optional: 4

EXERCISE 3 Use Blackline Master 4.1B during the discussion of Ms. Pascal's paths. Students will see this exercise again in this chapter, and they still may not find the correct solution now. Do not give away the answer yet, but see if the students have a better understanding of the problem's complexity and are beginning to formulate a strategy for a solution.

Exercises *Practicing Habits of Mind*

On Your Own

3. Pascal's Paths

Ms. Pascal likes to take a different route to work every day. She will quit her job the day she has to repeat a route she has already taken. The grid of streets below shows her home and her workplace. She only travels north and east and never backtracks. How many days will she work at this job?

Two paths are different if they are not the same everywhere. They might overlap on some pieces though, like the two valid Pascal paths shown below.

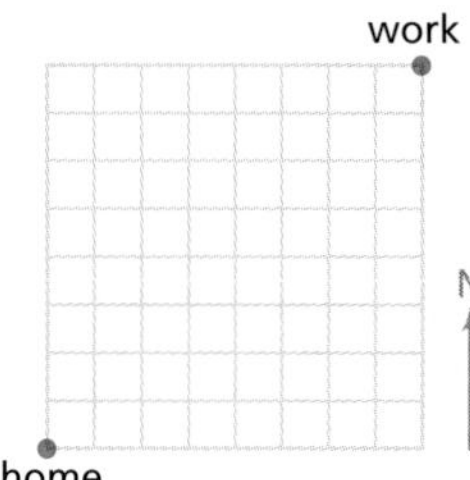

Again, here are some possible paths.

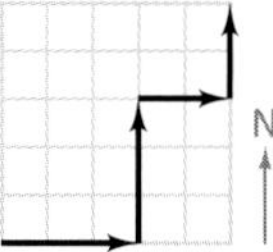

Here is a valid path.

This is also valid.

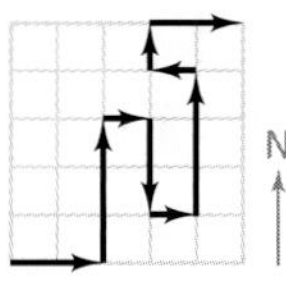

This is not a valid path.

Maintain Your Skills

4. The *Farey sequence of order n*, denoted F_n, is the set of all fractions from 0 to 1, inclusive, with denominators less than or equal to n. To write the sequence, write the fractions in lowest terms and arrange them in increasing order. For example, F_5, the Farey sequence of order 5, is

$$0, \frac{1}{5}, \frac{1}{4}, \frac{1}{3}, \frac{2}{5}, \frac{1}{2}, \frac{3}{5}, \frac{2}{3}, \frac{3}{4}, \frac{4}{5}, 1$$

a. Write out F_6, F_7, and F_8.

b. How many elements are in each of F_1 through F_8?

Answers

Exercises

3. 12,870 days

4. a. $F_6 = \left\{0, \frac{1}{6}, \frac{1}{5}, \frac{1}{4}, \frac{1}{3}, \frac{2}{5}, \frac{1}{2}, \frac{3}{5}, \frac{2}{3}, \frac{3}{4}, \frac{4}{5}, \frac{5}{6}, 1\right\}$

$F_7 = \left\{0, \frac{1}{7}, \frac{1}{6}, \frac{1}{5}, \frac{1}{4}, \frac{2}{7}, \frac{1}{3}, \frac{2}{5}, \frac{3}{7}, \frac{1}{2}, \frac{4}{7}, \frac{3}{5}, \frac{2}{3}, \frac{5}{7}, \frac{3}{4}, \frac{4}{5}, \frac{5}{6}, \frac{6}{7}, 1\right\}$

$F_8 = \left\{0, \frac{1}{8}, \frac{1}{7}, \frac{1}{6}, \frac{1}{5}, \frac{1}{4}, \frac{2}{7}, \frac{1}{3}, \frac{3}{8}, \frac{2}{5}, \frac{3}{7}, \frac{1}{2}, \frac{4}{7}, \frac{3}{5}, \frac{5}{8}, \frac{2}{3}, \frac{5}{7}, \frac{3}{4}, \frac{4}{5}, \frac{5}{6}, \frac{6}{7}, \frac{7}{8},\right.$

b. There are 2 elements in F_1, 3 elements in F_2, 5 elements in F_3, 7 elements in F_4, 11 elements in F_5, 13 elements in F_6, 19 elements in F_7, and 23 elements in F_8.

4.6 Permutations

In Investigation 4A, you developed your own strategies for solving counting problems. In this investigation, you will solve more complex problems, and see more formal counting methods and notations.

Do you remember the kindergarteners from Lesson 4.3? Recall that each kid was making a design by gluing four different shapes in a line. The four shapes were a square, a triangle, a circle, and a star. You counted the number of different designs possible.

Think about how to extend this problem. For instance, how many designs are possible if you could choose the four shapes from a larger set of shapes?

Go Online PHSchool.com

For a history of combinatorics, go to Web Code: bge-9031

For You to Do

1. Suppose the kindergarteners are gluing pictures of four different shapes in a line. In addition to a square, a triangle, a circle, and a star, they may use a diamond and an oval. How many designs are possible?

Developing Habits of Mind

Consider more than one strategy. Here are two strategies for solving Problem 1.

- Box strategy: Think of four boxes (a box for each position in a design). You can put any one of six shapes in the first box, and any one of the five remaining shapes in the second box (which five depends on the shape you picked for the first box). This gives $6 \cdot 5$ ways to start, with two more boxes to go.
- Cut off strategy: Make all possible designs that use all six shapes. Then cut off the last two shapes to get designs with just four shapes. Of course, you will get each four-shape design more than once.

□△○☆ ¦ ◇0
□△○☆ ¦ 0◇
□△○0 ¦ ◇☆
□△○0 ¦ ☆◇

For Discussion

2. Solve Problem 1 using the box strategy.
3. Solve Problem 1 using the cut off strategy.

In Problems 1–3, you chose four shapes from a set of six possible shapes and arranged them in some order. That is, you chose a *permutation.*

For You to Do

1. 360 designs

For Discussion

2. Check students' work.
3. Check students' work.

Lesson Overview

GOALS

- Develop and use formulas for finding the number of permutations of n objects, taken k at a time.
- Find the number of anagrams for a word.

Students begin this lesson by revisiting the kindergarten class from page 287. In that problem, students were asked how many ways the kindergartners could arrange four symbols in a line. Now they extend the problem to arranging six objects into the same four boxes.

CHECK YOUR UNDERSTANDING
- Core: 1, 2, 3, 4, 5, 6, 9, 10
- Optional: 7, 8, 11

MATERIALS
- graphing calculators
- Blackline Masters 4.6 A–B

HOMEWORK
- Core: 12, 13, 14, 15, 16, 17, 18, 21, 22, 23, 25
- Optional: 19, 20, 24, 26, 27

VOCABULARY
- anagram
- permutation
- ${}_nP_k$, number of permutations of n objects, taken k at a time

Launch

To launch this lesson, assign students to work on the For You to Do problems.

Explore

Developing Habits of Mind

You may want to use Blackline Master 4.6A on an overhead as you describe the strategies for solving the problem of selecting four shapes from the six available.

For Discussion

You probably want to begin this discussion by exploring how the strategies in the two problems differ.

PROBLEM 2 Make sure students use four boxes for this problem, one for each shape in the design.

PROBLEM 3 There are $6 \cdot 5 \cdot 4 \cdot 3 \cdot 2 \cdot 1 = 720$ designs that can be made with all six shapes. Now, if you cut off the last two shapes in each of these designs, you still have 720 designs, but some of them will repeat. If two designs have the first 4 shapes in common, they must also have the last two in common, just in a different order. Since there are only two ways the last two shapes can be ordered (one comes first, the other second), each of the designs must appear twice when the last two are cut off. There are $\frac{720}{2} = 360$ designs.

For Discussion

PROBLEM 5 This ${}_nP_k$, like all new notation, can cause trouble. Students want to do something to n and k, like add them. It takes some time and reinforcement to get students used to substituting the idea for the symbol. Some teachers address this in the following way: at random moments in the class, they just ask someone what, for example ${}_6P_4$ *means*. Then they ask someone else to evaluate ${}_6P_4$, explaining how the value is obtained. (This suggestion is only useful if it fits in with your teaching style. If not, never mind!)

Developing Habits of Mind

You can link the box strategy for figuring ${}_nP_k$ to the cut off strategy by adding $n - k$ boxes to the right of your string of k boxes. Next fill out these new boxes using the remaining $n - k$ elements from your basic set of distinct things. You can do this in $(n - k)!$ ways. In doing so you get the $n!$ ways to line up all of the n elements from your original set. Hence ${}_nP_k \cdot (n - k)! = n!$ and you have ${}_nP_k = n!/(n - k)!$, which you get from the cut off strategy.

Blackline Master 4.6B generalizes the discussion on Blackline Master 4.6A and concludes with the definition of permutation.

Definition

A permutation is a one-to-one function from a set to itself.

Think of this as a linear ordering of some (or all) elements. For example, consider the following function from the set $\{A, B, C, D, E\}$ to the set $\{A, B, C, D, E\}$.

$A \mapsto C$
$B \mapsto A$
$C \mapsto B$
$D \mapsto E$
$E \mapsto D$

In Problems 1–3 you had 6 shapes. You selected 4 of them and glued them in a linear order. The order you put them in is one permutation of the set of 4 shapes you chose. This is because you can make a one-to-one function from the set of 4 shapes to the same set of 4 shapes to represent the ordering. A different ordering is a different permutation.

When you select 4 shapes from a group of 6, you can write the total number of designs as ${}_6P_4$. This is the total number of permutations of 4 objects taken from a group of 6.

The number of different ways you can pick k things in order from a set of n distinct things is ${}_nP_k$.

For You to Do

4. a. What is ${}_6P_3$? **b.** What is ${}_6P_5$? **c.** What is ${}_6P_6$?
d. What is ${}_6P_k$? **e.** What is ${}_9P_4$? **f.** What is ${}_9P_5$?
g. What is ${}_9P_6$? **h.** What is ${}_9P_9$? **i.** What is ${}_9P_k$?

Habits of Mind

Visualize. It might help to think about lining up 6 different shapes. Line them up 3 at a time, 5 at a time, and so on.

For Discussion

5. What is a formula for ${}_nP_k$? Explain your answer.

Developing Habits of Mind

Think about it more than one way. Different strategies for solving the For You to Do problems lead to different (but equivalent!) formulas for ${}_nP_k$.

- Box strategy: You have k boxes. You can put any one of n items in the first box, any one of $(n - 1)$ in the second, and so on. When you come to the kth box you must choose from the $(n - k + 1)$ items remaining.

$$ {}_nP_k = \underbrace{n \cdot (n-1) \cdot \cdots \cdot (n-k+1)}_{k \text{ factors}} $$

- Cut off strategy: There are $n!$ ways to line up all n items. If you cut off the last $(n - k)$ items, you will have repeats of each permutation of n things taken k at a time. The number of repeats will be the same as the number of ways to rearrange the tails that you cut off, $(n - k)!$. You have to divide by this number to count each permutation only once.

$$ {}_nP_k = \frac{n!}{(n-k)!} $$

Answers

For You to Do

4. a. 120
b. 720
c. 720
d. $\frac{720}{(6-k)!}$
e. 3024
f. 15,120
g. 60,480
h. 362,880
i. $\frac{362{,}880}{(9-k)!}$

For Discussion

5. ${}_nP_k = \frac{n!}{(n-k)!}$; for possible explanations, see the Developing Habits of Mind that immediately follows this problem.

For You to Do

Show that each of the following is true.

6. $6 \cdot 5 \cdot 4 \cdot 3 = \frac{6!}{2!}$

7. $10 \cdot 9 \cdot 8 = \frac{10!}{7!}$

8. $100 \cdot 99 \cdot 98 \cdot 97 = \frac{100!}{96!}$

9. $100 \cdot 99 \cdot 98 \cdot \cdots \cdot (100 - k + 1) = \frac{100!}{(100 - k)!}$

10. $n(n - 1)(n - 2) \cdots (n - k + 1) = \frac{n!}{(n - k)!}$

Remember...

n! is the product of all of the integers from 1 to *n*.

Extending the Factorial Function

6! is defined as the descending product $6 \cdot 5 \cdot 4 \cdot 3 \cdot 2 \cdot 1$. To compute a factorial, you stop the descending products at 1. Using this definition, you cannot compute 0!. Since picking 0 objects from a set makes sense, it would also make sense for 0! to have a value. Since the descending-product definition does not apply, you can define 0! any way you wish. How many ways can you take 0 objects from a set? Only one way—not at all. So, you can define 0!=1.

Definition

$$0! = 1$$

This is not a deep mathematical result. It is merely a *definition*. The factorial of 0 is 1 because it is convenient to define it that way.

Here is a summary of how to count permutation (so far).

- ${}_nP_k$ is the number of ways you can line up k things in order picked from a set of n things. It is the number of permutations of n things taken k at a time.
- ${}_nP_k = n(n - 1)(n - 2) \cdots (n - k + 1)$
- ${}_nP_k = \frac{n!}{(n - k)!}$
- ${}_nP_n = n!$
- 0!=1

From the third formula in the list above, ${}_5P_5 = n! = 5!$ For the formulas to be consistent, then, the second formula must give this same result for ${}_5P_5$.

$$5! = {}_5P_5 = \frac{5!}{(5 - 5)!} = \frac{5!}{0!}$$

For the formulas to agree, it must be the case that 0! = 1. So, extending the factorial function in this way not only makes sense, but it is actually necessary for the counting formulas to work together.

Habits of Mind

Make strategic choices. In other words, you can extend this definition in a way that makes sense.

For You to Do

PROBLEMS 6–10 Suggest that students work from right to left, showing that the factorial expression equals the corresponding product.

For You to Do

6. $\frac{6!}{2!} = \frac{6 \cdot 5 \cdot 4 \cdot 3 \cdot (2 \cdot 1)}{(2 \cdot 1)} = 6 \cdot 5 \cdot 4 \cdot 3$

7. $\frac{10!}{7!} = \frac{10 \cdot 9 \cdot 8 \cdot (7 \cdot 6 \cdot 5 \cdot 4 \cdot 3 \cdot 2 \cdot 1)}{(7 \cdot 6 \cdot 5 \cdot 4 \cdot 3 \cdot 2 \cdot 1)} = 10 \cdot 9 \cdot 8$

8. $\frac{100!}{96!} = \frac{100 \cdot 99 \cdot 98 \cdot 97 \cdot (96!)}{96!} = 100 \cdot 99 \cdot 98 \cdot 97$

9. $\frac{100!}{(100 - k)!} = \frac{100 \cdot 99 \cdot \ldots \cdot (100 - k + 1)[(100 - k) \cdot (100 - k - 1) \cdot \ldots \cdot 2 \cdot 1]}{[(100 - k)(100 - k - 1) \cdot \ldots \cdot 2 \cdot 1]}$
$= 100 \cdot 99 \cdot \ldots \cdot (100 - k + 1)$

10. $\frac{n!}{(n - k)!} = \frac{n \cdot (n - 1) \cdot (n - 2) \cdot \ldots \cdot (n - k + 1)[(n - k) \cdot (n - k - 1) \cdot \ldots \cdot 2 \cdot 1]}{[(n - k) \cdot (n - k - 1) \cdot \ldots \cdot 2 \cdot 1]}$
$= n(n - 1)(n - 2) \cdots (n - k + 1)$

For You to Do

PROBLEM 11 Make sure students use 3 boxes, one for each digit of the number.

PROBLEM 12 As discussed in the Developing Habits of Mind section, either a 3-digit number has repeated digits or it does not. If you subtract the number of 3-digit numbers from the number of 3-digit numbers with no repeated digits, you have the number of 3-digit numbers with repeated digits. You have seen before that there are $9 \cdot 10 \cdot 10 = 900$ possible 3-digit numbers, so there must be $900 - 648 = 252$ 3-digit numbers that have repeated digits.

Indirect Counting

Sometimes it is easier to count objects that do not have a certain property than it is to count the objects that do. Suppose you know the total number of things in a set. Take away the number of things you do not want. You are left with only the number of things that you do want. In this way you are counting indirectly.

Habits of Mind

Find another way. Mathematicians often use clever shortcuts like this.

To see what is there, artists often look at what is not there.

For You to Do

11. How many three-digit numbers are there with no repeated digits?

12. How many three-digit numbers have repeated digits?

Developing Habits of Mind

Simplify complicated problems. Consider Problem 12. It is not obvious how to count the number of three-digit numbers with repeated digits. But you do know how to find the number of three-digit numbers with different digits. You also know how to find the total number of three-digit numbers. Using the answers to these two simpler problems, you can solve the more complicated one.

number of three-digit numbers with repeated digits =
number of all three-digit numbers −
number of those without repeated digits

Definition

An anagram is a rearrangement of the letters in a word or phrase.

For Discussion

13. How many different anagrams do the following words have?

a. TRIANGLE **b.** GULLIBLE

All sequences of letters are anagrams of themselves. For example, TRIANGLE is an anagram of TRIANGLE.

In the word "TRIANGLE," as in any 8-letter word with all different letters, every rearrangement of letters is a unique anagram. There are a total of 8! anagrams.

Suppose "GULLIBLE" looked like this.

$$GUL_1L_2IBL_3E$$

Then it would have 8! anagrams. Here are a few of these anagrams.

$$L_1L_2L_3EGUBI \quad L_2L_1L_3EGUBI \quad L_1L_3L_2EGUBI$$

Answers

For You to Do

11. 648 numbers

12. 252 numbers

For Discussion

13. a. 40,320 anagrams
b. 6720 anagrams

Of course, L's are not numbered, and you cannot tell these three anagrams apart without numbers. For any placement of L_1, L_2, and L_3, there are 3! ways to rearrange them without changing the placement of the other five letters. So you have to divide the number of rearrangements of 8 letters, 8!, by the number of ways to rearrange the L's. There are $\frac{8!}{3!}$ anagrams of the word "GULLIBLE."

For You to Do

14. How many different anagrams do the following words have?

a. ANACONDA **b.** HEDGEHOG

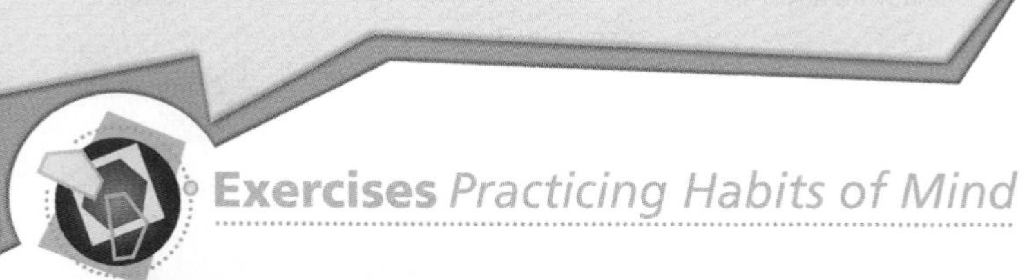

Exercises Practicing Habits of Mind

Check Your Understanding

1. Remember the factorial function.

$$n! = n(n-1)(n-2)\cdots 1$$

Explain why ${}_nP_n = n!$.

2. How many one-to-one functions from the set {place1, place2, place3, place4} to the set {a square, a triangle, a circle, a star, a diamond, an oval} are there?

3. How many one-to-one functions from the set $\{A, B, C, D\}$ to the set $\{1, 2, 3, 4, 5, 6\}$ are there?

4. In a class of 200 students, how many ways are there to choose a president, a vice-president, and a treasurer?

5. Consider all two-digit numbers.

a. How many two-digit numbers have all different digits? (Call these numbers *dull*).

b. How many two-digit numbers have repeated digits? (Call these numbers *funny*).

c. There is a big bag, with many pieces of paper inside. On each piece of paper, there is a two-digit number. All these numbers are different, and all possible two-digit numbers are in the bag. If someone takes out one piece of paper from that bag, is it more likely to be a dull number or a funny number? Explain.

Remember...

In a one-to-one function, two different inputs cannot correspond to the same output.

For You to Do

PROBLEM 14 There are 8! arrangements for the letters of the word ANACONDA, but the A's repeat three times and the N's repeat twice. Divide by the number of arrangements for each of these letters, to get $\frac{8!}{3! \cdot 2!} = 3360$ anagrams.

There are 8! arrangements for the letters of the word HEDGEHOG, but the H's, E's, and G's each appear twice. Divide by the number of arrangements for each of these letters, to get $\frac{8!}{2! \cdot 2! \cdot 2!} = 5040$ anagrams.

Wrap Up

The last discussion of anagrams of the words ANACONDA and HEDGEHOG provide a good wrap up to this lesson.

Assessment Resources

Lesson Quiz 4.6

1. A teacher wants to make a seating chart for a class of 15 students. The class has 8 girls and 7 boys.
   a. How many ways can the teacher choose five students to sit in the front row?
   b. If the teacher decides to put only boys in the front row, how many ways can she choose to do this?
2. How many anagrams does each word have?
   a. GRAPE b. APPLE
3. A computer assigns a password of 5 characters, where the first 2 characters are letters from the alphabet and the last 3 characters are numbers.
   a. How many passwords are possible?
   b. If you choose a password at random, what is the probability that it contains at least one letter A and at least one number 1?
   c. What is the probability your password has no repeated characters?
4. Jason rolls two number cubes. What is the probability that both number cubes show even numbers?

Exercises

HOMEWORK

- Core: 12, 13, 14, 15, 16, 17, 18, 21, 22, 23, 25
- Optional: 19, 20, 24, 26, 27

Check Your Understanding

EXERCISE 5 When going over the results of the three parts of this exercise, ask students what the probability is of drawing a dull number.

For You to Do

14. a. 3360 anagrams
b. 5040 anagrams

Exercises

1. Answers may vary. Sample: Since ${}_nP_k = \frac{n!}{(n-k)!}$ when $1 \le k \le n$, then ${}_nP_n = \frac{n!}{(n-n)!} = \frac{n!}{0!} = \frac{n!}{1} = n!$

2. 360 functions

3. 360 functions

4. 7,880,400 ways

5. a. 81 numbers
b. 9 numbers
c. Dull number; there are more dull numbers than funny numbers in the bag.

EXERCISE 9 Many students have played with anagrams before encountering them here. Encourage students to list out the anagrams before they try to apply any formulas, at first.

On Your Own

EXERCISES 18 AND 19 Notice that these exercises ask for probabilities and not for "how many ways." Check that students are giving probabilities for their answers.

6. Extend Exercise 5 and now consider all four-digit numbers.

There is another bag, also with many pieces of paper inside. On each piece of paper, there is a four-digit number. All these numbers are different, and all possible four-digit numbers are in the bag. If someone takes out one piece of paper from that bag, is it more likely to be a dull number or a funny number? Explain your reasoning.

7. Repeat Exercise 6 with five-digit numbers.

8. Repeat Exercise 6 with ten-digit numbers.

9. How many anagrams does each word have?

a. AGH **b.** AHA **c.** AAA

10. How many anagrams does each word have?

a. JOHN **b.** JILL **c.** PEEP
d. EEEK **e.** RRRR

11. How many anagrams does each word have?

a. BANANA **b.** BALLOON **c.** BORING

On Your Own

Exercises 12–17 refer to *attribute blocks.* Each block in a set of attribute blocks has

- one of two sizes (large or small)
- one of four colors (red, blue, green, or yellow)
- one of three shapes (described as square, circle, or triangle)

There is exactly one block with each combination of attributes. There is one large, green square, one small yellow circle, and so on.

12. How many pieces are there in a set of attribute blocks?

13. How many blue blocks are in a set?

14. How many large blocks are in a set?

Use the box strategy to solve Exercise 12. How many ways are there to pick an attribute for each box?

Begin each of Exercises 15–17 with all the attribute blocks in a bucket. You are to pick one or more blocks at random from the bucket. On each pick, you are equally likely to pick any block in the bucket.

15. Pick one block from the bucket. What is the probability that it is a green square?

16. Pick two blocks from the bucket. What is the probability that they are the same size?

Answers

6. Dull number; there are more dull numbers (4536) than funny numbers (4464) in the bag.

7. Funny number; there are more funny numbers (62,784) than dull numbers (27,216) in the bag.

8. Funny number; there are more funny numbers (8,996,734,080) than dull numbers (3,265,920) in the bag.

9. a. 6 anagrams
b. 3 anagrams
c. 1 anagram

10. a. 24 anagrams
b. 12 anagrams
c. 6 anagrams
d. 4 anagrams
e. 1 anagram

11. a. 60 anagrams
b. 1260 anagrams
c. 720 anagrams

12. 24 pieces

13. 6 blue blocks

14. 12 large blocks

15. $\frac{1}{12} \approx 8.3\%$

16. $\frac{11}{23} \approx 47.8\%$

17. Pick three blocks from the bucket. What is the probability that they are the same color?

18. Jim rolls two number cubes. What is the probability of the same number showing on both cubes?

19. Now Jim rolls three number cubes. What is the probability that at least two of three numbers showing are the same?

20. Tom and Jerry are playing a game. Tom rolls four number cubes. If all four numbers showing on the cubes are different, he wins. Otherwise, Jerry wins. Who do you think wins more often? Why do you think so?

21. How many different anagrams are there for the word NIMBLE?

22. How many different anagrams are there for the word MUMBLE?

23. **Write About It** How are Exercises 21 and 22 similar? Are they isomorphic?

24. How many different anagrams are there for the word MISSISSIPPI?

25. **Standardized Test Prep** At dinner, Ms. Fair tries to give portions of equal size to her four sons. The kids have a theory that whoever is served last gets less. They wrote out all possible orders that their mom could use. Ms. Fair followed the list, using each possible order exactly once. How often did the youngest son get his plate last?

A. 1 **B.** 3 **C.** 4 **D.** 6

Go Online PHSchool.com

For additional practice, go to **Web Code:** bga-0406

Maintain Your Skills

26. There are ten digits from 0–9. You are going to select an ATM PIN. The rules for these PINs differ from bank to bank. Assume that no valid PIN can have repeated digits. For each length given, find the number of possible ATM PINs.

a. one-digit **b.** two-digit
c. three-digit **d.** four-digit
e. five-digit **f.** ten-digit
g. n-digit

In the codes, order does matter. 012 is a different code from 201.

27. There are 26 letters from A to Z. You want to select an ATM PIN consisting of these letters. Assume that no valid PIN can have repeated letters. For each length given, find the number of possible ATM PINs.

a. one-letter **b.** two-letter
c. five-letter **d.** ten-letter
e. 26-letter **f.** n-letter

Order still matters. So GUM is a different code from MUG.

Additional Resources

PRINT RESOURCES
- Solution Manual
- Practice Workbook
- Assessment Resources
- Teaching Resources

TECHNOLOGY
- Interactive Textbook
- TeacherExpress CD-ROM
- ExamView CD-ROM
- PHSchool.com

Additional Practice

1. In a road race of 200 runners, how many different outcomes are there for first, second and third place?

2. Consider all four-digit numbers.
a. How many four-digit numbers have all different digits?
b. How many four-digit numbers have all the same digits?

3. How many anagrams does each word have?
a. SUNDAY **b.** YEARLY
c. EXCEED **d.** HAHAHA

4. You have a set of cards where each card has some combination of the following.
• one of five different colors (blue, green, purple, red, or orange)
• one of four different shapes on it (triangle, circle, square, or trapezoid)
• one of four different letters on it (E, F, G, or H)
There is exactly one card with each combination of characteristics.
a. How many cards are in the set?
b. How many red cards are in the set?
c. How many cards containing triangles are in the set?

5. On a test consisting of seven essay questions, students can choose to answer any three of them. How many choices do students have for a set of three essays?

6. A teacher wants to form an 8 person committee to represent the student body. She will choose 4 female students from the 25 females eligible. Then she will choose 4 male students from the 22 males eligible. In how many different ways can she form the new committee?

7. How many different words are possible from 3 K's and 7 L's? (Remember, we call such strings *words* even if they are meaningless.)

8. You have 15 cards numbered 1–15, and you randomly choose 4 cards.
a. How many different combinations of 4 cards are possible?
b. How many of the combinations contain the number 10?
c. How many of the combinations do not contain the number 10?

Practice: For Lesson 4.6, assign Exercises 1–4.

17. $\frac{10}{253} \approx 4\%$

18. $\frac{1}{6} \approx 16.7\%$

19. $\frac{4}{9} \approx 44.4\%$

20. Jerry; the probability of rolling 4 different number cubes is less than the probability of at least two number cubes being the same.

21. 720 anagrams

22. 360 anagrams

23. They are similar because they are anagrams of 6-letter words, but they are not isomorphic.

24. 34,650 anagrams

25. D

26. a. 10 codes **b.** 90 codes
c. 720 codes **d.** 5040 codes
e. 30,240 codes
f. 3,628,800 codes
g. When $n \leq 10$, there are ${}_{10}P_n$ possible n-digit codes. But, if $n > 10$, no ATM codes can be made.

27. a. 26 codes
b. 650 codes
c. 7,893,600 codes
d. 19,275,223,968,000 codes
e. 26! codes
f. When $n \leq 26$, there are ${}_{26}P_n$ possible n-letter codes. But, if $n > 26$, no ATM codes can be made.

Lesson Overview

GOALS

- Find a formula for the number of combinations of n objects, taken k at a time.
- Find the number of anagrams for a word.

This lesson introduces unordered groups with the game of SET®. From this, students develop techniques for counting combinations of cards and other objects by finding the number of ordered groupings and then dividing out by the possible orderings, drawing on their work with anagrams.

Students also learn to make arguments like this: to calculate the number of 5-person committees from a class of 26 people, pick a *distinguished person* in the class, say Melanie. A 5-person committee from a class of 26 either contains Melanie (so you have to pick four more from the remaining 25) or does not (so you have to pick all five from the remaining 25).

CHECK YOUR UNDERSTANDING

- Core: 1, 2, 3, 4, 9, 10, 11, 15, 18
- Optional: 5, 6, 7, 8, 12, 13, 14, 16, 17, 19, 20

MATERIALS

- graphing calculators
- Blackline Masters, MC12, 4.7A–B

HOMEWORK

- Core: 21, 22, 23, 24, 27, 28, 32, 33, 34, 35, 39
- Optional: 25, 26, 29, 30, 31, 38, 40
- Extension: 36, 37

VOCABULARY

- combination
- ${}_nC_k$, number of combinations of n objects, taken k at a time

Launch

Begin this class by describing the game of SET® and bring students into the first Discussion section.

Explore

Blackline Master 4.7A summarizes the rules for the game SET® and gives some examples. Color the shapes before using the master on an overhead.

4.7 Combinations

The game of SET® is a card game. Each card has four attributes:

shape:	ovals, squiggles, or diamonds
number:	one, two, or three of the shapes
color:	red, green, or purple
shading:	outlined, striped, or filled

The full deck has one card with each of the possible combinations of attributes. (All cards in a deck are different.)

The object of the game is to identify a SET of 3 cards from 12 cards laid out on a table.

A SET consists of three cards where each of the four attributes, looked at one by one, are either the same on each card or are different on all the cards. All the attributes must separately satisfy this rule. The shape must either be the same on the three cards of a set or all the shapes must be different on them. The colors on the three cards of a set must either be the same or all of them must be different, and so on.

For Discussion

1. How many cards are there in the whole deck?
2. In the problems below, you will need to describe different cards. It is time consuming to refer to a card as, for example, "a card with three, red, striped ovals." Think of a more efficient way to describe a card.

For You to Do

All cards in these triples are of the same color. Which ones are sets? Explain your answer.

3. 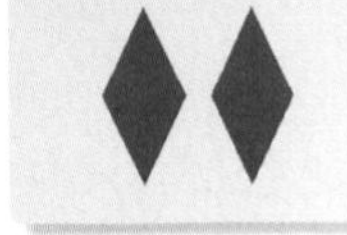 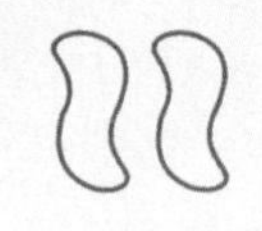 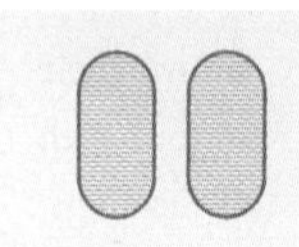

4. 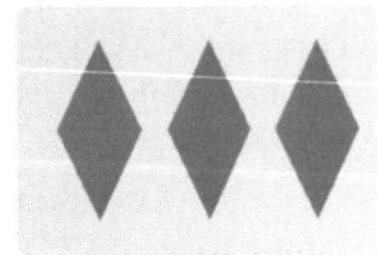 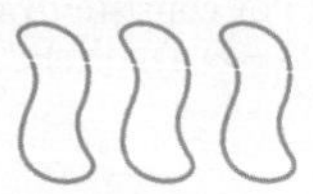 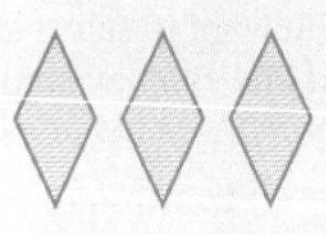

Answers

For Discussion

1. 81 cards
2. Check students' work.

For You to Do

3. Set; all have different shapes, all have 2 shapes, all have the same color, all have different shading.
4. Not a set; 2 cards have the same shapes while the other has different shapes.

5. 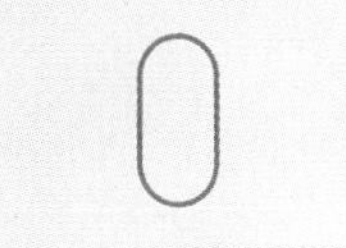  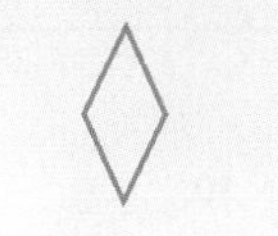

6. In this array of nine cards below, find all the sets.

 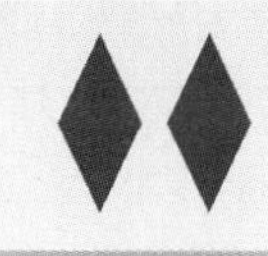 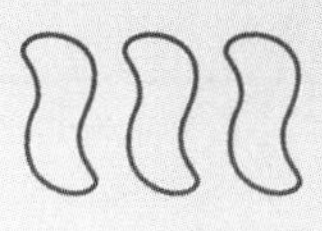

 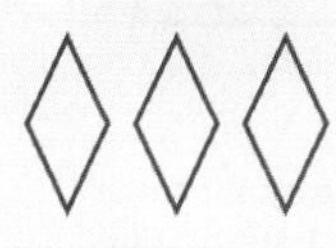 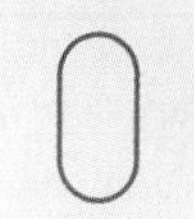

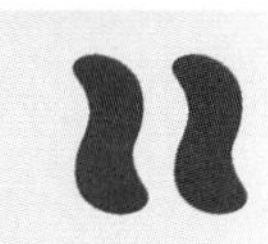 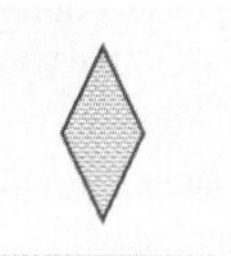 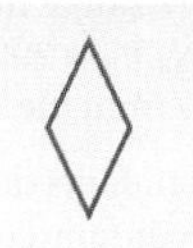

For Discussion

7. If you play SET with only the red, oval cards, then there would only be nine cards. How many different groups of three cards can you pick from nine cards?

Another question you can consider: How many of these groups of three are actually sets?

Here is a difference between objects in a group and objects in a line-up. Order does not matter for a group. Order does matter for a line-up. The number of combinations of objects in a group is less than the number of permutations of the same objects in a line-up.

Remember...

Remember, another word for "line-up" is *permutation*.

Definition

A subset of a set S is a combination of elements of S. You can think of a combination as being k things chosen from the set S, which itself has n elements.

The number of combinations of three cards from a deck of nine cards is written ${}_9C_3$. You say ${}_9C_3$ as, "9 choose 3."

In a combination, it does not matter how you arrange the elements.

For Discussion

PROBLEM 7 is aimed at getting students to think about how counting groups is different from counting permutations. Although some students may naturally gravitate toward developing a formula, this is not necessarily the expected outcome. Rather, students should use some of their general counting strategies to develop a strategy. If students are stuck, you may want to suggest looking at a smaller problem, like choosing a group of three cards from a deck of five cards.

Some ideas that might arise in the discussion:

- The order within a group of cards does not matter!
- There are ${}_9P_3 = 9 \cdot 8 \cdot 7$ ways to pick the three cards in order. Once they are chosen, any of the 3! ways to arrange those three cards would give you the same hand, so each hand gets counted 6 times. Therefore there are $\frac{9 \cdot 8 \cdot 7}{6} = 84$ ways to choose the three cards.
- There are six times as many permutations as combinations. Every group of three cards makes $3! = 6$ of the possible permutations.

5. Set; all have different shapes, all have 1 shape, all have the same color, all have the same shading.

6.

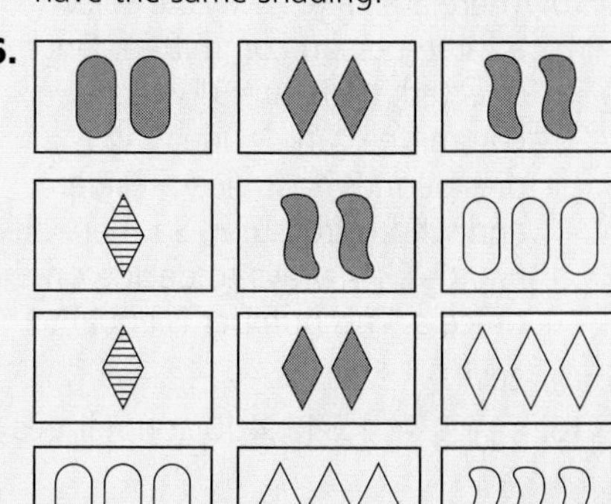

For Discussion

7. 84 groups

For You to Do

PROBLEM 8 There are $_9P_2 = 72$ permutations of 2 objects from a set of 9 objects. Since any combination of 2 of the objects has 2 permutations, there are $\frac{72}{2} = 36$ combinations of 2 objects from a set of 9 objects.

PROBLEM 9 As in the previous Discussion, there are $_9P_3 = 504$ permutations, and each combination of 3 accounts for $3! = 6$ permutations. There are $\frac{504}{6} = 84$ combinations of 3 objects from a set of 9.

PROBLEM 10 There are $_{12}P_2 = 132$ permutations of 2 objects from a set of 12. Since each combination of 2 objects accounts for 2 of the permutations, there are $\frac{132}{2} = 66$ combinations of 2 objects from a set of 12.

PROBLEM 11 Choosing to include 10 elements is the same as choosing NOT to include 2 of the elements. Therefore, $_{12}C_{10}$ can be thought of in two ways: (1) The number of combinations of 10 elements chosen from a set of 12, or (2) The number of combinations of 2 elements that are NOT chosen from the set of 12.

If you think of it the second way, it is clear why the answer is the same as in Problem 10. If you think of it the first way, then there are $_{12}P_{10}$ permutations of 10 objects chosen from the set of 12, and each group of 10 objects accounts for 10! of these permutations. The number of combinations is $\frac{_{12}P_{10}}{10!} = 66$.

For You to Do

PROBLEM 12 This expression can be thought of as the number of ways to choose 0 elements from a set of n elements.

PROBLEM 13 This expression can be thought of as the number of ways to choose n elements from a set of n elements.

PROBLEM 14 This expression can be thought of as the number of ways to choose 0 elements from a set of 0 elements.

For Discussion

PROBLEMS 15 AND 16 ask students to compare a permutation problem and a combination problem, both involving so many objects that they cannot list them out in a reasonable amount of time. This discussion may incorporate all of the concepts discussed in the previous combinations students have done, but the key concept to emphasize is the connection between permutations and combinations.

For You to Do

Find each number.

8. $_9C_2$ **9.** $_9C_3$ **10.** $_{12}C_2$ **11.** $_{12}C_{10}$

In general, the number of combinations of n objects chosen k at a time is $_nC_k$. The value of k can range from 0 to n.

For You to Do

Find each number.

12. $_nC_0$ **13.** $_nC_n$ **14.** $_0C_0$

Habits of Mind

Experiment. Try it with numbers!

To find a formula for $_nC_k$, consider the following.

In one class of 200 students, elections occur the following way. First, the students choose the president. Then, out of the remaining 199 students, they choose the vice-president. Finally, out of the remaining 198 students, they choose the treasurer. There are $_{200}P_3 = 200 \cdot 199 \cdot 198$ possible ways for the class to choose these 3 officers from the 200 students.

In another class of 200 students, the students decide first to elect a three-person committee. Then they let the committee members decide who among themselves will be president, vice-president, and treasurer.

For Discussion

15. Show that both election procedures lead to the same number of possible selections of the president, vice-president, and treasurer.

16. Suppose now that another class of 200 students is going to elect a committee of three students, but each person on the committee has the same role (no president, vice-president, or treasurer). How many different committees could the class form then?

The committee {Jan, Kyle, Mena} is the same as the committee {Mena, Jan, Kyle}.

To find a formula for $_nC_k$, analyze the two different procedures of electing a president, a vice-president, and a treasurer.

The first procedure gives you $_{200}P_3$ possible choices of a president, vice-president, and treasurer.

Think, "C for Combinations and for Committees—both are unordered choices."

In the second procedure, you obtain $_{200}C_3$ possible committees with 3 members. Then the committee members decide who will play which role. Any one of the three can be the president, either of the other two can be the vice-president. There is no choice except being treasurer for the third person.

That makes $3 \cdot 2 \cdot 1 = 3!$ possibilities at the second stage. The total number of possible choices for president, vice-president, and treasurer under this second procedure is, therefore,

$$_{200}C_3 \cdot 3!$$

Answers

For You to Do

8. 36

9. 84

10. 66

11. 66

For You to Do

12. 1 **13.** 1 **14.** 1

For Discussion

15. There are $_{200}C_3$ ways to select a three-person committee. Once selected, there are 3! ways a committee can decide who is president, who is vice-president, and who is treasurer. So there are $(_{200}C_3) \cdot 3!$ ways to decide on the officers. This number is equal to $_{200}P_3$.

16. $_{200}C_3 = 1{,}313{,}400$ committees

In the end, both procedures give the same number of possible choices for the three positions.

$$_{200}P_3 = {}_{200}C_3 \cdot 3!$$

Solving this equation for $_{200}C_3$, you arrive at the following formula.

$$_{200}C_3 = \frac{_{200}P_3}{3!} = \frac{200 \cdot 199 \cdot 198}{3 \cdot 2 \cdot 1} = 1{,}313{,}400$$

For You to Do

17. Show that the number of combinations $_nC_k$, is the number of permutations, $_nP_k$, divided by the number of permutations per combination, $_kP_k$. In other words,

$$_nC_k = \frac{_nP_k}{k!}$$

The result in Problem 17 is important enough to state as a theorem.

Theorem 4.2

$$_nC_k = \frac{_nP_k}{k!} = \frac{n!}{k!(n-k)!}$$

Proof You already proved the first part in Problem 17. The second part follows directly from the formula $_nP_k$.

$$\frac{_nP_k}{k!} = \frac{\frac{n!}{(n-k)!}}{k!} = \frac{n!}{k!(n-k)!}$$

Remember...

The formula for the number of permutations of n things taken k at time is

$$_nP_k = \frac{n!}{(n-k)!}$$

For Discussion

A board of directors consists of five people. They want to form a three-person subcommittee. Suppose the people on the board are

{Jason, John, Michelle, Alicia, Dan}

18. How many three-person committees include Dan?

19. How many three-person committees do not include Dan?

For You to Do

17. If you take any one combination of k elements selected from a set of n elements, there are $k!$ ways to line them up. So $_nC_k \cdot k! = {}_nP_k$. It follows that $_nC_k = \frac{_nP_k}{k!}$.

For Discussion

18. 6 committees

19. 4 committees

For You to Do

PROBLEM 17 You know $_nC_k = \frac{_nP_k}{k!}$, but you also know that $_kP_k = \frac{k!}{(k-k)!} = \frac{k!}{0!} = k!$, so $_nC_k = \frac{_nP_k}{k!} = \frac{_nP_k}{_kP_k}$.

For Discussion

PROBLEMS 18 AND 19 You may want to ask students, "How could you use your answer to these problems to count $_5C_3$?" The discussion leads nicely to the combinatorial proof. You do not need to wrap up this discussion until after you look at the Minds in Action dialog on the next page with students.

Minds in Action

You may wish to use Pascal's Triangle on Blackline Master MC12 following the discussion of Sasha's result. Illustrate some of the other properties of Pascal's Triangle shown on the master. Use this master throughout the remainder of the chapter as needed.

Minds in Action episode 12

Sasha is working on writing a proof to show that ${}_5C_3 = {}_4C_2 + {}_4C_3$.

Sasha I want to show that

$${}_5C_3 = {}_4C_2 + {}_4C_3$$

I could use the formula for ${}_nC_k$, but instead I'll use a combinatorial proof. In this problem, suppose I have the 5 people in the For Discussion problem:

{Jason, John, Michelle, Alicia, Dan}

and I want to pick a committee of 3. There are ${}_5C_3$ different committees I could make. Every one of these committees either contains Dan or doesn't. So,

$${}_5C_3 = \text{the number of committees that contain Dan} + \text{the number of committees that don't}$$

But if a committee contains Dan, I have to pick 2 more people from the remaining 4, and there are ${}_4C_2$ ways to do that. So,

$$\text{the number of committees that contain Dan} = {}_4C_2$$

And, if a committee doesn't contain Dan, I have to pick all 3 people from the remaining 4, and there are ${}_4C_3$ ways to do that:

$$\text{the number of committees that don't} = {}_4C_3$$

Therefore

$${}_5C_3 = {}_4C_2 + {}_4C_3$$

A combinatorial proof allows you to answer questions like these by telling a story. You can establish a formula by showing that each side of the formula represents a different way to count the same thing. You can simplify a complex algebraic identity by looking at it in the right way. Of course, finding the right way can be difficult at first, but it gets a lot easier with practice.

There is no reason to single out Dan. Sasha could have chosen any one of the five people.

You can visualize Sasha's proof using a diagram like this.

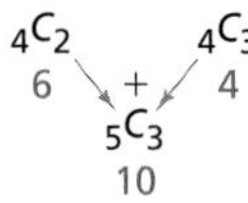

In fact, you could quickly create a table of the values of ${}_nC_k$.

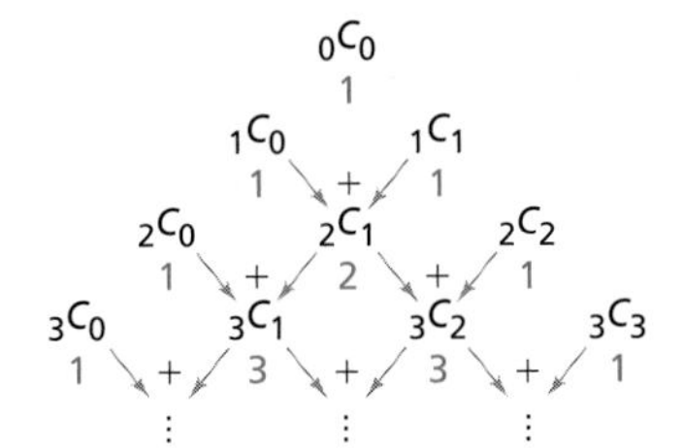

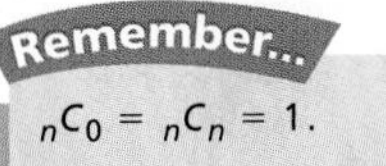

Remember...

${}_nC_0 = {}_nC_n = 1.$

Recall Pascal's Triangle.

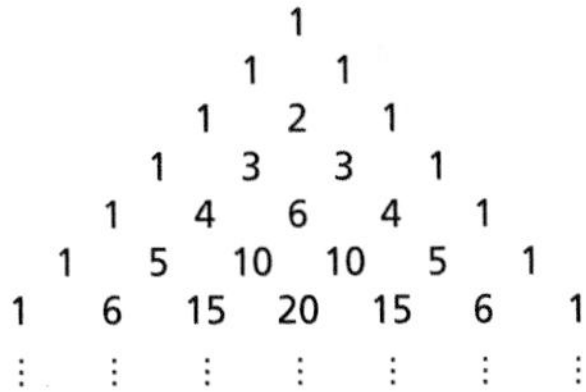

Remember...

Number the horizontal rows starting with 0 and number the first element in each row with a 0.

Remember that you can label an entry of Pascal's Triangle like this.

Recall that the top number n is the row number (starting with 0). The bottom number k is how far you go across in a row (starting with 0). For example, you can label the entries in the fifth row like this.

$$\binom{5}{0} \quad \binom{5}{1} \quad \binom{5}{2} \quad \binom{5}{3} \quad \binom{5}{4} \quad \binom{5}{5}$$

$$1 \quad 5 \quad 10 \quad 10 \quad 5 \quad 1$$

Using this labeling method, you can see the following connection between combinations and the entries of Pascal's Triangle.

Theorem 4.3 The Pascal-Combinations Connection

For any $n \geq 0$ and all k such that $0 \leq k \leq n$,

$$\binom{n}{k} = {}_nC_k$$

You will develop more details of the Pascal-Combinations Connection Theorem as you work through the exercises. You might want to read Sasha's storytelling proof again, after working a few exercises.

Wrap Up

These Pascal-Combinations Connections are often blurry for students! They will have plenty of opportunities in the next investigation to hammer down the connections. For now they should work on making sense of the Pascal-Combinations Connection.

Assessment Resources

Lesson Quiz 4.7

1. You must choose classmates to work on a group project with you. There are 9 boys and 7 girls from which to choose.
   a. How many ways can you choose three classmates?
   b. How many ways can you choose four classmates?
   c. How many ways can you choose 2 boys and 2 girls?

2. A baseball team consists of 17 players with jersey numbers 1 through 17. For every game the coach chooses 3 players to play in the outfield.
   a. How many ways can the coach choose three players?
   b. What is the probability that the coach chooses the person wearing number 15 to play outfield?
   c. What is the probability that the coach does not choose the person wearing number 15 to play outfield?

Exercises

HOMEWORK

- Core: 21, 22, 23, 24, 27, 28, 32, 33, 34, 35, 39
- Optional: 25, 26, 29, 30, 31, 38, 40
- Extension: 36, 37

Exercises *Practicing Habits of Mind*

Check Your Understanding

1. How many different committees of 4 people are possible in a class of 200 students?

2. A class of 200 students must form a committee of 4 people. Nobody wants to be elected. So instead the class is choosing $200 - 4 = 196$ students who can safely avoid serving on that committee. How many different groups of 196 students are possible out of 200 students?

3. Explain why ${}_{200}C_4 = {}_{200}C_{196}$.

4. Write the following using factorial notation.

   a. ${}_7P_3$ b. ${}_7C_3$

5. Consider ${}_7C_3$, the number of combinations of 7 things chosen 3 at a time. Show that ${}_7C_3$ is ${}_7P_3$ (the number of permutations of 3 things taken from a group of 7) divided by ${}_3P_3$ (the number of permutations per combination).

$${}_7C_3 = \frac{{}_7P_3}{3!}$$

6. Show that ${}_nC_k = {}_nC_{n-k}$, for $0 \le k \le n$.

7. Explain why ${}_{10}P_3 = 6 \cdot {}_{10}C_3$.

8. Explain why ${}_{10}C_3 = {}_{10}C_7$.

   Tell a story that would lead to this equation. Generalize this equation to a formula.

9. **Write About It** Explain the difference between what you count to get ${}_nP_k$ and what you count to get ${}_nC_k$.

10. June wants to read four books. To keep June's taste in reading secret, you will call these books simply "book 1," "book 2," "book 3," and "book 4." June is packing for her vacation and is deciding which of these books (if any) she should take with her.

    a. June decides to take exactly two books. How many choices does she have for which two books to take?

    b. Among these two-book choices, how many include book 1?

    c. Among the two-book choices, how many do not include book 1?

11. Give a combinatorial proof that ${}_7C_4 = {}_6C_3 + {}_6C_4$.

Habits of Mind

Understand the problem. Do not just show that the numbers are the same. Explain why there are 6 times as many permutations as there are combinations.

Answers

Exercises

1. 64,684,950 committees
2. 64,684,950 groups
3. For each distinct committee of 4 people you choose, you leave behind a distinct *non-committee* of 196 people. So, there are the same number of committees of 4 people and committees of 196 people.
4. **a.** ${}_7P_3 = \frac{7!}{4!}$ **b.** ${}_7C_3 = \frac{7!}{4! \cdot 3!}$
5. From the previous exercise, ${}_7C_3 = \frac{{}_7P_3}{3!} = \frac{{}_7P_3}{{}_3P_3}$. This makes sense, since every combination of 3 particular objects accounts for $3! = 6$ of the permutations of 3 of the 6 objects.
6. See back of book.
7. Every combination of 3 objects from a set of 10 can be arranged in $3! = 6$ ways (that is, has $3! = 6$ permutations). So, ${}_{10}C_3 \cdot 6$ is the number of possible permutations of 3 objects chosen from a set of 10, or ${}_{10}P_3$.
8. ${}_{10}P_3$ represents the number of subsets of 3 cards you can make from a set of 10 cards, and ${}_{10}C_7$ represents the number of subsets of 7 cards you can make from a set of 10 cards. But, every time you make a different subset of 3 cards, you leave behind a different group of seven cards - that is, there are as many subsets of 7 cards as there are of 3 cards: ${}_{10}C_3 = {}_{10}C_7$. The same argument would hold for any subset of k cards chosen from a set of n cards: ${}_nC_k = {}_nC_{n-k}$.
9. See back of book.
10. **a.** 6 choices
    b. 3 choices
    c. 3 choices
11. See back of book.

12. **a.** Complete the statement to make it true.

$$_{10}C_6 = {}_{?}C_6 + {}_{9}C_{??}$$

b. Prove the statement.

13. Give a combinatorial proof that for $0 < k < n$

$$_{n}C_k = {}_{n-1}C_{k-1} + {}_{n-1}C_k$$

Why does this result not apply when $k = 0$, or when $k = n$?

14. For any $n > 1$, explain the relationship between the expressions.

a. $_{n}C_0$ and $_{n-1}C_0$

b. $_{n}C_n$ and $_{n-1}C_{n-1}$

15. Recall this table from page 309.

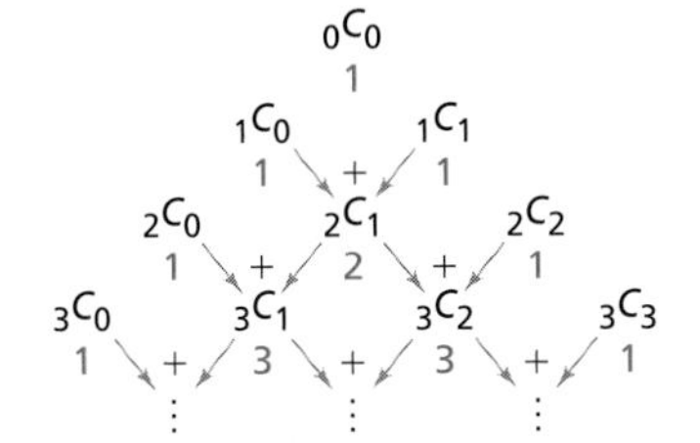

Copy the table. Then extend it by writing rows 4 through 10.

16. Explain why Theorem 4.3 is true.

17. What is a good definition of $\binom{5}{6}$? Explain your choice.

18. Wrigley High School's basketball team has ten players. The coach needs to choose five players to start in the next game. How many five-player combinations are possible?

In Exercise 18, choose the five starting players without regard to the positions they play.

19. A board of directors has eight members. They want to form several committees, but they are not sure how many members to use. The committee sizes will range from zero to eight members, inclusive. For each one of these sizes, find the number of committees possible.

20. Find a formula for the sum of the entries in any row of Pascal's Triangle.

On Your Own

21. Consider a list of ten problems. How many different assignments of exactly six problems are possible out of these ten problems?

Check Your Understanding

EXERCISE 17 continues the theme of extension, extending definitions in ways that make sense.

12. a. $_{10}C_6 = {}_9C_6 + {}_9C_5$.

b. Answers may vary. Sample: suppose we have a group of 10 people, including a person named Gill. We want to make a committee of 6 people From this group of 10. There are $_{10}C_6$ different committees we could make. However,

$_{10}C_6$ = number of possible committees Gill is on + number of committees Gill is not on

If Gill is on a committee, then there are 9 remaining people to fill the other 5 spots on the committee. So, there are $_9C_5$ different committees that can be made with Gill. If Gill is not on the committee, then the entire committee of 6 people needs to be chosen from the remaining 9 people. So, there are $_9C_6$ different committees that can be made without Gill. Thus:

$$_{10}C_6 = {}_9C_6 + {}_9C_5$$

13. See back of book.

14. a. $_nC_0 = {}_{n-1}C_0 = 1$

b. $_nC_n = {}_{n-1}C_{n-1} = 1$

15–16. See back of book.

17. Answers may vary. Sample: 0; check students' work.

18. 252 combinations

19. 1; 8; 28; 56; 70; 56; 28; 8; 1

20. 2^n

21. 210 assignments

On Your Own

EXERCISE 24 is typical of many in the set of exercises and leads to more general results later. Since it is a multi-part exercise, you may find it worth discussing parts of it during class. Blackline Master 4.7B graphically interprets the box strategy mentioned in the margin note as well as showing the table. Fill in the boxes using the box method and have students determine the numbers of each kind of subset.

22. In a homework set of ten problems, students can choose to skip any four. How many choices do students have for a set of four problems to omit?

23. Show that Exercises 21 and 22 are isomorphic.

24. a. How many subsets does $S = \{A, B, C, D, E\}$ have? Count the whole set and the empty set, too.

b. How many elements can a subset of S have?

c. Copy and complete the table.

Number of Elements in a Subset of S	Number of Subsets of S
0 (the empty set)	■
1	■
2	■
3	■
4	■
5 (the whole set)	■

d. The sum of the numbers in the second column must be the same as the number of subsets you found in part (a). Verify that they are the same.

Think of this as a "box problem." There are five boxes, one for each element of $\{A, B, C, D, E\}$. For a given subset, put a 1 in the box corresponding to an element if that element is in the subset. Put a 2 in the box if the element is not in the subset. How many ways are there to put 1's or 2's into the five boxes?

25. You have nine books, but there is only room for four of them on your shelf. In how many different ways can you line up four of the nine books on your shelf?

26. In how many different ways can a person choose four books from a pile of nine distinct best-sellers?

Make a connection. You can think of each function as describing one of June's possible book choices. (See Exercise 10.)

27. Consider all functions from the set $\{1, 2, 3, 4\}$ to the set {take, leave}. Two examples of such functions are shown below.

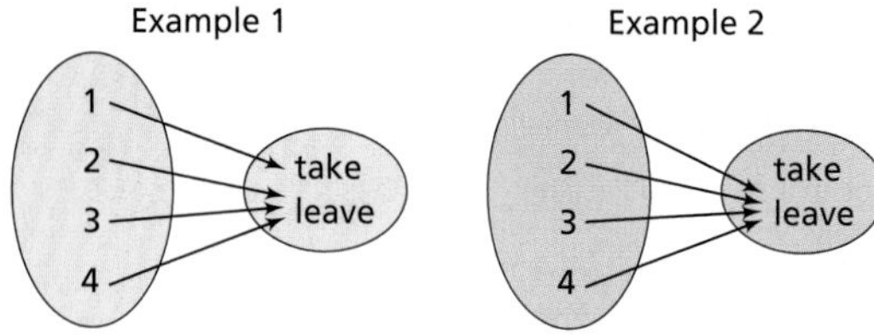

a. How many functions are there from the set $\{1, 2, 3, 4\}$ to the set {take, leave}?

b. How many of these functions do not have *take* as an output?

c. How many of these functions have *take* as an output for exactly one input? (Function A above is one of them.)

For additional practice, go to **Web Code:** bga-0407

Answers

22. 210 choices

23. Choosing 6 problems to complete is the same as choosing 4 problems *not* to complete.

24. a. 32 subsets

b. 0, 1, 2, 3, 4, or 5 elements

c.

Number of Elements in a Subset of *S*	Number of Subsets of *S*
0 (the empty set)	${}_5C_0 = 1$
1	${}_5C_1 = 5$
2	${}_5C_2 = 10$
3	${}_5C_3 = 10$
4	${}_5C_4 = 5$
5 (the whole set)	${}_5C_5 = 1$

d. $1 + 5 + 10 + 10 + 5 + 1 = 32$, so the table agrees with part (a).

25. 3024 ways

26. 126 ways

27. a. 16 functions

b. 1 function

c. 4 functions

d. 6 functions

e. 4 functions

f. 1 function

g. $1 + 4 + 6 + 4 + 1 = 16$

d. How many of these functions have *take* as an output for exactly two inputs?

e. How many of these functions have *take* as an output for exactly three inputs?

f. How many of these functions have *take* as an output all four inputs?

g. You counted all functions in part (a). Then, in parts (b)–(f), you counted them again, counting by the number of times *take* is an output of the function. Check whether you got the same total number of functions.

28. Michelle, Jenn and Suzi are in a class of 21 people.

a. How many committees of four are possible in this class?

b. How many of those four-person committees contain Suzi?

c. How many of those four-person committees do not contain Suzi?

d. How many of those four-person committees do not contain Suzi, but do contain both Michelle and Jenn?

Habits of Mind

Find another way. Some people prefer to solve a different problem instead: In how many ways can you choose three students that will escape this duty?

29. a. In how many ways can you choose two students out of five to write their homework solutions on the board?

b. How many five-letter "words" are possible using two N's and three E's?

c. In how many ways can you arrange two red chips and three blue chips in a line? (Chips of the same color are identical, so their order does not matter.)

d. Explain why the problems in parts (a) through (c) are isomorphic.

30. The director of a research laboratory wants to hire 5 new workers. She will choose 2 from the 12 chemists who applied. Then she will choose 3 from the 5 physicists who applied. In how many different ways can she hire the new workers?

31. Mr. Henkle chooses five students each day (at random) to write their homework solutions on the board. There are 12 students in his class.

a. Which entries in Pascal's Triangle will tell you how many different groups of 5 students Mr. Henkle could pick? How many groups are there?

b. Darren is in the class. Which entries in Pascal's Triangle will tell you how many groups contain Darren? How many groups are there that contain Darren?

c. If Darren is in class today, what is the probability that he will have to write his solution on the board?

32. Prove that

$$\binom{5}{0} + \binom{5}{1} + \binom{5}{2} + \binom{5}{3} + \binom{5}{4} + \binom{5}{5} = 2^5$$

28. a. 5985 committees
b. 1140 committees
c. 4845 committees
d. 153 committees

29. a. 10 ways
b. 10 ways
c. 10 ways
d. All these problems can be solved using the formula ${}_5C_2 = 10$.

30. 660 ways

31. a. $\binom{12}{5}$ or $\binom{12}{7}$; 792 groups
b. $\binom{11}{4}$ or $\binom{11}{7}$; 330 groups
c. $\frac{5}{12} \approx 41.7\%$

32. $\binom{5}{0} + \binom{5}{1} + \binom{5}{2} + \binom{5}{3} + \binom{5}{4} + \binom{5}{5} = 1 + 5 + 10 + 10 + 5 + 1 = 32 = 2^5$

EXERCISE 34 Although this exercise looks similar to Exercise 20 on page 311, students can now solve it using different methods.

EXERCISE 35 For part (b) of this exercise, some students might get 6 instead of 30, because they are forgetting that there are five possibilities for choosing one the first day.

EXERCISE 36 This is known as Vandermonde's Identity.

EXERCISE 37 will no longer be an Extension exercise for students after they see Newton's Difference Formula in Investigation 5B.

33. Explain how can you evaluate the sum

$$\binom{6}{0}+\binom{6}{1}+\binom{6}{2}+\binom{6}{3}+\binom{6}{4}+\binom{6}{5}+\binom{6}{6}$$

by using the sum

$$\binom{5}{0}+\binom{5}{1}+\binom{5}{2}+\binom{5}{3}+\binom{5}{4}+\binom{5}{5}$$

34. Prove that for all nonnegative integers, n,

$$\binom{n}{0}+\binom{n}{1}+\binom{n}{2}+\cdots+\binom{n}{n-2}+\binom{n}{n-1}+\binom{n}{n}=2^n$$

This is another pattern in Pascal's Triangle. The sum of the entries in the nth row in Pascal's Triangle is 2^n. When $n = 0$, the sum is really just the single entry $\binom{0}{0}$.

35. A local high school is hosting a talent competition. A selection committee will choose three performers to perform in front of the school. The students' vote determines who wins. To choose the three performers, the selection committee will watch five auditions the first day and four auditions the second day. They will select the performers at the end of each day.

a. Suppose the selection committee rejects all five candidates the first day. How many ways can they still pick three contestants?

b. In how many ways could they pick one person from the first group and two people from the second group?

c. In how many ways could they pick two people from the first group and one person from the second group?

d. In how many ways could they pick three people from the first group and no one from the second group?

e. In how many ways are there to pick three performers from the nine candidates?

In counting the ways to choose 10 singers from 100 people, does it matter whether the auditions happen in a single day?

Answers

33. The sum of the entries in row 6 of Pascal's Triangle is twice the sum of the entries in row 5.

34. Answers may vary. Sample: show that both sides of the equation are solutions to the same problem—how many subsets can be formed from a set of n distinct objects?

For $\binom{n}{0}+\binom{n}{1}+\binom{n}{2}+\cdots+\binom{n}{n-2}+\binom{n}{n-1}+\binom{n}{n}$, construct a table that counts the number of subsets by counting the number of subsets with no elements, then the number of subsets with one element, and continuing on until it counts the last possibility of a subset containing n elements. Since both 2^n and ${}_nC_0 + {}_nC_1 + nC_2 + \cdots + {}_nC_{n-2} + {}_nC_{n-1} + {}_nC_n$ both answer the same question, they must be equal to one another.

35. a. 4 ways

b. 30 ways

c. 40 ways

d. 10 ways

e. 84 ways

36. This exercise and Exercise 35 suggests the identity

$$\binom{m+n}{r}=\binom{m}{0}\binom{n}{r}+\binom{m}{1}\binom{n}{r-1}+\cdots+\binom{m}{k}\binom{n}{r-k}+\cdots+\binom{m}{r-1}\binom{n}{1}+\binom{m}{r}\binom{n}{0}$$

36. **Take It Further** A local high school is hosting a singing competition. A selection committee will choose four contestants to perform in front of the school. The students' vote determines who wins. To choose the four performers, the selection committee will listen to nine auditions the first day and eleven auditions the second day. They will select the performers at the end of each day. How many ways can the selection committee choose four performers?

Sasha and Derman are working on the problem above

Sasha Well, we did something exactly like this in Exercise 35. So it's going to be something like

$$\binom{9}{0}\binom{11}{4} + \binom{9}{1}\binom{11}{3} + \binom{9}{2}\binom{11}{2} + \binom{9}{3}\binom{11}{1} + \binom{9}{4}\binom{11}{0} = 4845$$

Derman Um . . . Sasha? Maybe this is crazy, but can't we just do $\binom{20}{4}$? I mean, there are twenty contestants, and the selection committee is choosing 4 . . .

Sasha That should be right, but—let's check. . . . You get the same answer. Hey! I wonder if there's an identity in here somewhere!

What's going on here?

37. **Take It Further** What is the sum of the squares of the entries in the nth row of Pascal's Triangle? Prove your result.

38. A four-digit number is *interesting* if it does not contain zero, and its digits are in decreasing order. For example, 9761 and 6531 are both interesting, but 9877 and 5678 are not. How many four-digit interesting numbers are there?

39. **Standardized Test Prep** There are 7 girls and 6 boys in a class. They want to make a committee of three students. There must be at least one boy and one girl on the committee. How many possible committees are there?

A. 126 **B.** 105 **C.** 231 **D.** 277

Habits of Mind

Look for a pattern. Try it with numbers!

Decreasing order means that each digit of a number is less than the previous one (to its left).

Maintain Your Skills

40. Suppose n is an integer with $n \geq 2$. You can define a polynomial function f with the property that f evaluated at n is $\binom{n}{2}$.

$$f(n) = \binom{n}{2} = \frac{n(n-1)}{2} = \frac{1}{2}n^2 - \frac{1}{2}n$$

a. Suppose n is an integer, with $n \geq 3$. Define a polynomial function g with the property that g evaluated at n is $\binom{n}{3}$.

b. Suppose n and k are integers, with $n \geq k$. Define a polynomial function h_k with the property that h_k evaluated at n is $\binom{n}{k}$.

Additional Resources

PRINT RESOURCES

- Solution Manual
- Practice Workbook
- Assessment Resources
- Teaching Resources

TECHNOLOGY

- Interactive Textbook
- TeacherExpress CD-ROM
- Exam View CD-ROM
- PHSchool.com

Additional Practice

1. In a road race of 200 runners, how many different outcomes are there for first, second and third place?

2. Consider all four-digit numbers.
   a. How many four-digit numbers have all different digits?
   b. How many four-digit numbers have all the same digits?

3. How many anagrams does each word have?
   a. SUNDAY b. YEARLY
   c. EXCEED d. HAHAHA

4. You have a set of cards where each card has some combination of the following.
   - one of five different colors (blue, green, purple, red, or orange)
   - one of four different shapes on it (triangle, circle, square, or trapezoid)
   - one of four different letters on it (E, F, G, or H)

   There is exactly one card with each combination of characteristics.
   a. How many cards are in the set?
   b. How many red cards are in the set?
   c. How many cards containing triangles are in the set?

5. On a test consisting of seven essay questions, students can choose to answer any three of them. How many choices do students have for a set of three essays?

6. A teacher wants to form an 8 person committee to represent the student body. She will choose 4 female students from the 25 females eligible. Then she will choose 4 male students from the 22 males eligible. In how many different ways can she form the new committee?

7. How many different words are possible from 3 K's and 7 L's? (Remember, we call such strings *words* even if they are meaningless.)

8. You have 15 cards numbered 1–15, and you randomly choose 4 cards.
   a. How many different combinations of 4 cards are possible?
   b. How many of the combinations contain the number 10?
   c. How many of the combinations do not contain the number 10?

Practice: For Lesson 4.7, assign Exercises 5–8.

37. $\binom{2n}{n}$; Show that:

$$\binom{n}{0}^2 + \binom{n}{1}^2 + \cdots + \binom{n}{n}^2 = \binom{2n}{n}$$

To see this, look at $\binom{2n}{n}$ as the number of ways to choose n objects from a collection of $2n$ objects, and split the $2n$ objects into 2 sets with n objects each. Choose:

n	from the first n objects leaving	0 from the rest
$n-1$	from the first n objects leaving	1 from the rest
$n-2$	from the first n objects leaving	2 from the rest
$\vdots$		
1	from the first n objects leaving	$n-1$ from the rest
0	from the first n objects leaving	n from the rest

Since $\binom{n}{k} = \binom{n}{n-k}$, then $\binom{n}{0}^2 + \binom{n}{1}^2 + \cdots + \binom{n}{n}^2 = \binom{2n}{n}$

38. 126 numbers

39. C

40. a. $g(n) = \frac{1}{6}n^3 - \frac{1}{2}n^2 + \frac{1}{3}n$ **b.** $h_k(n) = \frac{n(n-1)(n-2)\cdots(n-k+1)}{k!}$

Lesson Overview

GOAL

- Develop and use formulas for finding the number of permutations of n objects, taken k at a time.

This is a very short lesson aimed at giving students an opportunity to synthesize some of what they have learned in the previous lessons. This investigation has been pretty dense!

CHECK YOUR UNDERSTANDING
- Core: 1, 2, 4, 6
- Optional: 3
- Extension: 5

MATERIALS
- graphing calculators
- Blackline Master 4.7A

HOMEWORK
- Core: 7, 8, 9, 10, 11, 12, 13, 14, 15, 16, 17, 19
- Optional: 20
- Extension: 18

Launch

This lesson begins with a summary of some facts about permutations and combinations. Make sure that the summary makes sense to the students.

Explore

For You to Do

PROBLEM 1 In making a 4-digit number, the order of the digits matters. This problem can be solved using the permutation formula: ${}_6P_4 = 360$.

PROBLEM 2 On a committee, the order the people are chosen for the committee does not matter. The problem can be solved using the combination formula: ${}_{16}C_4 = 1820$.

PROBLEM 3 The order in which Mrs. Masse picks the students does not change the group that carries the table, so order does not matter. The problem can be solved using the combination formula: ${}_{23}C_4 = 8855$.

4.8 Putting It Together

Here are some basic facts on combinations and permutations that you have discovered and explored so far in this chapter.

Permutations	Combinations
Order matters: Count *X, Y, Z* and *X, Z, Y* as different cases.	Order does not matter: Count *X, Y, Z* and *X, Z, Y* as the same case.
Sample problem: There are 12 people in a class. In how many different ways could the class elect a president, vice-president, and a treasurer?	Sample problem: There are 12 people in a class. In how many different ways could the class pick 3 of them to wash the chalkboard?
${}_nP_k = \frac{n!}{(n-k)!}$	${}_nC_k = \frac{n!}{k!(n-k)!} = \binom{n}{k}$
${}_nP_k = (k!)\left({}_nC_k\right)$	${}_nC_k = \frac{{}_nP_k}{k!}$
${}_nP_k = n \cdot {}_{n-1}P_{k-1}, n > k > 0$	${}_nC_k = {}_{n-1}C_{k-1} + {}_{n-1}C_k, n > k > 0$

Now that you have a collection of formulas, it might be difficult to choose which one to use. As you solve the next set of problems, think about which formula works best in each case.

For You to Do

1. How many four-digit numbers can you make from the digits 1, 2, 3, 4, 5, and 6 if no repeats are allowed?
2. How many four-person committees are possible in a class of 16 people?
3. There are 23 students in a class. In how many ways can Mrs. Masse pick four students in the class to carry a table to the auditorium?

Do not be too eager to use formulas. If the problem has a twist, you might not be able to just apply a formula. It is important to remember what the formulas actually mean and how you derive them.

Example

Problem In this year's student council election, there are 3 positions for junior class representatives, and 4 positions for senior class representatives. There are 25 people running for junior class representative and 32 people running for senior class representative. How many different student councils are possible?

Answers

For You to Do

1. 360 numbers
2. 1820 committees
3. 8855 ways

Solution If there were only one position for the junior class and one position for the senior class, you could use the box strategy.

This is a good start for this problem. Earlier, when using the box strategy, you were choosing just one item for each box. Here you need to choose multiple items to put in the boxes.

The junior and senior elections need to be considered separately. You cannot just lump all 57 candidates together and choose 7 representatives from them.

Since the representative positions for each class are the same, order does not matter. The number of ways to elect 4 seniors from 32 candidates is $\binom{32}{4}$. For each of these outcomes there are $\binom{25}{3}$ ways to elect 3 juniors from 25 candidates. You can calculate the number of possible election results using the following formula.

$$\begin{aligned}\text{total ways} &= \begin{pmatrix}\text{number of ways}\\ \text{to elect 4 seniors}\end{pmatrix} \cdot \begin{pmatrix}\text{number of ways}\\ \text{to elect 3 juniors}\end{pmatrix}\\ &= \binom{32}{4} \cdot \binom{25}{3}\end{aligned}$$

The Birthday Problem

Do you remember the "birthday problem" from Getting Started?

> In Ms. Roskam's class of 25 students, two of them have the same birthday. The students are very surprised to discover this. Ms. Roskam tells them that it's actually a good bet that, in a random group of 25 students, at least two of them will share a birthday.
>
> Is Ms. Roskam right? Suppose you choose 25 people at random. What is the probability that at least two of them share a birthday? If you want to ensure that the probability is more than 50%, how many people must you choose?

Habits of Mind

Be efficient. It is often more convenient to write out the formula for your solution, before you actually make any calculations. This is because the numbers involved in combinatorics problems can become very large very quickly!

To solve the birthday problem, consider the function

$$f(\text{person}) = \text{person's birthday}$$

- How many possible outputs does this function have?
- What does it mean for this function to be one-to-one when the domain is a class of students?

For You to Do

PROBLEMS 4–7 For these problems and the subsequent Discussion, refer to the solution to the birthday problem in Lesson 4.5.

PROBLEMS 9 AND 10 For these problems and the subsequent Discussion, refer to the solution to the trains problem in Lesson 4.5.

Wrap Up

You might wrap up this lesson by asking students for examples of problems they can solve using permutations and examples of problems they can solve using combinations.

Assessment Resources

Lesson Quiz 4.8

1. Jess has seven different flowering plants that she wants to line up on the window sill. Each plant is a different color.
   a. In how many ways can she line up the plants?
   b. If she wants the white flowers and purple flowers to be at opposite ends of the line, in how many ways can she line up the plants?
   c. If she wants the pink and yellow flowers next to each other, in how many ways can she line up the plants?
2. In how many ways can you write 22 as a sum of three counting numbers?
3. You order a salad for lunch. There are three different sizes and six different dressings to choose from. There are also toppings of chicken, tuna, or salmon.
   a. How many salads can you make if you choose the size, one dressing, and one topping?
   b. How many salads can you make if you want chicken?
   c. If you get to choose either white bread or wheat bread with your salad, how many different salads with bread are possible?

For You to Do

4. How many functions are there from an m-element set to an n-element set?
5. How many one-to-one functions are there from an m-element set to an n-element set?
6. How many functions from an m-element set to an n-element set are not one-to-one?
7. How many functions from the set $\{1, 2, \dots, 24, 25\}$ to the set $\{1, 2, \dots, 364, 365\}$ are not one-to-one?

Could you find even a single one-to-one function if n is less than m?

For Discussion

8. How do Problems 4–7 help you solve the "birthday problem"?

Number Rods

You can use number rods to build "trains" that share a common length. A "train of length 5" is a row of rods that have a combined length of 5.

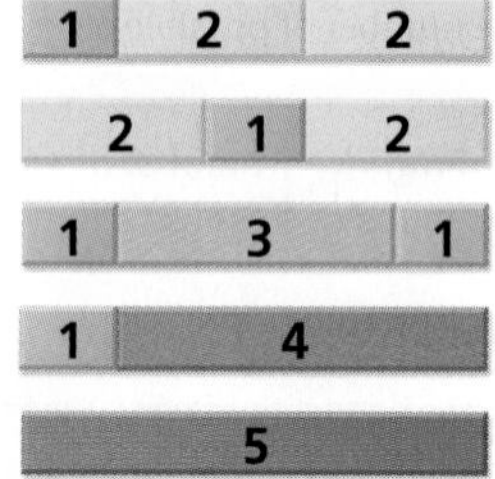

Notice that the 1–2–2 train and the 2–1–2 train contain the same rods. If you use identical rods in different orders, this makes different trains.

For You to Do

9. What are the minimum and maximum numbers of rods you can use for a train of length 3? Of length 6? Of length n?
10. Use a pile of rods to help you compile lists of all possible trains with lengths 2, 3, 4, and 5. Be sure you list each train once and only once.

For Discussion

11. Make a set of directions that explains how to list all the trains of any given length.
12. How many trains are there of length n? Write a proof to show your result is true for all integers $n > 0$.

Habits of Mind

Test your directions. Your directions should be an *algorithm*. A person (or computer) should be able to follow them without having to make any interpretations or add missing details. Test your directions by giving them to someone else. See if that person can use them to list all trains of length five.

Answers

For You to Do

4. n^m functions
5. 0 functions if $n < m$, $\frac{n!}{(n-m)!}$ functions if $n \geq m$
6. $n^m - \frac{n!}{(n-m)!}$ functions
7. $365^{25} - \frac{365!}{340!}$ functions

For Discussion

8. Answers may vary. Sample: the answer to Problem 4 finds that the total number of functions from the set $\{1, 2, \dots, 24, 25\}$ to the set $\{1, 2, \dots, 364, 365\}$ is 365^{25}. The answer to Problem 7 finds the number of those functions that are not one-to-one is $365^{25} - \frac{365!}{340!}$. Use those two numbers to calculate the probability that at least two people in a group of 25 have the same birthday.

For You to Do

9. minimum of 1 and maximum of 3; minimum of 1 and maximum of 6; minimum of 1 and maximum of n
10. length 2: 2, 1-1; length 3: 3, 2-1, 1-2, 1-1-1; length 4: 4, 3-1, 1-3, 2-2, 2-1-1, 1-2-1, 1-1-2, 1-1-1-1; length 5: 5, 4-1, 1-4, 3-2, 2-3, 3-1-1, 1-3-1, 1-1-3, 2-2-1, 2-1-2, 1-2-2, 2-1-1-1, 1-2-1-1, 1-1-2-1, 1-1-1-2, 1-1-1-1-1

For Discussion

11. Answers may vary. Sample: if $n = 1$, than there is exactly 1 train of length 1. Let n be a whole number greater than 1. Consider the set S $\{1, 2, 3, \dots, n-1\}$. Make a list

Exercises Practicing Habits of Mind

Check Your Understanding

1. Six friends went to the school dance together. In how many ways can they line up for a photo?
2. How many ways are there to arrange the letters in the word COMBINE?
3. How many four-digit numbers can you make from the digits 0, 1, 2, 3, 4, and 5 without repeating digits?
4. A class of 16 students wants to form a four-person committee consisting of two girls and two boys. There are nine boys and seven girls in the class. How many committees are possible?
5. Take It Further Six friends went to the school dance together. In how many ways can they line up for a photo if two of them, June and Mark, want to stay next to each other?
6. Suppose there are five women and four men in a room. In how many ways can they do each of the following?
   a. line up to have their picture taken
   b. line up to have their picture taken, if the men and women have to alternate
   c. line up if one of them, say Harry, refuses to stand at the beginning or at the end of the line
   d. line up in two rows, with all the women in the front row and all the men in the back row
   e. line up in two rows, with five people in the front row and four people in the back row

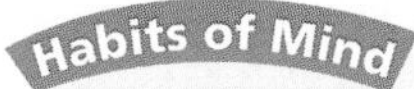

Be systematic. First, in how many ways can you choose the five people for the front row and the four people for the back row. Then, think about about how you can arrange the rows.

Exercises

HOMEWORK
- Core: 7, 8, 9, 10, 11, 12, 13, 14, 15, 16, 17, 19
- Optional: 20
- Extension: 18

of all the subsets of S (including the empty set and the set S itself). Write a string of $(n - 1)$ 1's connected by hyphens.

For a particular subset of S, change the hyphens in the positions denoted by the elements of the subset to + signs. Do the additions, keep the hyphens that were not changed, and you have the name of a train of length n. (For example, if you are listing trains of length 8, then $\{1, 2, 5\}$ is a subset of $\{1, 2, \dots, 7\}$. If you change the first, second and fifth hyphens in 1-1-1-1-1-1-1-1 to + sings, you get 1+1+1-1-1+1-1-1 which gives the train 3-1-2-1-1.) Use this procedure with each subset of S to get a list of all the trains of length n.

12. There are 2^{n-1} trains of length n; the procedure in Problem 11 shows that there is a one-to-one correspondence between subsets of $\{1, 2, \dots, n - 1\}$ and trains of length n. Hence, the total number of trains of length n is $\binom{n-1}{0} + \binom{n-1}{2} + \cdots + \binom{n-1}{n-1}$, and this sum is equal to 2^{n-1} as shown by the result proved in Exercise 34 of Lesson 4.7.

Exercises

1. 720 ways
2. 5040 ways
3. 300 numbers
4. 756 committees
5. 240 ways
6. a. 362,880 ways
   b. 2880 ways
   c. 282,240 ways
   d. 2880 ways
   e. 326,880 ways

On Your Own

7. A pizzeria has 3 sizes of pizza and 12 different toppings. How many ways are there to place the following orders?
   a. a pizza with exactly two toppings
   b. a pizza with at most two toppings
   c. a pizza
   d. a pizza with mushrooms and one additional topping
8. Are there more seven-digit numbers with a 1 in them than without a 1 in them? Explain.
9. There are nine points on a paper. No three of them are on the same line. How many different triangles can you draw using these points as vertices?
10. There are 14 airports in a country. You can go from any one of them to any other airport in the country by a direct flight. How many direct flights are there?
11. How many diagonals does a 14-sided polygon have?

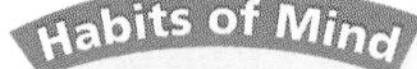

A diagonal of a polygon is a segment that connects two of the polygon's vertices but is not a polygon's side.

12. There are many ways that you can write 5 as a sum of counting numbers. Here are four:

$$\begin{aligned} 5 &= 1 + 4 \\ &= 5 \\ &= 2 + 1 + 1 + 1 \\ &= 1 + 2 + 1 + 1 \end{aligned}$$

How many different ways are there in all?

13. In how many ways can you write 20 as a sum of three counting numbers?
14. In how many ways can you put 20 quarters into three colored pockets (red, green, and blue) so that there is at least one coin in each pocket?
15. The apple flats at a farmers' market hold 20 apples each. Kim wants to fill her flat with three types of apples. She selects red delicious apples, then Granny Smith apples, and then Macintosh apples. Assuming she has at least one apple of each type, how many different assortments of these apples can she make?

Habits of Mind

Compare. Does Exercise 12 remind you of the trains problem in any way? How is it similar or different from the trains problem? Are they isomorphic?

Answers

On Your Own

7. **a.** 198 ways
   b. 237 ways
   c. 12,288 ways
   d. 33 ways
8. Yes; the number of seven-digit numbers is $9 \cdot 10^6 = 9{,}000{,}000$ and the number of seven-digit numbers without a 1 is $8 \cdot 9^6 = 4{,}215{,}528$, so the number of seven-digit numbers with a 1 is $9{,}000{,}000 - 4{,}215{,}528 = 4{,}748{,}472$.
9. 84 triangles
10. 182 flights
11. 77 diagonals
12. 16 ways
13. 171 ways
14. 171 ways
15. 171 assortments

16. There are 19 people and only 2 tickets to a concert. How many ways are there to choose which two people go to the concert?

17. Explain how Exercises 13 through 16 are all isomorphic.

18. Take It Further Look a little more closely at the game of SET. You may want to review the rules of the game on page 304. If you lay out 3 cards from the whole deck of SET, what is the probability that the cards would be a set?

19. Standardized Test Prep How many "trains" of length six can you build using only three number rods?

A. 5 **B.** 9 **C.** 10 **D.** 20

For additional practice, go to Web Code: bga-0408

How many different groups of three cards could you lay out from the deck? How many of them would make a set?

Maintain Your Skills

20. **a.** What is the coefficient of a^3b^1 in the expansion of $(a + b)^4$?

b. What other term has the same coefficient?

c. What is the coefficient of a^4b^1 in the expansion of $(a + b)^5$?

d. What other term has the same coefficient?

e. What is the coefficient of a^2b^3 in the expansion of $(a + b)^5$?

f. What other term has the same coefficient?

g. What is the coefficient of a^2b^4 in the expansion of $(a + b)^6$?

h. What other term has the same coefficient?

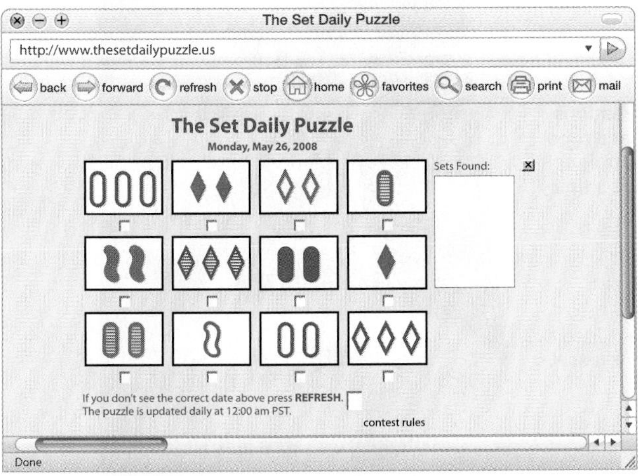

Can you find all six sets?

On Your Own

EXERCISE 18 Use Blackline Master 4.7A as needed.

Additional Resources

PRINT RESOURCES

- Solution Manual
- Practice Workbook
- Assessment Resources
- Teaching Resources

TECHNOLOGY

- Interactive Textbook
- TeacherExpress CD-ROM
- Exam View CD-ROM
- PHSchool.com

Additional Practice

1. A car dealership has seven vehicles each of a different color to line up on display in the showroom. Three of them are sedans and four of them are SUVs.
a. How many ways are there to line up the vehicles on display?
b. How many ways are there to line up the vehicles if all of the sedans must be together?
c. If the black SUV and the red sedan must be next to each other, how many ways are there to line up the vehicles?

2. A sandwich shop has five types of bread, four types of meat, and three different cheeses for sandwiches.
a. How many ways can you make a sandwich if you choose only one type of bread, meat, and cheese?
b. How many ways can you make a sandwich without cheese on it?
c. If your sandwich (made with bread, meat and cheese) is part of a combo meal with a choice of three different drinks, how many combo meals can you make?

3. There are 12 points on a piece of paper. No three of them are on the same line.
a. How many different triangles can you draw using these points as vertices?
b. How many different quadrilaterals can you draw using these points as vertices?

4. How many diagonals does a 12-sided polygon have?

5. Consider all the five-digit numbers that can be made using the numbers 1, 2, 3, 4, and 5.
a. How many total numbers are possible?
b. How many numbers are possible if no numbers can be repeated?

6. In how many ways can you write 18 as the sum of three counting numbers?

7. A softball team has 20 players, 12 boys and 8 girls.
a. How many ways can 9 players start the game if there must be 5 girls and 4 boys on the field?
b. How many ways can 9 players start the game if there must be 4 girls and 5 boys on the field?

Practice: For Lesson 4.8, assign Exercises 1–7.

16. 171 ways

17. These exercises involve choosing 2 objects from 19, so they all can be solved using the formula $\binom{19}{2}$.

18. $\frac{1}{79} \approx 1.3\%$

19. C

20. **a.** 4

b. the term containing a^1b^3

c. 5

d. the term containing a^1b^4

e. 10

f. the term containing a^3b^2

g. 15

h. the term containing a^4b^2

Mathematical Reflections

EXERCISES 6–8 At the start of the investigation, you may have assigned these as Questions 1–3 for students to think and write about.

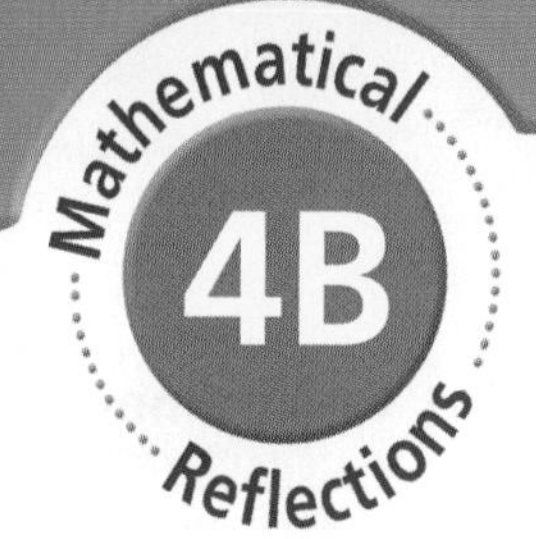

In this investigation, you learned how to count permutations (ordered choices) and combinations (unordered choices). You also learned how to count anagrams (ordered choices with repetition). The following questions will help you summarize what you have learned.

1. Find the probability that in a group of 35 students, at least 2 of them have the same birthday.
2. Explain why, for any integers n and k such that $0 \le k \le n$, ${}_nC_k = \binom{n}{k}$.
3. Show that ${}_nC_k = {}_nC_{n-k}$ for $0 \le k \le n$.
4. Explain why ${}_{10}P_4 = 24 \cdot {}_{10}C_4$.
5. Figure out whether there are more nine-digit numbers with a 1 in them, or if there are more nine-digit numbers without a 1 in them.
6. In how many ways can you pick three objects, in order, from a set of six distinct objects?
7. How many three-digit numbers are there that have repeated digits?
8. How many five-student committees are possible in a class of 26 students?

Vocabulary and Notation

In this investigation, you learned these terms. Make sure you understand what each one means and how to use it.

- **anagram**
- **combination**
- **permutation**
- **${}_nC_k$, number of combinations of n objects, taken k at a time**
- **${}_nP_k$, number of permutations of n objects, taken k at a time**

Horns play permutations of single notes.

Answers

Mathematical Reflections

1. about 81.4%
2. $\binom{n}{k}$, the kth entry of row n of Pascal's Triangle, can be defined by $\binom{n}{0} = \binom{n}{n} = 1$ and $\binom{n}{k} = \binom{n-1}{k-1} + \binom{n-1}{k}$. Observe that ${}_nC_k$ can also be defined by the same conditions. That is, ${}_nC_0 = {}_nC_n = 1$ and ${}_nC_k = {}_{n-1}C_{k-1} + {}_{n-1}C_k$. Therefore, $\binom{n}{k} = {}_nC_k$.
3. For $0 \le k \le n$,
$$\begin{aligned} {}_nC_{n-k} &= \frac{n!}{(n-k)![n-(n-k)]!} \\ &= \frac{n!}{(n-k)!k!} = \frac{n!}{k!(n-k)!} \\ &= {}_nC_k \end{aligned}$$
4. $24 \cdot {}_{10}C_4 = 24 \cdot \frac{10!}{4!6!} = \frac{10!}{6!} = {}_{10}P_4$
5. more nine-digit numbers with a 1 in them
6. 120 ways
7. 252 numbers
8. 65,780 committees

Mid-Chapter Test

Go Online PHSchool.com

For a mid-chapter test, go to Web Code: bga-0452

Multiple Choice

1. Here are three problems:

I. Ann has saved \$100. If she spends \$20 on CDs, how much money does she have left?

II. Bill earned \$100 last week, but he had to pay \$20 in taxes. What was the amount of Bill's paycheck?

III. Carla took a test in history that was worth 100 points. She lost 20 points for mistakes. What was her final grade on the test?

Which of the above problems are isomorphic?

A. I and II only **B.** I and III only

C. II and III only **D.** I, II, and III

2. How many three-digit numbers can you make using only the digits 1, 2, or 3?

A. 6 **B.** 8

C. 9 **D.** 27

3. The high school baseball team has three starting pitchers. The coach is making his pitching schedule for the first three games of the playoffs. If no pitcher can start twice, how many different options does he have?

A. 6 **B.** 8

C. 9 **D.** 27

4. The Town Council is going to choose two delegates. One will go to the state conference and one will go to the regional conference. There are 25 candidates for the two positions. Which expression represents the number of ways the council can choose the two delegates?

A. 25^2 **B.** $25 + 25$

C. $25 \cdot 24$ **D.** $25 + 24$

5. How many functions have inputs from the set $\{A, B, C, D\}$ and outputs from the set $\{1, 2, 3, 4, 5\}$?

A. 9 **B.** 20

C. 625 **D.** 1024

Open Response

6. Make up a problem that is isomorphic to the following problem.

Alice has to write a ten-page paper for her history class. So far, she has written six pages. How many more pages does she need to write?

7. How many three-digit numbers are possible with only the digits 0, 1, or 2? (Remember that the first digit of a three-digit number cannot be zero.)

8. For the early bird special at a local restaurant, you can choose one appetizer, one entree, and one dessert. There are five appetizers, six entrees, and four desserts. In how many ways can you choose your meal with the early bird special?

9. a. How many five-digit numbers are there?

b. How many five-digit numbers have 3 as the final digit?

10. a. How many functions are there from a two-element set to a four-element set?

b. How many of these functions are one-to-one?

c. How many of these functions are not one-to-one?

11. Describe what it means for two problems to be isomorphic.

Mid-Chapter Test

1. D

2. D

3. A

4. C

5. C

6. Answers may vary. Sample: John has \$10 and spends \$6 at the arcade. How much money does he have left?

7. 18 numbers

8. 120 ways

9. a. 90,000 numbers

b. 9000 numbers

10. a. 16 functions

b. 12 functions

c. 4 functions

11. Two problems are isomorphic if they can be solved using the same numbers and the same calculations.

Mid-Chapter Test

Assessment Resources

Mid-Chapter Test **page 1**

Multiple Choice

1. Consider the following problem:

Amy wants to paint a wall in her bedroom. If the wall has a height of 8 feet and a length of 12 feet, how many square feet does she have to cover with paint?

Which is isomorphic to the above problem?

A. Beth wants to fence in her garden. If the garden is 8 feet long and 12 feet wide, what length of fence does she need to go around the entire garden?

B. John has 8 coins and his friend has 12 coins. How many do they have altogether?

C. A triangle has a base of 16 feet and a height of 12 feet. What is its area?

D. A rectangle has a base of 12 feet and a height of 8 feet. What is its area?

2. How many three-digit numbers can you make that do not start with 7, 8 or 9?

A. 6561 **B.** 4374

C. 1296 **D.** 5103

3. How many one-to-one functions are there from a four-element set to a six-element set?

A. 24 **B.** 1296

C. 4096 **D.** 10

4. How many ways are there to arrange the letters in the word COLORADO?

A. 40,320 **B.** 6720

C. 13,440 **D.** 336

5. Chris wants to buy three new tropical fish to add to his fish tank. The pet store has 15 different tropical fish. How many ways can Chris choose three of them?

A. 2730 **B.** 455

C. 3375 **D.** 75

Also available: Form B

Mid-Chapter Test **page 2**

Open Response

6. For each of the following, find an isomorphic problem that you can solve using the given calculation.

a. $96 - (10 + 12) = 74$

b. $36 \div 4 = 9$

7. A bank assigns a 6-digit password using the following criteria.

- A password must contain four numbers and two letters.
- A password cannot contain two of the same letters.

a. How many passwords are possible?

b. How many passwords do not contain any repeated digits?

c. How many passwords start with the letter A?

8. Suppose a unique language consists of eight letters. No word in the language is more than five letters long. At most how many words can there be in such a language?

9. a. How many functions are there from a four-element set to a five-element set?

b. How many of these functions are one-to-one?

c. How many of these functions are not one-to-one?

10. How many anagrams does each word have?

a. EIGHTY **b.** TWENTY **c.** ELEVEN

11. Alicia has ten pairs of shoes including one pair of sneakers. She is packing for a trip and can only bring four pairs with her.

a. How many ways can she choose four pairs to bring with her?

b. How many of those four pair choices include her sneakers?

c. How many of those four pair choices do not include her sneakers?

Challenge Problem

12. A teacher needs at least five students to present their projects at the science fair. If there are 8 students to choose from, how many different groups of students can she choose?

Also available: Form B

Investigation Overview

The Binomial Theorem and its proofs demonstrate one of the many times when cross pollination of many disparate areas of mathematics yields a simple and elegant result. In this case, the areas of algebra, combinatorics, and geometry come together. The investigation begins with the Pascal's Path's problem from the very first lesson of the chapter, which pulls out another pattern from Pascal's Triangle: each entry represents the total number of paths to get to a particular intersection if you allow only north and east movements. One way of thinking about each path is to consider it a word made from the letters *N* and *E*. Students then examine these words as polynomials terms, which leads to the statement and proof of the Binomial Theorem.

One way to explain why Pascal's Triangle is so ubiquitous in mathematics is that many mathematical phenomena satisfy the two-term recurrence and the base case that determines the triangle. This investigation revisits the fact that the coefficients of $(a + b)^n$ provide yet another example of numbers that satisfy this recurrence.

You may wish to assign Questions 1–3 for students to think and write about during the investigation.

Learning Goals

- Apply counting strategies to solve the Pascal's Paths problem.
- Explain why the coefficients of a binomial expansion are found in Pascal's Triangle.
- See the entries of Pascal's Triangle from a variety of perspectives.

Habits and Skills

- Use combinations to find binomial coefficients.
- Use combinatorics to prove the Binomial Theorem.
- Recognize isomorphic problems.

Making Connections

In *Making Connections*, you will develop relationships among the coefficients of binomial expansions, Pascal's Triangle, and combinations.

By the end of this investigation, you will be able to answer questions like these.

1. What is the coefficient of the $x^{13}y^{37}$ term in the expansion of $(x + y)^{50}$?
2. What is the connection between the Pascal's Paths problem and the entries in Pascal's Triangle?
3. Why is the sum of the entries in row n of Pascal's Triangle 2^n?

You will learn how to

- apply counting strategies to solve the Pascal's Paths problem
- explain why the coefficients of a binomial expansion are found in Pascal's Triangle
- see the entries of Pascal's Triangle from a variety of perspectives

You will develop these habits and skills:

- Use combinations to find binomial coefficients.
- Use combinatorics to prove the Binomial Theorem.
- Recognize isomorphic problems.

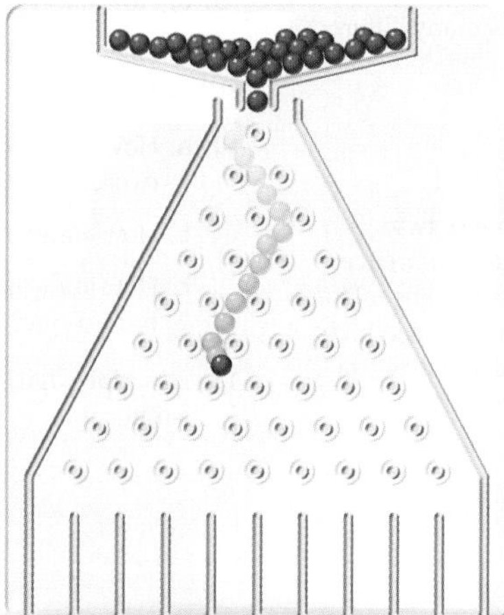

In this Galton box or "bean machine," a ball can fall to the right or left of each peg. Do you see a connection to Ms. Pascal and the routes she takes to work?

Investigation Road Map

LESSON 4.9, *Getting Started,* revisits the Pascal's Paths problem from the earlier Getting Started lessons.

LESSON 4.10, *Revisiting the Binomial Theorem,* shows students a proof of the Binomial Theorem using Pascal's Paths.

LESSON 4.11, *Connections,* looks at traditional problems about combinations, Pascal's Triangle entries, and binomial coefficients from multiple perspectives.

4.9 Getting Started

Recall the following problem that you have seen in the Getting Started lesson of the Investigations 4A and 4B.

Pascal's Path
Ms. Pascal likes to take a different route to work every day. She will quit her job the day she has to repeat a route she has already taken. The grid of streets below shows her home and her workplace. She only travels north or east and never back tracks. How many days will she work at this job?

Two paths are different if they are not the same everywhere. They might overlap on some pieces though, like the two valid Pascal paths shown below.

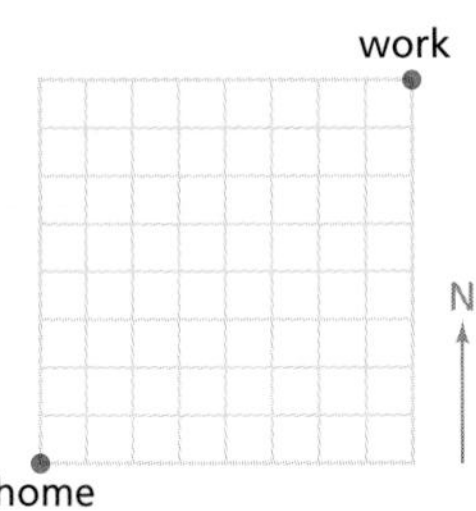

Again, here are some examples of some possible paths.

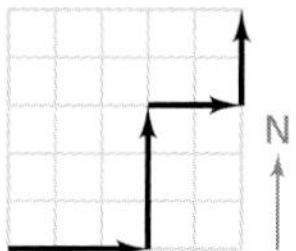

Here is a valid path.

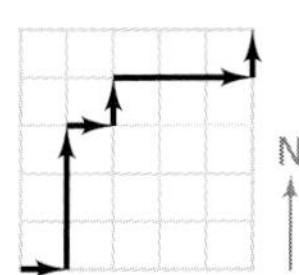

This is also valid.

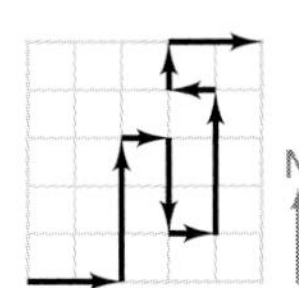

This is not a valid path.

For You to Explore

1. Jane invented a special way to describe a path. She wrote "N" if Ms. Pascal went north along a block and "E" if Ms. Pascal went east. For example, Jane wrote "EEEEEEEENNNNNNNN" to describe Ms. Pascal going eight blocks east and then eight blocks north.

   Describe how Jane could solve the Pascal's Paths problem using this approach.

2. Mark tried reasoning backward. "To get to work," Mark thought, "Ms. Pascal had to go through intersection A or through intersection B." So, Mark wanted to find the number of ways to reach A and the number of ways to reach B. Then he could add these two numbers.

   Describe how Mark could solve the Pascal's Paths problem using this approach.

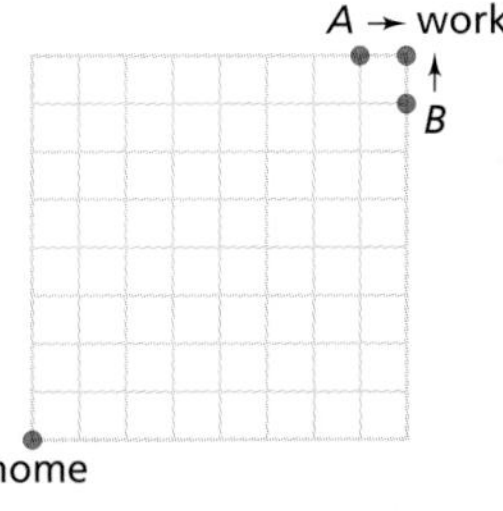

Answers

For You to Explore

1. Answers may vary. Sample: Jane would have to count all the 16-letter words that could be made of 8 E's and 8 N's. There are ${}_{16}C_8 = 12{,}870$ words so there are 12,870 paths.
2. Mark would have to record the number of ways to get to each intersection, as he works his way backwards.

Lesson Overview

GOALS

- Warm up to the ideas of the investigation.
- Apply counting strategies to solve the Pascal's Paths problem.

This Getting Started lesson breaks down the Pascal's Path's problem into smaller pieces.

FOR YOU TO EXPLORE
- Core: 1, 2, 3, 4, 5, 6, 7, 8, 9, 10
- Optional: none

MATERIALS
- graphing calculators
- Blackline Masters 4.1B, 4.9

HOMEWORK
- Core: 11, 12, 13, 14, 15, 17
- Optional: 16

Launch

To launch this lesson, assign students to work on the For You to Explore problems.

Explore

For You to Explore

Students will probably want to play with these problems before discussion any counting methods.

PROBLEM 2 Use Blackline Master 4.1B. Students should now see the problem as isomorphic to that of finding the number of permutations of eight E's and eight N's, as discussed in Problem 1. This method leads directly to the discussion of binomial expansions of $(E + N)^n$ which follows on page 326.

For You to Do

PROBLEM 8 Blackline Master 4.9 presents several different questions, concluding with a comparison to Problem 8c. It gives some hints after Questions 3 and 4, which you may want to keep covered until you discuss them. Instead of focusing on the solution, discuss the similarities. Have the students state the basic isomorphic problem.

Wrap Up

You might ask students to describe their counting methods.

3. Eventually Mark decides to start from the very beginning. He wants to write on each street intersection the number of different ways Ms. Pascal could reach that intersection. Copy the diagram, and help him to fill at least ten more spaces.

work

① ② ①

home

4. **a.** If Ms. Pascal travels only two blocks, how many different places might she end up?
   b. How many different paths two blocks long are there?
   c. Write down all different paths that are two blocks long using Jane's notation.

Do the numbers in Problem 3 remind you of something?

Suppose you are expanding the square of a binomial, $(E + N)^2$. You could expand it as follows.

$$(E + N)^2 = (E + N)(E + N) = E \cdot E + E \cdot N + N \cdot E + N \cdot N$$
$$= E^2 + 2EN + N^2$$

Stop to examine the expression before combining like terms.

$$E \cdot E + E \cdot N + N \cdot E + N \cdot N$$

Ignore the multiplication and addition symbols and you will notice four strings of letters.

EE, *EN*, *NE*, and *NN*

Do these strings look familiar? In Jane's notation, each of these four strings describes a valid Pascal path. Each path is two blocks long.

For You to Do

5. In expanding the square $(E + N)^2$, the monomials $E \cdot N$ and $N \cdot E$ are equal. The paths they describe bring you to the same place on the grid. Do equal monomials in the expansion of $(E + N)^k$ always describe paths that lead to the same place? Explain.
6. Expand $(E + N)^3$. How does this relate to Pascal paths of length three?
7. Expand $(E + N)^4$. How does this relate to Pascal paths of length four?
8. If you expand $(E + N)^5$ and add like terms, what is the coefficient in front of each of the following?
   a. E^5 **b.** E^4N **c.** E^3N^2
   d. E^2N^3 **e.** EN^4 **f.** N^5
   g. What is the sum of all the coefficients?
9. **a.** Show that if you expand $(E + N)^9$ and add like terms, the E^7N^2 and E^2N^7 terms have the same coefficient.
   b. What other monomials of this polynomial have equal coefficients?

Remember...

A monomial is a number or the product of a number and one or more variables. Any polynomial can be written as a sum of monomials.

Answers

3. See back of book.

4. a. 3 places **b.** 4 paths
c. *NE*, *EN*, *EE*, and *NN*

For You to Do

5. Yes; in equal monomials, the number of *E*'s will be equal, and the number of *N*'s will be equal.

6. $(E + N)^3 = (E + N)(E + N)^2$
$= (E + N)(EE + EN + NE + NN)$
$= EEE + EEN + ENE + ENN + NEE + NEN + NNE + NNN$

These eight monomials correspond exactly with the eight possible ways to go three blocks.

7. Use the same idea as in the last problem, the expansion gives:

$(E + N)^4 = EEEE + EEEN + EENE + EENN + ENEE + ENEN + ENNE$
$+ ENNN + NEEE + NEEN + NENE + NENN + NNEE$
$+ NNEN + NNNE + NNNN$

These sixteen monomials correspond exactly with the sixteen possible ways to go four blocks.

8. a. 1 **b.** 5 **c.** 10 **d.** 10
e. 5 **f.** 1 **g.** 32

9. a. Use the 9th row of Pascal's Triangle. The coefficients for the terms that contain E^7N^2 and E^2N^7 are both equal to 36.
b. E^9 and N^9, EN^8 and E^8N, E^3N^6 and E^6N^3, E^4N^5 and E^5N^4

10. **a.** In how many ways can Ms. Pascal reach the intersection four blocks north and three blocks east from her home?

b. Expand $(E + N)^7$. What is the coefficient of the E^3N^4 term?

c. Show that the two problems in parts (a) and (b) are isomorphic.

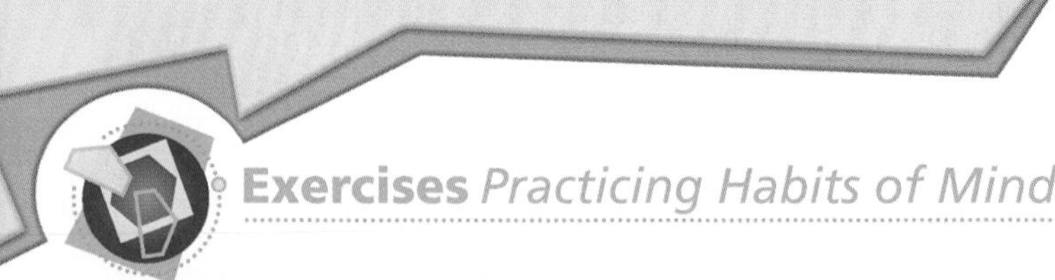

Exercises Practicing Habits of Mind

On Your Own

11. **a.** If Ms. Pascal only travels three blocks, in how many different places might she end up?

b. How many Pascal paths are three blocks long?

c. Write down all different paths three blocks long using Jane's notation.

d. In Jane's notation, how could you tell which ones lead to the same place?

12. **Write About It** Describe the connection between the Pascal's Paths problem and the entries in Pascal's Triangle.

13. **a.** How many blocks must Ms. Pascal travel to get to work?

b. How many different routes are there from Ms. Pascal's home to her workplace? You can use either Jane's or Mark's strategy to find the answer.

14. What is the sum of the coefficients of the polynomial $(E - N)^k$?

15. In how many ways can you make a string (a "word") fifteen symbols long using five U's, five F's, and five R's?

If the answer reminds you of the total number of Pascal paths of length *k*, or of the number of *k*-digit numbers consisting of 1's and 2's—you are on the right path!

Maintain Your Skills

16. If you expand $(E + N)^2$ you'll obtain

$$(E + N)^2 = E^2 + 2EN + N^2$$

The coefficients are 1, 2, and 1. The sum of the coefficients is $1 + 2 + 1 = 4$.

a. Find the sum of coefficients of the polynomial $(E + N)^3$.

b. Find the sum of coefficients of the polynomial $(E + N)^4$.

c. Find the sum of coefficients of the polynomial $(E + N)^k$.

Habits of Mind

Try a specific case. See what happens with both sides of this identity if $N = E = 1$.

Exercises

HOMEWORK

- Core: 11, 12, 13, 14, 15, 17
- Optional: 16

10. a. 35 ways **b.** 35

c. Think of $(E + N)^7$ as $(E + N)(E + N)(E + N)(E + N)(E + N)(E + N)(E + N)$. Then, all of the terms (before you combine like terms) can be found by appropriately choosing an *E* or an *N* from each parentheses and multiplying them together. As discussed previously, the coefficient for the term E^3N^4 is the total number of ways you can choose three *E*'s and four *N*'s from the parentheses (and then multiply them together). Ms. Pascal uses the same process to get to the intersection 4 blocks north and 3 blocks east. At each intersection, she can choose either north or east, and the first problem asks in how many ways can she choose 4 norths and 3 easts. So, each set of parentheses is like one of the 7 intersections Ms. Pascal encounters; each time we choose to multiply by *N* (or an *E*) she opts for north (or east). Since the same process applies to both, they are isomorphic.

Exercises

11. a. 4 places **b.** 8 paths

c. *EEE*, *EEN*, *ENE*, *NEE*, *ENN*, *NEN*, *NNE*, and *NNN*

d. If two of the paths written down have the same number of *N*'s (and therefore the same number of *E*'s), then they will lead to the same place.

12. The number of ways to get to a given intersection is given by entry *k* of row *n* of Pascal's Triangle (that is, $\binom{n}{k}$), where *n* is the total number of blocks required to get to the intersection and *k* is either the number of blocks north or the number of blocks east from "home."

13. a. 16 blocks **b.** 12,870 routes

14. 0

15. 756,756 ways

16. a. 8 **b.** 16 **c.** 2^k

Lesson Overview

GOAL

- Explain why the coefficients of a binomial expansion are found in Pascal's Triangle.

Students saw the Binomial Theorem in Algebra 2, but they probably want some review.

CHECK YOUR UNDERSTANDING
- Core: 1, 2, 3, 4
- Optional: 5

MATERIALS
- CAS
- graphing calculators
- Blackline Master MC12

HOMEWORK
- Core: 6, 7, 10
- Optional: 8, 11
- Extension: 9

Launch

You might begin by going over Problems 5–9 of the Getting Started lesson.

Explore

Use Blackline Master MC12 on an overhead to remind students of the structure of Pascal's Triangle.

4.10 Revisiting the Binomial Theorem

In Problems 5–9 of the Getting Started lesson, you saw some rather interesting connections between the numbers in Pascal's Triangle and the coefficients of $(a + b)^n$.

$(a + b)^0 = 1$	1
$(a + b)^1 = a + b$	1 1
$(a + b)^2 = a^2 + 2ab + b^2$	1 2 1
$(a + b)^3 = a^3 + 3a^2b + 3ab^2 + b^3$	1 3 3 1

This may have reminded you of the Binomial Theorem.

Theorem 4.4 The Binomial Theorem

For any integers n and k with $0 \le k \le n$,

$$(a+b)^n = \binom{n}{0}a^nb^0 + \binom{n}{1}a^{n-1}b^1 + \binom{n}{2}a^{n-2}b^2 + \cdots + \binom{n}{k}a^{n-k}b^k + \cdots + \binom{n}{n-1}a^1b^{n-1} + \binom{n}{n}a^0b^n$$

Now you can use the Pascal-Combinations connection from Investigation B to understand the Binomial Theorem.

Minds in Action **episode 13**

Sasha and Derman are looking at the Binomial Theorem.

Sasha This theorem shows the connection between finding the coefficients when you expand $(a + b)^n$ and counting problems like the exercises about committees in this chapter.

Derman But how are terms of a polynomial like people on a committee? We proved the Binomial Theorem last year and our proof didn't have anything to do with committees!

Sasha Let's look at $(a + b)^5$. It's really just

$$(a+b)(a+b)(a+b)(a+b)(a+b)$$

Derman Hold on, expanding that will take a while.

Sasha No, just think of doing the calculation. If you multiplied all this out, you'd get a sum of terms. You get each term by taking a letter from each of the five factors and multiplying them together.

Derman You mean, for example, you could take a from factors 1, 2, and 4 and b from factors 3 and 5? That would give you an a^3b^2.

Answers

For Discussion

1. There are $\binom{5}{0}$ ways to pick a 5 times and b 0 times, $\binom{5}{1}$ ways to pick a 4 times and b 1 time, $\binom{5}{2}$ ways to pick a 3 times and b 2 times, $\binom{5}{3}$ ways to pick a 2 times and b 3 times, $\binom{5}{4}$ ways to pick a 1 time and b 4 times, and $\binom{5}{5}$ ways to pick a 0 times and b 5 times. These numbers agree with the expanded form of $(a + b)^5$.

For You to Do

2. Using Sasha and Derman's idea, the coefficient of $a^{n-k}b^k$ in the expansion of $(a + b)^n$ is the number of ways to choose k b's (and therefore $n - k$ a's) from the n different sets of parentheses. Since there are $\binom{n}{k}$ ways to do this, the coefficient of $a^{n-k}b^k$ in the expansion of $(a + b)^n$ is $\binom{n}{k}$. Therefore,

$$(a+b)^n = \sum_{k=0}^{n}\binom{n}{k}a^{n-k}b^k$$

Sasha Yes, but you could also get an a^3b^2 by taking a from factors 1, 2, and 3 and b from factors 4 and 5.

Derman Oh! So the coefficient of a^3b^2 will be the number of the ways you can pick 3 factors of a and 2 factors of b.

Sasha And that is just the number of ways you can pick three things (three a's) from five factors. It's $\binom{5}{3}$.

Derman Right! That's the connection. But couldn't we also count this as the number of ways you can pick two things (two "b"s) from five factors? That's $\binom{5}{2}$.

Sasha Of course. But $\binom{5}{2}$ is the same as $\binom{5}{3}$ And the same idea applies to the other terms. You can pick no a's and five b's, one a and four b's, . . .

For Discussion

1. Use Sasha and Derman's argument to show that the Binomial Theorem works when applied to the expansion of $(a + b)^5$.

For You to Do

2. Explain how you could use a combinatorial proof to prove the Binomial Theorem for any $n > 0$.

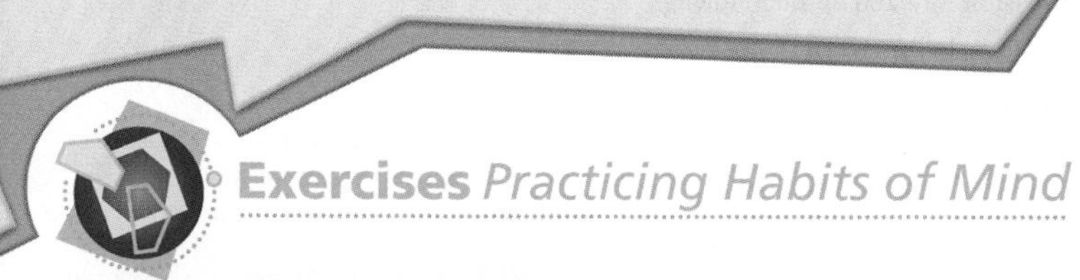

Exercises *Practicing Habits of Mind*

Check Your Understanding

1. Use the Binomial Theorem to expand each of the following. Use your CAS to verify your answers.
   - **a.** $(x + y)^7$
   - **b.** $(x + 2y)^5$
2. Consider the expansion of $(a + b)^{12}$.
   - **a.** What is the coefficient of the a^5b^7 term?
   - **b.** What other term(s) share this coefficient?
   - **c.** Which terms do not share their coefficients with any other terms?

Go Online PHSchool.com

For a history of the Binomial Theorem, go to **Web Code: bge-9031**

For Discussion

PROBLEM 1 The coefficient for the term x^3y^2 is $\binom{5}{3}$, because there are $\binom{5}{3}$ ways to choose 3 of the 5 parentheses from which to pick the 3 factors of x. Then, pick y from the remaining 2 parentheses to make the product x^3y^2. Likewise, the coefficient for x^4y is $\binom{5}{4}$, since you are choosing 4 of the 5 parentheses from which to pick the 4 factors of x, and the coefficient for x^5 is $\binom{5}{5}$, since you will pick x from 5 of the 5 parentheses.

Wrap Up

Wrap up by going over Problem 2.

Assessment Resources

Lesson Quiz 4.10

1. Determine the coefficient of each of the following terms in the expansion of $(x + y)^{35}$.
   - **a.** $x^{10}y^{25}$
   - **b.** x^3y^{32}
2. Write a polynomial that you can factor in the form $(a + b)^n$ where:
   - The constant term is not 1.
   - There exactly one variable, x.
   - There are at least 4 terms.
3. Use the Binomial Theorem to expand $(2x - 1)^6$.

Exercises

HOMEWORK

- Core: 6, 7, 10
- Optional: 8, 11
- Extension: 9

Exercises

1. a. $(x + y)^7 = x^7 + 7x^6y + 21x^5y^2 + 35x^4y^3 + 35x^3y^4 + 21x^2y^5 + 7xy^6 + y^7w$

b. $(x + 2y)^5 = x^5 + 10x^4y + 40x^3y^2 + 80x^2y^3 + 80xy^4 + 32y^5$

2. a. 792

b. the term containing a^7b^5

c. the term containing a^6b^6

Additional Resources

PRINT RESOURCES
- Solution Manual
- Practice Workbook
- Assessment Resources
- Teaching Resources

TECHNOLOGY
- Interactive Textbook
- TeacherExpress CD-ROM
- ExamView CD-ROM
- PHSchool.com

Additional Practice

1. Use the Binomial Theorem to expand each of the following.
   a. $(2x + y)^6$ b. $(x^2 + 3y)^5$

2. Determine the coefficient of each of the following terms in the expansion of $(x + y)^{40}$.
   a. x^2y^{38} b. $x^{24}y^{16}$
   c. $x^{34}y^6$ d. $x^{30}y^{10}$

3. a. Write a polynomial that you can factor in the form $(a + b)^n$ where:
   - The constant term is not 1.
   - There is exactly one variable, x.
   - There are at least 6 terms.

   b. Write a polynomial that you can factor in the form $(a + b)^n$ where:
   - The constant term is 1.
   - There is exactly one variable, x.
   - There are at least 5 terms.

4. Write an equivalent expression for each of the following.
   a. $(x - 2)^n$ b. $(y - z)^n$

5. How could you simplify the following sum? Let $n = 6$.

$$\sum_{k=0}^{n}\binom{n}{k}(-1)^k$$

What if n is 7 instead of 6? What if n is 12?

Practice: For Lesson 4.10, assign Exercises 1–5.

3. Determine the coefficient of each of the following terms in the expansion of $(x + y)^{50}$.

   a. $x^{13}y^{37}$ **b.** xy^{49} **c.** $x^{25}y^{25}$

4. How could you simplify the following sum? Let $n = 5$.

$$\sum_{k=0}^{n}\binom{n}{k}(-1)^k$$

What if n were 6 instead of 5? What if n were 11 instead of 5?

5. Write a polynomial that you can factor in the form $(a + b)^n$ where:
   - The constant term is not 1.
   - There is exactly one variable, x.
   - There are at least 5 terms.

   Switch polynomials with a partner. Factor your partner's polynomial.

Habits of Mind

Be efficient. You certainly should use your CAS to evaluate these, but do not ask your CAS to find all 51 terms! Use what you know to make the calculations easier.

On Your Own

6. **a.** Factor the expression $1 + 4x + 6x^2 + 4x^3 + x^4$.

   b. Evaluate the sum (without a calculator).

$$1 + 4 \cdot 2 + 6 \cdot 2^2 + 4 \cdot 2^3 + 2^4$$

   c. Explain how the two problems in parts (a) and (b) are connected.

7. Write an equivalent expression for each of the following.

   a. $(x - 1)^n$ **b.** $(a - b)^n$

8. Consider trinomial coefficients. What is the coefficient of the ab^2c term in the expansion of $(a + b + c)^4$?

9. **Take It Further** In the expansion of $(a + b + c + d + e)^{14}$, what is the coefficient of the $a^2b^3cd^5e^3$ term?

10. **Standardized Test Prep** What is the coefficient of the a^4b^3 term in the expansion of $(a - b)^7$?

    A. −56 **B.** 56 **C.** 168 **D.** −280

Go Online PHSchool.com

For additional practice, go to Web Code: bga-0410

Think about the combinatorial proof you used for the Binomial Theorem. In how many ways can you choose one a, two b's, and one c from the four factors?

Maintain Your Skills

11. Find the value of each sum. Look for shortcuts!

    a. $\sum_{k=0}^{6}\binom{6}{k}3^{n-k}$ **b.** $\sum_{k=0}^{6}\binom{6}{k}(-1)^k3^{n-k}$

Answers

3. a. $\binom{50}{13} = 354{,}860{,}518{,}600$

b. $\binom{50}{1} = 50$

c. $\binom{50}{25} = 126{,}410{,}606{,}437{,}752$

4. All sums are equal to 0.

5. Answers may vary. Sample: $32x^5 + 240x^4 + 720x^3 + 1080x^2 + 810x + 243$ (factors as $(2x + 3)^5$)

6. a. $(1 + x)^4$

b. 81

c. To evaluate the sum in part (b), replace x with 2 in the factored from of the polynomial in part (a) to get $(1 + 2)^4 = 3^4 = 81$.

7. a. $\binom{n}{0}x^n - \binom{n}{1}x^{n-1} + \binom{n}{2}x^{n-2} + \cdots + (-1)^k\binom{n}{k}x^{n-k} + \cdots + (-1)^{n-1}\binom{n}{n-1}x + (-1)^n\binom{n}{n}$

b. $\binom{n}{0}a^n - \binom{n}{1}a^{n-1}b + \binom{n}{2}a^{n-2}b^2 + \cdots + (-1)^k\binom{n}{k}a^{n-k}b^k + \cdots + (-1)^{n-1}\binom{n}{n-1}ab^{n-1} + (-1)^n\binom{n}{n}b^n$

8. 12

9. 10,090,080

10. D

11. a. 4096 **b.** 64

4.11 Connections

You now know several ways to get the numbers in Pascal's Triangle.

- Pascal's Triangle is a recursively generated number pattern.

$$\binom{0}{0}=1$$
$$\binom{1}{0}=1 \quad \binom{1}{1}=1$$
$$\binom{2}{0}=1 \quad \binom{2}{1}=2 \quad \binom{2}{2}=1$$
$$\binom{3}{0}=1 \quad \binom{3}{1}=3 \quad \binom{3}{2}=3 \quad \binom{3}{3}=1$$
$$\binom{4}{0}=1 \quad \binom{4}{1}=4 \quad \binom{4}{2}=6 \quad \binom{4}{3}=4 \quad \binom{4}{4}=1$$
$$\binom{5}{0}=1 \quad \binom{5}{1}=5 \quad \binom{5}{2}=10 \quad \binom{5}{3}=10 \quad \binom{5}{4}=5 \quad \binom{5}{5}=1$$

Notice that the numbering starts with 0. So, for example,

$$\binom{6}{0} = 1 \quad \text{and} \quad \binom{6}{1} = 6$$

You can write the recursive rule for generating the triangle using words.

> Each row starts and ends with a 1, and any interior element is the sum of the two above it.

You can also write this same rule using symbols.

$$\binom{n}{k} = \begin{cases} 1 & \text{if } k = 0 \text{ or if } k = n \text{ (each row starts and ends with 1)} \\ \binom{n-1}{k-1} + \binom{n-1}{k} & \text{if } 0 < k < n \text{ (an interior element is the sum of the two above it)} \end{cases}$$

See the TI-Nspire™ Handbook on p. 704 to learn how to model a recursively defined function of two variables.

- The entries in Pascal's Triangle count subsets. Suppose you have a set of five elements, say $\{A, B, C, D, E\}$. How many three-element subsets are there? There are $\binom{5}{3} = 10$. Here they are:

$\{A, B, C\}, \{A, B, D\}, \{A, B, E\}, \{A, C, D\}, \{A, C, E\},$
$\{A, D, E\}, \{B, C, D\}, \{B, C, E\}, \{B, D, E\}, \{C, D, E\}$

- The entries in Pascal's Triangle are the coefficients in $(a + b)^n$. The entries in the nth row are the coefficients in the expansion of $(a + b)^n$. More precisely,

$$(a+b)^n = \binom{n}{0}a^n + \binom{n}{1}a^{n-1}b + \binom{n}{2}a^{n-2}b^2 + \cdots + \binom{n}{n-1}ab^{n-1} + \binom{n}{n}b^n$$

Lesson Overview

GOAL

- See the entries of Pascal's Triangle from a variety of perspectives.

This short lesson gives students a chance to review all of the different ways they can look at Pascal's triangle. It is a recursively generated number pattern, as well as a method for counting subsets, binomial coefficients, and quotients of factorials. It is one thing for students to know that Pascal's triangle is somehow, vaguely related to all of these things, but the exercises in this lesson are designed to give students real experience of these connections.

CHECK YOUR UNDERSTANDING
- Core: 1, 2, 3, 4, 5, 6
- Optional: 7, 8

MATERIALS
- graphing calculators
- Blackline Master MC12

HOMEWORK
- Core: 9, 10, 11, 12, 14
- Optional: 15
- Extension: 13

Launch

Launch this lesson by going over the connections in this lesson with students.

Explore

You may want to use Blackline Master MC12 on an overhead. Use entries in the triangle as examples as you discuss each of the properties.

Wrap Up

You might wrap up by asking students to summarize what they have learned about Pascal's Triangle.

Assessment Resources

Lesson Quiz 4.11

1. Suppose you have a set of 10 elements.
 a. How many three-element subsets are there?
 b. How many four-element subsets are there?
 c. How many nine-element subsets are there?
 d. How many 10-element subsets are there? Use this answer to explain how to find $\binom{n}{n}$ for any whole number, n.

2. Use the expansion of $(x + y)^{17}$ to answer the following.
 a. How do the coefficients of the terms x^8y^9 and x^9y^8 compare?
 b. What is the coefficient of the term y^{17}?

Exercises

HOMEWORK

- Core: 9, 10, 11, 12, 14
- Optional: 15
- Extension: 13

- The entries in Pascal's Triangle are quotients of factorials. Recall there is an explicit formula for $\binom{n}{k}$ in terms of factorials.

$$\binom{n}{k} = \frac{n!}{k!(n-k)!}$$

So, for example,

$$\begin{aligned}\binom{12}{5} &= \frac{12!}{5!\,7!} \\ &= \frac{12\cdot 11\cdot 10\cdot 9\cdot 8\cdot 7\cdot 6\cdot 5\cdot 4\cdot 3\cdot 2\cdot 1}{(5\cdot 4\cdot 3\cdot 2\cdot 1)(7\cdot 6\cdot 5\cdot 4\cdot 3\cdot 2\cdot 1)} \\ &= \frac{12\cdot 11\cdot 10\cdot 9\cdot 8}{5\cdot 4\cdot 3\cdot 2\cdot 1} \\ &= 792\end{aligned}$$

- The entries in Pascal's Triangle are rational expressions. Sometimes it is useful to do the cancellations in the factorial expression. Then you can write $\binom{n}{k}$ as a product of fewer factors.

$$\begin{aligned}\binom{n}{k} &= \frac{n(n-1)(n-2)(n-3)\cdots(n-k+1)(n-k)\cdots 1}{k!(n-k)!} \\ &= \frac{n(n-1)(n-2)(n-3)\cdots(n-k+1)}{k!}\end{aligned}$$

One advantage of this expression over all the others is that n can be any number. In a sense, this expression extends the formula for entries in Pascal's Triangle from integers to real (or even complex) numbers. This will be important in the next chapter.

In the exercises for this lesson, you will spend time developing these connections.

Habits of Mind

Make strategic choices. Making this factorial formula hold for the cases $k = 0$ and $k = n$ is one of the reasons for defining $0!$ to be 1.

Habits of Mind

Extend an idea. The symbol $\binom{\pi}{3}$ doesn't make sense in the context of any of the other methods. However, using the formula for $\binom{n}{k}$ you get $\frac{\pi(\pi-1)(\pi-2)}{6}$

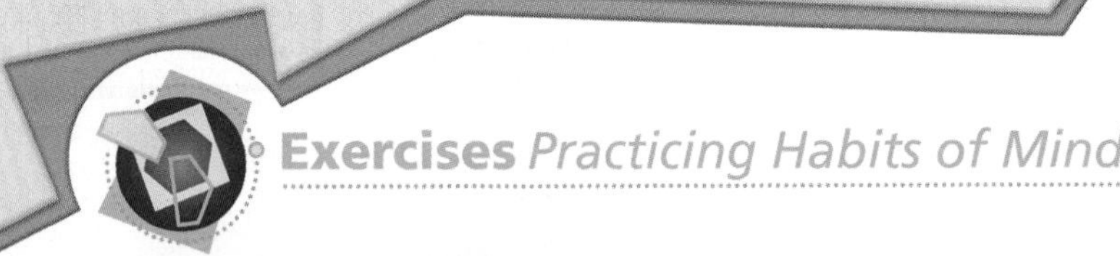

Exercises Practicing Habits of Mind

Check Your Understanding

1. Explain why the sum of the entries in row n of Pascal's Triangle is 2^n. Use the fact that Pascal's Triangle is a recursively generated number pattern.
2. Explain why the sum of the entries in row n of Pascal's Triangle is 2^n. Use the fact that entries in Pascal's Triangle count subsets.

Answers

Exercises

1. Start with row 0. $\binom{0}{0} = 1 = 2^0$. Observe that in row 1, $\binom{1}{0} + \binom{1}{1} = 1 + 1 = 2 = 2^1$. Next, because of the way Pascal's Triangle is recursively defined, the sum of row n is equal to twice the sum of row $n - 1$. Therefore, the sum of row 2 is twice the sum of row 1 or $2(2) = 2^2$. Likewise, the sum of row 3 is twice the sum of row 2 or 2^3. Continuing this reasoning, the sum of row n is 2^n.

2. Entry k in row n of Pascal's Triangle, ${}_nC_k$, is the number of subsets of size k that can be made from a set with n elements. Therefore, the sum of these entries represents the number of all subsets (the subsets of each possible size from 0 to n), which you already know is 2^n.

3. $\binom{n}{n}$ is the number of subsets of the set $\{1, 2, 3, \ldots, n\}$ containing all n elements and there is only one such subset (the set itself). Therefore, $\binom{n}{n} = 1$.

4. $\binom{n}{n} = \frac{n!}{n!0!} = \frac{n!}{n!} = 1$

5. You know that $\binom{n}{k} = {}_nC_k$ is the number of subsets of $\{1, 2, 3, \ldots, n\}$ that contain k elements. But for every k-element subset, there is a unique $(n - k)$-element subset consisting of the elements that are *not* included in the particular k-element subset. Also, for every $(n - k)$-element subset, there is a unique k-element subset consisting of the remaining elements. But this means that ${}_nC_k = {}_nC_{n-k}$, so $\binom{n}{k} = \binom{n}{n-k}$.

6. First, notice that $(a + b)^n = (b + a)^n$. But, according to the Binomial Theorem,

$$(a + b)^n = \sum_{k=0}^{n}\binom{n}{n-k}a^{n-k}b^k \text{ and}$$

$$(b + n)^n = \sum_{k=0}^{n}\binom{n}{n-k}b^{n-k}a^k.$$

3. Using the fact that entries in Pascal's Triangle count subsets, explain why $\binom{n}{n} = 1$.

4. Using the fact that entries in Pascal's Triangle are quotients of factorials, explain why $\binom{n}{n} = 1$.

5. Using the fact that entries in Pascal's Triangle count subsets, explain why $\binom{n}{k} = \binom{n}{n-k}$.

6. Using the fact that entries in Pascal's Triangle are the coefficients in $(a + b)^n$, explain why $\binom{n}{k} = \binom{n}{n-k}$.

7. Using the fact that entries in Pascal's Triangle count subsets, explain why $\binom{n}{1} = n$.

8. Using the fact that entries in Pascal's Triangle are the coefficients in $(a + b)^n$, explain why $\binom{n}{1} = n$.

On Your Own

9. Explain why the sum of the entries in row n of Pascal's Triangle is 2^n. Use the fact that the entries in Pascal's Triangle are the coefficients in $(a + b)^n$.

10. Using the fact that entries in Pascal's Triangle are coefficients in $(a + b)^n$, explain why $\binom{n}{n} = 1$.

11. Using the fact that entries in Pascal's Triangle are quotients of factorials, explain why $\binom{n}{k} = \binom{n}{n-k}$.

12. Using the fact that entries in Pascal's Triangle are quotients of factorials, explain why $\binom{n}{1} = n$.

13. **Take It Further** Using the fact that Pascal's Triangle is a recursively generated number pattern, explain why $\binom{n}{1} = n$.

14. **Standardized Test Prep** What is the value of x if ${}_{2008}C_x = {}_{2008}C_{x-4}$?

A. 1004 **B.** 1006 **C.** 1008 **D.** 2004

Go Online PHSchool.com

For additional practice, go to Web Code: bga-0411

Maintain Your Skills

15. Let $E = \binom{n}{0} + \binom{n}{2} + \binom{n}{4} + \cdots$ (the sum of all the even-entry terms of row n), and $O = \binom{n}{1} + \binom{n}{3} + \binom{n}{5} + \cdots$ (the sum of all the odd-entry terms of row n). How do E and O compare?

Additional Resources

PRINT RESOURCES
- Solution Manual
- Practice Workbook
- Assessment Resources
- Teaching Resources

TECHNOLOGY
- Interactive Textbook
- TeacherExpress CD-ROM
- ExamView CD-ROM
- PHSchool.com

Additional Practice

1. Consider a set with six elements.
   a. How many one-element subsets are there?
   b. How many three-element subsets are there?
   c. How many four-element subsets are there?

2. A set has three elements $\{a, b, c\}$.
   a. List all of the subsets.
   b. How many two-element subsets are there?
   c. List all of the two-element subsets.

3. Using the fact that Pascal's Triangle counts subsets, explain why $\binom{6}{6} = 1$.

4. A girl has eight different flowers. How many possible bouquets can she make if a bouquet can consist of any number of flowers?

5. Christa is forming a club of 5 members from the 20 eligible persons in her class. Assume that one of the 20 eligible persons is her teacher.
   a. How many clubs are possible?
   b. How many clubs are possible which include the teacher?
   c. How many clubs are possible which do not include the teacher?
   d. Explain how your three previous answers are related.

Practice: For Lesson 4.11, assign Exercises 1–5.

In the expansion of $(a + b)^n$, the coefficient of $a^{n-k}b^k$ is $\binom{n}{n-k}$, but in the expansion of $(b + a)^n$, the cofficient of $a^{n-k}b^k$ is $\binom{n}{k}$. Therefore, $\binom{n}{k} = \binom{n}{n-k}$.

7. $\binom{n}{1}$ is the number of one-element subsets of a set with n elements. Since there are n one-element subsets (containing each of the n elements individually), $\binom{n}{1} = n$.

8. $\binom{n}{1}$ is the cofficient of ab^{n-1} in the expansion of $(a + b)^n$. Since there are n ways to choose an a from the n parentheses, $\binom{n}{1} = n$.

9. The sum of the entries in row n of Pascal's Triangle is the sum of the coefficients in the expansion of $(a + b)^n$, which can be computed by evaluating $(a + b)^n$ when $a = b = 1$. Since $(1 + 1)^n = 2^n$, the sum of the entries of row n of Pascal's Triangle is 2^n.

10. $\binom{n}{n}$ is the coefficient of a^n in the expansion of $(a + b)^n$. Since there is only one way to get a^n when multiplying out the n $(a + b)$'s (choose a from each set of parentheses), $\binom{n}{n} = 1$.

11. $\binom{n}{k} = \frac{n!}{k!(n-k)!} = \frac{n!}{(n-k)!k!} = \binom{n}{n-k}$

12. $\binom{n}{1} = \frac{n!}{1!(n-1)!} = \frac{n!}{(n-1)!}$
$= \frac{n(n-1)(n-2)\cdots 3 \cdot 2 \cdot 1}{(n-1)(n-2)\cdots 3 \cdot 2 \cdot 1} = n$

13. $\binom{n}{1} = \binom{n-1}{1-1} = \binom{n-1}{1} =$
$\binom{n-1}{0} + \binom{n-1}{1} = 1 + n - 1 = n$

14. B

15. $E = O$

Mathematical Reflections

EXERCISES 6–8 At the start of the investigation, you may have assigned these as Questions 1–3 for students to think and write about.

In this investigation, you learned that the coefficients in the expansion of $(a + b)^n$ are

- **the numbers in the nth row of Pascal's Triangle**
- **the numbers of combinations when choosing from n elements**

The following questions will help you summarize what you have learned.

1. Using the fact that entries in Pascal's Triangle are the coefficients in $(a + b)^n$, explain why $\binom{n}{k} = \binom{n}{n-k}$.
2. Factor the expression $1 + 4x + 6x^2 + 4x^3 + x^4$.
3. Find the sum of the coefficients of the polynomial $(E + N)^6$.
4. Find the sum of the coefficients of the polynomial $(E - N)^k$.
5. Using the fact that entries in Pascal's Triangle are quotients of factorials, explain why $\binom{n}{k} = \binom{n}{n-k}$.
6. What is the coefficient of the $x^{13}y^{37}$ term in the expansion of $(x + y)^{50}$?
7. What is the connection between the Pascal's Paths problem and the entries in Pascal's Triangle?
8. Why is the sum of the entries in row n of Pascal's Triangle 2^n?

If you overlay Pascal's Triangle, you will see the number of different paths that get to each peg. In the end, the balls will fall into the bins, approximately in a *binomial distribution*.

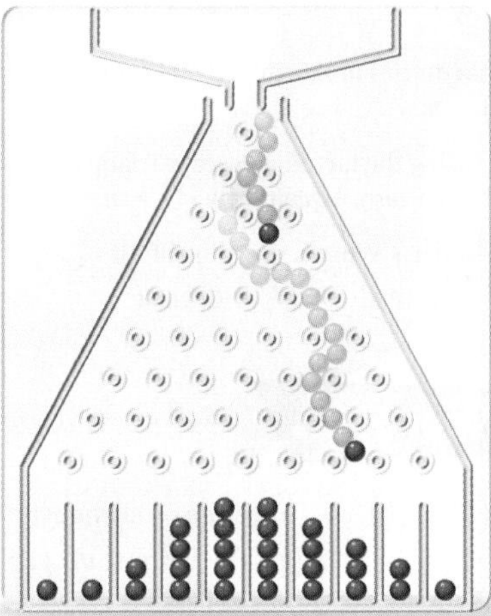

Answers

Mathematical Reflections

1. First, notice that $(a + b)^n = (b + a)^n$. But, according to the Binomial Theorem,

$$(a + b)^n = \sum_{k=0}^{n} \binom{n}{n-k} a^{n-k}b^k \text{ and}$$

$$(b + n)^n = \sum_{k=0}^{n} \binom{n}{n-k} b^{n-k}a^k.$$

In the expansion of $(a + b)^n$, the coefficient of $a^{n-k}b^k$ is $\binom{n}{n-k}$, but in the expansion of $(b + a)^n$, the cofficient of $a^{n-k}b^k$ is $\binom{n}{k}$. Therefore, $\binom{n}{k} = \binom{n}{n-k}$.

2. $(1 + x)^4$
3. 64
4. 0
5. $\binom{n}{k} = \frac{n!}{k!(n-k)!} = \frac{n!}{(n-k)!k!} = \binom{n}{n-k}$
6. 354,860,518,600
7. The number of ways to get to a location E blocks east and N blocks north is $\binom{N+E}{E} = \binom{N+E}{N}$, which is entry E (or N) of row $N + E$ of Pascal's Triangle.
8. Since entry k of row n in Pascal's triangle is the number of k-element subsets an n-element set has, the sum of the entries in row n of Pascal's triangle is the total number of subsets (of all sizes) an n-element set has. Since an n-element set has 2^n subsets, 2^n is the sum of the entries of row n of Pascal's Triangle.

Project: Using Mathematical Habits

The Simplex® Lock

The Simplex® lock is a mechanical pushbutton lock, with five buttons. Like most keyless locks, you enter a secret code by pushing the buttons. The one code that opens the lock is called "the combination" by most people.

The Simplex lock is unusual since you can push more than one button at the same time. For example, one possible combination is "2, then 1 and 4 at the same time, then 3."

In choosing a valid combination, you must follow two rules.

Rule 1 Each button may be used at most once. For example, "2, then 2 and 3 at the same time" is not a valid combination.

Rule 2 Each push may include any number of buttons, from one to five. For example, one valid combination is "hit all five buttons at once." But hitting all five buttons cannot be part of a larger combination because of rule 1.

It follows from these rules that in a combination there can be at most five distinct pushes. (Do you see why?) The rules allow for the null combination, in which you do not have to push any buttons at all. (The door is unlocked!)

Keep in mind that when you push two or more buttons at the same time, their order does not matter. That is, you *should not* count "2 and 3 together, then 5" and "3 and 2 together, then 5" as two distinct combinations.

1. How many lock combinations are there that use all of the buttons?
2. A company that sells this lock advertises that thousands of lock combinations are possible. Are they right?
3. How many lock combinations are there that use fewer than all the buttons? (*Hint:* Use your answer from Exercise 1 to count indirectly.)

To open a door with a Simplex lock, you need the correct permutation from all of the possible codes.

Go Online PHSchool.com

For more information on the Simplex Lock, go to Web Code: bge-9031

Project

1. 541 combinations
2. No, since only 1082 combinations are possible.
3. 541 combinations

Chapter 4 Review

For vocabulary review, go to Web Code: bgj-0451

In **Investigation 4A,** you learned to

- become familiar with what combinatorics means and the kinds of problems that you can solve using combinatorics
- develop your own strategies for systematic counting

The following questions will help you check your understanding.

1. Make up two isomorphic problems that you can solve this way:

$$28 + 2 \cdot 3 = 34$$

2. In how many different ways can you arrange the letters of the word CUBE?

3. a. How many functions have the inputs from the set $\{A, B, C, D\}$ and outputs from the set $\{2, 4, 6\}$?

b. Are any of these functions one-to-one? Explain your answer.

In **Investigation 4B,** you learned to

- develop and use formulas for finding the number of permutations ${}_nP_k$, of n objects taken k at a time
- use a formula for ${}_nC_k$, the number of combinations of n things taken k at a time
- find the number of anagrams for a given word

The following questions will help you check your understanding.

4. Elaine has six books that she is arranging according to color on a bookshelf.

a. How many ways can she arrange the six books if they are all different colors?

b. How many ways can she arrange the six books if 4 of them are the same color?

5. The 25 students in the Student Council want to form a 5-member prom committee.

a. How many committees are possible?

b. Suppose they want to appoint one of the five members as chairperson and another as the treasurer. How many committees can they make using this method?

6. How many anagrams does each word have?

a. FRAME **b.** MIRROR **c.** PAINTING

In **Investigation 4C,** you learned to

- apply counting strategies to solve the Pascal's Paths problem
- explain why you find the coefficients of a binomial expansion in Pascal's Triangle
- See the entries of Pascal's Triangle from a variety of perspectives

The following questions will help you check your understanding.

7. a. If Ms. Pascal only travels three blocks, in how many different places might she end up?

b. How many Pascal paths are three blocks long?

work

home

8. Consider the expansion of $(x + y)^{10}$.

a. What is the coefficient of the x^3y^7 term?

b. What is the coefficient of the x^9y term?

c. Which terms have 45 as their coefficient?

Answers

Chapter Review

1. See back of book.

2. 24 ways

3. a. 81 functions

b. No; since there are only 3 outputs and there are 4 inputs, at least one of the outputs will have to be used twice. In a one-to-one function, each input can be paired with one and only one input.

4. a. 720 ways **b.** 30 ways

5. a. 53,130 ways

b. 1,062,000 ways

6. a. 120 anagrams

b. 120 anagrams

c. 10,080 anagrams

7. a. 4 places

b. 8 paths

8. a. 120

b. 10

c. x^8y^2 and x^2y^8

Test

For a chapter test, go to Web Code: bga-0453

Multiple Choice

1. How many four-digit numbers can you make using the digits 0, 1, 2, or 3?
   A. 15 **B.** 16 **C.** 192 **D.** 256

2. Which expression is equivalent to $\frac{8!}{4!}$?
   A. 2!
   B. $8 \cdot 7 \cdot 6 \cdot 5$
   C. $8 \cdot 7 \cdot 6 \cdot 5 \cdot 4$
   D. $8 \cdot 7 \cdot 6 \cdot 5 \cdot 3 \cdot 2 \cdot 1$

3. How many anagrams does the word PEN have?
   A. 1 **B.** 3 **C.** 6 **D.** 27

4. Which of the following is not equal to ${}_8C_3$?
   A. $\binom{8}{3}$ **B.** $\frac{{}_8P_3}{3!}$ **C.** ${}_8C_5$ **D.** ${}_8P_3 \cdot 6$

5. What is the coefficient of a^9b^2 in the expansion of $(a+b)^{11}$?
   A. 9 **B.** 36 **C.** 55 **D.** 110

Open Response

6. Write the following using factorial notation and then find the value of the expression.
   a. ${}_6C_2$ **b.** ${}_6P_2$
   c. $\binom{6}{0}$ **d.** ${}_7P_7$
   e. ${}_8C_5 + {}_8C_6$

7. Ms. Smith's kindergarten class has 15 students, 8 girls and 7 boys.
   a. How many ways can the 8 girls line up for recess?
   b. How many ways can Ms. Smith choose 4 of her students to form a reading group?
   c. How many ways can she choose the reading group if there must be 2 boys and 2 girls in the group?

8. How many anagrams does each word have?
   a. EARTH
   b. MERCURY
   c. NEPTUNE

9. **a.** Write the first three terms in the expansion of $(a+b)^{24}$.
   b. Write the last three terms in the expansion of $(a+b)^{24}$.
   c. Write the term that does not share its coefficient with any other term.

10. How many three-digit numbers are there that have repeated digits?

Chapter Test

1. C 2. B 3. C
4. D 5. C

6. **a.** $\frac{6!}{2!4!} = 15$ **b.** $\frac{6!}{4!} = 30$
   c. $\frac{6!}{0!6!} = 1$ **d.** $7! = 5040$
   e. ${}_9C_6 = \frac{9!}{6!3!} = 84$ or $\frac{8!}{5!3!} + \frac{8!}{6!2!} = 84$

7. **a.** 40,320 ways
   b. 1365 ways
   c. 588 ways
8. **a.** 120 anagrams
   b. 2520 anagrams
   c. 1260 anagrams
9. **a.** $a^{24} + 24a^{23}b + 276a^{22}b^2$
   b. $276a^2b^{22} + 24ab^{23} + b^{24}$
   c. $2{,}704{,}156a^{12}b^{12}$
10. 252 numbers

Test

Assessment Resources

Chapter Test Form A page 1 of 3

Multiple Choice

1. How many four-digit numbers can you make using the digits 4, 5, 6 or 7?
   A. 126 **B.** 256
   C. 3024 **D.** 1024

2. A state issues a five-character license plate which has two letters and three numbers. How many license plates of this form are possible?
   A. 676,000 **B.** 468,000
   C. 576,000 **D.** 260,000

3. Which of the following is an expression for the number of functions from the set {1, 2, 3, ..., 19, 20} to the set {1, 2, 3, ..., 149, 150}?
   A. 20^{150} **B.** 150^{20}
   C. ${}_{150}P_{20}$ **D.** ${}_{150}C_{20}$

4. Suppose you have a deck of 24 cards, numbered 1 through 24. How many ways can you choose five different cards?
   A. 5,100,480 **B.** 7,962,624
   C. 40,204 **D.** 42,504

5. Ana is hanging some pictures in a row. She has seven pictures to hang in any order she pleases. How many different ways can Ana arrange the pictures?
   A. 823,543 **B.** 702,400
   C. 5040 **D.** 720

6. How many functions are there from the set {1, 2, 3, 4} to the set {small, medium, large}?
   A. 81 **B.** 64
   C. 24 **D.** 48

7. Jerry has seven different math books to line up on a shelf. If he wants the Geometry and Algebra books to be next to each other, in how many ways can he arrange the books?
   A. 5040 **B.** 2520
   C. 1440 **D.** 720

Also available: Form B

Chapter Test Form A page 2 of 3

8. If you expand $(x+y)^{62}$, what is the coefficient of the term $x^{58}y^4$?
   A. 1891 **B.** 2040
   C. 622,380 **D.** 557,845

9. Which of the following is the binomial expansion of $(2+y^2)^5$?
   A. $y^5 + 10y^4 + 40y^3 + 80y^2 + 80y + 32$
   B. $y^{10} + 10y^8 + 40y^6 + 80y^4 + 80y^2 + 32$
   C. $y^{10} - 10y^8 + 40y^6 - 80y^4 + 80y^2 - 32$
   D. $y^5 - 10y^4 + 40y^3 - 80y^2 + 80y^1 - 32$

10. There are eight points on a paper. No three of them are on the same line. How many different triangles can you draw using these points as vertices?
    A. 336 **B.** 512
    C. 56 **D.** 112

Open Response

11. Decide if the following pairs of problems are isomorphic. Explain.
    a. • Five friends each have $10. How much do they have altogether?
    • A regular pentagon has side lengths of 10 centimeters. What is its perimeter?
    b. • A square has a perimeter of 24 feet. What is the length of each side?
    • What is the area of a triangle with a base of 4 feet and a height of 12 feet?
    c. • A hockey goalie made 15 saves in the first game, 8 saves in the second game, and 12 saves in the third game. How many saves did he make in total for all three games?
    • A triangle has side lengths of 15 inches, 8 inches, and 12 inches. What is its perimeter?

12. **a.** How many ways are there to arrange the letters in the word HOMERUN?
    b. In how many different ways can you arrange the letters if M and E must be next to each other?
    c. In how many different ways can you arrange the letters if you want the arrangement to contain the word RUN?

13. **a.** How many functions are there from a five-element set to a seven-element set?
    b. How many of these functions are one-to-one?
    c. How many of these functions are not one-to-one?

Also available: Form B

Cumulative Review

Assessment Resources

Quarter Test — page 1

Multiple Choice

1. Let $f(x) = -x^3 + x^2 + 5x - 4$. Which of the following is the equation of the line secant to the graph of f through the points $(-2, f(-2))$ and $(3, f(3))$?
   A. $y = 2x - 4$ **B.** $y = x + 1$ **C.** $y = -x - 4$ **D.** $y = -2x + 1$

2. Which rational function has a graph with a vertical asymptote at $x = -7$?
   A. $f(x) = \frac{x^2 + 5x - 14}{x^2 + 4x - 21}$ **B.** $f(x) = \frac{x^2 - 7x - 18}{x^2 - 5x - 14}$
   C. $f(x) = \frac{x^2 - 7x - 18}{x^2 + 4x - 21}$ **D.** $f(x) = \frac{x^2 + 4x - 21}{x^2 - 5x - 14}$

3. Which of the following equations is true for all real x, without restriction?
   A. $\ln \frac{x}{5} = \ln x - \ln 5$ **B.** $\log_x 5 = \frac{\ln 5}{\ln x}$
   C. $e^{\ln x} = x$ **D.** $\ln e^x = x$

4. In the binomial expansion of $(4x + 2y)^4$, which of the following is the coefficient of the term x^3y?
   A. 384 **B.** 512 **C.** 256 **D.** 128

5. How many ways can you arrange the letters in the word "DOLPHIN", if the letters O and L must be next to one another?
   A. 1440 **B.** 720 **C.** 5040 **D.** 4020

6. A unique language consists of seven letters. No word in the language is more than 4 letters long. What is the maximum number of words that the language can contain?
   A. 2401 **B.** 399 **C.** 2800 **D.** 405

7. A baseball team has thirteen players. The coach needs to choose nine players to start the game. How many ways can the coach choose nine players?
   A. 525 **B.** 310 **C.** 220 **D.** 715

Quarter Test — page 2

Open Response

8. Suppose \$3150 is invested at 6.5% APR. Find the value of the investment after 3 years, under each of the following assumptions.
   a. annual compounding
   b. monthly compounding
   c. continuous compounding

9. Let $f(x) = e^x$. Find an equation for the line tangent to the graph of f at $(6, f(6))$.

10. Derive the formula $\log_b x = \frac{\ln x}{\ln b}$. Start by noting two ways to simplify the expression $\ln b^{\log_b x}$.

11. a. How many functions are there from a six-element set to an eight-element set?
    b. How many of these functions are one-to-one?

12. Taylor is arranging framed pictures in a straight line on the wall. There are six different pictures and each has a different color frame.
    a. In how many different ways can she arrange the pictures?
    b. In how many different ways can she arrange the pictures if she wants the blue-framed picture and the red-framed picture to be next to one another?
    c. In how many different ways can she arrange the pictures if she wants the blue picture to be at either end of the line?

13. Use the Binomial Theorem to expand the following.
    a. $(x - 2z)^4$ b. $(7 + y)^5$

Challenge Problem

14. Let $f(x) = qx^3 + rx^2 + sx + t$, and let the Taylor expansion of f about a be written in the form $f(x) = A + B(x - a) + C(x - a)^2 + D(x - a)^3$.
    a. Explain what the quantities t, A, and $A - Ba$ each tell you about the graph of f or the line tangent to the graph at $(a, f(a))$.
    b. Explain what B and s each tell you about the graph of f or one of its tangent lines.

Chapter 4 Cumulative Review

1. For each degree measure, find the corresponding radian measure.
   a. 330°
   b. 225°
   c. 240°
   d. 90°

2. Find all solutions to the equation $4\sin^2 x - 3 = 0$ for $0 \le x \le 2\pi$.

3. Find the period of the function $g(t) = 1 + \cos(2t)$.

4. Let z be a complex number where $|z| = 3$ and $\arg(z) = \frac{\pi}{3}$. Find z^4.

5. Let $x + yi = 4 \operatorname{cis} 150°$. Find x and y.

6. Evaluate $(-3 + 3i\sqrt{3})^3$.

7. Examine the graph of the function g below. List all of the roots of g.

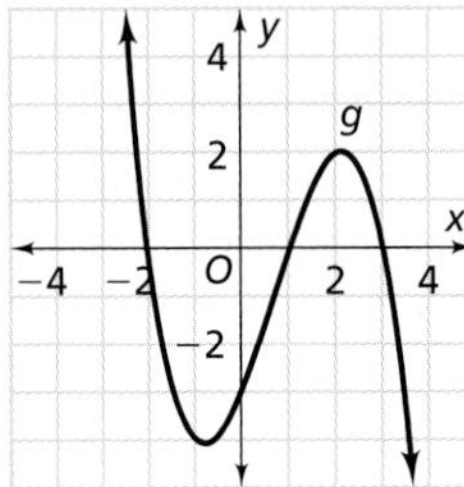

8. Consider the function $f(x) = \frac{x^2 - x - 12}{x^2 + x - 6}$.
   a. The graph of f has a horizontal asymptote. Find the equation of the horizontal asymptote.
   b. The graph of f has a vertical asymptote. Find the equation of the vertical asymptote.
   c. The graph of f has a hole. Find the coordinates of the hole.

9. Phoebe invests \$1000 at 9% APR. She wants to determine the interest earned by different compounding methods after one year. Copy and complete the table, rounding answers to the nearest penny.

	Compounding Periods	Amount of Interest
a.	yearly	■
b.	quarterly	■
c.	monthly	■
d.	daily	■
e.	continuously	■

10. Consider the function $f(x) = 2x^3 - 4x^2 + 1$. One point on the graph of f is (2, 1).
    a. Use geometry software to draw the graph of f. Plot the point $A(2, 1)$. Place a moveable point B on the graph of f to the right of A.
    b. Construct the secant line through A and B. Find the equation of this line.
    c. Let b be the x-coordinate of B. Write $m(A, B)$ as a polynomial in b using the formula $m(A, B) = \frac{f(b) - f(2)}{b - 2}$.
    d. Move B closer to A. What happens to the slope of the secant line?

11. Find constants A and B such that
$$\frac{9x - 1}{x^2 - 3x - 4} = \frac{A}{x + 1} + \frac{B}{x - 4}$$

12. Suppose that $f(x) = x^3 + 4x^2 - 7x - 12$ and $g(x) = 3x^2 - 8x + 2$. Expand the following in powers of $x - 2$.
    a. $f(x)$ b. $g(x)$
    c. $f(x) + g(x)$ d. $5g(x)$

Answers

Cumulative Review

1. a. $\frac{11\pi}{6}$ b. $\frac{3\pi}{4}$ c. $\frac{4\pi}{3}$ d. $\frac{\pi}{2}$
2. $\frac{\pi}{3}, \frac{2\pi}{3}, \frac{4\pi}{3}, \frac{5\pi}{3}$
3. π
4. $81 \operatorname{cis} \frac{4\pi}{3}$
5. $x = -2\sqrt{3}, y = 2$
6. 216
7. −2, 1, 3
8. a. $y = 1$ b. $x = 2$ c. $\left(-3, \frac{7}{5}\right)$
9. a. \$90.00 b. \$93.08 c. \$93.81 d. \$94.16 e. \$94.17
10. a. See back of book.
    b. $y = 2b^2x - 4b^2 + 1$
    c. $m = 2b^2$
    d. The slope gets closer and closer to 8.
11. $A = 2, B = 7$
12. a. $(x - 2)^3 + 10(x - 2)^2 + 21(x - 2) - 2$
    b. $3(x - 2)^2 + 4(x - 2) - 2$

13. The quadratic function $q(x) = 1 - x + \frac{x^2}{2}$ is a good approximation to $f(x) = e^{-x}$ when x is near 0.

a. Calculate $q(0.05)$ and $e^{-0.05}$ to five decimal places. What is the percent error for $q(0.05)$ as an approximation to $e^{-0.05}$?

b. Calculate $q(0.5)$ and $e^{-0.5}$ to five decimal places. What is the percent error for $q(0.5)$ as an approximation to $e^{-0.5}$?

c. Calculate $q(1)$ and e^{-1} to five decimal places. What is the percent error for $q(1)$ as an approximation to e^{-1}?

14. Write each of the following using factorial notation. Then find the value of the expression.

a. ${}_9C_3$

b. ${}_7P_2$

c. $\binom{7}{5}$

d. ${}_6C_0 + {}_6C_6$

15. For the expansion of $(u + v)^8$, find the coefficient of the specified term.

a. the first term

b. the last term

c. the u^5v^3 term

d. the u^4v^4 term

16. Find the number of anagrams that each word has.

a. LOBSTER

b. CHICKEN

c. DESSERT

d. APPETITE

17. The gymnastics team at Valley View College consists of 10 women and 8 men. The team is going to a statewide competition. Their bus can only hold twelve members of the team, so only some of them can go on the trip.

a. How many ways can they choose 6 women and 6 men to go on the trip?

b. How many ways can they choose 7 women and 5 men to go on the trip?

c. Suppose the captain of the women's squad and the captain of the men's squad must go on the trip. They want 7 women and 5 men, including the captains, to make the trip. How many ways can they choose who will go?

18. Three of the following are equal to each other. The fourth is not equal to any of the others. Which one is it?

a. ${}_{10}C_7$ **b.** $\binom{10}{3}$ **c.** $\frac{10!}{3!}$ **d.** $\frac{{}_{10}P_7}{3!}$

19. For the expansion of $(m + n)^{16}$, write the specified terms.

a. the first three terms

b. the last three terms

c. the middle term

20. Darlene is planning a summer vacation to the Caribbean. She can fly from her home to Miami on any one of four different airlines. From Miami, she can then board a ship belonging to any one of two cruise lines to the Bahamas. Once in the Bahamas, she can then rent a car from one of three car rental agencies, and can stay in any one of seven different hotels. In how many ways could she select a package consisting of an airline, a cruise line, a car rental agency, and a hotel?

Assessment Resources

Mid-year Test Form A — page 1

Multiple Choice

1. Simplify $\tan^{-1}\left(-2 \sin \frac{\pi}{3}\right)$.
   A. $-\frac{\pi}{6}$ B. $\frac{\pi}{3}$ C. $-\frac{\pi}{3}$ D. $\frac{\pi}{6}$

2. Find the minimum value of the function $H(t) = 5 \cos\left(t + \frac{\pi}{3}\right) - 3$.
   A. −8 B. −5 C. −3 D. 2

3. Use the addition formula for the cosine or sine function to find the exact value of $\sin \frac{\pi}{12}$.
   A. $\frac{\sqrt{6}}{4} - \frac{\sqrt{2}}{4}$ B. $\frac{\sqrt{3}}{4} - \frac{1}{4}$ C. $\frac{\sqrt{6}}{4} + \frac{\sqrt{2}}{4}$ D. $\frac{1}{4} + \frac{\sqrt{3}}{4}$

4. Suppose $z = \text{cis } 80°$. Find the smallest positive integer n so that z is an nth root of unity.
   A. 3 B. 5 C. 7 D. 9

5. Which rational function has a vertical asymptote at $x = 3$, a hole at $(2, -7)$, and a horizontal asymptote at $y = 4$?
   A. $f(x) = \frac{x^2 - 5x + 6}{4x^2 - 9x + 2}$ B. $g(x) = \frac{4x^2 - 9x + 2}{x^2 + x - 6}$
   C. $h(x) = \frac{4x^2 - 9x + 2}{x^2 - 5x + 6}$ D. $k(x) = \frac{x^2 + x - 6}{4x^2 - 9x + 2}$

6. An account earns 7.3% interest (APR), compounded continuously. If the initial deposit is $2605, what is the account balance after 5 years and 3 months?
   A. $3770.99 B. $3821.65 C. $3873.45 D. $3919.17

7. How many three-digit numbers can you make using the digits 0, 1, 2, 3, and 4?
   A. 64 B. 100 C. 125 D. 1024

8. What is the coefficient of a^2b^6 in the expansion of $(a + b)^8$?
   A. 15 B. 28 C. 56 D. 64

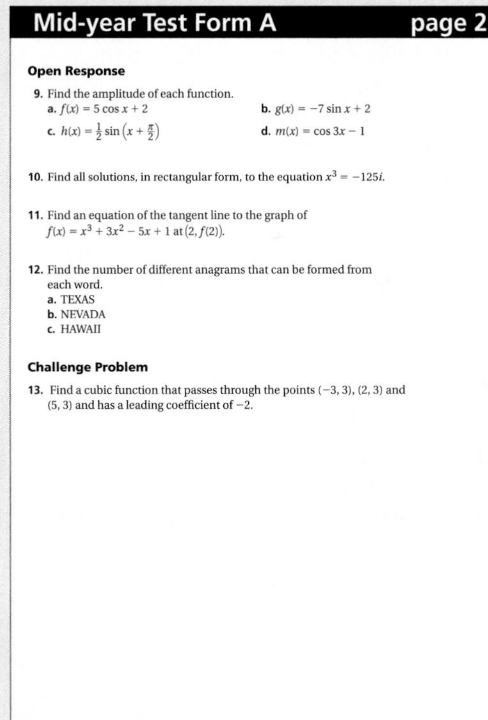

Mid-year Test Form A — page 2

Open Response

9. Find the amplitude of each function.
   a. $f(x) = 5 \cos x + 2$ b. $g(x) = -7 \sin x + 2$
   c. $h(x) = \frac{1}{2} \sin\left(x + \frac{\pi}{2}\right)$ d. $m(x) = \cos 3x - 1$

10. Find all solutions, in rectangular form, to the equation $x^3 = -125i$.

11. Find an equation of the tangent line to the graph of $f(x) = x^3 + 3x^2 - 5x + 1$ at $(2, f(2))$.

12. Find the number of different anagrams that can be formed from each word.
   a. TEXAS
   b. NEVADA
   c. HAWAII

Challenge Problem

13. Find a cubic function that passes through the points $(-3, 3)$, $(2, 3)$ and $(5, 3)$ and has a leading coefficient of -2.

Also available: Form B

c. $(x - 2)^3 + 13(x - 2)^2 + 25(x - 2) - 4$
d. $15(x - 2)^2 + 20(x - 2) - 10$

13. a. $q(0.05) \approx 0.95125$, $e^{-0.05} \approx 0.95123$; 0.0021%
b. $q(0.5) \approx 0.625$, $e^{-0.5} \approx 0.60653$; 3.0452%
c. $q(1) \approx 0.5$, $e^{-1} \approx 0.36788$; 35.9139%

14. a. $\frac{9!}{3!6!} = 84$ **b.** $\frac{7!}{5!} = 42$
c. $\frac{7!}{5!2!} = 21$ **d.** $\frac{6!}{0!6!} + \frac{6!}{6!0!} = 2$

15. a. 1 **b.** 1 **c.** 56 **d.** 70

16. a. 5040 **b.** 2520
c. 1260 **d.** 5040

17. a. 5880 ways **b.** 6720 ways
c. 5880 ways

18. C

19. a. $m^{16} + 16m^{15}n + 120m^{14}n^2$
b. $120m^2n^{14} + 16mn^{15} + n^{16}$
c. $12{,}870m^8n^8$

20. 168 ways

Chapter 5
Functions and Tables

This chapter focuses primarily on two ways to define functions: recursively and with closed-form rules. The first investigation looks at induction, one way to prove that a recursive rule and a closed-form rule agree for all inputs. The second investigation looks at how you can use Pascal's Triangle, a recursively-generated set of numbers, to find closed-form function definitions that fit tables. The third investigation looks at how to find closed-form function definitions for two specific situations: a two-term recurrence such as the one for Fibonacci numbers, and a recurrence defined by multiplying the previous term and then adding a constant. Students have seen this second recurrence before when dealing with car payments and bank balances.

Chapter Overview

INVESTIGATION 5A, *A New Method of Proof,* reviews recursive and closed-form function definitions, and shows how to use mathematical induction to justify that two such definitions for a function will *always* agree for any integer input.

INVESTIGATION 5B, *Fitting Functions to Tables,* has students explore difference tables and the connections between how difference tables and Pascal's Triangle are constructed, which leads to Newton's Difference Formula.

INVESTIGATION 5C, *Closed-Form and Recursive Definitions,* has students explore different rules used to recursively define functions, and methods used to find a closed-form function definition fitting the same rule.

For more information on the Investigations, see

- Chapter Road Map, pp. 340–341
- Investigation Road Maps, pp. 342, 370, 408

PROJECT The Project near the end of the chapter is optional. You can assign the Project at any time during the chapter depending on how often and how long you feel students should work on it.

Pacing Suggestions and Materials

Investigation 5A ***A New Method of Proof***

DAY	LESSON	HOMEWORK
1	5.1 Getting Started Core: 1, 2, 3a–d, 4 Optional: 5, 6a–c; Extension: 3e, 6d	Core: 7, 9, 10, 13 Optional: 8, 11, 12
2	5.2 Two Ways to Define a Function Core: 1, 2, 4, 6 Optional: 3, 5, 7, 8	Core: 9, 10, 12, 15, 17, 18 Optional: 11, 13, 14, 16, 19a–b; Extension: 1
3	5.3 Multistep Recursive Definitions Core: 1, 2, 3, 5 Optional: 4a–c, 6; Extension: 4d	Core: 7, 8, 10, 13, 14 Optional: 9a–c, 11, 12a–b; Extension: 9d, 12c
4	5.4 Mathematical Induction Core: 1, 3, 5, 7 Optional: 2, 4, 6; Extension: 8	Core: 9, 10, 13, 16, 17 Optional: 11, 12, 14, 18; Extension: 15
5	5.5 Ways to Think About Induction Core: 2, 3, 4 Optional: 1, 5	Core: 6, 8, 11, 12, 13a–b Optional: 7, 9, 10; Extension: 13c

Investigation 5B ***Fitting Functions to Tables***

DAY	LESSON	HOMEWORK
1	5.6 Getting Started Core: 1, 2, 3 Optional: 4	Core: 5, 6, 9 Optional: 7, 8, 10, 11
2	5.7 Properties of Difference Tables Core: 1, 4, 5 Optional: 3, 6; Extension: 2	Core: 7, 9, 10, 11, 13 Optional: 8, 14, 15; Extension: 12
3	5.8 The Pascal Connection Core: 1, 2, 4, 5 Optional: 3, 6	Core: 7, 8, 9, 13, 14 Optional: 10, 11; Extension: 12
4	5.9 Newton's Difference Formula Core: 1, 2, 3 Optional: 4, 5a, 7; Extension: 5b, 6	Core: 9, 10, 13, 15 Optional: 8, 12, 16; Extension: 11, 14
5	5.10 Sums of Powers Core: 1, 2, 3, 4a Optional: 5; Extension: 4b, 6	Core: 7, 10, 12, 13 Optional: 8, 9, 11

NOTES	MATERIALS
	• graphing calculators • Blackline Masters MC13, 5.1
	• graphing calculators • Blackline Masters MC13–14, 5.1
	• graphing calculators • number rods (optional) • Blackline Master MC13
You may want to take two days for this lesson. If you take two days, consider skipping Lesson 5.5.	• CAS (recommended) • graphing calculators • Blackline Master MC13
This lesson is optional.	• graphing calculators • Blackline Masters MC13, 5.5

NOTES	MATERIALS
	• graphing calculators • Blackline Masters MC13–14, 5.6A–B
Consider making a spreadsheet program available if calculators do not have one.	• graphing calculators • spreadsheet software • Blackline Masters 5.1, 5.7A–C
	• CAS • graphing calculators • Blackline Masters MC12, 5.7A, 5.7C, 5.8A–B
You may want to take two days for this lesson. If you take two days, consider skipping Lesson 5.10.	• CAS (recommended) • graphing calculators • Blackline Masters MC12, 5.9A–B
This lesson is optional.	• CAS (recommended) • graphing calculators • wood blocks (or other 3-D manipulatives) • Blackline Masters 5.10A–B

Mathematics Background

MATHEMATICAL INDUCTION The CME Project approach to mathematical induction varies from the traditional approach, and arises from a natural problem with technology. As seen in the Getting Started of Investigation 5A, there are recursive function definitions and closed-form function definitions that can agree for a long time. But when using technology, at some point the recursive definition fails. This begs the question of whether or not the recursive definition fails at that point, or if it is just the technology running out of memory.

And it is this question that is at the heart of mathematical induction. Students already have their base case in hand—many base cases, in fact. And their goal is to show that even if the technology fails at some k, if $f(k - 1) = g(k - 1)$, then $f(k) = g(k)$. This generalizes quickly to the statement of mathematical induction: armed with a base case, show that if $f(n - 1) = g(n - 1)$, then $f(n) = g(n)$.

When students who are using a more traditional approach to induction look at an induction step, they often ask the question, "Aren't I assuming what I am trying to prove here?" But the technology breakdown forces this upon them: they actually are trying to prove something for which they currently lack justification. This approach has been used successfully in classrooms for many years.

NEWTON'S DIFFERENCE FORMULA Newton's Difference Formula is a classical topic that connects many of the things students have learned to this point. In CME Project *Algebra 1*, students learned about difference tables, and how to find a function definition to fit a table with constant differences. In CME Project *Algebra 2*, students learned about more difference tables, including second and greater differences. Students also learned about Pascal's Triangle in Chapter 7 of CME Project *Algebra 2*.

This material ties these concepts together. You can use the top row of a difference table, along with function definitions built from Pascal's Triangle, to directly find a closed-form rule that fits a table. It is a beautiful result that also benefits from the use of CAS technology, as expressions such as

$$1 + 3\binom{x}{1} - 6\binom{x}{2} + 12\binom{x}{3}$$

are tedious to simplify.

Students may already know coming in that, for example, if second differences are constant, a quadratic fits the table, and its leading coefficient is half the constant difference. Newton's Difference Formula is a stronger version: it gives *all* the coefficients. And the explanation of why the formula works is based on the up-and-over rule, which students see in difference tables and Pascal's Triangle.

continued on p. 340c

continued from p. 340b

FIBONACCI NUMBERS Investigation 5C delves more deeply into the relationship between the closed-form definition and recursive definition for functions. One of the key functions is the recursive definition of Fibonacci numbers, something students have known for years.

This investigation shows how to find the closed-form definition for Fibonacci numbers, along with most recurrences in the form $f(n) = Af(n-1) + Bf(n-2)$. The closed-form definition is related to the roots of the quadratic $x^2 - x - 1 = 0$, and justifies why the ratio of consecutive Fibonacci numbers approaches the golden ratio.

Pacing Suggestions and Materials

Investigation 5C *Closed-Form and Recursive Definitions*

DAY	LESSON	HOMEWORK
1	5.11 Getting Started Core: 1, 2, 3 Optional: 4, 5	Core: 6, 7, 10, 11 Optional: 8, 9
2	5.12 Recurrences Core: 1, 3a–b, 4, 5 Optional: 2, 6, 7; Extension: 3c	Core: 8, 11a–b, 12, 14, 15 Optional: 9, 10; Extension: 11c, 13
3	5.13 $f(n) = Af(n-1) + Bf(n-2)$ Core: 1a–e, 2, 3, 7 Optional: 4, 5, 6; Extension: 1f	Core: 8, 9, 10, 12, 16, 17 Optional: 11; Extension: 13, 14, 15
4	5.14 $f(n) = Af(n-1) + B$ Core: 1, 2, 3 Optional: 4, 5; Extension: 6	Core: 7, 9, 10, 11, 14 Optional: 8, 15; Extension: 12, 13

NOTES	MATERIALS
	• graphing calculators • Blackline Masters MC7, 5.7C
	• CAS (recommended) • graphing calculators • Blackline Master 5.12
You may want to take two days for this lesson, especially to explore the Fibonacci closed form.	• graphing calculators • Blackline Master 5.13
	• CAS (recommended) • graphing calculators

Developing Students' Mathematical Habits

MODELING Students model and work with closed-form and recursive definitions of functions. They find closed-form definitions that agree with recursive definitions, determine whether two such definitions produce functions that are equivalent on the domain of the recursively-defined function, and use induction to prove that the functions agree.

MAKING THE CONNECTION Students are asked to connect the properties of Pascal's Triangle with properties of difference tables, and they use these connections to construct and verify functions that fit tables.

GENERALIZING Students learn to generalize a pattern that works for one function to a class of related functions.

DETECTING Students learn to detect whether a linear, polynomial, or exponential rule can approximate a table.

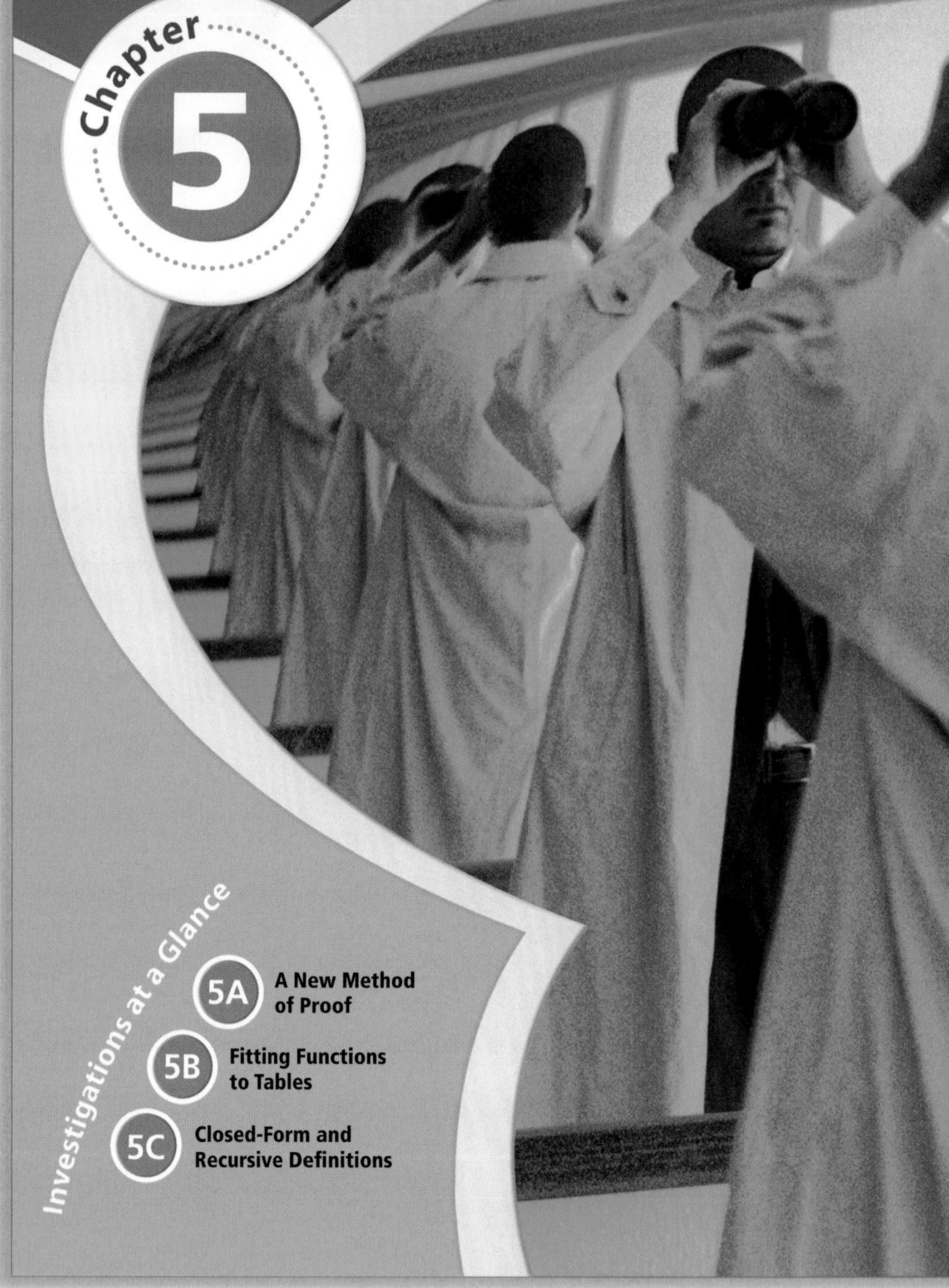

Chapter
5
Investigations at a Glance
5A A New Method of Proof
5B Fitting Functions to Tables
5C Closed-Form and Recursive Definitions

Chapter Road Map

INVESTIGATION 5A, *A New Method of Proof,* reminds students about defining functions recursively or with a closed form, and then focuses on when the two definitions agree. Mathematical induction is used to justify that two such rules will always agree for any integer input.

INVESTIGATION 5B, *Fitting Functions to Tables,* has students explore difference tables and learn about the connections between how difference tables are built and how Pascal's Triangle is constructed. These observations lead to Newton's Difference Formula, a method that can be used to find a function that fits a table.

INVESTIGATION 5C, *Closed-Form and Recursive Definitions,* has students explore different rules used to recursively define functions and methods used to find a closed-form function fitting the rule. This investigation includes a look at the closed-form functions for investment situations and for Fibonacci numbers, among others.

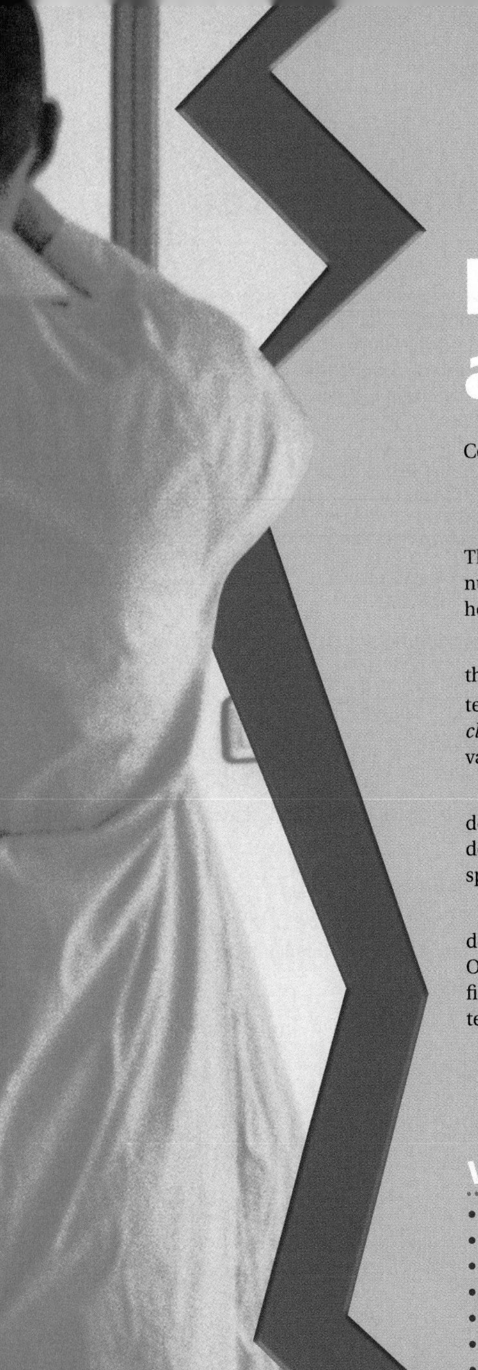

Functions and Tables

Consider the sequence

$$10, 11, 14, 19, 26, 35, \ldots$$

One person might say, "The sequence starts with 10. Then you add 1, add 3, add 5, and keep adding the odd numbers." This is a *recursive* description, one that tells you how to go from one value to the next.

A second person might say. "All the terms are 10 more than the squares of consecutive integers. Term 0 is 10, term 1 is 11, term 2 is 14, and term n is $n^2 + 10$." This is a *closed-form* description, one that tells you how to find any value directly.

Each description has its pros and cons. A recursive description is often more natural, but a closed-form description may prove more useful if you need to find a specific term.

But how might you check or prove that a recursive definition and a closed-form definition will always agree? Or, if you had only a recursive definition, how could you find a closed-form definition to directly calculate the 60th term? This chapter explores these questions.

Vocabulary

- base case
- closed-form definition
- difference table
- equilibrium point
- Fibonacci sequence
- functional equation
- hockey-stick property
- Mahler polynomials
- mathematical induction
- recurrence
- recursive definition
- two-term recurrence
- up-and-over property

Chapter Vocabulary and Notation

The following list gives key vocabulary and notation used in the chapter. Selected new vocabulary and notation items are shown in boldface on the student page.

- base case, p. 347
- closed-form definition, p. 346
- difference table, p. 374
- equilibrium point, p. 429
- Fibonacci sequence, p. 353
- functional equation, p. 412
- hockey-stick property, p. 375
- Mahler polynomials, p. 391
- mathematical induction, p. 360
- recurrence, p. 412
- recursive definition, p. 347
- two-term recurrence, p. 413
- up-and-over property, p. 375

Chapter Technology

CME Project *Precalculus* assumes that each student has access to a graphing calculator. It also recommends access to a computer algebra system (CAS) and to geometry software.

Support for the use of technology is available in the TI-Nspire™ Technology Handbook. See p. 704.

A list of technology used with important concepts in this chapter appears below. Students will need access to the functionality listed to develop complete understanding of these topics.

Function-Modeling Language

LESSON 5.1 Model a recursive function definition, p. 343.

LESSON 5.3 Model the Fibonacci sequence, p. 353.

LESSON 5.12 Model a recursive function definition in order to find a closed-form equivalent, p. 413.

Graphing Calculator

LESSON 5.3 Calculate values of a recursively-defined function, p. 352.

Spreadsheet Software

LESSON 5.7 Make a difference table using a spreadsheet, p. 374.

Investigation Overview

The concept of mathematical induction arises here from the differences between recursive definitions and closed-form definitions of functions. These functions can agree for a long time, but when using technology, at some point the recursive definition fails. This begs the question of whether or not the recursive function fails at that point, or if it is just the technology running out of memory.

This approach establishes clear base cases and a clear reason to want to prove the induction step. Most of the investigation focuses on the agreement of functions defined recursively and in closed form, but the last lesson explores other ways to use induction.

You may wish to assign Questions 1–3 for students to think and write about during the investigation.

Learning Goals

- Determine the domain on which two functions agree.
- Construct closed-form and recursive function definitions that fit a table.
- Compare the efficiency of different recursive definitions that generate the same function.
- Analyze multistep recursive definitions of functions.
- Verify that a closed-form and a recursive function definition agree at the first few inputs in a domain.
- Prove by induction that two function definitions agree for all inputs in an infinite domain.
- Apply induction to geometric proofs.

Habits and Skills

- Model and work with closed-form and recursive definitions of functions.
- Determine whether two functions agree for all inputs in a given set.
- Use patterns to write function definitions.
- Prove that two functions agree for all inputs in an infinite domain.

A New Method of Proof

In *A New Method of Proof*, you will describe functions recursively, by relating outputs to other outputs. You will determine when a function described this way agrees with a function described by a formula, or closed-form definition, which directly relates inputs to outputs. To prove that two functions agree for all shared inputs, you will use a powerful tool known as induction.

By the end of this investigation, you will be able to answer questions like these.

1. What are the differences between a closed-form definition and a recursive definition for a function?
2. How can you prove that a closed-form and a recursive function definition agree at each of infinitely many inputs?
3. What happens to the ratio of consecutive Fibonacci numbers?

You will learn how to

- determine the domain on which two functions agree
- verify that a closed-form and a recursive function definition agree at the first few inputs in a domain
- prove by induction that two function definitions agree for all inputs in an infinite domain

You will develop these habits and skills:

- Model and work with closed-form and recursive definitions of functions.
- Determine whether two functions agree for all inputs in a given set.
- Use patterns to write function definitions.
- Prove that two functions agree for all inputs in an infinite domain.

In a match-play golf tournament, the winner of each match advances to the next round. The number of players in each round follows a recursive rule.

Investigation Road Map

LESSON 5.1, *Getting Started,* shows examples of functions that agree on domains, including recursive and closed-form definitions for the same situation.

LESSON 5.2, *Two Ways to Define a Function,* reviews difference tables. Students explore the advantages and disadvantages of recursive and closed-form definitions.

LESSON 5.3, *Multistep Recursive Definitions,* looks at more complex recurrences and situations where a calculator runs out of memory while evaluating a function.

LESSON 5.4, *Mathematical Induction,* shows students how to set up and complete an inductive proof when a recursive and closed-form definition agree for all non-negative integers.

LESSON 5.5, *Ways to Think About Induction,* shows students other examples where inductive proof is used.

5.1 Getting Started

Activating Prior Knowledge

You already know that you can often describe a function in more than one way. On the other hand, sometimes you will be given two or more different function descriptions. If this happens, you need to be able to determine whether or not they describe the same function.

For You to Explore

Here is an input-output table for a function.

Input	Output
0	3
1	8
2	13
3	18
4	23

1. Takashi says that this table came from the function $T(n) = 5n + 3$.
   a. Does function T agree with the entire table?
   b. What does Takashi's function give for $T(20)$? For $T(500)$?
2. Christine says she has a different function for the table.

   Christine: You start with 3 and keep adding 5. Each output is 5 more than the one before it. And I can write that down. It's

   $$C(n) = \begin{cases} 3 & \text{if } n = 0 \\ C(n-1) + 5 & \text{if } n > 0 \end{cases}$$

   Christine: I'd put this in a calculator if it was more complicated.

   a. Does function C agree with the entire table?
   b. What does Christine's function give for $C(20)$? For $C(500)$?
3. Takashi and Christine would like to know if their functions are the same.
   a. Can you find any input where the two functions from Problems 1 and 2 behave differently?
   b. What are the domains of T and C?
   c. Explain why T and C are not identical functions.
   d. Find the largest set of inputs for which the two functions agree.
   e. **Take It Further** Prove that for any number in this set, T and C must give the same output.

See the TI-Nspire™ Handbook on p. 704 for how to model this definition in your FML (function modeling language).

Answers

For You to Explore

1. a. Yes
   b. 103; 2503
2. a. Yes
   b. 103; 2503
3. a. For negative numbers or fractions/decimals, $T(n)$ can be calculated but $C(n)$ is undefined.
   b. Domain of T = all real numbers; domain of C = all non-negative integers.
   c. Two functions with different domains cannot be equal.
   d. $\{0, 1, 2, \ldots\}$
   e.

$$\begin{cases} T(n) = 3 = C(n) & n = 0 \\ T(n+1) = 5(n+1) + 3 & \\ \qquad = (5n+3) + 5 & \\ \qquad = T(n) + 5 & n > 0 \end{cases}$$

Since the same relation holds between $T(n + 1)$ and $T(n)$ (when $n > 0$) as between $C(n + 1)$ and $C(n)$, and $T(0) = C(0)$, the functions will agree on this domain.

Lesson Overview

GOALS

- Warm up to the ideas of the investigation.
- Determine the domain on which two functions agree.

As always in a Getting Started lesson, there is no need to formalize these ideas today. Students meet all of the ideas again throughout the investigation. The goal of the lesson is to remind students about two different ways to define a function (closed-form and recursive), and introduce them to the possibility of agreement between those functions on a domain.

FOR YOU TO EXPLORE
- Core: 1, 2, 3a–d, 4
- Optional: 5, 6a–c
- Extension: 3e, 6d

MATERIALS
- graphing calculators
- Blackline Masters MC13, 5.1

HOMEWORK
- Core: 7, 9, 10, 13
- Optional: 8, 11, 12

Launch

Have students start on the problems right away.

Explore

For You to Explore

You may want to use the left side of Blackline Master 5.1 on an overhead while reviewing Takashi and Christine's discussion of the input-output table. The same table of inputs and outputs appears again in Lessons 5.2, 5.4 and 5.7.

PROBLEM 2 While some students will work out $C(500)$ naturally by adding fives, others may type the equation into the calculator and find that it cannot calculate $C(500)$ due to recursion depth. This is a good thing! These calculator failures are a good inroad to later discussions about mathematical induction.

PROBLEM 3 is the key problem of this Getting Started lesson. You can have a good argument in class over whether T and C are identical functions. They are not, due to their domains. In Minds in Action in Lesson 5.4, the characters argue over these same functions. Give students a chance to attack the problem, and perhaps some will build an argument that resembles induction.

PROBLEM 4 You may wish to provide copies of Blackline Master MC13 for students to tabulate functions.

PROBLEM 5 and the exercises that follow in On Your Own may remind some students of Lagrange Interpolation from CME Project *Algebra 2*. This is a desirable development. The simplest way to construct functions that agree at 1 and 4 is to add $A(x - 1)(x - 4)$ to any function.

PROBLEM 6 Most calculators or computer programs cannot calculate $B(36)$ given the original form of the function; test this ahead of time to be sure.

Note that On Your Own Exercises 11 and 12 reference this problem, so you might assign this problem as part of homework if you are also assigning either of those exercises.

Wrap Up

Consider wrapping up this lesson by discussing Problem 3, or have students build a similar example of two other functions that behave like C and T.

Exercises

HOMEWORK

- Core: 7, 9, 10, 13
- Optional: 8, 11, 12

You can make a handout from Blackline Master MC13 for students to use while working on the exercises.

4. For each of the following pairs of functions, find the largest set of inputs for which the two functions agree.

a. $f(x) = \frac{1}{x} + x, \quad g(x) = \frac{1 + x^2}{x}$

b. $f(x) = 3x + 2, \quad g(x) = 5x + 1$

c. $f(x) = 3x + 2, \quad g(x) = 3x + 7$

d. $f(x) = x, \quad g(x) = |x|$

e. $f(x) = x^2, \quad g(x) = x + 2$

f. $f(x) = x + 1, \quad g(x) =$ the next integer greater than x

5. Name two functions that agree only at the inputs 1 and 4.

6. Suppose you take out a \$12,000 car loan with a 6% APR compounded monthly, and your monthly payment is \$300 per month. You can recursively define a function B that gives your balance after n months:

$$B(n) = \begin{cases} 12{,}000 & \text{if } n = 0 \\ B(n-1) + \frac{0.06}{12}B(n-1) - 300 & \text{if } n > 0 \end{cases}$$

Why do you divide the interest rate by 12?

a. Use a calculator to find $B(6)$ to the nearest cent.

b. What happens if you try to calculate $B(36)$?

c. Redefine $B(n)$ by combining like terms, then calculate $B(36)$.

d. **Take It Further** What monthly payment amount would bring the balance to exactly zero after 36 months?

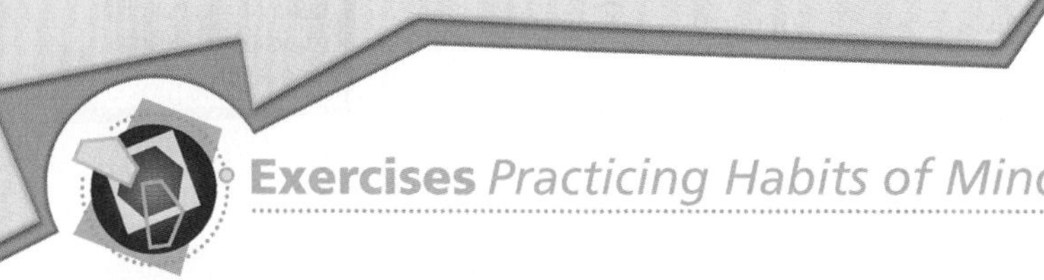

Exercises *Practicing Habits of Mind*

On Your Own

7. For each of the following pairs of functions, find the largest set of inputs for which the two functions agree.

a. $f(x) = x^2 - 9, \quad g(x) = (x + 3)(x - 3)$

b. $f(x) = \frac{x^2 - 16}{x - 4}, \quad g(x) = x + 4$

c. $f(x) = \sqrt{x^2}, \quad g(x) = x$

d. $f(x) = 3x + 2, \quad g(x) = 3x + 2 + (x - 1)(x - 2)(x - 3)$

Answers

4. a. $x =$ all real numbers, $x \neq 0$

b. $x = \frac{1}{2}$

c. Not equal for any value of x.

d. $x \geq 0$

e. $x = 2, x = -1$

f. $x =$ all integers

5. Answers may vary. Sample: $f(x) = A$ and $g(x) = A + (x - 1)(x - 4)$ where A is any expression.

6. a. \$10,541.88

b. Calculator runs out of memory.

c. \$2559.33

d. \$365.06

Exercises

7. a. $\mathbb{R}$

b. $\{x \mid x \neq 4\}$

c. $\{x \mid x \geq 0\}$

d. $\{1, 2, 3\}$

8. a. Answers may vary. Sample: $h(x) = A$ and $k(x) = A + (x - 1)(x - 2) \cdot (x - 3)(x - 4)(x - 5)$

b. Answers may vary. Sample: $m(x) = A$ and $n(x) = A + (x - 6)(x - 7) \cdot (x - 8)(x - 9)(x - 10)$

9. $T(n - 1) + 5$
$= 5(n - 1) + 3 + 5$
$= 5n - 5 + 3 + 5$
$= 5n + 3$
$= T(n)$

8. **a.** Find two functions h and k, defined on all of $\mathbb{R}$, that agree only for the set $\{1, 2, 3, 4, 5\}$.

   b. Find two functions m and n, defined on all of $\mathbb{R}$, that agree only for the set $\{6, 7, 8, 9, 10\}$.

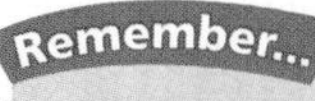

Remember...

$\mathbb{R}$ is the set of real numbers.

9. Takashi's function for the table was $T(n) = 5n + 3$. Show that for any n, $T(n)$ satifies the condition

$$T(n) = T(n - 1) + 5$$

10. **a.** Build a model of the function C from Problem 2 in your FML. Find the greatest value of n for which the model produces an output.

    b. What is the domain of C?

Use the form of the function in Problem 6 to answer the following questions.

11. Suppose you buy a \$10,000 car with a \$1000 down payment and take out a loan for the remaining \$9000 at 5% APR. You are to pay the loan off over 36 months. Find your monthly payment, to the nearest cent.

12. Suppose that the interest rate for the loan in Exercise 11 changes from 5% to 1.9%. How much money per month will you save? How much money will you save over the life of the loan?

Remember...

Enter 1.9% as a decimal number less than 1.

Maintain Your Skills

13. Below are recursive definitions of four functions. For each, tabulate the function using inputs from 0 to 5. Then find a closed-form definition that agrees with the table.

    a. $g(n) = \begin{cases} 5 & \text{if } n = 0 \\ g(n - 1) + 7 & \text{if } n > 0 \end{cases}$

    b. $t(n) = \begin{cases} 1 & \text{if } n = 0 \\ 2 \cdot t(n - 1) & \text{if } n > 0 \end{cases}$

    c. $k(x) = \begin{cases} -3 & \text{if } x = 0 \\ k(x - 1) + 4 & \text{if } x > 0 \end{cases}$

    d. $j(m) = \begin{cases} 0 & \text{if } m = 0 \\ j(m - 1) + m & \text{if } m > 0 \end{cases}$

On Your Own

EXERCISE 9 provides practice using the general replacement $f(n - 1)$, a useful skill when doing proof by induction.

EXERCISE 10 Skip this exercise if students do not have access to the appropriate technology. Also, expect multiple answers if students use different calculators or spreadsheet software.

10. a. Check students' work.

b. This does not change the domain of the function C.

11. \$269.74

12. \$12.35 saved per month; \$444.51 saved over the life of the loan.

13. a.

n	$g(n)$
0	5
1	12
2	19
3	26
4	33
5	40

$g(n) = 7n + 5$

b.

n	$t(n)$
0	1
1	2
2	4
3	8
4	16
5	32

$t(n) = 2^n$

c.

x	$k(x)$
0	−3
1	1
2	5
3	9
4	13
5	17

$k(x) = 4x - 3$

d.

m	$j(m)$
0	0
1	1
2	3
3	6
4	10
5	15

$j(m) = \frac{1}{2}m(m + 1)$

Lesson Overview

GOAL

- Construct closed-form and recursive function definitions that fit a table.

The purpose of this lesson is to reinforce the concepts in the Getting Started lesson: defining functions recursively or with a closed form. Students review difference tables and discover a connection between difference tables and recursively-defined functions.

CHECK YOUR UNDERSTANDING
- Core: 1, 2, 4, 6
- Optional: 3, 5, 7, 8

MATERIALS
- graphing calculators
- Blackline Masters MC13–14, 5.1

HOMEWORK
- Core: 9, 10, 12, 15, 17, 18
- Optional: 11, 13, 14, 16, 19a–b
- Extension: 19c

VOCABULARY
- base case
- closed-form definition
- recursive definition

Launch

Using the recursively-defined function C from the Getting Started lesson, give the value of one output, such as $C(13) = 68$, and ask students to calculate other nearby outputs, such as $C(14)$ or $C(11)$.

Explore

For Discussion

PROBLEM 1 Students should correctly find other function definitions that satisfy the recurrence, including $f(n) = 5n + C$ for any number C. With an advanced group, ask for other classes of function definitions that also satisfy this recurrence. (Answer: One form is $f(n) = 5n + C + \sin 2\pi n$.)

You may want to use one or both sides of Blackline Master 5.1 on an overhead while talking with students about the "+5" behavior of the function $f(n)$. The Δ notation, denoting the difference column, is introduced in Lesson 5.7.

5.2 Two Ways to Define a Function

When you look for a function that agrees with a table, it helps if you can see patterns in the outputs. As an example, consider this table from Lesson 5.1.

Input, n	Output, $f(n)$
0	3
1	8
2	13
3	18
4	23

You could say that each output is 3 more than 5 times the input, writing this as $n \mapsto 5n + 3$. A **closed-form definition** for a function f lets you find $f(n)$ for any input n by direct calculation.

But you might also notice that each output is 5 more than the previous output. In mathematical notation, this function f has the property that

Many people notice this pattern in the outputs before they find a function like $n \mapsto 5n + 3$.

$$f(1) = f(0) + 5 \quad (8 = 3 + 5)$$
$$f(2) = f(1) + 5 \quad (13 = 8 + 5)$$
$$f(3) = f(2) + 5 \quad (18 = 13 + 5)$$
$$f(4) = f(3) + 5 \quad (23 = 18 + 5)$$

In short, this statement is true for any n:

$$f(n) = f(n - 1) + 5$$

Developing Habits of Mind

Think about it more than one way. The rule $f(n) = f(n - 1) + 5$ has many interpretations.

- The output at n is the output at $n - 1$, plus 5.
- The output at n is 5 more than the output at $n - 1$.
- The output at n is 5 more than the previous output.
- Any output is 5 more than the previous output.

For Discussion

1. Is $f(n) = 5n + 3$ the only function that makes $f(n) = f(n - 1) + 5$ true for $n = 0, 1, 2, \ldots$? Explain.

Answers

For Discussion

1. No; answers may vary. Sample: There are other functions that match the recurrence, such as $f(n) = 5n + C$ for any number C.

In order to produce outputs, a rule like $f(n) = f(n-1) + 5$ has to have a place to start, called a **base case.** Once you know that f is a function for which $f(0) = 3$ and $f(n) = f(n-1) + 5$, you can find the output for any integer input greater than 0:

$$f(n) = \begin{cases} 3 & \text{if } n = 0 \\ f(n-1) + 5 & \text{if } n > 0 \end{cases}$$

This is called a **recursive definition** of f. It defines most of the outputs of f in terms of other outputs.

Example

Problem Suppose you know that

$$g(n) = g(n-1) + 7$$

and $g(99) = 496$. Calculate $g(100)$ and $g(101)$.

Solution Let $n = 100$. Then

$$g(100) = g(99) + 7$$

Since $g(99) = 496$, then $g(100) = 496 + 7 = 503$. Similarly, you can use $g(100) = 503$ to find $g(101) = 510$.

If you did not have a base case you would not be able to find $g(101)$—all you would know is that it is 7 more than $g(100)$.

For You to Do

2. Find the values of $f(104)$ and $f(97)$.

Suppose you need to find a function that fits this table:

n	$g(n)$
0	1
1	3
2	7
3	13
4	21
5	31

For You to Do

PROBLEM 2 Find the value of $f(104)$ by applying the recurrence four more times. (Answer: 531) Stepping backwards by sevens gives $f(97) = 496 - 7 - 7 = 482$.

For You to Do

2. $f(104) = 531$, $f(97) = 482$

Wrap Up

Consider wrapping up by discussing Exercise 3, or ask a student to build a table with a specific recursively-defined function in mind. Then have other students determine the function definition.

Assessment Resources

Lesson Quiz 5.2

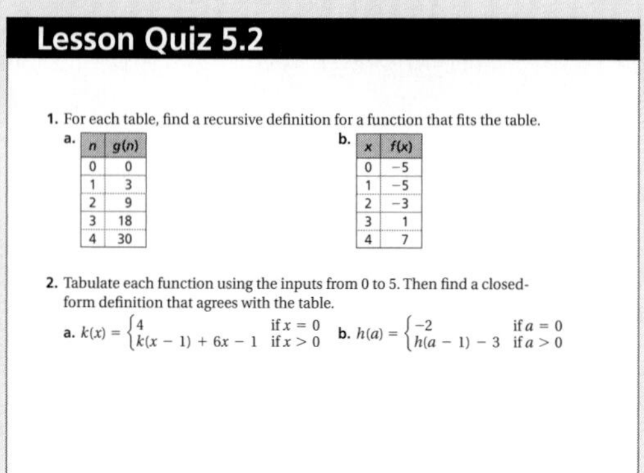
1. For each table, find a recursive definition for a function that fits the table.

a.

n	$g(n)$
0	0
1	3
2	9
3	18
4	30

b.

x	$f(x)$
0	−5
1	−5
2	−3
3	1
4	7

2. Tabulate each function using the inputs from 0 to 5. Then find a closed-form definition that agrees with the table.

a. $k(x) = \begin{cases} 4 & \text{if } x = 0 \\ k(x-1) + 6x - 1 & \text{if } x > 0 \end{cases}$ b. $h(a) = \begin{cases} -2 & \text{if } a = 0 \\ h(a-1) - 3 & \text{if } a > 0 \end{cases}$

One way to find a recursive definition that fits a table is to add a Δ column, containing the differences between successive outputs. For example, the first number in the difference column below is $3 - 1 = 2$.

n	$g(n)$	Δ
0	1	2
1	3	4
2	7	6
3	13	8
4	21	10
5	31	

The differences tell you what to add to go from one output to the next, which is perfect for defining a function recursively.

The difference table tells you that

$$\begin{aligned} g(1) &= g(0) + 2 \\ g(2) &= g(1) + 4 \\ g(3) &= g(2) + 6 \\ g(4) &= g(3) + 8 \\ g(5) &= g(4) + 10 \\ &\vdots \\ g(n) &= g(n-1) + \text{??} \end{aligned}$$

It appears that $g(n) = g(n-1) + 2n$. When you combine this equation with the base case $g(0) = 1$, you obtain a recursive definition for $g(n)$:

$$g(n) = \begin{cases} 1 & \text{if } n = 0 \\ g(n-1) + 2n & \text{if } n > 0 \end{cases}$$

This technique of using the difference column can be very helpful in finding recursive definitions.

Developing Habits of Mind

Make strategic choices. Which should you use: recursive or closed-form definitions? It depends. For some situations, such as the repayment of a loan, a recurvise definition is more natural. On the other hand, recursive definitions can really slow down a calculator or computer. In order to calculate the output at 100, it has to calculate the output at 99, and so on. A computer has to plod through all the unstacking until it gets to a base case. However, you may be able to see a pattern and write a closed-form definition that speeds up the calculation.

Exercises *Practicing Habits of Mind*

Check Your Understanding

For Exercises 1–7 find a recursive definition for a function that fits the table.

1.

n	$B(n)$
0	0
1	2
2	6
3	12
4	20

2.

n	$G(n)$
0	−7
1	−4
2	−1
3	2
4	5

3.

x	$K(x)$
0	1
1	2
2	5
3	10
4	17

4.

n	$\beta(n)$
0	0
1	1
2	3
3	6
4	10

5.

n	$\varepsilon(n)$
0	2
1	3
2	5
3	9
4	17

6.

n	$\kappa(n)$
0	0
1	1
2	4
3	9
4	16

7.

n	$\gamma(n)$
0	0
1	1
2	4
3	10
4	20

Habits of Mind

Represent a function. Model your functions in your FML.

Some of the functions have Greek letters as names. Here is how you say them:

β = beta
γ = gamma
ε = epsilon
κ = kappa

8. Recall the example from this lesson. Given only the rule $g(n) = g(n-1) + 7$ and the information that $g(99) = 496$, can you calculate $g(100.5)$? Explain.

Exercises

HOMEWORK

- Core: 9, 10, 12, 15, 17, 18
- Optional: 11, 13, 14, 16, 19a–b
- Extension: 19c

You can make copies of Blackline Masters MC13 and MC14 for students to use while working on the exercises.

Check Your Understanding

EXERCISE 4 This table contains the sum of the first n positive integers. Students encounter this same function in Exercise 18 of this lesson.

EXERCISE 8 This exercise speaks to the domain of functions defined recursively. If $g(99)$ is known, the recurrence can help find $g(n)$ for any integer, but no more.

Answers

Exercises

1. $B(n) = \begin{cases} 0 & n = 0 \\ B(n-1) + 2n & n > 0 \end{cases}$

2. $G(n) = \begin{cases} -7 & n = 0 \\ G(n-1) + 3 & n > 0 \end{cases}$

3.

$$K(x) = \begin{cases} 1 & x = 0 \\ K(x-1) + 2x - 1 & x > 0 \end{cases}$$

4. $\beta(n) = \begin{cases} 0 & n = 0 \\ \beta(n-1) + n & n > 0 \end{cases}$

5.

$$\varepsilon(n) = \begin{cases} 2 & n = 0 \\ \varepsilon(n-1) + 2^{n-1} & n > 0 \end{cases}$$

6.

$$\kappa(n) = \begin{cases} 0 & n = 0 \\ \kappa(n-1) + 2n - 1 & n > 0 \end{cases}$$

7.

$$\gamma(n) = \begin{cases} 0 & n = 0 \\ \gamma(n-1) + \frac{1}{2}n(n-1) & n > 0 \end{cases}$$

8. No. In the base case, n is an integer. Therefore, $g(n)$ is only defined for integer n.

On Your Own

EXERCISE 9 Students who mistakenly forget to add the previous balance (using 0.03 instead of 1.03) should get a result very close to 500. Ask them whether this is a reasonable result for the account.

EXERCISE 16 If you review this exercise, check for students using a difference table to generate the recursively-defined function.

Students should recognize this as the factorial function $f(n) = n!$. You might point out to students that factorial is not a closed-form function, since its definition

$$n! = 1 \cdot 2 \cdot 3 \cdots n$$

requires an increasing number of steps as n increases.

On Your Own

9. Anna used a \$500 deposit to open a savings account that earns 3% interest per year. Every year Anna deposits another \$500. She makes no withdrawals. Write a recursive function definition for the balance in Anna's savings account after n years. Use the definition to calculate the balance after 5 years.

For Exercises 10–13, tabulate the function using inputs from 0 to 5. Then find a closed-form definition that agrees with the table.

10. $h(a) = \begin{cases} 3 & \text{if } a = 0 \\ h(a-1) + 8 & \text{if } a > 0 \end{cases}$

11. $f(m) = \begin{cases} 0 & \text{if } m = 0 \\ f(m-1) + 2m & \text{if } m > 0 \end{cases}$

12. $c(m) = \begin{cases} 3 & \text{if } m = 0 \\ c(m-1) + m & \text{if } m > 0 \end{cases}$

13. $j(t) = \begin{cases} -1 & \text{if } t = 0 \\ j(t-1) + 2t & \text{if } t > 0 \end{cases}$

For Exercises 14–16, find a recursive definition for a function that fits the table.

14.

n	$T(n)$
0	1
1	3
2	9
3	27
4	81
5	243

15.

x	$Z(x)$
0	3
1	10
2	21
3	36
4	55

For additional practice, go to Web Code: bga-0502

Answers

9.

$$B(n) = \begin{cases} 0 & n = 0 \\ 1.03 \cdot B(n-1) + 500 & n > 0 \end{cases}$$

$B(5) = 2654.57$

10–13. See back of book.

14. $T(n) = \begin{cases} 1 & n = 0 \\ T(n-1) \cdot 3 & n > 0 \end{cases}$

15. $Z(x) = \begin{cases} 0 & x = 0 \\ Z(x-1) + 4x + 3 & x > 0 \end{cases}$

16.

n	$\Gamma(n)$
0	1
1	1
2	2
3	6
4	24
5	120

This letter Γ is capital "gamma."

17. **Standardized Test Prep** Define f as

$$f(n) = \begin{cases} 5 & \text{if } n = 0 \\ f(n-1) - 6 & \text{if } n > 0 \end{cases}$$

What is $f(5)$?

A. -34 **B.** 34 **C.** -25 **D.** 5

Maintain Your Skills

18. Let $S(n)$ be the sum of the first n positive integers, with $S(0) = 0$.
   a. Make a table for $S(n)$ using inputs from 0 to 6.
   b. Find a recursive function definition that fits this table.
   c. Find a closed-form function definition that fits this table.

19. Let $T(n)$ be the sum of the squares of the first n positive integers, with $T(0) = 0$.
   a. Make a table for $T(n)$ using inputs from 0 to 6.
   b. Find a recursive function definition that fits this table.
   c. **Take It Further** Find a closed-form function definition that fits this table.

As a check, $T(5) = 55$.

16. $\Gamma(n) = \begin{cases} 1 & n = 0 \\ n \cdot \Gamma(n-1) & n > 0 \end{cases}$

17. C

18. a.

n	$S(n)$
0	0
1	1
2	3
3	6
4	10
5	15
6	21

b. $S(n) = \begin{cases} 0 & n = 0 \\ S(n-1) + n & n > 0 \end{cases}$

c. $S(n) = \frac{1}{2}n(n+1)$

19. a. See back of book.

b.

$$T(n) = \begin{cases} 0 & n = 0 \\ T(n-1) + n^2 & n > 0 \end{cases}$$

c. $T(n) = \frac{1}{6}n(n+1)(2n+1)$

Maintain Your Skills

EXERCISE 18 This is the same table as Exercise 4 of this lesson, but students are also being asked for a closed form. Many creative methods are possible here, so this is a good exercise to review.

EXERCISE 19 The closed form is difficult to find; most students who do this use difference tables and techniques learned in CME Project *Algebra 2*. By the end of Investigation 5B, students find this closed form using Newton's Difference Formula.

Additional Resources

PRINT RESOURCES
- Solution Manual
- Practice Workbook
- Assessment Resources
- Teaching Resources

TECHNOLOGY
- Interactive Textbook
- TeacherExpress CD-ROM
- ExamView CD-ROM
- PHSchool.com

Additional Practice

For Exercises 1 and 2, find a recursive definition for a function that fits the table.

1.

n	$F(n)$
0	-2
1	1
2	7
3	16
4	28

2.

n	$G(n)$
0	2
1	5
2	9
3	14
4	20

3. Nicholas used \$800 to open a savings account that earns 4% interest per year. Every year Nicholas deposits another \$800. He makes no withdrawals. Write a recursive function definition for the balance in Nicholas's savings account after n years. Use the definition to calculate the balance after 10 years.

For Exercises 4 and 5, tabulate the function using inputs from 0 to 5. Then find a closed-form definition that agrees with the table.

4. $h(a) = \begin{cases} 2 & \text{if } a = 0 \\ h(a-1) + 7 & \text{if } a > 0 \end{cases}$

5. $f(n) = \begin{cases} -1 & \text{if } n = 0 \\ f(n-1) + 3n & \text{if } n > 0 \end{cases}$

6. Jack has a credit card balance of \$2500 and pays \$50 per month.
   a. With an APR of 16% compounded monthly, how much will Jack owe at the end of three years?
   b. The credit card company will allow Jack to make a minimum payment of 3.5% of the balance each month, instead of paying \$50. If Jack makes only the minimum payment, how much will he owe at the end of three years?
   c. Suppose Jack had a credit card with a lower APR of 12% compounded monthly. Repeat part (a) with this new interest rate. Determine how much money Jack would save by using the card with the lower interest rate.

7. Here is a recursive definition with a two-term rule.

$$P(n) = \begin{cases} 1 & \text{if } n = 0 \\ 3 & \text{if } n = 1 \\ P(n-2) + P(n-1) & \text{if } n > 1 \end{cases}$$

   a. Tabulate P for inputs from 0 to 10.
   b. Determine $P(20)$.
   c. Is $P(5.5)$ defined? Why or why not?

Practice: For Lesson 5.2, assign Exercises 1–5.

Lesson Overview

GOALS

- Compare the efficiency of different recursive definitions that generate the same function.
- Analyze multistep recursive definitions of functions.

This lesson looks at recursively-defined functions with multiple steps. You can rewrite some of these functions, such as the interest example given first, as simpler functions requiring fewer calculations. Others you cannot rewrite, such as the Fibonacci numbers. The lesson also discusses the implications of multistep recursion for calculator memory, including the reason why a multistep recursion returns an error more quickly.

CHECK YOUR UNDERSTANDING

- Core: 1, 2, 3, 5
- Optional: 4a–c, 6
- Extension: 4d

MATERIALS

- graphing calculators
- number rods (optional)
- Blackline Master MC13

HOMEWORK

- Core: 7, 8, 10, 13, 14
- Optional: 9a–c, 11, 12a–b
- Extension: 9d, 12c

VOCABULARY

- Fibonacci sequence

Launch

Begin today's lesson by reviewing Exercise 9 from Lesson 5.2, looking to see if students come up with the two functions *A* and *B* from the In-Class Experiment of this lesson.

Explore

In-Class Experiment

PROBLEM 1 The definitions agree at any input. On a calculator, $B(n)$ should find the outputs more quickly since it has fewer terms. See the lesson for more information about how much slower $A(n)$ finds the outputs.

5.3 Multistep Recursive Definitions

Some recursive definitions are simpler and more efficient than others.

In-Class Experiment

Exercise 9 in Lesson 5.2 asked you to find a recursive function definition for the balance in Anna's savings account. Anna deposits \$500 in the account each year. She earns 3% interest on any money already in the account.

Here are two recursive definitions that should generate the same function.

$$A(n) = \begin{cases} 500 & \text{if } n = 0 \\ A(n-1) + 0.03A(n-1) + 500 & \text{if } n > 0 \end{cases}$$

$$B(n) = \begin{cases} 500 & \text{if } n = 0 \\ 1.03B(n-1) + 500 & \text{if } n > 0 \end{cases}$$

1. Enter each definition into a calculator. Use each function to calculate the balance after 1 year, 2 years, 3 years, and 10 years. Do the definitions agree? Which definition finds the outputs more quickly?

How does a calculator or computer find $A(24)$ using the recursive definition of $A(n)$? It scans the definition and notes what should be done. It sees two places where it will need to compute $A(23)$.

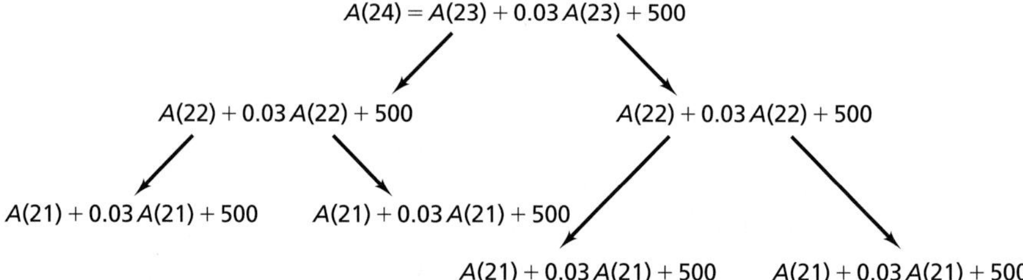

In each of the 2 computations of $A(23)$, the calculator needs to compute $A(22)$ twice, for a total of 4 times. It computes $A(21)$ 8 times, $A(20)$ 16 times, and so on. The total number of calculations required to find $A(24)$ is larger than what the calculator can handle.

The calculator will not notice that the two calculations of $A(23)$ are the same. The definition of $A(n)$ calls $A(n-1)$ twice. Combining like terms gives the $B(n)$ definition, which a calculator can use far more easily. $B(24)$ needs $B(23)$ once, which needs $B(22)$ once, and so on, until the calculator reaches $B(0)$, the base case.

Answers

In-Class Experiment

1. Yes; the definitions agree. $B(n)$ finds the outputs more quickly.

For Discussion

2. Find the first integer $n > 0$ for which $B(n)$ "gives up" (returns an error). What might you do if you really needed to calculate that value of $B(n)$?

While it is sometimes possible to combine terms to simplify a recursive definition, a recursive definition may depend on more than one previous term. One famous example is the **Fibonacci sequence,** in which each term is the sum of the previous two terms:

$$F(n) = \begin{cases} 0 & \text{if } n = 0 \\ 1 & \text{if } n = 1 \\ F(n-1) + F(n-2) & \text{if } n > 1 \end{cases}$$

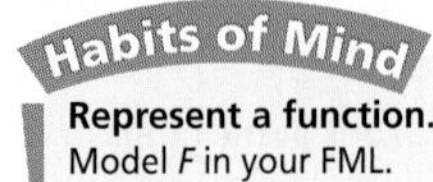

Represent a function. Model F in your FML.

For You to Do

3. Use a model of F to find the value of $F(10)$. Give a value of n where you do not expect the calculator to be able to find $F(n)$.

As you can see, a recursive definition sometimes needs two or more base cases to make the definition work. If a definition referred to $F(n)$ in terms of $F(n-4)$, there would need to be four base cases.

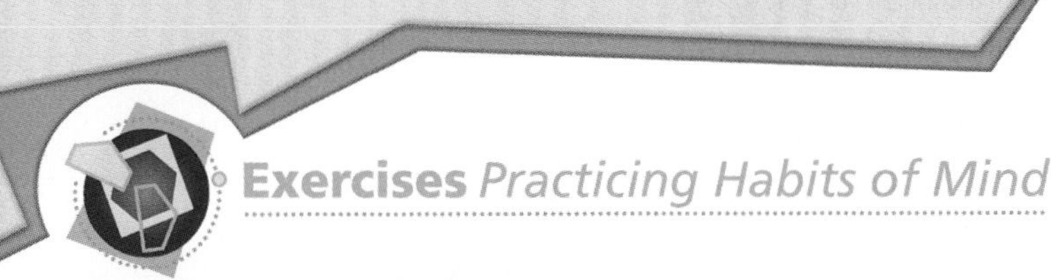

Exercises *Practicing Habits of Mind*

Check Your Understanding

1. Louis is paying down a credit card with a \$2000 balance. The credit card charges 18% annual interest, or 1.5% per month.
   a. Suppose Louis makes a payment of \$50 each month. Explain why this recursive function definition gives the balance on the credit card after n months.

$$B(n) = \begin{cases} 2000 & \text{if } n = 0 \\ B(n-1) - 50 + 0.015B(n-1) & \text{if } n > 0 \end{cases}$$

For Discussion

2. Answers may vary. Sample: $B(n)$ "gives up" on the TI-Nspire at $n = 75$. To figure out how $B(75)$ would be calculated, get to $B(74)$ then run the recursion once manually.

For You to Do

3. $F(10) = 55$

Exercises

1. a. The balance at $n = 0$ is \$2000 (initial balance), and in subsequent months the balance decreases by \$50 (monthly payment) and increases by 1.5% of the previous balance (monthly interest).

For Discussion

PROBLEM 2 Note that this integer is different on different technology. Students should use what they learned in Lesson 5.2 to calculate the function when the technology fails—find the value of the function at the last successful integer and then run the recursion once manually.

For You to Do

PROBLEM 3 Students should find $F(10) = 55$, and $F(n)$ may fail on a calculator shortly thereafter. Remind students that just because the calculator did not give an answer for some $F(n)$ does not mean it does not exist.

Wrap Up

Wrap up by working on or discussing Exercise 3, with a potential discussion leading to why the golden ratio emerges.

Assessment Resources

Lesson Quiz 5.3

1. Dustin is paying down a credit card with a \$4000 balance. The credit card charges 24% annual interest or 2% per month.
   a. Suppose Dustin makes a payment of \$120 each month. Find a recursive function definition that gives the balance on the credit card after n months.
   b. How much will Dustin owe on the card after 24 months?

2. Here is a recursive definition with a two-term rule.

$$F(n) = \begin{cases} 4 & \text{if } n = 0 \\ 6 & \text{if } n = 1 \\ 2F(n-1) - F(n-2) & \text{if } n > 1 \end{cases}$$

   a. Tabulate F for inputs from 0 through 10.
   b. Find $F(40)$.
   c. What is the domain of F?

Exercises

HOMEWORK

- Core: 7, 8, 10, 13, 14
- Optional: 9a–c, 11, 12a–b
- Extension: 9d, 12c

You can make copies of Blackline Master MC13 for students to use while working on the exercises.

Check Your Understanding

EXERCISE 1 Depending on the calculator or computer used, it may not be possible to calculate $B(24)$ without changing the function definition. This exercise is meant to closely follow the lesson's work on Anna's savings account.

EXERCISE 3 If time permits, you might dig into this exercise to find the value of r so that the ratio is constant. This leads to the equation $r^2 - r - 1 = 0$, which, to students' surprise, has two solutions.

This forms the heart of the arguments in Investigation 5C that lead to the closed form for Fibonacci numbers. Students see Fibonacci numbers frequently in this chapter.

EXERCISE 4 Investigation 5C explores the general form of this type of sequence, with any given starting values. Exercise 14 in this lesson provides a taste of the rules that govern such sequences.

EXERCISE 5 Some students may find $P(50)$ by using a calculator or computer, but most use the fact that the terms of $P(x)$ follow a repeating pattern. Point out to students that when $P(6) = P(0)$ and $P(7) = P(1)$, the rest must follow due to the fact that it is a two-term recurrence.

b. Determine the amount of money Louis will owe on this card after 6 months, 12 months, and 24 months.

c. Write a simpler recursive definition for B. Then use it to calculate $B(48)$.

2. The lesson suggests that the number of calculations required to find $A(24)$ is overwhelmingly large. How large, exactly? Remember to count all evaluations of any of $A(0)$ through $A(24)$ in your total.

Find a simpler way to obtain the sum of all of these numbers, rather than just adding them all.

3. Look at the ratios of consecutive Fibonacci numbers:

$$\frac{F(2)}{F(1)} = \frac{1}{1} = 1$$

$$\frac{F(3)}{F(2)} = \frac{2}{1} = 2$$

$$\frac{F(4)}{F(3)} = \frac{3}{2} = 1.5$$

a. For $1 \le n \le 10$, tabulate

$$\frac{F(n+1)}{F(n)}$$

b. Describe the behavior of the ratios. Are they approaching some number? Can you tell what number it might be?

4. The *Lucas numbers* use the same recursive rule as the Fibonacci numbers, but the base cases are $L(0) = 2$ and $L(1) = 1$.

a. Write the recursive definition of $L(n)$.

b. Calculate $L(10)$.

c. What happens to the ratio of consecutive Lucas numbers as n gets larger?

d. **Take It Further** Show that, in general, $L(n) = F(n-1) + F(n+1)$.

5. Here is another recursive definition with a two-term rule.

$$P(n) = \begin{cases} 2 & \text{if } n = 0 \\ 5 & \text{if } n = 1 \\ P(n-1) - P(n-2) & \text{if } n > 1 \end{cases}$$

a. Tabulate P for inputs from 0 to 10.

b. Determine the value of $P(50)$.

c. Is $P(2.5)$ defined? Why or why not?

d. What is the domain of P?

6. Here is an exponential function, the base of which is the golden ratio.

$$g(n) = \frac{1}{\sqrt{5}}\left(\frac{1+\sqrt{5}}{2}\right)^n$$

Make a table for g using inputs 0 to 10. Approximate the outputs to four decimal places.

Answers

1. b. $B(6) = 1875.41$; $B(12) = 1739.18$; $B(24) = 1427.33$

c. $B(n) = \begin{cases} 2000 & n = 0 \\ 1.015 \cdot B(n-1) - 50 & n > 0 \end{cases}$

$B(48) = 608.70$

2. $2^{25} - 1 = 33{,}554{,}431$

3. a. See back of book.

b. The ratios approach $\frac{1+\sqrt{5}}{2} \approx 1.618034$.

4. a. $L(n) = \begin{cases} 2 & n = 0 \\ 1 & n = 1 \\ L(n-1) + L(n-2) & n > 1 \end{cases}$

b. $L(10) = 123$

c. The ratio approaches $\frac{1+\sqrt{5}}{2} \approx 1.618034$, the golden ratio.

d.

$$\begin{aligned} L(n) &= L(n-1) + L(n-2) \\ &= F(2) \cdot L(n-1) + F(1) \cdot L(n-2) \\ &= F(3) \cdot L(n-2) + F(2) \cdot L(n-3) \\ &= F(4) \cdot L(n-3) + F(3) \cdot L(n-4) \\ &\vdots \\ &= F(n) \cdot L(1) + F(n-1) \cdot L(0) \\ &= F(n) + 2F(n-1) \\ &= F(n+1) + F(n-1) \end{aligned}$$

5. a. See back of book.

b. $P(50) = 3$

c. No, because $P(1.5)$ and $P(0.5)$ are not defined.

d. the set of non-negative integers

6.

n	$g(n)$
0	0.4472
1	0.7236
2	1.1708
3	1.8944
4	3.0652
5	4.9597
6	8.0249
7	12.9846
8	21.0095
9	33.9941
10	55.0036

On Your Own

7. Adrian has a credit card balance of \$1500 and pays \$50 per month.
   a. With an APR of 18% compounded monthly, how much will Adrian owe at the end of two years?
   b. The credit card company will allow Adrian to make a minimum payment of 2.5% of the balance each month, instead of paying \$50. If Adrian makes only the minimum payment, how much will he owe at the end of two years?

8. Adrian is considering switching to a credit card with an APR of 9.9% compounded monthly instead of 18%. Repeat Exercise 7 with this new interest rate. Determine how much money Adrian would save by using the card with the lower interest rate.

9. It is possible to count by 1's and 2's to any positive integer in more than one way, unless the integer is 1. For example, you can write 6 in many ways, including

$$6 = 2 + 2 + 2$$
$$6 = 2 + 1 + 1 + 1 + 1$$
$$6 = 1 + 1 + 2 + 1 + 1$$

(Note that you count different orders of the same number of 1's and 2's.)
   a. Show that there are two ways to count to 2.
   b. How many ways are there to count to 3? to 4? to 5? to 6?
   c. Describe a pattern in your results.
   d. **Take It Further** Explain why the pattern emerges and will continue to exist for any larger number.

Remember...

2 + 1 and 1 + 2 are different ways to count to 3.

10. Consider a new function that does a computation with three consecutive Fibonacci numbers. It takes the product of the greatest and least, and subtracts the square of the middle number:

$$s(n) = F(n + 1) \cdot F(n - 1) - (F(n))^2$$

   a. Tabulate this new function s using inputs from 1 to 10.
   b. Find a simpler function definition that agrees with your table.

If $n = 3$, then $F(3) = 2$, $F(2) = 1$, and $F(4) = 3$. So $s(3) = 3 \cdot 1 - 2^2 = -1$.

11. Consider a new function that does a computation with two consecutive Fibonacci numbers. It squares the greater number, subtracts the product of the two numbers, and subtracts the square of the lesser number:

$$t(n) = (F(n + 1))^2 - F(n + 1)F(n) - (F(n))^2$$

   a. Tabulate this new function t using inputs from 1 to 10.
   b. Find a simpler function definition that agrees with your table.

On Your Own

EXERCISE 9 If you have number rods available, this is a perfect exercise for their use. Students can see and justify the Fibonacci pattern much more easily using the rods.

EXERCISE 10 and the one that follows give some interesting rules that govern Fibonacci numbers.

7. a. \$712.58 **b.** \$1178.52

8. a. \$505.91 **b.** \$1000.06

9. a. 2 or 1 + 1

b. 3 ways to count to 3; 5 ways to count to 4; 8 ways to count to 5; 13 ways to count to 6

c. The number of ways to count to n is $F(n + 1)$ where $F(n)$ is the nth Fibonacci Number.

d. If W = ways to count to n, $W(n) = W(n - 1) + W(n - 2)$. Also, $W(1) = 1$ and $W(2) = 2$.

10. a.

n	$s(n)$
1	−1
2	1
3	−1
4	1
5	−1
6	1
7	−1
8	1
9	−1
10	1

b. $s(n) = (-1)^n$

11. a.

n	$t(n)$
1	−1
2	1
3	−1
4	1
5	−1
6	1
7	−1
8	1
9	−1
10	1

b. $t(n) = (-1)^n$

Maintain Your Skills

EXERCISE 14 In this exercise students observe the additive and multiplicative patterns in Fibonacci-like sequences. In part (a), the sequence's starting values are 10 times the starting values for Fibonacci, and so the results are all 10 times larger. In part (b), the sequence's starting values are 7 times the starting values for Fibonacci, adjusted one term. In part (c), the sequence's starting values are the sum of the first two sequences, and so are all the terms. (Ask if anyone notices this.) In part (d), the sequence is the generalization, but students should notice the original Fibonacci sequence in the coefficients of x and y.

Additional Resources

PRINT RESOURCES
- Solution Manual
- Practice Workbook
- Assessment Resources
- Teaching Resources

TECHNOLOGY
- Interactive Textbook
- TeacherExpress CD-ROM
- ExamView CD-ROM
- PHSchool.com

Additional Practice

For Exercises 1 and 2, find a recursive definition for a function that fits the table.

1.

n	$F(n)$
0	−2
1	1
2	7
3	16
4	28

2.

n	$G(n)$
0	2
1	5
2	9
3	14
4	20

3. Nicholas used \$800 to open a savings account that earns 4% interest per year. Every year Nicholas deposits another \$800. He makes no withdrawals. Write a recursive function definition for the balance in Nicholas's savings account after n years. Use the definition to calculate the balance after 10 years.

For Exercises 4 and 5, tabulate the function using inputs from 0 to 5. Then find a closed-form definition that agrees with the table.

4. $h(a) = \begin{cases} 2 & \text{if } a = 0 \\ h(a-1) + 7 & \text{if } a > 0 \end{cases}$

5. $f(n) = \begin{cases} -1 & \text{if } n = 0 \\ f(n-1) + 3n & \text{if } n > 0 \end{cases}$

6. Jack has a credit card balance of \$2500 and pays \$50 per month.
- **a.** With an APR of 16% compounded monthly, how much will Jack owe at the end of three years?
- **b.** The credit card company will allow Jack to make a minimum payment of 3.5% of the balance each month, instead of paying \$50. If Jack makes only the minimum payment, how much will he owe at the end of three years?
- **c.** Suppose Jack had a credit card with a lower APR of 12% compounded monthly. Repeat part (a) with this new interest rate. Determine how much money Jack would save by using the card with the lower interest rate.

7. Here is a recursive definition with a two-term rule.

$$P(n) = \begin{cases} 1 & \text{if } n = 0 \\ 3 & \text{if } n = 1 \\ P(n-2) + P(n-1) & \text{if } n > 1 \end{cases}$$

- **a.** Tabulate P for inputs from 0 to 10.
- **b.** Determine $P(20)$.
- **c.** Is $P(5.5)$ defined? Why or why not?

Practice: For Lesson 5.3, assign Exercises 6–7.

12. A function C satisfies the rule $C(n+2) = -C(n)$
- **a.** If you knew that $C(2) = -1$, could you find $C(n)$ for all nonnegative integers n? Explain.
- **b.** If you knew that $C(2) = -1$ and $C(5) = 0$, could you find $C(n)$ for all nonnegative integers n? Explain.
- **c.** **Take It Further** Regardless of the value of $C(2)$ or $C(5)$, calculate

$$\sum_{k=0}^{15} C(k)$$

Go Online PHSchool.com

For additional practice, go to **Web Code:** bga-0503

13. **Standardized Test Prep** Define C as

$$C(n) = \begin{cases} 1 & \text{if } n = 0 \\ -2 & \text{if } n = 1 \\ C(n-1) + C(n-2) & \text{if } n > 1 \end{cases}$$

What is $C(5)$?

A. −9 **B.** −4 **C.** 0 **D.** −7

Maintain Your Skills

14. Each of these functions has the same recursive rule as the Fibonacci numbers, but they are all different functions. Tabulate each function using inputs from 0 to 7.

a. $A(n) = \begin{cases} 0 & \text{if } n = 0 \\ 10 & \text{if } n = 1 \\ A(n-1) + A(n-2) & \text{if } n > 1 \end{cases}$

b. $B(n) = \begin{cases} 7 & \text{if } n = 0 \\ 7 & \text{if } n = 1 \\ B(n-1) + B(n-2) & \text{if } n > 1 \end{cases}$

c. $C(n) = \begin{cases} 7 & \text{if } n = 0 \\ 17 & \text{if } n = 1 \\ C(n-1) + C(n-2) & \text{if } n > 1 \end{cases}$

d. $D(n) = \begin{cases} x & \text{if } n = 0 \\ y & \text{if } n = 1 \\ D(n-1) + D(n-2) & \text{if } n > 1 \end{cases}$

For the last function, each new output will be in terms of x and y.

Answers

12. a. No; knowing a value of $C(2)$ allows you to find the value of $C(n)$ for even integers only.

b. Yes; knowing a value of $C(n)$ for one even and one odd integer will allow you to find $C(n)$ for all integers.

c. 0

13. D

14. a.

n	$A(n)$
0	0
1	10
2	10
3	20
4	30
5	50
6	80
7	130

5.4 Mathematical Induction

Here is the table from the start of Lesson 5.1.

Input	Output
0	3
1	8
2	13
3	18
4	23

You have seen two ways to define a function that could match the entries in such a table.

Closed-form definitions allow you to calculate an output directly from an input.

Recursive definitions allow you to calculate the output from some previous output.

These two functions both fit the table above, but have different definitions.

Closed form: $A(n) = 5n + 3$

Recursive:

$$B(n) = \begin{cases} 3 & \text{if } n = 0 \\ B(n-1) + 5 & \text{if } n > 0 \end{cases}$$

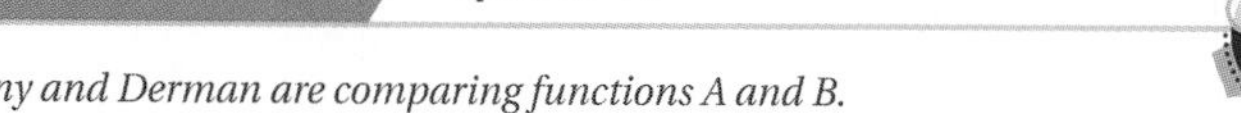

Minds in Action — episode 14

Tony and Derman are comparing functions A and B.

Tony So, I entered A and B in my calculator. They have the same table for a long time.

Derman What, forever?

Tony I'm not sure. I'll try some bigger numbers. Hey, B stopped working.

Derman Uh oh. When did that happen?

Tony I can narrow it down. $B(100)$ didn't work, but $B(30)$ did. Okay, $B(55)$ worked but $B(56)$ won't.

Derman So the functions only agree up to 55? That seems weird.

Tony I don't think the calculator's right. I'll bet if we used a different calculator or computer, we'd get different results.

Lesson Overview

GOALS

- Verify that a closed-form and a recursive function definition agree at the first few inputs in a domain.
- Prove by induction that two function definitions agree for all inputs in an infinite domain.

In this lesson, students see a proof by mathematical induction for the first time. The dialog is the core of the lesson and forms an argument based on comparing a closed-form function definition and a recursive function definition that agree until the recursively-defined function fails on a calculator. However, you can still use the recursive definition to go one more step.

If you imagine that the calculator stops working at some other point, you can carry out the proof again with a different number. This generalization suggests the use of a variable to show that if the functions are equal at $n - 1$, they must also be equal at n. This result, along with verification of the base cases, forms a proof by induction.

This lesson gives students some concrete practice with the concept before asking them to do more abstract proofs. The concept stays the same, however; if students can prove the induction step for $n = 100$ or $n = 1000$, they should be able to do it in general with a variable.

If you cover this lesson in two days, assign the Core exercises on the first day and the Optional exercises on the second day.

CHECK YOUR UNDERSTANDING
- Core: 1, 3, 5, 7
- Optional: 2, 4, 6
- Extension: 8

MATERIALS
- CAS (recommended)
- graphing calculators
- Blackline Master MC13

HOMEWORK
- Core: 9, 10, 13, 16, 17
- Optional: 11, 12, 14, 18
- Extension: 15

VOCABULARY
- mathematical induction

Launch

Have students read the dialog that begins on the first page of the lesson. Students should already be familiar with these two functions from the Getting Started lesson. Stop when Tony begins to argue that $B(56) = A(56)$ and see if a student comes up with the same line of reasoning.

b.

n	$B(n)$
0	7
1	7
2	14
3	21
4	35
5	56
6	91
7	147

c.

n	$C(n)$
0	7
1	17
2	24
3	41
4	65
5	106
6	171
7	277

d.

n	$D(n)$
0	x
1	y
2	$x+y$
3	$x+2y$
4	$2x+3y$
5	$3x+5y$
6	$5x+8y$
7	$8x+13y$

Explore

For You to Do

PROBLEM 1 The argument should be identical, except all numbers are one greater.

Derman All right, maybe we can convince ourselves B will still work after it breaks on the calculator. What do we know about $B(56)$?

Tony It's five more than $B(55)$. That's what the definition says.

Derman That means it's five more than $A(55)$, since $A(55)$ and $B(55)$ were equal. The calculator said so.

Tony So now I just have to show that 5 more than $A(55)$ is $A(56)$. I think I'll need to write this down.

$$\begin{aligned} B(56) &= B(55) + 5 && \textit{(this is how B is defined)} \\ &= A(55) + 5 && \textit{(B(55) = A(55)—calculator said so)} \\ &= (5 \cdot 55 + 3) + 5 && \textit{(this is how A is defined)} \\ &= (5 \cdot 55 + 5) + 3 && \textit{(basic rules of arithmetic)} \\ &= (5 \cdot 56) + 3 && \textit{(basic rules of arithmetic)} \end{aligned}$$

Derman Hey, I think you got it. That last thing is $A(56)$.

Tony So let's see, what did we do? If we're sure that $A(55)$ and $B(55)$ are equal, then $A(56)$ and $B(56)$ have to be equal.

Derman And $A(55)$ equals $B(55)$, because the calculator said so. What about $A(57)$ and $B(57)$?

For You to Do

1. Explain how Derman and Tony could show that $A(57) = B(57)$.

Tony I'm pretty sure there's nothing special about 55 or 56 here. If you believe me that A and B agree up to any number, I can show you that they'll agree at the next number.

Derman Okay, my favorite number is 123.

Tony Of course it is. All right, say I had a calculator that would tabulate both functions up to 123 and they agreed. But it ran out of memory at 124. I could say $A(123) = B(123)$, a fact you can check on your calculator. Then I'll show you that $A(124) = B(124)$, like this:

$$\begin{aligned} B(124) &= B(123) + 5 \\ &= A(123) + 5 \\ &= (5 \cdot 123 + 3) + 5 \\ &= (5 \cdot 123 + 5) + 3 \\ &= 5 \cdot 124 + 3 \\ &= A(124) \end{aligned}$$

Derman Seems like you could do this with any number, or even a variable. Then you could prove it always works.

Tony As long as you have some starting point to work from.

Derman Very smooth.

Answers

For You to Do

1. $B(57) = B(56) + 5$.
   Since $B(56) = A(56)$,
   $B(57) = A(56) + 5$.
   $B(57) = 5 \cdot 56 + 3 + 5 =$
   $5 \cdot 57 + 3 = A(57)$

For You to Do

2. Fill in reasons for each of the steps in Tony's calculation.
3. Repeat the argument using $A(n-1) = B(n-1)$ as a starting point and show that if $A(n-1) = B(n-1)$, then $A(n) = B(n)$.

Tony's method works for other functions. Consider this table.

n	$H(n)$
0	0
1	2
2	6
3	12
4	20

Here are two function definitions that fit the table, one closed-form and one recursive.

$$H(n) = n^2 + n$$

$$h(n) = \begin{cases} 0 & \text{if } n = 0 \\ h(n-1) + 2n & \text{if } n > 0 \end{cases}$$

When entering these functions into a calculator, use different letters instead of uppercase and lowercase.

Example

Problem Suppose you know that $H(100) = h(100)$. Prove that $H(101) = h(101)$.

Solution Write $h(101)$ in terms of $h(100)$, then expand using the fact that $h(100) = H(100)$. Expand $H(101)$ as well, to show that it and $h(101)$ are equal.

$$\begin{aligned} h(101) &= h(100) + 2(101) \\ &= H(100) + 2(101) \\ &= (100^2 + 100) + 2(100 + 1) \\ &= 100^2 + 100 + 2 \cdot 100 + 2 \\ &= 100^2 + 3 \cdot 100 + 2 \end{aligned}$$

$$\begin{aligned} H(101) &= 101^2 + 101 \\ &= (100 + 1)^2 + (100 + 1) \\ &= (100^2 + 2 \cdot 100 + 1) + (100 + 1) \\ &= 100^2 + 3 \cdot 100 + 2 \end{aligned}$$

$h(101)$ and $H(101)$ equal the same expression, so they must be equal.

For You to Do

PROBLEM 2 The steps should be similar to the proof for $A(56) = B(56)$.

PROBLEM 3 The same argument from Problem 2 applies. Point out to students that the use of $(n - 1)$ may make some numerical cleanup easier.

For You to Do

2. $B(124) = B(123) + 5$ (definition of B)
   $= A(123) + 5$ ($B(123) = A(123)$ verified by calculator)
   $= (5 \times 123 + 3) + 5$ (definition of A)
   $= (5 \times 123 + 5) + 3$ (associative property)
   $= 5 \times 124 + 3$ (arithmetic)
   $= A(124)$ (definition of A)
3. $B(n) = B(n-1) + 5$ (definition of B)
   $= A(n-1) + 5$ ($B(n-1) = A(n-1)$ given)
   $= (5(n-1) + 3) + 5$ (definition of A)
   $= (5n - 5 + 5) + 3$ (arithmetic)
   $= 5n + 3$ (arithmetic)
   $= A(n)$ (definition of A)

For You to Do

4. Repeat the process in the Example to show that if $h(n-1) = H(n-1)$, then $h(n) = H(n)$.

The statement "If $h(n-1) = H(n-1)$, then $h(n) = H(n)$" says that if these two functions agree at one integer, then they agree at the next one.

In the Example, the two functions are equal up to 100, so they are equal at 101, and that makes them equal at 102, and that makes them equal at 103, and so on. They are always equal for any nonnegative integer input.

This method of proof is called **mathematical induction.** You use it to show that a fact is true for some set of integers (typically positive or nonnegative ones). A proof by mathematical induction involves two parts:

Step 1 Show that the fact is true for the first few cases (often using tabulation by hand or by computer).

Step 2 Show that if the fact is true up to some integer $(n-1)$, it must also be true for n.

This course primarily uses mathematical induction to show that a closed-form definition and a recursive definition agree for all nonnegative integers. However, you can also use induction to prove facts about summations, to prove identities and inequalities, and even to prove theorems in geometry. Induction is a key element in many proofs, such as those for the Binomial Theorem and for the *Four-Color Theorem.*

See the next lesson for some other examples of inductive proofs. See page 366 for a statement of the Four-Color Theorem.

Exercises *Practicing Habits of Mind*

Check Your Understanding

For Exercises 1–4,

- Tabulate the function for integer inputs from 0 to 5.
- Find an alternative function definition that fits the table—for example, a recursive definition for Exercise 1 and a closed-form definition for Exercise 2.
- Suppose you have checked that your two functions agree up to 1000. Explain why they will agree at 1001.

For You to Do

PROBLEM 4 There are fewer steps, since expansion of $H(n)$ is not required; expansion of $H(n-1)$ is used.

Wrap Up

Discuss how to prove that the two functions generated from one of Exercises 1–4 agree, using induction with a variable.

Assessment Resources

Lesson Quiz 5.4

1. a. Tabulate the following function for integer inputs from 0 to 5.

$$k(n) = \begin{cases} 6 & \text{if } n = 0 \\ k(n-1) + 8 & \text{if } n > 0 \end{cases}$$

b. Find a closed-form function definition that fits the table.

c. Suppose you have checked that the functions agree up to 100. Explain why they will agree at 101.

2. Tabulate the two given functions for integer inputs from 0 to 5 to make sure they agree. If they do, use mathematical induction to show they will agree at any nonnegative integer.

$g(x) = x(2x + 1)$ $\quad$ $G(x) = \begin{cases} 0 & \text{if } x = 0 \\ G(x-1) + 4x - 1 & \text{if } x > 0 \end{cases}$

Exercises

HOMEWORK

- Core: 9, 10, 13, 16, 17
- Optional: 11, 12, 14, 18
- Extension: 15

Answers

For You to Do

4.
$$\begin{aligned} h(n) &= h(n-1) + 2n \\ &= H(n-1) + 2n \\ &= (n-1)^2 + (n-1) + 2n \\ &= n^2 - 2n + 1 + n - 1 + 2n \\ &= n^2 + n \\ &= H(n) \end{aligned}$$

Exercises

1.

a	M(a)
0	5
1	8
2	11
3	14
4	17
5	20

$$m(a) = \begin{cases} 5 & a = 0 \\ m(a-1) + 3 & a > 0 \end{cases}$$

$$\begin{aligned} m(1001) &= m(1000) + 3 \\ &= M(1000) + 3 \\ &= (3 \cdot 1000 + 5) + 3 \\ &= (3 \cdot 1000 + 3) + 5 \\ &= 3 \cdot 1001 + 5 \\ &= M(1001) \end{aligned}$$

2–4. See back of book.

5.

a	J(a)	j(a)
0	−7	−7
1	3	3
2	13	13
3	23	23

$$\begin{aligned} J(n+1) &= 10 \cdot (n+1) - 7 \\ &= 10n + 10 - 7 \\ &= 10n - 7 + 10 \\ &= J(n) + 10 \\ &= j(n) + 10 \\ &= j(n+1) \end{aligned}$$

1. $M(a) = 3a + 5$

2. $k(n) = \begin{cases} 3 & \text{if } n = 0 \\ k(n-1) + 7 & \text{if } n > 0 \end{cases}$

3. $j(n) = \begin{cases} 0 & \text{if } n = 0 \\ j(n-1) + (2n-1) & \text{if } n > 0 \end{cases}$

4. $f(x) = 2^x$

Exercises 5 through 8 each give two function definitions. Tabulate the functions to make sure they agree at the first few inputs. If they do, use mathematical induction to show they will agree at any nonnegative integer.

On your FML, use two different letters for the functions rather than an uppercase and lowercase letter.

5. $J(a) = 10a - 7$

$j(a) = \begin{cases} -7 & \text{if } a = 0 \\ j(a-1) + 10 & \text{if } a > 0 \end{cases}$

6. $F(x) = x^2$

$f(x) = \begin{cases} 0 & \text{if } x = 0 \\ f(x-1) + 2x - 1 & \text{if } x > 0 \end{cases}$

7. $G(n) = 4^n$

$g(n) = \begin{cases} 4 & \text{if } n = 0 \\ 4 \cdot g(n-1) & \text{if } n > 0 \end{cases}$

8. Take It Further

$S(x) = \frac{x(x+1)(2x+1)}{6}$

$s(x) = \begin{cases} 0 & \text{if } x = 0 \\ s(x-1) + x^2 & \text{if } x > 0 \end{cases}$

On Your Own

For Exercises 9–11,

- Tabulate the function for integer inputs from 0 to 5.
- Find an alternative function definition that fits the table—for example, a closed-form definition for Exercise 9.
- Suppose the two definitions agree up to 55. Explain why they will agree at 56.

9. $C(n) = \begin{cases} 4 & \text{if } n = 0 \\ C(n-1) + 7 & \text{if } n > 0 \end{cases}$

10. $D(n) = (n-1)^2$

You can make copies of Blackline Master MC13 for students to use while working on the exercises.

BACKGROUND FOR TEACHER Exercises 1–4 and 9–11 give students practice at constructing inductive proofs. None of these exercises ask students to carry out the general proof, but students get the flavor of the proof by justifying the induction step at a particular value of the input.

You might consider taking one of these exercises and demonstrating how to transition from the numeric induction step to the general version.

GOING FURTHER Exercises 5–8 and 12–15 ask students to prove by induction that the two function definitions agree. In some cases, they do not agree: you might ask students to "fix" one of the definitions and then restart the process.

ERROR PREVENTION If students are stuck on a proof, ask them to follow the process from the previous exercises using a numeric value. This process should lead them through the steps they need for the full proof.

Check Your Understanding

EXERCISE 8 Note that this is the function for the sum of squares that students find in Exercise 19 of Lesson 5.2. Students may want to use a CAS to deal with the algebra here, although clever students can get through faster if they do *not* expand the cubic numerator completely.

Investigation 5B covers this formula in more depth, including using a 3-dimensional model for the sum of squares.

8.

x	S(x)	s(x)
0	0	0
1	1	1
2	5	5
3	14	14

$$\begin{aligned} S(n+1) &= \frac{(n+1)(n+2)(2n+3)}{6} \\ &= \frac{1}{6}(n+1)(2n^2+7n+6) \\ &= \frac{1}{6}(n+1)[n(2n+1)+6n+6] \\ &= \frac{1}{6}n(n+1)(2n+1) + \frac{1}{6}(n+1)\cdot 6(n+1) \\ &= S(n) + (n+1)\cdot(n+1) \\ &= s(n) + (n+1)^2 \\ &= s(n+1) \end{aligned}$$

9–10. See back of book.

6.

x	F(x)	f(x)
0	0	0
1	1	1
2	4	4
3	9	9

$$\begin{aligned} f(n+1) &= f(n) + 2(n+1) - 1 \\ &= F(n) + 2n + 2 - 1 \\ &= n^2 + 2n + 1 \\ &= (n+1)^2 \\ &= F(n+1) \end{aligned}$$

7.

n	G(n)	g(n)
0	1	4
1	4	16
2	16	64
3	64	256

$G(n) \neq g(n)$

On Your Own

EXERCISE 15 This is the formula for the sum of cubes; remarkably, it is the square of the formula for the sum of integers. This formula is discussed further in Investigation 5B.

EXERCISE 16 Basically you are looking for students to explain the *domino theory* of induction. You could talk about this exercise as a lead-in to the next lesson.

Maintain Your Skills

EXERCISE 18 Students are asked to factor here, since they will then recognize the pattern. These polynomials play a large role in Investigation 5B, so this exercise is just a preview for now.

Additional Resources

PRINT RESOURCES
- Solution Manual
- Practice Workbook
- Assessment Resources
- Teaching Resources

TECHNOLOGY
- Interactive Textbook
- TeacherExpress CD-ROM
- ExamView CD-ROM
- PHSchool.com

Additional Practice

For Exercises 1 and 2:

a. Tabulate the functions for integer inputs 0 to 5.

b. Find a closed-form definition for Exercise 1 and a recursive definition for Exercise 2.

c. Suppose you have checked that your two functions agree up to 99. Explain why they will agree at 100.

1. $k(n) = \begin{cases} 4 & \text{if } n = 0 \\ k(n-1) + 8 & \text{if } n > 0 \end{cases}$

2. $M(a) = 4a - 2$

For Exercises 3–6, tabulate both functions to make sure they agree at the first few inputs. If they do, use mathematical induction to show they will always agree at any nonnegative integer.

3. $F(n) = 6n - 3$

$f(n) = \begin{cases} -3 & \text{if } n = 0 \\ f(n-1) + 6 & \text{if } n > 0 \end{cases}$

4. $G(x) = x^3$

$g(x) = \begin{cases} 0 & \text{if } x = 0 \\ g(x-1) + 3x - 2 & \text{if } x > 0 \end{cases}$

5. $K(x) = x(x + 2)$

$k(x) = \begin{cases} 0 & \text{if } x = 0 \\ k(x-1) + 2x + 1 & \text{if } x > 0 \end{cases}$

6. $P(n) = 3^n - 1$

$p(n) = \begin{cases} 0 & \text{if } n = 0 \\ 3p(n-1) + 2 & \text{if } n > 0 \end{cases}$

In Exercises 7–10, find (a) a closed-form function definition and (b) a recursive function definition. (c) Then use mathematical induction to show that your two functions must agree for all nonnegative integers.

7.

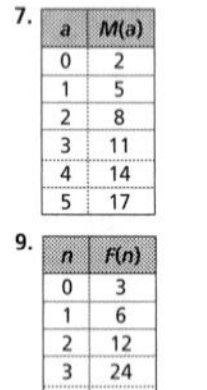

a	M(a)
0	2
1	5
2	8
3	11
4	14
5	17

8.

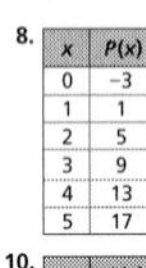

x	P(x)
0	-3
1	1
2	5
3	9
4	13
5	17

9.

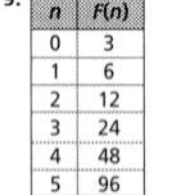

n	F(n)
0	3
1	6
2	12
3	24
4	48
5	96

10.

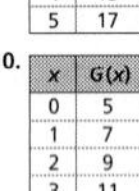

x	G(x)
0	5
1	7
2	9
3	11
4	13
5	15

Practice: For Lesson 5.4, assign Exercises 1–6.

11. $E(n) = \begin{cases} 0 & \text{if } n = 0 \\ E(n-1) + 4n & \text{if } n > 0 \end{cases}$

For Exercises 12–15, tabulate both functions to make sure they agree at the first few inputs. If they do, use mathematical induction to show they will always agree at any nonnegative integer.

12. $Q(a) = 3a + 2$

$q(a) = \begin{cases} 3 & \text{if } a = 0 \\ q(a-1) + 2 & \text{if } a > 0 \end{cases}$

13. $F(x) = x^2 + 3$

$f(x) = \begin{cases} 3 & \text{if } x = 0 \\ f(x-1) + 2x - 1 & \text{if } x > 0 \end{cases}$

14. $Z(n) = 2 \cdot 3^n$

$z(n) = \begin{cases} 2 & \text{if } n = 0 \\ 3 \cdot z(n-1) & \text{if } n > 0 \end{cases}$

15. **Take It Further**

$C(x) = \left(\frac{x(x+1)}{2}\right)^2$

$c(x) = \begin{cases} 0 & \text{if } x = 0 \\ c(x-1) + x^3 & \text{if } x > 0 \end{cases}$

For additional practice, go to **Web Code: bga-0504**

16. **Write About It** How does a proof by mathematical induction establish that two functions agree for all nonnegative integers?

17. **Standardized Test Prep** Define p as

$$p(n) = \begin{cases} 1 & \text{if } n = 0 \\ p(n-1) \cdot n & \text{if } n > 0 \end{cases}$$

Which of the following agrees with p for all nonnegative integers?

A. $P(n) = n^2$

B. $P(n) = \frac{n(n-1)}{2}$

C. $P(n) = 3n - 2$

D. $P(n) = n!$

Maintain Your Skills

18. Calculate each sum as an expression in x. Then factor each result (if possible).

a. $\sum_{k=0}^{x-1} 1$ **b.** $\sum_{k=0}^{x-1} k$ **c.** $\sum_{k=0}^{x-1} \frac{k(k-1)}{2}$ **d.** $\sum_{k=0}^{x-1} \frac{k(k-1)(k-2)}{6}$

Yes, expression (a) is just $1 + 1 + 1 \ldots$ But how many 1's are there?

Answers

11–15. See back of book.

16. Answers may vary. Sample: A proof by mathematical induction must provide one or more base cases as a starting point, and must prove conclusively that the process to go from one step to the next works. If both these conditions are met, the proof is complete since the base case implies the next one, which implies the next one, etc.

17. D

18. a. x

b. $\frac{x(x-1)}{2}$

c. $\frac{x(x-1)(x-2)}{6}$

d. $\frac{x(x-1)(x-2)(x-3)}{24}$

5.5 Ways to Think About Induction

Mathematical induction is a general method for proving a sequence of propositions—including arithmetic formulas, algebraic results, geometric facts, and more. Here is how it works.

Step 1 Set out the list of things you wish to prove.

Step 2 Show directly that the base cases are true.

Step 3 Prove that if the propositions are true for every case up to $(n - 1)$, then the nth proposition must be true.

The conclusion is that all propositions in the sequence must be true.

In your proofs so far, these steps have looked like this:

Step 1 The goal is to prove two functions agree for all integers $n \geq 0$.

Step 2 Use a table to check that the functions agree at the first few inputs, including the base cases.

Step 3 Show that if the two functions agree at $(n - 1)$, then they must agree at n.

The conclusion is that the two functions agree for all nonnegative integers.

Induction is like an infinite line of dominoes, set up so that if one falls, it will hit the next one, which will fall, and so on.

This statement is true:

> If domino $(n - 1)$ falls, it will hit domino n.
> So domino n will fall as well.

But the dominoes do not just fall automatically. To start the process, the first one must fall down. That is the base case.

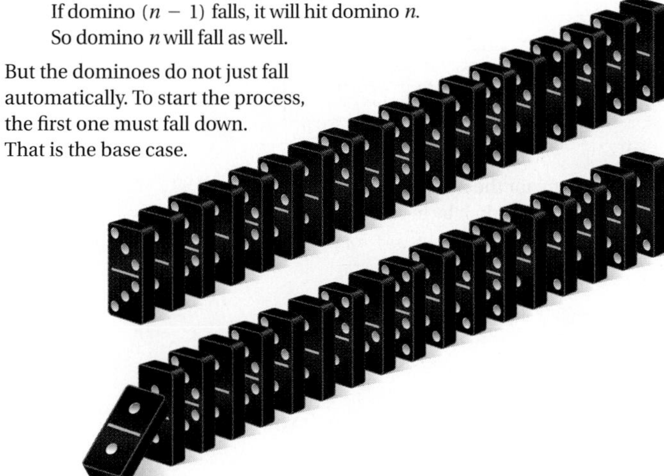

Now, this statement is true:

> If domino $(n - 1)$ falls, it will hit domino n. So domino n will fall as well. Domino 1 has fallen, so all the dominoes will fall.

Lesson Overview

GOAL

- Apply induction to geometric proofs.

This lesson introduces students to some additional situations where inductive reasoning is appropriate and useful, such as the Four-Color Theorem and finding the sum of the measures of the angles in a polygon. This lesson is optional, so if time is a factor, move on to Investigation 5B.

CHECK YOUR UNDERSTANDING

- Core: 2, 3, 4
- Optional: 1, 5

MATERIALS

- graphing calculators
- Blackline Masters MC13, 5.5

HOMEWORK

- Core: 6, 8, 11, 12, 13a–b
- Optional: 7, 9, 10
- Extension: 13c

Launch

Start with a discussion of Exercise 16 from the previous lesson, or dive into the In-Class Experiment.

Explore

In-Class Experiment

For the In-Class Experiment, you may wish to have students work in small groups. The goal is to have students gain experience that will help them understand induction.

You may want to use Blackline Master 5.5 on an overhead and fill it in as students give the answer for each number of vertices.

In-Class Experiment

Here is a geometric example. You can take a polygon and divide it into triangles by drawing diagonals, making sure none of the diagonals intersect each other.

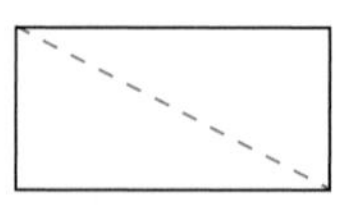
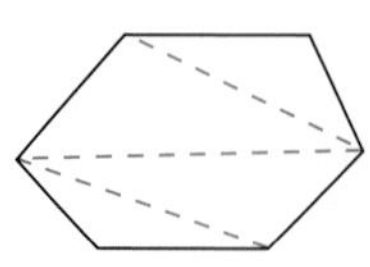
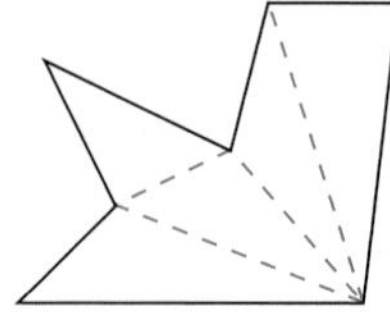

Remember...

A diagonal connects two non-adjacent vertices of the polygon.

1. Copy each polygon without the diagonals, and find a different way to divide it into triangles by drawing diagonals.
2. Did you get a different number of triangles than in the example? Is it possible to get a different number of triangles?
3. Copy and complete this table. You may need to draw a few more shapes to help you fill it in.

Number of Vertices	Number of Triangles You Can Form
3	1
4	■
5	■
6	■
7	■
8	■
9	■

Experiments can lead you to a conjecture for the number of triangles. But how could you prove you are right? You could do it by induction.

Answers

In-Class Experiment

1. Answers may vary. Sample:

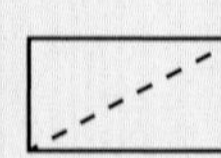
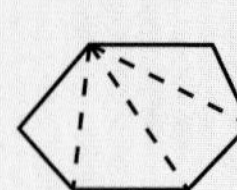

2. No; no

3.

Number of Vertices	Number of Triangles You Can Form
3	1
4	2
5	3
6	4
7	5
8	6
9	7

Example

Problem Prove that for a polygon with n vertices, the number of triangles formed by drawing a set of nonintersecting diagonals is $T(n) = n - 2$.

Solution

- Your base case is $n = 3$. Here the polygon IS a triangle (you cannot draw any diagonals). $T(3) = 3 - 2 = 1$, so your formula works when $n = 3$. For another base case, consider any quadrilateral. You can form $T(4) = 4 - 2 = 2$ triangles by drawing an interior diagonal.
- You assume that your statement holds for polygons having anywhere from 3 to $(n - 1)$ vertices. You must show that this implies that your formula holds for any polygon that has n vertices.

Consider a polygon P with $n > 3$ vertices. Pick two vertices that have an interior diagonal between them. Call these vertices v and v'. Draw the diagonal.

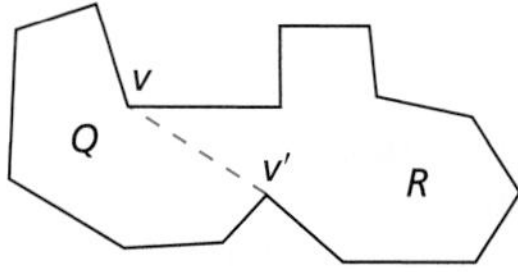

Polygon P has n vertices

This diagonal splits polygon P into two polygons, Q and R, having q and r vertices, respectively. Each of these polygons leaves out at least one vertex of P, and each has at least three vertices. So $3 \le q \le n - 1$ and $3 \le r \le n - 1$.

By assumption, Q divides into $q - 2$ triangles and R then divides into $r - 2$ triangles. Together, they make up polygon P, so

$$T(n) = (q - 2) + (r - 2) = q + r - 4$$

Now, comparing the number of vertices in Q and R to the number of vertices in P gives you

$$q + r = n + 2$$

because the vertices v and v' are counted twice (once in Q and once in R).

If you put the two equations together, you have

$$\begin{aligned} T(n) &= q + r - 4 \\ &= n + 2 - 4 \\ &= n - 2 \end{aligned}$$

This shows that if $T(k) = k - 2$ for $3 \le k \le n - 1$, then $T(n) = n - 2$. This completes your induction proof. You conclude:

$$T(n) = n - 2 \text{ for all integers } n \ge 3$$

Example

A subtlety is missing here: the diagonal in the induction step must lie inside the polygon. You can prove that such a diagonal exists, but that proof is also by induction! If students ask about this issue, you might restrict the proof (for the time being) to convex polygons, where all diagonals lie inside the polygon.

Wrap Up

Wrap up by demonstrating the proof of either Exercise 1 or Exercise 2, then assign the homework.

Assessment Resources

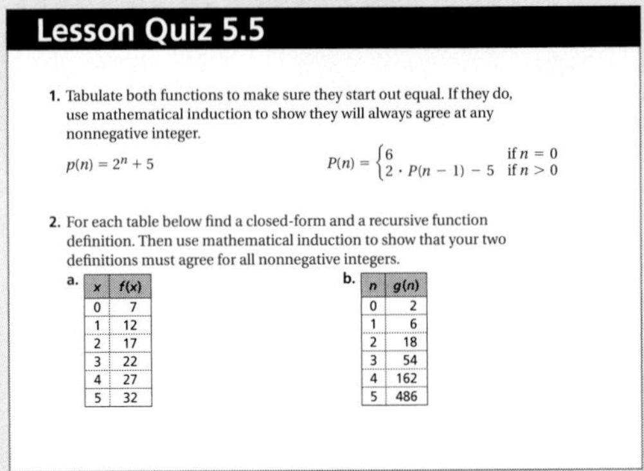

Lesson Quiz 5.5

1. Tabulate both functions to make sure they start out equal. If they do, use mathematical induction to show they will always agree at any nonnegative integer.

$p(n) = 2^n + 5$ $\quad\quad P(n) = \begin{cases} 6 & \text{if } n = 0 \\ 2 \cdot P(n-1) - 5 & \text{if } n > 0 \end{cases}$

2. For each table below find a closed-form and a recursive function definition. Then use mathematical induction to show that your two definitions must agree for all nonnegative integers.

a.

x	$f(x)$
0	7
1	12
2	17
3	22
4	27
5	32

b.

n	$g(n)$
0	2
1	6
2	18
3	54
4	162
5	486

Exercises

HOMEWORK
- Core: 6, 8, 11, 12, 13a–b
- Optional: 7, 9, 10
- Extension: 13c

You can make copies of Blackline Master MC13 for students to use while working on the exercises.

The induction arguments needed to show that recursive and closed-form definitions give functions that agree are usually short and clear. Other induction proofs, however, are long and complex. The proof of the Four-Color Theorem is an example of a complicated induction. This theorem says that if you have a map of countries that are all solid areas, without holes or separated colonies, then four colors suffice to color the map so that no two countries sharing a common border have the same color.

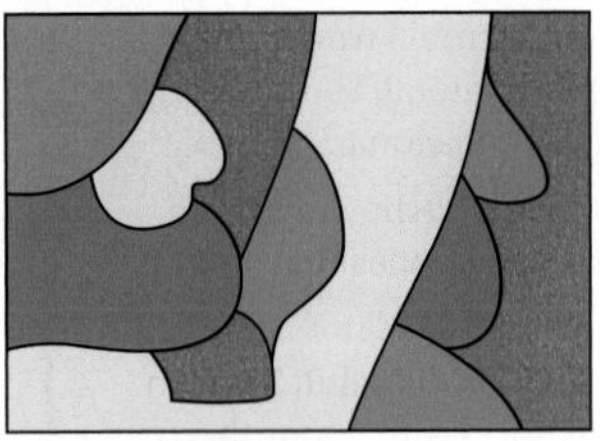

A four-color map

In 1852 Francis Guthrie, a mathematics student in England, conjectured that this was true. In 1890, Percy Heawood showed that no more than five colors are ever necessary, but the Four-Color Theorem remained unproven until 1976. Kenneth Appel and Wolfgang Haken of the University of Illinois established its truth using a computer to check over 1000 base cases. Then they proved the induction claim that if all the base cases were valid, the theorem must be true for all larger maps. As of 2008, the challenge of finding a proof that does not rely on a computer remains open.

If you try to color maps on your own, keep in mind that two regions which just meet at a point can share the same color. But regions with the same color cannot share a boundary that is a segment or curve.

For more problems on mathematical induction, go to **Web Code**: bge-9031

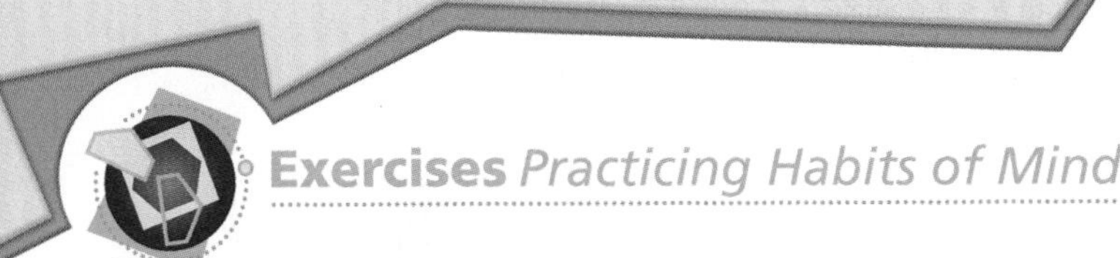

Check Your Understanding

For Exercises 1 and 2, tabulate both functions to make sure they agree at 0. If they do, use mathematical induction to show they will agree at any nonnegative integer.

1. $P(n) = 2^n + 2 \qquad p(n) = \begin{cases} 3 & \text{if } n = 0 \\ 2 \cdot p(n-1) - 2 & \text{if } n > 0 \end{cases}$

2. $H(x) = \dfrac{x(x+1)}{2} \qquad h(x) = \begin{cases} 0 & \text{if } x = 0 \\ h(x-1) + x & \text{if } x > 0 \end{cases}$

Answers

Exercises

1. $P(0) = 3 = p(0)$
$$\begin{aligned} P(n+1) &= 2^{n+1} + 2 \\ &= 2 \cdot 2^n + 2 \\ &= 2 \cdot (2^n + 2) - 4 + 2 \\ &= 2 \cdot P(n) - 2 \\ &= 2 \cdot p(n) - 2 \\ &= p(n+1) \end{aligned}$$

2. $H(0) = 0 = h(0)$
$$\begin{aligned} H(n+1) &= \frac{(n+2)(n+1)}{2} \\ &= \frac{n(n+1)}{2} + \frac{2(n+1)}{2} \\ &= 2 \cdot (2^n + 2) - 4 + 2 \\ &= H(n) + (n+1) \\ &= h(n) + (n+1) \\ &= h(n+1) \end{aligned}$$

3. Since a polygon containing n sides can be divided into $n - 2$ triangles, and the sum of the measures of the 3 angles of each triangle is 180°, the sum of the

3. Write About It Explain how you can use the results from the In-Class Experiment to justify this statement:

   In a polygon with n sides, the sum of the measures of the interior angles is $(n - 2) \cdot 180°$.

4. Theorem 5.1 is the Two-Color Theorem.

Theorem 5.1

Use straight lines extending infinitely in either direction to draw a map that divides the plane into any number of regions. Two colors are enough to color the map so that no two regions with a common border have the same color.

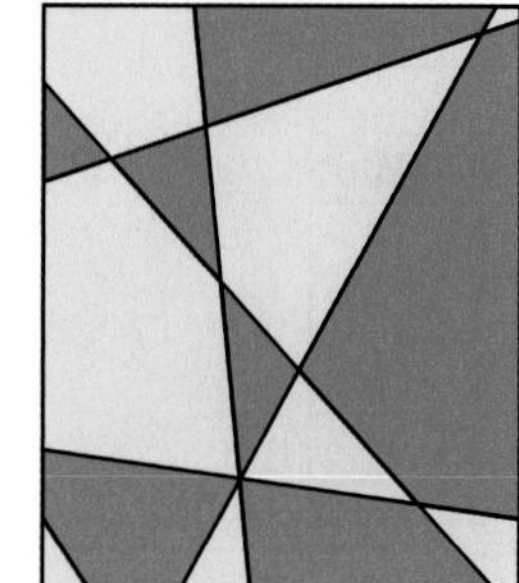

   a. Check a few base cases. Do two colors suffice to color the map if you draw only one line? If you draw two parallel lines? If you draw two intersecting lines? If you draw three lines?

   b. Suppose you know that up to some number $(n - 1)$ of lines, two colors will suffice. Prove that two colors suffice for n lines.

5. What's Wrong Here? Lester says that all sets of n horses are the same color. He offers this "proof":

   Lester: I need a base case, and that's $n = 1$. Obviously, all sets of 1 horse are the same color. Now I'm going to prove that if it's true for $n - 1$, it's true for n. Show me the n horses, and I set one off to the side and look at the rest. They must be the same color, since it's true for $n - 1$. Then I bring in the one I set off to the side and send another one off. Now those $n - 1$ horses are the same color, and of course it has to be the same color as the other set, since the horses that stayed in both times did not change colors. So all n horses are the same color, and by induction this is true for any n.

   What is wrong with this proof? It clearly cannot be sound, can it?

interior angles of a polygon with n sides is $(n - 2) \cdot 180°$.

4. a. In all four cases, the Two-Color Theorem would hold.

b. Suppose you have a coloring for $(n - 1)$ lines. Then add the nth line. On one side of this line, switch the color of everything; on the other side, leave it the same. Now, nothing on either side of the new line has the same color (since you only switched one side). And the coloring you had before means that everything else is still colored properly (since switching all colors from one to the other cannot make a coloring fail). So this gives a proper coloring for n lines, completing the induction step of the proof.

5. The "set one off to the side" argument in the inductive step assumes that the two sets of $n - 1$ horses have one or more horses in common, the horses that "stayed in both times." This assumption is false for $n = 2$, and so the claim that the $n - 1$ case implies the n case remains unproven.

Check Your Understanding

EXERCISE 3 Do not spend too much time on this exercise; most students should readily understand the result based on the triangles.

EXERCISE 4 If students have trouble with the general case, ask them to prove that if the theorem is true for $n = 5$, it is true for $n = 6$.

EXERCISE 5 Students may have difficulty finding the flaw in the argument. This is one reason to look at several base cases before proceeding to the induction step!

On Your Own

EXERCISES 6–11 each take some time, so consider assigning only a few.

Maintain Your Skills

EXERCISE 13 This exercise helps set the stage for Investigation 5B. This property of functions in the form

$$f(n) = \frac{n(n-1)(n-2)\cdots(n-k+1)}{k!}$$

is useful in finding the formulas for the sums of squares, cubes, and so forth.

BACKGROUND FOR TEACHER The sum from $k = 0$ to -1 of any function $g(k)$ equals zero because it has no terms, and the value of a sum with no terms is zero. You can also think of this convention as stemming from the fact that you can find the sum from $k = 0$ to $n - 1$ by subtracting the last term of the sum from $k = 0$ to n. The spirit of the convention is the same as the one that yields $x^0 = 1$ from the fact that $x^{(n-1)}$ is x^n divided by x.

Additional Resources

PRINT RESOURCES
- Solution Manual
- Practice Workbook
- Assessment Resources
- Teaching Resources

TECHNOLOGY
- Interactive Textbook
- TeacherExpress CD-ROM
- ExamView CD-ROM
- PHSchool.com

Additional Practice

For Exercises 1 and 2:

a. Tabulate the functions for integer inputs 0 to 5.
b. Find a closed-form definition for Exercise 1 and a recursive definition for Exercise 2.
c. Suppose you have checked that your two functions agree up to 99. Explain why they will agree at 100.

1. $k(n) = \begin{cases} 4 & \text{if } n = 0 \\ k(n-1) + 8 & \text{if } n > 0 \end{cases}$

2. $M(a) = 4a - 2$

For Exercises 3–6, tabulate both functions to make sure they agree at the first few inputs. If they do, use mathematical induction to show they will always agree at any nonnegative integer.

3. $F(n) = 6n - 3$
   $f(n) = \begin{cases} -3 & \text{if } n = 0 \\ f(n-1) + 6 & \text{if } n > 0 \end{cases}$

4. $G(x) = x^3$
   $g(x) = \begin{cases} 0 & \text{if } x = 0 \\ g(x-1) + 3x - 2 & \text{if } x > 0 \end{cases}$

5. $K(x) = x(x + 2)$
   $k(x) = \begin{cases} 0 & \text{if } x = 0 \\ k(x-1) + 2x + 1 & \text{if } x > 0 \end{cases}$

6. $P(n) = 3^n - 1$
   $p(n) = \begin{cases} 0 & \text{if } n = 0 \\ 3p(n-1) + 2 & \text{if } n > 0 \end{cases}$

In Exercises 7–10, find (a) a closed-form function definition and (b) a recursive function definition. (c) Then use mathematical induction to show that your two functions must agree for all nonnegative integers.

7.
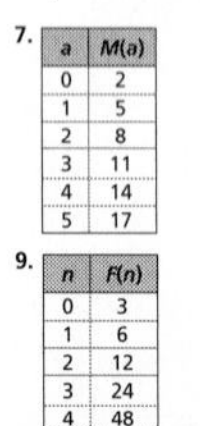

a	M(a)
0	2
1	5
2	8
3	11
4	14
5	17

8.
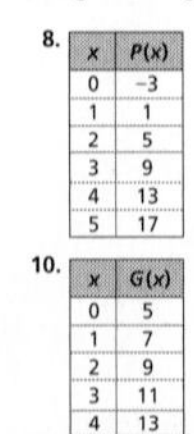

x	P(x)
0	−3
1	1
2	5
3	9
4	13
5	17

9.

n	F(n)
0	3
1	6
2	12
3	24
4	48
5	96

10.

x	G(x)
0	5
1	7
2	9
3	11
4	13
5	15

Practice: For Lesson 5.5, assign Exercises 7–10.

On Your Own

In Exercises 6–11, find a closed-form and a recursive function definition for the table. Then use mathematical induction to show that your two definitions must agree for all nonnegative integers.

6.

n	E(n)
0	2
1	4
2	6
3	8
4	10

7.

n	F(n)
0	1
1	4
2	7
3	10
4	13

8.

x	K(x)
0	1
1	2
2	5
3	10
4	17

For Exercise 6, the closed-form definition might be $E(n) = 2n + 2$. Find a recursive definition. Then use induction to prove the definitions must continue to agree for larger n.

9.

n	P(n)
0	1
1	3
2	9
3	27
4	81

10.

a	W(a)
0	1
1	$\frac{1}{2}$
2	$\frac{1}{4}$
3	$\frac{1}{8}$
4	$\frac{1}{16}$

11.

t	ε(t)
0	2
1	3
2	5
3	9
4	17

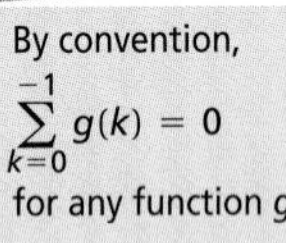

For additional practice, go to **Web Code:** bga-0505

12. **Standardized Test Prep** Which of the following does NOT play a role in inductive proof?
    A. assuming that the statement is true for all counting numbers through $(n - 1)$
    B. verifying that the statement is true for one or more base cases
    C. showing that the statement is true for all numbers between $(n - 1)$ and n
    D. showing that the statement must be true for the counting number n

Maintain Your Skills

13. Show that each of these is true.

a. $\displaystyle\sum_{k=0}^{n-1} k = \frac{n(n-1)}{2}$

b. $\displaystyle\sum_{k=0}^{n-1} \frac{k(k-1)}{2} = \frac{n(n-1)(n-2)}{6}$

c. **Take It Further** $\displaystyle\sum_{k=0}^{n-1} \frac{k(k-1)(k-2)}{6} = \frac{n(n-1)(n-2)(n-3)}{4!}$

By convention, $\displaystyle\sum_{k=0}^{-1} g(k) = 0$ for any function g.

Answers

6. $E(n) = 2n + 2$;

$$e(n) = \begin{cases} 2 & n = 0 \\ e(n-1) + 2 & n > 0 \end{cases}$$

$$\begin{aligned} E(n+1) &= 2(n+1) + 2 \\ &= 2n + 2 + 2 \\ &= E(n) + 2 \\ &= e(n) + 2 \\ &= e(n+1) \end{aligned}$$

7. $F(n) = 3n + 1$;

$$f(n) = \begin{cases} 1 & n = 0 \\ f(n-1) + 3 & n > 0 \end{cases}$$

$$\begin{aligned} F(n+1) &= 3(n+1) + 1 \\ &= 3n + 3 + 1 \\ &= 3n + 1 + 3 \\ &= F(n) + 3 \\ &= f(n) + 3 \\ &= f(n+1) \end{aligned}$$

8–11. See back of book.

12. C

13. See back of book.

In this investigation, you looked at recursive function definitions. You learned how to use induction to prove that two functions, one with a closed-form definition and one with a recursive definition, agree for an infinite number of inputs. The following questions will help you summarize what you have learned.

1. Define f recursively by

$$f(n) = \begin{cases} k & \text{if } n = 0 \\ f(n-1) + \frac{1}{3} & \text{if } n > 0 \end{cases}$$

If $f(20) = -3$, find the value of k.

2. Find a closed-form definition for a function that agrees with f for all integers $n \geq 0$.

$$f(n) = \begin{cases} 0 & \text{if } n = 0 \\ f(n-1) + 4n & \text{if } n > 0 \end{cases}$$

3. Use induction to show these two functions must agree for all integers $a \geq 0$.

$$J(a) = 8a - 5$$

$$j(a) = \begin{cases} -5 & \text{if } a = 0 \\ j(a-1) + 8 & \text{if } a > 0 \end{cases}$$

4. Derman says his calculator "broke" while finding $f(36)$ for this function:

$$f(n) = \begin{cases} 3 & \text{if } n = 0 \\ f(n-1) + 5 - 0.2f(n-1) & \text{if } n > 0 \end{cases}$$

What could Derman do to make it possible to calculate $f(36)$?

5. Find a recursive function definition that agrees with

$$f(n) = n^2 + 10$$

for any integer $n \geq 0$.

6. What are the differences between a closed-form definition and a recursive definition for a function?

7. How can you prove that a closed-form and a recursive function definition agree at each of infinitely many inputs?

8. What happens to the ratio of consecutive Fibonacci numbers?

Vocabulary

In this investigation, you learned these terms. Make sure you understand what each one means and how to use it.

- **base case**
- **closed-form definition**
- **Fibonacci sequence**
- **mathematical induction**
- **recursive definition**

Mathematical Reflections

EXERCISES 6–8 At the start of the investigation, you may have assigned these as Questions 1–3 for students to think and write about.

EXERCISE 8 Students may recognize this as the pattern from the Chapter Opener.

Mathematical Reflections

1. $-\frac{29}{3}$

2. $F(n) = 2n(n + 1)$

3. $J(0) = -5 = j(a)$

$$\begin{aligned} J(n+1) &= 8(n+1) - 5 \\ &= 8n + 8 - 5 \\ &= 8n - 5 + 8 \\ &= J(n) + 8 \\ &= j(n) + 8 \\ &= j(n+1) \end{aligned}$$

4–5. See back of book.

6.
- A closed-form definition typically has the domain of all real numbers, whereas a recursive definition has a domain of non-negative integers.
- A closed-form definition allows you to evaluate $f(n)$ directly, whereas a recursive definition requires the calculation of $f(n-1)$ in order to determine $f(n)$.

7–8. See back of book.

Investigation Overview

Newton's Difference Formula is a classical topic that connects difference tables, recursive rules, and Pascal's Triangle. Students have used difference tables since CME Project *Algebra 1*. Students learned about Pascal's Triangle in Chapter 7 of CME Project *Algebra 2* and Chapter 4 of this course.

This material ties it together. You can use the top row of a difference table, along with functions built from Pascal's Triangle, to directly find a closed-form rule that fits a table. Newton's Difference Formula benefits from the use of CAS technology, as expressions such as

$$1 + 3\binom{x}{1} - 6\binom{x}{2} + 12\binom{x}{3}$$

are tedious to simplify.

Students probably already know coming in that, for example, if second differences are constant, a quadratic fits the table, and its leading coefficient is half the constant difference. Newton's Difference Formula is a stronger version; it gives *all* the coefficients. And the explanation of why the formula works is based on the up-and-over rule students use in difference tables and Pascal's Triangle.

You may wish to assign Questions 1–3 for students to think and write about during the investigation.

Learning Goals

- Find a polynomial function that fits a difference table.
- Explain how the up-and-over-rule of difference tables relates to Pascal's Triangle.
- Quickly find rules for summations, like the sum of the first n squares.

Habits and Skills

- Connect the properties of Pascal's Triangle with properties of difference tables.
- Construct and verify functions that fit tables.
- Work with polynomials in normal and factored form.
- Work with summations.

Fitting Functions to Tables

In *Fitting Functions to Tables*, you will use a difference table to study a function. You will use numbers from the difference table and numbers from Pascal's Triangle to find a polynomial that fits a function table. You will use this method to find polynomials that describe sums of powers.

By the end of this investigation, you will be able to answer questions like these.

1. If the third differences in the table of a polynomial function are all 24, what can you say about that function?
2. What are the Mahler polynomials?
3. How can you use differences to find a polynomial function that fits a table?

You will learn how to

- find a polynomial function that fits a difference table
- explain how the up-and-over rule of difference tables relates to Pascal's Triangle
- quickly find rules for summations, like the sum of the first n squares

You will develop these habits and skills:

- Connect the properties of Pascal's Triangle with properties of difference tables.
- Construct and verify functions that fit tables.
- Work with polynomials in normal and factored form.
- Work with summations.

Charles Babbage (1791–1871) designed this difference engine, a mechanical device for using difference tables to calculate the outputs of polynomial functions.

Investigation Road Map

LESSON 5.6, *Getting Started,* explores methods of finding functions that fit tables and includes the construction of difference tables with multiple steps.

LESSON 5.7, *Properties of Difference Tables,* has students experiment with relationships in difference tables that are based on Pascal's Triangle.

LESSON 5.8, *The Pascal Connection,* formalizes the connections learned in Lessons 5.6 and 5.7. Students learn to extend a difference table.

LESSON 5.9, *Newton's Difference Formula,* presents Newton's Difference Formula and how to write a polynomial that fits a difference table.

LESSON 5.10, *Sums of Powers,* applies Newton's Difference Formula to summation situations, and shows that in the Mahler polynomial basis, a summation is just a shift.

5.6 Getting Started

In CME Project *Algebra 2*, you studied methods for fitting a function to a table. This investigation describes a method for fitting polynomials to tables where the inputs are the nonnegative integers. This method, known as Newton's Difference Formula, is more specific than some of the methods in *Algebra 2* (such as Lagrange Interpolation), but it has many theoretical applications and is closely connected to Pascal's Triangle.

For You to Explore

1. Find two different ways to fit a function to this table.

Input	Output
0	15
1	0
2	−9
3	−12
4	−9
5	0
6	15
7	36

2. **Write About It** Describe what you would do to find a polynomial function N, that fits this table.

x	$N(x)$
0	1
1	−1
2	11
3	49
4	125
5	251
6	439
7	701

3. Suppose you know that E is a quadratic function with an input-output table that starts like this.

x	$E(x)$	Δ
0	3	6
1	9	10
2	19	■
3	33	■
4	■	■
5	■	■
6	■	■
7	■	■
8	■	

Without finding the formula for $E(x)$, find the value of $E(8)$.

4. Here is a table for a function f, with a lot of information missing.

n	$f(x)$	Δ	Δ^2	Δ^3
0	0	1	6	6
1	■	■	■	6
2	8	■	■	6
3	■	■	■	6
4	■	■	■	6
5	■	■	■	6
6	■	■	■	
7	■	■		
8	■			

Find the value of $f(8)$.

Remember...

The Δ column contains the differences of consecutive outputs. The first two entries are filled in: $6 = 9 - 3$ and $10 = 19 - 9$.

The Δ^2 column contains the differences of the numbers in the Δ column, not the squares of those numbers.

Answers

1. Answers may vary. Samples:
   - Construct difference tables and then observe patterns in the Δ column.
   - Graph the function and observe the shape of the curve, x- and y-intercepts, etc.
   - Develop and solve a system of equations from the data given.
2. Answers may vary. Samples:
   - Construct difference tables and then observe patterns in the Δ column.
   - Graph the function and observe the shape of the curve, x- and y-intercepts, etc.
   - Develop and solve a system of equations from the data given.
3. $E(8) = 163$
4. $f(8) = 512$

Lesson Overview

GOAL

- Warm up to the ideas of the investigation.

As always in a Getting Started lesson, there is no need to formalize these ideas today. Students meet all of the ideas again throughout the investigation. The exercises in this short Getting Started focus on difference tables, especially the means to continue a difference table or directly calculate an output without finding the fitting function.

FOR YOU TO EXPLORE
- Core: 1, 2, 3
- Optional: 4

MATERIALS
- graphing calculators
- Blackline Masters MC13–14, 5.6A–B

HOMEWORK
- Core: 5, 6, 9
- Optional: 7, 8, 10, 11

Launch

Have students start on the problems right away.

Explore

For You to Explore

PROBLEM 1 Discuss this problem immediately after the students complete the For You to Explore section, looking especially for any methods that use differences. One goal here is to establish the connection between differences and the degree of a polynomial that fits a table.

PROBLEMS 3 AND 4 You may want to use Blackline Master 5.6A on an overhead and fill in the entries as students supply them, or you can hand out printed copies for students to do their own work on.

PROBLEM 3 Look for students to use the up-and-over property of difference tables here. If students have trouble, ask them to calculate the difference next to the 19 and then proceed. (Answer: 14) Since E is quadratic, the differences are linear; otherwise you could not possibly extend the difference column in any known pattern.

PROBLEM 4 Assign this problem as additional work for students who quickly finish the other problems. Later in this investigation you explore the top row of tables for functions like $y = x^3$.

Wrap Up

Discuss Problem 3 and ask students to calculate $E(20)$ directly; see if students mention a summation method. This prepares students for the up-and-over and hockey-stick methods in the next lesson.

Exercises

HOMEWORK

- Core: 5, 6, 9
- Optional: 7, 8, 10, 11

You can make copies of Blackline Masters MC13 and MC14 for students to use while working on the exercises.

On Your Own

EXERCISE 6 Review this exercise, and look for students seeing Pascal's Triangle in this table. The rows with 1-2-1 and 1-3-3-1 may be helpful for exposing the connections to Pascal's Triangle. Also look for students describing the up-and-over and hockey-stick rules, as well as the observation that the constant Δ^3 column generates a linear Δ^2 column and a quadratic Δ column.

You can use Blackline Master 5.6B on an overhead and fill in the entries as students supply them, or you can hand out printed copies for students to do their own work on.

EXERCISE 7 $P(x)$ is one of the Mahler polynomials. Later, students learn that $P(x)$ is equivalent to $\binom{x}{3}$, or $nCr(x, 3)$ on a CAS.

Exercises Practicing Habits of Mind

On Your Own

5. Calculate $f(8)$ without filling in anything else for the difference table at the right.

a	f(a)	Δ
0	17	9
1	■	−16
2	■	7
3	■	2
4	■	12
5	■	−8
6	■	−7
7	■	4
8	■	

6. The table at the right is for a cubic function P

a. Copy and complete the table.

b. Describe some patterns you see in the table.

x	P(x)	Δ	Δ²	Δ³
0	0	0	0	1
1	■	■	■	1
2	■	■	■	1
3	■	■	■	1
4	■	■	■	1
5	10	■	■	1
6	20	■	■	1
7	■	■	■	1
8	■	■	■	1

7. A cubic polynomial function P fits the input-output table from Exercise 6.

a. What are the zeros of this polynomial?

b. Write $P(x)$ in factored form, $P(x) = A(x - r_1)(x - r_2)(x - r_3)$.

8. Tabulate each function using inputs from 0 to 8. Then calculate difference columns until you find a constant column of differences.

a. $f(x) = 7x - 3$

b. $g(x) = x^2 - 5x + 4$

c. $h(x) = 10x^2 - 50x + 40$

d. $j(x) = 4x - x^2$

e. $k(x) = 4x - x^3$

f. $m(x) = 5x^3 - 20x$

Answers

Exercises

5. $f(8) = 20$

6. a. See back of book.

b. The third differences are constant and the values of $P(x)$ are all in Pascal's Triangle.

7. a. $x = 0, x = 1, x = 2$

b. $P(x) = \frac{1}{6}x(x - 1)(x - 2)$

8. a.

x	f(x)	Δ
0	−3	7
1	4	7
2	11	7
3	18	7
4	25	7
5	32	7
6	39	7
7	46	7
8	53	

b.

x	g(x)	Δ	Δ²
0	4	−4	2
1	0	−2	2
2	−2	0	2
3	−2	2	2
4	0	4	2
5	4	6	2
6	10	8	2
7	18	10	
8	28		

c–f. See back of book.

9. The table at the right is for N from Problem 2.

x	$N(x)$
0	1
1	−1
2	11
3	49
4	125
5	251
6	439
7	701

a. Build a complete difference table for N.

b. Using any method you like, find a closed-form definition for N.

EXERCISE 9 You refer to this difference table in the next lesson, so consider assigning this exercise.

It is unlikely that students will use the difference table to find the closed form for $N(x)$, and that is fine. Later in this investigation, students learn how to use the difference table to *quickly* find such a definition.

Maintain Your Skills

EXERCISES 10 AND 11 are related. The algebraic result of Exercise 10 matches the functions generated from the Δ column in Exercise 11. Students see this again in the investigation, but this is a chance for them to discover this property for themselves.

Maintain Your Skills

10. For each function $f(x)$, calculate and simplify the expression

$$f(x+1) - f(x)$$

a. $f(x) = x^2$

b. $f(x) = 7x - 3$

c. $f(x) = \frac{x(x-1)}{2}$

d. $f(x) = 2^x$

11. Copy each input-output table and fill in the Δ column. Then find a function that agrees with the outputs of the Δ column.

a.

Input	Output	Δ
0	0	■
1	1	■
2	4	■
3	9	■
4	16	■
5	25	

b.

Input	Output	Δ
0	−3	■
1	4	■
2	11	■
3	18	■
4	25	■
5	32	

c.

Input	Output	Δ
0	0	■
1	0	■
2	1	■
3	3	■
4	6	■
5	10	

d.

Input	Output	Δ
0	1	■
1	2	■
2	4	■
3	8	■
4	16	■
5	32	

9. a. See back of book.

b. $N(x) = 2x^3 + x^2 - 5x + 1$

10. a. $2x + 1$ **b.** 7

c. x **d.** 2^x

11. a.

Input	Output	Δ
0	0	1
1	1	3
2	4	5
3	9	7
4	16	9
5	25	

$\Delta f(x) = 2x + 1$

b.

Input	Output	Δ
0	−3	7
1	4	7
2	11	7
3	18	7
4	25	7
5	32	

$\Delta f(x) = 7$

c.

Input	Output	Δ
0	0	0
1	0	1
2	1	2
3	3	3
4	6	4
5	10	

$\Delta f(x) = x$

d.

Input	Output	Δ
0	1	1
1	2	2
2	4	4
3	8	8
4	16	16
5	32	

$\Delta f(x) = 2^x$

Lesson Overview

GOAL

- Find a polynomial function that fits a difference table.

This lesson reviews the important properties of difference tables. The up-and-over property is critical to the understanding of the connections between difference tables and Pascal's Triangle. Emphasize it more than anything else in the lesson. Consider moving quickly to the exercises where students get a chance to explore the Pascal connections.

CHECK YOUR UNDERSTANDING
- Core: 1, 4, 5
- Optional: 3, 6
- Extension: 2

MATERIALS
- graphing calculators
- spreadsheet software
- Blackline Masters 5.1, 5.7A–C

HOMEWORK
- Core: 7, 9, 10, 11, 13
- Optional: 8, 14, 15
- Extension: 12

VOCABULARY
- difference table
- hockey-stick property
- up-and-over property

Launch

Begin today's lesson by building a difference table for $f(x) = 5x + 3$ and see if students can use the table to justify the function rule.

You may want to use the right side of Blackline Master 5.1 on an overhead while explaining how a difference table works.

5.7 Properties of Difference Tables

One way to see whether a table could have come from a linear function is to compare changes in output to changes in input. If the ratio of the changes is constant, then a linear function fits the table.

Take this table, for example:

Input, x	Output, $M(x)$
0	3
1	8
2	13
3	18
4	23

$\frac{8-3}{1-0} = 5$, $\frac{13-8}{2-1} = 5$, $\frac{18-13}{3-2} = 5$, and so on. M is a linear function.

When the inputs are evenly spaced, making a **difference table** gives another way to explain whether a linear function fits the table. You can calculate differences by subtracting each output from the one before it. There are a few different possible notations, but one way is to write another column after the output and label it Δ for "difference":

See the TI-Nspire Handbook on p. 704 for a refresher on how to make a difference table using a spreadsheet.

x	$M(x)$	Δ
0	3	5
1	8	5
2	13	5
3	18	5
4	23	

Now you can describe the outputs using sums instead of ratios: $M(1)$ is $M(0) = 3$ plus the difference 5. The next output, $M(2)$, is 3 plus two 5's. You could calculate $M(4)$ as

$$3 + 5 + 5 + 5 + 5 = 3 + 4 \cdot 5$$

So $M(4)$ is 3 plus four 5's. In general, $M(n)$ is 3 plus n 5's. This general rule is written as $M(n) = 3 + 5n$.

For higher-degree polynomials, the entries in the difference column will not be constant, but there is hope—continue taking differences. The notation Δ^2 means the column of second differences, found by subtracting entries in the Δ column.

Here is a complete difference table for function N of Exercise 9 from Lesson 5.6:

x	$N(x)$	Δ	Δ^2	Δ^3	Δ^4	Δ^5	Δ^6	Δ^7
0	1	−2	14	12	0	0	0	0
1	−1	12	26	12	0	0	0	
2	11	38	38	12	0	0		
3	49	76	50	12	0			
4	125	126	62	12				
5	251	188	74					
6	439	262						
7	701							

Be efficient. This table might feel a little too complete. You can stop when you reach a constant column.

The highlighted 50, for example, is $126 - 76$.

For Discussion

1. Suppose the last two rows of this table were missing. How could you use the table to determine what belongs in those rows?
2. Copy the table. Circle the number 125. Then shade five numbers in the table, including the 1 at the top of the $N(x)$ column (the output column), that you could add to make 125.

The five numbers to shade are near one another in a systematic way.

These two properties of difference tables are named

- **Up-and-over:** Any number in the table (other than inputs) is the sum of two numbers—the number directly above it and the number directly to the right of the one above it.
- **Hockey stick:** Any number in the table (other than inputs) is the sum of the top value in its column and all the numbers above it in the column immediately to its right.

For You to Do

3. Find the values of A, B, and C in this difference table.

Input	Output	Δ	Δ^2
0	0	1	A
1	1	4	5
2	5	9	■
3	■	16	■
4	■	25	11
5	■	B	
6	C		

Answers

For Discussion

1. If the last two rows of the table were missing, you could fill in the numbers by adding together the number immediately above it and the number directly to the right of the one above it.
2. Shade 76, 38, 12, −2, and 1, so $76 + 38 + 12 - 2 + 1 = 125$.

For You to Do

3. $A = 3, B = 36, C = 91$

Explore

For Discussion

PROBLEM 1 should help students come up with the up-and-over property and the hockey-stick property. If the last two rows were missing, you could fill in the numbers by adding two numbers from the row above. The calculations give $439 = 251 + 188$ and $262 = 188 + 74$, and then $701 = 439 + 262$.

PROBLEM 2 The five numbers to shade are the 1 and, from the Δ column, −2, 12, 38, and 76. Overall, $125 = 1 + (-2) + 12 + 38 + 76$. This occurs because $125 = 49 + 76$, but $49 = 11 + 38$; so $125 = 11 + 38 + 76$. You can continue this process to the top row of the table.

You may want to use Blackline Master 5.7A on an overhead while working through this problem. This table for function N will appear again in Lessons 5.8 and 5.9.

For You to Do

PROBLEM 3 Using the difference rule, $A = 4 - 1 = 3$; using the up-and-over property, $B = 25 + 11 = 36$; using the hockey-stick property, $C = 5 + 9 + 16 + 25 + 36 = 91$ or, alternately, $C = 0 + 1 + 4 + 9 + 16 + 25 + 36 = 91$.

You may want to use Blackline Master 5.7B on an overhead and fill in the entries as students supply them.

In-Class Experiment

PROBLEMS 4 AND 5 Watch for students using variables for the original five numbers. This is a great way to come up with a generalization. Hopefully students recognize that the numbers 1, 4, 6, 4, 1 come from Pascal's Triangle. End your discussion of these problems with a quick review of Pascal's Triangle.

You might consider assigning these problems in class, discussing them, then assigning Exercise 4. Students should notice that the same numbers from Pascal's Triangle are used in the exercise.

Wrap Up

Carefully discuss Exercise 4, tracing the 125 back through the numbers above it. The In-Class Experiment should help here, since students worked with the same numbers in the same way. It is important that students have a chance to understand the connection to Pascal's Triangle before the formalization that follows in the next two lessons.

In-Class Experiment

Alice writes down five numbers, then adds consecutive pairs to form four numbers. She adds those four numbers in the same way. She continues adding until there is only one number left. Suppose her starting numbers are

$$1 \quad -2 \quad 14 \quad 12 \quad 0$$

Her second row reads

$$-1 \quad 12 \quad 26 \quad 12$$

4. What is Alice's final number?

5. Try the experiment with other starting numbers. How is the final number related to the original five numbers? Is there a formula?

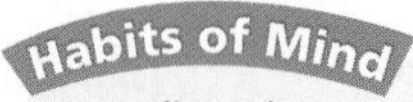

Habits of Mind

Generalize. What happens if you use variables to stand for the five numbers?

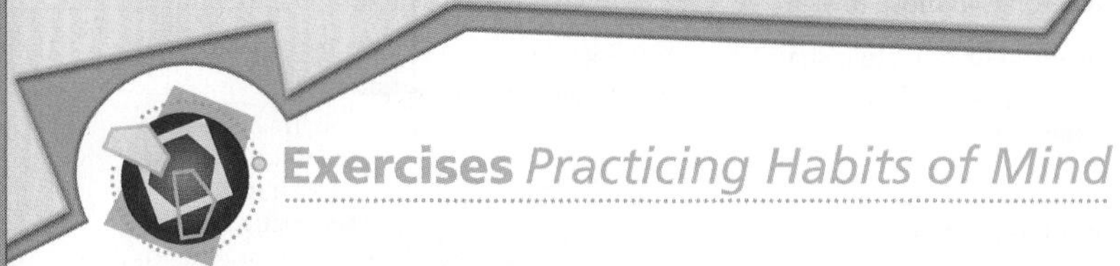

Exercises Practicing Habits of Mind

Check Your Understanding

1. a. Copy and complete this table for $f(x) = ax^2 + bx + c$.

Input, x	Output, $f(x)$	Δ	Δ^2
0	c	■	■
1	$a + b + c$	■	■
2	■	■	■
3	■	■	■
4	■	■	
5	■		

b. Use the table to write expressions for $\Delta f(x)$ and $\Delta^2 f(x)$ in terms of x. Write your expressions in normal form.

c. What does this exercise say about difference tables of quadratic functions?

Answers

In-Class Experiment

4. 125

5. If the starting numbers are a, b, c, d, and e, then the final number will be $a + 4b + 6c + 4d + e$.

Exercises

1. a.

Input, x	Output, $f(x)$	Δ	Δ^2
0	c	$a + b$	$2a$
1	$a + b + c$	$3a + b$	$2a$
2	$4a + 2b + c$	$5a + b$	$2a$
3	$9a + 3b + c$	$7a + b$	$2a$
4	$16a + 4b + c$	$9a + b$	
5	$25a + 5b + c$		

b. $\Delta f(x) = 2ax + (a + b)$
$\Delta^2 f(x) = 2a$

c. The Δ^2 column will contain a constant equal to twice the coefficient of the x^2 term of the function.

2. Take It Further

a. Copy and complete this difference table for the generic cubic function $f(x) = ax^3 + bx^2 + cx + d$.

Input, x	Output, $f(x)$	Δ	Δ^2	Δ^3
0	d	■	■	■
1	$a+b+c+d$	■	■	■
2	$8a+4b+2c+d$	■	■	■
3	■	■	■	
4	■	■		
5	$125a+25b+5c+d$			

b. Use the table to write expresssions for $\Delta f(x)$, $\Delta^2 f(x)$ and $\Delta^3 f(x)$ in terms of x. Write your expressions in normal form.

c. What does this exercise say about difference tables of cubic functions?

3. You have a table for an unknown function. You make a difference table, and find that all the second differences are 10.

a. A polynomial fits the table. What is the smallest degree it could have?

b. Is this the only kind of function that could fit the table? Explain.

Exercises 4–6 use function N from the lesson. Here is its complete difference table.

x	$N(x)$	Δ	Δ^2	Δ^3	Δ^4	Δ^5	Δ^6	Δ^7
0	1	−2	14	12	0	0	0	0
1	−1	12	26	12	0	0	0	
2	11	38	38	12	0	0		
3	49	76	50	12	0			
4	125	126	62	12				
5	251	188	74					
6	439	262						
7	701							

Assessment Resources

Lesson Quiz 5.7

1. Suppose you have a difference table for an unknown function. All of the second differences are 8.
   a. A polynomial fits the table. What is the smallest degree it could have? What would be the leading coefficient?
   b. Is this the only kind of function that could fit the table? Explain.

2. Use the difference table on the right to answer the following questions.
   a. Suppose you did not know that $F(4) = 174$. What two numbers in the $x = 3$ row could you add to get 174?
   b. Suppose you did not know those two numbers, either. Using the numbers in the $x = 2$ row, how could you get 174?

x	$F(x)$	Δ	Δ^2	Δ^3	Δ^4
0	−2	5	18	12	0
1	3	23	30	12	0
2	26	53	42	12	0
3	79	95	54	12	
4	174	149	66		
5	323	215			
6	538				

Exercises

HOMEWORK

- Core: 7, 9, 10, 11, 13
- Optional: 8, 14, 15
- Extension: 12

You can make copies of Blackline Master 5.7C for students to use while working on the exercises.

Check Your Understanding

EXERCISE 1 follows the discussion in the lesson about when the constant differences are found. For a quadratic, the second constant difference is twice the leading coefficient.

EXERCISE 2 asks students to follow the same process for a general cubic.

2. a.

Input, x	Output, $f(x)$	Δ	Δ^2	Δ^3
0	d	$a + b + c$	$6a + 2b$	$6a$
1	$a + b + c + d$	$7a + 3b + c$	$12a + 2b$	$6a$
2	$8a + 4b + 2c + d$	$19a + 5b + c$	$18a + 2b$	$6a$
3	$27a + 9b + 3c + d$	$37a + 7b + c$	$24a + 2b$	
4	$64a + 16b + 4c + d$	$61a + 9b + c$		
5	$125a + 25b + 5c + d$			

b. $\Delta f(x) = 3ax^2 + (3a + 2b)x + (a + b + c)$

$\Delta^2 f(x) = 6a(x + 1) + 2b$

$\Delta^3 f(x) = 6a$

c. The Δ^3 column entries of cubic functions are constant and equal to 6 times the coefficient of the cubed term.

3. a. degree 2

b. No; any function that equals zero at the x-values shown on the table could be added to a polynomial function that fits the table, and the resulting function would also fit the table.

EXERCISE 4 Discuss this exercise as a lead-in to the next lesson, which fleshes out the concepts established here. Make sure students recognize that the numbers from Pascal's Triangle appear here because of the up-and-over property.

EXERCISE 5 follows up on the previous one, so you might consider discussing Exercise 4 before students tackle this one. Both exercises are important for what is to come, so make sure students get a chance to work on them.

4. **a.** Suppose you did not know that $N(4) = 125$. What two numbers in the $x = 3$ row could you add to get 125?

b. Suppose you did not know those two numbers, either. How could you use the 11 and two 38's in the $x = 2$ row to get 125?

c. You could also use four numbers in the $x = 1$ row to get 125. How?

d. You could use five numbers in the $x = 0$ row to get 125. How?

5. Describe, as completely as possible, how to generate the value $N(5) = 251$ from the rows above it.

You can go all the way to the top, and describe $N(5)$ in terms of the numbers across the top row.

6. Without finding the closed-form definition for N, find a possible value for $N(10)$. Justify your claim. Can you write $N(10)$ in terms of the numbers in the top row?

On Your Own

7. Repeating the In-Class Experiment, Alice started with the four numbers below.

1000 100 10 1

She added consecutive pairs until there was only one number left.

a. What was the final number?

b. Repeat Alice's experiment with variable letters a, b, c, d as the starting numbers. What happens?

8. **Write About It** Describe, in your own words, why the up-and-over property works in a difference table. Include an example.

9. Here is a difference table with a lot of missing numbers.

Input, n	Output, $P(n)$	Δ
0	12	−5
1	■	−5
2	■	−5
3	■	−5
4	■	−5
5	■	−5
6	■	−5

For additional practice, go to Web Code: bga-0507

a. Calculate $P(6)$ and describe how you did it.

b. Assuming the Δ column entries continue to be -5, what will be the value of $P(97)$?

c. Find a closed-form definition for $P(n)$ that fits the table for $n \geq 0$.

Answers

4. **a.** $49 + 76$

b. $11 + 2 \cdot 38 + 38$

c. $-1 + 3 \cdot 12 + 3 \cdot 26 + 12$

d. $1 + 4 \cdot (-2) + 6 \cdot 14 + 4 \cdot 12 + 0$

5. Continue using the up-and-over property all the way up to the top row.

$251 = 1 + 5(-2) + 10 \cdot 14 + 10 \cdot 12 + 5 \cdot 0 + 1 \cdot 0$

6. $N(10) = 2051$; $N(10)$ could be written in terms of the numbers across the top row using the numbers in the tenth row of Pascal's triangle (i.e., $N(10) = a + 10b + 45c + 120d + 210e + 252f + 210g + 120h + 45i + 10j + k$).

7. **a.** 1331

b. $a + 3b + 3c + d$

8. The up-and-over property is based on the difference between consecutive outputs of a function: $\Delta f(x) = f(x + 1) - f(x)$.

10. According to its table, what might be the degree of the polynomial function N from Exercises 4–6. What might be its leading coefficient? Explain.

11. Here is a table for function g.

Input, n	Output, $g(n)$
0	0
1	1
2	14
3	45
4	100
5	185

a. Explain why g cannot be linear or quadratic.

b. If g is cubic, what is its leading coefficient?

12. **Take It Further**

a. Use the algebraic definition of the Δ operation, $\Delta f(x) = f(x + 1) - f(x)$, to prove that if f is a degree-n polynomial (with $n > 0$), then Δf is a polynomial with degree $n - 1$.

b. Show that if f is a degree-n polynomial, then $\Delta^n f$ must be constant and nonzero.

c. Prove that if f is a polynomial so that Δf is a polynomial with degree $n - 1$, then f has degree n.

13. **Standardized Test Prep** This is a difference table, partially filled in, for a polynomial function of degree 4.

Input	Output	Δ	Δ^2	Δ^3
0	■	■	−7	−2
1	■	−7	■	−1
2	−7	■	■	0
3	E	■	■	1
4	■	■	■	2

What is the value of E?

A. 6 **B.** −14 **C.** −21 **D.** −23

On Your Own

EXERCISES 10 AND 11 If the students worked on Exercise 3, they should answer these exercises quickly. If not, you might ask them to build difference tables for polynomials until they see a pattern. By the end of the investigation, you prove the general version of these observations.

EXERCISE 12 Note that to prove that a polynomial has a specific degree, students must show its leading coefficient *cannot* be zero.

9. a. $P(n) = -18;$
$P(n + 1) = P(n) + \Delta$

b. $P(97) = -473$

c. $P(n) = -5n + 12$

10. This table could represent a third-order polynomial (cubic function) with leading coefficient equal to one-sixth of the Δ^3 term, or 2.

11. a. The Δ and Δ^2 columns are not constant.

b. 1

12. a. $f(x) = x^n$

$\Delta f(x) = f(x + 1) - f(x)$

$= (x + 1)^n - x^n$

$= x^n + nx^{n-1} + \dfrac{n(n-1)}{2}x^{n-2}$

$+ \cdots - x^n = nx^{n-1} +$ terms of lower order

b. Each time you apply the Δ operator, you reduce the degree of the polynomial by 1.

c. Moving in the opposite direction from Δ^{n+1} to Δ^n increases the degree of the polynomial by 1.

13. D

Additional Resources

PRINT RESOURCES
- Solution Manual
- Practice Workbook
- Assessment Resources
- Teaching Resources

TECHNOLOGY
- Interactive Textbook
- TeacherExpress CD-ROM
- ExamView CD-ROM
- PHSchool.com

Additional Practice

1. Here is a difference table with a lot of missing numbers.

Input, n	Output, $P(n)$	Δ
0	10	−6
1		−6
2		−6
3		−6
4		−6
5		−6

   a. Calculate $P(5)$ and describe how you did it.
   b. Assuming the Δ column entries continue to be −6, what will be the value of $P(80)$?
   c. Find a closed-form definition for $P(n)$ that fits the table for $n \geq 0$.

2. To the right is a table for function g.
   a. Explain why g cannot be linear or quadratic.
   b. If g is cubic, what is its leading coefficient?

Input, n	Output, $g(n)$
0	2
1	3
2	16
3	52
4	126
5	247

3. Suppose f is a polynomial function with $f(0) = f(1) = 0$ and $f(2) = 3$.
   a. What is the minimum possible degree of f?
   b. Write a closed-form definition for f.
   c. Tabulate f and find the first and second differences.

4. Suppose g is a polynomial function of minimal degree with $g(x) = 0$ when $x = 0, 1, 2$ and $g(x) = 4$ when $x = 3$. Find $g(x)$ in factored form.

5. To the right is a difference table for $f(x) = 3^x$, an exponential function.
   a. Copy and complete the table.
   b. Express $f(3)$ in terms of the top row of your table.
   c. Express $f(4)$ in terms of the top row of your table.

x	$f(x)$	Δ	Δ^2	Δ^3	Δ^4
0					
1					
2					
3					
4					
5					
6					

Practice: For Lesson 5.7, assign Exercises 1–2.

Maintain Your Skills

14. Find a function that agrees with this difference table.

Input, x	Output, $f(x)$	Δ	Δ^2
0	3	4	2
1	■	■	2
2	■	■	2
3	■	■	2
4	■	■	
5	■		

Start by looking at the polynomials $f(x) = x^n$.

15. Find a function that agrees with this difference table.

Input	Output	Δ	Δ^2
0	m	n	p
1	■	■	p
2	■	■	p
3	■	■	p
4	■	■	
5	■		

You might find Exercise 1 helpful.

Answers

14. $f(x) = x^2 + 3x + 3$

15. $f(x) = \frac{p}{2}x^2 + \left(n - \frac{p}{2}\right)x + m$

5.8 The Pascal Connection

There is a connection between the differences you find in a difference table and the numbers in Pascal's Triangle.

For You to Do

The difference operator Δ turns a function into another function. If f is any function, Δf is another function, defined by

$$\Delta f(x) = f(x+1) - f(x)$$

Let $f(x) = x^2$, $g(x) = x^3$, and $h(x) = x^4$. Find a polynomial that defines each function.

1. Δf
2. Δg
3. Δh

Here is the difference table for N from the preceding lessons.

x	$N(x)$	Δ	Δ^2	Δ^3	Δ^4	Δ^5	Δ^6	Δ^7
0	1	−2	14	12	0	0	0	0
1	−1	12	26	12	0	0	0	
2	11	38	38	12	0	0		
3	49	76	50	12	0			
4	125	126	62	12				
5	251	188	74					
6	439	262						
7	701							

The value of $N(3)$ is given as 49. However, you can calculate $N(3)$ from the numbers above it, using the up-and-over property: $N(3) = 11 + 38$. But you can in turn calculate those numbers from the numbers above them, all the way to the top row of the table:

$$\begin{aligned} N(3) &= 49 \\ &= 11 + 38 \\ &= (-1 + 12) + (12 + 26) = -1 + 2 \cdot 12 + 26 \\ &= [1 + (-2)] + 2 \cdot (-2 + 14) + (14 + 12) \\ &= 1 + 3 \cdot (-2) + 3 \cdot 14 + 12 \end{aligned}$$

For You To Do

1. $\Delta f(x) = 2x + 1$
2. $\Delta g(x) = 3x^2 + 3x + 1$
3. $\Delta h(x) = 4x^3 + 6x^2 + 4x + 1$

Lesson Overview

GOAL

- Explain how the up-and-over rule of difference tables relates to Pascal's Triangle.

This lesson formalizes what students learned in the exercises of Lessons 5.6 and 5.7: how to extract the binomial coefficients from the calculations of outputs in a difference table.

CHECK YOUR UNDERSTANDING
- Core: 1, 2, 4, 5
- Optional: 3, 6

MATERIALS
- CAS
- graphing calculators
- Blackline Masters MC12, 5.7A, 5.7C, 5.8A–B

HOMEWORK
- Core: 7, 8, 9, 13, 14
- Optional: 10, 11
- Extension: 12

Launch

Have students start on the problems right away.

Explore

You may want to make copies of Blackline Masters 5.7A and MC12 for students to use for reference and to mark on.

For You to Do

PROBLEMS 1–3 Students may not immediately notice the emergence of numbers from Pascal's Triangle, so ask them to do all three problems.

Encourage students to manually expand $(x + 1)^n$, as this may remind them of patterns in Pascal's Triangle.

For You to Do

PROBLEM 4

Students quickly pick up on the idea that they should use only the necessary coefficients from within a row of Pascal's Triangle.

Here is the same information again, with a little more emphasis on coefficients.

$$\begin{aligned} N(3) &= \mathbf{1}\cdot 49 \\ &= \mathbf{1}\cdot 11 + \mathbf{1}\cdot 38 \\ &= \mathbf{1}\cdot(-1) + \mathbf{2}\cdot 12 + \mathbf{1}\cdot 26 \\ &= \mathbf{1}\cdot 1 + \mathbf{3}\cdot(-2) + \mathbf{3}\cdot 14 + \mathbf{1}\cdot 12 \end{aligned}$$

In short, you can calculate $N(3)$ using the top row of the difference table, multiplying by coefficients from Pascal's Triangle. Here is the same process for $N(4)$, using the up-and-over property.

$$\begin{aligned} N(4) &= \mathbf{1}\cdot 125 \\ &= \mathbf{1}\cdot 49 + \mathbf{1}\cdot 76 \\ &= \mathbf{1}\cdot(11+38) + \mathbf{1}\cdot(38+38) \\ &= \mathbf{1}\cdot 11 + \mathbf{2}\cdot 38 + \mathbf{1}\cdot 38 \\ &= \mathbf{1}\cdot(-1+12) + \mathbf{2}\cdot(12+26) + \mathbf{1}\cdot(26+12) \\ &= \mathbf{1}\cdot(-1) + \mathbf{3}\cdot 12 + \mathbf{3}\cdot 26 + \mathbf{1}\cdot 12 \\ &= \mathbf{1}\cdot[1+(-2)] + \mathbf{3}\cdot(-2+14) + \mathbf{3}\cdot(14+12) + \mathbf{1}\cdot(12+0) \\ &= \mathbf{1}\cdot 1 + \mathbf{4}\cdot(-2) + \mathbf{6}\cdot 14 + \mathbf{4}\cdot 12 + \mathbf{1}\cdot 0 \end{aligned}$$

Again, you can calculate the result using the top row of the difference table, multiplying by coefficients from Pascal's Triangle.

For You to Do

4. Write $N(5)$ and $N(6)$ as expressions based on the top row of the table, then verify that the values are correct.

Developing Habits of Mind

Understand the process. To find $N(10)$, you could say something like "Go to the 10th row of Pascal's Triangle and start writing out the numbers"—or you could use $\binom{n}{k}$ notation. The expression $\binom{5}{2}$, for example, designates the second number in the fifth row of Pascal's Triangle. Just remember that the top row is row number zero, and in each row the left-most entry is entry number zero.

$$\binom{0}{0} = 1$$
$$\binom{1}{0} = 1 \quad \binom{1}{1} = 1$$
$$\binom{2}{0} = 1 \quad \binom{2}{1} = 2 \quad \binom{2}{2} = 1$$
$$\binom{3}{0} = 1 \quad \binom{3}{1} = 3 \quad \binom{3}{2} = 3 \quad \binom{3}{3} = 1$$
$$\binom{4}{0} = 1 \quad \binom{4}{1} = 4 \quad \binom{4}{2} = 6 \quad \binom{4}{3} = 4 \quad \binom{4}{4} = 1$$
$$\binom{5}{0} = 1 \quad \binom{5}{1} = 5 \quad \binom{5}{2} = 10 \quad \binom{5}{3} = 10 \quad \binom{5}{4} = 5 \quad \binom{5}{5} = 1$$

These binomial coefficients are named for what happens when you expand expressions like $(x + y)^5$.

Answers

For You to Do

4. $N(5) = 1\cdot 1 + 5\cdot(-2) + 10\cdot 14 + 10\cdot 12 + 5\cdot 0 + 1\cdot 0 = 251$;

$N(6) = 1\cdot 1 + 6\cdot(-2) + 15\cdot 14 + 20\cdot 12 + 15\cdot 0 + 6\cdot 0 + 1\cdot 0 = 439$

For Discussion

5. $N(10) = 2051$; $N(20) = 16{,}301$

6. These are not the only possible answers. You could use Lagrange interpolation to set $N(10)$ or $N(20)$ to any number, and you could add any polynomial that vanishes on the table to produce the same difference table.

So, for example, you can write $N(5)$ as

$$N(5) = \binom{5}{0} \cdot 1 + \binom{5}{1} \cdot (-2) + \binom{5}{2} \cdot 14 + \binom{5}{3} \cdot 12$$

The notation used for binomial coefficients makes it clear how to find $N(10)$. Just replace all the 5's by 10's. You are done.

While $\binom{n}{k}$ is the standard mathematical notation, most calculators use nCr instead. For example, $nCr(5, 3)$ should return 10.

Why stop here? Why not continue to $\binom{5}{5}$?

For Discussion

5. Calculate $N(10)$ and $N(20)$ using this method.
6. Are these the only possible values for $N(10)$ and $N(20)$? Explain.

Exercises *Practicing Habits of Mind*

Check Your Understanding

1. a. Copy and complete this difference table for $a(x) = 3x^2 - 5x + 10$.

Input, x	Output, $a(x)$	Δ	Δ^2
0	10	■	■
1	8	■	■
2	12	■	■
3	■	■	■
4	■	■	■
5	■	■	
6	■		

b. Show how to find $a(5)$ from the numbers in the top row.

c. Calculate

$$10 \cdot \binom{6}{0} - 2 \cdot \binom{6}{1} + 6 \cdot \binom{6}{2}$$

Find these numbers in row 6 of Pascal's Triangle.

Exercises

1. a.

Input, x	Output, $a(x)$	Δ	Δ^2
0	10	−2	6
1	8	4	6
2	12	10	6
3	22	16	6
4	38	22	6
5	60	28	
6	88		

b. $a(5) = 1 \cdot 10 + 5 \cdot (-2) + 10 \cdot 6 = 60$

c. 88

For Discussion

PROBLEM 5 Watch for students asking if a generalization to $N(x)$ is possible; it is, but only if x is a nonnegative integer (for now).

PROBLEM 6 Note that these are not the only possible answers. You can use Lagrange Interpolation to set $N(10)$ or $N(20)$ to any number, and add any polynomial that vanishes on the table to produce the same difference table. You would only see the effects of such changes outside the scope of the table. The assumption that the constant third difference 12 in the table for $N(x)$ continues forever may not be valid.

If this assumption is not valid, then some later top-row Δ value is nonzero. If students do not catch on to this, there is no need to press it.

Wrap Up

Wrap up by reviewing Exercise 1, or by giving a table for a mystery function of your choosing (up to cubic) and asking students to extend the table.

Assessment Resources

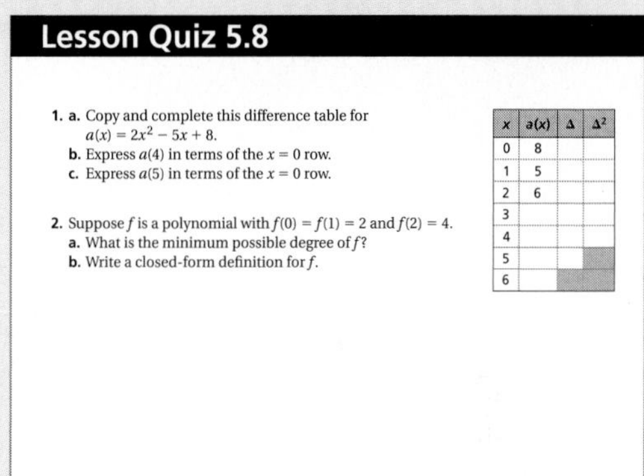

Lesson Quiz 5.8

1. a. Copy and complete this difference table for $a(x) = 2x^2 - 5x + 8$.
   b. Express $a(4)$ in terms of the $x = 0$ row.
   c. Express $a(5)$ in terms of the $x = 0$ row.

2. Suppose f is a polynomial with $f(0) = f(1) = 2$ and $f(2) = 4$.
   a. What is the minimum possible degree of f?
   b. Write a closed-form definition for f.

x	$a(x)$	Δ	Δ^2
0	8		
1	5		
2	6		
3			
4			
5			
6			

Exercises

HOMEWORK

- Core: 7, 8, 9, 13, 14
- Optional: 10, 11
- Extension: 12

You can make copies of Blackline Masters MC12 and 5.7C for students to use while working on the exercises.

Check Your Understanding

EXERCISE 2 previews the next lesson, where you find the polynomials that match $\binom{x}{k}$. Here, the result is $\binom{x}{2}$.

EXERCISE 3 Here, the result is $\binom{x}{3}$. You do more with this result in the next lesson.

EXERCISE 4 Alert students may realize before completing the table that they can find $T(8)$ based on the top row using the pattern set forth in this exercise. Students who do this understand the topic very well.

You can make copies of Blackline Master 5.8A for students to use while working on this exercise and the one that follows.

2. Suppose f is a polynomial function with $f(0) = f(1) = 0$ and $f(2) = 1$.

a. What is the minimum possible degree of f?

b. Write a closed-form definition for f

c. Copy and complete the table of first and second differences.

Input, x	Output, $f(x)$	Δ	Δ^2
0	0	■	■
1	0	■	■
2	1	■	■
3	■	■	■
4	■	■	■
5	■	■	
6	■		

3. Suppose g is a polynomial function of minimal degree with $g(x) = 0$ when $x = 0, 1, 2$ and $g(x) = 1$ when $x = 3$. Find $g(x)$ in factored form.

4. a. Find the values of $\binom{8}{0}$, $\binom{8}{1}$, and $\binom{8}{2}$.

Evaluate these using *nCr*, or find row 8 of Pascal's Triangle.

b. Copy and complete this table of differences.

n	$T(n)$	Δ	Δ^2
0	a	b	c
1	■	■	c
2	■	■	c
3	■	■	c
4	■	■	c
5	■	■	c
6	■	■	c
7	■	■	c
8	■	■	c

Answers

2. a. 2

b. $f(x) = \frac{1}{2}x(x - 1)$

c.

Input, x	Output, $f(x)$	Δ	Δ^2
0	0	0	1
1	0	1	1
2	1	2	1
3	3	3	1
4	6	4	1
5	10	5	
6	15		

3. $g(x) = \frac{x(x - 1)(x - 2)}{6}$

4. a. $\binom{8}{0} = 1$; $\binom{8}{1} = 8$; $\binom{8}{2} = 28$

b.

n	$T(n)$	Δ	Δ^2
0	a	b	c
1	$a + b$	$b + c$	c
2	$a + 2b + c$	$b + 2c$	c
3	$a + 3b + 3c$	$b + 3c$	c
4	$a + 4b + 6c$	$b + 4c$	c
5	$a + 5b + 10c$	$b + 5c$	c
6	$a + 6b + 15c$	$b + 6c$	c
7	$a + 7b + 21c$	$b + 7c$	c
8	$a + 8b + 28c$	$b + 8c$	c

5. Use your CAS to model $g(x) = \binom{x}{3}$.

a. Based on the degree of g, how many differences must you take before you arrive at a constant?

b. Copy and complete this difference table for g.

x	$g(x)$	Δ	Δ^2	Δ^3	Δ^4
0	■	■	■	■	■
1	■	■	■	■	■
2	■	■	■	■	■
3	■	■	■	■	■
4	■	■	■	■	
5	■	■	■		
6	■	■			
7	■				

c. Locate the outputs of g in Pascal's Triangle.

d. Locate the numbers in the Δ column in Pascal's Triangle.

6. Here is a difference table for $p(x) = 2^x$, an exponential function.

x	$p(x)$	Δ	Δ^2	Δ^3	Δ^4	Δ^5	Δ^6
0	1	■	■	■	■	■	■
1	2	■	■	■	■	■	
2	4	■	■	■	■		
3	8	■	■	■			
4	16	■	■				
5	32	■					
6	64						

a. Copy and complete the table.

b. Express $p(4)$ in terms of the top row of your table.

c. What is the sum of the numbers in row 6 of Pascal's Triangle?

Remember...

The 1 at the top of Pascal's Triangle is row 0.

EXERCISE 5 The table in this exercise is the same table referred to earlier in this lesson! This is a good exercise for all of the students to work on at once as an "aha." You explore these polynomials further in the next lesson.

EXERCISE 6 connects the difference tables to a familiar result: the sum of the numbers in each row of Pascal's Triangle is a power of two. This exercise sketches a proof of this fact.

You can make copies of Blackline Master 5.8B for students to use while working on this exercise.

5. a. 3

b.

x	$g(x)$	Δ	Δ^2	Δ^3	Δ^4
0	0	0	0	1	0
1	0	0	1	1	0
2	0	1	2	1	0
3	1	3	3	1	0
4	4	6	4	1	
5	10	10	5		
6	20	15			
7	35				

c. These numbers are along the third diagonal in Pascal's Triangle.

d. These numbers are along the second diagonal in Pascal's Triangle.

6. a.

x	$p(x)$	Δ	Δ^2	Δ^3	Δ^4	Δ^5	Δ^6
0	1	1	1	1	1	1	1
1	2	2	2	2	2	2	
2	4	4	4	4	4		
3	8	8	8	8			
4	16	16	16				
5	32	32					
6	64						

b. $p(4) = 1 \cdot 1 + 4 \cdot 1 + 6 \cdot 1 + 4 \cdot 1 + 1 \cdot 1$
$= 16$

c. 64

On Your Own

EXERCISE 7 Since this exercise does not specify a particular method, some students may find $h(x)$ using a system of equations (or, perhaps, the results from Exercise 15 in the previous lesson). If you discuss this exercise, focus on students who use the relationship to Pascal's Triangle developed in this lesson.

Note that some students solve the first two parts of this exercise without using the relationship of Pascal's Triangle, but part (c) really requires it (or the closed form for the quadratic). In the next lesson, students learn how to use the relationship in Pascal's Triangle to build closed-form definitions for functions that fit tables.

EXERCISE 9 Students should use differences here, but some will use a system of equations and a few may use function-fitting tools on the calculator. Demonstrate the differencing method if you discuss this exercise.

Maintain Your Skills

EXERCISE 14 is an extension of Exercise 4, using a cubic instead of a quadratic. If you review this exercise, point out the appearance of Pascal's Triangle coefficients in each row and column.

You can make copies of Blackline Master 5.8B for students to use while working on this exercise.

On Your Own

7. A quadratic function h has a table that starts like the one at the right.

Input, x	Output, $g(x)$	Δ	Δ^2
0	10	−18	6
1	−8	−12	6
2	−20	−6	6
3	−26	0	6
4	−26	6	6

a. Determine the value of $h(7)$.

b. Determine the value of $h(10)$.

c. Determine the value of $h(97)$.

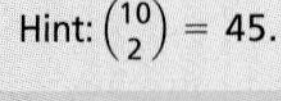

Hint: $\binom{10}{2} = 45$.

8. Kellie says that she can use the method in Exercise 7 to find $h(x)$ for any x.

Kellie: To do $h(97)$ I have to use a calculator unless I want to spend all day filling out a difference table or making a huge Pascal's Triangle. I can type

$$10 \cdot nCr(97, 0) - 18 \cdot nCr(97, 1) + 6 \cdot nCr(97, 2)$$

Kellie: But it looks like I should be able to do this for any number. So I just enter the entire expression at once, and it seems to work for any x:

$$h(x) = 10 \cdot nCr(x, 0) - 18 \cdot nCr(x, 1) + 6 \cdot nCr(x, 2)$$

a. Calculate $h(x)$ this way. Check that it gives the correct values for $h(1)$, $h(7)$, and $h(97)$.

b. Repeat Exercise 14 from Lesson 5.7 using this method.

9. a. Find a quadratic function f with $f(0) = 5$, $f(1) = -3$, and $f(2) = -15$.

b. Find a cubic function g with $g(0) = 5$, $g(1) = -3$, $g(2) = -15$, and $g(3) = -25$.

10. a. In this table, only the Δ column is given. Copy the table and fill in the output column, in a way that makes the numbers in the Δ column valid.

b. Now, find a second way to fill in the output column that also makes the numbers in the Δ column valid.

Input	Output	Δ
0	■	12
1	■	−6
2	■	−20
3	■	0
4	■	12
5	■	2
6	■	

Go Online PHSchool.com

For additional practice, go to Web Code: bga-0508

Answers

7. a. $h(7) = 10$ **b.** $h(10) = 100$
c. $h(97) = 26{,}200$

8. a. $h(x) = 10 \cdot \binom{x}{0} - 18 \cdot \binom{x}{1} + 6 \cdot \binom{x}{2}$; $h(7) = 10 \cdot \binom{7}{0} - 18 \cdot \binom{7}{1} + 6 \cdot \binom{7}{2} = 10 \cdot 1 - 18 \cdot 7 + 6 \cdot 21 = 10$;
$h(10) = 10 \cdot \binom{10}{0} - 18 \cdot \binom{10}{1} + 6 \cdot \binom{10}{2} = 10 \cdot 1 - 18 \cdot 10 + 6 \cdot 45 = 100$;
$h(97) = 10 \cdot \binom{97}{0} - 18 \cdot \binom{97}{1} + 6 \cdot \binom{97}{2} = 10 \cdot 1 - 18 \cdot 97 + 6 \cdot 4656 = 26{,}200$

b. $f(x) = 3 \cdot \binom{x}{0} + 4 \cdot \binom{x}{1} + 2 \cdot \binom{x}{2}$
$= 3 + 4x + 2 \cdot \frac{x(x-1)}{2}$
$= 3 + 4x + x^2 - x$
$= x^2 + 3x + 3$

9. a. $f(x) = -2x^2 - 6x + 5$
b. $f(x) = x^3 - 5x^2 - 4x + 5$

10. a. Answers may vary. Sample:

Input	Output	Δ
0	0	12
1	12	−6
2	6	−20
3	−14	0
4	−14	12
5	−2	2
6	0	

b. See back of book.

11. Find a function for which the difference column is always exactly twice the function output. In algebraic terms, $\Delta f(x) = 2f(x)$ for all x.

12. **Take It Further** Find a function for which the entries in the difference column are the Fibonacci numbers: 0, 1, 1, 2, ...

13. **Standardized Test Prep** This is the top row of the difference table for a certain cubic function.

Input, x	Output, $f(x)$	Δ	Δ^2	Δ^3
0	6	−2	3	1

What is $f(5)$?

A. 36 **B.** −36 **C.** 8 **D.** −8

Maintain Your Skills

14. **a.** Find the values of $\binom{7}{0}$, $\binom{7}{1}$, $\binom{7}{2}$, and $\binom{7}{3}$.

b. Copy and complete this table of differences.

n	$C(n)$	Δ	Δ^2	Δ^3
0	a	b	c	d
1	■	■	■	d
2	■	■	■	d
3	■	■	■	d
4	■	■	■	d
5	■	■	■	d
6	■	■	■	d
7	■	■	■	d

Leave room, since the expressions farther down will involve several variables.

Additional Resources

PRINT RESOURCES
- Solution Manual
- Practice Workbook
- Assessment Resources
- Teaching Resources

TECHNOLOGY
- Interactive Textbook
- TeacherExpress CD-ROM
- ExamView CD-ROM
- PHSchool.com

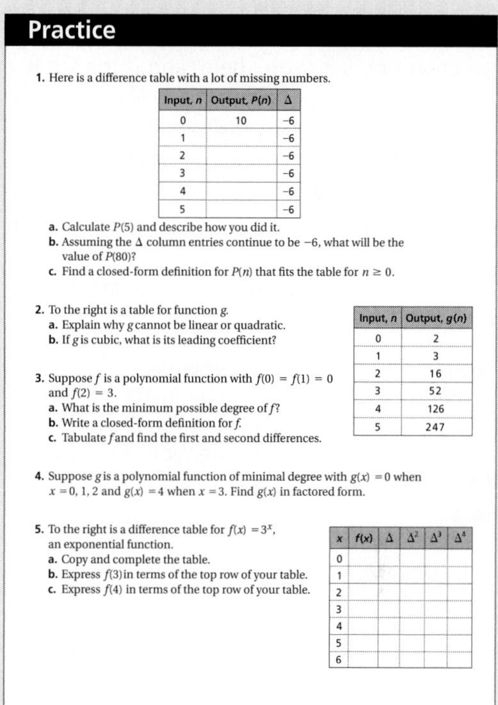

Practice

1. Here is a difference table with a lot of missing numbers.

Input, n	Output, $P(n)$	Δ
0	10	−6
1		−6
2		−6
3		−6
4		−6
5		−6

a. Calculate $P(5)$ and describe how you did it.
b. Assuming the Δ column entries continue to be −6, what will be the value of $P(80)$?
c. Find a closed-form definition for $P(n)$ that fits the table for $n \geq 0$.

2. To the right is a table for function g.
a. Explain why g cannot be linear or quadratic.
b. If g is cubic, what is its leading coefficient?

Input, n	Output, $g(n)$
0	2
1	3
2	16
3	52
4	126
5	247

3. Suppose f is a polynomial function with $f(0) = f(1) = 0$ and $f(2) = 3$.
a. What is the minimum possible degree of f?
b. Write a closed-form definition for f.
c. Tabulate f and find the first and second differences.

4. Suppose g is a polynomial function of minimal degree with $g(x) = 0$ when $x = 0, 1, 2$ and $g(x) = 4$ when $x = 3$. Find $g(x)$ in factored form.

5. To the right is a difference table for $f(x) = 3^x$, an exponential function.
a. Copy and complete the table.
b. Express $f(3)$ in terms of the top row of your table.
c. Express $f(4)$ in terms of the top row of your table.

x	$f(x)$	Δ	Δ^2	Δ^3	Δ^4
0					
1					
2					
3					
4					
5					
6					

Practice: For Lesson 5.8, assign Exercises 3–5.

11. $f(x) = A \cdot 3^x$

12. $f(x) = F(x + 1)$, where $F(x)$ is the xth Fibonacci number.

13. A

14. a. 1, 7, 21, and 35

b.

n	$C(n)$	Δ	Δ^2	Δ^3
0	a	b	c	d
1	$a + b$	$b + c$	$c + d$	d
2	$a + 2b + c$	$b + 2c + d$	$c + 2d$	d
3	$a + 3b + 3c + d$	$b + 3c + 3d$	$c + 3d$	d
4	$a + 4b + 6c + 4d$	$b + 4c + 6d$	$c + 4d$	d
5	$a + 5b + 10c + 10d$	$b + 5c + 10d$	$c + 5d$	d
6	$a + 6b + 15c + 20d$	$b + 6c + 15d$	$c + 6d$	d
7	$a + 7b + 21c + 35d$	$b + 7c + 21d$	$c + 7d$	d

Lesson Overview

GOAL

- Find a polynomial function that fits a difference table.

This lesson generalizes the technique of using binomial coefficients, switching from $\binom{10}{3}$ to $\binom{x}{3}$ polynomials. The rational-expression form of binomial coefficients is useful here, and is the form used by a CAS when typing something like *nCr*(*x*, 3). You can add together these polynomials, called the Mahler polynomials, to find polynomials that fit a difference table.

The method here is similar to generalization methods seen in previous courses: keep trying numbers until a clear pattern emerges, then use a variable to write the general expression.

CHECK YOUR UNDERSTANDING
- Core: 1, 2, 3
- Optional: 4, 5a, 7
- Extension: 5b, 6

MATERIALS
- CAS (recommended)
- graphing calculators
- Blackline Masters MC12, 5.9A–B

HOMEWORK
- Core: 9, 10, 13, 15
- Optional: 8, 12, 16
- Extension: 11, 14

VOCABULARY
- Mahler polynomials

Launch

Begin today's lesson with the example. Students should be able to find $f(10)$ using what they learned in the previous lesson.

5.9 Newton's Difference Formula

In the last lesson, you learned how to use the numbers across the top row of a difference table, along with binomial coefficients, to find the outputs of a polynomial function that fits the table. This lesson goes further, showing how to use the numbers across the top row to find an actual polynomial that defines a function that fits the table.

Example

Problem Here is a table for a cubic polynomial function f. Find $f(10)$.

x	$f(x)$
0	5
1	15
2	31
3	41
4	33
5	−5

Solution Build a difference table, looking for a constant difference. Since you know f to be cubic, the third differences should be constant.

x	$f(x)$	Δ	Δ^2	Δ^3
0	5	10	6	−12
1	15	16	−6	−12
2	31	10	−18	−12
3	41	−8	−30	
4	33	−38		
5	−5			

Now, because of the up-and-over property, you can find $f(10)$ using binomial coefficients by reading across the top row.

$$f(10) = \binom{10}{0} \cdot 5 + \binom{10}{1} \cdot 10 + \binom{10}{2} \cdot 6 + \binom{10}{3} \cdot (-12)$$

You can read the values of the binomial coefficients off of Pascal's Triangle or find them on a calculator using its *nCr* function.

$$f(10) = 1 \cdot 5 + 10 \cdot 10 + 45 \cdot 6 + 120 \cdot (-12) = -1065$$

For You to Do

1. Calculate $f(100)$, where f is the function from the Example.

You could use this method to calculate $f(n)$ for any nonnegative integer n. For example,

$$\begin{aligned}
f(3) &= 41 &&= \mathbf{1} \cdot 5 + \mathbf{3} \cdot 10 + \mathbf{3} \cdot 6 + \mathbf{1} \cdot (-12)\\
f(4) &= 33 &&= \mathbf{1} \cdot 5 + \mathbf{4} \cdot 10 + \mathbf{6} \cdot 6 + \mathbf{4} \cdot (-12)\\
f(5) &= -5 &&= \mathbf{1} \cdot 5 + \mathbf{5} \cdot 10 + \mathbf{10} \cdot 6 + \mathbf{10} \cdot (-12)\\
f(6) &= -85 &&= \mathbf{1} \cdot 5 + \mathbf{6} \cdot 10 + \mathbf{15} \cdot 6 + \mathbf{20} \cdot (-12)\\
f(7) &= -219 &&= \mathbf{1} \cdot 5 + \mathbf{7} \cdot 10 + \mathbf{21} \cdot 6 + \mathbf{35} \cdot (-12)
\end{aligned}$$

Here is a formula for $f(n)$ using binomial coefficients:

$$f(n) = \binom{n}{0} \cdot 5 + \binom{n}{1} \cdot 10 + \binom{n}{2} \cdot 6 + \binom{n}{3} \cdot (-12)$$

where 5, 10, 6, and -12 are the numbers across the top row of the difference table for f.

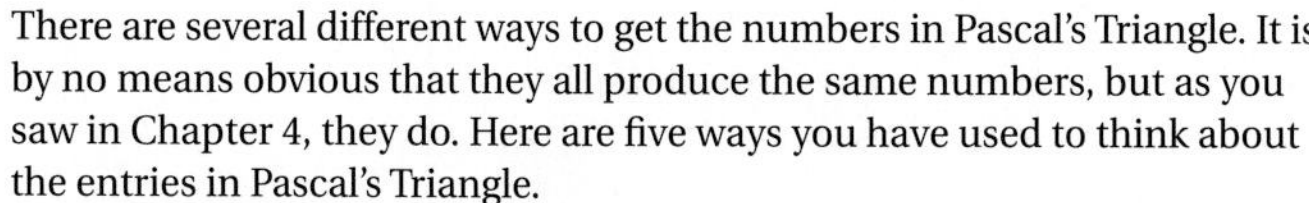

Think about it another way. This formula for $f(n)$ only appears to work for nonnegative integers. What about the other real numbers? Using Pascal's Triangle to find $\binom{\pi}{2}$ does not make sense. Or does it?

There are several different ways to get the numbers in Pascal's Triangle. It is by no means obvious that they all produce the same numbers, but as you saw in Chapter 4, they do. Here are five ways you have used to think about the entries in Pascal's Triangle.

- *Pascal's Triangle is a recursively generated number pattern.* In words: Each row starts and ends with 1. Any interior element is the sum of the two above it.

  In symbols:

$$\binom{n}{k} = \begin{cases} 1 & \text{if } k = 0 \text{ or if } k = n \text{ (each row starts and ends with 1)} \\ \binom{n-1}{k-1} + \binom{n-1}{k} & \text{if } 0 < k < n \text{ (an interior element is the sum of the two above it)} \end{cases}$$

Explore

You may want to use Blackline Masters MC12 and 5.9A as overheads or reference handouts while you talk about Mahler polynomials and Newton's Difference Formula, and while the students work the For You to Do problems.

For You to Do

PROBLEM 1 $f(100) = \binom{100}{0} \cdot 5 + \binom{100}{1} \cdot 10 + \binom{100}{2} \cdot 6 + \binom{100}{3} \cdot (-12) = -1{,}909{,}695$

Answers

For You to Do

1. $f(100) = -1{,}909{,}695$

- *The entries in Pascal's Triangle count subsets.* Suppose you have a set of five elements, say $\{A, B, C, D, E\}$. How many three-element subsets are there? There are $\binom{5}{3} = 10$. Here they are:

$$\{A, B, C\}, \{A, B, D\}, \{A, B, E\}, \{A, C, D\}, \{A, C, E\},$$
$$\{A, D, E\}, \{B, C, D\}, \{B, C, E\}, \{B, D, E\}, \{C, D, E\}$$

- *The entries in Pascal's Triangle are binomial coefficients.* The entries in the nth row are the coefficients in the expansion of $(a + b)^n$. More precisely,

$$\begin{aligned}(a+b)^n &= \binom{n}{0}a^n + \binom{n}{1}a^{n-1}b + \binom{n}{2}a^{n-2}b^2 + \cdots + \binom{n}{n-2}a^2b^{n-2} \\ &\quad + \binom{n}{n-1}ab^{n-1} + \binom{n}{n}b^n \\ &= \sum_{k=0}^{n}\binom{n}{k}a^{n-k}b^k\end{aligned}$$

- *The entries in Pascal's Triangle are quotients of factorials.* There is an explicit formula for $\binom{n}{k}$ in terms of factorials:

$$\binom{n}{k} = \frac{n!}{k!(n-k)!}$$

So, for example,

$$\begin{aligned}\binom{12}{5} &= \frac{12!}{5!7!} \\ &= \frac{12 \cdot 11 \cdot 10 \cdot 9 \cdot 8 \cdot 7 \cdot 6 \cdot 5 \cdot 4 \cdot 3 \cdot 2 \cdot 1}{5 \cdot 4 \cdot 3 \cdot 2 \cdot 1 \times 7 \cdot 6 \cdot 5 \cdot 4 \cdot 3 \cdot 2 \cdot 1} \\ &= \frac{12 \cdot 11 \cdot 10 \cdot 9 \cdot 8}{5 \cdot 4 \cdot 3 \cdot 2 \cdot 1} \\ &= 792\end{aligned}$$

Making this factorial formula hold for the cases $k = 0$ and $k = n$ is one of the reasons for defining $0!$ to be 1.

- *The entries in Pascal's Triangle are rational expressions.* Sometimes, it is useful to do the cancellations in the factorial expression and write $\binom{n}{k}$ as a product of factors:

$$\begin{aligned}\binom{n}{k} &= \frac{n(n-1)(n-2)(n-3)\cdots(n-k+1)(n-k)\cdots 1}{k!(n-k)!} \\ &= \frac{n(n-1)(n-2)(n-3)\cdots(n-k+1)}{k!}\end{aligned}$$

One advantage of this expression over all the others is that n need not be an integer. In a sense, this expression extends the formula for entries in Pascal's triangle from integers to real (or even complex) numbers. This is the way to think about it that is most useful for this chapter.

The symbol $\binom{\pi}{3}$ does not make sense in the context of any of the other methods. But here, it is just

$$\frac{\pi(\pi-1)(\pi-2)}{6}$$

Definition

The Mahler polynomials are the set of polynomials that match the binomial coefficients. The first few Mahler polynomials are

k	$\binom{x}{k}$ (Factored)	$\binom{x}{k}$ (Expanded)
0	1	1
1	x	x
2	$\frac{x(x-1)}{2!}$	$\frac{-x+x^2}{2}$
3	$\frac{x(x-1)(x-2)}{3!}$	$\frac{2x-3x^2+x^3}{6}$
4	$\frac{x(x-1)(x-2)(x-3)}{4!}$	$\frac{-6x+11x^2-6x^3+x^4}{24}$
5	$\frac{x(x-1)(x-2)(x-3)(x-4)}{5!}$	$\frac{24x-50x^2+35x^3-10x^4+x^5}{120}$

The examples so far show how you can use the Mahler polynomials, along with the numbers in the top row of a difference table, to find a function that fits the table. This is called Newton's Difference Formula.

Theorem 5.2 Newton's Difference Formula

Suppose you have a table with integer inputs from 0 to m:

Input	Output	Δ	Δ^2	Δ^3	...	Δ^m
0	a_0	a_1	a_2	a_3	...	a_m
1						
2						
3						
4						
5						
6						
⋮						
m						

A polynomial function that fits the table is

$$f(x) = \sum_{k=0}^{m} a_k \binom{x}{k}$$

Each $\binom{x}{k}$ is a Mahler polynomial.

For You to Do

PROBLEM 2 The polynomial is $p(x) = 0.5x^4 - 0.5x$. You might skip this problem for the sake of time.

GOING FURTHER You can extend this problem by asking students to find the polynomial instead of just its degree and leading coefficient. This is a good example of using a CAS to speed the work, as students can find $p(x)$ directly using a CAS and the *nCr* function.

Wrap Up

Review Exercises 1–3 and Exercise 16, which provides a key connection to the next lesson.

Assessment Resources

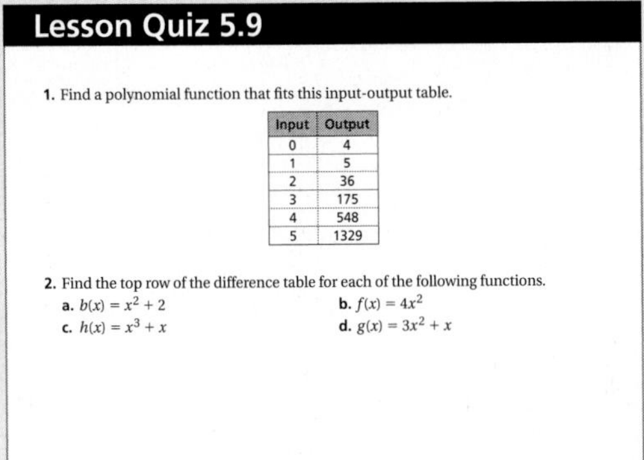

Lesson Quiz 5.9

1. Find a polynomial function that fits this input-output table.

Input	Output
0	4
1	5
2	36
3	175
4	548
5	1329

2. Find the top row of the difference table for each of the following functions.

a. $b(x) = x^2 + 2$
b. $f(x) = 4x^2$
c. $h(x) = x^3 + x$
d. $g(x) = 3x^2 + x$

Newton's Difference Formula explains the observations made previously about the degree and leading coefficient of a fitting polynomial. For example, consider this table for N:

x	$N(x)$	Δ	Δ^2	Δ^3	Δ^4	Δ^5	Δ^6	Δ^7
0	1	−2	14	12	0	0	0	0
1	−1	12	26	12	0	0	0	
2	11	38	38	12	0	0		
3	49	76	50	12	0			
4	125	126	62	12				
5	251	188	74					
6	439	262						
7	701							

Newton's Difference Formula says that you can find a function N that fits the table by reading across the top row of the difference table and multiplying each number by the corresponding Mahler polynomial.

$$N(x) = 1 \cdot 1 + (-2) \cdot x + 14 \cdot \frac{x(x-1)}{2} + 12 \cdot \frac{x(x-1)(x-2)}{6}$$

Without expanding, you know that this polynomial must be cubic, since it will have a nonzero x^3 term and no higher-degree term. Moreover, the coefficient of the x^3 term is $\frac{12}{6} = 2$. This term alone controls the degree and leading coefficient of N (why?).

For You to Do

2. Find the degree and leading coefficient of the lowest-degree polynomial function that fits this table.

x	$p(x)$
0	0
1	0
2	7
3	39
4	126
5	310
6	645
7	1197

3. Find a cubic function that matches the table from the Example in this lesson.

Answers

For You to Do

2. leading coefficient: $\frac{1}{2}$; degree: 4
3. $f(x) = -2x^3 + 9x^2 + 3x + 5$

Exercises *Practicing Habits of Mind*

Check Your Understanding

1. The first few Mahler polynomials are

$$\binom{x}{0} = 1$$
$$\binom{x}{1} = x$$
$$\binom{x}{2} = \frac{x(x-1)}{2}$$
$$\binom{x}{3} = \frac{x(x-1)(x-2)}{3!}$$

List the next three Mahler polynomials. Then write a general rule for the kth Mahler polynomial.

2. Find a polynomial function that fits this input-output table.

Input	Output
0	6
1	5
2	24
3	99
4	290
5	681

3. If you made a difference table for each of the following functions, what would the top row look like?

a. $a(x) = x^2$ **b.** $b(x) = 2x^2$ **c.** $c(x) = x^3$

d. $d(x) = 2x^3$ **e.** $e(x) = x^3 + x^2$

4. Derman wonders how a difference table could help if the inputs started from a different number. How might you find a function that fits this table?

Input	Output
3	3
4	−1
5	−1
6	3
7	11
8	23
9	39

Exercises

HOMEWORK

- Core: 9, 10, 13, 15
- Optional: 8, 12, 16
- Extension: 11, 14

Check Your Understanding

EXERCISE 3 If you discuss this exercise, talk about the relationships between the different tables. For example, the row for $b(x)$ is twice the row for $a(x)$. See Exercise 16 for a related exercise.

Exercises

1. $\binom{x}{4} = \frac{x(x-1)(x-2)(x-3)}{4!}$

$\binom{x}{5} = \frac{x(x-1)(x-2)(x-3)(x-4)}{5!}$

$\binom{x}{6} = \frac{x(x-1)(x-2)(x-3)(x-4)(x-5)}{6!}$

In general, the kth Mahler polynomial is

$$\binom{x}{k} = \frac{x(x-1)(x-2)\cdots(x-k+1)}{k!}$$

2. $f(n) = n^4 + 3n^2 - 5n + 6$

3. **a.** 0, 1, 2
b. 0, 2, 4
c. 0, 1, 6, 6
d. 0, 2, 12, 12
e. 0, 2, 8, 6

4. Method 1: Work backwards to build a difference table for all values of the function between 0 and 9, then use the top row to determine the function.

$$f(x) = 39 \cdot \binom{x}{0} - 16 \cdot \binom{x}{1} + 4 \cdot \binom{x}{2} = 2x^2 - 18x + 39$$

Method 2: Pretend the inputs start at 0 and find $g(x) = 2x^2 - 6x + 3$. Then replace x with $x - 3$ and expand to obtain $g(x - 3) = f(x) = 2x^2 - 18x + 39$.

5. The algebraic definition of the Δ operator is that

$$\Delta f(x) = f(x + 1) - f(x)$$

a. Show that if $f(x) = \binom{x}{3}$, then $\Delta f(x) = \binom{x}{2}$. In other words, the Δ of the third Mahler polynomial is the second Mahler polynomial.

b. **Take It Further** Show that, in general, if $f(x) = \binom{x}{k}$, then $\Delta f(x) = \binom{x}{k-1}$.

You will need the general form for $\binom{x}{k}$ first.

6. **Take It Further** An interesting result comes from multiplying the numbers in a row of Pascal's Triangle by powers of integers. For example, take the row 1, 3, 3, 1 and multiply each number by powers of 4:

$$1 \times 1 = 1$$
$$4 \times 3 = 12$$
$$16 \times 3 = 48$$
$$64 \times 1 = 64$$

The total is $125 = 5^3$.

a. Build a difference table for $g(x) = 5^x$, and then show that you can write 125 as the sum given above.

b. Show that, in general, $\sum_{k=0}^{n} 4^k \binom{n}{k} = 5^k$

c. Generalize this result to any power:

$$\sum_{k=0}^{n} p^k \binom{n}{k} = (p+1)^k$$

7. Kei says that if the entries in the difference column of a table are all zero, the function must be constant.

Kei: If all the Δ's are 0, that means all the outputs have to be the same number. It has to be a constant function, like $f(x) = 5$.

Is he right? If so, explain why. If not, sketch the graph of a function where $f(x + 1) - f(x)$ is always zero but f is not constant.

Answers

5. a. If $f(x) = \binom{x}{3}$,

$$\Delta f(x) = f(x+1) - f(x)$$
$$= \binom{x+1}{3} - \binom{x}{3}$$
$$= \frac{(x+1)x(x-1)}{6} - \frac{x(x-1)(x-2)}{6}$$
$$= \frac{x(x-1)}{6}[(x+1) - (x-2)]$$
$$= \frac{x(x-1)}{6} \cdot 3$$
$$= \frac{x(x-1)}{2}$$
$$= \binom{x}{2}$$

b. If $f(x) = \binom{x}{k}$,

$$\Delta f(x) = f(x+1) - f(x)$$
$$= \binom{x+1}{k} - \binom{x}{k}$$
$$= \frac{(x+1)x(x-1)\cdots(x-k+2)}{k!} - \frac{x(x-1)(x-2)\cdots(x-k+1)}{k!}$$
$$= \frac{x(x-1)\cdots(x-k+2)}{k!} \cdot [(x+1) - (x-k+1)]$$
$$= \frac{x(x-1)\cdots(x-k+2)}{k!} \cdot k$$
$$= \frac{x(x-1)\cdots(x-k+2)}{(k-1)!}$$
$$= \binom{x}{k-1}$$

6. a.

x	g(x)	Δ	Δ^2	Δ^3
0	1	4	16	64
1	5	20	80	320
2	25	100	400	
3	125	500		
4	625			

$$g(3) = 1 \cdot \binom{3}{0} + 4 \cdot \binom{3}{1} + 16 \cdot \binom{3}{2} + 64 \cdot \binom{3}{3} = 125$$

b–c. See back of book.

On Your Own

8. Let $f(x) = 2x^3 + 5x^2 - x - 17$. Find a function for which the outputs are the fourth differences, $\Delta^4 f$.

9. The table below gives the sums of the squares of integers from 0 to n for each n.

n	Sum of Squares
0	0
1	1
2	5
3	14
4	30
5	55
6	91

Use Mahler polynomials and a difference table to find a closed-form definition for $S(n)$, the sum of the squares from 0 to n.

10. Find a closed-form definition for $C(n)$, the sum of the cubes from 0 to n.

As a challenge, try doing this without a calculator. Factoring helps.

11. **Take It Further** Find a rule for the sum of fifth powers from 0 to n.

12. Derman has a follow-up question after Exercise 4.

Derman: I changed the input numbers, but not the outputs. Is it still possible to find a function that fits this table?

Input	Output
0	3
5	−1
10	−1
15	3
20	11
25	23
30	39

You could answer this if the inputs went 0, 1, 2, 3, ..., so the question is how to change that answer so that it works for this table instead.

How could you use Mahler polynomials to find a function that fits this table?

13. Here is a function with a curious definition.

$$D(n) = \begin{cases} 1 & \text{if } n = 0 \\ 0 & \text{if } n \neq 0 \end{cases}$$

a. Explain how you know D cannot be a polynomial function.

b. Build a difference table for D and describe its top row.

On Your Own

EXERCISE 8 This is a little bit of a trick question, but should only take a minute or two.

EXERCISE 9 If you discuss this exercise, be sure to point out the interval 0 to n. There is a discussion in the next lesson about how to use a difference table to generate a sum from 0 to $n - 1$, and how to adjust the result to work for the interval 0 to n.

7. Incorrect; a periodic function such as $f(x) = 5 + \sin 2\pi x$ would have a difference table with $\Delta = 0$. If f is a polynomial function, then it must be constant.

8. $f(x) = 2x^3 + 5x^2 - x - 17$

9. $S(n) = \dfrac{n(n+1)(2n+1)}{6}$

10. $C(n) = \dfrac{n^2(n+1)^2}{4}$

11. $F(n) = \dfrac{n^2(n+1)^2(2n^2+2n-1)}{12}$

12. Start by constructing a difference table:

Input	Output	Δ	Δ^2
0	3	−4	4
5	−1	0	4
10	−1	4	4
15	3	8	4
20	11	12	4
25	23	16	
30	39		

Since the inputs grow by fives rather than one, $\frac{x}{5}$ grows by one. Therefore, substitute $\frac{x}{5}$ for x:

$$f(x) = 3\binom{x/5}{0} - 4\binom{x/5}{1} + 4\binom{x/5}{2}$$

$$= 3 \cdot 1 - 4 \cdot \frac{x}{5} + 4 \cdot \frac{\frac{x}{5}\left(\frac{x}{5} - 1\right)}{2}$$

$$= \frac{2}{25}x^2 - \frac{6}{5}x + 3$$

13. a. A polynomial can only have a finite number of roots.

b. See back of book.

Maintain Your Skills

EXERCISE 16 This exercise gives a way to convert from the normal polynomial basis $(1, x, x^2)$ to the Mahler polynomial basis. Some things (especially things in difference tables) are more easily done in the Mahler basis, as seen in the next lesson on sums of powers.

Consider having students complete the table in class, then discuss what the table means and any patterns they find.

You can make copies of Blackline Master 5.9B for students to use with this exercise.

GOING FURTHER You can use this table to quickly build a difference table for any polynomial up to degree 5. For example, if $f(x) = 2x^3 + 4x$, its difference row is twice the row for x^3 (0, 1, 6, 6) plus four times the row for x (0, 1). So the difference row is 0, 6, 12, 12. This could lead students to think about or build a table to convert in the other direction, which is another interesting exercise. (See Exercise 6 in the next lesson.)

Additional Resources

PRINT RESOURCES
- Solution Manual
- Practice Workbook
- Assessment Resources
- Teaching Resources

TECHNOLOGY
- Interactive Textbook
- TeacherExpress CD-ROM
- ExamView CD-ROM
- PHSchool.com

Additional Practice

1. Find a polynomial function that fits this input-output table.

Input	Output
0	2
1	1
2	10
3	35
4	82
5	157

2. If you made a difference table for each of the following functions, what would the top row look like?
a. $f(x) = 3x^2$ **b.** $g(x) = x^2 + x$
c. $h(x) = 3x^3$ **d.** $k(x) = x^4$

3. Let $f(x) = 3x^3 - 4x^2 + 2x - 12$. Find a function for which the outputs are the fourth differences, $\Delta^4 f$.

4. a. Make a difference table for $g(x) = 2x^4$.
b. Write
$$\sum_{k=0}^{n-1} 2k^4$$
in terms of Mahler polynomials.

5. For each sum, find a formula in terms of n.
a. $\sum_{k=0}^{n-1} 4$ **b.** $\sum_{k=0}^{n-1} 2k$
c. $\sum_{k=0}^{n-1} (k^2 + 2k)$ **d.** $\sum_{k=0}^{n-1} 2k^2$

6. Define f recursively as
$$f(n) = \begin{cases} 6 & \text{if } n = 0 \\ f(n-1) + 2n + 4 & \text{if } n > 0 \end{cases}$$
Find a closed-form definition for $f(n)$ for any nonnegative integer n.

Practice: For Lesson 5.9, assign Exercises 1–3.

14. **Take It Further** You can use the function D to prove an interesting fact about Pascal's Triangle:

In any row of Pascal's Triangle, the sum of the even terms $\binom{n}{0}, \binom{n}{2}, \ldots$ is equal to the sum of the odd terms $\binom{n}{1}, \binom{n}{3}, \ldots$.

Prove this using D and its difference table.

15. **Standardized Test Prep** Identify the next value in the row of Pascal's Triangle that begins

1 10 45 ...

A. 55 **B.** 80 **C.** 120 **D.** 10

Go Online PHSchool.com

For additional practice, go to Web Code: bga-0509

Maintain Your Skills

16. Copy and complete this table, which gives the top row of the difference table for each polynomial from $f(x) = x^0 = 1$ to $f(x) = x^5$. You found some of the entries in Exercise 3. Describe any patterns you notice in this table.

$f(x)$	$\binom{x}{0} = 1$	$\binom{x}{1} = x$	$\binom{x}{2} = \frac{x(x-1)}{2!}$	$\binom{x}{3} = \frac{x(x-1)(x-2)}{3!}$	$\binom{x}{4}$	$\binom{x}{5}$
1	1	–	–	–	–	–
x	0	1	–	–	–	–
x^2	■	■	■	–	–	–
x^3	■	■	■	■	–	–
x^4	■	■	■	■	■	–
x^5	■	■	■	■	■	■

Finding a smooth function that fits a table is the mathematical equivalent of fitting a flexible plank to a rigid frame.

Answers

14. Using the top row of the previous exercise:

$$D(6) = \binom{6}{0} - \binom{6}{1} + \binom{6}{2} - \binom{6}{3} + \binom{6}{4} - \binom{6}{5} + \binom{6}{6}$$

Since $D(6) = 0$ by definition:

$$0 = \binom{6}{0} - \binom{6}{1} + \binom{6}{2} - \binom{6}{3} + \binom{6}{4} - \binom{6}{5} + \binom{6}{6}$$

and

$$\binom{6}{1} + \binom{6}{3} + \binom{6}{5} = \binom{6}{0} + \binom{6}{2} - \binom{6}{4} + \binom{6}{6}$$

15. C

16. See back of book.

5.10 Sums of Powers

Recall the following sums.

$$\sum_{k=0}^{n-1} k = \frac{n(n-1)}{2}$$

$$\sum_{k=0}^{n-1} k^2 = \frac{n(n-1)(2n-1)}{6}$$

$$\sum_{k=0}^{n-1} k^3 = \frac{n^2(n-1)^2}{4}$$

$$\sum_{k=0}^{n-1} k^4 = \frac{n(n-1)(2n-1)(3n^2-3n-1)}{30}$$

$$\sum_{k=0}^{n-1} k^5 = \frac{n^2(n-1)^2(2n^2-2n-1)}{12}$$

In CME Project *Algebra 2*, the sums ran from 0 to *M*. Replace all the *n*'s here by $M + 1$'s and you have sums from 0 to *M*.

How did anyone find these formulas? In this lesson you will use Newton's Difference Formula to find formulas for the sums of squares, cubes, or any power.

Example

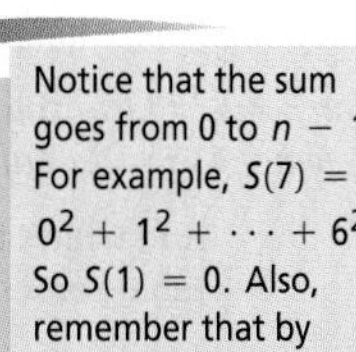

Problem Find a rule for the function *S* defined as

$$S(n) = \sum_{k=0}^{n-1} k^2$$

Then calculate $S(101)$.

Solution Calculate $S(n)$ for the first few integers, then build a difference table.

n	$S(n)$	Δ	Δ^2	Δ^3
0	0	0	1	2
1	0	1	3	2
2	1	4	5	2
3	5	9	7	2
4	14	16	9	
5	30	25		
6	55			

Notice that the sum goes from 0 to $n - 1$. For example, $S(7) = 0^2 + 1^2 + \cdots + 6^2$. So $S(1) = 0$. Also, remember that by convention,

$$\sum_{k=0}^{-1} k^2 = 0$$

Lesson Overview

GOAL

- Quickly find rules for summations, like the sum of the first *n* squares.

This optional lesson applies Newton's Difference Formula to summations. Since the Δ operation and summation undo one another, the function being summed shows up in the column of first differences. Therefore, the formulas for summations are simple to write when using Mahler polynomials; then a CAS or algebra legwork calculates a formula for the summation rule.

CHECK YOUR UNDERSTANDING
- Core: 1, 2, 3, 4a
- Optional: 5
- Extension: 4b, 6

MATERIALS
- CAS (recommended)
- graphing calculators
- wood blocks (or other 3-D manipulatives)
- Blackline Masters 5.10A–B

HOMEWORK
- Core: 7, 10, 12, 13
- Optional: 8, 9, 11

Launch

Begin today's lesson with the example, and have students find a formula for the sum of squares. Then compare the result to Exercise 10 in the previous lesson. Ask students to show how the two results are related, and why they are different. (Answer: The example runs from 0 to $(n - 1)$, while the homework exercise runs from 0 to n.)

You may want to use Blackline Master 5.10A as an overhead or reference handout while you talk about the difference tables for functions $S(n)$ and $g(n)$.

Explore

For Discussion

PROBLEM 1 Look for students to mention induction and wonder, "If the function works up to $n - 1$, does it work for n?" The proof here is time-consuming, but an advanced class should be able to handle it. Or, some students may notice that the first difference is quadratic, so a cubic fits.

Newton's Difference Formula states that you can find a rule for S using the top row of the difference table and the Mahler polynomials:

$$S(n) = 0 \cdot 1 + 0 \cdot n + 1 \cdot \frac{n(n-1)}{2} + 2 \cdot \frac{n(n-1)(n-2)}{6}$$

$S(n)$ in expanded form is $S(n) = \frac{1}{3}n^3 - \frac{1}{2}n^2 + \frac{1}{6}n$. Then $S(101) = 338{,}350$, which is also the sum of the squares $0^2 + 1^2 + 2^2 + \cdots + 100^2$.

For Discussion

1. This function fits the table for S, but how might you prove that they will always agree?

Minds in Action episode 15

Sasha and Tony are studying the difference table for S.

Tony Hey Sasha, I noticed something strange about the table from the example.

Sasha What's that?

Tony It's got the table for x^2 buried inside it.

Sasha Huh? What do you mean?

Tony Look. I can just cover the $S(n)$ column with my pencil. Check out what's left.

Tony covers the output column of the table for S, leaving the input and Δ columns.

n	Δ	Δ^2	Δ^3
0	0	1	2
1	1	3	2
2	4	5	2
3	9	7	2
4	16	9	
5	25		
6			

And what's interesting to me is the whole table comes from sums of squares.

Sasha Wait, I think this makes sense. The Δ column should be the squares; that's just the way the function was built. It reminds me of the hockey-stick property, where you add up all the numbers.

Tony I see what you mean. And the $n - 1$ makes it line up right, otherwise there wouldn't be a zero at the top. I wonder what we could use this for.

Sasha Well, look across the top row of the difference table you've got. The covered-up one.

Tony 0-1-2. That's the top row for x^2. We've done that before.

Sasha Okay, now uncover that $S(n)$ column.

Answers

For Discussion

1. proof by induction

Tony uncovers it .

n	$S(n)$	Δ	Δ^2	Δ^3
0	0	0	1	2
1	0	1	3	2
2	1	4	5	2
3	5	9	7	2
4	14	16	9	
5	30	25		
6	55			

Tony Ahh, 0-0-1-2. They're almost the same, except you add a zero in front. I'll bet we could do this with other functions. Do we have top rows for other functions?

Sasha Yes, and it's not hard to make more.

You will be asked to "make more" in the exercises.

Doing It With Sums

You can use Newton's Difference Formula to find polynomial formulas for sums of powers. And you can use sums of powers to build polynomials that fit any table (in which the inputs form an arithmetic sequence). To see how, consider the mystery function g. What could a formula for g be?

n	$g(n)$
0	1
1	−2
2	1
3	10
4	25
5	46
6	73

Here is the table with two difference columns.

n	$g(n)$	Δ	Δ^2
0	1	−3	6
1	−2	3	6
2	1	9	6
3	10	15	6
4	25	21	6
5	46	27	
6	73		

So there is a linear polynomial that produces the Δ column, namely $6n - 3$.

n	Δ	Δ^2
0	−3	6
1	3	6
2	9	6
3	15	6
4	21	6
5	27	

You might be able to make some progress on g, now that you are equipped with this formula for the first differences.

n	$g(n)$	$\Delta = 6n - 3$
0	1	$-3 = 6 \cdot 0 - 3$
1	−2	$3 = 6 \cdot 1 - 3$
2	1	$9 = 6 \cdot 2 - 3$
3	10	$15 = 6 \cdot 3 - 3$
4	25	$21 = 6 \cdot 4 - 3$
5	46	$27 = 6 \cdot 5 - 3$
6	73	

To get the entry in the Δ column for an input of n, start with −3 and add n 6's.

To see where $g(5)$ comes from, use the hockey-stick property, replacing each number in the Δ column by the calculation that led to it.

n	$g(n)$	$\Delta = 6n - 3$
0	1	**−3**
1	2	**3**
2	1	**9**
3	10	**15**
4	25	**21**
5	46	27
6	73	

$$g(5) = 1 + \boxed{-3} + \boxed{3} + \boxed{9} + \boxed{15} + \boxed{21}$$

$$= 1 + \boxed{6 \cdot 0 - 3} + \boxed{6 \cdot 1 - 3} + \boxed{6 \cdot 2 - 3} + \boxed{6 \cdot 3 - 3} + \boxed{6 \cdot 4 - 3}$$

Now, group "like terms."

$$g(5) = 1 + 6(0 + 1 + 2 + 3 + 4) + [(-3) + (-3) + (-3) + (-3) + (-3)]$$
$$= 1 + 6(0 + 1 + 2 + 3 + 4) + 5(-3)$$

Similarly,

$$g(6) = 1 + 6(0 + 1 + 2 + 3 + 4 + 5) + [(-3) + (-3) + (-3) + (-3) + (-3) + (-3)]$$
$$= 1 + 6(0 + 1 + 2 + 3 + 4 + 5) + 6(-3)$$

And, in general, a function g that agrees with the table will have the property that

$$g(n) = 1 + 6(0 + 1 + 2 + 3 + 4 + 5 + \cdots + (n - 1)) + n(-3)$$

Now, use the formula for the sum of the first n integers.

$$0 + 1 + 2 + 3 + \cdots + (n - 1) = \frac{n(n-1)}{2}$$

So, you have

$$g(n) = 1 + 6(0 + 1 + 2 + 3 + 4 + 5 + \cdots + (n - 1)) + n(-3)$$
$$= 1 + 6\left(\frac{n(n-1)}{2}\right) - 3n$$
$$= 3n^2 - 6n + 1$$

You can check that this fits the table.

If you work through some more examples, it becomes clear that a constant first difference requires you to add up n identical constants. A constant second difference requires you to add up the first n integers. It turns out that a constant third difference requires you to add up the first n squares. And in general, a constant difference in the mth column requires that you are able to add up the first $n(m - 1)^{\text{st}}$ powers. This gives you another perfectly good method for "resolving" difference tables, now that you have nice formulas for sums of powers.

For You to Do

2. Use this method to find a function that agrees with this table.

Input	Output
0	5
1	15
2	31
3	41
4	33
5	−5

Answers

For You to Do

2. $f(x) = -2x^3 + 9x^2 + 3x + 5$

Wrap Up

Wrap up by reviewing Exercises 1 and 3, or by giving students a difficult summation such as

$$\sum_{k=0}^{n-1} N(k)$$

where N is the cubic function students worked with earlier in this investigation.

Assessment Resources

Lesson Quiz 5.10

1. **a.** Make a difference table for $f(x) = 5x^2$, using inputs from 0 to 6.
   b. Write $\sum_{k=0}^{n-1} 5k^2$ in terms of Mahler polynomials.

2. For each sum, find a formula in terms of n.
   a. $\sum_{k=0}^{n-1} 8$ **b.** $\sum_{k=0}^{n-1} 2k^3$

3. Define the function g recursively as
$$g(x) = \begin{cases} 5 & \text{if } x = 0 \\ g(x-1) + 4x + 2 & \text{if } x > 0 \end{cases}$$
Find a closed-form definition for $g(x)$ for any nonnegative integer.

Exercises

HOMEWORK

- Core: 7, 10, 12, 13
- Optional: 8, 9, 11

Check Your Understanding

EXERCISE 1 is a straightforward exercise, but if students have difficulty, lead them through it. Some students may need extra time to understand the concept of shifting to find the sum.

EXERCISE 2 Some students just use difference tables to do this, while others wisely use the fact that $\sum 6k^2 = 6\sum k^2$. This exercise ties into Exercise 5, as the 6 sums of squares are used to form the solid block.

EXERCISE 4 follows up on the formula given for resolving difference tables at the end of the lesson. Part (b) effectively acts as a proof by induction that the formula is correct.

Exercises *Practicing Habits of Mind*

Check Your Understanding

1. a. Use a difference table to show that

$$k^3 = 0\binom{k}{0} + 1\binom{k}{1} + 6\binom{k}{2} + 6\binom{k}{3}$$

b. Find a closed form for the sum below.

$$\sum_{k=0}^{n-1} k^3$$

2. Calculate this sum as a function of n.

$$\sum_{k=0}^{n-1} 6k^2$$

Factor the result.

3. a. Make a difference table for $f(x) = x^4$.

b. Write

$$\sum_{k=0}^{n-1} k^4$$

in terms of the Mahler polynomials.

c. Show that

$$\sum_{k=0}^{n-1} k^4 = \frac{n(n-1)(2n-1)(3n^2-3n-1)}{30}$$

4. Carlos says he found a formula for the sum of fourth powers that is different from the one in Exercise 3.

Carlos: I searched the Internet for "sum of 4th powers," and the first hit that came back gave this formula:

$$S_4(n) = \frac{n(n+1)(2n+1)(3n^2+3n-1)}{30}$$

Carlos: It's really close to what came from Exercise 3, but it's not the same.

a. Explain the discrepancy between Carlos' formula and the one in Exercise 3.

b. **Take It Further** Show that

$$\frac{n(n-1)(2n-1)(3n^2-3n-1)}{30} + n^4 = \frac{n(n+1)(2n+1)(3n^2+3n-1)}{30}$$

Answers

Exercises

1. a.

k	k^3	Δ	Δ^2	Δ^3
0	0	1	6	6
1	1	7	12	6
2	8	19	18	6
3	27	37	24	
4	64	61		
5	125			

b. $\dfrac{n^2(n-1)^2}{4}$

2. $n(n-1)(2n-1)$

3. a. See back of book.

b. $\displaystyle\sum_{k=0}^{n-1} k^4 = 0\cdot\binom{n}{1} + 1\cdot\binom{n}{2} + 14\cdot\binom{n}{3} + 36\cdot\binom{n}{4} + 24\cdot\binom{n}{5}$

c. $\displaystyle\sum_{k=0}^{n-1} k^4 = \frac{n(n-1)}{2} + 14\cdot\frac{n(n-1)(n-2)}{6} + 36\cdot\frac{n(n-1)(n-2)(n-3)}{24} + 24\cdot\frac{n(n-1)(n-2)(n-3)(n-4)}{120}$

4. a. Substitute $(n-1)$ for n and the formulas are the same.

b. Write n^4 as $\frac{30n^4}{30}$ and factor both sides to demonstrate that these two expressions are equal.

5. You can model the formula for the sum of the first n squares with blocks of wood.

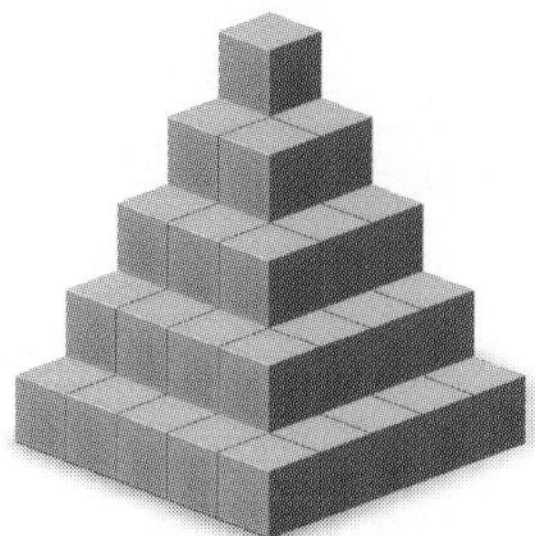

The small cube at the top of the shape is 1 inch per side.

a. Explain why the volume of the shape, in cubic inches, is

$$1^2 + 2^2 + 3^2 + 4^2 + 5^2$$

b. Show how to assemble six blocks in this shape to form a solid box (or, better yet, build it). Then, find the dimensions of the box.

c. Generalize this process to show that

$$1^2 + 2^2 + 3^2 + \cdots + n^2 = \frac{n(n+1)(2n+1)}{6}$$

6. **Take It Further** You can use the table in Exercise 16 of Lesson 5.9 to rewrite polynomials containing the usual powers of x $(1, x, x^2, x^3, \ldots)$ in terms of the Mahler polynomials $1, x, \frac{x(x-1)}{2}, \frac{x(x-1)(x-2)}{6}, \ldots$. But what about the other direction, converting from Mahler polynomials back to powers of x? For example,

$$\frac{x(x-1)}{2} = \frac{1}{2}x^2 - \frac{1}{2}x$$

Copy and complete this table, which describes the conversion.

$f(x)$	1	x	x^2	x^3	x^4	x^5
$\binom{x}{0}$	1	–	–	–	–	–
$\binom{x}{1}$	0	1	–	–	–	–
$\binom{x}{2}$	0	$-\frac{1}{2}$	$\frac{1}{2}$	–	–	–
$\binom{x}{3}$	■	■	■	■	–	–
$\binom{x}{4}$	■	■	■	■	■	–
$\binom{x}{5}$	■	■	■	■	■	■

Describe any patterns you find in this table, or any relationships between this table and the table for conversion to Mahler polynomials.

EXERCISE 5 is a great exercise to do in class with appropriate materials, such as wood blocks. Students likely have seen the staircase argument for the sum of the first n integers in the past, and the same concept is used here (with volume instead of area). This particular exercise does not tie in directly with the rest of the lesson, but is appropriate for the topic and a fun activity.

EXERCISE 6 If time permits, use matrix algebra to show that this table (as a 6-by-6 matrix) is the inverse of the table in Exercise 16 of Lesson 5.9. This is an amazing result, but you can explain it by talking about systems of equations and how the tables are constructed.

You can make copies of Blackline Master 5.10B for students to use with this exercise.

5. a. The volume is made up of five smaller shapes: $5 \times 5 \times 1$, $4 \times 4 \times 1$, $3 \times 3 \times 1$, $2 \times 2 \times 1$, and $1 \times 1 \times 1$. $V = 1^2 + 2^2 + 3^2 + 4^2 + 5^2$

b. $5 \times 6 \times 11$

c. The dimensions of the box are n by $(n + 1)$ by $(2n + 1)$. Since six congruent shapes were used to build the box, the volume of each shape is $V = \frac{n(n+1)(2n+1)}{6}$, which also equals $1^2 + 2^2 + 3^2 + 4^2 + 5^2$.

6.

$f(x)$	1	x	x^2	x^3	x^4	x^5
$\binom{x}{0}$	1	-	-	-	-	-
$\binom{x}{1}$	0	1	-	-	-	-
$\binom{x}{2}$	0	$-\frac{1}{2}$	$\frac{1}{2}$	-	-	-
$\binom{x}{3}$	0	$\frac{1}{3}$	$-\frac{1}{2}$	$\frac{1}{6}$	-	-
$\binom{x}{4}$	0	$-\frac{1}{4}$	$\frac{11}{24}$	$-\frac{1}{4}$	$\frac{1}{24}$	-
$\binom{x}{5}$	0	$\frac{1}{5}$	$-\frac{5}{24}$	$-\frac{7}{24}$	$-\frac{1}{12}$	$\frac{1}{120}$

Patterns: Reciprocals of the factorial numbers appear along the diagonal; within each row, the terms always alternate signs; the x column contains reciprocals of all positive integers in an alternating positive/negative pattern. This matrix is the inverse of the matrix from Exercise 16 in Lesson 5.9.

On Your Own

EXERCISE 7 addresses the additive and multiplicative properties of sums. The result from part (e) is the sum of the results of parts (b)–(d).

EXERCISE 9 As with the wood-block exercise, this is a nice exercise to do in class, although it is not directly tied to the nature of the topic. You can also use it to remind students about inductive proof as seen in Investigation 5A.

On Your Own

7. For each sum, find a formula in terms of n.

a. $\sum_{k=0}^{n-1} 3$ **b.** $\sum_{k=0}^{n-1} k$ **c.** $\sum_{k=0}^{n-1} 5k$

d. $\sum_{k=0}^{n-1} k^2$ **e.** $\sum_{k=0}^{n-1} (k^2 + 5k + 3)$

How many 3's are there in part (a)?

8. The sum of cubes from 0^3 through $(n-1)^3$ is a perfect square:

$$\sum_{k=0}^{n-1} k^3 = \left(\frac{n(n-1)}{2}\right)^2$$

Interestingly, the fraction $\frac{n(n-1)}{2}$ is the sum of the integers from 0 through $(n-1)$, which means that

$$\sum_{k=0}^{n-1} k^3 = \left(\sum_{k=0}^{n-1} k\right)^2$$

Verify this claim for 0 through 10 by tabulating each sum.

9. For an ingenious proof that the sum in Exercise 8 is always a perfect square, start by actually creating the square. Here is the square for the sum $1^3 + 2^3 = (1 + 2)^2$.

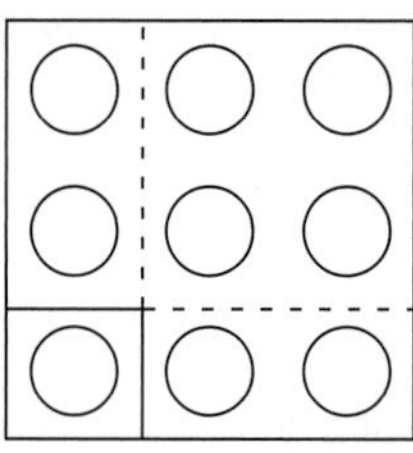

a. Show how you could add three 3-by-3 squares to this pattern to make a 6-by-6 square.

b. Show how you could add four 4-by-4 squares to the 6-by-6 square to make a 10-by-10 square. You will need to cut one of the four squares in some way.

c. Show how you could add five 5-by-5 squares to make a 15-by-15 square.

d. In general, if n is odd, show how you can add n n-by-n squares to the pattern, justifying that they fit the existing pattern.

e. In general, if n is even, show how you can also add n n-by-n squares to the pattern, cutting one of the n squares.

f. What type of proof is this? Is the proof complete based on what you have done in this exercise?

Answers

7. a. $3n$

b. $\frac{n(n-1)}{2}$

c. $\frac{5n(n-1)}{2}$

d. $\frac{n(n-1)(2n-1)}{6}$

e. $\frac{n(n-1)(2n-1)}{6} + \frac{5n(n-1)}{2} + 3n$

8. See back of book.

9. a.

o	o	o	o	o	o
o	o	o	o	o	o
o	o	o	o	o	o
o	o	o	o	o	o
o	o	o	o	o	o
o	o	o	o	o	o

b–d. See back of book.

10. Define f recursively as

$$f(n) = \begin{cases} 8 & \text{if } n = 0 \\ f(n-1) + 2n + 5 & \text{if } n > 0 \end{cases}$$

Use what you have learned in this investigation to find a closed-form definition for $f(n)$ for any nonnegative integer n.

11. Generalize the result of Exercise 10 to find a closed-form equivalent for this recursive definition

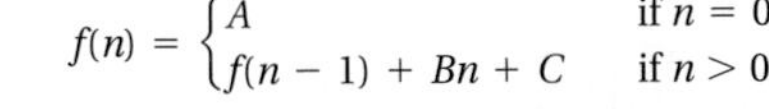

$$f(n) = \begin{cases} A & \text{if } n = 0 \\ f(n-1) + Bn + C & \text{if } n > 0 \end{cases}$$

12. Standardized Test Prep In the table, output $f(n)$ is the sum of $(n + 1)$ consecutive odd numbers beginning with some number $s = f(0)$.

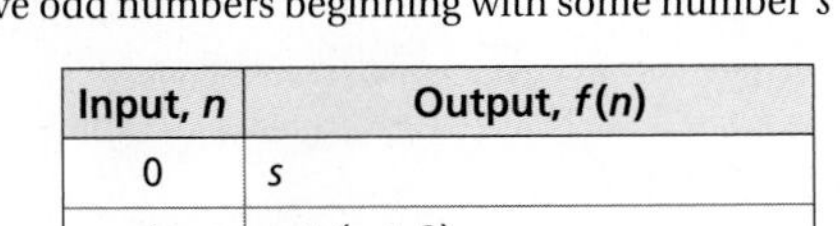

Input, n	Output, $f(n)$
0	s
1	$s + (s + 2)$
2	$s + (s + 2) + (s + 4)$
3	$s + (s + 2) + (s + 4) + (s + 6)$

Supposing s to be given, which of the following is a closed-form definition of $f(n)$, with $n \geq 0$?

A. $(n + 1)(n + s)$ **B.** $n(n + s)$ **C.** $n(n - s)$ **D.** $(n - 1)(n + s)$

Go Online PHSchool.com

For additional practice, go to Web Code: bga-0510

Maintain Your Skills

13. For each recursively-defined function, find a value of C that makes f a constant function. (So $f(1)$ must equal $f(0)$, etc.)

a. $f(n) = \begin{cases} C & \text{if } n = 0 \\ 2f(n-1) - 3 & \text{if } n > 0 \end{cases}$

b. $f(n) = \begin{cases} C & \text{if } n = 0 \\ 4f(n-1) - 24 & \text{if } n > 0 \end{cases}$

c. $f(n) = \begin{cases} C & \text{if } n = 0 \\ 0.75f(n-1) + 3 & \text{if } n > 0 \end{cases}$

d. $f(n) = \begin{cases} C & \text{if } n = 0 \\ 1.005f(n-1) - 300 & \text{if } n > 0 \end{cases}$

e. Let n be even. The previous square will be $\frac{n(n-1)}{2}$ on a side if the pattern works to this point. You want to add $\frac{n-1}{2}$ squares to each edge, a total of $n - 1$ squares but since n is even, this can only be done by cutting one square in half first. One more square fits in the corner to complete the pattern, and the new large square has side: $\frac{n(n-1)}{2} + n = \frac{n(n+1)}{2}$.

f. This is proof by induction. The proof is complete since it has several defined base cases and each step is justified as long as the previous steps were.

10. $f(n) = n^2 + 6n + 8$

11. $f(n) = A + Cn + B \cdot \frac{n(n-1)}{2}$

12. A

13. a. $C = 3$ **b.** $C = 8$

c. $C = 12$ **d.** $C = 60{,}000$

Maintain Your Skills

EXERCISE 13 previews some of the ideas students see in the next investigation.

Additional Resources

PRINT RESOURCES
- Solution Manual
- Practice Workbook
- Assessment Resources
- Teaching Resources

TECHNOLOGY
- Interactive Textbook
- TeacherExpress CD-ROM
- ExamView CD-ROM
- PHSchool.com

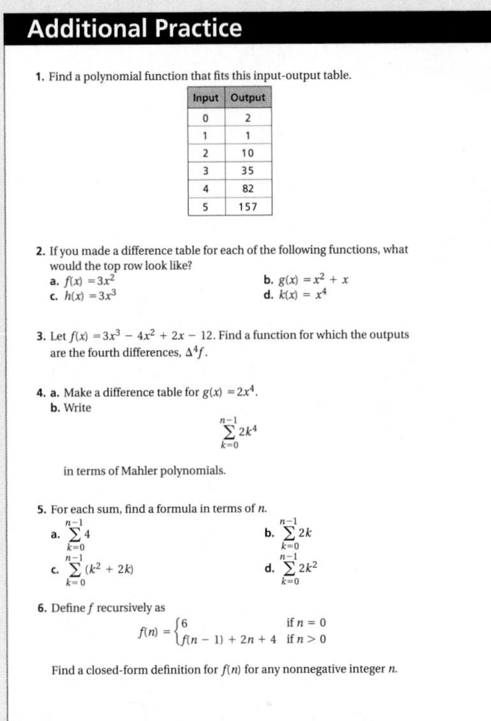

Additional Practice

1. Find a polynomial function that fits this input-output table.

Input	Output
0	2
1	1
2	10
3	35
4	82
5	157

2. If you made a difference table for each of the following functions, what would the top row look like?
   a. $f(x) = 3x^2$ b. $g(x) = x^2 + x$
   c. $h(x) = 3x^3$ d. $k(x) = x^4$

3. Let $f(x) = 3x^3 - 4x^2 + 2x - 12$. Find a function for which the outputs are the fourth differences, $\Delta^4 f$.

4. a. Make a difference table for $g(x) = 2x^4$.
   b. Write $$\sum_{k=0}^{n-1} 2k^4$$ in terms of Mahler polynomials.

5. For each sum, find a formula in terms of n.
   a. $\sum_{k=0}^{n-1} 4$ b. $\sum_{k=0}^{n-1} 2k$
   c. $\sum_{k=0}^{n-1} (k^2 + 2k)$ d. $\sum_{k=0}^{n-1} 2k^2$

6. Define f recursively as
$$f(n) = \begin{cases} 6 & \text{if } n = 0 \\ f(n-1) + 2n + 4 & \text{if } n > 0 \end{cases}$$
Find a closed-form definition for $f(n)$ for any nonnegative integer n.

Practice: For Lesson 5.10, assign Exercises 4–6.

Mathematical Reflections

EXERCISES 6–8 At the start of the investigation, you may have assigned these as Questions 1–3 for students to think and write about.

In this investigation, you studied functions with difference tables that contain a column of constants. You described any such function with a polynomial by using Newton's Difference Formula. You applied this formula to sums of powers. The following questions will help you summarize what you have learned.

1. Find a polynomial function that fits this table.

x	$f(x)$
0	5
1	17
2	37
3	65
4	101

2. Find a polynomial function S that satisfies

$$S(n) = \sum_{k=0}^{n-1} (k+1)(k-1)$$

3. Build a table that no linear, quadratic, or cubic function will fit. Explain why none of them can fit the table.
4. Find a function f for which $\Delta f(x) = 9f(x)$ for all x.
5. Let $g(x) = x^4$. Find rules for Δg and $\Delta^2 g$.
6. If the third differences in the table of a polynomial function are all 24, what can you say about that function?
7. What are the Mahler polynomials?
8. How can you use differences to find a polynomial function that fits a table?

Vocabulary

In this investigation, you learned these terms. Make sure you understand what each one means and how to use it.

- **difference table**
- **hockey-stick property**
- **Mahler polynomials**
- **up-and-over property**

Answers

Mathematical Reflections

1. $f(x) = 4x^2 + 8x + 5$
2. $S(x) = \dfrac{x(2x - 3x - 5)}{6}$
3. Answers may vary. Sample: As long as the fourth difference or later is nonzero, the function cannot be a polynomial with degree less than or equal to 3.
4. $f(x) = A \cdot 10^x$
5. $\Delta g(x) = 4x^3 + 6x^2 + 4x + 1$; $\Delta^2 g(x) = 12x^2 + 24x + 14$
6. The function is cubic with a coefficient of the cubes term equal to 4.
7. The Mahler polynomials are the set of polynomials that match the binomial coefficients, written as: $\binom{x}{k} = \dfrac{x(x-1)(x-2)\cdots(x-k+1)}{k!}$
8. Take the top row of a difference table and multiply each number in the top row by the corresponding Mahler polynomial. Simplify the expression.

Mid-Chapter Test

For a mid-chapter test, go to Web Code: bga-0552

Multiple Choice

1. Let $f(x) = 3x - 7$. Let $g(x) = 3x - 7 - 2x(x + 1)$. What is the set of inputs for which the two functions are equal?

A. $\{-1\}$ **B.** $\{0, 1\}$
C. $\{-1, 0\}$ **D.** $\{-1, 0, \frac{7}{3}\}$

2. Let h be defined recursively by

$$h(n) = \begin{cases} a & \text{if } n = 0 \\ h(n-1) + 2n + 5 & \text{if } n > 0 \end{cases}$$

If $h(3) = 31$, find a.

A. 1 **B.** 4 **C.** 11 **D.** 13

3. Here is a partially completed difference table for a function p.

x	p(x)	Δ	Δ²	Δ³
0	3	0	4	6
1	3	4	10	6
2	■	B	■	6
3	■	■	A	6

Find the value of $A + B$.

A. 22 **B.** 24 **C.** 36 **D.** 42

4. Let

$$S(n) = \sum_{k=0}^{n-1} k^3$$

What is $S(3)$?

A. 3 **B.** 5 **C.** 9 **D.** 36

5. Let the function f be defined by $f(x) = x^2 + x$. Which of the following is a closed-form definition for Δf?

A. $\Delta f = x^2 + x - 1$ **B.** $\Delta f = x^2 + 3x + 2$
C. $\Delta f = 2x + 2$ **D.** $\Delta f = x + 1$

Open Response

6. Find a recursively defined function that agrees with $f(n) = 2n^2 + 3$ for all nonnegative integers n.

7. Use induction to show that these two functions agree for all nonnegative integers.

$$M(n) = 3n - 2$$

$$m(n) = \begin{cases} -2 & \text{if } n = 0 \\ m(n-1) + 3 & \text{if } n > 0 \end{cases}$$

8. A quadratic function w has a table that starts like the one below.

Input, x	Output, w(x)	Δ	Δ²
0	7	2	10
1	9	12	10
2	21	22	10

a. Determine the value of $w(8)$.
b. Determine the value of $w(100)$.

9. Find a polynomial that fits the input-output table.

Input	Output
0	−5
1	−3
2	−1
3	7
4	27
5	65

10. Find a formula for each sum in terms of n.

a. $\sum_{k=0}^{n-1} 3k$ **b.** $\sum_{k=0}^{n-1} (k^2 + 1)$

Mid-Chapter Test

1. C **2.** B **3.** C
4. C **5.** C
6.

$$F(n) = \begin{cases} 3 & n = 0 \\ F(n-1) + 4n - 2 & n > 0 \end{cases}$$

7. $M(0) = -2 = m(0)$

$$\begin{aligned} M(N+1) &= 3(N+1) - 2 \\ &= 3N + 3 - 2 \\ &= 3N - 2 + 3 \\ &= M(N) + 3 \\ &= m(N) + 3 \\ &= m(N+1) \end{aligned}$$

8. a. $w(8) = 303$
b. $w(100) = 49{,}707$

9. $f(x) = x^3 - 3x^2 + 4x - 5$

10. a. $\frac{3n(n-1)}{2}$

b. $\frac{n(2n^2 - 3n + 7)}{6}$

Mid-Chapter Test

Assessment Resources

Mid-Chapter Test page 1

Multiple Choice

1. Define the function f as $f(x) = x^2 + x$. Define the function g as $g(x) = x^2 + x + 3(x-2)(x-1)(x+4)$. What is the set of inputs for which the two functions are equal?
A. $\{-1, 0\}$ **B.** $\{-4, 1, 2, 3\}$ **C.** $\{-2, -1, 4\}$ **D.** $\{-4, 1, 2\}$

2. Define the function j recursively as

$$j(n) = \begin{cases} a & \text{if } n = 0 \\ j(n-1) + 10 & \text{if } n > 0 \end{cases}$$

If $j(4) = 60$, find a.
A. 0 **B.** 6 **C.** 10 **D.** 20

3. Here is a partially completed difference table for a function q.

x	q(x)	Δ	Δ²
0	−8	−1	6
1	−9	5	6
2			6
3			6
4		A	6

Find the value of A.
A. 23 **B.** 26 **C.** 29 **D.** 34

4. Let

$$S(n) = \sum_{k=0}^{n-1} 4k$$

Find $S(4)$.
A. 10 **B.** 12 **C.** 24 **D.** 44

5. Define the function f as $f(x) = 2x^2 - 3x + 1$. Which of the following is a closed-form definition for Δf?
A. $\Delta f = 0$ **B.** $\Delta f = 4x - 1$
C. $\Delta f = -2x + 4$ **D.** $\Delta f = 4x^2 + 4x + 4$

Mid-Chapter Test page 2

Open Response

6. Find a recursively defined function that agrees with $f(n) = n^2 + n + 1$ for all nonnegative integers n.

7. Use induction to show that these two functions agree for all nonnegative integers.

$$H(n) = 4n + 1$$

$$h(n) = \begin{cases} 1 & \text{if } n = 0 \\ h(n-1) + 4 & \text{if } n > 0 \end{cases}$$

8. A cubic function has a table that starts this way.

Input, x	Output, c(x)	Δ	Δ²	Δ³
0	2	−1	−4	6
1	1	−5	2	6
2	−4	−3	8	6

a. Determine the value of $c(10)$.
b. Determine the value of $c(25)$.

9. Find a polynomial that fits the input-output table.

Input	Output
0	3
1	6
2	25
3	60
4	111
5	178

10. Find a formula for each sum in terms of n.
a. $\sum_{k=0}^{n-1} 6k$ **b.** $\sum_{k=0}^{n-1} (k^2 - 1)$

11. If the third differences in the table of a polynomial are all 24, what is true about that polynomial?

Also available: Form B

Investigation Overview

This investigation looks more deeply at the relationship between the closed-form and recursive definitions for two types of recurrences: two-term recurrences such as the rule that generates Fibonacci numbers, and affine recurrences (multiply-and-add) which form the basis for loan and annuity calculations.

One of the highlights of this investigation is deriving the closed form for Fibonacci numbers, along with other recurrences in the form $f(n) = Af(n-1) + Bf(n-2)$. The closed form is generated from the quadratic equation $x^2 - x - 1 = 0$, which justifies the fact that the ratio of consecutive Fibonacci numbers approaches the golden ratio.

You may wish to assign Questions 1–3 for students to think and write about during the investigation.

Learning Goals

- Find general classes of functions that fit a recurrence.
- Relate a solution for a two-term recurrence to a quadratic polynomial.
- Calculate the monthly payment for a car loan and write a general rule for all such problems.

Habits and Skills

- Generalize a pattern that works for one function to a class of related functions.
- Solve linear systems.
- Detect whether you can approximate a table by a linear, polynomial, or exponential rule.
- Represent a function with a table, a graph, or an equation.
- Find equilibrium points for repeated operations.

Closed-Form and Recursive Definitions

In *Closed-Form and Recursive Definitions*, you will find closed-form equivalents for recursively-defined functions. You will also study relationships similar to the relationship that defines the Fibonacci numbers.

By the end of this investigation, you will be able to answer questions like these.

1. What methods are available for deciding if a linear, polynomial, or exponential rule fits a table?
2. How can you find a closed-form function definition that satisfies a two-term recurrence?
3. What is the monthly payment for a three-year car loan for $15,000, taken out at 5% APR?

You will learn how to

- find general classes of functions that fit a recurrence
- relate a solution for a two-term recurrence to a quadratic polynomial
- calculate the monthly payment for a car loan and write a general rule for all such problems

You will develop these habits and skills:

- Generalize a pattern that works for one function to a class of related functions.
- Solve linear systems.
- Decide whether you can approximate a table by a linear, polynomial, or exponential rule.
- Represent a function with a table, a graph, or an equation.
- Find equilibrium points for repeated operations.

Car dealers will arrange loans for their customers, but you can also get a car loan directly from a bank. Rates may vary, so it pays to check out all your options.

Investigation Road Map

LESSON 5.11, *Getting Started,* has students look at two-term recurrences like the Fibonacci numbers and extract regularity from the recurrence. For example, if a function f satisfies the recurrence, then so will $k \cdot f$ for any constant k.

LESSON 5.12, *Recurrences,* revisits situations where closed-form and recursive definitions of functions are applied, and shows students what tools are available to help determine functions that match data.

LESSON 5.13, $f(n) = Af(n-1) + Bf(n-2)$, has students find closed forms for the two-term recurrence $f(n) = Af(n-1) + Bf(n-2)$ and determine why the solution is the sum of two exponential functions.

LESSON 5.14, $f(n) = Af(n-1) + B$, has students find closed forms for the recurrence $f(n) = Af(n-1) + B$ and determine the correct monthly payment for a car loan using several methods.

5.11 Getting Started

Activating Prior Knowledge
Exploring New Ideas

In earlier courses, you learned how to find functions with closed-form definitions that agree with functions like

$$f(n) = \begin{cases} 3 & \text{if } n = 0 \\ f(n-1) + 5 & \text{if } n > 0 \end{cases}$$

or

$$g(n) = \begin{cases} 3 & \text{if } n = 0 \\ g(n-1) + 5n + 2 & \text{if } n > 0 \end{cases}$$

or

$$h(n) = \begin{cases} 7 & \text{if } n = 0 \\ 3h(n-1) & \text{if } n > 0 \end{cases}$$

In this investigation, you will learn how to find closed-form equivalents for other kinds of recursive function definitions.

Habits of Mind

Recall what you know. Function f has constant first differences, so you can find a linear function that agrees with it. Function g has constant second differences, so you can find a quadratic function that agrees with it. Function h has constant ratios, so you can find an exponential function that agrees with it.

For You to Explore

1. Consider the recurrence

$$f(n) = f(n-1) + f(n-2)$$

This is not enough to define a function completely. You also need the initial terms $f(0)$ and $f(1)$.

For each pair of numbers below,

- Tabulate the function up to $f(8)$.
- Describe any patterns you find, either by examining the outputs of a single function or by comparing the functions with each other.

a. $f(0) = 1, f(1) = 3$ **b.** $f(0) = 5, f(1) = 15$ **c.** $f(0) = 2, f(1) = -2$
d. $f(0) = 7, f(1) = 13$ **e.** $f(0) = 3, f(1) = 17$

An equation like $f(n) = f(n-1) + f(n-2)$ is called a *recurrence*. More about this later in the investigation.

2. Consider the recurrence

$$f(n) = 2f(n-1) + 3f(n-2)$$

Again, this is not enough to define a function. For each pair of numbers below,

- Tabulate the function up to $f(8)$.
- Describe any patterns you find, either by examining the outputs of a single function or by comparing the functions with each other.
- Find a closed-form definition for a function that fits the table.

a. $f(0) = 1, f(1) = 3$ **b.** $f(0) = 5, f(1) = 15$ **c.** $f(0) = 2, f(1) = -2$
d. $f(0) = 7, f(1) = 13$ **e.** $f(0) = 3, f(1) = 17$

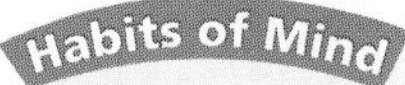

Experiment. FML models allow you to experiment with the functions.

Answers

For You to Explore

1–2. See back of book.

Lesson Overview

GOAL

- Warm up to the ideas of the investigation.

As always in a Getting Started lesson, there is no need to formalize these ideas today. Students meet all of the ideas again throughout the investigation. The exercises give students opportunities to work with recurrences and attempt to find situations where closed forms are available.

FOR YOU TO EXPLORE
- Core: 1, 2, 3
- Optional: 4, 5

MATERIALS
- graphing calculators
- Blackline Masters MC7, 5.7C

HOMEWORK
- Core: 6, 7, 10, 11
- Optional: 8, 9

Launch

Have students start on the problems right away.

Explore

For You to Explore

You may want to make copies of Blackline Master 5.7C for students to use while working the problems.

PROBLEM 1 Students should quickly recognize the relationship between part (a) and part (b), but you might need to prod them to recognize the relationship among part (b), part (c), and part (d). (Answer: All the terms starting from 7, 13, . . . are the sums of the terms from 5, 15 . . . and 2, −2, . . .) The fact that if two functions work for this type of recurrence, then their sums work, is key to the discovery of closed forms for two-term recurrences like the one in this problem, or the one in the next problem.

PROBLEM 2 Some students may have trouble with the rule for part (c), which is $f(n) = -2(-1)^n$. If students do not see the last two patterns, make sure they filled in correct values to $f(8)$. Students are very likely to see the sum and difference patterns after recognizing the similarity between the part (b) table and the tables from part (d) or part (e).

For You to Explore

PROBLEM 3 Consider skipping the last two parts of this problem, or assigning them only to students who complete the other parts of the problem quickly.

PROBLEM 4 Encourage students to use exact improper fractions, as it leads them more quickly to the Fibonacci relationship.

Wrap Up

Review the exercises, especially Exercise 3; it is prominent in Lesson 5.13.

Exercises

HOMEWORK

- Core: 6, 7, 10, 11
- Optional: 8, 9

On Your Own

EXERCISE 6 Students may or may not notice that the numbers used here are the same as those used in Exercise 3, but this is a key to understanding why the results include the numbers 5 and 2. This exercise talks about the *ratios* of successive outputs of the function in Exercise 3 (and is the reason the letter *r* represents this function). Knowing that the ratio is approaching 5 is one reason to consider an exponential function to fit the output of a recurrence like the one in Exercise 3.

3. Consider a function r that satisfies the recurrence

$$r(n) = 7r(n-1) - 10r(n-2)$$

For each of the following, find a closed-form definition for a function that agrees with r. For the first two, start by tabulating the function r.

a. $r(0) = 1,\ r(1) = 5$ **b.** $r(0) = 1,\ r(1) = 2$ **c.** $r(0) = 2,\ r(1) = 7$

d. $r(0) = 0,\ r(1) = 3$ **e.** $r(0) = 5,\ r(1) = 16$ **f.** $r(0) = m,\ r(1) = n$

You might tabulate each function first, until you find a clear relationship.

4. Start with the number 1. Take its reciprocal and add 1. Take the reciprocal of the result, and add 1. Continue the process, taking the reciprocal of the result and adding 1.

a. Explain why the following definition captures the above description.

$$f(n) = \begin{cases} 1 & \text{if } n = 0 \\ \frac{1}{f(n-1)} + 1 & \text{if } n > 0 \end{cases}$$

b. Find the exact value of $f(n)$ for each n from 0 to 10.

c. Does $f(n)$ approach a limit as n grows without bound?

5. Define B as the 2-by-2 matrix

$$B = \begin{pmatrix} 0 & 1 \\ 1 & 1 \end{pmatrix}$$

Find B^n for $n = 1, 2, 3, 4, 5$, and 6. Describe what is happening.

Do not let the calculator have all the fun.

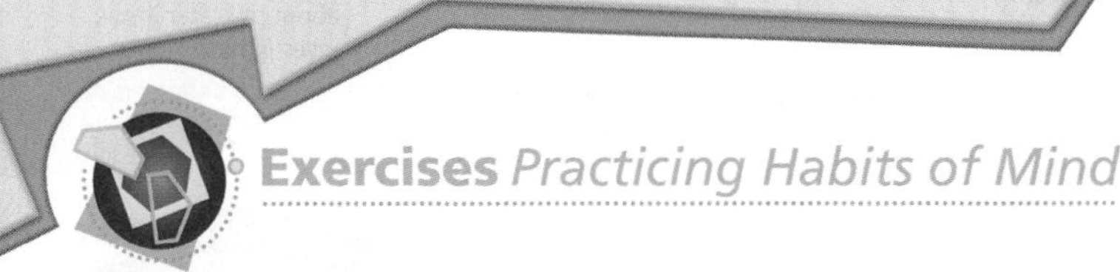

Exercises Practicing Habits of Mind

On Your Own

6. Start with the number $\frac{7}{2}$. Take its reciprocal, multiply by -10, and add 7. Take the reciprocal of the result, multiply by -10, and add 7. Continue this process, taking the reciprocal of the result, multiplying by -10, and adding 7.

a. Explain why the following definition captures the above description.

$$r(n) = \begin{cases} \frac{7}{2} & \text{if } n = 0 \\ \frac{-10}{r(n-1)} + 7 & \text{if } n > 0 \end{cases}$$

b. Find the value of $r(n)$, expressed as a fraction, for each n from 0 to 6.

c. Does $r(n)$ approach a limit as n grows without bound?

d. See if you can find other behaviors using other values for $r(0)$.

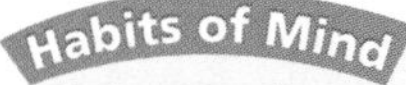

Make strategic choices. It is probably best to express $r(n)$ as an improper fraction throughout, since it is simpler to calculate the reciprocal.

Answers

3. a. $r(x) = 5^x$

b. $r(x) = 2^x$

c. $r(x) = 5^x + 2^x$

d. $r(x) = 5^x - 2^x$

e. $r(x) = 2 \cdot 5^x - 3 \cdot 2^x$

f. $r(x) = \left(\frac{n-2m}{3}\right) \cdot 5^x - \left(\frac{5m-n}{3}\right) \cdot 2^x$

4. a. The function defined matches the description.

b. See back of book.

c. Yes, it approaches 1.618.

5. $B^1 = \begin{pmatrix} 0 & 1 \\ 1 & 1 \end{pmatrix}$ $B^2 = \begin{pmatrix} 1 & 1 \\ 1 & 2 \end{pmatrix}$

$B^3 = \begin{pmatrix} 1 & 2 \\ 2 & 3 \end{pmatrix}$ $B^4 = \begin{pmatrix} 2 & 3 \\ 3 & 5 \end{pmatrix}$

$B^5 = \begin{pmatrix} 3 & 5 \\ 5 & 8 \end{pmatrix}$ $B^6 = \begin{pmatrix} 5 & 8 \\ 8 & 13 \end{pmatrix}$

Successive powers of B appear to contain consecutive numbers in the Fibonacci sequence.

Exercises

6. a. The function defined matches the description in the problem.

b. See back of book.

c. Yes, it approaches 5.

d. Except for $r(0) = 2$, $r(n) \to 5$ as n grows without bound. $r(0) = 2$ repeatedly returns 2.

7. a. Sketch the graphs of these two equations on the same axes.

$$y = x$$

$$y = -\frac{10}{x} + 7$$

b. Where do the graphs intersect?

c. What happens if, instead of $\frac{7}{2}$, you use the x-coordinate of one of the intersection points for $r(0)$ in Exercise 6?

8. Pick a number, any number. Divide it by 2 and add 1, then divide the result by 2 and add 1. Continue this process, dividing the result by 2 and adding 1.

a. What do you get after 10 iterations?

b. Do the successive outputs approach a limit?

c. Try to find other possible behaviors using different starting numbers.

9. Pick a number, any number. Multiply it by 2 and add 1, then multiply the result by 2 and add 1. Continue this process, multiplying the result by 2 and adding 1.

a. What do you get after 10 iterations?

b. Do the successive outputs approach a limit?

c. Try to find other possible behaviors using different starting numbers.

10. Find all numbers x such that

$$x^n = 7x^{n-1} - 10x^{n-2}$$

for all integers $n > 1$.

Maintain Your Skills

11. For each recurrence, find an initial value $f(0)$ that makes $f(n) = f(0)$ for all n. For example, for $f(n) = 3f(n-1) - 12$ the value is 6, because if $f(0) = 6$, then $f(1) = 3 \cdot 6 - 12 = 6$, and then $f(2) = 6$, and so on.

a. $f(n) = 2f(n-1)$

b. $f(n) = 2f(n-1) + 3$

c. $f(n) = 0.5f(n-1) + 10$

d. $f(n) = 0.8f(n-1) + 3000$

e. $f(n) = 1.005f(n-1) - 350$

f. $f(n) = Af(n-1) + B$

EXERCISE 7 You can make copies of Blackline Master MC7 for students to use with this exercise.

EXERCISE 9 The last lesson of this investigation covers the behavior seen in this exercise and the following one in more detail. Specifically, you determine when results approach a limit, and the value of that limit in terms of variables in the situation. In general, the behavior of $f(n) = Af(n-1) + B$ approaches a limit whenever $|A| < 1$.

EXERCISE 10 This method is a key component in solving the two-term recurrence $f(n) = Af(n-1) + Bf(n-2)$, as it finds all possible bases for exponential $f(n) = b^n$. You show that if the quadratic equation $x^2 = Ax + B$ has roots r and s, the closed-form function is $f(n) = Cr^n + Ds^n$ for some constants C and D determined by the initial conditions.

7. a.

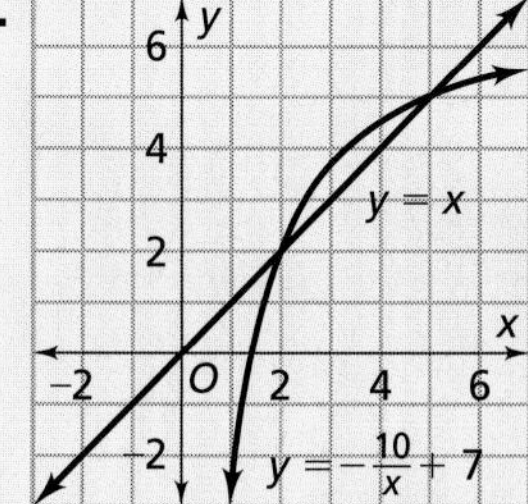

b. (2, 2) and (5, 5)

c. If $r(0) = 2$, then $r(n) = 2$, for all n. If $r(0) = 5$, then $r(n) = 5$ for all n. Both functions are constant.

8. a. Check students' work.

b. The outputs appear to be approaching 2.

c. The long-term behavior of the outputs seems independent of the starting number. They always approach 2.

9. a. Check students' work.

b. The outputs do not approach any number as a limit and depend strongly on the starting number.

c. The starting number −1 creates outputs that are all equal to −1. Increasing or decreasing the starting number creates outputs that approach infinity or negative infinity, respectively.

10. $x = 2$, $x = 5$

11. a. 0 **b.** −3 **c.** 20 **d.** 15,000 **e.** 70,000 **f.** $\frac{B}{1-A}$

Lesson Overview

GOAL

- Find general classes of functions that fit a recurrence.

This lesson reminds students about situations they encountered where recurrences and closed forms are both involved. The main goal is for students to identify that linear, polynomial, and exponential rules can all emerge from recurrences.

CHECK YOUR UNDERSTANDING
- Core: 1, 3a–b, 4, 5
- Optional: 2, 6, 7
- Extension: 3c

MATERIALS
- CAS (recommended)
- graphing calculators
- Blackline Master 5.12

HOMEWORK
- Core: 8, 11a–b, 12, 14, 15
- Optional: 9, 10
- Extension: 11c, 13

VOCABULARY
- functional equation
- recurrence
- two-term recurrence

Launch

Review Problems 1 and 2 from the Getting Started lesson if you have not already done so. Then introduce some examples of recurrences like the ones presented in the Facts and Notation section.

5.12 Recurrences

In your studies, you have encountered recursive definitions for functions, sequences, and series. Examples include Problems 2 and 4 and Exercise 11 from Lesson 5.11. Here are some others.

- The function that gives the sum of the first n squares is

$$S(n) = \begin{cases} 0 & \text{if } n = 0 \\ S(n-1) + n^2 & \text{if } n > 0 \end{cases}$$

- The function that gives the monthly balance on a loan of \$10,000 at 5% APR with a monthly payment of \$520 is

$$b(n) = \begin{cases} 10000 & \text{if } n = 0 \\ \left(1 + \frac{0.05}{12}\right) \cdot b(n-1) - 520 & \text{if } n > 0 \end{cases}$$

- The function that gives the Fibonacci numbers is

$$F(n) = \begin{cases} 0 & \text{if } n = 0 \\ 1 & \text{if } n = 1 \\ F(n-1) + F(n-2) & \text{if } n > 1 \end{cases}$$

The goal of this investigation is to develop some general purpose tools for finding closed-from equivalents for such definitions, and for proving that the closed-form functions actually do agree with the recursively defined functions.

Facts and Notation

- A **functional equation** tells how various outputs of a function are related. For example,

$$f(2x) = (f(x))^2$$

is a functional equation. Not every function satisfies this equation. But $r(x) = 3^x$ does, because

$$\begin{aligned} r(2x) &= 3x^2 \\ &= (3^x)^2 \\ &= (r(x))^2 \end{aligned}$$

- A **recurrence** is a special kind of functional equation that tells how the output of a function at integer n is related to the outputs at integers less than n. Examples include the recurrences that are satisfied by

arithmetic sequences. For example,

$$f(n) = f(n-1) + 3$$

Habits of Mind

Develop your understanding. A functional equation is an equation whose "variable" is a function. What are some other functions that satisfy this functional equation?

More complicated recurrences include the functional equations satisfied by binomial coefficients, and the function that gives the balance on a loan at the end of each month.

Geometric sequences. For example,

$$f(n) = 3f(n-1)$$

Fibonacci numbers.

$$f(n) = f(n-1) + f(n-2)$$

A recurrence like the last one, which defines the output at n in terms of the outputs at $n-2$ and $n-1$, is called a **two-term recurrence.**

As you saw in Lesson 5.1, a recurrence is not enough to define a function. You also need one or more base cases. For example, to complete the definition of an arithmetic sequence, you have to give the value for $f(0)$. See Problem 3 of Lesson 5.11 for an example of how different base cases produce different functions that satisfy the same recurrence.

The problem for this investigation is as follows.

Problem

a. Characterize all functions that satisfy a given recurrence.

b. Given base cases, find (if possible) a closed-form definition that satisfies the recurrence.

Suppose you have a recursive function definition. Here are some useful methods for finding a closed-form equivalent.

- **Model the recursive definition in your FML.** This gives you a computational model, with which you can experiment. You can look at outputs, look for patterns in the outputs, tabulate the model, graph it, and so on.
- **Tabulate the function.** Search the table for patterns. Make a difference table. If the third differences are constant, there is a cubic fit. Look at the ratios. If the successive ratios are constant, there is an exponential fit. Look at how the length of the string of digits grows. Rapid growth may point to a closed form based on an exponential function.
- **Graph the function.** For a recursively defined function, the domain is probably positive integers, in which case you will have to use a scatter plot. The shape of the plot can reveal whether the function is linear, exponential, or polynomial. A graph that looks quadratic would lead you to try a quadratic fit.
- **Use what you know from previous chapters and courses.** For example, you can write a recurrence like

  $$f(n) = 3f(n-1) + 2$$

  as

  $$f(n) = \mathcal{A}_{(3,2)}(f(n-1))$$

  where $\mathcal{A}_{(a,b)}(x) = ax + b$. In *Algebra 2* you learned how to "unstack" such recurrences using the iteration formula

  $$\mathcal{A}^{(n)}_{(a,b)} = \mathcal{A}\left(a^n, b\left(\frac{a^n-1}{a-1}\right)\right)$$

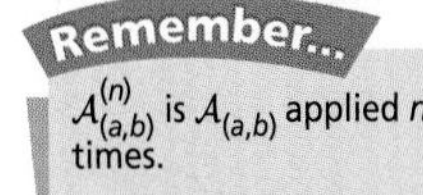

$\mathcal{A}^{(n)}_{(a,b)}$ is $\mathcal{A}_{(a,b)}$ applied n times.

Explore

Problem

Remind students that the recurrence can only give a general form, while the base cases determine the specific instance of that form. Typically, then, they use the base cases to solve an equation (or a system of equations) to determine the coefficients in the solution.

In-Class Experiment

Watch for students using a table or graph to help them answer these questions. Also, consider skipping some parts or emphasizing others.

For Discussion

PROBLEMS 6–9 Answers will vary. You might consider assigning only Problems 6 and 7 here.

Wrap Up

Review Exercise 3, or build a similar two-term recurrence such as

$$f(n) = 8f(n-1) - 15f(n-2)$$

A ratio table is most helpful to see that the ratio of consecutive terms approaches 5. Here a closed form is

$$f(n) = h \cdot 5^n + j \cdot 3^n$$

Assessment Resources

Lesson Quiz 5.12

1. Define the function p recursively as

$$p(x) = \begin{cases} 54 & \text{if } x = 0 \\ \frac{2}{3}p(x-1) & \text{if } x > 0 \end{cases}$$

a. Calculate $p(4)$.
b. Find a closed-form definition for a function that agrees with p.
c. Find the value of the sum $\sum_{k=0}^{\infty} p(k)$.

2. Define the function f recursively as

$$f(x) = 3f(x-1)$$

with $f(0) = 2$.
a. Find a closed-form definition for a function that agrees with f.
b. Find the value of the sum $\sum_{k=0}^{10} f(k)$.

A recurrence like

$$f(n) = f(n-1) + 5^n$$

unstacks to a geometric series. You know how to sum those.

In-Class Experiment

Use the methods above, or anything else you like, to find closed-form equivalents for the following functions.

1. $f(n) = \begin{cases} 3 & \text{if } n = 0 \\ f(n-1) + 7 & \text{if } n > 0 \end{cases}$

2. $f(n) = \begin{cases} 3 & \text{if } n = 0 \\ 7f(n-1) & \text{if } n > 0 \end{cases}$

3. $f(n) = \begin{cases} 3 & \text{if } n = 0 \\ 4f(n-1) - 6 & \text{if } n > 0 \end{cases}$

4. $f(n) = \begin{cases} 1 & \text{if } n = 0 \\ 3 & \text{if } n = 1 \\ 5f(n-1) - 6f(n-2) & \text{if } n > 1 \end{cases}$

5. $f(n) = \begin{cases} 2 & \text{if } n = 0 \\ 5 & \text{if } n = 1 \\ 5f(n-1) - 6f(n-2) & \text{if } n > 1 \end{cases}$

For Discussion

What kind of recurrence relation will each type of function satisfy?

6. linear
7. exponential
8. quadratic
9. degree-n polynomial

Computers that Prove Theorems

Babbage's difference engine performed calculations to find specific numerical outputs of polynomial functions. Today, computers can produce induction proofs of general theorems, like the identity

$$\sum_{k=1}^{n} k^4 = \frac{n^5}{5} + \frac{n^4}{2} + \frac{n^3}{3} - \frac{n}{30}$$

Even more surprisingly, computers can discover and prove new identities, ones which mathematicians had not previously suspected.

For more information on computer-based proofs, go to **Web Code**: bge-8031

Answers

In-Class Experiment

1. $f(n) = 7n + 3$
2. $f(n) = 3 \cdot 7^n$
3. $f(n) = 4^n + 2$
4. $f(n) = 3^n$
5. $f(n) = 2^n + 3^n$

For Discussion

6. $f(n) = f(n-1) + k$
7. $f(n) = f(n-1) \cdot k$
8. $f(n) = f(n-1) + An + B$
9. $f(n) = f(n-1) + p(n)$, where $p(n)$ is a polynomial of degree $(n-1)$

Exercises *Practicing Habits of Mind*

Check Your Understanding

1. Define function f recursively as

$$f(n) = \begin{cases} K & \text{if } n = 0 \\ 3f(n-1) & \text{if } n > 0 \end{cases}$$

Suppose also that $f(5) = 100$.

a. Calculate $f(6)$ and $f(4)$.

b. Find the value of K.

c. Find a closed-form definition for a function that agrees with f.

2. Define function g recursively, by

$$g(n) = \begin{cases} 64 & \text{if } n = 0 \\ \frac{3}{4}g(n-1) & \text{if } n > 0 \end{cases}$$

a. Calculate $g(4)$.

b. Find a closed-form definition for a function that agrees with g.

c. Find the value of this sum.

$$\sum_{j=0}^{\infty} g(j)$$

d. Approximate the value of this sum to four decimal places.

$$\sum_{j=0}^{100} g(j)$$

3. **a.** Find the bases for two different exponential functions $h(n) = a^n$ and $j(n) = b^n$ that satisfy the recurrence

$$f(n) = 10f(n-1) - 24f(n-2)$$

b. For your functions h and j in part (a), define

$$k(n) = 5h(n) + 8j(n)$$

Show that k also satisfies the recurrence

$$f(n) = 10f(n-1) - 24f(n-2)$$

c. **Take It Further** Suppose a function r satisfies the recurrence given above, and $r(0) = 3$ and $r(1) = 8$. Find a closed-form definition for a function that agrees with r.

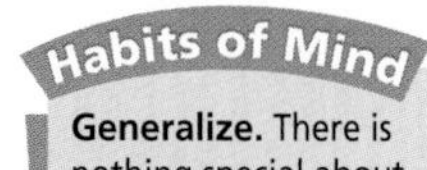

Generalize. There is nothing special about 5 and 8 here.

Exercises

HOMEWORK

- Core: 8, 11a–b, 12, 14, 15
- Optional: 9, 10
- Extension: 11c, 13

Check Your Understanding

EXERCISE 1 If you discuss this exercise, mention briefly that $f(n) = 100 \cdot 3^{n-5}$ is a good closed-form definition since the initial value was given as $f(5)$ rather than $f(0)$.

EXERCISE 2 Use this exercise to remind students how to find the sum of a geometric series, which is handy throughout this investigation.

EXERCISE 3 previews the process for a two-term recurrence, the focus of the next lesson. So, give them a chance with this one, but do not look for mastery.

Exercises

1. a. $f(6) = 300$; $f(4) = \frac{100}{3}$

b. $K = \frac{100}{243}$ or $\frac{100}{3^5}$

c. $f(n) = 100 \cdot 3^{n-5}$

2. a. $g(4) = 20.25$

b. $g(n) = 64 \cdot \left(\frac{3}{4}\right)^n$

c. 256

d. 256.0000

3. a. $h(n) = 4^n$; $j(n) = 6^n$

b.
$$\begin{aligned} 10k(n-1) - 24k(n-2) &= 10(5 \cdot 4^{n-1} + 8 \cdot 6^{n-1}) - 24(5 \cdot 4^{n-2} + 8 \cdot 6^{n-2}) \\ &= 50 \cdot 4^{n-1} + 80 \cdot 6^{n-1} - 120 \cdot 4^{n-2} - 192 \cdot 6^{n-2} \\ &= 50 \cdot 4^{n-1} + 80 \cdot 6^{n-1} - 30 \cdot 4 \cdot 4^{n-2} - 32 \cdot 6 \cdot 6^{n-2} \\ &= 50 \cdot 4^{n-1} + 80 \cdot 6^{n-1} - 30 \cdot 4^{n-1} - 32 \cdot 6^{n-1} \\ &= 20 \cdot 4^{n-1} + 48 \cdot 6^{n-1} \\ &= 5 \cdot 4 \cdot 4^{n-1} + 8 \cdot 6 \cdot 6^{n-1} \\ &= 5 \cdot 4^n + 8 \cdot 6^n \\ &= k(n) \end{aligned}$$

c. $r(n) = 5 \cdot 4^n - 2 \cdot 6^n$

EXERCISE 4 is suspiciously simple, but later exercises follow the same pattern with more complicated recurrences.

EXERCISE 5 This method, based on the fixed point, is one way to get closed-form function definitions that agree with recursive ones in the form $f(x) = Af(x - 1) + B$, like those used for annuities and loan payments. This exercise serves as a preview to the material on annuities and loan payments later in this investigation.

EXERCISE 7 You can make copies of Blackline Master 5.12 for students to use with this exercise.

4. Suppose f is a function that satisfies the recurrence $f(n) = 2f(n - 1)$.

a. Find a value b for $f(0)$ that makes f a constant function.

b. Judy starts with $f(0)$ a distance of 16 units away from b. That is, $|f(0) - b| = 16$. How far away from b is $f(1)$? $f(2)$?

5. Josue considers the more complicated recurrence

$$j(n) = 2j(n - 1) + 3$$

a. What base case $j(0) = b$ makes j a constant function?

b. Josue starts with $j(0)$ a distance of 16 units away from b. How far away from b is $j(1)$? $j(2)$?

6. Consider function g from Exercise 2.

a. Find $\lim_{n \to \infty} g(n)$.

b. How far away from this limit is $g(0)$? $g(1)$? $g(2)$?

7. Consider the recurrence

$$r(x) = \frac{3}{4}r(x - 1) + 10$$

a. Find a closed-form definition for a function that agrees with r if $r(0) = 40$.

b. Copy and complete the following table for the base case $r(0) = 104$.

n	$r(n)$	Δ	÷
0	104	■	■
1	■	■	■
2	■	■	■
3	■	■	■
4	■	■	■
5	■	■	■
6	■	■	■
7	■	■	
8	■		

The ÷ column consists of the ratios of successive entries in the Δ column—the ratios of successive differences.

Answers

4. a. $b = 0$

b. $f(1)$ is 32 away from b and $f(2)$ is 64 away from b.

5. a. $b = -3$

b. $j(1)$ is 32 away from b and $j(2)$ is 64 away from b.

6. a. 0

b. $g(0)$ is 64 away from the limit, $g(1)$ is 48 away from the limit, $g(2)$ is 36 away from the limit.

7. a. $r(x) = 40$

b.

n	$r(n)$	Δ	÷
0	104	−16	0.75
1	88	−12	0.75
2	76	−9	0.75
3	67	−6.75	0.75
4	60.25	−5.0625	0.75
5	55.1875	−3.7969	0.75
6	51.3906	−2.8477	0.75
7	48.5430	−2.1357	
8	46.4072		

On Your Own

8. Establish the following identity.

$$(1 + r + r^2 + r^3 + \cdots + r^{n-1})(1 - r) = 1 - r^n$$

So, for any number $r \neq 1$,
$1 + r + r^2 + r^3 + \cdots + r^{n-1} = \frac{1 - r^n}{1 - r}$

9. Write About It The formula for the sum of an infinite geometric series when $|r| < 1$ is

$$\sum_{k=0}^{\infty} r^k = \frac{1}{1 - r}$$

Why is $|r| < 1$ required? Why does this formula not work for $|r| \geq 1$?

10. Define function f recursively as

$$f(x) = 4f(x - 1)$$

with $f(0) = 3$.

a. Find a closed-form definition for a function that agrees with f.

b. Find the value of

$$\sum_{k=0}^{10} f(k)$$

11. a. Find the bases for two different exponential functions $h(n) = a^n$ and $j(n) = b^n$ that satisfy the recurrence

$$f(n) = 11f(n - 1) - 24f(n - 2)$$

b. For your functions h and j in part (a), define

$$k(n) = 7h(n) - 2j(n)$$

Show that k also satisfies the recurrence

$$f(n) = 11f(n - 1) - 24f(n - 2)$$

c. Take It Further Suppose a function r satisfies the recurrence given above and $r(0) = 5$ and $r(1) = 10$. Find a closed-form definition for a function that agrees with r.

Habits of Mind

Generalize. There is nothing special about 7 and −2 here.

12. Here is a recurrence.

$$f(n) = 5f(n - 1) - 6f(n - 2)$$

For each sequence below, decide whether or not the sequence could be consecutive outputs of a function that satisfies the recurrence.

a. 1, 2, 4, 8, 16, 32

b. 1, 3, 9, 27, 81, 243

c. 2, 5, 13, 35, 97, 275

d. 1, 4, 16, 64, 256, 1024

e. 0, 0, 0, 0, 0, 0

f. $a + b$, $2a + 3b$, $4a + 9b$, $8a + 27b$, $16a + 81b$, $32a + 243b$

g. 7, 13, 23, 37, 47, 13

Go Online PHSchool.com

For additional practice, go to **Web Code:** bga-0512

On Your Own

EXERCISE 12 Point out to students that the sequence in part (f) is a times the first plus b times the second. This is the general tactic that is used in the next lesson: find two exponential functions that satisfy the recursive definition, then show that you can solve any initial values by a times the first exponential function plus b times the second.

8. Expand the left side to $1 + r^2 + r^3 + \cdots + r^{n-1}$, then multiply by -1 to get $-1 - r^2 - r^3 - \ldots - r^{n-1}$. Adding together these terms leaves just $(1 - r^n)$ as the result of the expansion.

9. If $|r| > 1$, then the terms get infinitely larger, not smaller.

10. a. $f(n) = 3 \cdot 4^n$

b. 4,194,303

11. a. $h(n) = 3^n$, $j(n) = 8^n$

b.
$$\begin{aligned}
11k(n-1) - 24k(n-2) &= 11(7 \cdot 3^{n-1} - 2 \cdot 8^{n-1}) - 24(7 \cdot 3^{n-2} + 2 \cdot 8^{n-2}) \\
&= 77 \cdot 3^{n-1} - 22 \cdot 8^{n-1} - 168 \cdot 3^{n-2} + 48 \cdot 2^{n-2} \\
&= 77 \cdot 3^{n-1} - 22 \cdot 8^{n-1} - 56 \cdot 3 \cdot 3^{n-2} + 6 \cdot 8 \cdot 8^{n-2} \\
&= 77 \cdot 3^{n-1} - 22 \cdot 8^{n-1} - 56 \cdot 3^{n-1} - 6 \cdot 8^{n-1} \\
&= 21 \cdot 3^{n-1} - 16 \cdot 8^{n-1} \\
&= 7 \cdot 3 \cdot 3^{n-1} + 2 \cdot 8 \cdot 8^{n-1} \\
&= 7 \cdot 3^n + 2 \cdot 8^n \\
&= k(n)
\end{aligned}$$

c. $r(n) = 6 \cdot 3^n - 8^n$

12. a. yes **b.** yes **c.** yes **d.** no
e. yes **f.** yes **g.** yes

Maintain Your Skills

EXERCISE 15 You can do this exercise efficiently by using the calculator and spreadsheet interaction on the nSpire. On one screen, define (and redefine) $t(n)$, while a second screen has an input-output and ratio table. Students may want to add extra columns such as the result of $t(n) - 3^n$ to find the other part of the closed form.

This exercise may take a while. You might consider only assigning one or two parts. The closed form in Part (c) is the simplest to identify, since it involves powers of 10. Still, not all students find the closed form here, and you should consider this exercise a chance for students to figure out the rules governing closed forms before the formality of the next lesson.

Additional Resources

PRINT RESOURCES
- Solution Manual
- Practice Workbook
- Assessment Resources
- Teaching Resources

TECHNOLOGY
- Interactive Textbook
- TeacherExpress CD-ROM
- ExamView CD-ROM
- PHSchool.com

Additional Practice

1. Define function f recursively as

$$f(n) = \begin{cases} c & \text{if } n = 0 \\ 2 \cdot f(n-1) & \text{if } n > 0 \end{cases}$$

Suppose also that $f(4) = 80$.
a. Calculate $f(3)$ and $f(5)$.
b. Find the value of c.
c. Find a closed-form definition for a function that agrees with f.

2. Define function g recursively as

$$g(x) = \begin{cases} 12 & \text{if } x = 0 \\ \frac{1}{3}g(x-1) & \text{if } x > 0 \end{cases}$$

a. Calculate $g(6)$.
b. Find a closed-form definition for a function that agrees with g.
c. Find the value of this sum.

$$\sum_{k=0}^{\infty} g(k)$$

3. Define f recursively as

$$f(x) = 5 \cdot f(x-1)$$

with $f(0) = 10$.
a. Find a closed-form definition for a function that agrees with f.
b. Find the value of

$$\sum_{k=0}^{10} f(k)$$

4. Here is a recurrence.

$$f(n) = 3f(n-1) - 2f(n-2)$$

For each sequence below, decide whether or not the sequence could be consecutive outputs of a function that satisfies the recurrence.
a. 0, 1, 3, 7, 15, 31
b. 0, a, $3a$, $4a$, $6a$, $10a$
c. 2, 3, 5, 7, 9, 11
d. 10, 15, 55, 135, 295, 615

Practice: For Lesson 5.12, assign Exercises 1–4.

13. **Take It Further** Find a closed-form definition for a function f that generates the sequence from Exercise 12g,

$$7, 13, 23, 37, 47, 13, \ldots$$

and continues to satisfy the recurrence

$$f(n) = 5f(n-1) - 6f(n-2)$$

14. **Standardized Test Prep** This is the top row of the difference table for a polynomial function of degree 4.

Input, n	Output, $f(n)$	Δ	Δ^2	Δ^3	Δ^4
0	z	r	m	c	1

Which of the following is the $n = 3$ row?

a.

3	$z + 3r$	$r + 3m$	$m + 3c$	$c + 3$	1

b.

3	$4z + 2r + m$	$4r + 2m + c$	$4m + 2c + 1$	$4c + 2$	1

c.

3	z^3	r^3	m^3	c^3	1

d.

3	$z + 3r + 3m + c$	$r + 3m + 3c + 1$	$m + 3c + 3$	$c + 3$	1

Maintain Your Skills

15. Given each recursively-defined function,
- Tabulate t using inputs from 0 to 7.
- Describe what is happening to the ratio of consecutive terms as the input grows.
- Find a closed-form definition for a function that agrees with t.

a. $t(n) = 5t(n-1) - 6t(n-2)$, with $t(0) = 2$ and $t(1) = 5$
b. $t(n) = 3t(n-1) + 10t(n-2)$, with $t(0) = 2$ and $t(1) = 3$
c. $t(n) = 13t(n-1) - 30t(n-2)$, with $t(0) = 2$ and $t(1) = 13$
d. $t(n) = -7t(n-1) - 12t(n-2)$, with $t(0) = 2$ and $t(1) = -7$
e. $t(n) = 7t(n-1) - 12t(n-2)$, with $t(0) = 2$ and $t(1) = 7$
f. $t(n) = 6t(n-1) + 40t(n-2)$, with $t(0) = 2$ and $t(1) = 6$

Habits of Mind

Look for a pattern. All the closed-form definitions will be similar. If you can find one, it will be easier to find the others.

Answers

13. $f(n) = 8 \cdot 2^n - 3^n$ **14.** D

15. a.

n	$t(n)$
0	2
1	5
2	13
3	35
4	97
5	275
6	793
7	2315

The ratio of consecutive terms is approaching 3.
$f(n) = 2^n + 3^n$

5.13 $f(n) = Af(n-1) + Bf(n-2)$

What can you say about a function that satisfies this recurrence?

$$f(n) = 7f(n-1) - 10f(n-2)$$

For the sake of illustration, try to find a closed-form definition for a function that agrees with g, which is f with base cases specified as shown:

$$g(n) = \begin{cases} 4 & \text{if } n = 0 \\ 11 & \text{if } n = 1 \\ 7g(n-1) - 10g(n-2) & \text{if } n > 1 \end{cases}$$

Start by building a model for g and tabulating it:

n	$g(n)$
0	4
1	11
2	37
3	149
4	673
5	3221
6	15,817
7	78,509
8	391,393
9	1,954,661
10	9,768,697
11	48,834,269
12	244,152,913
13	1,220,727,701
14	6,103,564,777
15	30,517,676,429
16	152,588,087,233
17	762,939,846,341
18	3,814,698,052,057
19	19,073,487,900,989
20	95,367,434,786,353

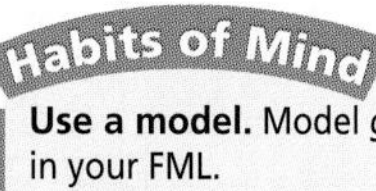

Use a model. Model g in your FML.

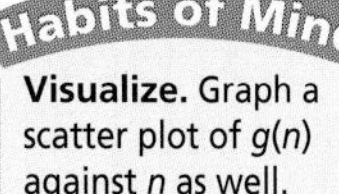

Visualize. Graph a scatter plot of $g(n)$ against n as well.

Lesson Overview

GOAL

- Relate a solution for a two-term recurrence to a quadratic polynomial.

This lesson targets two-term recurrences, and gives reasons why their closed forms are the sum of exponentials. Concentrate on the characteristic polynomial, whose roots are the bases of the exponentials.

CHECK YOUR UNDERSTANDING

- Core: 1a–e, 2, 3, 7
- Optional: 4, 5, 6
- Extension: 1f

MATERIALS

- graphing calculators
- Blackline Master 5.13

HOMEWORK

- Core: 8, 9, 10, 12, 16, 17
- Optional: 11
- Extension: 13, 14, 15

Launch

Begin today's lesson by reviewing Exercise 15 from the previous lesson, and see if students came up with any closed forms or generalizations.

You may want to use Blackline Master 5.13 as an overhead as you walk the students through the tabulation of function g.

b.

n	$t(n)$
0	2
1	3
2	29
3	117
4	641
5	3093
6	15,689
7	77,997

The ratio of consecutive terms is approaching 5. $f(n) = 5^n + (-2)^n$

c.

n	$t(n)$
0	2
1	13
2	109
3	1027
4	10,081
5	100,243
6	1,000,729
7	10,002,187

The ratio of consecutive terms is approaching 10. $f(n) = 10^n + 3^n$

d–f. See back of book.

The length of the digit strings suggests exponential growth. To test this, add a column with the ratios of consecutive terms.

n	$g(n)$	$\frac{g(n+1)}{g(n)}$
0	4	2.75
1	11	3.36364
2	37	4.02703
3	149	4.51678
4	673	4.78603
5	3221	4.91059
6	15,817	4.96358
7	78,509	4.98533
8	391,393	4.99411
9	1,954,661	4.99764
10	9,768,697	4.99906
11	48,834,269	4.99962
12	244,152,913	4.99985
13	1,220,727,701	4.99994
14	6,103,564,777	4.99998
15	30,517,676,429	4.99999
16	152,588,087,233	5.00000
17	762,939,846,341	5.00000
18	3,814,698,052,057	5.00000
19	19,073,487,900,989	5.00000
20	95,367,434,786,353	

Depending on your system, you may get slightly different numbers for the ratios. The constant 5 is an approximation—the actual ratio is very close to 5.

It looks as if the growth is "almost exponential." In fact, it looks as if the function $n \mapsto 5^n$ is close to a solution. What is going on?

Tabulate $n \mapsto 5^n$ next to g.

The answer is hinted at in Exercise 3 in Lesson 5.12. There are exponential functions of the form $n \mapsto a^n$ that satisfy the recurrence

$$g(n) = 7g(n-1) - 10g(n-2)$$

but they do not satisfy the base cases

$$g(0) = 4 \text{ and } g(1) = 11$$

But all is not lost. By transforming the exponential solutions a little, you can get a closed-form definition for a function that agrees with g. Here is how:

Suppose $n \mapsto a^n$ satisfies the recurrence

$$g(n) = 7g(n-1) - 10g(n-2)$$

Then $a^n = 7a^{n-1} - 10a^{n-2}$ for all integers $n \geq 2$.

Since the base of an exponential function cannot be 0, you can divide both sides by a^{n-2}. You get

$$a^2 = 7a - 10$$

This is a quadratic equation. So, if $n \mapsto a^n$ satisfies the recurrence, a must be a root of the quadratic equation

$$a^2 - 7a + 10 = 0$$

The roots of this equation are 2 and 5 (there is the 5 again). Just to be sure, check it out:

The polynomial $x^2 - 7x + 10$ is called the *characteristic polynomial* for the recurrence $g(n)$.

For You to Do

Show the following for all integers $n \geq 2$.

1. $2^n = 7 \cdot 2^{n-1} - 10 \cdot 2^{n-2}$
2. $5^n = 7 \cdot 5^{n-1} - 10 \cdot 5^{n-2}$

But not only does $n \mapsto 2^n$ satisfy the recurrence, so does the more general exponential function $n \mapsto k \cdot 2^n$, for any number k. To see this, multiply both sides of the equation

$$2^n = 7 \cdot 2^{n-1} - 10 \cdot 2^{n-2}$$

by k. If you distribute the k on the right side, you get

$$k \cdot 2^n = 7 \cdot k \cdot 2^{n-1} - 10 \cdot k \cdot 2^{n-2}$$

So, $n \mapsto k \cdot 2^n$ satisfies the recurrence

$$g(n) = 7 \cdot g(n-1) - 10 \cdot g(n-2)$$

Similarly, any function of the form $n \mapsto j \cdot 5^n$ for some constant j will also satisfy the recurrence.

Minds in Action — episode 16

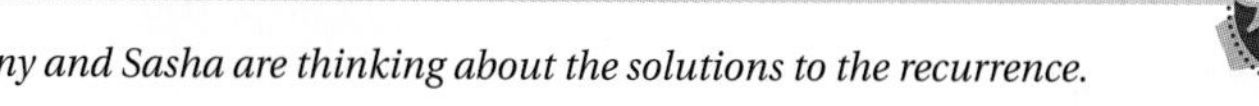

Tony and Sasha are thinking about the solutions to the recurrence.

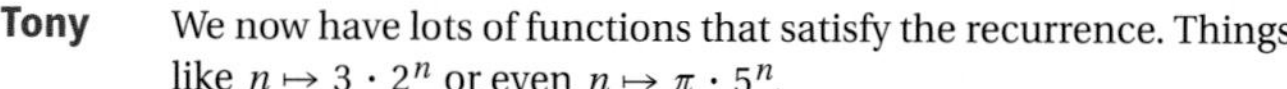

Tony We now have lots of functions that satisfy the recurrence. Things like $n \mapsto 3 \cdot 2^n$ or even $n \mapsto \pi \cdot 5^n$.

Sasha But none of them satisfy the base cases. They can't, because, for example, $j \cdot 5^n$ is j when $n = 0$, so j would have to be 4 if the first base case is true.

Tony And $j \cdot 5^n$ is $5j$ when $n = 1$, so if $j = 4$, $5j$ is 20. The second base case says it has to be 11. No good.

Answers

For You to Do

1. $2^n = 7 \cdot 2^{n-1} - 10 \cdot 2^{n-2}$
$= 7 \cdot 2^{n-1} - 5 \cdot 2 \cdot 2^{n-2}$
$= 7 \cdot 2^{n-1} - 5 \cdot 2^{n-1}$
$= 2 \cdot 2^{n-1}$
$= 2^n$

2. $5^n = 7 \cdot 5^{n-1} - 10 \cdot 5^{n-2}$
$= 7 \cdot 5^{n-1} - 2 \cdot 5 \cdot 5^{n-2}$
$= 7 \cdot 5^{n-1} - 2 \cdot 5^{n-1}$
$= 5 \cdot 5^{n-1}$
$= 5^n$

Enter Derman, who stares at the board.

Derman Why not do both? Do some 5^n's and some 2^n's. It would be $n \mapsto k \cdot 2^n + j \cdot 5^n$. Now you have two variables—I bet you can find k and j that make the function 4 at 0 and 11 at 1.

Sasha Two equations and two unknowns. I think he's on to something.

Tony Yes, but now it probably won't satisfy the recurrence.

Sasha Maybe it will. They each work by themselves. Look—take the two expressions and add down.

Sasha writes on the board.

$$\begin{array}{rcccl} & k \cdot 2^n & = & 7 \cdot k \cdot 2^{n-1} & - \quad 10 \cdot k \cdot 2^{n-2} \\ + & j \cdot 5^n & = & 7 \cdot j \cdot 5^{n-1} & - \quad 10 \cdot j \cdot 5^{n-2} \\ \hline & k \cdot 2^n + j \cdot 5^n & = & 7(k \cdot 2^{n-1} + j \cdot 5^{n-1}) & - \quad 10(k \cdot 2^{n-2} + j \cdot 5^{n-2}) \end{array}$$

Tony So, the sum of the two solutions will be another solution. Nice.

Derman See? I told you it would work.

Tony Don't worry, we believed you. Now we can find k and j to make the base cases work. Let's see—our closed form is $n \mapsto k \cdot 2^n + j \cdot 5^n$. If n is 0, we want this to be 4, so $k \cdot 2^0 + j \cdot 5^0 = 4$. That's just

$$k + j = 4$$

And when $n = 1$, the output is $k \cdot 2^1 + j \cdot 5^1$. We want this to be 11, so

$$2k + 5j = 11$$

Derman See? Two equations in two unknowns, like Sasha said. I told you it would work.

Sasha Fine, fine. Now we solve the system

$$\begin{aligned} k + j &= 4 \\ 2k + 5j &= 11 \end{aligned}$$

and we get $k = 3$ and $j = 1$. Looks like the closed form is

$$h(n) = 3 \cdot 2^n + 5^n$$

Tony I'll check it against the table . . . It worked!

Derman No doubt!

For You to Do

3. Show that Sasha, Tony and Derman's function h and the original function g agree for the domain of g. That is, show that the two functions

$$h(n) = 3 \cdot 2^n + 5^n \text{ and } g(n) = \begin{cases} 4 & \text{if } n = 0 \\ 11 & \text{if } n = 1 \\ 7g(n-1) - 10g(n-2) & \text{if } n > 1 \end{cases}$$

agree for all nonnegative integers n.

> The natural domain of h is all of $\mathbb{R}$, while g is defined only for nonnegative integers.

Embedded in the above example is a general method for solving any two-term recurrence. You will give a precise description of the method in Exercise 6.

And Sasha's "add down" insight leads to another useful result.

Theorem 5.3 Closure of Solutions

If two functions r and s satisfy the two-term recurrence

$$f(n) = Af(n-1) + Bf(n-2)$$

then so does any linear combination

$$t(n) = k \cdot r(n) + j \cdot s(n)$$

where k and j are real numbers.

> **Remember...**
> A linear combination of x and y is $ax + by$, where a and b are real numbers.

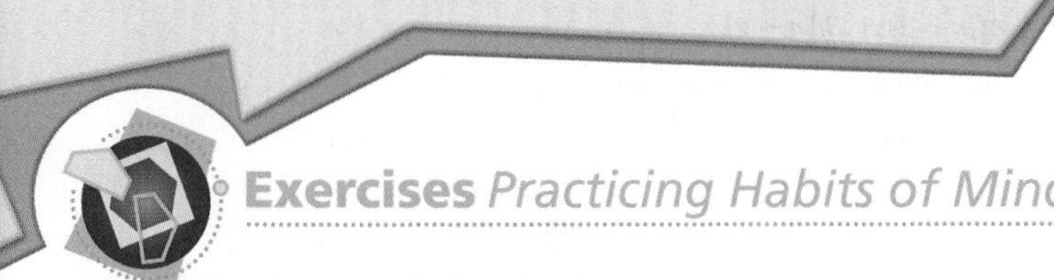

Exercises *Practicing Habits of Mind*

Check Your Understanding

1. The two-term recurrence

$$f(n) = 7f(n-1) - 10f(n-2)$$

is satisfied by any function in the form $f(n) = A \cdot 2^n + B \cdot 5^n$. Each of the sequences below satisfies the recurrence. For each sequence, calculate the next two terms. Then find the values of A and B.

a. 4, 14, 58, ...
b. 0, −3, −21, ...
c. 4, 11, 37, ...
d. 0, 1, 7, ...
e. 1, 0, −10, ...
f. **Take It Further** $x, y, -10x + 7y, \ldots$

> **Habits of Mind**
> **Generalize.** How can you use the other sequences in this exercise to help with part (f)?

Answers

For You to Do

3. $7(3 \cdot 2^{n-1} + 5^{n-1})$
$- 10(3 \cdot 2^{n-2} + 5^{n-2})$
$= (21 \cdot 2^{n-1} - 30 \cdot 2^{n-2})$
$+ (7 \cdot 5^{n-1} - 10 \cdot 5^{n-2})$
$= (21 \cdot 2^{n-1} - 15 \cdot 2^{n-1})$
$+ (7 \cdot 5^{n-1} - 2 \cdot 5^{n-1})$
$= 6 \cdot 2^{n-1} + 5 \cdot 5^{n-1}$
$= 3 \cdot 2^n + 5^n$
$= h(n)$

Exercises

1. a. 266 and 1282; $A = 2, B = 2$
b. −117 and −609; $A = 1, B = -1$
c. 149 and 673; $A = 3, B = 1$
d. 39 and 203; $A = -\frac{1}{3}, B = \frac{1}{3}$
e. −70 and −390; $A = \frac{5}{3}, B = -\frac{2}{3}$
f. $-70x + 39y$ and $-390x + 203y$; $A = \dfrac{5x - y}{3}, B = \dfrac{y - 2x}{3}$

Explore

For You to Do

PROBLEM 3 You can verify the base cases $n = 0$ and $n = 1$ directly. The induction step looks very similar to what Sasha drew in the dialog, using the specific numbers $k = 3$ and $j = 1$. The goal is to show that $h(n) = 7h(n-1) - 10h(n-2)$ for $n \geq 2$; in other words, show that

$$3 \cdot 2^n + 5^n = 7(3 \cdot 2^{n-1} + 5^{n-1}) - 10(3 \cdot 2^{n-2} + 5^{n-2})$$

Students were asked to do similar work in part (b) of Exercise 3 in Lesson 5.12, and are asked in the upcoming exercises to do this type of work.

Wrap Up

Give students a two-term recurrence they have not seen before, such as

$$f(n) = 13f(n-1) - 36f(n-2)$$

with initial conditions $f(0) = 5$, $f(1) = 35$, and have them construct the closed form

$$f(n) = 2 \cdot 4^n + 3 \cdot 9^n$$

Or explore the Fibonacci closed form (Exercise 7).

Assessment Resources

Lesson Quiz 5.13

1. Find a closed-form definition for a function that agrees with h.

$$h(a) = \begin{cases} 4 & \text{if } a = 0 \\ 14 & \text{if } a = 1 \\ 7h(a-1) - 12h(a-2) & \text{if } a > 1 \end{cases}$$

2. Consider the two-term recurrence

$$f(n) = 11f(n-1) - 18f(n-2)$$

a. Show that 2^n satisfies the recurrence.
b. Find a closed-form definition for f if the initial conditions are $f(0) = 6$ and $f(1) = 33$.

Exercises

HOMEWORK
- Core: 8, 9, 10, 12, 16, 17
- Optional: 11
- Extension: 13, 14, 15

Check Your Understanding

EXERCISE 1 Look for any student solving the general case first, rather than repeatedly solving the 2-by-2 system of equations.

EXERCISE 2 The proofs here should help students understand the connection between quadratics and the corresponding solutions to recurrences. The sum and product results are fundamental to the proofs and explain why both 10^n and 3^n can solve the recurrence.

EXERCISE 7 is the key exercise of the lesson; students are being asked to generate the Binet formula for Fibonacci numbers. Students who understand the prior exercises, especially the ones which do not factor, may have immediate success with this.

If you feel your students are not ready, assign the On Your Own exercises, then return to do this one in class. This exercise is definitely one to give students a chance to solve; those who do should be very satisfied with what they have accomplished!

GOING FURTHER You might also point out that this exercise explains why the ratio of successive Fibonacci numbers approaches the golden ratio. As n gets higher, the second term approaches zero since $\frac{1-\sqrt{5}}{2}$ is between -1 and 1, so $f(n)$ gets closer and closer to the powers of the golden ratio.

2. Consider the two-term recurrence

$$g(n) = 13g(n-1) - 30g(n-2)$$

a. What two numbers have a sum of 13 and a product of 30?

b. Show that $g(n) = 10^n$ satisfies the recurrence.

c. Show that $g(n) = 3^n$ satisfies the recurrence.

d. Show that $g(n) = 10^n + 3^n$ satisfies the recurrence.

That is, show that $10^n = 13 \cdot 10^{n-1} - 30 \cdot 10^{n-2}$ for any integer $n \geq 2$.

3. Find a closed-form definition for a function that agrees with t.

$$t(n) = \begin{cases} 5 & \text{if } n = 0 \\ 19 & \text{if } n = 1 \\ 8t(n-1) - 15t(n-2) & \text{if } n > 1 \end{cases}$$

4. Define function t by

$$t(n) - 10t(n-1) + 21t(n-2) = 0$$

with $t(0) = 2$ and $t(1) = 10$. Find a closed-form equivalent for t.

Make a connection. What connection is there between this and $x^2 - 10x + 21$?

5. Find different exponential functions $h(n) = a^n$ and $j(n) = b^n$ that satisfy the two-term recurrence

$$f(n) = 2f(n-1) + f(n-2)$$

Use the quadratic formula.

6. **Write About It** Describe a method for finding a closed form (in terms of A and B) for a function that satisfies the two-term recurrence

$$f(n) = Af(n-1) + Bf(n-2)$$

7. The Fibonacci numbers are the outputs of the function f defined by

$$f(n) = f(n-1) + f(n-2)$$

with the initial conditions $f(0) = 0$ and $f(1) = 1$. Find a closed-form equivalent for f.

On Your Own

8. Function f satisfies the recurrence

$$f(n) = 9f(n-1) - 20f(n-2)$$

Find a closed-form equivalent for f if

a. $f(0) = 2$ and $f(1) = 9$

b. $f(0) = 20$ and $f(1) = 90$

Answers

2. a. 10 and 3

b. $13 \cdot 10^{n-1} - 30 \cdot 10^{n-2}$
$= 13 \cdot 10^{n-1} - 3 \cdot 10 \cdot 10^{n-2}$
$= 13 \cdot 10^{n-1} - 3 \cdot 10^{n-1}$
$= 10 \cdot 10^{n-1}$
$= 10^n$

c. $13 \cdot 3^{n-1} - 30 \cdot 3^{n-2}$
$= 13 \cdot 3^{n-1} - 10 \cdot 3 \cdot 3^{n-2}$
$= 13 \cdot 3^{n-1} - 10 \cdot 3^{n-1}$
$= 3 \cdot 3^{n-1}$
$= 3^n$

d. $13(10^{n-1} + 3^{n-1}) - 30(10^{n-2} + 3^{n-2})$
$= (13 \cdot 10^{n-1} - 30 \cdot 10^{n-2}) + (13 \cdot 3^{n-1} - 30 \cdot 3^{n-2})$
See proofs in parts (b) and (c) to complete the proof.

3. $t(n) = 3 \cdot 3^n + 2 \cdot 5^n$

4. $t(n) = 3^n + 7^n$

5. $h(n) = (1+\sqrt{2})^n$, $j(n) = (1-\sqrt{2})^n$

6. Answers may vary. Sample: Use the quadratic equation $x^2 = Ax + B$ to find the two roots that are used to determine the closed form. Either root of the equation $x^2 - Ax - B = 0$ can be the base.

7. $f(n) = \dfrac{\left(\frac{1+\sqrt{5}}{2}\right)^n - \left(\frac{1-\sqrt{5}}{2}\right)^n}{\sqrt{5}}$

8. a. $f(n) = 4^n + 5^n$

b. $f(n) = 10(4^n + 5^n)$

9. Consider the two-term recurrence $f(n) = 8f(n-1) - 12f(n-2)$.

   a. Why might you guess that an exponential function would satisfy the recurrence?

   b. Show that $f(n) = 6^n$ satisfies this recurrence.

   c. Find a closed-form definition for f if the initial conditions are $f(0) = 2$ and $f(1) = 8$.

   d. Find a closed-form definition for f if the initial conditions are $f(0) = 5$ and $f(1) = 26$.

10. Find a closed-form equivalent for a function f that fits this table by first determining a two-term recurrence that the function satisfies.

x	$f(x)$
0	2
1	10
2	36
3	152
4	592
5	2400

11. Suppose f satisfies the recurrence $f(n) = 6f(n-1) - 7f(n-2)$.

   a. Show that if $f(0) = 1$ and $f(1) = 3 + \sqrt{2}$, then $f(2) = (3 + \sqrt{2})^2$.

   b. Find both possible values of b that make $f(n) = b^n$ satisfy the recurrence.

   c. If $f(0) = 2$ and $f(1) = 6$, find a closed-form definition for f.

   d. If $f(0) = 0$ and $f(1) = 1$, find a closed-form definition for f.

12. Find a closed-form definition for the function $L(n) = L(n-1) + L(n-2)$ with $L(0) = 2$ and $L(1) = 1$. This function generates the Lucas numbers

$$2, 1, 3, 4, 7, 11, \ldots$$

13. **Take It Further** Define function f by

$$f(n) = 4f(n-1) - 13f(n-2)$$

with $f(0) = 2$ and $f(1) = 4$.

   a. Tabulate f using inputs from 0 to 8.

   b. Find a closed-form equivalent for f using the techniques from this lesson. What is different about this exercise? Does the process still work?

14. **Take It Further** Suppose f satisfies the recurrence

$$f(n) = 19f(n-2) - 30f(n-3)$$

Find a closed-form definition for f if $f(0) = 8$, $f(1) = 3$, and $f(2) = 79$.

For additional practice, go to Web Code: bga-0513

On Your Own

EXERCISE 10 You might remind students that there is more than one possible function f that fits the table, but the two-term recurrence leads to a specific closed-form definition.

This is a fairly difficult exercise, since the recurrence is unknown. Consider asking students to determine the recurrence as a separate exercise.

EXERCISE 11 The solution method here is similar to Exercise 7 on the Fibonacci numbers.

EXERCISE 14 requires students to think about how they can extend the rules for two-term recurrences. In general, closed forms for three-term recurrences are difficult to find due to the difficulty of solving cubic equations. Here, the equation has three integer roots, so students can find the form more directly.

9. a. Answers may vary. Sample: One way would be to tabulate $f(n)$ and notice that a common ratio between terms emerges, suggesting that this ratio might fit the recurrence.

b. $8 \cdot 6^{n-1} - 12 \cdot 6^{n-2}$
$= 8 \cdot 6^{n-1} - 2 \cdot 6 \cdot 6^{n-2}$
$= 8 \cdot 6^{n-1} - 2 \cdot 6^{n-1}$
$= 6 \cdot 6^{n-1}$
$= 6^n$

c. $f(n) = 6^n + 2^n$

d. $f(n) = 4 \cdot 6^n + 2^n$

10. $f(n) = \frac{7}{3} \cdot 4^n - \frac{1}{3} \cdot (-2)^n$

11. a. $f(2) = 6(3 + \sqrt{2}) - 7(1)$
$= 11 + 6\sqrt{2}$
$= (3 + \sqrt{2})^2$

b. $b_1 = 3 + \sqrt{2}$, $b_2 = 3 - \sqrt{2}$

c. $f(n) = (3 + \sqrt{2})^n + (3 - \sqrt{2})^n$

d. $f(n) = \frac{1}{2\sqrt{2}} \cdot ((3 + \sqrt{2})^n - (3 - \sqrt{2})^n)$

12. $L(n) = \left(\frac{1 + \sqrt{5}}{2}\right)^n + \left(\frac{1 - \sqrt{5}}{2}\right)^n$

13 a.

n	$f(n)$
0	2
1	4
2	−10
3	−92
4	−238
5	244
6	4070
7	13,108
8	−478

b. $f(n) = (2 + 3i)^n + (2 - 3i)^n$
The process still works, but the difference is that $f(n)$ uses complex numbers.

14. $f(n) = 5 \cdot 2^n + 3^n + 2 \cdot (-5)^n$

EXERCISE 15 closes a loophole, addressing the issue of a double root in the quadratic characteristic polynomial. The solution is similar to how you deal with a double root in the method of partial fractions.

Maintain Your Skills

EXERCISE 17 may be a review of material students learned in an earlier course, so use this exercise as a gauge to see if students need a refresher.

Additional Resources

PRINT RESOURCES
- Solution Manual
- Practice Workbook
- Assessment Resources
- Teaching Resources

TECHNOLOGY
- Interactive Textbook
- TeacherExpress CD-ROM
- ExamView CD-ROM
- PHSchool.com

Additional Practice

1. The two-term recurrence

$$f(n) = 4f(n-1) - 3f(n-2)$$

is satisfied by any function in the form $f(n) = A \cdot 1^n + B \cdot 3^n$. Each of the sequences below satisfies the recurrence. For each sequence, calculate the next two terms. Then find the values of A and B.

a. 5, 11, 29, . . .
b. 3, 5, 11, . . .
c. 10, 18, 42, . . .
d. −2, 2, 14, . . .

2. Function g satisfies the recurrence

$$g(n) = 8g(n-1) - 12g(n-2)$$

Find a closed-form equivalent for g if

a. $g(0) = 2$ and $g(1) = 8$
b. $g(0) = 10$ and $g(1) = 40$

3. Consider the two-term recurrence

$$f(n) = 9f(n-1) - 18f(n-2)$$

a. What two numbers have a sum of 9 and a product of 18?
b. Show that $f(n) = 3^n$ satisfies the recurrence.
c. Show that $f(n) = 6^n$ satisfies the recurrence.

4. Nicholas invests \$600 every year in a savings account. Each year he also earns 4% on the money currently invested. Find a closed-form definition for a function that gives the amount of money in Nicholas's account after n years.

5. Michaela wants to save money to buy a house. She estimates she can save \$7000 a year toward a down payment.
a. How much can Michaela expect to have in her account in three years if the money in her account grows by 7% each year?
b. How much more would Michaela have in her account in three years at 10% growth each year instead of 7%?

6. a. Find the correct monthly payment on a \$12,000 car loan taken at 8% APR for 36 months.
b. Find the correct monthly payment on a \$22,000 car loan taken at 9% APR for 48 months.

Practice: For Lesson 5.13, assign Exercises 1–3.

15. Take It Further There is a special case of recurrences in the form $f(n) = Af(n-1) + Bf(n-2)$. One such recurrence is

$$f(n) = 2f(n-1) - f(n-2)$$

a. Describe the function with starting conditions $f(0) = 3$ and $f(1) = 8$.
b. Describe the function with starting conditions $f(0) = 10$ and $f(1) = 0$.
c. Describe the function in general for all functions that satisfy this recurrence.
d. Describe the function in general for all functions that satisfy the similar recurrence.

$$f(n) = 6f(n-1) - 9f(n-2)$$

16. Standardized Test Prep Consider the following function.

$$f(n) = \begin{cases} 0 & \text{if } n = 0 \\ 1 & \text{if } n = 1 \\ f(n-1) + f(n-2) & \text{if } n > 1 \end{cases}$$

Which statement is correct?

A. $f(2n) = 2(f(n-1) + f(n-2))$
B. $f(2n) = f(2(n-1)) + f(2(n-2))$
C. $f(2n) = f(2n-1) + f(2n-2)$
D. $f(2n) = f(2n-2) + f(2n-3)$

Maintain Your Skills

17. The Martinez family buys a house. They get a 15-year mortgage at a low rate of 6% APR. This means that what they owe at the end of the year is 6% more than what they owed at the start of the year. After the interest is added, the family reduces what they owe by making a payment. The family owes \$200,000 to start.

a. If the Martinez family pays \$12,000 every year, explain why the function B gives their balance after n years.

$$B(n) = \begin{cases} 200{,}000 & \text{if } n = 0 \\ 1.06B(n-1) - 12{,}000 & \text{if } n > 0 \end{cases}$$

For simplicity, calculate interest and payment once per year, rather than once per month.

b. If the Martinez family pays \$12,000 every year, will they pay off the mortgage in 15 years? If not, how much is left at the end? What if they pay \$13,000? \$14,000? \$15,000? Look for a pattern.
c. If the family pays D dollars every year, how much is left at the end in terms of D?
d. Determine the exact amount the Martinez family should pay per year to leave a \$0 balance on the mortgage at the end.

Answers

15. a. Outputs follow the form $f(n) = 5n + 3$.
b. Outputs follow the form $f(n) = -10n + 10$.
c. Any function in the form $f(n) = pn + q$ satisfies the recurrence.
d. The general closed form is $f(n) = (An + B) \cdot 3^n$.

16. C

17. a. The initial balance would be \$200,000. The 1.06 term adds the 6% interest and the \$12,000 payment is deducted each year.
b. No; \$200,000; no; \$176,724 no; \$153,448; no; \$130,172. The value after 15 years appears to be dropping linearly.
c. $B = 479{,}312 - 23.276D$
d. \$20,592.55

5.14 $f(n) = Af(n-1)+B$

The right strategy for solving a recurrence depends on the form of the recurrence. Lesson 5.13 showed how combining two exponential solutions to a recurrence of the form $f(n) = Af(n-1) + Bf(n-2)$ produces yet another solution. In this lesson, you will draw on skills developed earlier to solve recurrences of the form $f(n) = Af(n-1) + B$.

Minds in Action episode 17

Sasha and Tony are looking at the newspaper.

Tony All these car ads make me think of the monthly payment function we figured out last year.

Sasha If you think about it, we were solving a recurrence. Remember this problem?

> Suppose you want to buy a car that costs \$10,000. You can put \$1000 down, so you would borrow \$9000. The interest rate is 5%. The dealer wants the loan paid off in three years. Will a monthly payment of \$250 pay off the loan?

Tony Yes, I remember what we did. We figured out a function b that gave us the balance at the end of month n with a monthly payment of 250 dollars. Then we figured out $b(36)$ and saw if it was 0. The function definition was recursive:

$$b(n) = \begin{cases} 9000 & \text{if } n = 0 \\ \left(1 + \frac{0.05}{12}\right)b(n-1) - 250 & \text{if } n > 0 \end{cases}$$

We didn't get 0, but then we adjusted the monthly payment to make $b(36)$ come out to be 0.

Sasha And later, we unstacked this and got a formula for the monthly payment. But wait. If we think about it in terms of recurrence relations, the recurrence looks like

$$b(n) = Ab(n-1) + B$$

Maybe we can use what we did for monthly payments to solve any recurrence of this form.

Remember...

What you owe at the end of the month is what you owed at the start of the month plus $\frac{1}{12}$th of the year's interest on that amount, minus the monthly payment.

What is the actual monthly payment?

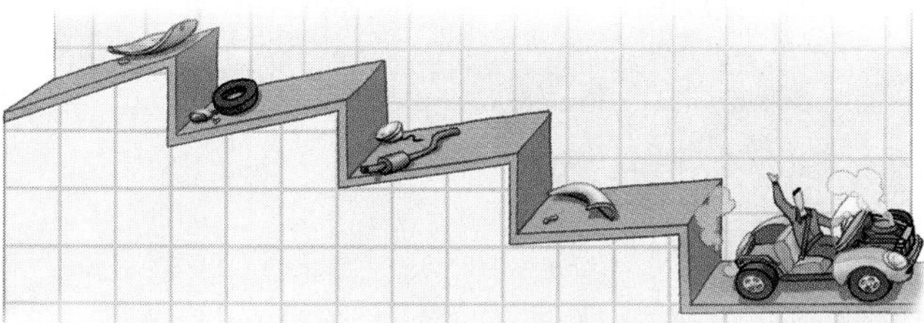

Lesson Overview

GOAL

- Calculate the monthly payment for a car loan and write a general rule for all such problems.

This lesson revisits the monthly-payment problem as a recurrence in the form $f(n) = Af(n-1) + B$, solving the general case. The problems present multiple paths to the result, including a path that looks at how far away outputs are from an equilibrium point, a value of $f(n)$ that repeats. Relative to the equilibrium point, these functions are purely exponential.

CHECK YOUR UNDERSTANDING
- Core: 1, 2, 3
- Optional: 4, 5
- Extension: 6

MATERIALS
- CAS (recommended)
- graphing calculators

HOMEWORK
- Core: 7, 9, 10, 11, 14
- Optional: 8, 15
- Extension: 12, 13

VOCABULARY
- equilibrium point

Launch

Review Exercise 17 from the previous lesson, or launch directly into the dialog that starts the lesson.

Explore

Developing Habits of Mind

Skip the language of affine transformations unless students covered this material in CME Project *Algebra 2*. Students have used and will continue to use the geometric series expansion, which is a good way of understanding the resulting closed form given as Theorem 5.4.

If students are having trouble, take them through a numeric example without evaluating; they will see which numbers they can combine in what ways.

For Discussion

PROBLEM 1 The last step in the Developing Habits of Mind gives

$f(n) = A^n f(0) + B(A^{n-1} + A^{n-2} + \cdots + A + 1)$

Now use the formula for the sum of a geometric series to condense the sum.

$$f(n) = A^n f(0) + B\left(\frac{A^n - 1}{A - 1}\right)$$

Finally, note that $f(0) = p$ is given as a base case, so

$$f(n) = A^n \cdot p + B\left(\frac{A^n - 1}{A - 1}\right)$$

Developing Habits of Mind

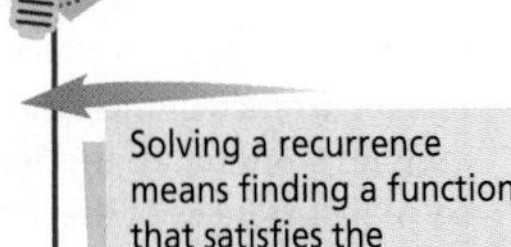

Consider more than one strategy. There are two methods from CME Project *Algebra 2* to solve the recurrence

$$f(n) = Af(n - 1) + B$$

- You could use affine transformations. If $\mathcal{A}_{(a,b)}(x) = ax + b$, then the recurrence is

$$f(n) = \mathcal{A}_{(A,B)}(f(n - 1))$$

But then

$$f(n - 1) = \mathcal{A}_{(A,B)}(f(n - 2))$$

and

$$f(n - 2) = \mathcal{A}_{(A,B)}(f(n - 3))$$

and so on, so that

$$f(n) = \mathcal{A}^n_{(A,B)}(f(0))$$

where $\mathcal{A}^n_{(A,B)}$ is the nth iteration of $\mathcal{A}_{(A,B)}$. In CME Project *Algebra 2*, you derived a formula for the nth iteration of an affine transformation.

- If you did not want to use the language of affine transformations, you could just unstack the recurrence:

$$\begin{aligned} f(n) &= Af(n - 1) + B \\ &= A(Af(n - 2) + B) + B = A^2 f(n - 2) + AB + B \\ &= A^2(Af(n - 3) + B) + AB + B = A^3 f(n - 3) + A^2B + AB + B \\ &\vdots \\ &= A^n f(0) + B(A^{n-1} + A^{n-2} + \cdots + A + 1) \end{aligned}$$

The rightmost sum is a geometric series. You know a formula for that.

Solving a recurrence means finding a function that satisfies the recurrence at every input in the function's domain.

For Discussion

1. Finish one or both of these derivations to prove the following theorem.

Theorem 5.4 ***Closed-form equivalent for $f(n) = Af(n - 1) + B$***

Define f by

$$f(n) = \begin{cases} p & \text{if } n = 0 \\ Af(n - 1) + B & \text{if } n > 0 \end{cases}$$

Then for nonnegative integer inputs, a closed-form equivalent for f is

$$f(n) = A^n \cdot p + B\left(\frac{A^n - 1}{A - 1}\right)$$

Here, p is a number, the base case.

Answers

For Discussion

1. $f(n) = A^n f(0) + B(A^{n-1} + A^{n-2} + \cdots + A + 1)$ Using the formula for the sum of a geometric series to condense the sum: $f(n) = A^n \cdot p + B\left(\frac{A^n - 1}{A - 1}\right)$.

For You to Do

Tristen buys a car. The car costs \$12,000. The financing is 6% APR, or 0.5% monthly. A car payment is due every month for 36 months.

2. Find Tristen's car payment, to the nearest cent.
3. Using the same term and interest rate, construct a function m so that $m(C)$ is the monthly payment for a car that costs C dollars.

How could a CAS help you do this without guesswork?

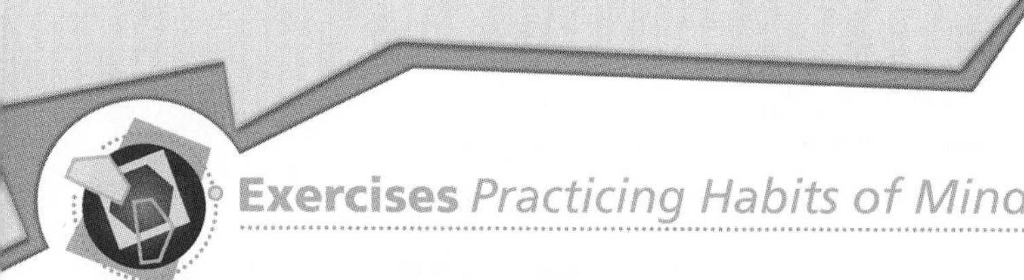

Exercises *Practicing Habits of Mind*

Check Your Understanding

1. Jess invests \$500 every year in a savings account. Each year she also earns 3% on the money currently invested. Find a closed-form definition for a function that gives the amount of money in Jess's account after n years.
2. Generalize the result from Exercise 1. Suppose Jess invests D dollars per year in a savings account that earns a rate of r per year (as a decimal, not a percent). Find a function B that gives the balance of Jess's account after n years.
3. A local environmental group claims that 20% of the trees in Woodville are being cut down each year. Authorities have decided to plant 3000 trees every year to try and counteract this effect.
   a. Suppose there are 25,000 trees in Woodville to start. Determine how many trees there will be each year for the next seven years, rounding to the nearest tree.
   b. Make a scatter plot with number of trees on the vertical axis and years on the horizontal axis.
   c. Find an *equilibrium point*, the number of trees that will remain constant year-to-year after a certain number of iterations of this process.
   d. How many more trees than the equilibrium point does Woodville have at the start? After one year, how many more trees than the equilibrium point are there? After two years? After three? Look for a pattern.
   e. Find a closed-form definition for $T(n)$, the number of trees in Woodville after n years.

An equilibrium point is a repeating value of an iteration. If $f(n) = f(n-1) = C$, then C is an equilibrium point.

For You to Do

2. \$365.06
3. $m(C) = \dfrac{1.005^n \cdot C \cdot 0.005}{1.005^n - 1}$

Exercises

1. $B(n) = 500\left(\dfrac{1.03^n - 1}{0.03}\right)$
2. $B(n) = D\left(\dfrac{(1 + r)^n - 1}{r}\right)$

3. a.

Years, n	Trees, $T(n)$
0	25,000
1	23,000
2	21,400
3	20,120
4	19,096
5	18,277
6	17,621
7	17,097

b–e. See back of book.

For You to Do

PROBLEM 3 Use the result from Theorem 5.4, and set the balance equal to zero for payment m and initial balance C dollars:

$$0 = (1.005)^n \cdot C - m\left(\frac{1.005^n - 1}{0.005}\right)$$

Then solve for m in terms of C.

Note that $m(C)$ is directly proportional to C, so (for example) a car twice as expensive has twice the monthly payment.

Wrap Up

Review any methods students have used to solve the monthly payment problem or the general recurrence.

Assessment Resources

Lesson Quiz 5.14

1. Katie invests \$1000 every year in a savings account. Each year she also earns 4% interest on the money currently invested. Find a closed-form definition for a function that gives the amount of money in Katie's account after n years.
2. Jack takes out a loan for \$20,000 with 6% yearly interest compounded monthly. He will pay it off in monthly installments of \$500.
   a. Determine how much Jack will owe each month for the first year.
   b. Find a closed-form definition for $P(n)$, the amount of money Jack owes after n months.
3. Define the function f by the recurrence

$$f(n) = 1.075f(n-1) + C$$

with $f(0) = 325,000$. Find C if 325,000 is the equilibrium point for f, the value of $f(n)$ that produces a constant output.

Exercises

HOMEWORK

- Core: 7, 9, 10, 11, 14
- Optional: 8, 15
- Extension: 12, 13

Check Your Understanding

EXERCISE 1 If students have trouble with this exercise, suggest that they write the expression for $B(1)$, $B(2)$, and so on without actually computing the balance. This will help them see the pattern.

EXERCISE 2 If students get stuck here, encourage them to follow another numeric example in the style of Exercise 1. If students can describe how the work is done there, they should be able to generalize.

Note that this result is used in Exercise 7, so review this exercise before assigning the homework.

EXERCISE 3 This perspective (comparing to an equilibrium point) can help students quickly find closed forms for these situations, as the function is exponential relative to the equilibrium point.

EXERCISE 6 The algebra of this exercise is not overly challenging; what is challenging is the concept that each term is A (here, $1 + r$) times as far from the equilibrium point as the term before it. The equilibrium value is simple to calculate, and students have calculated this at least twice before (including Exercise 4).

On Your Own

EXERCISE 7 One purpose here is for students to recognize that over the long term, the effect of these rate changes is more than just a proportional percentage. The change from 10% to 12% gives more than a proportional (20%) change in the resulting balance.

4. Define function f by the recurrence

$$f(n) = 1.065f(n-1) + B$$

with $f(0) = 200{,}000$. Find B if 200,000 is the equilibrium point for f, the value of $f(0)$ that produces a constant output.

5. Show that the equilibrium point for the recurrence

$$f(n) = Af(n-1) + B$$

is

$$n = \frac{B}{1-A}$$

6. **Take It Further** The general form for a car payment or mortgage comes from the recurrence

$$f(n) = (1+r)f(n-1) - P$$

Given $f(0) = B$ (the starting balance), the goal is to find the correct value of P so that $f(a) = 0$ where a is the length of the loan and r is the interest rate expressed as a decimal.

   a. Find the equilibrium point of f in terms of P and r.

   b. How far is the starting balance B from the equilibrium point?

   c. How far away from the equilibrium point is $f(1)$? $f(2)$? $f(n)$?

   d. Write a closed-form definition for f in terms of B, P, r, and n.

   e. Solve the equation $f(n) = 0$ to find a function for the monthly payment P in terms of the initial balance B, the rate r, and the number of payments n.

On Your Own

7. At 30 years old, Drew estimates he can save \$5000 per year toward retirement. Use the result from Exercise 2 to answer these questions.

   a. How much can Drew expect to have in his retirement account at age 65 if he assumes that each year, the money in his account will grow by 10%?

   b. How much more would Drew have in his retirement account at age 65 at 12% growth instead of 10%?

   c. How much less would Drew have in his retirement account at age 65 at 8% growth instead of 10%?

10% growth per year is a reasonable average when investing in commodities such as stocks. The actual percentage varies year-to-year but a fixed percentage is usually used when estimating long-term results like this one.

Answers

4. $B = -13{,}000$

5. If x is an equilibrium point, then $f(n) = x$ for all n. Therefore:

$$x = Ax + B$$
$$x - Ax = B$$
$$x(1-A) = B$$
$$x = \frac{B}{1-A}$$

6. a. $\frac{P}{r}$

   b. $B - \frac{P}{r}$

   c. $f(1)$ is $(1+r)\left(B - \frac{P}{r}\right)$ away from the equilibrium point.

   $f(2)$ is $(1+r)^2\left(B - \frac{P}{r}\right)$ away from the equilibrium point.

   $f(n)$ is $(1+r)^n\left(B - \frac{P}{r}\right)$ away from the equilibrium point.

   d. $f(n) = \frac{P}{r} + (1+r)^n\left(B - \frac{P}{r}\right)$

   e. $P = \dfrac{Br(1+r)^n}{(1+r)^n - 1}$

7. a. \$1,355,121.84

   b. \$803,195.64

   c. \$493,537.82

8. Define f recursively as

$$f(n) = \begin{cases} P & \text{if } n = 0 \\ Af(n-1) + B & \text{if } n > 0 \end{cases}$$

a. Tabulate f for inputs from 0 to 4.

b. Find a closed-form equivalent for f.

9. Consider Tristen's situation with a \$12,000 car loan at 6% APR for 36 months. The recursive definition for Tristen's balance is

$$B(n, p) = \begin{cases} 12{,}000 & \text{if } n = 0 \\ 1005B(n-1, p) - p & \text{if } n > 0 \end{cases}$$

a. Use the results from the previous exercise to write $f(36)$ in terms of p, the monthly payment.

b. Find the correct monthly payment to the nearest cent.

> If 6% is the APR, what is the monthly interest rate?

10. a. Find the correct monthly payment on a \$10,000 car loan taken at 9% APR for 48 months,

b. Find the correct monthly payment on a \$20,000 car loan with the same terms. What happens to the monthly payment?

11. **Write About It** Prove the following theorem.

Theorem 5.5 Monthly Payments

On a loan for C dollars taken out for n months with an APR of i percent compounded monthly, the monthly payment is m dollars where

$$m = \frac{q^n(q-1)}{q^n - 1}C$$

and $q = 1 + \frac{i}{1200}$.

12. **Take It Further** In this investigation you explored two-term recurrences in the form

$$f(n) = Af(n-1) + Bf(n-2)$$

A related form is

$$f(n) = Af(n-1) + Bf(n-2) + Cf(n-3)$$

Consider the three-term recurrence

$$f(n) = 10f(n-1) - 31f(n-2) + 30f(n-3)$$

a. Show that $f(n) = 2^n$ satisfies this recurrence.

b. Find two other exponential functions that satisfy the recurrence.

c. If $f(0) = 4$, $f(1) = 16$, and $f(2) = 74$, find a closed-form definition for f.

EXERCISE 9 provides a second method of solving the monthly payment problem, which is different from the method seen in the Check Your Understanding exercises that relies on the equilibrium point. Both methods are valuable and lead to the same result.

ERROR PREVENTION Watch out for students making the mistake of letting $B = p$ instead of $B = -p$.

EXERCISE 10 If students work on the general form here, have them explain why the general form implies the doubling behavior seen in this exercise.

8. a.

n	$f(n)$
0	P
1	$AP + B$
2	$A^2P + AB + B$
3	$A^3P + A^2B + AB + B$
4	$A^4P + A^3B + A^2B + AB + B$

b. $f(n) = A^nP + B\left(\frac{A^n - 1}{A - 1}\right)$

9. a. $f(36) = 1.005^{36} \cdot 12{,}000 - p\left(\frac{1.005^{36} - 1}{0.005}\right)$

b. \$365.06

10. a. \$248.85

b. \$497.70; it doubles.

11. $f(n) = pA^n + B\left(\frac{A^n - 1}{A - 1}\right)$, $A = q$, $p = C$, $m = -b$

$f(n) = Cq^n - m\left(\frac{q^n - 1}{q - 1}\right)$

The monthly payment is determined at $f(n) = 0$.

$0 = Cq^n - m\left(\frac{q^n - 1}{q - 1}\right)$

$m\left(\frac{q^n - 1}{q - 1}\right) = Cq^n$

$m = \frac{Cq^n(q - 1)}{q^n - 1}$

12. a. $10 \cdot 2^{n-1} - 31 \cdot 2^{n-2} + 30 \cdot 2^{n-3}$
$= 10 \cdot 2^{n-1} - 31 \cdot 2^{n-2} + 15 \cdot 2^{n-2}$
$= 10 \cdot 2^{n-1} - 16 \cdot 2^{n-2}$
$= 10 \cdot 2^{n-1} - 8 \cdot 2^{n-1}$
$= 2 \cdot 2^{n-1}$
$= 2^n$

b. $f(n) = 3^n$ and $f(n) = 5^n$

c. $f(n) = 2 \cdot 2^n - 3^n + 3 \cdot 5^n$

Additional Resources

PRINT RESOURCES
- Solution Manual
- Practice Workbook
- Assessment Resources
- Teaching Resources

TECHNOLOGY
- Interactive Textbook
- TeacherExpress CD-ROM
- ExamView CD-ROM
- PHSchool.com

Additional Practice

1. The two-term recurrence

$$f(n) = 4f(n-1) - 3f(n-2)$$

is satisfied by any function in the form $f(n) = A \cdot 1^n + B \cdot 3^n$. Each of the sequences below satisfies the recurrence. For each sequence, calculate the next two terms. Then find the values of A and B.

a. 5, 11, 29, . . .
b. 3, 5, 11, . . .
c. 10, 18, 42, . . .
d. −2, 2, 14, . . .

2. Function g satisfies the recurrence

$$g(n) = 8g(n-1) - 12g(n-2)$$

Find a closed-form equivalent for g if

a. $g(0) = 2$ and $g(1) = 8$
b. $g(0) = 10$ and $g(1) = 40$

3. Consider the two-term recurrence

$$f(n) = 9f(n-1) - 18f(n-2)$$

a. What two numbers have a sum of 9 and a product of 18?
b. Show that $f(n) = 3^n$ satisfies the recurrence.
c. Show that $f(n) = 6^n$ satisfies the recurrence.

4. Nicholas invests $600 every year in a savings account. Each year he also earns 4% on the money currently invested. Find a closed-form definition for a function that gives the amount of money in Nicholas's account after n years.

5. Michaela wants to save money to buy a house. She estimates she can save $7000 a year toward a down payment.

a. How much can Michaela expect to have in her account in three years if the money in her account grows by 7% each year?
b. How much more would Michaela have in her account in three years at 10% growth each year instead of 7%?

6. a. Find the correct monthly payment on a $12,000 car loan taken at 8% APR for 36 months.
b. Find the correct monthly payment on a $22,000 car loan taken at 9% APR for 48 months.

Practice: For Lesson 5.14, assign Exercises 4–6.

13. Take It Further Find a three-term recurrence that this sequence satisfies. Then find a closed-form definition for a function that satisfies the recurrence and agrees with the sequence.

$$1, 5, 105, 965, 10065, 99725, 1000665$$

14. Standardized Test Prep Find, to the nearest penny, the monthly payment on a $12,000 loan at 6% APR, paid off over 36 months.

A. $362.97 **B.** $365.06 **C.** $368.44 **D.** $370.60

For additional practice, go to **Web Code: bga-0514**

Maintain Your Skills

15. Consider the recurrence

$$f(n) = 3f(n-1) - 300$$

a. Show that 150 is an equilibrium point for f. That is, if $f(n-1) = 150$, then $f(n) = 150$.

b. Suppose $f(0)$ is 1000 greater than the equilibrium point. How much greater than the equilibrium point is $f(1)$? $f(2)$? $f(3)$? $f(n)$?

What is the monthly payment on a $12,000 car loan at 6% APR, paid off over 36 months?

Answers

13. $f(n) = \begin{cases} 1 & n = 0 \\ 5 & n = 1 \\ 9f(n-1) + 16f(n-2) - 60f(n-3) & n > 1 \end{cases}$

$F(n) = 10^n + (-3)^n - 2^n$

14. B

15. a. Calculate directly: if $f(n-1) = 150$ then $f(n) = 3 \cdot 150 - 300 = 150$.

b. $f(1)$ is 3000 greater than the equilibrium point.
$f(2)$ is 9000 greater than the equilibrium point.
$f(3)$ is 27,000 greater than the equilibrium point.
$f(n)$ is $1000 \cdot 3^n$ greater than the equilibrium point.

In this investigation you studied recursive relationships. You found closed polynomial and exponential forms for them. The following questions will help you summarize what you have learned.

1. Every day, Melissa takes 50 mg of prescription medication. Each day, her body metabolizes and removes 20% of the medicine present.
   a. Explain why the recurrence $f(n) = 0.8f(n-1) + 50$ models the amount of medicine in Melissa's body, day by day.
   b. Melissa begins the treatment with no medicine in her body: $f(0) = 0$. Tabulate f for days 0 through 10. Plot the results.
   c. What appears to be happening in the long run?
2. Oscar buys a house. He takes out a 15-year mortgage on the $200,000 cost of the house. The interest rate is 6.5% per year. Oscar considers an interest-only loan. In this type of loan, he would pay only the exact amount of the interest.
   a. If Oscar had an interest-only loan, how much would he pay each year?
   b. Instead, Oscar pays $16,000 per year. Write a recursive definition for the loan balance after n years. What is the balance after 15 years?
   c. Determine the annual payment Oscar should make to pay off his mortgage in 15 years.
3. The Fibonacci numbers satisfy the recurrence $f(n) = f(n-1) + f(n-2)$ with $f(0) = 0$ and $f(1) = 1$. The ratio of consecutive Fibonacci numbers approaches the golden ratio $\phi = \frac{1+\sqrt{5}}{2}$.
   The numbers that satisfy the recurrence $g(n) = 2g(n-1) + 2g(n-2)$ with $g(0) = 0$ and $g(1) = 1$ have a similar property, but approach a different ratio. Find the exact value of this ratio.
4. What methods are available for deciding if a linear, polynomial, or exponential rule fits a table?
5. How can you find a closed-form function definition that satisfies a two-term recurrence?
6. What is the monthly payment for a three-year car loan for $15,000, taken out at 5% APR?

Vocabulary

In this investigation, you learned these terms. Make sure you understand what each one means and how to use it.

- **equilibrium point**
- **functional equation**
- **recurrence**
- **two-term recurrence**

Mathematical Reflections

EXERCISES 4–6 At the start of the investigation, you may have assigned these as Questions 1–3 for students to think and write about.

Mathematical Reflections

1. a. Since her body removes 20% of the medicine, 80% remains from one day to the next. Then 50 mg is added, therefore the recurrence is $f(n) = 0.8f(n-1) + 50$ with the base case of $f(0) = 0$.
b. See back of book.
c. The values approach an equilibrium point of 250 mg.

2. a. $13,000
b. $b(n) = \begin{cases} 200{,}000 & n = 0 \\ 1.065b(n-1) - 16{,}000 & n > 0 \end{cases}$
$b(15) = \$127{,}453$
c. $21,270.56

3. $1 + \sqrt{3}$

4. Answers may vary. Sample: Good methods include making a difference table or ratio table, looking at a graph, or inspecting the pattern and number of digits in the outputs.

5. Answers may vary. Sample: Determine the quadratic equation whose two roots are used to determine the closed form. The two roots r_1 and r_2 of the quadratic lead to the closed form $f(n) = k \cdot r_1^n + j \cdot r_2^n$.

6. $449.56

Project

In this project, students try to find quick ways to determine the number of different rhyme schemes that are possible given poems of different numbers of lines. Through the project, they will hopefully see how this project relates to the project from Chapter 4. It is recommended that students who work on this project also work on the project from Chapter 4.

EXERCISE 3 Students' organization of work is key here to seeing the overall structure.

EXERCISE 4 Watch for students answering 3 or 5 here: students answering 3 do not recognize that they can use the next letter, while students answering 5 do not recognize that they can use only the next letter.

EXERCISE 5 Some students will want to answer this exercise without following this process, and that is fine; some other great ideas may come of this.

EXERCISE 6 Hopefully, students will use patterns to extend the table. It is definitely a bigger challenge to find the 203 six-line schemes by enumeration.

You may want to use Blackline Master 5.14 on an overhead and fill in the entries as students supply them.

EXERCISE 9 Some problems for further study: how are the numbers in the Simplex table related to the Mahler polynomials?

BACKROUND FOR TEACHER The numbers in the rhyme scheme table are called Stirling numbers of the second kind, and have several other mathematical applications.

Project: Using Mathematical Habits

Rhyme Schemes

The *rhyme scheme* of a poem dictates the pattern of rhyming lines the poem uses. For example, here is a five-line limerick:

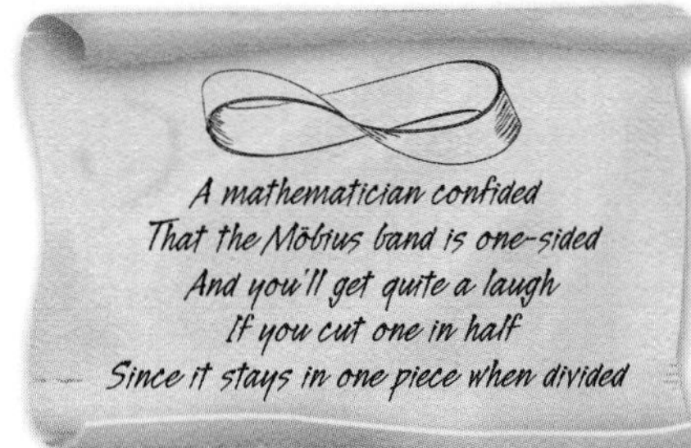

A mathematician confided
That the Möbius band is one-sided
And you'll get quite a laugh
If you cut one in half
Since it stays in one piece when divided

The rhyme scheme of this poem is AABBA. This means that the first, second, and fifth line all rhyme. The third and fourth line also rhyme. The letters are always assigned in alphabetical order, so it would not be correct to call this same meter BBAAB or even ZZYYZ.

Here are some other possible rhyme schemes for five-line poems:

- AAAAA. Here, all five lines rhyme.
- ABCAB. Here, lines 1 and 4 rhyme, and lines 2 and 5 rhyme. Line 3 does not rhyme with any other.
- ABCDD. Only lines 4 and 5 rhyme.
- ABCDE. No lines rhyme.

The lettering must be in alphabetical order. The first line is always A, and any time a new line does not rhyme with any other, it gets assigned the next letter in the alphabet.

1. Find or write a short poem. Detail its rhyme scheme.
2. Find all the rhyme schemes for
   a. two-line poems.
   b. three-line poems.
3. Find all the rhyme schemes for four-line poems. Think about how to organize your work to guarantee that you have found them all.
4. A five-line poem's rhyme scheme starts with ABCB. How many possible rhyme schemes are there for the entire poem?
5. Use the tactics of Exercise 4 to find the number of rhyme schemes for five-line poems.
6. Copy and complete this table with the number of different rhyme schemes of different types. (For example, the table says that there are 15 different five-line rhyme schemes that use only the two letters A and B, and 65 different six-line rhyme schemes using exactly four letters.) Look for patterns that help you extend the table.

Lines ↓ / Letters Used	1	2	3	4	5	6
1	1	–	–	–	–	–
2	1	1	–	–	–	–
3	1	3	1	–	–	–
4	■	■	■	■	–	–
5	■	15	■	■	1	–
6	■	■	■	65	■	■

7. Describe and explain some patterns found in the table of Exercise 6.
8. How many 7-line rhyme schemes are there?
9. Find a relationship between the situation in this project and the situation with the Simplex Lock in Chapter 4.

Answers

Project

1. Check students' work.
2. **a.** AA, AB
   b. AAA, AAB, ABA, ABB, ABC
3. AAAA, AAAB, AABA, AABB, AABC, ABAA, ABAB, ABAC, ABBA, ABBB, ABBC, ABCA, ABCB, ABCC, ABCD

   A number tree helps, starting with A at the top and drawing branches for each possible next letter until all of the combinations are shown.
4. 4
5. 52
6.

Lines↓/Letters Used	1	2	3	4	5	6
1	1	-	-	-	-	-
2	1	1	-	-	-	-
3	1	3	1	-	-	-
4	**1**	**7**	**6**	**1**	-	-
5	**1**	15	**25**	**10**	1	-
6	**1**	**31**	**90**	65	**15**	**1**

7. • The first column is always equal to 1 since the only pattern is to repeat A.
   • Each value in the diagonal is equal to one since there is only one way to arrange x letters into x lines in alphabetical order.
   • Each row adds up to the total number of rhyme schemes for x-line poems.
8. 877
9. Answers may vary. Sample: Both situations involve sequential selections from a finite set of elements.

5 Review

Go Online PHSchool.com — For vocabulary review, go to Web Code: bga-0551

In **Investigation 5A,** you learned to

- determine the domain on which two functions agree
- verify that a closed-form and a recursive function definition agree at the first few inputs in a domain
- prove by induction that two function definitions agree for all inputs in an infinite domain

The following questions will help you check your understanding.

1. For each of the following pairs of functions, find the largest set of inputs for which the two functions are equal.

   a. $f(x) = x - \frac{1}{x}$, $g(x) = \frac{x^2 - 1}{x}$

   b. $f(x) = \frac{x^2 - 1}{x + 1}$, $g(x) = x - 1$

   c. $f(x) = 3x - 5$, $g(x) = 3x - 5 + x(x - 8)$

   d. $f(x) = |x|$, $g(x) = -|x|$

2. Tabulate each function below using inputs from 0 to 5, then find a function with a closed-form definition that agrees with the table.

   a. $f(x) = \begin{cases} 4 & \text{if } x = 0 \\ f(x-1) + 5 & \text{if } x > 0 \end{cases}$

   b. $g(x) = \begin{cases} 5 & \text{if } x = 0 \\ 2 \cdot f(x-1) & \text{if } x > 0 \end{cases}$

3. Define G and g as

   $G(x) = x^2 + 2$

   $g(x) = \begin{cases} 2 & \text{if } x = 0 \\ g(x-1) + 2x - 1 & \text{if } x > 0 \end{cases}$

   a. Tabulate the functions to make sure they start out equal.

   b. Show that if $G(21) = g(21)$, then $G(22) = g(22)$.

   c. Use mathematical induction to show G and g will always agree for any nonnegative integer inputs.

In **Investigation 5B,** you learned to

- find a polynomial function that fits a difference table
- explain how the up-and-over property of difference tables relates to Pascal's Triangle
- quickly find rules for summations, like the sum of the first n squares

The following questions will help you check your understanding.

4. Find the values of A, B, and C in the difference table.

Input	Output	Δ	Δ²
0	7	−2	A
1	5	4	6
2	9	10	6
3	■	■	6
4	■	■	6
5	■	B	
6	C		

Review

1. a. x = all real numbers, $x \neq 0$.
   b. x = all real numbers, $x \neq -1$
   c. $x = 0, x = 8$ d. null set

2. a.

x	f(x)
0	4
1	9
2	14
3	19
4	24
5	29

$f(x) = 5x + 4$

b.

x	g(x)
0	5
1	10
2	20
3	40
4	80
5	160

$g(x) = 5 \cdot 2^n$

3. a.

x	G(x)	g(x)
0	2	2
1	3	3
2	6	6
3	11	11
4	18	18
5	27	27

b. $g(22) = g(21) + (2 \cdot 22 - 1)$
$= G(21) + (2 \cdot 21 + 2 - 1)$
$= (21^2 + 2) + 2 \cdot 21 + 1$
$= 21^2 + 2 \cdot 21 + 1 + 2$
$= (21+1)^2 + 2$
$= 22^2 + 2$
$= G(22)$

c. $g(n) = g(n - 1) + (2 \cdot n - 1)$
$= G(n - 1) + 2 \cdot (n - 1) + 2 - 1$
$= (n - 1)^2 + 2 + 2n - 2 + 2 - 1$
$= (n - 1)^2 + 2n + 1 + 2$
$= (n - 1 + 1)^2 + 2$
$= n^2 + 2$
$= G(n)$

4. $A = 6$, $B = 28$, $C = 85$

Review continued

5. Here is a table for a function G.

x	$G(x)$
0	−4
1	0
2	22
3	74
4	168
5	316
6	530
7	822

 a. Build a complete difference table for G.

 b. Find a polynomial function that agrees with this table.

6. Use a difference table to find a closed-form equivalent for

$$S(n) = \sum_{k=0}^{n-1} (k^2 + 2)$$

In **Investigation 5C,** you learned to

- find general classes of functions that fit a recurrence
- relate a solution to a two-term recurrence to a quadratic polynomial.
- calculate the monthly payment for a car loan and write a general rule for all such problems

The following questions will help you check your understanding.

7. Define f recursively as

$$f(n) = 0.75f(n-1) + 15$$

 with $f(0) = 10$.

 a. Tabulate f for $n = 0$ to $n = 5$.

 b. What is the equilibrium point?

 c. How far away from the equilibrium point is $f(0)$? $f(1)$? $f(2)$?

 d. Write a closed-form equivalent for f.

8. Function f satisfies the recurrence

$$f(n) = 9f(n-1) - 14f(n-2)$$

 a. Find both possible values of b that make $f(n) = b^n$ satisfy the recurrence.

 b. If $f(0) = 2$ and $f(1) = 9$, find a closed-form definition for f.

9. Find the correct monthly payment on a \$25,000 car loan taken out at 6% APR for 60 months.

Answers

5. a.

x	$G(x)$	Δ	Δ^2	Δ^3
0	−4	4	18	12
1	0	22	30	12
2	22	52	42	12
3	74	94	54	12
4	168	148	66	12
5	316	214	78	
6	530	292		
7	822			

b. $G(x) = 2x^3 + 3x^2 - x - 4$

6. $S(n) = \frac{1}{3}n^3 - \frac{1}{2}n^2 + \frac{13}{6}n$

7. a.

n	$f(n)$
0	10
1	22.5
2	31.875
3	38.906
4	44.180
5	48.135

b. 60

c. $f(0)$ is 50 away from the equilibrium point, $f(1)$ is 37.5 away, and $f(2)$ is 28.125 away.

d. $f(n) = -50 \cdot 0.75^n + 60$

8. a. $b = 2$ and $b = 7$

b. $f(n) = 2^n + 7^n$

9. \$483.32

Test

Go Online PHSchool.com — For a chapter test, go to Web Code: bga-0553

Multiple Choice

1. Define H recursively as

$$H(n) = \begin{cases} -3 & \text{if } n = 0 \\ 4 \cdot H(n-1) + 1 & \text{if } n > 0 \end{cases}$$

Find $H(2)$.

A. -43 **B.** -11 **C.** 13 **D.** 45

2. Define f and g as

$$f(x) = x^2 + 7$$
$$g(x) = x^2 + 7 + x(x-3)(x+5)$$

What is the largest set on which f and g agree?

A. $\{1, 3, 5\}$ **B.** $\{-5, 0, 3\}$
C. $\{-5, 3\}$ **D.** $\{-3, 0, 5\}$

3. At the right is a partial table for a function f. Use the table to find $f(4)$.

x	f(x)	Δ
0	5	2
1	■	10
2	■	−8
3	■	12

A. 4 **B.** 9
C. 16 **D.** 21

4. Here is the first line of a difference table for a cubic function g.

x	g(x)	Δ	Δ²	Δ³
0	3	1	−4	6

Find $g(8)$.

A. 6 **B.** 44 **C.** 235 **D.** 249

5. Let f be a function that satisfies the recurrence.

$$f(n) = 3 \cdot f(n-1) - 4 \cdot f(n-2)$$

Which of the following cannot be a sequence of consecutive outputs of f?

A. 1, 2, 2, −2, −14, −34 **B.** 2, 4, 4, −4, −28, −68
C. −1, 5, 19, 37, 37, −37 **D.** 1, 4, 8, 8, −8, −56

Open Response

6. Use induction to show that these two functions must agree for all integers $n \geq 0$.

$$H(n) = 5n + 2$$
$$h(n) = \begin{cases} 2 & \text{if } n = 0 \\ h(n-1) + 5 & \text{if } n > 0 \end{cases}$$

7. Find a polynomial function that fits this table.

x	m(x)
0	−1
1	−4
2	−7
3	2
4	35
5	104

8. Find a closed-form definition for

$$S(n) = \sum_{k=0}^{n-1} (k^2 + k)$$

a. by using a difference table.

b. by using the formulas for $\sum_{k=0}^{n-1} k^2$ and $\sum_{k=0}^{n-1} k$.

9. Define f recursively as

$$f(x) = 0.6f(x-1) + B$$

with $f(0) = 80$.

a. If $B = 35$, what is the equilibrium point?

b. Find the value of B if the equilibrium point is 100.

10. Find the bases for two exponential functions $h(n) = a^n$ and $j(n) = b^n$ that satisfy the recurrence

$$f(n) = 5f(n-1) - 6f(n-2)$$

11. How can differences be used to find a polynomial that matches a table?

Test

Assessment Resources

Chapter Test Form A page 1 of 2

Multiple Choice

1. Define the function H recursively as

$$H(n) = \begin{cases} 5 & \text{if } n = 0 \\ -3 \cdot H(n-1) + 2 & \text{if } n > 0 \end{cases}$$

Find $H(3)$.
A. −121 B. −31 C. −3 D. 17

2. Define f and g as

$$f(x) = x - 2$$
$$g(x) = x - 2 + 4(x-1)(x-5)$$

What is the largest set on which f and g agree?
A. {1, 5} B. {0, 1, 5} C. {1, 2, 5} D. {0, 1, 2, 5}

3. Here is a partial table for a function f.

x	f(x)	Δ
0	3	5
1		8
2		−2
3		7
4		1
5		9

Use the table to find $f(5)$.
A. 8 B. 9 C. 22 D. 31

4. Here is the first line of a difference table for a cubic function h.

x	h(x)	Δ	Δ²	Δ³
0	−1	3	2	12

Find $h(7)$.
A. 21 B. 482 C. 483 D. 1322

5. Here is a recurrence.

$$f(n) = 2 \cdot f(n-1) + 3 \cdot f(n-2)$$

Which of the following sequences could be consecutive outputs of a function that satisfies the recurrence?
A. {1, 2, 8, 26, 80} B. {2, 7, 25, 89, 317}
C. {−1, 1, 2, 7, 23, 53} D. {1, 5, 13, 41, 121}

Also Available: Form B

Test

1. A **2.** B **3.** D
4. C **5.** C

6. $h(n) = h(n-1) + 5$
$= H(n-1) + 5$
$= 5(n-1) + 2 + 5$
$= 5n - 5 + 2 + 5$
$= 5n + 2$

7. $m(x) = 2x^3 - 6x^2 + x - 1$

8. a. $S(n) = \frac{1}{3}n^3 - \frac{1}{3}n$
b. $S(n) = \frac{1}{3}n^3 - \frac{1}{3}n$

9. a. 87.5
b. $B = 40$

10. 2 and 3

11. Answers may vary. Sample: Use the top row of the difference table and multiply each number in the top row by the corresponding Mahler polynomial.

Chapter 6
Analytic Geometry

In this chapter, students prove geometric theorems using coordinates and vectors, revisit topics from geometry and algebra 2 courses, and investigate the conic sections. They again find that by making connections between algebra and geometry, they learn more about both ways of thinking. In Chapter 2: Complex Numbers, students saw that as soon as they had a graphical representation of the complex numbers, they could understand more about how they worked. Students developed new conjectures about the geometry of the complex plane, and used algebra to prove their conjectures. They also made conjectures about algebraic relationships, and used geometry to prove these conjectures. A similar synergy takes place here, as students explore the added value that the coordinate plane gives to both algebra and geometry.

Vector methods make even more connections between geometry and algebra. The vector perspective is a different way to look at the coordinate plane. It simplifies many kinds of calculations and leads to some really elegant solutions to geometry questions. Students connect much of what they learned about matrix algebra to the rest of the mathematics that they are learning. By seeing the same ideas in many different ways, they come to a deeper understanding of mathematics as a discipline.

Chapter Overview

INVESTIGATION 6A, *Coordinate Geometry*, has students investigate more connections between algebra and geometry by using algebraic techniques to prove geometric results.

INVESTIGATION 6B, *Conic Sections*, has students explore the conic sections from many different perspectives.

INVESTIGATION 6C, *Vector Algebra and Geometry*, has students use matrix algebra to operate on vectors and use vector methods to connect algebra and geometry.

For more information on the Investigations, see

- Chapter Road Map, pp. 438–439
- Investigation Road Maps, pp. 440, 464, 500

PROJECT The Project near the end of the chapter is optional. You can assign the Project at any time during the chapter depending on how often and how long you feel students should work on it.

DAILY PLANNER DAILY PLANNER DAILY PL

Pacing Suggestions and Materials

Investigation 6A *Coordinate Geometry*

DAY	LESSON	HOMEWORK
1	6.1 Getting Started Core: 1, 2, 3, 4 Optional: none; Extension: 5	Core: 6, 7, 8, 10, 11 Optional: 12, 13a–e; Extension: 9, 13f
2	6.2 Equations as Point-Testers Core: 1, 2, 3, 4 Optional: 5, 6a–d; Extension: 6e	Core: 7, 8, 9, 10, 11, 13 Optional: 14; Extension: 12
3	6.3 Coordinates and Proof Core: 1, 2, 3, 4, 5 Optional: none; Extension: 6	Core: 7, 8, 9, 11, 13, 14 Optional: 10; Extension: 12
4	6.4 The Power of a Point Core: 1, 2, 3, 4 Optional: none; Extension: 5	Core: 6, 7, 8, 9, 12 Optional: 13; Extension: 10, 11

Investigation 6B *Conic Sections*

DAY	LESSON	HOMEWORK
1	6.5 Getting Started Core: 1, 2, 3, 4 Optional: none; Extension: 5	Core: 6, 7, 8, 9 Optional: 10
2	6.6 Slicing Cones Core: 1, 2, 4a–b, 5 Optional: 3; Extension: 4c	Core: 6, 7, 8, 9, 10, 12 Optional: 13; Extension: 11
3	6.7 Conics at the Origin Core: 1, 2, 3, 4, 5 Optional: none; Extension: 6	Core: 7, 8, 9, 10, 13 Optional: 12, 14; Extension: 11
4	6.8 Conics Anywhere Core: 1, 2, 3, 5, 6 Optional: 4; Extension: 7	Core: 8, 9, 11, 12, 13, 15 Optional: 10, 14, 16
5	6.9 They Are All the Same Core: 1, 2, 3, 4, 5 Optional: none; Extension: 6, 7	Core: 8, 9, 10, 11, 12, 14 Optional: 15; Extension: 13

NOTES	MATERIALS
	• CAS (optional) • graph paper • graphing calculators • Blackline Masters MC7, 6.1
	• graph paper • graphing calculators • Blackline Masters MC7, 6.2A–C
	• graph paper • graphing calculators • Blackline Masters MC7, 6.2B
	• graph paper • graphing calculators • Blackline Masters M C7, MC8, 6.4

NOTES	MATERIALS
	• graph paper • graphing calculators • modeling clay/dough (optional) • string (optional) • Blackline Master MC7
	• graph paper • graphing calculators • models of conic sections (optional) • Blackline Masters MC7, 6.6A–B
You may want to take two days for this lesson.	• graph paper • graphing calculators • Blackline Masters MC7, 6.6B
	• graph paper • graphing calculators • Blackline Master MC7
	• geometry software • graph paper • graphing calculators • Blackline Masters MC7, 6.6B, 6.9

Mathematics Background

COORDINATE GEOMETRY Graphing in all four of the CME Project courses focuses on the close connection between an equation and its graph. An equation is the *point-tester* for its graph, so if and only if the coordinates of a point satisfy an equation, is that point on the graph of that equation. In this chapter, students work with equations in two variables, but the same rule holds.

Students also revisit their study of Euclidean geometry through coordinates. They saw some of this in Chapter 7 of CME Project *Geometry*, but the ideas are extended here. Through the use of coordinate methods, students prove geometric theorems with algebra. Theorems, including the concurrence of medians in a triangle, the midline theorem for triangles, and many other classical results, are derived using coordinate methods and basic facts such as the formulas for locating the midpoint of a segment, calculating the distance between two points, and slope relationships in parallel and perpendicular lines.

With computer algebra systems, mathematicians have proven extremely intricate geometric results using algebraic methods. Algebra allows for a much more extensive investigation of "centers" in triangles, including the familiar centroid, in-center, circumcenter, and others. It defines a triangle center as a point whose location depends on the location of the triangle vertices and/or the measures of the triangle's angles. One of the CME Project authors wrote her thesis on "special points" in the trapezoid. She considers points that are invariant for permutations of the vertices. One example is the baricenter, because it does not depend on the order in which you use the vertices and all of the vertices contribute in the same way to its location. She goes on to find properties of these "special points" and proves theorems about them until she has enough information about them to select four independent special points and reconstruct the trapezoid that defined them.

CONIC SECTIONS Imagine an infinite double-cone in space—two congruent cones with a common axis touching apex to apex. Slice into that cone with a plane. Depending on the direction of the plane, you get different kinds of curves including ellipses, parabolas, and hyperbolas. These curves are the conic sections. In Investigation 6B, students investigate these curves in detail.

For each class of curves, students learn a locus definition—a description of the points in the curve based on a property they share. A locus definition of a parabola, for example, is the set of all points that are equidistant from a given line and a given point not on that line. Students see that the curve defined

continued on p. 438c

continued from p. 438b

by this type of locus definition is, in fact, the same curve you get when you slice the cone, through an argument involving Dandelin spheres. A Dandelin sphere is a sphere inscribed in the cone which is tangent to the slicing plane. The argument hinges on the fact that if two different things are both tangent to a sphere, the two points of tangency are the same distance from the center of the sphere.

You can also think of each conic section as the graph of an equation in two variables, and students learn that they can write all the equations of the conic sections in the form

$$rx^2 + ty^2 + ux + vy + w = 0$$

Different classes of curves have different relationships among the coefficients in this standard equation. For example, if a curve is a parabola, then either r or t must equal zero. Students see what these equations look like when the curve is centered at the origin and then when it is moved away via an affine transformation. This common standard equation for all the conic sections suggests that all conic sections are the same in some sense. Students explore this notion both through projective geometry and *eccentricity*.

VECTOR METHODS Another way to bring algebra to bear on geometric problems is through vector methods. Students were first introduced to these ideas in Chapter 7 of CME Project *Geometry*, and vector concepts are revisited and deepened here. The basic idea is to introduce an algebraic structure on $\mathbb{R}^2$—to define algebraic operations on points in the plane so that you can add them to each other or scale them by a factor. Then students interpret the results of these operations geometrically. For example, students interpret the sum of two points as the process of completing the parallelogram which has these two points and the origin as three of its vertices. The fourth vertex is the sum of the two points. They interpret the scaling of a point as dilating the vector from the origin to the point in question by the scale factor. The scaled point is the head of the scaled vector, whose tail is still at the origin.

These geometric interpretations allow for some really elegant geometric arguments. For example, the midpoint of a segment is just the "average" of its endpoints, and similarly, the centroid of a triangle is the average of its vertices. Students also develop a generalization of midpoint—the point $(1 - k)A + kB$ is k of the way from A to B along $\overline{AB}$. If k is $\frac{1}{2}$, then this is the midpoint, but if k is $\frac{1}{3}$, for example, this is the trisection point closest to A. This idea allows students to prove that the three medians of a triangle are concurrent, and that the point of concurrency cuts each median into two pieces, one twice as long as the other.

Pacing Suggestions and Materials

Investigation 6C *Vector Algebra and Geometry*

DAY	LESSON	HOMEWORK
1	6.10 Getting Started Core: 1, 2, 3, 4 Optional: none	Core: 5, 6, 7, 8 Optional: 9
2	6.11 Ordered Pairs, Points, and Vectors Core: 1, 3, 4, 5 Optional: 2	Core: 6, 7, 10, 12, 13 Optional: 8, 11; Extension: 9
3	6.12 Vector Equations of Lines Core: 1, 2, 3, 4, 6 Optional: 5, 7, 8	Core: 9, 10, 11, 13, 16, 18 Optional: 14, 15, 19, 20, 21; Extension: 12, 1
4	6.13 Affine Combinations and Geometry Core: 1, 2, 3, 4, 5 Optional: 6; Extension: 7	Core: 8, 9, 13, 14 Optional: 11; Extension: 10, 12

NOTES	MATERIALS
	• graph paper • graphing calculators • Blackline Master MC7
	• graph paper • graphing calculators • Blackline Master MC7
	• geometry software (optional) • graph paper • graphing calculators • Blackline Master MC7
	• graph paper • graphing calculators

There are two ways to represent an ordered pair on the geometric plane (or an *n*-tuple in *n*-dimensional space): as a point and as a vector. The representation as a vector is trickier, because (as you will see) many different vectors are associated with the same ordered pair. However, it is this very ability to represent an ordered pair many ways that makes matrix algebra methods so powerful for geometry.

The use of *n*-tuple matrices to treat *n*-dimensional space ($n = 2$ for the plane, $n = 3$ for physical space) has become so common that there has been a transfer of terminology. Historically, vectors were geometric objects (arrows). To most mathematicians today, the *n*-tuples themselves are the vectors. So, when the matrices in question are *n*-tuples (1-row or 1-column matrices), mathematicians refer to *vector algebra*, not matrix algebra—especially when applied to geometry.

Of course, mathematicians want to draw pictures, so they sometimes refer to *algebraic* vectors when they are thinking *n*-tuples, and *geometric* vectors when they are drawing arrows. Or they just use "vector" and let context tell you what they mean.

However, so far the students in CME Project courses studied vectors as geometric objects only, and it would do no good to suddenly switch. This course usually refers to matrix algebra, not vector algebra, and only uses the word vector when there is an arrow around. But you will see that, more and more, each arrow is associated with a single ordered pair of numbers rather than with a pair of points at the tail and head. This ordered pair is the *displacement*, the amount that the arrow goes over and up.

Developing Students' Mathematical Habits

STRATEGIC CHOICE OF COORDINATE SYSTEM Students learn that by choosing the "generic" coordinates carefully, they can simplify their algebraic calculations and see more meaning in them.

REASONING BY CONTINUITY Students investigate how a slicing plane intersects a double cone at different angles, cutting off different conic sections. As the eccentricity changes, the conic sections change from ellipse to parabola to hyperbola.

ABSTRACTION When working with vectors, students are suddenly calculating with things that are not numbers, but the operations behave in much the same way.

Chapter Road Map

INVESTIGATION 6A, *Coordinate Geometry,* makes more connections between algebra and geometry by using algebraic techniques to prove geometric results. However, instead of demonstrating specific instances of geometric theorems through coordinates, students learn to choose strategic coordinate systems to construct general proofs of geometric results.

INVESTIGATION 6B, *Conic Sections,* explores the conic sections from many different perspectives. Students see these curves as the intersection of a plane with an infinite double cone, as a collection of points with specific distance relationships with points and lines, and as graphs of equations in two variables. They make connections among all these different representations as they compare and contrast the curves and their equations.

INVESTIGATION 6C, *Vector Algebra and Geometry,* uses the matrix algebra students learned previously to operate on vectors, which are ordered pairs in the plane or ordered

Analytic Geometry

The connections between geometry and algebra are a pathway to apply mathematics to the real world. View experimental data through a mathematical lens and you can link graphs to numerical data and see a relationship. Using this relationship, you can predict future behavior or even discover underlying physical laws of nature.

For example, tie a mass to a spring and wait until it stops moving. Displace the mass by a distance d, and use a stopwatch to find the time it takes for the mass to move through one complete oscillation (up and down and back to the starting place). You will see that this time remains constant. That is because the force on the object is always equal to kx. where k is a constant that depends on the spring you are using and x is the current distance of the object from its equilibrium position. Robert Hooke (1635–1703) discovered the law by matching an equation to the picture formed by graphing numerical data about the position of masses tied to springs.

Vocabulary and Notation

- **affine combination**
- **centroid**
- **conic sections**
- **convex combination**
- **coordinatize**
- **Dandelin sphere**
- **directrix**
- **double cone, $z^2 = x^2 + y^2$**
- **eccentricity**
- **ellipse**
- **focus, foci**
- **head and tail of a vector**
- **hyperbola**
- **locus**
- **major axis**
- **minor axis**
- **parabola**
- **parameter**
- **point-tester**
- **power of a point, $\Pi(P)$**
- **signed power of a point, $\Pi_S(P)$**
- **vector, $\overrightarrow{AB}$**

triples in three-space. Students use vector methods to connect to geometry, which results in even more synergy between algebra and geometry. As they learn to visualize the geometric results of algebraic operations on vectors, students understand more about the properties of those operations, and through vector methods they come upon completely new ways to think about geometric proofs in the coordinate plane. Students find vector methods to be especially valuable because they translate much more easily to three-dimensional space than traditional coordinate methods.

Chapter Vocabulary and Notation

The following list gives key vocabulary and notation used in the chapter. Selected new vocabulary and notation items are shown in boldface on the student page.

- affine combination, p. 518
- apex, p. 468
- axis, p. 468
- centroid, p. 519
- concurrent, p. 519
- conic sections, p. 468
- convex combination, p. 518
- coordinatize, p. 450
- Dandelin sphere, p. 472
- dilation, p. 507
- directrix, p. 472
- double cone, $z^2 = x^2 + y^2$, p. 449
- eccentricity, p. 495
- ellipse, p. 469
- focus, foci, p. 470
- generator, p. 468
- head and tail of a vector, p. 503
- hyperbola, p. 469
- locus, p. 470
- major axis, p. 477
- median, p. 519
- midline, p. 456
- minor axis, p. 477
- parabola, p. 469
- parallelogram, p. 450
- parameter, p. 512
- parametric equations, p. 512
- perpendicular bisector, p. 445
- point-tester, p. 444
- power of a point, $\Pi(P)$, p. 458
- rhombus, p. 453
- scalar, p. 501
- scaling, p. 505
- signed power of a point, $\Pi_S(P)$, p. 459
- trapezoid, p. 456
- vector, $\overrightarrow{AB}$, p. 503
- vector equations, p. 511
- vertex, p. 477

Chapter Technology

CME Project *Precalculus* assumes that each student has access to a graphing calculator. It also recommends access to a computer algebra system (CAS) and to geometry software.

Support for the use of technology is available in the TI-Nspire™ Technology Handbook. See p. 704.

A list of technology used with important concepts in this chapter appears below. Students will need access to the functionality listed to develop complete understanding of these topics.

Computer Algebra System

CHAPTER 6 PROJECT Expand a sum of products of polynomials, p. 528.

Geometry Software

LESSON 6.6 Graph conic sections, p. 470.

LESSON 6.9 Study conic sections, p. 493.

Graphing Calculator

LESSON 6.8 Graph a second-degree equation in x and y, p. 487.

CHAPTER 6 PROJECT Graph conic sections, p. 526.

Investigation Overview

In this investigation, students form deeper associations between geometry and algebra by using the Cartesian coordinate system to bring measurement to geometric objects and relationships. Students review formulas for distance, midpoint, and slope from previous courses, and use this knowledge to prove geometric results in the coordinate plane. They also review the process of *completing the square* to find the center and radius of a circle, and explore the *signed power of a point* with respect to a circle.

Students also begin to think about graphs of functions in two variables, such as $x^2 + y^2 = r^2$ and $x^2 - y^2 = k$, and produce some graphs of functions like these in two and three dimensions. In the next investigation, they examine these graphs more closely as *conic sections* and use distance relationships to develop locus definitions for these graphs.

You may wish to assign Questions 1–3 for students to think and write about during the investigation.

Learning Goals

- Sketch the graphs of equations in two variables.
- Use distance and slope relationships to prove geometric results.
- Evaluate and use the signed power of a point with respect to a circle.

Habits and Skills

- Use equations as point-testers for graphs.
- Visualize collections of points that meet particular conditions—points that satisfy a distance relationship, points with the same signed power with respect to a given circle, and so on.
- Choose coordinate systems strategically to facilitate calculation and proof.

Coordinate Geometry

In *Coordinate Geometry*, you will reap the benefits of the insight of Rene Descartes. His coordinate system lets you transform geometric problems into algebraic problems. Then you will use algebra to solve those problems.

By the end of this investigation, you will be able to answer questions like these.

1. What is the set of points equidistant from the x-axis and the point $(0, 4)$?
2. How can you use coordinates to show that the diagonals of a parallelogram bisect each other?
3. How can you find the center and radius of a circle with an equation written in normal form?

You will learn how to

- sketch the graphs of equations in two variables
- use distance and slope relationships to prove geometric results
- evaluate and use the signed power of a point with respect to a circle

You will develop these habits and skills:

- Use equations as point-testers for graphs.
- Visualize collections of points that meet particular conditions—points that satisfy a distance relationship, points with the same signed power with respect to a given circle, and so on.
- Choose coordinate systems strategically to facilitate calculation and proof.

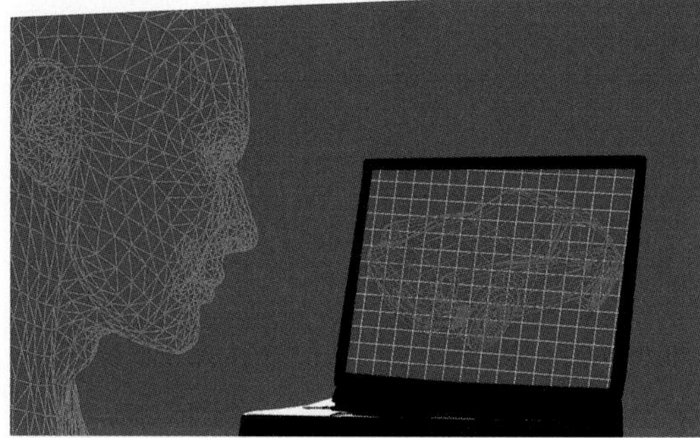

Artists and engineers employ digital wire frame models to represent three dimensional objects. The surface and underlying structure of the item is first coordinatized. Then the animator uses powerful computer software to study, manipulate, or bring the entity to virtual life.

Investigation Road Map

LESSON 6.1, *Getting Started,* has students use a grid, similar to the one used to depict the multiplication table in CME Project *Algebra 1,* to visualize graphs of equations in two variables.

LESSON 6.2, *Equations as Point-Testers,* uses equations as point-testers for graphs of two-variable functions, and reviews basic distance and slope formulas.

LESSON 6.3, *Coordinates and Proof,* develops strategies for choosing a coordinate system to simplify the calculations associated with a geometric proof.

LESSON 6.4, *The Power of a Point,* extends the idea of *power of a point* with respect to a circle using coordinates.

6.1 Getting Started

In CME Project *Algebra 1*, you explored versions of the addition and multiplication tables placed upon a coordinate grid. Here is the multiplication table.

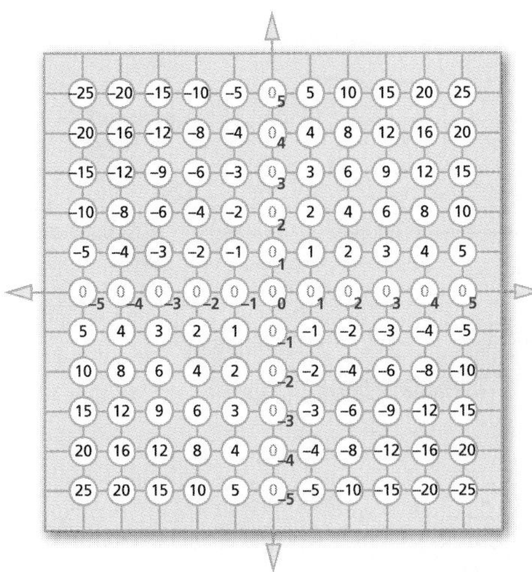

You can use the coordinate grid to visualize the outputs of any two-variable function, such as $f(x, y) = x^2 - y^2$.

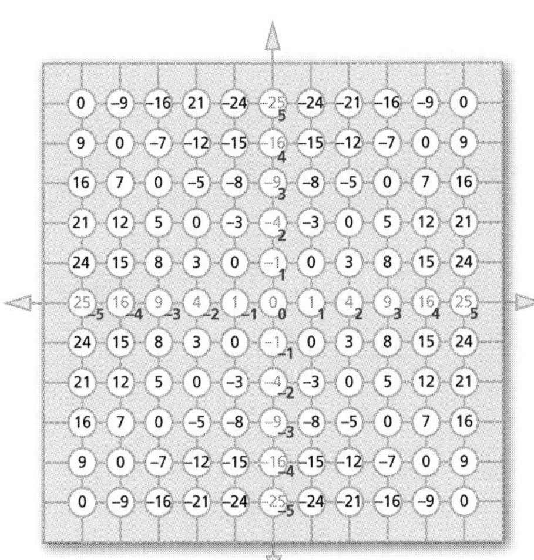

Lesson Overview

GOAL

- Warm up to the ideas of the investigation.

CME Project *Algebra 1* gave students a different way to look at the multiplication table. It is set up in a way similar to the Cartesian coordinate grid. At any lattice point (x, y) there is a blank circle, in which students write the product xy. From a figure like this, students find all the points (x, y) which have a given product, such as 24. By extending this idea a bit, students can plot these lattice points on a traditional coordinate system and connect them with a smooth curve to visualize the graph of the equation $xy = 24$. And, it is not just the product xy that they can write in the blank circle. In this lesson, students put $x^2 - y^2$ into these circles instead, and use the new picture as a tool to sketch a graph of an equation, such as $x^2 - y^2 = 9$.

In this Getting Started lesson, students also work problems that preview upcoming lessons. Later lessons will formalize many of the topics in these problems. For now, let students explore them and develop their own methods.

FOR YOU TO EXPLORE

- Core: 1, 2, 3, 4
- Optional: none
- Extension: 5

MATERIALS

- CAS (optional)
- graph paper
- graphing calculators
- Blackline Masters MC7, 6.1

HOMEWORK

- Core: 6, 7, 8, 10, 11
- Optional: 12, 13a–e
- Extension: 9, 13f

Launch

Have your students jump right into the problems. You may want to give them copies of Blackline Master 6.1 to use for Problem 1 and Exercise 6.

Explore

As students are working, clarify the process of creating a grid other than the familiar multiplication table grid. Explain that each circle has an x and a y value associated with it, because each circle is on a point (x, y) of the coordinate grid. Students can substitute these x and y values into any two-variable expression to make a special grid for that expression. In the multiplication table, the expression is just xy. They used a similar grid for the addition table. You can use *any* expression in x and y to generate values to fill the circles.

You may wish to use the Blackline Master MC7 on an overhead or to provide copies for students to use in this lesson. It will be useful whenever students are asked to graph.

For You to Explore

PROBLEM 1 The grid from CME Project *Algebra 1* may help students visualize the graphs of equations in two variables. They already used this idea to solve sum-product problems to aid in factoring. Blackline Master 6.1 reproduces this grid. You may wish to provide copies to your students to use with their homework.

PROBLEM 3 Make sure that students notice the switch in variables. Rather than make a brand-new grid, encourage them to figure out how to use the one they have.

PROBLEM 5 Some students may struggle with sketching a three-dimensional graph. You might suggest that they think about using shading, color, or even contour lines. The graphs they drew for Problems 2 and 3 are contour lines for this three-dimensional graph.

Wrap Up

If students are able to complete the core For You to Explore problems, have them continue with the On Your Own exercises. Listen to your students to gain information about their backgrounds. Are they using the words *hyperbola*, or *point-tester*? Do any students recognize the power of a point calculation in Exercise 11?

Exercises

HOMEWORK

- Core: 6, 7, 8, 10, 11
- Optional: 12, 13a–e
- Extension: 9, 13f

On Your Own

EXERCISES 6 Graphs of this equation are much more familiar to your students, which is why the students work with equations of the form $x^2 - y^2$ in class, and you assign Exercises 6 and 7 as homework.

EXERCISE 8 As with the previous system, students can use the graphs to see the number and approximate value of solutions. In this exercise students often miss one or more of the intersections.

EXERCISE 9 Later students will encounter the equation $z^2 = x^2 + y^2$, and see how to use this double cone to visualize conic sections.

EXERCISE 10 Hopefully, your students remember the mathematical habit they first encountered in CME Project *Algebra 1*: the equation is the point-tester for the graph. Rather than graphing the circle and these points, they should substitute the coordinates of each point into the equation and see if the result is a true statement.

For You to Explore

1. Use the grid for f to find several solutions to the equation $x^2 - y^2 = 9$.
2. Use the grid to help draw an accurate graph of the equation $x^2 - y^2 = 9$.
3. Use the grid to help draw an accurate graph of the equation $y^2 - x^2 = 5$.
4. Find all solutions to this system of equations.
$$x^2 - y^2 = 9$$
$$x + y = 5$$
5. **Take It Further** Use the grid to help you draw a reasonable sketch of the graph of this equation.
$$z = x^2 - y^2$$

You may need to find other points besides the ones in the grid.

The *z*-axis is perpendicular to the *xy*-plane, and passes through the origin.

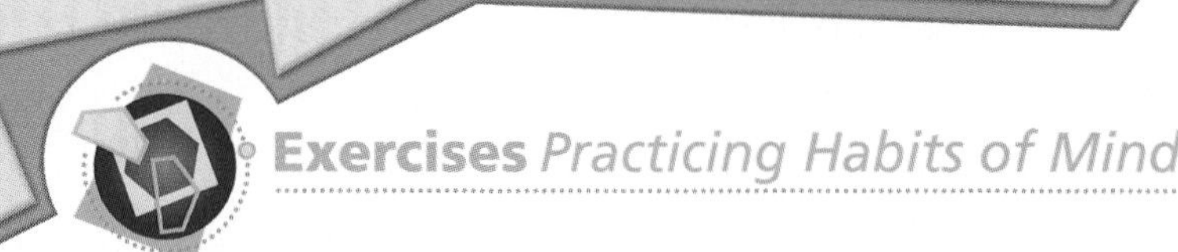

Exercises *Practicing Habits of Mind*

On Your Own

6. Build a grid similar to the one for $f(x, y) = x^2 - y^2$ for the function g defined as
$$g(x, y) = x^2 + y^2$$
7. Use the grid to help draw an accurate graph of the equation $x^2 + y^2 = 17$.
8. Solve this system of equations.
$$x^2 + y^2 = 17$$
$$x^2 - y^2 = 9$$
9. **Take It Further** Draw a rough three-dimensional sketch of the graph of this equation.
$$z = x^2 + y^2$$
10. The graph of the equation $x^2 + y^2 = 13$ is a circle. For each point listed below, determine whether or not it is on this circle.
    a. (3, 2) **b.** (2, −3) **c.** (0, 4) **d.** $(2\sqrt{3}, -1)$
    e. Write About It Describe how you would determine if any point (x, y) is on this circle.

Answers

For You to Explore

1. Answers may vary. Sample: (3, 0), (−3, 0), (5, 4), (5, −4), (−5, −4), and others. Any value of x with $|x| \geq 3$ has two corresponding y values.

2–3. See back of book.

4. $x = 3.4, y = 1.6$
5. See back of book.

Exercises

6–7. See back of book.

8. $(\sqrt{13}, 2), (\sqrt{13}, -2), (-\sqrt{13}, 2), (-\sqrt{13}, -2)$
9. See back of book.
10. **a.** yes **b.** yes **c.** no **d.** yes
    e. Any point (x, y) satisfying the equation $x^2 + y^2 = 13$ is on the circle.

11. Here is the graph of two chords of the circle given by the graph of the equation $x^2 + y^2 = 13$.

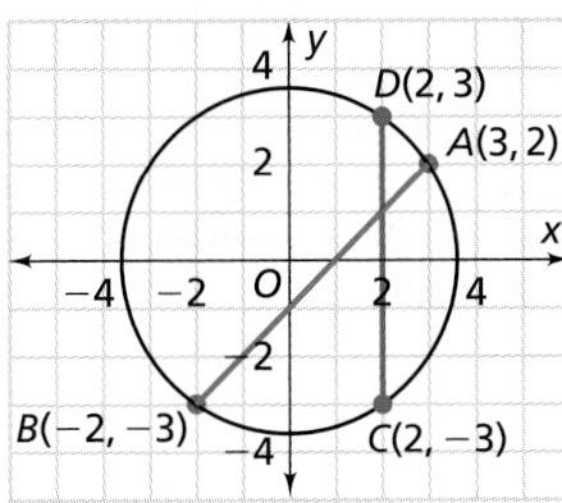

a. Find an equation for the line containing $A(3, 2)$ and $B(-2, -3)$.

b. Find an equation for the line containing $C(2, -3)$ and $D(2, 3)$.

c. Find the coordinates of the point of intersection X of the two chords.

d. Show that the following statement is true by calculating the length of each chord.

$$AX \cdot BX = CX \cdot DX$$

12. Here is the graph of two chords of the circle given by the graph of the equation $x^2 + y^2 = 25$.

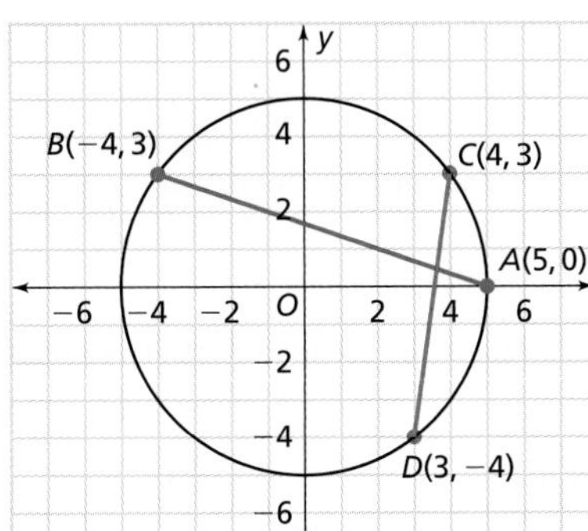

a. Find an equation for the line containing $A(5, 0)$ and $B(-4, 3)$.

b. Find an equation for the line containing $C(4, 3)$ and $D(3, -4)$.

c. Find the coordinates of the point of intersection X of the two chords.

d. Show that the following statement is true by calculating the length of each chord.

$$AX \cdot BX = CX \cdot DX$$

Maintain Your Skills

13. For each statement, write an expression that matches the description.

a. the slope between (2, 4) and (x, y)

b. the distance from the origin (0, 0) to (x, y)

c. the distance from (2, 4) to (x, y)

d. the distance from (3, 0) to (x, y), plus the distance from (−3, 0) to (x, y)

e. the distance from (x, y) to the line with equation $y = -3$

f. **Take It Further** the distance from (x, y) to the line with equation $x + y = 10$

11. a. $y = x - 1$

b. $x = 2$

c. (2, 1)

d. $AX = \sqrt{2}$, $BX = 4\sqrt{2}$, $CX = 4$, $DX = 2$, therefore $AX \cdot BX = CX \cdot DX = 8$

12. a. $y = -\frac{1}{3}x + \frac{5}{3}$

b. $y = 7x - 25$

c. $\left(\frac{40}{11}, \frac{5}{11}\right)$

d. $AX = \frac{5}{11}\sqrt{10}$, $BX = \frac{28}{11}\sqrt{10}$, $CX = \frac{20}{11}\sqrt{2}$, $DX = \frac{35}{11}\sqrt{2}$, therefore $AX \cdot BX = CX \cdot DX = \frac{1400}{121}$

13. a. $\frac{y-4}{x-2}$

b. $\sqrt{x^2 + y^2}$

c. $\sqrt{(x-2)^2 + (y-4)^2}$

d. $\sqrt{(x-3)^2 + y^2} + \sqrt{(x+3)^2 + y^2}$

e. $|y + 3|$

f. $\frac{|x + y - 10|}{\sqrt{2}}$

EXERCISE 11 When you assign this exercise and the next, there is no need to remind students about power of a point yet. They will see more examples in later lessons.

EXERCISE 12 is not much more difficult than Exercise 6, but students will take longer due to the uglier numbers involved. Students might want to use a CAS for the distance calculations, so you might consider asking them to build a function on the CAS for calculating the distance between points.

Maintain Your Skills

EXERCISE 13 helps prepare students to understand the locus definitions of conic sections, covered later in this chapter.

Lesson Overview

GOAL

- Sketch the graphs of equations in two variables.

In this lesson, students review the idea that an equation is the *point-tester* for its graph. In other words, if the coordinates of a point on the plane satisfy an equation, then that point is on the graph of that equation. Students do not even need to know how to completely graph an equation to decide if a particular point is on its graph—they just substitute the coordinates of the point into the equation and see if the result is a true statement.

Investigation 6B uses this familiar point-tester concept to develop the locus definitions for conic sections. For example, a parabola is the set of all points that are equidistant from a given point and a given line that does not pass through the point. Students write a point-tester equation based on this information using what they know about finding the distance between two points and the distance between a point and a line. (The lines used for this purpose in this course are generally vertical or horizontal so that the distance calculations are reasonable.)

In this lesson, students also review some basic distance and slope formulas from previous courses and use them to make calculations that will lead to proofs of geometric results as the investigation continues.

CHECK YOUR UNDERSTANDING
- Core: 1, 2, 3, 4
- Optional: 5, 6a-d
- Extension: 6e

MATERIALS
- graph paper
- graphing calculators
- Blackline Masters MC7, 6.2A–C

HOMEWORK
- Core: 7, 8, 9, 10, 11, 13
- Optional: 14
- Extension: 12

VOCABULARY
- double cone, $z^2 = x^2 + y^2$
- perpendicular bisector
- point-tester

Launch

Begin today's lesson with the For You to Do section. Use Blackline Master 6.2A on an overhead as you discuss the Facts and Notation section.

Explore

For You to Do

PROBLEM 1 Some students may not remember the distance formula, but since it is printed just a little further down the page, that should not be an issue.

PROBLEM 2 Some students may be uncomfortable with the absolute value graph because it is not one of the familiar basic graphs that they have studied. Encourage them to work it out on their own.

6.2 Equations as Point-Testers

In CME Project *Algebra 1*, you learned that graphs are point-testers. The graph of an equation is the set of the points on the Cartesian plane that make the equation true. Sometimes you can describe a graph using words, and sometimes by its shape and some key points. If you can write an equation that captures all the characteristics of the graph, that equation will be an equation for the graph.

For You to Do

1. Find an equation describing the points (x, y) that are 5 units away from $(3, 4)$.
2. Sketch a graph of all points (x,y) in the plane satisfying the equation $|y - 2| = 3$.

Facts and Notation

Here are some useful formulas from previous courses.

- *Distance formula*: The distance between points $A(x_1, y_1)$ and $B(x_2, y_2)$ is

$$d(A, B) = \sqrt{(x_2 - x_1)^2 + (y_2 - y_1)^2}$$

- *Midpoint formula*: The midpoint of the segment between points $A(x_1, y_1)$ and $B(x_2, y_2)$ is

$$M(A, B) = \left(\frac{x_1 + x_2}{2}, \frac{y_1 + y_2}{2}\right)$$

- *Slope formula*: The slope between points $A(x_1, y_1)$ and $B(x_2, y_2)$ is

$$m(A, B) = \frac{y_2 - y_1}{x_2 - x_1}$$

- *Perpendicular slopes*: Two lines in the plane are perpendicular if the product of their slopes is -1, or if one line is vertical and the other is horizontal.

This assumes that $x_1 \neq x_2$. What happens if $x_1 = x_2$?

Remember...

In your geometry class, you proved that if the slope of a line ℓ is m (with $m \neq 0$), then the slope of any line perpendicular to ℓ is $-\frac{1}{m}$.

Answers

For You To Do

1. $(x - 3)^2 + (y - 4)^2 = 25$

2.

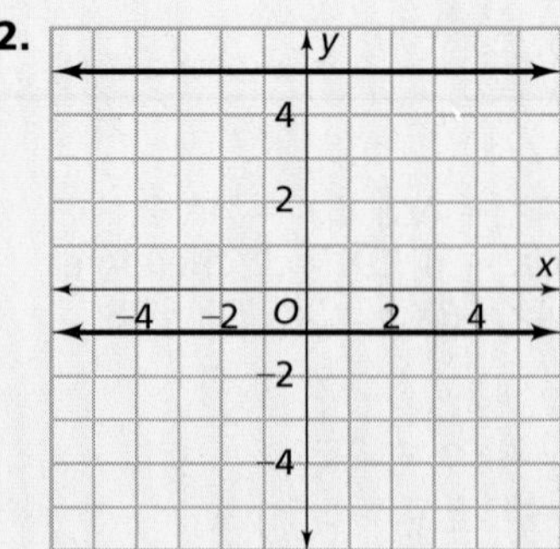

Example 1

Problem Find an equation for the set of points equidistant from (5, 2) and (11, 0).

Solution

Method 1 Use the distance formula. Consider any point (x, y) on the graph. Its distance from (5, 2) must equal its distance from (11, 0).

$$\text{distance from } (x, y) \text{ to } (5, 2) = \text{distance from } (x, y) \text{ to } (11, 0)$$

$$\sqrt{(x-5)^2 + (y-2)^2} = \sqrt{(x-11)^2 + y^2}$$

This is a valid equation but you can simplify it. Since the expressions under the radicals are nonnegative (why?), squaring both sides will not introduce any new solutions.

$$\begin{aligned} (x-5)^2 + (y-2)^2 &= (x-11)^2 + y^2 \\ x^2 - 10x + 25 + y^2 - 4y + 4 &= x^2 - 22x + 121 + y^2 \\ -10x - 4y + 29 &= -22x + 121 \\ -4y &= -12x + 92 \\ y &= 3x - 23 \end{aligned}$$

Method 2 Use the geometric observation that the solution will be the equation of the perpendicular bisector of the segment connecting (5, 2) and (11, 0).

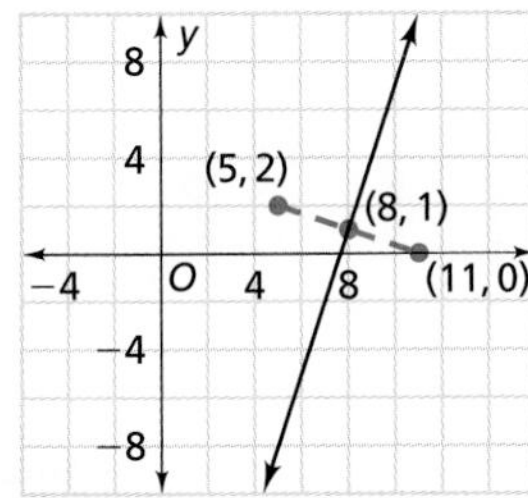

The perpendicular bisector must pass through the midpoint (8, 1) and be perpendicular to the segment. The slope between (5, 2) and (11, 0) is $-\frac{1}{3}$, so the slope of the perpendicular bisector is 3. One equation for the perpendicular bisector is $y - 1 = 3(x - 8)$. This equation is equivalent to $y = 3x - 23$ as found earlier.

Remember...

If you write the equation of a line in the form $y - k = m(x - h)$, the line passes through the point (h, k) and has slope m.

Example 2

Problem Find an equation for the set of points that are equidistant from the origin and the line with equation $y = 2$.

Solution Take an arbitrary point (x, y). Its distance to the origin is $\sqrt{x^2 + y^2}$. Its distance from the line with equation $y = 2$ is $|y - 2|$.

Examples 1 and 2

Spend time as needed going over these completed examples. Make sure students understand the problems. As necessary, help them develop detailed solutions. Use Blackline Master MC7 on an overhead as needed.

Wrap Up

Finish today's class by going over the core Check Your Understanding exercises as time allows. Exercises 7 and 8 from the On Your Own exercise set will use the results from Exercise 4, so cover this exercise if possible.

Assessment Resources

Lesson Quiz 6.2

1. a. Write a point-tester that is true for any point (x, y) 4 units away from the line with equation $y = 6$.
   b. Sketch the graph of all points (x, y) that are 4 units away from the line with equation $y = 6$.

2. Consider the triangle with vertices at $A(0, 6)$, $B(4, -4)$, and $C(10, 8)$.
   a. Find an equation for the perpendicular bisector of $\overline{AB}$.
   b. Find an intersection for the perpendicular bisectors of $\overline{AB}$ and $\overline{BC}$.
   c. Find the equation of the median from C to $\overline{AB}$.

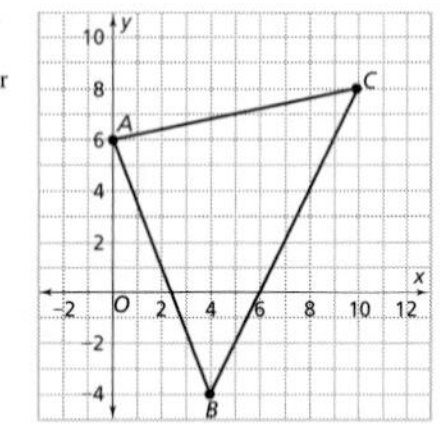

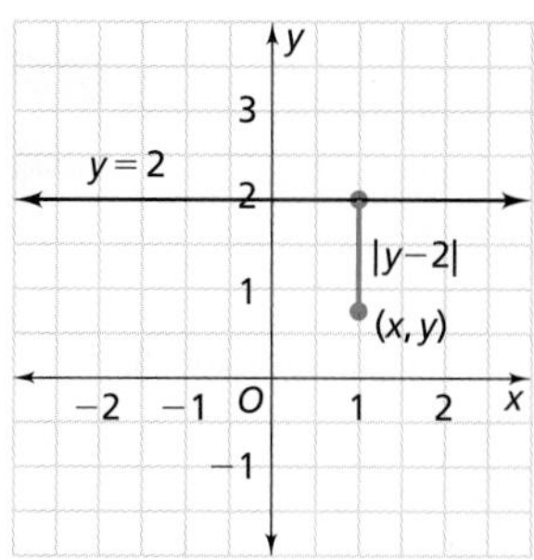

The set of points equidistant from both satisfies the equation $\sqrt{x^2 + y^2} = |y - 2|$. Simplify and solve for y.

$$\sqrt{x^2 + y^2} = |y - 2|$$
$$x^2 + y^2 = (y - 2)^2$$
$$x^2 + y^2 = y^2 - 4y + 4$$
$$x^2 + 4y = 4$$
$$y = -\tfrac{1}{4}x^2 + 1$$

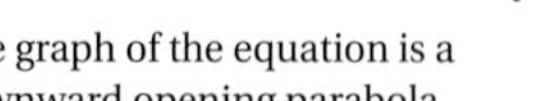

The graph of the equation is a downward opening parabola.

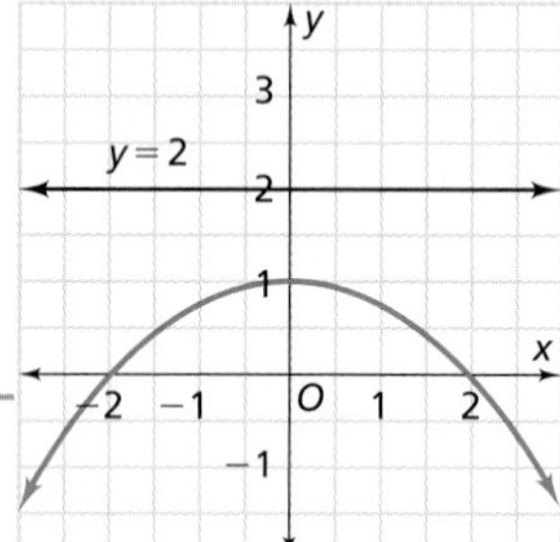

Habits of Mind

Understand the process. Why is it legal to square both sides?

Developing Habits of Mind

Establish a process. The intersection of the graphs of two equations is the set of points that satisfies both of their equations. For example, the Getting Started lesson for this investigation asked you to find the intersection of the graphs of the equations $x^2 - y^2 = 9$ and $x + y = 5$. You can solve this algebraically. Note that you can factor $x^2 - y^2$.

$$(x + y)(x - y) = 9$$

But $x + y = 5$ is known, so $x - y$ must equal 1.8. Then a system of equations emerges.

$$x + y = 5$$
$$x - y = 1.8$$

You can solve this system of equations by many methods, including adding the two equations together. The solution $x = 3.4$, $y = 1.6$ is the only intersection of the two graphs.

Answers

Exercises

1. a. $|y - 2| = 3$

b.

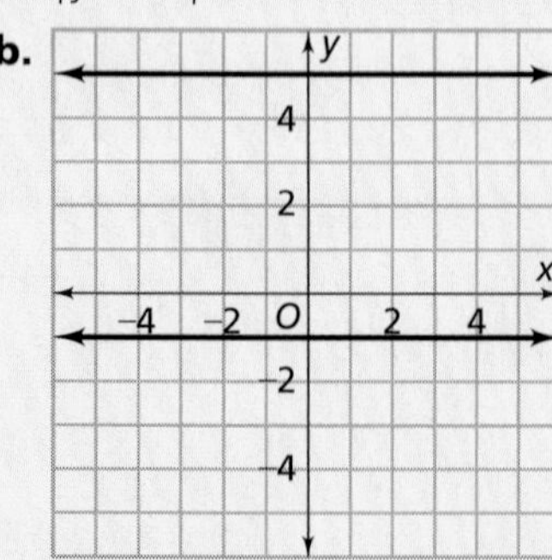

2. a. no

b. yes

c. If $a < 0$, this point must be closer to the y-axis than to $(4, 0)$ since $(4, 0)$ will be on the opposite side of the axis. Therefore, the distances could never be equal.

d. $y^2 = 8x - 16$

3. a. No; the distance from $(5, 3)$ to $(15, 0)$ is $\sqrt{109}$, and the distance from $(5, 3)$ to $(6, 0)$ is $\sqrt{10}$.

b. $(9, 0)$ and $(-3, 0)$

c. $36 = (x - 3)^2 + y^2$

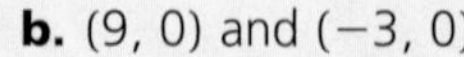

d.

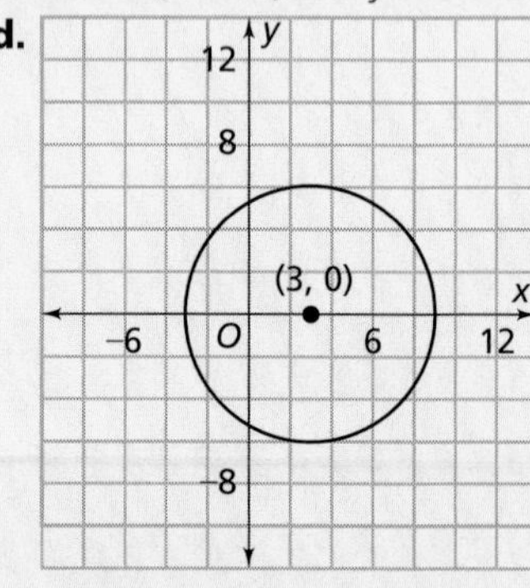

Exercises *Practicing Habits of Mind*

Check Your Understanding

1. **a.** Write a point-tester that is true for any point (x, y) 3 units away from the line with equation $y = 2$.

   b. Sketch the graph of all points (x, y) that are 3 units away from the line with equation $y = 2$.

2. Consider the set of all points (x, y) that are the same distance away from $(4, 0)$ as they are from the y-axis.

   a. Determine whether $(3, 3)$ is in this set of points.

   b. Determine whether $(10, 8)$ is in the set.

   c. Explain why any point (a, b) with $a < 0$ cannot be in this set of points.

   d. Write a point-tester that is true for any point (x, y) equidistant from $(4, 0)$ and the y-axis.

3. You have learned that the set of points equidistant from two given points in the plane is a line. But now, consider the set of points that are twice as far away from $(15, 0)$ as they are from $(6, 0)$.

   a. Is $(5, 3)$ in this set? Justify your answer.

   b. Find the two points on the x-axis that are in this set.

   c. Write a point-tester equation that you can use to determine whether any point (x, y) is in this set.

   d. Sketch the graph of the point-tester equation.

4. A triangle has vertices $A(2, 0)$, $B(6, -2)$, and $C(8, 4)$.

   a. Find an equation for the perpendicular bisector of $\overline{AB}$.

   b. Find an equation for the perpendicular bisector of $\overline{AC}$.

   c. Find the intersection of the two perpendicular bisectors.

5. Point-testers can be useful to find equations in three-dimensional space. Consider the set of points exactly 5 units away from the point $(2, 3, 4)$.

   a. Find five points that are in this set.

   b. Find five points that are not in this set.

   c. Write a point-tester equation that you can use to determine whether any point (x, y, z) is in this set of points.

Exercises

HOMEWORK
- Core: 7, 8, 9, 10, 11, 13
- Optional: 14
- Extension: 12

Many exercises in Lessons 6.2, 6.3, and 6.13 refer to the definitions summarized on Blackline Master 6.2B. Make your own marks on an overhead of the master to indicate equal sides and angles.

Check Your Understanding

EXERCISE 1 Some students may have an easier time visualizing this three-dimensional situation as an infinitely long cylinder of radius 2 with the line with equation $y = 2$ as a central axis.

EXERCISE 2 provides an early exposure to the locus definition of a parabola. In this definition, the point in question is called the *focus* of the parabola, and the line is the *directrix*. There is no need to formalize this now, though.

EXERCISE 3 The result surprises many students, especially the fact that it is a circle; most expect a line. Also, watch for students who mistakenly switch the "2" in the distance equation. The distance from (15, 0) should equal double the distance from (6, 0). Students who continue to struggle should test points until they see the behavior.

EXERCISE 5 Hopefully, students will realize that this is a description of a sphere, although they may not have encountered its equation in three-dimensional coordinate space yet.

4. a. $y = 2x - 9$

b. $y = -\frac{3}{2}x + \frac{19}{2}$

c. $\left(\frac{37}{7}, \frac{11}{7}\right)$

5. a. Answers may vary. Any (x, y, z) fitting the equation $5 = \sqrt{(x-2)^2 + (y-3)^2 + (z-4)^2}$ is in this set. Samples: $(7, 3, 4)$, $(2, 3, 9)$, $(2, 0, 0)$, $(-2, 0, 4)$, and $(2, -2, 4)$.

b. Answers may vary. Any (x, y, z) not fitting the equation in part (a) is not part of this set.

c. $(x-2)^2 + (y-3)^2 + (z-4)^2 = 25$

EXERCISE 6 Students may have trouble visualizing this as a plane. If they remember that the set of all points that are equidistant from two points in a plane is the perpendicular bisector of the segment with the two points as endpoints, they may visualize several perpendicular bisectors in three-space and see that they all lie in a plane. Finding the point-tester is more of an algebraic challenge, and unless your students have some experience with three-dimensional graphing, they may not recognize the resulting equation as the equation of a plane.

On Your Own

EXERCISE 8 Students already proved that the three medians of a triangle must all intersect in a single point, but they should appreciate seeing the numbers work out in a specific occurrence.

EXERCISE 10 The proof requires completing the square, so judge whether students will feel comfortable with the technique. You might consider reviewing the process, since students will use the technique frequently in the next two investigations.

6. Consider the set of points in space that are the same distance from the origin (0, 0, 0) as they are from the point (2, 4, 6).

a. In the plane, the set of points equidistant from two points would be a line. What kind of shape should it be in space?

b. Determine whether or not (3, 7, −1) is in this set of points.

c. What equation would you use to check to see if (x, y, z) is in this set of points? Simplify the equation as much as possible.

d. Use the point-tester from part (c) to determine whether or not the point (15, 4, −3) is in this set of points.

e. **Take It Further** Sketch the graph of all points in this set.

On Your Own

7. Exercise 4 looked at the perpendicular bisectors of $\triangle ABC$.

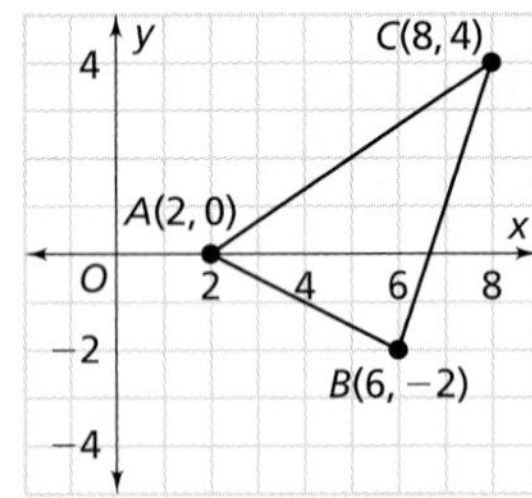

a. Find an equation for the perpendicular bisector of $\overline{BC}$.

b. Find an intersection for the perpendicular bisectors of $\overline{AB}$ and $\overline{BC}$.

8. Find equations for the three medians of $\triangle ABC$. Show that the three medians intersect in one point.

Remember... A median of a triangle is a segment connecting a vertex to the midpoint of the opposite side.

9. As in the Getting Started lesson, build a grid for the function h,

$$h(x, y) = x^2 + y^2 - 4x + 2y - 4$$

if $-5 \leq x \leq 5$, $-5 \leq y \leq 5$.

10. **a.** Use the grid from Exercise 9 to describe the graph of the equation

$$x^2 + y^2 - 4x + 2y - 4 = 0$$

b. Prove that your description in part (a) is correct.

You may need to add or subtract terms from each side.

Answers

6. **a.** a plane

b. Yes, this point is part of the set.

c. $x + 2y + 3z = 14$

d. Yes, this point is part of the set.

e. See back of book.

7. **a.** $y = -\frac{1}{3}x + \frac{10}{3}$

b. $\left(\frac{37}{7}, \frac{11}{7}\right)$

8. $y = \frac{1}{5}x - \frac{2}{5}$; $y = -4x + 22$; $y = \frac{5}{4}x - 6$; the point $\left(\frac{16}{3}, \frac{2}{3}\right)$ is on all three lines.

9. See back of book.

10. **a.** The graph is a circle centered at (2, −1) with radius 3.

b. $x^2 + y^2 - 4x + 2y - 4 = 0$

$(x^2 - 4x + 4) + (y^2 + 2y + 1) = 9$

$(x - 2)^2 + (y + 1)^2 = 9$

$\sqrt{(x - 2)^2 + (y + 1)^2} = 3$

This equation matches the distance formula for any point 3 units from (2, −1).

11. Consider the equation in three variables

$$z^2 = x^2 + y^2$$

a. Find several points (x, y, z) that are on the graph of this equation.

b. Suppose $z = 5$. Describe the set of x and y values that make the equation true.

c. Suppose $z = 11$. Describe the set of x and y values that make the equation true.

d. Suppose $z = -11$. Describe the set of x and y values that make the equation true.

e. Suppose $z = 0$. Describe the set of x and y values that make the equation true.

f. Sketch the graph of $z^2 = x^2 + y^2$ as accurately as you can.

For additional practice, go to Web Code: bga-0602

12. **Take It Further** The graph of $z^2 = x^2 + y^2$ is sometimes called a *double cone.*

a. What kind of figure does slicing the double cone perpendicular to the z-axis (say, with the plane with equation $z = 5$) produce?

b. What is the graph that results when the plane with equation $x = 3$ slices the double cone?

c. Find what other shapes might be possible with other slices. Give some examples.

An equation for the plane that contains the point $(0, 0, c)$ is $z = c$. Similarly, an equation for the plane that contains the point $(a, 0, 0)$ is $x = a$.

13. **Standardized Test Prep** Which of the following is an equation for the set of points equidistant from (2, 3) and (6, 1)?

A. $\sqrt{(x-2)^2 + (y-3)^2} = \sqrt{(x-6)^2 + (y-1)^2}$

B. $\frac{y-3}{x-2} = \frac{y-1}{x-6}$

C. $y - 3 = -\frac{1}{2}(x - 2)$

D. $2x + 3y = 6x + y$

Maintain Your Skills

14. The *centroid* of a triangle is the intersection of its medians. Given the three vertices of $\triangle ABC$, find its centroid.

a. $A(0, 0)$, $B(10, 0)$, $C(2, 9)$

b. $A(0, 0)$, $B(10, 0)$, $C(2, -9)$

c. $A(0, 0)$, $B(100, 0)$, $C(20, 90)$

d. $A(1, 2)$, $B(10, 11)$, $C(19, 5)$

e. $A(0, 0)$, $B(3a, 0)$, $C(3b, 3c)$

f. $A(x_1, y_1)$, $B(x_2, y_2)$, $C(x_3, y_3)$

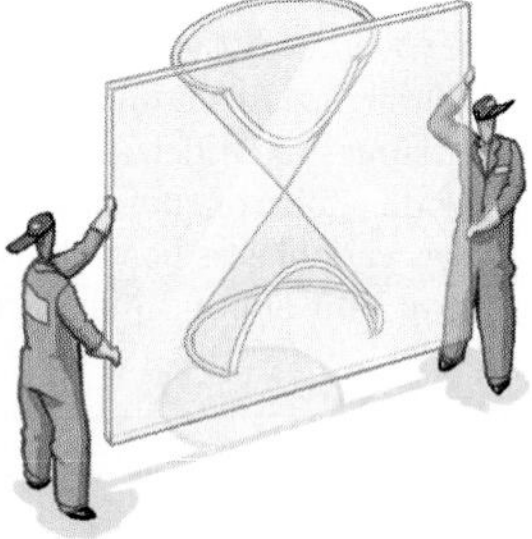

11. a. Answers may vary. Sample: (5, 3, 4), (−4, 4, 0), and (13, 12, 5) (note Pythagorean triples)
b. Circle centered at (0, 0) with radius 5
c. Circle centered at (0, 0) with radius 11
d. Circle centered at (0, 0) with radius 11
e. A single point at the origin.
f. See back of book.

12. a. A circle, unless $z = 0$, in which case the figure would be a single point
b. The graph is a hyperbola.
c. Answers may vary. Sample: a nearly horizontal slice will yield an ellipse. A diagonal slice will yield a parabola.

13. A

14. a. (4, 3) b. (4, −3)
c. (40, 30) d. $(a + b, c)$
e. $\left(\frac{x_1 + x_2 + x_3}{3}, \frac{y_1 + y_2 + y_3}{3}\right)$

EXERCISES 11 AND 12 In these exercises, students visualize slices of the double cone for the first time. They develop this idea further in Investigation 6B on conic sections. Exercise 11 leads immediately to Exercise 12, which is the foundation for Investigation B. It may be worthwhile to work through the exercise in class, using Blackline Master 6.2C on an overhead.

Maintain Your Skills

EXERCISE 14 After working several parts of this exercise, students may notice that the centroid is the average of the three vertices of the triangle. While they can do all parts of this exercise by finding the intersection of the medians, it is more likely that students will look for shortcuts. Students may also already know the median result from their work in a geometry course.

Additional Resources

PRINT RESOURCES	TECHNOLOGY
• Solution Manual	• Interactive Textbook
• Practice Workbook	• TeacherExpress CD-ROM
• Assessment Resources	• ExamView CD-ROM
• Teaching Resources	• PHSchool.com

Additional Practice

1. a. Write a point-tester that is true for any point (x, y) 4 units away from the line with equation $y = 3$.
b. Sketch the graph of all points (x, y) that are 4 units away from the line with equation $y = 3$.

2. Consider the set of all points (x, y) that are the same distance away from (6, 0) as they are from the y-axis.
a. Determine whether the point (6, 6) is in this set of points.
b. Determine whether the point (8, 12) is in this set of points.
c. Write a point-tester that is true for any point (x, y) equidistant from (6, 0) and the y-axis.

3. A triangle has vertices $A(2, 6)$, $B(-2, 2)$, and $C(4, 2)$.
a. Find an equation for the perpendicular bisector of $\overline{AB}$.
b. Find an equation for the perpendicular bisector of $\overline{AC}$.
c. Find the intersection of the two perpendicular bisectors.

4. Consider the set of points in space that are the same distance from the origin (0, 0, 0) as they are from the point (3, −5, 8).
a. Determine whether or not $\left(\frac{1}{3}, 0, 6\right)$ is in this set of points.
b. Write a point-tester equation to determine whether any point (x, y, z) is in this set of points. Simplify the equation as much as possible.

5. a. Find an equation for the set of all points that are equidistant from (4, 3) and (7, 0).
b. Sketch the graph of all points (x, y) that are equidistant from (4, 3) and (7, 0).

6. a. Find an equation for the set of all points that are equidistant from the point (0, 3) and the line with equation $y = 4$.
b. Sketch the graph of all points (x, y) that are equidistant from (0, 3) and the line $y = 4$.

Practice: For Lesson 6.2, assign Exercises 1–6.

Lesson Overview

GOAL

- Use distance and slope relationships to prove geometric results.

In this lesson, students see some strategies for choosing a coordinate system that serves a particular purpose. For example, suppose that you want to prove a result for all triangles. How can you set up a triangle in the coordinate plane so that it is a general triangle (not necessarily a right triangle or an isosceles triangle—not necessarily anything more than a triangle), but so that you are not overwhelmed by a large number of variables every time you want to make a calculation? The Minds in Action dialog demonstrates this particular situation. In this lesson and its exercises, students will practice techniques for *coordinatizing* different shapes in the plane.

CHECK YOUR UNDERSTANDING

- Core: 1, 2, 3, 4, 5
- Optional: none
- Extension: 6

MATERIALS

- graph paper
- graphing calculators
- Blackline Masters MC7, 6.2B

HOMEWORK

- Core: 7, 8, 9, 11, 13, 14
- Optional: 10
- Extension: 12

VOCABULARY

- coordinatize
- midline
- parallelogram
- rhombus
- trapezoid

Launch

Begin today's lesson with the first For You to Do problem. You may wish to use Blackline Master MC7 on an overhead to illustrate the discussion.

Explore

For You to Do

PROBLEM 1 If it suits your class, you may want to assign the three different proofs to different groups of students, and then let each group present their solution to the rest of the class.

6.3 Coordinates and Proof

In this lesson, you will learn how to use coordinate methods to prove geometric facts. For example, consider quadrilateral *ABCD* in the plane.

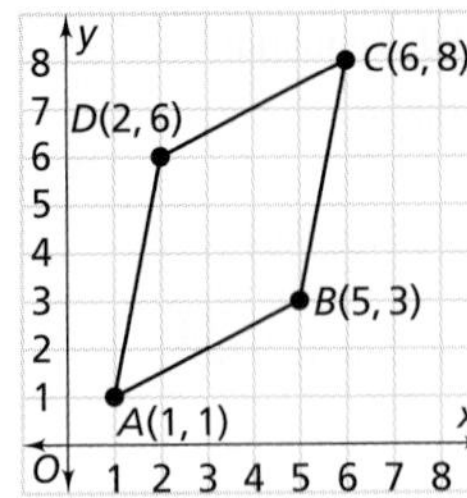

If you wanted to prove that it is a parallelogram you could use any of the following approaches.

- If a quadrilateral has pairs of opposite sides that are parallel, then it is a parallelogram.
- If a quadrilateral has pairs of opposite sides that are congruent, then it is a parallelogram.
- If a quadrilateral has one pair of opposite sides that are congruent and parallel, then it is a parallelogram.

For You to Do

1. Pick one of the three approaches above. Then use it to show that the quadrilateral *ABCD* is a parallelogram.

To prove something more generally, *coordinatize* a geometric shape by making a general version in the coordinate plane. For example, a general parallelogram might look like as follows.

If a general parallelogram lies in the plane, you can define the coordinates however you like. So, define the origin to be one of the vertices. Let one of the sides lie along the *x*-axis. But be careful not to overdefine the shape. For example, if you already defined $Q(0, a)$, point S in the parallelogram cannot be defined as (a, b). That assumes too much about where S is located. A good choice of coordinates is one that needs as few variables as possible, but does not assume any more about the shape than is necessary.

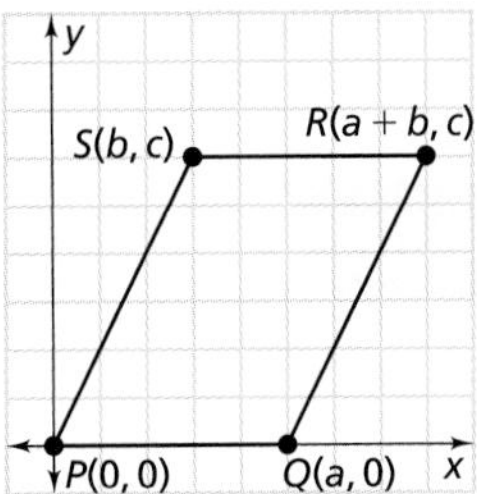

Answers

For You to Do

1. - The slopes of $\overline{AB}$ and $\overline{DC}$ are both equal to $\frac{1}{2}$ and the slopes of $\overline{AD}$ and $\overline{BC}$ are both equal to 5. Since each pair of opposite sides is parallel, this must be a parallelogram.
   - The lengths of $\overline{AB}$ and $\overline{DC}$ are both $\sqrt{20}$ and the lengths of $\overline{AD}$ and $\overline{BC}$ are both $\sqrt{26}$. Since each pair of opposite sides is congruent, this must be a parallelogram.
   - Using the two proofs above, either pair of sides can be shown to be parallel and congruent.

Minds in Action episode 18

Derman and Sasha are coordinatizing $\triangle EON$.

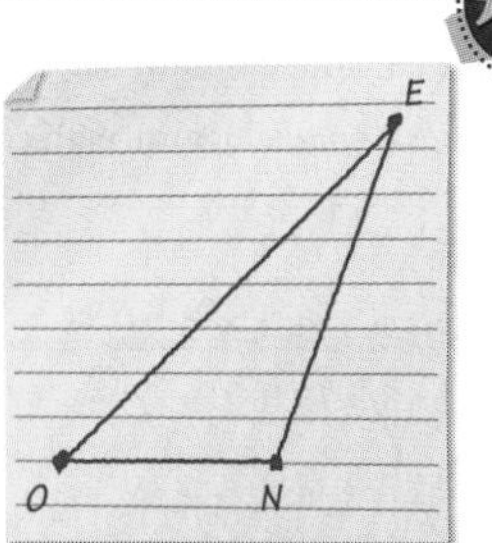

Derman What about a general triangle like this one?

Sasha So how do you want to label the points?

Derman Why not just use six letters? Make the vertices $O(a, b)$, $N(c, d)$, and $E(e, f)$.

Sasha I think we can do it with fewer variables. We can put the axes wherever we want, so let's put point O at the origin. Then we can place $\overline{ON}$ on the x-axis. Point N would have y-coordinate 0, so say its coordinates are $(c, 0)$.

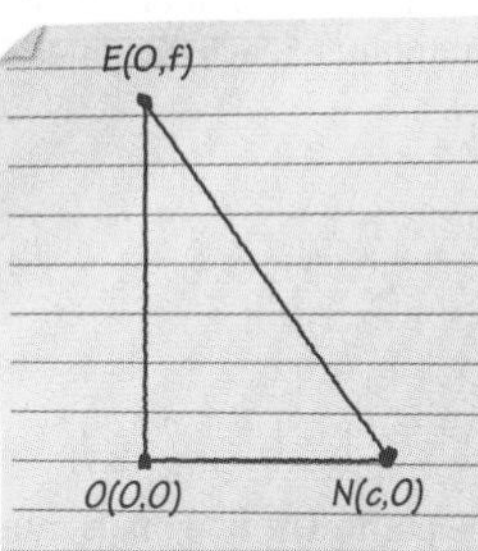

Derman I can do that with the y-axis, too. Line it up with $\overline{OE}$. Then E has x-coordinate 0!

Sasha Wait a minute! If you line up $\overline{ON}$ with the x-axis and $\overline{OE}$ with the y-axis, then something is wrong. Just draw it.

Derman Okay.

Derman Oh. I get it now. I forced $\angle EON$ to be a right angle. I'll bet these would be useful coordinates for a right triangle, though.

Sasha You're right. But this is the way our general triangle should look.

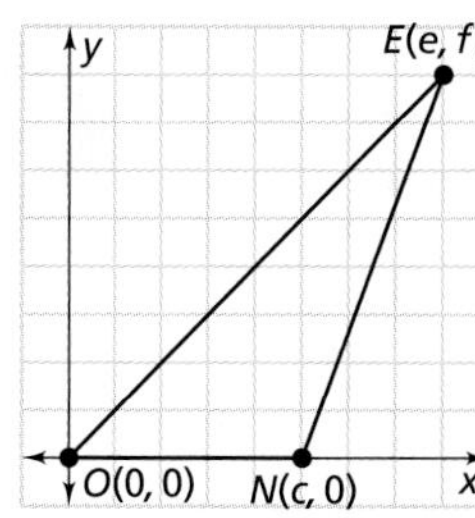

Coordinatizing lets you use formulas to obtain other information about the shape.

Minds in Action

You may wish to assign students Minds in Action roles and present the conversation to the class. This is more effective if you assign the roles one class day prior to the "performance." Urge the students to "get into" their parts by using their own words instead of memorizing lines.

Developing Habits of Mind

Have students connect the habits of mind with the ways they have used their minds in prior mathematics work and/or in life outside the classroom.

Example 1

Problem Show that the diagonals of a parallelogram bisect each other.

Solution Here is a diagram for a general parallelogram, with coordinates labeled.

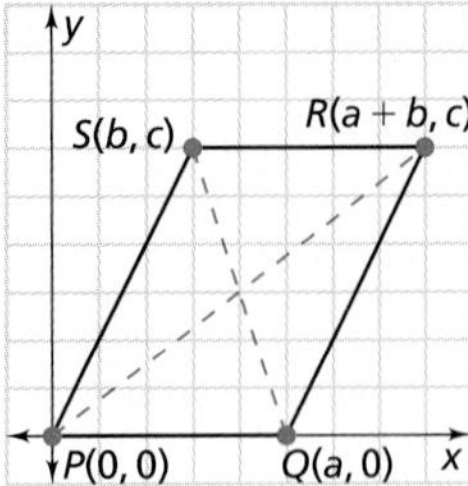

The diagonals bisect each other if their midpoints are the same. So, use the midpoint formula to find the midpoint of each diagonal.

The midpoint of diagonal $\overline{PR}$ is

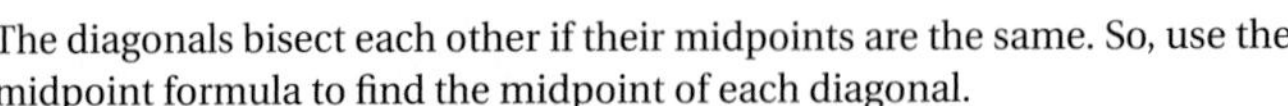

$$\left(\frac{0 + (a + b)}{2}, \frac{0 + c}{2}\right) = \left(\frac{a + b}{2}, \frac{c}{2}\right)$$

The midpoint of diagonal $\overline{QS}$ is

$$\left(\frac{a + b}{2}, \frac{0 + c}{2}\right) = \left(\frac{a + b}{2}, \frac{c}{2}\right)$$

The two midpoints are the same point. The diagonals must intersect at the point $\left(\frac{a + b}{2}, \frac{c}{2}\right)$. This common midpoint means that the diagonals bisect one another.

Habits of Mind

Prove. How do these coordinates guarantee that *PQRS* is a parallelogram?

Developing Habits of Mind

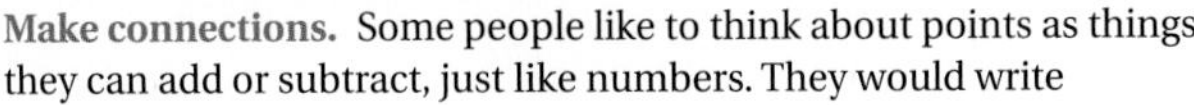

Make connections. Some people like to think about points as things they can add or subtract, just like numbers. They would write

$$(3, 7) + (11, 5) = (14, 12)$$

If you think of points this way, finding a midpoint is just like averaging the points. The average of (3, 7) and (11, 5) is

$$\frac{(3, 7) + (11, 5)}{2} = (7, 6)$$

And, as you saw, (7, 6) is the midpoint of the segment from (3, 7) to (11, 5).

This algebra of points can come in handy, and matches up with the matrix concepts of addition and scalar multiplication. You will revisit these concepts in Investigation C.

For You to Do

2. Plot the points $A(3, 7)$ and $B(11, 5)$ on graph paper. Then calculate and plot $P = \frac{3}{4}(3, 7) + \frac{1}{4}(11, 5)$. How could you describe the location of P relative to points A and B?

Example 2

Problem Prove that the diagonals of a rhombus are perpendicular.

Solution A *rhombus* is a quadrilateral with four congruent sides. Start with a diagram for a general parallelogram.

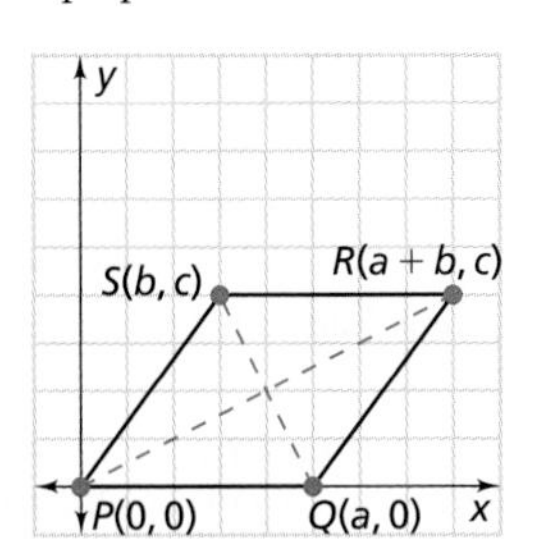

Since $PQRS$ is a rhombus, $PQ = PS$. So $a = \sqrt{b^2 + c^2}$. Or, $a^2 = b^2 + c^2$.

The slope of diagonal $\overline{PR}$ is $\frac{c}{a+b}$. The slope of diagonal $\overline{QS}$ is $\frac{-c}{a-b}$. These slopes are perpendicular if their product is -1.

$$\frac{c}{a+b} \cdot \frac{-c}{a-b} = \frac{-c^2}{a^2 - b^2}$$

Since $a^2 = b^2 + c^2$

$$\frac{-c^2}{a^2 - b^2} = \frac{-c^2}{(b^2 + c^2) - b^2} = \frac{-c^2}{c^2} = -1$$

The product of the slopes of the diagonals is -1, so they are perpendicular.

Habits of Mind

Reason logically. The fact that a rhombus has four congruent sides tells you that it is also a parallelogram. Why?

Or, relabel a as $\sqrt{b^2 + c^2}$, then continue. The proof will be messier, though.

For You to Do

The proof above only holds if neither of the diagonals is vertical (has undefined slope). However, the way you set up the coordinates means that a vertical diagonal will have interesting consequences.

3. What would the coordinates of the vertices of rhombus $PQRS$ have to be if the diagonal $\overline{QS}$ were vertical? What do these coordinates imply about $PQRS$?

4. What would the coordinates of the vertices of rhombus $PQRS$ have to be if the diagonal $\overline{PR}$ were vertical? What do these coordinates imply about $PQRS$?

Example 2

Spend time as needed going over this completed example. Make sure students understand the problem. As necessary, help them develop the detailed solution.

Answers

For You to Do

2.

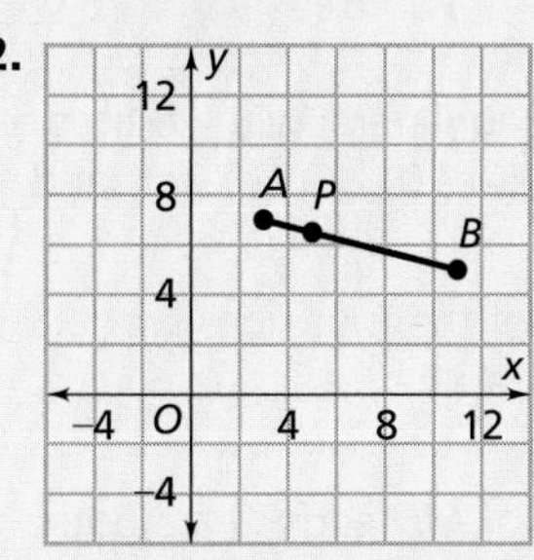

Point P lies on $\overline{AB}$ $\frac{1}{4}$ of the way from A to B.

3. This would be a rhombus that has collapsed down to a line segment with endpoints at (0, 0) and (2a, 0).

4. This would be a rhombus that has collapsed down to a single point at the origin.

Developing Habits of Mind

Use Blackline Master 6.2B to review the definition of median if desired.

Wrap Up

Finish today's class by giving students time to work on the core Check Your Understanding exercises. If time allows, go over some of the solutions. You may want to make a special effort to go over Exercise 5. It points out a common problem that students encounter—Joey assumes what he is trying to prove.

Assessment Resources

Lesson Quiz 6.3

1. **a.** Find four coordinate pairs to represent the vertices of a square.
   b. Prove that the diagonals of a square are equal in length.

2. A parallelogram has three of its vertices at the points $(-2, 8)$, $(1, 2)$, and $(3, 6)$. (See figure.) Find a set of possible coordinates for the fourth vertex.

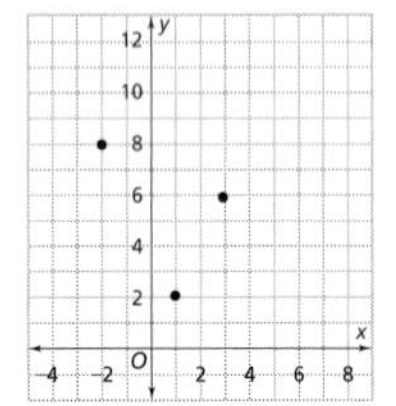

3. Consider the triangle with vertices $A(2, 8)$, $B(2, 0)$, $C(10, 0)$.
   a. Show the triangle is isosceles.
   b. Find an equation that gives the median from B to $\overline{AC}$.
   c. Show that the median from B to side $\overline{AC}$ is also the perpendicular bisector of $\overline{AC}$.

Developing Habits of Mind

Make strategic choices. The choice of coordinates is often influenced by what you are trying to prove. If you are trying to prove a statement about medians, it may make more sense to label a triangle as follows.

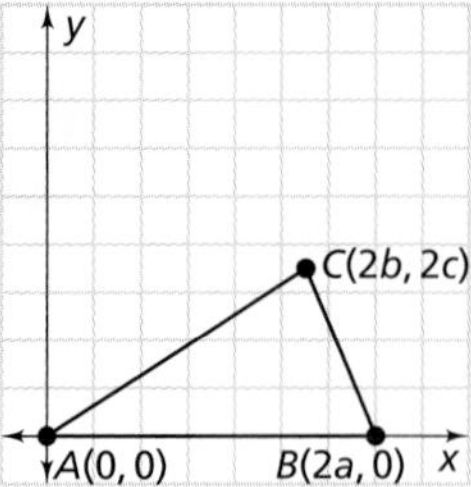

This makes working with medians a little easier, since the midpoints will not have fractional coordinates.

If your geometric shape has a line of symmetry, one choice is to place the line of symmetry on an axis. Here is one way to coordinatize an isosceles triangle.

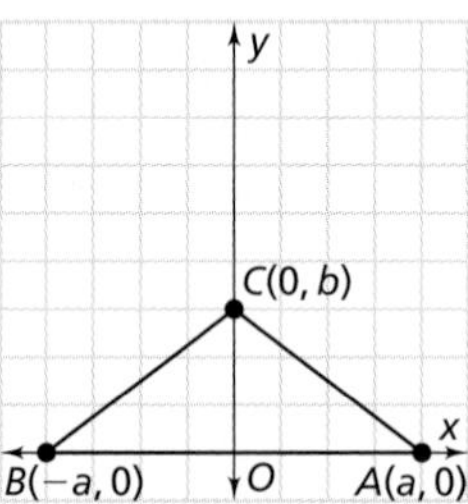

It takes some practice to develop the knack for choosing a convenient set of coordinates. You want your choice to make the calculations easier, but you do not want to introduce any extra assumptions, as Derman did in episode 18 on page 451. Try to think about what you are trying to prove and how to get there. A good choice of coordinates can reduce the work of the proof.

The massive cables of the Golden Gate Bridge, as with most suspension bridges, form parabolic arcs.

Answers

Exercises

1. **a.** Answers may vary. Sample: $A(0, 0)$, $B(a, 0)$, $C(a, b)$, $D(0, b)$
   b. Using the coordinates from part (a), find the length of the diagonal using the distance formula:

$$AC = \sqrt{(a-0)^2 + (b-0)^2}$$
$$= \sqrt{a^2 + b^2}$$
$$BD = \sqrt{(a-0)^2 + (0-b)^2}$$
$$= \sqrt{a^2 + (-b)^2} = \sqrt{a^2 + b^2}$$

2. 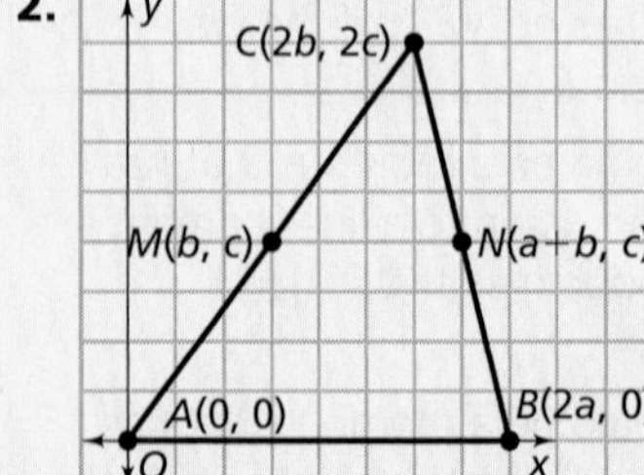

The midpoint of AC is $M(b, c)$ and the midpoint of BC is $N(a + b, c)$.

The length of segment MN, which joins the midpoints of sides AC and BC, is a.

The length of side AB is $2a$, which is twice that of MN.

Both segments are horizontal, therefore parallel, which completes the proof.

3. Assume quadrilateral with vertices at $A(0, 0)$, $B(2a, 0)$, $C(2b, 2c)$, and $D(2d, 2e)$.

Midpoints of the four sides are $M(a, 0)$, $N(a + b, c)$, $P(b + d, c + e)$, $Q(d, e)$.

The slopes of MN and PQ are both $\frac{c}{b}$ and the slopes of NP and MQ are both

Exercises *Practicing Habits of Mind*

Check Your Understanding

1. **a.** Find four coordinate pairs to represent the vertices of a rectangle.
   b. Prove that the diagonals of a rectangle are equal in length.
2. Use coordinates to prove the *Midline Theorem*:

   The segment joining the midpoints of two sides of a triangle is parallel to the third side. Its measure is equal to half the measure of the third side.

Remember...
You first proved the Midline Theorem in your geometry course.

3. Prove that if you connect the midpoints of the sides of any quadrilateral, the resulting quadrilateral is a parallelogram.

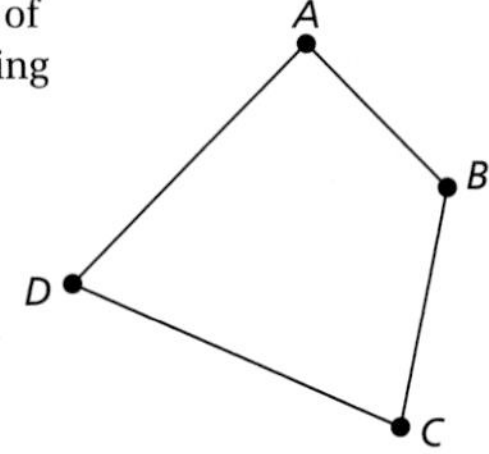

For additional practice, go to **Web Code**: bga-0603

4. Determine what type of quadrilateral results when you connect the midpoints of the sides of a rectangle. Prove your result.
5. **What's Wrong Here?** Joey says that he can quickly prove that the diagonals of a rhombus are perpendicular.

   Joey: I used the symmetry of the rhombus. The diagonals ended up being right on the axes. Then of course the diagonals are perpendicular. They're the axes.

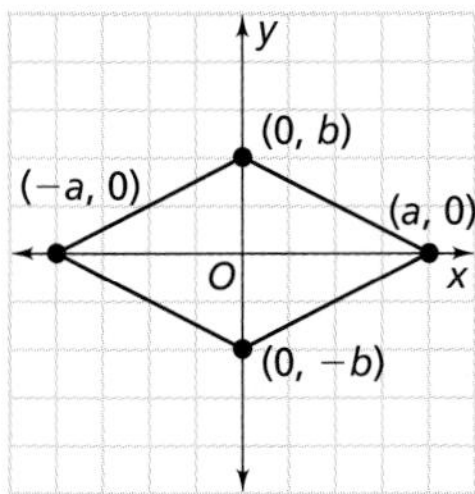

   What is wrong with Joey's reasoning?

6. **Take It Further** Prove that if the diagonals of a parallelogram are perpendicular, then the parallelogram is a rhombus.

Exercises

HOMEWORK
- Core: 7, 8, 9, 11, 13, 14
- Optional: 10
- Extension: 12

Check Your Understanding

EXERCISE 1 This is a fairly simple independent exercise in coordinatization for students to try on their own. Even if they do not place one of their rectangle's vertices at the origin, the calculations are not impossible as long as they align their rectangle with the axes. If you go over this exercise in class, you may even want to contrast such a coordinate system with one where a vertex is at the origin. Other students may also use the symmetry of the rectangle to set up their coordinates.

EXERCISE 2 This is a situation where selecting the original coordinates to be multiples of 2, using points like $(2a, 0)$, can make the end result easier to manage. Not all students will pick up on this tactic right away, and that is fine. The overall concept is that different choices of coordinates can lead to more or less work later.

EXERCISE 5 Joey is right that the rhombus has two lines of symmetry, but can he justify his assumption that the two lines of symmetry are perpendicular? By placing them on the coordinate axes, he made this assumption. It does work out to be true, but his argument assumes what he is trying to prove.

$\frac{e}{d-a}$. Therefore, since the slopes of both pairs of opposite sides are equal, this must be a parallelogram.

4. rhombus

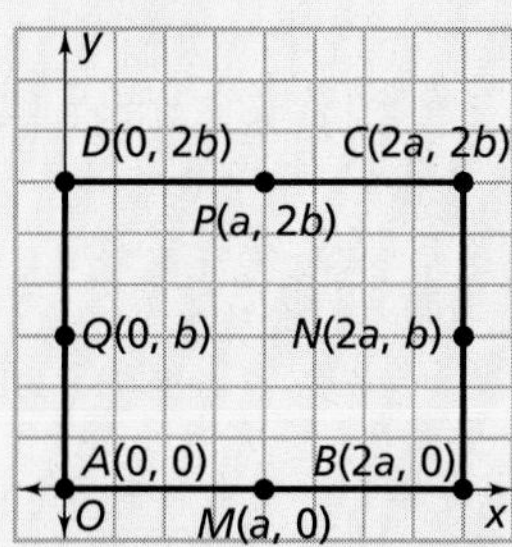

Assume rectangle with vertices at $A(0, 0)$, $B(2a, 0)$, $C(2a, 2b)$, $D(0, 2b)$.

Midpoints of the four sides are $M(a, 0)$, $N(2a, b)$, $P(a, 2b)$, $Q(0, b)$.

Similar to the previous problem, the slopes of MN and PQ are equal and the slopes of NP and MQ are equal. Therefore, since the slopes of both pairs of opposite sides are equal, this must be a parallelogram. Also, since $MN = NP$, $MNPQ$ is a rhombus.

5. Answers may vary. Sample: Joey assumes that the two lines of symmetry of the rhombus are perpendicular. He does this by placing them along the axes. It would be alright for Joey to place one line of symmetry on the axis, then prove the other must lie along the axis as well. But by building the rhombus in this way, Joey has assumed what he is trying to prove, which is invalid.
6. See back of book.

On Your Own

EXERCISE 9 Students familiar with trigonometry can do this exercise with only one variable. No matter what the side length of the equilateral triangle is, all of its angles must measure 60°.

EXERCISE 10 Some students will get stuck on the coordinate setup. There is more than one good setup. Students who want to put one vertex at the origin may have trouble deciding where to put the last two vertices.

Additional Resources

PRINT RESOURCES
- Solution Manual
- Practice Workbook
- Assessment Resources
- Teaching Resources

TECHNOLOGY
- Interactive Textbook
- TeacherExpress CD-ROM
- ExamView CD-ROM
- PHSchool.com

Additional Practice

1. a. Find four coordinate pairs to represent the vertices of a square.
   b. Prove that the diagonals of a square are perpendicular.

2. a. In the figure on the right, $\triangle CAB$ is an isosceles triangle with sides $\overline{AB}$ and $\overline{CA}$ of equal length. Set coordinates for points A and B.
   b. Show that the median $\overline{AD}$, where D is a point on $\overline{CB}$, is the perpendicular bisector of $\overline{CB}$.

3. The graph of the equation
   $x^2 + y^2 - 6x - 10y - 47 = 0$ is a circle.
   a. Find the center of the circle.
   b. Find the radius of the circle.
   c. Sketch the graph of the circle.
   d. Find the exact coordinates of all intercepts.

4. a. Find the signed power of a point $P(6, -3)$ with respect to the circle
   $$(x - 4)^2 + (y + 6)^2 = 16$$
   b. Find another point with the same signed power as $(6, -3)$ with respect to the circle
   $$(x - 4)^2 + (y + 6)^2 = 16$$
   c. Repeat parts (a) and (b) for the point $(12, -4)$.

5. Calculate the value of $f(x, y) = (x + 7)^2 + (y - 4)^2 - 36$ for each set of inputs.
   a. $x = 0, y = 2$ b. $x = -8, y = 5$
   c. $x = -1, y = 4$ d. $x = 4, y = 0$

Practice: For Lesson 6.3, assign Exercises 1–2.

On Your Own

7. Coordinatize a general square.

8. In this figure, $\triangle ABC$ is a right triangle and point D is the midpoint of hypotenuse $\overline{BC}$. Set coordinates for points B and C, then prove that $AD = BD = CD$.

9. a. Coordinatize a general equilateral triangle.
   b. Prove that in an equilateral triangle, any median is also a perpendicular bisector.

10. a. Coordinatize an *isosceles trapezoid*, a trapezoid with congruent non-parallel sides.
    b. Prove that the diagonals of an isosceles trapezoid are equal in length, but do not bisect each other.

11. Use coordinates to prove that the length of the *midline of a trapezoid* is the average of the lengths of its two bases.

12. **Take It Further** Coordinatize a regular hexagon centered at the origin. Use only one variable.

13. **Standardized Test Prep** Given a parallelogram with three of its vertices at the points (1, 5), (5, –1), and (2, 2), which of the following could not be the fourth vertex?

    A. (6, –4) **B.** (4, 2) **C.** (3, 2) **D.** (–2, 8)

Habits of Mind

Make strategic choices. You can do this with only one variable.

Remember...

The *midline* of a trapezoid is a segment connecting the midpoints of the two nonparallel sides. For the trapezoid given, the midline connects the midpoint of $\overline{AD}$ with the midpoint of $\overline{BC}$.

Maintain Your Skills

14. The graph of the equation
    $$x^2 + y^2 - 8x + 10y + 24 = 0$$
    is a circle centered at the point $(4, -5)$. For each point listed below, determine whether or not it is on the graph of the circle.

    a. $(4, -1)$ **b.** $(5, -1)$ **c.** $(8, -6)$
    d. $(8, 0)$ **e.** $(0, 0)$ **f.** $(3, -9)$

Answers

7. Answers may vary. Sample: $A(0, 0)$, $B(s, 0)$, $C(s, s)$, $D(0, s)$

8. Answers may vary. Sample: $B(2b, 0)$, $C(0, 2c)$, $D(b, c)$

$AD = \sqrt{b^2 + c^2}$

$BD = \sqrt{(2b - b)^2 + (0 - c)^2}$
$= \sqrt{b^2 + c^2}$

$CD = \sqrt{(0 - b)^2 + (2c - c)^2}$
$= \sqrt{b^2 + c^2}$

All three lengths are the same.

9–12. See back of book.

13. C

14. a. no
b. yes
c. yes
d. no
e. no
f. yes

6.4 The Power of a Point

Consider a circle with center (h, k) and radius r. If you picked any point (x, y), how would you decide whether it was on the circle? You can find a point-tester for a circle by calculating the distance from (x, y) to the center, which must equal r.

$$\sqrt{(x-h)^2 + (y-k)^2} = r$$
$$(x-h)^2 + (y-k)^2 = r^2$$

This second equation is the *center-radius form* for a circle. Equations for circles are not always in this form. You can use the method of *completing the square* to rewrite an equation of a circle in this form.

Example 1

Problem The graph of the equation

$$x^2 + y^2 - 10x + 14y - 26 = 0$$

is a circle. Find its center and radius.

Solution You can identify the center and radius if the equation is in the form

$$(x-h)^2 + (y-k)^2 = r^2$$

Start by moving terms to make the result appear as follows.

$$(x^2 - 10x \quad) + (y^2 + 14y \quad) = 26$$

Now find constants that produce perfect square trinomials. For the first term this constant is $\left(-\frac{10}{2}\right)^2 = 25$. For the second term this constant is $\left(\frac{14}{2}\right)^2 = 49$. Add these constants to each side of the equation.

$$(x^2 - 10x + \mathbf{25}) + (y^2 + 14y + \mathbf{49}) = 26 + \mathbf{25} + \mathbf{49}$$

Factor each expression in parentheses.

$$(x-5)^2 + (y+7)^2 = 100$$

The center is $(5, -7)$ and the radius is $\sqrt{100} = 10$.

Remember...

This technique is called completing the square because you add the number that produces a complete perfect square trinomial.

For You to Do

1. Find the center and radius for the circle with equation $x^2 + y^2 + 12x - 8y + 3 = 0$.
2. Find the center for the circle with equation $x^2 + y^2 + 50x - 18y + 100 = 0$.
   Can you do this without completing the square? Explain.

For You to Do

1. Center is $(-6, 4)$ and radius is 7.
2. Center is $(-25, 9)$. You can do this by dividing the coefficients of the x and y terms by 2 and multiplying the result by -1.

Lesson Overview

GOAL

- Evaluate and use the signed power of a point with respect to a circle.

Students briefly review the Power of a Point Theorem they proved in CME Project *Geometry*:

> Given a point P, a circle, and any line through P that intersects the circle in two points A and B. Then the product $PA \cdot PB$ is a constant, no matter what line you choose. This quantity is called the power of point P with respect to the circle, $\Pi(P)$.

The lesson extends this idea to define the *signed power of a point*. Given a point P and a circle, if the distance from the center of the circle to P is d and the radius of the circle is r, then the signed power of P, $\Pi_s(P)$ is equal to $d^2 - r^2$. The absolute value of this quantity is equal to the power of P, and for a circle with equation $x^2 + y^2 + Cx + Dy + E = 0$ and a point P with coordinates (a, b), $\Pi_s(P) = a^2 + b^2 + aC + bD + E$. Students learn this new definition and use it to prove further results.

CHECK YOUR UNDERSTANDING
- Core: 1, 2, 3, 4
- Optional: none
- Extension: 5

MATERIALS
- graph paper
- graphing calculators
- Blackline Masters MC7, MC8, 6.4

HOMEWORK
- Core: 6, 7, 8, 9, 12
- Optional: 13
- Extension: 10, 11

VOCABULARY
- power of a point, $\Pi(P)$
- signed power of a point, $\Pi_s(P)$

Launch

Start today's lesson by discussing the point-tester for the graph of a circle with center (h, k) and radius r. You may want to see if students remember the technique for *completing the square* by asking them to find the center and radius of a different circle than the one in Example 1.

Explore

EXAMPLE 1 Before class, prepare the graph of the circle on an overhead using Blackline Master MC7 or MC8.

For You to Do

PROBLEM 2 Students learn that they can read the coordinates of the center of a circle from its equation in normal form. Later, they use this technique to find the center and then use the signed power of that center to determine the radius without ever finishing the completing-the-square calculation.

THEOREM 6.1 Blackline Master 6.4 reproduces the theorem and its two corollaries. You may wish to display these results on an overhead as you discuss each of them.

For Discussion

PROBLEM 3 To find the power of a point P that lies on the circle, draw a line through both P and the center. It intersects the circle in two points, A, which coincides with P, and B. The power of P is $PA \cdot PB$. $PB = 2r$ where r is the radius of the circle, and $PA = 0$, because P and A coincide, so the power of P is 0.

In CME Project *Geometry*, you discovered the *Power of a Point Theorem.*

Theorem 6.1 Power of a Point

Given a point P and a circle, take any line through P that intersects the circle in two points A and B. Then $PA \cdot PB$ is constant, no matter what line you choose through P. This constant is called the power of the point P. The power is a function of the point, so write the power of P as $\Pi(P)$.

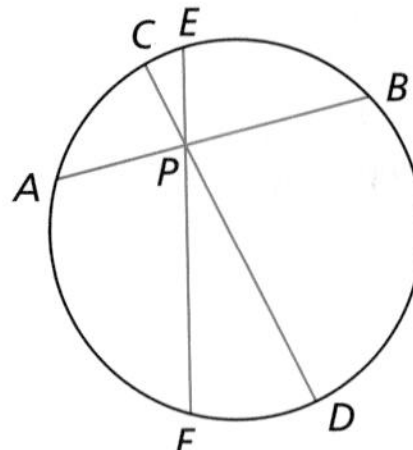

$PA \cdot PB = PC \cdot PD = PE \cdot PF$

For an exploration activity on power of a point, go to Web Code: bge-9031

Here are two corollaries.

Corollary 6.1.1

Inside a circle, the power of a point d units away from the center of a circle with radius r is $r^2 - d^2$.

Corollary 6.1.2

Outside a circle, the power of a point d units away from the center of a circle with radius r is $d^2 - r^2$.

For Discussion

3. Suppose point P is on the circle. What is its power?

Here is a proof of Corollary 6.1.1.

Proof The Power of a Point Theorem applies to any line through P that intersects the circle at two points. So, pick $\overleftrightarrow{OP}$, where O is the center of the circle.

This line intersects the circle at points A and B. Since $OP = d$, and $\overline{AB}$ is a diameter, you know the lengths PA and PB: $PA = r + d$ and $PB = r - d$. The power of point P with respect to the circle is

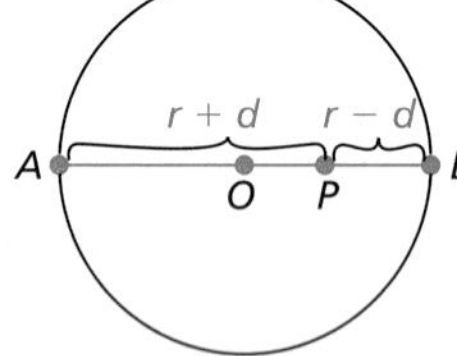

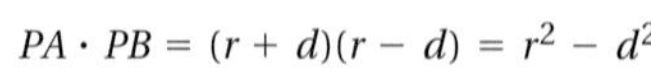

$$PA \cdot PB = (r + d)(r - d) = r^2 - d^2$$

Answers

For Discussion

3. If point P is on the circle, its power is zero.

You will prove Corollary 6.1.2 in Exercise 1 below. Note that the two rules are nearly identical. Also, the quantity $d^2 - r^2$ is invariant for any point P. This quantity is negative for points inside the circle and positive for points outside the circle. Now name this quantity.

Definition

Given point P, d units from the center of a circle of radius r. The signed power of point P with respect to the circle is given by

$$\Pi_S(P) = d^2 - r^2$$

Example 2

Problem Calculate the signed power of each point with respect to the circle with equation

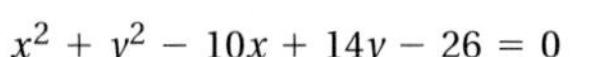

$$x^2 + y^2 - 10x + 14y - 26 = 0$$

a. $(8, -3)$ **b.** $(-1, 1)$ **c.** $(5, -7)$

d. $(5, 18)$ **e.** (x, y)

Solution Earlier, you showed that the center of this circle is $(5, -7)$ and its radius is 10. For each point, calculate $d^2 - r^2$, where d is its distance from the center, and r is the radius (10).

a. The distance from $(8, -3)$ to $(5, -7)$ is $\sqrt{3^2 + 4^2} = 5$, so the signed power is $5^2 - 10^2 = -75$. If a chord $\overline{AB}$ of this circle passes through $P(8, -3)$, the product of PA and PB will be 75.

b. The distance from $(-1, 1)$ to $(5, -7)$ is $\sqrt{6^2 + 8^2} = 10$, so the signed power is $10^2 - 10^2 = 0$. This point is on the circle.

c. This point is the center, so its signed power is $0^2 - 10^2 = -100$.

d. The distance from $(5, 18)$ to $(5, -7)$ is 25, so the signed power is $25^2 - 10^2 = 525$.

e. The distance from (x, y) to $(5, -7)$ is

$$\sqrt{(x-5)^2 + (y+7)^2}$$

The signed power of point (x, y) is

$$(x-5)^2 + (y+7)^2 - 100$$

Expanding and collecting terms gives

$$(x^2 - 10x + 25) + (y^2 + 14y + 49) - 100$$
$$x^2 + y^2 - 10x + 14y - 26$$

Amazing! This is exactly the left side of the equation that defines the circle.

You generalize the process in Example 2.

Example 2

Use the graph you created for Example 1 to illustrate this example.

Wrap Up

As time allows, go over the core Check Your Understanding exercises with your class. You may want to point out Exercise 4 as a nice example of reasoning by continuity.

Assessment Resources

Lesson Quiz 6.4

1. The graph of the equation $x^2 + y^2 - 4x + 10y - 20 = 0$ is a circle.
   a. Find the center and radius of the circle.
   b. Sketch a graph of the circle.
   c. Find the exact coordinates of all intercepts.

2. Consider the circle given by $(x - 1)^2 + (y + 3)^2 = 25$.
   a. Find the signed power of point $P(3, 2)$ with respect to the circle.
   b. Find two other points with the same signed power as $P(3, 2)$ with respect to the circle.

3. Calculate the value of $f(x, y) = (x + 4)^2 + (y - 7)^2 - 36$ for each set of inputs.
   a. $x = -2, y = 4$ b. $x = -8, y = 10$ c. $x = -4, y = 13$

Theorem 6.2

The signed power of point $P(x, y)$ with respect to the circle with equation $x^2 + y^2 + Cx + Dy + E = 0$ is

$$\Pi_S(P) = x^2 + y^2 + Cx + Dy + E$$

If you want to, you can write the equation that defines the circle as $\Pi_S(P) = 0$.

Developing Habits of Mind

Find another way. Given a specific circle, what is the minimum value that the signed power can have. And where does this value occur? The signed power is $d^2 - r^2$. Since r is fixed, the signed power is smallest when $d = 0$. This d is the distance to the center, so the signed power takes on its minimum value at the center of the circle. The minimum value is $-r^2$.

This gives an interesting way to find the center and radius of a circle based on its equation in normal form. For example, take the circle with equation

$$x^2 + y^2 - 16x + 22y - 344 = 0$$

If you were finding the center and radius by completing the square, you would look at the coefficients of the linear x and y terms and write an equation that looked like this:

$$(x - 8)^2 + (y + 11)^2 = \text{something}$$

The center of this circle is $(8, -11)$. You can quickly find the center for any circle this way. Then, use the signed power calculation to find the radius. The signed power of the center $(8, -11)$ is

$$\Pi_S(8, 11) = 8^2 + (-11)^2 - 16(8) + 22(-11) - 344 = -529$$

This value is equal to $-r^2$, so the radius is $\sqrt{529} = 23$. The signed power of a point allows you to find the center and radius for a circle with an equation in normal form without having to finish completing the square.

Let P be the point of intersection of the chopsticks. Can you find the power of a point P with respect to the rim of the plate?

Answers

Exercises

1.

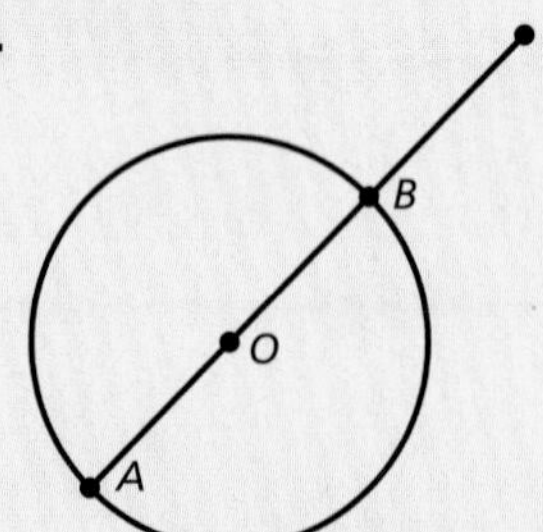

Consider point P outside the circle.

Pick $\overleftrightarrow{OP}$ where O is the center of the circle so that $OP = d$ and AB *is a diameter.*

$PA = d + r$ and $PB = d - r$, therefore the power of point P with respect to the circle is:

$PA \cdot PB = (d + r)(d - r) = d^2 - r^2$

2. **a.** Center is $(-3, 4)$and radius is 7.

   b.

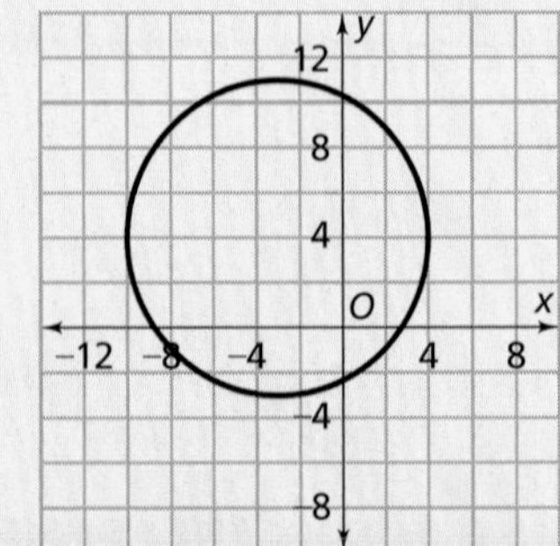

   c. The two x-intercepts are $(-3 + \sqrt{33}, 0)$ and $(-3 - \sqrt{33}, 0)$.

   The two y-intercepts are $(0, 4 + 2\sqrt{10})$ and $(0, 4 - 2\sqrt{10})$.

3. **a.** 24
   b. 24
   c. $(4, 4)$ and $(-3, -3)$; $P = 24$

4. As the intersection points get closer together, the line through P comes closer and closer to being a tangent of the circle. If PA is the tangent to the circle, then $(PA)^2$ equals the power of point P. This means that if point P is d units away from the center of

Exercises *Practicing Habits of Mind*

Check Your Understanding

1. Prove Corollary 6.1.2.

   Outside a circle, a point d units away from the center of a circle with radius r has power $d^2 - r^2$.

2. The graph of the equation $x^2 + y^2 + 6x - 8y - 24 = 0$ is a circle.

   a. Find the center and radius of the circle.

   b. Sketch the graph of the circle.

   c. Find the exact coordinates of all intercepts.

3. The point $P(0, 0)$ lies inside the circle from Exercise 2. Several chords of the circle defined by the graph of $x^2 + y^2 + 6x - 8y - 24 = 0$ pass through the origin.

   a. One such chord lies along the x-axis. Calculate the power of P with respect to this circle using this chord.

   b. Calculate the power of P using the chord that lies along the y-axis.

   c. Find the two intersection points of the circle with the line with equation $y = x$. Use these intersections to calculate the power of P.

4. **Write About It** The Power of a Point Theorem applies to any line drawn through a point P that intersects a circle twice. What happens when P is outside the circle and the intersection points get closer together? How could you rephrase the Power of a Point Theorem to address this situation?

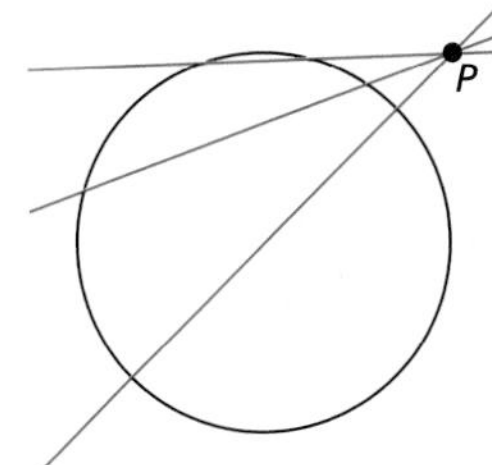

5. **Take It Further** Find the two intersection points of the circle from Exercise 3 with the line with equation $y = kx$. Then show that the power of $P(0, 0)$ with respect to this circle is independent of k.

Exercises

HOMEWORK

- Core: 6, 7, 8, 9, 12
- Optional: 13
- Extension: 10, 11

Check Your Understanding

EXERCISE 1 Make sure that students notice that the statement in this exercise refers to the original definition of power of a point, not to the new definition of signed power of a point.

EXERCISE 3 is designed to help students see that the power of a point is actually invariant. A related Take It Further problem follows as Exercise 5.

the circle, and $d > r$, the length of the tangent from P to the circle is $\sqrt{d^2 - r^2}$.

5. Set $y = kx$ in the equation $x^2 + y^2 + 6x - 8y - 24 = 0$:

$$x^2 + (kx)^2 + 6x - 8kx - 24 = 0$$

$$(k^2 + 1)x^2 + (6 - 8k)x - 24 = 0$$

$$x = \frac{8k - 6 \pm \sqrt{(6 - 8k)^2 - 4(k^2 + 1)(-24)}}{2(k^2 + 1)}$$

$$x = \frac{4k - 3 \pm \sqrt{40k^2 - 24k + 33}}{k^2 + 1}$$

Since the values of y are k times the values of x, the two intersections are at:

$$\left(\frac{4k - 3 \pm \sqrt{40k^2 - 24k + 33}}{k^2 + 1},\ k \cdot \frac{4k - 3 \pm \sqrt{40k^2 - 24k + 33}}{k^2 + 1}\right)$$

To determine the power of P, find the distance between $(0, 0)$ and (x, kx):

$$\sqrt{x^2 + (kx)^2} = \sqrt{(k^2 + 1)x^2}$$
$$= |x|\sqrt{k^2 + 1}$$

The product of the two distances is $k^2 + 1$ multiplied by the two x-coordinates.

$$= \frac{4k - 3 + \sqrt{40k^2 - 24k + 33}}{k^2 + 1} \cdot \frac{4k - 3 - \sqrt{40k^2 - 24k + 33}}{k^2 + 1} \cdot (k^2 + 1)$$

$$= \frac{(4k - 3)^2 - (40k^2 - 24k + 33)}{k^2 + 1}$$

$$= \frac{16k^2 - 24k + 9 - (40k^2 - 24k + 33)}{k^2 + 1}$$

$$= \frac{-24k^2 - 24}{k^2 + 1}$$

$$= \frac{-24(k^2 + 1)}{k^2 + 1} = -24$$

(which is independent of k)

On Your Own

EXERCISE 7 Since points with the same signed power are the same distance from the center of the circle, some of your students will see immediately that concentric circles with this common center are contour lines for the signed power of a point function.

EXERCISE 10 Make sure students consider the cases when the circles are concentric, intersecting, and nonintersecting. This problem is a lot easier to do algebraically than geometrically!

Additional Resources

PRINT RESOURCES	TECHNOLOGY
• Solution Manual	• Interactive Textbook
• Practice Workbook	• TeacherExpress CD-ROM
• Assessment Resources	• ExamView CD-ROM
• Teaching Resources	• PHSchool.com

Additional Practice

1. a. Find four coordinate pairs to represent the vertices of a square.
   b. Prove that the diagonals of a square are perpendicular.

2. a. In the figure on the right, $\triangle CAB$ is an isosceles triangle with sides $\overline{AB}$ and $\overline{CA}$ of equal length. Set coordinates for points A and B.
   b. Show that the median $\overline{AD}$, where D is a point on $\overline{CB}$, is the perpendicular bisector of $\overline{CB}$.

3. The graph of the equation $x^2 + y^2 - 6x - 10y - 47 = 0$ is a circle.
   a. Find the center of the circle.
   b. Find the radius of the circle.
   c. Sketch the graph of the circle.
   d. Find the exact coordinates of all intercepts.

4. a. Find the signed power of a point $P(6, -3)$ with respect to the circle
   $$(x - 4)^2 + (y + 6)^2 = 16$$
   b. Find another point with the same signed power as $(6, -3)$ with respect to the circle
   $$(x - 4)^2 + (y + 6)^2 = 16$$
   c. Repeat parts (a) and (b) for the point $(12, -4)$.

5. Calculate the value of $f(x, y) = (x + 7)^2 + (y - 4)^2 - 36$ for each set of inputs.
   a. $x = 0, y = 2$ b. $x = -8, y = 5$
   c. $x = -1, y = 4$ d. $x = 4, y = 0$

Practice: For Lesson 6.4, assign Exercises 3–5.

On Your Own

6. Find the signed power of point $P(6, 5)$ with respect to the circle
$$(x - 3)^2 + (y + 1)^2 = 25$$

7. Find some other points with the same signed power as $P(6, 5)$ with respect to the circle
$$(x - 3)^2 + (y + 1)^2 = 25$$

8. Calculate the value of $f(x, y) = (x - 3)^2 + (y + 1)^2 - 25$ for each set of inputs.
   a. $x = 6, y = 5$ **b.** $x = 9, y = -4$ **c.** $x = 0, y = -7$ **d.** $x = -3, y = 2$

9. If C is the center of a circle with radius r, explain why the signed power of C with respect to the circle is $-r^2$.

10. **Take It Further** Given two circles, describe the set of points that have the same signed power with respect to both circles. Does your answer change depending on how the circles are positioned?

11. **Take It Further** Prove Theorem 6.1 in general. In other words, show that the signed power of a point $P(a, b)$ with respect to the circle with equation $x^2 + y^2 + Cx + Dy + E = 0$ is
$$\Pi_S(P) = a^2 + b^2 + aC + bD + E$$

12. **Standardized Test Prep** Which of the following is the center of the circle with equation $x^2 + y^2 + 4x - 2y = 0$?
   A. $(4, -2)$ **B.** $(-4, 2)$ **C.** $(2, -1)$ **D.** $(-2, 1)$

Go Online PHSchool.com

For additional practice, go to Web Code: bga-0604

Maintain Your Skills

13. Let the point X be the intersection of chords $\overline{AB}$ and $\overline{CD}$ inside a circle.
   a. If $AX = 4$, $BX = 6$, $CX = 9$, find DX.
   b. If $AX = 8$, $BX = 6$, $CX = 9$, find DX.
   c. If $AX = 4$, $BX = 6$, $CX = 18$, find DX.
   d. If $AX = 4$, $BX = 6$, $CX = c$, find DX.
   e. If $AX = 4$, $BX = 6$, find the smallest possible length of chord $\overline{CD}$.

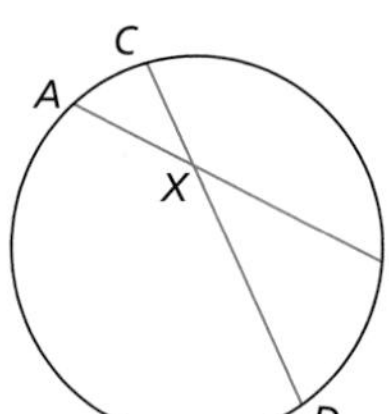

Answers

6. 20

7. Answers may vary. Any point satisfying the equation $(x - 3)^2 + (y + 1)^2 = 45$ will have the same signed power.

8. a. 20
b. 20
c. 20
d. 20

9. See back of book.

10. The set of points that have the same signed power with respect to both circles is a line. This is the case no matter how the circles are positioned.

11. See back of book.

12. D

13. a. $DX = \frac{8}{3}$
b. $DX = \frac{16}{3}$
c. $DX = \frac{4}{3}$
d. $DX = \frac{24}{c}$
e. $CD = 4\sqrt{6}$

In this investigation, you found equations that characterized descriptions of various point sets. You used coordinate methods to prove geometric facts. You investigated the signed power of a point. The following questions will help you summarize what you have learned.

1. Which points with integer coordinates lie on the circle with equation $x^2 + y^2 = 25$?
2. Which of the following points lie on the ellipse with equation $\frac{(x-3)^2}{16} + \frac{(y+1)^2}{12} = 1$?
   a. $(-1, -1)$ **b.** $(3, -1)$ **c.** $(1, 2)$
3. For which values of x can the equation $\frac{(x-h)^2}{a^2} - \frac{(y-k)^2}{b^2} = 1$ be true?
4. Prove the following consequence of the Pythagorean Theorem: *The sum of the squares of the lengths of the diagonals of a parallelogram is equal to the sum of the squares of the lengths of its four sides.*
5. Determine the power of the point (16, 6) with respect to the circle $(x-4)^2 + (y+3)^2 = 25$.
6. What is the set of points equidistant from the x-axis and the point (0, 4)?
7. How can you use coordinates to show that the diagonals of a parallelogram bisect each another?
8. How can you find the center and radius of a circle with an equation written in normal form?

Vocabulary and Notation

In this investigation, you learned these terms and symbols. Make sure you understand what each one means and how to use it.

- **coordinatize**
- **double cone, $z^2 = x^2 + y^2$**
- **midline**
- **parallelogram**
- **point-tester**
- **perpendicular bisector**
- **power of a point, $\Pi(P)$**
- **rhombus**
- **signed power of a point, $\Pi_S(P)$**
- **trapezoid**

Mathematical Reflections

EXERCISES 6–8 At the start of the investigation, you may have assigned these as Questions 1–3 for students to think and write about.

Mathematical Reflections

1. (5, 0), (3, 4), (4, 3), (0, 5), (−3, 4), (−4, 3), (−5, 0), (−3, −4), (−4, −3), (0, −5), (3, −4), (4, −3)
2. **a.** yes
   b. no
   c. yes
3. $x \geq h + a$ or $x \leq h - a$
4. See back of book.
5. 200
6. $x^2 - 8y + 16 = 0$
7. Assume a parallelogram with vertices at $(0, 0)$, $(c, 0)$, (a, b), and $(a + c, b)$. The diagonals of the parallelogram are the line segment with endpoints $(0, 0)$ and $(a + c, b)$ and the line segment with endpoints $(c, 0)$ and (a, b). The midpoint of both of these line segments is $\left(\frac{a+c}{2}, \frac{b}{2}\right)$. Since these line segments share a midpoint, by definition they bisect each other.
8. See back of book.

Investigation Overview

The investigation opens with students considering the intersection of a plane with various three-dimensional solids. Visualizing the slices and describing them in different ways helps students deal with the material that follows.

Then the investigation introduces the three families of conic sections: *parabolas, ellipses,* and *hyperbolas*. Students define each of these in a number of ways: as an intersection of a plane with an infinite double cone, as a locus of points in the plane, and as points satisfying an equation—the conic's point-tester. Again, the investigation extends the associations between geometry and algebra.

By investigating the general form equation for each conic, students learn to identify its geometric properties and special features. By using the translation equations they learned in earlier courses, they transform the basic equations away from the origin to more general cases.

Students discover other properties of conics by inspecting the general form second-degree equation in x and y

$$rx^2 + ty^2 + ux + vy + w = 0$$

and identifying the coefficients. Another distinguishing feature of a conic section is its *eccentricity*, which students consider in several different approaches.

You may wish to assign Questions 1–3 for students to think and write about during the investigation.

Learning Goals

- Visualize each of the conic sections as the intersection of a plane with an infinite double cone.
- Give a locus definition for each of the conic sections.
- Identify the equations for the graphs of the conic sections, and sketch their graphs.

Habits and Skills

- Visualize the effect of different angles of intersection of a plane with an infinite double cone.
- Make connections between the different definitions of each type of conic section.
- Reason by continuity to make connections between the different types of conic section.

Conic Sections

In *Conic Sections*, you will study circles, ellipses, parabolas, and hyperbolas from visual, verbal, geometrical, and analytical viewpoints.

By the end of this investigation, you will be able to answer questions like these.

1. How do you slice an infinite double cone with a plane to get a parabola?
2. What is the locus definition of a hyperbola?
3. What kind of conic section do you get when you graph $x^2 + 16y^2 - 8x + 64y + 64 = 0$? How can you identify the conic section from its equation?

You will learn how to

- visualize each of the conic sections as the intersection of a plane with an infinite double cone
- give a locus definition for each of the conic sections
- identify the equations for the graphs of the conic sections, and sketch their graphs

You will develop these habits and skills:

- Visualize the effect of different angles of intersection of a plane with an infinite double cone.
- Make connections between the different definitions of each type of conic section.
- Reason by continuity to make connections between the different types of conic section.

Parabolic curves form the surfaces of radio telescopes, freeway overpass arches, field microphones, solar ovens, and these reflectors of a solar electric generating system.

Investigation Road Map

LESSON 6.5, *Getting Started,* helps students visualize the intersections of planes and solids and think about the graphs of equations in two variables.

LESSON 6.6, *Slicing Cones,* formally defines each conic section as an intersection of a plane with an infinite double cone and as a locus of points.

LESSON 6.7, *Conics at the Origin,* introduces the general forms for the equation of each type of conic section and shows how to extract critical features from the equations.

LESSON 6.8, *Conics Anywhere,* examines the equations for conic sections that do not have the coordinate axes as lines of symmetry.

LESSON 6.9, *They Are All the Same,* reveals a single class of equations that encompasses all the conic sections

6.5 Getting Started

The intersection of a plane and a solid gives you a cross section of the solid. It is a challenging visualization habit to determine what cross section shapes are possible for different solids.

For You to Explore

1. Consider a cube.

When you take a planar slice through the cube (a smooth cut with a knife), what possible shapes could you make?

> Consider the boundary of the cut as the shape of the slice. One possible shape for the slice is a square, but there are a lot more.

2. Consider a sphere.

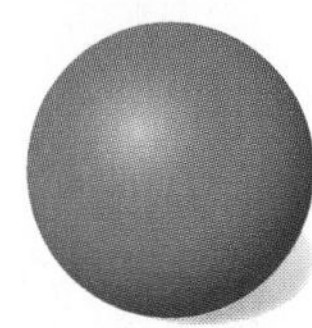

When you take a planar slice through the sphere, what possible shapes could you make?

3. Consider a cone that extends forever from its tip.

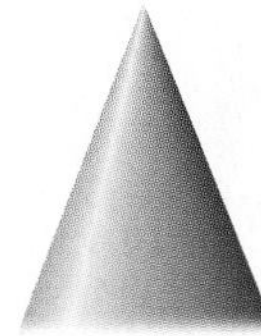

When you take a planar slice through the cone, what possible shapes could you make?

4. Sketch the graph of each equation.

   a. $x^2 + y^2 = 16$
   b. $x^2 - y^2 = 16$
   c. $4x^2 + y^2 = 16$
   d. $x^2 + y = 16$

5. **Take It Further** Find and graph an equation for the set of points $\frac{4}{5}$ times as far from (5, 2) as they are from the line $x = 14$.

Lesson Overview

GOAL

- Warm up to the ideas of the investigation.

Students begin to think about three-dimensional shapes and how a plane can cut these shapes, previewing the idea of conic sections as planar slices of an infinite double cone. They also begin to graph equations in two variables, previewing the work they will do in graphing conics and associating conics with a general form equation.

FOR YOU TO EXPLORE

- Core: 1, 2, 3, 4
- Optional: none
- Extension: 5

HOMEWORK

- Core: 6, 7, 8, 9
- Optional: 10

MATERIALS

- graph paper
- graphing calculators
- modeling clay/dough (optional)
- string (optional)
- Blackline Master MC7

Launch

Have students jump right into the For You to Explore problems. These involve some visualization in three dimensions, which is difficult for many people. You may also find that some of your students really enjoy this activity. Their strength in visualization is a real asset to them as they continue in this investigation.

You may want to provide some modeling materials to help with this lesson. For example, you might have students use modeling clay or dough. Use string or dental floss for cutting through clay to model a plane slicing through a shape. You can also get cubes and cones made from synthetic materials that students can cut if you are able to also provide acceptable cutting tools, or if students can do the work at home. Sometimes it helps to hold and look at a solid shape, so you might provide some boxes or other objects in the shapes described. However, if you have a commercial model that explicitly shows the conic sections, you should probably put it away for now. Students need some experience honing their three-dimensional visualization skills.

Explore

You may wish to use the Blackline Master MC7 on an overhead or to provide copies for students to use in this lesson. It will be useful throughout this investigation whenever students are asked to graph.

continued on p. 466

Answers

For You to Explore

1. Answers may vary. Samples: square, rectangle, non-rectangular parallelogram, triangle, pentagon, hexagon, single point, line segment
2. circle
3. Answers may vary. Samples: circle, ellipse, parabola, a single point, a ray
4. See back of book.
5. $\frac{(x+11)^2}{400} + \frac{(y-2)^2}{144} = 1$

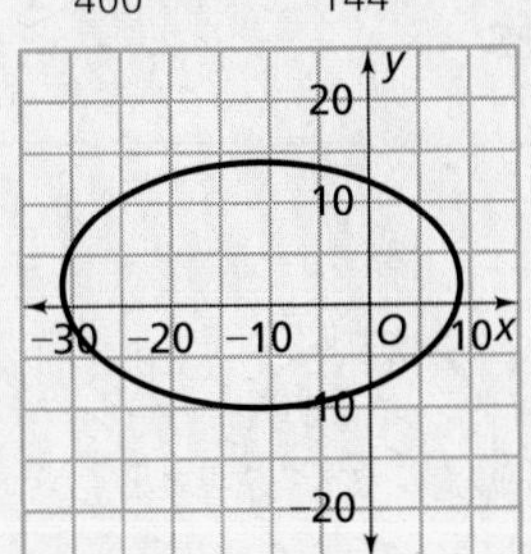

continued from p. 465

For You to Explore

As students are working, listen for descriptions or thoughts you would like students to share with the class. For example, one student may approach Problem 1 by thinking about the number of edges of the cube a plane could intersect. Another student may have a clever way of making a visualization more concrete, such as, "Just think about cutting an orange—you get a circle if you cut all the way through. It could be a small one or one through the center of the orange, but it is a circle."

PROBLEM 1 Encourage students to look at a few possibilities here, but make sure to leave time to talk about the cone.

PROBLEM 2 Again, make sure to leave time to talk about the cone. This exercise should not take as long as the exercise about the cube.

PROBLEM 3 If possible, use clay models to help students see the slices. The ellipse is especially interesting to see, but requires a good, clean cut. Many students will not distinguish between the parabola and hyperbola at this point, and that is fine; the distinction will be clearer when students think about the infinite double cone.

PROBLEM 4 You can use this problem as an introduction to the four conic sections; also see Exercises 7 and 8 in the On Your Own section.

Some students may be more comfortable with the graphs in this problem than the visualization experiments, just as some of your students may be energized by thinking in three dimensions. However, these equations are not in a form that students can type directly into a graphing calculator. Spend a little time talking about how to get a graphing calculator to show the graphs of equations like these and consult the TI-Nspire Technology Handbook p. 704 for further hints. Another point to note is that if the scale is not the same for the x and y axes, graphs that are not circles might look like circles, and graphs that are circles might not look like circles.

Exercises *Practicing Habits of Mind*

On Your Own

6. Find all solutions to the following equation.

$$\sqrt{x - 12} + \sqrt{x - 7} = 5$$

7. Sketch the graph of each equation.

a. $x^2 + y^2 = 25$

b. $(x - 3)^2 + y^2 = 25$

c. $(x + 3)^2 + y^2 = 25$

d. $(x - 1)^2 + (y + 4)^2 = 25$

e. $\frac{x^2}{5^2} + \frac{y^2}{5^2} = 1$

8. Sketch the graph of each equation.

a. $x^2 + y^2 = 1$

b. $\frac{x^2}{4^2} + \frac{y^2}{4^2} = 1$

c. $\frac{x^2}{3^2} + \frac{y^2}{5^2} = 1$

d. $\frac{x^2}{3^2} + \frac{y^2}{2^2} = 1$

e. $9x^2 + 25y^2 = 225$

Remember...

Equations are point-testers. Find some points that make the equations true.

This whispering gallery is in the Cincinnati Museum Center. To concentrate sound of one point in the hall, architects make use of the reflective properties of one of the conics. As you work through this investigation, can you guess which one?

Wrap Up

Depending on how much time your class spent working with models in three dimensions, you may need to make sure they are ready to tackle the graphing exercises in tonight's homework. Remind students that equations are point-testers for their graphs. To graph an equation, they only need to find coordinate pairs that satisfy the equation.

Answers

Exercises

6. $x = 16$

7. a.

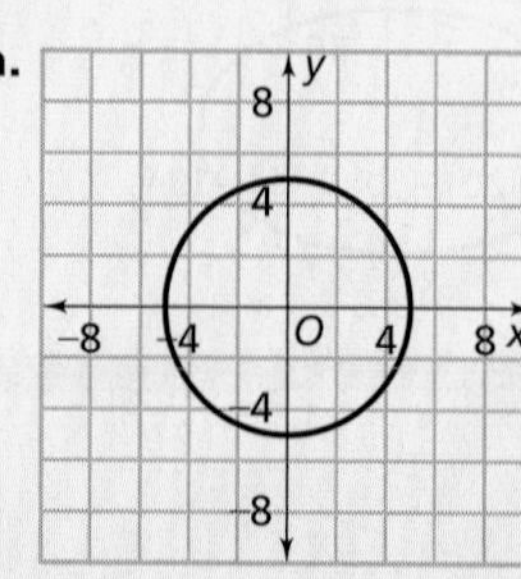

b–e. See back of book.

8. a.

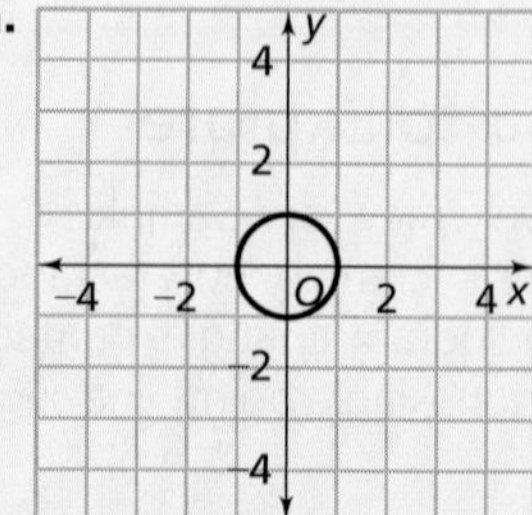

b–e. See back of book.

9. You are on a camping trip. As you are returning from a hike in the woods, you see that your tent is on fire. Luckily, you are holding an empty bucket and you are near a river. You plan to run to the river to fill the bucket and then run to the tent.

Students of the CME Project curriculum always carry a bucket when hiking.

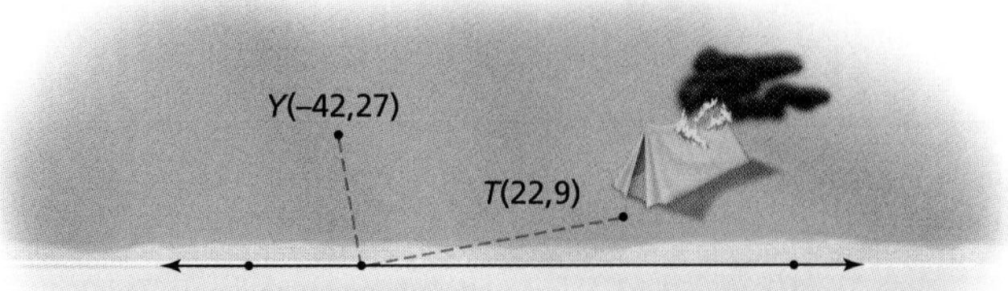

a. In CME Project *Geometry*, you found the shortest total path by reflecting your position Y over the line of the river's edge and connecting the reflected image Y' to T with a straight line. The intersection of that line and the river's edge is the point P that minimizes the path. Explain why this method produces the shortest path.

b. You also looked at contour lines for this situation. A contour line is the collection of all points P for which the path Y–P–T has the same length. What shapes are the contour lines for the burning tent problem? Why?

c. How is the contour line that contains the optimum point P that you found in part (a) positioned in relation to you, the river, and the tent? Why?

Maintain Your Skills

10. Find all solutions to the following equation.

$$\sqrt{x + 10} + \sqrt{x + 31} = 7$$

Exercises

HOMEWORK

- Core: 6, 7, 8, 9
- Optional: 10

On Your Own

EXERCISE 6 The process in this exercise is similar to the process you use to find the equation of an ellipse or a hyperbola, since each involves the sum or difference of square roots (via the distance formula).

EXERCISE 7 reviews students' understanding of equations for circles, along with the rules for translating them. These translation rules apply to ellipses, parabolas, and hyperbolas.

EXERCISE 8 These graphs follow the same transformation behavior for general functions. Students with experience in these topics may latch onto this method for graphing. Thus, an ellipse is a transformation of the unit circle $x^2 + y^2 = 1$ and any hyperbola is a transformation of one of the unit hyperbolas, $x^2 - y^2 = 1$ or $y^2 - x^2 = 1$.

Maintain Your Skills

EXERCISE 10 Watch for students saying that there is no solution since x is negative; the entire term under the radical must be negative for the square root to be undefined.

9. a. If the river were between you and the tent, it would be easy to find the best point to fill the bucket, because you would just run straight for the tent. By reflecting your actual position over the line of the river's edge you guarantee that $Y'P = YP$ for all points P along the river. That is because points on the line of reflection are mapped to themselves and the length of a segment is unchanged by reflection. In other words, you have found a way to see this problem as though the river is between you and the tent.

b. The contour lines are ellipses, because they are a set of points where the sum of the distance from the two foci (the points Y and T) is constant.

c. See back of book.

10. $x = -6$

Lesson Overview

GOALS

- Visualize each of the conic sections as the intersection of a plane with an infinite double cone.
- Give a locus definition for each of the conic sections.

The conic sections—ellipses, parabolas, and hyperbolas, are formally defined both as intersections between a plane and an infinite double cone and as a locus of points. A locus definition gives a set of properties. The set of points with these properties is on the curve defined by the locus. These two types of definition are very different, so it is okay if students do not immediately accept that the curves defined in each way are the same. The lesson presents an argument involving Dandelin spheres for why the cone intersection definition gives the same curve as the locus definition for an ellipse. Interested students may want to research the Dandelin sphere connections for the cone and locus definitions of parabolas and hyperbolas as well.

CHECK YOUR UNDERSTANDING

- Core: 1, 2, 4a–b, 5
- Optional: 3
- Extension: 4c

MATERIALS

- graph paper
- graphing calculators
- models of conic sections (optional)
- Blackline Masters MC7, 6.6A–B

HOMEWORK

- Core: 6, 7, 8, 9, 10, 12
- Optional: 13
- Extension: 11

VOCABULARY

- apex
- axis
- conic sections
- Dandelin sphere
- directrix
- ellipse
- focus, foci
- generator
- hyperbola
- locus
- parabola

Launch

Look back at students' work from the previous lesson in visualizing planar slices through a cone. If students identified points, triangles, circles, ellipses, and parabolas as possible intersections, then they are ready to move fairly quickly through much of the description at the beginning of this lesson and get right into the In-Class Experiment.

Most students will not see a distinction between a planar slice of a cone whose intersection is a parabola and another whose intersection is one branch of a hyperbola. They are not visualizing an infinite double cone. Relate the intersections that students found for cones with the intersections they visualize for this infinite double cone, but spend the majority of the time thinking about how to tell when the intersection has two branches or only one.

Many students do not feel confident about their ability to sketch in three-dimensions. Encourage

6.6 Slicing Cones

The theory of **conic sections** ties together algebra, geometry, and the analysis of functions. In this lesson, you start with the geometry and lay the foundations for the connections with other parts of mathematics.

Picture a line in space, fixed at one point, while another point on the line moves along a circle.

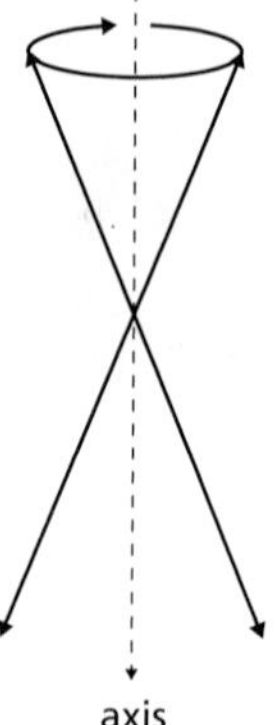

The fixed point is the cone's *apex*. The rotating line is called the *generator* of the cone. The line through the apex perpendicular to the circle is the cone's *axis*.

The surface made by the moving line is an infinite double cone. Now picture a plane passing through the cone.

The plane slices the cone in a curve. That curve is a conic section. You get different kinds of curves depending on how the plane slices the cone.

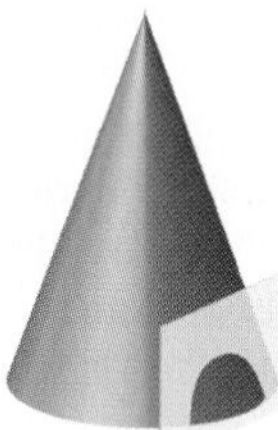

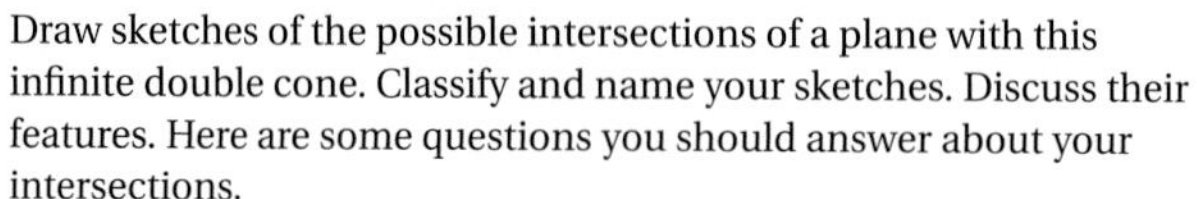

In-Class Experiment

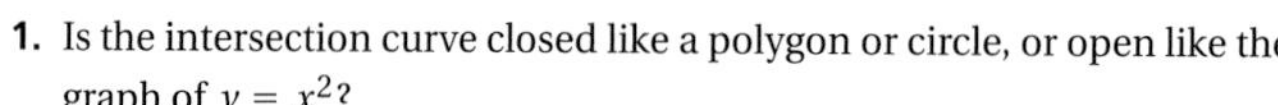

Draw sketches of the possible intersections of a plane with this infinite double cone. Classify and name your sketches. Discuss their features. Here are some questions you should answer about your intersections.

1. Is the intersection curve closed like a polygon or circle, or open like the graph of $y = x^2$?
2. Does the intersection curve have two branches like the graph of $xy = 1$ or is it a single connected curve?
3. Does the intersection curve have any symmetry?

Answers

In-Class Experiment

1. The intersection is closed for an ellipse. It is open for a parabola and a hyperbola.
2. The hyperbola has two branches. The parabola and ellipse are single continuous curves.
3. All the intersection curves are symmetric about a central axis. The ellipse and hyperbola are also symmetric about an axis perpendicular to the central at the center and are thus symmetric about the center.

The intersection curves look like curves you have encountered before in Algebra 1, Geometry, or Algebra 2. And it turns out that they are the same curves.

Facts and Notation

- **The curve you get by slicing the cone with a plane that intersects only one branch of the cone is an ellipse.**
- **The curve you get by slicing the cone with a plane that is parallel to its generator is a parabola.**
- **The curve you get by slicing the cone with a plane that intersects both branches of the cone is a hyperbola.**

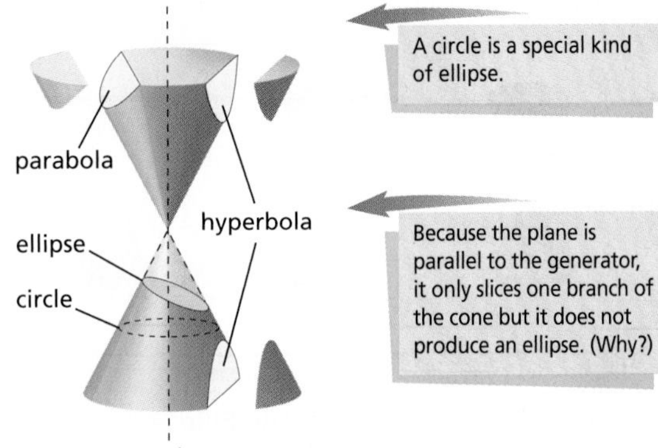

A circle is a special kind of ellipse.

Because the plane is parallel to the generator, it only slices one branch of the cone but it does not produce an ellipse. (Why?)

It should not be obvious to you that the curve you get when you slice a cone parallel to its generator is exactly the same kind curve as the one you get when you graph $y = x^2$. Or that the oval conic section is the same kind of curve as the oval you get when you graph $4x^2 + 9y^2 - 36 = 0$. Or that the conic section called "hyperbola" has the same kind of shape as the graph of $xy = 1$. One purpose of the lessons in this investigation is to see why this is the case.

Developing Habits of Mind

Visualize. Here is an interesting thought experiment: Picture a fixed line ℓ in space, outside a cone and between the apex and the base. The line ℓ is parallel to the base of the cone. Next imagine a single plane that contains ℓ and rotates around ℓ. The plane starts out perpendicular to the axis of the cone, cutting the cone in a circle. Then it rotates down, creating a family of ellipses (increasing in size) until it is parallel to the generator, producing a parabola. It continues its rotation down, creating hyperbolas until it is parallel to the generator again (now on the opposite side of the cone).

them to give it a shot, and to supplement their sketches with descriptions. The In-Class Experiment provides a good list of properties to think about when describing these planar slices. Throughout this lesson, models of the conic sections as slices of this infinite double cone are very helpful. If students made models to show planar slices of cones in the previous lesson, use those models in today's class. If you cannot get or make models, you may want to draw some intersections on transparencies you make from Blackline Master 6.6A.

Explore

In-Class Experiment

PROBLEM 1 A plane intersects the double cone in closed curves that are circles and ellipses if the plane's slope is shallower than the slope of the generating line. Open curves, including parabolas and hyperbolas, result if the slicing plane's slope is the same as or "steeper" than the slope of the generating line. A single point, which you could consider as closed, is another possible shape for the intersection of a plane and a double cone. A line through the apex, or two lines intersecting at the apex, could also result from the intersection. You could consider these shapes open.

PROBLEM 2 If the slope of the slicing plane is steeper than the slope of the generating line, it cuts the cone in an intersection which has two separate pieces. However, if the plane contains the axis of the double cone, the intersection curve is two lines intersecting at the apex of the cone. Even though this type of intersection does not have two *separate* pieces (they touch at the apex) it is not considered a single continuous curve. That is because you cannot draw this kind of an X-shape in a single motion without lifting your pencil.

PROBLEM 3 All possible intersection curves have some kind of symmetry. The circles (and the point) have infinitely many lines of symmetry, each passing through their center. The center of an intersecting curve which is a circle (or a point) must lie on the axis of the double cone. Ellipses and hyperbolas have two lines of symmetry, and parabolas have one line of symmetry.

Most of your students should be very familiar with circles, ellipses, and parabolas. They may be less familiar with the hyperbola. You might remind students of some of the properties of this type of curve by showing the basic graph of $y = \frac{1}{x}$ as an example of a hyperbola.

DEFINITION Use Blackline Master 6.6B here and on page 472 to help explain these vital definitions. Use Blackline Master MC7 to illustrate the locus definitions.

In some sense, these conic sections are all the same. You will look more carefully at this idea in Lesson 6.9.

Where did the names "ellipse," "parabola," and "hyperbola" come from? They bear a striking resemblance to the English language terms "ellipsis," "parable," and "hyperbole." This is not a coincidence—you will see the connections in Lesson 6.9.

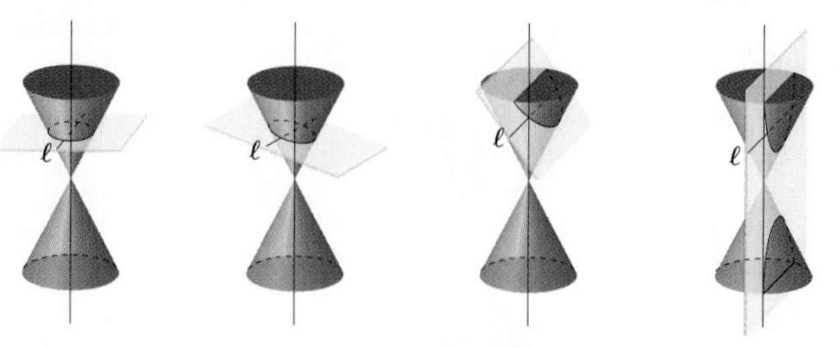

Locus Definitions for Conics: The Ellipse

In CME Project *Geometry*, you defined an ellipse with a pin and string construction. Suppose F_1 and F_2 are two fixed points—the **foci** of the ellipse—and you have a fixed length, say s. Then the ellipse with foci F_1 and F_2 and string length s is the set (locus) of all points P such that $PF_1 + PF_2 = s$.

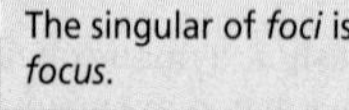

The singular of *foci* is *focus*.

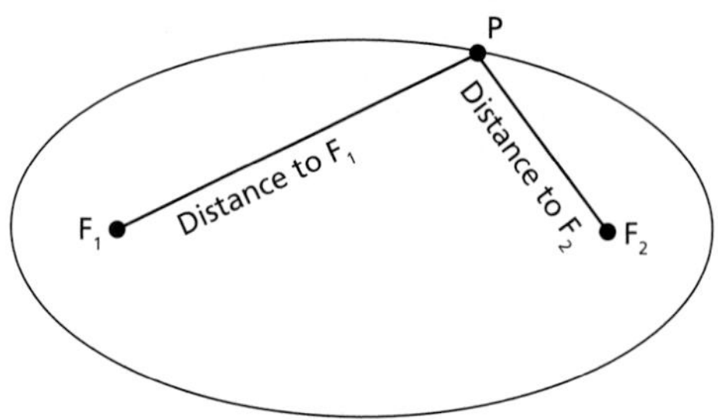

distance to F_1 + distance to F_2 = a constant

For You to Do

4. You can draw half of an ellipse by taking a string of length s and pinning its ends to F_1 and F_2. Then use a pencil to pull the string tight and trace the curve by moving the pencil, keeping tension on the string. Try it. How does the string length affect the size of the ellipse? How does the distance between the foci affect the size of the ellipse?

See the TI-Nspire™ Handbook on p. 704 for instructions about using the pin and string idea to make an ellipse with your geometry software.

Answers

For You to Do

4. For two fixed foci (the pins or thumbtacks), the longer the string or larger the string length, the larger the ellipse. For a fixed string length, an increase in the distance between the foci does not change the length of the ellipse but decreases its width.

You may also have a feeling that a section of a cone sliced by a plane that only cuts one branch of the cone and is not parallel to the generator is an ellipse.

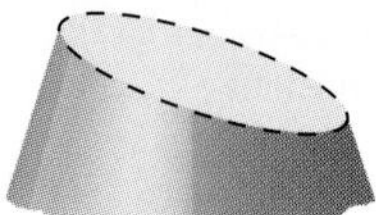

A proof by the French mathematician Germinal Dandelin shows why this is so. Begin with a cone that a plane has passed through. Now imagine placing two spheres in this cone. Put the first one into the top of the cone, big enough so it just touches the sides of the cone and just touches the plane in only one spot—it is tangent to both the cone and the plane. Then put a larger sphere into the cone under the ellipse. Again make this sphere just the right size, so it is tangent to the cone and to the plane of the ellipse.

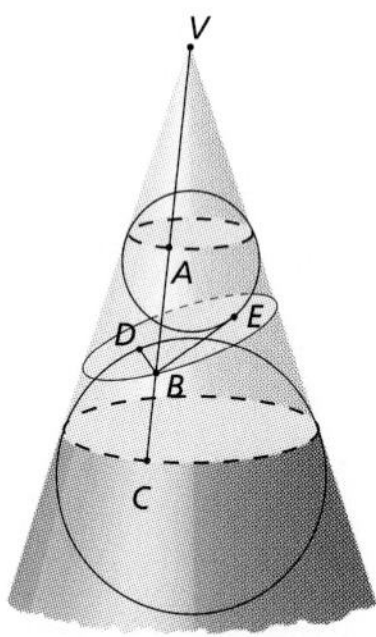

Pass a straight line down the surface of the cone, beginning at the apex *V*. Label the points of intersection with the smaller sphere, the plane, and the larger sphere *A*, *B*, and *C* in the figure above. Point *D* is the point where the larger sphere is tangent to the plane. Point *E* is the point where the smaller sphere is tangent to the plane. $BA = BE$ because $\overrightarrow{BA}$ and $\overrightarrow{BE}$ each emanates from *B* and are tangent to the smaller sphere.

For this same reason $BC = BD$, because both $\overrightarrow{BC}$ and $\overrightarrow{BD}$ are tangent to the larger sphere.

No matter what line you choose to draw from *V*, the lengths *VA* and *VC* are invariant. Note that since this is so, *AC*, the difference between *VA* and *VC*, is also invariant. Also note that $AC = BA + BC$. Since $BA = BE$ and $BC = BD$ then $BA + BC = BD + BE$. $BA + BC$ is constant so this means that $BD + BE$ must also be constant. So an ellipse must be a set of all points in the plane, such that the sum of the distances from two fixed points (*E* and *D*) remains constant.

Remember...

Given a circle and a point *P* outside the circle, the two segments from *P* tangent to the circle are equal in length. Rotating this gives a sphere with the same property.

Wrap Up

Investigate the locus definitions of hyperbola and parabola at the end of today's lesson. Have students think about how they can locate points based on these definitions, and their implications for symmetry. Something else to consider is the minimum amount of information you need to construct one of these curves. If you know the two foci for an ellipse or a hyperbola, you still do not know enough to completely determine the graph; many ellipses or hyperbolas have the same two foci. However, if you know the focus and directrix for a parabola, its graph is completely determined.

If possible, give students time to work on the core Check Your Understanding exercises. The more students make connections between a locus definition and the curve that it defines, the more they will understand the symmetry of each curve and how to determine the equation for each type of graph.

Assessment Resources

Lesson Quiz 6.6

1. Consider foci $F_1(4, 0)$ and $F_2(-4, 0)$, and the distance $s = 12$.
   a. Find the two values of b so that $(0, b)$ is on the ellipse.
   b. Find the two values of a so that $(a, 0)$ is on the ellipse.

2. a. Find an equation of the parabola with focus $(2, 0)$ and directrix with equation $x = 5$.
   b. Find two points on the parabola found in part (a).

3. Suppose a hyperbola has foci $F_1(2, 0)$ and $F_2(-2, 0)$, and the fixed difference $d = 3$.
   a. Find two points on the hyperbola.
   b. Write an equation you could use to test whether or not any point (x, y) is on the hyperbola.

Locus Definitions for Conics: The Parabola and the Hyperbola

There are similar ways to show that the other two conics have locus properties.

- A hyperbola is the set of points such that the absolute value of the difference of the distances from two fixed points is constant.

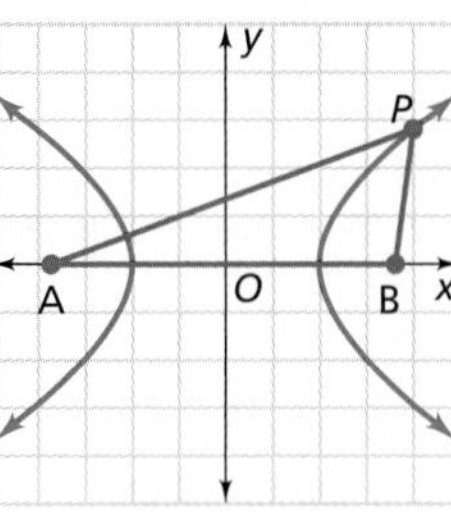

$|PA - PB| = \text{Constant}$

- A parabola is the set of points equidistant from a fixed point and a line.

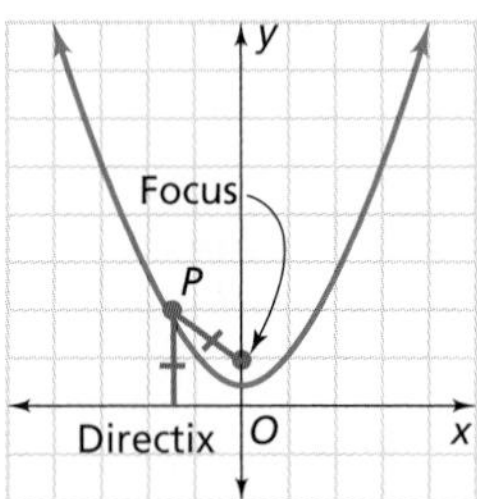

Dandelin showed that the cone slices that you call parabola and hyperbola are the same ones that satisfy the locus descriptions above, using the same idea of putting spheres around the slicing planes. The spheres are now called Dandelin spheres. The arguments are the same in spirit, but they are considerably more complicated.

See the TI-Nspire Handbook on p. 704 for instructions to use the locus definition to draw a hyperbola and a parabola in your dynamic geometry environment.

Why did you not need the absolute value in the definition of the ellipse?

A hyperbola has two foci. A parabola has only one. The fixed line in the parabola definition is called its **directrix.**

Exercises *Practicing Habits of Mind*

Check Your Understanding

1. **a.** Using the pin-and-string model, draw an ellipse that closely resembles a circle.

   b. Using the same string but different pin locations, draw an ellipse that does not resemble a circle.

   c. Where might you place the pins to draw a circle?

   The locus definition of an ellipse uses two points F_1 and F_2, the foci, and a distance s. The ellipse is the set of points P with $PF_1 + PF_2 = s$.

2. Consider foci $F_1(3, 0)$ and $F_2(-3, 0)$, and the distance $s = 10$.

   a. Find the two values of b so that $(0, b)$ is on the ellipse.

   b. Find the two values of a so that $(a, 0)$ is on the ellipse.

   c. Is the point $(2, 3)$ on the ellipse? Explain how you know.

   d. Write an equation that you could use to test whether or not any point (x, y) is on the ellipse.

3. The lesson shows what the two Dandelin spheres look like after slicing a double-cone to produce an ellipse. Suppose you slice a double cone to produce a circle. Describe what the two Dandelin spheres look like. Also, describe the points where the Dandelin spheres touch the sliced circle.

Go Online PHSchool.com

For more information on Dandelin's spheres, go to **Web Code:** bge-9031

4. By its locus definition, a hyperbola is the set of points such that the absolute value of the difference of the distances from two fixed points is constant. Suppose the two points are $F_1 = (3, 0)$ and $F_2 = (-3, 0)$, with the fixed difference $d = 4$.

   a. Find five points that are on this hyperbola.

   b. Sketch a graph of the hyperbola.

   c. **Take It Further** Find an equation for the graph of the hyperbola.

5. **What's Wrong Here?** Joachim decides to make a hyperbola with fixed points $A(3, 0)$ and $B(-3, 0)$, and the fixed difference $d = 10$. But he is having trouble finding points that work. Why?

On Your Own

6. On the coordinate plane, a parabola has focus $(1, 0)$ and directrix with equation $x = -1$. Which of these points is on the parabola?

   A. $(1, 1.5)$ **B.** $(1.5, 2.5)$ **C.** $(2.25, 3)$ **D.** $(9, 36)$

Exercises

HOMEWORK
- Core: 6, 7, 8, 9, 10, 12
- Optional: 13
- Extension: 11

Check Your Understanding

EXERCISE 1 is a good exercise to model with geometry software, as students can see the effects of moving the pins (foci) immediately. Geometry software may not allow you to put the pins in the exact same location, but you can put them close enough to make the point that a circle is a special kind of ellipse.

EXERCISE 2 is about the point-tester concept, so do not expect students to simplify the distance result all the way out.

EXERCISE 4 Building the equation of the hyperbola is tougher, since students may want to start from $|PA - PB| = d$. This is a tough starting point, since it is necessary to square both sides. Encourage students to start from $PA - PB = d$, or equivalently $PA = PB + d$, then look at how the second case $PA = PB - d$ is resolved with the same equation.

EXERCISE 5 The reverse is true for an ellipse; the string length must be more than the distance between the foci in order to generate an ellipse. For hyperbolas, the fixed difference must be *less* than the distance between the foci. You can prove both of these facts with the Triangle Inequality Theorem.

On Your Own

EXERCISE 6 This exercise helps students set up a point-tester equation for the parabola.

Answers

Exercises

1. **a.** Check students' work. The pins should be placed fairly close together.

   b. Check students' work. The pins should be placed far apart, a little shorter than the string length s but larger than $\frac{s}{2}$.

   c. Place both pins in the same spot.

2. **a.** 4, −4

   b. 5, −5

   c. No; the sum of the distances between this point and the foci does not equal 10.

   d. $\sqrt{(x-3)^2 + y^2} + \sqrt{(x+3)^2 + y^2} = 10$

3–5. See back of book.

6. **a.** no

   b. no

   c. yes

   d. no

EXERCISE 7 Use the equation $x = \frac{1}{4}y^2$ to test students' points. You might challenge students to come up with points that no one does, and justify that their points are still on the parabola.

EXERCISE 9 Some students may solve this exercise incidentally while working on the previous exercises.

EXERCISE 10 You can use this form to quickly find the endpoints of the axes of an ellipse.

Additional Resources

PRINT RESOURCES
- Solution Manual
- Practice Workbook
- Assessment Resources
- Teaching Resources

TECHNOLOGY
- Interactive Textbook
- TeacherExpress CD-ROM
- ExamView CD-ROM
- PHSchool.com

Additional Practice

1. The locus definition of an ellipse uses two points F_1 and F_2, the foci, and a distance s. The ellipse is the set of points P with

$$PF_1 + PF_2 = s$$

Consider the foci $F_1(6, 0)$ and $F_2(-6, 0)$, and the distance $s = 20$.
a. Find the two values of b so that $(0, b)$ is on the ellipse.
b. Find the two values of a so that $(a, 0)$ is on the ellipse.
c. Is the point $(2, 5)$ on the ellipse? Explain how you know.

2. Find three points on the parabola with focus $(0, 2)$ and directrix with equation $y = -3$.

3. a. Find c if $(3, c)$ is on the parabola with focus $(2, 0)$ and directrix with equation $x = -4$.
b. Find b if $(b, 4)$ is on the parabola with focus $(2, 0)$ and directrix with equation $x = -4$.
c. Find an equation of the parabola with focus $(2, 0)$ and directrix with equation $x = -4$.

4. Consider the ellipse $144x^2 + 16y^2 = 2304$.
a. Show that this ellipse passes through the point $(0, 12)$.
b. Find three other points on the ellipse.
c. Show that the length of the major axis is 24.
d. The foci of the ellipse are $(c, 0)$ and $(-c, 0)$. Find the value of c.
e. Sketch the graph of this ellipse.

5. The graph of the equation $9x^2 - 4y^2 = 81$ is a hyperbola.
a. Show that the points $(3, 0)$ and $(-3, 0)$ are on the hyperbola.
b. If $x = 4$, find approximate values of y to four decimal places.
c. If $x = 12$, find approximate values of y to four decimal places.
d. As x grows larger, what relationship is there between the x- and y-coordinates of points on the hyperbola?

Practice: For Lesson 6.6, assign Exercises 1–3.

7. Find three points on the parabola with focus $(1, 0)$ and directrix with equation $x = -1$. Do not use points listed in Exercise 6.

8. Find a given each condition.

a. $(1, a)$ is on the parabola with focus $(1, 0)$ and directrix with equation $x = -1$.

b. $(a, 1)$ is on the parabola with focus $(1, 0)$ and directrix with equation $x = -1$.

9. Find an equation of the parabola with focus $(1, 0)$ and directrix with equation $x = -1$.

10. One equation for an ellipse with foci $(3, 0)$ and $(-3, 0)$ and string length $s = 10$ is

$$\sqrt{(x-3)^2 + y^2} + \sqrt{(x+3)^2 + y^2} = 10$$

a. Write another equation that must also be true but only involves a single square root. Proceed as follows. Move one square root to the other side. Square both sides. Simplify the equation as much as possible.

b. Show that you can simplify the equation above to

$$\frac{x^2}{25} + \frac{y^2}{16} = 1$$

11. **Take It Further** In Exercise 2 you found an equation for an ellipse with foci $(3, 0)$ and $(-3, 0)$ and string length $s = 10$.

a. Find an equation for the ellipse with the same foci, but leave string length as a variable s.

b. If $s = 20$, find several points on the ellipse.

c. Sketch the graph of the ellipse when $s = 20$.

d. Sketch the graph of the ellipse when $s = 8$.

e. Sketch the graph when $s = 6$.

12. **Standardized Test Prep** Which of the following points is on the parabola with focus $(3, 4)$ and directrix $y = 5$?

A. $(-3, 4)$ **B.** $(0, 0)$ **C.** $(3, 3)$ **D.** $(5, 4)$

Habits of Mind

Represent the situation. Equations are point testers.

Go Online PHSchool.com

For additional practice, go to **Web Code:** bga-0606

Maintain Your Skills

13. Sketch the graph of each equation.

a. $x^2 + y^2 - 2x + 4y - 4 = 0$

b. $x^2 + y^2 - 2x + 4y = 0$

c. $x^2 + y^2 - 2x + 4y + 4 = 0$

d. $x^2 + y^2 - 2x + 4y + 5 = 0$

e. $x^2 + y^2 - 2x + 4y + 9 = 0$

Answers

7. Answers may vary. Accept any points satisfying the equation $x = \frac{1}{4}y^2$.

8. a. $a = 2, -2$

b. $a = \frac{1}{4}$

9. $x = \frac{1}{4}y^2$

10. a. Answers may vary. Sample:
$3x + 25 = 5\sqrt{(x+3)^2 + y^2}$.

b. $3x + 25 = 5\sqrt{(x+3)^2 + y^2}$

$(3x + 25)^2 = 25\left((x+3)^2 + y^2\right)$

$9x^2 + 150x + 625 = 25(x^2 + 6x + 9 + y^2)$

$9x^2 + 150x + 625 = 25x^2 + 150x + 225 + 25y^2$

$400 = 16x^2 + 25y^2$

$\frac{x^2}{25} + \frac{y^2}{16} = 1$

11–13. See back of book.

6.7 Conics at the Origin

The words *ellipse, parabola,* and *hyperbola* showed up in your previous courses in another context. You gave these names to graphs of certain equations. In this lesson, you will find general forms for equations for each of the conics when you put them on the coordinate plane. These equations will connect to the curves you already know about.

Equations for Parabolas

You already found an equation for one parabola in Exercise 9 from the previous lesson. Suppose $c \neq 0$. Consider the parabola with focus $(0, c)$ and directrix with equation $y = -c$.

In the figures that accompany this derivation, $c > 0$. The same derivation works if $c < 0$. Try it.

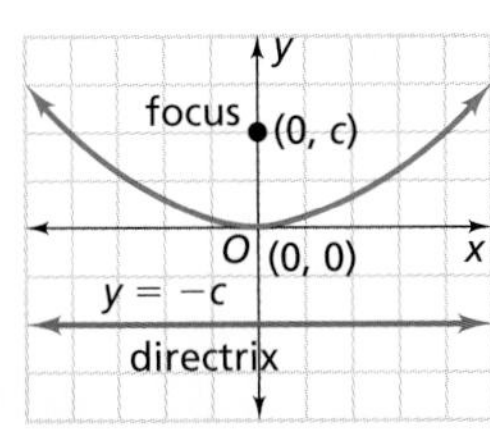

The origin is on this parabola because it is equidistant from the focus and the directrix. In fact, the parabola looks like the graph of a quadratic function with vertex $(0, 0)$.

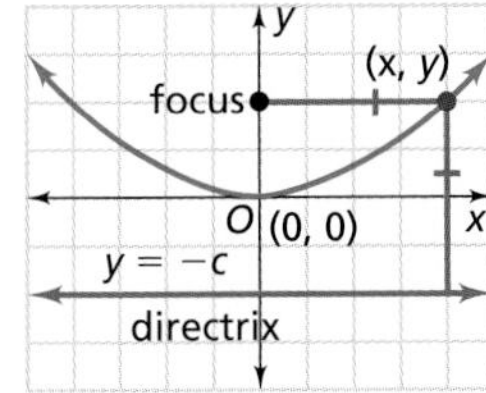

What is the point-tester for this graph? You want the distance from (x, y) to the point $(0, c)$ to be the same as the distance from (x, y) to the line $y = -c$. That gives you

$$\sqrt{x^2 + (y - c)^2} = |y + c|$$

This is fine as a point-tester. For example, $(2c, c)$ is on the graph because

$$\sqrt{(2c)^2 + (c - c)^2} = |c + c|$$

as you can check.

For You to Do

1. Find all values of x so that (x, c) is on the parabola.

For You to Do

1. $x = 2c$ or $x = -2c$

Lesson Overview

GOAL

- Identify the equations for the graphs of the conic sections, and sketch their graphs.

In this lesson, students use the locus definitions from the previous lesson along with the distance formula to write point-testers for their graphs. They see how to locate key features of each conic section by looking at the equation of its graph, and eventually see that all the equations have similar forms.

Depending on your students, you may want to spend more than one class period on this lesson. There are many details to consider in each of these graphs, and it is nice to spend time with each type of conic section. One way to divide the lesson is to work on parabolas and ellipses the first day, and then cover hyperbolas and the common form of the general equation the next day. If you spend two days on the lesson, you may also want to put greater emphasis on the asymptotes of the hyperbola. Exercises 4 and 8 work on this concept.

One common misunderstanding that students develop, upon learning that hyperbolas have asymptotes, is to assume that parabolas must have asymptotes, too. It is often difficult for students to see why this is not the case. Think about the graph of $y = x^2$. If it had an asymptote, then its slope would eventually approach some constant value. That does not happen, because the slope of the parabola is always increasing. For each step of 1 unit to the right, the step up in y value is bigger. At this point, students may think that it must have a vertical asymptote, which is a line with equation $x = c$. If that were the case, the value of the function would be undefined for $x = c$. However, $y = x^2$ is defined for all real numbers. This lack of an asymptote is still likely to bother some students, though.

CHECK YOUR UNDERSTANDING
- Core: 1, 2, 3, 4, 5
- Optional: none
- Extension: 6

MATERIALS
- graph paper
- graphing calculators
- Blackline Masters MC7, 6.6B

HOMEWORK
- Core: 7, 8, 9, 10, 13
- Optional: 12, 14
- Extension: 11

VOCABULARY
- major axis
- minor axis
- vertex

Launch

Begin today's lesson by using the locus definition of the parabola to make a point-tester for the graph of a parabola with focus $(0, c)$ and directrix $y = -c$. Although this is worked out in the text, you and your class may want to develop this independently from the book.

Explore

You may wish to use Blackline Master 6.6B here and later in the discussion to review the locus definitions for the conics. Use Blackline Master MC7 to illustrate the discussion.

For You to Do, p. 475

PROBLEM 1 Some of your students may conclude that since the vertex of this parabola is at the origin, the *y*-axis is a line of symmetry for the parabola, so for any point (x, y) on the graph, the point $(-x, y)$ is also on the graph.

You can simplify the equation in ways that will make it look familiar.

$\sqrt{x^2 + (y - c)^2} = \lvert y + c \rvert$	Square both sides.
$x^2 + (y - c)^2 = (y + c)^2$	Expand.
$x^2 + y^2 - 2cy + c^2 = y^2 + 2cy + c^2$	Cancel and simplify.
$x^2 = 4cy$	

Theorem 6.3

An equation for the parabola with focus $(0, c)$ and directrix with equation $y = -c$ is

$$x^2 = 4cy$$

This should look familiar. In earlier courses, you wrote it as

$$y = \frac{1}{4c}x^2$$

So, your parabola is the graph of the quadratic function $f(x) = \frac{1}{4c}x^2$.

Example

Problem A favorite quadratic curve has equation $y = x^2$.

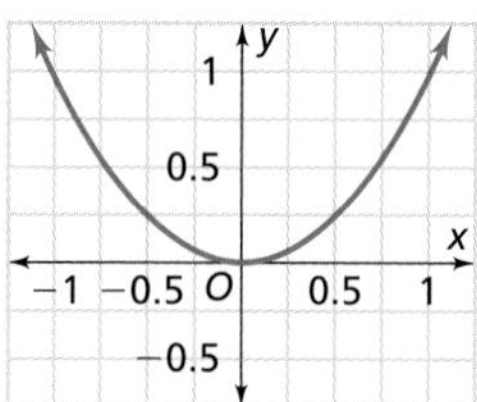

It has a focus and directrix. What are they?

Solution You can read the information from the general equation

$$x^2 = 4cy$$

In this equation, $4c = 1$ so $c = \frac{1}{4}$. Hence the focus of the standard parabola is $\left(0, \frac{1}{4}\right)$ and its directrix has equation $y = -\frac{1}{4}$.

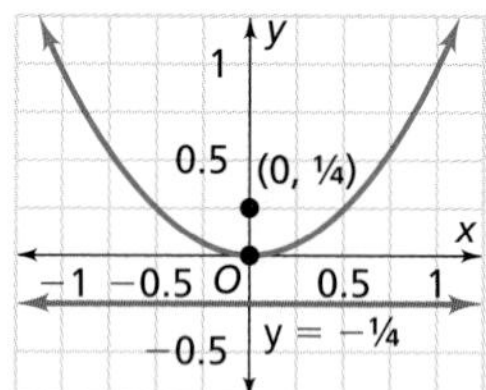

For Discussion

2. Find the equation of the parabola with focus $(c, 0)$ and directrix with equation $x = -c$.

Equations for Ellipses

Suppose an ellipse has foci $(c, 0)$ and $(-c, 0)$ and has string length is s.

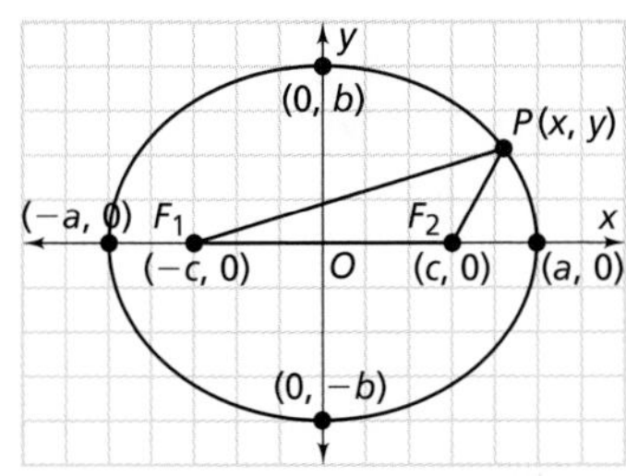

Remember...

An ellipse is the set of points such that the sum of the distances to two fixed foci is constant.

Facts and Notation

- **The center of the ellipse is the origin.**
- **The ellipse has two lines of symmetry. They intersect the interior of the ellipse in two segments. The longer segment is called the major axis for the ellipse and the shorter segment is called the minor axis.**
- **The endpoints of the axes for the ellipse are sometimes called the vertices of the ellipse. Label the vertices $(a, 0)$, $(-a, 0)$, $(0, b)$ and $(0, -b)$.**
- **For any point P on the ellipse with foci F_1 and F_2 and string length s, $PF_1 + PF_2 = s$.**

Habits of Mind

Explore the possibilities. Can an ellipse have major and minor axes of the same length?

What is the point-tester for this ellipse? The "sum of distances is constant" becomes, in this notation

$$\sqrt{(x-c)^2 + y^2} + \sqrt{(x+c)^2 + y^2} = 2a$$

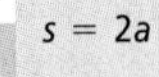

$s = 2a$

This is a perfectly good point-tester, but you can simplify it. Isolate the radicals.

$$\sqrt{(x-c)^2 + y^2} = 2a - \sqrt{(x+c)^2 + y^2}$$

Square both sides.

$$(x-c)^2 + y^2 = 4a^2 - 4a\sqrt{(x+c)^2 + y^2} + (x+c)^2 + y^2$$

For Discussion

PROBLEM 2 You can use the locus definition and the distance formula to get this point tester.

$$\sqrt{(x-c)^2 + y^2} = |x + c|$$

Simplify to get

$$(x-c)^2 + y^2 = (x+c)^2$$
$$x^2 - 2cx + c^2 + y^2 = x^2 + 2cx + c^2$$
$$y^2 = 4cx$$

Another way to think about it, though, is to realize that this focus and directrix are the same as those for $y = \frac{1}{4c}x^2$, but the roles for x and y are reversed. You could hypothesize that this is the parabola with equation $x = \frac{1}{4c}y^2$, and then check your hypothesis.

Answers

For Discussion

2. $x = \frac{1}{4c}y^2$

Expand a little and isolate again.

$$x^2 - 2cx + c^2 + y^2 = 4a^2 - 4a\sqrt{x^2 + 2cx + c^2 + y^2} + x^2 + 2cx + c^2 + y^2$$

so

$$-4cx - 4a^2 = -4a\sqrt{x^2 + 2cx + c^2 + y^2}$$

or

$$cx + a^2 = a\sqrt{x^2 + 2cx + c^2 + y^2}$$

Now square both sides once more.

$$c^2x^2 + 2a^2cx + a^4 = a^2x^2 + 2a^2cx + a^2c^2 + a^2y^2$$

The $2a^2cx$ cancels. You can rearrange terms to look like this.

$$a^4 - a^2c^2 = (a^2 - c^2)x^2 + a^2y^2$$

or

$$a^2(a^2 - c^2) = (a^2 - c^2)x^2 + a^2y^2$$

But $a^2 = b^2 + c^2$, so $a^2 - c^2 = b^2$. So the equation simplifies to

$$a^2b^2 = b^2x^2 + a^2y^2$$

It is often useful to divide both sides of this equation by a^2b^2 to get

$$1 = \frac{x^2}{a^2} + \frac{y^2}{b^2}$$

Habits of Mind

Understand the process. Each of these steps is reversible (as long as *a* and *c* are not negative). Make sure you understand why.

Habits of Mind

Make connections. Looking at this equation, you might also recognize it as a scaling of the unit circle by a factor of *a* horizontally and *b* vertically.

Theorem 6.4

The ellipse with foci $(c, 0)$ and $(-c, 0)$ and string length $2a$ has equation

$$1 = \frac{x^2}{a^2} + \frac{y^2}{b^2} \quad \text{where} \quad b^2 = a^2 - c^2.$$

Developing Habits of Mind

Understand the process. A careful proof of this theorem would require you to show that you did not gain or lose any points when you went from the raw point-tester to the equation in the theorem. There is some work to do here, because you squared both sides of the equation twice, making it possible for extra solutions to creep in. Make sure every step is reversible.

For Discussion

3. Discuss what happens to the graph of the equation $1 = \frac{x^2}{a^2} + \frac{y^2}{b^2}$ as a gets closer and closer to b.
4. Find an equation for the ellipse with foci at $(0, c)$ and $(0, -c)$ and string length $2a$.

Equations for Hyperbolas

Consider a hyperbola with foci $F_1(c, 0)$ and $F_2(-c, 0)$ defined by the condition

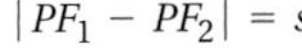

$$|PF_1 - PF_2| = s$$

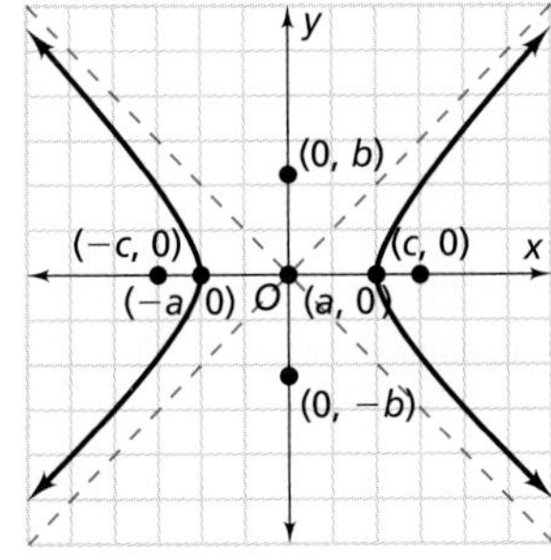

Facts and Notation

- **The points $(a, 0)$ and $(-a, 0)$ are the *vertices* of the hyperbola. Therefore, $s = 2a$. The segment connecting the vertices is the hyperbola's *major axis*.**
- **The constant b is defined by the equation $a^2 + b^2 = c^2$.**

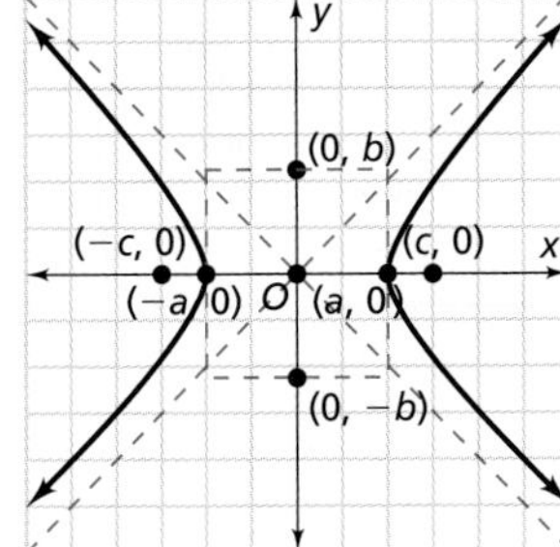

You can construct b by creating a rectangle around the origin with sides parallel to the axes, one side of length $2a$, and diagonals of length $2c$. The vertical side of the rectangle is $2b$. The segment connecting $(0, b)$ to $(0, -b)$ is the hyperbola's *minor axis*.

The diagonals of this little rectangle have an interesting relationship to the hyperbola. You will explore that relationship in the exercises.

For Discussion

PROBLEM 3 As the value of a gets closer and closer to b in this equation, its graph will get closer and closer to the graph of the circle $x^2 + y^2 = b^2$.

PROBLEM 4 This is the same situation as the previous ellipse, but the foci are on the y-axis rather than the x-axis. So this is a congruent ellipse, but with x and y reversed. Its equation is

$$1 = \frac{y^2}{a^2} + \frac{x^2}{a^2 - c^2}$$

Answers

For Discussion

3. The graph gets closer and closer to the graph of a circle with radius b.
4. $\frac{y^2}{a^2} + \frac{x^2}{b^2} = 1$

Wrap Up

If you choose to cover this lesson in one day, you may not have a great deal of time to go over the core Check Your Understanding exercises with students.

If you are spending two days on this lesson, then assign Check Your Understanding Exercises 1, 2, and 3 the first day, and Exercises 4 and 5 the second day. (You can assign any of homework Exercises 7, 9, 10, 11, 13, and 14 the first day, and 8 and 12 with any remaining exercises on the second.) If you find yourself with extra time, you can preview the next lesson's material by asking students to figure out the equation of a translation of one of their ellipses.

Assessment Resources

Lesson Quiz 6.7

1. The ellipse $36x^2 + 16y^2 = 576$ has its center at the origin and passes through the point (0, 6).
   a. Find three other points on this ellipse.
   b. Find the length of the major axis.
   c. The foci of this ellipse are $(0, c)$ and $(0, -c)$. Find the value of c.

2. a. Find an equation for the parabola with focus (0, −4) and directrix with equation $y = 2$.
   b. Find two points on the parabola.
   c. Sketch the graph of the parabola.

3. Consider the hyperbola with equation $\frac{x^2}{9} - \frac{y^2}{16} = 1$. Find the foci of the hyperbola.

The point-tester for the hyperbola is $|PF_1 - PF_2| = 2a$. In terms of coordinates, this translates into

$$\left|\sqrt{(x+c)^2 + y^2} - \sqrt{(x-c)^2 + y^2}\right| = 2a$$

This is a perfectly good point-tester. But you can simplify it considerably using exactly the same algebraic technique that you used to derive the equation of the ellipse. You will take care of the details in Exercise 12.

Well, there is one complication that you did not have with the ellipse: the absolute value. But you can avoid this by treating one branch of the hyperbola at a time. In the end, both equations come out the same.

Theorem 6.5

The hyperbola with foci $(c, 0)$ and $(-c, 0)$ and constant difference $2a$ has equation

$$1 = \frac{x^2}{a^2} - \frac{y^2}{b^2}$$

where $b^2 = c^2 - a^2$.

Developing Habits of Mind

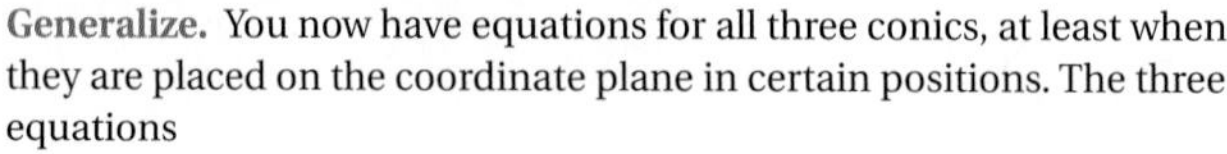

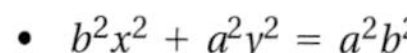

Generalize. You now have equations for all three conics, at least when they are placed on the coordinate plane in certain positions. The three equations

- $b^2x^2 + a^2y^2 = a^2b^2$,
- $b^2x^2 - a^2y^2 = a^2b^2$, and
- $x^2 = 4cy$

are all special cases of the following general quadratic equation in two variables.

$$rx^2 + sxy + ty^2 + ux + vy + w = 0$$

where r, s, t, u, v, and w are real numbers. In the next lesson, you will show that if $s = 0$, the equation's graph is a conic with axis parallel to one of the coordinate axes. In fact, a very simple calculation with two numbers will tell you what kind of a conic it is. In the project for this chapter, you will show that even if $s \neq 0$, the graph is a conic, although its axis is not horizontal or vertical.

Habits of Mind

Find relationships. This predictive power—being able to tell the shape of a graph from a simple calculation—is something that mathematicians prize.

For You to Do

5. Find the values of r, s, t, u, v, and w in each of the three equations above.

Answers

For You to Do

5. Equation 1:
   $r = b^2, s = 0, t = a^2,$
   $u = 0, v = 0, w = -a^2b^2$
   Equation 2:
   $r = b^2, s = 0, t = -a^2, u = 0,$
   $v = 0, w = -a^2b^2$
   Equation 3:
   $r = 1, s = 0, t = 0, u = 0,$
   $v = -4c, w = 0$

Exercises

1. a. $25 \cdot (0)^2 + 169 \cdot (5)^2 = 169 \cdot 25 = 4225$
   b. Answers may vary. Accept any points satisfying the equation $\frac{x^2}{169} + \frac{y^2}{5} = 1$.
   c. The major axis is formed by the points (13, 0) and (–13, 0). The distance between these points is 26.
   d. $c = 12$
   e.

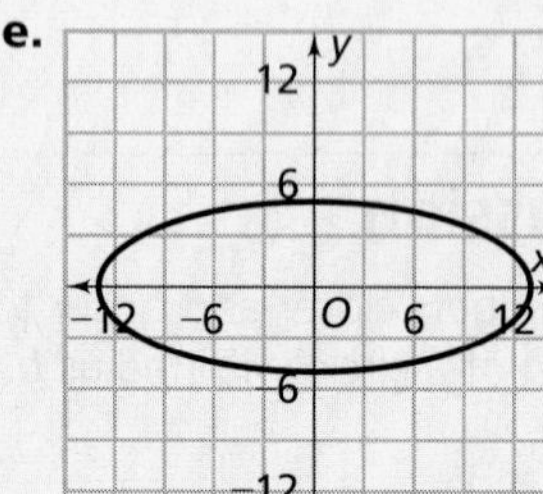

2. a. Answers may vary. Accept any points satisfying the equation $\frac{x^2}{9} + \frac{y^2}{25} = 1$.

Exercises *Practicing Habits of Mind*

Check Your Understanding

1. Many different ellipses have centers at the origin and pass through the point $(0, 5)$.
   a. Show that the ellipse with equation $25x^2 + 169y^2 = 4225$ passes through $(0, 5)$.
   b. Find four other points on the ellipse from part (a).
   c. Show that the length of the major axis is 26.
   d. The foci of this ellipse are $(c, 0)$ and $(-c, 0)$. Find the value of c.
   e. Sketch a graph of this ellipse.

2. The ellipse with equation $25x^2 + 9y^2 = 225$ also has its center at the origin and passes through $(0, 5)$.
   a. Find four other points on this ellipse.
   b. Show that the length of the major axis is 10.
   c. The foci of this ellipse are $(0, c)$ and $(0, -c)$. Find the value of c.
   d. Sketch a graph of this ellipse.

3. **Write About It** Describe, as completely as possible, how to find the foci and sketch the graph of
$$1 = \frac{x^2}{a^2} + \frac{y^2}{b^2}$$
Be careful to describe cases where $a > b$, $a = b$, and $a < b$.

4. The graph of the equation $y^2 - 9x^2 = 36$ is a hyperbola.
   a. Show that the points $(0, 6)$ and $(0, -6)$ are on the hyperbola.
   b. If $x = 1$, find approximate values of y to four decimal places.
   c. If $x = 5$, find approximate values of y to four decimal places.
   d. If $x = 100$, find approximate values of y to four decimal places.
   e. As x grows larger, what relationship is there between the x- and y-coordinates of points on the hyperbola?

Exercises

HOMEWORK
- Core: 7, 8, 9, 10, 13
- Optional: 12, 14
- Extension: 11

Check Your Understanding

EXERCISE 2 Watch for students assuming that the major axis is horizontal. The major axis for an ellipse is always the longer direction. However, the major axis for a hyperbola may be shorter. One helpful reminder to students is that for both an ellipse and a hyperbola, the major axis is always collinear with the foci.

b. The major axis is formed by the points $(0, 5)$ and $(0, -5)$. The distance between these points is 10.

c. $c = 4$

d.

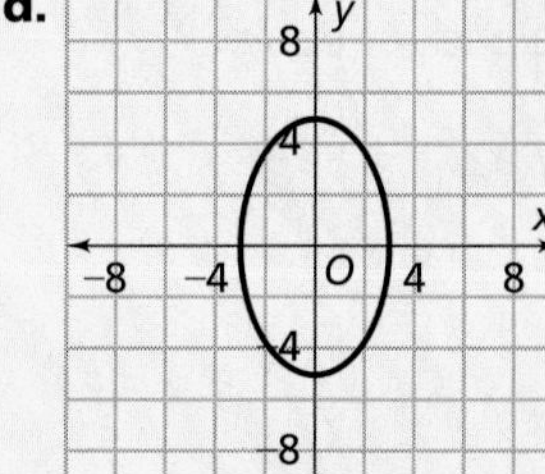

3. The graph will pass through the points $(a, 0)$, $(-a, 0)$, $(0, b)$, and $(0, -b)$.

If $a = b$, then this graph is a circle centered at the origin.

If $a > b$, the graph is an ellipse with major axis along the x-axis with foci at $(\pm\sqrt{a^2 - b^2}, 0)$.

If $a < b$, the graph is an ellipse with major axis along the y-axis with foci at $(0, \pm\sqrt{b^2 - a^2})$.

4. a. $y^2 - 9x^2 = 36$

$(\pm 6)^2 - 9 \cdot (0)^2 = 36$

b. $y = \pm 6.7082$

c. $y = \pm 16.1555$

d. $y = \pm 300.0600$

e. As x grows larger, the ratio of $\frac{y}{x}$ approaches 3 or -3 and the points on the hyperbola approach asymptotes defined by the lines $y = 3x$ and $y = -3x$.

EXERCISE 5 Some students may think of the degenerate hyperbola as an extreme close-up of the graph. The graphs in parts (a) and (b) are getting closer and closer to the origin, and the graph in part (c) actually reaches it. You might also ask students what they think $y^2 - 9x^2 = -1$ looks like, if time permits.

EXERCISE 6 There are several different valid forms for the answer to part (a) of this exercise, but this is one reason why the standard form $rx^2 + sxy + ty^2 + ux + vy + w = 0$ exists. It is difficult to draw an accurate sketch of this parabola, though a rough sketch is quite simple using the geometric definition: plot the focus, plot the directrix, and go. If students plot this parabola by rotating the page, there is a potential teachable moment: this parabola is congruent to a parabola that points upward from the origin (in the form $y = ax^2$), but which one is it? The distance between focus and vertex determines it uniquely.

On Your Own

EXERCISE 8 provides one explanation of why asymptotes behave the way they do. You can find another explanation in Exercise 5, which looks at a similar equation with the 1 replaced by 0. In this case, the graph is the asymptote lines.

5. In Exercise 4, you worked with the equation

$$y^2 - 9x^2 = 36$$

A slight change to this equation can produce very different results.

a. Sketch the graph of $y^2 - 9x^2 = 9$. How is the graph similar to the one from Exercise 4. How is it different?

b. Sketch the graph of $y^2 - 9x^2 = 1$.

c. Sketch the graph of $y^2 - 9x^2 = 0$.

Habits of Mind

Recall what you know. What techniques can you use when one side of an equation is set equal to zero?

6. Take It Further The following equation gives the distance from a point (x, y) to the line with equation $x + y = 10$.

$$D = \frac{|x + y - 10|}{\sqrt{2}}$$

a. Find an equation for the parabola with focus at the origin and with directrix with equation $x + y = 10$.

b. Find the two points on the graph with x-coordinate -5.

c. Sketch the graph of this parabola.

Go Online PHSchool.com

For additional practice, go to **Web Code:** bga-0607

On Your Own

7. Find an equation for the parabola with focus $(-2, 0)$ and directrix with equation $x = 2$.

8. The graph of the following equation is a hyperbola.

$$\frac{x^2}{16} - \frac{y^2}{9} = 1$$

a. If (x, y) is on this hyperbola, then so are $(-x, y)$, $(-x, -y)$ and $(x, -y)$. Explain.

b. Copy and complete this table to find the nonnegative value of y for each value of x. Approximate your results to four decimal places.

x	y
3	undefined
4	0
5	■
6	■
8	■
10	■
20	■
40	■
100	■
1000	■

Answers

5. See back of book.

6. a. $x^2 - 2xy + y^2 + 20x + 20y - 100 = 0$

b. $(-5, 5)$ and $(-5, 35)$

c. See back of book.

7. $x = -\frac{1}{8}y^2$

8. a. If (x, y) is on the hyperbola, then $\frac{x^2}{16} - \frac{y^2}{9} = 1$. If x is replaced by $-x$, the value of $\frac{x^2}{16}$ will not change. If y is replaced by $-y$, the value of $\frac{y^2}{9}$ will not change. Therefore, the value will equal 1 and all of these points are on the hyperbola.

b. See back of book.

c. As x grows larger, what relationship is there between the x- and y-coordinates of points on the hyperbola?

9. Show that every point on the graph of $y = x^2$ is equidistant from the focus $(0, \frac{1}{4})$ and the directrix with equation $y = -\frac{1}{4}$.

10. Consider the equation $1 = \frac{x^2}{9} + \frac{y^2}{4}$.
   a. Find all values of x if $(x, 0)$ is on the graph of the equation.
   b. Find all values of y if $(0, y)$ is on the graph of the equation.
   c. Sketch the graph of the equation.
   d. Find all values of x if (x, x) is on the graph of the equation.
   e. Find three points that are close to being on the graph but not actually on it.

11. **Take It Further** An ellipse has foci $(8, -6)$ and $(-6, 8)$ and string length 20.
   a. Show that this ellipse passes through the origin.
   b. Find the center of the ellipse.
   c. Find the endpoints of the major axis.
   d. Find an equation of the ellipse.
   e. Sketch the graph of the ellipse.

The major axis contains the foci. It has the same length as the string length.

12. Prove Theorem 6.5, which gives an equation for a hyperbola.

13. **Standardized Test Prep** Which of the following are the foci of the ellipse with equation $\frac{x^2}{25} + \frac{y^2}{9} = 1$?

   A. $(-1, 0), (1, 0)$ B. $(-2, 0), (2, 0)$
   C. $(-3, 0), (3, 0)$ D. $(-4, 0), (4, 0)$

Maintain Your Skills

14. Each of these is the equation of a parabola. For each, find the coordinates of the focus and an equation of the directrix.
   a. $y = \frac{1}{4}x^2$ b. $x = \frac{1}{4}y^2$ c. $y = -\frac{1}{4}x^2$
   d. $x = -\frac{1}{4}y^2$ e. $y = 2x^2$ f. $x = 2y^2$

EXERCISE 12 There are many steps to this proof, but most are identical to the steps for the ellipse proof. One key step is recognizing that the theorem gives the relationship $b^2 = c^2 - a^2$, a different relationship than the one for an ellipse. If students have trouble near the end, encourage them to combine like terms, noting that a and c are fixed values.

Additional Resources

PRINT RESOURCES
- Solution Manual
- Practice Workbook
- Assessment Resources
- Teaching Resources

TECHNOLOGY
- Interactive Textbook
- TeacherExpress CD-ROM
- ExamView CD-ROM
- PHSchool.com

Additional Practice

1. The locus definition of an ellipse uses two points F_1 and F_2, the foci, and a distance s. The ellipse is the set of points P with

$$PF_1 + PF_2 = s$$

Consider the foci $F_1(6, 0)$ and $F_2(-6, 0)$, and the distance $s = 20$.
   a. Find the two values of b so that $(0, b)$ is on the ellipse.
   b. Find the two values of a so that $(a, 0)$ is on the ellipse.
   c. Is the point $(2, 5)$ on the ellipse? Explain how you know.

2. Find three points on the parabola with focus $(0, 2)$ and directrix with equation $y = -3$.

3. a. Find c if $(3, c)$ is on the parabola with focus $(2, 0)$ and directrix with equation $x = -4$.
   b. Find b if $(b, 4)$ is on the parabola with focus $(2, 0)$ and directrix with equation $x = -4$.
   c. Find an equation of the parabola with focus $(2, 0)$ and directrix with equation $x = -4$.

4. Consider the ellipse $144x^2 + 16y^2 = 2304$.
   a. Show that this ellipse passes through the point $(0, 12)$.
   b. Find three other points on the ellipse.
   c. Show that the length of the major axis is 24.
   d. The foci of the ellipse are $(c, 0)$ and $(-c, 0)$. Find the value of c.
   e. Sketch the graph of this ellipse.

5. The graph of the equation $9x^2 - 4y^2 = 81$ is a hyperbola.
   a. Show that the points $(3, 0)$ and $(-3, 0)$ are on the hyperbola.
   b. If $x = 4$, find approximate values of y to four decimal places.
   c. If $x = 12$, find approximate values of y to four decimal places.
   d. As x grows larger, what relationship is there between the x- and y-coordinates of points on the hyperbola?

Practice: For Lesson 6.7, assign Exercises 4–5.

8. c. The ratio $\frac{y}{x}$ approaches $\frac{3}{4}$.

9. Distance to focus

$$= \sqrt{x^2 + \left(x^2 - \tfrac{1}{4}\right)^2}$$
$$= \sqrt{x^2 + x^4 - \tfrac{1}{2}x^2 + \tfrac{1}{16}}$$
$$= \sqrt{\left(x^2 + \tfrac{1}{4}\right)^2}$$
$$= \left|x^2 + \tfrac{1}{4}\right|$$
$$= x^2 + \tfrac{1}{4}$$

Distance to directrix $= x^2 + \frac{1}{4}$

10. a. $x = \pm 3$ **b.** $y = \pm 2$
c. See back of book.
d. $x = \pm\frac{6\sqrt{13}}{13}$
e. Answers may vary. Accept any points that do not satisfy the equation, but come close.

11. a. The distance from point (0, 0) to both foci is equal to 10 and the string length of the ellipse is 20, therefore (0, 0) lies on the ellipse.
b. (1, 1)
c–e. See back of book.

12–14. See back of book.

Lesson Overview

GOAL

- Identify the equations for the graphs of the conic sections, and sketch their graphs.

Now that students can use the properties of a conic section centered at the origin to write its equation, they are ready to think about the equations of translations of these graphs. These equations behave in the same way as any basic graph, so you may be able to move through this material very quickly. Similarly, students practice "completing the square" to rewrite an equation that is in normal form in a form with easily identifiable characteristics and graph type. If your students are comfortable with completing the square, this will not seem very new to them.

CHECK YOUR UNDERSTANDING

- Core: 1, 2, 3, 5, 6
- Optional: 4
- Extension: 7

MATERIALS

- graph paper
- graphing calculators
- Blackline Master MC7

HOMEWORK

- Core: 8, 9, 11, 12, 13, 15
- Optional: 10, 14, 16

Launch

You might begin today's lesson by seeing how much your students remember about translations of basic graphs. Ask them to write the equation of a circle of radius 5 centered at the origin. (Answer: $x^2 + y^2 = 25$) Then ask them to write the equation of a circle of radius 5 centered at the point (3, 4). (Answer: $(x - 3)^2 + (y - 4)^2 = 25$) Check their equations and talk about the relationships you see. The equations are the same, except in the equation for the circle centered at (3,4), you replace every instance of x by $x - 3$, and you replace every instance of y by $y - 4$. In translating the circle to the right 3 units and up 4 units, you are working with bigger x and y values, so you have to subtract the difference to keep equality in the equation for the graph.

Students who struggle with translations of graphs often develop some techniques that step around understanding the change in variables. You may hear things like, "Every time I think I am going to add 3, it turns out I am supposed to subtract. So now, I just go with the opposite of what I think it is going to be and I am always right." You may have to accept coping techniques like these for now, but encourage students to keep checking points and *trying* to understand what is going on.

6.8 Conics Anywhere

In this lesson, you will look at equations for conics where the center (or vertex, for the parabola) is not at the origin.

You looked at various affine transformations of parabolas in CME Project *Algebra 2*. The ideas here are exactly the same. It is easiest to understand the general methods through examples.

Example 1

Problem Find equation of the ellipse $\mathcal{E}$ with foci at (3, 16) and (3, −8) and with string length 26.

Solution The situation looks like this.

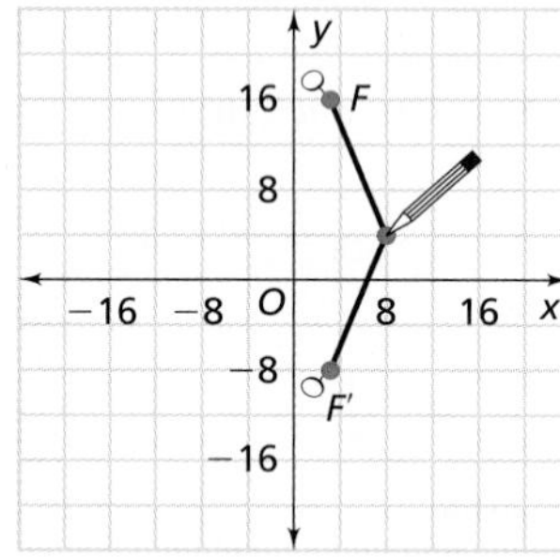

The center of an ellipse is the midpoint of the segment connecting its foci, so the center of this ellipse is (3, 4). The major axis is vertical and the distance from the center to each focus is $c = 12$. Since the string length is 26, $a = 13$ and the vertices are at $(3, 4 + 13) = (3, 17)$ and $(3, 4 - 13) = (3, -9)$.

Since $a^2 = b^2 + c^2$, $b = 5$. So the minor axis connects (−2, 4) to (8, 4).

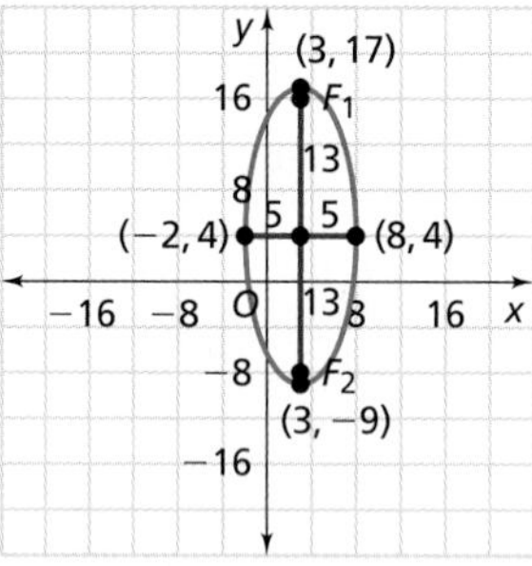

This ellipse $\mathcal{E}$ is a translation of an ellipse $\mathcal{E}'$, centered at the origin with foci located at (0, 12) and (0, −12) and string length 26.

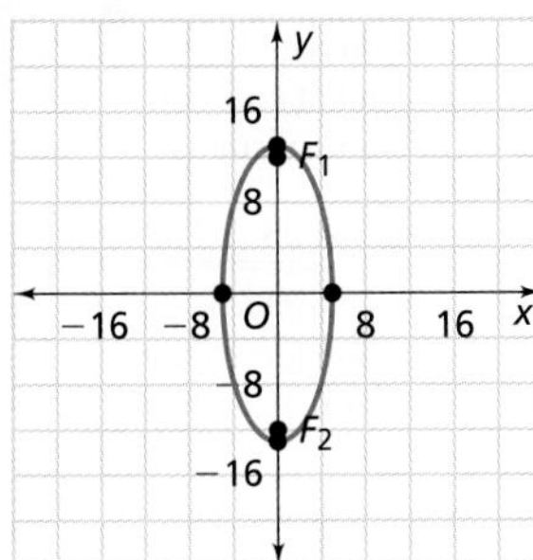

You already know how to find an equation of ellipse centered at the origin. An equation for $\mathcal{E}$ is

$$\frac{x^2}{25} + \frac{y^2}{169} = 1$$

How can you use this equation to find an equation of the ellipse centered at (3, 4)? Notice that the distance from any point (x, y) to (3, 16) is the same as the distance from $(x - 3, y - 4)$ to $(3 - 3, 16 - 4) = (0, 12)$. (Why?) Similarly, the distance from any point (x, y) to $(3, -8)$ is the same as the distance from $(x - 3, y - 4)$ to $(3 - 3, -8 - 4) = (0, -12)$. So, the sum of the distances from (x, y) to (3, 16) and $(3, -8)$ is the same as the sum of the distances from $(x - 3, y - 4)$ to (0, 12) and $(0, -12)$. In particular, it follows that (x, y) is on $\mathcal{E}$ if and only if $(x - 3, y - 4)$ is on $\mathcal{E}'$.

So, the point-tester for $\mathcal{E}$ is "See if $(x - 3, y - 4)$ is on $\mathcal{E}'$." That is the same as "See if $(x - 3, y - 4)$ satisfies the equation for $\mathcal{E}'$." In other words, check to see if

$$\frac{(x-3)^2}{25} + \frac{(y-4)^2}{169} = 1$$

So this is an equation for the ellipse $\mathcal{E}$.

Habits of Mind

Use what you know. You have done translations of basic graphs for quite a while now. Conic sections work the same way.

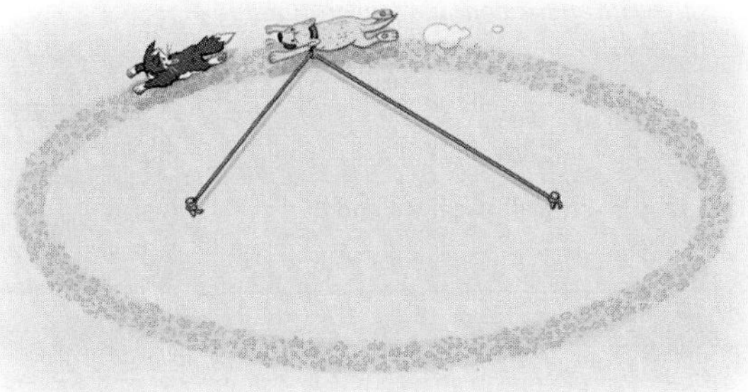

Explore

For Discussion

PROBLEM 1 If you have not yet discussed the asymptotes of a hyperbola and you would like to, recall students' work on Exercises 4 and 8 from Lesson 6.7. They found that for very large or small values of x, the hyperbola approaches (but does not touch) two lines. These lines have slopes $\frac{b}{a}$ and $-\frac{b}{a}$ and pass through the center of the hyperbola. If you sketch a small rectangle with width $2a$ and height $2b$ centered at the center of the hyperbola, the asymptotes contain its diagonals. The asymptotes of a hyperbola are very helpful if you want to sketch an accurate graph. For this hyperbola, the asymptotes pass through (6, 1) and have slopes $\frac{3}{4}$ and $-\frac{3}{4}$. The equations of these lines are $3x - 4y = 14$ and $3x + 4y = 22$.

Developing Habits of Mind

Simplify complicated problems. In the above example, you could have gone right to the locus definition. The point $P = (x, y)$ is on $\mathcal{E}$ if and only if the sum of the distances from P to the foci is 26, so the point-tester is

$$\sqrt{(x-3)^2 + (y-16)^2} + \sqrt{(x-3)^2 + (y+8)^2} = 26$$

To simplify this, you would have to face some hefty algebra (similar to what you did in the proof of Theorem 6.4). But using the translation idea reduces the problem to one you have already solved and eliminates the need for the complex calculations.

Of course, some people love to do algebraic calculations. If you are one of them, go ahead and see if you get the same equation as you got in the example.

For Discussion

1. Suppose $F_1 = (1, 1)$ and $F_2 = (11, 1)$. Find an equation of the hyperbola defined by

$$|PF_1 - PF_2| = 8$$

Minds in Action episode 19

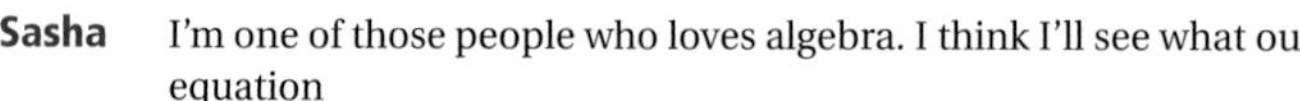

Tony and Sasha are looking at the example above

Sasha I'm one of those people who loves algebra. I think I'll see what our equation

$$\frac{(x-3)^2}{25} + \frac{(y-4)^2}{169} = 1$$

looks like if I expand everything and put it in normal form.

Tony Be my guest.

Sasha pulls out some chalk and begins to write on the board. A few minutes later, she smiles at her work.

Sasha I get

$$169x^2 - 1014x + 25y^2 - 200y - 2304 = 0$$

Tony I wonder how we could have graphed the ellipse if we had been given this equation.

Habits of Mind

Find a process. How would you help Tony answer his question?

Answers

For Discussion

1. $\frac{(x-6)^2}{16} - \frac{(y-1)^2}{9} = 1$

Example 2

Problem Is the graph of

$$9y^2 + 18y - 16x^2 + 64x - 199 = 0$$

a conic? If so, what kind is it?

Solution Complete the square in x and y on the left side so that you can write the equation in terms of $x - r$ and $y - s$ for some constants r and s.

$$\begin{aligned} 9y^2 + 18y - 16x^2 + 64x - 199 &= 0 \\ 9y^2 + 18y - 16x^2 + 64x &= 199 \\ 9(y^2 + 2y + ?) - 16(x^2 - 4x + ??) &= 199 + 9 \cdot ? - 16 \cdot ?? \\ 9(y^2 + 2y + 1) - 16(x^2 - 4x + 4) &= 199 + 9 \cdot 1 - 16 \cdot 4 \\ 9(y+1)^2 - 16(x-2)^2 &= 199 + 9 - 64 \\ 9(y+1)^2 - 16(x-2)^2 &= 144 \end{aligned}$$

So the equation is

$$9(y+1)^2 - 16(x-2)^2 = 144$$

Divide both sides by 144 to get

$$\frac{(y+1)^2}{16} - \frac{(x-2)^2}{9} = 1$$

The graph is a hyperbola with center $(2, -1)$.

See the TI-Nspire Handbook on p. 704 for ideas about how to use your calculator to graph the equation.

Developing Habits of Mind

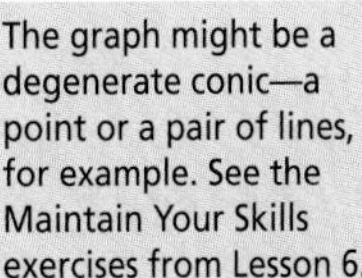

Generalize. This method will work on any equation of the form

$$rx^2 + ty^2 + ux + vy + w = 0$$

and the result will tell you what kind of a conic the graph is. When you complete the square on the left side and simplify, you will get an equation of the form

$$r(x - h)^2 + t(x - k)^2 = c$$

for constants h, k, and c.

The graph might be a degenerate conic—a point or a pair of lines, for example. See the Maintain Your Skills exercises from Lesson 6.6.

Example 2

If your students need practice graphing hyperbolas, you can go through the process of graphing this equation. Students should notice that since the x^2 term is subtracted from the y^2 term, this hyperbola will open up and down rather than left and right. The vertices of this hyperbola are at (2, 3) and (2, −5), its foci are at (2, 4) and (2, −6).

If you want to cover graphing the asymptotes of a hyperbola, this is another place to bring up that topic. Have students construct a rectangle that is $2a = 6$ units wide and $2b = 8$ units high centered at the center of the hyperbola. This rectangle has corners (5, 3), (5, −5), (−1, 3), and (−1, −5). The lines containing the diagonals of this rectangle are the asymptotes of the hyperbola. If you also want students to find the equations of these lines, they have slopes $\frac{4}{3}$ and $-\frac{4}{3}$ and both pass through the point (2, −1). One way to write the equations for the asymptotes is

$$y + 1 = \frac{4}{3}(x - 2) \text{ and } y + 1 = -\frac{4}{3}(x - 2)$$

For Discussion

PROBLEMS 2–4 These three statements are all true. As students have seen, if the equation is only quadratic in one of the variables, its graph is a parabola. If x is the quadratic, it opens up or down, if y is the quadratic, it opens left or right. When both x and y are quadratic, they either have the same sign and the graph is an ellipse, or they have opposite signs and the graph is a hyperbola. The process of completing the square means that any linear terms or constants do not affect the shape of the graph, only its position.

Wrap Up

As you assign Check Your Understanding and On Your Own exercises, consider the goals that you must meet for state or district standards. Such standards are usually fairly explicit about what your students should know, and this lesson may take them beyond the scope of those requirements. Similarly, they may need to know how to sketch detailed graphs and to show all the features, including some that are de-emphasized in this book. You should also consider your own and your students' mathematical taste. If they are enjoying the process of creating these graphs, they are gaining valuable practice in algebraic manipulation and making more robust associations between equations and graphs.

You may wish to provide copies of Blackline Master MC7 to your students to use on their homework.

For Discussion

Suppose the conic is not degenerate. Discuss each statement.

2. If either r or t is 0, the graph is a parabola.
3. If r and t have the same sign, the graph is an ellipse.
4. If r and t have opposite signs, the graph is a hyperbola.

A little more work produces the following classification theorem.

To a mathematician a classification theorem is truly a thing of beauty.

Theorem 6.6

The graph of

$$rx^2 + ty^2 + ux + vy + w = 0$$

is a (possibly degenerate) conic. In fact, the nature of the conic is determined by the sign of rt:

- **If $rt > 0$, the graph is an ellipse.**
- **If $rt = 0$, the graph is a parabola.**
- **If $rt < 0$, the graph is a hyperbola.**

For You to Do

5. How can you tell from the equation if the graph is a circle?
6. How can you tell from the equation if the graph is a single point?

Educators and scientists use ripple tanks to discover and demonstrate the additive and subtractive properties of combinations of waves in a shallow basin of water. Here the spreading rings of drops of liquid produce interference patterns. Such patterns are the common conic sections you studied in this chapter.

Answers

For Discussion

2. True. If either r or t is zero, then one of the squared variables will drop out and the resulting equation is a parabola.
3. True. If r and t have the same sign, the graph is an ellipse.
4. True. If r and t have opposite signs, the graph is a hyperbola.

For You to Do

5. The graph is a circle if $r = t$.
6. The graph is a single point if $r = t \neq 0$ and when you complete the square you get something of the form $r(x - h)^2 + t(y - k)^2 = 0$.

Exercises

1. **a.** (3, 2)

   b.

x	y
6	undefined
7	2
8	4.25
9	5.3541
11	7.1962
13	8.8739
23	16.6969
43	31.8496
103	76.9400
1003	751.9940

   c. The graph becomes asymptotic to the line $y - 2 = \frac{3}{4}(x - 3)$.

2. **a.**

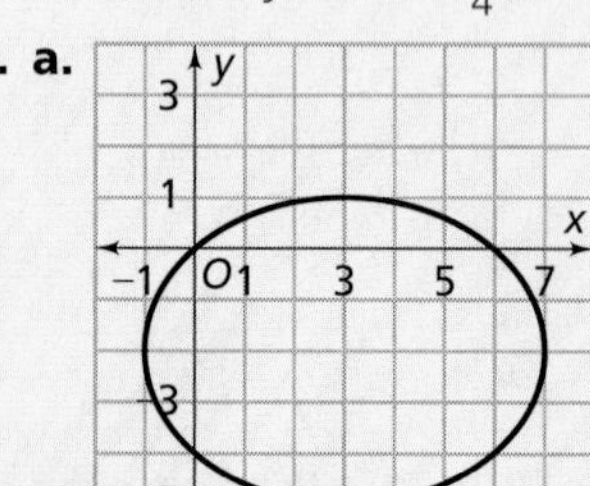

   b. no

Exercises *Practicing Habits of Mind*

Check Your Understanding

1. The graph of the following equation is a hyperbola.

$$\frac{(x-3)^2}{16} - \frac{(y-2)^2}{9} = 1$$

The hyperbola is related to the one from Exercise 8 of Lesson 6.7.

a. What is the center of the hyperbola?

b. Copy and complete this table to find the nonnegative value of y for each value of x. Approximate your results to four decimal places.

x	y
6	undefined
7	2
8	■
9	■
11	■
13	■
23	■
43	■
103	■
1003	■

c. As x grows larger, what relationship is there between the x- and y-coordinates of points on the hyperbola?

2. The graph of the equation

$$9(x-3)^2 + 16(y+2)^2 = N$$

depends on the value of N.

a. Sketch the graph when $N = 144$.

b. Does the ellipse you drew in part (a) pass through the origin?

c. Sketch the graph when $N = 36$.

d. Sketch the graph when $N = 0$.

e. Sketch the graph when $N = -144$.

f. Find all values of N such that the graph passes through the point $(13, -1)$.

Assessment Resources

Lesson Quiz 6.8

1. a. Is the graph of

$$16x^2 - 96x + 9y^2 + 72y + 144 = 0$$

a conic? If so, what kind is it?

b. Sketch the graph of the equation.

2. a. Is the graph of

$$36x^2 - 432x + 16y^2 + 64y + 1360 = 0$$

a conic? If so, what kind is it?

b. Sketch the graph of the equation.

3. An ellipse is centered at (2, 4), and (8, 4) is one of its foci.

a. Find the coordinates of the other focus.

b. If the point (10, 4) is on the ellipse, find the length of the major axis.

Exercises

HOMEWORK

- Core: 8, 9, 11, 12, 13, 15
- Optional: 10, 14, 16

Check Your Understanding

EXERCISE 1 This investigation does not place much emphasis on asymptotes, but this exercise can serve as a jumping-off point to a discussion about them. You can also use Exercise 6 to explore them.

c.

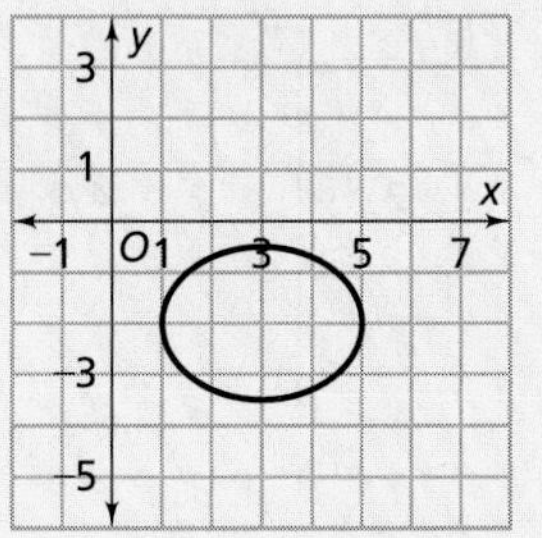

d.

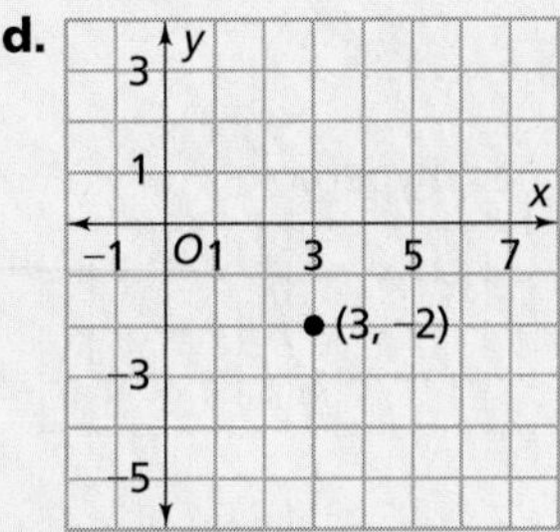

e. No graph, since the equation has no solution.

f. $N = 916$

EXERCISE 3 Watch for students adding 64 instead of subtracting—the most common error in completing the square. Another common error is forgetting about the product—students making this mistake will add 9 and 16 to the right side instead of the appropriate product.

EXERCISE 4 Watch for students quickly answering "ellipse," especially if they use the $rt > 0$ property. It is good that they are using the property, but they still must check against degenerate cases. Completing the square takes care of this.

EXERCISE 5 is a good exercise to review with the class, since they may want to use this technique on other exercises to check their graphs.

EXERCISE 6 As mentioned, this is a good jumping-off point into asymptotes, and helps explain why the asymptotes behave the way they do. If students are unclear, show the graph of

$$\frac{(x-3)^2}{16} - \frac{(y-2)^2}{9} = \frac{1}{16}$$

It is still a hyperbola but much closer to the two lines.

EXERCISE 7 Even if you do not assign this exercise, it is useful to show students that the graph of $y = \frac{1}{x}$ is a rotated hyperbola.

3. a. Is the graph of $25x^2 - 4y^2 + 150x + 32y + 61 = 0$ a conic? If so, what kind is it?

b. Sketch the graph of the equation.

4. a. Is the graph of $4x^2 + 25y^2 - 16x + 250y + 641 = 0$ a conic? If so, what kind is it?

b. Sketch the graph of the equation.

5. The graph of $\frac{(x+3)^2}{4} - \frac{(y-2)^2}{16} = 1$ is not the graph of a function, but it can be the union of two function graphs.

a. Solve the equation above for $(y-2)^2$.

b. Why is it not possible to uniquely solve for y?

c. Write y as two functions. Plot each function. Then combine them to sketch the entire hyperbola.

6. Sketch an accurate graph of these two equations on the same axes.

$$\frac{(x-3)^2}{16} - \frac{(y-2)^2}{9} = 1$$

$$\frac{(x-3)^2}{16} - \frac{(y-2)^2}{9} = 0$$

7. Take It Further Find an equation of a hyperbola that is the graph of all points P with

$$|PF_1 - PF_2| = 2\sqrt{2}$$

with foci $F_1 = (\sqrt{2}, \sqrt{2})$ and $F_2 = (-\sqrt{2}, -\sqrt{2})$.

On Your Own

8. Explain why the equation $\frac{(x+5)^2}{16} + \frac{(y-3)^2}{9} = -1$ has no graph, but the equation $\frac{(x+5)^2}{16} - \frac{(y-3)^2}{9} = -1$ does.

9. Consider the equation

$$\frac{(x-11)^2}{36} + \frac{(y+14)^2}{25} = 1$$

a. What possible values of x could make the equation true? Explain.

b. What possible values of y could make the equation true?

Try to do this without graphing the ellipse. What must be true about the entire x term?

For additional practice, go to **Web Code:** bga-0608

Answers

3. a. Yes; hyperbola

b.

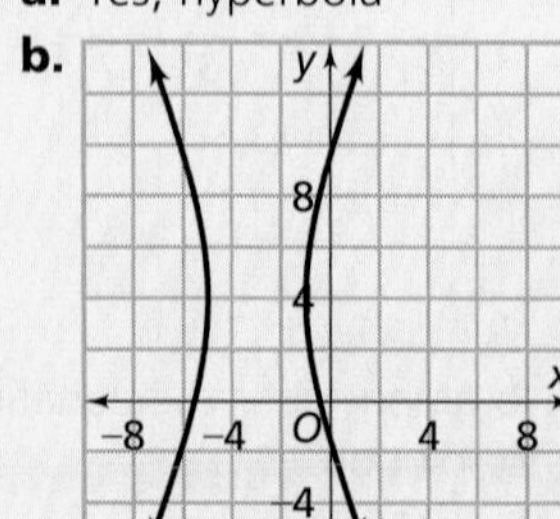

4. a. No; this equation is a single point.

b.

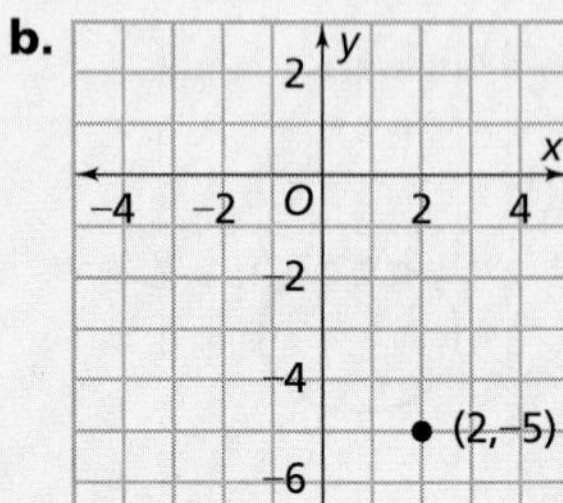

5–6. See back of book.

7. $y = \frac{1}{x}$

8. See back of book.

10. Consider the equation $\frac{(x+9)^2}{49} - \frac{(y-5)^2}{16} = 1$.

a. What possible values of x could make the equation true? Explain.

b. What possible values of y could make the equation true?

11. Find the coordinates of the foci of the ellipse with equation

$$36x^2 + 11y^2 - 288x - 110y + 455 = 0$$

12. **What's Wrong Here?** Pam thought about stretching an ellipse.

Pam: You can stretch these ellipses in any direction, and everything moves along. If you double the length of an axis, I think you'll double the distance between the foci, too.

a. Give an example that shows Pam's conjecture is not correct.

b. Can you stretch an ellipse to double the distance? Explain.

13. An ellipse is centered at (3, 5) and (10, 5) is one of its foci.

a. Find the coordinates of the other focus.

b. If the point (1, 17) is on the ellipse, find the length of the major and minor axes. Find an equation for the ellipse.

14. Show algebraically that the sum of the distances from (x, y) to (3, 16) and (3, −8) is the same as the sum of the distances from $(x - 3, y - 4)$ to (0, 12) and (0, −12).

15. **Standardized Test Prep** Which of the following is a hyperbola with foci at (3, 4) and (3, −4) and vertices 6 units apart?

A. $\frac{(x-3)^2}{9} - \frac{(y-4)^2}{16} = 1$ **B.** $\frac{(x-3)^2}{9} - \frac{y^2}{7} = 1$

C. $\frac{(y-4)^2}{9} - \frac{x^2}{16} = 1$ **D.** $\frac{y^2}{9} - \frac{(x-3)^2}{7} = 1$

Maintain Your Skills

16. An ellipse has center (2, −1) and one vertex is (6, −1).

a. Find the coordinates of the other vertex.

b. Find the foci if (2, 0) is one of the endpoints of the minor axis.

c. Find the foci if (2, 1) is one of the endpoints of the minor axis.

d. Find the foci if (2, 2) is one of the endpoints of the minor axis.

e. Find the foci if (2, 3) is one of the endpoints of the minor axis.

f. Find the foci if (2, 4) is one of the endpoints of the minor axis.

9. a. $5 \le x \le 17$

b. $-19 \le y \le -9$

10. a. $x \le -16$ or $x \ge -2$

b. $y =$ all real numbers

11. (4, 10) and (4, 0)

12. a. Answers may vary. Sample: Doubling the length of the major axis will more than double the distance between the foci.

b. Yes; doubling both axes at the same time will produce a dilated copy of the original ellipse, and the distance between the foci would then be doubled as well (along with all of the other scaling).

13. a. (−4, 5)

b. Length of major axis = 28; length of minor axis = $14\sqrt{3}$; $\frac{(x-3)^2}{196} + \frac{(y-5)^2}{147} = 1$

14. See back of book.

15. D

16. a. (−2, −1)

b. $(2 \pm \sqrt{15}, -1)$

c–f. See back of book.

On Your Own

EXERCISE 10 In this exercise, students develop some intuition about the values each term must have in an ellipse or hyperbola. It helps to explain why the hyperbola has the "gap" that an ellipse does not have: it is the area where the positive term would be less than 1, making the negative term impossible.

EXERCISE 11 Watch for students saying that the foci are horizontal: they need to recognize that the longer of the two axes contains the foci. Here, the second term (the y term) has the larger denominator, so the foci lie vertically along the major axis.

Maintain Your Skills

EXERCISE 16 Use caution with part (f): it looks similar to the other parts, but it is a contradiction because it implies that the minor axis is longer.

Additional Resources

PRINT RESOURCES
- Solution Manual
- Practice Workbook
- Assessment Resources
- Teaching Resources

TECHNOLOGY
- Interactive Textbook
- TeacherExpress CD-ROM
- ExamView CD-ROM
- PHSchool.com

Additional Practice

1. The graph of the following equation is a hyperbola.

$$\frac{(x-4)^2}{36} - \frac{(y-6)^2}{16} = 1$$

a. What is the center of the hyperbola?

b. Copy and complete the table on the right to find the nonnegative value y for each value x. Approximate your results to two decimal places.

x	y
6	
8	
10	
20	
40	
80	
160	
1000	

2. **a.** Is the graph of $64x^2 + 196y^2 - 128x - 1176y - 10{,}716 = 0$ a conic? If so, what kind is it?

b. Sketch the graph of the equation.

3. **a.** Is the graph of $9x^2 - 16y^2 - 36x + 160y - 508 = 0$ a conic? If so, what kind is it?

b. Sketch the graph of the equation.

4. Find the eccentricity of the ellipse given by each equation.

a. $\frac{x^2}{81} + \frac{y^2}{100} = 1$ **b.** $\frac{x^2}{81} + \frac{y^2}{9} = 1$ **c.** $\frac{x^2}{81} + \frac{y^2}{17} = 1$

5. The set of points 2 times as far from (2, 4) as they are from the graph of $x = -4$ is a hyperbola.

a. Find its center, vertices, and foci.

b. Find its eccentricity.

c. Sketch the graph of the hyperbola.

6. The set of points 3.5 times as far from (−1, −2) as they are from the graph of $y = 5$ is a hyperbola. Find its eccentricity.

7. A hyperbola has foci (7, 3) and (−5, 3). One endpoint of the major axis is (−2, 3).

a. Find the eccentricity of the hyperbola.

b. Find an equation of the hyperbola.

c. Sketch the graph of the hyperbola.

Practice: For Lesson 6.8, assign Exercises 1–3.

Lesson Overview

GOAL

- Identify the equations for the graphs of the conic sections, and sketch their graphs.

This lesson develops *eccentricity* as a measure of any conic section. Students begin by considering the locus definition of the parabola, and seeing that if they change the parameters of the definition slightly, they get curves that resemble conic sections. By analyzing this idea algebraically, they see that the curves *are* conic sections. The exercises reinforce this concept.

CHECK YOUR UNDERSTANDING
- Core: 1, 2, 3, 4, 5
- Optional: none
- Extension: 6, 7

MATERIALS
- geometry software
- graph paper
- graphing calculators
- Blackline Masters MC7, 6.6B, 6.9

HOMEWORK
- Core: 8, 9, 10, 11, 12, 14
- Optional: 15
- Extension: 13

VOCABULARY
- eccentricity

Launch

If you plan to use the dynamic geometry sketch described in the In-Class Experiment, consider your class's facility with programming in this type of environment. Some teachers are more comfortable programming the sketch themselves (following the detailed instructions in the TI-Nspire Technology Handbook p. 704) and then having students download the complete program from the teacher's computer. Other teachers assign the programming as homework and then give students time to check each other's programs (and help debug them) at the beginning of class. You might even have an interested student who will volunteer to write the program for everyone to download. You might choose to do this experiment as a class demonstration if you do not have the resources for students to run the program themselves. It is also possible to do this lesson without using geometry software, but you will need to do more sketching and students will have to take your word for how things behave as the ratio changes.

Even if you use the dynamic geometry software, Blackline Master MC7 may still be useful.

Explore

Review the locus definitions for the conics by using Blackline Master 6.6B on an overhead.

6.9 They Are All the Same

In Lesson 6.6, you saw each of the conics as a planar slice of an infinite double cone. The only difference between the different types of conic was the position of the slicing plane. This lesson shows another way to see the conics as in some sense the same. All of them come from a single class of equations.

The locus definition of a parabola is the set of points that are equidistant from a point F (the focus) and a line d (the directrix).

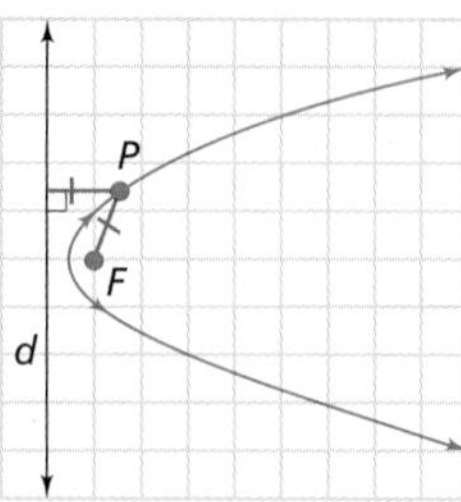

Another way to say that $PF = Pd$ is to say that $\frac{PF}{Pd} = 1$.

Pd means the distance from *P* to the line *d*, measured along the perpendicular from *P* to *d*.

Developing Habits of Mind

Experiment. Mathematicians like to tweak definitions. What would the curve look like if $\frac{PF}{Pd}$ were 2 instead of 1? What would it look like if the ratio were $\frac{1}{2}$? Experimenting with definitions like this often leads to new connections.

In-Class Experiment

You can set up an experiment in your geometry software in which you can control a slider and then produce the set of all points P so that the ratio of $\frac{PF}{Pd}$ is the length of the slider (a nonnegative real number). Here are some snapshots of such an experiment.

See the TI-Nspire Handbook on p. 704 for instructions on how to build the experiment.

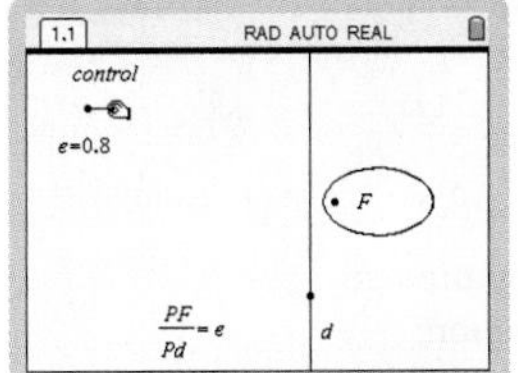

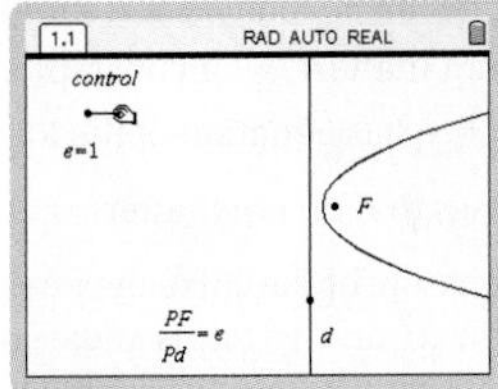

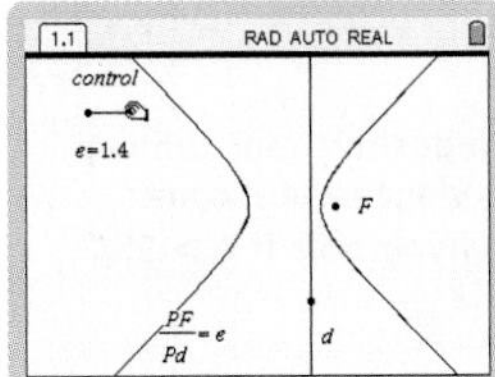

You know that when $e = 1$, the curve is a parabola. (Why?) But it sure looks as if other values of e produce conics, too. Before you see if this is so, experiment some with the sketch.

The letter e is used for the ratio for reasons that will become apparent in the exercises. But this has nothing to do with the constant e from Chapter 3.

1. For what values of e do the curves seem to be ellipses? Hyperbolas? Parabolas?
2. Experiment with the distance between the directrix and the focus. How does that affect things?

Just because something looks like a conic does not mean that it is a conic. To find out, you can use the algebra. Set up the situation on a coordinate plane. Then translate the locus definition into coordinates.

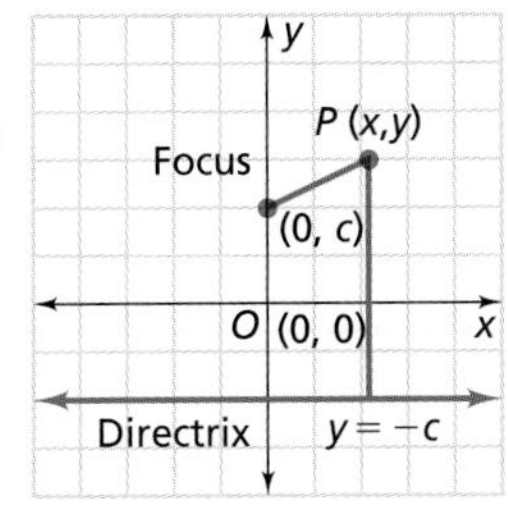

Suppose the focus is $(0, c)$ and the directrix has equation $y = -c$.

What is the point-tester? $P(x, y)$ is on the curve if and only if the distance from (x, y) to $(0, c)$ is e times the distance from (x, y) to the graph of $y = -c$.

$\frac{PF}{Pd} = e$ is the same as $PF = e \cdot Pd$.

But the distance from (x, y) to $(0, c)$ is $\sqrt{x^2 + (y - c)^2}$ and the distance from (x, y) to the graph of $y = -c$ is $|y - (-c)| = |y + c|$.

(Why?) So, the point tester is $\sqrt{x^2 + (y - c)^2} = e|y + c|$.

Answers

In-Class Experiment

1. Answers may vary. Samples: for $e = 2$, the curve is a hyperbola; for $e = \frac{1}{2}$, the curve is an ellipse; for $e = 1$, the curve is a parabola.
2. Check students' work.

In-Class Experiment

See the TI-Nspire Technology Handbook on page 704 for help building this dynamic geometry sketch.

PROBLEM 1 When the ratio e is 1, the curve is a parabola, because this situation matches the locus definition of the parabola. You are finding all the points that are equidistant from the focus and the directrix. If the ratio is less than one, the curve looks like an ellipse, and when it is greater than one, the curve looks like a hyperbola.

PROBLEM 2 The distance between the directrix and focus changes the location and center of the curves, but not their shape.

THEOREM 6.7 If you would like to give a proof of this theorem, it follows from Theorem 6.6. The coefficient of the x^2 term is 1 and the coefficient of the y^2 term is $1 - e^2$, so their product is $1 - e^2$. This quantity is positive if $e < 1$. If the product is positive, the curve is an ellipse. If $e = 1$, this quantity is zero, so the curve is a parabola. And finally, if $e > 1$, then $1 - e^2$ is negative and the curve is a hyperbola.

For Discussion

PROBLEM 3 Student responses will vary. It is not necessary to spend a great deal of time on this discussion, but your goal is to help students make associations that will help them remember how the eccentricity determines the conic section.

Wrap Up

Finish today's lesson by going over the core Check Your Understanding exercises. This should give students a deeper understanding of eccentricity and how it affects each of the conic sections.

Assessment Resources

Lesson Quiz 6.9

1. Find the eccentricity of the ellipse given by each equation.
   a. $\frac{x^2}{64} + \frac{y^2}{16} = 1$
   b. $\frac{x^2}{64} + \frac{y^2}{4} = 1$
   c. $\frac{x^2}{16} + \frac{y^2}{144} = 1$
   d. $\frac{x^2}{121} + \frac{y^2}{25} = 1$
2. The set of points twice as far from $(-5, 8)$ as they are from the graph of $y = 2$ is a hyperbola.
   a. Find its center.
   b. Find its eccentricity.
3. The set of points 3 times as far from $(18, 3)$ as they are from the graph of $x = 2$ is a hyperbola. Find its eccentricity.
4. A hyperbola has foci $(3, 8)$ and $(-5, 8)$. One endpoint of the major axis is $(-2, 8)$. Find the eccentricity of this hyperbola.
5. An ellipse has foci $(1, 4)$ and $(1, -6)$. One endpoint of the major axis is $(1, -8)$. Find the eccentricity of this ellipse.

This is fine as a point-tester. But you can simplify the equation in ways that will make it look familiar. Remember, thanks to Theorem 6.6, if you know that the equation is a polynomial in x and y of degree 2 set equal to 0, you only need the coefficients of x^2 and y^2 to tell which conic the graph will be.

$\sqrt{x^2 + (y - c)^2} = e\lvert y + c\rvert$	Square both sides.
$x^2 + (y - c)^2 = e^2(y + c)^2$	Expand.
$x^2 + y^2 - 2cy + c^2 = e^2y^2 + 2e^2cy + e^2c^2$	Cancel and simplify.
$x^2 + (1 - e^2)y^2 + \text{(things that do not matter)} = \text{a constant}$	

So, the set of all points P so that $\frac{PF}{Pd} = e$ has equation of the form

$$x^2 + (1 - e^2)y^2 + \text{(things that do not matter)} = 0$$

You know from Theorem 6.6 that the nature of the curve depends on the sign of the product of the coefficients of the x^2 and y^2 terms in the equation: $rt = 1 \cdot (1 - e^2) = 1 - e^2$. This leads to the following classification theorem.

Habits of Mind

Understand the process. $|x|^2 = x^2$ (Why?)

Theorem 6.7

Let F be a fixed point, d be a fixed line, and e be a positive real number. The set of points P such that $\frac{PF}{Pd} = e$ is a (possibly degenerate) conic. It is an ellipse if $e < 1$, a parabola if $e = 1$, and a hyperbola if $e > 1$.

Habits of Mind

Verify a conjecture. So, what the experiment suggested was true. The curve defined by $\frac{PF}{Pd} = e$ is always a conic.

Developing Habits of Mind

Make connections. Theorem 6.7 is one reason for the names *ellipse, parabola,* and *hyperbola.* If you check a dictionary you will discover that the words *ellipsis, parable,* and *hyperbole* have roughly these meanings in English.

- **ellipsis:** fall short—something is missing
- **parable:** fall beside—usually a story that illustrates a message
- **hyperbole:** fall beyond—an exaggeration

The theorem says that the curve is

- an ellipse if e "falls short" of 1.
- a parabola if e "falls beside" 1.
- a hyperbola e "falls beyond" 1.

In English, the symbol "..." is used to denote that something is missing, usually from a quotation and it is called an *ellipsis.* For example, "Now is the winter of our discontent..." means that the writer has cut this Shakespeare quotation before the end of the sentence.

For Discussion

3. Give an example of an English sentence that exhibits ellipsis, parable, or hyperbole.

Answers

For Discussion

3. Check students' answers.

Exercises *Practicing Habits of Mind*

Check Your Understanding

Some ellipses are flatter than others. One way to measure this is the **eccentricity,** the ratio of the distance between the foci, called the focal distance, to the distance between the vertices. Define the eccentricity by the ratio $\frac{c}{a}$.

1. Find the eccentricity of the ellipse given by each equation.

   a. $\frac{x^2}{25} + \frac{y^2}{16} = 1$ b. $\frac{x^2}{25} + \frac{y^2}{9} = 1$ c. $\frac{x^2}{25} + \frac{y^2}{24} = 1$ d. $\frac{x^2}{25} + \frac{y^2}{100} = 1$

2. Find an equation of an ellipse with center (8, 0), focus (6, 0), and eccentricity $\frac{1}{2}$.

3. The set of points P with the ratio $\frac{PF}{Pd} = \frac{1}{2}$ using focus $F(6, 0)$ and the y-axis as directrix forms a conic section. Find its equation. Find its center.

Remember...

For an ellipse, $a^2 = b^2 + c^2$ where a is half the major axis length, b is half the minor axis length, and c is half the distance between the foci.

The definition of eccentricity given above also applies to hyperbolas. The eccentricity is still the focal distance divided by the distance between the vertices, also expressed as $\frac{c}{a}$.

4. The set of points 1.5 times as far from (3, 5) as they are from the graph of $x = -2$ is a hyperbola.

   a. Find its center, vertices, and foci.

   b. Find its eccentricity.

   c. Sketch the graph of the hyperbola.

5. The set of points 3 times as far from (−3, 4) as they are from the graph of $y = -4$ is a hyperbola. Find its eccentricity.

6. **Take It Further** Given focus $F(0, 1)$ and directrix d given by $x = -1$. A conic section is defined by the points P with $\frac{PF}{Pd} = e$.

   a. If $e = 1$, how do you know that the conic is a parabola?

   b. If $e < 1$ show that the conic is an ellipse with eccentricity e.

   c. If $e > 1$ show that the conic is a hyperbola with eccentricity e.

Exercises

1. a. $\frac{3}{5}$ b. $\frac{4}{5}$ c. $\frac{1}{5}$ d. $\frac{\sqrt{3}}{2}$

2. $\frac{(x-8)^2}{16} + \frac{y^2}{12} = 1$

3. $\frac{(x-8)^2}{16} + \frac{y^2}{12} = 1$; (8, 0)

4. a. Center = (−6, 5); vertices = (−12, 5) and (0, 5); foci = (−15, 5) and (3, 5)

   b. $e = 1.5$

   c.

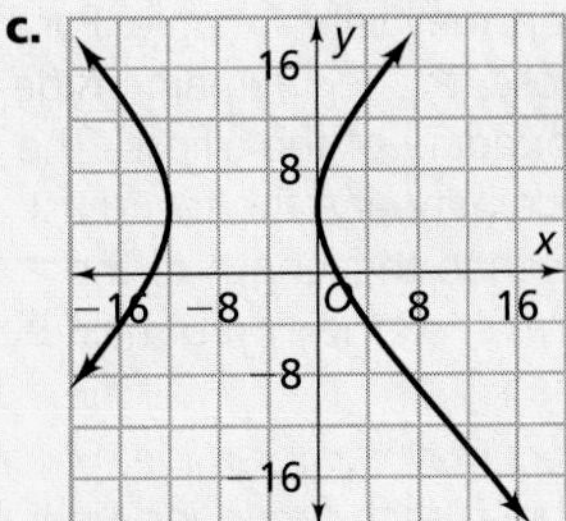

5. $e = 3$

6. See back of book.

Exercises

HOMEWORK

- Core: 8, 9, 10, 11, 12, 14
- Optional: 15
- Extension: 13

Check Your Understanding

EXERCISE 1 While this exercise does not ask students to graph the ellipses, you might ask students to do this to try and develop an intuition for eccentricity. For example, an ellipse with eccentricity 0.2 looks a lot like a circle.

EXERCISE 3 This is an important exercise: students should recognize this as the ellipse from Exercise 2. The eventual goal is for students to realize that eccentricity is a parallel definition to the ratio e defined in the lesson. Asking students to find the center gives them the chance to put the ellipse equation in the form most likely used in the previous exercise.

EXERCISE 4 As with the previous exercise, an important point is that the 1.5 shows up as both $\frac{PF}{Pd}$ and the eccentricity. Let students discover the relationship on their own; it is formalized in Exercise 6.

EXERCISE 6 There are other ways to do this exercise, such as locating the vertices and foci without finding the full equation. You can simplify much of the messy algebra here by using a generic numeric value and following it through. The steps are not much different from the steps in the prior exercises, but carrying the variable around makes it much more of a challenge.

This lesson has presented eccentricity in several different ways. Use Blackline Master 6.9 to review the different interpretations and show how they are related.

EXERCISE 7 shows another way in which ellipses and parabolas are related. One side route to take here is to talk about the path an object follows when tossed in the air. Typically you say the path is a parabola, but actually it is an ellipse: the same as the orbit of the moon, for example. But since you only see a far corner of an ellipse with a very high eccentricity, it behaves almost exactly like a parabola.

On Your Own

EXERCISE 8 With the geometric model presented in the lesson, there is no conic for $e = 0$. It shrinks to a point. This other eccentricity model helps deal with the situation. On the flip side, there is no way to deal with $\frac{c}{a} = 1$ for a parabola, since a parabola has only one focus. The geometric model helps deal with that situation. The key idea here is that circles and parabolas are special/more rare than ellipses and hyperbolas. If you randomly cut a conic, you are far more likely to get an ellipse or hyperbola.

EXERCISE 10 The higher the eccentricity, the wider the branching in the hyperbola. The asymptotes of this hyperbola have slopes $\pm\sqrt{35}$.

EXERCISE 12 The solution here presents an alternate method that some students may prefer, especially for those who are particularly strong at proportional reasoning.

EXERCISE 13 can help some students cement the idea that they can think of all the conics as coming from one core equation. This is also a good exercise to assign if you used geometric software to model the conics.

7. Take It Further Graph the ellipse with a graphing window of $-5 \le x \le 5$, $-5 \le y \le 5$.

$$\frac{x^2}{49} + \frac{(y - 100)^2}{10{,}000} = 1$$

a. What do you notice?

b. Find another ellipse that behaves similarly.

On Your Own

8. What is the eccentricity of a circle? Explain.

9. a. Explain why the eccentricity of an ellipse must always be less than 1.

b. Explain why the eccentricity of a hyperbola must always be greater than 1.

10. A hyperbola has foci $(5, 5)$ and $(-7, 5)$. One endpoint of the major axis is $(-2, 5)$.

a. Find an eccentricity of this hyperbola.

b. Find an equation of the hyperbola.

c. Sketch the graph of the hyperbola.

11. Which of these is an equation of an ellipse?

A. $4x^2 + 1 = 9y^2$

B. $4x + 6y + x^2 - y^2 = 36$

C. $4x^2 + 9y + 8x - 36 = 0$

D. $-16x + 8y + 4x^2 + 8y^2 - 25 = 0$

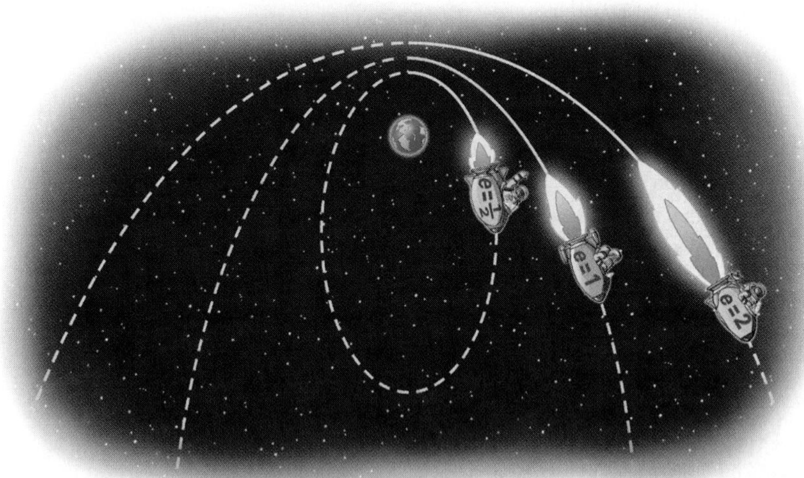

Answers

7.

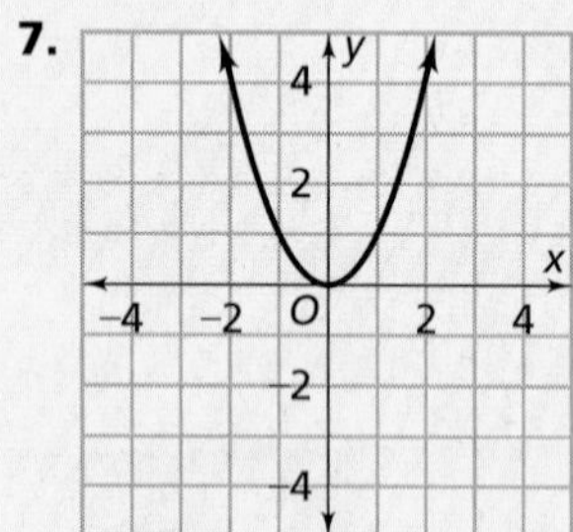

a. The graph looks very similar to $y = x^2$.

b. Check students' work. The ellipse must have a very high eccentricity and a vertex at $(0, 0)$.

8. 0; the two foci of an ellipse come together to the same point to form a circle. Based on the definition of eccentricity, with the numerator equal to the distance between the foci, it must be equal to zero since there is no distance between the foci of a circle.

9. a. Answers may vary. Sample: For an ellipse, the foci remain inside the boundary of the ellipse. The distance between the foci must be less than the length of the major axis, so their ratio must be less than 1.

b. Answers may vary. Sample: For a hyperbola, each focus lies within its branch. The distance from one vertex to the other must be less than the distance from one focus to the other. Therefore the ratio of the distances must be greater than 1.

10. a. $e = 6$

b. $\frac{(x + 1)^2}{1} - \frac{(y - 5)^2}{35} = 1$

c.

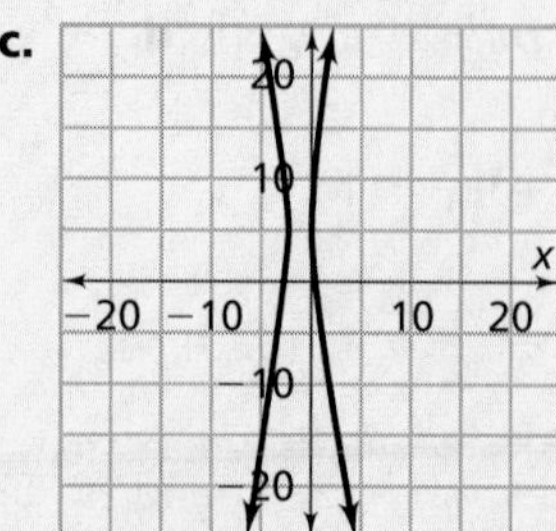

11. D

12. The set of points that are twice as far from (3, 7) as they are from the y-axis is a hyperbola. Find the other focus of this hyperbola.

13. **Take It Further** As seen in the lesson, fix focus point F and directrix line d, then vary the ratio $\frac{PF}{Pd}$ to produce different conic sections. One focus of the conic stays in place. But ellipses and hyperbolas have two foci: what happens to the other focus?

    a. As the ratio $\frac{PF}{Pd}$ approaches zero, what does the other focus move toward?

    b. As the ratio $\frac{PF}{Pd}$ gets larger toward 1, what does the other focus move toward?

    c. What happens when the ratio equals 1?

    d. As the ratio continues to grow, what does the other focus move toward?

14. **Standardized Test Prep** Which of the following could be the eccentricity of an ellipse with a focus at (5, 0), vertex at (7, 0), and directrix $x = 12$?

    A. $\frac{2}{5}$ B. $\frac{5}{7}$ C. $\frac{5}{12}$ D. $\frac{7}{12}$

Go Online PHSchool.com

For additional practice, go to Web Code: bga-0609

Maintain Your Skills

15. The orbit of every planet is an ellipse. Each elliptical orbit has the sun as one focus and some eccentricity e. This table gives the length of the major axis and the eccentricity for each planet's orbit.

Planet	Major Axis Length (million km)	Eccentricity e
Mercury	115.8	0.2056
Venus	216.4	0.0068
Earth	299.2	0.0167
Mars	455.9	0.0934
Jupiter	1556.8	0.0484
Saturn	2853.5	0.0542
Uranus	5741.9	0.0472
Neptune	8996.5	0.0086

a. Which planet's orbit is most like a circle? the least like a circle?

b. For each planet, determine how far away the sun is from the center of the planet's orbit.

Kepler proved this fact about the planets in the early 17th Century. Orbits of comets may be parabolic or even hyperbolic.

Remember...

The sun is a focus of the ellipse. The eccentricity is known.

Additional Resources

PRINT RESOURCES
- Solution Manual
- Practice Workbook
- Assessment Resources
- Teaching Resources

TECHNOLOGY
- Interactive Textbook
- TeacherExpress CD-ROM
- ExamView CD-ROM
- PHSchool.com

Additional Practice

1. The graph of the following equation is a hyperbola.

$$\frac{(x-4)^2}{36} - \frac{(y-6)^2}{16} = 1$$

   a. What is the center of the hyperbola?

   b. Copy and complete the table on the right to find the nonnegative value y for each value x. Approximate your results to two decimal places.

x	y
6	
8	
10	
20	
40	
80	
160	
1000	

2. a. Is the graph of $64x^2 + 196y^2 - 128x - 1176y - 10{,}716 = 0$ a conic? If so, what kind is it?

   b. Sketch the graph of the equation.

3. a. Is the graph of $9x^2 - 16y^2 - 36x + 160y - 508 = 0$ a conic? If so, what kind is it?

   b. Sketch the graph of the equation.

4. Find the eccentricity of the ellipse given by each equation.

   a. $\frac{x^2}{81} + \frac{y^2}{100} = 1$ b. $\frac{x^2}{81} + \frac{y^2}{9} = 1$ c. $\frac{x^2}{81} + \frac{y^2}{17} = 1$

5. The set of points 2 times as far from (2, 4) as they are from the graph of $x = -4$ is a hyperbola.

   a. Find its center, vertices, and foci.

   b. Find its eccentricity.

   c. Sketch the graph of the hyperbola.

6. The set of points 3.5 times as far from (−1, −2) as they are from the graph of $y = 5$ is a hyperbola. Find its eccentricity.

7. A hyperbola has foci (7, 3) and (−5, 3). One endpoint of the major axis is (−2, 3).

   a. Find the eccentricity of the hyperbola.

   b. Find an equation of the hyperbola.

   c. Sketch the graph of the hyperbola.

Practice: For Lesson 6.9, assign Exercises 4–7.

12. (−5, 7)

13. a. The second focus shrinks toward the first focus.

b. The second focus moves further and further away from the first focus along the major axis.

c. When $\frac{PF}{Pd} = 1$, the graph is a parabola, and there is no second focus.

d. When $\frac{PF}{Pd} > 1$, the graph is a hyperbola and the other focus can be found inside the other branch of the hyperbola.

14. A

15. a. Venus has the most circular orbit; Mercury has the least circular orbit.

b.

Planet	Sun to Orbit Center (million km)
Mercury	11.904
Venus	0.736
Earth	2.498
Mars	21.291
Jupiter	37.675
Saturn	77.330
Uranus	135.509
Neptune	38.685

Mathematical Reflections

EXERCISES 6–8 At the start of the investigation, you may have assigned these as Questions 1–3 for students to think and write about.

In this investigation, you sliced a cone to get a conic section—a circle, an ellipse, a parabola, or a hyperbola. You described each conic section verbally as a locus of points, or algebraically by an equation. Then, given an equation, you described its graph as a conic section. The following questions will help you summarize what you have learned.

1. Determine an equation (in the form $y = a(x - h)^2 + k$) for the parabola having focus (1, 2) and directrix the x-axis.
2. Find the center, foci, and the lengths of the major and minor axes of the ellipse having equation $16x^2 - 64x + 25y^2 + 50y = 311$.
3. We know from Theorem 6.6 that the graph of the equation $rx^2 + ty^2 + ux + vy + w = 0$ is a conic. In order for the conic to be a circle, what must be the relationship between r and t?
4. **a.** In order for the graph of the equation $2x^2 + cy^2 + 4x + 4cy + f = 0$ to be an ellipse, what must be true about the value of c?
   b. In order for the graph of the equation $2x^2 + cy^2 + 4x + 4cy + f = 0$ to be a nondegenerate ellipse, what must be true about the value of f?
5. Explain how you know that the graph of the equation $x^2 + y^2 - 2x + 4y + 5 = 0$ is a degenerate conic.
6. How do you slice an infinite double cone with a plane to get a parabola?
7. What is the locus definition of a hyperbola?
8. What kind of conic section do you get when you graph $x^2 + 16y^2 - 8x + 64y + 64 = 0$? How can you identify the conic section from its equation?

Vocabulary

In this investigation, you learned these terms. Make sure you understand what each one means and how to use it.

- **apex**
- **axis**
- **conic sections**
- **Dandelin sphere**
- **directrix**
- **eccentricity**
- **ellipse**
- **focus, foci**
- **generator**
- **hyperbola**
- **locus**
- **major axis**
- **minor axis**
- **parabola**
- **vertex**

Answers

Mathematical Reflections

1. $y = \frac{1}{4}(x - 1)^2 + 1$
2. Center $= (2, -1)$; foci $= (-1, -1)$ and $(5, -1)$; length of major axis: 10; length of minor axis: 8
3. $r = t \neq 0$
4. **a.** $c > 0$ and $c \neq 2$
   b. $f < 2 + 4c$
5. After completing the square to express the equation in the form $\frac{(x-h)^2}{a^2} + \frac{(y-k)^2}{b^2} = 1$, the right side of the equation is equal to zero. In other words, there is only one solution to the equation, the point $(1, -2)$.
6. Slice the double cone so that the plane is parallel to the generator of the cone and intersects only one branch of the cone.
7. A hyperbola is the set of points such that the absolute value of the difference of the distances from two fixed points (the foci) is constant.
8. It is an ellipse, because the x^2 and y^2 terms both have non-zero coefficients that have the same sign.

Mid-Chapter Test

1. C **2.** B **3.** D **4.** B **5.** A

6. **a.** $y = \frac{1}{2}x - \frac{1}{2}$
   b. $y = -\frac{2}{5}x - \frac{3}{5}$
   c. $\left(-\frac{1}{9}, -\frac{4}{9}\right)$

Mid-Chapter Test

Go Online PHSchool.com

For a mid-chapter test, go to Web Code: bga-0652

Multiple Choice

1. The graph of $x^2 + y^2 = 53$ is a circle. Determine which point does not lie on the circle.

   A. $(-1, 2\sqrt{13})$ B. $(-2, 7)$

   C. $(-5, 3)$ D. $(\sqrt{8}, 3\sqrt{5})$

2. Find the equation of the line that represents the set of points that are equidistant from $(0, 6)$ and $(12, 2)$.

   A. $y = -\frac{1}{3}x + 9$ B. $y = 3x - 14$

   C. $y = -3x + \frac{9}{3}$ D. $y = \frac{1}{3}x + \frac{4}{3}$

3. Find an equation of a parabola with focus $(0, 8)$ and directrix $y = -8$.

   A. $y = -\frac{1}{8}x^2$ B. $y = \frac{1}{16}x^2$

   C. $y = \frac{1}{8}x^2$ D. $y = \frac{1}{32}x^2$

4. The graph of $9x^2 - 36x - 4y^2 + 40y - 100 = 0$ is a conic. Determine the type of conic.

   A. circle B. hyperbola

   C. ellipse D. parabola

5. Find the eccentricity of the ellipse with equation $\frac{x^2}{100} + \frac{y^2}{36} = 1$.

   A. $\frac{4}{5}$ B. $\frac{1}{8}$ C. $\frac{2}{5}$ D. $\frac{1}{6}$

Open Response

6. A triangle has vertices at $A(-5, 2)$, $B(-1, -6)$, and $C(3, 4)$.
   a. Find the perpendicular bisector of $\overline{AB}$.
   b. Find the perpendicular bisector of $\overline{BC}$.
   c. Find the point of intersection of the two perpendicular bisectors.

7. The graph of the equation $x^2 + y^2 - 4x + 12y + 24 = 0$ is a circle.
   a. Find the center and radius of the circle.
   b. Sketch the graph of the circle.

8. The graph of $9x^2 - 16y^2 = 144$ is a hyperbola.
   a. Find the intercepts.
   b. Find the foci.
   c. Sketch the graph of the hyperbola, and label the intercepts and foci.

9. An ellipse is centered at $(1, 2)$ with one of its foci at $(13, 2)$ and one of its vertices at $(14, 2)$.
   a. Find the coordinates of the other focus.
   b. Write an equation of the ellipse.
   c. Sketch the graph of the ellipse.

10. Find the coordinates of the foci of the ellipse with equation $51x^2 + 100y^2 + 612x - 800y - 1664 = 0$.

11. The set of points twice as far from the point $(4, 6)$ as from the line $x = -2$ is a hyperbola.
    a. Find the center, foci, and vertices.
    b. Find the eccentricity.
    c. Sketch the graph of the hyperbola.

Mid-Chapter Test

Assessment Resources

Mid-Chapter Test **page 1 of 2**

Multiple Choice

1. The graph of $x^2 + y^2 - 6x + 10y + 18 = 0$ is a circle. Find the radius of the circle.

   A. $3\sqrt{2}$ B. 4 C. 3 D. $2\sqrt{13}$

2. Find the signed power of point $P(1, -1)$ with respect to the circle with equation $(x + 2)^2 + (y - 3)^2 = 49$.

   A. -24 B. -25 C. $2\sqrt{6}$ D. 25

3. The graph of the following equation is a hyperbola.

   $$\frac{x^2}{25} - \frac{y^2}{144} = 1$$

   Find the coordinates of the foci.

   A. $(0, 13), (0, -13)$ B. $(\sqrt{119}, 0), (-\sqrt{119}, 0)$

   C. $(0, 12), (0, -12)$ D. $(13, 0), (-13, 0)$

4. Find the equation of the parabola with focus $(0, -6)$ and directrix $y = 6$.

   A. $x^2 = -24y$ B. $y = 24x^2$ C. $y = -\frac{1}{2}x^2$ D. $y = -\frac{1}{6}x^2$

5. Find the eccentricity of the ellipse with equation $\frac{x^2}{25} + \frac{y^2}{75} = 1$.

   A. $\sqrt{3}$ B. $\frac{\sqrt{6}}{2}$ C. $\frac{2}{3}$ D. $\frac{\sqrt{6}}{3}$

Open Response

6. Find the equation of the line, in the form $y = Ax + B$, that represents the set of points that are equidistant from $(-3, 5)$ and $(1, -3)$.

7. The graph of the equation $9x^2 - 25y^2 = 225$ is a hyperbola. Find the foci.

8. An ellipse has foci $(-2, -4)$ and $(8, -4)$. One endpoint of the major axis is $(10, -4)$. Find an equation for this ellipse.

Also available: Form B

7. a. Center: $(2, -6)$; radius: 4

b.

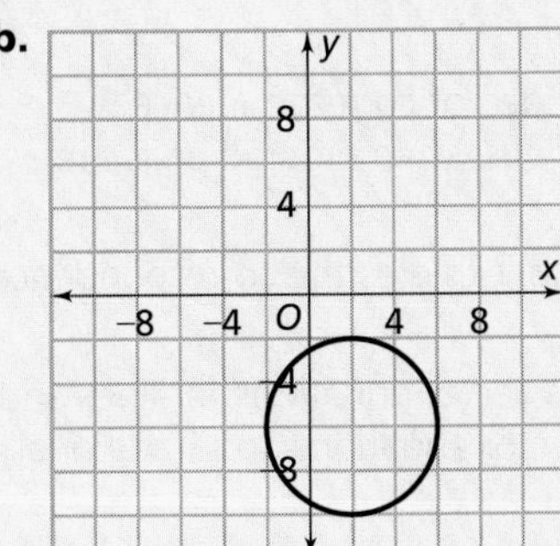

8. a. No y-intercepts; x-intercepts: $(-4, 0)$, $(4, 0)$

b. $(-5, 0)$, $(5, 0)$

c.

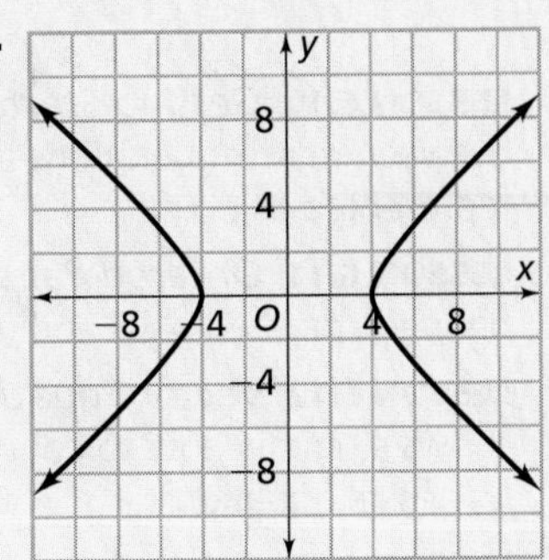

9. a. $(-11, 2)$

b. $\frac{(x - 1)^2}{169} + \frac{(y - 2)^2}{25} = 1$

c.

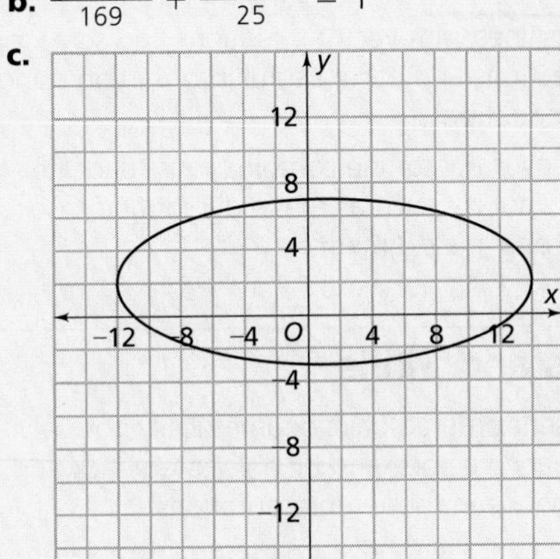

10. $(1, 4)$ and $(-13, 4)$

11. a. Center: $(-4, 6)$; vertices: $(-8, 6)$, $(0, 6)$; foci: $(-12, 6)$, $(4, 6)$

b. $e = 2$

c. See back of book.

Investigation Overview

This investigation applies matrix algebra to geometry, in particular, the algebra of ordered pairs, or *vectors*, using the definitions of addition and scalar multiplication for matrices of any size.

In some sense, this is an extension of the traditional analytic geometry of Descartes. However, it is also more. Matrix notation makes it easier to apply algebra to geometry than traditional analytic geometry. This is especially noticeable in three (and higher) dimensions; the traditional notation grows more complex while matrix notation does not. However, only occasional exercises in this investigation deal with three dimensions. It mostly uses the more familiar two dimensions to make students comfortable using matrix ideas in geometry. (Also, there are occasional exercises relating this approach to the geometric representation of complex numbers seen in Chapter 2.)

The overarching goal of this investigation is to continue to strengthen in the student's mind the interplay between algebra and geometry. In this case, the connection is between matrix algebra and geometry. A second goal is to continue to develop the students' facility and comfort with matrix algebra. In particular, they should begin to think of matrices, especially ordered pairs, as *objects in themselves* rather than a mere bookkeeping device to record several variables (mostly x and y in this investigation) at the same time.

You may wish to assign Questions 1–3 for students to think and write about during the investigation.

Learning Goals

- Interpret sums and scalar multiples of ordered pairs geometrically.
- Express lines with vector equations and solve for intersections and other useful information using these equations.
- Use convex and affine combinations to locate specific points, such as the midpoint and trisection points of a line segment.

Habits and Skills

- Represent ordered pairs geometrically both as points and vectors, and be able to go back and forth between these representations.
- Reason logically to prove geometry theorems using vector methods.
- Look at geometric figures in a new way to see vector relationships.

Vector Algebra and Geometry

In *Vector Algebra and Geometry*, you will study the simple but immensely useful notion of a vector. A vector, which you will define in terms of size and direction, has numerous applications in mathematics and the physical sciences. For geometry, vectors provide another vehicle for proof.

By the end of this investigation, you will be able to answer questions like these.

1. How can you interpret the matrix operations of sum and scalar product geometrically?
2. Why might it be useful to write an equation of a line in vector form?
3. How can you use vectors to prove that the medians of a triangle are concurrent?

You will learn how to

- interpret sums and scalar multiples of ordered pairs geometrically
- express lines with vector equations and solve for intersections and other useful information using these equations
- use convex and affine combinations to locate specific points, such as the midpoint and trisection points of a line segment

You will develop these habits and skills:

- Represent ordered pairs geometrically both as points and vectors, and be able to go back and forth between these representations.
- Reason logically to prove geometry theorems using vector methods.
- Look at geometric figures in a new way to see vector relationships.

A crosswind landing (Pilots refer to it as "crabbing.") vividly illustrates the vector effects of strong winds on the heading of even a large airliner.

Investigation Road Map

LESSON 6.10, *Getting Started,* previews the key idea of correspondence between matrix operations and geometric operations when ordered pairs are represented as points.

LESSON 6.11, *Ordered Pairs, Points, and Vectors,* explores the correspondence between ordered pairs and (geometric) vectors.

LESSON 6.12, *Vector Equations of Lines,* defines vector equations for lines and shows students how to convert between these vector equations and traditional Cartesian equations.

LESSON 6.13, *Affine Combinations and Geometry,* introduces the important expression $(1 - k)P + kQ$, the affine combination of points P and Q, and uses matrix algebra to prove various classical geometry theorems.

6.10 Getting Started

Ordered pairs represent points in the coordinate plane. You first learned to calculate with points in CME Project *Geometry*. But you can also think about ordered pairs as a special type of matrix. Calculations you perform on matrices such as $2U$, $U + V$, and $V - 3U$ should have geometric meaning as well. In this investigation, you will learn how to go back and forth between the algebra and geometry of ordered pairs.

Use graph paper on these exercises. You need to plot the points accurately to see some of the patterns.

Habits of Mind

Extend the process. These ideas can also be applied to ordered triples for three dimensions, or any number of dimensions.

For You to Explore

1. Let $U = (3, 1)$, $V = (2, 4)$. On graph paper, plot the points $(0, 0)$, U, V, and $U + V$. Connect the points with line segments. What kind of figure is it? Will a different choice for U and V produce a different kind of figure?

2. Let $U = (1, 0)$ and $V = (0, 1)$. Plot the following points, labeling each one. For each part, use a clean sheet of graph paper.
   a. $U,\ 2U,\ 3U,\ (-1)U,\ (-3)U$
   b. $V,\ V + U,\ V + 2U,\ V + 3U,\ V + (-1)U,\ V - 3U$
   c. $U,\ U + V,\ U + 2V,\ U + 3V,\ U + (-1)V,\ U - 3V$
   d. $U,\ V,\ \frac{U + V}{2},\ \frac{1}{4}U + \frac{3}{4}V,\ \frac{2}{3}U + \frac{1}{3}V$
   e. $U,\ V,\ -U + 2V,\ -\frac{1}{2}U + \frac{3}{2}V,\ 2U - V,\ 1.5U - 0.5V$
   f. $jU + kV$ where j, k are all integer pairs with $j = 0, 1, 2, 3$ and $k = 0, 1, 2, 3$
   g. Explain why you can represent any point on the plane as $aU + bV$ for some scalars a and b.

3. Do Exercise 2, parts (a) through (e), over again, but now let $U = (3, 2)$ and $V = (-1, 3)$. Do the patterns you observed in that exercise continue to hold? What are the patterns?

4. Let $U = (1, 0)$, $V = (0, 1)$, and $W = (-1, -1)$. Plot all the following on the same piece of graph paper.
   a. The triangle with corners U, V, W
   b. The point $\frac{U + V + W}{3}$
   c. The line segment from U to $\frac{V + W}{2}$
   d. The line segment from V to $\frac{U + W}{2}$
   e. The line segment from W to $\frac{U + V}{2}$
   f. $\frac{1}{2}U + \frac{1}{4}V + \frac{1}{4}W,\ \frac{1}{4}U + \frac{1}{2}V + \frac{1}{4}W$

Remember...

A scalar is a real number. Multiplying by a scalar is different from multiplying by a matrix.

Answers

For You to Explore

1.

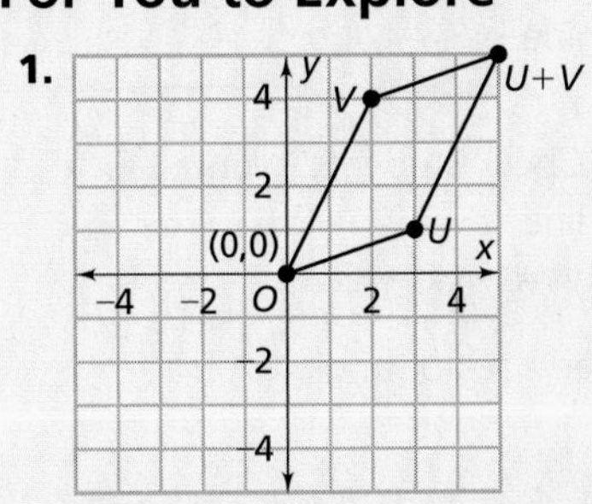

This is a graph of a parallelogram. If $\overline{OU}$ and $\overline{OV}$ are perpendicular, the resulting figure is a rectangle. If U, V, and $(0, 0)$ are collinear, the resulting figure is a line segment.

2. a.

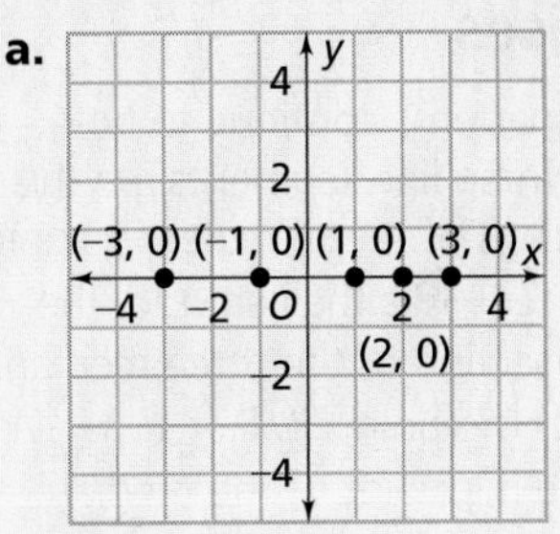

b–g. See back of book.

3–4. See back of book.

Lesson Overview

GOAL

- Warm up to the ideas of the investigation.

This Getting Started lesson introduces some of the key ideas of the investigation without formalizing the purpose or the conclusions. Students use their prior knowledge that every ordered pair represents a point. They plot many points with matrix algebra notation and begin to get a sense of how the algebraic combinations relate to positions on the plane.

FOR YOU TO EXPLORE
- Core: 1, 2, 3, 4
- Optional: none

MATERIALS
- graph paper
- graphing calculators
- Blackline Master MC7

HOMEWORK
- Core: 5, 6, 7, 8
- Optional: 9

VOCABULARY
- scalar

Launch

Have the students start on the core For You to Explore problems after reading the introduction.

Explore

You may want to have some students present their solutions to some of the problems. As students are working, ask them if they have identified any patterns. Ask them where they think the investigation will go with these patterns.

You may wish to use the Blackline Master MC7 on an overhead or to provide copies for students to use in this lesson.

For You to Explore

PROBLEM 1 In Lesson 6.3, students used slope and length relationships to prove that this figure is a parallelogram.

PROBLEM 2 Parts (c) through (e) are important to understanding the vector equation of a line. If you are short on discussion time, focus on these parts.

BACKGROUND FOR TEACHER The vectors (1, 0) and (0, 1) form a basis in two dimensions. If you can show that you can build the vectors (1, 0) and (0, 1), then you can build any (*p*, *q*). The same concept applies in any number of dimensions.

PROBLEM 3 You may wish to limit how much of Problem 2 the students do over. Have them concentrate on observing and describing the patterns this time. One pattern they may notice is that the line of part (b) is parallel to the line of part (a), which will help with the vector equation of a line.

Wrap Up

Students have seen transformations in each of their previous CME Project courses. They have seen the algebra of points before in CME Project *Geometry*, along with the vector equation of a line. Take some time today to see how much students remember from previous courses and to assess the depth of coverage they will need on upcoming topics.

Exercises

HOMEWORK
- Core: 5, 6, 7, 8
- Optional: 9

On Your Own

EXERCISE 6 gives students the equation of a line in vector form. After plotting the points that result from a few different values of t, students should see that they are collinear. Since they have the coordinates of several points on this line, they should not have trouble finding its equation.

EXERCISE 7 Students should see that this line is parallel to the line from Exercise 6. It is a dilation with scale factor 2, centered at the origin, which is another way to explain why the slope is unchanged but the y-intercept doubles.

Maintain Your Skills

EXERCISE 9 Multiplication by one of the matrices of the form $\begin{pmatrix} a & 0 \\ 0 & a \end{pmatrix}$ has the effect of scaling a point by a.

Exercises *Practicing Habits of Mind*

On Your Own

5. Let U and V be as in Exercise 4. Now let $W = (2, 5)$. Repeat the calculations of Exercise 4. Do the patterns you observed in that exercise continue to hold?

6. Consider the infinite set of points $(1, 2) + t(2, -1)$. where t is any real number.

a. Plot a few of these points for different values of t.

b. The set of points determines a geometric object. Find the object.

c. Find an equation for this geometric object in terms of x and y.

7. Consider the infinite set of points $2((1, 2) + t(2, -1))$, where t is any real number.

a. Plot a few of these points for different values of t.

b. The set of points determines a geometric object. Find the object.

c. Find an equation for this geometric object in terms of x and y.

8. Consider the quadrilateral at the right.

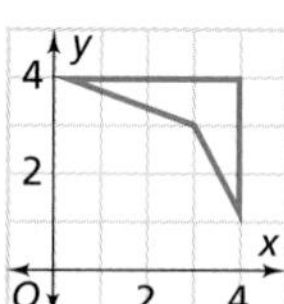

a. If you scale all the points on the perimeter of the figure by $\frac{1}{2}$, what figure do you get? Draw it on graph paper.

b. If, instead, you scale all the points by -1, you get another figure. Sketch the figure.

c. Draw the figure which, if you scale it by a factor of 2, you get the quadrilateral in the diagram.

Remember...

Scaling a matrix M by k means multiplying each coordinate by k, to get kM. For example, scaling the ordered pair (2, 3) by $\frac{1}{2}$, produces the ordered pair $\left(1, \frac{3}{2}\right)$.

Maintain Your Skills

9. Calculate the result of each matrix multiplication.

a. $\begin{pmatrix} 3 & 0 \\ 0 & 3 \end{pmatrix}\begin{pmatrix} 5 \\ 7 \end{pmatrix}$ **b.** $\begin{pmatrix} -2 & 0 \\ 0 & -2 \end{pmatrix}\begin{pmatrix} 5 \\ 7 \end{pmatrix}$ **c.** $\begin{pmatrix} 10 & 0 \\ 0 & 10 \end{pmatrix}\begin{pmatrix} 2 \\ -9 \end{pmatrix}$ **d.** $\begin{pmatrix} 1 & 0 \\ 0 & 1 \end{pmatrix}\begin{pmatrix} 13 \\ -6 \end{pmatrix}$

e. Describe the effect of multiplying any 2×1 matrix by the matrix $\begin{pmatrix} a & 0 \\ 0 & a \end{pmatrix}$.

Answers

Exercises

5. The patterns continue to hold. The three line segments are the medians of the triangle. The point $\frac{U + V + W}{3}$ is the centroid, the intersection of the three median lines. The point $\frac{1}{2}U + \frac{1}{4}V + \frac{1}{4}W$ is the midpoint of the median line from U to $\frac{V + W}{2}$. The point $\frac{1}{4}U + \frac{1}{2}V + \frac{1}{4}W$ is the midpoint of the median line from V to $\frac{U + W}{2}$.

6. a. Check students' work.
b. line
c. $y = -\frac{1}{2}x + \frac{5}{2}$

7. a. Check students' work.
b. line
c. $y = -\frac{1}{2}x + 5$

8–9. See back of book.

6.11 Ordered Pairs, Points, and Vectors

There is a strong tie between algebra and geometry. In CME Project *Geometry*, you applied algebra to geometry by thinking of points as ordered pairs. Ordered pairs are just a special type of matrix, so you can apply the algebra of matrices to geometric concepts.

The main operations you learned for matrices are addition, multiplication, and scalar multiplication. You will see how to represent these operations geometrically when the matrices are ordered pairs.

Remember...

You first learned about matrices in CME Project *Algebra 2*.

Adding Points

To add two points, $A(a, b)$ and $D(c, d)$ it makes sense to simply add them the way you add two matrices—find the sum of each pair of corresponding coordinates. This gives you the sum $A + D = (a + c, b + d)$. If you look at a picture that shows A, D, $A + D$, and the origin, you can see that these four points are the vertices of a parallelogram. The sum $A + D$ completes the parallelogram determined by O, A, and D.

You can also think of A as a point and D as a displacement. Then a point plus a vector equals a point.

Remember...

In Lesson 6.3, you proved that this figure is a parallelogram.

For You to Do

A vector PQ is an arrow with tail at point P and head at point Q. Call it $\overrightarrow{PQ}$. Two vectors are equivalent if they have the same displacement $D = (c, d)$. Or they have the same displacement if they move horizontally c units and vertically d units.

1. If $\overrightarrow{AB}$ has displacement $(2, 3)$ and $A = (1, -1)$, what is B? Draw a picture, or use graph paper.
2. If $\overrightarrow{CD}$ has displacement $(2, 3)$ and $D = (-2, 5)$, what is C?
3. If $P = (0, 3)$ and $Q = (1, -2)$, find the displacement of $\overrightarrow{PQ}$. Find the displacement of $\overrightarrow{QP}$.
4. Let

$$O = (0, 0),\quad A = (1, 3),\quad B = (3, 2),\quad C = (5, 1)$$

Determine which of the following vectors are equivalent.

$$\overrightarrow{OA},\ \overrightarrow{OB},\ \overrightarrow{OC},\ \overrightarrow{AB},\ \overrightarrow{AC},\ \overrightarrow{BC}$$

Lesson Overview

GOAL

- Interpret sums and scalar multiples of ordered pairs geometrically.

You can think of an ordered pair of real numbers (a, b) as a point (a location in the coordinate plane) and as a vector (an arrow from the origin to that point). You can also think of it as a characteristic of the infinitely many vectors that are all equivalent to (a, b)—all the vectors that go over a and up b from wherever they start. This means that you are thinking of (a, b) as representing a displacement. It is the interplay of these representations that actually provides the power.

Students have already seen the same geometric interpretations of addition and scalar multiplication in Chapter 2, and in CME Project *Geometry* and *Algebra 2*. The goal here is for the students to practice using all the representations and to talk clearly about them.

CHECK YOUR UNDERSTANDING

- Core: 1, 3, 4, 5
- Optional: 2

MATERIALS

- graph paper
- graphing calculators
- Blackline Master MC7

HOMEWORK

- Core: 6, 7, 10, 12, 13
- Optional: 8, 11
- Extension: 9

VOCABULARY

- dilation
- head and tail of a vector
- scaling
- vector, $\overrightarrow{AB}$

Launch

Begin today's lesson with the For You to Do on the first page of the lesson. You may wish to use Blackline Master MC7 on an overhead throughout the presentation of the lesson.

For You to Do

1. (3, 2)
2. (−4, 2)
3. (1, −5) and (−1, 5)
4. $\overrightarrow{AB}$ and $\overrightarrow{BC}$

Explore

For Discussion

PROBLEM 5 The equations $B = A + D$, $A = B - D$ and are all correct. $D = B - A$ is the "right" equation if you are testing different vectors for equivalence, because they are equivalent if they have the same displacement. $B = A + D$ is the "right" equation if you are modeling addition. $A = B - D$ is the "right" equation if you are modeling subtraction. You can summarize $D = B - A$ with a little ditty, "Head minus tail gives displacement."

Developing Habits of Mind

Think about it more than one way. If $\overrightarrow{AB}$ and $\overrightarrow{PQ}$ have the same displacement, are they the same vector or different vectors?

In this course, they are considered to be different vectors but equivalent.

Other people say they are the same vector, because to them it is the displacement that is actually the vector. In this view, $\overrightarrow{AB}$ and $\overrightarrow{PQ}$ are just different pictures of the same thing.

You can think of it whichever way works best for you. Vectors are meant to help you locate points. So long as you have a mental picture that allows you to start with ordered pairs A and D and to get to ordered pair $A + D$, you are all set.

There is one thing everyone agrees on: If you label a vector by a single ordered pair D, that pair represents the displacement. If you label a vector by two ordered pairs A and B, they are the points at the tail and head.

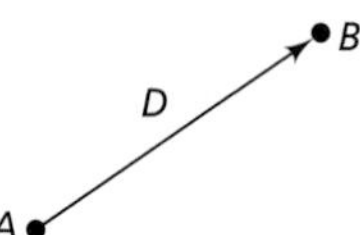

When you refer to the vector $D = (c, d)$, that means the vector displacement has c over and d up. Usually, context makes it clear which vector with that displacement you intend.

For Discussion

5. In the figure above, viewing A, B, and D as matrices that you add and subract, find an equation that relates A, B, and D.

Scalar Multiplication

In-Class Experiment

6. On graph paper, copy the corners P, Q, and R of the figure below.

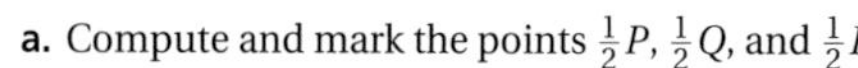

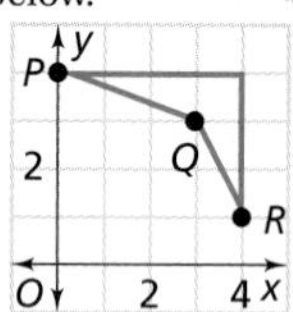

a. Compute and mark the points $\frac{1}{2}P$, $\frac{1}{2}Q$, and $\frac{1}{2}R$.

b. Draw the vectors from the origin to P, Q, and R.

c. Draw the vectors from the origin to $\frac{1}{2}P$, $\frac{1}{2}Q$, and $\frac{1}{2}R$.

Answers

For Discussion

5. $B = A + D$, $A = B - D$, $D = B - A$

In Class Experiment

6.

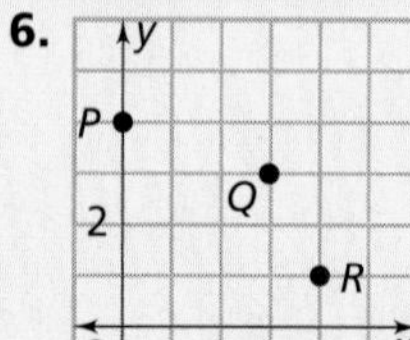

a.

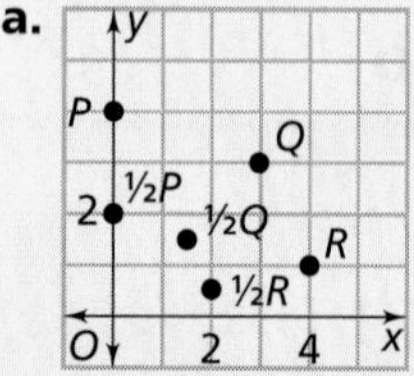

b.

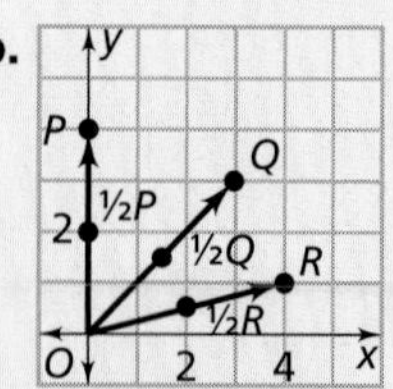

d. Compute and mark the points $(-1)P$, $(-1)Q$, and $(-1)R$.

e. Draw the vectors from the origin to $(-1)P$, $(-1)Q$, and $(-1)R$.

f. Find the relationship between A and kA when they are interpreted as points.

g. Find the relationship between A and kA when they are interpreted as displacements of vectors with tails at the origin.

You explored the effect of scaling, or dilation, in CME Project—*Geometry.* You can explain it with similar triangles. Here is the result of scaling point D and vector $\overrightarrow{OD}$ by the factor $k = 2$.

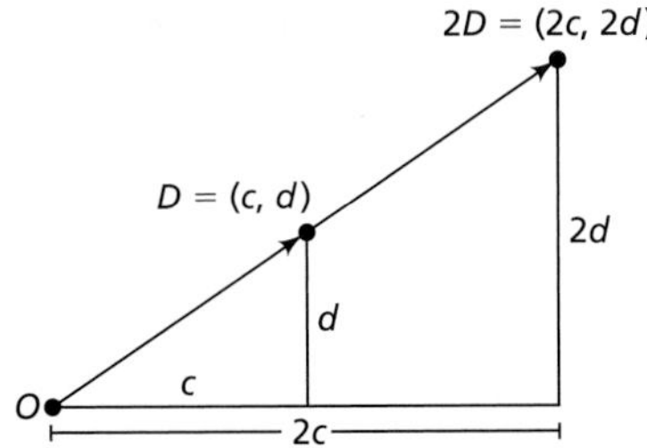

The vectors $\overrightarrow{OD}$ and $\overrightarrow{O(2D)}$ have the same slope $\frac{d}{c}$. Also, $\overrightarrow{O(2D)}$ is twice as long.

So $\overrightarrow{O(2D)} = 2\overrightarrow{OD}$.

Here is the result when using the scaling factor $k = 0.7$.

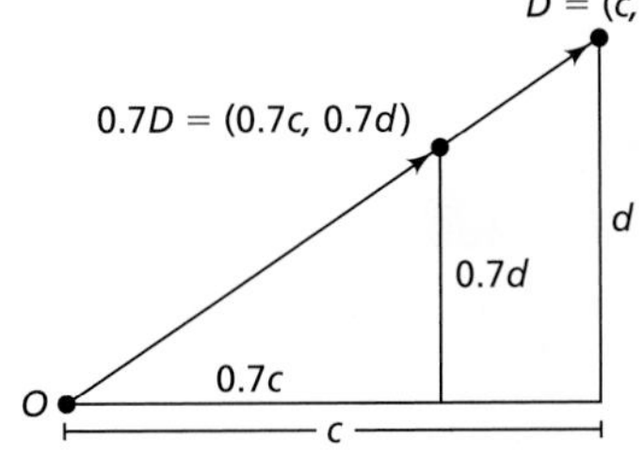

The slopes of the vectors are the same (the vectors are parallel) and the ratio of lengths is still the scaling factor (now 0.7). The resulting picture is smaller since $|k| < 1$.

Finally, here is a picture for $k = -1$. The tails of the vectors do not have to be at the origin. They can be at any point P. Then $D = (c, d)$ is the displacement and the name D appears along the vector rather than at the end.

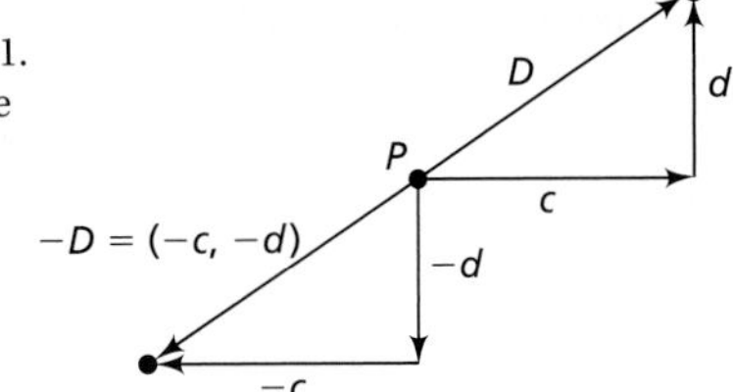

Remember...

If two vectors have the same direction, they have the same slope but they must also have the same orientation. $(1, -1)$ and $(-1, 1)$ have the same slope and length, but they point in opposite directions.

As before, the slopes of vectors D and $kD = -D$ are the same. This time the lengths are the same, but the directions are opposite. D and $-D$ are not the same vector: two vectors have the same displacement if and only if they have the same length and the same direction.

f. If the coordinates of A are (x, y), then the coordinates of kA are (kx, ky).

g. The vector from O to kA is a dilation by a factor of k of the vector from O to A.

c.

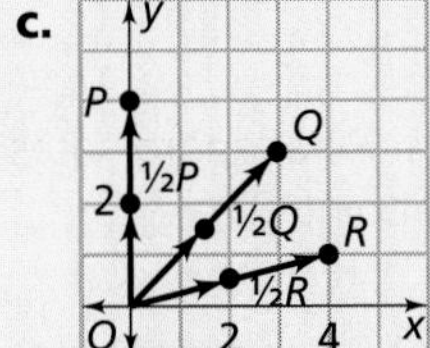

d.

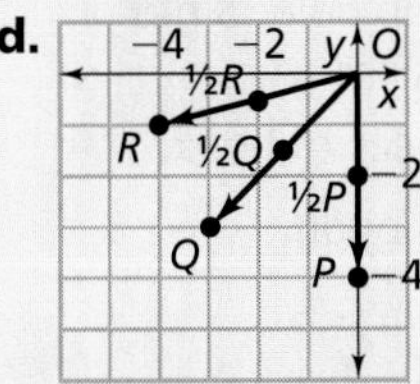

e.

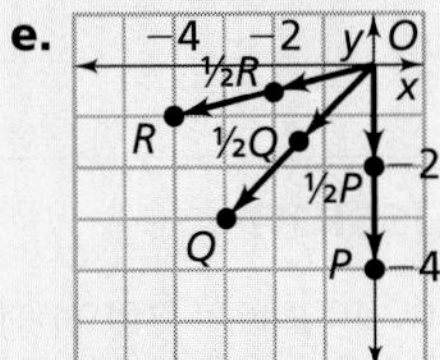

For Discussion

PROBLEM 7 This is the first appearance of lines in vector form, the main topic of the next lesson. This problem really is for classroom discussion, because different students think of it in different ways, depending on their mental image for the matrix sum $A + D$. Perhaps the discussion will change some minds about which mental image is best, at least for thinking about lines.

Wrap Up

Finish today's lesson by going over the core Check Your Understanding exercises as time allows. Be sure that students are able to visualize the sum of two vectors geometrically, and understand that all vectors with the same displacement are equivalent. The distinction between displacement and slope is difficult for some students to express, so have them generate examples of vectors that have the same slope, but different displacements, such as (2, 3) and (−2, −3).

Assessment Resources

Lesson Quiz 6.11

1. a. If a vector equivalent to (8, 5) has its tail at the point (−1, 3), find the coordinates of its head.
   b. If a vector equivalent to (2, 7) has its head at the point (12, 9), find the coordinates of its tail.

2. Consider the vectors $U = (-4, 6)$ and $V = (5, 3)$, both with tails at the origin.
   a. Find $U + V$.
   b. Dilate U with center (0, 0) by a factor of 2.
   c. Dilate V with center (0, 0) by a factor of −3.

Exercises

HOMEWORK
- Core: 6, 7, 10, 12, 13
- Optional: 8, 11
- Extension: 9

Check Your Understanding

EXERCISE 1 The distinctions between slope, direction, and displacement is subtle. You may want to ask students to generate several vectors that have the same slope as some particular vector. If they do not come up with examples that have opposite orientation or different length, you may need to suggest such vectors. Eventually, students will understand that any two vectors that have the same direction must have the same slope and orientation, and that any two vectors that have the same displacement must have the same direction and length.

For Discussion

Consider a point P and a vector D.

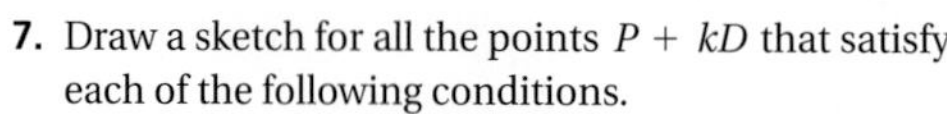

7. Draw a sketch for all the points $P + kD$ that satisfy each of the following conditions.
   a. k slides along from 0 to 2.
   b. k slides along from 0 to −2.
   c. k increases from some very large negative number to some very large positive number.

P

D

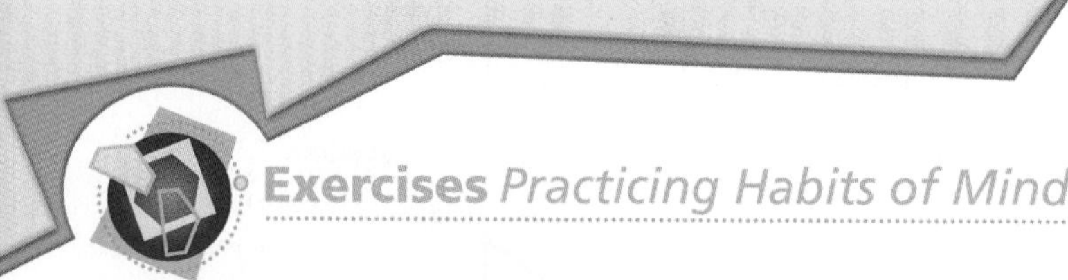

Check Your Understanding

1. Suppose two vectors $\overrightarrow{PQ}$ and $\overrightarrow{RS}$ are equivalent. That means that the two vectors have the same displacement, $D = (c, d)$.
   a. Show that $\overrightarrow{PQ}$ and $\overrightarrow{RS}$ have the same slope.
   b. Show that $\overrightarrow{PQ}$ and $\overrightarrow{RS}$ have the same length.
   c. Describe how can you be sure that $\overrightarrow{PQ}$ and $\overrightarrow{RS}$ have the same direction.

Remember...
Direction includes both the slope and the orientation of the vector.

2. Suppose that $\overrightarrow{PQ}$ and $\overrightarrow{RS}$ have the same direction and length. Prove that $Q - P = S - R$.
3. Find the coordinates of the fourth point if you complete the figure at the right to form a parallelogram.

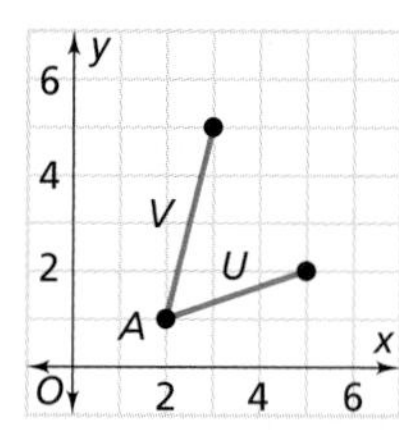

Answers

For Discussion

7. a. The line segment from point P to point $P + 2D$, traversed in that order.
   b. The line segment from point P to point $P - 2D$, traversed in that order. This is on the same line as the first segment, but going in the opposite direction from P
   c. The line through P with direction D, or at least a very large part of it.

Exercises

1. Assume point P has coordinates (x, y). Then point Q has coordinates $(x + c, y + d)$.

   Assume point R has coordinates (m, n). Then point S has coordinates $(m + c, n + d)$.

   a–c. See back of book.
2. See back of book.
3. (6, 6)

4. Find the coordinates of the fourth point if you complete the figure to form a parallelogram.

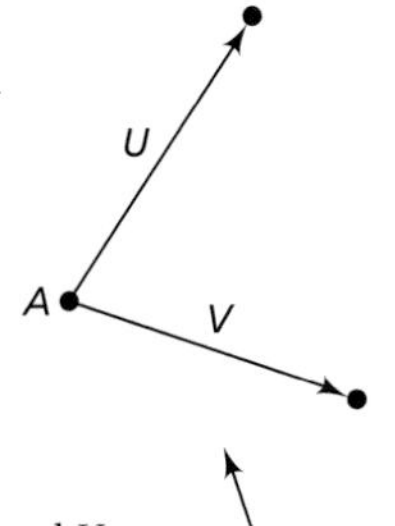

This time there is no grid, so the answer should be in terms of *A*, *U*, and *V*.

5. This picture shows two vectors *U* and *V*. Copy and draw the sum $U + V$.

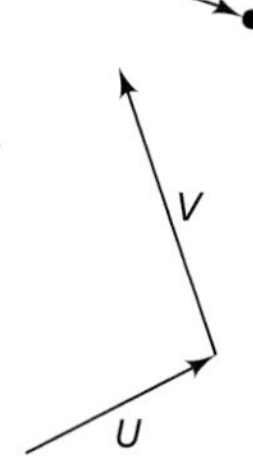

On Your Own

6. a. If a vector equivalent to (a_1, a_2) has its tail at the point (t_1, t_2), find the coordinates of its head.

   b. If a vector equivalent to (a_1, a_2) has its head at the point (h_1, h_2), find the coordinates of its tail.

7. Consider any closed polygon, like the one at the right. View each side as a vector, with the directions shown. Find the sum of these vectors.

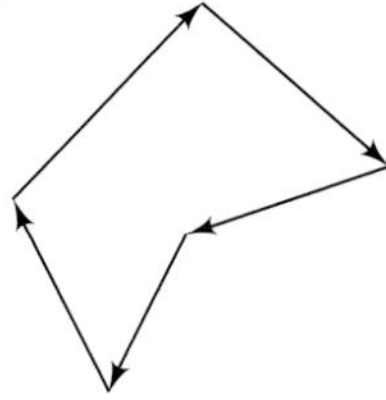

8. A *dilation* is any geometric transformation that expands or contracts the plane (or space) using some particular point as its center. The diagram below illustrates a dilation with center $A(1, 4)$ by a factor of 2. *S* is the figure made up of three line segments.

   Use graph paper to complete the following.

   a. Draw *S* and dilate it with center *A* by a factor of 3.

   b. Dilate *S* with center *A* by a factor of $\frac{1}{2}$.

   c. Dilate *S* with center *A* by a factor of -1.

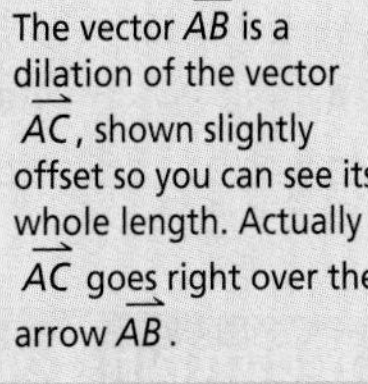

The vector $\overrightarrow{AB}$ is a dilation of the vector $\overrightarrow{AC}$, shown slightly offset so you can see its whole length. Actually $\overrightarrow{AC}$ goes right over the arrow $\overrightarrow{AB}$.

9. **Take It Further** Consider a dilation with center *A* by a factor of *k* as in Exercise 8. If you dilate point *B* to point *C*, find a formula for *C* in terms of *A*, *B*, and *k*.

EXERCISES 4 AND 5 In these exercises students work to develop a geometric picture of vector addition.

On Your Own

EXERCISE 8 When vectors have their tails at the center of dilation, it is easier to see what happens to them and to accept that the length of the scaled vector is the length of the original vector multiplied by the scale factor. What if the center of dilation is not at the tail of the vector, though? Think about the vector $\overrightarrow{OP}$ where *O* is the origin and *P* is the point (4, 0). How is it impacted by a dilation by a factor of 3 with center *A*?

To get from *A* to *O*, you move left 1 and down 4, so to get from *A* to the *image* of *O* after this dilation, you move left 3 and down 12. The image of *O*, *O′* is (−2, −8). To get from *A* to *P*, you move right 3 and down 4, so to move from *A* to the image of *P* after this dilation, you move right 9 and down 12. The image of *P*, *P′*, is (10, −8). The vector $\overrightarrow{O'P'}$ still has the same direction (horizontal, left to right) but its length is now 12 and it is no longer along the *x*-axis, but 8 units below it.

4. $A + U + V$

5.

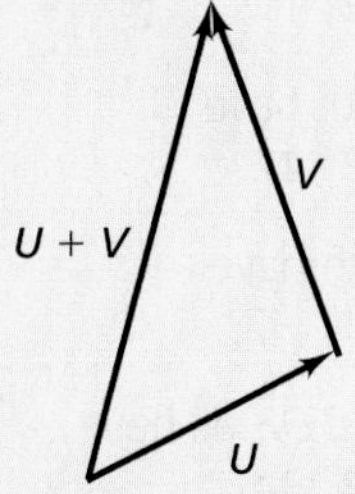

6. a. $(t_1 + a_1, t_2 + a_2)$

b. $(h_1 - a_1, h_2 - a_2)$

7. (0, 0)

8. a.

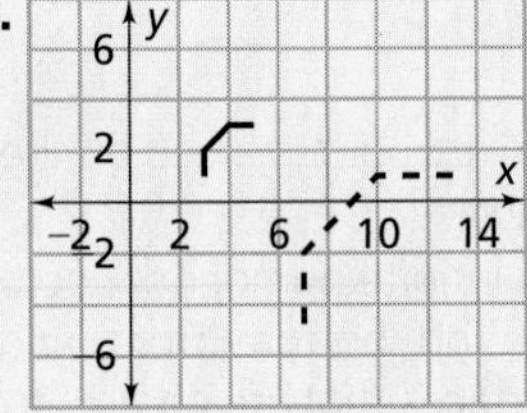

b–c. See back of book.

9. $C = (1 - k)A + kB$

EXERCISE 10 Many students find visualization in three dimensions difficult. You might suggest that they use some kind of a box (a square tissue box would work nicely) and a pencil to help them see what is going on here. They can visualize the coordinate axes using the box as a reference, and then place the pencil to represent the vector, using the point of the pencil as the head of the vector.

Maintain Your Skills

EXERCISE 13 Students should find the displacement of each vector and match any that have the same displacement.

Additional Resources

PRINT RESOURCES
- Solution Manual
- Practice Workbook
- Assessment Resources
- Teaching Resources

TECHNOLOGY
- Interactive Textbook
- TeacherExpress CD-ROM
- ExamView CD-ROM
- PHSchool.com

Additional Practice

1. Find the coordinates of the fourth point to complete the figure at the right to form a parallelogram.

2. a. If a vector equivalent to (8, 9) has its tail at the point (2, 4), find the coordinates of its head.
   b. If a vector equivalent to (−3, 7) has its head at the point (−5, 12), find the coordinates of its tail.

3. Use the graph at the right of vectors U and V to find the following dilations.
   a. Find the head and tail of the resulting vector when U is dilated with center A and by a factor of 4.
   b. Find the head and tail of the resulting vector when V is dilated with center A and by a factor of $\frac{1}{2}$.
   c. Find the head and tail of the resulting vector when V is dilated with center A and by a factor of −2.

4. Find the slope of the line that is the graph of each of the following equations.
   a. $X = (3, 4) + t(5, 2)$
   b. $X = (2, 4) + t(6, 7)$
   c. $X = (1, 3) + t(5, 0)$
   d. $X = (4, 7) + t(2, 1)$

5. Find a vector equation for each of the following.
   a. the graph of $y = \frac{2}{7}x + 3$
   b. the graph of $y - 4 = 2(x + 6)$
   c. the graph of $\frac{x}{3} + \frac{y}{4} = 2$
   d. the graph of $y = -\frac{1}{3}x + 6$

6. Two people start running at the same time. Person A starts at (0,0) and runs with a velocity of (10, 1). Person B starts at (−5, −5) and runs with a velocity of (9, 1).
   a. Determine if the paths of the two runners intersect. Will the two runners crash?
   b. Repeat part (a), except Person B starts at (2, 2).
   c. Repeat part (a), except Person B has velocity (11, 2).

Practice: For Lesson 6.11, assign Exercises 1–3.

10. Consider the unit cube with one corner at point (0, 0, 0) and the opposite corner at point (1, 1, 1). See the figure.

a. Consider $U = (1, 0, 0)$. As a point, find where U is located on the surface of this cube.

b. There are many vectors equivalent to U on the surface of the cube. Describe them.

c. Now consider $V = (0, 1, 1)$. As a point, find where V is located.

d. Describe all vectors equivalent to V lying entirely on the surface of the cube.

e. Represent the sums $U + V$ and $V + U$ on this cube.

11. Find the displacements of the diagonals of the parallelogram at the right.

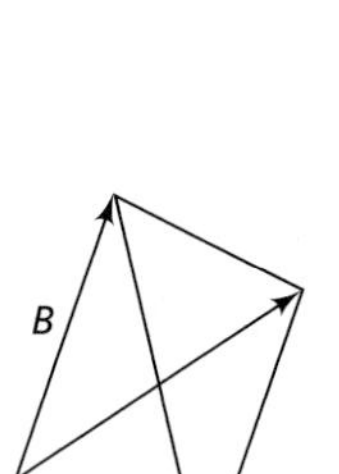

For additional practice, go to Web Code: bga-0611

12. Standardized Test Prep Given U is the vector (−3, 4) and V is the vector (2, 3) as shown. Which of the following represents the bold vector (a, b)?

A. (−1, −1) **B.** (3, −4)

C. (−5, 1) **D.** (5, −1)

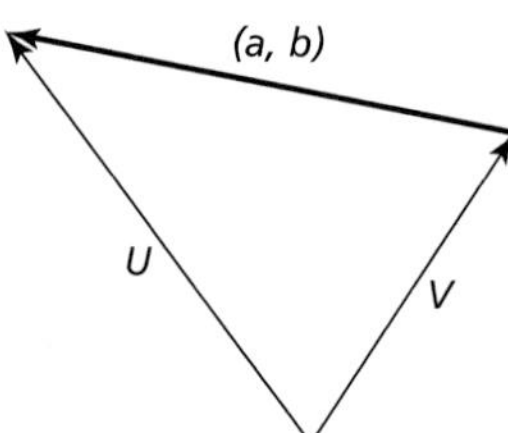

Maintain Your Skills

13. In the figure at the right, identify all vectors with the same displacement.

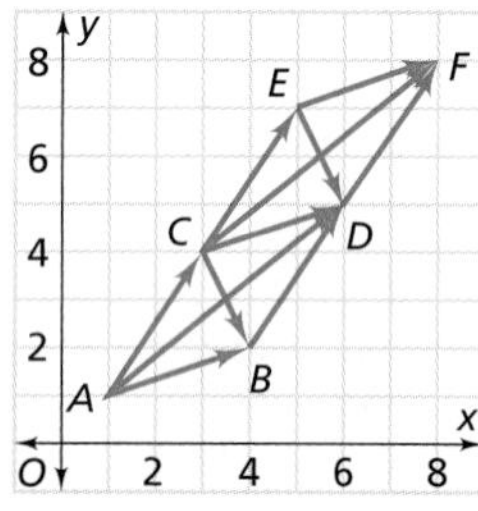

You could also phrase this question as, "Find all equivalent vectors." Some people would even say, "Find all vectors that are the same."

Answers

10. a. the red point marked on the figure

b. an infinite number of vectors on the top, bottom, front, and back surfaces that are parallel to U

c. top, left, forward corner

d. the vector with tail at (1, 0, 0) and head at (1, 1, 1)

e. (1, 1, 1)

11. $A + B$ and $A - B$

12. C

13. $\overrightarrow{AB}$, $\overrightarrow{CD}$, and $\overrightarrow{EF}$, all have displacement (3, 1).

$\overrightarrow{AD}$ and $\overrightarrow{CF}$ both have displacement (5, 4).

$\overrightarrow{CB}$ and $\overrightarrow{ED}$ both have displacement (1, −2).

$\overrightarrow{AC}$, $\overrightarrow{CE}$, $\overrightarrow{BD}$, and $\overrightarrow{DF}$ all have displacement (2, 3).

6.12 Vector Equations of Lines

Here is one way to think of a straight line: start at a point P and change position in some fixed direction. You can write the point P as an ordered pair. If you write the direction as a vector, you can do the same with it. This way of thinking leads to a vector equation for lines.

Minds in Action — episode 20

Tony and Sasha have been asked to figure out an equation for a typical point X on the line through point P with direction vector D.

Tony Okay, we start at P and change position in direction D. That makes sense. Look at this picture.

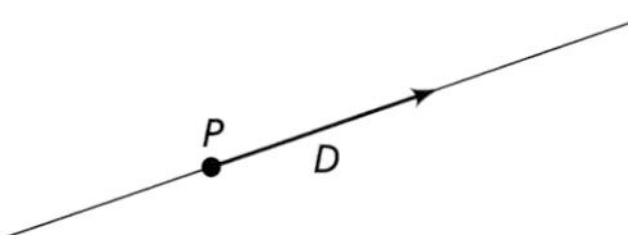

Sasha So long as any amount can mean both positive and negative amounts. Otherwise we just get a ray.

Tony We're supposed to write an equation for a typical point X on the line. Here it is.

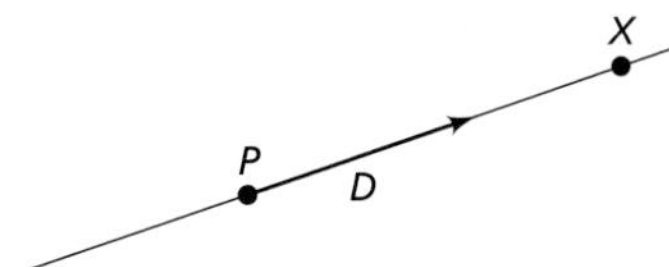

Sasha Or it could be on the other side, like this

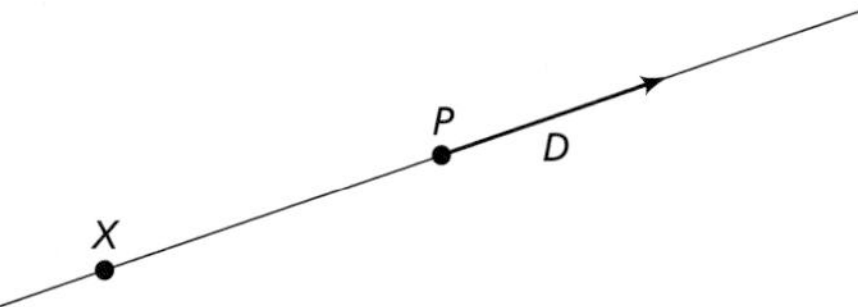

Tony Or it could be in close, like this.

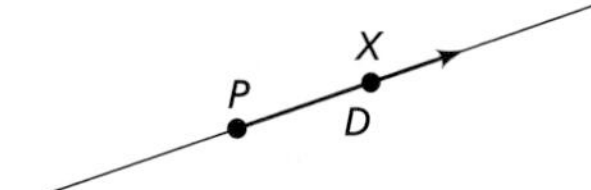

Lesson Overview

GOAL

- Express lines with vector equations and solve for intersections and other useful information using these equations.

This lesson is based on such a simple idea—you get a line when you start somewhere and go any amount in a fixed direction—that you wonder how one studied lines in Algebra 1 without talking about it. Maybe it sounds too fuzzy to be the basis of precise algebra. But it works fine in the vector algebra world.

Students first saw the vector equation of a line in CME Project *Geometry*, and they also saw how lines in three-dimensional space are simple to define if you use vector equations.

CHECK YOUR UNDERSTANDING
- Core: 1, 2, 3, 4, 6
- Optional: 5, 7, 8

MATERIALS
- geometry software (optional)
- graph paper
- graphing calculators
- Blackline Master MC7

HOMEWORK
- Core: 9, 10, 11, 13, 16, 18
- Optional: 14, 15, 19, 20, 21
- Extension: 12, 17

VOCABULARY
- parameter
- parametric equations
- vector equations

Launch

Have students act out the Minds in Action dialog between Tony and Sasha.

Explore

Minds in Action

You can also model this situation in a dynamic geometry program. Define a fixed point P, a vector D not connected to it, and a changeable segment. Define the length of this segment as k. Then as you change the length of the segment, you can plot the point $Q = P + kD$. See what happens for values of k close to zero or negative values. If you trace Q, students will see what the line through P with direction vector D looks like.

Sasha Whatever. The vector D just has to be scaled to get all the way from P to X. So I think it's kD instead of D.

Tony Hey, that's it, the part I was missing. From the last lesson, a point plus a vector is a point. You get from P to X by adding the vector kD. So $X = P + kD$. I think we're done!

Sasha Maybe. You like that point plus vector stuff, but I don't think that way. I want it to be all vectors. Plus, I like vectors from the origin, not just left out there anywhere. And I think they should be named by their tails and heads.

Tony Picky, picky. OK, let's see if we can do it that way. Maybe start with this?

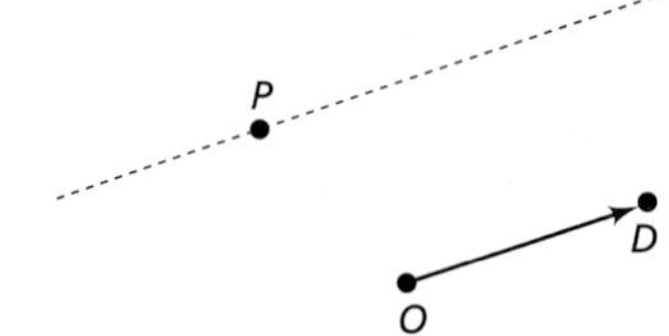

Sasha Yeah, but get some multiples kD in there too. I'll draw them a little to the side so I can see them.

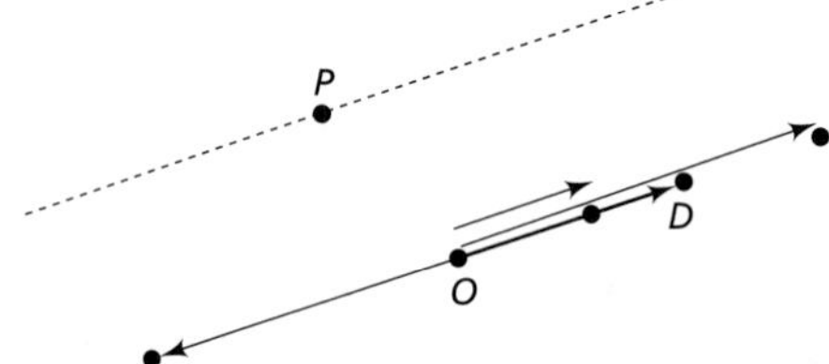

Tony OK, now we've got to translate them to P, draw in $\overrightarrow{OP}$, and add head to tail.

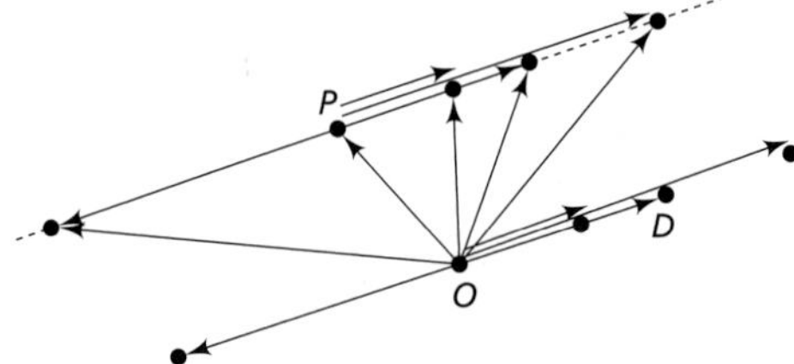

Sasha Now we're cooking. The arrows between the two lines are the sums of P and kD. The points at the ends of those arrows are the points on the line. So now it makes sense to me, $X = P + kD$.

Tony Hey, what if we use your method, but add in the other order $kD + P$. Let's see, I think we get this.

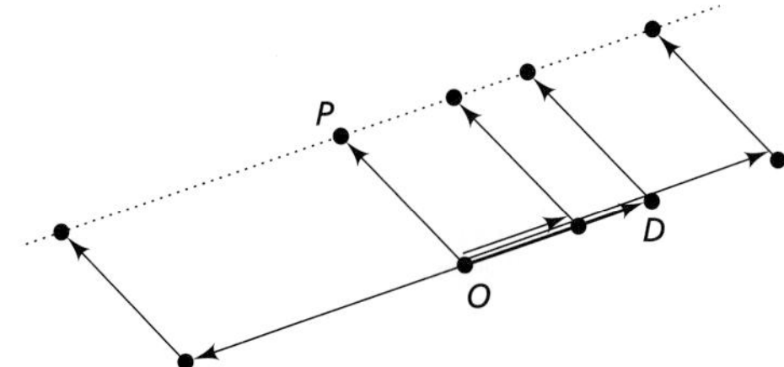

Sasha I like that. You haven't drawn in the sum vectors, but maybe it's clearer that way. You can see that you start with a line through the origin determined by the vector D. Then you translate the whole thing by vector P, getting a new line with the same direction but through the point P.

$X = P + kD$ is called a *vector equation of a line*, or the line expressed in vector form. You may replace the scalar k by the letter t, since t usually stands for a variable while k stands for a constant.

What are good letters to use for real-number variables? The letters x and y are out since they are coordinates of X. So t is a good choice, as are s, u, and v.

For You to Do

1. How would you write a vector equation of a line through two points P and Q? What direction vector would you use? Try out your idea, by finding a vector equation for the line through $P(-1, 4)$ and $Q(2, -2)$. Make sure both of these points satisfy your equation.

Recall that equations are point-testers. This is true for vector equations of lines as well.

Example 1

Problem Consider the line with vector equation $X = (1, 3) + t(2, -3)$.

a. Name two points on the line.

b. Determine if $(4, -1)$ is on this line.

c. Determine if $(-1, 6)$ is on this line.

Solution

a. Pick t to be any real number. For example, the choice $t = 0$ gives the base point $P = (1, 3)$. The choice $t = 1$ yields $(1, 3) + (2, -3) = (3, 0)$.

b. Substitute $(4, -1)$ for X to get the two real-number equations

$$4 = 1 + 2t$$
$$-1 = 3 - 3t$$

Example

Spend time as needed going over this completed example. Make sure students understand the problem. As necessary, help them develop the detailed solution.

Answers

For You to Do

1. $X = (-1, 4) + t(3, -6)$

The first equation's solution is $t = \frac{3}{2}$. Substituting this t into the second equation does not work. So $(4, -1)$ fails the test. It is not on the line.

c. This time the two equations are

$$-1 = 1 + 2t$$
$$6 = 3 - 3t$$

The first yields $t = -1$, which does satisfy the second equation. So point $(-1, 6)$ passes the test. It is on the line.

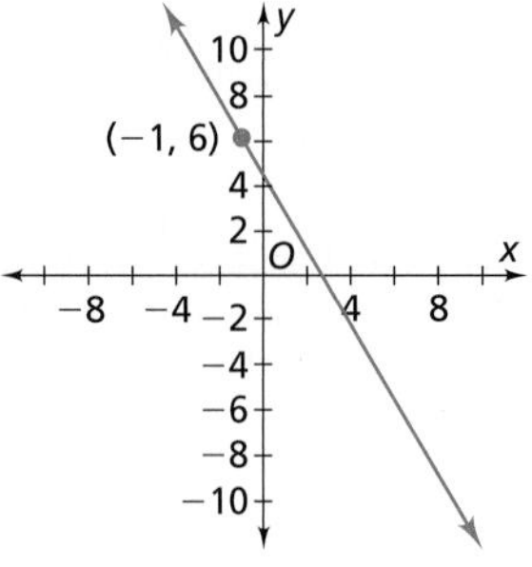

The vector form of a line has an extra variable, the t. This is called a **parameter.** It does not stand for a physical coordinate, the way x and y do. In mathematics, a parameter is a variable that does not appear in the picture but somehow determines what does appear.

Vector equations for lines are sometimes called *parametric equations* for lines.

So why is the vector form useful? Offhand, it seems that vector form only adds complication—the extra variable t.

The reason it is useful is that t can represent time and describe movement along the line.

Example 2

Problem Two test cars start racing along straight lines in a flat desert. Suppose Car 1 starts at (0, 0) and travels with constant velocity (25, 40). That means, in each time unit, Car 1 travels (25, 40) from where it was. (To make the speeds in this example somewhat realistic, let the units for distance be kilometers and the units for time be hours.) Suppose Car 2 starts at the same time at (10, 25) and travels with velocity vector (30, 45).

Do the paths of the cars intersect? Do the cars crash?

Solution At time t, Car 1 is at $(0, 0) + t(25, 40)$ and Car 2 is at $(10, 25) + t(30, 45)$.

To make sense of these equations, track Car 1's position for the first few hours. At $t = 0$, Car 1 is at $(0, 0)$. In one hour it moves along a vector equivalent to $(25, 40)$, so it reaches $(0, 0) + 1(25, 40)$. In 2 hours it has gone twice as far, so it reaches $(0, 0) + 2(25, 40)$. In general, after t hours it is at $(0, 0) + t(25, 40)$.

t does not have to be an integer.

Set the locations of the two cars equal and solve.

$$(0, 0) + t(25, 40) = (10, 25) + t(30, 45)$$

If you write this out as two separate real-number equations, this is

$$0 + 25t = 10 + 30t$$
$$0 + 40t = 25 + 45t$$

which simplifies to

$$-5t = 10$$
$$-5t = 25$$

Clearly there is no solution that gives the same t for both equations.

But what does this mean? The two things you set equal are the positions of the cars at the same time t. No solution means there is no time t at which the cars are at the same place. So they do not crash.

How do you determine whether their paths intersect? Are there different times at which they pass through the same spot? In other words, is there a solution to

$$(0, 0) + t(25, 40) = (10, 25) + s(30, 45)$$

The expression on the left is the position of Car 1 at time t. The expression on the right is the position of Car 2 at time s. You do not know yet what these times are, or if there are times at which the location for both cars is the same, but you can solve and find out. Again, write out the real-number equations.

$$0 + 25t = 10 + 30s$$
$$0 + 40t = 25 + 45s$$

which simplifies to

$$-30s + 25t = 10$$
$$-45s + 40t = 25$$

Solve this system to give the solution $s = 3,\ t = 4$.

The paths intersect, but the cars pass through the intersection an hour apart—Car 2 at hour 3 and Car 1 at hour 4.

For You to Do

2. Find the intersection point for the cars' paths. Show that this point is on both lines according to their vector equations.

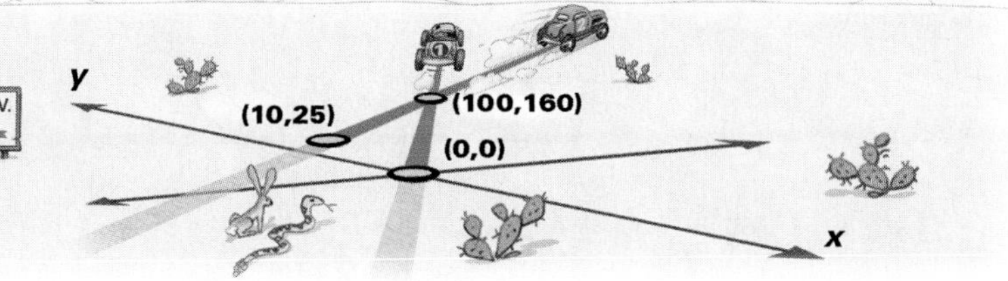

Answers

For You to Do

2. Using $t = 4$ and $s = 3$ from the example:

$(0, 0) + 4(25, 40) = (100, 160)$

$(10, 25) + 3(30, 45) = (100, 160)$

These cars' paths intersect at $(100, 160)$.

Wrap Up

Have students discuss the pros and cons of vector equations for lines relative to the types of equations they already know. One disadvantage is that a *unique* form for such an equation does not exist, so it takes a little work to decide whether two vector equations represent the same line. An advantage is that vector equations allow you to think about time and traveling along a line. The exercises about racing cars, which ask both whether the two paths cross and whether the cars crash, get at this idea.

Assessment Resources

Lesson Quiz 6.12

1. Consider the line with vector equation $X = (2, 5) + t(-4, 2)$.
   a. Test whether the point $(5, 7)$ is on the line.
   b. Test whether the point $(4, 4)$ is on the line.

2. Find a vector equation for each of the following.
   a. the graph of $y = \frac{4}{5}x + 7$
   b. the graph of $\frac{x}{2} + \frac{y}{4} = 1$

3. Let L be the line through $(4, 6)$ with direction vector $(2, -1)$. Find y such that $(-2, y)$ is on L.

Exercises

HOMEWORK
- Core: 9, 10, 11, 13, 16, 18
- Optional: 14, 15, 19, 20, 21
- Extension: 12, 17

Check Your Understanding

You may want to provide copies of Blackline Master MC7 to your students to use on their homework.

EXERCISE 2 You might spend some time looking at several different correct answers to this exercise.

EXERCISE 8 recalls the idea of scaling a *point*. Scaling a point X moves it along the line connecting the point to the origin, because it scales the vector $\overrightarrow{OX}$.

Exercises *Practicing Habits of Mind*

Check Your Understanding

1. Consider the line with vector equation $X = (1, 2) + t(3, 4)$. Test whether the points $(4, 6)$, $(-5, -5)$, and $(13, 18)$ are on the line.
2. Consider the line with parametric equation $X = (1, 0) + t(1, 2)$. Find a Cartesian equation of this line.
3. Find the slope of the line that is the graph of each of the following equations.
   a. $X = (1, 2) + t(3, 4)$
   b. $X = (1, 2) + t(4, 3)$
   c. $X = (1, 2) + t(6, 8)$
   d. $X = P + t(3, 4)$ for any point P
4. Find a vector equation for each of the following.
   a. the graph of $y = \frac{3}{2}x + 1$
   b. the graph of $(y - 3) = 4(x - 5)$
   c. the graph of $\frac{x}{2} + \frac{y}{3} = 1$
   d. the line through the points $(-2, 3)$ and $(3, 1)$
5. Let L be the line through $(2, 3)$ with direction vector $(3, -1)$. Find y such that $(-6, y)$ is on L.
6. Are there any lines in the plane that do not have a vector equation?
7. Give a general procedure for determining whether two vector equations

$$X = P + tD \quad \text{and} \quad X' = P' + tD'$$

   describe the same line.
8. Consider the line with equation $X = (4, 3) + t(2, 1)$.
   a. Sketch the line.
   b. Now dilate all the points on the line by 2 with the origin as the center of the dilation. Sketch the result.
   c. Explain why this proves that the scaled set of points is also a line and is parallel to the original line.

Answers

Exercises

1. $(4, 6)$: yes; $(-5, -5)$: no; $(13, 18)$: yes

2. $y = 2x - 2$

3. a. $\frac{4}{3}$ **b.** $\frac{3}{4}$ **c.** $\frac{4}{3}$ **d.** $\frac{4}{3}$

4. a. Answers may vary. Sample: $X = (0, 1) + t(2, 3)$
b. Answers may vary. Sample: $X = (5, 3) + t(1, 4)$
c. Answers may vary. Sample: $X = (0, 3) + t(2, -3)$
d. Answers may vary. Samples: $X = (-2, 3) + t(5, -2)$, $X = (3, 1) + t(5, -2)$

5. $y = \frac{17}{3}$

6. no

7. For the lines to be the same, D' must be a scalar multiple of D (i.e., the lines are parallel). Once you know that the lines are parallel, check to see if P' is on the first line. If that turns out to be true, the lines are identical, since a line is uniquely determined by a point and a slope.

8. a.

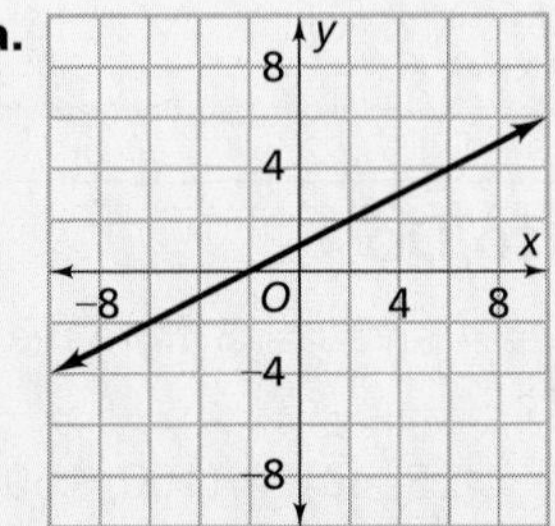

On Your Own

9. Find a vector equation for the line through the points $(2, 3)$ and $(-1, 4)$.

10. A line has vector equation $X = P + tD$. Determine P and D if when $t = 0$, $X = (2, 3)$, and when $t = 1$, $X = (4, 5)$.

11. A line has vector equation $X = P + tD$. Determine P and D if when $t = 1$, $X = (2, -1)$, and when $t = 2$, $X = (4, 3)$.

12. **Take It Further** Consider the curve with vector equation $X = (1, 2) + t^3(2, -1)$.
    - **a.** Find some points on this curve by using several values of t.
    - **b.** Plot the curve. Describe the curve you graphed.
    - **c.** Consider the curve given by the equation $X = (1, 2) + t^2(2, -1)$. Determine if this is the same set of points as $X = (1, 2) + t^3(2, -1)$.

13. Consider the two cars racing in the desert from the lesson. Recall that Car 1 starts at $(0, 0)$ and travels with velocity $(25, 40)$. That remains true in all the parts below, but the information on Car 2 changes.
    - **a.** Suppose Car 2 starts at the same time at $(-10, -10)$ and travels with velocity vector $(30, 45)$. Determine if the paths of the cars intersect. Determine if the cars crash.
    - **b.** Repeat part (a), except Car 2 starts at $(10, 10)$.
    - **c.** Repeat part (a), except Car 2 has velocity $(30, 48)$.
    - **d.** Repeat part (a), except Car 2 starts at $(30, 55)$ an hour later.

14. A vector equation of a line, $X = P + tD$, is unchanged in three dimensions. A line is still determined by a point and a direction but now X, P, D are triples. Let L' be the line through $(1, 2, 1)$ in the direction $(2, -1, 3)$. Find z such that $(5, 0, z)$ is on L'.

15. Two airplanes fly along straight lines. At time t airplane 1 is at $(75, 50, 25) + t(5, 10, 1)$ and airplane 2 is at $(60, 80, 34) + t(10, 5, -1)$.
    - **a.** Determine if the airplanes collide.
    - **b.** Determine if their flight paths intersect.

16. Which of the lines given by the following equations are the same? Explain.
    - $X = (1, -1) + t(3, 6)$
    - $X = (10, 17) + t(1, 3)$
    - $X = (10, 17) + s(1, 2)$

Go Online PHSchool.com

For additional practice, go to Web Code: bga-0612

The same is not true of Cartesian equations. Neither $y = mx + b$ nor $ax + by + cz = d$ is an equation of a line in three dimensions.

On Your Own

EXERCISES 10 AND 11 At first glance, these exercises may look as though they are asking students to find the vector equation of a line through two points. However, students are being asked to find a *particular* vector equation. For example, in Exercise 10, points (2, 3) and (4, 5) are certainly on the line. That line has a lot of different vector equations that are all valid, such as $X = (4, 5) + t(2, 2)$. But this equation does not satisfy the conditions, because when $t = 0$, $X \neq (4,5)$.

EXERCISE 13 In part (c) of this exercise, some students may find that the two cars are traveling along parallel paths and stop there, deciding that they cannot crash. You may need to remind them that two lines have the same slope if they are parallel *or* if they are the same line. Two cars traveling in the same direction along the same road can crash if the car in front is slower than the car behind it.

b.

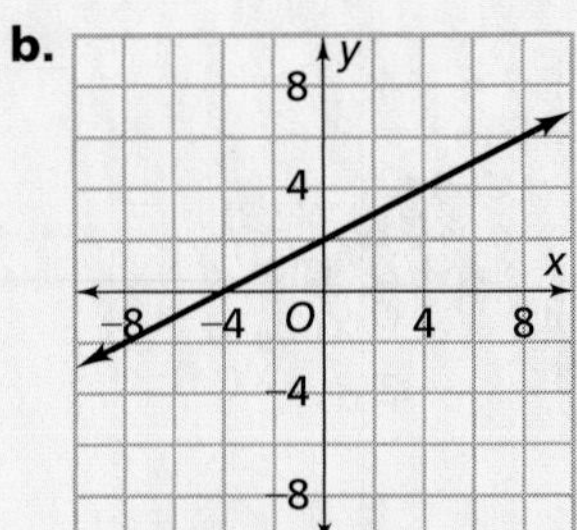

c. The direction vector is scaled, but the direction is not changed. Since the two lines have the same direction vector, they must be parallel.

9. Answers may vary. Sample: $X = (2, 3) + t(-3, 1)$

10. $P = (2, 3), D = (2, 2)$

11. $P = (0, -5), D = (2, 4)$

12. a. Answers may vary. Samples:

t	$x = (1, 2) + t^3(2, -1)$
-1	$(-1, 3)$
0	$(1, 2)$
1	$(3, 1)$
2	$(17, -6)$

b. This graph is a line.

c. No, since t^2 is never negative you cannot obtain all points on the line to the left of $(1, 2)$.

13. a–d. See back of book.

14. $z = 7$

15. a. no **b.** yes

16. See back of book.

Maintain Your Skills

EXERCISES 19 AND 20 These exercises lead to the fact that with vector algebra, you can express midpoints, trisection points, and other points that cut a segment into pieces with a specific ratio.

Additional Resources

PRINT RESOURCES
- Solution Manual
- Practice Workbook
- Assessment Resources
- Teaching Resources

TECHNOLOGY
- Interactive Textbook
- TeacherExpress CD-ROM
- ExamView CD-ROM
- PHSchool.com

Additional Practice

1. Find the coordinates of the fourth point to complete the figure at the right to form a parallelogram.

2. a. If a vector equivalent to (8, 9) has its tail at the point (2, 4), find the coordinates of its head.
   b. If a vector equivalent to (−3, 7) has its head at the point (−5, 12), find the coordinates of its tail.

3. Use the graph at the right of vectors U and V to find the following dilations.
   a. Find the head and tail of the resulting vector when U is dilated with center A and by a factor of 4.
   b. Find the head and tail of the resulting vector when V is dilated with center A and by a factor of $\frac{1}{2}$.
   c. Find the head and tail of the resulting vector when V is dilated with center A and by a factor of −2.

4. Find the slope of the line that is the graph of each of the following equations.
   a. $X = (3, 4) + t(5, 2)$
   b. $X = (2, 4) + t(6, 7)$
   c. $X = (1, 3) + t(5, 0)$
   d. $X = (4, 7) + t(2, 1)$

5. Find a vector equation for each of the following.
   a. the graph of $y = \frac{2}{7}x + 3$
   b. the graph of $y - 4 = 2(x + 6)$
   c. the graph of $\frac{x}{3} + \frac{y}{4} = 2$
   d. the graph of $y = -\frac{1}{3}x + 6$

6. Two people start running at the same time. Person A starts at (0,0) and runs with a velocity of (10, 1). Person B starts at (−5, −5) and runs with a velocity of (9, 1).
   a. Determine if the paths of the two runners intersect. Will the two runners crash?
   b. Repeat part (a), except Person B starts at (2, 2).
   c. Repeat part (a), except Person B has velocity (11, 2).

Practice: For Lesson 6.12, assign Exercises 4–6.

17. **Take It Further** You can think of a plane in three-space this way: You start at some base point P and move in each of two directions D_1 and D_2. Find a vector equation for a plane.

18. **Standardized Test Prep** Given U is the vector $(-3, 4)$ and V is the vector $(-1, 1)$. Which of the following points is on the line $U + tV$?
    A. (0, 1) **B.** (−3, −4) **C.** (−4, −3) **D.** (−1, 1)

Maintain Your Skills

19. Consider the line with equation $X(t) = (1, 0) + t(-1, 1)$. Now consider X as a function of t.
    a. Explain why the graph of $X(t)$ is the line through (1, 0) and (0, 1).
    b. Using graph paper, plot the following points, labeling them with the names given here.
    $$X(0), X(1), X\left(\tfrac{1}{2}\right), X\left(\tfrac{1}{3}\right), X\left(\tfrac{2}{3}\right), X(2), X(3), X(-1)$$

Writing $X(t)$, instead of just X, allows each point on the line to be identified with the value of the parameter for that point.

20. Consider the line with equation $Y(t) = (0, 1) + t(1, -1)$.
    a. Explain why this is the same line as in Exercise 19.
    b. Using graph paper, plot the following points, labeling them with the names given here.
    $$Y(0), Y(1), Y\left(\tfrac{1}{2}\right), Y\left(\tfrac{1}{3}\right), Y\left(\tfrac{2}{3}\right), Y(2), Y(3), Y(-1)$$

21. Let P and Q be two points in the plane. Explain where each of the following points is located relative to P and Q.
    a. $\frac{1}{2}P + \frac{1}{2}Q$
    b. $\frac{1}{3}P + \frac{2}{3}Q$
    c. $\frac{2}{3}P + \frac{1}{3}Q$
    d. $\frac{4}{5}P + \frac{1}{5}Q$
    e. $2P - Q$
    f. $3P - 2Q$

If you are having trouble, pick some sample points for P and Q and calculate the others.

Even though the cars' paths intersect, the cars arrived at different times, thus avoiding a collision.

Answers

17. $X = P + sD_1 + tD_2$ where D_1 and D_2 are two different directions (not parallel).

18. A

19. a. The base point for $X(t)$ is (1, 0) and the direction vector (−1, 1) goes from (1, 0) to (0, 1), so both of these points are on the same line.

b.

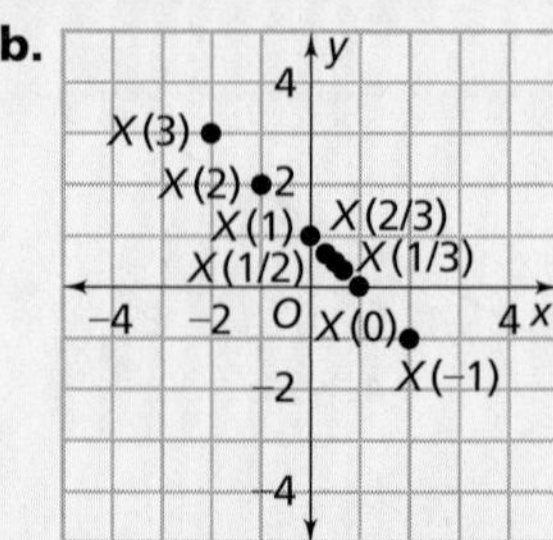

20–21. See back of book.

6.13 Affine Combinations and Geometry

A vector equation of a line has another advantage. You can use it to identify points in a particular position relative to given point.

Example 1

Problem Show that the midpoint of points A and B is $\frac{1}{2}(A + B)$.

Solution On the line determined by A and B, the midpoint will be halfway from A to B. Start at A and translate (displace) by half of $\overrightarrow{AB}$. The displacement of $\overrightarrow{AB}$ is $B - A$. So the midpoint M is

$$A + \tfrac{1}{2}(B - A) = A + \tfrac{1}{2}B - \tfrac{1}{2}A = \tfrac{1}{2}(A + B)$$

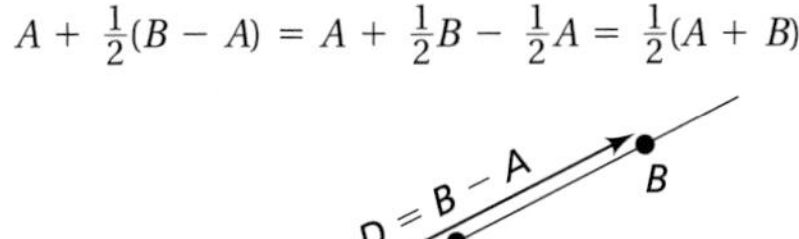

If a and b are numbers, their mean is given by $\frac{1}{2}(a + b)$.

The midpoint is halfway from A to B. There is nothing special about half. What if you wanted to go $\frac{1}{3}$ of the way from A to B?

Example 2

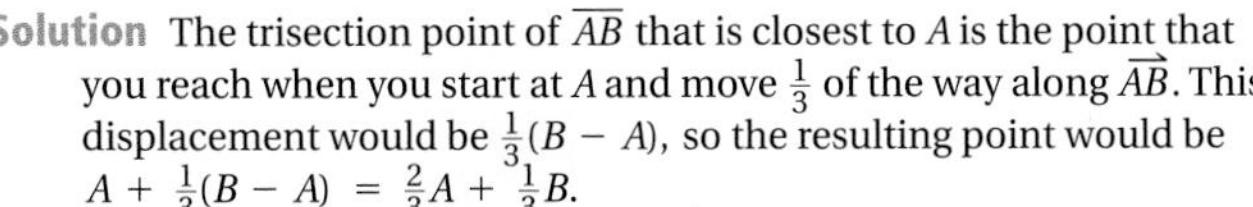

Problem Find a formula similar to the midpoint formula, but for the *trisection* points of a segment.

Solution The trisection point of $\overline{AB}$ that is closest to A is the point that you reach when you start at A and move $\frac{1}{3}$ of the way along $\overrightarrow{AB}$. This displacement would be $\frac{1}{3}(B - A)$, so the resulting point would be $A + \frac{1}{3}(B - A) = \frac{2}{3}A + \frac{1}{3}B$.

But there are two trisection points. You also want to find the point that is $\frac{2}{3}$ of the way from A to B. That would be the same as starting at B and finding the point $\frac{1}{3}$ of the way to A, so the two endpoints change roles in the formula. The second trisection point will be $B + \frac{1}{3}(A - B) = \frac{2}{3}B + \frac{1}{3}A$.

This idea could work for any real number k between 0 and 1.

Lesson Overview

GOAL

- Use convex and affine combinations to locate specific points, such as the midpoint and trisection points of a line segment.

In Chapter 7 of CME Project *Geometry*, students first saw the "algebra of points." If your students used a different geometry curriculum, they may not have seen this before, so you may want to spend a bit more time discussing what it means to add two points or to scale a point by a factor k. Some of the terminology (convex, affine) is new no matter what. But the payoff is worth it. In the end, students will look at an expression such as $-P + 2Q$ or $\frac{1}{3}A + \frac{2}{3}B$, interpret it as a point, and know exactly where it is relative to points P and Q (or A and B).

Then, in the second half of the lesson, students apply this knowledge to proving various classical geometry theorems. The proofs are simpler than the classical Euclidean proofs. Whether this impresses the students depends on how much they know about the classical proofs. And of course, the particular choice of theorems is due to the fact that you can prove them with these vector methods.

How natural the proofs in this lesson will seem to students depends in part on how accustomed they are to thinking about vectors in terms of their displacements. If they see $\overrightarrow{AB}$ will they know immediately that in a vector equation of a line from point A through point B, they should use $D = B - A$? They will if they have come to represent vectors by default in terms of their displacements instead of their endpoints. It is a bigger step if the only vector they naturally associate with ordered pair D is $\overrightarrow{OD}$. Since this chapter gives students and teachers some leeway in their choice of how to think about vectors, this lesson may vary in difficulty depending on what your class has done. There are some teacher notes about this later in the lesson.

CHECK YOUR UNDERSTANDING

- Core: 1, 2, 3, 4, 5
- Optional: 6
- Extension: 7

MATERIALS

- graph paper
- graphing calculators

HOMEWORK

- Core: 8, 9, 13, 14
- Optional: 11
- Extension: 10, 12

VOCABULARY

- affine combination
- centroid
- concurrent
- convex combination
- median

Launch

Go right to work on Example 1, which justifies the midpoint formula using vector algebra. Then continue to the generalization of the midpoint formula to the arbitrary affine combination

continued on p. 518

continued from p. 517

$(1 - k)A + kB$. Understanding that this point is "k of the way" from A to B, and what that means, is crucial if the students are to succeed at the proofs in the second half of the lesson. Insist that the students think about this and talk about it.

Explore

Example 1, p. 517

Students may suggest a simpler picture and slightly amended computation:

$$\begin{aligned} M &= A + \tfrac{1}{2}\overrightarrow{AB} \\ &= A + \tfrac{1}{2}(B - A) \\ &= A + \tfrac{1}{2}B - \tfrac{1}{2}A \\ &= \tfrac{1}{2}B - \tfrac{1}{2}A \\ &= \tfrac{1}{2}(A + B) \end{aligned}$$

It depends on how you think about vectors. If for you (and your class) the displacement *is* the vector and so all arrows with the same displacement are *the same* vector, then you can indeed write $\overrightarrow{AB} = B - A$ and $\frac{1}{2}\overrightarrow{AB} = \frac{1}{2}(B - A)$. With this interpretation $\overrightarrow{AB}$ is simply another name for the vector $B - A$, a name that identifies it as having a picture with an arrow that goes from point A to point B.

But if you think of vectors with the same displacement as *equivalent*, rather than equal, and the vector as the particular arrow, not the displacement, then you cannot write $\overrightarrow{AB} = B - A$ because these things are not equal at all. You cannot even write $\frac{1}{2}\overrightarrow{AB}$ because the only legal names for vectors are names that identify a tail and head. Earlier parts of CME Project use the latter approach (equivalence). This lesson noted earlier that there are actually these two approaches, and you and your students may have adopted the former. However, the text is written so that it makes sense under both approaches.

In any event, at some point it is quite likely that a student will write something like $\frac{1}{2}\overrightarrow{AB} = \frac{1}{2}(B - A)$ and you will have to discuss whether this is really in agreement with how you have been using the concepts and notation. If you want to force the issue, assign Exercise 12. You can also allow students to have a "flexible," more-informal interpretation that they can formalize in later courses that use vectors.

For Discussion

It is fun for the students to defend their answers in terms of their intuitive meaning of "k of the way" but they need to understand that in the

For You to Do

1. Show that, for any points A and B, the point k of the way from A to B is
$$(1 - k)A + kB$$

Actually, nothing in the algebra of this exercise requires k to be between 0 and 1. For any real number k, define *k of the way from A to B* to mean the point $A + k(B - A) = (1 - k)A + kB$. For instance, going twice the way from A to B ($k = 2$) means $A + 2(B - A) = A + (B - A) + (B - A)$, the point you get to when you go all the way from A to B and then go as far again.

For Discussion

Pick two points A and B and find the point with the following property.

2. 1.5 of the way from A to B
3. -1 of the way from A to B
4. 3 of the way from A to B
5. 0 of the way from A to B

The point $C = (1 - k)A + kB$ has a special name. If $0 \le k \le 1$, C is called a **convex combination** of A and B, because it is on the line segment between them. For any k whatsoever, C is called an **affine combination** of A and B, because C is on the line determined by A and B. Indeed,

- The line segment $\overline{AB}$ is the set of all points $(1 - k)A + kB$ for $0 \le k \le 1$.
- The line $\overleftrightarrow{AB}$ is the set of all points $(1 - k)A + kB$ for all real numbers k.

Remember...

Affine is just a fancy word for linear.

Vector Proofs of Geometry Theorems

Vector geometry, especially affine combinations, leads to algebraic proofs of many geometry theorems.

Example 3

Problem Prove the Midline Theorem. Let $\triangle ABC$ be any triangle. Let P and Q be the midpoints of sides $\overline{AB}$ and $\overline{BC}$, respectively. Then $\overline{PQ}$ is parallel to $\overline{AC}$ and half as long.

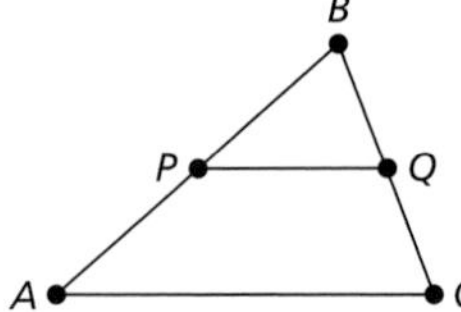

Answers

For You to Do

1. $A + k(B - A) = A - kA + kB$
$= (1 - k)A + kB$

For Discussion

2. Beyond B along $\overleftrightarrow{AB}$, half as far again as the distance from A to B.
3. Beyond A along $\overleftrightarrow{AB}$, as far as A is from B.
4. Beyond B along $\overleftrightarrow{AB}$, twice as far again as the distance from A to B.
5. A

on Show that $\overrightarrow{PQ}$ is parallel to and half as long as $\overrightarrow{AC}$ by relating their isplacements. Specifically, show that $Q - P = \frac{1}{2}(C - A)$.

Jse convex combinations: $P = \frac{1}{2}(A + B)$ and $Q = \frac{1}{2}(B + C)$. Then

$$Q - P = \frac{1}{2}(B + C) - \frac{1}{2}(A + B) = \frac{1}{2}C - \frac{1}{2}A = \frac{1}{2}(C - A)$$

ince $Q - P = \frac{1}{2}(C - A)$, $\overline{PQ}$ is half as long and in the same direction s $\overline{AC}$.

You to Do

rove: In $\triangle ABC$, if P is k of the way from A to B, and Q is k of the way from to B, then $\overline{PQ}$ is parallel to $\overline{AC}$. Also determine the ratio of PQ and AC.

Jow consider a famous theorem. A line segment from a vertex of a triangle the midpoint of the opposite side is called a **median.** A set of lines or egments are **concurrent** if they share a common point. For two lines to be oncurrent is pretty common, but for three or more lines to be concurrent always surprising.

rem 6.8

n any triangle, the three medians are concurrent. Moreover, on each edian the common point is $\frac{2}{3}$ the distance from the vertex to the pposite side.

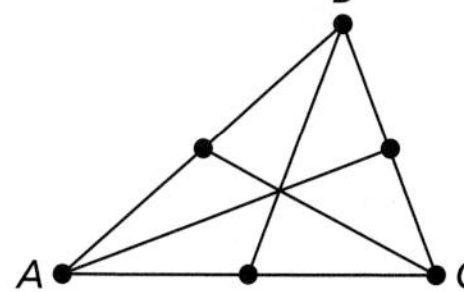

his common point is called the centroid of the triangle.

First, mark the midpoints as convex combinations.

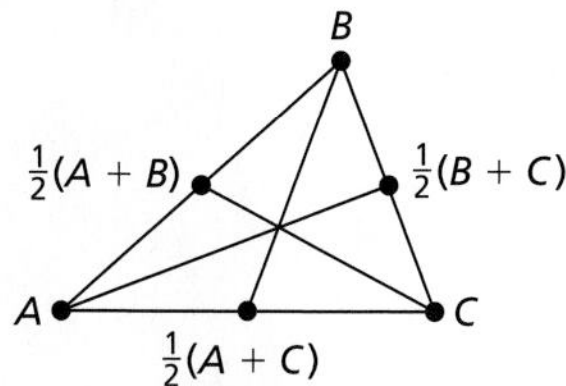

For You to Do

6. $Q - P = ((1 - k)C + kB) - ((1 - k)A + kB) = (1 - k)(C - A)$

So $\overline{PQ}$ is parallel to $\overline{AC}$ and $1 - k$ as long.

end it is the definition that counts: P is k of the way if $P = A + k\overrightarrow{AB} = (1 - k)A + kB$
The vector expression on the left is the easier one to intuit, but the one on the right is the simpler one for computations, and the one that is important in the theorems to come in this lesson.

Wrap Up

You might have the students explain the proofs of Theorem 6.8 and Theorem 6.9 to each other, in their own words. Then go over the core Check Your Understanding exercises as time allows.

Assessment Resources

Lesson Quiz 6.13

1. a. Verify that the figure below is a rhombus by showing that all four sides are equivalent.
   b. Compute the midpoint of the diagonal $\overline{PR}$.
   c. Compute the midpoint of the diagonal $\overline{SQ}$.

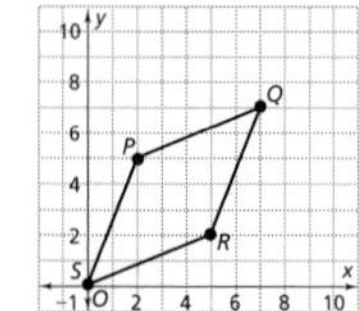

2. Given the arbitrary triangle *DEF* below, show that the centroid or point of intersection of all three medians is $\frac{2}{3}$ the distance from each vertex to the opposite side.

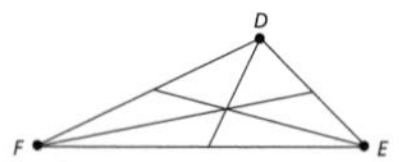

Next, compute the point $\frac{2}{3}$ of the way from A to $\frac{1}{2}(B + C)$.

$$\left(1 - \tfrac{2}{3}\right)A + \tfrac{2}{3}\left(\tfrac{1}{2}(B + C)\right) = \tfrac{1}{3}A + \tfrac{1}{3}B + \tfrac{1}{3}C$$

You can make similar computations for the other medians. The same simplified form, $\frac{1}{3}(A + B + C)$, appears for each. This is the same point for all three medians, so it is a point of concurrency.

Here is one more example. This one makes use of the assumption of parallel lines.

Remember...

The name *centroid* turns out to be doubly appropriate. It is geometrically and algebraically central. What could be more central to *A, B, C* than their average?

Theorem 6.9

In any parallelogram, the diagonals bisect each other.

Proof Let *ABCD* be a parallelogram, as shown.

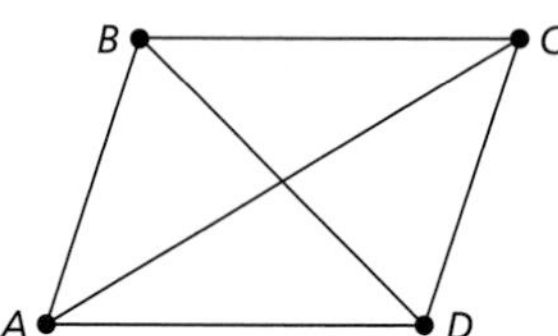

The proof requires showing that the midpoints of the diagonals are the same, so start by calculating each midpoint as an affine combination. The midpoint of $\overline{AC}$ is $\frac{1}{2}(A + C)$. The midpoint of $\overline{BD}$ is $\frac{1}{2}(B + D)$. The two expressions do not even involve the same letters.

But this is a parallelogram. In a parallelogram, opposite sides are parallel and equal in length. That means $\overrightarrow{AB}$ and $\overrightarrow{DC}$ are equivalent. So $B - A = C - D$. Add $A + D$ to both sides and divide by 2.

$$B - A = C - D$$
$$B + D = A + C$$
$$\tfrac{1}{2}(B + D) = \tfrac{1}{2}(A + C)$$

So the two midpoints are the same point, and the diagonals bisect each other.

Notice that with the vector algebra methods introduced so far, you can prove theorems about parallel lines and ratios of lengths. There are many other kinds of theorems you can prove with vector algebra, for instance, theorems about figures with right angles. But these require additional features of vector algebra that you have not seen yet.

Parallelogram faces and intersecting diagonals are conspicuous features of the remarkable Puerta de Europa office buildings in Madrid, Spain. The towers are mirror images of each other and lean at a striking 15°.

Answers

Exercises

1. **a.** $\overrightarrow{AB} = B - A = (3, 1) - (0, 0) = (3, 1)$. Similarly, $\overrightarrow{DC} = C - D = (4, 5) - (1, 4) = (3, 1)$. Therefore, sides $\overline{AB}$ and $\overline{DC}$ are parallel and equal in length, and *ABCD* must be a parallelogram.
   b. (2, 2.5)
   c. (2, 2.5)
2. Answers may vary. Samples:
   - Find the midpoints of two opposite sides, say $\overline{AB}$ and $\overline{CD}$, draw the "midline" segment between them, and take the midpoint of that segment:
   $$\frac{\frac{1}{2}(A + B) + \frac{1}{2}(C + D)}{2} = \frac{A + B + C + D}{4}$$
   - Draw both diagonals and mark the midpoints of each. Now take the midpoint of the segment between them:
   $$\frac{\frac{1}{2}(A + C) + \frac{1}{2}(B + D)}{2} = \frac{A + B + C + D}{4}$$
3. **a.** They bisect each other. The midpoint of $\overline{PR}$ is:
   $$\frac{P + R}{2} = \frac{\frac{1}{2}(A + B) + \frac{1}{2}(C + D)}{2} = \frac{A + B + C + D}{4}$$
   The midpoint of $\overline{QS}$ is also $\frac{A + B + C + D}{4}$. So the two lines intersect at their midpoints, bisecting each other.
   b. They are parallel and equal in length. Prove that $Q - P = R - S$ to show that these are equivalent vectors:
   $$Q - P = \frac{B + C}{2} - \frac{B + A}{2} = \frac{C - A}{2}$$
   $$R - S = \frac{C + D}{2} - \frac{A + D}{2} = \frac{C - A}{2}$$

Exercises *Practicing Habits of Mind*

Check Your Understanding

1. a. Verify that the figure shown below is a parallelogram by showing that opposite sides are equivalent.
   b. Compute the midpoint of the diagonal $\overline{AC}$
   c. Compute the midpoint of the diagonal $\overline{BD}$.

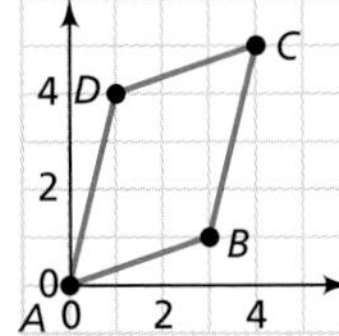

2. Consider any quadrilateral $ABCD$. Describe a method to construct the point $\frac{A+B+C+D}{4}$.

3. Let P, Q, R, and S be the midpoints of the sides of an arbitrary quadrilateral $ABCD$.

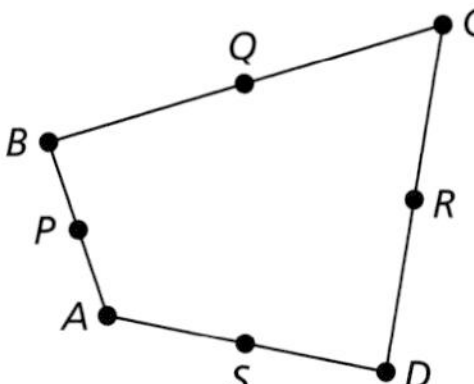

   a. Make a conjecture about the intersection of $\overline{PR}$ and $\overline{QS}$, then prove it.
   b. Make a conjecture about $\overline{PQ}$ and $\overline{RS}$, then prove it.

4. Let $A = (1, 3)$ and $B = (4, 2)$.
   a. Plot the points

$$A, \quad B, \quad A + B, \quad A + \tfrac{1}{2}B, \quad \tfrac{3}{2}A, \quad \tfrac{3}{2}B$$

   b. Verify that $A + \frac{1}{2}B$ is the midpoint of the segment from A to $(A + B)$.
   c. Show that no matter how you choose A and B, $A + \frac{1}{2}B$ is the midpoint of the segment from A to $(A + B)$.
   d. Show that no matter how you choose A and B, $A + \frac{1}{2}B$ is a trisection point of the segment from $\frac{3}{2}A$ to $\frac{3}{2}B$.

Exercises

HOMEWORK

- Core: 8, 9, 13, 14
- Optional: 11
- Extension: 10, 12

Check Your Understanding

EXERCISE 1 Students have already seen a proof of the theorem that states the diagonals of a parallelogram bisect each other. So some of them may compute the midpoint of the first diagonal and then cite the theorem to justify their claim that the midpoint of the second diagonal is the same. Others will do the computation of the midpoint of the second diagonal anyway, and be comforted when it comes out to be the same point. They will use the exercise as a check of their point-computation skills.

EXERCISE 2 It may seem a little out of place to ask students to figure out a construction that will give a point defined in terms of point algebra here. The purpose of this exercise is really to have students consider a geometric interpretation of the expression $\frac{A+B+C+D}{4}$. What does it mean? Where is this point in relation to the four points A, B, C, and D?

EXERCISE 3 You might remind students of the related work in Investigation 6A.

The vectors are equivalent, so $\overline{PQ}$ and $\overline{RS}$ are equal in length and parallel.

4. a.

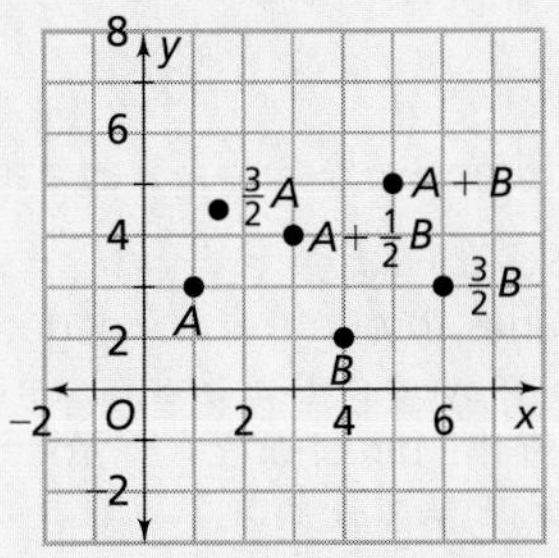

b. $\frac{1}{2}[A + (A + B)] = \frac{1}{2}[(1, 3) + (5, 5)] = (3, 4) = (1, 3) + \frac{1}{2}(4, 2)$

c. The midpoint of the segment from A to $(A + B)$ is $\frac{A + (A + B)}{2} = A + \frac{1}{2}B$.

d. For any points C, D, the trisection point of $\overline{CD}$ closer to C is $\frac{2}{3}C + \frac{1}{3}D$. Therefore, the trisection point closer to $\frac{3}{2}A$ of the segment from $\frac{3}{2}A$ to $\frac{3}{2}B$ is $\frac{2}{3}\left(\frac{3}{2}A\right) + \frac{1}{3}\left(\frac{3}{2}B\right) = A + \frac{1}{2}B$.

5. In triangle ABC, let P be the trisection point of $\overline{AB}$ closer to A. Let Q be the trisection point of $\overline{AC}$ closer to A. Let S be the intersection point of $\overline{BQ}$ and $\overline{CP}$.

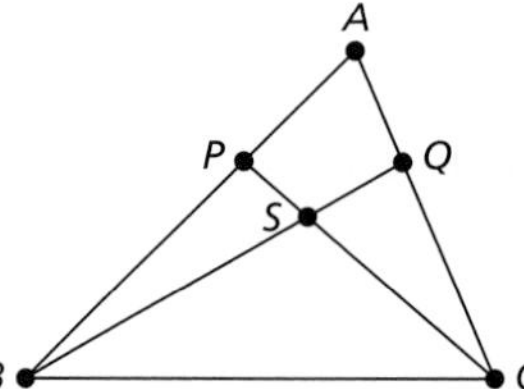

a. In what ratio does S divide $\overline{PC}$?

b. In what ratio does S divide $\overline{QB}$?

c. Prove that S is on the median from A (the line segment from A to the midpoint of $\overline{BC}$).

d. In what ratio does S divide this median line?

6. Here is another proof that the diagonals of a parallelogram bisect each other. Instead of naming the vertices A, B, C, and D, label just one point and label two different sides with their direction vectors.

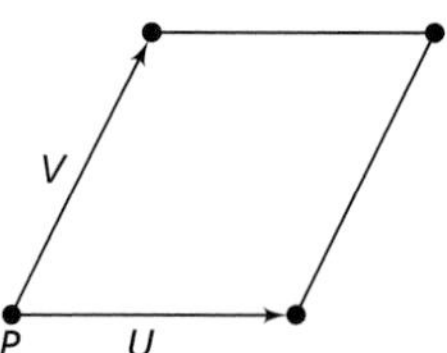

Name all the vertices of the parallelogram in terms of these labels, then compute the midpoints of the two diagonals.

7. **Take It Further** Prove that if both pairs of opposite sides of a quadrilateral are parallel, then both pairs are also equal in length. Explain why you can start with the following figure.

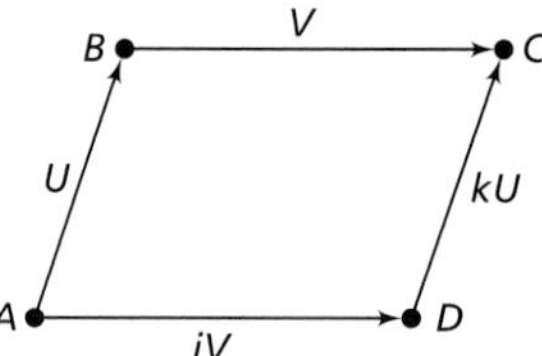

Answers

5. a. 1 to 3
   b. 1 to 3
   c. The quarter point of $\overline{PC}$, the quarter point of $\overline{QB}$, and the midpoint of the median, are all $\frac{1}{2}A + \frac{1}{4}B + \frac{1}{4}C$. Therefore, they are all the same point.
   d. S bisects the median line.

6. The parallelogram can be fully labeled using the given information:

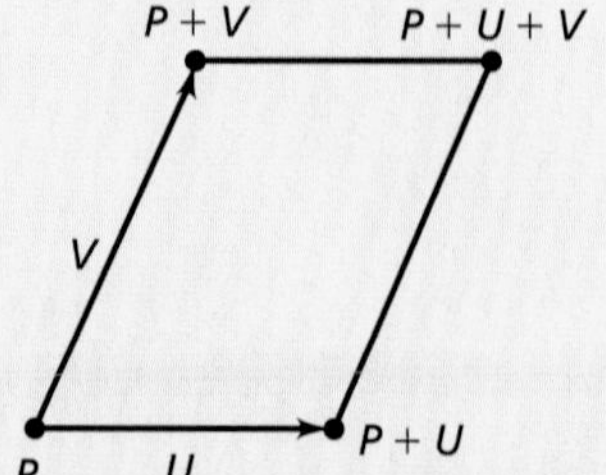

The midpoint of both diagonals is $P + \frac{1}{2}(U + V)$, so the diagonals bisect each other.

7. Two sides are parallel if the direction vector for one is a scalar multiple of the direction vector for the other. So the figure includes the givens. To show that opposite sides have equal length, you have to show that $k = j = 1$. By the parallelogram law,

$$U + V = jV + kU$$

$$(1 - k)U = (j - 1)V$$

But since U and V are not parallel, the only way two multiples of them could be equal is if the coefficients are 0. That is

$$(1 - k) = (j - 1) = 0$$

Which implies $k = j = 1$ as desired.

8. $(1 - k)A + kB = A + k(B - A)$. If k varies through all nonnegative numbers, you get all points starting at A in the direction of B. You get beyond B when $k > 1$.

On Your Own

8. The ray $\overrightarrow{AB}$ is the infinite halfline starting at point A, going straight through B, and continuing forever. Explain why the set of points on this ray is

$$(1 - k)A + kB, \quad k \geq 0 \qquad \text{or} \qquad A + k(B - A), \; k \geq 0$$

9. Let A, B, and C be the vertices of a triangle.

a. Show that you can represent every point D inside the triangle is in the form $aA + bB + cC$, where $a, b, c > 0$ and $a + b + c = 1$. Such a sum is called a *three-way convex combination.*

b. Assuming the conditions in part (a), where in the triangle is $aA + bB + cC$ if exactly one of a, b, or c is 0? If exactly two of a, b, or c are 0?

If D is in the interior, draw a segment from some vertex, through D, to the opposite side. Call the intersection point with the opposite side E.

10. Take It Further A *tetrahedron* is a solid in three dimensions with four vertices. See the figure. In a triangle you can draw a line from each vertex to the midpoint of the opposite side. Also, you know that the medians all intersect in a point.

In a tetrahedron you can picture drawing a line segment from each vertex to the centroid of the opposite face. Determine if these four lines also intersect in a point. Prove your result.

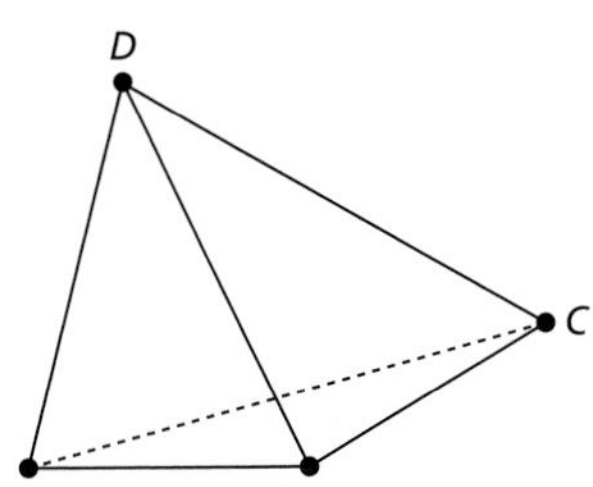

11. Start with an arbitrary triangle ABC. Draw the line segment from A to the midpoint of $\overline{BC}$. but then extend it equally far outside the triangle to P. Locate Q using B and R using C similarly, as in the figure. Conjecture and prove a result about $\triangle PQR$.

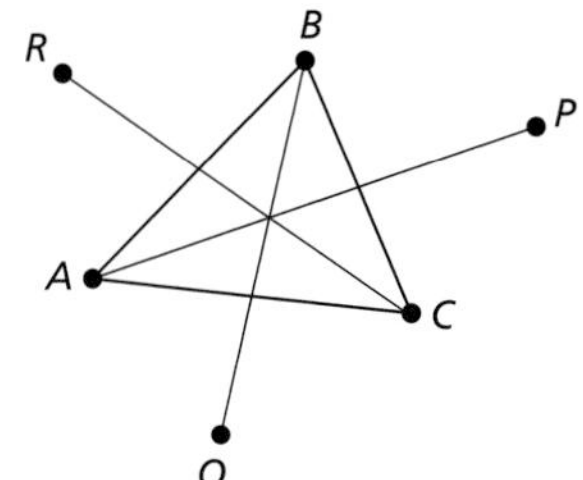

Go Online PHSchool.com

For additional practice, go to Web Code: bga-0613

On Your Own

EXERCISE 10 Building models can really help students visualize this result.

EXERCISE 11 Many students are able to understand k of the way best for $0 \leq k \leq 1$, and find values of k greater than 1 problematic. Encourage them to sketch the situation as they think about it.

10. Yes, all four intersect three-fourths of the way from the vertex to the centroid of the other side. The intersection point is $\frac{A + B + C + D}{4}$.
$\frac{A + B + C + D}{4} = \frac{1}{4}A + \frac{3}{4}\left(\frac{B + C + D}{3}\right)$

11. See back of book.

9. a. Given point D inside the triangle. Draw a line from vertex A through D to E on side $\overline{BC}$. Since E is between B and C, E is a convex combination of B and C, and $E = (1 - k)B + kC$ for some k with $0 < k < 1$. Because D is some convex combination of A and E, then $D = (1 - j)A + jE$ for some j with $0 < j < 1$. By substitution, $D = (1 - j)A + j(1 - k)B + jkC$. These coefficients, $1 - j$, $j(1 - k)$, jk, are a, b, c. All of these must be positive, and $(1 - j) + j(1 - k) + jk = 1 - j + j - jk + jk = 1$

b. Suppose $c = 0$. Then the point D is a convex combination of A and B and so is on the perimeter on side $\overline{AB}$. In general, if exactly one of a, b, c is 0, then the point is on the perimeter.

For the case of two zero coefficients, if $b = c = 0$, then $a = 1$ and the point is A. If two coefficients are zero, the point is a vertex.

EXERCISE 12 is a nice exercise to model with geometry software.

Additional Resources

PRINT RESOURCES
- Solution Manual
- Practice Workbook
- Assessment Resources
- Teaching Resources

TECHNOLOGY
- Interactive Textbook
- TeacherExpress CD-ROM
- ExamView CD-ROM
- PHSchool.com

Additional Practice

1. a. Verify that the figure shown at the right is a parallelogram by showing that the opposite sides are equivalent.
   b. Compute the midpoint of $\overline{XZ}$.
   c. Compute the midpoint of $\overline{WY}$.

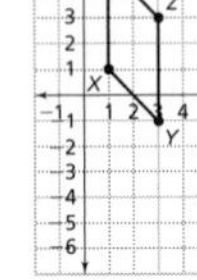

2. Assume $ABCD$ is any trapezoid where $\overline{AG}$ is parallel to $\overline{CD}$, P is the midpoint of $\overline{AD}$, and Q is the midpoint of $\overline{BC}$. Prove that $\overline{PQ}$ is parallel to $\overline{AB}$ and $\overline{CD}$ and that $\frac{AB + CD}{2} = PQ$.

3. Let $A = (2, 4)$ and $B = (8, 12)$.
   a. Plot the points $A, B, A + \frac{1}{4}B, A + \frac{1}{2}B, \frac{3}{2}A, 2A$.
   b. Verify that $A + \frac{1}{4}B$ is the midpoint of the segment from A to $\left(A + \frac{1}{2}B\right)$.
   c. Verify that $\frac{3}{2}A$ is the midpoint of the segment from A to $2A$.

4. Use vector geometry to prove that the diagonals of a rhombus bisect each other.

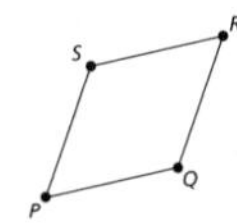

5. Use the vector identity $A + B + C + D = 0$ to prove that the midpoints of a quadrilateral form a parallelogram.

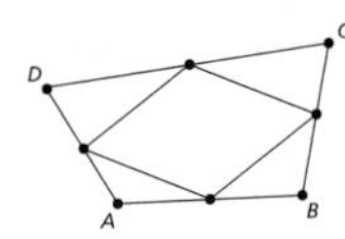

Practice: For Lesson 6.13, assign Exercises 1–5.

12. **Take It Further** Draw an arbitrary quadrilateral $ABCD$. Place a point P anywhere you like, as in the figure below. Construct a segment through A with P as an endpoint and A as its midpoint. Begin at the endpoint X of this new segment and construct another segment, this time with B as the midpoint. Continue doing this until you construct a segment with D as the midpoint. Label the finishing point Q in the figure.

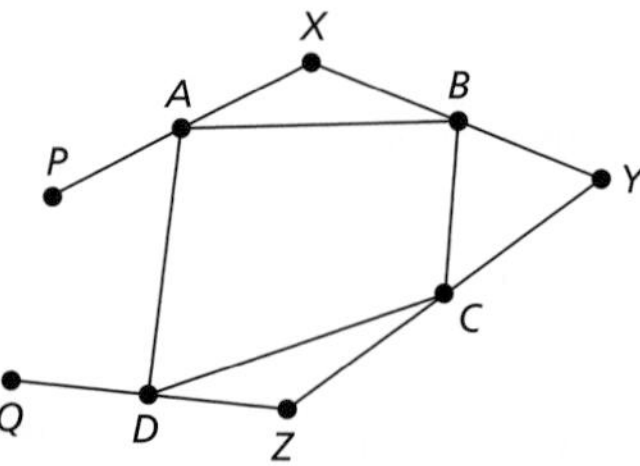

   a. Draw $\overrightarrow{QP}$. If you change P's location, $\overrightarrow{QP}$ changes location but not displacement. That is, $P - Q$ is constant, independent of the value of P. Prove this.

   $P - Q$ is not independent of the values of A, B, C, and D.

   b. When does $Q = P$? In light of part (a), the answer depends only on the original quadrilateral $ABCD$, not on P.

13. **Standardized Test Prep** Given the diagram as shown, which of the following represents the point $\frac{3}{7}$ of the way along the bold vector from the tip of V toward the tip of U?

   A. (0, 1) **B.** (−3, −4)
   C. (−4, −3) **D.** (−1, 1)

U
V
(0, 0)

Maintain Your Skills

14. So far you have seen affine combinations of points. There are also affine combinations of sets. Let P be a point and S a set of points. Then $(1 - k)P + kS$ is the set of all points $(1 - k)P + kQ$, where $Q \in S$.

   On a piece of graph paper, mark P and draw S from the following figure. Then determine the sets below.

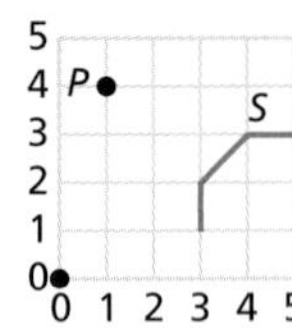

   a. $\frac{1}{2}P + \frac{1}{2}S$ (this is a convex combination of P and S)

   b. $\frac{1}{4}P + \frac{3}{4}S$ c. $\frac{3}{2}P - \frac{1}{2}S$ d. $-P + 2S$

Answers

12. a. Since X is an affine combination of P and A with $k = 2$, then

$$X = -P + 2A$$

and similarly

$$\begin{aligned} Y &= -X + 2B \\ Z &= -Y + 2C \\ Q &= -Z + 2D \\ &= -(-Y + 2C) + 2D \\ &= Y - 2C + 2D \\ &= (-X + 2B) - 2C + 2D \\ &= -X + 2B - 2C + 2D \\ &= -(-P + 2A) + 2B - 2C + 2D \\ &= P - 2(A - B + C - D) \end{aligned}$$

So $P - Q = 2(A - B + C - D)$, which is independent of the location of P.

b. when $ABCD$ is a parallelogram

13. C

14.

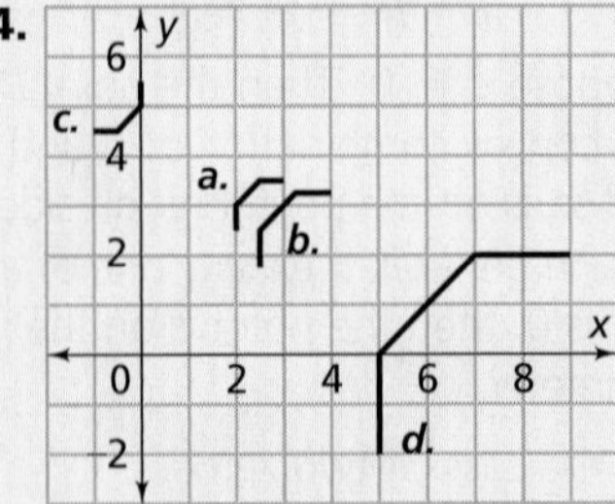

In this investigation, you expressed familiar geometric ideas in terms of vectors. You applied the basic rules of vector algebra to prove geometric facts. The following questions will help you summarize what you have learned.

1. Express the line containing the points $A(3, -1)$ and $B(5, 9)$ in vector form.
2. The vectors $U = (a, 0)$ and $V = (b, c)$ define the quadrilateral $ABCD$, with vertices $A(b, c)$, $B(a + b, c)$, $C(a, 0)$, and $D(0, 0)$. Express the diagonals of $ABCD$ in terms of vectors U and V.
3. Use vector methods to prove that quadrilateral $ABCD$ with vertices $A(0, 0)$, $B(5, 0)$, $C(8, 4)$, and $D(3, 4)$ is a rhombus. Confirm that its diagonals are perpendicular.
4. Determine which, if any, of the following vector equations have the same graph as $X = (1, -3) + t(3, 4)$.
   - $X = (1, -3) + t(6, 8)$
   - $X = (-1, 3) + t(-3, -4)$
   - $X = (7, 5) + t(3, 4)$
5. Given points $A(2, 5)$ and $B(6, -3)$, let M be the midpoint of $\overline{AB}$. Find the midpoint of $\overline{MB}$.
6. How can you interpret the matrix operations of sum and scalar product geometrically?
7. Why might it be useful to write an equation of a line in vector form?
8. How can you use vectors to prove that the medians of a triangle are concurrent?

Vocabulary

In this investigation, you learned these terms. Make sure you understand what each one means and how to use it.

- **affine combination**
- **centroid**
- **concurrent**
- **convex combination**
- **dilation**
- **head and tail of a vector**
- **median**
- **parameter**
- **parametric equations**
- **scaling**
- **vector, $\overrightarrow{AB}$**
- **vector equations**

Mathematical Reflections

EXERCISES 6–8 At the start of the investigation, you may have assigned these as Questions 1–3 for students to think and write about.

8. Given ΔABC, develop an equation for each of the three median lines in vector form, then solve the system of three equations to show that there is a unique point in common.

Mathematical Reflections

1. Answers may vary. Samples: $X = (3, -1) + t(10, 2)$ and $X = (5, 9) + t(10, 2)$.
2. $\overrightarrow{DB} = U + V$, $\overrightarrow{AC} = U - V$ or $\overrightarrow{CA} = V - U$
3. Compute the lengths of the 4 sides of the quadrilateral to determine that $AB = BD = CD = AC = 5$. Since all 4 sides have the same length, $ABDC$ is a rhombus.
4. the first equation and the third equation
5. $(5, -1)$
6. You can interpret the sum of two matrices geometrically as adding two vectors with tails at the origin and heads at the coordinates given by the row entries. A scalar product is a dilation with center at the origin.
7. Writing the equation of a line in vector form enables you to represent time and describe movement along the line.

Project

The basic idea of this project is to analyze the graph of the *general quadratic*

$$rx^2 + sxy + ty^2 + ux + vy + w = 0$$

It turns out that the graph is always a conic (possibly degenerate), and that you can tell the nature of the conic from the sign of $4rt - s^2$. Students build some very good intuitions by carefully working through Exercises 1–14.

To complete the entire project, students should know the results from the Chapter 4 project from CME Project *Algebra 2*. If they have not done this project, you could work through or simply state those results (below) with a few examples and tell students to use the results in the rest of the project. Or, you might just want to assign Exercises 1–14 and leave it at that.

The complete project really does tie many loose ends together, however. Here are the prerequisites from *Algebra 2:*

Students need to know properties of trace, transpose, and determinant for a 2 × 2 matrix

$$\begin{pmatrix} a & b \\ c & d \end{pmatrix}$$

Determinant

1. $\det\begin{pmatrix} a & b \\ c & d \end{pmatrix} = \begin{vmatrix} a & b \\ c & d \end{vmatrix} = ad - bc$
2. $\det AB = \det A \det B$
3. $\det A^{-1} = \frac{1}{\det A}$

Transpose

1. ${}^t\begin{pmatrix} a & b \\ c & d \end{pmatrix} = \begin{pmatrix} a & c \\ b & d \end{pmatrix}$
2. ${}^t(AB) = {}^tB\,{}^tA$

Trace

1. $\text{Tr}\begin{pmatrix} a & b \\ c & d \end{pmatrix} = a + d$
2. $\text{Tr}(A) = \text{Tr}({}^tA)$
3. $\text{Tr}(AB) = \text{Tr}(BA)$

Project: Using Mathematical Habits

The General Quadratic

In this chapter, you learned that the graph of any equation of the form

$$rx^2 + ty^2 + ux + vy + w = 0$$

is a conic. And you can tell what kind of conic you have by the sign of rt. You proved the following theorem.

Theorem 6.6

The graph of

$$rx^2 + ty^2 + ux + vy + w = 0$$

is a (possibly degenerate) conic. In fact, the nature of the conic is determined by the sign of rt:

- **If $rt > 0$, the graph is an ellipse.**
- **If $rt = 0$, the graph is a parabola.**
- **If $rt < 0$, the graph is a hyperbola.**

The equation

$$rx^2 + ty^2 + ux + vy + w = 0$$

is a quadratic equation in x and y. But it is not the most general one. The general quadratic in x and y is of the form

$$rx^2 + sxy + ty^2 + ux + vy + w = 0$$

The degree of each term is at most 2, the degree of each of the terms rx^2, sxy and ty^2 is 2, the degree of each of ux and vy is 1, and the degree of w is 0.

In this project, you will generalize Theorem 6.6. Start out by graphing these equations. Use any method you like. See the TI-Nspire™ Technology Handbook on page 704 for ideas about how to graph these equations.

1. $x^2 - xy + y^2 = 1$

2. $x^2 - xy + y^2 = 4$

3. $x^2 + xy + y^2 = 1$

4. $x^2 + xy + y^2 = 4$

5. $41x^2 - 24xy + 34y^2 = 51$

6. $41x^2 - 24xy + 34y^2 = 90$

7. $5x^2 + 15xy + 2y^2 = 8$

8. $5x^2 - 10xy + 5y^2 - 10y = 8$

9. $9x^2 + 24xy + 16y^2 = 49$

10. $xy = 1$

11. $xy = -1$

12. $13x^2 + 10xy + 13y^2 = 47$

13. $13x^2 + 10xy + 13y^2 = 0$

14. Write and Reflect Make your own quadratic equation graph gallery.

a. Sketch or generate 10 particularly interesting graphs of quadratic equations in two variables, in addition to the ones above.

b. Give an equation for each graph.

c. Describe what you find interesting about each graph. Make believe you are preparing a guided tour in an art museum, except the pictures are graphs of quadratic equations in two variables. Try adding some linear terms to some of the ones you graphed above.

Graphing all these equations gives some evidence that the graph of a general quadratic is a (possibly degenerate) conic. (Can you tell what kind of conic you will get from the equation before you graph it?) For equations with a nonzero xy term, the conic seems to be rotated—its axes are not parallel to the coordinate axes.

Answers

Project

1. $x^2 - xy + y^2 = 1$

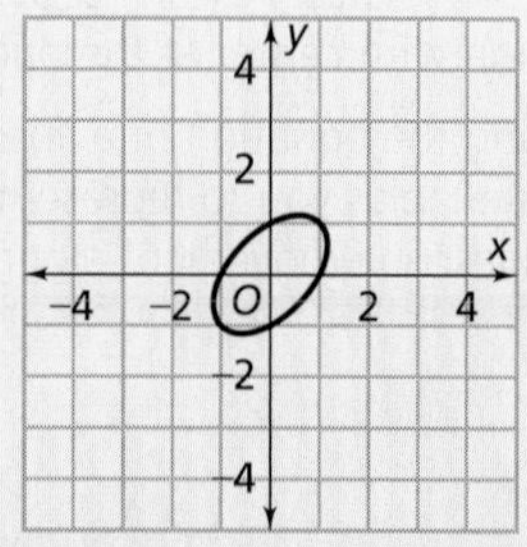

2. $x^2 - xy + y^2 = 4$

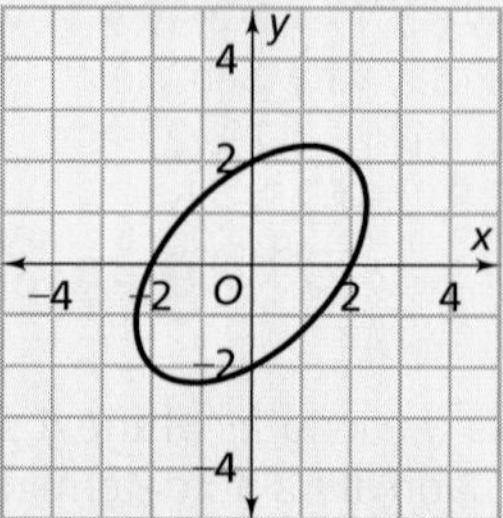

3–12. See back of book.

13. (0, 0)

14. Check students' work.

It seems as though the graph of the general quadratic is a conic. Assume that this is true and reason from that assumption. Sometimes, when you do this, you get to a place that tells you that your assumption is, in fact, correct. And even when this does not happen, you often get to a place that shows how to refine your assumption so that it is correct.

The strategy is to start with an equation, say

$$41x^2 - 24xy + 34y^2 = 51 \qquad (1)$$

and assume that its graph is a rotated conic. If that is so, by how much should you rotate the graph so that its axes are parallel to the x and y axes? Another way to ask the question is, "How should you transform x and y to x' and y' so that the equation in x' and y' that corresponds to (1) has no xy-term?"

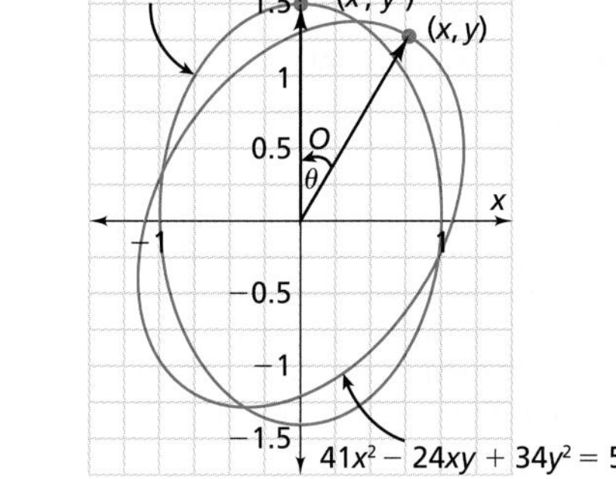

In the picture above, you have the graph of

$$41x^2 - 24xy + 34y^2 = 51$$

The graph looks like an ellipse (see Exercise 5). If you rotate the ellipse counterclockwise about the origin through some angle θ (that you need to find), you can turn the ellipse "upright." So, if (x, y) is any point on the original ellipse, and (x', y') is the image of (x, y) under a rotation about the origin through θ, (x', y') will satisfy an equation with no xy-term of the form

$$r(x')^2 + t(y')^2 = w$$

for numbers r, t, and w, because this is form of the equation of an upright ellipse centered at the origin. The question is how to find the precise angle θ that does the trick. This requires that you figure out how to rotate points about the origin.

15. Find x' and y' in terms of x and y if you obtain (x', y') from (x, y) by each of the given rotations.

a. 90° counterclockwise about the origin

b. 45° counterclockwise about the origin

c. counterclockwise through an angle of $\cos^{-1}\frac{3}{5}$ about the origin

d. counterclockwise through an angle of $\cos^{-1}\frac{5}{13}$ about the origin

e. counterclockwise through an angle of θ about the origin

16. a. Show that if

$$R_\theta = \begin{pmatrix} \cos\theta & -\sin\theta \\ \sin\theta & \cos\theta \end{pmatrix}$$

and if

$$\begin{pmatrix} x' \\ y' \end{pmatrix} = R_\theta \begin{pmatrix} x \\ y \end{pmatrix}$$

then you can obtain (x', y') from (x, y) by a counterclockwise rotation through an angle θ about the origin.

EXERCISE 15 There are many ways to derive the rotation formulas. One that you might want to encourage is through the use of complex numbers.

Suppose $P = (x, y)$ is a point in $\mathbb{R}^2$. If you want to rotate P through an angle of θ about the origin, think of P as a point $x + iy$ in $\mathbb{C}$, multiply it by cisθ, and then convert back from $\mathbb{C}$ to $\mathbb{R}^2$. The result is

$$x' = \cos\theta\ x - \sin\theta\ y$$
$$y' = \sin\theta\ x + \cos\theta\ y$$

or

$$\begin{pmatrix} x' \\ y' \end{pmatrix} = \begin{pmatrix} \cos\theta & -\sin\theta \\ \sin\theta & \cos\theta \end{pmatrix}\begin{pmatrix} x \\ y \end{pmatrix}$$

EXERCISE 16 Geometrically, $R_{-\theta}$ "undoes" the rotation carried out by R_θ.

15. a. $x' = -y,\ y' = x$

b. $x' = \frac{\sqrt{2}}{2}(x - y)$,

$y' = \frac{\sqrt{2}}{2}(x + y)$

c. $x' = \frac{3}{5}x - \frac{4}{5}y,\ y' = \frac{4}{5}x + \frac{3}{5}y$

d. $x' = \frac{5}{13}x - \frac{12}{13}y,\ y' = \frac{12}{13}x + \frac{5}{13}y$

e. $x' = x\cos\theta - y\sin\theta$,

$y' = x\sin\theta + y\cos\theta$

16. a. Multiplying this matrix yields:

$$\begin{pmatrix} x' \\ y' \end{pmatrix} = \begin{pmatrix} \cos\theta & -\sin\theta \\ \sin\theta & \cos\theta \end{pmatrix}\begin{pmatrix} x \\ y \end{pmatrix}$$

$x' = x\cos\theta - y\sin\theta$

$y' = x\sin\theta + y\cos\theta$

This matches the answer from part (e) of Exercise 15 above.

b. Show that

$$(R_\theta)^{-1} = {}^tR_\theta = R_{-\theta}$$

(Recall that ${}^tA$ denotes the transpose of the matrix A.)

Study this example.

Problem Analyze the graph of

$$41x^2 - 24xy + 34y^2 = 51 \qquad (1)$$

Solution The equation (1) can be written as

$$(xy)\begin{pmatrix} 41 & -12 \\ -12 & 34 \end{pmatrix}\begin{pmatrix} x \\ y \end{pmatrix} = 51$$

You would like to change variables via rotation through some angle θ

$$\begin{pmatrix} x' \\ y' \end{pmatrix} = \begin{pmatrix} \cos\theta & -\sin\theta \\ \sin\theta & \cos\theta \end{pmatrix}\begin{pmatrix} x \\ y \end{pmatrix}$$

so that the resulting equation in x' and y' has no xy-term. Solve the equation

$$\begin{pmatrix} x' \\ y' \end{pmatrix} = R_\theta\begin{pmatrix} x \\ y \end{pmatrix}$$

for the old variables by multiplying both sides of this equation by the inverse of R_θ.

$$(R_\theta)^{-1}\begin{pmatrix} x' \\ y' \end{pmatrix} = \begin{pmatrix} x \\ y \end{pmatrix}$$

or

$$\begin{pmatrix} \cos\theta & \sin\theta \\ -\sin\theta & \cos\theta \end{pmatrix}\begin{pmatrix} x' \\ y' \end{pmatrix} = \begin{pmatrix} x \\ y \end{pmatrix}$$

or

$$\cos\theta x' + \sin\theta y' = x$$
$$-\sin\theta x' + \cos\theta y' = y \qquad (2)$$

Just to remove clutter, let $m = \cos\theta$ and $n = \sin\theta$. Substitute (2) in (1):

$$41(mx' + ny')^2 - 24(mx' + ny')(-nx' + my') + 34(-nx' + my')^2 = 51 \qquad (3)$$

Using a CAS to expand the left side, the coefficient of $x'y'$ is

$$-24m^2 + 14mn + 24n^2$$

So, you want this to be 0. That is, you want

$$-24m^2 + 14mn + 24n^2 = 0$$

One solution is (0, 0), but that does not help. (Why?) So, assume $m \neq 0$ and divide both sides by m^2 to get an equation in $\frac{n}{m} = \tan\theta$.

$$-24 + 14\left(\frac{n}{m}\right) + 24\left(\frac{n}{m}\right)^2 = 0$$

Fingers crossed, hope that the roots of this are real. They are. (Is this an accident?) You find that

$$\tan\theta = \frac{3}{4} \quad \text{or}$$

$$\tan\theta = -\frac{4}{3}$$

Either will work because you can rotate in two directions to make the graph sit straight. Pick $\tan\theta = \frac{3}{4}$ so that

$$\cos\theta = \frac{4}{5}$$

and

$$\sin\theta = \frac{3}{5}$$

From here, you can get the equation of the rotated conic. It is all an algebraic calculation.

17. Find the equation of the rotated conic.

18. Carry out this analysis for the equation from Exercise 2

$$x^2 - xy + y^2 = 4$$

If you work out a few more examples, a certain rhythm develops in the calculations, one that allows you to carry out an analysis of the general quadratic, leading to a general classification theorem. The key idea is that you can write the expression

$$rx^2 + sxy + ty^2$$

as

$$(xy)\begin{pmatrix} r & \frac{s}{2} \\ \frac{s}{2} & t \end{pmatrix}\begin{pmatrix} x \\ y \end{pmatrix}$$

Answers

16. b. If $R_\theta = \begin{pmatrix} \cos\theta & -\sin\theta \\ \sin\theta & \cos\theta \end{pmatrix}$, then

$$(R_\theta)^{-1}\begin{pmatrix} \cos\theta & -\sin\theta \\ \sin\theta & \cos\theta \end{pmatrix}^{-1} = \begin{pmatrix} \cos\theta & \sin\theta \\ -\sin\theta & \cos\theta \end{pmatrix}$$

$${}^tR_\theta = \begin{pmatrix} \cos\theta & -\sin\theta \\ \sin\theta & \cos\theta \end{pmatrix}^T = \begin{pmatrix} \cos\theta & \sin\theta \\ -\sin\theta & \cos\theta \end{pmatrix}$$

$$R_{-\theta} = \begin{pmatrix} \cos(-\theta) & -\sin(-\theta) \\ \sin(-\theta) & \cos(-\theta) \end{pmatrix} = \begin{pmatrix} \cos\theta & \sin\theta \\ -\sin\theta & \cos\theta \end{pmatrix}$$

17. $50x^2 + 25y^2 = 51$

18. $\cos\theta = \frac{\sqrt{2}}{2}$, $\sin\theta = \frac{\sqrt{2}}{2}$;

$\frac{1}{2}x^2 + \frac{3}{2}y^2 = 4$

19. 1. $x^2 - xy + y^2 = 1$

$$\delta = \frac{4 \cdot 1 \cdot 1 - (-1)^2}{4} = \frac{3}{4}$$

$\delta > 0$, therefore the graph is an ellipse.

2. $x^2 - xy + y^2 = 4$

$$\delta = \frac{4 \cdot 1 \cdot 1 - (-1)^2}{4} = \frac{3}{4}$$

$\delta > 0$, therefore the graph is an ellipse.

3. $x^2 + xy + y^2 = 1$

$$\delta = \frac{4 \cdot 1 \cdot 1 - 1^2}{4} = \frac{3}{4}$$

$\delta > 0$, therefore the graph is an ellipse.

4. $x^2 + xy + y^2 = 4$

$$\delta = \frac{4 \cdot 1 \cdot 1 - 1^2}{4} = \frac{3}{4}$$

$\delta > 0$, therefore the graph is an ellipse.

5. $41x^2 - 24xy + 34y^2 = 51$

$$\delta = \frac{4 \cdot 41 \cdot 34 - (-24)^2}{4} = 1250$$

$\delta > 0$, therefore the graph is an ellipse.

Through a rotation, you can transform the matrix to one of the form

$$\begin{pmatrix} r' & 0 \\ 0 & t' \end{pmatrix}$$

If you keep track of the algebra, you will find that you need to find θ so that

$$R_\theta \begin{pmatrix} r & \frac{s}{2} \\ \frac{s}{2} & t \end{pmatrix} (R_\theta)^{-1} = \begin{pmatrix} r' & 0 \\ 0 & t' \end{pmatrix}$$

You saw in the investigation that the sign of $r't'$ determines the nature of a conic. But this is the determinant of the right side. So, it is also the determinant of the left side. By a result in your earlier algebra course this determinant is the same as the determinant of the middle matrix on the left side—that is

$$rt - \left(\frac{s}{2}\right)^2$$

Technical details remain, but this is the basic idea behind the full classification theorem.

Theorem 6.10

The graph of

$$rx^2 + sxy + ty^2 + ux + vy + w = 0$$

depends only on the determinant

$$\delta = \begin{vmatrix} r & \frac{s}{2} \\ \frac{s}{2} & t \end{vmatrix} = rt - \left(\frac{s}{2}\right)^2 = \frac{4rt - s^2}{4}$$

More precisely,

- **If $\delta < 0$, the graph is a (possibly degenerate) hyperbola.**
- **If $\delta = 0$, the graph is a (possibly degenerate) parabola.**
- **If $\delta > 0$, the graph is a (possibly degenerate) ellipse.**

19. Verify the theorem for each of the examples in Exercises 1–13.

20. **Take It Further** Prove Theorem 6.10.

6. $41x^2 - 24xy + 34y^2 = 90$

$$\delta = \frac{4 \cdot 41 \cdot 34 - (-24)^2}{4} = 1250$$

$\delta > 0$, therefore the graph is an ellipse.

7. $5x^2 + 15xy + 2y^2 = 8$

$$\delta = \frac{4 \cdot 5 \cdot 2 - 15^2}{4} = -46.25$$

$\delta < 0$, therefore the graph is a hyperbola.

8. $5x^2 - 10xy + 5y^2 - 10y = 8$

$$\delta = \frac{4 \cdot 5 \cdot 5 - (-10)^2}{4} = 0$$

$\delta = 0$, therefore the graph is a parabola.

9. $9x^2 + 24xy + 16y^2 = 49$

$$\delta = \frac{4 \cdot 9 \cdot 16 - 24^2}{4} = 0$$

$\delta = 0$, therefore the graph is a parabola.

10. $xy = 1$

$$\delta = \frac{4 \cdot 0 \cdot 0 - 1^2}{4} = -\frac{1}{4}$$

$\delta < 0$, therefore the graph is a hyperbola.

11. $xy = -1$

$$\delta = \frac{4 \cdot 0 \cdot 0 - (-1)^2}{4} = -\frac{1}{4}$$

$\delta < 0$, therefore the graph is a hyperbola.

12. $13x^2 + 10xy + 13y^2 = 47$

$$\delta = \frac{4 \cdot 13 \cdot 13 - 10^2}{4} = 144$$

$\delta > 0$, therefore the graph is an ellipse.

13. $13x^2 + 10xy + 13y^2 = 0$

$$\delta = \frac{4 \cdot 13 \cdot 13 - 10^2}{4} = 144$$

$\delta > 0$, therefore the graph is an ellipse (degenerate).

20. See back of book.

Answers

Chapter Review

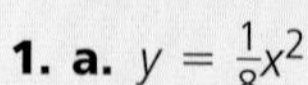

1. a. $y = \frac{1}{8}x^2$

b.

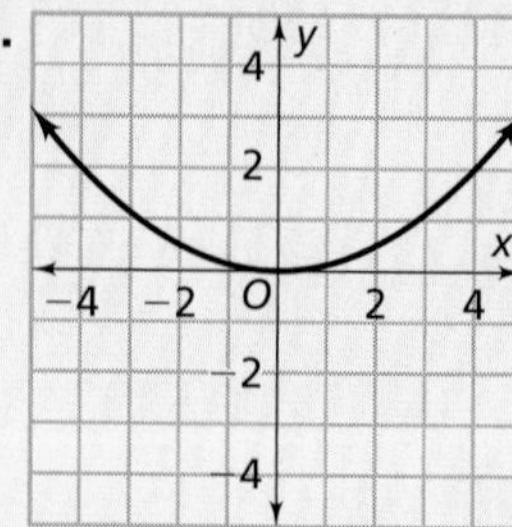

2. a. Let the vertices of the trapezoid be $A(0, 0)$, $B(b, 0)$, $C(c, h)$, and $D(d, h)$, where $\overline{AB}$ and $\overline{CD}$ are the parallel sides. Let M be the midpoint of $\overline{AD}$ and N be the midpoint of $\overline{BC}$.

b. The slopes of $\overline{MN}$, $\overline{AB}$, $\overline{CD}$ are all 0, so they are all parallel.

3. a. The center is $(-2, 6)$ and the radius is 3.

b.

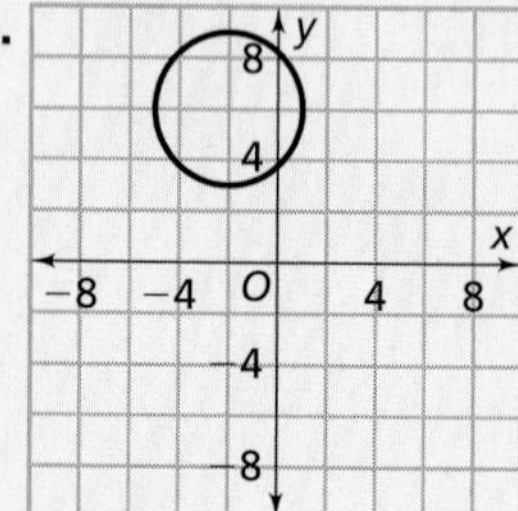

c. 16

d. −7

4. a. $y = \frac{1}{8}x^2$

b.

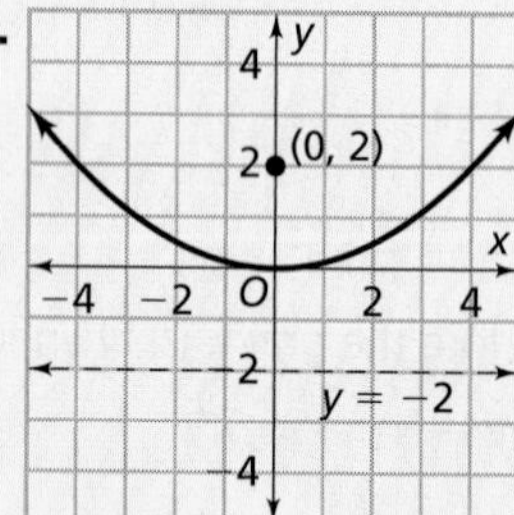

5. a. $e = \frac{3}{5}$

b. $(0, -2)$ and $(0, 6)$

c. $\frac{x^2}{25} + \frac{(y-2)^2}{16} = 1$

d.

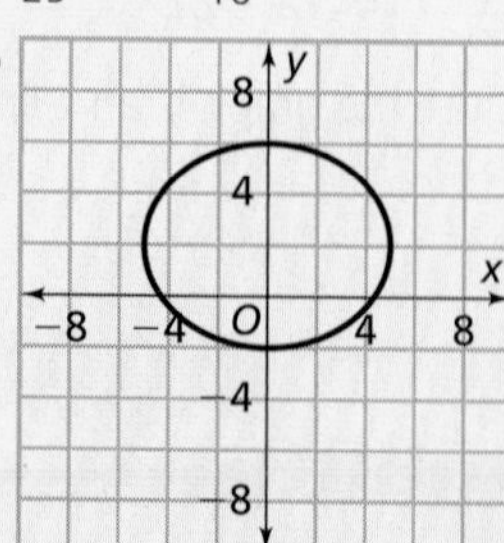

6. • $9x^2 - 4y^2 - 36x - 8y - 4 = 0$

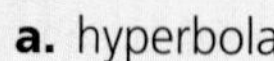

a. hyperbola

b. Center $(2, -1)$; foci $(2 \pm \sqrt{13}, -1)$

c. $e = \frac{\sqrt{13}}{2} \approx 1.803$

d.

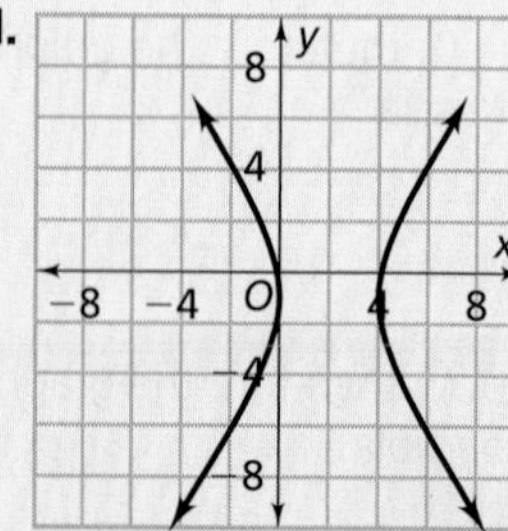

• $9x^2 + y^2 + 54x + 4y + 76 = 0$

a. ellipse

b. Center $(-3, -2)$; foci $(-3, -2 \pm \sqrt{8})$

c. $e = \frac{\sqrt{8}}{3} \approx 0.943$

d.

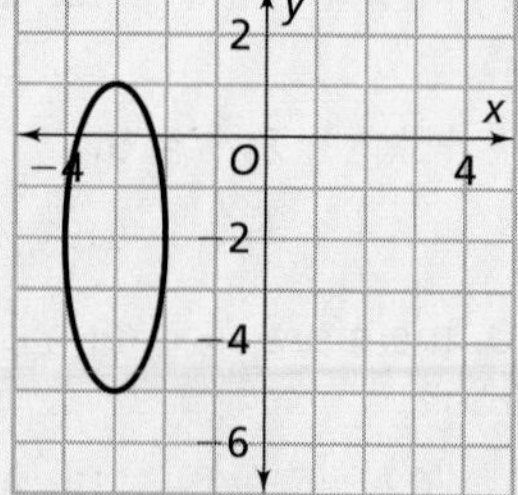

Chapter 6 Review

For vocabulary review, go to Web Code: bgj-0651

In **Investigation 6A,** you learned to

- sketch the graphs of equations in two variables
- use distance and slope relationships to prove geometric results
- evaluate and use the signed power of a point with respect to a circle

The following questions will help you check your understanding.

1. a. Find an equation for the set of points equidistant from the point $(0, 2)$ and the line with equation $y = -2$.

b. Sketch a graph of all points satisfying the equation.

2. a. Coordinatize a trapezoid.

b. Prove that the midline of the trapezoid is parallel to its bases.

3. The graph of $x^2 + y^2 + 4x - 12y + 31 = 0$ is a circle.

a. Find the center and the radius of the circle.

b. Sketch the graph of the circle.

c. Find the signed power of point $P(2, 3)$ with respect to the circle.

d. Find the signed power of point $Q(-1, 7)$ with respect to the circle.

In **Investigation 6B,** you learned to

- visualize each of the conic sections as the intersection of a plane with an infinite double cone
- give a locus definition for each of the conic sections
- identify the equations for the graphs of the conic sections, and sketch their graphs

The following questions will help you check your understanding.

4. A parabola has focus $(0, 2)$ and directrix with equation $y = -2$.

a. Find an equation of the parabola.

b. Sketch the graph of the parabola. Graph and label the focus and the directrix.

5. An ellipse has foci $(-3, 2)$ and $(3, 2)$. One endpoint of the major axis is $(5, 2)$

a. Find the eccentricity of the ellipse.

b. Find the endpoints of the minor axis.

c. Find an equation of the ellipse.

d. Sketch the graph of the ellipse.

6. Consider the following equations.

- $9x^2 - 4y^2 - 36x - 8y - 4 = 0$
- $9x^2 + y^2 + 54x + 4y + 76 = 0$

a. Identify the graph of each equation (circle, parabola, ellipse, or hyperbola).

b. Find the coordinates of the center and foci.

c. Find the eccentricity.

d. Sketch the graph of the equation.

In **Investigation 6C,** you learned to

- interpret sums and scalar multiples of ordered pairs geometrically
- express lines with vector equations and solve for intersections and other useful information using these equations
- use convex and affine combinations to locate specific points, such as the midpoint and trisection points of a line segment

The following questions will help you check your understanding.

7. Let $A = (3, 4)$, $B = (-2, 0)$, and $C = (1, -4)$.

a. Plot and label the points A, B, $A + B$, $A + 2B$, and $A - B$.

b. Find the displacement of $\overrightarrow{AB}$. Find the displacement of $\overrightarrow{BA}$.

c. If $\overrightarrow{CD}$ has displacement $(4, 2)$, find D.

d. If $\overrightarrow{DC}$ has displacement of $(4, 2)$, find D.

8. a. Find a vector equation for the line through the points $(1, 3)$ and $(5, 2)$.

b. Name two points on this line.

c. Determine if the point $(-7, 5)$ is on this line.

d. Find the point of intersection of this line with the graph of $X = (-2, 6) + s(1, -1)$.

9. Let $A = (-1, -4)$, $B = (9, 2)$, and $C = (1, 5)$ be the vertices of a triangle.

a. Find the trisection points for side $\overline{AC}$.

b. Find the centroid of the triangle.

c. Point P is k of the way from A to B. Find P if $k = \frac{1}{4}$.

d. Point P is k of the way from A to B. Find P if $k = 2$.

9. a. $\left(-\frac{1}{3}, -1\right)$ and $\left(\frac{1}{3}, 2\right)$

b. $(3, 1)$

c. $P = \left(\frac{3}{2}, -\frac{5}{2}\right)$

d. $P = (19, 8)$

7. a. $A + B = (1, 4)$, $A + 2B = (-1, 4)$, $A - B = (5, 4)$

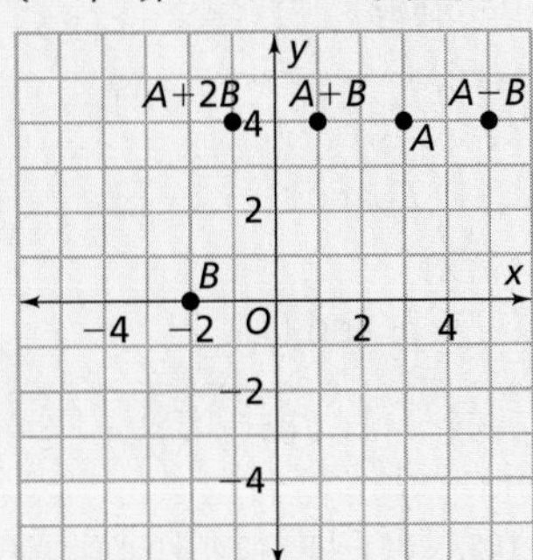

b. The displacement of $\overrightarrow{AB}$ is $(-5, -4)$. The displacement of $\overrightarrow{BA}$ is $(5, 4)$.

c. $D = (5, -2)$

d. $D = (-3, -6)$

8. a. $X = (1, 3) + t(4, -1)$ or $X = (5, 2) + t(-4, 1)$.

b. Answers may vary. Samples: $(9, 1)$ and $(-3, 4)$

c. yes

d. $(1, 3)$

Test

Assessment Resources

Chapter Test Form A page 1

Multiple Choice

1. Find an equation for the set of points equidistant from the points $(-6, 5)$ and $(2, 1)$.
   A. $y = 2x + 4$ B. $y = -\frac{1}{2}x + 2$ C. $y = 2x + 7$ D. $y = \frac{1}{2}x + 4$

2. The length of the major axis of an ellipse is 50. The length of the minor axis is 14. Find the eccentricity of the ellipse.
   A. $\frac{24}{25}$ B. 0.28 C. $\frac{25}{7}$ D. $\frac{32}{25}$

3. Which of the following is NOT a vector equation for the line through the points $(-3, 5)$ and $(5, 1)$?
   A. $X = (-3, 5) + t(8, -4)$ B. $X = (5, 1) + t(-4, 2)$
   C. $X = (5, 1) + t(-8, -4)$ D. $X = (-3, 5) + t(4, -2)$

4. Let $U = (2, 3)$ and $V = (-1, 5)$. Find $\frac{1}{4}U + \frac{3}{4}V$.
   A. $\left(\frac{5}{4}, -3\right)$ B. $\left(\frac{1}{2}, 4\right)$ C. $\left(\frac{5}{4}, \frac{7}{2}\right)$ D. $\left(-\frac{1}{4}, \frac{9}{2}\right)$

5. Given $\triangle RST$, determine which of the following must lie on a line from R to the midpoint of $\overline{ST}$.
   A. $\frac{2}{3}R + \frac{1}{3}(S + T)$ B. $\frac{1}{3}R + \frac{2}{3}\left(\frac{1}{2}(S + T)\right)$
   C. $R + S + T$ D. $\frac{1}{2}R + \frac{1}{2}(S + T)$

Open Response

6. The graph of the equation $x^2 + y^2 - 8x + 6y = 0$ is a circle.
   a. Calculate the signed power of the point $P(2, -5)$ and describe its location with respect to the circle.
   b. Calculate the signed power of the point $P(2, 2)$ and describe its location with respect to the circle.

7. Consider the set of points that are equidistant from the point $(0, 3)$ and the line with equation $y = -1$.
   a. Write an equation that describes this set of points.
   b. Determine if this equation represents a conic. If it does, state what kind of conic.
   c. Sketch the graph of this set of points.

Also available: Form B

Test

Go Online PHSchool.com For a chapter test, go to Web Code: bga-0653

Multiple Choice

1. Determine the equation in the form $y = a(x - h)^2 + k$ for the parabola having focus $(3, 4)$ and directrix the x-axis.
   A. $y = 8(x - 4)^2 + 3$
   B. $y = \frac{1}{4}(x - 3)^2 + 4$
   C. $y = \frac{1}{8}(x - 3)^2 + 2$
   D. $y = 3(x - 4)^2 + \frac{1}{2}$

2. Find the type of conic given by the equation $12x^2 + 2y^2 - 72x + 20y - 206 = 0$.
   A. circle
   B. ellipse
   C. hyperbola
   D. parabola

3. A hyperbola has foci $(4, 6)$ and $(-8, 6)$ and one endpoint of the major axis is $(-1, 6)$. Find the eccentricity of the hyperbola.
   A. 6 B. $\frac{1}{8}$ C. 8 D. $\frac{1}{6}$

4. Determine which of the following is an equation of a degenerate conic.
   A. $(x - 2)^2 + (y + 5)^2 = 49$
   B. $x^2 + y^2 - 4x + 14y + 53 = 0$
   C. $\frac{(x - 3)^2}{16} + \frac{(y - 1)^2}{12} = 1$
   D. $x^2 - 4y^2 - 6x + 40y + 18 = 0$

5. Determine which of the following points is on the graph of $X = (-1, 4) + t(2, 6)$.
   A. $(1, 8)$
   B. $(5, 20)$
   C. $(-1, -3)$
   D. $(-5, -8)$

6. Find a vector equation for the line through the points $(4, 7)$ and $(-3, 9)$.
   A. $X = (0, 4) + t(4, 7)$
   B. $X = (1, 2) + t(-7, 2)$
   C. $X = (4, 7) + t(-7, 2)$
   D. $X = (-3, 9) + t(4, 7)$

7. Determine which of the points would form a parallelogram with the three points on the graph.

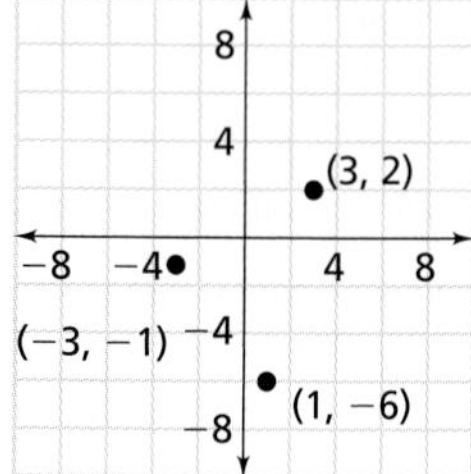

   A. $(0, 2)$
   B. $(-1, 6)$
   C. $(-1, 7)$
   D. $(-2, 4)$

8. An ellipse has foci $(10, -4)$ and $(-4, 10)$. Find the coordinates of the center.
   A. $(3, 3)$
   B. $(-6, 6)$
   C. $(-3, 6)$
   D. $(7, 7)$

9. Consider the line with parametric equation $X = (3, -1) + t(-1, 5)$. Which of the following is a Cartesian equation for the line?
   A. $y = \frac{1}{5}x + 3$
   B. $y = -\frac{1}{5}x + 1$
   C. $y = 5x + 3$
   D. $y = -5x + 14$

Answers

Chapter Test

1. C
2. B
3. A
4. B
5. D
6. C
7. C
8. A
9. D
10. B

11. a. Radius: 15; center: $(-2, 13)$
    b. -200; the point is inside the circle.
    c. 0; the point is on the circle.
12. a. Yes; ellipse
    b.

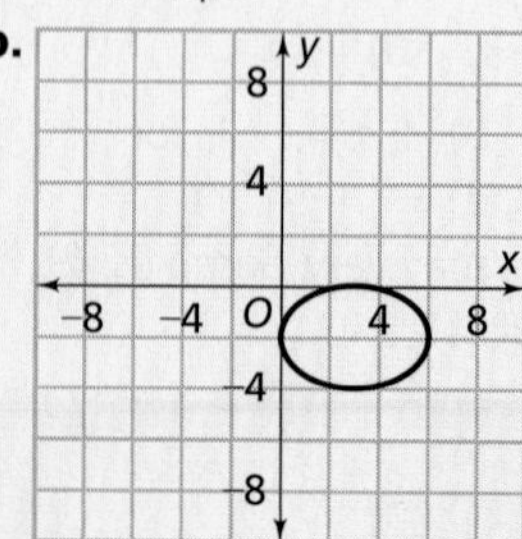

13. a. $y^2 = 16x - 32$
    b. parabola
14. a. vertical
    b. $(-1, -9)$
    c. $(-1, 7)$ and $(-1, -13)$
15. a. $(1, 2)$
    b. $(-9, 2)$ and $(11, 2)$
    c. $\frac{(x - 1)^2}{100} + \frac{(y - 2)^2}{64} = 1$
16. a. no
    b. Yes; Car A at hour 2 and Car B at hour 3

10. A hyperbola is centered at $(-6, 4)$ and has foci $(-11, 4)$ and $(-1, 4)$. Find which of the equations gives this hyperbola.

A. $\frac{(x+4)^2}{16} - \frac{(y-6)^2}{9} = 1$

B. $\frac{(x+6)^2}{16} - \frac{(y-4)^2}{9} = 1$

C. $\frac{(x-6)^2}{16} - \frac{(y+4)^2}{9} = 1$

D. $\frac{(x-6)^2}{9} - \frac{(x+4)^2}{16} = 1$

Open Response

11. The graph of the equation

$$x^2 + y^2 + 4x - 26y - 52 = 0$$

is a circle.

a. Find the radius and center of the circle.

b. Calculate the signed power of the point $(1, 17)$ and describe its location with respect to the circle.

c. Calculate the signed power of the point $(7, 25)$ and describe its location with respect to the circle.

12. Consider the equation

$$4x^2 + 9y^2 - 24x + 36y + 36 = 0$$

a. Determine if this equation represents a conic. If it does, state what kind of conic.

b. Sketch the graph of the equation.

13. Consider the set of points that are equidistant from the point $(6, 0)$ and the line with equation $x = -2$.

a. Write an equation that describes this set of points.

b. Determine what type of conic this set describes.

14. An ellipse is centered at $(-1, -3)$ with a focus at $(-1, 3)$ and eccentricity $\frac{3}{5}$.

a. Find the major axis of the ellipse.

b. Find the coordinates of the other focus.

c. Find the vertices of the ellipse.

15. An ellipse has foci $(-5, 2)$ and $(7, 2)$ and string length 20.

a. Find the center of the ellipse.

b. Find the coordinates of the vertices.

c. Write an equation of the ellipse.

16. Two cars drive along straight, flat lines. At time t, Car A is at $(80, 60) + t(10, 15)$ and Car B is at $(40, 15) + t(20, 25)$.

a. Determine if the cars collide. If they do, find at what time.

b. Determine if their paths intersect. If they do, find at what time each car passes the intersection point.

17. Consider the equation $\frac{(x-4)^2}{144} - \frac{(y+7)^2}{81} = 1$.

a. Find what type of conic is given by the graph of this equation.

b. Find the center and foci.

c. Sketch the graph of the equation.

18. Let L be the line through $(4, 6)$ with direction vector $(2, -5)$. Find y so that $(-2, y)$ is on L.

19. Consider the lines given by the equations $X = (2, 5) + t(-1, -3)$ and $Y = (1, 4) + t(6, -2)$.

a. Graph both lines.

b. Determine if these lines are parallel, perpendicular, or neither.

Chapter Test Form A page 2

8. Two hikers walk along two straight, flat trails. At time t, Hiker A is at $(2, 19) + t(4, 3)$ and Hiker B is at $(4, 10) + t(6, 8)$.
   a. Determine if the hikers meet. If they do, find at what time this occurs.
   b. Determine if the hikers' paths intersect. If they do, find the intersection point and find at what time each hiker passes the intersection point.

9. Let L be the line through $(-4, 7)$ with direction vector $(2, -3)$. For each of the following ordered pairs, find y so that the point is on L.
   a. (x, y) for a given real number x
   b. $(-10, y)$
   c. $(0, y)$
   d. $(6, y)$

10. Find the centroid of $\triangle ABC$ given below.

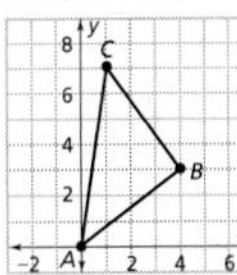

Challenge Problem

11. Define the difference of two vectors $U - V$ as the vector combination $U + (-1)V$.
   a. Let U and V be the direction vectors (a, b) and (c, d), respectively. Show that the direction vectors $U - V$ and $V - U$ are opposites.
   b. Interpret the result from part (a) in terms of the diagonals of a parallelogram.

Also available: Form B

17. a. hyperbola

b. Center: $(4, -7)$; foci: $(-11, -7)$ and $(15, -7)$

c.

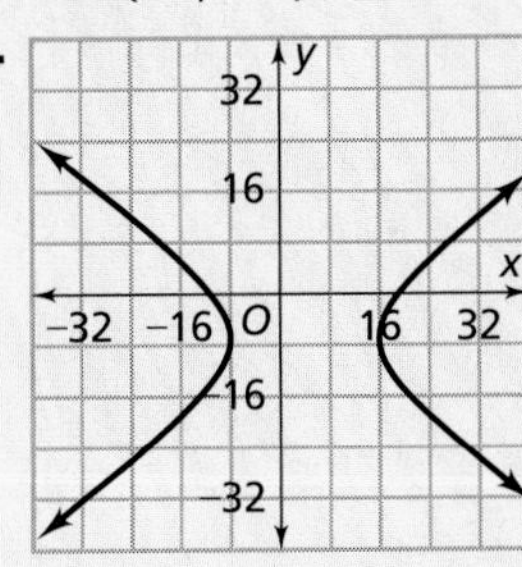

18. 21

19. a.

b. perpendicular

Cumulative Review

Assessment Resources

Quarter Test page 1 of 3

Multiple Choice

1. Suppose you want to prove by mathematical induction that the function $G(n) = 3n^2 + n$ agrees at all nonnegative integer inputs with the function

$$g(n) = \begin{cases} 0 & \text{if } n = 0 \\ 4 & \text{if } n = 1 \\ 2g(n-1) - g(n-2) + 6 & \text{if } n > 1 \end{cases}$$

With which assumption do you begin the inductive step of the proof?
A. $g(1) = 3(1)^2 + 1$ B. $g(n) = 3n^2 + n$
C. $g(n-1) = 3(n-1)^2 + n$ D. $g(k) = 3k^2 + k$ for $k \le (n-1)$

2. Which of the following is a Mahler polynomial?
A. $2x^2$ B. $\frac{x(x-1)}{2}$ C. $\frac{(x+1)(x-1)}{6}$ D. $-x + x^2$

3. How many solutions does the recurrence $f(n) = 5f(n-1)$ have?
A. one B. two C. three D. infinitely many

4. Find an equation for the parabola having focus $(4, -1)$ and directrix with equation $y = -5$.
A. $y = \frac{1}{8}(x-4)^2 - 3$ B. $y = \frac{x^2}{8} + x - 5$
C. $y = \frac{1}{8}(x-4)^2 - 1$ D. $y = 8(x-4)^2 - 5$

5. Determine which of the following is an equation of a degenerate conic.
A. $4(x+1)^2 + 9(y-1)^2 = 1$ B. $(x-2)^2 - 9(y+1)^2 = 9$
C. $x^2 + y^2 + 6x - 4y + 13 = 0$ D. $6x^2 - 24x - y + 21 = 0$

6. Consider the line with parametric equation $X = (-5, 2) + t(2, 1)$. Which of the following is a Cartesian equation for the line?
A. $y = \frac{x}{2} + \frac{9}{2}$ B. $y = -\frac{x}{2} - \frac{1}{2}$ C. $y = -\frac{3}{7}x - \frac{1}{7}$ D. $y = -\frac{2}{5}x - 2$

7. Find the signed power of the point $P(-1, -1)$ with respect to the circle $(x+2)^2 + (y-3)^2 = 16$.
A. 9 B. −3 C. 1 D. −11

Chapter 6

Cumulative Review

1. Find all solutions to the equation $\tan^2 x - 3 = 0$ on $0 \le x \le 2\pi$.

2. A device monitors and regulates the air moisture in a greenhouse. It varies throughout the day according to the equation

$$h = 88.5 + 3.7 \sin \tfrac{\pi}{12}(t - 9)$$

where h is the humidity, in percent, and t is the number of hours after midnight, $0 \le t \le 24$.

   a. Find the maximum humidity and when it occurs.
   b. Find the minimum humidity and when it occurs.
   c. Find the difference between the maximum and minimum values.

3. Simplify the expression.

$$\left(-\tfrac{\sqrt{2}}{2} + i\tfrac{\sqrt{2}}{2}\right)^5$$

4. Consider the identity $\cos(2t) = 2\cos^2 t - 1$.
   a. Let $s = 2t$ so that $t = \frac{s}{2}$. Find an identity for $\cos\frac{s}{2}$.
   b. Use your result in part (a) to find an exact value for cos 15°.
   c. Use your result in part (a) to find an exact value for cos 22.5°.

5. Expand each of the following in powers of $x - 2$.
   a. x^2 b. x^3 c. x^4

6. Find the solution to each equation to three decimal places using logarithms.
   a. $e^x = 5$ b. $e^x = 0.5$
   c. $e^x = 2$ d. $2^x = 5$

7. Lowe High School's student senate has 12 members.
   a. Find the number of ways the senate can choose a 6-member Activities Committee.
   b. Find the number of ways this committee can be formed if they first choose one of the six members as a chairperson.

8. Find the coefficient of the specified term in the expansion of $(a + b)^{10}$.
   a. the a^8b^2 term b. the a^5b^5 term
   c. the a^3b^7 term d. the b^{10} term

9. Let h be defined recursively by

$$h(n) = \begin{cases} -2 & \text{if } n = 0 \\ 2 \cdot h(n-1) + 3n & \text{if } n > 0 \end{cases}$$

Find each of the following values.
   a. $h(1)$ b. $h(2)$ c. $h(3)$ d. $h(4)$

10. Here is the first row of a difference table for a cubic function f. Find $f(4)$.

x	f(x)	Δ	Δ²	Δ³
0	6	2	−3	4

11. Find the set of numbers for which the functions $f(x) = -3x^2 + 2$ and $g(x) = -3x^2 + 2 + x(x-2)(x+3)$ are equal.

12. Here is a partial difference table for a function c. Find $c(4)$.

Input x	Output c (x)	Δ	Δ²	Δ³
0	−8	2	−3	4
1	■	−1	1	4
2	■	■	5	4
3	■	■	■	4

Answers

Cumulative Review

1. $\frac{\pi}{3}, \frac{2\pi}{3}, \frac{4\pi}{3}, \frac{5\pi}{3}$
2. a. 92.2%; 3:00 P.M.
   b. 84.8%; 3:00 A.M.
   c. 7.4%
3. $\frac{\sqrt{2}}{2} - i\frac{\sqrt{2}}{2}$
4. a. $\cos\frac{s}{2} = \pm\sqrt{\frac{\cos s + 1}{2}}$ Determine the proper sign (+ or −) from the context of the problem.
   b. $\frac{\sqrt{2} + \sqrt{6}}{4}$
   c. $\frac{\sqrt{2 + \sqrt{2}}}{2}$
5. a. $(x-2)^2 + 4(x-2) + 4$
   b. $(x-2)^3 + 6(x-2)^2 + 12(x-2) + 8$
   c. $(x-2)^4 + 8(x-2)^3 + 24(x-2)^2 + 32(x-2) + 16$
6. a. 1.609 b. −1.609
   c. 0.693 d. 2.322
7. a. 924 b. 5544
8. a. 45 b. 252
   c. 120 d. 1
9. a. −1 b. 4
   c. 17 d. 46
10. 12
11. {−3, 0, 2}
12. −2

13. Let the function h be defined by $h(x) = x^3 - 2x$. Find a polynomial that agrees with Δh.

14. Use mathematical induction to show that the functions G and g given here must agree for all integers $n \geq 0$.

$$G(n) = 4n - 3$$

$$g(n) = \begin{cases} -3 & \text{if } n = 0 \\ g(n-1) + 4 & \text{if } n > 0 \end{cases}$$

15. The graph of the equation

$$x^2 + y^2 - 4x + 6y - 12 = 0$$

is a circle.

a. Find the center and radius of the circle.

b. Sketch the graph of the circle.

c. Find the exact coordinates of all intercepts.

16. The point $P(0, 0)$ lies inside the circle in Exercise 15. Several chords of the circle defined by the graph of

$$x^2 + y^2 - 4x + 6y - 12 = 0$$

pass through the origin.

a. One such chord lies along the x-axis. Calculate the power of P with respect to this circle using this chord.

b. Find the two intersection points of the circle with the line with equation $y = x$.

c. Use the points found in part (b) to calculate the power of P.

17. Find an equation of the parabola with focus $(0, 2)$ and directrix with equation $y = -2$.

18. The graph of the equation

$$\frac{(x-2)^2}{4} + \frac{(y-3)^2}{k} = 1$$

depends on the value of k. Find the value of k, or the conditions for k, such that the graph of the equation is the specified conic section.

a. a circle

b. an ellipse (but not a circle)

c. a hyperbola

19. Find the eccentricity of the conic section given by each equation.

a. the hyperbola $\frac{x^2}{16} - \frac{y^2}{9} = 1$

b. the ellipse $\frac{x^2}{16} + \frac{y^2}{9} = 1$

c. the parabola $\frac{x^2}{16} - y = 0$

20. Find a vector equation for each line.

a. the graph of $y + 3 = -2(x - 1)$

b. the graph of $y = \frac{2}{5}x + 4$

c. the line through the points $(3, 2)$ and $(6, -4)$

Quarter Test

Open Response

8. Use induction to show that these two definitions agree for all nonnegative integers.

$$Q(n) = -2n + 7$$

$$q(n) = \begin{cases} 7 & \text{if } n = 0 \\ q(n-1) - 2 & \text{if } n > 0 \end{cases}$$

9. Find a closed-form definition for a quadratic polynomial function that fits the table.

Input	Output	Δ	Δ^2
0	−4	−1	3
1	−5	2	3
2	−3	5	3

10. Find a closed-form function definition that agrees for all nonnegative integers with the function

$$f(n) = \begin{cases} 17 & \text{if } n = 0 \\ -f(n-1) + 3 & \text{if } n > 0 \end{cases}$$

11. An ellipse has vertices at $(-3, -2)$ and $(9, -2)$ and one focus at $(7, -2)$.

a. Write an equation for the ellipse.

b. Sketch the graph of the ellipse.

12. Determine the eccentricity e of each conic.

a. $9x^2 - 36y^2 = 324$

b. $9x^2 + 36y^2 = 324$

13. $\Delta h = 3x^2 + 3x - 1$

14. $n = 0$:

$G(0) = -3 = g(0)$

Assume k:

$$\begin{aligned} G(k) = 4k - 3 &= g(k) \\ 4k - 3 &= g(k-1) + 4 \\ g(k-1) &= 4k - 7 \end{aligned}$$

Show $k + 1$:

$$\begin{aligned} G(k+1) = 4k + 1 &\stackrel{?}{=} g(k+1) \\ 4k + 1 &\stackrel{?}{=} g(k) + 4 \\ g(k) &\stackrel{?}{=} g(k+1) - 4 \\ g(k+1) &= g(k) + 4 \end{aligned}$$

15. a. Center: $(2, -3)$; radius: 5

b.

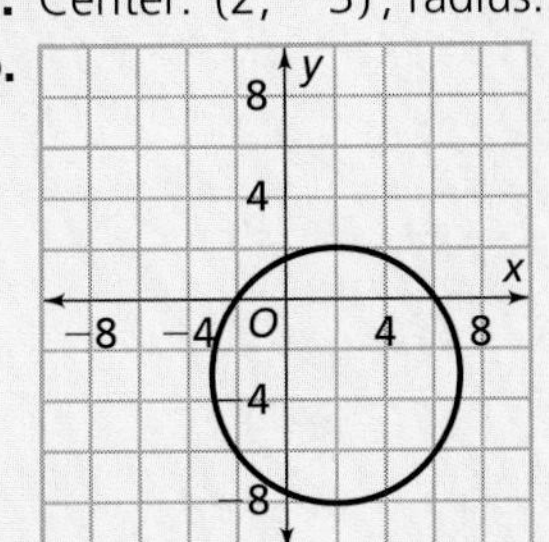

c. $(6, 0)$, $(0, -3 + \sqrt{21})$, $(-2, 0)$, $(0, -3 - \sqrt{21})$

16. a. -12

b. $(2, 2)$, $(-3, -3)$

c. -12

17. $y = \frac{1}{8}x^2$

18. a. $k = 4$

b. $k > 0$, $k \neq 4$

c. $k < 0$

19. a. $\frac{5}{4}$ b. $\frac{\sqrt{7}}{4}$ c. 1

20. a. $X = (1, -3) + t(1, -2)$

b. $X = (0, 4) + t(5, 2)$

c. $X = (3, 2) + t(1, -2)$

Chapter 7
Probability and Statistics

In this chapter, students apply their knowledge of combinatorics to calculate theoretical probabilities in various situations. They develop the idea of a probability distribution and work with several different kinds of distributions, including uniform and binomial. They learn properties of statistical distributions, including the Central Limit Theorem and algebraic properties of standard deviation and variance. They also use a generating polynomial as a tool for representing a discrete distribution.

Chapter Overview

INVESTIGATION 7A, *Probability and Polynomials,* formalizes the language used to describe probability experiments and shows students how to calculate and make sense of expected value as a statistical measure of these experiments.

INVESTIGATION 7B, *Expectation and Variation,* asks students to calculate expected value, variance, and standard deviation, and to draw conclusions about the algebraic structure of these functions.

INVESTIGATION 7C, *The Normal Distribution,* gives students a chance to develop an informal understanding of the Central Limit Theorem and to use the normal distribution.

For more information on the Investigations, see

- Chapter Road Map, pp. 536–537
- Investigation Road Maps, pp. 538, 572, 602

PROJECT The Project near the end of the chapter is optional. You can assign the Project at any time during the chapter depending on how often and how long you feel students should work on it.

Pacing Suggestions and Materials

Investigation 7A ***Probability and Polynomials***

DAY	LESSON	HOMEWORK
1	7.1 Getting Started Core: 1, 2, 3, 4 Optional: none	Core: 5, 6, 7, 8 Optional: 9, 10
2	7.2 Probability and Pascal's Triangle Core: 1, 2, 3, 4 , 5 Optional: none; Extension: 6	Core: 8, 9, 10, 11, 12, 14 Optional: 7, 15; Extension: 13
3	7.3 Polynomial Powers Core: 1, 2, 3, 4, 5, 6 Optional: none	Core: 7, 8, 9, 11, 12, 13 Optional: 14, 15; Extension: 10
4	7.4 Expected Value Core: 1, 2, 3, 4, 6, 7 Optional: 5	Core: 8, 9, 10, 12, 13, 14, 15, 16 Optional: 17; Extension: 11, 18
5	7.5 Lotteries Core: 1, 2, 3, 4, 6 Optional: none; Extension: 5	Core: 7, 8, 9, 11, 12 Optional: 10, 13a; Extension: 13b

Investigation 7B ***Expectation and Variation***

DAY	LESSON	HOMEWORK
1	7.6 Getting Started Core: 1, 2, 3 Optional: none	Core: 4, 5 Optional: 8; Extension: 6, 7
2	7.7 Variance and Standard Deviation Core: 1, 2, 3, 4, 5, 8 Optional: 6; Extension: 7	Core: 9, 10, 11, 12, 13, 14, 16 Optional: 17; Extension: 15
3	7.8 Adding Variances Core: 1, 2, 3, 4, 5, 6 Optional: 7	Core: 8, 9, 11, 12, 13, 14, 15 Optional: 16, 17; Extension: 10, 18
4	7.9 Repeated Experiments Core: 1, 2, 3, 4, 6a–b Optional: none; Extension: 6c, 7	Core: 8, 9, 10, 12, 13, 14 Optional: 15, 16; Extension: 11
5	7.10 Bernoulli Trials Core: 1, 2, 3, 4, 5, 6 Optional: 7; Extension: 8	Core: 9a-c, 10, 11, 12, 14 Optional: 15; Extension: 9d, 13

NOTES	MATERIALS
	• CAS (recommended) • graphing calculators • pennies (optional) • Blackline Master MC12
	• CAS (recommended) • graphing calculators • number cubes in two different colors • pennies • Blackline Masters MC12, 7.2
	• CAS (recommended) • graphing calculators • Blackline Master 7.2
	• CAS (recommended) • graphing calculators • Blackline Masters MC12, 7.2
	• graphing calculators • Blackline Master 7.5

NOTES	MATERIALS
	• graphing calculators • Blackline Masters 7.6A–C
	• graphing calculators • number cubes (optional) • tape (optional) • Blackline Master 7.7
	• graphing calculators • Blackline Master 7.7
	• computers with Internet access (optional) • graphing calculators • Blackline Master 7.7
	• graphing calculators

Mathematics Background

POLYNOMIALS AS A BOOKKEEPING DEVICE Students use polynomials for many different purposes in CME Project courses, but now they come across the *generating polynomial*, which is a new step in abstraction. Usually in a polynomial, x represents something. It can be an unknown that you need to solve for, as in the equation $3x - 5 = 13$. It can be the input for a function, as in $f(x) = x^2 - 3x + 2$. In that case, it can take on any value in the domain of the function and produce an output.

However, in a generating polynomial, x does not really represent anything. You can use the polynomial $x^1 + x^2 + x^3 + x^4 + x^5 + x^6$ to generate the frequencies of outcomes when rolling a standard number cube and keeping track of the sum of the results. The powers of x represent the outcomes—the numbers on the faces of the number cube. The coefficients are all equal, because each of the outcomes is equally likely. (You could also give each term the coefficient $\frac{1}{6}$ for the probability of each outcome. Raising that polynomial to powers generates the probabilities of the outcomes, rather than just their frequencies.) The only reason x is there is to provide a base for all the powers, because the laws of exponents provide the relationship needed for this idea to work. $x^a \cdot x^b = x^{a+b}$, and if you get an a the first time you roll the number cube, and a b on your second roll, your total is $a + b$ for those two throws.

Here is an example. The experiment is, "Roll three standard number cubes and record the sum." Because you are throwing three number cubes, you want to raise the number cubes polynomial to the third power. Here is the expansion:

$$(x^1 + x^2 + x^3 + x^4 + x^5 + x^6)^3 = x^3 + 3x^4 + 6x^5 + 10x^6 + 15x^7 + 21x^8 + 25x^9 + 27x^{10} + 27x^{11} + 25x^{12} + 21x^{13} + 15x^{14} + 10x^{15} + 6x^{16} + 3x^{17} + x^{18}$$

The sum of the coefficients is 216, because there are 216 equally-likely outcomes in this experiment, from 1,1,1 for a sum of 3, up to 6,6,6 for a sum of 18. The powers in the expansion range from 3 to 18 to reflect these possible sums. The coefficients represent the frequency of each corresponding outcome. Since the coefficient of the x^6 term is 10, there are 10 ways to get a sum of 6 by throwing three number cubes.

Without this polynomial power method, you would have to figure the number of ways to get a sum of 6 on three number cubes. Usually, you would do it by making a systematic list like this:

(1, 1, 4) (1, 2, 3) (1, 3, 2)

(1, 4, 1) (2, 1, 3) (2, 2, 2) (2, 3, 1)

(3, 1, 2) (3, 2, 1) (4, 1, 1)

continued on p. 536c

continued from p. 536b

It is difficult to be sure you have found all the possibilities, and for events that include a larger number of outcomes the task is even more difficult. The polynomial gives us the number of outcomes for each of the possible sums with a simple (for a CAS) polynomial expansion.

You can use the expansion to calculate the probability of throwing a sum of 6 on three number cubes as $\frac{10}{216}$. You can also calculate more complex probabilities, such as the probability of throwing a sum that is divisible by 3. To do this, find the sum of all the coefficients in the expansion for terms with exponents divisible by 3 and divide by the total number of outcomes.

$$\frac{1 + 10 + 25 + 25 + 10 + 1}{216} = \frac{72}{216} = \frac{1}{3}$$

The x in the polynomial and in the expansion is just a placeholder, something that is there so that you can capitalize on the properties of exponents and have a convenient way (if you have a CAS) to calculate probabilities.

ALGEBRAIC STRUCTURE OF STATISTICS One habit of mind that is present throughout the CME Project curriculum is the practice of investigating the algebraic structure of new functions. In this chapter, students learn to calculate the expected value, variance, and standard deviation of a random variable. Since they have spent some time with CME Project, they probably wonder immediately about the algebraic structure of these new functions.

Some functions are additive, so that $f(x + y) = f(x) + f(y)$. Some functions are multiplicative, so that $f(xy) = f(x) \cdot f(y)$. Students see that for a random variable, Z, defined as the sum of two independent random variables, $Z = X + Y$, the expected value and variance are both additive. (Students also discover that the standard deviation is not additive.)

$$E(Z) = E(X) + E(Y) \text{ and } V(Z) = V(X) + V(Y)$$

However, for a random variable W defined as the product of two independent random variables, $W = XY$, although the expected value is multiplicative, the variance is not.

CONNECTIONS TO CALCULUS Early on in this chapter, students make frequency histograms. These histograms show a bar for each of the possible outcomes for an experiment, and the height of each bar represents the frequency for the outcome. Students change these into probability histograms by making the height of each bar equal to the probability of that outcome instead of the frequency. Another change takes place when students begin to think of the outcomes of a probability experiment as inputs to a *random variable*. For each outcome, the random variable returns a number. Then, the

DAILY PLANNER DAILY PLANNER DAILY PL

Pacing Suggestions and Materials

Investigation 7C *The Normal Distribution*

DAY	LESSON	HOMEWORK
1	7.11 Getting Started Core: 1, 2, 3, 4 Optional: none	Core: 5, 6, 7, 8, 9 Optional: 10, 11a–b, 12; Extension: 11c
2	7.12 The Central Limit Theorem Core: 1a–b, 2, 3, 4, 6 Optional: 5a–d, 7; Extension: 1c, 5e	Core: 8, 9, 10, 13, 14 Optional: 11, 15; Extension: 12
3	7.13 The Normal Distribution Core: 1, 2, 3, 4, 5 Optional: none; Extension: 6	Core: 7, 8, 9, 10, 13 Optional: 11, 12, 14

NOTES	MATERIALS
	• CAS (recommended) • graph paper • graphing calculators • Blackline Masters MC8, MC9
	• graphing calculators • Blackline Master 7.12
	• graphing calculators • Blackline Master 7.13

histogram represents the possible outcomes for the random variable (all numbers) with a bar the height of the probability of that outcome. This is a probability distribution for the random variable.

Due to the way it is constructed, the sum of the areas of all the bars in a probability distribution is 1. Also, the sum of the areas of all the bars for outcomes that are part of an event (such as rolling a sum divisible by 3 with three number cubes) is the probability for that event. In other words, in a probability distribution, area is probability.

Probability distributions for large numbers of trials of an experiment often look eerily similar to each other, even if the experiments on which they are based are quite different. As the number of trials of an experiment increases, the probability distribution for the random variable that represents the sum of all the results often looks like the ubiquitous bell-curve of the normal distribution. In fact, the Central Limit Theorem says

> Let X be a random variable with mean μ and standard deviation σ. The distribution for the sum of the outputs of X over n experiments is more and more closely approximated by $N(\mu n, \sigma\sqrt{n})$ as n grows larger.

So you can use the normal curve to approximate the probability distribution for a large number of trials of an experiment. And area is probability. So to find probabilities using the normal curve, you have to have a way to find the area under this curve. In this course, students use pre-programmed functions on their calculators to find the area under the normal curve, but eventually (as previewed in Chapter 8) they use calculus to find the integral.

Using the normal curve to approximate a probability distribution is actually a really nice introduction to the idea of finding the area under a curve. It even includes a preview of the idea of approximating a curved area with a number of thin bars and finding their sum.

Developing Students' Mathematical Habits

ALGEBRAIC REASONING Students picture the result of a complex calculation without actually carrying it out in detail, and use patterns in the form of the calculation to draw conclusions.

LOGICAL REASONING By connecting the result of calculations back to the context of the problem, students draw conclusions about probability situations.

VISUALIZATION After looking at probability distributions for a series of repeated independent trials of a probability experiment in several different contexts, students see similarities between the graphs and use this to gain an intuitive understanding of the Central Limit Theorem.

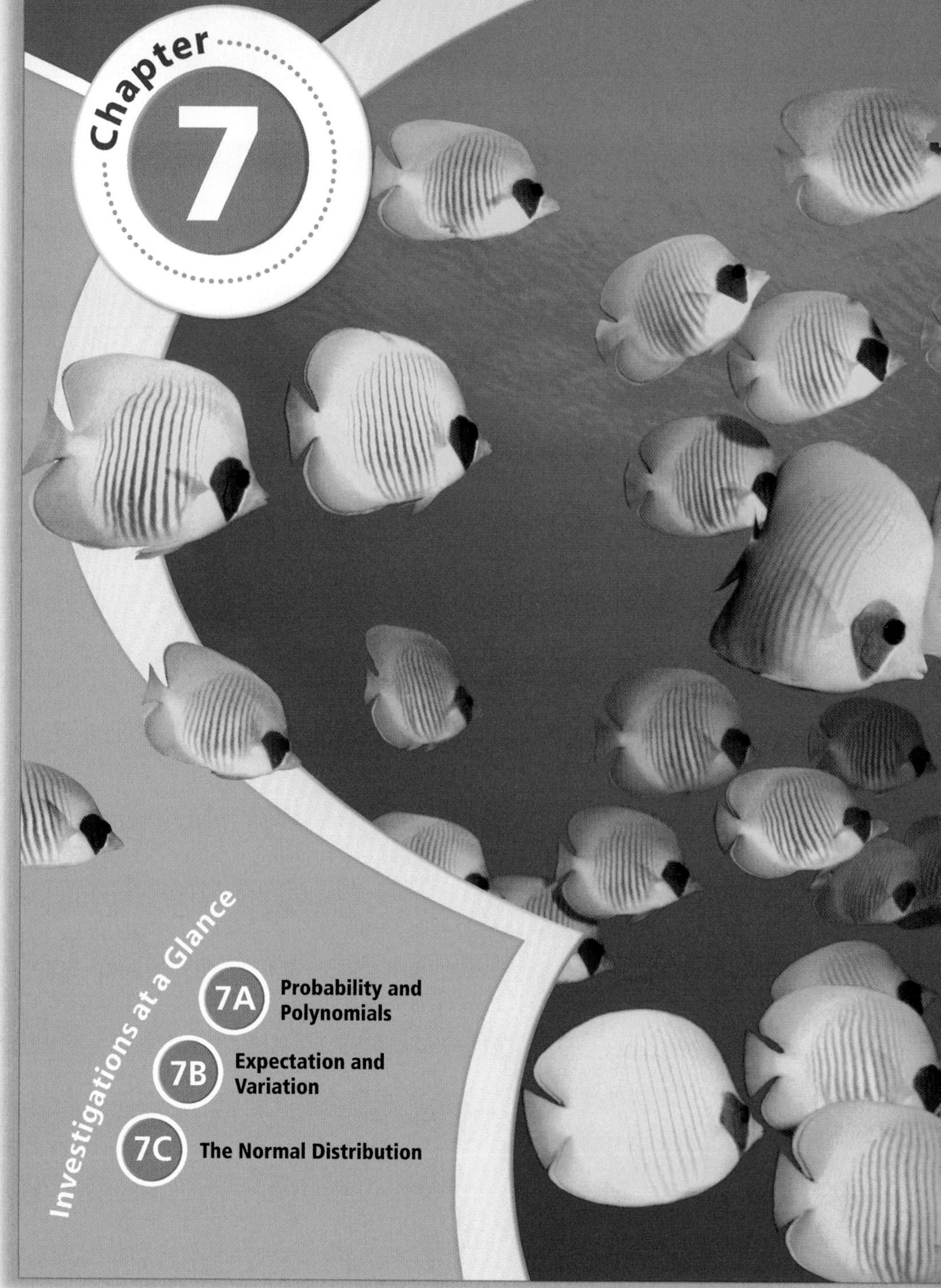

Chapter Road Map

INVESTIGATION 7A, *Probability and Polynomials,* formalizes the language used to describe probability experiments. Students learn to calculate and make sense of expected value as a statistical measure of these experiments. Students also create and use generating polynomials to calculate frequencies and probabilities.

INVESTIGATION 7B, *Expectation and Variation,* asks students to calculate expected value, variance, and standard deviation, and to draw conclusions about the algebraic structure of these functions. Students also explore Bernoulli trials and see how formulas for expected value and variance can be simplified in this restricted environment.

Probability and Statistics

Although there is much variation between individuals, populations are often quite consistent. Probability and statistics allow you to quantify a population and make predictions about it.

In this picture of a school of fish, you see that this fish can be yellow or red but the yellow occurs more frequently. Is that true of this type of fish in general or just this school of fish? You can use probability and statistics to quantify this information accurately.

Vocabulary and Notation

- **Bernoulli trial**
- **confidence interval**
- **cumulative density function**
- **event**
- **expected value, $E(X)$**
- **experimental probability**
- **frequency, $|A|$**
- **independent**
- **mean absolute deviation**
- **mean squared deviation, or variance, σ^2**
- **mutually exclusive**
- **normal distribution, $N(\mu, \sigma)$**
- **probability density function**
- **probability histogram**
- **random variable**
- **root mean squared deviation, or standard deviation, σ**
- **sample space**
- **theoretical probability**
- **z-score**

INVESTIGATION 7C, *The Normal Distribution,* gives students a chance to develop an informal understanding of the Central Limit Theorem. By looking at probability distributions for some very different probability experiments, students see that as the number of trials of each experiment increases, the distributions come to resemble each other more and more. Eventually, the distributions all come to resemble the bell-shaped curve of the normal distribution. Students learn to use the normal distribution as an approximation of one of their own distributions and calculate with it.

Chapter Vocabulary and Notation

The following list gives key vocabulary and notation used in the chapter. Selected new vocabulary and notation items are shown in boldface on the student page.

- Bernoulli trial, p. 596
- confidence interval, p. 615
- cumulative density function, p. 619
- deviation, p. 575
- event, p. 542
- expected value, $E(X)$, p. 556
- experimental probability, p. 592
- frequency, p. 549
- independent, p. 544
- mean absolute deviation, p. 576
- mean squared deviation, or variance, σ^2, p. 576
- mutually exclusive, p. 544
- normal distribution, $N(\mu,\sigma)$, p. 608
- outcome, p. 542
- probability density function, p. 619
- probability distribution, p. 607
- probability histogram, p. 603
- probability of an event, p. 542
- random variable, p. 555
- root mean squared deviation, or standard deviation, σ, p. 576
- sample space, p. 542
- spread, p. 575
- theoretical probability, p. 592
- unit normal distribution, $N(0, 1)$, p. 617
- *z*-score, p. 598
- $|A|$ (the number of outcomes in event A), p. 542

Chapter Technology

CME Project Precalculus assumes that each student has access to a graphing calculator. It also recommends access to a computer algebra system (CAS) and to geometry software.

Support for the use of technology is available in the TI-Nspire™ Technology Handbook. See p. 704.

A list of technology used with important concepts in this chapter appears below. Students need access to the functionality listed to develop complete understanding of these topics.

Computer Algebra System

LESSON 7.1 Expand a binomial raised to a power, p. 539.

LESSON 7.3 Expand a polynomial raised to a power, p. 549.

Graphing Calculator

LESSON 7.12 Find a probability predicted by the normal distribution, p. 615.

LESSON 7.13 Approximate a binomial probability predicted by a normal distribution, p. 620.

Spreadsheet Software

LESSON 7.8 Calculate the expected value, p. 584.

Investigation Overview

This investigation begins with an introduction (or review) of basic probability vocabulary and calculation. Students see how to apply what they learned about combinatorics in Chapter 4 to simple probability experiments. Then they learn a very powerful technique for calculating frequencies and probabilities in situations with a large number of trials. They model a probability experiment with a polynomial, such as $t + h$ for a coin flip or $x^1 + x^2 + x^3 + x^4 + x^5 + x^6$ for rolling a number cube. Then students learn how to read the coefficients of the expansion of powers of these specially-constructed polynomials to calculate frequency or probability. With this new tool, they move on to calculate expected value and analyze some more complex probability experiments, including lotteries.

You may wish to assign Questions 1–3 for students to think and write about during the investigation.

Learning Goals

- Calculate probabilities of simple random events.
- Build a set of equally likely outcomes for a probability experiment.
- Find a polynomial to model a probability experiment and interpret expansions of its powers.
- Calculate the expected value of a random variable.

Habits and Skills

- Visualize the process of a probability experiment in order to count its outcomes.
- Reason from definitions, such as *mutually exclusive* and *independent*, and apply them to probability situations.
- Understand the domains and ranges of various functions related to probability, including random variables, frequency, expected value, and probability functions.

Probability and Polynomials

In *Probability and Polynomials,* you will learn basic probability definitions and rules. You will discover connections between probability and Pascal's Triangle. You will model a variety of experiments with polynomials. You will calculate the likelihood of each outcome in an experiment, and also predict the average outcome of an experiment.

By the end of this investigation, you will be able to answer questions like these.

1. If you are to roll four number cubes, what is the probability they sum to 12?
2. What is expected value?
3. How can you use polynomials to solve probability problems?

You will learn how to

- calculate probabilities of simple random events
- build a set of equally likely outcomes for a probability experiment
- find a polynomial to model a probability experiment and interpret expansions of its powers
- calculate the expected value of a random variable

You will develop these habits and skills:

- Visualize the process of a probability experiment in order to count its outcomes.
- Reason from definitions, such as for *mutually exclusive* and *independent,* and apply them to probability situations.
- Understand the domains and ranges of various functions related to probability, including random variables, frequency, expected value, and probability functions.

Investigation Road Map

LESSON 7.1, *Getting Started,* asks students to list possible outcomes of simple experiments and makes connections to Pascal's triangle and powers of polynomials.

LESSON 7.2, *Probability and Pascal's Triangle,* has students formalize connections between probability calculations and combinatorial techniques.

LESSON 7.3, *Polynomial Powers,* has students model a probability experiment with a polynomial and model multiple trials with powers of that polynomial.

LESSON 7.4, *Expected Value,* introduces the idea of expected value. Students learn to avoid some common pitfalls with expected value and to interpret their results.

LESSON 7.5, *Lotteries,* teaches students to calculate probabilities and expected value in common lottery and raffle situations.

7.1 Getting Started

Activating Prior Knowledge
Exploring New Ideas

Considering all possible outcomes is a good habit when calculating probabilities. If you know all possible outcomes in an experiment, you can find the likelihood of any particular outcome occurring.

For You to Explore

1. When you flip a coin three times, there are eight possible outcomes. For example, one outcome is heads-tails-heads. Write out the eight outcomes. Determine how many outcomes are in each category.

   a. no heads **b.** one head **c.** two heads **d.** three heads

2. There are 16 possible outcomes when you flip a coin four times. For example, one outcome is heads-tails-heads-heads. Write out the 16 outcomes. Determine how many outcomes are in each category.

   a. no heads **b.** one head **c.** two heads
   d. three heads **e.** four heads

3. You are to flip a coin five times.

   a. Write down the ten different ways you could flip two heads and three tails.

   b. What is the probability that you flip two heads and three tails?

4. Expand each of these expressions.

   a. $(t + h)^2$ **b.** $(t + h)^3$ **c.** $(t + h)^4$ **d.** $(t + h)^5$

One of the outcomes is "heads, tails, tails, heads, tails" but you might prefer to write it as HTTHT.

See the TI-Nspire™ Handbook on p. 704, for instructions on how to expand these expressions with a CAS.

If the survival rate for turtle eggs is 38%, how many are expected to hatch from a nest of 120 eggs?

Answers

For You to Explore

1. HHH, HHT, HTH, THH, HTT, THT, TTH, TTT
   a. 1 outcome **b.** 3 outcomes
   c. 3 outcomes **d.** 1 outcome
2. HHHH, HHHT, HHTH, HTHH, THHH, HHTT, HTHT, HTTH, THHT, THTH, TTHH, HTTT, THTT, TTHT, TTTH, TTTT
   a. 1 outcome **b.** 4 outcomes
   c. 6 outcomes **d.** 4 outcomes
   e. 1 outcome
3. **a.** HHTTT, HTHTT, HTTHT, HTTTH, THHTT, THTHT, THTTH, TTHHT, TTHTH, TTTHH
   b. $\frac{10}{32} = \frac{5}{16}$
4. **a.** $t^2 + 2th + h^2$
   b. $t^3 + 3t^2h + 3th^2 + h^3$
   c. $t^4 + 4t^3h + 6t^2h^2 + 4th^3 + h^4$
   d. $t^5 + 5h^4t + 10h^3t^2 + 10h^2t^3 + 5ht^4 + h^5$

Lesson Overview

GOAL

- Warm up to the ideas of the investigation.

In this Getting Started lesson, you have a chance to see how much your students know or remember about some common probability situations. Although they do not compute probabilities yet, they visualize the results of various probability experiments and list outcomes. Some students may apply their knowledge of combinatorics to count the ways that certain outcomes can occur rather than making complete lists. Encourage this habit, but allow students to adopt it when they are ready and understand how to proceed.

FOR YOU TO EXPLORE
- Core: 1, 2, 3, 4
- Optional: none

MATERIALS
- CAS (recommended)
- graphing calculators
- pennies (optional)
- Blackline Master MC12

HOMEWORK
- Core: 5, 6, 7, 8
- Optional: 9, 10

Launch

Have your students jump right in to the problems. If you like, you can let students use real coins as they work on the coin flipping problems.

You might want to make a connection between flipping one coin five times and flipping five coins at once, because these two experiments may seem very different to your students.

Explore

For You to Explore

As students are working, keep track of the different strategies they are using for an end of class discussion.

PROBLEM 1 The first few questions here may remind students of Pascal's Triangle, so watch for that. If it comes up, remind students about the triangle and its numbers.

PROBLEM 2 Watch for students using the results from Problem 1 here; this is good! Other students may recognize the Pascal numbers emerging from the results, which is the other desired result.

PROBLEM 3 If you discuss this problem, mention the utility of writing the probability as $\frac{10}{32}$ even though you can reduce it.

PROBLEM 4 You may prefer that your students do this by hand instead of using a CAS, but it takes a lot longer. Students should recognize that the same numbers show up here as in the coin-flipping questions, and they may have trouble seeing this result if they expand by hand.

Wrap Up

As you go over the For You to Explore problems, let students share their solution methods. Discuss advantages and disadvantages of each method. Look for shortcuts or ways to make a method more efficient. Make connections between different methods. Ask students how Problem 4 connects to the work they did in the previous three problems.

Exercises

HOMEWORK
- Core: 5, 6, 7, 8
- Optional: 9, 10

On Your Own

EXERCISE 5 Some students may find this exercise disconnected from the work of the lesson, especially those who do not see a connection to Problem 4. When you discuss the homework, take some time to discuss how some students were able to use Pascal's triangle in later exercises.

This exercise refers to Pascal's Triangle, so you may want to use Blackline Master MC12 on an overhead. Then review other exercises—such as Problems 1–4—in terms of the rows of Pascal's Triangle.

EXERCISE 6 Not all students get this right. Encourage those having trouble to start with a simpler problem, like the ones encountered in the For You To Explore problems.

EXERCISE 7 introduces a problem discussed throughout this chapter, the probability that two integers picked at random do not share a common factor.

EXERCISES 8 AND 9 Students learn how to answer the "exactly this many heads" and "exactly this many ones" questions in Lesson 7.10. For now, ask for a guess and have students save or remember that guess for later. Do ask them to explain their guess. Reasons that relate to the problem situation or prior experiences are more valuable than accurate guesses that students cannot explain or justify.

Maintain Your Skills

EXERCISE 10 If students get stuck on this exercise or do not know how to start, a prompt such as, "What is the largest square number in this set?" may help.

Exercises *Practicing Habits of Mind*

On Your Own

5. Write out the first eight rows of Pascal's Triangle. Count your rows so that the third row is

1 3 3 1

6. Determine the probability that if you flip a coin eight times, you will flip exactly four heads and four tails. Explain in detail how you arrived at your answer.

7. a. Picture two spinners that are equally likely to land on any integer between 1 and 5, inclusive. List all 25 ways the spinners could land if you spin them both.

> Here is one way: first spinner 3, second spinner 4. And here is another, different way: first spinner 4, second spinner 3.

b. Find the probability that the two numbers spun do not share a common factor greater than 1.

c. Repeat parts (a) and (b) for two spinners that are equally likely to land on any integer between 1 and 6, inclusive. For this, there are 36 outcomes.

d. Repeat parts (a) and (b) for two spinners that are equally likely to land on any integer between 1 and 7, inclusive.

8. a. If you flip a fair coin 240 times, how many heads would you expect?

b. Guess the probability of getting exactly this many heads.

9. a. If you roll a fair number cube 240 times, how many ones would you expect?

b. Guess the probability of getting exactly this many ones.

> You may assume that a number cube has the numbers 1 through 6 on its faces, unless stated otherwise.

Maintain Your Skills

10. For each value of n, you are to pick an integer at random from 1 to n. What is the probability it will be a perfect square?

a. $n = 10$ **b.** $n = 100$ **c.** $n = 1000$ **d.** $n = 10{,}000$

e. What is happening "in the long run" (as n grows larger without bound)?

Answers

Exercises

5.

```
                1
              1   1
            1   2   1
          1   3   3   1
        1   4   6   4   1
      1   5  10  10   5   1
    1   6  15  20  15   6   1
  1   7  21  35  35  21   7   1
1   8  28  56  70  56  28   8   1
```

6. $\frac{70}{256}$; there are 70 ways to toss 4 heads and 4 tails in 8 throws, $\binom{8}{4} = 70$. The total number of possible ways to toss 8 coins is $2^8 = 256$.

7–9. See back of book.

10. a. $\frac{3}{10}$ **b.** $\frac{10}{100}$ or $\frac{1}{10}$

c. $\frac{31}{1000}$ **d.** $\frac{100}{10{,}000}$ or $\frac{1}{100}$

e. Answers may vary. Sample: The probability appears to approach zero as n grows.

7.2 Probability and Pascal's Triangle

In this section you will learn some basic definitions and rules of probability. If you have not done so already, start to think about how you can count the possible outcomes of experiments more efficiently.

In-Class Experiment

Here are four similar games.

Game 1: Flip two coins. If you get exactly two heads, you win.

Game 2: Flip three coins. If you get exactly two heads, you win.

Game 3: Flip four coins. If you get exactly two heads, you win.

Game 4: Flip five coins. If you get exactly two heads, you win.

1. Which game gives you the greatest probability of winning?

You can use probability theory to determine how likely it is that an event will occur. Consider a multiple-choice question with five options. Only one is right. If you guess randomly, the probability of getting the correct answer is $\frac{1}{5}$. The probability of getting an incorrect answer is $\frac{4}{5}$.

Example

Problem Roll two different-colored number cubes. Find the probability of each event.

a. At least one number cube shows a 5.

b. The sum of the numbers is exactly 5.

Solution One way to proceed is to write out the *sample space*, the entire list of possible outcomes. Since each number cube has 6 possible outcomes, there are 36 total outcomes for this experiment.

	1	2	3	4	5	6
1	(1,1)	(1,2)	(1,3)	(1,4)	**(1,5)**	(1,6)
2	(2,1)	(2,2)	(2,3)	(2,4)	**(2,5)**	(2,6)
3	(3,1)	(3,2)	(3,3)	(3,4)	**(3,5)**	(3,6)
4	(4,1)	(4,2)	(4,3)	(4,4)	**(4,5)**	(4,6)
5	**(5,1)**	**(5,2)**	**(5,3)**	**(5,4)**	**(5,5)**	**(5,6)**
6	(6,1)	(6,2)	(6,3)	(6,4)	**(6,5)**	(6,6)

In-Class Experiment

1. Game 2 and Game 3 have the highest probability of winning, $\frac{3}{8}$.

Lesson Overview

GOALS

- Calculate probabilities of simple random events.
- Build a set of equally likely outcomes for a probability experiment.

This lesson defines many basic probability terms and demonstrates them with specific experiments. Students grapple with ways to make lists of equally-likely outcomes for different situations and understand that this is different from making a list of all the different outcomes that could occur. You may encounter some basic probability misconceptions. For example, students often believe that if you flip a coin 40 times and get 40 heads, that you are somehow more likely to get tails on your 41st flip. In other words, somehow the result of the 41st flip *depends* on the first 40 results. Another difficulty to watch out for is when students confuse numbers of results with numerical results. What does a particular value mean? Is it a result of a number cube throw, or the number of times you have gotten a particular number cube result?

CHECK YOUR UNDERSTANDING

- Core: 1, 2, 3, 4, 5
- Optional: none
- Extension: 6

MATERIALS

- CAS (recommended)
- graphing calculators
- number cubes in two different colors
- pennies
- Blackline Masters MC12, 7.2

HOMEWORK

- Core: 8, 9, 10, 11, 12, 14
- Optional: 7, 15
- Extension: 13

VOCABULARY

- event
- independent
- mutually exclusive
- outcome
- probability of an event
- sample space
- $|A|$ (the number of outcomes in event A)

Launch

Begin today's lesson with the In-Class Experiment. You may want students to try playing the games briefly. Students should notice a key fact; if the elements in a sample space are the number of possible heads, they are *not* equally likely, but if the elements in a sample space are the results of the flips, such as {HH, HT, TH, TT} for the two-coin experiment, then they *are* equally likely.

Explore

In-Class Experiment

PROBLEM 1 Students should use their results from the Getting Started lesson to help them with this problem. Check for students' general understanding

continued on p. 542

continued from p. 541

of probability. Some students may think Game 2 is 1 out of 4 and not 3 out of 8 (a student may think there are four equally-likely outcomes, 0 through 3 heads). Other students may think Game 4 has the greatest probability of winning since more outcomes are successful (10), not considering that there are many more outcomes in general. Encourage students to *not* simplify the probabilities immediately, especially not to a decimal. It helps them to see patterns; the pattern here is that the numerators are all the triangular numbers (1, 3, 6, 10) while the denominators are increasing powers of 2 (4, 8, 16, 32). Games 2 and 3 both have the same probability of winning, larger than the probability of winning either Game 1 or Game 4.

Example

Beginning with this Example, this lesson frequently refers to the outcomes resulting from rolling two number cubes. Blackline Master 7.2 reproduces the table of individual outcomes of this experiment and the table of the sums of the numbers on the cubes. Use the master wherever needed.

a. The 11 highlighted outcomes have at least one 5. So, the probability of rolling at least one 5 is

$$P\,(\text{at least one } 5) = \frac{\text{number of successful outcomes}}{\text{total number of outcomes}} = \frac{11}{36}$$

b. Make a second table showing the sums of the numbers on the two number cubes.

+	1	2	3	4	5	6
1	2	3	4	5	6	7
2	3	4	5	6	7	8
3	4	5	6	7	8	9
4	5	6	7	8	9	10
5	6	7	8	9	10	11
6	7	8	9	10	11	12

The 4 highlighted outcomes each show a sum of 5. So, the probability of rolling a sum of exactly 5 is $\frac{4}{36}$ or $\frac{1}{9}$.

For You to Do

2. Find the probability that when rolling two number cubes, the sum is less than or equal to 5.

Several definitions come in handy when talking about probability problems.

Definitions

The sample space is a set. Its elements are outcomes.

An event is a subset of the sample space, a set of outcomes. $|A|$ denotes the number of outcomes in event A.

$P(A)$, the probability of an event A, is the number of outcomes in A, divided by the number of outcomes in the sample space S.

$$P(A) = \frac{\text{number of outcomes in } A}{\text{total number of outcomes}} = \frac{|A|}{|S|}$$

An *outcome* could be anything, such as "rolling a 3" or "heads, heads, tails." The situation determines the appropriate outcomes.

This definition of probability depends on the assumption that all outcomes in the sample space are equally likely. You cannot use this definition when the outcomes are not equally likely.

When rolling a number cube, there are six outcomes in the sample space, all equally likely. One outcome is "roll the number 5." An event might be "roll a prime number." There are three outcomes in this event, so $P(\text{roll a prime number}) = \frac{3}{6}$ or $\frac{1}{2}$.

Often, there are shortcuts to counting either the number of outcomes in an event, or the number of outcomes in the sample space. The sample space for rolling two number cubes has $6 \times 6 = 36$ outcomes since there are six ways each number cube can land.

Answers

For You to Do

2. $\frac{10}{36}$ or $\frac{5}{18}$

Minds in Action episode 21

Derman and Sasha are working on Game 4 from the In-Class Experiment.

Derman We want to find the probability of getting exactly two heads when you flip five coins.

Sasha All right, so we need to know the number of outcomes with exactly two heads, and the total number of outcomes in the sample space.

Derman I think the probability should be 1 out of 6.

Sasha Oh?

Derman Well, you could get 0 heads, 1 head, 2, 3, 4, or 5 heads. Six ways it could happen. It's 1 out of 6.

Sasha Wait, wait, wait. That's not going to work, those things would have to be equally likely. But I'm not convinced that they are.

Derman Well, flipping a coin is equally likely: heads or tails.

Sasha Right. So start from there. Five coin flips.

Derman The total number of outcomes is . . . I think it's 32, 2 to the fifth.

Sasha That's a much better sample space. The probability's got to be something out of 32, then. Now we just have to figure out how many of those 32 outcomes have exactly two heads.

Derman I'll make a list . . .

HHTTT	TTTHH	THTHT
HTHTT	HTTTH	HTTHT
THHTT	THTTH	TTHHT

Derman Nine! It's nine out of 32.

Sasha You missed one: TTHTH. It's ten.

Derman It's hard to know the list is complete. There must be a better way to count these.

Sasha It's two H's out of a total of five spots.

Derman Ohh . . . just like a combination! From Chapter 4, I know that 10 is in Pascal's Triangle.

Sasha Hey, nice. Five flips and two H's. So the number of ways should be 5 choose 2, which is 10.

Derman So the probability is 10 out of 32. Guess it wasn't 1 out of 6 after all.

Remember...

The notation for "five choose 2" is $\binom{5}{2}$ or $_5C_2$. You can calculate it as $\frac{5!}{2! \cdot 3!}$.

Minds in Action

You may wish to assign students Minds in Action roles and present the conversation to the class. This is more effective if you assign the roles one class day prior to the "performance." Urge the students to "get into" their parts by using their own words instead of memorizing lines.

Developing Habits of Mind

This section establishes the relationship between binary outcomes and entries in Pascal's Triangle. You might want to put Blackline Master MC12 on an overhead and use other rows as examples, much as this section uses row 5.

DEFINITIONS After you cover the definitions of *mutually exclusive* and *independent*, you may want to ask students to describe some events that are *not* mutually exclusive or some events that are *not* independent of each other. For example, the events "roll two number cubes and get an even sum," and "roll two number cubes and get a sum less than 3." are not mutually exclusive.

To find events that are not independent, you need to think about situations with inherent "memory." For example, if you have a bag containing 5 blue marbles and 1 green marble, and you remove one marble at random and record its color and then remove a second marble, the probabilities for the color of the second marble *depend* on the color of the first marble. If the first marble you remove is green, the probability that the second marble is green is now zero. However, if the first marble is blue, the probability that the second marble is green is $\frac{1}{5}$.

Developing Habits of Mind

Look for relationships. The connection to probability can also explain a property about the sum of the numbers in a row of Pascal's Triangle. Consider row 5:

$$1 \quad 5 \quad 10 \quad 10 \quad 5 \quad 1$$

When you toss five coins, these numbers show up as the number of ways to get 0 heads, 1 head, 2 heads, and so on. For example, the probability of getting no heads when you flip five coins is $\frac{1}{32}$, since there is 1 successful outcome out of 32 total. Now look at the sum of all the probabilities.

$$\frac{1}{32} + \frac{5}{32} + \frac{10}{32} + \frac{10}{32} + \frac{5}{32} + \frac{1}{32}$$

If you toss five coins, you have to get *some* number of heads from 0 to 5. If you add up the probability of getting 0 heads, 1 head, 2 heads, 3 heads, 4 heads, and 5 heads, you have covered all the possibilities. Also, there is no overlap between these events. When you count the number of heads, the answer cannot be 2 *and* 4. So, the sum of these probabilities must be 1.

$$\frac{1}{32} + \frac{5}{32} + \frac{10}{32} + \frac{10}{32} + \frac{5}{32} + \frac{1}{32} = 1$$

This happens with any row of Pascal's Triangle. The sum of the numbers in the nth row of Pascal's Triangle is 2^n, which equals the total number of outcomes when tossing n coins.

For You to Do

3. Which is more likely, flipping exactly 3 heads in 10 coin flips, or flipping exactly 4 heads in 5 coin flips?

Here are two additional terms that apply to events.

Definitions

Two events A and B are mutually exclusive if they do not share any outcomes in the same sample space: whenever $P(A \text{ and } B) = 0$. If A and B are mutually exclusive, then $P(A \text{ or } B) = P(A) + P(B)$.

Two events A and B are independent if the result from one event has no effect on the other. If A and B are independent, then $P(A \text{ and } B) = P(A) \cdot P(B)$.

Consider rolling a single number cube. Rolling a 5 and rolling a 6 are mutually exclusive: you cannot do both at once. To find the probability of rolling a 5 or 6, add the probabilities of rolling each.

$P(5 \text{ and } 6) = 0$
$P(5 \text{ or } 6) = P(5) + P(6)$

Consider rolling two number cubes. The probability of rolling a 5 on the first number cube is $\frac{1}{6}$. The probability of rolling a 6 on the second number

Answers

For You to Do

3. Flipping exactly 4 heads in 5 coin flips is more likely than 3 heads in 10 coin flips.

cube is also $\frac{1}{6}$. These events are independent: the result for the second number cube does not rely in any way on the result for the first number cube. So, the probability of rolling a 5 on the first number cube and a 6 on the second number cube is $\frac{1}{6} \cdot \frac{1}{6} = \frac{1}{36}$.

Developing Habits of Mind

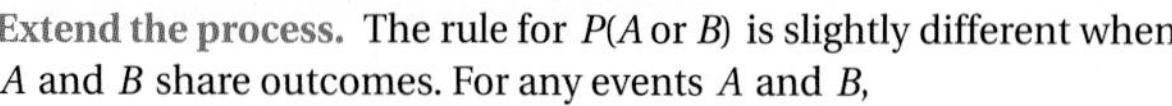

Extend the process. The rule for $P(A \text{ or } B)$ is slightly different when A and B share outcomes. For any events A and B,

$$P(A \text{ or } B) = P(A) + P(B) - P(A \text{ and } B)$$

One way to look at this is with a Venn diagram.

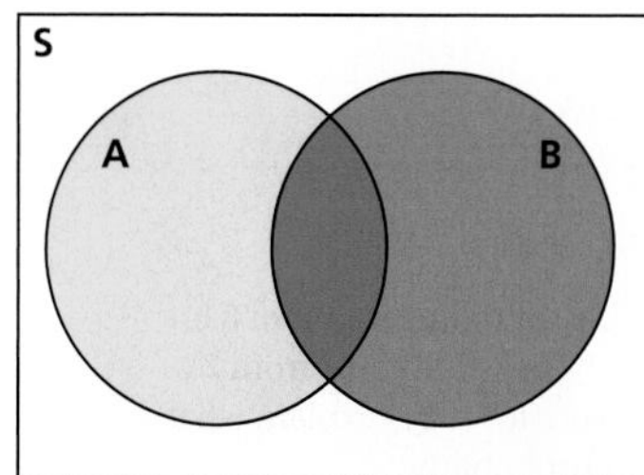

Let S be the sample space. In the diagram, the entire yellow circle represents event A. The entire blue circle represents event B. The green intersection of the two circles (where the yellow and blue overlap) represents the event (A and B). The union of the two circles represents the event (A or B).

In the diagram, this union is the part that is either yellow or blue, or is both yellow and blue. How could you compute the area of this colored region? You cannot just add the area of the entire yellow circle and the area of the entire blue circle. If you were to do this, you would double-count the middle green area, where the two circles intersect. So, subtract that green area from the sum and you will get the correct area.

Note that if A and B are mutually exclusive, $P(A \text{ and } B) = 0$. Then you do not have to take the intersection into account. This makes sense, since for mutually exclusive events $P(A \text{ or } B) = P(A) + P(B)$.

You can find probabilities for more than two overlapping events by using the inclusion-exclusion principle. For three events A, B, and C, first add the probabilities of the events. Next subtract all the intersections of pairs of events. Then add back in the intersection of *triples* of events.

$$\begin{aligned} P(A \text{ or } B \text{ or } C) = & \ P(A) + P(B) + P(C) \\ & - P(A \text{ and } B) - P(A \text{ and } C) - P(B \text{ and } C) \\ & + P(A \text{ and } B \text{ and } C) \end{aligned}$$

What happens if A, B, and C are mutually exclusive?

You can extend this principle to find probabilities for any number of overlapping events.

Wrap Up

Finish today's class by going through the sequence of core Check Your Understanding exercises. These exercises are designed to help students figure out how to use the entries in Pascal's triangle effectively to compute probabilities. By relating probabilities to the coefficients in a polynomial expansion, students prepare for the next lesson in this investigation.

Assessment Resources

Lesson Quiz 7.2

1. Determine each probability.
   a. P(flip two coins, both tails)
   b. P(flip three coins, all 3 tails)
   c. P(roll a number cube and get a 3 or a 6)
   d. P(roll two number cubes and get a sum of 7)

2. Consider flipping a coin eight times.
   a. How many total outcomes are in the sample space?
   b. How many different ways are there for the result to be 3 heads and 5 tails?
   c. How many different ways are there for the result to be 4 heads and 4 tails?

3. Find the probability that if you flip 10 coins, you will get exactly 4 heads and 6 tails.

Exercises

HOMEWORK
- Core: 8, 9, 10, 11, 12, 14
- Optional: 7, 15
- Extension: 13

Check Your Understanding

Use Blackline Masters 7.2 and MC12 as you see fit while discussing the exercises.

EXERCISE 2 illustrates a very common misconception, and also helps explain to students why they should start from basic situations like single coin flips or single number cube rolls.

EXERCISE 3 parallels the dialog from this lesson. Students learn that there are 15 ways by using Pascal's Triangle, as the next exercise reminds them.

EXERCISE 5 is, to an extent, a preview of what is coming next. It also reviews the Binomial Theorem, reminding students of the connection between binomial expansion and combinations.

EXERCISE 6 is difficult for students now, but much easier after the investigation. You might consider revisiting this exercise later. A similar question is asked in the Mathematical Reflections for this investigation.

On Your Own

EXERCISE 7 Give students a few minutes in class to think or talk about it. You could also give a sample game, such as the one described in the solution to this exercise, to give students some idea of what to look at.

Exercises *Practicing Habits of Mind*

Check Your Understanding

1. Determine each probability.

a. P(flip 1 coin, heads)

b. P(flip 2 coins, both heads)

c. P(roll a number cube and get an odd number)

d. P(roll a number cube and get an even number)

e. P(roll a number cube and get a negative number)

f. P(roll two number cubes and get a sum of 2)

g. P(roll two number cubes and get a sum greater than 2)

2. **What's Wrong Here?** Russ says that the probability of rolling a sum of 8 on two number cubes should be $\frac{1}{11}$, since there are 11 possible sums from 2 to 12. "It works for one number cube, so it should work for two." Explain what is wrong with his reasoning, and find the correct probability.

3. If you flip a coin six times, how many different ways are there for the result to be 2 heads and 4 tails? Write them out.

4. Calculate the value of $\binom{6}{2}$. Explain how your result relates to the work in Exercise 3.

5. Use the expansion of $(t + h)^6$ to find the total number of ways you could flip 3 heads and 3 tails in a sequence of six coin tosses.

6. **Take It Further** Suppose you are to roll a number cube three times. Find the probability that the sum of the numbers will be 8.

On Your Own

7. Make a game where the probability of winning is about $\frac{1}{3}$. Explain clearly how the game is played, and what the winning condition is. The best games are simple to play but complex in their potential outcomes.

So, one game would be "Roll a number cube. If it comes up 1 or 2, you win." But you can make something more interesting!

8. You flip a coin eight times.

a. Explain why there are 256 outcomes in the sample space.

b. What is the most likely number of heads? How likely is it to occur?

9. Find the probability that if you flip nine coins, you will get exactly six heads and three tails.

Answers

Exercises

1. a. $\frac{1}{2}$ **b.** $\frac{1}{4}$ **c.** $\frac{1}{2}$ **d.** $\frac{1}{2}$
e. 0 **f.** $\frac{1}{36}$ **g.** $\frac{35}{36}$

2. The results are not equally likely. There are 5 ways to roll a sum of 8 on two dice out of 36 outcomes; $\frac{5}{36}$

3. 15; HHTTTT, HTHTTT, HTTHTT, HTTTHT, HTTTTH, THHTTT, THTHTT, THTTHT, THTTTH, TTHHTT, TTHTHT, TTHTTH, TTTHHT, TTTHTH, TTTTHH

4. $\binom{6}{2} = 15$; this represents 15 ways to pick two items from a group of six.

5. 20, the coefficient of the t^3h^3 term

6. $\frac{21}{216}$ or $\frac{7}{72}$

7. Check students' work.

8. a. $2^8 = 256$ because each coin can be heads or tails (2 choices), so the choices are multiplied.

b. 4 heads; $\binom{8}{4} = \frac{70}{256}$

9. $\frac{84}{512}$ or 16.4%

10. In a carnival game, you roll a standard number cube and flip a coin. The coin has a 0 on one side, and a 5 on the other side. Your score is the sum of the values that appear on the number cube and the coin.

   a. You win the game if you score 10 points or more. Find the probability that you win the game.

   b. The man running the carnival says that every score from 1 to 11 is equally likely. Is he right? Explain.

11. Consider the set S of ordered pairs (x, y) such that x and y are both integers between 1 and 8, inclusive, and $x \geq y$.

   a. How many such ordered pairs are there?

   b. If you are to pick an ordered pair (x, y) at random, what is the probability that x and y do not have any common factor greater than 1?

   c. In the coordinate plane, plot all the ordered pairs (x, y) in S that do not have any common factor greater than 1.

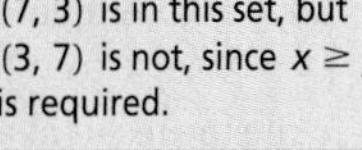

(7, 3) is in this set, but
(3, 7) is not, since $x \geq y$
is required.

12. Repeat Exercise 11 with the integer pairs satisfying $1 \leq y \leq x \leq 9$.

13. **Take It Further** Flip a coin 10 times, keeping score as follows. If you flip heads, you get one point. If you flip tails, you are in "danger." If you flip tails twice in a row, you "bust," lose all your points, and the game ends.

   a. What is the probability you survive all ten flips without busting?

   b. What is the average score players achieve in this game?

14. **Standardized Test Prep** In the sample space for rolling two number cubes, how many outcomes will have neither a one nor a two on either cube?

   A. 16 **B.** 18 **C.** 20 **D.** 24

For additional practice, go to **Web Code:** bga-0702

Maintain Your Skills

15. This is F_5, the *Farey sequence* of order 5:

$$\frac{0}{1}, \frac{1}{5}, \frac{1}{4}, \frac{1}{3}, \frac{2}{5}, \frac{1}{2}, \frac{3}{5}, \frac{2}{3}, \frac{3}{4}, \frac{4}{5}, \frac{1}{1}$$

F_5 is all fractions from 0 to 1, inclusive, with denominators less than or equal to 5. It is written in increasing order with fractions in lowest terms.

Find the number of elements in F_n. Copy and complete the table for n from 1 to 10, inclusive. Describe any patterns you find.

n	Number of elements in F_n
1	2
2	3
3	■
4	■
5	11

10. a. $\frac{2}{12}$ or $\frac{1}{6}$

b. No; there are two ways to get a score of 6, while there is only one way to get every other score.

11. a. 36

b. $\frac{22}{36}$ or $\frac{11}{18}$

c.

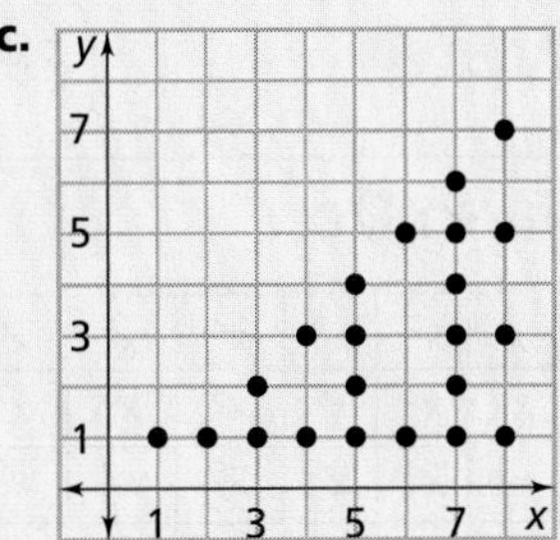

12–15. See back of book.

On Your Own

EXERCISE 12 Students should not do this exercise from scratch; rather they should use their result from Exercise 11 as a starting point.

EXERCISE 13 Students should notice the Fibonacci relationship. One relationship not found as quickly is that all the "number of ways" listed in the table are found in Pascal's Triangle! A nice identity emerges relating the numbers in Pascal's Triangle to the Fibonacci numbers. For example,

$$13 = \binom{6}{0} + \binom{5}{1} + \binom{4}{2} + \binom{3}{3}$$

and any such number built this way is a Fibonacci number.

Maintain Your Skills

EXERCISE 15 More questions relating to the Farey sequence are in future Maintain Your Skills sections. These questions align with the ones about the probability of two numbers not sharing a common factor. If you plan to have students do future problems about the Farey sequence, assign this exercise.

Additional Resources

PRINT RESOURCES
- Solution Manual
- Practice Workbook
- Assessment Resources
- Teaching Resources

TECHNOLOGY
- Interactive Textbook
- TeacherExpress CD-ROM
- Exam View CD-ROM
- PHSchool.com

Additional Practice

1. a. If you flip a coin five times, how many different ways are there for the result to be 3 heads and 2 tails? Write them out.
   b. Calculate the value of $\binom{5}{3}$. Explain how it relates to the work in part (a).

2. Consider flipping a coin eight times.
   a. Find the probability you will get exactly five heads and three tails.
   b. Find the probability you will get exactly four heads and four tails.

3. In a game, you roll a standard number cube and flip a coin. The coin has the number 2 on one side, and 6 on the other side. Your score is the sum of the values that appear on the number cube and the coin flip.
   a. You win the game if you score 8 points or more. Find the probability that you win.
   b. You get to roll the number cube and flip the coin a second time if you score 5. Find the probability that you score 5.
   c. Are all the scores from 3 to 12 equally likely? Explain.

4. A six-sided number cube has the numbers 1, 2, 4, 6, 6, and 8 on its faces.
   a. Find a polynomial that models one roll of this number cube.
   b. In three rolls, what is the most likely sum? How likely is it?

5. A spinner with five equal wedges has the numbers 0, 3, 4, 5, and 7.
   a. Find a polynomial that models one spin.
   b. What is the most likely sum of the numbers after four spins? How likely is it?

6. A board game has a spinner with the numbers 1 through 6 on it. All numbers are equally likely in a single spin. As you near the end of the game, there are nine more spaces left to move.
   a. Find the probability that you spin at least a nine in two spins.
   b. Find the probability that you spin at least a nine in three spins.
   c. Find the probability that you spin less than a nine in three spins.

Practice: For Lesson 7.2, assign Exercises 1–3.

Lesson Overview

GOAL

- Find a polynomial to model a probability experiment and interpret expansions of its powers.

In this lesson, students relate the coefficients in the expansion of specially-constructed polynomials to the frequency and probability of various outcomes in probability experiments. This algebraic connection, together with a CAS, gives students the ability to find probabilities in situations where the sample space is too large for them to list in any practical way. Students revisit "expansion boxes," a technique they learned for expanding polynomials in CME Project *Algebra 1*. If some of your students did not take Algebra 1 with this program, you may want to give some brief examples using expansion boxes to multiply polynomials, such as $(x - 1)(x^3 + x^2 + x + 1)$.

The expansion box provides a place to write the product of each term from the first factor and each term from the second factor.

$\times$	1	x	x^2	x^3
-1	-1	$-x$	$-x^2$	$-x^3$
x	x	x^2	x^3	x^4

Now, by combining like terms (which lie along diagonal lines in the table), students find the normal form for this product, which is $x^4 - 1$.

CHECK YOUR UNDERSTANDING
- Core: 1, 2, 3, 4, 5, 6
- Optional: none

MATERIALS
- CAS (recommended)
- graphing calculators
- Blackline Master 7.2

HOMEWORK
- Core: 7, 8, 9, 11, 12, 13
- Optional: 14, 15
- Extension: 10

VOCABULARY
- frequency

Launch

If necessary, review (or introduce) expansion boxes. A brief introduction is all that is necessary, because students only use it in Problem 1.

Explore

For You to Do

PROBLEM 1 See if students draw the connection between the expansion and the table from Lesson 7.2 used for the sum of two number cubes. If not, you may want to discuss this connection.

PROBLEM 2 Use Blackline Master 7.2 to help solve the problem.

7.3 Polynomial Powers

You can use Pascal's Triangle to quickly count the number of each type of outcome for coin-flip experiments. But what about other experiments, like rolling a number cube or answering multiple-choice questions? This lesson explores the use of polynomials to solve probability problems.

For You to Do

1. Copy and complete the expansion box below to find the expanded form of $(x + x^2 + x^3 + x^4 + x^5 + x^6)^2$.

   Write the result in ascending powers of x.

$\cdot$	x	x^2	x^3	x^4	x^5	x^6
x	■	■	■	■	■	■
x^2	■	■	x^5	■	■	■
x^3	■	■	■	■	■	■
x^4	■	■	■	■	■	■
x^5	■	x^7	■	■	■	■
x^6	■	■	■	■	■	x^{12}

2. When you roll two number cubes, what is the probability that the sum of the numbers will be exactly 5?

Remember...

You first used expansion boxes in CME Project *Algebra 1* as a way to keep track of all the terms when you were multiplying two expressions.

Developing Habits of Mind

Recognize a similar process. Consider the table from Lesson 7.2, with the 36 possible outcomes for the sum when rolling two number cubes.

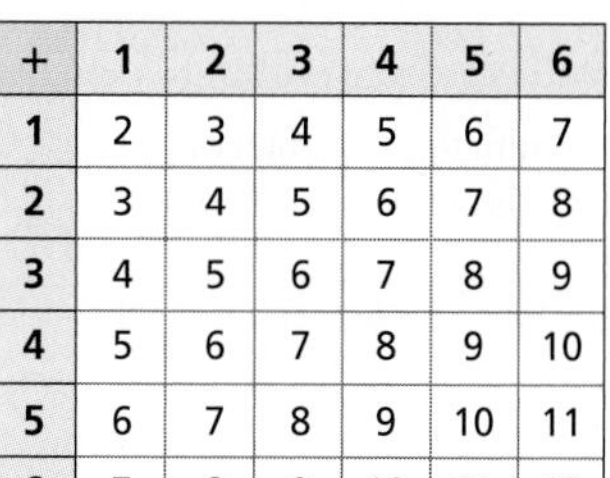

+	1	2	3	4	5	6
1	2	3	4	5	6	7
2	3	4	5	6	7	8
3	4	5	6	7	8	9
4	5	6	7	8	9	10
5	6	7	8	9	10	11
6	7	8	9	10	11	12

This table and the one from For You To Do are nearly identical, and they should be! Think about how you might get an x^5 in the expansion: multiply two terms like x^2 and x^3, or x^4 and x^1. In all, there are four ways to do

Answers

For You to Do

1.

$\cdot$	x	x^2	x^3	x^4	x^5	x^6
x	x^2	x^3	x^4	x^5	x^6	x^7
x^2	x^3	x^4	x^5	x^6	x^7	x^8
x^3	x^4	x^5	x^6	x^7	x^8	x^9
x^4	x^5	x^6	x^7	x^8	x^9	x^{10}
x^5	x^6	x^7	x^8	x^9	x^{10}	x^{11}
x^6	x^7	x^8	x^9	x^{10}	x^{11}	x^{12}

2. $\frac{4}{36}$ or $\frac{1}{9}$

this. Now think about how you get a 5 from the sum of the numbers on two cubes: roll a 2 and a 3, or a 4 and a 1. There are four ways to do this, too. It works because when you multiply polynomials, you are adding exponents.

So, you can use the polynomial $(x + x^2 + x^3 + x^4 + x^5 + x^6)$ to model the results when rolling a number cube with the numbers 1 through 6 on it.

Consider this frequency chart, listing the number of ways to get each sum when rolling two number cubes:

Roll	2	3	4	5	6	7	8	9	10	11	12
Frequency	1	2	3	4	5	6	5	4	3	2	1

The **frequency** of an event A is the number of outcomes in A. The frequency of the event "roll a sum of 10 on two number cubes" is 3, since there are 3 different outcomes with sum 10. In shorthand, $|A| = 3$.

Compare it to the result when squaring the polynomial that models a number cube roll:

$$(x + x^2 + x^3 + x^4 + x^5 + x^6)^2 =$$

$$1x^2 + 2x^3 + 3x^4 + 4x^5 + 5x^6 + 6x^7 + 5x^8 + 4x^9 + 3x^{10} + 2x^{11} + 1x^{12}$$

The expansion gives the same frequency information. There is one way to make x^2, two ways to make x^3, and so on. The table analyzing the sample space is really the same as the expansion box multiplying the polynomials.

Polynomials come in handy when exploring sample spaces that are too complex to list by hand. The sample space for rolling two number cubes has 36 outcomes, but the sample space for rolling four number cubes has $6^4 = 1296$ outcomes. This is tough to build by hand, but a CAS can quickly perform the corresponding polynomial expansion.

See the TI-Nspire Handbook on p. 704, for details on how to expand polynomials.

$$(x + x^2 + x^3 + x^4 + x^5 + x^6)^4 =$$
$$x^{24} + 4x^{23} + 10x^{22} + 20x^{21} + 35x^{20} + 56x^{19}$$
$$+ 80x^{18} + 104x^{17} + 125x^{16} + 140x^{15} + 146x^{14} + 140x^{13}$$
$$+ 125x^{12} + 104x^{11} + 80x^{10} + 56x^9 + 35x^8 + 20x^7 + 10x^6 + 4x^5 + x^4$$

This expansion gives a lot of information. For example, there are exactly 80 ways to roll a sum of 18 on four number cubes. Since there are $6^4 = 1296$ outcomes, $P(\text{rolling a sum of 18}) = \frac{80}{1296}$.

PROBLEM 3 Since all the numbers doubled, the most common outcome doubles to 30. It is useful to verify the result on a CAS. As a related question, ask about a spinner with 2, 3, 4, 4, 9; all these numbers are 1 larger, so the most common outcome on four spins is 19 (15 + 4).

PROBLEM 4 $f(1) = 625$, the total number of outcomes. This works in many other situations, such as the number cubes polynomial. It also works on the expanded form, since the expanded form is still the same function.

Example

A spinner has five wedges of equal area. The wedges are labeled with the numbers 1, 2, 3, 3, and 8.

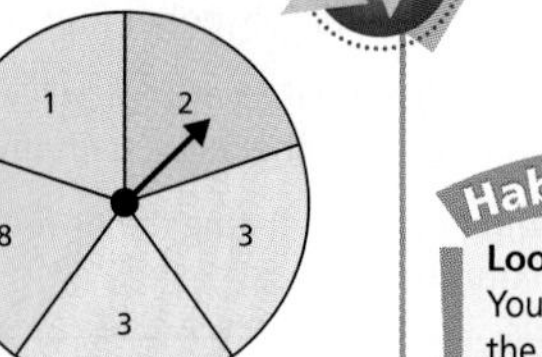

Problem What is the most likely sum of the numbers from four spins. How likely is it?

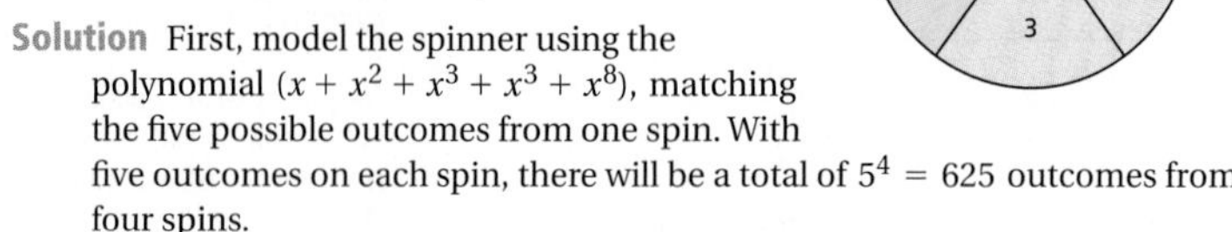

Solution First, model the spinner using the polynomial $(x + x^2 + x^3 + x^3 + x^8)$, matching the five possible outcomes from one spin. With five outcomes on each spin, there will be a total of $5^4 = 625$ outcomes from four spins.

Expand the polynomial to the fourth power.

$$(x + x^2 + x^3 + x^3 + x^8)^4 =$$

$$x^{32} + 8x^{27} + 4x^{26} + 4x^{25} + 24x^{22} + 24x^{21} + 30x^{20}$$
$$+ 12x^{19} + 6x^{18} + 32x^{17} + 48x^{16} + 72x^{15} + 52x^{14} + 36x^{13}$$
$$+ 28x^{12} + 36x^{11} + 56x^{10} + 56x^9 + 49x^8 + 28x^7 + 14x^6 + 4x^5 + x^4$$

Each coefficient is the frequency for a specific sum, indicated by the exponent. The greatest coefficient is 72. There are 72 ways to make a sum of 15. The probability of this sum occuring is $\frac{72}{625}$, since there are $5^4 = 625$ total outcomes.

Habits of Mind

Look for a relationship. You could also write the polynomial as $(x + x^2 + 2x^3 + x^8)$. What does the coefficient 2 mean here?

For You to Do

3. A second similar spinner has the numbers 2, 4, 6, 6, 16. What is the most likely sum from four spins?

4. Let $f(x) = (x + x^2 + x^3 + x^3 + x^8)^4$. What is the value of $f(1)$?

You can model other situations using polynomials as well. To model a coin flip, use the polynomial $(t + h)$ as seen in Lesson 7.1. Look at this expansion:

$$(t + h)^5 = t^5 + 5t^4h + 10t^3h^2 + 10t^2h^3 + 5th^4 + h^5$$

You can interpret this as, "There is one way to get five tails, then five ways to get four tails and one head, then ten ways to get three tails and two heads . . ."

To model a multiple-choice question with one right answer and three wrong answers use the polynomial $(r + w + w + w)$, or $(r + 3w)$. Here is another expansion:

$$(r + 3w)^5 = r^5 + 15r^4w + 90r^3w^2 + 270r^2w^3 + 405rw^4 + 243w^5$$

Habits of Mind

Represent the situation. An appropriate choice of letters can be helpful. Here, you use t and h for tails and heads. You use r and w for right and wrong answers.

Answers

For You to Do

3. 30

4. 625

You can use the expression to show that on five questions, there are 270 different ways to get exactly two right and three wrong answers. The total number of outcomes in the sample space is the sum of the coefficients.

$$1 + 15 + 90 + 270 + 405 + 243 = 1024 = 4^5$$

So, $P(\text{2 right and 3 wrong}) = \frac{270}{1024} \approx 0.2637$.

Developing Habits of Mind

Extend the process. The polynomials you have seen so far are helpful in counting outcomes, but you can use a variation to calculate the probability directly. For example, by raising $(r + 3w)$ to powers, you can see how many ways there are to get right and wrong answers to a multiple-choice test. But the probability of getting a question right is $\frac{1}{4} = 0.25$ and the probability of getting it wrong is $\frac{3}{4} = 0.75$.

By raising $(0.25r + 0.75w)$ to the nth power, you can see the probabilities of the different events when guessing at n questions.

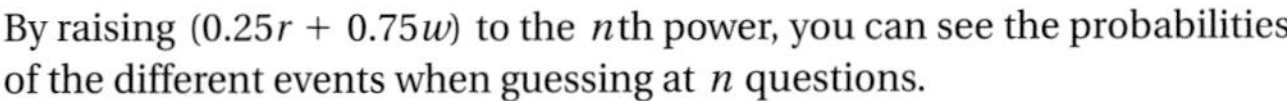

Consider the expansion of $(0.25r + 0.75w)^5$.

$$0.000977r^5 + 0.014648r^4w + 0.087891r^3w^2 + 0.263672r^2w^3 + 0.395508rw^4 + 0.237305w^5$$

Expand using the Binomial Theorem or a CAS.

Now each coefficient gives the probability of each event occurring, rather than its frequency. The probability of getting 2 right and 3 wrong is the coefficient of the r^2w^3 term.

You can also obtain more information by evaluating the polynomial. For example, take the polynomial for rolling a number cube, $p(x) = x + x^2 + x^3 + x^4 + x^5 + x^6$. The output $p(1) = 6$ gives the total number of outcomes. Also, $(p(1))^3$ equals $6^3 = 216$. This is the total number of outcomes when rolling three number cubes.

But consider $p(-1) = 0$ and how it is built term by term. Let $x = -1$. Then $x^k = 1$ if k is even and $x^k = -1$ if k is odd. So, $p(-1) = 0$ means there are just as many even numbers on a number cube as odd numbers.

Now look at $(p(-1))^4$. It also equals zero, but models the sum of four number cubes. So, there are just as many ways to roll an odd sum from four number cubes as an even sum. This is pretty surprising, but you can verify it using the expansion on page 549. In fact, it must be true no matter how many number cubes are thrown.

One important thing to remember is that the method of polynomial powers is useful when performing the same experiment several times. Experiments involving coins, number cubes, and spinners are good examples. Picking a committee or drawing balls out of a bingo machine are not good examples, since the experiment changes over time. To see this, think about drawing a bingo number. When you draw that number, you remove it from the machine. You have fewer numbers for the next draw.

Wrap Up

Have students work on the Check Your Understanding exercises. This sequence of exercises increases in difficulty, giving students more and more responsibility for formulating the solution each time. In Exercise 1, students interpret an already worked-out expansion. In Exercise 2, students need to see the connection between the power to which the polynomial is raised and the number of number cubes in the experiment. In Exercise 3, students have a new type of number cube to contend with, so they have to consruct their own polynomial to model it. In Exercise 4, they see how to deal with outcomes that are not equally likely. Exercise 5 asks them to interpret an expansion with this new situation, emphasizing the meaning of substitutions. And finally, in Exercise 6, students deal with a totally new situation, answering different types of questions.

Assessment Resources

Lesson Quiz 7.3

1. An unusual number cube has the numbers 1, 2, 4, 6, 9, and 10 on its faces.
   a. Find a polynomial that models one roll of this number cube.
   b. In three rolls, what is the most likely sum? How likely is it?

2. A board game has a spinner with the numbers 4, 5, 6, 7 and 8. Each number is equally likely.
   a. Find the probability that you spin a total of at least 13 in just two spins.
   b. Find the probability that you spin a 10 or less in just two spins.
   c. Find the probability of spinning exactly an 11 in just two spins.

3. A spinner has four numbers 0, 3, 4, and 4.
   a. Find a polynomial to model one spin.
   b. What is the mostly likely sum after four spins? How likely is it?

Exercises

HOMEWORK
- Core: 7, 8, 9, 11, 12, 13
- Optional: 14, 15
- Extension: 10

Check Your Understanding

EXERCISE 2 is a good question for further study, since it is possible to get the answer $\frac{1}{2}$ in many ways, not all of them intuitive.

EXERCISE 3 is a good one to test the concepts of the lesson.

EXERCISE 6 As mentioned, the last part may take a while to calculate without use of a CAS function that transforms a polynomial into a list, or removes the lesser terms from the polynomial. Once you remove the lower terms, let $x = 1$ to calculate the sum of the coefficients.

On Your Own

EXERCISE 7 When you review this exercise, show both the direct use of the polynomial expansion, and the relationship to the example in this lesson. Since each number on this spinner is 1 less than the numbers from the example, the most likely sum is 4 less. All sums for four spins are 4 less, with probability equal to the example.

Exercises *Practicing Habits of Mind*

Check Your Understanding

1. The polynomial on page 549 gives the distribution of possible sums for rolling four number cubes.
   a. Build a histogram showing the frequency for each outcome, from 4 to 24.
   b. Explain why there are exactly as many ways to roll a sum of 5 as there are ways to roll a sum of 23.

2. Suppose you roll three number cubes. Calculate the probability that the sum of the numbers will be greater than 10.

3. On an unusual number cube the "1" face has a 10 instead.
   a. Find a polynomial that models one roll of this number cube.
   b. In four rolls, what is the most likely sum? How likely is it?

The six faces on this number cube have the numbers 2, 3, 4, 5, 6, and 10.

4. On another number cube the "6" face has a 5 instead.
   a. Explain why the polynomial $p(x) = x + x^2 + x^3 + x^4 + 2x^5$ models one roll of this number cube.
   b. In four rolls, what is the most likely sum? How likely is it?

The six faces on this number cube have the numbers 1, 2, 3, 4, 5, and 5.

5. Consider the number cube from Exercise 4 and its corresponding polynomial p.
   a. Expand $q(x) = (p(x))^2$. What does q represent?
   b. Find the value of $q(1)$.
   c. There are 36 outcomes when rolling this number cube twice. How many more ways are there to roll an even sum than an odd sum?
   d. Find the value of $q(-1)$.

6. A board game has a spinner with the numbers 1 through 10 on it. All numbers are equally likely. As you near the end of the game, you have 18 spaces left to move.
   a. Find the probability that you spin a total of *at least* 18 on just two spins.
   b. Find the probability that you spin a total of *at least* 18 on three spins.
   c. Find the probability that you spin a total of *at least* 18 on four spins.

Answers

Exercises

1. a. See back of book.

b. To roll a 5, the only possible roll is the four variations of 1-1-1-2. To roll a 23, the only possible roll is the four variations of 6-6-6-5. Also, the frequencies appear symmetric on either side of 14.

2. $\frac{1}{2}$

3. a. $x^2 + x^3 + x^4 + x^5 + x^6 + x^{10}$

b. 20; $\frac{95}{1296}$

4. a. Answers may vary. Sample: $2x^5$ represents the two faces with 5 on them, while the other exponents indicate single faces with 1 through 4 on them.

b. 13; $\frac{164}{1296}$

5–6. See back of book.

On Your Own

For additional practice, go to Web Code: bga-0703

7. A spinner has the five numbers 0, 1, 2, 2, and 7.
   a. Find a polynomial to model one spin.
   b. What is the most likely sum of the numbers from four spins? How likely is it?

8. Avery takes a multiple-choice test with six questions. There are five choices per question. He guesses at each question.
   a. What is the probability that Avery guesses correctly on the first question? on the second question?
   b. What is the probability that Avery guesses correctly on all six questions?
   c. Write a polynomial expansion to model this situation.
   d. Find the probability that Avery guesses correctly on exactly two of the six questions.

9. A local market has a prize wheel. Lucky customers can spin the wheel to win free fish. On one spin, it is possible to win 1 fish, 2 fish, 3 fish, or 10 fish.
   a. What is the average number of fish the market can expect to give away, per spin?
   b. Three customers spin the wheel. What is the most likely total number of fish that they win? How likely is this?

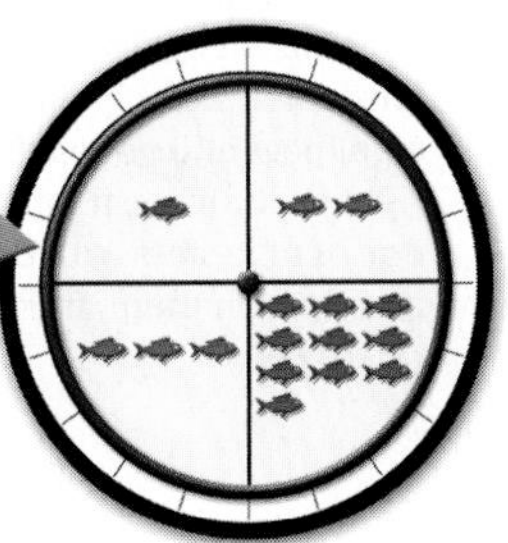

10. **Take It Further** Ten customers spin the Wheel of Fish from Exercise 9. Find the probability that the total number of fish they win is even.

11. Use a coordinate grid with $1 \le x \le 10$, $1 \le y \le 10$. Plot all 55 points with integer coordinates (x, y) in this range with $x \ge y$. Use one color if the two numbers share a common factor greater than 1. Use a second color if they do not.

12. You are to choose two integers x and y between 1 and 10, inclusive, with $x \ge y$. Use your plot from Exercise 11. Determine the probability that the pair of integers will have no common factor greater than 1.

13. **Standardized Test Prep** Which of the following is the sum of the entries in the 12th row of Pascal's Triangle?

    A. 12! B. 6^6 C. 2^{12} D. ${}_{12}P_2$

Maintain Your Skills

14. Write out F_{10}, the Farey sequence of order 10.

15. Take a coordinate grid with $0 \le x \le 10$, $0 \le y \le 10$. Plot all points (x, y) in this range where the fraction $\frac{y}{x}$ is in F_{10}, the Farey sequence of order 10. Compare the results to Exercise 11.

Remember...

The *Farey sequence* of order *n* is all fractions between 0 and 1 in lowest terms with denominators less than or equal to *n*, written from least to greatest.

7. a. $1 + x + 2x^2 + x^7$

b. 11; $\frac{72}{625} = 0.115$

8. a. 0.2; 0.2

b. $(0.2)^6 = 0.000064$

c. $(0.2r + 0.8w)^6$

d. $\frac{768}{3125} = 0.24576$

9. a. 4

b. 14; with probability $\frac{9}{64}$

10. $\frac{1}{2}$

11. See back of book.

12. $\frac{32}{55}$

13. C

14. $\frac{0}{1}, \frac{1}{10}, \frac{1}{9}, \frac{1}{8}, \frac{1}{7}, \frac{1}{6}, \frac{1}{5}, \frac{2}{9}, \frac{1}{4}, \frac{2}{7}, \frac{3}{10},$
$\frac{1}{3}, \frac{3}{8}, \frac{2}{5}, \frac{3}{7}, \frac{4}{9}, \frac{1}{2}, \frac{5}{9}, \frac{4}{7}, \frac{3}{5}, \frac{5}{8}, \frac{2}{3},$
$\frac{7}{10}, \frac{5}{7}, \frac{3}{4}, \frac{7}{9}, \frac{4}{5}, \frac{5}{6}, \frac{6}{7}, \frac{7}{8}, \frac{8}{9}, \frac{9}{10}, \frac{1}{1}$

15. See back of book.

EXERCISE 8 This follows the Developing Habits of Mind section at the end of the lesson, using $(0.2r + 0.8w)$ for five choices instead of the four-choice version given.

EXERCISE 9 Some students may assume that 12 fish is the most likely answer, since the average is 4 fish per spin. This is, in general, not true. For example, it is not even possible to give away 8 fish in two spins. It is worthwhile to make a spinner for this game so that students can experiment with it a bit, or even so that you can demonstrate it when going over this and other Wheel of Fish exercises.

Maintain Your Skills

EXERCISES 14 AND 15 These exercises are two more in the continuing series of exercises on the Farey sequence. If you want to assign them, it is best if students did the exercises in previous lessons.

Additional Resources

PRINT RESOURCES
- Solution Manual
- Practice Workbook
- Assessment Resources
- Teaching Resources

TECHNOLOGY
- Interactive Textbook
- TeacherExpress CD-ROM
- ExamView CD-ROM
- PHSchool.com

Additional Practice

1. a. If you flip a coin five times, how many different ways are there for the result to be 3 heads and 2 tails? Write them out.
   b. Calculate the value of $\binom{5}{3}$. Explain how it relates to the work in part (a).

2. Consider flipping a coin eight times.
   a. Find the probability you will get exactly five heads and three tails.
   b. Find the probability you will get exactly four heads and four tails.

3. In a game, you roll a standard number cube and flip a coin. The coin has the number 2 on one side, and 6 on the other side. Your score is the sum of the values that appear on the number cube and the coin flip.
   a. You win the game if you score 8 points or more. Find the probability that you win.
   b. You get to roll the number cube and flip the coin a second time if you score 5. Find the probability that you score 5.
   c. Are all the scores from 3 to 12 equally likely? Explain.

4. A six-sided number cube has the numbers 1, 2, 4, 6, 6, and 8 on its faces.
   a. Find a polynomial that models one roll of this number cube.
   b. In three rolls, what is the most likely sum? How likely is it?

5. A spinner with five equal wedges has the numbers 0, 3, 4, 5, and 7.
   a. Find a polynomial that models one spin.
   b. What is the most likely sum of the numbers after four spins? How likely is it?

6. A board game has a spinner with the numbers 1 through 6 on it. All numbers are equally likely in a single spin. As you near the end of the game, there are nine more spaces left to move.
   a. Find the probability that you spin at least a nine in two spins.
   b. Find the probability that you spin at least a nine in three spins.
   c. Find the probability that you spin less than a nine in three spins.

Practice: For Lesson 7.3, assign Exercises 4–6.

Lesson Overview

GOAL

- Calculate the expected value of a random variable.

This lesson formalizes the idea of *expected value*, which is a way to predict the average result of many trials of a probability experiment. Students begin to think of the result of a probability experiment as a number, and develop the idea of *random variable*. A random variable is a function that takes outcomes as inputs and returns a number. Students sum the products of the probability of each outcome with the value that the random variable returns for that outcome to find the expected value. All of this theory, however, is made much more concrete through examples of games.

CHECK YOUR UNDERSTANDING
- Core: 1, 2, 3, 4, 6, 7
- Optional: 5

MATERIALS
- CAS (recommended)
- graphing calculators
- Blackline Masters MC12, 7.2

HOMEWORK
- Core: 8, 9, 10, 12, 13, 14, 15, 16
- Optional: 17
- Extension: 11, 18

VOCABULARY
- expected value, $E(X)$
- random variable

Launch

Begin today's lesson with the description of the Plinko game in the In-Class Experiment. There are many websites that provide a simulation of this game, so you might want to have students play with a simulation to develop some experience with it.

Explore

In-Class Experiment

PROBLEM 2 It is possible to solve this problem without a polynomial, but it is a good idea to show the use of a polynomial like $(\ell + r)^8$ for the lefts and rights.

PROBLEM 6 On average, the per-chip win is

$$10000 \cdot \frac{70}{256} + 0 \cdot \frac{112}{256} + 1000 \cdot \frac{56}{256} + 500 \cdot \frac{16}{256} + 100 \cdot \frac{2}{256} \approx 2985.16$$

The phrasing of this question is key to understanding expected value. Students often think the expected value must be one of the values, and getting them to think in the "long term" can help them recognize that the expected value is a weighted average.

7.4 Expected Value

The expected value for a game is how much you could expect to win per game, on average. It is not necessarily the most likely amount you would win in any one game. Instead, if you played many times over, your average score would approach this expected value in the long run.

In-Class Experiment

On game shows and at school carnivals, the game of Plinko is a often favorite. Suppose on one game show all the player has to do is drop a chip, and they can win up to $10,000. Here is a simplified version of the Plinko board:

Whenever the chip hits a peg, it has a 50-50 chance of going left or right as it falls. After the chip has hit eight pegs and gone left or right eight times, it falls into one of nine slots with dollar amounts on them, from $0 to $10,000.

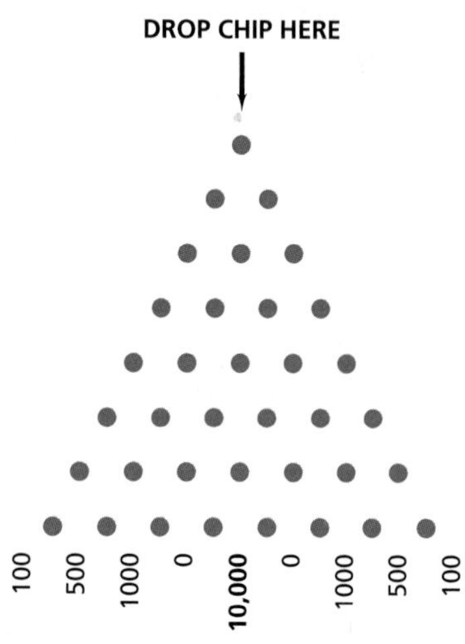

1. Describe the relationship between the falling chip and coin flipping.
2. Write a polynomial, raised to a power, to model this game.
3. Find the probability that the chip falls into the center slot for a $10,000 win.
4. Find the probability that the chip falls into a $0 slot. Note there are two such slots.
5. What is the probability of winning $1000? $500? $100?
6. How much, on average, would you win per chip if you were to keep playing this game for a long, long time?

The sample space here has 256 outcomes. Why?

Answers

In-Class Experiment

1. The falling Plinko chip is similar to flipping a coin, because at each peg, the chip has a 50% chance of going to the right and a 50% chance of going to the left. What it already has done has no impact on what it will do next.
2. $(r + \ell)^8$
3. 0.27344
4. 0.4375
5. 0.21875; 0.0625; 0.0078125
6. $2985.16

Minds in Action episode 22

A student is thinking about the last problem from the In-Class Experiment.

Wendy Let me answer a simpler question first: let's say you paid me \$10,000 if I flip a coin heads, and \$0 if it's tails. I've got a $\frac{1}{2}$ chance to make heads, so it should be \$5000 per flip, on average.

So now let me look at this bigger problem. I'll focus on the \$10,000 first. Every time I drop a chip, there's a $\frac{70}{256}$ chance of getting the 10 grand. If you sat me there all day dropping chips, I can find the average by multiplying.

$$\$10{,}000 \cdot \frac{70}{256} \approx \$2734$$

So if everything else was zeros, that would be my average.

But I could win some smaller amounts of money. There's a $\frac{56}{256}$ chance of hitting \$1000. I'll do the same thing:

$$\$1000 \cdot \frac{56}{256} \approx \$219$$

So, I'll build a table for all the options.

Win	Probability	Win × Probability
\$10,000	$\frac{70}{256}$	\$2734
\$1000	$\frac{56}{256}$	\$219
\$500	$\frac{16}{256}$	\$31
\$100	$\frac{2}{256}$	\$1
\$0	whatever	\$0

I'm not sure what to do now, I think I'll just add the dollar values. On average, I'd expect to win around \$2985 per chip, if you let me sit there all day and drop chips. Not a bad day's work.

Often, it makes sense to assign a number to each outcome of an experiment, such as "3" instead of "rolling a 3 on the number cube," or "2" instead of "heads, tails, heads, tails, tails" or "10,000" instead of "the chip falls in the middle slot." Each set of these numerical assignments is a random variable, and typically uses a capital letter like X or Y.

Wendy's method calculates the *expected value* of a random variable.

A **random variable** is a function whose inputs are outcomes, and whose outputs are numbers.

Example

Spend time as needed going over this completed example. Make sure students understand the problem. As necessary, help them develop the detailed solution.

Definition

The expected value of a random variable X is the sum when each value of X is multiplied by its probability. The typical notation is $E(X)$.

$$E(X) = \sum_i x_i \cdot p_i$$

where the x_i are the values of the random variable, and the p_i are the probabilities of the values, respectively. An alternative notation is

$$E(X) = \sum_i s_i \cdot P(X = s_i)$$

where $P(X = s_i)$ is the probability that the random variable X takes on the value s_i.

Remember...

$\sum_i x_i \cdot p_i$ means to add the products of all the different possible x's and their corresponding p's. It is the same as writing $\sum_{i=1}^{n} x_i \cdot p_i$ There are n different outcomes, so there are n products to add.

The definition is a mouthful, but the Plinko game is a good example. For the Plinko board, each x_i is a dollar value. Each p_i is the probability of hitting that value.

Example

Problem Toss five coins. What is the expected value for the number of heads?

Solution Define a random variable H as the number of heads in 5 coin tosses. This experiment has 32 outcomes. List the possible values of H, along with the probability for each.

Remember...

A random variable takes in outcomes and returns numbers. For example, one outcome is a = "heads, tails, heads, tails, tails." The random variable H takes in that outcome and returns the number 2, $H(a) = 2$.

Number of Heads	Probability
0	$\frac{1}{32}$
1	$\frac{5}{32}$
2	$\frac{10}{32}$
3	$\frac{10}{32}$
4	$\frac{5}{32}$
5	$\frac{1}{32}$

Calculate expected value. Multiply each value of H by its probability. Then add the results.

Number of Heads	Probability	Product
0	$\frac{1}{32}$	0/32
1	$\frac{5}{32}$	5/32
2	$\frac{10}{32}$	20/32
3	$\frac{10}{32}$	30/32
4	$\frac{5}{32}$	20/32
5	$\frac{1}{32}$	5/32
Total		**80/32**

The expected value is $\frac{80}{32}$, which simplifies to $\frac{5}{2}$.

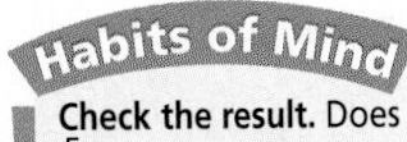

Check the result. Does $\frac{5}{2}$ make sense as the average number of heads when flipping five coins?

Developing Habits of Mind

Use a different process. You might have thought about the Plinko game in a different way. You could add up all the money you would win from each path. There are 2 ways to win \$100, 16 ways to win \$500, 56 ways to win \$1000, and 70 ways to win \$10,000. The total winnings from all the different paths is

$$2 \cdot \$100 + 16 \cdot \$500 + 56 \cdot \$1000 + 70 \cdot \$10{,}000 = \$764{,}200$$

This is the total value for all 256 paths, so the average would have to be

$$\frac{\$764{,}200}{256} \approx \$2985.16$$

This gives the correct result! Both methods are valid. It comes down to whether you prefer to count probabilities or frequencies. The result Wendy comes up with is

$$\frac{2}{256} \cdot \$100 + \frac{16}{256} \cdot \$500 + \frac{56}{256} \cdot \$1000 + \frac{70}{256} \cdot \$10{,}000$$

The distributive law shows that both these results must be identical. So, you can also calculate the expected value by taking the sum of all the outputs from the random variable, then dividing by the total number of outcomes. The expected value is the mean result from the random variable.

For example, the expected value of the numeric result when rolling one number cube is the mean of the numbers on the six faces.

$$\frac{1+2+3+4+5+6}{6} = 3.5$$

Minds in Action

In Investigation 7B, you follow up on the idea that expected value multiplies across repeated trials of the experiment. For now, watch for students building an intuition that this should be true.

LEADING QUESTION What is the expected value of 5 Plinko chips? (Answer: If each Plinko chip is worth \$2985, then 5 chips are worth \$14,925.)

Wrap Up

As time allows, have students work on the core Check Your Understanding exercises. Exercises 1 and 2 are good ones for students to act out as part of their process. When you act out the situation, it is much easier to see that you cannot have exactly one or exactly three people in the wrong chairs, than if you are just trying to count possibilities. When you go over these exercises, emphasize Exercise 4. Many students confuse the range of allowable values for probabilities with the range of allowable values for expected value.

Assessment Resources

Lesson Quiz 7.4

1. A bag contains ten coins worth different values. There are three \$10 coins, four \$20 coins, two \$50 coins, and one \$75 coin. You choose one coin at random.
   a. What is the probability you choose a \$75 coin?
   b. What is the expected value, in dollars, of the coin?

2. A spinner has the numbers 3, 4, 5, 6 and 7. All numbers are equally likely.
   a. Find the expected value for the sum of two spins.
   b. Find the expected value for the sum of three spins.

3. Dan is taking an 8-question multiple choice test, with five choices for each question. He guesses at each question. Find the expected value for the number of questions Dan gets right when taking the test.

Minds in Action episode 23

Tony and Derman look at Exercise 9 from Lesson 7.3.

Tony So, it's a wheel with 1, 2, 3, and 10 fish on it. And we want to know the average from one spin.

Derman I'll just add and divide. The sum is . . . 16. So the average is 4.

Tony Sounds good. Now what about two spins?

Derman I think it's going to be 8. Two times four. Two spins, 4 fish each?

Tony I'm not sure it works that way. Let's just write out the sample space. There are only 16 ways it can go.

Derman A table it is.

+	1	2	3	10
1	2	3	4	11
2	3	4	5	12
3	4	5	6	13
10	11	12	13	20

Tony Cool. I'm going to add all these numbers then divide by 16. Since the sample space is small, I won't bother making a frequency table.

The sum is 128. So, the expected value for two spins is 128 over 16 . . . hey, you were right! It is 8.

Derman It was bound to happen sometime. If I'm right, for three spins the expected value should be 12. The table's going to be a mess!

Tony Well, we should use a polynomial power instead. The outcomes are 1, 2, 3, and 10, so the polynomial for one spin should be

$$(x^1 + x^2 + x^3 + x^{10})$$

Derman Isn't x^1 just x?

Tony I like writing x^1, it makes it more clear where it came from. I'd do that for x^0 instead of writing 1.

Derman Fair enough. And we raise that to the third power, since it's three spins. Expand that and . . .

Tony Let's write that out.

For You to Do

7. Complete the work from the dialog. Write out the expansion of $(x^1 + x^2 + x^3 + x^{10})^3$, then use it to show that the expected value for three spins is 12.

Answers

For You to Do

7. $x^{30} + 3x^{23} + 3x^{22} + 3x^{21} + 3x^{16} + 6x^{15} + 9x^{14} + 6x^{13} + 3x^{12} + x^9 + 3x^8 + 6x^7 + 7x^6 + 6x^5 + 3x^4 + x^3$; $3 \times \frac{1 + 2 + 3 + 10}{4} = 3 \times \frac{16}{4} = 3 \times 4 = 12$

Exercises *Practicing Habits of Mind*

Check Your Understanding

Alice, Bev, Craig, and Dawn sit at a table for four in no particular order. Rey, the host of the party, tells them their seats are assigned at the table and shows them the chart.

1. a. What is the probability that all four of them are already in the right seat?

b. What is the probability that all four of them are in the *wrong* seat?

2. On average, how many of the four will be sitting in the right seat?

3. Suppose a Plinko board has a center hole worth $20,000.

DROP CHIP HERE

100 500 1000 0 20,000 0 1000 500 100

Find the average amount a player will win, per chip, in the long run.

Habits of Mind

Make a list. There are 24 possible ways for the four guests to sit down. Do you see why there are 24 possible outcomes? Try listing them.

This is another way to say, "Calculate the expected value" for this new version of the game.

4. What's Wrong Here? Daisuke had trouble calculating the expected number of heads when tossing three coins.

Daisuke: I built the table with each outcome and its probability, then added it up. I got the probabilities from the Getting Started lesson. I could use Pascal's Triangle to get them, too.

Number of Heads	*Probability*	*Product*
0	$\frac{1}{8}$	$\frac{0}{8}$
1	$\frac{3}{8}$	$\frac{3}{8}$
2	$\frac{3}{8}$	$\frac{6}{8}$
3	$\frac{1}{8}$	$\frac{3}{8}$
Total		$\frac{12}{8}$

Daisuke: But it doesn't make sense to me to get $\frac{12}{8}$ as the answer: that's one and a half, and I thought probability was never supposed to be more than one.

What would you say to Daisuke? Has he made a mistake in the calculation?

Exercises

HOMEWORK

- Core: 8, 9, 10, 12, 13, 14, 15, 16
- Optional: 17
- Extension: 11, 18

Check Your Understanding

You might find Blackline Masters 7.2 and MC12 useful in discussing several of the exercises. Exercise 4, for instance, mentions Pascal's Triangle but Blackline Master MC12 might also be helpful in Exercise 5. Exercises 10 and 11 refer to the number cube outcomes so you could use Blackline Master 7.2 if you discuss them.

EXERCISE 2 If time and technology permit, examine this problem more deeply with more seats (or fewer seats). Amazingly, the average number of correctly seated people never changes, it is always 1. One informal reason for this result is that each seat is correctly filled with probability $\frac{1}{n}$, and there are n seats.

EXERCISE 3 is a fairly straightforward exercise for students if they follow the expected value calculation.

EXERCISE 4 Students often believe that expected values are between 0 and 1, because they are not distinguishing between expected value and probability. This is a very common misconception. If students fall into this trap, have them work with situations where the results are nowhere near the 0-to-1 range of probabilities.

Exercises

1. a. $\frac{1}{24}$

b. $\frac{9}{24}$ or $\frac{3}{8}$

2. 1

3. $5719.53

4. There is nothing wrong with Daisuke's calculation. His mistake was in the interpretation of his results. Expected value is not a probability and can be greater than 1. $\frac{12}{8}$ represents the number of heads expected when you toss 3 coins.

EXERCISE 5 The result here previews an important result in Investigation 7B, that expectation adds. Here, the expected value for each question is 0.2, so the expected value for all six questions is $0.2 \cdot 6 = 1.2$.

EXERCISE 7 As with Exercise 5, this result previews an important idea in Investigation 7B. The result here is 4 times as large as the result for one spin.

On Your Own

EXERCISE 8 is another exercise previewing the concept of adding expectation. Students are likely to have a good intuition for the answer here.

EXERCISE 9 follows up on the example in this lesson. Students can use an expansion or Pascal's Triangle to calculate the probabilities.

EXERCISE 10 If you review this problem, point out the pattern in the expected values! Students catch on to this, developing an intuition for the ideas in Investigation 7B.

EXERCISE 11 Students may not think to use polynomials here. This is not relevant to the rest of the chapter, so do not give this exercise much emphasis.

EXERCISE 14 and the following one are messy in that they generally require enumeration of the 120 cases. While there are ways to speed up the process, they are not simple to find. You might split this exercise among several students, or offer it as optional credit.

5. Avery is taking a six-question multiple choice test, with five choices for each question. He guesses at each question.

a. Expand the polynomial $(0.2r + 0.8w)^6$. What do the results represent?

b. Find the expected value for the number of questions Avery gets right when taking the test.

6. Three customers spin the Wheel of Fish as seen in Exercise 9 on page 553.

a. Use a polynomial expansion to find the frequency of each outcome.

b. Find the probability that the market will give away fewer than 10 total fish to these three customers.

On one spin, the possible outcomes are 1, 2, 3, and 10 fish.

7. Find the expected value for the total number of fish the market gives away when four customers spin the Wheel of Fish.

On Your Own

8. In this lesson's In-Class Experiment, you calculated the expected value for dropping one Plinko chip. Now suppose you drop five chips.

a. What is the expected value, in dollars, for the first chip? the second chip? the third chip?

b. What is the expected value for the total earned from all five chips?

For additional practice, go to **Web Code:** bga-0704

9. Find the expected value for the number of heads when tossing six coins.

10. a. Find the expected value for the sum when rolling two number cubes.

b. Find the expected value for the sum when rolling three number cubes.

11. Take It Further

a. Find the expected value for the *product* when rolling two number cubes.

b. Find the expected value for the product when rolling three number cubes. How could you use a polynomial here?

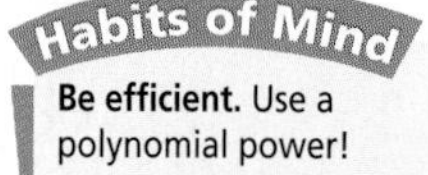

Be efficient. Use a polynomial power!

Answers

5. a. See back of book.

b. 1.2

6. a. $(x^1 + x^2 + x^3 + x^{10})^3$
$= x^{30} + 3x^{23} + 3x^{22} + 3x^{21} + 3x^{16} + 6x^{15} + 9x^{14} + 6x^{13} + 3x^{12} + x^9 + 3x^8 + 6x^7 + 7x^6 + 6x^5 + 3x^4 + x^3$

b. $\frac{27}{64} = 0.421875$

7. 16

8. a. \$2985.16; \$2985.16; \$2985.16

b. \$14,925.80

9. 3

10. a. 7

b. 10.5

11. a. $\frac{441}{36} = 12.25$

b. $\frac{9261}{216} = 42.875$; expand $(x^1 + x^2 + x^3 + x^4 + x^5 + x^6)^3$ to find the frequency of each outcome.

Suppose a friend gives you five envelopes, each with a different address on it. You are to put one of five different letters in each envelope. But you have no idea which letter is for which person, so you stuff them in at random.

12. What is the probability that all five envelopes contain the right letter?

13. What is the probability that exactly four envelopes contain the right letter?

14. What is the probability that all five envelopes contain the wrong letter?

15. Find the expected value for the number of letters correctly addressed.

This exercise is in the same style as Exercises 1 and 2. You might want to think of this as five people and five seats.

16. **Standardized Test Prep** A student randomly guesses on a true-false combinatorics test with five questions. Which of the following is the probability that the student will score at least 80%?

A. $\frac{5}{32}$ **B.** $\frac{3}{16}$ **C.** $\frac{1}{4}$ **D.** $\frac{1}{2}$

Maintain Your Skills

17. Copy and complete this table using your work from previous lessons.

n	Number of Elements in F_n	Relatively Prime Pairs
1	2	■
2	■	■
3	■	4
4	■	■
5	11	■
6	■	■
7	■	18
8	■	■
9	■	■
10	33	■

Here, F_n is the Farey sequence of order n. *Relatively prime pairs* refers to the number of pairs that have no common factors greater than 1 as plotted in Exercise 11 on page 553.

18. **Take It Further** Find the number of elements in F_{30}, the Farey sequence of order 30. Your goal is only to find the number of elements, not list them all.

Habits of Mind

Look for relationships. Look for a simpler method than writing out the entire sequence F_{30}.

12. $\frac{1}{120}$

13. 0

14. $\frac{44}{120}$ or $\frac{11}{30}$

15. 1

16. A

17. See back of book.

18. 279

EXERCISE 15 See Exercise 11 in the next lesson for a final follow-up. In the end, the number of gifts does not matter; the expected value is always 1. In Investigation 7B students learn that the variance for this data is *also* always 1!

Maintain Your Skills

EXERCISE 17 This may be the first time some students recognize the connection between the two functions.

EXERCISE 18 If students have trouble with this exercise, ask them to build a difference table for the number of elements in each Farey sequence. They may see the pattern emerge; each Farey sequence adds $\phi(n)$ more numbers, where ϕ is Euler's function that counts how many numbers less than n are relatively prime to n. For example, F_{11} has 10 more elements than F_{10}, while F_{12} has only 4 more elements than F_{11}.

One nice extension is to look at this data in a scatter plot; it nearly forms a quadratic and is fit well by one. In the end, a quadratic with leading coefficient $\frac{3}{\pi^2}$ closely fits F_n!

Additional Resources

PRINT RESOURCES
- Solution Manual
- Practice Workbook
- Assessment Resources
- Teaching Resources

TECHNOLOGY
- Interactive Textbook
- TeacherExpress CD-ROM
- ExamView CD-ROM
- PHSchool.com

Additional Practice

1. Jonah has five different plants and five pots, each labeled with one of the plant names. He does not know the correct name of each plant so he randomly puts one plant in each pot.
  a. What is the probability that all five of the plants are in the pot with the correct name?
  b. What is the probability that all five of the plants are in a pot with the wrong name?
  c. On average, how many of the five will be in the correct pot?

2. A game show has a spinner with the numbers 0, 3, 4, 5, and 10 in equally likely wedges. Whatever number a contestant spins is awarded in hundreds of dollars (example: if a 5 is spun, the contestant wins $500).
  a. What is the expected value of prize money awarded to a contestant that spins once?
  b. What is the expected value of prize money awarded to a contestant that spins twice?
  c. Find the probability that less than $700 in prize money will be given away in one spin.

3. A 5-ball lottery has 35 numbered balls. A player selects five numbers. A machine draws five balls at random.
  a. Copy and complete this frequency table.
  b. Find the expected value for the number of balls a player will correctly match in the 5-ball lottery.

Matches	Frequency
0 correct	
1 correct	
2 correct	
3 correct	
4 correct	
5 correct	1

4. A 6-ball lottery is played with 80 balls to pick from. A player wins a prize in this lottery if they get at least 3 of the 6 numbers right. What is the probability of winning a prize in this lottery?

5. A bag contains 12 black coins and 8 white coins. Erika picks one coin. After returning the coin to the bag and remixing the coins, she reaches in a second time and picks one coin. If Erika is paid as shown in the table, what is the expected value of the amount she will win?

Outcome	Payout
Two black	loses $5
One black, one white	wins $10
Two white	wins $25

Practice: For Lesson 7.4, assign Exercises 1–2.

Lesson Overview

GOAL

- Calculate the expected value of a random variable.

In this lesson, students learn how to calculate the probabilities and expected values for various common types of lotteries. This work helps to solidify their understanding of the meaning of expected value and give them practice in combinatorics. They also examine the effects of slight changes to the lottery rules on the expected value and interpret their findings as profit for the entity running the lottery.

CHECK YOUR UNDERSTANDING
- Core: 1, 2, 3, 4, 6
- Optional: none
- Extension: 5

MATERIALS
- graphing calculators
- Blackline Master 7.5

HOMEWORK
- Core: 7, 8, 9, 11, 12
- Optional: 10, 13a
- Extension: 13b

Launch

Begin today's lesson by letting your students tell you what they know about lotteries. You could bring in (or ask them to bring in) descriptions of some of the lotteries being run in your area. You might want to make a list of conjectures and questions that students have, and note when these are investigated in the lesson.

Work through the scratch ticket situation at the beginning of the lesson with your class. Make distinctions between frequency and probability, and identify the payouts as the value of the random variable for each outcome. Help your students make sense of the vocabulary in this investigation by translating lottery terms into more formal mathematical language.

Blackline Master 7.5 is a blank lottery table. Use only the columns required by the example or problem. There is room for up to a dozen different matches. Cover up or shade in the columns, rows, or cells that you do not need. Label the last row you use as "Total." You may wish to provide copies to your students for use in class or on their homework.

7.5 Lotteries

One application of expected value is a lottery. There are several different kinds of lotteries. In some lotteries, expected value can be directly calculated, while others require an approach based on combinations.

Scratch Tickets

State lotteries print batches of tickets, some of which are prize winners. Players pay to get a ticket. Most tickets lose, but some tickets are worth hundreds or thousands of dollars.

Here is the distribution from a scratch ticket game where each ticket costs $1.

Payout	Frequency
$1	163,500
$2	62,800
$4	20,945
$8	4,189
$12	4,189
$50	5,621
$100	128
$1,000	4
$0 (lose)	995,324
Total	**1,256,700**

Most of the tickets lose. Only a small percentage give the player more money than the price of the ticket.

How much is the average ticket worth in this game? To find this, calculate the expected value.

The random variable is the dollar value (payout) of the ticket, from 0 to 1000. The sample space is all 1,256,700 tickets. The expected value is the sum of each payout, multiplied by its probability.

Payout	Frequency	Product
1	163,500	163,500
2	62,800	125,600
4	20,945	83,780
8	4,189	33,512
12	4,189	50,268
50	5,621	281,050
100	128	12,800
1,000	4	4,000
0 (lose)	995,324	0
Total	**1,256,700**	**754,510**

The expected value is $\frac{754{,}510}{1{,}256{,}700}$, very close to 60 cents. This lottery ticket actually costs $1, so roughly 60% of the money paid for tickets is returned to players as prizes, while 40% is kept by the state that runs this lottery.

Example

In a 6-ball lottery a player picks six numbers, from 1 to 42. Then a machine draws six balls at random from a set of 42 numbered balls. The order of the drawing does not matter. The amount the player wins depends on how many of the numbers match numbers on their ticket.

The sample space has $\binom{42}{6} = 5{,}245{,}786$ elements.

This table shows the possible outcomes and their frequencies.

Matches	Frequency	Payout
0 correct	1,947,792	$0 (loss)
1 correct	2,261,952	$0 (loss)
2 correct	883,575	$0 (loss)
3 correct	142,800	$1
4 correct	9,450	$75
5 correct	216	$1,500
6 correct	1	$2,000,000 jackpot
Total	**5,245,786**	

Problem A ticket in this lottery costs $1. Find the expected value for one ticket.

Solution Multiply the frequencies by the payouts.

Matches	Frequency	Payout	Product
0 correct	1,947,792	0	0
1 correct	2,261,952	0	0
2 correct	883,575	0	0
3 correct	142,800	1	142,800
4 correct	9,450	75	708,750
5 correct	216	1,500	324,000
6 correct	1	2,000,000	2,000,000
Total	**5,245,786**		**3,175,550**

Note that the majority of the payouts go to the single jackpot winner (if there is one). Overall the expected value is

$$\frac{3{,}175{,}550}{5{,}245{,}786} \approx 0.6054$$

The $1 ticket is worth just over 60 cents, so the lottery earns an average profit of nearly 40 cents per dollar played.

For You to Do

1. Suppose the lottery is considering changing the rules to give a $5 prize for 3 numbers correct. What would happen to the expected value of a ticket? Would the lottery still be profitable for whoever is running it?

Habits of Mind

Use what you know. Try modifying the information from the table.

Combinatorics and Lotteries

You can determine the frequencies in the previous example by counting combinations. Picture the 42 balls in the lottery drawing. The player picks 6 numbers, dividing the 42 balls into two categories: 6 that they want to see, and 36 others that they do not want to see.

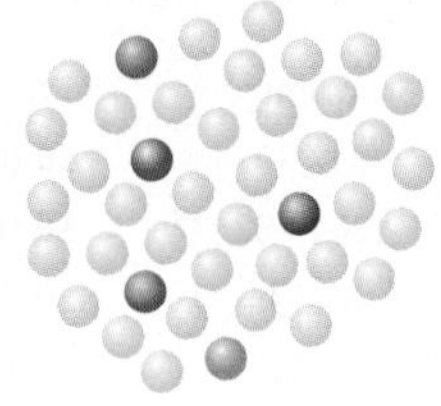

Suppose you want to know how many different ways there are to get exactly four balls correct in the lottery drawing. Well, out of the 6 balls the player wants to see, the machine draws 4. That can happen $\binom{6}{4}$ ways. But the machine also draws 2 of the "other" balls. That can happen $\binom{36}{2}$ ways. So, the number of ways to get exactly four balls correct is

$$\binom{6}{4} \cdot \binom{36}{2} = 15 \cdot 630 = 9450$$

You can use this approach for any count between 0 and 6.

Matches	Frequency
0 correct	$\binom{6}{0} \cdot \binom{36}{6} = 1{,}947{,}792$
1 correct	$\binom{6}{1} \cdot \binom{36}{5} = 2{,}261{,}952$
2 correct	$\binom{6}{2} \cdot \binom{36}{4} = 883{,}575$
3 correct	$\binom{6}{3} \cdot \binom{36}{3} = 142{,}800$
4 correct	$\binom{6}{4} \cdot \binom{36}{2} = 9{,}450$
5 correct	$\binom{6}{5} \cdot \binom{36}{1} = 216$
6 correct	$\binom{6}{6} \cdot \binom{36}{0} = 1$

Remember...

You can calculate combinations like $\binom{36}{2}$ using the nCr function on a calculator, or by using the factorial formula:

$$\binom{n}{k} = \frac{n!}{k!(n-k)!}$$

Note that the total number of outcomes is $\binom{42}{6}$ since there are 42 balls and 6 are picked. This leads to a theorem about combinations.

Theorem 7.1 ***Vandermonde's Identity***

Let $r \leq n$ be nonnegative integers. Then

$$\binom{n}{r} = \sum_{k=0}^{r} \binom{r}{k} \cdot \binom{n-r}{r-k}$$

This method can be used to analyze most ball-drawing lottery games.

Answers

For You to Do

1. Increase; yes, the new expected value would be 71 cents.

Developing Habits of Mind

Study the difference. Larger multi-state lotteries now exist, typically using these rules:

- First, a machine draws five balls from a set.
- Second, another machine draws the sixth ball (the "bonus ball") from a second set of balls, a completely different group.

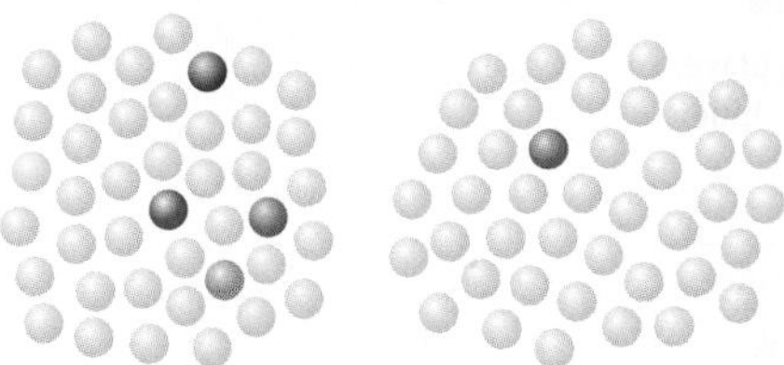

In order to win the jackpot, the player must get all five regular balls correct, plus the bonus ball. What effect does the existence of the bonus ball have on the sample space? Consider a game with 42 balls for the regular drawing, and a new set of 42 balls for the "bonus."

The size of the sample space becomes

$$\binom{42}{5} \cdot \binom{42}{1}$$

since 5 balls are chosen from the first set of 42, then 1 ball is chosen from the second set. While it may not seem like much of a difference, this has a huge effect on the size of the sample space.

$$\text{sample space for 6-ball lottery} = \binom{42}{6} = 5{,}245{,}786$$

$$\text{sample space with bonus ball} = \binom{42}{5} \cdot \binom{42}{1} = 35{,}728{,}056$$

The sample space is roughly 7 times bigger. It is much less likely a player will win. As of April 2008, one multi-state lottery had a sample space of over 146 million, while another had a sample space of over 175 million!

Think about flipping a coin 27 times in a row, and having all 27 coin flips come up heads. This would happen once every 134 million tries. In other words, flipping 27 heads in a row is *more* likely to happen than buying a winning ticket in either of these multi-state lotteries.

For Discussion

2. A multi-state lottery could increase its sample space by adding more balls to either the regular pool or the "bonus" pool. How many more regular-pool balls would be needed to double the sample space? How many more "bonus" balls would be needed to double the sample space?

For Discussion

2. To more than double the sample size of a 6-ball lottery with 42 regular balls, you would need to add 6 regular balls. To more than double the size of a lottery with one "bonus" ball, you would need to add 42 additional bonus balls. The second bonus ball would increase the sample space more than 20 times its original size.

Explore

Discussion

PROBLEM 2 Students may be surprised by the results; adding a ball to the regular pool increases the sample space quickly, while adding balls to the "bonus" pool only increases the sample space proportionally. One reason for this is that $\binom{n}{1} = n$ is a linear function, while $\binom{n}{5}$ is a fifth-degree polynomial (as learned in Chapter 5). Therefore, $\binom{n}{5}$ grows much more quickly when n is large enough.

Amazingly, only 6 more regular-pool balls are needed to more than double the sample space, while 42 more "bonus" balls are needed. Adding regular-pool balls is a tactic typically used by lotteries to increase their maximum jackpot value without a large impact on the outward appearance of their game.

Wrap Up

If you made a list of questions and conjectures at the beginning of the lesson, return to it now. See which have been resolved. For those unresolved issues, evaluate whether or not your students have enough mathematics background to investigate. Some of the students' questions may have been non-mathematical. For example, students may have asked whether state-run lotteries should be considered ethical. Encourage interested students to write a response to these questions. If your class has debated ethics, you might ask them to respond to the statement, "Lotteries are taxes on people who do not know math."

As you go over the core Check Your Understanding exercises, make certain that students can distinguish between probability and expected value, and between probability and frequency. These distinctions often trip up students.

Assessment Resources

Lesson Quiz 7.5

1. A 4-ball lottery has 36 numbered balls. A player selects four numbers. Then, four of the balls are drawn by a machine.
   a. Copy and complete this frequency table.
   b. Find the expected value for the number of balls a player will correctly match.

Matches	Frequency
0 correct	
1 correct	
2 correct	
3 correct	
4 correct	

2. Consider a 6-ball lottery with 36 balls. A player selects 6 balls. Then six of the balls are drawn by a machine. Find the expected value for the number of balls that a player will correctly match.

3. A school raffle offers these prizes: Each ticket costs $4. What is the school's profit if every ticket is sold?

Payout	Frequency
$100	10
$15	50
$0 (lose)	940

Exercises

HOMEWORK
- Core: 7, 8, 9, 11, 12
- Optional: 10, 13a
- Extension: 13b

Check Your Understanding

EXERCISE 2 has a surprising result, and one that continues to preview the concept that expectation adds. Watch for students giving a fractional answer here, the decimal 0.4545 is not helpful in detecting the pattern.

EXERCISE 3 The total number of outcomes is also given by $\binom{55}{5} \cdot 42$, due to the way the lottery balls are pulled. If you review this exercise, point out how amazingly low these numbers are; 30 cents on the dollar is only half what most state lottery games return in prizes, and those are not all that great either.

Exercises *Practicing Habits of Mind*

Check Your Understanding

1. A 5-ball lottery has 55 numbered balls. A player selects five numbers. Then, five of the balls are drawn by a machine.

   Copy and complete this frequency table.

Matches	Frequency
0 correct	■
1 correct	1,151,500
2 correct	■
3 correct	■
4 correct	■
5 correct	1

2. Find the expected value for the number of balls a player will correctly match in the 5-ball lottery presented in Exercise 1.

3. Suppose an interstate lottery has a 5-ball component with 55 balls, and then a bonus ball from a separate set of 42 balls. This table lists the payouts for this lottery.

Ticket Type	Frequency	Payout
5 balls + bonus	1	Jackpot
5 balls + no bonus	41	\$200,000
4 balls + bonus	250	\$10,000
4 balls + no bonus	10,250	\$100
3 balls + bonus	12,250	\$100
3 balls + no bonus	502,250	\$7
2 balls + bonus	196,000	\$7
1 ball + bonus	1,151,500	\$4
Bonus only	2,118,760	\$3
Losing ticket	142,116,660	\$0
Total outcomes	**146,107,962**	

   The base jackpot for this lottery is \$16,000,000. Find the expected value of a \$1 ticket in this lottery.

Answers

Exercises

1.

Matches	Frequency
0 correct	2,118,760
1 correct	1,151,500
2 correct	196,000
3 correct	12,250
4 correct	250
5 correct	1

2. $\frac{5}{11}$

3. The expected return for a \$1 ticket is $\frac{44,800,030}{146,107,962} = 0.30662$. This Lottery pays 30 cents in prizes for every dollar it takes in.

4. The jackpot in the game from Exercise 3 may grow as high as $100 million!

   a. Suppose the jackpot is worth m million dollars. Find the expected value of a ticket, in terms of m.

   b. If the jackpot is $100 million, what is the expected value of a ticket?

   c. How high must the jackpot be for the expected value to be greater than $1 per ticket?

The jackpots that lotteries report are actually much more than the money that they pay out or that a player would get. A player has to pay taxes on winnings. Also, the lottery pays the jackpot over many years, not all up front. In fact, it is rare for the jackpot to grow above $100 million in most lotteries.

5. **Take It Further** A second multistate lottery has a 5-ball component with 56 balls, and then a bonus ball from a separate set of 46 balls.

   Copy and complete this table for the frequency of each payout.

Ticket Type	Frequency	Payout
5 balls + bonus	1	Jackpot
5 balls + no bonus	■	$250,000
4 balls + bonus	■	$10,000
4 balls + no bonus	11,475	$150
3 balls + bonus	■	$150
3 balls + no bonus	■	$7
2 balls + bonus	■	$10
1 ball + bonus	■	$3
Bonus only	■	$2
Losing ticket	171,306,450	$0
Total outcomes	**175,711,536**	

   Then, find the expected value of a $1 ticket at the base jackpot of $12 million.

6. A state-run raffle offers a number of prizes. A total of 500,000 tickets are available. Each ticket costs $20. These prizes are available:

Payout	Frequency
$1,000,000	4
$100,000	5
$10,000	8
$5,000	8
$1,000	500
$100	2000
$0 (lose)	497,475

   Find the expected value of a $20 raffle ticket.

4. a. $\frac{1{,}000{,}000m + 28{,}800{,}030}{146{,}107{,}962} =$ $0.006844m + 0.197115$, where m is the number of millions

b. 0.88154; the expected return is 88 cents for a $1 ticket.

c. greater than $117,308,932

5. See back of book.

6. The expected return per ticket is $10.64.

EXERCISE 4 If your students are interested, this is a good place to discuss the actual value of a large jackpot. If the reported jackpot is $300 million, the actual value is closer to $80 million. Multistate lotteries offer a "lump-sum" payment that is typically 40–50% of the reported jackpot, and the winner is responsible for state and federal income taxes.

On Your Own

EXERCISE 7 Point out to students that any one ball is $\frac{1}{7}$ likely to be picked, since there are 6 picks from a set of 42. If each ball is $\frac{1}{7}$ likely to be picked, and there are six picks…

EXERCISE 8 You may want to have students consider what happens to the profitability of the game if not all of the tickets are sold. After all, it is difficult to sell 65 million tickets at $20 each. What is the "worst-case" scenario for the state if they sell only half of these tickets? What is the "best-case" scenario? What would the state expect to happen? Another discussion point is that scratch ticket games have a greater potential for fraud. Tickets are either winners or losers, and it might be possible for employees at the manufacturing plant to have some prior knowledge. It is also true that the winning tickets are delivered to particular locations, and after delivery, only customers at those locations can win.

On Your Own

7. Consider the 6-ball lottery with 42 balls from this lesson. Find the expected value for the number of balls that a player will correctly match.

8. Consider the following prize distribution from a large scratch ticket game.

Payout	Frequency
$10,000,000	10
$1,000,000	130
$25,000	130
$10,000	1,820
$1,000	33,670
$500	109,200
$200	336,700
$100	1,791,335
$50	1,310,400
$40	2,620,800
$25	7,862,400
$20	7,862,400
$0 (lose)	43,585,545
Total tickets	**65,520,000**

a. Find the expected value of one ticket.

b. Each ticket costs $20. If all tickets are sold, how much profit will be made by the state running this lottery?

9. A 6-ball lottery in Italy is the largest of its kind with 90 balls to pick from. A player wins a prize in this lottery if they get at least 3 of the 6 numbers right. What is the probability of winning a prize in this lottery?

10. Use the Internet to find information on a lottery or scratch ticket game. Determine the expected value on a ticket in that game.

Go Online PHSchool.com

For additional practice, go to Web Code: bga-0705

Answers

7. $\frac{6}{7}$

8. a. $\frac{1,110,353,500}{65,530,000} \approx 16.9468$; the expected value of one ticket is about $16.95.

b. $200,046,500

9. $P(\text{win}) = \frac{1,958,475}{622,614,630}$

≈ 0.003146

10. Check students' work.

11. Suppose a friend gives you six envelopes, each with a different address on it. You are to put one of six different letters in each envelope. But you have no idea which letter is for which person, so you stuff them in at random. You hope at least some of the envelopes contain the correct letter.

This frequency table lists the number of different permutations with 0 correct envelopes, 1 correct, and so on.

Number Correct	Frequency
0	265
1	264
2	135
3	40
4	15
5	0
6	1

a. What is the total number of outcomes in this sample space?

b. Find the expected value for the number of correct envelopes.

12. **Standardized Test Prep** A bag contains 16 red chips and 4 blue chips. Amy picks one chip. After returning the chip to the bag and remixing the chips, she reaches in a second time and picks one chip. If Amy is paid as shown in the table, what is the expected value of the amount she will win?

Outcome	Payout
Two blue	wins $10
One blue, one red	wins $1
Two red	loses $1

A. loses at least $1 **B.** loses less than $1 **C.** Breaks even
D. wins less than $1 **E.** wins at least $1

Maintain Your Skills

13. The numbers 7, 21, and 35 appear in the 7th row of Pascal's Triangle. These numbers are unusual in that they form an arithmetic sequence: add 14 to 7 to get 21, then add another 14 to get 35. Or, put another way, 21 is the mean of 7 and 35.

a. Find the next time this occurs in Pascal's Triangle.

b. **Take It Further** If $\binom{n}{k}$ is the mean of $\binom{n}{k-1}$ and $\binom{n}{k+1}$, find a relationship between n and k.

11. a. 720
b. 1

12. D

13. a. $\binom{14}{4} = 1001$, $\binom{14}{5} = 2002$, $\binom{14}{6} = 3003$

b. Answers may vary. Sample: $n + 2$ must be a perfect square, and $2k - n$ must equal the square root of $n + 2$. So, $k = \frac{\sqrt{n+2} + n}{2}$.

EXERCISE 11 This result is even more surprising if you connect it back to Exercises 12 through 15 in the previous lesson. The expected value in that situation was also 1, even though there were five envelopes instead of six.

Maintain Your Skills

EXERCISE 13 Some students approach this exercise by doing the second part first. If they find algebraic calculation more appealing than constructing Pascal's triangle and searching for a pattern, this is where they may start, and that is fine.

Additional Resources

PRINT RESOURCES
- Solution Manual
- Practice Workbook
- Assessment Resources
- Teaching Resources

TECHNOLOGY
- Interactive Textbook
- TeacherExpress CD-ROM
- ExamView CD-ROM
- PHSchool.com

Additional Practice

1. Jonah has five different plants and five pots, each labeled with one of the plant names. He does not know the correct name of each plant so he randomly puts one plant in each pot.
a. What is the probability that all five of the plants are in the pot with the correct name?
b. What is the probability that all five of the plants are in a pot with the wrong name?
c. On average, how many of the five will be in the correct pot?

2. A game show has a spinner with the numbers 0, 3, 4, 5, and 10 in equally likely wedges. Whatever number a contestant spins is awarded in hundreds of dollars (example: if a 5 is spun, the contestant wins $500).
a. What is the expected value of prize money awarded to a contestant that spins once?
b. What is the expected value of prize money awarded to a contestant that spins twice?
c. Find the probability that less than $700 in prize money will be given away in one spin.

3. A 5-ball lottery has 35 numbered balls. A player selects five numbers. A machine draws five balls at random.
a. Copy and complete this frequency table.
b. Find the expected value for the number of balls a player will correctly match in the 5-ball lottery.

Matches	Frequency
0 correct	
1 correct	
2 correct	
3 correct	
4 correct	
5 correct	1

4. A 6-ball lottery is played with 80 balls to pick from. A player wins a prize in this lottery if they get at least 3 of the 6 numbers right. What is the probability of winning a prize in this lottery?

5. A bag contains 12 black coins and 8 white coins. Erika picks one coin. After returning the coin to the bag and remixing the coins, she reaches in a second time and picks one coin. If Erika is paid as shown in the table, what is the expected value of the amount she will win?

Outcome	Payout
Two black	loses $5
One black, one white	wins $10
Two white	wins $25

Pract ce: For Lesson 7.5, assign Exercises 3–5.

Mathematical Reflections

EXERCISES 6–8 At the start of the investigation, you may have assigned these as Questions 1–3 for students to think and write about.

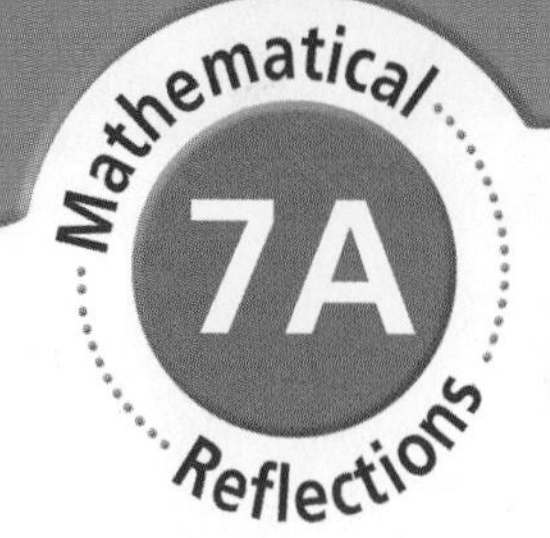

In this investigation, you calculated probabilities using Pascal's Triangle and polynomial powers. You also learned about expected value and its uses. The following questions will help you summarize what you have learned.

1. How can you use the expansion of $(t + h)^5$ to find the probability of getting exactly two heads on five coin tosses?
2. a. Al wins a game if he flips a coin heads, and rolls less than a six on a number cube. What is the probability that Al wins the game?

   b. Beth wins a game if she flips a coin tails, or (after flipping heads) if she rolls a six on a number cube. What is the probability that Beth wins the game?
3. A wheel has the numbers 5 through 100 on it, in multiples of 5. What is the expected value of one spin of this wheel?
4. A 5-ball state lottery uses 49 balls. What is the probability of getting exactly four of the five balls correct?
5. A wheel has the numbers 1, 2, 3, and 6 on it. After spinning the wheel four times, what is the most likely total?
6. If you are to roll four number cubes, what is the probability they sum to 12?
7. What is expected value?
8. How can you use polynomials to solve probability problems?

Vocabulary and Notation

In this investigation, you learned these terms and symbols. Make sure you understand what each one means and how to use it.

- **event**
- **expected value, $E(X)$**
- **frequency, $|A|$**
- **independent**
- **mutually exclusive**
- **outcome**
- **probability of an event**
- **random variable**
- **sample space**

If the survival rate for a hatchling to make it to the sea is 32%, how many in a group of 46 are expected to reach the sea?

Answers

Mathematical Reflections

1. Divide the coefficient of the h^2t^3 term by the number of possible outcomes.
2. a. $\frac{5}{12}$

   b. $\frac{7}{12}$
3. 52.5
4. 0.00011537
5. 12
6. $\frac{125}{1296} = 0.09645$
7. The expected value of a random variable X is the sum when each value of X is multiplied by its probability.
8. Polynomials can be used to model results, and they are useful when the questions are too complex to list the outcomes by hand.

Mid-Chapter Test

For a mid-chapter test, go to Web Code: bga-0752

Multiple Choice

1. If you flip a coin six times, how many possible outcomes are there?

   A. 12 B. 32
   C. 36 D. 64

2. What is the probability of flipping exactly three heads if you flip a coin six times?

   A. $\frac{5}{16}$ B. $\frac{1}{2}$
   C. $\frac{1}{6}$ D. $\frac{3}{64}$

3. A number cube has the numbers 2, 4, 6, 8, 10, and 12. Which polynomial models one roll of this cube?

   A. $x^1 + x^2 + x^3 + x^4 + x^5 + x^6$
   B. $2x^1 + 4x^2 + 6x^3 + 8x^4 + 10x^5 + 12x^6$
   C. $x^2 + x^4 + x^6 + x^8 + x^{10} + x^{12}$
   D. $2(x^2 + x^4 + x^6 + x^8 + x^{10} + x^{12})$

4. A spinner has four wedges of equal area with the numbers 2, 3, 5, and 6. If you spin twice, what is the probability that the sum of the spins is 8?

   A. $\frac{1}{9}$ B. $\frac{1}{2}$
   C. $\frac{1}{4}$ D. $\frac{1}{3}$

5. You play a game by flipping a coin three times. If you flip three heads you win $20. If you flip two heads, you win $10. If you flip only one head you win nothing. If you flip no heads you must pay $5. What is the expected value of your winnings?

   A. $10 B. $3.50
   C. $0 D. $6.25

6. Michaela is taking a five-question test where she is matching words with their definitions. If she just guesses, what is the probability that she gets 100%?

   A. $\frac{1}{3125}$ B. $\frac{1}{120}$
   C. $\frac{1}{25}$ D. $\frac{1}{5}$

Open Response

7. If you roll two number cubes, determine the following probabilities.
   a. rolling a sum of 7
   b. rolling a sum of 1
   c. rolling a sum greater than or equal to 10

8. A box contains five coins. Two of the coins are worth $100, one of the coins is worth $50, another coin is worth $25, and the last coin is worth $5. You reach in and randomly choose a coin.
   a. What is the probability of choosing a coin worth $100?
   b. Calculate the expected value for this experiment.
   c. Calculate the expected value if someone adds a sixth, worthless coin to the box.

9. A lottery has 36 numbered balls, and a player must select five numbers. Then, five of the balls are picked. Matching all five of the numbers wins the jackpot.
   a. How many total combinations of five numbers are possible?
   b. How many ways can a player match three of the five numbers?
   c. What is the probability of winning the jackpot?

10. A lottery is played by choosing four numbers out of 80 numbers.
    a. Copy and complete the table.

Matches	Frequency	Payout
0 correct	■	$0
1 correct	■	$5
2 correct	■	$500
3 correct	■	$5,000
4 correct	■	$25,000

    b. A ticket for this lottery costs $10. What is the expected value for one ticket?

Mid-Chapter Test

1. D
2. A
3. C
4. C
5. D
6. B
7. a. $\frac{1}{6}$ b. 0 c. $\frac{1}{6}$
8. a. $\frac{2}{5}$ b. $56 c. $46.67
9. a. 376,992
   b. 4650
   c. $\frac{1}{376,992}$
10. a.

Matches	Frequency	Payout
0 correct	1,282,975	$0
1 correct	281,200	$5
2 correct	17,100	$500
3 correct	304	$5,000
4 correct	1	$25,000

    b. $7.27

Mid-Chapter Test

Assessment Resources

Mid-Chapter Test page 1

Multiple Choice

1. Suppose you roll three six-sided number cubes and find the sum. How many possible outcomes are there?

   A. 18 B. 36
   C. 216 D. 729

2. If you flip a coin eight times, what is the probability of flipping exactly 5 heads?

   A. $\frac{1}{256}$ B. $\frac{1}{128}$
   C. $\frac{5}{32}$ D. $\frac{7}{32}$

3. A spinner has four equal wedges containing the numbers 3, 3, 4, 5, and 8. Which polynomial models one spin of this spinner?

   A. $1 + x^3 + x^4 + x^5 + x^8$
   B. $2x^3 + x^4 + x^5 + x^8$
   C. $2x^3 + 2x^4 + x^5 + x^8$
   D. $x + 2x^3 + x^4 + x^5 + x^8$

4. A number cube has the numbers 2, 3, 4, 5, 7 and 10 on its faces. If you are to roll twice, what is the probability that the sum of the faces rolled is 7?

   A. $\frac{1}{18}$ B. $\frac{1}{14}$
   C. $\frac{1}{9}$ D. $\frac{1}{6}$

5. A game involves selecting a ticket from a bag and winning the prize amount on the ticket. A bag contains ten tickets. There are four tickets worth $5. There are also three tickets worth $10, two tickets worth $25, and one ticket worth $50. If you reach in and pull out one ticket, what is the expected value of your winnings?

   A. $10.50 B. $12.00
   C. $15.00 D. $22.50

6. Samantha is taking a six-question test where she is matching words with their definitions. If she just guesses, what is the probability that she gets 100%?

   A. $\frac{1}{720}$ B. $\frac{1}{120}$
   C. $\frac{1}{36}$ D. $\frac{1}{6}$

Also available: Form B

Mid-Chapter Test page 2

Open Response

7. If you roll two number cubes, determine the following probabilities.
   a. rolling a sum of 12
   b. rolling a sum of 6
   c. rolling a number less than or equal to 5

8. A box contains seven coins. Three of the coins are worth $10. Two of the coins are worth $20. One of the coins is worth $50 and another coin is worth $100. You reach in and randomly choose a coin.
   a. What is the probability of choosing the $100 coin?
   b. Calculate the expected value for this experiment.
   c. Calculate the expected value if someone adds an eighth worthless coin to the box.

9. A lottery has 32 numbered balls, and a player must select five numbers. Then a machine picks five of the balls. Matching all five of the numbers wins the jackpot.
   a. How many total combinations of five numbers are possible?
   b. How many ways can a player match two of the five numbers?
   c. What is the probability of winning the jackpot?

10. A lottery is played by choosing four numbers out of 75 numbers.
    a. Copy and complete the table.

Matches	Frequency	Payout
0 correct		$0
1 correct		$80
2 correct		$800
3 correct		$8000
4 correct		$80,000

    b. Find the expected value of a ticket in this lottery.

Also available: Form B

Investigation Overview

Expected value for a random variable is a measure of its central tendency. Over many trials of a probability experiment, the values of the random variable cluster around the expected value. And if the trials are independent and the outcomes are equally likely, the expected value is equal to the mean of the possible values of the random variable. So if you graph the value of the random variable over repeated trials of an experiment, you know the approximate location of the center of that distribution.

However, to produce a complete description of the distribution you expect for a random variable, you also need to have some way to talk about the spread of the data. How closely does it cluster around the expected value? If you have a way of figuring out the spread of the data from the parameters of the probability experiment, then you can judge the relevance of the expected value as a predictor of future behavior.

You may wish to assign Questions 1–3 for students to think and write about during the investigation.

Learning Goals

- Calculate expected value, mean absolute deviation, variance, and standard deviation.
- Calculate statistics for compound events, including repeated experiments.
- Identify Bernoulli trials and compute related statistics.

Habits and Skills

- Interpret statistics in order to compare two data sets or make predictions.
- Understand $\sum$ notation and apply $\sum$ theorems.
- Reason deductively to prove relationships in statistics such as the "machine formula."

Expectation and Variation

In *Expectation and Variation*, you will learn how to calculate an interval of values that you are likely to obtain when you perform an experiment involving data.

By the end of this investigation, you will be able to answer questions like these.

1. How can you calculate the standard deviation for a large set of data?
2. What happens to the mean, variance, and standard deviation if an experiment is repeated a second time?
3. What is the mean and standard deviation for the number of heads on 400 coin flips?

You will learn how to

- calculate expected value, mean absolute deviation, variance, and standard deviation
- calculate statistics for compound events, including repeated experiments
- identify Bernoulli trials and compute related statistics

You will develop these habits and skills:

- Interpret statistics in order to compare two data sets or make predictions.
- Understand Σ notation and apply Σ theorems.
- Reason deductively to prove relationships in statistics such as the "machine formula."

When flipping coins, you expect to get about half heads and half tails. The actual number of heads and tails cannot be predicted but the amount of variation can be calculated.

Investigation Road Map

LESSON 7.6, *Getting Started,* has students perform a probability experiment and record the results in a histogram.

LESSON 7.7, *Variance and Standard Deviation,* introduces formal calculations for variance and standard deviation. Students prove the *machine formula*.

LESSON 7.8, *Adding Variances,* shows students that variance is additive.

LESSON 7.9, *Repeated Experiments,* has students apply the result from the previous lesson to large numbers of trials of probability experiments.

LESSON 7.10, *Bernoulli Trials,* formally introduces Bernoulli trials, which are experiments with two outcomes—success and failure.

7.6 Getting Started

Here is an opportunity to explore how well you would do if you guessed at every question on a multiple-choice test.

For You to Explore

1. On a separate piece of paper, take this multiple-choice test. For each of the 20 questions, select choice A, B, C, D, or E. Only one answer is correct. After the test, your class can compile the scores and build a histogram of the data.

   Oops, the questions are missing. Good luck!

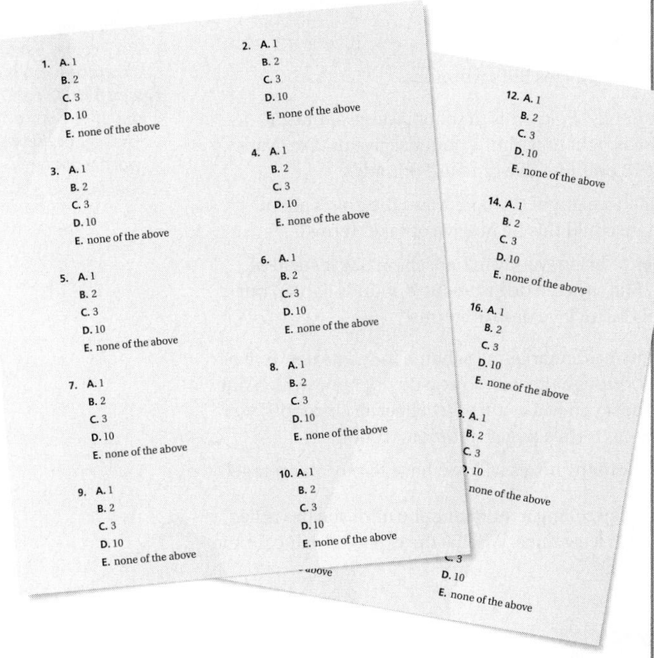

2. On average, how many questions would you expect each person in your class to get right? Explain.

3. **a.** Build a histogram for the number of questions each person in your class answered correctly.

   b. What percent of the class got between 2 and 6 correct, inclusive?

Lesson Overview

GOAL

- Warm up to the ideas of the investigation.

This lesson explores topics in probability. Students take a completely random multiple-choice test. It is random because the questions are not given. Then they are asked to think about this situation. How many questions should they expect to get right? What does the data look like for the class as a whole? They produce a histogram for the class results, and think about what the shape of that histogram tells them about the data. In the exercises, they consider some probability experiments and situations involving randomness and think about how they could make predictions about the results. This work prepares them for a more formal study of expected value and variance. Students are not expected to know formal methods to calculate answers to these exercises, but the exercises preview the work of the investigation.

FOR YOU TO EXPLORE
- Core: 1, 2, 3
- Optional: none

MATERIALS
- graphing calculators
- Blackline Masters 7.6A–C

HOMEWORK
- Core: 4, 5
- Optional: 8
- Extension: 6, 7

Launch

Have students first complete the For You to Explore section. This is a multiple-choice test with no questions so they must choose their answers at random. Then have them swap papers and call out the answers so they can grade each other's papers. A possible answer key is ABEAABADBAADCECCE CBD, but you can make your own.

Investigation 7B opens with a guessing, multiple choice quiz (with answers similar to the Wheel of Fish on page 533). The test form, as seen in the textbook, appears on Blackline Masters 7.6A and 7.6B. To save paper, a one page form is given as Blackline Master 7.6C. Copy before class and distribute to the students.

Explore

For You to Explore

PROBLEM 1 Score the test using the above answer key. Or make your own solution key, but do not follow a pattern such as ABCDEABCDE and so on. If more than one class takes the "test," use a different solution key for each class to avoid the possibility of students exchanging a list of the correct answers.

Answers

For You to Explore

1. Answers may vary. Note that students are to use their answers in Problems 2 and 3.
2. 4; answers may vary. Sample: a person has a $\frac{1}{5} = 20\%$ probability of answering each question correctly. 20% of 20 questions is 4.
3. **a–b.** Check students' work.

Wrap Up

Look back at the data from your class, and discuss it in connection with any conjectures that the class made. Depending on your class, you may want to do further trials of the test-taking experiment to test their conjectures, or modify the experiment and see how the modifications impact the result. You might also choose to have students continue on to the On Your Own exercises, with opportunities for class or small group discussion.

In any case, remind students that when they do a Getting Started lesson, they may not know how to approach some of the questions being asked. That is certainly the case in this lesson. What matters is that students are able to explain their reasoning in a way that shows they made sense of the situation. Students are not expected to know how to calculate answers to the exercises in this set; they are just expected to think about them and make predictions based on their thoughts and impressions.

Exercises

HOMEWORK
- Core: 4, 5
- Optional: 8
- Extension: 6, 7

On Your Own

EXERCISE 5 The purpose here is to show that variance adds, regardless of the calculation. Students may be surprised by this, initially calculating that the second answer is within 1 pound. If students have trouble here, explain the extreme ranges of the books and dog.

EXERCISE 6 There is a connection here to the sum of the harmonic series, since you write the number of picks required as

$$\frac{6}{6} + \frac{6}{5} + \frac{6}{4} + \frac{6}{3} + \frac{6}{2} + \frac{6}{1}$$

or 6 times the sum of the harmonic series up to $\frac{1}{6}$.

GOING FURTHER You might ask about 10 toy robots, or an entire set of collectible cards (say, 750). The same logic applies but the calculation requires sum notation.

EXERCISE 7 This situation is isomorphic to the toy robot exercise. Hopefully, students who work on both discover this for themselves.

Maintain Your Skills

EXERCISE 8 reminds students about summation notation, and the last part is the calculation of standard deviation. You might ask students to do this without the sum feature of the calculator.

Exercises *Practicing Habits of Mind*

On Your Own

4. Bill is a contestant on a game show. On this show, Bill gets a random integer n between 1 and 75. He then guesses whether the next number (picked from the remaining numbers) will be higher or lower. If Bill is correct, he wins \$100 times the new number. Bill's plan is to win as much money as possible. Determine whether Bill should pick higher or lower in each of the following cases.

a. $n = 25$ **b.** $n = 38$ **c.** $n = 39$ **d.** $n = 42$

e. Describe a strategy that maximizes Bill's winnings.

So, he wins only \$300 if a 3 comes out after a correct guess, but he wins \$6,700 if a 67 comes out after a correct guess. The higher numbers are worth a lot more!

5. Nancy estimates that the books she carries to school weigh about 25 pounds. Nancy figures she is right to within 3 pounds, give or take. Nancy's dog Woody weighs about 18 pounds, give or take 2 pounds.

a. Nancy says the combined weight of the books and the dog is about 43 pounds. How accurate could this be in "give or take" terms?

b. One day, Nancy decides to bring Woody in her school bag instead of books (a lighter load!). She says the dog is about 7 pounds lighter, but how accurate could this be in "give or take" terms?

6. **Take It Further** A company has a marketing scheme to sell its new line of toy robots. You cannot see through the box, so you do not know which one of the six equally likely robots you will get. If you collect all six robots, you can connect them together to form a larger "ultimate" robot.

To collect all six robots, how many boxes will you have to buy on average?

7. **Take It Further** Bree will keep rolling a number cube until she has rolled each number (1 through 6) at least once. What is the expected value for the number of times Bree will roll?

Maintain Your Skills

8. Calculate each sum.

a. $\sum_{k=1}^{9} k$ **b.** $\sum_{k=1}^{9} k^2$ **c.** $\sum_{k=1}^{9} \frac{k^2}{9}$

d. $\sum_{k=1}^{9} \frac{(k-5)^2}{9}$ **e.** $\sqrt{\sum_{k=1}^{9} \frac{(k-5)^2}{9}}$

Answers

Exercises

4. a. higher **b.** higher
c. higher **d.** higher
e. Bill should go higher for $n \leq 53$, and lower for $n \geq 54$.

5. a. The range of combined weights is 38 to 48 pounds, so about 43 pounds is accurate give or take 5 pounds.

b. The maximum possible difference is 12 pounds (28–16), and the minimum possible difference is 2 pounds. The guess of "about" 7 pounds lighter is accurate, give or take 5 pounds.

6. 14.7

7. 14.7

8. a. 45 **b.** 285
c. $\frac{285}{9} = \frac{95}{3} = 31.667$
d. 6.67
e. 2.58

7.7 Variance and Standard Deviation

When you do an experiment repeatedly, it is likely that your results will cluster around the expected value of the experiment. You can measure how well they cluster by calculating the standard deviation.

In-Class Experiment

As the winner of a contest, you get to pick one of three spinners and spin it. You will earn \$1 multiplied by the number you spin.

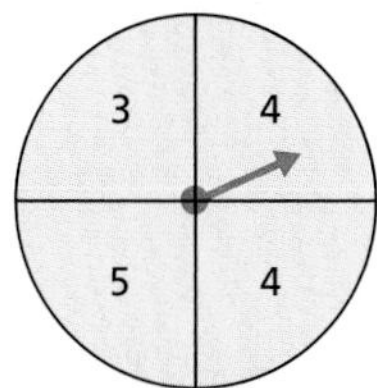

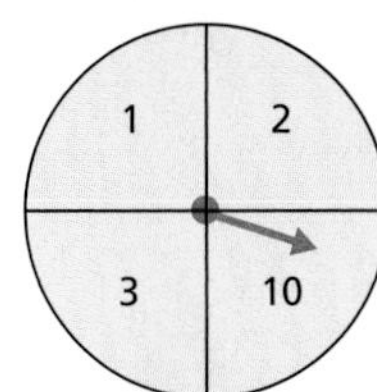

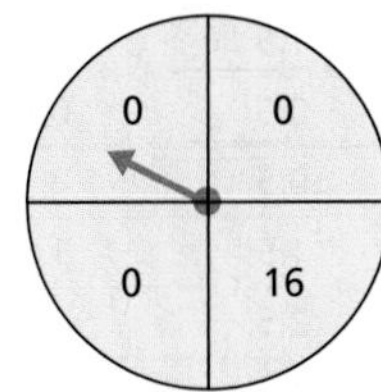

1. For each spinner, calculate the expected value of the spin. Which spinner would you choose? Explain your choice. Would your answer change if you were spinning for \$10,000 multiplied by the spin?

Suppose for a random variable X, the n outputs x_1 through x_n are all equally likely. Then, as you learned in Investigation 7A, the expected value $E(X)$ is equal to the mean $\overline{x}$.

$$E(X) = \frac{x_1 + x_2 + \cdots + x_n}{n} = \frac{\sum_i x_i}{n} = \overline{x}$$

With equally likely outcomes, the expected value and the mean are interchangeable. So, both $E(Y)$ and $\overline{y}$ denote the expected value for random variable Y with equally likely outcomes.

The three spinners in the In-Class Experiment each have the same expected value. But there are major differences in the **spread** of each. Most measures of spread start by calculating the **deviation** of each result from the mean. For example, if X is the random variable corresponding to the value on one number cube roll, its possible values are 1, 2, 3, 4, 5, and 6. Its mean is $\overline{x} = 3.5$. The table at the right calculates the deviations for each result.

x	Deviation $x - \overline{x}$
1	−2.5
2	−1.5
3	−0.5
4	0.5
5	1.5
6	2.5

Deviation may be positive, negative, or zero.

In-Class Experiment

1. 4; 4; 4; check students' work.

Lesson Overview

GOAL

- Calculate expected value, mean absolute deviation, variance, and standard deviation.

This lesson formally introduces calculations for variance and standard deviation. Students begin with an experiment which asks them to compare the results of three different probability experiments that all have the same mean, but different spread. This gives them some experience in evaluating spread and gauging its impact on an experiment. Then they learn how to calculate deviations from the mean (expected value) and three different measures of spread derived from it.

CHECK YOUR UNDERSTANDING

- Core: 1, 2, 3, 4, 5, 8
- Optional: 6
- Extension: 7

MATERIALS

- graphing calculators
- number cubes (optional)
- tape (optional)
- Blackline Master 7.7

HOMEWORK

- Core: 9, 10, 11, 12, 13, 14, 16
- Optional: 17
- Extension: 15

VOCABULARY

- deviation
- mean absolute deviation
- mean squared deviation, or variance, σ^2
- root mean squared deviation, or standard deviation, σ
- spread

Launch

Begin today's lesson with the In-Class Experiment. Depending on your class, you may want to use spinner blanks to make the spinners described in the experiment and have students try a few rounds of the game just to get a feel for it. Then have students calculate the expected value for each spinner. Give them a chance to discuss their choices and explain their rationales, but do not get bogged down in the discussion. It is okay for some of these questions to remain open for now, and many of them involve non-mathematical issues such as personal risk tolerance.

The calculation of the variance and standard deviation can be both confusing and tedious. Use Blackline Master 7.7 throughout the presentation to help make the process routine and more accurate. At first, use only the first few columns, but the table expands as you progress through this lesson and the next. There is room for up to a dozen values of x; cover up or shade in the columns, rows, or cells that you do not need. Label the last row used as "Total." You may wish to provide copies to your students for use in class or on their homework.

Explore

In-Class Experiment, p. 575

PROBLEM 1 Students should find that all of the expected values are the same, so the choice comes down to risk and spread. The first spinner is the safest, while the last spinner is the most risky. Try not to spend a lot of time on this, since the goal is to expose students to the concept of spread.

For You to Do

2. For each spinner in the In-Class Experiment, calculate the deviations from the mean. Then calculate the sum of the deviations.

Three common measures of spread arise from deviations. You can use these measures to judge how wide a distribution is, or to compare distributions. A larger spread means the distribution is wider.

The first measure of spread is the **mean absolute deviation.** Calculate it by finding the absolute value of each deviation, then finding the mean of these numbers.

x	Deviation $x - \overline{x}$	$\lvert x - \overline{x} \rvert$
1	−2.5	2.5
2	−1.5	1.5
3	−0.5	0.5
4	0.5	0.5
5	1.5	1.5
6	2.5	2.5
	Total	**9**

The mean absolute deviation for one number cube roll is $\frac{9}{6} = \frac{3}{2} = 1.5$.

The second measure is the **mean squared deviation.** Calculate it by finding the square of each deviation, then finding the mean of these numbers.

x	Deviation $x - \overline{x}$	$(x - \overline{x})^2$
1	−2.5	6.25
2	−1.5	2.25
3	−0.5	0.25
4	0.5	0.25
5	1.5	2.25
6	2.5	6.25
	Total	**17.5**

The mean squared deviation for one number cube roll is $\frac{17.5}{6} = \frac{35}{12} \approx 2.917$. Note that you can express the mean squared deviation as

$$\frac{\sum_i (x_i - \overline{x})^2}{n}$$

The third measure is the **root mean squared deviation.** Calculate it by finding the square root of the mean squared deviation. The root mean squared deviation for one number cube roll is approximately 1.708.

Habits of Mind

Understand the process. For each of these measures of spread, the name will tell you how to calculate it.

Answers

For You to Do

2. Spinner 1: −1, 0, 0, 1; 0;
Spinner 2 : −3, −2, −1, 6; 0;
Spinner 3: −4, −4, −4, 12; 0

Developing Habits of Mind

Reason about calculations. Why would anyone use the root mean squared deviation if it is just the square root of another measure? The biggest reason is units. Squaring changes the units, so the mean squared deviation is not in the same units. Consider the second spinner from the In-Class Experiment, with outcomes 1, 2, 3, and 10 and mean 4. Include the units (dollars).

Payout x	Deviation $x - \bar{x}$	$(x - \bar{x})^2$
\$1	−3 dollars	9 square dollars
\$2	−2 dollars	4 square dollars
\$3	−1 dollar	1 square dollar
\$10	6 dollars	36 square dollars
	Total	**50 square dollars**

The mean squared deviation is $\frac{50}{4} = 12.5$ square dollars! By taking the square root, the result is in dollars again.

Of the three measures of spread, the last two are so common that they have shorter names. **Variance** is the shorter, more common name for mean squared deviation. **Standard deviation** is the common name for root mean squared deviation. You may want to remember the longer names, because they reveal the calculations involved and make an underlying relationship more clear:

Standard deviation is the square root of variance

See the TI-Nspire Handbook on p. 704 for details on how to calculate variance and standard deviation.

Standard deviation is a good measure of the spread of data. Most data will be within one standard deviation of the mean. For example, the mean height for adult women is 63.5 inches. The standard deviation is 2.5 inches. Most adult women are between 61 and 66 inches tall. 61 and 66 are each one standard deviation away from the mean of 63.5.

Definitions

The *variance* σ^2 for a data set $\{x_1, x_2, \ldots, x_n\}$ is given by

$$\sigma^2 = \frac{\sum_i (x_i - \bar{x})^2}{n}$$

where $\bar{x}$ is the mean of the data set.

The *standard deviation* σ for a data set is the square root of the variance and is given by

$$\sigma = \sqrt{\frac{\sum_i (x_i - \bar{x})^2}{n}}$$

For Discussion

PROBLEM 3 Note to students that $\overline{x^2}$ is different from $\overline{x}^2$. A numeric example should be enough here.

Wrap Up

For the first four Check Your Understanding exercises, you might have students put masking tape over the numbers on standard number cubes and make the non-standard number cubes described in the exercises. Then they can get a little experience with them to make their calculations more concrete. Go over the core Check Your Understanding exercises as time allows.

Assessment Resources

Lesson Quiz 7.7

For each spinner listed below, calculate the following.

a. the mean
b. the mean absolute deviation
c. the variance
d. the standard deviation

1. A spinner with the numbers 3, 4, 7, 10, and 11, where each number is equally likely.
2. A spinner with the numbers 2, 2, 4, 5, and 7, where each number is equally likely.
3. A spinner with the numbers 0, 2, 3, 4, and 4, where each number is equally likely.

4. Consider the data set {2, 3, 3, 4, 7, 8, 8, 10, 12, 12}. Find the following.
a. mean
b. mean absolute deviation
c. variance
d. standard deviation

These same formulas apply when you view the data as the outputs of a random variable X (rather than as just a set of outcomes). If the outputs xi are all equally likely, the expected value $E(X)$ is equal to the mean $\overline{x}$. So, you can write the variance as

$$V(X) = E((X - E(X))^2)$$

A short formula for variance exists: variance is "the mean of the squares minus the square of the mean." Often, this is easier to calculate. For a number cube roll of 1 through 6 consider the following calculations.

When you compute the variance using this easier calculation, you are using the "machine formula."

- The *mean of the squares* is $(1 + 4 + 9 + 16 + 25 + 36)$ divided by 6, which is $\frac{91}{6}$.
- The *square of the mean* is $\left(\frac{7}{2}\right)^2 = \frac{49}{4}$.
- The difference between these is $\frac{91}{6} - \frac{49}{4} = \frac{35}{12}$. This is the same value for the variance that you calculated using the mean squared deviation.

Below is a proof that this short formula follows from the definition of mean squared deviation, by using binomial expansion and some properties of sums.

Proof

$$\begin{aligned}
\frac{\sum_i (x_i - \overline{x})^2}{n} &= \frac{\sum_i (x_i^2 - 2x_i\overline{x} + \overline{x}^2)}{n} \\
&= \sum_i \frac{x_i^2}{n} - 2\sum_i \frac{x_i\overline{x}}{n} + \sum_i \frac{\overline{x}^2}{n} \\
&= \sum_i \frac{x_i^2}{n} - 2\overline{x}\sum_i \frac{x_i}{n} + \overline{x}^2\sum_i \frac{1}{n} \\
&= \sum_i \frac{x_i^2}{n} - 2\overline{x}^2 + \overline{x}^2 \\
&= \sum_i \frac{x_i^2}{n} - \overline{x}^2 \\
&= \overline{x^2} - \overline{x}^2
\end{aligned}$$

For Discussion

3. For each step in the deviation of the machine formula, give a justification. Why is it okay to pull $\overline{x}$ out of the sum? Where does the $\overline{x}^2$ come from in the middle term? How does the $\sum_i \frac{1}{n}$ just disappear?

Answers

For Discussion

3. Expansion of binomial, sum rules, constants can be pulled out, evaluation of sums, simplification of like terms, definition of mean; $\overline{x}$ is a constant; $\sum_{i=1}^{n} \frac{x_i}{n} = \overline{x}$; $\sum_{i=1}^{n} \frac{1}{n} = 1$

Exercises *Practicing Habits of Mind*

Check Your Understanding

A standard number cube has the numbers 1 through 6. You know from this lesson that the numbers on the faces have the following statistics.

mean $\bar{x} = 3.5$

mean absolute deviation $= 1.5$

mean squared deviation (variance) $\sigma^2 = \frac{35}{12} \approx 2.917$

root mean squared deviation (standard deviation) $\sigma = \sqrt{\frac{35}{12}} \approx 1.708$

For each nonstandard number cube listed below, calculate each of these:

a. the mean
b. the mean absolute deviation
c. the variance
d. the standard deviation

1. A number cube with the numbers 2, 3, 4, 5, 6, 7

2. A number cube with the numbers 2, 4, 6, 8, 10, 12

3. A number cube with the numbers 1, 2, 3, 4, 5, 5

4. A number cube with the numbers 3, 3, 3, 3, 3, 3

5. Write About It

a. When you add a constant c to each element in a data set, what happens to the mean, mean absolute deviation, variance, and standard deviation? Give an additional example using a new data set.

b. When you multiply each element of a data set by a constant k, what happens to the mean, mean absolute deviation, variance, and standard deviation? Give an additional example using a new data set.

Exercises

1. a. 4.5 **b.** 1.5 **c.** 2.917 **d.** 1.708

2. a. 7 **b.** 3 **c.** 11.667 **d.** 3.4156

3. a. 3.3333 **b.** 1.3333 **c.** 2.2222 **d.** 1.4907

4. a. 3 **b.** 0 **c.** 0 **d.** 0

5. a. The mean increases by c, but the mean absolute deviation, variance, and standard deviation are unchanged. Answers may vary. Sample: compare the example data set 1, 2, 3, 4, 5, 6 with the data set from Exercise 1. The mean increases by 1, but the other values are the same.

b. The mean, mean absolute deviation, and standard deviation are multiplied by k, and the variance is multiplied by k^2. Answers may vary. Sample: compare the example data set 1, 2, 3, 4, 5, 6 with the data from Exercise 2. The mean, mean absolute deviation, and standard deviation were multiplied by 2. The variance was multiplied by 4.

Exercises

HOMEWORK

- Core: 9, 10, 11, 12, 13, 14, 16
- Optional: 17
- Extension: 15

Check Your Understanding

EXERCISE 1 Only the mean changes when all numbers on the number cube increase by one.

EXERCISE 2 When the numbers on the number cube double, all statistics double except the variance, which is multiplied by $2^2 = 4$.

EXERCISE 3 The numbers on this number cube are close to those on the standard number cube, but they are a little smaller (no 6), so the mean is smaller. They are also closer to each other (range 1 to 5 instead of 1 to 6), so the mean absolute deviation, variance, and standard deviation are all smaller.

EXERCISE 4 Here, all the numbers on the number cube are identical, so there is zero variance. With only one possible result, the mean is equal to that result.

EXERCISE 5 Students should use the results of the number cube examples here, but also should be able to construct their own.

EXERCISE 6 Since these calculations are always the same, this is a good opportunity to use a spreadsheet to standardize the calculations. Note that this is a time-consuming exercise that you should skip if students do not have enough time to work through it. A later lesson in this investigation refers to the values produced here. Using the results later, students find that the mean is near 4, and the standard deviation is near 1.789. The actual results from this data are quite close. The actual results from your own class's data (see Exercise 11) are probably not as close, but should show similarities.

EXERCISE 7 Since there are many calculations to analyze in this exercise, you might ask students to work out the results for adding **c** to each data value, rather than assigning both parts.

EXERCISE 8 There is no need to press here for students to see that the mean and variance double, since the next lesson covers that. But if it comes up in discussion, mention it as a preview.

On Your Own

EXERCISE 10 The next lesson points out the pattern with the mean and variance, but note here that all the statistics go up except the mean absolute deviation, which stays constant.

6. This frequency table gives the results when 500 students took the 20-question multiple choice test from the Getting Started lesson.

Score	Frequency
0	5
1	34
2	74
3	100
4	100
5	85
6	59
7	29
8	10
9	4
10+	0

Find the mean and standard deviation for this data.

This is a data set with 500 elements! Think about how you might simplify the calculation. Since this is a frequency table, the mean is not the average of 5, 34, 74, . . . , but the mean of 0, 0, 0, 0, 0, 1, 1, 1, 1, . . . , 8, 9, 9, 9, 9.

7. **Take It Further** Use algebra and what you know about sums to prove the claims made in Exercise 5.

8. When you roll two standard number cubes, there are 36 possible outcomes. Calculate the mean, mean absolute deviation, variance, and standard deviation for the sum of the numbers rolled for all 36 possible outcomes. Compare to the results from the numbers on one number cube.

On Your Own

9. Define a random variable for a coin flip as follows. The random variable X equals 1 if the coin flip is heads. It equals 0 if the coin flip is tails.

a. Calculate $E(X)$, the expected value for X.

b. Calculate the deviation for X for each possible outcome.

c. Calculate the mean absolute deviation, the variance, and the standard deviation for the number of heads on one coin flip.

How often will $X = 1$? How often will $X = 0$? Remember, deviation can be negative.

10. Define a random variable for two coin flips as follows. The random variable Y equals 2 if both coins are heads, 1 if exactly one coin is heads, and 0 if both coins are tails.

a. Calculate $E(Y)$, the expected value for Y.

b. Calculate the deviation for Y for each of the four outcomes.

c. Calculate the mean absolute deviation, the variance, and the standard deviation for the number of heads on two coin flips.

Answers

6. 3.96; 1.8018

7. a–b. See back of book.

8. 7; $\frac{35}{18}$; $\frac{35}{6}$; 2.415; the mean and variance are doubled and the standard deviation is $\sqrt{2}$ times as large. The mean absolute deviation is larger by factor of $\frac{35}{27}$ which does not seem to be part of the pattern.

9. a. $\frac{1}{2}$

b. $\frac{1}{2}$ and $-\frac{1}{2}$

c. $\frac{1}{2}$; $\frac{1}{4}$; $\frac{1}{2}$

10. a. 1

b. 1, 0, 0, −1

c. $\frac{1}{2}$; $\frac{1}{2}$; $\frac{\sqrt{2}}{2}$

11. Your class should have data for the 20-question test from the Getting Started lesson. Each element in the data set is the number of correct answers for a particular student. For your class's data, find the mean, mean absolute deviation, variance, and standard deviation.

This might be a good place to use the machine formula for variance: the mean of the squares, minus the square of the mean.

12. Consider this set of 16 sums from Derman's table in Lesson 7.4.

+	1	2	3	10
1	2	3	4	11
2	3	4	5	12
3	4	5	6	13
10	11	12	13	20

a. Build a second table with each element's deviation from the mean.

b. Find the mean absolute deviation and the mean squared deviation for the 16 sums.

c. Which is larger, the mean absolute deviation or the standard deviation?

13. **What's Wrong Here?** Dani thinks that adding deviations is useful.

Dani: Why do we have to do absoiute value or squaring? It seems like we should be able to just find the deviations from the mean, then add them up. Done, and done.

Make an argument to convince Dani that adding the deviations is not a helpful calculation.

14. Find the mean, mean absolute deviation, variance, and standard deviation for the data set {1, 2, 3, 4, 5, 6, 7, 8, 9, 10}.

Go Online PHSchool.com

For additional practice, go to **Web Code: bga-0707**

15. **Take It Further** In terms of n, find formulas for the mean, mean absolute deviation, variance, and standard deviation for the data set $\{1, 2, 3 \ldots, n\}$.

16. **Standardized Test Prep** The table shows the frequency of each score possible in a game. Find the (mean, variance) for the score.

A. $\left(-\frac{1}{3}, \frac{10}{3}\right)$ B. $\left(-\frac{1}{3}, \frac{25}{3}\right)$

C. $\left(-1, \frac{10}{3}\right)$ D. $\left(-1, \frac{25}{3}\right)$

Score	Frequency
−5	2
0	1
1	2
2	1

Maintain Your Skills

17. Find the variance for each data set.

a. {1, 1, 1, 2, 2, 11}

b. {1, 1, 1, 8, 8, 11}

c. {1, 1, 1, 11, 11, 11}

d. $\{1, 1, 1, n, n, 11\}$

11. Check students' work.

12. a.

	1	2	3	10
1	−6	−5	−4	3
2	−5	−4	−3	4
3	−4	−3	−2	5
10	3	4	5	12

b. $\frac{9}{2}$; 25

c. standard deviation

13. Answers may vary. Sample: The sum of the deviations is always zero. It is not a useful statistic.

14. 5.5; 2.5; 8.25; 2.87

15. $\frac{n+1}{2}$; $\begin{cases} \frac{n}{4}, & \text{if } n \text{ is even} \\ \frac{n}{4} - \frac{1}{4n}, & \text{if } n \text{ is odd} \end{cases}$; $\frac{n^2-1}{12}$; $\sqrt{\frac{n^2-1}{12}}$

16. D

17. a. 13

b. 17

c. 25

d. $\frac{2n^2 - 14n + 137}{9}$

EXERCISE 12 It turns out that for *any* data, the standard deviation is larger than the mean absolute deviation, but it is difficult to prove this result.

Maintain Your Skills

EXERCISE 17 Students gain experience calculating variance, but they also have the chance to find the general pattern here. This is not a particularly useful result on its own, because it is not likely that you would ever come across a data set consisting of three ones, one eleven, and two more numbers which are identical. Still, this kind of exercise does appeal to many students. They enjoy the detective work involved in noticing a pattern and finding a function to match it. And that skill is widely applicable in mathematics.

Additional Resources

PRINT RESOURCES
- Solution Manual
- Practice Workbook
- Assessment Resources
- Teaching Resources

TECHNOLOGY
- Interactive Textbook
- TeacherExpress CD-ROM
- ExamView CD-ROM
- PHSchool.com

Additional Practice

For each nonstandard number cube listed in Exercises 1–3 below, calculate each of these:

a. the mean b. the mean absolute deviation
c. the variance d. the standard deviation

1. A number cube with numbers 2, 4, 6, 10, 12, 14
2. A number cube with numbers 1, 2, 4, 5, 7, 8
3. A number cube with 5, 10, 15, 20, 25, 30
4. A spinner has 5 equal wedges with the numbers 2, 4, 6, 7, and 8. If you spin twice there are 25 possible outcomes. Calculate the mean, mean absolute deviation, variance, and standard deviation for the sums of the numbers spun for all 25 possible outcomes.
5. Define a random variable for two coin flips as follows. The random variable Y equals 2 if both coins are tails, 1 if exactly one coin is tails, and 0 if both coins are heads.
   a. Calculate $E(Y)$, the expected value for Y.
   b. Calculate the deviation for Y for each the four outcomes.
   c. Calculate the mean absolute deviation, the variance, and the standard deviation for two coin flips.
6. Consider two spinners with five equal wedges, each with different numbers. Spinner A has the numbers 2, 2, 3, 4 and 5. Spinner B has the numbers 4, 5, 5, 6 and 7. Let X be the random variable defined as the sum of the values when spinning A and B once each.
   a. Build a table of the 10 possible values of X.
   b. Find the mean, variance, and standard deviation of X.
7. Consider two number cubes with different numbers on their faces:
   Cube 1: 1, 3, 3, 5, 6, 7
   Cube 2: 2, 4, 5, 6, 7, 8
   a. Find the mean, variance, and standard deviation for the results when rolling Cube 1 once.
   b. Find the mean, variance, and standard deviation for the results when rolling Cube 2 once.
   c. If you roll both number cubes at once, there are 36 outcomes. Find the mean, variance, and standard deviation for the sums when rolling the two number cubes.

Practice: For Lesson 7.7, assign Exercises 1–5.

Lesson Overview

GOAL

- Calculate statistics for compound events.

In this lesson, students practice calculating mean (expected value), variance, and standard deviation. Along the way they see that if a random variable Z is defined as the sum of two other random variables X and Y, then both the mean and the variance are additive. In symbols, $\overline{Z} = \overline{X} + \overline{Y}$ and $V(Z) = V(X) + V(Y)$. Students prove this fact using the "machine formula" from Lesson 7.7 and various summation theorems. Depending on how familiar your students are with summation notation and the formulas for computing sums, you may need to produce a list of theorems and show a few examples if you decide to cover this proof in class.

CHECK YOUR UNDERSTANDING
- Core: 1, 2, 3, 4, 5, 6
- Optional: 7

MATERIALS
- graphing calculators
- Blackline Master 7.7

HOMEWORK
- Core: 8, 9, 11, 12, 13, 14, 15
- Optional: 16, 17
- Extension: 10, 18

Launch

Begin today's lesson with the In-Class Experiment. The calculations are fairly straightforward, so focus the discussion on comparing the results.

Use Blackline Master 7.7 as needed throughout the discussion.

Explore

In-Class Experiment

PROBLEM 3 After students find the results for the combined data, ask them to look for patterns in the results. Students are likely to find the additive result for mean and variance; they may suspect that the mean absolute deviation is the maximum of the two spinners (it is not). The standard deviation does not have a discernible pattern.

Alternately, have students read the Minds in Action dialogue, which follows up on the work in the In-Class Experiment.

7.8 Adding Variances

You can view two separate experiments as one big experiment. If you do, there is a way to combine information about the two experiments to find the expected value and variance of the one big experiment.

In-Class Experiment

Here are two spinners. One is from the previous lesson, and the other one is a new one.

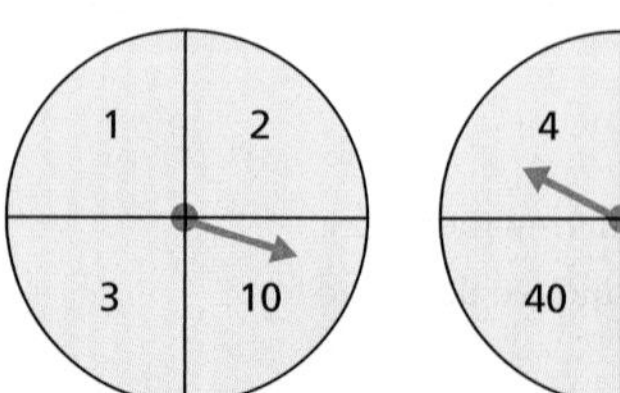

In this game, you spin each spinner once. Let Z be the random variable defined by the sum of the values on the two spinners.

1. Find the mean, mean absolute deviation, mean squared deviation, and root mean squared deviation for the values when spinning each spinner.
2. Use polynomial expansion to quickly find the 16 possible values for the random variable Z.
3. Find the mean, mean absolute deviation, mean squared deviation, and root mean squared deviation for Z.

Remember...

The mean squared deviation and the root mean squared deviation are more commonly called the *variance* and *standard deviation.*

An investment manager adds variances to find the overall risk of an investment portfolio.

Answers

In-Class Experiment

1. Spinner 1: 4; 3; 12.5; 3.54;
   Spinner 2: 36; 24; 808; 28.43
2. Z: {90, 83, 82, 81, 50, 43, 42, 41, 30, 23, 22, 21, 14, 7, 6, 5}
3. 40; 24; 820.5; 28.644

Minds in Action episode 24

Sasha and Derman are working on the In-Class Experiment.

Derman Let's start playing the game.

Sasha Derman! We can't do this by playing. We'd have to play thousands of times. This is about what will happen *on average.*

Derman So, how are we supposed to do that?

Sasha Come on, Derman. You can look back at the last lesson if you've forgotten how to find any of these things.

Derman Alright, I'm going to find the mean for each spinner by averaging. The mean for the first spinner is 4. The mean for the second spinner is 36. So, the mean for Z, when you add them, should be 40.

Sasha That seems like it makes sense.

Derman I'm making a list of the 16 possible results . . . hey, it worked!

Sasha That was a good idea.

Derman Alright, on to the next one. The mean absolute deviation for the first spinner is 3 . . . and for the second spinner is 24 . . . so for Z it should be 27.

Sasha Did you calculate it?

Derman I added 3 and 24.

Sasha Let's just check, I'm not so sure this time. Unfortunately . . . you lose. It's 24, not 27.

Derman What? It worked for the mean, it's supposed to work on everything. Do it again.

Sasha Derman. It's still 24. I think it only works for the mean. Not everything adds like that.

Derman Alright, alright, what about the variance?

Sasha The variance for the first spinner is 12.5. The variance for the second spinner is 808.

Derman So the variance for Z will be 820.5.

Sasha You wish. You can't just add these things.

Derman Au contraire. *I* win. It *is* 820.5. Exactly.

Sasha, baffled, performs the calculation.

Sasha Wow! You're kidding me. I can't believe that worked. Does that always work? That would be amazing. I've gotta see why.

Sasha and Derman suspect that mean and variance are additive.

Example

Problem Find the mean and variance for the sum when tossing two standard number cubes. Compare to the mean and variance for the value from tossing one number cube.

Solution You calculated the mean and variance for one number cube in Lesson 7.7. The mean is 3.5. The variance is $\frac{35}{12} \approx 2.917$.

For the sum of the numbers on two number cubes, expand the polynomial $(x + x^2 + x^3 + x^4 + x^5 + x^6)^2$ or make a table of the 36 outcomes in the sample space, as you did in Investigation 7A.

+	1	2	3	4	5	6
1	2	3	4	5	6	7
2	3	4	5	6	7	8
3	4	5	6	7	8	9
4	5	6	7	8	9	10
5	6	7	8	9	10	11
6	7	8	9	10	11	12

Determine the expected value by building a frequency table as in Lesson 7.4.

Sum	Frequency	Product
2	1	2
3	2	6
4	3	12
5	4	20
6	5	30
7	6	42
8	5	40
9	4	36
10	3	30
11	2	22
12	1	12
Total	**36**	**252**

See the TI-Nspire Handbook on p. 704 for help in using a spreadsheet to perform these calculations.

The expected value is $\frac{252}{36} = 7$.

Use a similar table to calculate the mean squared deviation. Here, multiply each squared deviation by the frequency of the outcome.

Sum	Frequency	Deviation $x - \bar{x}$	Deviation^2	Freq · Dev.^{2}
2	1	−5	25	25
3	2	−4	16	32
4	3	−3	9	27
5	4	−2	4	16
6	5	−1	1	5
7	6	0	0	0
8	5	1	1	5
9	4	2	4	16
10	3	3	9	27
11	2	4	16	32
12	1	5	25	25
Total	**36**			**210**

The variance (mean squared deviation) is $\frac{210}{36} = \frac{35}{6} \approx 5.833$.

Note that both the mean and variance for the sums when rolling two number cubes are exactly double the mean and variance for the values of one number cube.

Habits of Mind

Visualize. Think about what the table might look like if it had 36 rows so each outcome had its own line. The result for ways to roll a 4 is multiplied by three, since there are three ways to roll a 4. The result for 11 is multiplied by two, since there are two ways an outcome of 11 can occur.

For You to Do

4. Take a guess at the mean and variance for the sums of the numbers when rolling three number cubes.

Proving It

The proofs that mean and variance add are complicated. Keep this picture in mind for what the combined sample space looks like when the sample spaces of two random variables X and Y are combined:

+	x_1	x_2	$\dots$	x_n
y_1	$x_1 + y_1$	$x_2 + y_1$	$\dots$	$x_n + y_1$
y_2	$x_1 + y_2$	$x_2 + y_2$	$\dots$	$x_n + y_2$
y_3	$x_1 + y_3$	$x_2 + y_3$	$\dots$	$x_n + y_3$
$\vdots$	$\vdots$	$\vdots$	$\ddots$	$\vdots$
y_m	$x_1 + y_m$	$x_2 + y_m$	$\dots$	$x_n + y_m$

Answers

For You to Do

4. Answers may vary. Sample: The mean is 10.5, and the variance is 8.75.

Wrap Up

Depending on whether or not you choose to go over the proof of Theorem 7.2 in detail, you may have time for students to work on the core Check Your Understanding exercises. The key piece of knowledge for students to take away from this lesson is that if a random variable Z is equal to the sum of two independent random variables X and Y, then the mean of Z is equal to the sum of the means of X and Y, and the variance of Z is equal to the sum of the variances of X and Y. Emphasize that these results do not hold if the variables do not satisfy the conditions.

Assessment Resources

Lesson Quiz 7.8

1. Consider a number cube with the numbers 0, 2, 5, 6, 8, and 9 on its faces.
   a. Find a polynomial that models one roll of this number cube.
   b. Find the mean for the sums when rolling this number cube three times.
   c. Using the mean, find the variance and standard deviation for the sums when rolling this number cube three times.

2. Consider two spinners. Spinner A has the numbers 1, 2, 3, 4, and 5. Spinner B has the numbers 3, 5, 7, 8, and 9. On both spinners, each number is equally likely.
   a. Find the mean for the sum of the results when spinning Spinners A and B once.
   b. Find the variance and standard deviation for the sum of the results when spinning Spinners A and B once.
   c. Find the mean of spinning Spinner B twice.
   d. Find the variance and standard deviation when spinning Spinner B twice.

Theorem 7.2

Let Z be the random variable defined by adding the results of independent random variables X and Y. Then

- **The expected value, or mean, of Z is the sum of the expected values for X and Y, and**
- **The variance, or mean squared deviation, of Z is the sum of the variances for X and Y.**

Proof First, prove the property for the mean. Let $\overline{x}$ be the mean for X with n outcomes and $\overline{y}$ be the mean for Y with m outcomes. (See the table on page 585.) Of the mn outcomes for Z, each value x_1 through x_n occurs m times, one for each y-pairing. Each value y_1 through y_m occurs n times. So, the mean for random variable Z is as follows.

$$\begin{aligned}\overline{z} &= \frac{m(x_1 + x_2 + \cdots + x_n) + n(y_1 + y_2 + \cdots + y_m)}{mn} \\ &= \frac{m(x_1 + x_2 + \cdots + x_n)}{mn} + \frac{n(y_1 + y_2 + \cdots + y_m)}{mn} \\ &= \frac{(x_1 + x_2 + \cdots + x_n)}{n} + \frac{(y_1 + y_2 + \cdots + y_m)}{m} \\ &= \overline{x} + \overline{y}\end{aligned}$$

The proof for the variance uses the machine formula from Lesson 7.7. You want to show that $V(Z) = V(X) + V(Y)$. But the machine formula states that the variance is the mean of the squares less the square of the means. So, the goal is to show that

$$\overline{z^2} - \overline{z}^2 = \left(\overline{x^2} - \overline{x}^2\right) + \left(\overline{y^2} - \overline{y}^2\right)$$

Rewrite $\overline{z}$ as $\overline{x} + \overline{y}$ and expand. The left side becomes

$$\begin{aligned}\overline{z^2} - \overline{z}^2 &= \overline{z^2} - (\overline{x} + \overline{y})^2 \\ &= \overline{z^2} - \left(\overline{x}^2 + 2\overline{x} \cdot \overline{y} + \overline{y}^2\right)\end{aligned}$$

Think about how to calculate $\overline{z^2}$. First square each possible value of Z. Then add the squares and divide by mn at the end. Each value of Z is of the form $x_i + y_j$ for some i and j, so its square is $x_i^2 + 2x_iy_j + y_j^2$. Think about how many times each number appears. The number of terms is mn. Each x_i^2 appears m times, each y_j^2 appears n times, and every possible pair of x_iy_j occurs once. So,

$$\begin{aligned}\overline{z^2} &= \frac{m\left(\sum_i x_i^2\right) + n\left(\sum_j y_j^2\right) + 2\sum_i \sum_j x_iy_j}{mn} \\ &= \frac{\sum_i x_i^2}{n} + \frac{\sum_j y_j^2}{m} + 2\frac{\sum_i \sum_j x_iy_j}{mn} \\ &= \overline{x^2} + \overline{y^2} + 2\overline{xy}\end{aligned}$$

Remember...

$\overline{x}$ is the same as $E(X)$, the expected value of the random variable X. For example, if X is the value when rolling a number cube, $\overline{x} = E(X) = 3.5$.

Habits of Mind

Try a specific case. This proof may seem clearer if you try working it out completely for a small example, say $m = 3$ and $n = 4$.

When you see $\sum_i \sum_j x_i y_j$, that means that you sum all the products x_iy_j over all i and j, in other words, match every x_i with every y_j.

$$\overline{z^2} - \bar{z}^2 = \overline{x^2} + \overline{y^2} + 2\overline{xy} - \bar{x}^2 - 2\bar{x} \cdot \bar{y} - \bar{y}^2$$
$$= (\overline{x^2} + \bar{x}^2) + (\overline{y^2} - \bar{y}^2) + 2\overline{xy} - 2\bar{x} \cdot \bar{y}$$
$$= V(X) + V(Y) + 2\overline{xy} - 2\bar{x} \cdot \bar{y}$$

This is very close to what you want to show. However, you still need to show that $\overline{xy} = \bar{x} \cdot \bar{y}$ (the mean of the product is the product of the means). This is true whenever X and Y are independent random variables. The proof of this fact is left as Exercise 14. Once this is known, the proof is complete: the variance of Z is the sum of the variances of X and Y.

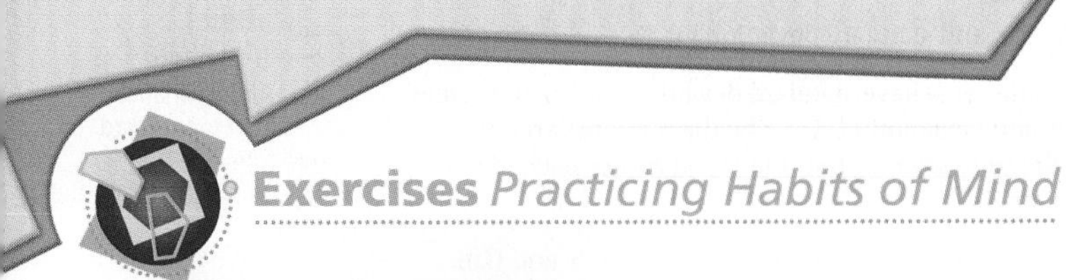

Exercises *Practicing Habits of Mind*

Check Your Understanding

1. a. Use a polynomial power to write a frequency table for the sums when rolling three number cubes.

b. Find the mean for the sums when rolling three number cubes.

c. Using the mean, find the variance and standard deviation for the sums when rolling three number cubes.

d. How many times as large is the variance for the sums for three number cubes than the variance for one number cube?

e. How many times as large is the standard deviation for the sums for three number cubes than the standard deviation for the values from rolling one number cube?

2. Find the mean, variance, and standard deviation for the values when spinning each spinner.

a. Spinner A

b. Spinner B

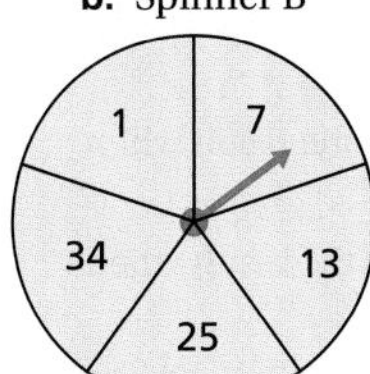

c. Spinner C

Exercises

HOMEWORK

- Core: 8, 9, 11, 12, 13, 14, 15
- Optional: 16, 17
- Extension: 10, 18

Check Your Understanding

EXERCISE 1 Make sure students see the results of the last two parts of this exercise; they preview the core concept of the next lessons. You can speed up the work on variance by using a spreadsheet, or by noticing that the second half of the table is identical to the first half.

EXERCISE 2 is a prerequisite for the next few exercises.

Answers

Exercises

1. a. See back of book.

b. 10.5

c. $\frac{35}{4}; \frac{\sqrt{35}}{2}$

d. The variance for 3 number cubes $\left(\frac{35}{12}\right)$ is 3 times the variance for 1 number cube $\left(\frac{35}{4}\right)$.

e. The standard deviation is $\sqrt{3}$ times larger for 3 number cubes than the standard deviation for one number cube.

2. a. 7; 25; 5

b. 16; 144; 12

c. 18; 256; 16

EXERCISE 3 Spinners A and B have been constructed with "nice" numbers, in order to trigger recognition. In particular, the "5-12-13" relationship between the different standard deviations comes from the $\sigma_1^2 + \sigma_2^2 = \sigma^2$ relationship of the variances.

EXERCISE 4 Again, the standard deviations follow a Pythagorean triple, this time 12-16-20.

EXERCISE 5 Watch for students claiming the answer is 23; refer them to the previous exercises. Standard deviations do not add!

This exercise uses another Pythagorean triple, 8-15-17. You might point out to students that this does not usually occur; standard deviation is usually not an integer.

EXERCISE 6 In general, mean absolute deviation does not add. This is one reason that variance has become the standard calculation, and mean absolute deviation has become less and less commonly used.

On Your Own

EXERCISE 8 Two number cubes that combine in the same frequencies as two standard number cubes are called "Sicherman dice". The result from part (c) is identical to the data in the example for this lesson. The Sicherman dice are the only other number cubes with this property, which you can prove with the factorization of $(x + x^2 + x^3 + x^4 + x^5 + x^6)^2$.

3. Consider spinners A and B from Exercise 2. Let X be the random variable defined as the sum of the values when spinning A and B once each.

a. Build a table of the 10 possible values of X.

b. Find the mean, variance, and standard deviation of X.

4. Consider spinners B and C from Exercise 2. Let Y be the random variable defined as the sum of the values when spinning B and C once each.

a. Build a table of the 25 possible outcomes, and the value of Y for each.

b. Find the mean, variance, and standard deviation for Y.

5. Suppose the values on Spinner D have standard deviation 8. Also, the values on Spinner E have standard deviation 15. Let Z be the random variable defined as the sum of the values when spinning D and E once each. What is the standard deviation for Z?

Remember...

Recall how variance is related to standard deviation.

6. a. Calculate the mean absolute deviation for each spinner A, B, and C in Exercise 2.

b. Calculate the mean absolute deviation for X, the random variable for the resulting sum of spinning A and B.

c. Calculate the mean absolute deviation for Y, the random variable for the resulting sum of spinning B and C.

d. What pattern, if any, emerges for the mean absolute deviation of the combined spinners?

7. Write About It The additive property of variance is sometimes called the "Pythagorean Theorem of Statistics." Why do you suppose this is, in light of the results from Exercises 3 through 5?

On Your Own

8. Consider two number cubes with different numbers on their faces:

Cube 1: 1, 2, 2, 3, 3, 4

Cube 2: 1, 3, 4, 5, 6, 8

a. Find the mean, variance, and standard deviation for the result when rolling Cube 1 once.

b. Find the mean, variance, and standard deviation for the result when rolling Cube 2 once.

c. If you roll both number cubes at once, there are 36 outcomes. Find the mean, variance, and standard deviation for the sum when rolling the two number cubes.

Answers

3. a.

+	1	7	13	25	34
2	3	9	15	27	36
12	13	19	25	37	46

b. 23; 169; 13

4. a.

+	1	7	13	25	34
10	11	17	23	35	44
10	11	17	23	35	44
10	11	17	23	35	44
10	11	17	23	35	44
50	51	57	63	75	84

b. 34; 400; 20

5. 17

6. a. Spinner A: 5; Spinner B: 10.8; Spinner C: 12.8

b. 11.2

c. 16.32

d. Answers may vary. Sample: There is not an obvious pattern in the relationships of the mean absolute deviation of the combined spinners.

7. Answers may vary. Sample: If the original standard deviations are a and b, and the new standard deviation is c. The numbers for the standard deviation are in the relationship, $a^2 + b^2 = c^2$.

8. a. $\frac{5}{2}$; $\frac{11}{12}$; $\frac{\sqrt{33}}{6}$

b. $\frac{9}{2}$; $\frac{59}{12}$; $\frac{\sqrt{177}}{6}$

c. 7; $\frac{35}{6}$; $\sqrt{\frac{35}{6}} \approx 2.415$

9. Here is an experiment: Roll a standard number cube. Spin Spinner A from Exercise 2. Then, add the numbers that result.

Find the mean, variance, and standard deviation for each of the 12 possible outcomes.

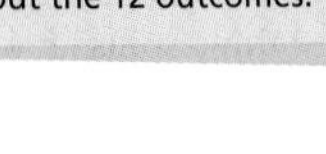

See if you can do this exercise without writing out the 12 outcomes.

10. **Take It Further** Kevin is challenged to roll a sum of 15 from standard number cubes. He can choose how many number cubes to roll. How many number cubes gives Kevin the best chance of rolling a sum of 15?

11. **What's Wrong Here?** Cayle looked at the data from Exercise 12 in Lesson 7.7:

+	1	2	3	10
1	2	3	4	11
2	3	4	5	12
3	4	5	6	13
10	11	12	13	20

Cayle: I know this data comes from two spins of that fish wheel with 1, 2, 3, 10 on it. And I know the standard deviation for one spin is about 3.54. So, the standard deviation for two spins should be 3.54 + 3.54, just over 7. But I am *not* getting that answer! I've checked it three times.

Explain what went wrong here, and how the correct standard deviation could be calculated.

12. Jane is designing a game of chance for her school's Random Fair. It costs 50 cents to play Jane's game. The player flips a coin. Then the player rolls a number cube. If the player gets heads on the coin flip, the number cube result is multiplied by 20 cents. That money is the prize. If the player gets tails on the coin flip, though, the number cube result is multiplied by 5 cents. Although everyone takes away some money, most people do not make back the price of the game.

   a. List the sample space for Jane's game as a set of equally likely outcomes.

   b. Calculate the expected value for Jane's game. Will Jane's game make money for the fair over time?

   c. Calculate the variance and standard deviation for Jane's game.

   d. **What's Wrong Here?** Jane wants to check her variance calculation by computing it two ways. In the first way, she uses the data and the machine formula. In the second way, she adds the variance for one coin flip to the variance for one number cube roll. The two methods do not give the same result. Where did Jane go wrong?

For additional practice, go to Web Code: bga-0708

EXERCISE 9 If you review this exercise, emphasize the method of adding variance. The sample space is small enough to enumerate, but the method of adding variance is necessary for larger sets.

EXERCISE 11 One difficulty with nice results in mathematics is that students often want to generalize them. You see students behaving as though non-linear functions are linear ($\sqrt{x+y} = \sqrt{x} + \sqrt{y}$), and now that they have seen that the expected value and variance are additive, they probably assume (at least sometimes) that the standard deviation is additive, too.

EXERCISE 12 It is difficult for some students to see that the two events in Jane's game—flipping a coin and rolling a number cube—are not independent. After all, the result of the coin flip does not influence the result of the number cube throw. However, the real outcome is the amount of money the player gets back at the end of the turn. From that perspective, the way the roll of the number cube is *scored* does depend on the result of the coin flip.

ERROR PREVENTION It is very common for students to forget about conditions for a result unless they see exercises in which those conditions are absent and the result fails. This exercise is meant to remind students that unless the events are independent, the variance rule does not work.

9. 10.5; $\frac{335}{12}$; $\sqrt{\frac{335}{12}} \approx 5.284$

10. 4

11. The variances add, but standard deviations do not. The new standard deviation is the square root of the new variance. The original variance is 12.5, so the new variance is 25. The new standard deviation is 5.

12. a. −45, −40, −35, −30, −30, −25, −20, −10, 10, 30, 50, 70

b. −6.25 cents; yes, the game will make money over time.

c. 1308.854; 36.18

d. The first method is correct. The second method does not work, because the random variables are not independent. The results of the coin flip affect the results of the roll of the number cube.

Maintain Your Skills

These Maintain Your Skills exercises require students to think about the infinite set of the integers in a way that allows them to compute probabilities.

EXERCISE 16 In thinking about divisibility by 2 and/or by 5, you can think just about the integers 1 through 10 (= 2 × 5). In that smaller set, you see all the possibilities *in the same ratios* as in the entire set of integers. That is because within the set of integers from 1 through 10 you see all the possible combinations of remainder after division by 2 and 5. The integers from 11 through 20 (and every other set of ten consecutive integers cut sequentially before or after the set from 1 to 10) goes through the same cycle of remainders.

Additional Resources

PRINT RESOURCES
- Solution Manual
- Practice Workbook
- Assessment Resources
- Teaching Resources

TECHNOLOGY
- Interactive Textbook
- TeacherExpress CD-ROM
- ExamView CD-ROM
- PHSchool.com

Additional Practice

For each nonstandard number cube listed in Exercises 1–3 below, calculate each of these:

a. the mean
b. the mean absolute deviation
c. the variance
d. the standard deviation

1. A number cube with numbers 2, 4, 6, 10, 12, 14

2. A number cube with numbers 1, 2, 4, 5, 7, 8

3. A number cube with 5, 10, 15, 20, 25, 30

4. A spinner has 5 equal wedges with the numbers 2, 4, 6, 7, and 8. If you spin twice there are 25 possible outcomes. Calculate the mean, mean absolute deviation, variance, and standard deviation for the sums of the numbers spun for all 25 possible outcomes.

5. Define a random variable for two coin flips as follows. The random variable Y equals 2 if both coins are tails, 1 if exactly one coin is tails, and 0 if both coins are heads.
   a. Calculate $E(Y)$, the expected value for Y.
   b. Calculate the deviation for Y for each the four outcomes.
   c. Calculate the mean absolute deviation, the variance, and the standard deviation for two coin flips.

6. Consider two spinners with five equal wedges, each with different numbers. Spinner A has the numbers 2, 2, 3, 4 and 5. Spinner B has the numbers 4, 5, 5, 6 and 7. Let X be the random variable defined as the sum of the values when spinning A and B once each.
   a. Build a table of the 10 possible values of X.
   b. Find the mean, variance, and standard deviation of X.

7. Consider two number cubes with different numbers on their faces:
   Cube 1: 1, 3, 3, 5, 6, 7
   Cube 2: 2, 4, 5, 6, 7, 8
   a. Find the mean, variance, and standard deviation for the results when rolling Cube 1 once.
   b. Find the mean, variance, and standard deviation for the results when rolling Cube 2 once.
   c. If you roll both number cubes at once, there are 36 outcomes. Find the mean, variance, and standard deviation for the sums when rolling the two number cubes.

Practice: For Lesson 7.8, assign Exercises 6–7.

13. The variance for one spin of the Wheel of Fish with the numbers 1, 2, 3, and 10 is 12.5.
    a. Calculate the variance and standard deviation for the sum of two spins.
    b. Calculate the variance and standard deviation for the sum of three spins.
    c. Verify that your answers to part (b) are correct by calculating the sum of three spins for all 64 outcomes, then calculating the variance for the data.

14. Consider the following table for the product of independent random variables X and Y.

$\cdot$	x_1	x_2	$\ldots$	x_n
y_1	$x_1 \cdot y_1$	$x_2 \cdot y_1$	$\ldots$	$x_n \cdot y_1$
y_2	$x_1 \cdot y_2$	$x_2 \cdot y_2$	$\ldots$	$x_n \cdot y_2$
y_3	$x_1 \cdot y_3$	$x_2 \cdot y_3$	$\ldots$	$x_n \cdot y_3$
$\vdots$	$\vdots$	$\vdots$	$\ddots$	$\vdots$
y_m	$x_1 \cdot y_m$	$x_2 \cdot y_m$	$\ldots$	$x_n \cdot y_m$

Show that the mean of the products is the product of the means for the original random variables. That is,

$$\overline{xy} = \overline{x} \cdot \overline{y}$$

This completes the proof given in the lesson.

15. **Standardized Test Prep** For a random positive integer less than 1001, what is the probability that the number is neither divisible by 2 nor 5?
    A. 0.1 **B.** 0.4 **C.** 0.5 **D.** 0.6

Maintain Your Skills

16. Suppose you are to pick an integer at random. Find the probability of each event.
    a. The number is not divisible by 2.
    b. The number is not divisible by 5.
    c. The number is neither divisible by 2 nor 5.
    d. The number is divisible by 2 *or* 5 (or both).

17. Suppose you are to pick an integer at random. Find the probability that it is divisible by 4 or 13 (or both).

18. **Take It Further** Find some other values of p and q so that $\frac{p}{q}$ is the probability that an integer chosen at random is divisible by p or q (or both).

Answers

13. a. 25; 5

b. 37.5; $\sqrt{37.5} \approx 6.124$

c. $(x^1 + x^2 + x^3 + x^{10})^3 = x^{30} + 3x^{23} + 3x^{22} + 3x^{21} + 3x^{16} + 6x^{15} + 9x^{14} + 6x^{13} + 3x^{12} + x^9 + 3x^8 + 6x^7 + 7x^6 + 6x^5 + 3x^4 + x^3$; the variance is 38.19397.

14. See back of book.

15. B

16. a. $\frac{1}{2}$

b. $\frac{4}{5}$

c. $\frac{2}{5}$

d. $\frac{3}{5}$

17. $\frac{4}{13}$

18. Answers may vary. Sample: $p = 8$ and $q = 57$

7.9 Repeated Experiments

Suppose you define a random variable Z as the sum of two independent random variables X and Y. In the previous lesson, you learned that the mean and variance of Z are the sum of the means and variances of X and Y. This knowledge can help you quickly calculate important statistics, especially the standard deviation for many consecutive trials of the same kind of experiment.

For Discussion

1. Suppose you flip 100 coins. What is the average number of heads you would expect? Would 40 heads seem reasonable? What about 65 heads?

In-Class Experiment

2. Flip 100 coins and count the total number of heads. Record your data along with all other data the class collects. What percent of the data was between 40 and 60 heads, inclusive? between 45 and 55 heads?

In Exercise 9 in Lesson 7.7 you found the mean, variance, and standard deviation for one coin flip. Recall for that experiment, a head counts as 1. A tail counts as 0. The mean is $\frac{1}{2}$, the variance is $\frac{1}{4}$, and the standard deviation is $\sqrt{\frac{1}{4}} = \frac{1}{2}$.

For two coin flips, there are four possible outcomes: HH, HT, TH, and TT. The mean number of heads is 1, which is twice the mean for one coin flip. This table calculates the variance:

Here, "HT" means that the first flip is heads, and the second flip is tails. HT and TH are two different outcomes.

Outcome	Number of Heads	Deviation	Deviation^2
HH	2	1	1
HT	1	0	0
TH	1	0	0
TT	0	−1	1
4 outcomes			2

The variance is $\frac{2}{4} = \frac{1}{2}$, which is twice the variance for one coin flip. The standard deviation is the square root of the variance, so it is $\sqrt{\frac{1}{2}} = \frac{\sqrt{2}}{2} \approx 0.707$.

For Discussion

1. 50; answers may vary. Sample: yes, no

In-Class Experiment

2. Check students' work.

Lesson Overview

GOAL

- Calculate statistics for repeated experiments.

In this lesson, students confront the difference between theoretical probability, which is computed based on the conditions of the experiment, and experimental probability, which is computed based on the results of doing the experiment some number of times. These two probabilities are rarely identical, but as the number of trials increases, the experimental probability approaches the theoretical probability. For larger numbers of trials, the mean grows faster than the standard deviation. Since most of the data is within one standard deviation of the mean, the proportion of data outside this range decreases as the number of trials increases.

CHECK YOUR UNDERSTANDING
- Core: 1, 2, 3, 4, 5, 6a–b
- Optional: none
- Extension: 6c, 7

HOMEWORK
- Core: 8, 9, 10, 12, 13, 14
- Optional: 15, 16
- Extension: 11

MATERIALS
- computers with Internet access (optional)
- graphing calculators
- Blackline Master 7.7

VOCABULARY
- experimental probability
- theoretical probability

Launch

Begin today's lesson with the For Discussion problem. Tease out students' current understanding of what the theoretical mean and standard deviation imply in evaluating the likelihood of particular experimental results. Emphasize that although most of the time the experimental results fall within one standard deviation of the mean, it is still not impossible to flip a coin 100 times and get 100 heads. It is just very unlikely! (In other words, if you compute the theoretical probability of 100 heads in 100 flips, it is $\left(\frac{1}{2}\right)^{100}$, which is a very small number, but not equal to zero.)

Throughout today's lesson, keep in mind the distinction between theoretical values and experimental values, and make the distinction explicit for students.

Explore

For Discussion

PROBLEM 1 Move through this discussion quickly. Students should come up with 50 as the expected number of heads, and will probably reject 65 as unreasonable. The experiment shows that an answer of 40 is not very reasonable either; there is only about a 3% chance that the number of heads is 40 or less.

In-Class Experiment, p. 591

PROBLEM 2 There are computer simulations of coin flipping available on the web that you might use to speed up this experiment. Many calculators also have a random number generator that you can program to simulate a coin-flipping experiment. See the TI-Nspire Technology Handbook on p. 704 in the back of this book for help in programming such a simulation.

For You to Do

PROBLEM 3 Some students prefer using the frequency setup from Lesson 7.8, while others use the model of listing out the outcomes. Either way is fine.

Help students interpret what this means for experimental results when flipping three coins. Most of the time, their results are within $\frac{3}{4}$ of 1.5, giving a range of "reasonable results" from 0.75 to 2.25. Since 0, 1, 2, and 3 are the only possible results for this experiment, this means that most of the time, you get either 1 or 2 heads. With a small number of trials, you are not really gaining a lot from this interpretation, but when you look ahead to the reasonable results for 100 coin flips, you can see more of a benefit. You can predict that most of the time your results are between 45 and 55, which is a much narrower range within the scope of the experiment.

For You to Do

3. Consider three coin flips, with eight possible outcomes. Verify that the variance of the number of heads is exactly $\frac{3}{4}$.

Each coin flip adds $\frac{1}{2}$ to the mean number of heads tossed, and $\frac{1}{4}$ to the variance. The additive rules for mean and variance give these results for the number of heads in n coin flips:

$$\text{mean: } \frac{1}{2}n$$

$$\text{variance: } \frac{1}{4}n$$

$$\text{standard deviation: } \sqrt{\frac{1}{4}n} = \frac{1}{2}\sqrt{n}$$

In Lesson 7.7, you learned that most data will be within one standard deviation of the mean.

For 100 coin flips, the standard deviation for the number of heads is $\frac{1}{2}\sqrt{100} = 5$. Most of the time you flip 100 coins, the number of heads will be between 45 and 55, one standard deviation away from the mean.

In a theoretical statistics course, you would prove that most of the data will be within one standard deviation of the mean. For now, your experiments should be enough.

Did most of your class flip between 45 and 55 heads in the In-Class Experiment? Did everyone?

The fact that mean and variance add can help you make similar observations about other repeated experiments. While most data will fall within one standard deviation of the mean, results outside this interval are likely.

Two Kinds of Probability

As you learned in Investigation 7A, the probability of an event is the number of outcomes in that event, divided by the total number of outcomes in the sample space. This is known as **theoretical probability.** You use this kind of probability when the properties of an experiment are clear.

But many probability questions are not clear-cut. What is the probability that it will rain tomorrow? What is the probability that Teri will make her next free throw? In many cases where randomness is present, you have no way to determine the exact properties of the experiment. In these situations, experimental probability is all you can compute.

Go Online
PHSchool.com

For exploration of theoretical and experimental probability, go to **Web Code:** bge-9031

The **experimental probability** of an event is the number of times the event occurred, divided by the number of trials. If Teri has made 37 of 50 free throws, the experimental probability is $\frac{37}{50} = 0.74$. You might say that Teri has a 74% chance of making her next free throw. Experimental probability is more prone to change than theoretical probability. Maybe Teri had especially good or bad luck on her 50 shots. The greater the number of trials, the more accurate an experimental probability becomes.

Answers

For You to Do

3.

x_i	Frequency, f	$x_i \cdot f$	$(x_i)^2$	$(x_i)^2$? f
3	1	3	9	9
2	3	6	4	12
1	3	3	1	3
0	1	0	0	0
	8	12		24

So the mean is $\frac{12}{8} = 1.5$ and the mean of the squares is $\frac{24}{8} = 3$. The variance is $3 - (1.5)^2 = 0.75$. So the variance is $\frac{3}{4}$.

Developing Habits of Mind

Make connections. The result of a random experiment is rarely exactly equal to the expected value. If you flip 100 coins, getting exactly 50 heads is pretty unlikely. But the properties of mean and standard deviation can explain an important concept. Over time, experimental probability will come closer and closer to theoretical probability.

Equaling the expected value may even be impossible. It's impossible to roll a number cube and get 3.5, but that is the expected value.

As the number of trials grows, the mean and standard deviation are both growing, because the mean and the variance (the square of the standard deviation) are additive. But the mean grows by the factor n. Also, the standard deviation grows by the factor $\sqrt{n}$. This means that the ratio

$$\frac{\text{standard deviation}}{\text{mean}}$$

gets smaller as n grows. Consider 100 coin flips. The mean number of heads is 50. The standard deviation is 5 heads. Most of the time you flip 100 coins, the results will fall between $50 - 5 = 45$ and $50 + 5 = 55$ heads.

Now consider 2500 coin flips. The mean number of heads is 1250, and the standard deviation is 25 heads. Most of the time when you flip 2500 coins, the results will fall between $1250 - 25 = 1225$ and $1250 + 25 = 1275$ heads.

Habits of Mind

Make strategic choices. Why is 2500 flips a better choice here than 1000?

The spread is widening, but only when you consider the number of heads. If you consider the ratio of heads, the spread is narrowing. Most of the time you flip 100 coins, the ratio of heads will be between 0.45 and 0.55. But for 2500 flips, this spread narrows:

$$\frac{1225}{2500} \leq \text{ratio of heads} \leq \frac{1275}{2500}$$

$$0.49 \leq \text{ratio of heads} \leq 0.51$$

So most of the time you flip 2500 coins, you will get between 49% and 51% heads. If you continue to increase the number of coin flips, you can get the numbers as close to 50% as you like.

For You to Do

4. What is the mean and standard deviation for the number of heads in 10,000 coin flips? Most of the time, the percentage of heads would be within what range?

For You to Do

4. 5000; 50; 49.5% and 50.5%

Wrap Up

How are your students doing with these ideas? Are they comfortable with the assumption that most of the time the results of a probability experiment are within one standard deviation of the mean? In the exercises, when students are asked whether a result is "typical" or "reasonable," they should judge using this standard.

The distinction between experimental and theoretical probability is a very thorny one for some students, and it can take a long time for it to solidify. That is okay. For now, students just need to understand that when they use the properties of an experiment to figure out the probability, they are using theoretical probability. When they use actual results from doing the experiment to compute probability, they are using experimental probability.

Assessment Resources

Lesson Quiz 7.9

1. Teresa answers four multiple-choice questions, each with five options. She guesses at each answer. She scores a 1 if she is right, a 0 if she is wrong.
  a. Find the mean, variance, and standard deviation for the scores on four questions.
  b. What is the probability that Teresa scores a 0 on all four questions?

2. Find the variance and standard deviation for the numbers of heads when flipping 280 coins.

3. You spin a wheel with the numbers 30, 40, 45, 60, and 65 on it. Find the mean, variance, and standard deviation for the total scores from spinning the wheel
  a. twice. **b.** four times.

Exercises

HOMEWORK

- Core: 8, 9, 10, 12, 13, 14
- Optional: 15, 16
- Extension: 11

Many of the exercises involve calculating the mean, variance, and standard deviation. Although most of the exercises have small sets of data, use Blackline Master 7.7 on an overhead or provide copies to your students as needed.

Check Your Understanding

EXERCISE 3 Some students still want to enumerate or use a polynomial power here, and that is fine. They catch on to the speedier method once they see other students giving the same answer much more quickly.

EXERCISE 4 With 20 questions, enumeration is tedious, but the method of multiplying still works. Students have now determined the theoretical mean and standard deviation for the multiple-choice test from the Getting Started lesson.

EXERCISE 6 previews some concepts with standard deviation in Investigation 7C. For now, students are becoming familiar with the idea that "most" data fall within 1 standard deviation of the mean. Here, the mean is 18 (half of 36 flips). Later, students learn that for situations that are close to the normal distribution, about 68% of data fall within 1 standard deviation of the mean.

EXERCISE 7 Students who correctly answer this question have effectively completed the main goal of the next lesson.

On Your Own

EXERCISE 8 Point out to students that with 4 spins, the standard deviation doubles. For 100 spins, it increases by a factor of 10. A student should be able to explain why this happens due to the variance property.

EXERCISE 12 The answer here is subject to interpretation. 600 is unusual as it is more than 1 standard deviatian from the mean, but it is not more than 2 standard deviations from the mean. If students have questions, suggest 2 or 3 standard deviations as a boundary. Lesson 7.13 addresses this topic in detail.

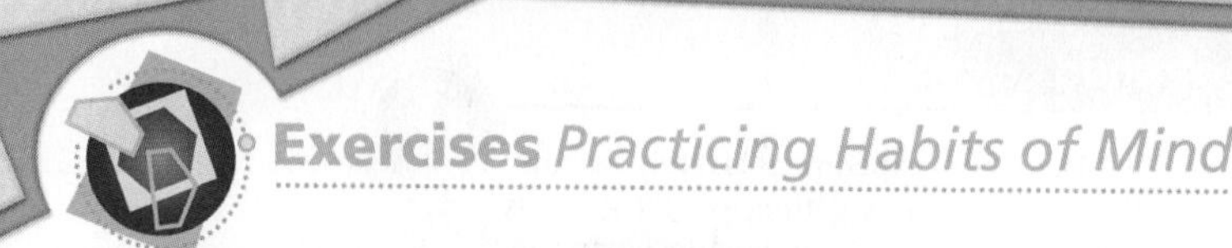

Exercises *Practicing Habits of Mind*

Check Your Understanding

1. Avery answers one multiple-choice question with five options. He guesses. He scores a 1 if he is right, a 0 if he is wrong. Find the mean, variance, and standard deviation for the score on one question.

2. Avery answers two multiple-choice questions, still five options, still guessing.
   - **a.** What is the probability that Avery scores a 2? a 1? a 0?
   - **b.** Find the mean, variance, and standard deviation for the score on two questions.

3. Find the mean, variance, and standard deviation for the score on three multiple-choice questions with five options each.

4. A multiple-choice test has 20 questions, each with five options. Find the mean, variance, and standard deviation for the score on all 20 questions.

5. Find the variance and standard deviation for the number of heads when flipping each of the following.
   - **a.** one coin
   - **b.** two coins
   - **c.** four coins
   - **d.** nine coins
   - **e.** 100 coins

6. You flip a coin 36 times. The result is 10 heads and 26 tails.
   - **a.** Find the standard deviation for the number of heads tossed when flipping 36 coins.
   - **b.** Is it particularly unusual to get only 10 heads? Use the standard deviation to decide.
   - **c.** **Take It Further** Suppose you are to flip a fair coin 36 times. Find the probability that you get exactly 10 heads and 26 tails.

7. **Take It Further** An experiment has probability of success p.
   - **a.** Find the mean, variance, and standard deviation for the number of successes in one such experiment (in terms of p).
   - **b.** Find the mean, variance and standard deviation for the number of successes in n such experiments (in terms of n and p).

Check that your answers are correct for $p = \frac{1}{2}$. What if $p = 0$?

Answers

Exercises

1. $\frac{1}{5}$; 0.16; 0.4
2. **a.** $\frac{1}{25}, \frac{8}{25}, \frac{16}{25}$
   b. 0.4; 0.32; $\sqrt{0.32} \approx 0.566$
3. 0.6; 0.48; $\sqrt{0.48} \approx 0.693$
4. 4; 3.2; $\sqrt{3.2} \approx 1.789$
5. **a.** $\frac{1}{4}, \frac{1}{2}$
   b. $\frac{1}{2}$; $\sqrt{0.5} \approx 0.707$
   c. 1; 1
   d. $\frac{9}{4}, \frac{3}{2}$
   e. 25; 5
6. **a.** 3
   b. Answers may vary. Sample: Yes, it is unusual; most results should be in the range 18 ± 3, between 15 and 21. Only 10 heads is far outside this range.
   c. 0.003699 or 0.37%
7. **a.** p; $p(1 - p)$; $\sqrt{p(1 - p)}$
   b. np; $np(1 - p)$; $\sqrt{np(1 - p)}$

On Your Own

8. A spinner has the numbers 25, 50, 75, and 100. Find the variance and standard deviation for the sum of each number of spins.

a. one spin　**b.** two spins　**c.** four spins　**d.** 100 spins

9. Find the variance and standard deviation for the number of sixes you get when rolling each number of number cubes.

a. one number cube　**b.** two number cubes

c. four number cubes　**d.** nine number cubes

e. n number cubes

10. You roll a number cube 50 times. The sum of the rolls is 165. Is this a particularly unusual result? Use the standard deviation to decide.

11. Take It Further

a. You are to roll n number cubes and count the number of sixes. Find the smallest integer n so that the standard deviation is an integer.

b. You are to roll n number cubes and sum the results. Find the smallest positive integer n so that the standard deviation is an integer.

12. A board game has a spinner with numbers 1 to 10.

a. Find the mean and standard deviation when spinning this spinner 100 times.

b. Would it be unlikely for you to get a total of 600 in 100 spins? Explain.

13. Write About It In a new promotion, 100 people will spin the Wheel of Fish for prizes. The manager of the market is hoping that no more than 500 fish will be given away. Is this a likely outcome? Use the standard deviation to decide.

14. Standardized Test Prep For each play of a game, the mean is 1 and the standard deviation is 1. Which of the following pairs of numbers represents the (mean, standard deviation) for 100 plays?

A. (1, 100)　**B.** (10, 100)　**C.** (100, 1)　**D.** (100, 10)

Go Online PHSchool.com

For additional practice, go to **Web Code:** bga-0709

Remember...

The Wheel of Fish has the numbers 1, 2, 3, 10 on it. The mean for one spin is 4, and the variance is 12.5.

Maintain Your Skills

15. You are to roll five number cubes. Find the probability that you roll

a. no sixes.　**b.** exactly one six.

c. exactly two sixes.　**e.** more than two sixes.

16. Expand $\left(\frac{1}{6}s + \frac{5}{6}n\right)^5$. How can you use this expansion to help answer the questions in Exercise 15?

8. a. 781.25; 27.95
b. 1562.5; 39.53
c. 3125; 55.90
d. 78,125; 279.51

9. a. 0.1389; 0.3727
b. 0.2778; 0.5270
c. 0.5556; 0.7454
d. 1.25; 1.118
e. $\frac{5n}{36}, \frac{\sqrt{5n}}{6}$

10. Answers may vary. Sample: The mean for one roll of the number cube is 3.5 and the variance is $\frac{35}{12}$. For 50 rolls of the number cube the mean is 175 and the variance is $50 \cdot \frac{35}{12} (\approx 145.8)$ and the standard deviation is 12.08. Most of the time 50 number cubes are rolled the results will be in the range 175 ± 12, from 163 to 187. Since 165 is in this range it is not an unusual result.

11. a. 180
b. 420

12–16. See back of book.

Maintain Your Skills

EXERCISES 15 AND 16 ask students to think about how to count the possibilities, applying their work in combinatorics. For example, to compute the probability of rolling exactly two sixes, students picture the five number cubes in the problem. They need to choose which two show a six, and there are $\binom{5}{2} = 10$ ways to do that. Then once they know that, they need to compute the probability that the number cubes show three non-sixes and two sixes, which is $\left(\frac{5}{6}\right)^3 \cdot \left(\frac{1}{6}\right)^2 = \frac{125}{7776}$.

Some students are bothered by the kind of language that is usually used with this kind of calculation. Phrases such as "choose which two number cubes show a six," sound as though there is choice in the matter rather than randomness. It is helpful to remind students that they are counting the number of ways it is possible to roll two sixes. That is not a random act—they are listing every possible way it could happen.

Additional Resources

PRINT RESOURCES
- Solution Manual
- Practice Workbook
- Assessment Resources
- Teaching Resources

TECHNOLOGY
- Interactive Textbook
- TeacherExpress CD-ROM
- ExamView CD-ROM
- PHSchool.com

Additional Practice

1. Caitlin answers three multiple-choice questions with four options. She guesses. She scores a 4 if she is right, a 0 is she is wrong.
a. What is the probability that Caitlin scores a 4? an 8? a 0?
b. Find the mean, variance, and standard deviation for scores on three questions.
c. Suppose Caitlin has to answer eight questions. Find the mean, variance, and standard deviation for scores on eight questions.

2. You spin a spinner with the numbers 10, 12, 15, 18 and 20 on it. Find the variance and standard deviation for the total scores from spinning the spinner the following number of times.
a. once　**b.** twice
c. five times　**d.** 100 times

3. You roll a standard number cube 100 times and the sum of the rolls is 600. Is this a particularly unusual result? Use the standard deviation to decide.

4. a. Find the mean and standard deviation for the numbers of twos you would get when rolling 360 number cubes.
b. If you rolled 360 number cubes and got only 25 twos, would that be a surprising result or within reasonable limits?

5. Two-fifths of the students at a high school participate in athletics. Fifty students are surveyed at random. Find the mean and standard deviation for the numbers of students who will say they participate in athletics.

6. Jack takes a 15-question multiple-choice test by guessing at the answers. Each question has four choices, so each answer has probability $p = 0.25$ of being correct.
a. Write an expression that represents the probability of getting all of the questions correct.
b. What is the probability of getting all of the questions wrong?
c. Find the probability of getting exactly 5 questions out of 15 correct.
d. Find the probability of getting exactly 10 questions out of 15 correct.

7. Consider two independent Bernoulli trials. The first has probability of success $p = 0.3$. The second has probability of success $q = 0.4$.
a. Find the probability that both trials are successful.
b. Find the probability that neither trial is successful.
c. Find the probability that exactly one trial is successful.

Practice: For Lesson 7.9, assign Exercises 1–3.

Lesson Overview

GOAL

- Identify Bernoulli trials and compute related statistics.

This lesson defines Bernoulli trials—experiments with exactly two outcomes, often referred to as "success" and "failure." By reducing the number of outcomes to two, you simplify the counting. You only need to worry about two probabilities, and they sum to 1. Students first work with tables, and then see how combinatorics and polynomial expansions can lead to considerable shortcuts.

CHECK YOUR UNDERSTANDING

- Core: 1, 2, 3, 4, 5, 6
- Optional: 7
- Extension: 8

MATERIALS

- graphing calculators

HOMEWORK

- Core: 9a–c, 10, 11, 12, 14
- Optional: 15
- Extension: 9d, 13

VOCABULARY

- Bernoulli trial
- *z*-score

Launch

Begin today's lesson with the definition of a Bernoulli trial. Have students give other examples of Bernoulli trials, or examples of experiments which are not Bernoulli trials. For this second set of examples, ask students to frame the experiment differently, so that there is a way to see it as a Bernoulli trial. As an example of an experiment that is not a Bernoulli trial, students might suggest, "Toss five number cubes and count the number of sixes." That experiment has 6 possible outcomes, so students are correct that it is not a Bernoulli trial. You can reframe it as, "Toss five number cubes. You succeed if you get more than two sixes." Now it is a Bernoulli trial with only two outcomes—success and failure.

7.10 Bernoulli Trials

A **Bernoulli trial** is an experiment with two outcomes, *success* and *failure.* You have seen several examples of Bernoulli trials: flipping a coin heads, answering a multiple-choice question correctly, rolling a six. A Bernoulli trial has a probability of success p, so the probability of failure is $1 - p$.

Habits of Mind

Look for a relationship. Why must the probability of failure be $1 - p$?

Example 1

Problem Consider a Bernoulli trial with probability of success $p = 0.2$. In three trials, what is the probability of exactly two successes?

Solution

Method 1 Write out all eight possible outcomes. Determine the probability of each. Then, add the probabilities that have exactly two successes. Use S for success and F for failure.

Outcome	Probability	Product
SSS	$0.2 \cdot 0.2 \cdot 0.2$	0.008
SSF	$\mathbf{0.2 \cdot 0.2 \cdot 0.8}$	**0.032**
SFS	$\mathbf{0.2 \cdot 0.8 \cdot 0.2}$	**0.032**
SFF	$0.2 \cdot 0.8 \cdot 0.8$	0.128
FSS	$\mathbf{0.8 \cdot 0.2 \cdot 0.2}$	**0.032**
FSF	$0.8 \cdot 0.2 \cdot 0.8$	0.128
FFS	$0.8 \cdot 0.8 \cdot 0.2$	0.128
FFF	$0.8 \cdot 0.8 \cdot 0.8$	0.512

The probability is the sum for all the outcomes with exactly two successes: 0.096, or 9.6%.

Method 2 Use combinatorics to identify the number of different outcomes, with exponents that correspond to the number of successes and failures.

For this experiment, there are $\binom{3}{2} = 3$ different orderings for 2 successes and 1 failure. Each success has probability 0.2, while each failure has probability 0.8. The probability for exactly two successes is

$$\binom{3}{2} \cdot (0.2)^2 \cdot (0.8)^1 = 0.096$$

In general, the probability of exactly k successes in n trials for this experiment is given by

$$\binom{n}{k} \cdot (0.2)^k \cdot (0.8)^{n-k}$$

since there are k successes and $(n - k)$ failures.

Some examples of Bernoulli trials with probability of success 0.2: correctly answering a multiple-choice question with 5 choices, spinning a 1 or 2 on a spinner with 1–10, or a baseball player getting a hit.

Method 3 The binomial $(0.2s + 0.8f)$ models one trial. Raising this binomial to the third power gives all the probabilities:

$$(0.2s + 0.8f)^3 = 0.008s^3 + 0.096s^2f + 0.384sf^2 + 0.512f^3$$

The probability of two successes and one failure can be read by looking at the coefficient of the s^2f term. The coefficient is 0.096.

For Discussion

1. Given $p = 0.2$ as in Example 1, find the probability that there will be at least one success in the three trials. Is there more than one way to do this?

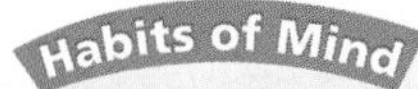

Make strategic choices. This way, the sum of the values for n trials will be the number of successes.

To calculate the mean and variance for a Bernoulli trial, assign 1 as the value of a success and 0 as the value of a failure. Using the calculation method from Lesson 7.4, find the mean by multiplying each value by its probability. The probability of a success is p. The probability of a failure is $(1 - p)$.

Value	Probability	Product
1 (success)	p	p
0 (failure)	$1 - p$	0
Total		p

The mean for a single Bernoulli trial is the probability of its success. Since the mean is additive, in n trials the expected number of successes will be np. For example, on a 20-question multiple-choice test with 5 choices per question, you would expect (on average) to get 4 out of 20 if you were completely guessing throughout the test.

$n = 20$ and $p = 0.2$, so $np = 4$.

What about variance? Variance is mean squared deviation. Here, the deviation is taken from the mean p. Each squared deviation is multiplied by its probability.

Result	Deviation	Deviation^2	Probability	Product
1 (success)	$1 - p$	$(1 - p)^2$	p	$p(1 - p)^2$
0 (failure)	$-p$	p^2	$1 - p$	$p^2(1 - p)$
Total				$p(1 - p)$

This result for variance matches earlier results. For a coin flip, the variance is $0.5(1 - 0.5) = 0.25$. If an outcome is impossible ($p = 0$) or guaranteed ($p = 1$), the variance is zero.

Since variance is additive, in n trials the variance is $np(1 - p)$. As before, the standard deviation is the square root of the variance.

Answers

For Discussion

1. 0.488; Answers may vary. Sample: one way to find the probability is to consider all the cases where there is at least one success.

$$\binom{3}{1}(0.2)^1(0.8)^2 + \binom{3}{2}(0.2)^2(0.8)^1 + \binom{3}{3}(0.2)^3(0.8)^0$$

$$= 3 \cdot 0.2 \cdot 0.64 + 3 \cdot 0.04 \cdot 0.8 + 1 \cdot 0.008 \cdot 1 = 0.488$$

An alternative method would be to consider the cases where there is not at least one method of success and subtract the probability from 1.

Explore

For Discussion

PROBLEM 1 The probability is 0.488, and is found by adding all the outcomes with 1, 2, or 3 successes. A simpler method, though, is to subtract the probability of no successes from 1.

GOING FURTHER Ask students to come up with a general formula here for different p-values; the general formula is

$$1 - (1 - p)^3$$

Wrap Up

As time allows, go over the core Check Your Understanding exercises with your class. Exercises 1 and 2 ask students to revisit questions they first tried to answer back in Exercises 8 and 9 from the Getting Started lesson for Investigation 7A. Have students think about these questions from their current perspective before they go back and examine their original ideas. What have they learned so far about calculating probabilities?

Assessment Resources

Lesson Quiz 7.10

1. a. Find the mean and standard deviation for the number of sixes you would see when rolling 180 number cubes.
   b. What is the probability of rolling exactly 25 sixes?

2. Two independent Bernoulli trials are performed. The first has probability of success $p = 0.35$. The second has probability of success $q = 0.15$.
   a. Find the probability that both trials are successful.
   b. Find the probability that neither trial is successful.
   c. Find the probability that exactly one trial is successful.

3. Isobel takes a 25-question multiple-choice test. She guesses at each question. Each question has probability $p = 0.2$ of being correct.
   a. Write an expression that gives the probability of getting all 25 questions correct.
   b. Find the probability of getting all 25 questions wrong.
   c. Find the probability of getting exactly 5 questions correct.

Facts and Notation

Consider a Bernoulli trial with probability of success p. In n trials, the mean, variance, and standard deviation for the number of successes are as follows.

$$\text{mean } \bar{x} = np$$

$$\text{variance } \sigma^2 = np(1 - p)$$

$$\text{standard deviation } \sigma = \sqrt{np(1 - p)}$$

These formulas all rely on the fact that mean and variance are additive.

Habits of Mind

Try a specific case. With $n = 20$ and $p = 0.2$ like a 20-question multiple-choice test, $\bar{x} = 4$ and $\sigma \approx 1.789$. Most people guessing on this test will get between 2 and 6 correct.

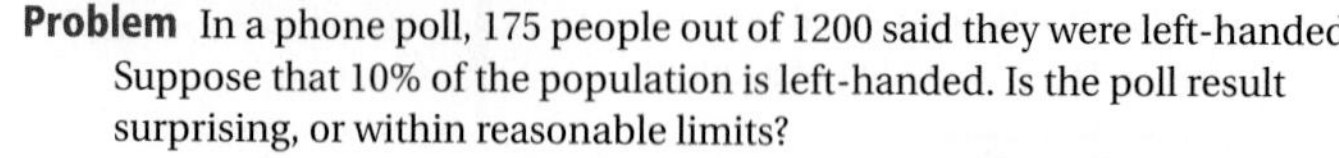

Example 2

Problem In a phone poll, 175 people out of 1200 said they were left-handed. Suppose that 10% of the population is left-handed. Is the poll result surprising, or within reasonable limits?

Solution This can be considered a Bernoulli trial with probability $p = 0.1$, tested 1200 times. Calculate the mean and standard deviation for the numbers of people expected to answer that they are left-handed.

$$\text{mean } \bar{x} = 1200 \cdot 0.1 = 120$$

$$\text{standard deviation } \sigma = \sqrt{1200 \cdot 0.1 \cdot 0.9} = 6\sqrt{3} \approx 10.39$$

So, most of the time the poll is run, you would expect the result to be within 120 ± 10.39 because most of the data will fall within one standard deviation of the mean. The upper bound here is just over 130. But the actual poll result was 175. This is well outside the expected range, so the poll result is very surprising.

One statistic that can be useful to calculate is the **z-score,** the number of standard deviations away from the mean. For Example 2, the z-score of the phone poll is approximately

$$\frac{175 - 120}{10.39} \approx 5.29$$

Since most data fall within one standard deviation of the mean, a z-score this high is very unusual. It is more than five standard deviations from the mean. This result suggests that the premise that only 10% of people are left-handed might not be correct or that the sample in the poll was not representative of the general population.

Hypothesis testing is a branch of statistics that deals with these types of claims.

Exercises *Practicing Habits of Mind*

Check Your Understanding

1. For Exercise 8 in Lesson 7.1, you guessed the probability of tossing exactly 120 heads and 120 tails on 240 coin flips.
   a. Use the formula given in this lesson to find this probability to four decimal places.
   b. How does your answer compare to the guess you made previously?

2. For Exercise 9 in Lesson 7.1, you guessed the probability of rolling exactly 40 ones on 240 number cubes rolls.
   a. Use the formula given in this lesson to find this probability to four decimal places.
   b. How does your answer compare to the guess you made previously?

3. a. Find the mean and standard deviation for the number of sixes you would get when rolling 240 number cubes.
   b. If you rolled 240 number cubes and got only 20 sixes, would that be a surprising result or within reasonable limits?

4. In the Getting Started lesson, you took a 20-question multiple-choice test by guessing. Each answer had probability $p = 0.2$ of being correct.
   a. Explain why the probability of getting all 20 questions correct is $(0.2)^{20}$.
   b. Find the probability of getting all 20 questions wrong.
   c. Use the formula given in this lesson to find the probability of getting exactly 3 questions out of 20 correct.
   d. What percentage of your class actually got exactly 3 questions out of 20 correct?

5. a. Write the definition for a function f where the output is the probability of getting exactly n questions correct on the 20-question test from the Getting Started lesson.
   b. Copy and complete the table for n from 0 to 10.

n	$f(n)$
0	■
1	■
2	■
3	■
4	■
5	■
6	■
7	■
8	■
9	■
10	■

See the TI-Nspire Handbook on p. 704 for information on how to build the table for Exercise 5.

6. Expand the polynomial $(0.2r + 0.8w)^{20}$. Find the coefficient of the r^3w^{17} term. What is its significance?

7. Show algebraically that $p(1 - p)^2 + p^2(1 - p) = p(1 - p)$.

8. **Take It Further** Consider a Bernoulli trial with probability of success p. Build tables similar to the ones on page 597 that show that the mean for the number of successes in two trials is $2p$, and the variance is $2p(1 - p)$.

Exercises

HOMEWORK
- Core: 9a–c, 10, 11, 12, 14
- Optional: 15
- Extension: 9d, 13

Check Your Understanding

EXERCISE 1 and the one that follows revisits questions from weeks earlier that students can now answer definitively.

EXERCISE 2 This answer is larger due to the lower variance of the number cube rolls. Lower variance means a tighter spread, so each value is proportionally higher (near the mean).

EXERCISE 3 A question in Investigation 7C asks about the likelihood of this result.

EXERCISE 5 If time permits, compare these theoretical results to the results from the actual test the class took.

EXERCISE 6 is a direct consequence of the Binomial Theorem.

Answers

Exercises

1. a. 0.0514
   b. Check students' work.
2. a. 0.0690
   b. Check students' work.
3. a. 40; 5.7735
   b. Answers may vary. Sample: This is an unusual result. Most of the results should be from 40 ± 5.7735. This is roughly from 34 to 46. Getting only 20 sixes is far outside this range.
4. a. Each question has $p = 0.2$ probability of getting a correct answer. They are independent of one another, so the probability of getting n consecutive questions right is 0.2^n.
   b. 0.0115 or 1.15%
   c. 0.2054 or 20.54%
   d. Check students' work.
5. a. $f(n) = \binom{20}{n}(0.20)^n(0.8)^{(20-n)}$
   b.

n	$f(n)$
0	0.0115
1	0.0576
2	0.1369
3	0.2054
4	0.2182
5	0.1746
6	0.1091
7	0.0545
8	0.0222
9	0.0074
10	0.0020

6. 0.2054; the coefficient is the probability of getting 3 correct and 17 wrong answers.

7–8. See back of book.

On Your Own

EXERCISE 9 This algebraic legwork serves as verification for the results earlier in the investigation; mean and variance add for independent events.

EXERCISE 11 Some students have trouble seeing why 14 is the best choice; consider simplifying the game to 2 number cubes. Once they see why 7 is the best choice for this simpler game, they should be able to step to the larger problem. Remind students about polynomial powers if they do not recall the earlier exercise.

EXERCISE 12 Hopefully students are surprised by the result here! The next exercise helps explain this.

EXERCISE 13 explains why Game 2 is easier to win. Its standard deviation is smaller, so it has a narrower spread. More of its results equal 12 than equal 14 in Game 1.

Maintain Your Skills

EXERCISE 15 The ridiculous height of 7 feet in part (f) is included to give students a sense of especially high or low *z*-scores.

Additional Resources

PRINT RESOURCES
- Solution Manual
- Practice Workbook
- Assessment Resources
- Teaching Resources

TECHNOLOGY
- Interactive Textbook
- TeacherExpress CD-ROM
- ExamView CD-ROM
- PHSchool.com

Additional Practice

1. Caitlin answers three multiple-choice questions with four options. She guesses. She scores a 4 if she is right, a 0 is she is wrong.
   a. What is the probability that Caitlin scores a 4? an 8? a 0?
   b. Find the mean, variance, and standard deviation for scores on three questions.
   c. Suppose Caitlin has to answer eight questions. Find the mean, variance, and standard deviation for scores on eight questions.

2. You spin a spinner with the numbers 10, 12, 15, 18 and 20 on it. Find the variance and standard deviation for the total scores from spinning the spinner the following number of times.
   a. once
   b. twice
   c. five times
   d. 100 times

3. You roll a standard number cube 100 times and the sum of the rolls is 600. Is this a particularly unusual result? Use the standard deviation to decide.

4. a. Find the mean and standard deviation for the numbers of twos you would get when rolling 360 number cubes.
   b. If you rolled 360 number cubes and got only 25 twos, would that be a surprising result or within reasonable limits?

5. Two-fifths of the students at a high school participate in athletics. Fifty students are surveyed at random. Find the mean and standard deviation for the numbers of students who will say they participate in athletics.

6. Jack takes a 15-question multiple-choice test by guessing at the answers. Each question has four choices, so each answer has probability $p = 0.25$ of being correct.
   a. Write an expression that represents the probability of getting all of the questions correct.
   b. What is the probability of getting all of the questions wrong?
   c. Find the probability of getting exactly 5 questions out of 15 correct.
   d. Find the probability of getting exactly 10 questions out of 15 correct.

7. Consider two independent Bernoulli trials. The first has probability of success $p = 0.3$. The second has probability of success $q = 0.4$.
   a. Find the probability that both trials are successful.
   b. Find the probability that neither trial is successful.
   c. Find the probability that exactly one trial is successful.

Practice: For Lesson 7.10, assign Exercises 4–7.

On Your Own

9. Consider two independent Bernoulli trials. The first has probability of success p. The second has probability of success q.
   a. Find the probability that both trials are successful.
   b. Find the probability that neither trial is successful.
   c. Find the probability that exactly one trial is successful.
   d. Take It Further Find the mean and variance for the total number of successes for the two Bernoulli trials.

Here are two carnival games involving number cubes.

Game 1 Call a number, then roll four number cubes. If the sum from the four number cubes is exactly the number you called, you win.

Game 2 Call a number, then roll 72 number cubes. If the number of sixes rolled is exactly the number you called, you win.

10. Make a quick guess: which game is easier to win, and why?

11. What number gives you the best chance to win Game 1. How likely are you to win with this number?

12. What number gives you the best chance to win Game 2. How likely are you to win with this number?

13. Take It Further Find the mean and standard deviation for each experiment.
   a. the sum when rolling four number cubes
   b. the number of sixes when rolling 72 number cubes

14. Standardized Test Prep For a Bernoulli trial with probability of success p, the variance is $p(1 - p)$. What value of p gives the maximum variance?

A. $\frac{1}{4}$ **B.** $\frac{1}{2}$ **C.** $\frac{2}{3}$ **D.** 1

Go Online PHSchool.com

For additional practice, go to Web Code: bga-0710

Maintain Your Skills

15. The mean height for an adult woman is 63.5 inches (5 feet $3\frac{1}{2}$ inches), with a standard deviation of 2.5 inches. For each height, calculate the *z*-score.
   a. 5 feet 6 inches **b.** 5 feet 1 inch **c.** 5 feet 8 inches
   d. 6 feet **e.** 4 feet 11 inches **f.** 7 feet
   g. x inches

The *z*-score may be any real number. It can be positive, negative, or zero.

Answers

9. a. pq
b. $(1 - p)(1 - q)$
c. $p + q - 2pq$
d. $p + q$; $p(1 - p) + q(1 - q)$

10. Check students' work.

11. 14; $\frac{146}{1296} \approx 0.1127 \approx 11.27\%$

12. 12; $\binom{72}{12}\left(\frac{1}{6}\right)^{12}\left(\frac{5}{6}\right)^{60} \approx 0.1253 \approx 12.53\%$

13. a. 14; about 3.4157
b. 12; about 3.1623

14. B

15. a. 1
b. −1
c. 1.8
d. 3.4
e. −1.8
f. 8.2
g. $\frac{x - 63.5}{2.5}$

Mathematical Reflections

EXERCISES 6–8 At the start of the investigation, you may have assigned these as Questions 1–3 for students to think and write about.

In this investigation, you calculated variance and standard deviation, which give you some sense of how much your results vary from the average outcome, or expected value, of an experiment. You then tailored these calculations to repeated experiments and Bernoulli trials. The following questions will help you summarize what you have learned.

1. If you guess on a 25-question multiple-choice test with five options, what is the expected number of correct answers? What is the standard deviation?
2. Find the variance for this set: $\{1, 2, 5, 7, 10, 11\}$.
3. A number cube has the numbers 1, 2, 2, 3, 3, and 4 on it. Find the mean, variance, and standard deviation for each random variable.
   a. the value of one roll of this number cube
   b. the sum of two rolls of this number cube
4. Find the mean and standard deviation for the number of successes in 600 Bernoulli trials with probability of success $p = 0.3$.
5. You are to roll 15 number cubes. Find the probability of getting no more than two sixes.
6. How can you calculate the standard deviation for a large set of data?
7. What happens to the mean, variance, and standard deviation if an experiment is repeated a second time?
8. What is the mean and standard deviation for the number of heads on 400 coin flips?

Vocabulary and Notation

In this investigation, you learned these terms and symbols. Make sure you understand what each one means and how to use it.

- **Bernoulli trial**
- **experimental probability**
- **mean absolute deviation**
- **mean squared deviation, or variance, σ^2**
- **root mean squared deviation, or standard deviation, σ**
- **spread**
- **theoretical probability**
- ***z*-score**

Mathematical Reflections

1. 5; 2
2. 14
3. a. 2.5; $\frac{11}{12}$; 0.9574
   b. 5; $\frac{11}{6}$; 1.3540
4. 180; 11.2250
5. 0.5322
6. Answers may vary. Sample: The machine formula (the mean of the squares, minus the square of the mean) can be used to calculate the variance, then the standard deviation is the square root of the variance.
7. The mean and variance double, and the standard deviation is multiplied by $\sqrt{2}$.
8. 200; 10

Investigation Overview

In this investigation, students continue to investigate what happens to random variables as the number of trials of an experiment gets larger and larger. They begin by constructing probability histograms rather than frequency histograms so that they have a bar graph where the total area of all the bars is 1. Then they see that, as they increase the number of trials, the shapes of these probability histograms all look more and more like each other—taking on the shape of a bell curve. This is a consequence of the Central Limit Theorem, and although the proof of this theorem is beyond the scope of a high school course, students can see its effect. They learn to write equations for the normal distribution given the mean and standard deviation for a random variable, and learn how to use it to find approximations for probabilities, especially when the number of trials is so large that the theoretical probabilities are difficult to calculate. Students also learn a rule for the percentage of values in a normal distribution that are within one, two, or three standard deviations from the mean, and interpret this rule in many contexts.

You may wish to assign Questions 1–3 for students to think and write about during the investigation.

Learning Goals

- Make a probability histogram.
- Write an equation for a normal distribution given its mean and standard deviation.
- Use an appropriate normal distribution to find approximate probabilities.

Habits and Skills

- Visualize the effect on a probability histogram of increasing the number of trials.
- Understand the consequences of the Central Limit Theorem and apply it correctly.
- Interpret and solve probability questions using appropriate normal distributions.

The Normal Distribution

In *The Normal Distribution*, you will learn that if you repeat an experiment a large number of times, the graph of the average outcomes is approximately the shape of a bell curve. You will understand Central Limit Theorem, one of the central theorems of statistics.

By the end of this investigation, you will be able to answer questions like these.

1. What is the Central Limit Theorem?
2. Why is the normal distribution so common?
3. What is the probability of rolling 10% or fewer sixes if you roll 1000 number cubes?

You will learn how to:

- make a probability histogram
- write an equation for a normal distribution given its mean and standard deviation
- use an appropriate normal distribution to find approximate probabilities

You will develop these habits and skills:

- Visualize the effect on a probability histogram of increasing the number of trials.
- Understand the consequences of the Central Limit Theorem and apply it correctly.
- Interpret and solve probability questions using appropriate normal distributions.

By design, the Empire State Building is a lightning rod. It is struck by lightning about 100 times a year. Some years lightning will strike the building fewer times and other years it will strike the building more times. The distribution of the number of lightning strikes to the building per year follows a bell curve.

Investigation Road Map

LESSON 7.11, *Getting Started,* has students construct probability histograms, instead of frequency histograms, for various situations. Students begin to compare these probability distributions for different events and for increasing numbers of trials.

LESSON 7.12, *The Central Limit Theorem,* introduces the Central Limit Theorem. Students notice that many different probability histograms look similar to each other and become even more similar to each other and to a bell-shaped curve as the number of trials increase. Then students learn to approximate these histograms with a normal distribution and compute the error in the type of approximation.

LESSON 7.13, *The Normal Distribution,* has students learn to write equations for normal distributions and to use their calculators to evaluate these equations to find approximations of various probabilities for experiments with large numbers of trials. Students learn the 68-95-99.7 rule to estimate probablities for data.

7.11 Getting Started

A **probability histogram** is similar to a regular histogram, except each bar height (and area) is the probability of achieving each result, instead of the frequency of the result. For example, here is the probability histogram for the number of heads when tossing three coins:

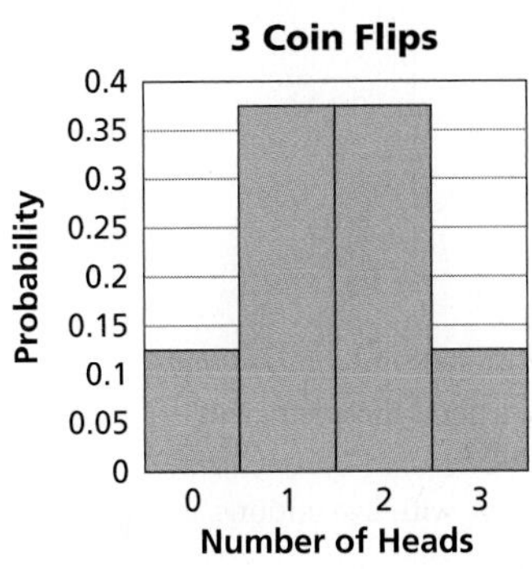

The probability of getting 1 head in 3 tosses is $\frac{3}{8} = 0.375$, so that is the height and area of the bar in the histogram. What is the probability of getting at least 1 head in 3 tosses?

Probability histograms look the same as frequency histograms, but the height of each bar must be between 0 and 1. The sum of all bars' heights (and areas) is exactly 1.

For You to Explore

1. In Exercise 1 on page 552, you made a frequency histogram for the distribution of sums when rolling four number cubes.

   Copy the diagram below. Make a probability histogram for the distribution of sums when rolling four number cubes. For example, the probability of rolling a sum of exactly 17 is $\frac{104}{1296} \approx 0.0802$.

The least possible sum is 4. The greatest is 24.

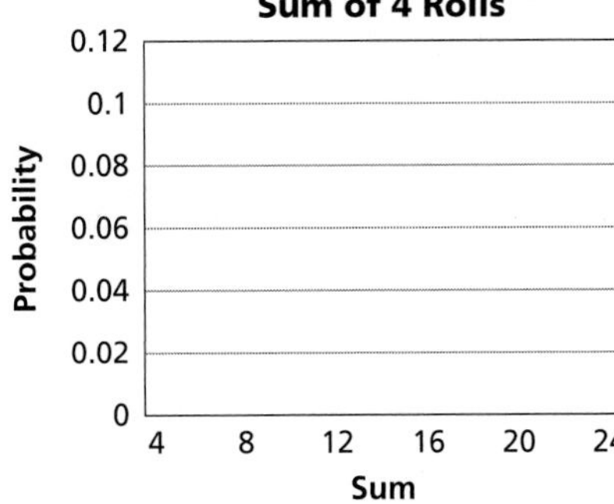

Answers

For You to Explore

1.

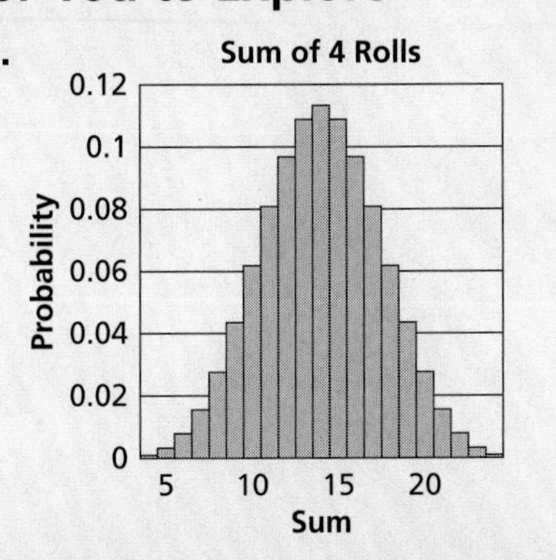

Lesson Overview

GOALS

- Warm up to the ideas of the investigation.
- Make a probability histogram.

In this lesson, students learn to make a probability histogram. Since they have already made frequency histograms, this just involves changing the height of the bars in the frequency histogram so they are equal to the probability, creating a histogram in which the total area of all the bars is equal to one. Students compare histograms for the same experiment but with different numbers of trials. Over the course of this exercise set, they see a pattern begin to emerge—for a large number of trials, it seems that *any* probability histogram resembles a bell-shaped curve.

FOR YOU TO EXPLORE

- Core: 1, 2, 3, 4
- Optional: none

MATERIALS

- CAS (recommended)
- graph paper
- graphing calculators
- Blackline Masters MC8, MC9

HOMEWORK

- Core: 5, 6, 7, 8, 9
- Optional: 10, 11a–b, 12
- Extension: 11c

VOCABULARY

- probability histogram

Launch

Begin today's lesson by defining *probability histogram*. Emphasize the association between area and probability in such a graph.

Explore

For You to Explore

As students work on the For You to Explore problems, see if they notice similarities between their graphs for Problems 1, 2, and 4. Since Lesson 7.12 presents the answers to these three problems first thing, consider assigning these problems to students without reference to the book.

You may find Blackline Master MC8 or MC9 useful in making the probability histograms in this lesson and the next.

PROBLEM 3 and the next review parts of Investigation 7B, and should help to cement the concepts. The overall perspective developed in this Getting Started lesson is that all three histograms students build are significantly similar.

PROBLEM 4 The Binomial Theorem is used often enough that some students may decide to define a calculator function like

$$\text{prob}(p, n, k) = \binom{n}{k} \cdot p^k \cdot (1 - p)^{n-k}$$

This may be a helpful suggestion for some of your students. Overall, continue to emphasize the solution by polynomial powers, which is an extension of the Binomial Theorem.

Wrap Up

If possible, compare results from Problems 1, 2, and 4 as a class. As time allows give students a chance to work on the On Your Own exercises.

2. When flipping 10 coins, there are 1024 possible outcomes.

Copy the diagram below. Make a probability histogram for the distribution of the number of heads when flipping 10 coins. For example, the probability of flipping exactly 2 heads is $\frac{45}{1024} \approx 0.0439$.

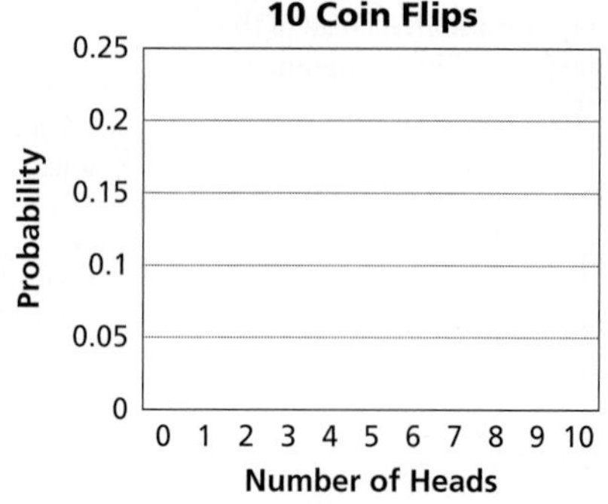

3. When the expression $(0.2r + 0.8w)^{20}$ is expanded, what is the coefficient of the r^2w^{18} term? What might this coefficient signify?

4. A multiple-choice test has 20 questions, each question with five options. Only one option is correct.

Copy the diagram below. Make a probability histogram for the distribution of the number of questions you would get correct by guessing at random. For example, the probability of getting all 20 questions wrong is about 0.0115.

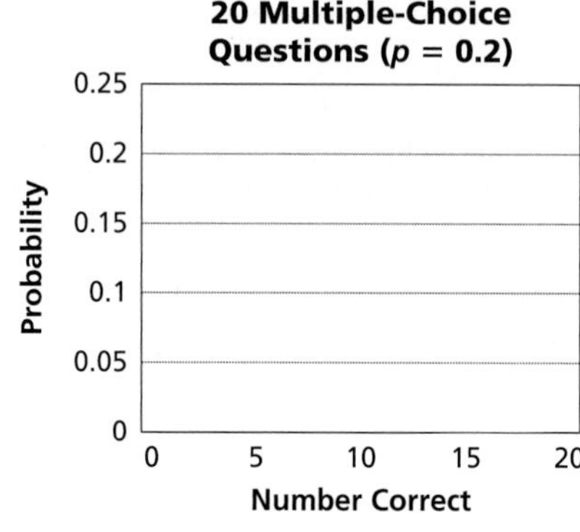

Answers

2.

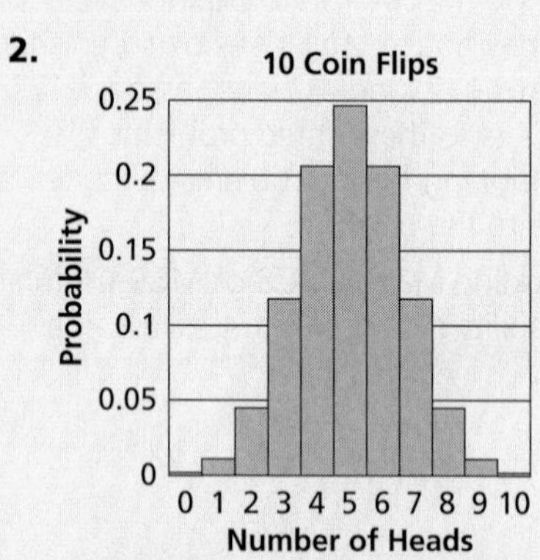

3. 0.1369; the coefficient of r^2w^{18} is the probability of getting exactly 2 successes with probability $p = 0.2$ in 20 trials.

4.

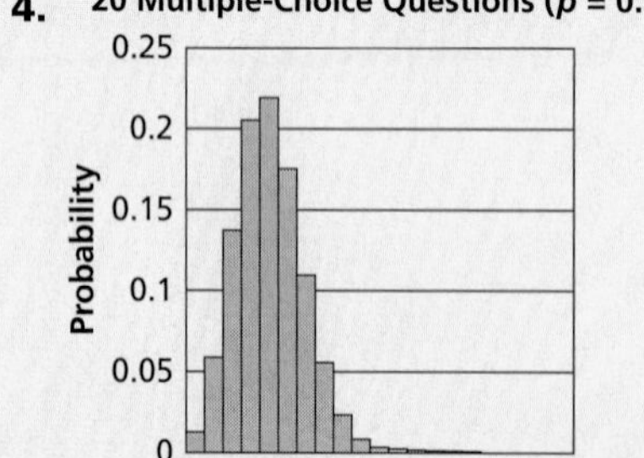

Exercises *Practicing Habits of Mind*

On Your Own

5. Expand the following polynomial.

$$\left(\frac{1}{6}x + \frac{1}{6}x^2 + \frac{1}{6}x^3 + \frac{1}{6}x^4 + \frac{1}{6}x^5 + \frac{1}{6}x^6\right)^4$$

a. Find the coefficient of the x^{17} term to four decimal places.

b. What is the sum of all the coefficients?

6. Build a probability histogram for the number of heads when flipping

a. two coins. **b.** four coins. **c.** five coins.

7. Flip ten coins and write down the number of heads that result. Repeat this experiment thirty times and tabulate the results.

Use a cup. Scoop the 10 coins into the cup, and drop them.

Number of Heads	Frequency
0	■
1	■
2	■
3	■
4	■
5	■
6	■
7	■
8	■
9	■
10	■

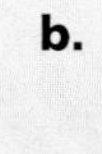

8. a. Make a probability histogram for your data from Exercise 7.

b. **Write About It** Compare your probability histogram to the one from Exercise 2. What might explain the differences between the two histograms?

9. The probability that Todd makes a free throw is 0.642. In a game, Todd attempts ten free throws. Assuming each free throw is an independent event, find the probability that Todd makes

a. exactly 7 out of 10 free throws.

b. exactly 8 out of 10 free throws.

c. more than 8 out of 10 free throws.

Exercises

HOMEWORK

- Core: 5, 6, 7, 8, 9
- Optional: 10, 11a–b, 12
- Extension: 11c

On Your Own

EXERCISE 6 If students have trouble with this exercise, ask them to construct a frequency histogram first, then divide the bars' heights by the size of the sample space.

EXERCISE 7 Exercise 1 in the next lesson asks students to compile this data into one class set. The class set should have results that are far closer to the theoretical results from Problem 2.

EXERCISE 8 You might ask students to compare their histograms; they may be surprised how different they are, and start looking for consistent behavior. There are very few extreme results (0, 1, 9, 10) and there are almost always a good number of 4's, 5's, and 6's. You see this behavior later in the combined class set.

Exercises

5. a. $\frac{13}{162} \approx 0.0802$ **b.** 1

6. a.

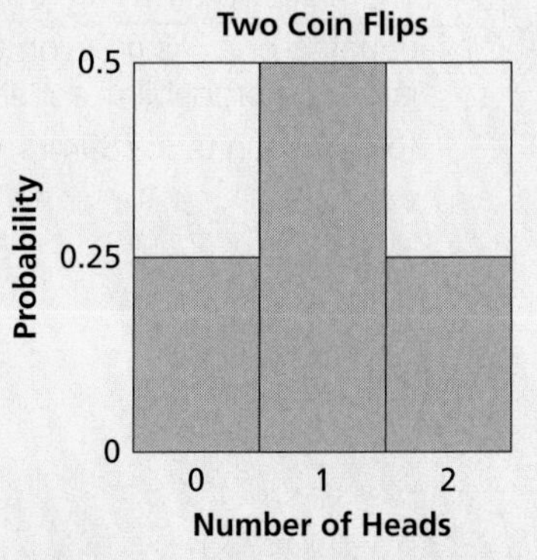

b.

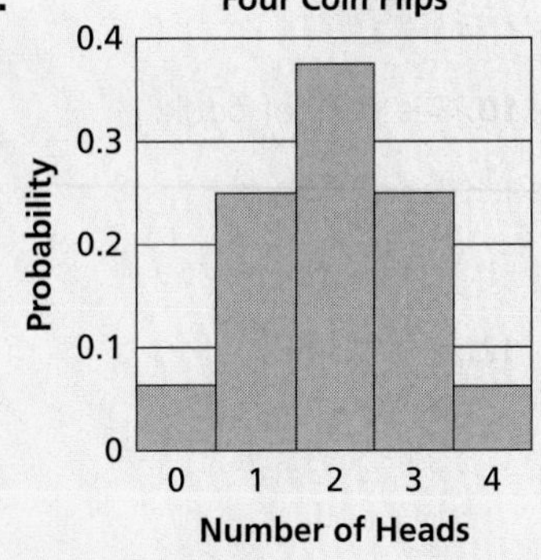

c.

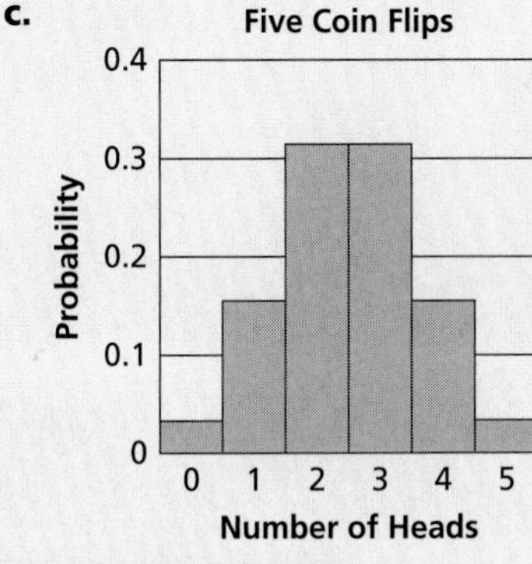

7. Check students' work.

8. a–b. Check students' work.

9. a. 0.2475
b. 0.1664
c. 0.0782

EXERCISE 11 You can use similar techniques to find the probability of being dealt a specific kind of 5-card poker hand, but note that the 5 poker cards are not independent as are the rolls of a number cube.

Maintain Your Skills

EXERCISE 12 The form $\left(\frac{n-1}{n}\right)^n$ is very similar to the way we define *e* (if *n* is allowed to grow toward infinity), which may be worth a brief investigation.

10. Copy and complete this table for the function

$$f(n) = \binom{10}{n} \cdot (0.642)^n \cdot (0.358)^{10-n}$$

Give each answer to four decimal places.

n	*f(n)*
0	■
1	■
2	■
3	■
4	■
5	■
6	■
7	■
8	■
9	■
10	■

11. When you roll five number cubes, what is the probability of each event?

a. All five number cubes show the same number.

b. All five number cubes show different numbers.

c. **Take It Further** Exactly four number cubes show the same number.

Maintain Your Skills

12. **a.** When rolling a number cube, there is a 1 in 6 chance of rolling a two. Find the probability, to four decimal places, that you roll the number cube six times and never get a two.

b. The spinner in a board game has numbers from 1 through 10, so there is a 1 in 10 chance of spinning a 2. Find the probability, to four decimal places, that you spin this spinner ten times and never get a 2.

c. When rolling two number cubes, there is a 1 in 36 chance of rolling a sum of two. Find the probability, to four decimal places, that you roll the pair of number cubes 36 times and never get a sum of two.

d. If an experiment with probability of success $\frac{1}{n}$ is run n times, find the probability that none of the n trials will be successful. As n increases, what happens in the long run to this probability?

Answers

10. See back of book.

11. a. 0.0001

b. 0.0926

c. 0.0193

12. a. 0.3349

b. 0.3487

c. 0.3627

d. $\binom{n}{0}\left(\frac{1}{n}\right)^0\left(\frac{n-1}{n}\right)^n$

The first two terms are both equal to one. As *n* becomes large the probability appears to approach 0.3678944, which is e^{-1}.

7.12 The Central Limit Theorem

In the Getting Started lesson, you made the probability histogram for several different probability distributions: rolls of a number cube, coin flips, and multiple-choice tests.

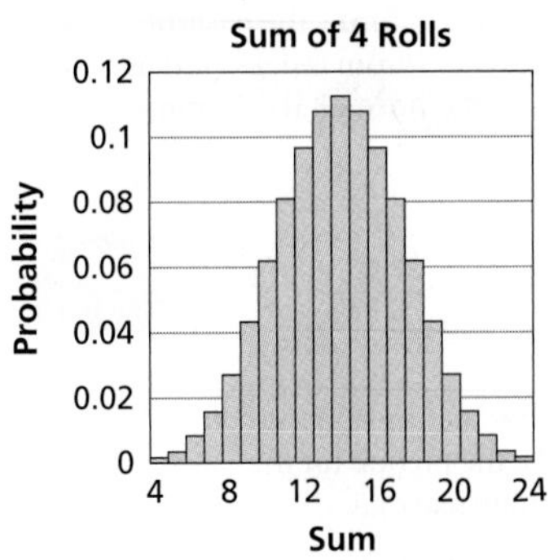

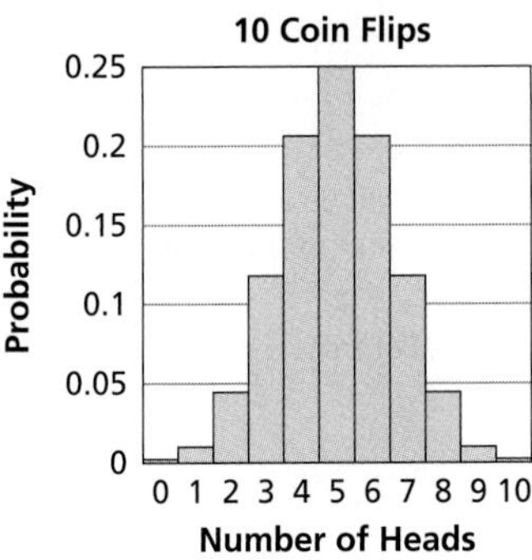

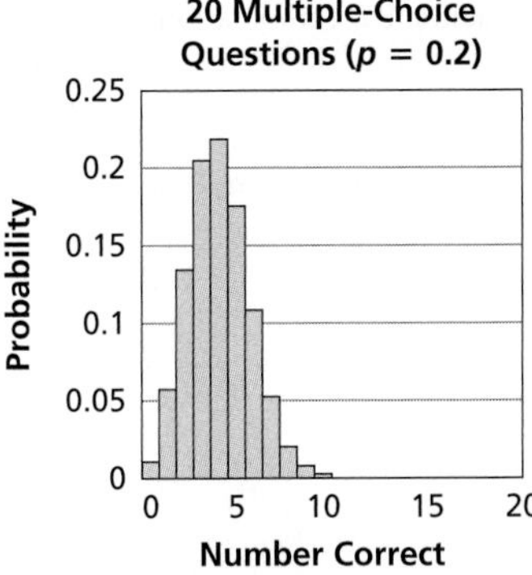

A **probability distribution** is a function that assigns a probability to each numeric output of a random variable. For example, if X is the sum of four number cubes, the probability distribution gives $P(X = 17) \approx 0.0802$.

All three are the distributions of sums. The second distribution is the sum of 1's and 0's for the heads and tails of the flips. The third is the sum of 1's and 0's for the right and wrong answers.

Lesson Overview

GOAL

- Write an equation for a normal distribution given its mean and standard deviation.

In this lesson, students look at how probability distributions change as the number of trials increase. They see that even in situations as odd as spinning the Wheel of Fish, the distributions smooth out to a similar bell shape. This similarity between probability distributions in very different situations is quite noticeable, and gives students the experience they need to accept the Central Limit Theorem. The actual proof of this theorem is well beyond the scope of a high school course, but if your students have "seen it happen for themselves" they are more likely to accept it. By working to construct the different distributions shown in the dialogue in this lesson, students gain a better understanding of what a "large" number of trials might mean.

CHECK YOUR UNDERSTANDING
- Core: 1a-b, 2, 3, 4, 6
- Optional: 5a-d, 7
- Extension: 1c, 5e

MATERIALS
- graphing calculators
- Blackline Master 7.12

HOMEWORK
- Core: 8, 9, 10, 13, 14
- Optional: 11, 15
- Extension: 12

VOCABULARY
- confidence interval
- normal distribution, $N(\mu, \sigma)$
- probability distribution

Launch

Begin today's lesson by going over the probability histograms students made in Problems 1, 2, and 4 in the Getting Started lesson. Pictures of the graphs are shown at the beginning of this lesson. Ask students to describe any similarities they see among these graphs if you have not already had this discussion. Then proceed to the first For You to Do problem.

Explore

For You to Do

PROBLEM 1 The probability is the sum of the areas of the last nine bars in the histogram, roughly one-third the total area. Since the total area is 1, then the probability is about $\frac{1}{3}$. If students make a more detailed graph, they might be able to make a more accurate estimate. The probability is $\frac{435}{1296} \approx 0.3356$, though, so $\frac{1}{3}$ is pretty close!

For You to Do

1. Use the first probability histogram on the previous page to estimate the probability of rolling higher than 15 as the sum of four number cubes.

All three histograms show very similar shapes, even though the original experiments are quite different from one another. The same "bell curve" emerges, no matter what you started from. This concept forms the basis of the Central Limit Theorem, which states that the results from repeated trials of an experiment approach a specific distribution: the **normal distribution.**

Minds in Action episode 25

Derman and Tony are comparing the three histograms shown above.

Derman I don't trust this. Sure, the number cubes picture and the coin picture look similar, but I don't feel like the picture for the multiple-choice questions looks anything like that.

Tony Really? It's a little squished to one side, but that's because the questions aren't 50–50.

Derman Maybe with more questions?

Tony Alright, let's do 50 questions instead of 20.

Derman So . . . the probability of getting n questions right on a 50-question test. Each question has a 20% chance of getting it right, 80% chance of getting it wrong.

Tony There was a formula for this in Lesson 7.10. For k successes in 50 questions it's going to be

$$\binom{50}{k} \cdot (0.2)^k \cdot (0.8)^{50-k}$$

Derman Nice, but I have to keep entering different k values.

Tony Then define it as a function on the calculator. For combinations, use "nCr."

See the TI-Nspire Handbook on p. 704 for details on programming this function into your calculator.

Derman Oh, very nice!

Tony Now I take all these answers and plot them as a histogram. This might take a moment . . .

After some calculating . . .

Tony Check it out.

Answers

For You to Do

1. Answers may vary. Sample: $\frac{1}{3}$; the probability is approximately 0.3356.

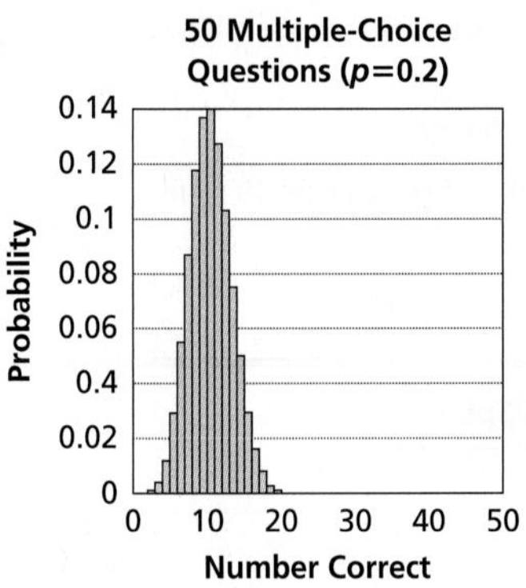

Tony I probably should've stopped at 20. Looks like it's really hard to get 20 out of 50 by guessing.

Derman And the mean is 10. That looks a lot more like the others. What if I start from something else, like The Wheel of Fish? It's got 1, 2, 3, and 10 on it. That's a mess, there's no way it's going to look like this picture.

Tony Use a polynomial. Each number is $\frac{1}{4}$ likely, so the polynomial for one spin is

$$(0.25x + 0.25x^2 + 0.25x^3 + 0.25x^{10})$$

Then raise that to some power. Might need to be a pretty high power to see a curve.

Derman Cool, I can get all the percentages for 10 spins by raising that to the 10th power and reading off the coefficients. I'll tell you tomorrow how I did. I'm still totally unconvinced.

Tony Good luck.

The next day . . .

Derman Look at this histogram for the 10 spins!

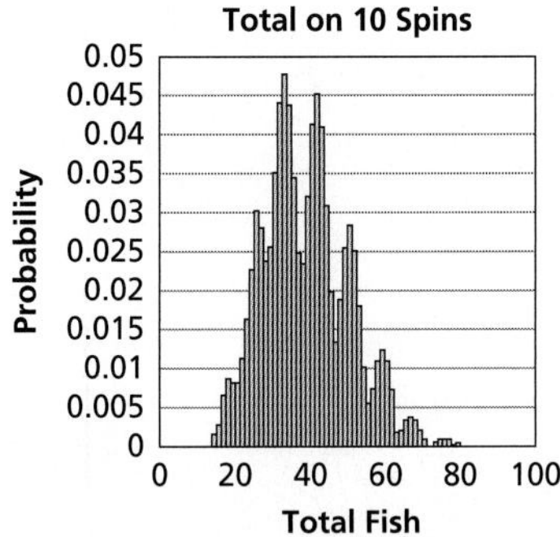

See the TI-Nspire Hand book on p. 704 for details on how Derman might have made this plot.

Derman It's like there's one big bell curve with the peaks. Then each peak has its own baby bell curve inside it.

Tony Wow, you've really given this a lot of thought.

Derman I know! I wasn't convinced about the overall shape for 10 spins, so I did it all again for 25 spins.

Tony And?

Derman Bam!

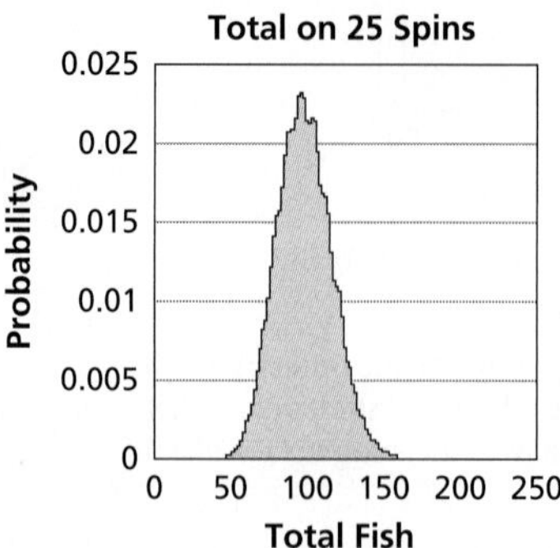

Derman And look where the biggest peak is: right at 100! Which is where it should be. The expected value is 4, times 25 spins.

Tony Hmm. That seems true for all of these. The coin flip peak is at 5 out of 10, the multiple choice peak is at 10 out of 50 . . . neat.

Derman I'm convinced. So when do we learn about this bell curve?

Habits of Mind

Visualize. The "bars" are much harder to see now, but the height at $n = 97$ is the probability that the sum for 25 spins is exactly 97. The total area of the shape is 1, since that is the total area of all the bars.

Developing Habits of Mind

Make a model. The histograms shown seem to be taking the shape of a bell curve like this one:

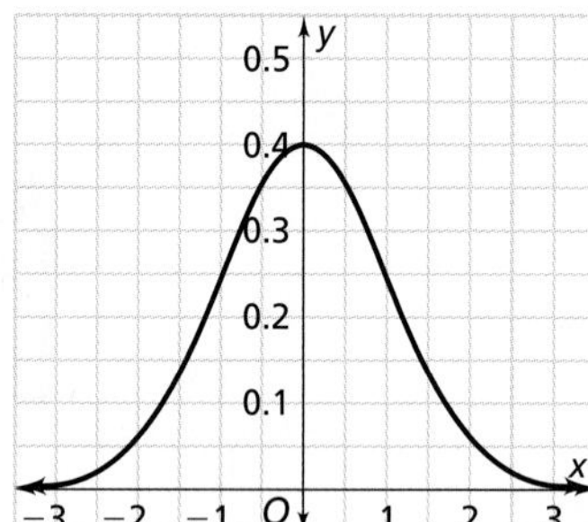

The function that defines this curve is a probability distribution called a *normal distribution.* The graph shows a normal distribution for a random variable with mean 0 and standard deviation 1. By stretching and shifting, you can construct a general normal distribution with any desired mean μ and any standard deviation σ. The notation for such a normal distribution is $N(\mu, \sigma)$.

The normal distribution gives you a close approximation for the behavior of repeated experiments. For example, on 25 spins of the spinner from the dialog, the mean is 100 and the standard deviation is $\sqrt{1250}$, or about 35. The behavior of this experiment can be approximated by $N(100, \sqrt{1250})$.

Similarly, the number of heads on 10 coin flips can be approximated by $N\left(5, \frac{\sqrt{10}}{2}\right)$ since those are the mean and standard deviation for the number of heads on 10 coin flips. Here is the probability histogram for the number of heads on 10 coin flips. It is overlaid with the graph of $N\left(5, \frac{\sqrt{10}}{2}\right)$, the corresponding normal distribution.

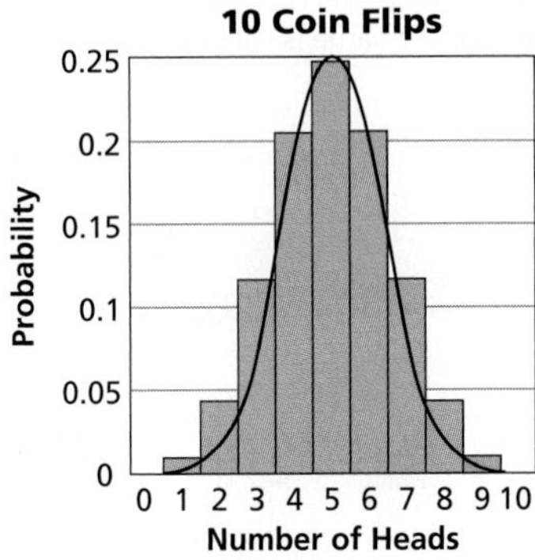

$P(a \le X \le b)$ is the probability that the value of random variable X is between a and b, inclusive. This probability equals the area that is under the curve of the distribution function and is between the two vertical lines $x = a$ and $x = b$.

Most calculators have a function for displaying or defining a normal distribution $N(\mu, \sigma)$.

See the TI-NSpire Handbook on p. 704 for details on defining normal distributions.

Note that the normal distribution is an approximation of the probability histogram. The normal distribution is pretty accurate. It becomes even more accurate as the number of trials increases. In the end, the normal distribution is a single powerful tool that you can use to answer many different types of questions.

For You to Do

2. Find the mean and standard deviation for the sum when rolling four number cubes. Then use a calculator to display the normal distribution that has this mean and standard deviation.

Here is the Central Limit Theorem. A proof of this theorem is beyond the scope of this book. It would be part of an advanced college course in statistics.

For You to Do

PROBLEM 2 When students display a graph of a normal curve, they need to choose an appropriate window so they can see the curve. If you show the graph in a standard window, it appears quite flat, as its height is always less than one. You may want to spend some time making sure that students see how to evaluate and graph this function with their calculators. Use the TI-Nspire Technology Handbook on p. 704 as a resource.

Answers

For You to Do

2. 14; 3.4; Check students' work.

Wrap Up

The end of this lesson contains a great deal of material for discussion. You might choose to work with students so that they really understand the relationship between the two different forms of the Central Limit Theorem. The paragraph following this theorm is also an interesting one, because it gets to the heart of the idea that over a large number of trials of a probability experiment, the mean of the observed results (the experimental probability) approaches the theoretically expected mean. The Historical Perspective on the next page raises another issue. If you *do not* approach the mean you expect to approach over a large number of trials for a coin or a number cube, maybe the coin or number cube is somehow not fair.

In any case, you can follow your students' interests in this discussion. Emphasize the fact that over a large number of trials, the results you observe should conform to a pattern—the normal distribution, the expected theoretical mean, or the properties of the ideal fair coin or number cube.

As time allows, let students work on the core Check Your Understanding exercises. If you compiled class data for Exercise 7 from Lesson 7.11, you might choose to analyze it together now by working on Exercise 1 as a class. Then you can relate your class data to the normal curve approximation in Exercise 2.

Assessment Resources

Lesson Quiz 1.9

1. A spinner has the numbers 1, 2, 2, 4, 5, 5, and 7. Each number is equally likely to be spun.
   a. Build a probability histogram for the outcome of one spin.
   b. Build a probability histogram for the outcome of the sum of two spins.

2. The probability that a hockey goalie makes a save is 0.87. In a game, the opposing team makes 18 attempts to score a goal. Assuming each attempt at a goal is an independent event, find the probability that the goalie makes
   a. exactly 12 saves.
   b. no less than 16 saves.

3. Suppose you flip 500 coins and count the number of heads. According to de Moivre's findings, give the range that should include roughly 68% of the data.

Exercises

HOMEWORK

- Core: 8, 9, 10, 13, 14
- Optional: 11, 15
- Extension: 12

Theorem 7.3 Central Limit Theorem

Let X be a random variable with mean μ and standard deviation σ. The distribution for the sum of the outputs of X over n experiments is more and more closely approximated by $N(\mu n, \sigma\sqrt{n})$ as n grows larger.

Often, people rephrase the Central Limit Theorem in terms of the mean of the results, rather than the sum. The statement is quite similar:

Let X be a random variable with mean μ and standard deviation σ. The distribution for the mean of the outputs of X over n experiments is more and more closely approximated by $N\left(\mu, \frac{\sigma}{\sqrt{n}}\right)$ as n grows larger.

The statement about the mean is interesting, since the standard deviation drops toward zero as n increases. As you perform an experiment many times and look at the average of the results, the observed mean should get closer and closer to the theoretically expected mean. Try rolling 100 number cubes: the average roll should be close to 3.5. Try rolling 1000 number cubes: the average roll should be even closer to 3.5. The same is true for coin flips, for spins, for any repeated experiment.

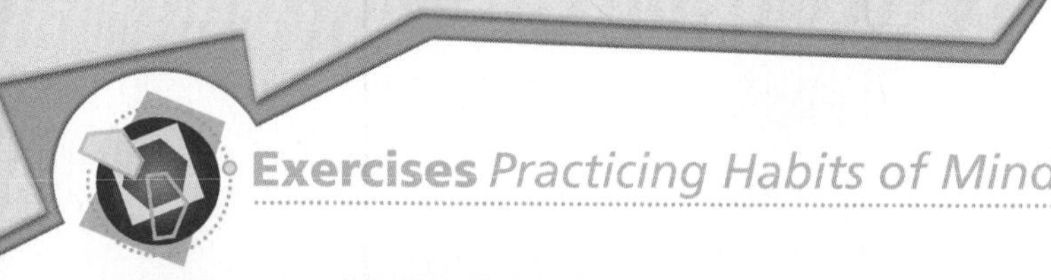

Exercises *Practicing Habits of Mind*

Check Your Understanding

1. **a.** As a class, compile the data generated from Exercise 7 from Lesson 7.11. Build a probability histogram for the class data.
   b. Write About It Compare the probability histogram for the class data to the theoretical distribution given on page 607.
   c. Take It Further Calculate the mean and standard deviation for the class data. Compare it to the theoretical prediction.

Answers

Exercises

1. a–c. Check students' work.

2. In this lesson, you learned that the distribution $N\left(5, \frac{\sqrt{10}}{2}\right)$ closely models the distribution for the number of heads when flipping 10 coins.

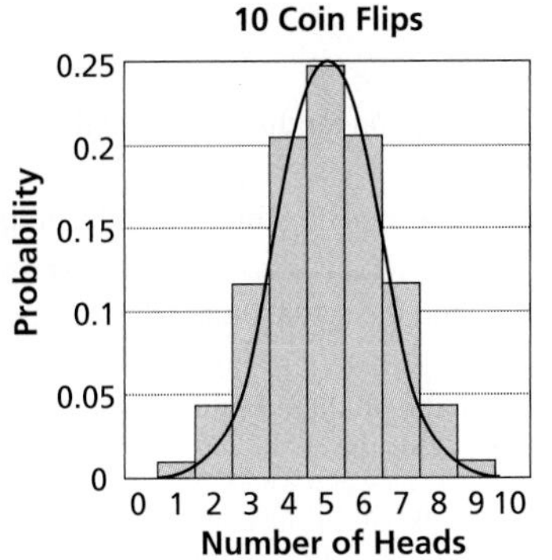

The theoretical distribution has mean 5 and standard deviation $\frac{\sqrt{10}}{2}$.

a. Using a calculator, find the value predicted by the distribution for the probability of flipping exactly 4 heads.

b. Find the actual probability of flipping exactly 4 heads on 10 coin tosses.

c. Find the percent error between the predicted value and the actual probability of flipping 4 heads on 10 coin tosses.

d. Find the percent error between the predicted value and the experimental probability that you found for your class in Exercise 1.

On many calculators, this is normpdf$\left(4, 5, \frac{\sqrt{10}}{2}\right)$ See the TI-Nspire Handbook on p. 704 for more information.

Historical Perspective

The first person to explore the normal distribution was Abraham de Moivre, the same person whose famous theorem appears in Chapter 2 of this book. De Moivre's work is motivated by what he called "Problems of Chance."

> Altho' the Solution of Problems of Chance often require that several Terms of the Binomial $(a + b)^n$ be added together, nevertheless in very high Powers the thing appears so laborious, and of so great a difficulty, that few people have undertaken that Task . . .

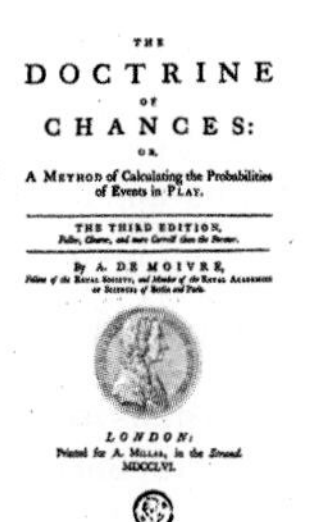

THE
DOCTRINE
OF
CHANCES:
OR,
A Method of Calculating the Probabilities of Events in Play.
THE THIRD EDITION,
By A. DE MOIVRE,
LONDON:

De Moivre went on to determine the equation for the normal distribution, and provided some computations. The most well-known of these computations is that for a normal distribution, about 68.3% of data falls within one standard deviation from the mean. He then gives a specific example: 3600 fair "Experiments" (with 50% likelihood).

> Hence $\frac{1}{2}n$ will be 1800, and $\frac{1}{2}\sqrt{n} = 30$, then the Probability of the Event's neither appearing oftner than 1830 times, nor more rarely than 1770, will be 0.682688.

De Moivre goes on to say how his concepts could be used to decide whether a coin was fair: continue flipping it long enough, and the observed probability from its results should come closer and closer to 50–50. If not, the coin must be unfair in some way.

2. a. 0.2066
b. 0.2051
c. 0.73%
d. Check students' work.

Check Your Understanding

EXERCISE 1 If you would like to bypass the compilation step, use this data that comes from 27 students (810 total trials).

Result	Frequency
0	0
1	9
2	34
3	121
4	167
5	185
6	159
7	109
8	21
9	5
10	0

EXERCISE 3 As the number of samples increases, the normal approximation approaches the actual probability. Another example appears in Lesson 7.13, with the probability of exactly 5000 heads in 10,000 coin tosses. There, the predicted value is accurate to within 0.01%.

EXERCISE 5 If time does not permit students to do the work here, consider showing the results from 2, 3, 4, and 10 spins on Blackline Master 7.12 as an overhead. It is remarkable how few spins are needed to approach a bell curve, even though the initial results from 1 or 2 spins look almost nothing like a bell curve.

EXERCISE 6 After doing this exercise, you might refer students to the histogram Derman builds for 25 spins, and mark the endpoints of the range given in this exercise.

EXERCISE 7 The range from 46 to 54 has probability 0.6318, so the range from 45 to 55 is the narrowest range (centered at the mean) that includes at least 68% of the data.

3. **a.** Find the mean and standard deviation for the number of heads when flipping 100 coins.
   b. Find the value predicted by the normal distribution for the probability of flipping exactly 43 heads.
   c. Use the Binomial Theorem to find the actual probability of flipping exactly 43 heads.
   d. Find the percent error between the predicted value and the actual probability of flipping exactly 43 heads.
4. De Moivre described the experiment of flipping 3600 coins and counting the number of heads. He said that roughly 68% of the time, the actual number of heads will be within one standard deviation of the mean.
   a. Find the mean and standard deviation for the number of heads when flipping 3600 coins.
   b. If the number of coins was doubled to 7200, what would happen to the mean? the standard deviation?
   c. For 7200 coin flips, find an interval that includes roughly 68% of the data.
5. A spinner has the numbers 1, 1, 2, and 4 on its four wedges.

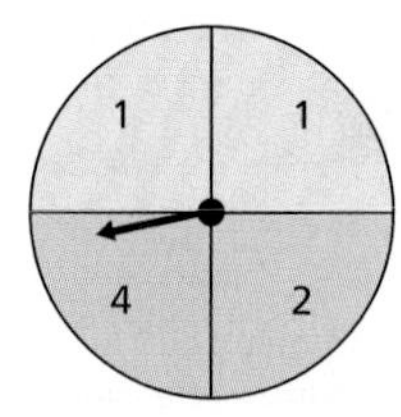

Build a probability histogram for each experiment.
   a. one spin of the spinner
   b. sum of two spins
   c. the sum of three spins
   d. the sum of four spins
   e. Take It Further the sum of ten spins

Habits of Mind

Represent the situation. The polynomial $0.25s^4 + 0.25s^2 + 0.5s$ might be helpful in this exercise.

6. The Minds in Action dialog in this lesson refers to 25 spins of the Wheel of Fish with the numbers 1, 2, 3, and 10 on it.
   a. Find the mean and standard deviation for the sum of all 25 spins.
   b. Find a range that includes roughly 68% of the data.

One spin of the Wheel of Fish has mean 4, variance 12.5, and standard deviation $\sqrt{12.5}$.

7. Suppose you flip 100 coins and count the number of heads.
   a. Using de Moivre's findings, give a range that should include roughly 68% of the data.
   b. Using the Binomial Theorem, find the actual probability that the total number of heads will be in this range.

Answers

3. a. 50; 5 **b.** 0.2995
c. 0.0301 **d.** 0.41%

4. a. 1800; 900
b. mean doubles to 3600; standard deviation is multiplied by $\sqrt{2}$ to 42.43
c. 3558 to 3642

5. a.

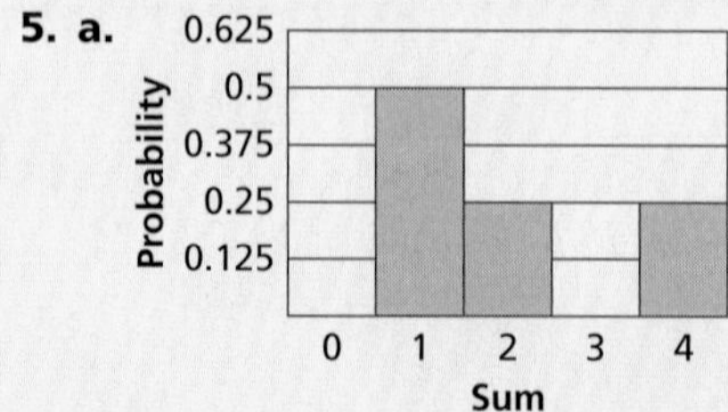

b.

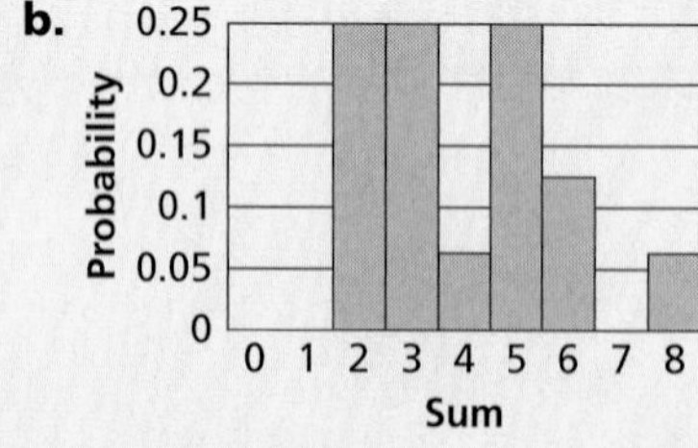

c. See back of book.

d.

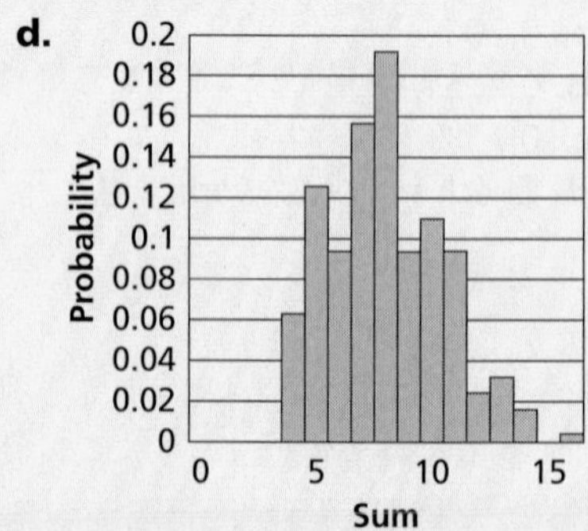

On Your Own

8. One of de Moivre's other findings is that for experiments that are approximated by a bell curve, roughly 95% of the data falls within two standard deviations of the mean. The range of values within two standard deviations of the mean is the 95% **confidence interval.**

   a. Find a 95% confidence interval for the number of heads when flipping 3600 coins.

   b. Find a 95% confidence interval for the number of heads when flipping 100 coins.

   c. Find a 95% confidence interval for the total in 25 spins of the Wheel of Fish from Exercise 6.

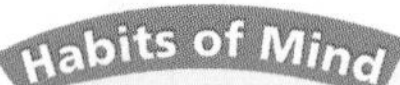

If the mean is 100 and the standard deviation is 20, a 95% confidence interval is from 60 to 140. This assumes and requires that the distribution is close to a bell curve.

9. Hannah is a "300 hitter" in softball. She gets a hit on each at-bat with probability $p = 0.3$. Assume each at-bat is an independent Bernoulli trial.

   a. Find the mean and standard deviation for the numbers of hits Hannah gets in 60 at-bats.

   b. For 60 at-bats, find a 95% confidence interval for Hannah's batting average, found by dividing the number of hits by the number of at-bats.

   c. For a full season of 600 at-bats, find a 95% confidence interval for Hannah's batting average.

Habits of Mind

Use a different process. You could find a confidence interval for the number of hits, then divide by 60.

10. a. Repeat Exercise 9 for Sally, a "250 hitter" who gets a hit with probability $p = 0.25$.

    b. **Write About It** Describe how your results show that Sally could outhit Hannah over a short time period, but is much less likely to do so for an entire season.

11. Todd makes free throws with probability of success $p = 0.642$.

    a. Find the mean and standard deviation for the number of successes in 100 free throws.

    b. Find a 95% confidence interval for the number of free throws Todd will make in 100 tries.

    c. Use a normal approximation to estimate, to six decimal places, the probability that Todd makes exactly 70 out of 100 free throws.

    d. Use the Binomial Theorem to find, accurate to six decimal places, the probability that Todd makes exactly 70 out of 100 free throws.

Go Online PHSchool.com

For additional practice, go to Web Code: bga-0712

On a calculator, you might do this using normpdf (70, μ, σ) where μ and σ are the mean and standard deviation you found in part (a).

On Your Own

EXERCISE 8 The next lesson explores confidence intervals again. This topic is central in a full statistics course.

EXERCISE 9 If students do not round off they get slightly different answers, which is fine. The next exercise shows the effect of a full season for players of different abilities; in the short run, a "250 hitter" might play better than a "300 hitter," but it is much less likely for a full year.

EXERCISE 10 In a softball season, the league leaders in batting average at the start of the season often have outlandish averages like 0.420 or 0.450; this never lasts. This is a consequence of this short-term versus long-term concept; only a truly great hitter could maintain 0.420 for an entire season, while a lesser hitter could just be lucky for a little while. And with hundreds of softball players, *someone* is almost sure to be lucky for a little while.

e.

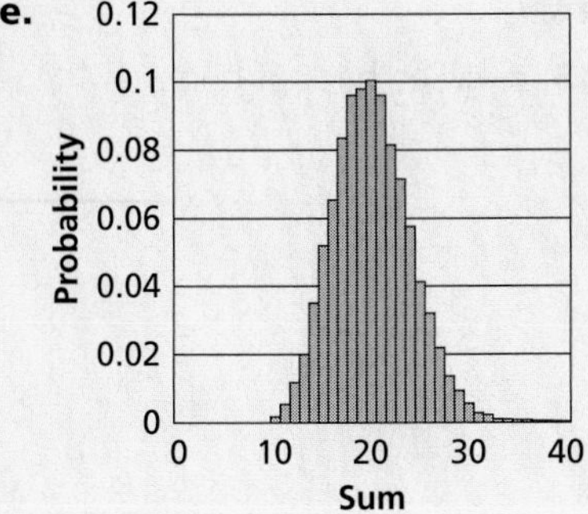

6. a. 100; 17.68
b. 82 to 118

7. a. 45 to 55 heads
b. $\sum_{k=45}^{55} \binom{100}{k} \cdot 0.5^k \cdot 0.5^{100-k} \approx 0.7287$

8. a. 1740 to 1860 heads
b. 40 to 60 heads
c. 65 to 135

9. a. 18; 3.55
b. 0.183 to 0.417
c. 0.263 to 0.337

10. a. 15; 3.35; 0.133 to 0.367; 0.215 to 0.285
b. Answers may vary. Sample: For 60 at-bats, Hannah's and Sally's confidence intervals overlap a lot. The area of overlap is from 0.183 to 0.367. The overlap is much smaller for 600 at-bats, from 0.263 to 0.285. While it is still possible for Sally to outhit Hannah, it is less likely over the course of a full season.

11. a. 64.2; 4.79
b. 55 to 74 free throws
c. 0.040029
d. 0.040915

EXERCISE 12 Some students may complain here that it is not exactly 95%, and that is fine—the actual confidence interval for 2 standard deviations is 95.4% anyway. The rest of the error here is due to the rounding that occurs when applying the continuous normal distribution to a discrete situation; it is impossible for Todd to make 73.7 free throws, so you round the endpoint up to 74.

EXERCISE 13 For Bernoulli experiments, the convention is to use the normal approximation only when $np > 5$ *and* $n(1 - p) > 5$. So if $p = 0.1$ is the probability of success, the normal approximation is accurate only when $n > 50$.

Maintain Your Skills

EXERCISE 15 This exercise shows another nice example of a probability distribution that starts out looking quite different from the normal distribution, but after only a few repeats of the experiment, smoothes out to a bell-shaped graph.

Additional Resources

PRINT RESOURCES
- Solution Manual
- Practice Workbook
- Assessment Resources
- Teaching Resources

TECHNOLOGY
- Interactive Textbook
- TeacherExpress CD-ROM
- ExamView CD-ROM
- PHSchool.com

Additional Practice

1. a. Find the mean and standard deviation for the numbers of heads when flipping 150 coins.
   b. Find the value predicted by the normal distribution for the probability of flipping exactly 72 heads.
   c. Use the Binomial Theorem to find the actual probability of flipping exactly 72 heads.
   d. Find the percent error between the predicted value and the actual probability of flipping exactly 72 heads.

2. A spinner has the numbers 1, 2, 3, and 6 on its four wedges. Build a probability histogram for each experiment.
   a. one spin of the spinner
   b. the sum of two spins
   c. the sum of three spins

3. Suppose you flip a coin 300 times and count the number of heads.
   a. Using de Moivre's findings, give a range that should include roughly 68% of the data.
   b. Using the Binomial Theorem, find the actual probability that the total number of heads will be in this range.

4. a. Find a 95% confidence interval for the number of heads when flipping 4000 coins.
   b. Find a 95% confidence interval for the number of heads when flipping 120 coins.
   c. Find a 95% confidence interval for the total in 20 spins of a spinner with numbers 1, 3, 5, 6 and 7 on it.

5. Nicholas is a "350 hitter" in baseball. He gets a hit on each at-bat with probability $p = 0.35$. Assume each at-bat is an independent Bernoulli trial.
   a. Find the mean and standard deviation for the numbers of hits Nicholas gets in 40 at-bats.
   b. Find the probability that in 20 at-bats Nicholas will get exactly 8 hits.
   c. For 80 at-bats, find a 95% confidence interval for Nicholas's batting average, found by dividing the number of hits by the number of at-bats.
   d. For a full season of 550 at-bats, find a 95% confidence interval for Nicholas's batting average.

Practice: For Lesson 7.12, assign Exercises 1–5.

12. **Take It Further** Use the Binomial Theorem to find the probability that Todd makes between x and y free throws in 100 tries, where x and y are the ends of the confidence interval you found in Exercise 11.

13. **What's Wrong Here?** Andrea said she got an unexpected result when thinking about the Central Limit Theorem.

Andrea: It says it should work for just about anything, so I picked a spinner that has 1 through 10 on it. I made a table for two spins and built the probability histogram.

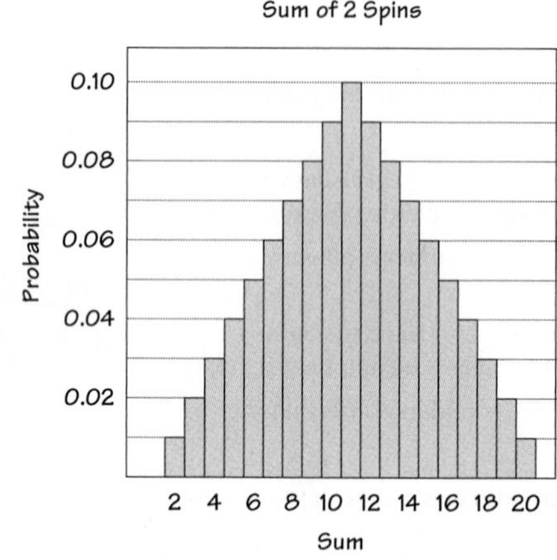

But it's a triangle shape. The lesson says this is supposed to look like a bell curve, but to me it doesn't look anything like that.

What would you say to Andrea in this situation to help?

14. **Standardized Test Prep** A spinner with 12 has the numbers 1–12 in equal wedges. What is the probability that the sum of two spins is 13?

A. $\frac{1}{18}$ **B.** $\frac{1}{13}$ **C.** $\frac{1}{12}$ **D.** $\frac{1}{8}$

Maintain Your Skills

15. A number cube has 1, 2, 3, 4, 5, and 5 on its faces. Build a probability histogram for the sum of the number for each of the following experiments.

a. two rolls

b. three rolls

c. four rolls

Remember...
You can use a polynomial power to help calculate the results.

Answers

12. Answers may vary. Sample: 0.963090, about 96% of the time Todd will make between 55 and 74 free throws.

13. Answers may vary. Sample: Andrea is not including enough spins for a bell curve to emerge. The Central Limit Theorem states that this occurs as n grows larger, but $n = 2$ is not large enough to see the behavior emerging. The "bell curve" behavior emerges when you use more spins.

14. C

15. a–c. See back of book.

7.13 The Normal Distribution

In Lesson 7.12, you saw the importance of the normal distribution. The heights, weights, and life expectancies of people are (typically) normally distributed. This lesson explores the graphs and properties of the normal distribution.

Each normal distribution is characterized by its mean μ and standard deviation σ. The notation for the distribution is $N(\mu, \sigma)$. The **unit normal distribution** has mean 0 and standard deviation 1.

$$N(0, 1) = \frac{1}{\sqrt{2\pi}} e^{\frac{-x^2}{2}}$$

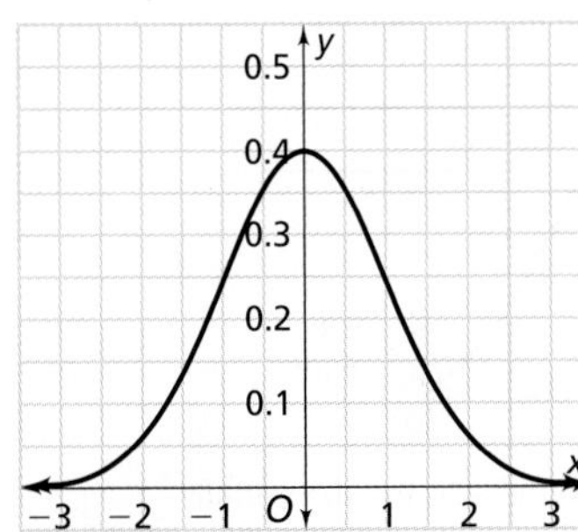

The equation for the normal distribution has the property that the total area between the curve and the x-axis is 1. This is very similar to the probability histograms in the Getting Started lesson where the total area of all the bars is exactly 1. It may help to picture many small-width bars on the above graph, between the curve and the x-axis.

In Chapter 8, you will learn some techniques for estimating an area like this.

Since the total area under the curve is 1, the unit normal distribution measures probability. Other normal distributions are shifted in ways that preserve this total area, so that they too are useful in answering questions about probability.

Consider a normal distribution with mean 0 and standard deviation σ.

$$N(0, \sigma) = \frac{1}{\sigma} \cdot \frac{1}{\sqrt{2\pi}} e^{\frac{-\left(\frac{x}{\sigma}\right)^2}{2}}$$

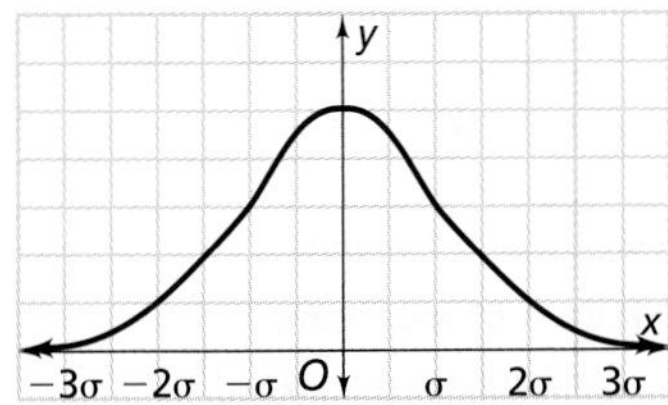

Note that this graph is σ times as wide as the unit normal distribution and x has been replaced by $\frac{x}{\sigma}$. This results in a horizontal stretch (for $\sigma < 1$). But the total area under this curve must still be equal to 1 if it is going to serve

Lesson Overview

GOAL

- Use an appropriate normal distribution to find approximate probabilities.

This lesson refines students' understanding of the Central Limit Theorem by looking closely at how to construct an appropriate normal distribution to approximate the data for a random variable with mean μ and standard deviation σ. Students see how to draw conclusions based on the 68-95-99.7 rule. They also learn how to use their calculators to calculate the height of the normal curve at a specific value and the area under the normal curve for a range of values. They interpret and make sense of these calculator results in the context of the original situations.

CHECK YOUR UNDERSTANDING

- Core: 1, 2, 3, 4, 5
- Optional: none
- Extension: 6

MATERIALS

- graphing calculators
- Blackline Master 7.13

HOMEWORK

- Core: 7, 8, 9, 10, 13
- Optional: 11, 12, 14

VOCABULARY

- cumulative density function
- probability density function
- unit normal distribution, $N(0, 1)$

Launch

Start today's lesson by discussing how to use transformations to construct a normal distribution with a given mean and standard deviation from the unit normal distribution which has a mean of 0 and a standard deviation of 1. If it has been a while since your students performed transformations in the plane, you may want to do a parallel transformation of the graph of $y = x^2$, so students can see how each change to the equation transforms *that* graph.

Then look at the normal distribution graph marked with percentages of the data. Remind students that in a probability distribution, the area under the curve gives the probability. Together with the 68-95-99.7 rule, this picture helps students visualize probabilities in a normal distribution.

FACTS AND NOTATION Blackline Master 7.13 includes the graph of the normal distribution and the information given in this section. Use it on an overhead whenever necessary in this lesson and in the exercises.

as a measure of probability. That means that a corresponding vertical shrink (also by a factor of σ) is done. The factor of $\frac{1}{\sigma}$ in front has this result. So by stretching the curve in the x direction and shrinking it in the y direction, the graph of $N(0, \sigma)$ still has a total area of 1 between its curve and the x-axis.

A horizontal shift of μ units to the right will center this graph at the mean. You can make an equation that has this kind of graph by replacing x in the previous equation by $x - \mu$. This gives you the equation for $N(\mu, \sigma)$, the normal distribution with mean μ and standard deviation σ:

$$N(\mu, \sigma) = \frac{1}{\sigma} \cdot \frac{1}{\sqrt{2\pi}} e^{\frac{-\left(\frac{x-\mu}{\sigma}\right)^2}{2}}$$

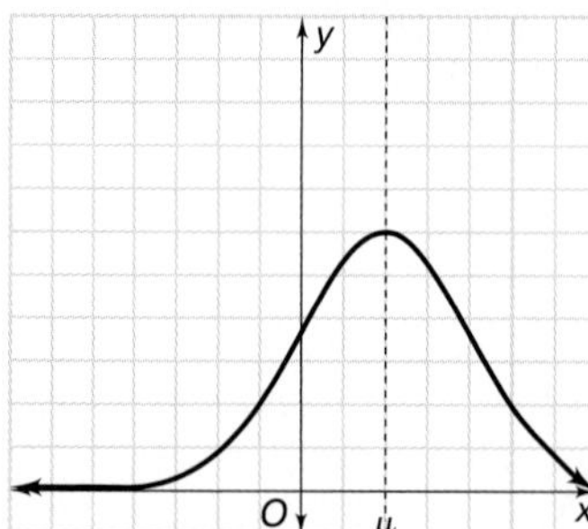

Note that the graph has shifted along the horizontal axis, but the overall shape of the bell curve has not changed.

It is possible to find the area between any two x-values under a normal curve. This graphic shows several important percents:

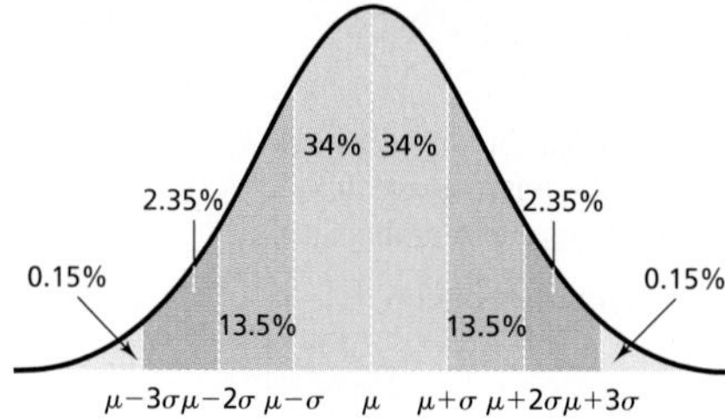

Adding these percents gives the following facts about normal distributions.

Facts and Notation

For a normal distribution, approximately

- **68% of the data lie within one standard deviation of the mean.**
- **95% of the data lie within two standard deviations of the mean.**
- **99.7% of the data lie within three standard deviations of the mean.**

For You to Do

Adult women's heights are normally distributed, with a mean of 63.5 inches and a standard deviation of 2.5 inches.

1. Approximately what percent of women have height between 61 inches and 66 inches?
2. Give a range in which approximately 99.7% of all women's heights should lie.

You can use a calculator to find the area under a normal distribution. On many calculators, the name for the function is normCdf. Its four inputs are the lower and upper boundaries, then the mean and standard deviation of the distribution. The output is a decimal between 0 and 1, giving the area under the curve.

See the TI-Nspire Handbook p. 704 Appendix for more information.

normCdf $(-2, 2, 0, 1) = 0.9545$
(the 95% rule)

normCdf $(60, 72, 63.5, 2.5) = 0.9189$
(the percent of women with height between 5 feet and 6 feet)

Developing Habits of Mind

Explore relationships. There are two functions for working with normal distributions: normPdf and normCdf. Each has a different use.

Use the PDF, short for **probability density function,** when approximating values in a matching histogram. The approximate percentage of women with height 5 feet 5 inches is given by

normPdf $(65, 63.5, 2.5) = 0.13329$

Approximately 13.3% of adult women have a height of 5 feet, 5 inches.

Think of this one as the height of the histogram bar at 65 inches. The normal distribution gives an approximation for what the real bar's height should be.

Use the CDF, short for **cumulative density function** to find the area under the normal curve between two values. It gives the percentage of values that fall within a range.

normCdf $(60, 65, 63.5, 2.5) = 0.64499$

Approximately 64.5% of adult women have heights between 5 feet and 5 feet 5 inches.

Think of this one as the total area of all the bars between 60 and 65 inches The normal distribution's CDF gives the total area under the curve in this range, which should be close to the total area of the bars in that range.

You will see more about finding the area under a curve in Chapter 8. This concept, called the *integral,* is one of the foundations of calculus. The CDF is the integral of the PDF.

Explore

For You to Do

PROBLEMS 1 AND 2 These problems should help students begin to interpret the percentages in the 68-95-99.7 rule.

Answers

For You to Do

1. 68%
2. 56 to 71 inches

Wrap Up

To make sure that students know how to choose between the normCdf and normPdf functions on their calculators to answer probability questions and know how to interpret the results, you might discuss these functions before having students get to work on the exercises. Ask students to give examples of the type of questions they would answer using each of these functions. They should expect to use normCdf when they are trying to find the probability that a random variable is within some particular range, and to use normPdf when they want to know the probability that a random variable is equal to some particular value. You could also mention that the 68-95-99.7 rule is only helpful when the given range is close to one, two, or three standard deviations away from the mean.

As students work on the core Check Your Understanding exercises, questions about these functions may still come up even if you have discussed them as a class. It takes some experience actually using these functions for students to feel comfortable knowing they have chosen the right one and are interpreting the results correctly.

Assessment Resources

Lesson Quiz 7.13

1. The test scores from a class are normally distributed with a mean of 76 and a standard deviation of 4 points.
   a. Approximately what percentage of the test scores are between 72 and 80?
   b. Give a range in which approximately 99.7% of the test scores should lie.
2. Use the normal CDF to find the approximate probability of getting 48% or fewer heads when tossing each of the following.
   a. 400 coins
   b. 5500 coins
3. It is believed that 70% of a town's population is in favor of a new playground being built. A poll is given out to 1200 people in the town asking what they think about a new playground. Find a 95% confidence interval for the percentage of people who will say they are in favor of the playground being built.

Exercises

HOMEWORK

- Core: 7, 8, 9, 10, 13
- Optional: 11, 12, 14

Check Your Understanding

EXERCISE 3 leads into the next exercise; as the number of tosses increases, it becomes more and more likely for the percentage of heads to be within the 49–51% range. This is one of the effects described by DeMoivre, and ties into the exercises from the previous lesson about batting average.

Example

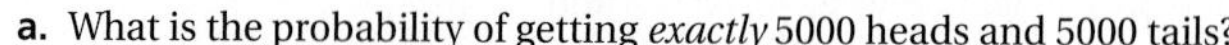

Problem An experiment consists of tossing a coin 10,000 times.

a. What is the probability of getting *exactly* 5000 heads and 5000 tails?

b. What is the probability of getting between 4900 and 5100 heads?

Solution

a. According to the Binomial Theorem, the result should be

$$\binom{10000}{5000}(0.5)^{5000}(0.5)^{5000}$$

Most calculators cannot find the result for the binomial. It is too large a number to hold. So, approximate by using a normal curve. For one coin flip, the mean for the number of heads is $\frac{1}{2}$. The variance is $\frac{1}{4}$. For 10,000 coin flips, the mean is $10{,}000 \cdot \frac{1}{2} = 5000$ and the variance is $10{,}000 \cdot \frac{1}{4} = 2500$. The standard deviation is the square root of the variance, or 50. The 10,000 coin flips are approximated by $N(5000, 50)$.

> You could also use the formulas given in Lesson 7.10.

Use the normPdf function to approximate the probability of getting exactly 5000 heads:

normPdf(5000, 5000, 50) = 0.007979

You have about a 0.8% chance of getting exactly 5000 heads when you flip 10,000 coins.

> The actual value is about 0.00797865, while the normal approximation gives 0.00797885. Extremely close!

b. Using the standard deviation of 50, 4900 and 5100 are exactly two standard deviations away from the mean of 5000. Apply the 68-95-99.7 rule: you have about a 95% chance of getting between 4900 and 5100 heads when you flip 10,000 coins.

Or you could use normCdf.

normCdf(4900, 5100, 5000, 50) = 0.9545

Exercises *Practicing Habits of Mind*

Check Your Understanding

1. The Intelligence Quotient, or IQ, is a score given as the result of an intelligence test. Adult IQ is normally distributed with mean 100 and standard deviation 15.
   a. About what percentage of adults have IQ between 85 and 115?
   b. About what percentage of adults have IQ between 70 and 130?
   c. About what percentage of adults have IQ above 130?

Go Online PHSchool.com

For more information on normal distribution, go to **Web Code:** bge-9031

2. Adult men's heights are normally distributed, with a mean of 69 inches and a standard deviation of 3 inches.
   a. Approximately what percent of men have heights between 66 and 72 inches?
   b. Give a range in which approximately 99.7% of all men's heights should lie.
3. a. Find the mean and standard deviation for the number of heads when tossing 2500 coins.
   b. Find the approximate probability of getting 49% or fewer heads when tossing 2500 coins.
4. Use the normal CDF to find the approximate probability of getting 49% or fewer heads when tossing each of the following.
   a. 100 coins
   b. 400 coins
   c. 900 coins
   d. 2500 coins
   e. 10,000 coins
   f. 40,000 coins
   g. 1,000,000 coins
5. Exercise 3 in Lesson 7.10 asked this question:

   If you rolled 240 number cubes and got only 20 sixes, would that be a surprising result or within reasonable limits?

   Use a normal distribution to approximate the number of sixes when rolling 240 number cubes. Find the approximate probability that the number of sixes recorded is 20 or fewer.
6. **Take It Further** For normally distributed data, the range within two standard deviations of the mean is the 95% confidence interval. However, other confidence intervals can be calculated by changing the number of standard deviations. Determine, to two decimal places, how many standard deviations are needed for each of the following.
   a. 50% confidence interval
   b. 68% confidence interval
   c. 90% confidence interval
   d. 99% confidence interval

Answers

Exercises

1. **a.** 68%
   b. 95%
   c. 2.5%
2. **a.** 68%
   b. 60 to 78 inches
3. **a.** 1250; 25
   b. 16%
4. **a.** 0.42074
   b. 0.344578
   c. 0.274253
   d. 0.158655
   e. 0.022750
   f. 0.000032
   g. 0
5. using the binomial theorem: 0.00013475, using the normal CDF: 0.00026605
6. **a.** 0.675
   b. 1
   c. 1.65
   d. 2.58

EXERCISE 4 The same idea can apply to any percentage approaching 50%. Interested students might try it with 49.9% to see that it still works. The experimental probability approaches the theoretical probability to any desired degree of accuracy—it just takes longer.

EXERCISE 5 You can explain the wide gap in the two answers by the fact that you are looking at the very edge of the distribution, where it may not behave as much like a bell curve. Both the exact and predicted answers show that the situation is very rare, however.

EXERCISE 6 Students may discover a function that calculates these numbers; it is invNorm on the nSpire. The graph of the *pr* function described in the solution is quite nice, and includes (roughly) the points (1, 0.68), (2, 0.95), and (3, 0.997).

On Your Own, p. 622

EXERCISE 8 Show students the estimate that uses the graph of the normal distribution. Students with a good sense of working with area are more prepared for working with integrals in Chapter 8 or a calculus course.

EXERCISE 9 and the next exercise suggest the "plus or minus 3%" reported in polling. In reality, the opposite occurs; the results of the phone poll give the best guess at the mean of the real population statistic. Such a discussion is better suited for a full statistics course, which is why the questions are phrased in this manner. But the same concepts apply; polling 500 people randomly on a topic should give roughly the same margin of error. Most news reports that give such margins are giving a 95% confidence interval based on the size of the polling sample.

EXERCISE 10 Note that quadrupling the sample size cuts the margin of error in half. This is one reason why most polls do not use more than a few thousand. You need a much larger sample to get more accuracy, and an extra-large poll is less likely to be sufficiently random to be believed.

EXERCISE 11 As the number of trials grows, the mean grows as n but the standard deviation is only growing as $\sqrt{n}$. This is what forces the action; the size of the confidence interval grows, but its size as a proportion (or percentage) actually shrinks. There is no limit to how small this can get, and it is another way of showing that experimental probability approaches theoretical probability.

EXERCISE 12 Do not spend much time dealing with the issue of using 114.5 and 125.5 as endpoints here (versus 115 and 125). For discrete data, this can matter significantly (and does here). This topic is typically treated more deeply in a full statistics course and you should explore it only if time permits and students are curious about it. A good leading

continued on p. 622

continued from p. 621

example is to use the normal CDF to estimate the probability of exactly 120 heads on 240 flips; use the endpoints 119.5 and 120.5 and the result is quite accurate.

Maintain Your Skills

EXERCISE 14 As with the previous examples, this is an illustration of the Central Limit Theorem; the higher the number of rolls, the more the histogram looks like a normal distribution. For example, here is the probability histogram for the sum when rolling 10 of these number cubes:

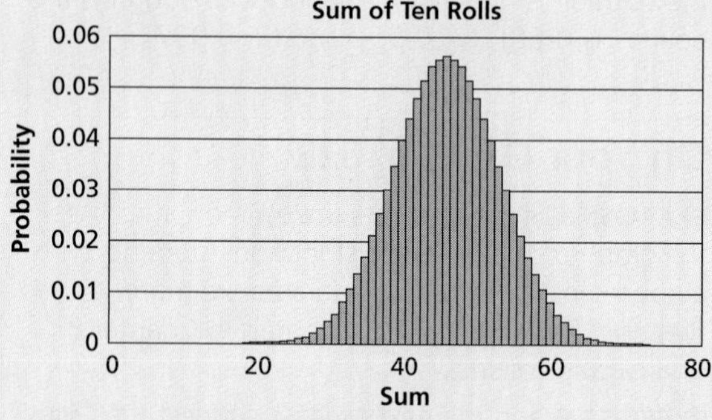

Additional Resources

PRINT RESOURCES
- Solution Manual
- Practice Workbook
- Assessment Resources
- Teaching Resources

TECHNOLOGY
- Interactive Textbook
- TeacherExpress CD-ROM
- ExamView CD-ROM
- PHSchool.com

Additional Practice

1. The weights of adult cats are normally distributed with a mean of 14 pounds and a standard deviation of 3 pounds.
   a. Approximately what percent of cats have a weight between 11 and 17 pounds?
   b. Approximately what percent of cats have a weight between 14 and 20 pounds?
   c. Give a range in which approximately 99.7% of all cat's weights should lie.

2. a. Find the mean and standard deviation for the numbers of heads when tossing 1600 coins.
   b. Find the approximate probability of getting 47.5% or fewer heads when tossing 1600 coins.

3. Use the normal CDF to find the approximate probability of getting 49% or fewer heads when tossing each of the following.
   a. 200 coins b. 1200 coins
   c. 3500 coins d. 12,000 coins
   e. 20,000 coins f. 50,000 coins

4. It is believed that 70% of people own a pet. Suppose that a survey about pet ownership is randomly given to 800 people.
   a. Find the mean and standard deviation for the numbers of people (out of 800) who will say they own a pet.
   b. Find a 95% confidence interval for the percentage of people who will say they own a pet.
   c. A wider survey of pet ownership involves 4000 people. Find a 95% confidence interval for the percentage of people who say they own a pet.

5. Use the normal distribution to approximate the number of sixes when rolling 600 number cubes. Find, approximately, the probability that the number of sixes recorded is 80 or fewer.

Practice: For Lesson 7.13, assign Exercises 1–5.

On Your Own

7. a. Using the values from Exercise 2, find the approximate percent of men with heights between 5 feet and 6 feet.

b. Find the approximate percent of men with height 5 feet 11 inches.

8. Revisit Exercise 13 from Lesson 7.9.

> In a new promotion, 100 people will spin the Wheel of Fish for prizes. The manager of the market is hoping that no more than 500 fish will be given away. Is this a likely outcome?

Use the normal curve's CDF to find the probability that more than 500 fish will be given away by the market.

The Wheel of Fish has the values 1, 2, 3, and 10 on it. One spin has mean 4 and variance 12.5.

9. It is believed that 60% of the population is now in favor of Proposition 1338. Suppose a pollster questions 500 people.

a. Find the mean and standard deviation for the number of people (out of 500) who will say they are in favor of Proposition 1338.

b. Find a 95% confidence interval for the percentage of people who will say they are in favor of Proposition 1338.

10. A wider poll of Proposition 1338 involves 2000 people. Find a 95% confidence interval for the percentage of people who will say they are in favor of Proposition 1338.

11. Show that for Bernoulli trials, when the number of trials is multiplied by 4, the 95% confidence interval is twice as wide, but is half as wide if expressing the proportion of observed successes.

Go Online PHSchool.com

For additional practice, go to **Web Code:** bga-0713

12. When tossing 240 coins, find the probability that the number of heads will be between 115 and 125, inclusive.

13. Standardized Test Prep In an experiment, you are to toss 100 coins and record the proportion that land heads. What is the standard deviation of the experiment?

A. 0.025 **B.** 0.05 **C.** 0.1 **D.** 0.25

Maintain Your Skills

14. A number cube has the faces 1, 3, 4, 5, 6, and 8. Build a probability histogram for the sum of the rolls in each experiment.

a. two rolls **b.** three rolls **c.** four rolls

Remember... You can use a polynomial power to help calculate the results.

Answers

7. a. 84%

b. 0.106483, about 10.6% are 5 feet, 11 inches.

8. 0.21%

9. a. 300; 10.95

b. 55.6% to 64.4%

10. 57.8% to 62.2%

11. See back of book.

12. 52.2%

13. B

14. a.

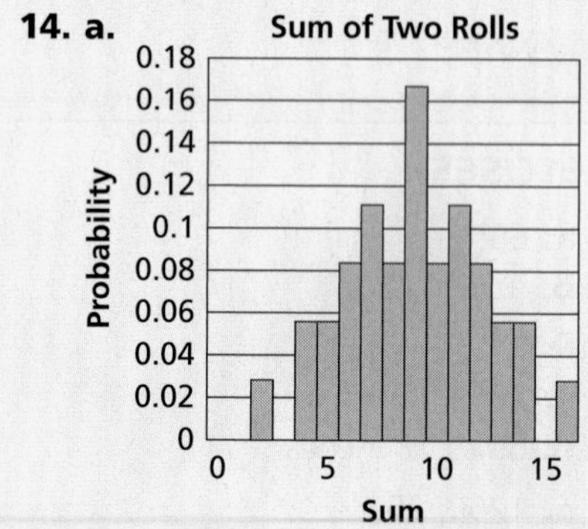

b–c. See back of book.

In this investigation, you learned about the normal distribution, $N(\mu, \sigma)$, a function that approximates the average outcomes of a large number of repeated experiments. People call it a bell curve because of the shape of its graph. The following questions will help you summarize what you have learned.

1. Make a probability histogram for the number of heads when flipping eight coins.
2. A number cube has the numbers 1, 2, 2, 3, 3, and 4 on it. Find a 95% confidence interval for the sum when rolling this number cube 132 times.
3. Give some examples of situations where a normal distribution could apply. Give some examples of where a normal distribution could not apply.
4. Approximate the probability of getting between 190 and 210 heads when flipping 400 coins.
5. Todd shoots free throws with a probability of success $p = 0.642$. In a season, Todd shoots 164 free throws. Use the normal approximation to find the probability that Todd makes at least 110 free throws in a season.
6. Approximately what percentage of women's heights are between 5 feet 3 inches and 5 feet 9 inches? Recall the mean of women's heights is 63.5 inches. The standard deviation is 2.5 inches.
7. What is the Central Limit Theorem?
8. Why is the normal distribution so common?
9. What is the probability of rolling 10% or fewer sixes if you roll 1000 number cubes?

Vocabulary and Notation

In this investigation, you learned these terms and symbols. Make sure you understand what each one means and how to use it.

- **confidence interval**
- **cumulative density function**
- **normal distribution, $N(\mu, \sigma)$**
- **probability density function**
- **probability distribution**
- **probability histogram**
- **unit normal distribution, $N(0, 1)$**

Mathematical Reflections

EXERCISES 7–9 At the start of the investigation, you may have assigned these as Questions 1–3 for students to think and write about.

Mathematical Reflections

1.

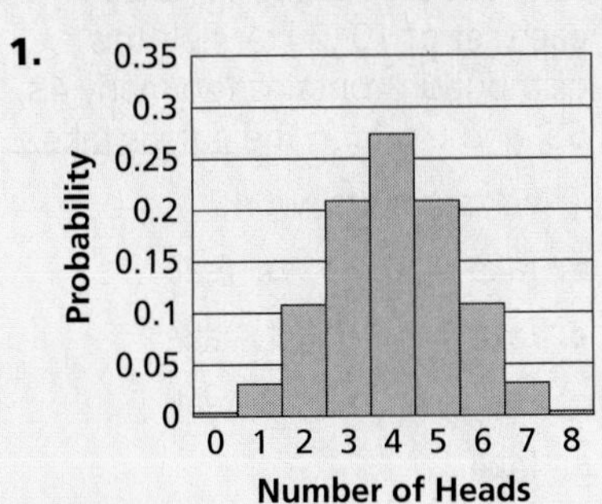

2. 308 to 352

3. Answers may vary. Sample: Situations where the normal distribution applies include: heights, weights, lifespan, and manufacturing (product size or defects). Situations where the normal distribution does not apply include: single-instance events such as rolling one number cube, personal income, or city population, or any situation with a low or limited number of possible outcomes.

4. about 68%

5–9. See back of book.

Project

It is hard to be completely random. This project asks students to make truly random data, but also to try and make a believable fake.

EXERCISE 3 is the meat of the project; press students to come up with a clear test. Also, some tests are comparisons (which of these two is real, and which is fake?), while others are applied to any new list. Encourage students to find more than one test and improve the ones they make.

Project: Using Mathematical Habits

Faking the Flips

It is hard to be completely random. This project will ask you to make truly random data, but also to try to make a believable fake.

1. *Fake* the results of flipping a coin 240 times as a sequence of 1's and 0's. Write heads as 1, tails as 0, and make the order of the fake flips clear. Do not use any computer, calculator, or anything that could be used to make the random numbers.
2. Now, *make* the results of flipping a coin 240 times. Write heads as 1, tails as 0, and make the order of the real flips clear. Seriously, make it: flip a coin 240 times and write down the results as a sequence. Use the same format you used when making the fake results so that only you will know which result is real and which is fake.
3. Make a test you could use to decide whether a list someone gives you is real or fake.
4. Exchange lists with a classmate and run your test on their lists. Did your test correctly decide which was real and which was fake?
5. Use your test on each of these seven data sets to decide whether each is real or fake.

a.

1 0 0 1 0 1 1 1 1 0 0 0 1 1 0 1 0 0 0 1 0
1 0 1 0 0 0 0 1 1 0 1 0 0 1 0 1 0 0 0 1 1
1 0 1 0 1 1 0 1 0 1 1 0 0 0 1 1 0 1 0 0 0
1 0 0 0 1 0 1 0 0 1 0 1 1 0 0 0 0 1 0 1 1
1 0 0 0 1 0 1 1 0 0 0 1 1 1 1 0 1 0 0 1 1
1 1 1 0 0 1 1 0 0 0 0 1 1 1 1 0 0 1 1 0 0
0 0 1 1 0 0 0 1 1 1 1 0 0 0 1 1 0 1 0 1 0
0 0 0 0 1 0 1 1 0 0 0 1 1 1 1 1 1 0 0 1 0
0 1 0 0 1 1 0 0 1 1 1 0 1 0 1 1 0 0 1 0
0 1 1 0 0 1 1 0 1 0 1 1 1 1 0 0 0 1 0 1
1 0 1 0 0 0 1 1 1 1 0 1 0 1 1 0 0 1 1 0
1 0 0 1 1 0 1 0 0 1 1 0 0 1 0 0 1 0 0 1

b.

0	0	1	0	0	1	0	1	1	0	1	0
0	1	1	1	1	1	0	1	0	0	1	0
0	0	1	1	1	0	1	0	1	1	1	1
0	0	1	1	1	1	1	0	0	0	0	0
0	0	0	0	1	1	0	1	0	0	1	0
0	0	0	1	1	1	1	0	1	1	0	0
0	1	0	0	1	0	0	1	0	0	0	0
1	0	1	0	0	1	0	0	0	0	0	1
0	1	1	0	1	1	1	0	0	1	1	1
1	1	0	1	0	0	1	0	0	0	1	1
1	0	0	1	0	0	1	1	1	1	1	0
1	0	0	1	0	1	0	0	1	1	0	0
1	1	1	0	1	1	1	1	1	1	1	0
1	0	0	1	1	1	1	1	0	1	0	1
0	1	0	0	0	1	1	1	1	1	0	0
0	1	1	1	1	1	1	0	0	0	0	1
1	0	1	0	1	0	0	0	1	1	0	1
1	1	0	0	1	1	0	1	1	0	0	0
1	1	1	0	1	1	0	1	0	0	1	0
1	0	1	0	0	0	0	0	0	1	1	1

c.

0 0 1 0 0 1 1 0 0 0 1 1 1 1 1 0 1 0 0 1 0 1 1 0
1 1 1 0 0 1 1 0 0 0 1 1 1 0 1 1 0 1 0 1 1 0 0 1
0 1 0 1 1 1 0 1 0 0 1 1 0 1 0 1 0 1 1 0 1 0 0 0
1 0 1 1 0 1 1 0 0 1 1 1 1 1 1 0 0 1 0 1 1 0 1 0
0 0 0 0 0 0 1 0 0 1 0 1 1 0 1 1 0 1 0 0 1 1 1 1
0 1 1 0 1 0 1 1 1 1 0 1 0 0 0 0 1 0 1 0 1 0 1 0
0 1 0 1 0 1 0 1 0 1 1 1 0 0 0 1 0 0 1 0 1 0 0 0
1 0 0 1 1 1 0 1 1 0 1 0 1 1 0 0 1 0 1 0 0 1 0 1
0 1 0 0 1 0 0 0 1 1 1 0 1 0 0 1 0 1 0 1 0 1 1 1
1 1 0 0 1 0 0 1 1 1 0 0 0 1 0 0 0 0 0 0 1 0 1 1

Answers

Chapter Project

1. Check students' work.
2. Check students' work.
3. Answers may vary. Sample: Count the longest "run" of ones or zeros, and the list with the longer run is probably the real one. Alternatively, count the total number of times that the list switches from 0 to 1 or back, which should be about 120. If it is too far from 120, it is probably the fake. Another possibility is to count the number of ones in each set of 10 (24 sets). If this distribution contains too many 4's, 5's, and 6's, then the data is fake.
4. Check students' work.
5. **a.** fake **b.** real
   c. fake **d.** fake
   e. real **f.** real
   g. fake
6. Check students' work.

d.

```
0 0 1 0 0 1 0 1 1 0 0 0 1 0 1 0 0 1 1 1 0 1 1 0 0 1 1 0 1 1
0 1 1 1 0 0 1 0 0 1 1 1 0 1 1 0 0 0 1 0 0 1 1 0 0 1 0 0 0 0
0 1 1 1 1 1 0 0 0 0 1 0 0 0 1 1 1 0 1 1 0 0 1 0 1 0 0 1 1 0
0 0 0 0 0 1 1 0 1 0 0 0 1 1 0 1 1 0 0 1 0 1 1 1 0 1 0 0 0 1
1 0 0 1 1 0 1 1 0 0 0 1 0 0 1 0 1 1 1 0 1 0 0 1 0 1 0 0 1 1
1 0 0 1 1 0 1 0 1 1 1 0 1 1 0 0 0 1 1 1 0 0 1 0 1 1 0 1 0 1
0 1 1 0 0 1 1 0 0 1 1 1 0 1 0 1 0 0 1 1 1 1 1 1 0 0 1 0 0 1
0 1 1 1 1 1 1 0 0 0 1 0 0 1 1 0 1 0 0 1 0 0 1 0 1 1 1 0 1 0
```

e.

```
0001  0001  0110  1100  1100  1110
0100  0010  1100  0111  0001  1111
1110  0110  0001  1000  1111  0110
0110  1000  0010  1010  0110  1001
0111  0001  0110  0000  0100  1110
0110  0010  1011  1110  0101  0100
0100  0101  0001  0010  0101  0101
0100  1010  0000  0010  0001  1010
1101  0010  0100  1011  1110  1111
1111  0011  0011  1010  1100  1000
```

f.

```
111010110011011111111101
111111101011010010000000
010000100000110011000010
000011010010101010101011
110101011101000010110010
111000000000101110111101
011011001000101010101001
100000100111000011011100
101101011001001100111010
101100101001111001100000
```

g.

→

```
1 1 0 0 0 0 1 0 1 1 0 1
0 0 1 1 1 0 0 1 0 0 0 0
1 1 1 0 0 1 0 0 1 1 1 1
0 0 1 1 0 0 0 1 0 1 1 1
0 1 1 0 0 1 0 0 0 1 1 0
0 1 1 1 1 0 0 1 0 1 1 0
1 0 0 0 0 1 0 1 1 1 1 0
0 1 1 0 0 1 0 0 0 0 1 1
1 0 0 1 0 1 1 1 0 0 0 0
1 1 0 1 0 1 1 1 0 0 1 0
0 0 1 0 0 0 1 1 0 1 0 0
1 1 1 0 1 1 0 0 0 1 1 1
1 1 1 1 0 0 1 0 1 0 0 0
1 1 0 0 1 0 1 1 1 1 0 0
1 0 1 1 0 1 0 0 0 0 1 1
0 1 0 0 0 0 1 1 0 1 0 0
1 0 1 1 1 0 1 0 0 0 0 0
1 0 1 1 1 0 0 1 0 1 1 1
0 0 1 0 0 0 1 1 0 1 1 1
0 0 1 0 0 0 1 1 0 1 0 0
```

6. Using what you have learned from testing real and fake data, construct a more believable fake set of 240 coin flips.

Chapter 7 Review

Go Online PHSchool.com — For vocabulary review go to Web Code: bgj-0751

In **Investigation 7A,** you learned to

- calculate probabilities of simple random events.
- determine a set of equally likely outcomes for a probability experiment.
- find a polynomial to model a probability experiment and interpret expansions of its powers.
- calculate the expected value of a random variable.

The following questions will help you check your understanding.

1. In a game you are to roll a pair of regular octahedrons each with eight faces numbered 1–8.

a. Write out the sample space for this experiment.

b. What is the probability of rolling two 5's?

c. What is the probability of rolling exactly one 5?

d. What is the probability that the sum of the numbers on the faces is 9?

2. A game spinner has three colors, red, green, and blue. Each is equally likely. Expand $(r + b + g)^3$ to find the probability of getting two reds and one green when you spin three times.

3. A local high school is holding a raffle to raise money for extracurricular activities at the school. They plan to sell 1000 tickets. There will be one prize of \$500, 2 prizes of \$200, and 5 prizes of \$100. What is the expected value of one ticket?

In **Investigation 7B,** you learned to

- calculate expected value, mean absolute deviation, variance, and standard deviation.
- calculate statistics for compound events, including repeated experiments.
- identify Bernoulli trials and compute statistics using the specialized formulas for this case.

The following questions will help you check your understanding.

4. At a recent family reunion, Carla recorded the ages of the ten children, aged 1–9, who were attending. She built the following table:

Age x	Frequency
1	2
2	1
4	3
5	1
7	2
9	1

Calculate each statistic.

a. the mean

b. the mean absolute deviation

c. the variance

d. the standard deviation

5. Karen and Joe each have a spinner. The numbers on Karen's spinner are 1, 2, 4, and 6. The numbers on Joe's spinner are 3, 5, 7, and 11. They each are to spin and then add the numbers that result. Find the mean, variance, and standard deviation for the 16 possible outcomes.

Answers

Chapter Review

1. a. See back of book.

b. $\frac{1}{64}$

c. $\frac{14}{64} = \frac{7}{32}$

d. $\frac{8}{64} = \frac{1}{8}$

2. $\frac{3}{27} = \frac{1}{9}$

3. \$1.40

4. a. 4.4

b. 2.08

c. 6.44

d. 2.53772

5. The mean is 9.75. The variance is 12.4375. The standard deviation is approximately 3.52668.

6. Using Karen's spinner from Exercise 5, find the mean, variance, and standard deviation for the sum of each number of spins.

   a. one spin

   b. four spins

   c. ten spins

   d. 100 spins

7. A local bus company advertises that your bus will be on time 85% of the time. If you are to take the bus 40 days, find the mean, variance, and standard deviation for the number of times the bus will be on time.

In **Investigation 7C,** you learned to

- make a probability histogram.
- write an equation for a normal distribution given its mean and standard deviation.
- use an appropriate normal distribution to find approximate probabilities.

The following questions will help you check your understanding.

8. Consider this experiment: Place four balls labeled with the numbers 1, 1, 2, and 3 in a bag. Draw one ball, record its number and replace it. Draw again, record the number of the ball. Add the two numbers. Make a probability histogram for the sum of the two numbers.

9. Use the container and numbered balls from Exercise 8. Make 10 draws from the container, recording the number, and replacing the ball after each draw. Find a 95% confidence interval for the sum of the 10 numbers.

10. In each at-bat, Jon has a 26% chance of getting a hit. This year, he will have approximately 180 at-bats. Use the normal approximation to find the probability that Jon will have 50 or more hits.

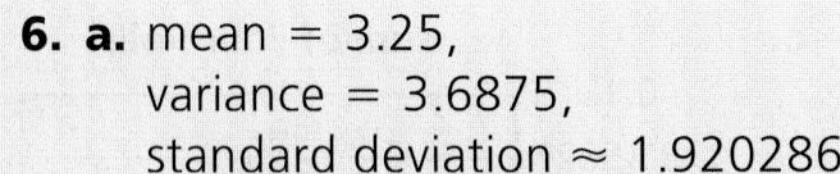

6. a. mean = 3.25, variance = 3.6875, standard deviation ≈ 1.920286

b. mean = 13, variance = 14.75, standard deviation ≈ 3.84057

c. mean = 32.5, variance = 36.875, standard deviation ≈ 6.072479

d. mean = 325, variance = 368.75, standard deviation ≈ 19.20286

7. The mean is 34 days. The variance is 5.1. The standard deviation is approximately 2.25832.

8.

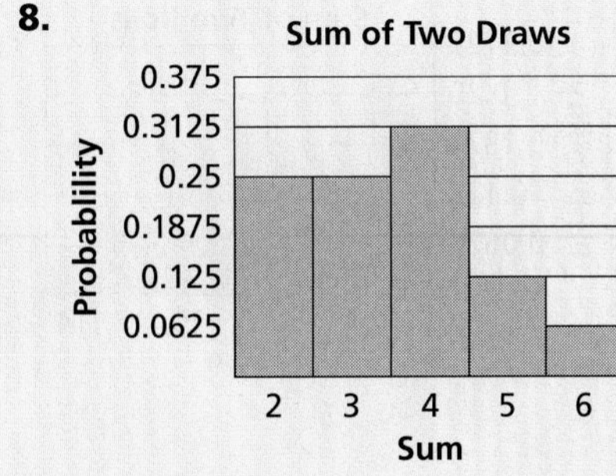

9. 12.256 to 22.744

10. 29%

Test

Assessment Resources

Test Form A page 1 of 4

Multiple Choice

1. If you are to toss a coin seven times, what is the expected value for the number of heads you would get?
   A. 3 B. 3.5
   C. 4 D. 4.5

2. Consider the following two spinners with five equal wedges.
   Spinner A: 2, 3, 4, 5, and 8
   Spinner B: 4, 5, 6, 8, and 9
   What is the expected value for the sum when you spin the two spinners?
   A. 7.8 B. 8.8
   C. 9.8 D. 10.8

3. The probability that a batter gets a hit is $p = 0.4$. What is the probability that in 24 at-bats the batter will get exactly nine hits?
   A. 0.16 B. 0.26
   C. 0.38 D. 0.42

4. A hospital recorded lengths of newborn babies for a 3-month period and found them to be normally distributed. The data indicated that the average length of newborns was 20 inches with a standard deviation of 2.5 inches. What percent of babies born during that three-month period had a length between 15 inches and 25 inches?
   A. 34% B. 68%
   C. 81.5% D. 95%

5. A number cube has the numbers 3, 3, 4, 6, 7, and 10 on its faces. Calculate the mean μ and the standard deviation σ for one roll.
   A. $\mu = 5.5; \sigma = 2.5$ B. $\mu = 5.5; \sigma = 7.5$
   C. $\mu = 5; \sigma = 2.5$ D. $\mu = 5; \sigma = 7$

Also available: Form B

Test

For a chapter test, go to Web Code: bga-0753

Multiple Choice

1. If you are to toss a coin five times, what is the expected value for the number of tails flipped?
   A. 2 B. 2.5
   C. 3 D. 3.5

2. Consider the following two spinners with five equal spaces.
   Spinner A: 1, 3, 5, 6, 7
   Spinner B: 2, 4, 5, 7, 8
   What is the expected value for the sum when you spin the two spinners?
   A. 10.2 B. 8
   C. 5 D. 9.6

3. The probability a batter gets a hit is $p = 0.3$. What is the probability that in eight at-bats the batter will get exactly four hits? Round to two decimal places.
   A. 0.14 B. 0.31
   C. 0.01 D. 0.25

4. At a local dealership, the average selling prices of new cars are normally distributed. On average a new car sells for $23,000 with a standard deviation of $3500. What percent of cars sell between $25,000 and $30,000? Round to four decimal places.
   A. 0.1023 B. 0.2157
   C. 0.4772 D. 0.2615

5. A number cube has the numbers 2, 3, 5, 7, 8, and 11 on its faces. Calculate the mean μ and standard deviation σ for one roll, to three decimal places.
   A. $\mu = 7; \sigma = 4.021$
   B. $\mu = 6; \sigma = 3.055$
   C. $\mu = 7; \sigma = 3.282$
   D. $\mu = 6; \sigma = 3.155$

6. A multiple-choice test has 28 questions each with four choices. If you randomly guess, what is the average number of questions you expect to get correct?
   A. 4 B. 14 C. 7 D. 10

7. Find a 95% confidence interval for the number of tails when you flip a coin 400 times.
   A. (180, 220) B. (190, 210)
   C. (195, 205) D. (200, 220)

8. A spinner contains the numbers 1, 1, 2, 2, 4, and 6 in equal wedges. Which polynomial models the sum of three spins?
   A. $(x^1 + x^2 + x^4 + x^6)^3$
   B. $(2x^1 + 2x^2 + x^4 + x^6)^3$
   C. $(x^1 + x^2 + 2x^4 + 2x^6)^3$
   D. $(3x^1 + 3x^2 + 3x^4 + 3x^6)^3$

Open Response

9. You play a game where you roll a number cube. Each time you roll a six you win. Round off answers to two decimal places.
   a. What is the probability that you never win?
   b. What is the probability that you win exactly twice?
   c. What is the average number of wins in ten rolls?

10. A game involves rolling a standard number cube and spinning a spinner with the numbers 2, 3, and 5 in equal wedges. Then sum the two results.
    a. How many equally-likely outcomes are in this sample space?
    b. What is the probability of getting a sum of 7?
    c. What is the probability of getting a sum of 12?

Answers

Chapter Test

1. B **2.** D **3.** A **4.** D

5. B **6.** C **7.** A **8.** B

9. a. 0.16 **b.** 0.29 **c.** 1.67

10. a. 18 **b.** $\frac{1}{6}$ **c.** 0

11. a. $(x^1 + x^2 + x^3 + x^4 + x^5 + x^6 + x^7 + x^8)^2$
b. $\frac{5}{64}$ **c.** $\frac{15}{64}$ **d.** 9

12. a. 63,562,800
b. 9,900
c. 4,115,100

13. a.

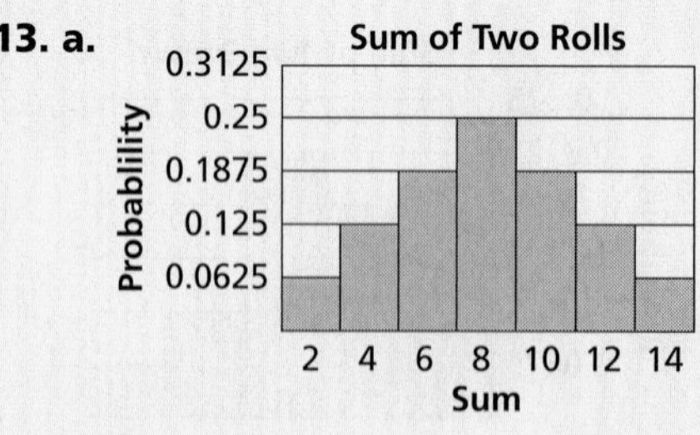

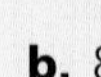

b. 8

c.

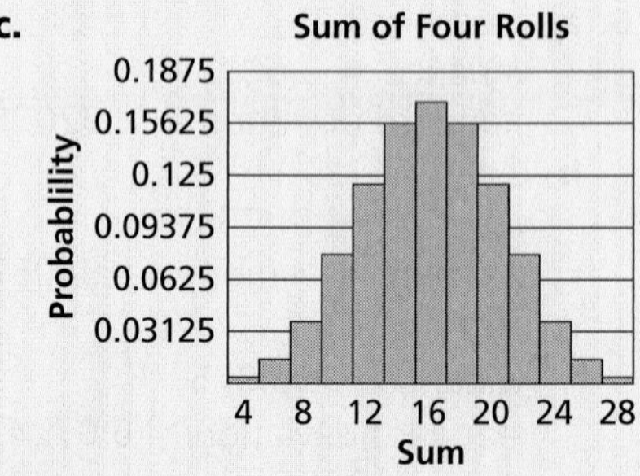

d. 16

14. a. 20
b. 3.87
c. 0.063

11. You have two decks of eight cards. The cards in each deck are labeled one through eight. You pick a card from each deck and find their sum.
   a. Find a polynomial to model the sum.
   b. What is the probability of getting a sum of exactly six?
   c. What is the probability of getting a sum greater than or equal to twelve?
   d. Which sum is most likely to occur?

12. To play a certain lottery, a player chooses five numbers from the numbers 1–50 and then chooses a bonus number from the numbers 1–30.
   a. How many different tickets are possible?
   b. How many ways can a player match three numbers plus the bonus number?
   c. How many ways can a player match two numbers, but not the bonus number?

13. A spinner has the numbers 1, 3, 5, and 7.
   a. Build a probability histogram for the sum of two spins.
   b. In two spins, what sum is most likely?
   c. Build a probability histogram for the sum of four spins.
   d. In four spins, what sum is most likely?

14. In a hockey shootout the probability a player will score a goal is $p = 0.25$. If the player takes 80 shots, find the following.
   a. the mean for the number of goals
   b. the standard deviation for the number of goals scored
   c. the probability that the player will score exactly 16 goals

15. Test scores from an 11th grade class are normally distributed with a mean of 77 and a standard deviation of 3.2.
   a. Approximately what percentage of students received a grade between 80 and 85?
   b. What percent of students received a grade less than 70?
   c. Give a range of scores in which approximately 99.7% of all students' scores should lie.

16. A friend tells you that his password is a five-digit number containing the digits 1, 2, 4, 5, and 8. He then asks you to guess his password.
   a. How many possible passwords are there?
   b. What is the probability that your guess has none of the digits in the correct place?
   c. What is the probability that two of the digits are in the correct place?
   d. What is the probability that you correctly guess his password?

17. A lottery is played by choosing six numbers from the set 1–42, with payouts as shown.

Matches	Frequency	Prize
0 correct	■	\$0
1 correct	■	\$0
2 correct	■	\$2
3 correct	■	\$10
4 correct	■	\$50
5 correct	■	\$20,000
6 correct	■	\$1,000,000

   a. Copy and complete the table.
   b. What is the probability of matching exactly four numbers?
   c. What is the probability of winning the million dollar prize?
   d. Find the expected value of one ticket.

Test Form A page 2 of 4

6. At a high school, it is estimated that 30% of students participate in the marching band. A survey about the marching band is randomly distributed to 650 students. Find a 95% confidence interval for the number of students who will say they are in the marching band.
   A. (170, 210) B. (172, 218)
   C. (200, 220) D. (180, 200)

7. A multiple-choice test has 30 questions, each with five choices. If you randomly guess at each question, what is the expected value for the number of questions you get right?
   A. 5 B. 5.5
   C. 6 D. 7

8. A spinner contains the numbers 1, 3, 3, 4, 4, and 5 in six equal wedges. Which polynomial models the sum of three spins?
   A. $(1 + x^3 + x^4 + x^5)^3$ B. $(x + x^3 + x^4 + x^5)^3$
   C. $(1 + 2x^3 + 2x^4 + x^5)^3$ D. $(x + 2x^3 + 2x^4 + x^5)^3$

Open Response

9. You play a game where you roll a standard number cube 12 times. Each time you roll a one, you win. Round off answers to two decimal places.
   a. What is the probability that you never win?
   b. What is the probability that you win exactly four times?
   c. What is the expected value for the number of wins you will have in 12 rolls?

10. A game involves rolling a standard number cube and spinning a spinner with the numbers 2, 4, 5, and 6 in equal wedges. Then sum the two results.
   a. How many equally likely outcomes are in this sample space?
   b. What is the probability of getting a sum of 7?
   c. What is the probability of getting a sum of 10?

11. You have two decks of seven cards. The cards in each deck are labeled one through seven. You pick a card from each deck and find their sum.
   a. Find a polynomial to model the sum.
   b. What is the probability of getting a sum of exactly eight?
   c. Which sum is most likely to occur?

Also available: Form B

15. a. 0.1674
b. 0.0139
c. (67.4, 86.6)

16. a. 120
b. $\frac{44}{120}$ or $\frac{11}{30}$
c. $\frac{20}{120}$ or $\frac{1}{6}$
d. $\frac{1}{120}$

17. a.

Matches	Frequency	Payout
0 correct	1,947,792	\$0
1 correct	2,261,952	\$0
2 correct	883,575	\$2
3 correct	142,800	\$10
4 correct	9450	\$50
5 correct	216	\$20,000
6 correct	1	\$1,000,000

b. $\frac{9450}{5{,}245{,}786} \approx 0.0018$
c. $\frac{1}{5{,}245{,}786}$
d. \$1.71

Chapter 8
Ideas of Calculus

There are many ways to introduce students to the ideas that underlie calculus, because calculus has so many origins and employs several different ways of thinking. One route into calculus involves the mathematics of motion, looking at ways to make sense of notions like "instantaneous velocity." Another, the one that CME Project *Precalculus* follows, looks at the age-old problem of calculating areas of irregular shapes. There are also more modern stylizations of these approaches (finding the slope of the tangent to a graph at a point, for example). The idea here is to give an experiential introduction to calculus.

The work in this chapter is computationally intense. Students will probably use their calculators to do the arithmetic, but you may want to convince them that understanding here comes from abstracting off patterns from the calculations, making them mechanical, and seeing how they evolve. As the well-known mathematician Glenn Stevens would say, "Don't let the calculator have all the fun."

Chapter Overview

INVESTIGATION 8A, ***Finding Areas of Shapes,*** reviews the area of familiar shapes and has students think about how to find the areas of irregular or "curvy" shapes.

INVESTIGATION 8B, ***Finding Areas Under Curves,*** has students look at Cavalieri's method and Fermat's method for finding the area under the graph of $y = x^m$ between $x = a$ and $x = b$ for any positive integer m.

INVESTIGATION 8C, ***A Function Emerges,*** has students look at the area under the graph of $y = x^m$ between $x = a$ and $x = b$ for any integer m, and in particular, for $m = -1$.

For more information on the Investigations, see

- Chapter Road Map, pp. 630–631
- Investigation Road Maps, pp. 632, 652, 674

PROJECT The Project near the end of the chapter is optional. You can assign the Project at any time during the chapter, depending on how often and how long you feel students should work on it.

DAILY PLANNER DAILY PLANNER DAILY PL

Pacing Suggestions and Materials

Investigation 8A *Finding Areas of Shapes*

DAY	LESSON	HOMEWORK
1	8.1 Getting Started Core: 1, 2, 5, 6, 7 Optional: 3, 4, 8, 9, 10	Core: 11, 14, 15 Optional: 12, 13
2	8.2 Areas of Blobs Core: 1, 3, 4 Optional: 2, 5	Core: 7, 9 Optional: 10; Extension: 6, 8
3	8.3 Finding the Area Under $y = x^2$ Core: 1, 3 Optional: 4, 5; Extension: 2	Core: 6, 9, 10 Optional: 8, 11; Extension: 7

Investigation 8B *Finding Areas Under Curves*

DAY	LESSON	HOMEWORK
1	8.4 Getting Started Core: 1, 2, 3, 4, 5, 6, 7, 8, 9, 10 Optional: none	Core: 11, 13, 14 Optional: 12
2	8.5 Cavalieri's Approach Core: 2, 3, 5, 8 Optional: 1, 4, 6, 9; Extension: 7	Core: 11, 12, 14 Optional: 10, 13, 15
3	8.6 Fermat's Big Idea Core: 1, 2, 3, 4 Optional: 5, 6, 7, 8	Core: 9, 11, 13, 14, 15, 23 Optional: 10, 12, 16, 17, 18, 20, 24, 25 Extension: 19, 21, 22

NOTES	MATERIALS
	• Blackline Master 8.1
This is a short lesson.	• Blackline Masters MC8, MC9, 8.2
You may want to take one and a half or two days for this lesson.	• CAS (recommended) • graphing calculators • Blackline Masters 8.3A–B

NOTES	MATERIALS
	• CAS (recommended) • graphing calculators • Blackline Masters 8.4A–B
You may want to take two days for this lesson.	• CAS (recommended) • graphing calculators • Blackline Master 8.5
	• CAS (recommended) • graphing calculators

Mathematics Background

LIMITS AND CONTINUITY: Suppose you want to find the area of the region bounded by the graph of $y = x^2$ in the first quadrant between the vertical lines with equations $x = a$ and $x = b$.

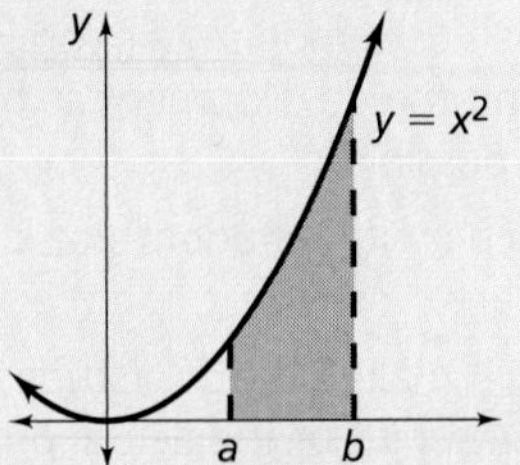

One way to do it is to approximate the area by dividing the *x*-axis between *a* and *b* into *n* pieces (of equal length, say) and erecting a rectangle over each piece whose height is the *y*-coordinate of the point on the curve above the left endpoint of each base. The sum of the areas of the rectangles approximates the area you want. Furthermore, as *n* increases, the sequence of approximations gets better and better, but is always a little less than the area you want. And you can do the same thing with the sequence of rectangles whose heights are the *y*-coordinates of the points on the curve above the right endpoint of each base. This gives a sequence of approximations that also gets better and better, and each approximation is a little bigger than the area you want.

Now, if the two sequences converge to the same limit, your area, always a little bigger than the terms in one sequence and a little less than the terms in the other, is that common limit.

You might wonder about continuity. Well, you already use it implicitly when you imagine a number sandwiched between two sequences that approach each other. But it comes up in other ways, too. For example, it turns out that some of the approximation techniques do not work when *a* is 0; you cannot use them directly to find the area from $x = 0$ to, say, $x = 1$ under $y = x^2$. But you can use them to find the area from $x = a$ to $x = 1$ for any small number *a*, as close to 0 as you want. If you assume that small changes in *a* produce small changes in the area (that is, the area from $x = a$ to $x = 1$ is a continuous function of *a*), then you can use this continuity to get the area from $x = 0$ to $x = 1$.

HISTORY By the way, more rigorous treatments of area have tipped this reasoning upside down, like many historical evolutions of mathematical ideas. More advanced courses define the area of the shape as the common limit, if it exists. Historically, mathematicians viewed area as something to find that is sandwiched between two calculated numbers. Using a modern approach, mathematicians view area as something to discover that is sandwiched between two sequences. CME Project *Precalculus*

continued on p. 630c

continued from p. 630b

takes the historical approach. So that is the program: use sequences of areas of things you can find to approximate and then find areas of more general things.

JUSTIFICATION Why use this approach?

- This approach uses modern algebraic techniques while keeping the development as historically accurate as possible.
- This approach limits a student's task to that of finding the area.
- This approach makes use of a student's intuition to capture the spirit of the actual proof. The arguments are not airtight proofs; instead, they invoke intuition about limits, continuity, and area.
- This approach develops the intuition of students. It gives them the foundation for developing a more formal and precise understanding of limits in a later course.

This approach has two additional benefits. First, it is historically significant. Second, it makes nice use of the results in Chapter 7 of CME Project *Algebra 2*, and Chapter 3 of this book.

Pacing Suggestions and Materials

Investigation 8C *A Function Emerges*

DAY	LESSON	HOMEWORK
1	8.7 Getting Started Core: 1, 2 Optional: none	Core: 3, 4, 5, 6 Optional: 7, 8, 9, 10
2	8.8 The Area Under $y = \frac{1}{x}$ Core: 1, 2, 3, 4 Optional: 5, 6; Extension: 7, 8, 9, 10	Core: 11, 12, 13, 15, 16 Optional: 17; Extension: 14
3	8.9 Properties of the Function $\mathcal{L}$ Core: 2, 3, 4, 5 Optional: 1	Core: 7, 8, 9, 10 Optional: 6, 11
4	8.10 The Area Under $f(x) = e^x$ Core: 1, 4, 6 Optional: 2, 3, 5; Extension: 7	Core: 11 Optional: 8, 9, 10, 12

NOTES	MATERIALS
	• CAS (recommended) • graphing calculators • Blackline Master 8.7
You may want to take two days for this lesson.	• CAS (recommended) • graphing calculators • Blackline Master 8.8
You may want to take two days for this lesson.	• CAS (recommended) • graphing calculators • Blackline Master 8.9
	• CAS (recommended) • graphing calculators

Developing Students' Mathematical Habits

APPROXIMATION One of the most satisfying insights this chapter offers is that approximating can lead to exact answers.

PASSING TO THE LIMIT: This chapter revisits the work on limits from Chapter 7 of CME Project *Algebra 2* and Chapter 3 of this book—using the notion that you can get as "close as you want" to the limit of a sequence.

REASONING BY CONTINUITY If you think of the area under the graph of $y = x^2$ from 1 to some number a as a function of a, it is reasonable to suppose that this function is continuous—that small changes in a produce small changes in the area. This chapter builds and uses this intuition throughout.

Chapter Road Map

INVESTIGATION 8A, *Finding Areas of Shapes,* begins by having students look at the areas of familiar shapes. Students then think about how to find the areas of irregular shapes. For example, students think about how to find the area of their hand and how to find the area under the graph of $y = x^2$ between $x = 0$ and $x = 1$.

INVESTIGATION 8B, *Finding Areas Under Curves,* extends what students have learned by having them look at areas under the graph of $y = x^m$ between $x = a$ and $x = b$ for any positive integer m. In fact, students look at two different ways of finding these areas. First, students study Cavalieri's method of dividing the interval $[a, b]$ into equally sized rectangles, which leads to formulas for the sums of powers. Second, students look at Fermat's method of dividing an interval with a geometric sequence, which bypasses the need for summation formulas.

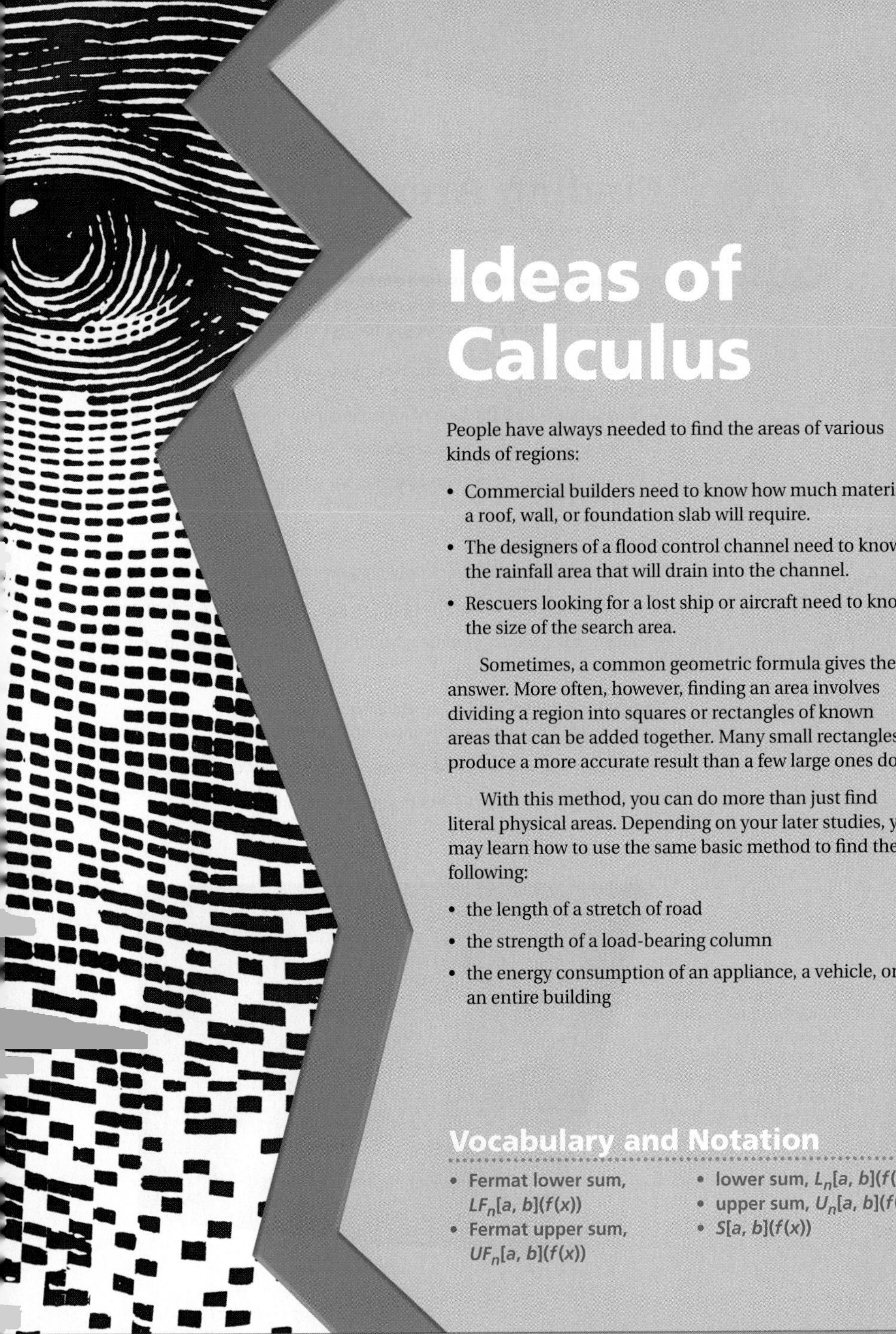

People have always needed to find the areas of various kinds of regions:

- Commercial builders need to know how much material a roof, wall, or foundation slab will require.
- The designers of a flood control channel need to know the rainfall area that will drain into the channel.
- Rescuers looking for a lost ship or aircraft need to know the size of the search area.

Sometimes, a common geometric formula gives the answer. More often, however, finding an area involves dividing a region into squares or rectangles of known areas that can be added together. Many small rectangles produce a more accurate result than a few large ones do.

With this method, you can do more than just find literal physical areas. Depending on your later studies, you may learn how to use the same basic method to find the following:

- the length of a stretch of road
- the strength of a load-bearing column
- the energy consumption of an appliance, a vehicle, or an entire building

Vocabulary and Notation

- Fermat lower sum, $LF_n[a, b](f(x))$
- Fermat upper sum, $UF_n[a, b](f(x))$
- lower sum, $L_n[a, b](f(x))$
- upper sum, $U_n[a, b](f(x))$
- $S[a, b](f(x))$

Chapter Vocabulary and Notation

The following list gives key vocabulary and notation used in the chapter. Selected new vocabulary and notation items are shown in boldface on the student page.

- Fermat lower sum, $LF_n[a, b](f(x))$, p. 663
- Fermat upper sum, $UF_n[a, b](f(x))$, p. 664
- lower sum, $L_n[a, b](f(x))$, p. 647
- upper sum, $U_n[a, b](f(x))$, p. 645
- $S[a, b](f(x))$, p. 647

Chapter Technology

CME Project *Precalculus* assumes that each student has access to a graphing calculator. It also recommends access to a computer algebra system (CAS) and to geometry software.

Support for the use of technology is available in the TI-Nspire™ Technology Handbook. See p. 704.

A list of technology used with important concepts in this chapter appears below. Students will need access to the functionality listed to develop complete understanding of these topics.

Computer Algebra System

LESSON 8.3 Write a program to compute upper and lower area approximations, p. 648.

LESSON 8.5 Find a closed-form expression for an area approximation, p. 661.

Function-Modeling Language

PROJECT Model a recursive function definition, p. 696.

Graphing Calculator

LESSON 8.3 Use Archimedes' method to approximate an area, p. 646.

LESSON 8.8 Use Fermat's method to approximate an area, p. 677.

INVESTIGATION 8C, *A Function Emerges,* extends students' intuition further by looking at areas under the graph of $y = x^m$ between $x = a$ and $x = b$ for any integer m. This gets interesting for $m = -1$, as a new "mystery function" $\mathcal{L}(a)$ is defined to be the area under the graph of $y = \frac{1}{x}$ between $x = 1$ and $x = a$. Students work with this function, and eventually see that $\mathcal{L}(a) = \ln a$.

Investigation Overview

This investigation introduces a rhythm repeated throughout the next two investigations. It asks students to compute lower and upper approximations for areas. In the third lesson, students compute lower and upper sums for the area under $y = x^2$ with a few subdivisions. Then they increase the number of subdivisions, looking at how the calculations of the approximations change. This leads to a general form for the lower and upper sums in terms of n, the number of subdivisions. Finally, students investigate what happens to these general forms as n gets very large. They find that they can make the lower sums and the upper sums as close as they want to the same number. Since the area is sandwiched between these two sums, the area is that number.

This is all standard fare for first courses in calculus. There are several things that are different about the treatment in CME Project *Precalculus*:

- Students move very slowly from explicit numerical calculations to general forms. Calculus courses often do not have time for this, but it is important for students to experience how the numerical approximations change as the number of subdivisions increases. More importantly, students experience how these approximations do not change; while the numerical value of the sums gets closer to a limit, the algebraic form of the sums is always the same (the sum of squares from 1 to n, for example).
- Students build directly on the summation formulas. Sums are just discrete integrals.
- Students learn some of the history of ideas that went into the solution of the problem of finding areas under polynomial functions.

You may wish to assign Questions 1–3 for students to think and write about during the investigation.

Learning Goals

- Estimate the areas of irregularly-shaped objects.
- Estimate the area under the graph of $y = x^2$ between $x = 0$ and $x = 1$.
- Calculate the area under the graph of $y = x^2$ between $x = 0$ and $x = 1$ exactly.

Habits and Skills

- Use rectangles to estimate the areas of irregular shapes.
- Use approximation to find areas to any desired level of accuracy.
- Use the formula for the sum of squares to find areas.

Finding Areas of Shapes

You already know how to find areas of lots of shapes. In *Finding Areas of Shapes*, you will look at the problem of finding areas of irregularly-shaped blobs, and you will begin to find areas under curves.

By the end of this investigation, you will be able to answer questions like these.

1. How can you find the area of an irregularly-shaped figure?
2. How can you estimate the area under a curve?
3. What is the area of the region under the graph of $y = x^2$ from $x = 0$ to $x = 1$?

You will learn how to

- estimate the areas of irregularly-shaped objects
- estimate the area under the graph of $y = x^2$ between $x = 0$ and $x = 1$
- calculate the area under the graph of $y = x^2$ between $x = 0$ and $x = 1$ exactly

You will develop these habits and skills:

- Use rectangles to estimate the areas of irregular shapes.
- Use approximation to find areas to any desired level of accuracy.
- Use the formula for the sum of squares to find areas.

By now you know how to find the areas of simple geometric shapes. But how would you find the area of a more complicated shape? How would you find the area of a piece of land with irregular boundaries? No simple formula, like $A = s^2$ or $A = \pi r^2$, will tell you the area of this island.

Investigation Road Map

LESSON 8.1, *Getting Started,* has students experiment with finding the areas of irregularly shaped objects.

LESSON 8.2, *Areas of Blobs,* teaches students practical techniques for finding areas of "blobs."

LESSON 8.3, *Finding the Area Under $y = x^2$,* shows students a technique for finding the area under the graph of $y = x^2$.

8.1 Getting Started

Activating Prior Knowledge
Exploring New Ideas

You use linear measurements to help you find areas. You can use areas of familiar shapes to help you estimate areas of other shapes.

For You to Explore

1. Copy the two shapes below. Cut them out, and without taking any measurements, decide which has the greater area.

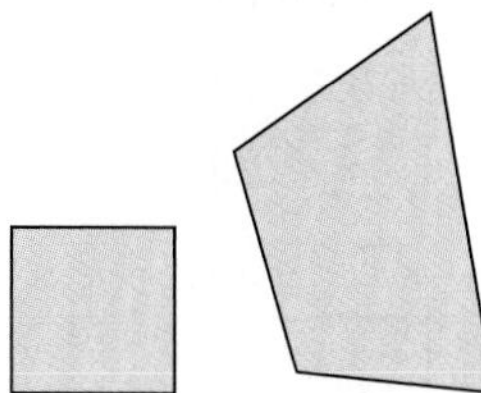

   a. How did you compare the areas?
   b. What properties of area did you use?
   c. How accurate is your method?
   d. Would it work for any two shapes?

2. Now suppose that you are allowed to measure. Then, for instance, you can find the area of a square by just measuring its side length and using the formula for the area of a square $(A = s^2)$.

   Thousands of years ago, mathematicians developed formulas for the areas of simple regions, like squares, rectangles, parallelograms, and triangles.

   Find the areas of the figures below.

   a. 2, 2, 2, 2
   b. 7, 2, 2, 7
   c. 5, 5, 4, 6
   d. 6, 2, 2, 2, 6, 2
   e. 3
   f. 9, 6, 5, 6, 9

Answers

For You to Explore

1. The shape on the left (the square) has a smaller area.
   a. Answers may vary. Sample: It is possible to fit one shape inside the other, so the first shape has less area.
   b. Answers may vary. Sample: If one shape fits inside another it has less area.
   c. Check students' work.
   d. No; there will probably be cases where it is hard to determine which shape has less area.
2. a. 4
   b. 14
   c. 12
   d. 16
   e. 9π
   f. 45

Lesson Overview

GOAL

- Warm up to the ideas of the investigation.

This lesson has several goals. First, students get back into the spirit of finding areas of shapes, which they may not have done since their geometry course. Second, they start to think about how to find areas of irregular or curvy shapes. Third, they start to think about how to find the area of a region bounded by graphs of lines on a Euclidean plane.

FOR YOU TO EXPLORE
- Core: 1, 2, 5, 6, 7
- Optional: 3, 4, 8, 9, 10

MATERIALS
- Blackline Master 8.1

HOMEWORK
- Core: 11, 14, 15
- Optional: 12, 13

Launch

To launch this lesson, assign students to work on the For You to Explore problems.

Explore

For You to Explore

PROBLEM 1 This problem reviews some basic assumptions about area:

- If a figure is cut up and the pieces are rearranged, the area does not change.
- Congruent figures have the same area.
- If one figure fits completely inside another (or you can cut it up to do so), its area is smaller.

You can provide copies of Blackline Master 8.1 for students to cut out the shapes and do the area comparison.

PROBLEM 4 The message of part (i) is that perimeter does not determine area.

3. Suppose you have geometry software that can display the distance between any two selected points.

   a. Could you use this software to find the area of a square? If so, how? If not, why not?

   b. Could you use this software to find the area of a regular hexagon? If so, how? If not, why not?

   c. Could you use this software to find the area of a circle? If so, how? If not, why not?

4. For each shape, develop a formula for its area, if possible, using only the labeled measurements. Explain how you did it, or why it is not possible.

a.
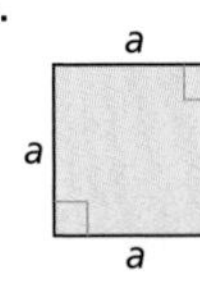

b.
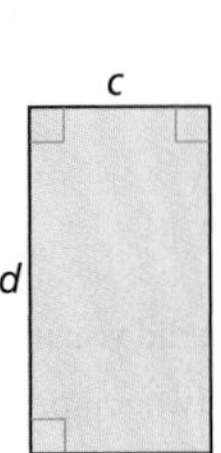

c.
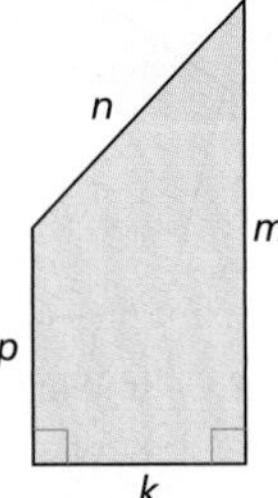

d.
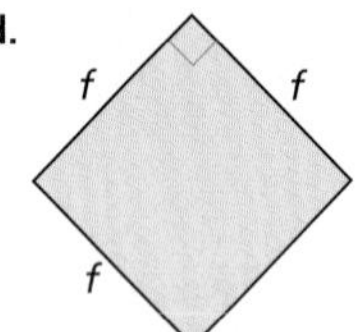

e.
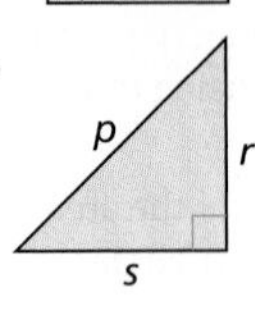

f.
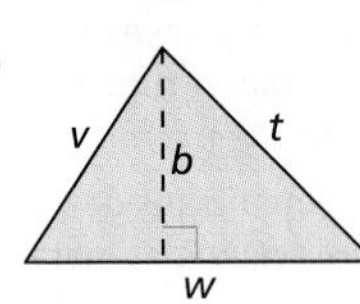

g.
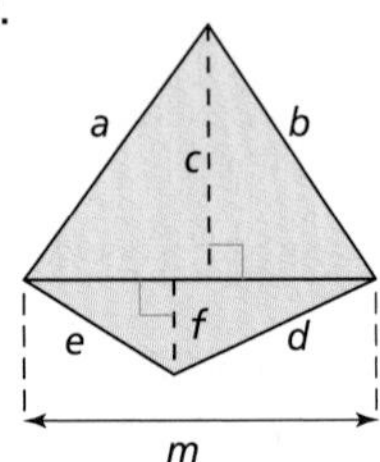

h.
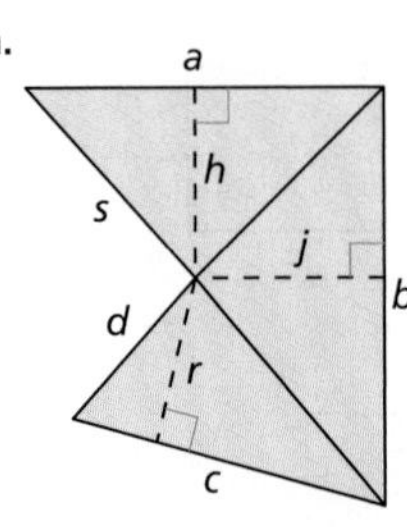

i.
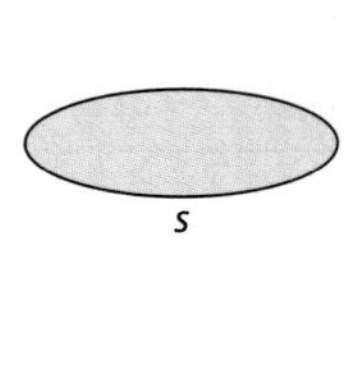

In part (i), s is the perimeter of the shape.

5. **Write About It** The palm of your hand is a nice example of an irregular shape with a curvy boundary.

   a. Think of a way to estimate the area of the palm of your hand.

   b. Explain how you came up with the estimate. How accurate do you think it is?

   c. Do you think your estimate is greater than or less than the actual area of the palm of your hand? Why do you think so?

Answers

3. a. Yes; by clicking on two adjacent vertices and measuring the length of one side then squaring that length

b. Yes; you can use the lengths of sides of any triangles to find its area, then use addition and subtraction of areas of triangles to find the area of a hexagon.

c. Yes; by clicking on the circle's center and any point on the circle, you have the circle's radius. Squaring the radius and then multiplying by π gives you the area.

4. a. a^2 **b.** $c \cdot d$ **c.** $\frac{p+m}{2} \cdot k$

d. There is not enough information provided to determine the area; the unlabeled side does not have a determined length.

e. $\frac{1}{2}r \cdot s$ **f.** $\frac{1}{2}b \cdot w$

g. $\frac{1}{2}m \cdot (c + f)$ **h.** $\frac{1}{2}(ah + bj + cr)$

i. There is not enough information provided to determine the area; if the shape is transformed to become longer and narrower while the length of its edge is not changed, the area will still become smaller.

5. a. Answers may vary, but they should contain something about comparing the palm with a shape whose area can be computed. Tracing the palm on grid paper, then counting unit squares contained within the trace, is a useful technique.

b–c. Answers may vary. Sample: Using the idea of a grid from part (a), count all of the squares that lie inside the outline and multiply by the area of an individual square. The result will be an estimate less than the actual area. If you count all the squares inside and partially inside the outline and multiply by the area of an individual square, the estimate will be greater than the actual area.

In Exercises 6–9,

a. graph the function f.

Then, for each pair of lines with the given equations, find the area of the region enclosed by the lines, the graph of f, and the x-axis.

b. $x = 0$ and $x = 1$ **c.** $x = 0$ and $x = 2$

d. $x = 0$ and $x = 10$ **e.** $x = 0$ and $x = n$

6. $f(x) = x$ **7.** $f(x) = 2x$

8. $f(x) = 10x$ **9.** $f(x) = kx,\ k > 0$

10. How does the area of the region under the graph of $f(x) = kx$ between 0 and n compare to the area under the curve $f(x) = x$ between 0 and n?

For shorthand, you may refer to the area in Problem 6b simply as "the area under the curve $y = x$ between 0 and 1."

PROBLEMS 6–9 Students are just finding areas of right triangles here, but the point is to start thinking about areas of regions defined by graphs of functions.

Wrap Up

Wrap up the lesson by going over Problem 5. This problem is useful for the rest of the chapter.

Exercises

HOMEWORK

- Core: 11, 14, 15
- Optional: 12, 13

Exercises Practicing Habits of Mind

On Your Own

11. Find the areas of these regular polygons in terms of a and b.

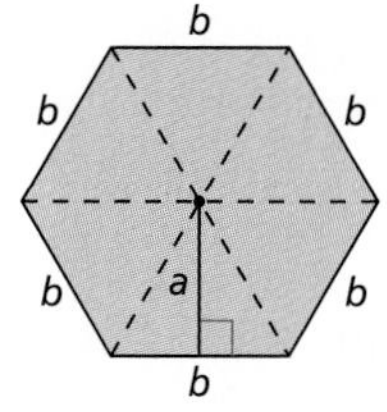

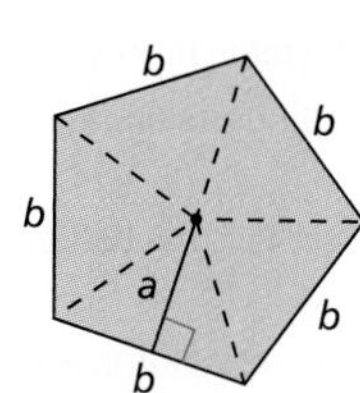

12. Prove that the area of a regular polygon is equal to half the product of its perimeter and the distance from its center to a side: $A = \frac{1}{2}Pa$.

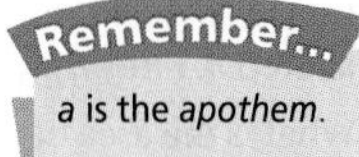

a is the *apothem*.

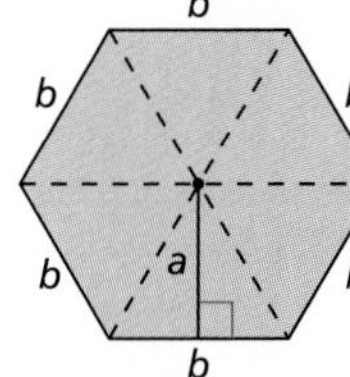

6. a.

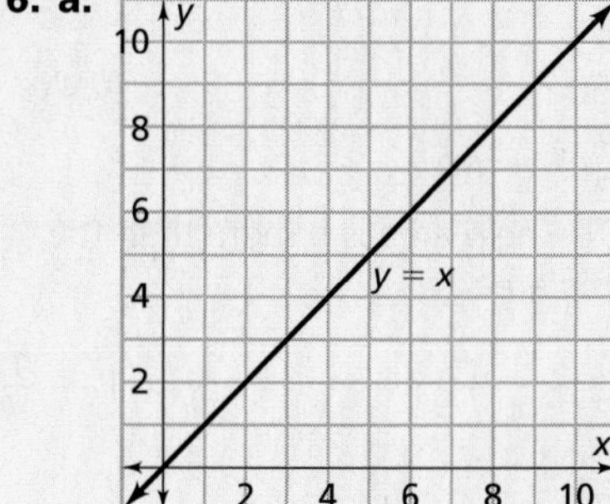

b. $\frac{1}{2}$ **c.** 2 **d.** 50 **e.** $\frac{1}{2}n^2$

7. a.

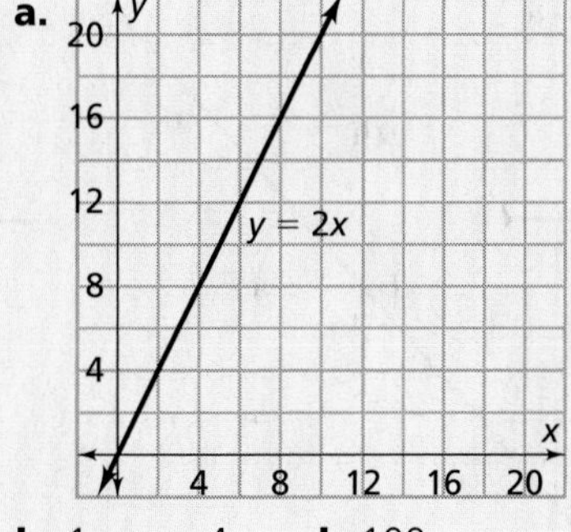

b. 1 **c.** 4 **d.** 100 **e.** n^2

8. a.

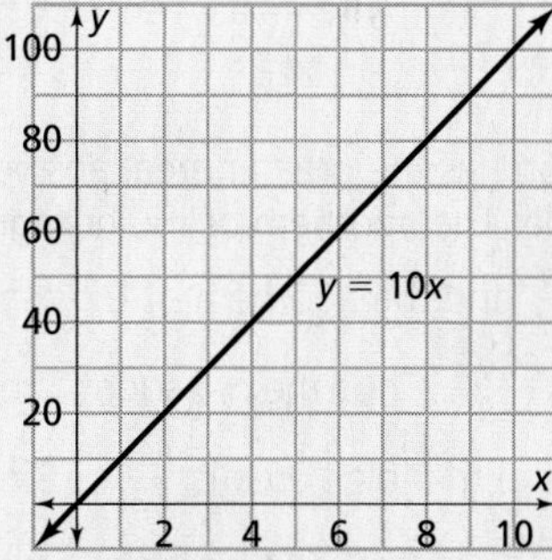

b. 5 **c.** 20 **d.** 500 **e.** $5n^2$

9. a. Answers may vary, but graphs should all be of lines through the origin having positive slope (like the graphs given in Exercises 6–8).

b. $\frac{1}{2}k$ **c.** $2k$ **d.** $50k$ **e.** $\frac{1}{2}kn^2$

10. See back of book.

Exercises

11–12. See back of book.

Maintain Your Skills

EXERCISE 14 Students may remember a similar exercise from CME Project *Geometry* or CME Project *Algebra 2*, but it is a useful exercise to get back into the habit of summing areas.

13. Below are two regular polygons with the same perimeters. Which one has the greater area? Why do you think so?

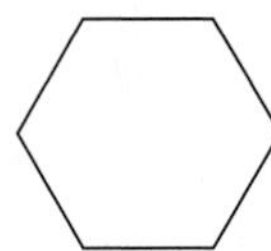

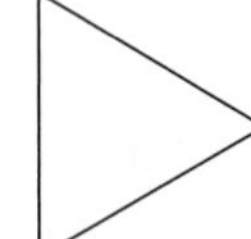

14. Graph the function defined by $f(x) = x + 1$.

a. What is the area of the region under the graph of $y = x + 1$ between 0 and 1?

b. What is the area of the region under the graph of $y = x + 1$ between 0 and 10?

c. What is the area of the region under the graph of $y = x + 1$ between 0 and n $(n \geq 0)$?

d. How does the area of the region under the graph of $y = x + 1$ between 0 and n compare to the area under the graph of $y = x$ between 0 and n $(n \geq 0)$?

Maintain Your Skills

15. Start with a blank sheet of paper.

Step 1 Tear the sheet in half. Put one half on the table in front of you.

Step 2 Tear the piece you are still holding in half on the table. Put one half on top of the piece from Step 1.

Step 3 Tear the piece you are still holding in half. Put one half on top of the piece from Step 1 and Step 2.

Step 4 Continue this process until the piece you are holding is too small to tear.

a. Let the area of the original paper be 1 and A_n the total area in your stack at Step n. Find A_n.

b. What is the area of the piece of paper in your hand at Step n?

Answers

13. The hexagon has the greater area; answers may vary. Sample: The apothem of the hexagon has length $\frac{P\sqrt{3}}{12}$, and the apothem of the triangle has length $\frac{P^2\sqrt{3}}{18}$. Thus the hexagon's area is $\frac{P^2\sqrt{3}}{24}$ and the triangle's area is $\frac{P^2\sqrt{3}}{36}$. Since $\frac{P^2\sqrt{3}}{24} > \frac{P^2\sqrt{3}}{36}$, the hexagon has the greater area.

14.

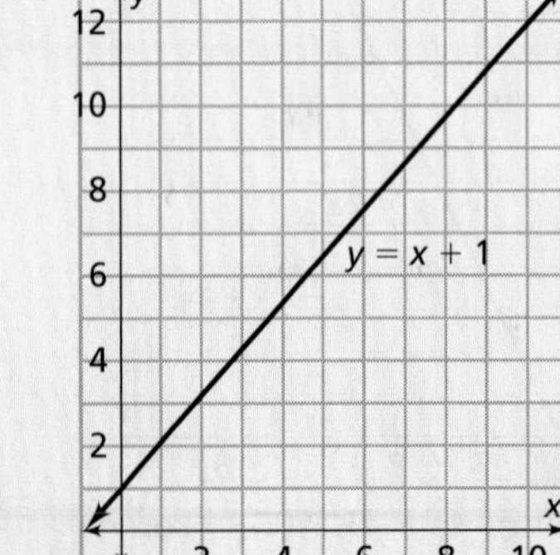

a. $1\frac{1}{2}$

b. 60

c. $\frac{1}{2}n^2 + n$

d. The new area is n more than the old area.

15. a. $\frac{1}{2} + \frac{1}{4} + \frac{1}{8} + \cdots + \frac{1}{2^n} = 1 - \frac{1}{2^n}$

b. $\frac{1}{2^n}$

8.2 Areas of Blobs

To find the area of any figure made only of straight lines, you can divide it into triangles and find the area of each triangle. But what if you are not dealing just with straight lines? What if you are looking for the area of an irregular shape?

In Problem 5 of Lesson 8.1, you thought about how to find the area of your hand. One common way to estimate areas of irregular figures is to "trap" the areas between inner and outer areas using the squares in a grid. The inner area is the lower approximation, A_{lower}. The outer area is the upper approximation, A_{upper}.

Here is an outline of the palm of a child's hand on a 1-inch grid.

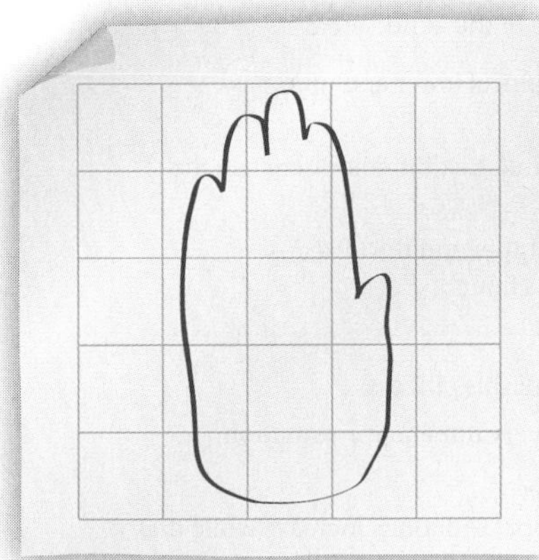

You can count the squares that are completely inside the outline. This gives a lower bound, $A_{lower} = 3$. You can also count the squares that touch the outline anywhere. This gives an upper bound, $A_{upper} = 15$.

Since each of the 1 inch-by-1 inch squares in the grid has an area of 1 square inch, you can also report your result in square inches:

$$A_{lower} = 3 \text{ in.}^2 \text{ and } A_{upper} = 15 \text{ in.}^2$$

So the area of the hand is between 3 in.^{2} and 15 in.^{2}:

$$3 \text{ in.}^2 < \text{area of hand} < 15 \text{ in.}^2$$

An estimate that the area is between 3 in.^{2} and 15 in.^{2} is not very good. How can you get a better estimate?

Lesson Overview

GOAL

- Estimate the areas of irregularly-shaped objects.

This lesson assumes there is an area of an object (a hand, say), and that you are trying to find it. Many analysis textbooks define area as the limit of the lower and upper approximations. The treatment in this lesson is not as rigorous, but it saves a lot of fussiness. (Later lessons in the chapter say more about this.)

CHECK YOUR UNDERSTANDING

- Core: 1, 3, 4
- Optional: 2, 5

MATERIALS

- Blackline Masters MC8, MC9, 8.2

HOMEWORK

- Core: 7, 9
- Optional: 10
- Extension: 6, 8

Launch

Before beginning this lesson with the In-Class Experiment, you might remind students of their own methods of approximating the area of a hand in Problem 5 of the previous lesson.

Explore

You may want to make an overhead from Blackline Master 8.2 and use it to illustrate the process of estimating a hand's area by counting 1-inch squares. You can either copy the outlined hand in the lesson or use your own hand.

In-Class Experiment

This In-Class Experiment gives students an opportunity to work on obtaining better and better approximations for the area of an irregular figure. As the grid becomes finer, the estimate of the area gets better.

You can make handout copies of Blackline Master 8.2 for students to use with the In-Class Experiment. If you prefer not to have students take the time to turn the 1-inch grid into a $\frac{1}{2}$-inch grid and the $\frac{1}{2}$-inch grid into a $\frac{1}{4}$-inch grid, you can instead have them transfer the hand outline onto copies of Blackline Masters MC8 and MC9.

For Discussion

PROBLEM 4 You might ask students to use each of the methods and compare answers.

Wrap Up

Wrap the lesson with a discussion of Exercises 3 and 4 in the Check Your Understanding section.

Assessment Resources

Lesson Quiz 8.2

1. In this lesson, you showed that, for a given grid

$$A_{\text{lower}} < \text{area of hand} < A_{\text{upper}}$$

You also showed that a finer grid improves the approximation. For any natural number n, let LA_n be the lower approximation for a $\frac{1}{n}$-inch grid and UA_n be the upper approximation for a $\frac{1}{n}$-inch grid.

a. How do LA_n and LA_{n+1} compare?
b. How do UA_n and UA_{n+1} compare?
c. Write a single compound inequality showing the relationships among LA_n, LA_{n+1}, UA_n, UA_{n+1}, and "area of hand."

2. In this lesson, you used a grid of squares to approximate the area of a hand. What if, instead of squares, a repeating pattern of equilateral triangles were used, with the length of a triangle's side equal to the length of the side of a square? Would the approximation be as good, or better, or worse? Explain your answer.

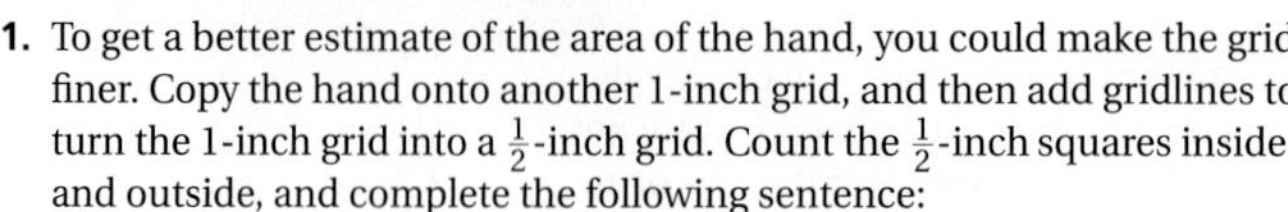

In-Class Experiment

1. To get a better estimate of the area of the hand, you could make the grid finer. Copy the hand onto another 1-inch grid, and then add gridlines to turn the 1-inch grid into a $\frac{1}{2}$-inch grid. Count the $\frac{1}{2}$-inch squares inside and outside, and complete the following sentence:

$$\blacksquare \text{ in.}^2 < \text{area of hand} < \blacksquare \text{ in.}^2$$

Explain why this grid gives you a better estimate for the area of the hand.

> What is the area of a square with $\frac{1}{2}$-inch sides?

2. To get an even better estimate for the area of the hand, you could make the grid finer still. On another sheet with the hand on a 1-inch grid, make the grid into a $\frac{1}{4}$-inch grid, count the squares inside and outside, and complete the following sentence:

$$\blacksquare \text{ in.}^2 < \text{area of hand} < \blacksquare \text{ in.}^2$$

Explain why this grid improves the estimate of the hand's area.

> What is the area of a square with $\frac{1}{4}$-inch sides?

3. In the lesson so far, you have found three pairs of lower and upper approximations of the area of the hand.
   a. Which squares do you need to count to find the difference between the upper and lower approximations, $A_{\text{upper}} - A_{\text{lower}}$?
   b. Explain why the difference between the upper and the lower approximations decreases as the grid gets finer.

Here are some important observations about this process:

- Every lower approximation is less than every upper approximation.

$$A_{\text{lower}} < A_{\text{upper}}$$

- With successive refinement, the lower approximations increase while the upper approximations decrease.
- The difference between the upper approximations and the lower approximations gets smaller as the grid gets finer.

For Discussion

Here are two ways to get a single numerical estimate for the area of the hand, rather than using upper and lower estimates:

- Average the lower and upper estimates.
- For each square that is not completely inside the hand, estimate the fraction of the square that is inside the hand and add the corresponding fractional area (rather than the whole square's worth) to the running total.

4. Using either or both of these methods, estimate the area of the hand at the beginning of this lesson (use the finest of the grids you have already made).

> Using these methods, can you tell whether your estimate of the area is over or under the exact value?

Answers

In Class Experiment

1. Answers may vary due to the impreciseness of making a $\frac{1}{2}$-inch grid, but should be close to $5.75 \text{ in.}^2 < \text{area of hand} < 13 \text{ in.}^2$. This is a better estimate than with a 1″ grid because you eliminated some wasted area from the upper bound and added some missing area to the lower area bound.

2. Answers may vary due to the impreciseness of making a $\frac{1}{4}$-inch grid, but should be close to $7.1875 \text{ in.}^2 < \text{area of hand} < 10.75 \text{ in.}^2$. The reason for the improvement in the estimate is the same as the reason in Problem 1.

3. a. the squares that are only partially covered by the hand
   b. When the grid gets finer, the lower approximation becomes larger while the upper approximation becomes smaller, so the difference between them decreases.

Exercises *Practicing Habits of Mind*

Check Your Understanding

1. Below is the same hand you saw earlier in this lesson, on the same 1-inch grid, with the fingers spread. Does the area change? Does the perimeter change? Explain your answer.

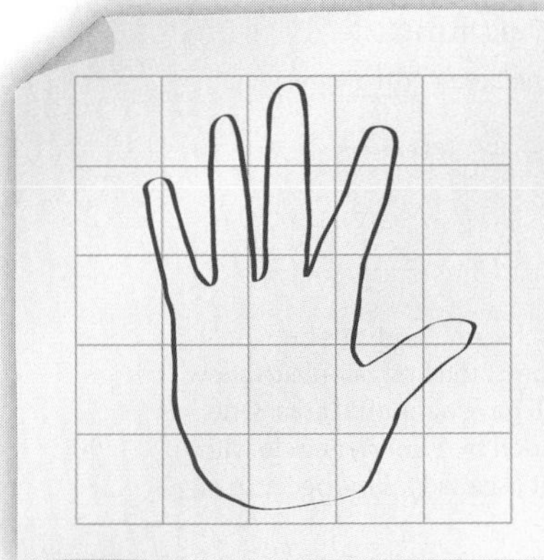

2. How would you estimate the perimeter of the hand in Exercise 1?
3. Trace your own hand on a 1-inch grid like the one you used in class, and answer the following questions. Do not spread your fingers.
   a. How many squares are totally inside your hand?
   b. How many squares touch your hand anywhere?
   c. Complete the mathematical statement.
   $$■ \text{ in.}^2 < \text{area of hand} < ■ \text{ in.}^2$$
   d. Estimate the area of your hand. Explain how you arrived at this estimate.
4. Change the grid used in Exercise 3 from 1-inch to $\frac{1}{2}$-inch.
   a. How many squares are totally inside your hand?
   b. How many squares touch your hand anywhere?
   c. Complete the mathematical statement.
   $$■ \text{ in.}^2 < \text{area of hand} < ■ \text{ in.}^2$$
   d. Estimate the area of your hand. Explain how you arrived at this estimate.
   e. Which grid, 1-inch or $\frac{1}{2}$-inch, is more useful in approximating the area of your hand? Why?

Exercises

HOMEWORK
- Core: 7, 9
- Optional: 10
- Extension: 6, 8

You can give the students copies of Blackline Masters 8.2 and MC9 to use as they work the exercises.

Check Your Understanding

EXERCISE 1 reinforces the independence of perimeter and area

EXERCISE 4 To change the grid, students can just draw "halfway" horizontal and vertical lines on the grid from the previous exercise.

For Discussion

4. Check students' work.

Exercises

1. No; yes; the area of the hand does not change by spreading the fingers, but the perimeter is larger because it now includes both sides of every finger.

2. Answers may vary. Sample: Use string to carefully match the perimeter of the hand, then measure the length of string needed.

3. Check students' work.

4. Check students' work.

Maintain Your Skills

EXERCISE 10 is computationally intense, but it is fun to strategize on how to think about it to minimize computation.

5. Use the upper and lower approximation process to estimate the area of a unit circle.

a. Draw a circle with a 1-inch radius on a 1-inch grid. Write the upper and the lower approximations of the area. Find the average.

b. How close to the actual area of the unit circle is the average found in part (a)?

c. Write the upper and the lower approximations of the area, this time using a $\frac{1}{2}$-inch grid. Find the average.

d. How close to the actual area is the average found in part (c)?

e. What size grid would allow you to estimate the area to the nearest hundredth of a square inch? Explain.

On Your Own

6. Take It Further The area of a circle with radius r is πr^2, and π is an irrational number. Hippocrates of Chios was one of the first people to show that a figure bounded by curved sides could still have a rational area. One of his examples was the shape below. It is bounded by a quarter circle with radius OB and a half circle with diameter AB. It is called a *lune* because of its resemblance to a crescent moon.

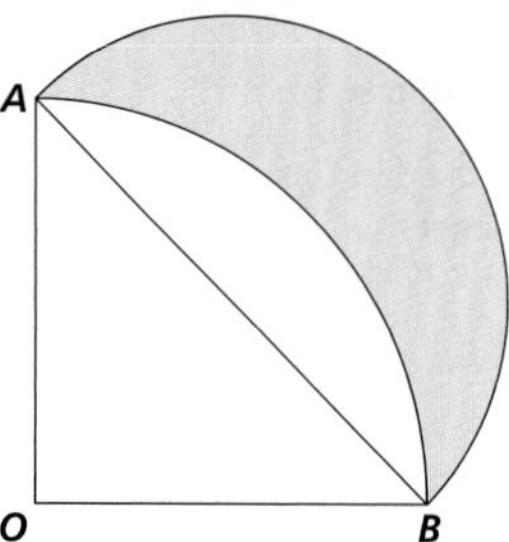

The Lune of Hippocrates

Around 430 B.C. Hippocrates showed that the area of this lune is equal to the area of triangle AOB. To do so, he first showed that the area of the circle with radius OB is twice as big as the area of the circle with diameter AB. (He did not actually find either of these areas.)

Using the area formulas you know, prove that the area of the shaded region is equal to the area of triangle AOB.

Answers

5.

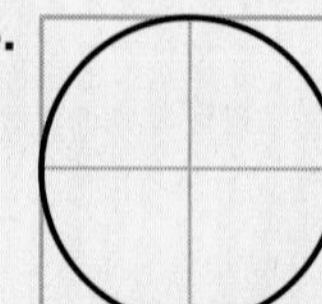

a. For a unit circle, $A_{lower} = 0$, $A_{upper} = 4$, and $A_{average} = 2$.

b. The actual area of a unit circle is π in.^{2}, so the error in part (a) is $(\pi - 2)$ in.^{2}, which is a little more than 36%.

c. Using the $\frac{1}{2}''$ grid, $A_{lower} = 1$, $A_{upper} = 4$, and $A_{average} = \frac{5}{2}$. Therefore, 1 in.^{2} < actual area < 4 in.^{2}, with the average of $\frac{5}{2}$ in.^{2}.

d. The error from part (b) is $\left(\pi - \frac{5}{2}\right)$ in.^{2}, which is slightly more than 20%.

e. A grid with squares of side 0.001 in. would be fine enough.

6. The area of the quarter circle with radius OB is $\frac{1}{4}\pi \cdot |OB|^2$ and the area of the half circle with diameter AB is $\frac{1}{2}\pi \cdot \left(\frac{|AB|}{2}\right)^2 = \frac{1}{2}\pi\frac{|AB|^2}{4}$. These two areas are equal since $|AB|^2 = 2|OB|^2$ by the Pythagorean Theorem. The lune is the half circle with the overlap of the half circle and quarter circle removed. The area of the lune then must be equal to the area of the quarter circle with the overlap removed, which is just the area of triangle AOB.

7. a. A dart is most likely to land in the "You win" region (assuming the board always gets hit) because the area of this region takes up more than half of the board.

b. The probability is equal to the area of the "You win" region $\left(\frac{1}{4}\pi\right)$ divided by the area of the dartboard (1), which equals $\frac{1}{4}\pi$.

7. Suppose you have a strange dartboard, like the one shown. You win if your dart lands in the section of the square below the arc. You lose if it lands in the section of the square above the arc.

You win

Assume that the arc is part of a circle of radius 1.

Suppose you throw darts so they hit the dartboard randomly.

a. In what region is the dart more likely to land? Why?

b. What is the probability of the dart landing in the "You win" region? How do you know?

8. **Take It Further** Write a computer program to do the following.

For some given number of trials,

- pick a random x value between 0 and 1
- pick a random y value between 0 and 1
- if $x^2 + y^2 < 1$, score a point (it is in the "You win" region of Exercise 7)

Return the total count of points divided by the total number of trials.

a. The output of this "Monte Carlo" program is a number. What does this number represent?

b. You can estimate the area of a quarter of the unit circle using this method. Explain how.

c. Can you tell if the estimate is too big or too small? Explain.

Monte Carlo is a European tourist destination, known for its casinos.

9. **Standardized Test Prep** An octagon is shown below, drawn on 1-cm graph paper. Using the method of complete squares, which of the following would be the upper approximation of the area of the figure?

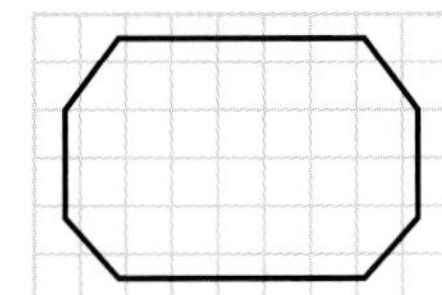

A. 48 cm^2 **B.** 50 cm^2 **C.** 52 cm^2 **D.** 54 cm^2

Go Online
PHSchool.com

For additional practice, go to **Web Code:** bga-0802

Maintain Your Skills

10. Draw a circle of radius 6 inches. Approximate its area using a grid with the following sizes.

a. 1 inch **b.** $\frac{1}{2}$ inch **c.** $\frac{1}{4}$ inch **d.** $\frac{1}{8}$ inch

Describe any patterns you see in your estimates.

Additional Resources

PRINT RESOURCES
- Solution Manual
- Practice Workbook
- Assessment Resources
- Teaching Resources

TECHNOLOGY
- Interactive Textbook
- TeacherExpress CD-ROM
- ExamView CD-ROM
- PHSchool.com

Additional Practice

1. Consider the irregular pentagon shown on a $\frac{1}{4}$-inch grid at the right. Estimate its area by answering the following.
   a. How many squares are totally inside the figure?
   b. How many squares touch the figure anywhere?
   c. Complete the mathematical statement: ___ $in.^2$ < area of pentagon < ___ $in.^2$
   d. Estimate the area of the pentagon. Explain how you arrived at this estimate.

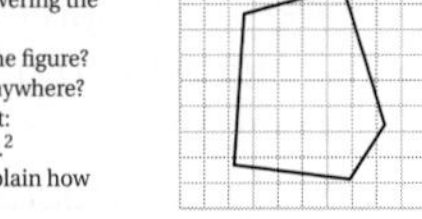

2. Consider the irregular pentagon from Exercise 1 on a "grid" of something other than squares, such as triangles, parallelograms, or hexagons. Could you use the new grid to approximate the pentagon's area? Explain.

3. Use the upper and lower approximation process to estimate the area of a circle with a radius of 3 inches.
   a. Draw a circle with a 3-inch radius on a $\frac{1}{2}$-inch grid. Write the upper and lower approximations of the area. Find the average.
   b. How close to the actual area of a circle is the average found in part (a)?
   c. Write the upper and lower approximations of the area, this time using a $\frac{1}{4}$-inch grid. Find the average.
   d. How close to the actual area is the average found in part (c)?

4. Consider the two shapes shown below.
   a. Using the strategy of counting squares, for which shape would you probably get a closer approximation of the area? Explain.
   b. Based on your answer for part (a), what strategy would you need to use to get a better area approximation for the other shape?

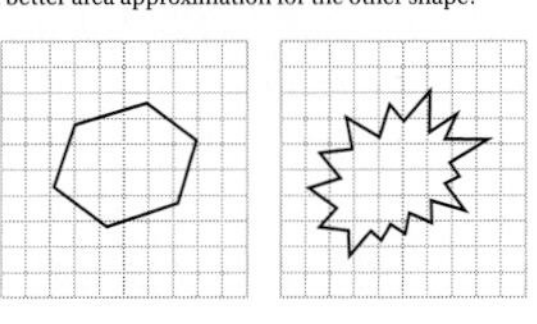

Practice: For Lesson 8.2, assign Exercises 1–4.

8. Answers may vary. Sample:

```
function: area(n)
m ← 0
repeat n
    x ← random (0, 1);
    y ← random (0, 1);
    if (x^2 + y^2 < 1) then
        m ← m + 1;
    area ← m/n
```

a. Outputs represent the experimental probability (after n trials) that a point randomly chosen from the square with vertices (0, 0), (0, 1), (1, 1) and (1, 0) will also belong to the quarter of the unit circle lying in the first quadrant. For large n, this value represents a good approximation of the actual probability that a randomly chosen point from the square lies in the quarter circle.

b. The probability that a point randomly chosen from the square will also belong to the quarter of the unit circle is the ratio of the area of the quarter circle to the area of the square. Since the area of the square is equal to 1, the probability is equal to the area of the quarter circle. Being an approximation of the probability, the output is also an approximation of the area of the quarter circle.

c. Since there is no pattern to how pairs are selected, this method cannot tell you if the estimate is too big or too small.

9. B

10. a. 72 $in.^2$

b. 90 $in.^2$

c. 103.5 $in.^2$

d. 109.125 $in.^2$

Answers may vary; Sample: approximations get closer to the actual value of the circle.

Lesson Overview

GOALS

- Estimate the area under the graph of $y = x^2$ between $x = 0$ and $x = 1$.
- Calculate the area under the graph of $y = x^2$ between $x = 0$ and $x = 1$ exactly.

This lesson introduces a version of how Archimedes used lower and upper sums to calculate the area of the region under the graph of $y = x^2$. Throughout the lesson, ask students to pay attention to the form of the sums they build, seeing how sums are similar as the number of subdivisions changes.

CHECK YOUR UNDERSTANDING
- Core: 1, 3
- Optional: 4, 5
- Extension: 2

MATERIALS
- CAS (recommended)
- graphing calculators
- Blackline Masters 8.3A–B

HOMEWORK
- Core: 6, 9, 10
- Optional: 8, 11
- Extension: 7

VOCABULARY
- lower sum, $L_n[a, b](f(x))$
- upper sum, $U_n[a, b](f(x))$
- $S[a, b](f(x))$

Launch

Launch with the first For You to Do section.

Explore

For You to Do

PROBLEM 2 You can give the students copies of Blackline Master 8.3A to use while working this problem.

8.3 Finding the Area Under $y = x^2$

When you are estimating the area of a blob, usually the best you can do is to put an irregular shape on a grid and approximate the area by counting squares to get upper and lower approximations. But if you know the equations of the boundary of your region, you can sometimes use another method to do much better.

For You to Do

Look at the area of the shaded region below the graph of $y = x^2$ from $x = 0$ to $x = 1$. Call this area A.

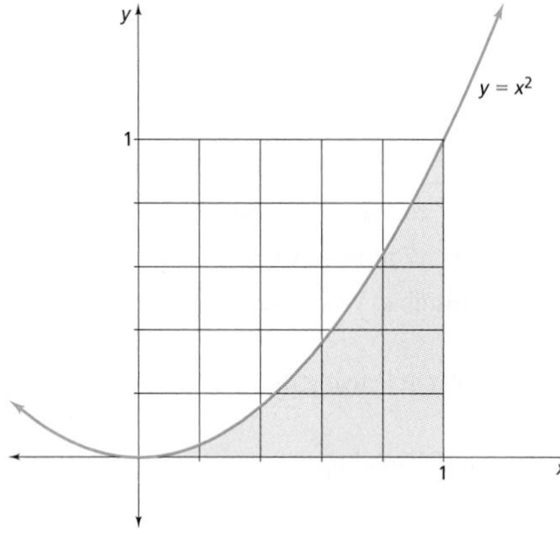

1. Write down a guess for the area of A.
2. Use the "counting squares" method from the previous lesson to estimate the area under the curve between $x = 0$ and $x = 1$. (You will need a couple of graphs of the function $y = x^2$ on graph paper for this problem.)

Sometimes A refers to a region, and sometimes it refers to the area of the region. Watch for context.

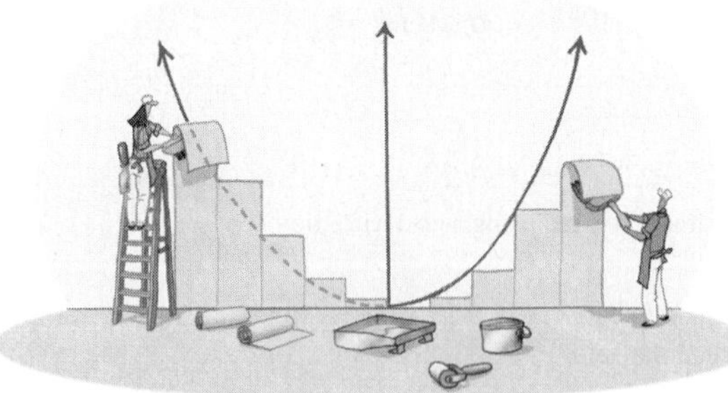

Answers

For You to Do

1. Answers may vary but should be less than $\frac{1}{2}$.
2. Answers may vary and depend on the fineness of the chosen grid. Samples:
   - For the $\frac{1}{2}$-inch grid: $0 < A < \frac{3}{4}$.
   - For the $\frac{1}{4}$-inch grid: $\frac{3}{16} < A < \frac{1}{2}$.

Minds in Action episode 26

Sasha and Derman are trying to approximate the area under the graph of $y = x^2$ from $x = 0$ to $x = 1$.

Derman Aren't you getting tired of all this square counting? I get that we keep getting better estimates with smaller and smaller grids, but it's kind of slow!

Sasha Well, I was thinking that we haven't really used all the information we have. We actually know something about this shape—we can describe it with equations. Look at these pictures:

Sasha draws the following graphs.

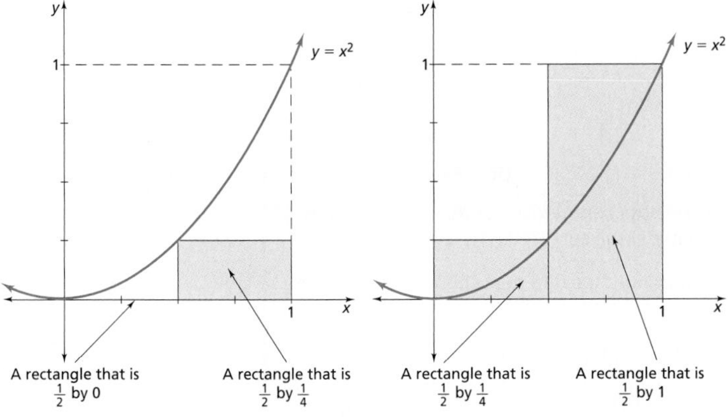

Sasha I'll calculate the lower sum. There are two rectangles, even though we can't see one of them. Its area is zero, and the other rectangle has area $\frac{1}{8}$. The total area is $\frac{1}{8}$.

Derman Oh sure, take the easy one. For the upper sum, the first rectangle has area $\frac{1}{8}$, and the second has area $\frac{1}{2}$. The total area of both rectangles is $\frac{5}{8}$.

Sasha So we have trapped the area between $\frac{1}{8}$ and $\frac{5}{8}$. Maybe a good estimate would be the average of the two. Can we do better?

Derman Oh, no. This is going to be like smaller and smaller grids, isn't it?

Sasha Well, I'm guessing smaller and smaller intervals, at least.

Minds in Action

You may wish to assign students Minds in Action roles and present the conversation to the class. This is more effective if you assign the roles one class day prior to the "performance." Urge the students to "get into" their parts by using their own words instead of memorizing lines.

For Discussion

The pictures below use four rectangles to give better lower and upper sums.

3. Find the lower and upper sums.

4. What is a good estimate for A, based on these sums?

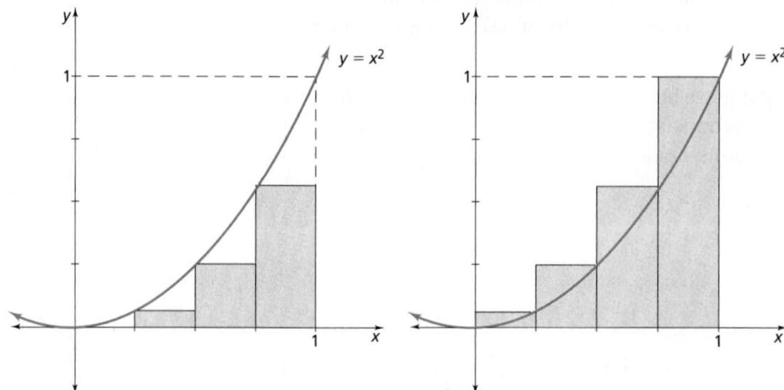

Lower sum Upper sum

5. Does the average of the lower and upper sums give you an estimate that is too big or too small for the area under the curve? Why?

6. The pictures below say something about the difference between the upper sum and the lower sum.

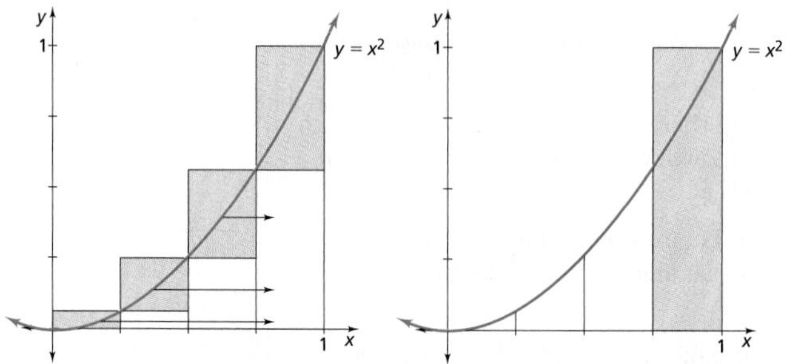

As you divide the interval [0, 1] into more and more pieces (in other words, as you use more and more subdivisions), what happens to the difference between the upper sum and the lower sum? How small can you make that difference? Explain your answer.

The notation [0,1] means the interval from 0 to 1, including the endpoints.

7. The graph of $y = x^2$ is increasing on the interval [0, 1]. How does this relate to the x-values used to set the heights of the lower-sum rectangles? What about the upper-sum rectangles? How would you set the heights of the lower- and upper-sum rectangles for a decreasing function?

Answers

For Discussion

3. The lower sum is

$$\frac{1}{4} \cdot 0 + \frac{1}{4} \cdot \frac{1}{16} + \frac{1}{4} \cdot \frac{1}{4} + \frac{1}{4} \cdot \frac{9}{16} = \frac{7}{32}$$

The upper sum is

$$\frac{1}{4} \cdot \frac{1}{16} + \frac{1}{4} \cdot \frac{1}{4} + \frac{1}{4} \cdot \frac{9}{16} + \frac{1}{4} \cdot 1 = \frac{15}{32}$$

4. A good estimate for the area is the average of the lower and the upper sums which is $\frac{11}{32}$.

5. The estimate is too big. The average of the upper and the lower rectangle on the same interval is the trapezoid with the same base, and the graph of $y = x^2$ is always below the trapezoid's upper edge.

Minds in Action — episode 27

Sasha and Derman wonder if they can do better.

Derman Okay, we're estimating and estimating. But how can we find the area exactly?

Sasha We know that the exact area under the curve is somewhere between the lower sum and the upper sum:

lower sum $\leq$ *area under the curve* $\leq$ *upper sum*

Let's use the equation of the curve to write an expression for the upper and lower sums, and maybe we can make some progress.

Here is a handy notation for saying "the upper approximation of the area under the curve $y = x^2$ from $x = 0$ to $x = 1$ with 6 subdivisions."

$$U_6[0, 1](x^2)$$

Example

Problem Calculate $U_6[0, 1](x^2)$, the upper approximation for the area under $y = x^2$ from $x = 0$ to $x = 1$ with 6 subdivisions.

Solution

Start by calculating the areas of each of the 6 rectangles.

	Base	Height	Area
1st rectangle	$\frac{1}{6}$	$\left(\frac{1}{6}\right)^2$	$\frac{1}{6} \times \left(\frac{1}{6}\right)^2 = \frac{1^2}{6^3}$
2nd rectangle	$\frac{1}{6}$	$\left(\frac{2}{6}\right)^2$	$\frac{1}{6} \times \left(\frac{2}{6}\right)^2 = \frac{2^2}{6^3}$
3rd rectangle	$\frac{1}{6}$	$\left(\frac{3}{6}\right)^2$	$\frac{1}{6} \times \left(\frac{3}{6}\right)^2 = \frac{3^2}{6^3}$
4th rectangle	$\frac{1}{6}$	$\left(\frac{4}{6}\right)^2$	$\frac{1}{6} \times \left(\frac{4}{6}\right)^2 = \frac{4^2}{6^3}$
5th rectangle	$\frac{1}{6}$	$\left(\frac{5}{6}\right)^2$	$\frac{1}{6} \times \left(\frac{5}{6}\right)^2 = \frac{5^2}{6^3}$
6th rectangle	$\frac{1}{6}$	$\left(\frac{6}{6}\right)^2$	$\frac{1}{6} \times \left(\frac{6}{6}\right)^2 = \frac{6^2}{6^3}$

To obtain the expression for the upper approximation, add up the areas of all six rectangles:

$$U_6[0, 1](x^2) = \frac{1}{6^3} + \frac{2^2}{6^3} + \frac{3^2}{6^3} + \frac{4^2}{6^3} + \frac{5^2}{6^3} + \frac{6^2}{6^3}$$
$$= \frac{1}{6^3}(1^2 + 2^2 + 3^2 + 4^2 + 5^2 + 6^2)$$

Here, a formula for the sum of consecutive squares comes in handy.

$$\frac{1}{6^3}(1^2 + 2^2 + 3^2 + 4^2 + 5^2 + 6^2) = \frac{1}{6^3} \cdot \frac{6 \cdot 7 \cdot 13}{6} \approx 0.4212963$$

Remember...

$$\sum_{k=1}^{n} k^2 = \frac{n(n+1)(2n+1)}{6}$$

You obtained this formula in Lesson 5.10, Exercise 5.

Example

Spend time as needed going over this completed example. Make sure students understand the problem. As necessary, help them develop the detailed solution.

6. Since the interval is [0, 1] and $y = x^2$, the difference between the upper and lower sums is the area of the last rectangle in the upper sum, which is equal to the reciprocal of the number of subintervals, n. As the number of subintervals grows, this difference gets smaller and can be made, by proper choice of n, as close to 0 as desired.

7. For an increasing function on the subinterval $[a, b]$, the height of the lower-sum rectangle is $f(a)$ and the height of the upper-sum rectangle is $f(b)$.

For a decreasing function, $f(a)$ is the height of the upper-sum rectangle and $f(b)$ is the height of the lower-sum rectangle.

For You to Do

PROBLEM 8. a. $U_7[0, 1](x^2)$

$$= \frac{1^2}{7^3} + \frac{2^2}{7^3} + \frac{3^2}{7^3} + \frac{4^2}{7^3} + \frac{5^2}{7^3} + \frac{6^2}{7^3} + \frac{7^2}{7^3}$$
$$= \frac{1}{7^3}(1^2 + 2^2 + 3^2 + 4^2 + 5^2 + 6^2 + 7^2)$$
$$= \frac{1}{7^3} \cdot \frac{7 \cdot 8 \cdot 15}{6}$$
$$= \frac{140}{343}$$
$$= \frac{20}{49}$$
$$\approx 0.4081633$$

PROBLEM 8. b. $U_8[0, 1](x^2)$

$$= \frac{1^2}{8^3} + \frac{2^2}{8^3} + \frac{3^2}{8^3} + \frac{4^2}{8^3} + \frac{5^2}{8^3} + \frac{6^2}{8^3} + \frac{7^2}{8^3} + \frac{8^2}{8^3}$$
$$= \frac{1}{8^3}(1^2 + 2^2 + 3^2 + 4^2 + 5^2 + 6^2 + 7^2 + 8^2)$$
$$= \frac{1}{8^3} \cdot \frac{8 \cdot 9 \cdot 17}{6}$$
$$= \frac{204}{512}$$
$$= \frac{51}{128}$$
$$\approx 0.3984375$$

PROBLEM 9 You may want to use Blackline Master 8.3B on an overhead and fill it in as students supply the entries, or you may want to hand out copies for students to complete individually.

For You to Do

8. a. Write an expression for $U_7[0, 1](x^2)$, the upper sum with 7 subdivisions. Use a calculator to approximate the value of this expression.

b. Write an expression for $U_8[0, 1](x^2)$, the upper sum with 8 subdivisions. Use a calculator to approximate the value of this expression.

9. To see how the upper sum changes when the number of subdivisions grows, copy and complete the table.

Upper Sums for Different Numbers of Subdivisions

Number of Subdivisions, n	Upper Sum, $U_n[0, 1](x^2)$	Approximate Value
6	$\frac{1}{6^3}(1^2 + 2^2 + 3^2 + 4^2 + 5^2 + 6^2)$	■
7	$\frac{1}{7^3}(1^2 + 2^2 + 3^2 + 4^2 + 5^2 + 6^2 + 7^2)$	■
8	■	■
9	■	■
⋮	⋮	⋮
15	■	■
⋮	⋮	⋮
n	■	

10. In Problem 9, you obtained the formula for the upper sum if the number of subdivisions is n. Find a closed form for this sum.

Using the closed form you just found, you can simplify the expression for U_n:

$$U_n = \frac{1}{n^3} \cdot \frac{n(n+1)(2n+1)}{6}$$
$$= \frac{2n^3 + 3n^2 + n}{6n^3} \qquad \text{Multiply out the numerator.}$$
$$= \frac{2n^3}{6n^3} + \frac{3n^2}{6n^3} + \frac{n}{6n^3} \qquad \text{Break it up into a sum of 3 fractions.}$$
$$= \frac{1}{3} + \frac{1}{2n} + \frac{1}{6n^2} \qquad \text{Reduce.}$$

You can write $U_n[0, 1](x^2)$ as U_n if the interval and function are clear from the context.

Answers

For You to Do

8. a. $U_7[0, 1](x^2)$

$$= \frac{1^2}{7^3} + \frac{2^2}{7^3} + \frac{3^2}{7^3} + \frac{4^2}{7^3} + \frac{5^2}{7^3} + \frac{6^2}{7^3} + \frac{7^2}{7^3}$$
$$\approx 0.4081633$$

b. $U_8[0, 1](x^2)$

$$= \frac{1^2}{8^3} + \frac{2^2}{8^3} + \frac{3^2}{8^3} + \frac{4^2}{8^3} + \frac{5^2}{8^3} + \frac{6^2}{8^3} + \frac{7^2}{8^3} + \frac{8^2}{8^3}$$
$$\approx 0.3984375$$

9. See back of book.

10. $U_n[0, 1](x^2)$

$$= \frac{1}{n^3}\sum_{i=1}^{n} i^2$$
$$= \frac{1}{n^3} \frac{n(n+1)(2n+1)}{6}$$

Developing Habits of Mind

Reason about calculations. What happens to $U_n = \frac{1}{3} + \frac{1}{2n} + \frac{1}{6n^2}$ as n becomes larger and larger?

You can prove that the area under the curve $y = x^2$ between 0 and 1 is not bigger than $\frac{1}{3}$.

Method 1: $U_n[0, 1](x^2) = \frac{1}{3} + \frac{1}{2n} + \frac{1}{6n^2}$. So you can think of U_n as $\frac{1}{3}$ plus something. This "something" term is

$$\frac{1}{2n} + \frac{1}{6n^2}$$

To make U_n a more accurate approximation (closer to A), you choose more and more subdivisions. As you do this, n becomes much, much larger and the "something" term becomes much, much smaller, until it is practically 0. (Check this out for yourself.) This means that the upper sum is getting closer and closer to $\frac{1}{3}$. Since A cannot be greater than any upper sum, A can be no greater than $\frac{1}{3}$.

Method 2: Suppose that A is greater than $\frac{1}{3}$, and see what happens

- If A is greater than $\frac{1}{3}$, it must be greater than $\frac{1}{3}$ by some amount, say, 0.01.
- You can choose n big enough so that the "something" term, $\frac{1}{2n} + \frac{1}{6n^2}$, is less than 0.01.
- The n you just chose makes A greater than an upper sum.

$$\begin{aligned} A &= \frac{1}{3} + 0.01 \\ &> \frac{1}{3} + \frac{1}{2n} + \frac{1}{6n^2} \\ &= U_n[0, 1](x^2) \end{aligned}$$

- However, this cannot be, since A is no greater than any upper sum. So, A cannot be greater than $\frac{1}{3}$.

Can the area be less than $\frac{1}{3}$? Consider the lower sums. Just as for upper sums, you can use a handy notation for "the lower approximation of the area under the curve $y = x^2$ from $x = 0$ to $x = 1$ with 6 subdivisions":

$$L_6[0, 1](x^2)$$

For You to Do

11. Just as you did for upper sums, obtain a closed form for $L_n[0, 1](x^2)$.
12. What number do the lower sums approach as n becomes very large?
13. Show that the actual area cannot be less than $\frac{1}{3}$.

To avoid cumbersome repetition, from now on the expression $S[0, 1](x^2)$ will denote the area under the curve $y = x^2$ between $x = 0$ and $x = 1$.

For You to Do

11. $L_n[0, 1](x^2) = \frac{1}{3} - \frac{1}{2n} + \frac{1}{6n^2}$

12. $\frac{1}{3}$

13. Answers may vary. Sample:
$L_n[0, 1](x^2)$ is always $\frac{1}{3}$ minus something. The something by which $L_n[0, 1](x^2)$ falls short is $\left(\frac{1}{2n} - \frac{1}{6n^2}\right)$. You can make this quantity as small as you want (but still positive) by making n large enough. The actual area A is always greater than any lower sum.

Assume that A is less than $\frac{1}{3}$. Then it is smaller than $\frac{1}{3}$ by some amount, say 0.001:

$$A = \frac{1}{3} - 0.001$$

But then you could make the difference between $L_n[0, 1](x^2)$ and $\frac{1}{3}$ less than 0.001, by making n large enough.

$$\frac{1}{3} - L_n[0, 1](x^2) < 0.001$$

or

$$\frac{1}{3} - 0.001 < L_n[0, 1](x^2)$$

For such an n, the area is smaller than the lower sum, and that cannot happen. Therefore, A is not less than $\frac{1}{3}$.

Wrap Up

To wrap up this lesson, go over Exercise 1 in the Check Your Understanding section.

Assessment Resources

Lesson Quiz 8.3

1. a. Calculate $U_8[0, 1](x^2)$, the upper approximation for the area under the graph of $y = x^2$ from 0 to 1 with 8 subdivisions.
   b. Calculate the lower approximation for the area under the graph of $y = x^2$ from 0 to 1 with 8 subdivisions.
   c. Calculate the average of your answers to parts (a) and (b). The exact area is $\frac{1}{3}$. What is the percent error of the average-based estimate?

2. Use 8 subdivisions to find both an upper and a lower approximation for the area under each curve between 0 and 1.
   a. $y = 2x^2$ b. $y = 3x^2$ c. $y = 4x^2$

3. Based on your answers to Exercises 1 and 2, make a conjecture about approximations of the area under the graph of $y = nx^2$ from 0 to 1, where n is a positive integer, compared to approximations for $y = x^2$.

Exercises

HOMEWORK
- Core: 6, 9, 10
- Optional: 8, 11
- Extension: 7

For Discussion

14. What is the exact value of $S[0, 1](x^2)$? Explain your reasoning.

Minds in Action episode 28

Sasha and Derman reach their goal.

Derman Isn't it kind of amazing, Sasha? We got the exact answer as a result of approximating!

Sasha Well, it took a lot of approximating.

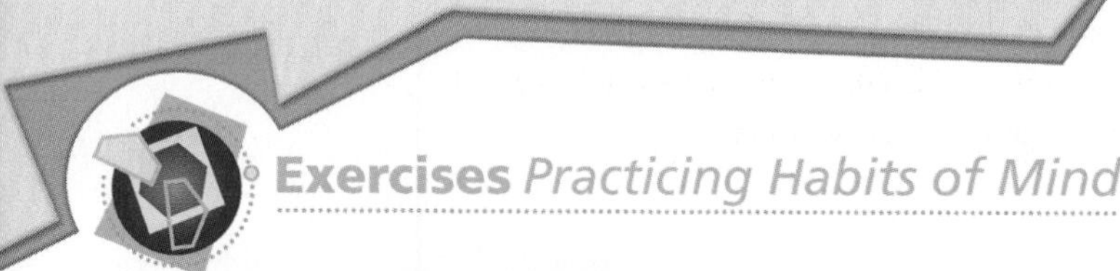

Exercises Practicing Habits of Mind

Check Your Understanding

1. **Write About It** Write an algorithm so that someone, given the number of subdivisions, could calculate the lower and upper sums for $f(x) = x^2$. It might start like this:
   - Divide the interval $[0, 1]$ into the specified number of equal pieces.
   - First find the lower sum. On each piece, build a rectangle with that base and height equal to. . . .

2. **Take It Further** Turn the algorithm you wrote in Exercise 1 into one or more programs on your graphing calculator or CAS. The programs should take an input n (the number of subdivisions) and output the lower sum, the upper sum, their average, and their difference.
   a. Test your programs with $n = 2, 4,$ and 8 to make sure you get the same answers you did with your hand calculations.
   b. Run your program with several other inputs, including 10, 200, and 1000.
   c. How many subdivisions do you need to put the lower approximation within 0.01 of the actual area? Within 0.001? Remember that the actual area is $\frac{1}{3}$.

Answers

For Discussion

14. $\frac{1}{3}$; since the exact value is greater than $\frac{1}{3}$ and less than $\frac{1}{3}$, it is exactly $\frac{1}{3}$.

Exercises

1. Answers may vary. However, the following are essential to any algorithm.
- Divide the interval [0, 1] into the given number of equal pieces.
- For the lower sum: on each piece, build a rectangle with that base and height equal to the value of the function for the left-hand endpoint.
- For the upper sum: on each piece, build a rectangle with that base and height equal to the value of the function for the right-hand endpoint.
- To compute either sum, add up the areas of all respective rectangles.

2. Answers may vary. Sample:
program: sums (n, L, U, A, D)
input: n (number of subdivisions),
output: L (lower sum),
U (upper sum),
A (their average)
D (their difference)

$L \leftarrow 0;$
$U \leftarrow 0;$
$base = \frac{1}{n};$
for $i = 1$ to n

$$L \leftarrow L + \frac{(i-1)^2}{n^2} \cdot base;$$

$$U \leftarrow U + \frac{i^2}{n^2} \cdot base;$$

$A \leftarrow 0.5(L + U)$
$D \leftarrow U - L$

a–b. See back of book.

c. Since the actual area lies between $U_n[0, 1](x^2)$ and $L_n[0, 1](x^2)$ and their difference is $\frac{1}{n}$, n must be such that $\frac{1}{n} < 0.01$. Therefore, any $n > 100$ will make $L_n[0, 1](x^2)$ within 0.01 of the actual area. Similarly, $n > 1000$ ensures that $L_{1000}[0, 1](x^2)$ is within 0.001 of the actual area.

3. On page 646, you simplified and analyzed the upper sum for the area under the graph of $y = x^2$ between $x = 0$ and $x = 1$. Here is another way to simplify it:

$$\frac{1}{6} \cdot \frac{n(n+1)(2n+1)}{n^3} = \frac{1}{6} \cdot \left(1 + \frac{1}{n}\right) \cdot \left(2 + \frac{1}{n}\right)$$

a. Verify that this equation is an identity.

b. Analyze the final expression to determine what number it approaches when n becomes very large.

4. **a.** Using the method of Exercise 3, find the number that $L_n[0, 1](x^2)$ approaches as n becomes very large.

b. Does this method give you the same value for the area under the curve $y = x^2$ between 0 and 1 as the method described on page 646?

5. Consider the claim that it is not necessary to bother with both lower and upper sums. Someone might reason that if you know that the difference between the upper and the lower sums approaches zero, you can safely conclude that the limit of, say, the upper sum is the area you are looking for.

a. For $f(x) = x^2$, does the difference between the upper and the lower sums approach zero? How do you know?

b. Do you agree with the general claim? Explain why or why not.

Historical Perspective

Archimedes was the first to use the methods in this lesson, though he never used S for area, nor did he use U_n and L_n. Generally, if you tried to read the original works of famous mathematicians, you would find it very difficult. This is because mathematical notation has changed dramatically over the centuries. Even the way we think about things has changed. For ease of understanding, this chapter uses modern notation and, in some cases, updated presentation. However, it is faithful to the basic ideas of the early masters of mathematics, so you can enjoy and appreciate what they did.

Unlike U_n and L_n, however, S is related to a historically important mathematical symbol: $\int$, for *integral*. Around 1675, Gottfried Wilhelm Leibniz invented this symbol and used it in the very same way we are using S. The symbol $\int$ denoted the area under a curve. Leibniz had the same approach to the area problem as we are using here. In fact, $\int$ is an elongated S and stands for *sum*. The area under the curve is the limit of the sum of the areas of the ever-increasing number of ever-narrowing rectangles. Leibniz used $\int$ while laying the foundations of the branch of mathematics called *calculus*.

Check Your Understanding

EXERCISES 1 AND 2 are technology-dependent in the sense that the algorithms and programs that you develop depend on the technology you are using. Whatever you use, try to make the programs mimic the actual calculations the students are doing by hand. In this way, writing the program supports the all-important mechanization of calculating upper and lower sums.

3. a. $\frac{1}{6} \cdot \frac{n(n+1)(2n+1)}{n^3}$

$= \frac{1}{6} \cdot \frac{n}{n} \cdot \frac{n+1}{n} \cdot \frac{2n+1}{n}$

$= \frac{1}{6} \cdot 1 \cdot \left(\frac{n}{n} + \frac{1}{n}\right) \cdot \left(\frac{2n}{n} + \frac{1}{n}\right)$

$= \frac{1}{6}\left(1 + \frac{1}{n}\right)\left(2 + \frac{1}{n}\right)$

b. As n gets larger and larger, $1 + \frac{1}{n}$ approaches 1, and $2 + \frac{1}{n}$ approaches 2. Therefore, $\frac{1}{6}\left(1 + \frac{1}{n}\right)\left(2 + \frac{1}{n}\right)$ approaches $\frac{1}{6} \cdot 1 \cdot 2 = \frac{1}{3}$.

4. a. $\frac{1}{3}$

b. yes

5. a. The difference between the upper and lower sums is $\frac{1}{n}$; it approaches 0 as n gets larger and larger.

b. yes; Check students' work.

Additional Resources

PRINT RESOURCES
- Solution Manual
- Practice Workbook
- Assessment Resources
- Teaching Resources

TECHNOLOGY
- Interactive Textbook
- TeacherExpress CD-ROM
- ExamView CD-ROM
- PHSchool.com

Additional Practice

1. One way to approximate $S[0, 1](x^3)$ is to find $U_n[0, 1](x^3)$, the upper sum for n subdivisions between 0 and 1. When you do this, you find that $U_n[0, 1](x^3) = \frac{1}{n^4} \cdot (1^3 + 2^3 + 3^3 + \cdots + n^3)$.
   a. Show that another way to write this is $\frac{1}{n^4} \cdot \frac{n^2(n+1)^2}{4}$.
   b. Simplify the result in part (a).
   c. Use the result in part (b) to approximate $S[0, 1](x^3)$ using $n = 100$.
   d. Use the result in part (b) to approximate $S[0, 1](x^3)$ using $n = 1000$.

2. Another way to write the result in Exercise 1 is $\frac{1}{n^4} \cdot \frac{n^2(n+1)^2}{4} = \frac{1}{4} \cdot \left(1 + \frac{1}{n}\right)^2$.
   a. Verify that this is an identity.
   b. What happens to the fraction on the right as n gets very large?
   c. What value does the answer to part (b) suggest for $S[0, 1](x^3)$?

3. For n subdivisions, the lower sum for the area under the graph of $y = x^2$ between 0 and 1 is $L_n[0, 1](x^2) = \frac{1}{n^3} \cdot \frac{n(n-1)(2n-1)}{6}$. Here is another way to simplify it:
$$\frac{1}{n^3} \cdot \frac{n(n-1)(2n-1)}{6} = \frac{1}{6} \cdot \left(1 - \frac{1}{n}\right) \cdot \left(2 - \frac{1}{n}\right)$$
   a. Verify that this is an identity.
   b. Analyze the final expression to determine what number it approaches when n becomes very large.

4. a. Describe a method for finding upper and lower approximations of the area under the graph of $y = 3 - x$ from 0 to 3, using three subdivisions along the y-axis instead of the x-axis.
   b. Calculate the upper and lower approximations.
   c. Explain how you would generalize the method to n subdivisions.
   d. Explain how you would use subdivisions along the y-axis to find the area under the graph of $y = 4 - x^2$ from $x = 0$ to $x = 2$.

5. a. Consider a cone with height and radius both equal to 3 cm. Describe a method for finding upper and lower approximations of the volume of the cone, using three subdivisions of the cone's central vertical axis.
   b. Calculate the upper and lower approximations, and find the average of the two.
   c. Compare your answers in part (b) to the exact volume of the cone. What is the percent error of the average-based estimate?

Practice: For Lesson 8.3, assign Exercises 1–5.

On Your Own

6. a. Find $S[0, 2](x^2)$.
   b. Find $S[0, a](x^2)$, where $a > 0$.
   c. Find $S[a, b](x^2)$, where $0 < a < b$.

7. **Take It Further** Prove the following result, first established by Archimedes. Draw a horizontal line that intersects the graph of $y = ax^2$ $(a > 0)$ at points A and B. The area of the parabolic section (the area of the shaded region above the parabola and below $\overline{AB}$) is $\frac{4}{3}$ of the area of triangle AOB.

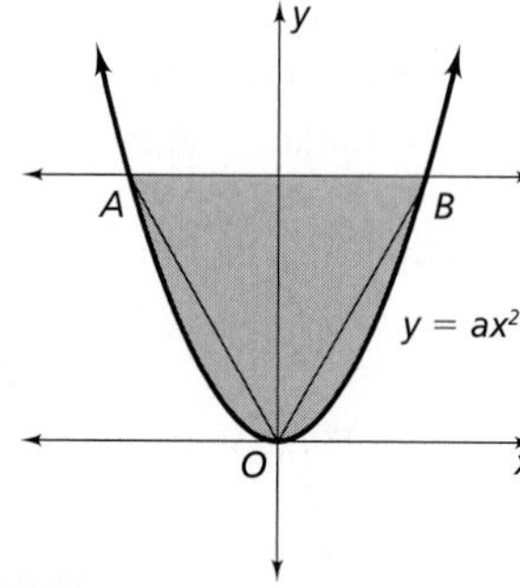

For additional practice, go to Web Code: bga-0803

8. In the next investigation, you will learn methods for finding areas under other curves. For each of the following, use subdivisions to find an estimate for the area under the curve between 0 and 1.
   a. $y = x^3$
   b. $y = x^4$
   c. $y = x^5$

9. **Standardized Test Prep** Using four equal intervals, which of the following would be the upper sum approximation of the area bounded by the graphs of $y = 0$, $y = \frac{1}{x}$, $x = 1$, and $x = 5$?
   A. $\frac{52}{25}$
   B. $\frac{25}{12}$
   C. $\frac{21}{10}$
   D. $\frac{29}{20}$

Maintain Your Skills

10. Find each area.
   a. $S[0, 1](2x^2)$
   b. $S[0, 1](3x^2)$
   c. $S[0, 1]\left(\frac{1}{2}x^2\right)$
   d. $S[0, 1](cx^2)$, where $c > 0$

11. Find a general formula for $S[a, b](cx^2)$, where $c > 0$, and $0 < a < b$.

Answers

6. a. $S[0, 2](x^2) = \frac{8}{3}$
   b. $S[0, a](x^2) = \frac{a^3}{3}$ where $a > 0$
   c. $\frac{b^3 - a^3}{3}$ (for $0 < a < b$)

7. Let A_T represent the area of $\triangle AOB$ and A_P be the area of the parabolic segment. You need to show that $A_T = \frac{3}{4} \cdot A_P$.
   Let point B have coordinates (b, ab^2). Because the parabola is symmetric about the y-axis,
   $A_T = 2 \cdot$ (area of the triangle that lies in the first quadrant)
   $= 2 \cdot \left(\frac{1}{2} \cdot b \cdot ab^2\right)$
   $= ab^3$
   Similarly,
   $A_P = 2 \cdot$ (area of the segment that lies in the first quadrant)
   $= 2 \cdot$ (area of the enclosing rectangle $- S[0, b](ax^2)$)
   $= 2 \cdot \left(b \cdot ab^2 - \frac{ab^3}{3}\right)$
   from problem 14 on page 648
   $= \frac{4ab^3}{3}$
   From these calculations, $A_T = \frac{3}{4}A_P$.

8. Answers may vary. Samples:
   a. approximately $\frac{1}{4}$
   b. approximately $\frac{1}{5}$
   c. approximately $\frac{1}{6}$

9. D

10. a. $\frac{2}{3}$
   b. 1
   c. $\frac{1}{6}$
   d. $\frac{c}{3}$

11. $S[a, b](cx^2) = \frac{c \cdot (b^3 - a^3)}{3}$

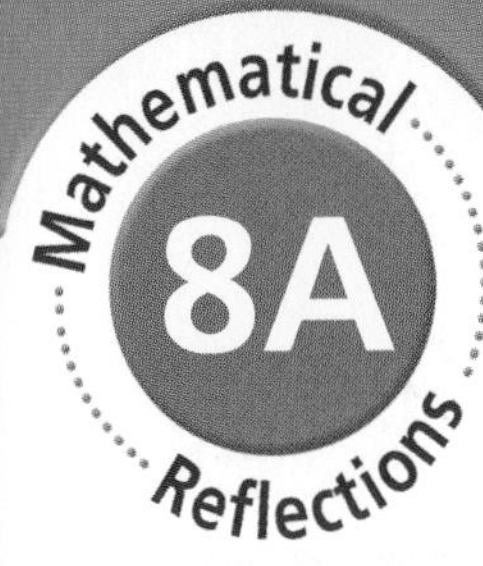

In this investigation, you approximated the areas of irregular shapes and regions under curves by using squares or rectangles. You applied the approximation method to the area under the graph of $y = x^2$. You found better and better approximations until you were able to state the exact area. The following questions will help you summarize what you have learned.

1. Describe Archimedes' method for finding the area under the curve $y = x^2$ between 0 and 1.
2. When you use Archimedes' method, what happens to the difference between the lower and upper sums as the number of subdivisions gets bigger? Why does this happen?
3. How can you find the area of an irregularly-shaped figure?
4. How can you estimate the area under a curve?
5. What is the area of the region under the graph of $y = x^2$ from $x = 0$ to $x = 1$?

Vocabulary and Notation

In this investigation, you learned these terms and symbols. Make sure you understand what each one means and how to use it.

- **lower sum, $L_n[a, b](f(x))$**
- **$S[a, b](f(x))$**
- **upper sum, $U_n[a, b](f(x))$**

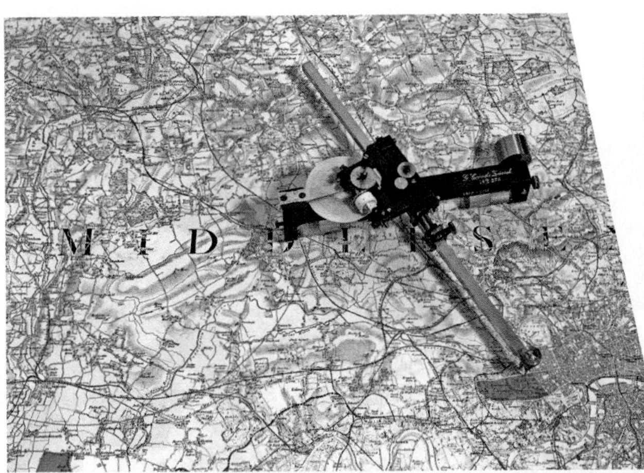

A planimeter, or mechanical integrator, is a device for measuring the area of a shape by tracing its outline. Geographers use planimeters to measure the areas of map regions. In the leather and textile industries, purchasers and production managers use planimeters to find the areas of irregularly-shaped pieces of material.

Mathematical Reflections

EXERCISES 3–5 At the start of the investigation, you may have assigned these as Questions 1–3 for students to think and write about.

Mathematical Reflections

1. Divide [0,1] into n subintervals of equal length by using points on the x-axis whose x-coordinates are $\frac{0}{n}, \frac{1}{n}, \frac{2}{n}, \frac{3}{n}, \dots, \frac{n-1}{n}, \frac{n}{n} = 1$. Find the lower estimate $L_n[0, 1](x^2)$ by adding the areas of the n rectangles whose left sides have heights $\left(\frac{i}{n}\right)^2$ (for $i = 0, 1, 2, \dots, n - 1$) and whose bases have length $\frac{1}{n}$. Find the upper estimate $U_n[0, 1](x^2)$ by adding the area of the n rectangles whose right sides have heights $\left(\frac{i}{n}\right)^2$ (for $i = 1, 2, 3, \dots, n$) and whose bases have length $\frac{1}{n}$. Find the limits of these estimates as $n \to \infty$. These limits will be the same, and their common value is the area under $y = x^2$ between 0 and 1.
2. The difference approaches 0; for n subintervals of [0, 1], the difference is $\frac{1}{n}$, and $\frac{1}{n} \to 0$ as $n \to \infty$.
3. Answers may vary. Sample: Trace the figure on grid paper. Get a low estimate by counting all the grid squares whose interiors lie entirely inside the figure, then multiply the count by the area of a grid square. Get a high estimate by counting all the grid squares whose interiors lie entirely or partially inside the figure, then multiply the count by the area of a grid square. You can get a better estimate of the area if you use the average of the low and high estimates.
4. Answers may vary. Sample: Apply the method described in the answer for Exercise 1.
5. $\frac{1}{3}$

Investigation Overview

In this investigation, students find and prove a conjecture that the area from 0 to 1 under $y = x^m$ is $\frac{1}{m+1}$. To complete the proof of this conjecture, they use a closed form for $\sum_{k=0}^{n} k^m$ as a function of m. They apply their results to other intervals using the geometry of the graph of $y = x^m$ instead of the upper and lower sum process.

The difficulty with this approach is that the calculations get much more complex as the degree of the polynomial goes up. Fermat had a brilliant idea that allowed him to calculate upper and lower sums for any x^m with m an integer, without having to sum m^{th} powers. Cavalieri summed areas of rectangles, all of which had the same size base ($\frac{1}{n}$ for n subdivisions). In essence he divided the interval along the x-axis under the curve into an arithmetic sequence. Fermat divided the interval into a geometric sequence, so that the rectangles all had different size bases. This complication makes the calculation much easier, because the upper and lower sums are then geometric series.

This simplification is not without cost. For one thing, you need to work with the "basic" interval [1, 2] instead of [0, 1]. Since you want to divide the interval $[a, b]$ into a geometric sequence

$$a, ar, ar^2, \ldots, ar^n = b$$

a cannot equal 0. (Fermat actually did work with the interval [0, 1], but that adds a technical consideration that he got around with some delicate arguments about limits.) The second difficulty is one that every geometry teacher knows; students have an easy time thinking about dividing a segment into equal pieces, but they sometimes have difficulty thinking about dividing a segment into *proportional* pieces.

You may wish to assign Questions 1–3 for students to think and write about during the investigation.

Learning Goals

- Find the area under the graph of $y = x^3$ between $x = 0$ and $x = 1$.
- Calculate the area under the graph of $y = x^m$ between $x = 0$ and $x = 1$ for any positive integer m.

Habits and Skills

- Use closed forms for $\sum_{k=1}^{n} k^m$ to find areas.
- Use a historical perspective to make sense of the most important ideas of calculus.
- Use a CAS to make short work of complicated calculations.

Finding Areas Under Curves

In *Finding Areas Under Curves,* you will learn how Cavalieri extended Archimedes' result to find the area under the graph of $y = x^m$, for integers $m = 2$ through 9. You will also learn Fermat's variation of this method, which allows you to find the area for any positive integer m.

By the end of this investigation, you will be able to answer questions like these.

1. What is a closed-form expression for the function defined by $F(b) = S[1, b](x^3)$, where $b > 1$?
2. What is a closed-form expression for the function defined by $F(b) = S[1, b](x^4)$, where $b > 1$?
3. What is Fermat's approach to finding the area under the graph of $y = x^m$ between $x = 0$ and $x = 1$?

You will learn how to

- find the area under the graph of $y = x^3$ between $x = 0$ and $x = 1$
- calculate the area under the graph of $y = x^m$ between $x = 0$ and $x = 1$ for any positive integer m

You will develop these habits and skills:

- Use closed forms for $\sum_{k=1}^{n} k^m$ to find areas.
- Use a historical perspective to make sense of the most important ideas of calculus.
- Use a CAS to make short work of complicated calculations.

You could estimate the area of this traffic roundabout by superimposing a grid and counting squares. But as you will learn in this investigation, there is a more elegant method that gives the area exactly.

Investigation Road Map

LESSON 8.4, *Getting Started,* has students experiment with finding upper and lower sums for $y = x^3$ and other functions.

LESSON 8.5, *Cavalieri's Approach,* shows students one way of computing $S[0, 1](x^m)$ for some positive integers m.

LESSON 8.6, *Fermat's Big Idea,* shows students another method of computing $S[0, 1](x^m)$ for any positive integer m.

8.4 Getting Started

If you can find the area under the graph of $y = x^2$ so successfully, perhaps you can use the same methods on other curves. In fact, you can, and sometimes with surprising results.

For You to Explore

Start with $y = x^3$.

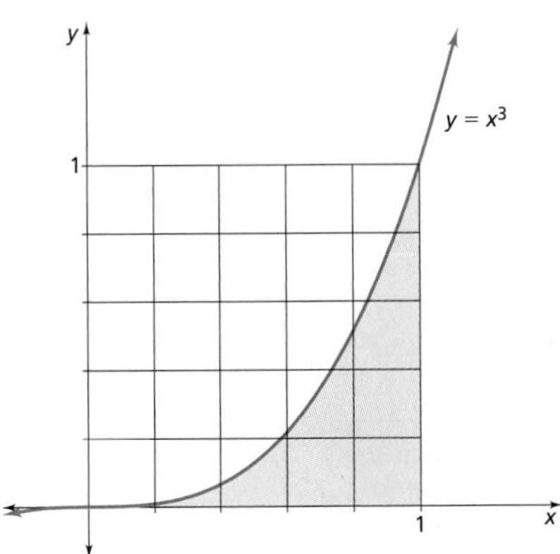

1. Before you do any calculations, how do you expect the area under the graph of $y = x^3$ to compare with the area under the graph $y = x^2$ between $x = 0$ and $x = 1$? Which is greater? Why? Write down a guess for the area under $y = x^3$, and explain your thinking.
2. Estimate $S[0, 1](x^3)$ by computing a few lower or upper approximations. Does your estimate confirm your guess from Problem 1?

   To find the exact area under $y = x^2$, you wrote the expression for the upper sum with the number of subdivisions n, and you used the formula for the sum of the squares,

$$\sum_{k=1}^{n} k^2 = 1^2 + 2^2 + \cdots + n^2 = \frac{n(n+1)(2n+1)}{6}$$

You can find the areas under the other curves using the same general approach. You may need to use some of the other formulas for sums of powers, from Chapter 5.

Lesson Overview

GOALS

- Warm up to the ideas of the investigation.
- Find the area under the graph of $y = x^3$ between $x = 0$ and $x = 1$.

In this Getting Started lesson, students find the exact value of $S[0, 1](x^3)$. It is very unusual to assign all of the problems in a For You to Explore section as core problems. With the help of this streamlined set of exercises, students calculate $S[0, 1](x^3)$ on their own with some scaffolding. In the homework, students use geometric intuition to find areas under other curves.

FOR YOU TO EXPLORE

- Core: 1, 2, 3, 4, 5, 6, 7, 8, 9, 10
- Optional: none

MATERIALS

- CAS (recommended)
- graphing calculators
- Blackline Masters 8.4A–B

HOMEWORK

- Core: 11, 13, 14
- Optional: 12

Launch

To launch this lesson, assign students to work on the For You to Explore problems.

Explore

For You to Explore

PROBLEMS 1–4 run through the approximation process for $y = x^3$.

You can give the students copies of Blackline Master 8.4A to use while working Problem 2.

Answers

For You to Explore

1. On the interval $[0, 1]$ the graph of $y = x^2$ is above the graph of $y = x^3$, so the area under $y = x^3$ should be smaller than the area under $y = x^2$.
2. See back of book.

PROBLEM 5 You may want to use Blackline Master 8.4B on an overhead and fill it in as students supply the entries, or you may want to hand out copies for students to complete individually.

PROBLEM 7 There is no need to talk about limits here. You might ask, though, how many subdivisions you need to get the upper sums within 0.001 of $\frac{1}{4}$.

Wrap Up

Before assigning homework, allow students some time to discuss and summarize their findings.

3. Find the base, height, and area of each rectangle. Then write the expression for $U_4[0, 1](x^3)$ by adding the four areas.

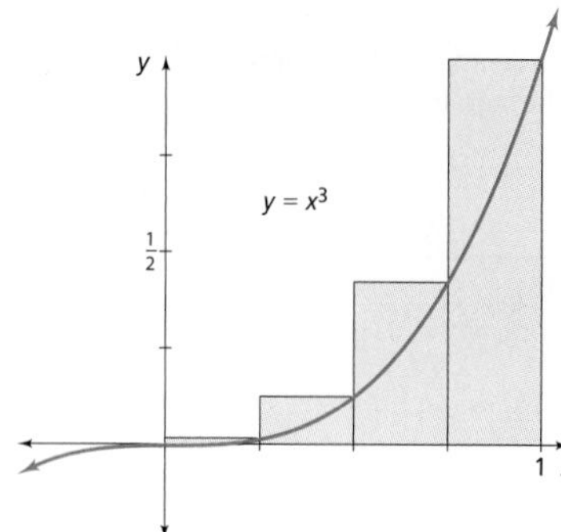

4. Write the expression for $U_5[0, 1](x^3)$, the upper approximation when the number of subdivisions is 5.

5. Copy and complete the table to see how the upper approximations change as the number of subdivisions increases.

Number of Subdivisions, n	Upper Sum Approximation for Different Numbers of Subdivisions, $U_n[0, 1](x^3)$
4	■
5	■
6	■
7	■
⋮	⋮
15	■
⋮	⋮
n	■

6. Find a closed form for $U_n[0, 1](x^3)$.
7. What happens to $U_n[0, 1](x^3)$ as n becomes large?
8. Find a closed form for $L_n[0, 1](x^3)$.
9. What happens to $L_n[0, 1](x^3)$ as n becomes large?
10. **Write About It** What is the exact value of $S[0, 1](x^3)$? Explain your reasoning.

Answers

3.

	Base	Height	Area
1st rectangle	$\frac{1}{4}$	$\left(\frac{1}{4}\right)^3$	$\frac{1}{4}\times\left(\frac{1}{4}\right)^3$
2nd rectangle	$\frac{1}{4}$	$\left(\frac{2}{4}\right)^3$	$\frac{1}{4}\times\left(\frac{2}{4}\right)^3$
3rd rectangle	$\frac{1}{4}$	$\left(\frac{3}{4}\right)^3$	$\frac{1}{4}\times\left(\frac{3}{4}\right)^3$
4th rectangle	$\frac{1}{4}$	$\left(\frac{4}{4}\right)^3$	$\frac{1}{4}\times\left(\frac{4}{4}\right)^3$

$$U_4[0, 1](x^3) = \frac{1}{4}\cdot\left(\frac{1}{4}\right)^3 + \frac{1}{4}\cdot\left(\frac{2}{4}\right)^3 + \frac{1}{4}\cdot\left(\frac{3}{4}\right)^3 + \frac{1}{4}\cdot\left(\frac{4}{4}\right)^3 = \frac{25}{64}$$

4. $$U_5[0, 1](x^3) = \frac{1}{5}\cdot\left(\frac{1}{5}\right)^3 + \frac{1}{5}\cdot\left(\frac{2}{5}\right)^3 + \frac{1}{5}\cdot\left(\frac{3}{5}\right)^3 + \frac{1}{5}\cdot\left(\frac{4}{5}\right)^3 + \frac{1}{5}\cdot\left(\frac{5}{5}\right)^3 = \frac{9}{25}$$

5. See back of book.

6. $$U_n[0, 1](x^3) = \frac{1}{n^4}\cdot\sum_{i=1}^{n} i^3 = \frac{n^2(n+1)^2}{4n^4} = \frac{1}{4} + \frac{1}{2n} + \frac{1}{4n^2}$$

7. As n becomes larger, $U_n[0, 1](x^3)$ approaches $\frac{1}{4}$.

8. $$L_n[0, 1](x^3) = \frac{1}{n^4}\cdot(0^3 + 1^3 + \cdots + (n - 1^3)) = \frac{1}{4} - \frac{1}{2n} + \frac{1}{4n^2}$$

9. As n becomes larger, $L_n[0, 1](x^3)$ approaches $\frac{1}{4}$.

10. The exact value of $S[0, 1](x^3)$ is $\frac{1}{4}$; the upper and lower sums both approach this value when n becomes large.

Exercises *Practicing Habits of Mind*

On Your Own

11. How can you find $S[0, 1](\sqrt{x})$? The picture below may help.

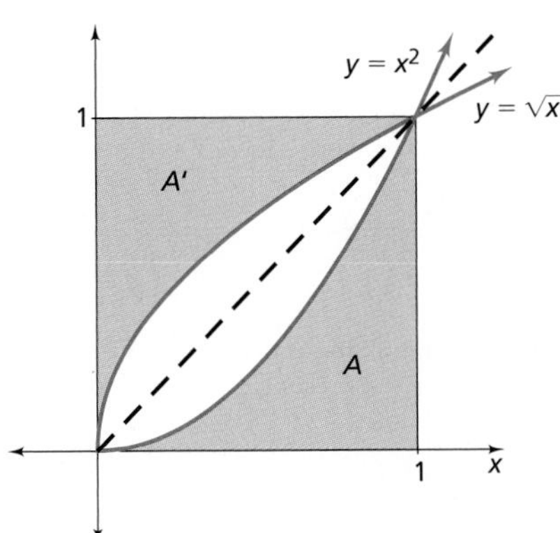

a. What is the relationship between the graphs of $y = x^2$ and $y = \sqrt{x}$?

b. How do the areas of A and A' compare? Explain your answer.

c. Find $S[0, 1](\sqrt{x})$.

12. Find $S[0, 1](\sqrt[3]{x})$.

13. In Investigation 8A, you found that $S[0, 1]\,(x^2) = \frac{1}{3}$. Use that fact to find the following areas.

a. $S[-1, 0](x^2)$

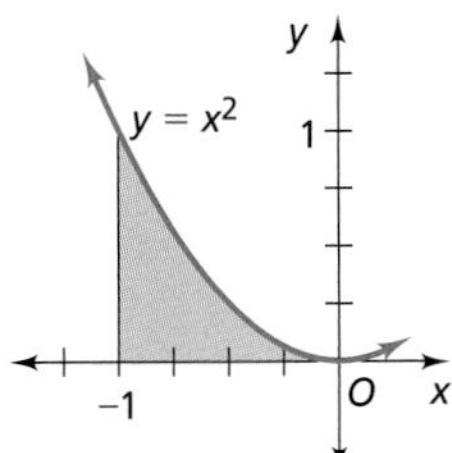

b. $S[0, 1](x^2 + 1)$ **c.** $S[-1, 1](x^2)$ **d.** $S[-1, 1](x^2 + 1)$

You do not need to use upper and lower sums in any of the exercises. Drawing the graph of a function might help.

Exercises

HOMEWORK
- Core: 11, 13, 14
- Optional: 12

Exercises

11. a. The graphs of $y = x^2$ and $y = \sqrt{x}$ are reflections of each other across the line $y = x$.

b. $A = A'$; answers may vary. Sample: the area between $y = x^2$ and $y = x$ is equal to the area between $y = \sqrt{x}$ and $y = x$, so the areas of the shaded regions are equal.

c. $\frac{2}{3}$

12. $\frac{3}{4}$

13. a. $\frac{1}{3}$

b. $1\frac{1}{3}$

c. $\frac{2}{3}$

d. $2\frac{2}{3}$

Use $S[0, 1](x^2) = \frac{1}{3}$ to find the areas.

e. $S[-1, 1](1 - x^2)$

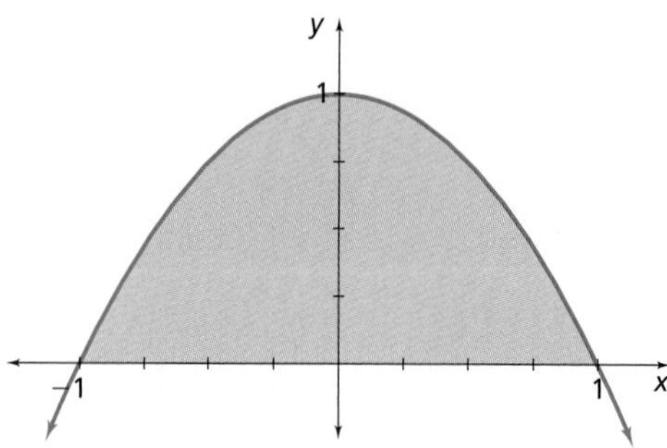

f. The area above the graph of $y = x^2$ and below the graph of $y = 1$.

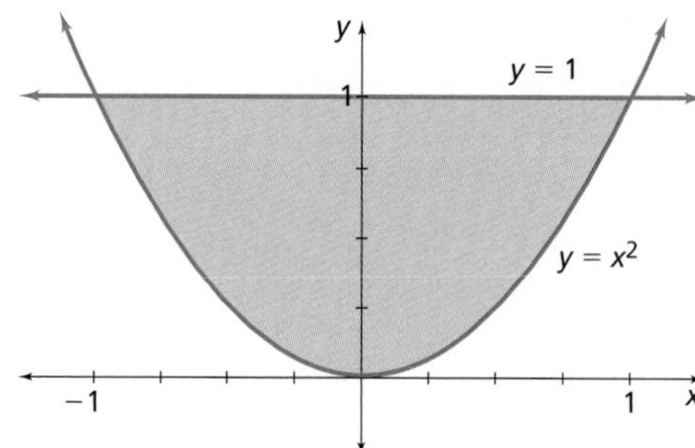

g. The area of the closed region between the x-axis and the graph of $y = x^2 - 1$.

h. The area of the closed region in the first quadrant between the graph of $y = x^2$ and $y = x^3$. (Use your answer to Problem 10 on page 654.)

Maintain Your Skills

14. Remember the identity $1 + r + r^2 + r^3 + \cdots + r^n = \frac{1 - r^{n+1}}{1 - r}$ from CME Project *Algebra 2*? Use it to find each of the following sums.

a. $1 + 5 + 5^2 + 5^3 + 5^4 + \cdots + 5^{12}$

b. $1 + \frac{1}{2} + \left(\frac{1}{2}\right)^2 + \left(\frac{1}{2}\right)^3 + \cdots + \left(\frac{1}{2}\right)^{10}$

c. $1 + 0.1 + (0.1)^2 + (0.1)^3 + \cdots + (0.1)^8$

Answers

13. e. $1\frac{1}{3}$

f. $1\frac{1}{3}$

g. $1\frac{1}{3}$

h. $\frac{1}{12}$

14. a. 305,175,781.25

b. $\frac{2047}{1024} = 2 - \frac{1}{2^{10}}$

c. 1.11111111

8.5 Cavalieri's Approach

In Lesson 8.4, you found $S[0, 1](x^3)$. You also know $S[0, 1](x^2)$ from the last investigation. You can find $S[0, 1](x^m)$ for other values of m, as well.

For You to Do

1. Find $S[0, 1](x^0)$.
2. Find $S[0, 1](x)$.
3. Is $S[0, 1](x^4)$ less than or greater than $S[0, 1](x^3)$? Explain.

You are now ready to look for a pattern and come up with a conjecture about $S[0, 1](x^m)$.

For Discussion

Complete the following statements.

4. $S[0, 1](x^0) = \blacksquare$
5. $S[0, 1](x^1) = \blacksquare$
6. $S[0, 1](x^2) = \blacksquare$
7. $S[0, 1](x^3) = \blacksquare$
8. Based on the pattern, make a conjecture about $S[0, 1](x^4)$.
9. Make a conjecture about $S[0, 1](x^m)$, for any positive integer m. How would you find $S[0, 1](x^m)$? Describe what you would need to know and what you would need to do.

You have a conjecture about the area under any curve $y = x^m$. However, a conjecture and a proven theorem are not the same thing. Around 1630, Bonaventura Cavalieri (1598–1647) turned his attention to this problem, extending Archimedes' result $S[0, 1](x^2) = \frac{1}{3}$ to find $S[0, 1](x^m)$ for $m > 2$.

For more information about Cavalieri, go to Web Code: bge-9031

Cavalieri proved that

$$S[0, 1](x^2) = \frac{1}{3}$$
$$S[0, 1](x^3) = \frac{1}{4}$$
$$S[0, 1](x^4) = \frac{1}{5}$$
$$S[0, 1](x^5) = \frac{1}{6}$$
$$\vdots \qquad \vdots$$

all the way up to $S[0, 1](x^9) = \frac{1}{10}$. Then he quit.

For You to Do

1. $S[0, 1](x^0) = 1$
2. $S[0, 1](x^1) = \frac{1}{2}$
3. On the interval $[0, 1]$ the graph of $y = x^4$ is below the graph of $y = x^3$, so the area under $y = x^4$ is smaller than the area under $y = x^3$.

For Discussion

4. $S[0, 1](x^0) = 1$
5. $S[0, 1](x^1) = \frac{1}{2}$
6. $S[0, 1](x^2) = \frac{1}{3}$
7. $S[0, 1](x^3) = \frac{1}{4}$
8. It seems that $S[0, 1](x^4)$ should equal $\frac{1}{5}$.
9. The pattern implies that $S[0, 1](x^m) = \frac{1}{m + 1}$, at least when m is a positive integer.

Lesson Overview

GOAL

- Calculate the area under the graph of $y = x^m$ between $x = 0$ and $x = 1$ for any positive integer m.

In this lesson, students find $S[0, 1](x^m)$ for positive integer values of m. In addition, the lesson previews an important idea from calculus that is essential to understanding the Fundamental Theorem of Calculus. It defines a new function G in terms of an old one f by the rule

$$G(x) = S[0, x](f(x))$$

The Fundamental Theorem says, (very) roughly, that the derivative of G is f. There is no need to go into that here, but students really stumble on this idea in calculus, and the primary difficulty is that they are not used to defining a function as a running accumulation of another function. So this lesson introduces it here as a simple case. Students previewed these ideas in Chapter 7 of CME Project *Algebra 2*.

Later in the chapter, the material on the natural logarithm uses this idea, so it is important to spend some time on it now.

CHECK YOUR UNDERSTANDING
- Core: 2, 3, 5, 8
- Optional: 1, 4, 6, 9
- Extension: 7

MATERIALS
- CAS (recommended)
- graphing calculators
- Blackline Master 8.5

HOMEWORK
- Core: 11, 12, 14
- Optional: 10, 13, 15

Launch

Jump right into the first For You to Do section.

Explore

For You to Do

PROBLEM 1 The graph of $y = x^0$ is the line $y = 1$ (except when $x = 0$, since 0^0 is undefined). Therefore $S[0, 1](x^0)$ is 1 unit, the area of the unit square.

PROBLEM 2 The area under the curve $y = x$ between 0 and 1 is the area of an isosceles right triangle with legs of length 1.

For Discussion

PROBLEM 11

$$U_n[0, 1](x^2) = \frac{1}{n^3} \cdot \sum_{k=1}^{n} k^2 = \frac{1}{n^3} \cdot \frac{n(n+1)(2n+1)}{6} = \frac{2n^3 + 3n + n}{6n^3} = \frac{1}{3} + \frac{1}{2n} + \frac{1}{6n^2}$$

$$U_n[0, 1](x^3) = \frac{1}{n^4} \cdot \sum_{k=1}^{n} k^3 = \frac{1}{n^4} \cdot \frac{n^2(n+1)^2}{4} = \frac{n^4 + 2n^3 + n^2}{4n^4} = \frac{1}{4} + \frac{1}{2n} + \frac{1}{4n^2}$$

To find out why Cavalieri did not go beyond the case $y = x^9$, consider what is involved in finding a general formula for $S[0, 1](x^m)$. In essence, Cavalieri tried to continue the upper- and lower-sum game that Archimedes had used so successfully to find the area under $y = x^2$, some 1800 years earlier.

For Discussion

10. Using the same methods you used for $U_n[0, 1](x^2)$ and $U_n[0, 1](x^3)$ discuss every line in this calculation.

$$\begin{aligned} U_n[0, 1](x^m) &= \tfrac{1}{n} \cdot \left(\tfrac{1}{n}\right)^m + \tfrac{1}{n} \cdot \left(\tfrac{2}{n}\right)^m + \tfrac{1}{n} \cdot \left(\tfrac{3}{n}\right)^m + \cdots + \tfrac{1}{n} \cdot \left(\tfrac{n}{n}\right)^m \\ &= \tfrac{1}{n} \cdot \tfrac{1^m}{n^m} + \tfrac{1}{n} \cdot \tfrac{2^m}{n^m} + \tfrac{1}{n} \cdot \tfrac{3^m}{n^m} + \cdots + \tfrac{1}{n} \cdot \tfrac{n^m}{n^m} \\ &= \frac{1^m}{n^{m+1}} + \frac{2^m}{n^{m+1}} + \frac{3^m}{n^{m+1}} + \cdots + \frac{n^m}{n^{m+1}} \\ &= \frac{1}{n^{m+1}}(1^m + 2^m + 3^m + \cdots + n^m) \\ &= \frac{1}{n^{m+1}} \sum_{k=1}^{n} k^m \end{aligned}$$

Why is it okay to pull the $\frac{1}{n^{m+1}}$ out of the sum?

So, to find a general closed form for $U_n[0, 1](x^m)$, Cavalieri needed to first find a general closed form for

$$\sum_{k=1}^{n} k^m$$

For Discussion

11. Use the general result of the last discussion and the closed forms you know for

$$\sum_{k=1}^{n} k^2 \quad \text{and} \quad \sum_{k=1}^{n} k^3$$

to find closed forms for $U_n[0, 1](x^2)$ and $U_n[0, 1](x^3)$. Check these with the closed forms you obtained earlier.

Habits of Mind

Try a specific case. It is nice to check general results in special cases where you know the answer. It gives you confidence.

At this point, it seemed that there was nothing to stop Cavalieri from finding $S[0, 1](x^m)$ for all positive integers m. All he needed to do was to find a general closed form for $\sum_{k=1}^{n} k^m$. Unfortunately, that is easier said than done. However, Cavalieri was able to find closed forms for specific values of m.

Answers

For Discussion

10. $U_n[0, 1](x^m) = \frac{1}{n} \cdot \left(\frac{1}{n}\right)^m + \frac{1}{n} \cdot \left(\frac{2}{n}\right)^m + \frac{1}{n} \cdot \left(\frac{3}{n}\right)^m + \cdots + \frac{1}{n} \cdot \left(\frac{n}{n}\right)^m$ (summing up the areas of the approximating rectangles)

$= \frac{1}{n} \cdot \frac{1^m}{n^m} + \frac{1}{n} \cdot \frac{2^m}{n^m} + \frac{1}{n} \cdot \frac{3^m}{n^m} + \cdots + \frac{1}{n} \cdot \frac{n^m}{n^m}$ (using algebra)

$= \frac{1^m}{n^{m+1}} + \frac{2^m}{n^{m+1}} + \frac{3^m}{n^{m+1}} + \cdots + \frac{n^m}{n^{m+1}}$ (multiplying fractions)

$= \frac{1}{n^{m+1}}(1^m + 2^m + 3^m + \cdots + n^m)$ (factoring out a common term)

$= \frac{1}{n^{m+1}} \sum_{k=1}^{n} k^m$ (using summation notation)

11. $U_n[0, 1](x^2) = \frac{1}{3} + \frac{1}{2n} + \frac{1}{6n^2}$

$U_n[0, 1](x^3) = \frac{1}{4} + \frac{1}{2n} + \frac{1}{4n^2}$

You could go on to find $S[0, 1](x^5)$ using exactly the same method as above. But there is no need to stop there. You could calculate $S[0, 1](x^m)$, for $m = 6, 7, 8,$ and so on.

As you know from Chapter 5, getting the formulas for the sums of powers involves some pretty hefty algebra, and things get more complicated quickly as powers get bigger. The fact that Cavalieri was able to work his way all the way up to $m = 9$ is a tribute to his perseverance and algebraic skills. The surprising thing is not that he quit after dealing with the case $m = 9$ (to find that $S[0, 1](x^9) = \frac{1}{10}$), but rather that he did not call it quits much earlier. Remember, Cavalieri did not have a CAS.

Developing Habits of Mind

Find another way. Cavalieri was hampered by the complicated closed forms for sums of powers. Later mathematicians paved the way for modern CAS technology, which allows one to easily generate such closed forms.

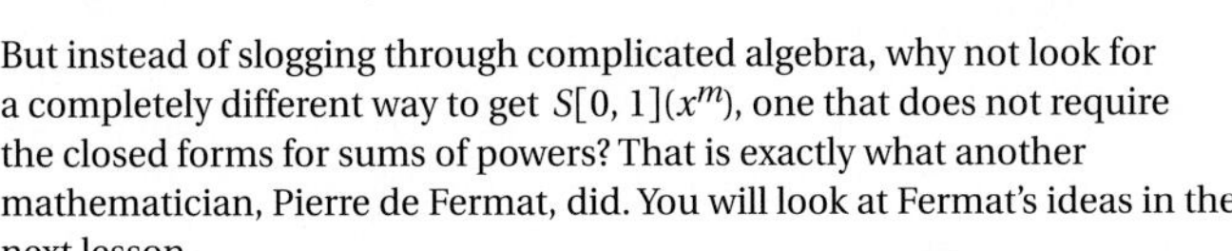

But instead of slogging through complicated algebra, why not look for a completely different way to get $S[0, 1](x^m)$, one that does not require the closed forms for sums of powers? That is exactly what another mathematician, Pierre de Fermat, did. You will look at Fermat's ideas in the next lesson.

Mathematicians love to build on what they know and to take it to another level. Now that you know how to find $S[0, 1](x^2)$, you also know how to find $S[1, 2](x^2)$, $S[1, 3](x^2)$, $S[1, 6](x^2)$, and in general, $S[1, b](x^2)$ for any integer b where $b > 1$. Mathematicians immediately see this as a function of b and start to wonder about its properties.

For You to Do

12. Copy and complete the table for the function $b \mapsto S[1, b](x^2)$.

b	Area under $y = x^2$ from 1 to b, $S[1, b](x^2)$
2	■
3	■
4	■
5	■
6	■

For You to Do

PROBLEM 12 You may want to use Blackline Master 8.5 on an overhead and fill it in as students supply the entries, or you may want to hand out copies for students to complete individually.

Wrap Up

Wrap up with a discussion of the Developing Habits of Mind section in this investigation, which motivates the next lesson.

Assessment Resources

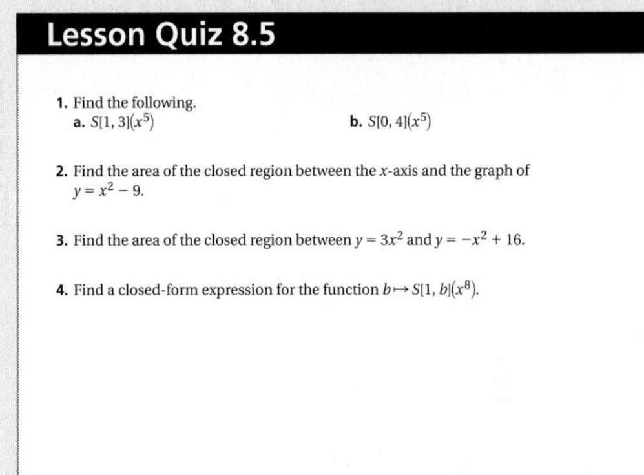

Lesson Quiz 8.5

1. Find the following.
   a. $S[1, 3](x^5)$ b. $S[0, 4](x^5)$
2. Find the area of the closed region between the x-axis and the graph of $y = x^2 - 9$.
3. Find the area of the closed region between $y = 3x^2$ and $y = -x^2 + 16$.
4. Find a closed-form expression for the function $b \mapsto S[1, b](x^8)$.

For You to Do

12.

b	Area under $y = x^2$ from 1 to b, $S[1, b](x^2)$
2	$S[1, 2](x^2) = \frac{7}{3} \approx 2.333$
3	$S[1, 3](x^2) = \frac{26}{3} \approx 8.666$
4	$S[1, 4](x^2) = \frac{63}{3} \approx 21$
5	$S[1, 5](x^2) = \frac{124}{3} \approx 41.333$
6	$S[1, 6](x^2) = \frac{215}{3} \approx 71.667$

Think of the graph of $y = x^2$, with a point b moving along the x-axis. $S[1, b](x^2)$ is the area bounded by the graph, the x-axis, the vertical line through $(1, 0)$ and the vertical line through $(b, 0)$.

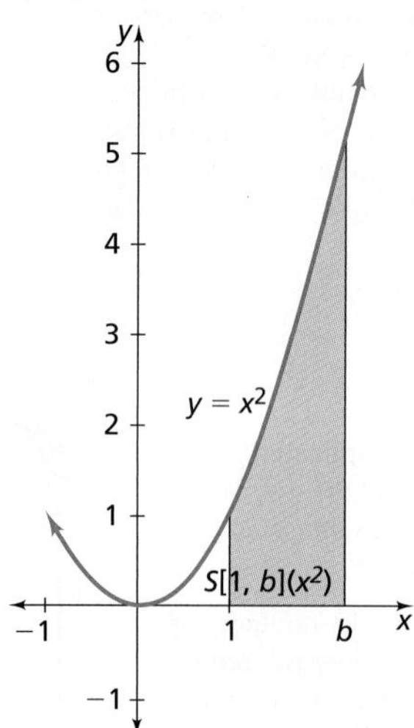

For Discussion

The table you completed in Problem 12 is for the function $G(b) = S[1, b](x^2)$.

13. Find a closed-form expression for G.

14. In the table, b takes on only positive integer values. Can b be something else, for example, 2.7 or $7\frac{1}{3}$? Explain.

15. Sketch the graph of G between 1 and 6.

Answers

For Discussion

13. $G(b) = \frac{b^3 - 1}{3}$

14. Yes; b can be any real number greater than 1. It makes sense to talk about the area under the graph of $y = x^2$ (which is defined for all real numbers) from $x = 1$ to $x = b$. Also, the derivation of $S[1, b](x^2) = \frac{b^3 - 1}{3}$ had no restrictions on b other than it being a real number.

15. The graph of G

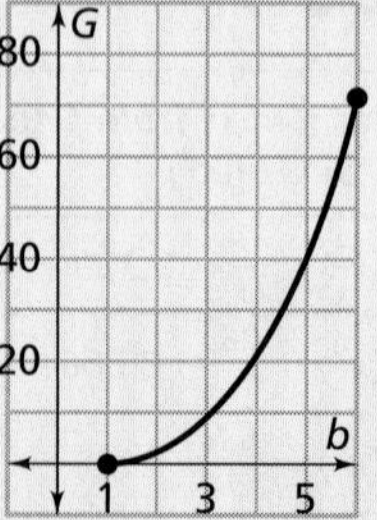

Exercises *Practicing Habits of Mind*

Check Your Understanding

1. Even with a CAS, the algebra of sum identities is substantial. Obtain a closed-form expression for

$$U_n[0, 1](x^5)$$

and find the exact value of

$$S[0, 1](x^5)$$

2. There are at least two ways to come up with a conjecture for $S[0, 1](\sqrt[m]{x})$:

- Use $\frac{1}{m}$ instead of m in the formula you developed in this lesson.
- Use the symmetry of the graphs of $y = x^m$ and $y = \sqrt[m]{x}$.

a. What formula for the upper sum do you get from each of these methods? Are the formulas equivalent?

b. Is there any value of m for which your formula does not work?

3. Find $S[1, 2](x^4)$.

4. Make a conjecture about the value of $S[1, 2](x^m)$ where m is a positive integer.

5. Find the area of the closed region between the x-axis and the graph of $y = x^2 - 1$.

6. Find the area of the closed region between the graphs of $y = x^4$ and $y = 2 - x^2$.

7. **Take It Further** Find a value of k for which the area in the first quadrant between the graphs of $y = x^k$ and $y = x^{k+1}$ is less than 0.01.

8. Find a closed-form expression for the function $b \mapsto S[1, b](x^3)$.

9. Find a closed-form expression for the function $b \mapsto S[1, b](x^4)$.

On Your Own

10. Fill in the details for the derivation of $S[0, 1](x^4)$.

a. Substitute $m = 4$ into the general formula for the upper sum of the area from the discussion in this lesson,

$$U_n[0, 1](x^m) = \frac{1}{n^{m+1}} \sum_{k=1}^{n} k^m$$

Exercises

HOMEWORK

- Core: 11, 12, 14
- Optional: 10, 13, 15

Exercises

1. $\frac{1}{6}$

2. a. • $S[0, 1](x^{\frac{1}{m}}) = \dfrac{1}{\frac{1}{m} + 1} = \dfrac{m}{m + 1}$

• $S[0, 1](\sqrt[m]{x})$
$= 1 - S[0, 1](x^m)$
$= 1 - \dfrac{1}{m + 1} = \dfrac{m}{m + 1}$

The formulas are equivalent.

b. The formula does not work for $n = -1$.

3. $\frac{31}{5}$

4. $\dfrac{2^{m+1} - 1}{m + 1}$

5. $\frac{4}{3}$

6. $\frac{44}{15}$

7. any integer k greater than 8

8. $\dfrac{b^4 - 1}{4}$

9. $\dfrac{b^5 - 1}{5}$

10. a. $U_n[0, 1](x^4) = \frac{1}{n^5} \cdot \sum_{k=1}^{n} k^4$

Additional Resources

PRINT RESOURCES
- Solution Manual
- Practice Workbook
- Assessment Resources
- Teaching Resources

TECHNOLOGY
- Interactive Textbook
- TeacherExpress CD-ROM
- ExamView CD-ROM
- PHSchool.com

Additional Practice

1. Obtain a closed form for $U_n[0, 1](x^6)$ and find the exact value of $S[0, 1](x^6)$. Use the formula

$$\sum_{k=1}^{n} k^6 = \frac{n(n+1)(2n+1)(3n^4+6n^3-3n+1)}{42}$$

2. Explain how knowing $S[0, 1](x^2)$ makes it easier to find $S[1, b](x^2)$ for any integer b where $b > 1$.

3. Find each of the following.
a. $S[1, 2](x^3)$ **b.** $S[1, 3](x^3)$
c. $S[1, 4](x^4)$ **d.** $S[1, 5](x^4)$

4. Find the area of the closed region between the x-axis and the graph of $y = x^2 - 4$.

5. Find the area of the closed region between the x-axis and the graph of $y = x^3 + 8$ from -2 to 0.

6. Find the area of the closed region between the graphs of $y = x^2$ and $y = -x^2 + 8$.

7. Find a closed-form expression for the function $b \mapsto S[1, b](x^5)$.

8. Find a closed-form expression for the function $b \mapsto S[1, b](x^6)$.

9. Find the area of the closed region in the first quadrant between the graphs of $y = x^2$ and $y = x^4$

10. Find the area of the closed region in the first quadrant between the graphs of $y = \sqrt{x}$ and $y = x^3$.

11. Find the area of the region above the graph of $y = x$ and below the graph of $y = x^2$ between $x = 2$ and $x = 3$.

12. Explain how you would find the area of the region above the graph of $y = -x^2$ and below the graph of $y = x$ between $x = 1$ and $x = 3$. Note that part of the region lies below the x-axis.

Practice: For Lesson 8.5, assign Exercises 1–12.

b. What happens to the upper sum as you increase the number of subdivisions?

c. Determine the exact value of $S[0, 1](x^4)$.

11. Find $S[1, 2](x^3)$. To do so, you could
- work out the upper and lower sums $U_n[1, 2](x^3)$ and $L_n[1, 2](x^3)$
- determine what happens to the sums, $U_n[1, 2](x^3)$ and $L_n[1, 2](x^3)$, when n becomes larger and larger
- draw a conclusion about $S[1, 2](x^3)$

Or you might use a different method.

12. Find the area of the closed region in the first quadrant between the graphs of $y = x^2$ and $y = x^3$.

13. Find the area of the closed region between the graphs of $y = x^2$ and $y = \sqrt{x}$.

14. **Standardized Test Prep** The graphs of $f(x)$ and $g(x)$ are as shown. Which of the following gives the area of the shaded region?

A. $[f(x) - g(x)](b - a)$
B. $[g(x) - f(x)](b - a)$
C. $S[a,b](f(x)) - S[a,b](g(x))$
D. $S[a,b](g(x)) - S[a,b](f(x))$

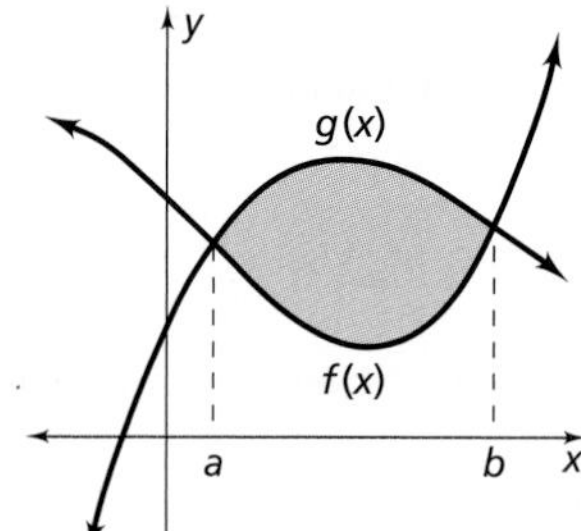

Go Online PHSchool.com

For additional practice, go to Web Code: bga-0805

Maintain Your Skills

15. a. Draw the graphs of $y = x$, $y = 2x$, $y = 3x$ and $y = 4x$ between 0 and 1.

b. Find the area of the region above the graph of $y = x$ and below the graph of $y = 2x$ between $x = 0$ and $x = 1$.

c. Find the area of the region above the graph of $y = x$ and below the graph of $y = 3x$ between $x = 0$ and $x = 1$.

d. Find the area of the region above the graph of $y = x$ and below the graph of $y = 4x$ between $x = 0$ and $x = 1$.

e. Make a conjecture about the area between the graph of $y = x$ and the graph of $y = mx$ $(m > 1)$ between $x = 0$ and $x = 1$.

Answers

10. b. As n gets larger, $U_n[0, 1](x^4)$ approaches $\frac{1}{5}$.

c. $S[0, 1](x^4) = \frac{1}{5}$

11. $3\frac{3}{4}$

12. $\frac{1}{12}$

13. $\frac{1}{3}$

14. D

15. a.

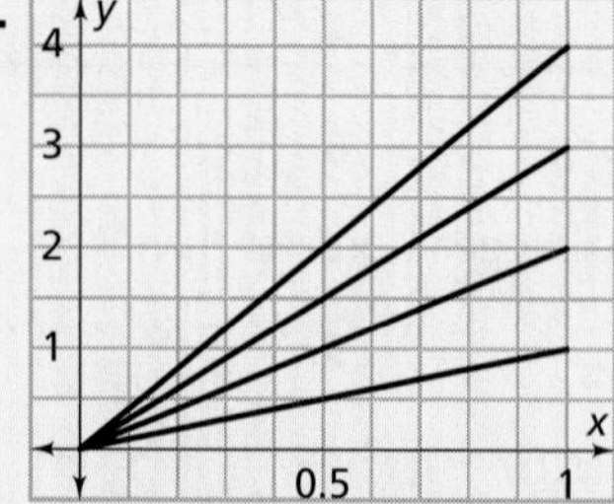

b. $\frac{1}{2}$ **c.** 1

d. $\frac{3}{2}$ **e.** $\frac{m - 1}{2}$

8.6 Fermat's Big Idea

Just about the time Cavalieri was patiently working his way up the curves $y = x^m$ one m at a time, Pierre de Fermat took a new and original approach to the same problem.

When Cavalieri calculated upper and lower sums, he always divided his intervals on the x-axis into equal parts. For example, the coordinates of Cavalieri's points of the interval [1, 2] for 5 subdivisions would be

$$1, 1\tfrac{1}{5}, 1\tfrac{2}{5}, 1\tfrac{3}{5}, 1\tfrac{4}{5}, 2$$

Fermat's big idea was to do subdivisions with unequal intervals. He suggested dividing an interval with a geometric sequence. For the same interval [1, 2] and the same number of subdivisions, Fermat would use the following points of subdivision:

$$1, r, r^2, r^3, r^4, r^5 \qquad \text{where } r^5 = 2$$

Here, r is a number between 1 and 2, such that $r^5 = 2$.

Cavalieri divided the interval up into an arithmetic sequence. This one has first term 1 and common difference $\frac{1}{5}$.

Remember...

Terms in a geometric sequence have a common ratio.

For Discussion

1. Find approximate values for the above Fermat points of subdivision (the number of subdivisions is 5). Plot the points on a number line.
2. Write the sequence of Fermat points for the interval [1, 2] with 6 subdivisions. Plot the points on a number line.
3. Write the sequence of Fermat points for the interval [1, 2] with 10 subdivisions. Plot the points on a number line.
4. Explain how the lengths of the subintervals change as the number of subdivisions grows.

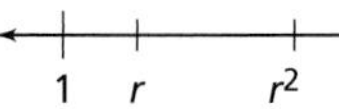

1 r r^2 . . . r^{n-1} $r^n = 2$

5. Write algebraic expressions and approximate values for r in the Fermat subdivision of the interval [1, 2], if the number of subdivisions, n, is

   a. 20 **b.** 40 **c.** 80
6. What number does r approach as the number of subdivisions grows?

Note that although n and r change, r^n remains equal to 2.

Fermat's method is very similar to the method of Archimedes and Cavalieri. However, Fermat could solve problems that Cavalieri and Archimedes could not.

Here is some handy notation for Fermat's method.

Fermat lower sum $= LF_n[a, b](f(x))$: the lower approximation of the area under the curve $f(x)$ from $x = a$ to $x = b$ when the number of

Lesson Overview

GOAL

- Calculate the area under the graph of $y = x^m$ between $x = 0$ and $x = 1$ for any positive integer m.

This lesson shows how, in one fell swoop, to use the Fermat sums to find $S[1, 2](x^m)$ for all positive integers m.

CHECK YOUR UNDERSTANDING
- Core: 1, 2, 3, 4
- Optional: 5, 6, 7, 8

MATERIALS
- CAS (recommended)
- graphing calculators

HOMEWORK
- Core: 9, 11, 13, 14, 15, 23
- Optional: 10, 12, 16, 17, 18, 20, 24, 25
- Extension: 19, 21, 22

VOCABULARY
- Fermat lower sum, $LF_n[a, b](f(x))$
- Fermat upper sum, $UF_n[a, b](f(x))$

Launch

Begin the lesson with the first For Discussion section.

Explore

For Discussion

Use the For Discussion problems to elicit conversation about the key ideas in the introduction to this lesson.

For Discussion

1. $1, r = \sqrt[5]{2} \approx 1.1487, r^2 \approx 1.3195, r^3 \approx 1.5157, r^4 \approx 1.7411$, and $r^5 = 2$

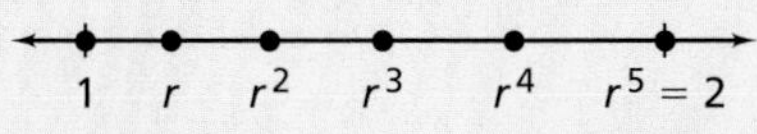

1 r r^2 r^3 r^4 $r^5 = 2$

2. $1, r = \sqrt[6]{2} \approx 1.1225, r^2 \approx 1.2599, r^3 = \sqrt{2} \approx 1.4142, r^4 \approx 1.5874, r^5 \approx 1.7818$, and $r^6 = 2$

1 r r^2 r^3 r^4 r^5 $r^6 = 2$

3. $1, r = \sqrt[10]{2} \approx 1.0178, r^2 = \sqrt[5]{2} \approx 1.1487, r^3 \approx 1.2311, r^4 \approx 1.3195, r^5 = \sqrt{2} \approx 1.4142, r^6 \approx 1.5157, r^7 \approx 1.6245, r^8 \approx 1.7411, r^9 \approx 1.8661$, and $r^{10} = 2$

1 r r^2 r^3 r^4 r^5 r^6 r^7 r^8 r^9 $r^{10} = 2$

4. Answers may vary. Sample: As you go from left to right, the points spread out since the lengths of the subintervals also form a geometric sequence with the same ratio of successive terms.

5. a. $r = \sqrt[20]{2} \approx 1.0353$

b. $r = \sqrt[40]{2} \approx 1.0175$

c. $r = \sqrt[80]{2} \approx 1.0087$

6. r seems to approach 1 as the number n of subintervals grows.

For You to Do

PROBLEM 7 Since the number of subdivisions is 3, $r = \sqrt[3]{2}$.

$$\begin{aligned} LF_3[1, 2](x^2) &= 1^2 \cdot (r - 1) + r^2 \cdot (r^2 - r) \\ &\quad + (r^2)^2 \cdot (r^3 - r^2) \\ &= 1 \cdot (r - 1) + r^2 \cdot (r(r - 1)) \\ &\quad + r^4 \cdot (r^2(r - 1)) \\ &= (r - 1) + r^3 \cdot (r - 1) + r^6 \cdot (r - 1) \\ &= (r - 1)(1 + r^3 + r^6) \\ &= \left(\sqrt[3]{2} - 1\right)(1 + 2 + 4) \\ &\approx 1.8194 \end{aligned}$$

$$\begin{aligned} UF_3[1, 2](x^2) &= r^2 \cdot (r - 1) + (r^2)^2 \cdot (r^2 - r) \\ &\quad + (r^2)^3 \cdot (r^3 - r^2) \\ &= r^2 \cdot (r - 1) + r^4 \cdot (r(r - 1)) \\ &\quad + r^6 \cdot (r^2(r - 1)) \\ &= r^2 \cdot (r - 1) + r^5 \cdot (r - 1) \\ &\quad + r^8 \cdot (r - 1) \\ &= (r - 1)(r^2 + r^5 + r^8) \\ &= \left(\sqrt[3]{2} - 1\right)\left(\left(\sqrt[3]{2}\right)^2 + \left(\sqrt[3]{2}\right)^5 \right. \\ &\quad \left. + \left(\sqrt[3]{2}\right)^8\right) \\ &\approx 2.8882 \end{aligned}$$

So, the area under $y = x^2$ from 1 to 2 is greater than 1.8194 and less than 2.8882.

Fermat subdivisions is n. **Fermat upper sum** $= UF_n[a, b](f(x))$: the upper approximation of the area under the graph of the function $f(x)$ from $x = a$ to $x = b$ when the number of Fermat subdivisions is n.

Say "Fermat lower sub n" and "Fermat upper sub n."

You find $LF_n[a, b](f(x))$ and $UF_n[a, b](f(x))$ the same way you found $L_n[a, b](f(x))$ and $U_n[a, b](f(x))$, namely by summing the area of the n rectangles formed by subdividing the interval $[a, b]$. The difference between the method of Fermat and that of Cavalieri is that the bases of the rectangles in Fermat's method form a geometric sequence.

For You to Do

7. Find an estimate for the area under the graph of $y = x^2$ from 1 to 2 using Fermat's method with 3 subdivisions.

$$■ < S[1, 2](x^2) < ■$$

Example

Problem Calculate the Fermat lower sum for the area under the graph of $y = x^3$ from $x = 1$ to $x = 2$ with 3 subdivisions.

	Base	Height	Area
1st rectangle	$r - 1$	1	$1(r - 1)$
2nd rectangle	$r^2 - r$	r^3	$r^3(r^2 - r)$
3rd rectangle	$r^3 - r^2$	$(r^2)^3$	$r^6(r^3 - r^2)$

Solution With three subdivisions, the Fermat points will be $1, r, r^2, r^3 = 2$, and the Fermat lower sum is

$$\begin{aligned} LF_3[1, 2](x^3) &= 1(r - 1) + r^3(r^2 - r) + (r^2)^3(r^3 - r^2) \\ &= 1(r - 1) + r^3(r(r - 1)) + r^6(r^2(r - 1)) \\ &= 1(r - 1) + r^4(r - 1) + r^8(r - 1) \\ &= (r - 1)(1 + r^4 + r^8) \\ &= (r - 1)(1 + r^4 + (r^4)^2) \end{aligned}$$

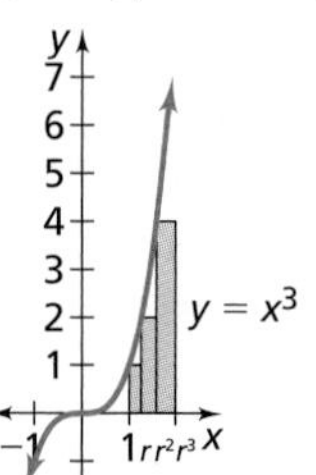

Answers

For You to Do

7. $1.8194 < S[1, 2](x^2) < 2.8882$

For You to Do

8. Show that when you increase the number of subdivisions to four, the Fermat points are $1, r, r^2, r^3, r^4 = 2$ and the Fermat lower sum is

$$LF_4[1,2](x^3) = (r-1)(1 + r^4 + (r^4)^2 + (r^4)^3)$$

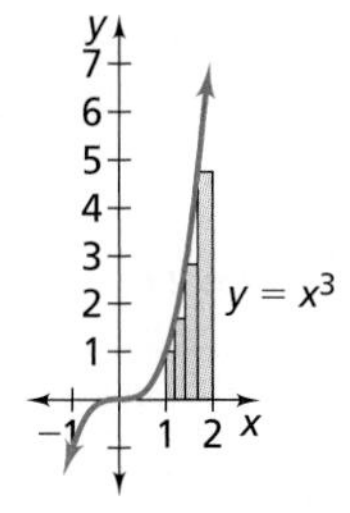

Similarly, for five subdivisions, the Fermat points are $1, r, r^2, r^3, r^4, r^5 = 2$, and the Fermat lower sum is

$$LF_5[1,2](x^3) = (r-1)(1 + r^4 + (r^4)^2 + (r^4)^3 + (r^4)^4)$$

Now look at the changes in $LF[1,2](x^3)$, as you increase the number of subdivisions:

$$LF_3[1,2](x^3) = (r-1)(1 + r^4 + (r^4)^2)$$
$$LF_4[1,2](x^3) = (r-1)(1 + r^4 + (r^4)^2 + (r^4)^3)$$
$$LF_5[1,2](x^3) = (r-1)(1 + r^4 + (r^4)^2 + (r^4)^3 + (r^4)^4)$$

Note that the value of r is different in each of these.

For each new subdivision, you add another term to the geometric sequence of terms. Since there is a formula for summing the terms of a geometric sequence of any length, using Fermat's method you can find a closed form for the lower sum (and the upper sum, too) for any number of subdivisions.

For Discussion

9. What is $LF_n[1,2](x^3)$?

Thus far, Fermat's method looks almost exactly like that of Cavalieri and Archimedes. Remember, their trouble was finding a closed form for the upper and lower sums when using large numbers of subdivisions for functions of the form x^m where m was bigger than 2. Fermat avoided this problem by dividing the interval with a geometric sequence. He knew that in finding the upper and lower sum he would be summing the terms of a geometric sequence. Geometric sequences are easy to sum.

$$1 + q + q^2 + \ldots + q^{n-1} = \frac{q^n - 1}{q - 1}$$

This works for any ratio $q \neq 1$ and any number of terms n. In choosing this subdivision, Fermat avoided Cavalieri's difficulty finding closed forms for $\sum_{k=1}^{n} k^m$.

For You to Do

8. $$\begin{aligned} LF_4[1,2](x^3) &= 1(r-1) + r^3(r^2 - r) + ((r^2)^3(r^3 - r^2) + ((r^3)^3)(r^4 - r^3) \\ &= 1(r-1) + r^3(r(r-1)) + r^6(r^2(r-1)) + r^9(r^3(r-1)) \\ &= 1(r-1) + r^4(r-1) + r^8(r-1) + r^{12}(r-1) \\ &= (r-1)(1 + r^4 + r^8 + r^{12}) \\ &= (r-1)(1 + r^4 + (r^4)^2 + (r^4)^3) \end{aligned}$$

For Discussion

9. $LF_n[1,2](x^3) = (r-1)(1 + r^4 + (r^4)^2 + (r^4)^3 + (r^4)^4 + (r^{n-1})^{n-1})$

In Lesson 8.5, you used Archimedes' method to find that the area under the graph of $y = x^2$ from $x = 1$ to $x = 2$, $S[1, 2](x^2)$, was $\frac{7}{3}$. By first using Fermat's method on an example that you already know the answer to, you can avoid making mistakes, and you can reassure yourself that it really works.

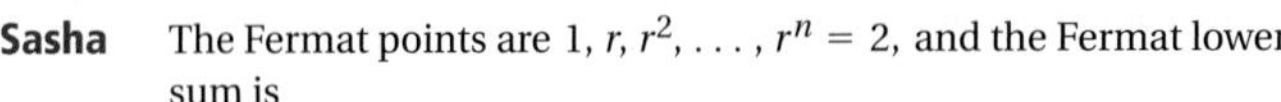

Sasha and Derman are working on writing a general expression for the Fermat lower sum for the area under the graph of $y = x^2$ from $x = 1$ to $x = 2$, with n subdivisions, $LF_n[1, 2](x^2)$. They want to know if the lower sum approach $\frac{7}{3}$ as the number of subdivisions, n, increases.

Sasha The Fermat points are $1, r, r^2, \ldots, r^n = 2$, and the Fermat lower sum is

$$LF_n[1, 2](x^2) = 1(r - 1) + r^2(r^2 - r) + (r^2)^2(r^3 - r^2) + \cdots + (r^{n-1})^2(r^n - r^{n-1})$$

Derman Oh, not this thing again. . . . Didn't we just do this calculation? Now we have to do it again?

Sasha Hey, you're right! We did just do this calculation. And by the same reasoning,

$$LF_n[1, 2](x^2) = (r - 1)(1 + r^3 + r^6 + \cdots + (r^3)^{n-1})$$

Derman Can you use one of your "favorite identities"?

Sasha Of course.

$$\begin{aligned} LF_n[1, 2](x^2) &= \left(\frac{(r^3)^{((n-1)+1)} - 1}{r^3 - 1}\right)(r - 1) && \text{The formula for summing geometric sequences} \\ &= \left(\frac{r^{3n} - 1}{r^3 - 1}\right)(r - 1) \\ &= \left(\frac{2^3 - 1}{r^3 - 1}\right)(r - 1) && r^n = 2 \\ &= \left(\frac{7}{r^3 - 1}\right)(r - 1) \\ &= \left(\frac{7}{(r - 1)(r^2 + r + 1)}\right)(r - 1) && \text{Factor } (r^4 - 1). \\ &= \frac{7}{r^2 + r + 1} && (r - 1) \text{ cancels (note that } r \neq 1). \end{aligned}$$

As n increases, r gets closer and closer to 1 but is always a little greater than 1. So as you increase the number of subdivisions, $\frac{7}{r^2 + r + 1}$ gets closer and closer to $\frac{7}{1 + 1 + 1} = \frac{7}{3}$.

Derman So as n becomes larger and larger, $LF_n[1, 2](x^2)$ gets closer and closer to $\frac{7}{3}$.

For You to Do

10. Write a general expression for $UF_n[1, 2](x^2)$.

11. What number does $UF_n[1, 2](x^2)$ approach as n becomes large? Why?

12. Use your answer to Problem 11 to find $S[1, 2](x^2)$.

So, to sum up, using Fermat's method gives $S[1, 2](x^3) = \frac{7}{3}$. That is the same result you get using Archimedes' method.

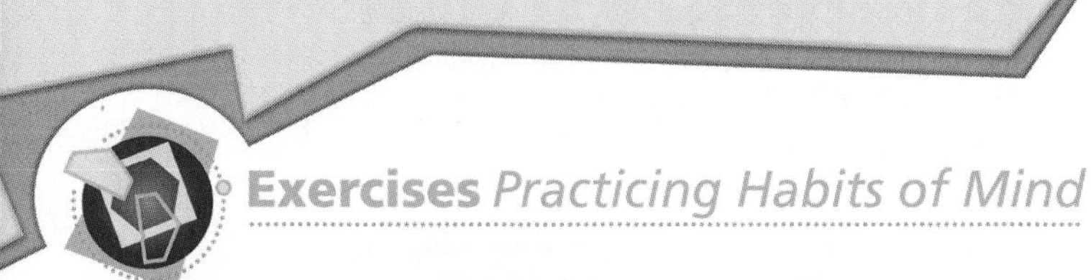

Exercises *Practicing Habits of Mind*

Check Your Understanding

1. Why does Fermat's method not work for the interval [0, 1]?

2. Use the following steps to find the Fermat lower sum for $S[1, 2](x^m)$ for any positive integer m.

a. For n subdivisions, write down expressions for the first three and the last three Fermat points in the subdivision.

b. Copy and complete the table.

Fermat Lower Sum for $y = x^m$, $LF_n[1, 2](x^m)$

	Base	Height	Area
1st rectangle	$r - 1$	1	$1(r - 1)$
2nd rectangle	$r^2 - r = r(r - 1)$	r^m	$r^{m+1}(r - 1)$
3rd rectangle	$r^3 - r^2 = r^2(r - 1)$	$(r^2)^m = r^{2m}$	$r^{2(m+1)}(r - 1)$
4th rectangle	$r^4 - r^3 = r^3(r - 1)$	■	■
⋮	⋮	⋮	⋮
nth rectangle	■	■	■

c. Add the areas of these rectangles to obtain an expression for the Fermat lower sum $LF_n[1, 2](x^m)$.

d. Use the formula for the geometric series to obtain the closed form.

e. What happens to $LF_n[1, 2](x^m)$ when you increase the number of subdivisions?

As n increases, r approaches 1. Remember that $r^n = 2$.

Answers

For You to Do

10. $UF_n[1, 2](x^2) = \frac{7r^2}{r^2 + r + 1}$

11. As n increases, r approaches 1 and $UF_n[1, 2](x^2)$ approaches $\frac{7 \cdot 1^2}{1^2 + 1 + 1} = \frac{7}{3}$.

12. Since $UF_n[1, 2](x^2)$ and $LF_n[1, 2](x^2)$ both approach $\frac{7}{3}$ as n increases, $S[1, 2](x^2) = \frac{7}{3}$.

Exercises

1. 0 cannot be the leftmost point of the interval, since the second point must be r times the leftmost point and $0 \cdot r = 0$.

2. a. $1, r = \sqrt[n]{2}, r^2, \ldots, r^{n-2}, r^{n-1}, r^n = 2$

b–c. See back of book.

d. $LF_n[1, 2](x^m) = \frac{2^{m+1} - 1}{\sum_{i=0}^{m} r^i}$

e. It approaches $\frac{2^{m+1} - 1}{m + 1}$.

For You to Do

PROBLEM 10

$$\begin{aligned}
UF_n[1, 2](x^2) &= r^2 \cdot (r - 1) + (r^2)^2 \cdot (r^2 - r) \\
&\quad + (r^2)^3 \cdot (r^3 - r^2) \\
&\quad + \cdots + (r^2)^n \cdot (r^n - r^{n-1}) \\
&= r^2 \cdot (r - 1) + r^5 \cdot (r - 1) \\
&\quad + r^8 \cdot (r - 1) \\
&\quad + \cdots + r^{3n-1} \cdot (r - 1) \\
&= (r^2 + r^5 + r^8 + \cdots + r^{3n-1}) \cdot \\
&\quad (r - 1) \\
&= r^2(1 + r^3 + (r^3)^2 + \cdots + (r^3)^{n-1}) \cdot \\
&\quad (r - 1) \\
&= r^2 \cdot \frac{(r^3)^{((n-1)+1)} - 1}{r^3 - 1} \cdot (r - 1) \\
&= r^2 \cdot \frac{r^{3n} - 1}{r^3 - 1} \cdot (r - 1) \\
&= r^2 \cdot \frac{2^3 - 1}{r^3 - 1} \cdot (r - 1) \\
&= r^2 \cdot \frac{7}{(r - 1)(r^2 + r + 1)} \cdot (r - 1) \\
&= \frac{7r^2}{r^2 + r + 1}
\end{aligned}$$

You can show that $\frac{7r^2}{r^2 + r + 1}$ is always a little greater than $\frac{7}{3}$, since its reciprocal is always a little less than $\frac{3}{7}$.

Wrap Up

You might wrap up by asking students to think about how to extend to find $S[1, 2](x^m)$ where m is any integer. This previews the next investigation.

Assessment Resources

Lesson Quiz 8.6

1. a. Identify the Fermat points for a lower approximation of the area between $x = 2$ and $x = 4$ under the graph of $y = x^2$, using four rectangles.

b. Complete the table below.

	Base	Height	Area
1st rectangle			
2nd rectangle	$2\sqrt[4]{4} - 2\sqrt[4]{2} = 2\sqrt[4]{2}(\sqrt[4]{2} - 1)$		
3rd rectangle		$(2\sqrt[4]{4})^2$	
4th rectangle			$8(\sqrt[4]{8})^3(\sqrt[4]{2} - 1)$

c. Using a calculator, add up the areas of the rectangles to obtain the value of the Fermat lower sum $LF_4[2,4](x^2)$.

2. a. A closed-form expression for $LF_n[2,4](x^2)$ is $\frac{8(2^3 - 1)}{(2^{\frac{1}{n}})^2 + (2^{\frac{1}{n}}) + 1}$.

What happens to $LF_n[2,4](x^2)$ when you increase the number of subdivisions?

b. What is $S_n[2,4](x^2)$?

Exercises

HOMEWORK

- Core: 9, 11, 13, 14, 15, 23
- Optional: 10, 12, 16, 17, 18, 20, 24, 25
- Extension: 19, 21, 22

3. Find the Fermat upper sum, $UF_n[1, 2](x^m)$, for any positive integer m.

4. Use your results from Exercises 2 and 3 to prove the general formula for all positive integers m.

$$S[1, 2](x^m) = \frac{1}{m+1}(2^{m+1} - 1)$$

5. a. Use Fermat's method to find the formula for $LF_n[3, 6](x^m)$ by subdividing the segment $[3, 6]$ with the points $3, 3r, 3r^2, 3r^3, \ldots, 3r^n = 6$.

   b. What happens to $LF_n[3, 6](x^m)$ as you increase the number of subdivisions?

6. a. Use Fermat's method to find the formula for $LF_n[2, 3](x^m)$ by subdividing the segment $[2, 3]$ with the points $2, 2r, 2r^2, 2r^3, \ldots, 2r^n = 3$.

   b. What happens to $LF_n[2, 3](x^m)$ as you increase the number of subdivisions?

7. a. Use Fermat's method to find the formula for $LF_n[2, 6](x^m)$ by subdividing the segment $[2, 6]$ with the points $2, 2r, 2r^2, 2r^3, \ldots, 2r^n = 6$.

   b. What happens to $LF_n[2, 6](x^m)$ as you increase the number of subdivisions?

8. **Write About It** For each of the above exercises, you can show that the upper sum and the lower sum approach the same value, as you increase the number of subdivisions. You may have noticed that

$$S[2, 6](x^m) = S[2, 3](x^m) + S[3, 6](x^m)$$

Is it always true that

$$S[a, c](x^m) = S[a, b](x^m) + S[b, c](x^m)$$

where $0 < a < b < c$? Explain.

On Your Own

9. Copy and complete the expressions in parts (a)–(c).

   a. $LF_3[1, 2](x^5) = (r - 1)(\blacksquare)$

   b. $LF_5[1, 2](x^5) = (r - 1)(\blacksquare)$

   c. $LF_8[1, 2](x^5) = (r - 1)(\blacksquare)$

   d. In terms of r, what is the common ratio in the geometric series which you placed inside the parentheses in parts (a)–(c)?

Note that the value of r is different in each of these.

Answers

3. See back of book.

4. Since the actual area, $S[1, 2](x^m)$, lies between $LF_n[1, 2](x^m)$ and $UF_n[1, 2](x^m)$ for each n and both the lower and upper sums approach $\frac{2^{m+1} - 1}{m+1}$ as n gets larger, $S[1, 2](x^m) = \frac{2^{m+1} - 1}{m+1}$.

5. a. $LF_n[3, 6](x^m) = \frac{6^{m+1} - 3^{m+1}}{1 + r + \cdots + r^m}$

   b. As the number of subdivisions increases, each of $r, r^2, r^3, \ldots, r^m$ approaches 1, and $LF_n[3, 6](x^m)$ approaches $\frac{1}{m+1} \cdot (6^{m+1} - 3^{m+1})$.

6. a. $LF_n[2, 3](x^m) = \frac{1}{1 + r + r^2 + r^3 + \cdots + r^m} \cdot (3^{m+1} - 2^{m+1})$

   b. As the number of subdivisions increases, $LF_n[2, 3](x^m)$ approaches $\frac{1}{m+1} \cdot (3^{m+1} - 2^{m+1})$.

7. a. $LF_n[2, 6](x^m) = \frac{1}{1 + r + r^2 + r^3 + \cdots + r^m} \cdot (6^{m+1} - 2^{m+1})$

   b. As the number of subdivisions increases, $LF_n[2, 6](x^m)$ approaches $\frac{1}{m+1} \cdot (6^{m+1} - 2^{m+1})$.

8. When $0 < a < b < c$, this is true because of the additive property of area. Suppose A is the region under $y = x^m$ between a and b, B is the region under $y = x^m$ between b and c, and C is the region under $y = x^m$ between a and c. Then since the union of A and B is C and since A and B have no overlap, the area of C is the sum of the areas of A and B. That is, $S[a, c](x^m) = S[a, b](x^m) + S[b, c](x^m)$.

9. a. $1 + r^6 + (r^6)^2$

   b. $1 + r^6 + (r^6)^2 + (r^6)^3 + (r^6)^4$

   c. $1 + r^6 + (r^6)^2 + (r^6)^3 + (r^6)^4 + (r^6)^5 + (r^6)^6 + (r^6)^7$

   d. The ratio is always r^6.

10. Justify each step in the calculations of $LF_3[1, 2](x^3)$ in the example in this lesson.

11. Use the following steps to find Fermat lower sum of $y = x^2$ from $x = 1$ to $x = 2$ with 5 subdivisions:

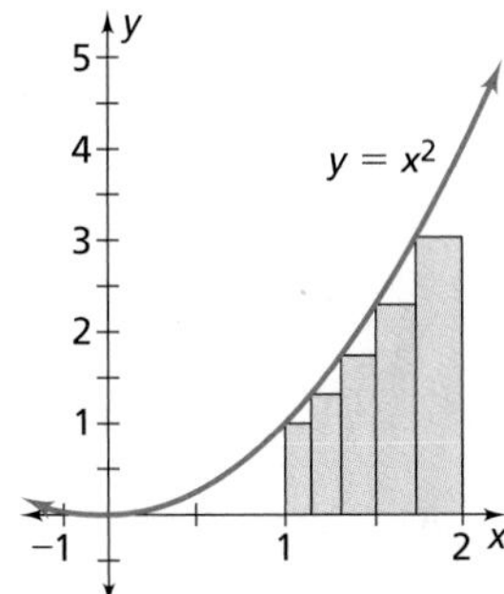

a. Write the expression for the sum of the areas of all five rectangles.

$$LF_5[1, 2](x^2) = \blacksquare$$

b. Use the formula for the geometric series to write the closed form for the Fermat lower sum.

c. Calculate r and the value of $LF_5[1, 2](x^2)$.

12. Repeat the steps of Exercise 11 for $n = 10$. Describe how the Fermat lower sum changes with this increase in the number of subdivisions.

13. Copy and complete the expressions in parts (a)–(c).

a. $LF_3[1, 2](x^4) = (r - 1)(\blacksquare)$

b. $LF_4[1, 2](x^4) = (r - 1)(\blacksquare)$

c. $LF_7[1, 2](x^4) = (r - 1)(\blacksquare)$

d. In terms of r, what is the common ratio in the geometric series which you placed inside the parentheses in parts (a)–(c)?

14. Use Fermat's method to find $S[1, 2](x^4)$.

15. Use Fermat's method to find $S[1, 3](x^4)$.

16. Find a general formula for $S[1, a](x^4)$ (where $a \geq 1$) using Fermat's method.

17. Find a general formula for $S[1, a](x^m)$ (where $a > 1$, and m is a positive integer) using Fermat's method.

Remember...

$$1 + q + \cdots + q^{n-1} = \frac{q^n - 1}{q - 1}$$

EXERCISES 11 AND 12 Remind students that the area under the graph of $y = x^2$ from $x = 1$ to $x = 2$, $S[1, 2](x^2)$ is $\frac{7}{3}$.

10. $LF_3[1, 2](x^3) = 1(r - 1) + r^3(r^2 - r) + ((r^2)^3)(r^3 - r^2)$
(the sum of rectangle areas)
$= 1(r - 1) + r^3(r(r - 1)) + r^6(r^2(r - 1))$
(factoring out powers of r)
$= 1(r - 1) + r^4(r - 1) + r^8(r - 1)$
(multiplying powers of r)
$= (r - 1)(1 + r^4 + r^8)$
(factoring out $r - 1$)
$= (r - 1)(1 + r^4 + (r^4)^2)$
(representing r^8 as $(r^4)^2$)

11. a. $LF_5[1, 2](x^2) = (r - 1) \cdot (1 + r^3 + (r^3)^2 + (r^3)^3 + (r^3)^4)$

b. $LF_5[1, 2](x^2) = \dfrac{r^{15} - 1}{r^2 + r + 1}$

c. Using $r = \sqrt[5]{2} \approx 1.1487$,
$LF_5[1, 2](x^2) = \dfrac{7}{(\sqrt[5]{2})^2 + \sqrt[5]{2} + 1} \approx 2.0183$

12. Using $r = \sqrt[10]{2} \approx 1.0718$,
$LF_{10}[1, 2](x^2) \approx 2.1736$

13. a. $1 + r^5 + (r^5)^2$

b. $1 + r^5 + (r^5)^2 + (r^5)^3$

c. $1 + r^6 + (r^5)^2 + (r^5)^3 + (r^5)^4 + (r^5)^5 + (r^5)^6$

d. The ratio is always r^5.

14. $S[1, 2](x^4) = \dfrac{2^5 - 1}{5} = \dfrac{31}{5}$

15. $S[1, 3](x^4) = \dfrac{3^5 - 1}{5} = \dfrac{242}{5}$

16. $S[1, a](x^4) = \dfrac{a^5 - 1}{5}$

17. $S[1, a](x^m) = \dfrac{a^{m+1} - 1}{m + 1}$

Additional Resources

PRINT RESOURCES
- Solution Manual
- Practice Workbook
- Assessment Resources
- Teaching Resources

TECHNOLOGY
- Interactive Textbook
- TeacherExpress CD-ROM
- ExamView CD-ROM
- PHSchool.com

Additional Practice

1. a. Copy and complete the table below. It describes the rectangles for a Fermat-method upper approximation of the area between $x = 1$ and $x = 3$ under the graph of $y = x^m$, for any positive integer m.

	Base	Height	Area
1st rectangle	$r-1$	r^m	$r^m(r-1)$
2nd rectangle	$r^2 - r = r(r-1)$	r^{2m}	$r^{2m+1}(r-1)$
3rd rectangle			
4th rectangle			
⋮	⋮	⋮	⋮
nth rectangle			

   b. Add the areas of these rectangles to obtain an expression for the Fermat upper sum $UF_n[1, 3](x^m)$.
   c. Use the formula for the geometric series to obtain the closed form.
   d. What happens to r in the denominator of $UF_n[1, 3](x^m)$ when you increase the number of subdivisions?
   e. What is $S_n[1, 3](x^m)$?

2. Use Fermat's method to find $S[2, 4](x^2)$.

3. Use Fermat's method to find $S[2, 5](x^2)$.

4. Find a general formula for $S[2, b](x^2)$, where $b > 1$, using Fermat's method.

5. Prove that $S[a, ab](x^m) = a^{m+1}S[1, b](x^m)$ for $a \geq 1$. Start by finding the Fermat lower sum $LF_n[a, ab](x^m)$.

6. To find $S[a, 1](x^2)$, the area below the graph of $y = x^2$ from a to 1, for $0 < a < 1$, proceed as follows.
   a. First, choose the Fermat points as $a, ar, ar^2, \ldots, ar^n = 1$. Add up the areas of the corresponding rectangles to obtain an expression for the Fermat lower sum $LF_n[a, 1](x^2)$.
   b. Use the formula for the geometric series to obtain the closed form.
   c. What happens to $LF_n[a, 1](x^2)$ when you increase the number of subdivisions? What is $S[a, 1](x^2)$?

Practice: For Lesson 8.6, assign Exercises 1–6.

18. a. Use Fermat's method to find the formula for $LF_n[5, 10](x^m)$ by subdividing the segment $[5, 10]$ with the points

$$5, 5r, 5r^2, 5r^3, \ldots, 5r^n = 10$$

   b. What happens to $LF_n[5, 10](x^m)$ as you increase the number of subdivisions?

19. **Take It Further** Derive the formula for $S[a, b](x^m)$ where $1 < a < b$, using your knowledge of $S[1, b](x^m)$.

Go Online PHSchool.com

For additional practice, go to Web Code: bga-0806

20. a. Find $S\left[\frac{1}{a}, 1\right](x^5)$ if
   - $a = 2$
   - $a = 4$
   - $a = 8$
   - $a = 100$

   b. What happens to $S\left[\frac{1}{a}, 1\right](x^5)$ as a becomes larger and larger?
   c. What is the value of $S[0, 1](x^5)$? Explain.

21. **Take It Further** Find a general formula for $S\left[\frac{1}{a}, 1\right](x^5)$ for any integer $a > 1$, by using the Fermat points for n subdivisions of the interval $\left[\frac{1}{a}, 1\right]$.

22. **Take It Further** Find $S[0, 1](x^m)$ using Fermat's method.

23. **Standardized Test Prep** Using Fermat's geometric sequence to determine the intervals, which of the following represents the upper estimate $UF_4[1, 16]\left(\frac{1}{x}\right)$?

   A. $\frac{15}{8}$ B. 4 C. 8 D. 15

Maintain Your Skills

24. Find algebraic expressions for the Fermat points for each of the following.
   a. 3 subdivisions of the interval $[1, a]$
   b. 6 subdivisions of the interval $[1, a]$
   c. n subdivisions of the interval $[1, a]$

In part (c), the first 3 and last 3 points are enough.

25. The following steps describe a method for subdividing the interval $[0, 1]$. Try it out.
   a. Divide each of the Fermat points you found in Exercise 24c for n subdivisions of $[1, a]$ by a. This gives you the Fermat points for the interval $\left[\frac{1}{a}, 1\right]$.
   b. What happens to $\frac{1}{a}$ as a becomes larger and larger? What interval does $\left[\frac{1}{a}, 1\right]$ approach, as a becomes larger and larger?

Answers

18. a. $LF_n[5, 10](x^m) = \dfrac{10^{m+1} - 5^{m+1}}{\sum\limits_{i=0}^{m} r^i}$

b. It approaches $5^{m+1} \cdot \dfrac{2^{m+1} - 1}{m + 1}$.

19. $S[a, b](x^m) = \dfrac{b^{m+1} - a^{m+1}}{m + 1}$

20. a.

a	$S\left[\frac{1}{a},1\right](x^5) = \frac{1}{6}\cdot\left(1-\left(\frac{1}{a}\right)^6\right)$
2	$= 0.1640625$
4	≈ 0.1666260
8	≈ 0.1666660
100	$\approx \frac{1}{6}$

b. As a gets larger, $\frac{1}{a}$ approaches 0, and so $\left[\frac{1}{a}, 1\right]$ approaches $[0, 1]$. Therefore, $S\left[\frac{1}{a}, 1\right](x^5)$ approaches $S[0, 1](x^5)$. Also as a gets larger, $\frac{1}{6} \cdot \left(1 - \left(\frac{1}{a}\right)^6\right)$ approaches $\frac{1}{6}$.

c. From part (b) it follows that $S[0, 1](x^5) = \frac{1}{6}$.

21. $S\left[\frac{1}{a}, 1\right](x^5) = \frac{1}{6} \cdot \left(1 - \left(\frac{1}{a}\right)^6\right)$

22. $S[0, 1](x^m) = \dfrac{1}{m + 1}$

23. B

24. a. $1, a^{\frac{1}{3}}, a^{\frac{2}{3}}, a$

b. $1, a^{\frac{1}{6}}, a^{\frac{1}{3}}, a^{\frac{1}{2}}, a^{\frac{2}{3}}, a^{\frac{5}{6}}, a$

c. numbers of the form $\left(\sqrt[n]{a}\right)^k = a^{\frac{k}{n}}$, where k is an integer satisfying $0 \leq k \leq n$

25. a. $\frac{1}{a}, \frac{r}{a}, \frac{r^2}{a}, \ldots, \frac{r^{n-2}}{a}, \frac{r^{n-1}}{a}, \frac{r^n}{a} = \frac{a}{a} = 1$, where $r = \sqrt[n]{a}$

b. As a gets larger, $\frac{1}{a}$ approaches 0, and the interval $\left[\frac{1}{a}, 1\right]$ approaches the interval $[0, 1]$.

In this investigation, you followed the historical approach taken by two mathematicians to find the areas under certain curves. The following questions will help you summarize what you have learned.

1. Calculate $S[1, a](x^m)$.
2. Find the area of the closed region between the x-axis and the graph of $y = x^2 - 1$.
3. What is a closed-form expression for the function defined by $F(b) = S[1, b](x^3)$, where $b > 1$?
4. What is a closed-form expression for the function defined by $F(b) = S[1, b](x^4)$, where $b > 1$?
5. What is Fermat's approach to finding the area under the graph of $y = x^m$ between $x = 0$ and $x = 1$?

Vocabulary and Notation

In this investigation, you learned these terms and symbols. Make sure you understand what each one means and how to use it.

- **Fermat lower sum, $LF_n[a, b](f(x))$**
- **Fermat upper sum, $UF_n[a, b](f(x))$**

In calculus, you learn to calculate the surface area of curved, three-dimensional objects like this sculpture by Piet Hein.

Mathematical Reflections

EXERCISES 3–5 At the start of the investigation, you may have assigned these as Questions 1–3 for students to think and write about.

Mathematical Reflections

1. $\frac{a^{m+1} - 1}{m + 1}$
2. $\frac{4}{3}$
3. $F(b) = \frac{b^4 - 1}{4}$
4. $F(b) = \frac{b^5 - 1}{5}$
5. Answers may vary. Sample: Use the Fermat points for n subdivisions of the interval $\left[\frac{1}{a}, 1\right]$. Find $LF_n\left[\frac{1}{a}, 1\right](x^m)$ and $UF_n\left[\frac{1}{a}, 1\right](x^m)$. Show that these approach the same limit as $n \to \infty$, and use this limit for $S\left[\frac{1}{a}, 1\right](x^m)$. Then examine what happens to $S\left[\frac{1}{a}, 1\right](x^m)$ as $a \to \infty$ to find $S[0, 1](x^m)$.

Mid-Chapter Test

Assessment Resources

Mid-Chapter Test **page 1**

Multiple Choice

1. What is the value of $U_4[1, 5](x^2)$, the upper sum approximation of the area under the graph of $y = x^2$ between 1 and 5?
   A. 54 B. 30 C. 75 D. 27

2. Which of the following estimates for the area under the graph of $y = 4 - x^2$ between 0 and 2 will have the largest error?
   A. $L_4[0, 2](4 - x^2)$ B. $L_8[0, 2](4 - x^2)$
   C. $U_8[0, 2](4 - x^2)$ D. The average of $L_8[0, 2](4 - x^2)$ and $U_8[0, 2](4 - x^2)$

3. Which sum represents $L_4\left[0, \frac{\pi}{2}\right](\sin x)$, the lower sum approximation of the area under the graph of $y = \sin x$ between 0 and $\frac{\pi}{2}$ using 4 subdivisions?
   A. $\frac{1}{4}\sin\frac{\pi}{8} + \frac{1}{4}\sin\frac{\pi}{4} + \frac{1}{4}\sin\frac{3\pi}{8} + \frac{1}{4}\sin\frac{\pi}{2}$ B. $\frac{\pi}{8}\sin\frac{\pi}{8} + \frac{\pi}{8}\sin\frac{\pi}{4} + \frac{\pi}{8}\sin\frac{3\pi}{8} + \frac{\pi}{8}\sin\frac{\pi}{2}$
   C. $\frac{1}{4}\sin 0 + \frac{1}{4}\sin\frac{\pi}{8} + \frac{1}{4}\sin\frac{\pi}{4} + \frac{1}{4}\sin\frac{3\pi}{8}$ D. $\frac{\pi}{8}\sin 0 + \frac{\pi}{8}\sin\frac{\pi}{8} + \frac{\pi}{8}\sin\frac{\pi}{4} + \frac{\pi}{8}\sin\frac{3\pi}{8}$

4. Which sum represents $U_4\left[0, \frac{\pi}{2}\right](\sin x)$, the upper sum approximation of the area under the graph of $y = \sin x$ between 0 and $\frac{\pi}{2}$ using 4 subdivisions?
   A. $\frac{1}{4}\sin\frac{\pi}{8} + \frac{1}{4}\sin\frac{\pi}{4} + \frac{1}{4}\sin\frac{3\pi}{8} + \frac{1}{4}\sin\frac{\pi}{2}$ B. $\frac{\pi}{8}\sin\frac{\pi}{8} + \frac{\pi}{8}\sin\frac{\pi}{4} + \frac{\pi}{8}\sin\frac{3\pi}{8} + \frac{\pi}{8}\sin\frac{\pi}{2}$
   C. $\frac{1}{4}\sin 0 + \frac{1}{4}\sin\frac{\pi}{8} + \frac{1}{4}\sin\frac{\pi}{4} + \frac{1}{4}\sin\frac{3\pi}{8}$ D. $\frac{\pi}{8}\sin 0 + \frac{\pi}{8}\sin\frac{\pi}{8} + \frac{\pi}{8}\sin\frac{\pi}{4} + \frac{\pi}{8}\sin\frac{3\pi}{8}$

Open Response

5. a. Compute $U_2[0, 2](x^3)$, the upper sum approximation (using 2 subdivisions) of the area under the graph of $y = x^3$ between 0 and 2.
   b. Compute $U_4[0, 2](x^3)$, the upper sum approximation (using 4 subdivisions) of the area under the graph of $y = x^3$ between 0 and 2.
   c. Without calculating the area, which of these two approximations do you think will be closer to the exact area? Explain.

Also available: Form B

Mid-Chapter Test

For a mid-chapter test, go to Web Code: bga-0852

Multiple Choice

1. What is the value of $L_4[1, 5](x^2)$, the lower sum approximation of the area under the graph of $y = x^2$ between 1 and 5?
   A. 54 B. 30 C. 7.5 D. 15

2. Which of the following estimates will be closest to the area under the graph of $y = \sqrt{x}$ between 0 and 4?
   A. $L_4[0, 4](\sqrt{x})$
   B. $U_{10}[0, 4](\sqrt{x})$
   C. $L_{10}[0, 4](\sqrt{x})$
   D. the average of $L_{10}[0, 4](\sqrt{x})$ and $U_{10}[0, 4](\sqrt{x})$

3. Which sum represents $L_4\left[0, \frac{\pi}{2}\right](\cos x)$, the lower sum approximation of the area under $y = \cos x$ between 0 and $\frac{\pi}{2}$ using 4 subdivisions?
   A. $\frac{1}{4}\cos\frac{\pi}{8} + \frac{1}{4}\cos\frac{\pi}{4} + \frac{1}{4}\cos\frac{3\pi}{8} + \frac{1}{4}\cos\frac{\pi}{2}$
   B. $\frac{\pi}{8}\cos\frac{\pi}{8} + \frac{\pi}{8}\cos\frac{\pi}{4} + \frac{\pi}{8}\cos\frac{3\pi}{8} + \frac{\pi}{8}\cos\frac{\pi}{2}$
   C. $\frac{1}{4}\cos 0 + \frac{1}{4}\cos\frac{\pi}{8} + \frac{1}{4}\cos\frac{\pi}{4} + \frac{1}{4}\cos\frac{3\pi}{8}$
   D. $\frac{\pi}{8}\cos 0 + \frac{\pi}{8}\cos\frac{\pi}{8} + \frac{\pi}{8}\cos\frac{\pi}{4} + \frac{\pi}{8}\cos\frac{3\pi}{8}$

4. Which sum represents $U_4\left[0, \frac{\pi}{2}\right](\cos x)$, the upper sum approximation of the area under $y = \cos x$ between 0 and $\frac{\pi}{2}$ using 4 subdivisions?
   A. $\frac{1}{4}\cos\frac{\pi}{8} + \frac{1}{4}\cos\frac{\pi}{4} + \frac{1}{4}\cos\frac{3\pi}{8} + \frac{1}{4}\cos\frac{\pi}{2}$
   B. $\frac{\pi}{8}\cos\frac{\pi}{8} + \frac{\pi}{8}\cos\frac{\pi}{4} + \frac{\pi}{8}\cos\frac{3\pi}{8} + \frac{\pi}{8}\cos\frac{\pi}{2}$
   C. $\frac{1}{4}\cos 0 + \frac{1}{4}\cos\frac{\pi}{8} + \frac{1}{4}\cos\frac{\pi}{4} + \frac{1}{4}\cos\frac{3\pi}{8}$
   D. $\frac{\pi}{8}\cos 0 + \frac{\pi}{8}\cos\frac{\pi}{8} + \frac{\pi}{8}\cos\frac{\pi}{4} + \frac{\pi}{8}\cos\frac{3\pi}{8}$

Open Response

5. a. Compute $U_2[0, 2](\sqrt{x})$, the upper sum approximation (using 2 subdivisions) of the area under $y = \sqrt{x}$ between 0 and 2. Express your answer exactly. Then approximate your answer to 3 decimal places.
   b. Compute $U_4[0, 2](\sqrt{x})$, the upper sum approximation (using 4 subdivisions) of the area under $y = \sqrt{x}$ between 0 and 2. Express your answer exactly. Then approximate your answer to 3 decimal places.
   c. Without calculating the area, which of these two approximations do you think will be closer to the exact area? Explain.

6. a. Recall that $U_4[0, 2](4 - x^2)$ is the upper sum approximation of the area under the curve $y = 4 - x^2$ between 0 and 2 using four subdivisions. Copy the graph below, and sketch the rectangles whose areas make up $U_4[0, 2](4 - x^2)$.

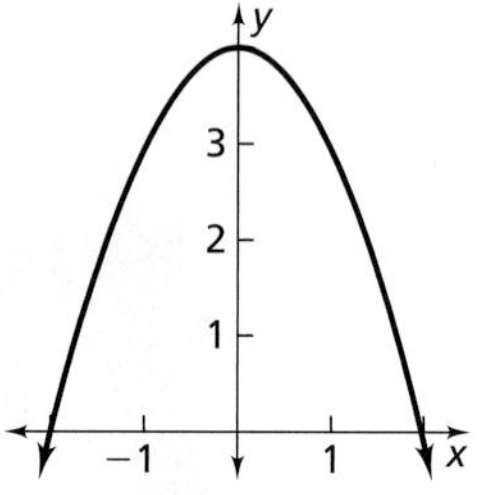

   b. Compute $U_4[0, 2](4 - x^2)$.
   c. On another copy of the same graph, sketch the rectangles the areas of which make up $L_4[0, 2](4 - x^2)$, the lower sum approximation of the area under the curve $y = 4 - x^2$ between 0 and 2 using four subdivisions.

Answers

Mid-Chapter Test

1. B
2. D
3. B
4. D
5. a. $1 + \sqrt{2}$; 2.414
   b. $\frac{2 + 3\sqrt{2} + \sqrt{6}}{4}$; 2.173
   c. $U_4[0, 2](\sqrt{x})$; $U_4[0, 2](\sqrt{x})$ is less than the other approximation and uses more subdivisions than the other approximation.

6. a.

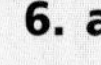

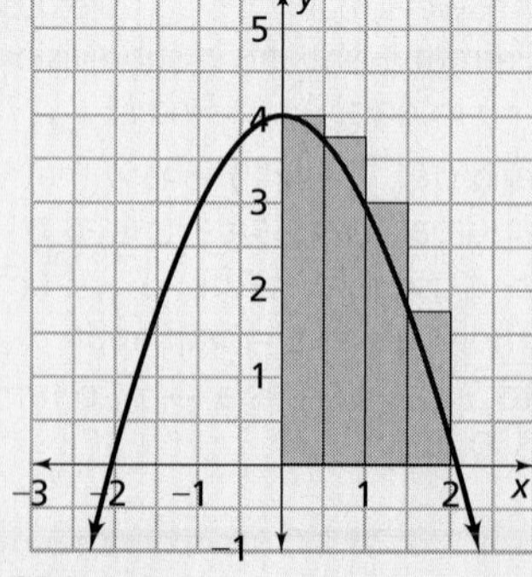

b. $\frac{25}{4}$, or 6.25

c.

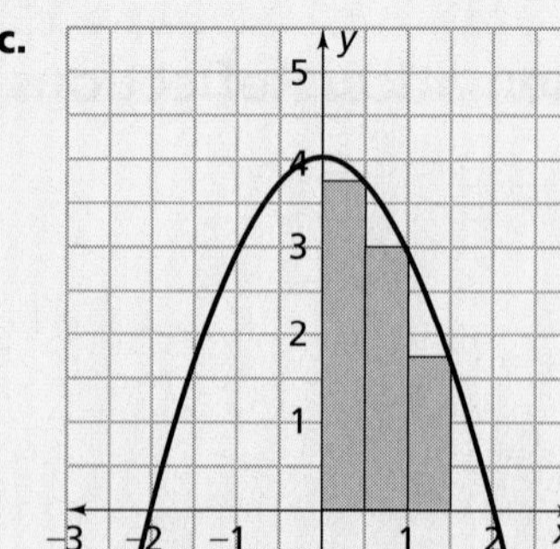

d. $\frac{17}{4}$, or 4.25

e. $\frac{21}{4}$, or 5.25

d. Compute $L_4[0, 2](4 - x^2)$.

e. Compute the average of $L_4[0, 2](4 - x^2)$ and $L_4[0, 2](4 - x^2)$ to get a third approximation of the area.

7. The graphs of $y = x^2$ and $y = 4 - x^2$ are shown below.

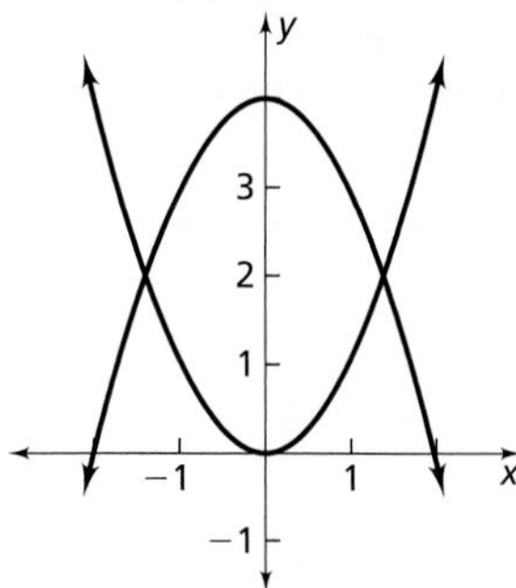

The area of the region under $y = x^2$ between -2 and 2 is $\frac{16}{3}$. Use that information to compute each of the following and explain your answers.

a. the area under $y = x^2$ between 0 and 2

b. the area under $y = 4 - x^2$ between 0 and 2

Challenge Problem

8. Using Fermat's method with n subdivisions, the endpoints of the subdivisions are $1, r, r^2, r^3, \dots, r^n$, where $r^n = 5$.

a. Compute $UF_n[1, 5](x^3)$, the upper sum approximation.

b. What value does $UF_n[1, 5](x^3)$ approach as n becomes larger?

c. Compute $LF_n[1, 5](x^3)$, the lower sum approximation.

d. What value does $LF_n[1, 5](x^3)$ approach as n becomes larger?

e. Compute $S[1, 5](x^3)$.

Mid-Chapter Test page 2

6. a. Recall that $U_4[-2, 0](4 - x^2)$ is the upper sum approximation of the area under the curve $y = 4 - x^2$ between -2 and 0 using four subdivisions. On the graph to the right, sketch the rectangles whose areas make up $U_4[-2, 0](4 - x^2)$.

b. Compute $U_4[-2, 0](4 - x^2)$.

c. On the graph to the right, sketch the rectangles whose areas make up $L_4[-2, 0](4 - x^2)$, the lower sum approximation of the area under the curve $y = 4 - x^2$ between -2 and 0 using four subdivisions.

d. Compute $L_4[-2, 0](4 - x^2)$.

e. Compute the average of $U_4[-2, 0](4 - x^2)$ and $L_4[-2, 0](4 - x^2)$ to get a third approximation of the area.

7. The graphs of $y = x^2$ and $y = 9 - x^2$ are shown below. The area of the region under $y = x^2$ between 0 and 3 is 9. Use that information to compute each of the following (being sure to explain your answer).

a. The area under $y = x^2$ between -3 and 3.

b. The area under $y = 9 - x^2$ between -3 and 3.

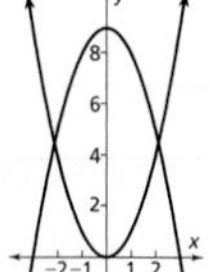

Challenge Problem

8. In this Exercise, you will use Fermat's Method to compute the area under the curve $y = x^3$ between 1 and 3. Using Fermat's method with n subdivisions, the endpoints of the subdivisions will be $1, r, r^2, r^3, \dots, r^n$, where $r^n = 3$.

a. Compute $UF_n[1, 3](x^3)$, the upper sum approximation.

b. What value does $UF_n[1, 3](x^3)$ approach as n gets larger?

c. Compute $LF_n[1, 3](x^3)$, the lower sum approximation.

d. What value does $LF_n[1, 3](x^3)$ approach as n gets larger?

e. Compute $S[1, 3](x^3)$.

Also available: Form B

7. a. $\frac{8}{3}$; by symmetry, the area between -2 and 0 is equal to the area beteen 0 and 2 and hence equal to $\frac{1}{2} \cdot \frac{16}{3}$.

b. $\frac{16}{3}$; the area is equal to the area of the 2-by-4 rectangle bounded by $x = 0$, $x = 2$, $y = 0$ and $y = 4$ minus the area of the region bounded by $y = 4$, the graph, and $x = 2$. This difference is, by symmentry and part (a), $8 - \frac{8}{3}$.

8. a. $\dfrac{624r^3}{r^3 + r^2 + r + 1}$, where $r = \sqrt[n]{5}$

b. 156

c. $\dfrac{624}{r^3 + r^2 + r + 1}$, where $r = \sqrt[n]{5}$

d. 156

e. 156

Investigation Overview

Students have now established the formula

$$S[1, 2](x^m) = \frac{1}{m+1}(2^{m+1} - 1)$$

for positive integers m. This investigation asks the question, "What happens if m is a negative integer?" Clearly, the formula cannot hold if $m = -1$, because the denominator $m + 1$ is undefined. But what if $m \neq -1$? The Getting Started lesson shows that the same formula (and the same calculation that produces it) goes through unchanged.

The next lesson begins the investigation of the case $m = -1$, and goes on to show

$$\log_e(a) = S[1, a]\left(\frac{1}{x}\right)$$

There is a split in approaches to the natural logarithm in calculus books. Some books define the natural logarithm as a function given by an area calculation. In this approach, e emerges as the input to the natural logarithm that produces an output of 1. In CME Project *Precalculus*, students have already met e, but in this investigation, they see e and the logarithm to the base e in a new context—area.

You may wish to assign Questions 1–3 for students to think and write about during the investigation.

Learning Goals

- Develop formulas for calculating $S[1, a](x^m)$ where m is any integer.
- Investigate a mysteriously familiar function, $\mathcal{L}(a)$.
- Find the area under the graph of $y = e^x$ between $x = 0$ and $x = 1$.

Habits and Skills

- Use properties of a mystery function to identify the function.
- Use areas under curves to gain new perspectives on familiar functions.

A Function Emerges

In *A Function Emerges*, you will extend your work from the previous two investigations. You will learn how to calculate the area under the graph of $y = x^m$, where m can be any integer. You will also examine the area under the graph of $y = e^x$.

By the end of this investigation, you will be able to answer question like these.

1. What is the value of $S[1, 2](x^{-2})$?
2. What is the value of $S[1, 2](x^{-1})$?
3. What is the value of $S[0, 1](e^x)$?

You will learn how to

- develop formulas for calculating $S[1, a](x^m)$ where m is any integer
- investigate a mysteriously familiar function, $\mathcal{L}(a)$
- find the area under the graph of $y = e^x$ between $x = 0$ and $x = 1$

You will develop these habits and skills:

- Use properties of a mystery function to identify the function.
- Use areas under curves to gain new perspectives on familiar functions.

The mystery function in this chapter is useful in radiocarbon dating of archeological specimens.

Investigation Road Map

LESSON 8.7, *Getting Started,* investigates extending the formula $S(1, 2)(x^m) = \frac{1}{m+1}(2^{m+1} - 1)$ to integers $m \neq -1$.

LESSON 8.8, *The Area Under $y = \frac{1}{x}$,* has students calculate $S[a, b]\left(\frac{1}{x}\right)$ for $1 \leq a < b$. Students also encounter a theorem that states that if $1 \leq a < b$, then $S[a, b]\left(\frac{1}{x}\right) = S[ta, tb]\left(\frac{1}{x}\right)$.

LESSON 8.9, *Properties of the Function $\mathcal{L}$,* has students work with the function $\mathcal{L}(a) = S[a, b]\left(\frac{1}{x}\right)$.

LESSON 8.10, *The Area Under $f(x) = e^x$,* has students approximate the area under the curve $f(x) = e^x$ using Archimedes' method of upper and lower sums.

8.7 Getting Started

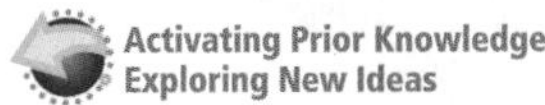

In the previous investigation, you developed and proved a formula for finding the area under the graph of $y = x^m$ between $x = 1$ and $x = 2$:

$$S[1, 2](x^m) = \frac{1}{m+1}(2^{m+1} - 1)$$

While working on this formula, you considered only nonnegative integers m. In many situations in mathematics, one of the ways to find out something new is to try to extend the result you already know.

There is actually a more general formula, for the area on any interval $[a, b]$, $1 \le a < b$: $S[a, b](x^m) = \frac{1}{m+1}(b^{m+1} - a^{m+1})$

For You to Explore

1. The goal in this problem is to answer the following question:

   When $m = -2$, does the formula $S[1, 2](x^m) = \frac{1}{m+1}(2^{m+1} - 1)$ give the correct area under the curve $y = x^{-2}$ between $x = 1$ and $x = 2$?

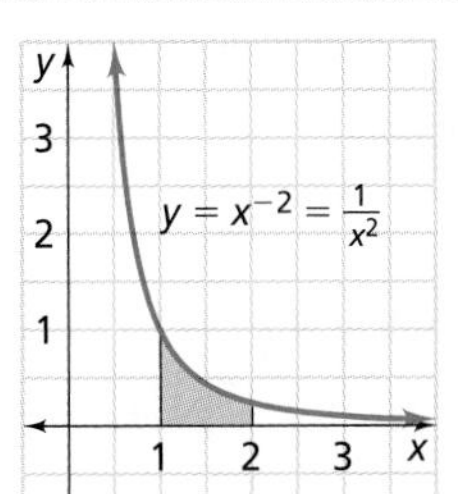

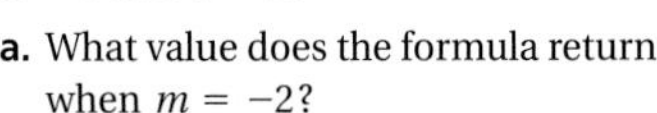

   a. What value does the formula return when $m = -2$?

   b. Copy and complete the following table.

Fermat Upper Sum for $y = x^{-2}$, $UF_n[1, 2](x^{-2})$

	Base	Height	Area
1st rectangle	$r - 1$	1	$1(r - 1)$
2nd rectangle	$r^2 - r = r(r - 1)$	r^{-2}	$r^{-1}(r - 1)$
3rd rectangle	■	■	■
4th rectangle	■	■	■
⋮	⋮	⋮	⋮
nth rectangle	■	■	■

   c. Why does this table give an upper sum, as opposed to a lower sum?

   d. Add the areas to find $UF_n[1, 2](x^{-2})$.

   e. What is the limit of $UF_n[1, 2](x^{-2})$ as n becomes larger and larger?

   f. Find $LF_n[1, 2](x^{-2})$.

   g. What is the limit of $LF_n[1, 2](x^{-2})$ as n becomes larger and larger?

   h. What is $S[1, 2](x^{-2})$?

2. Try to derive a general formula for $S[1, 2](x^m)$ in a way that works for all integer values (negative and nonnegative) of m. If a step of the derivation is not allowed for some value of m, explain why, and then describe all values of m for which your general formula does hold.

Habits of Mind

Reason logically. You know from the start that there will be trouble with $\frac{1}{m+1}(2^{m+1} - 1)$ if you try to replace m with -1. But studying the derivation shows you exactly where things go wrong.

Lesson Overview

GOAL

- Warm up to the ideas of the investigation.

In this lesson, students find $S[1, 2](x^{-2})$.

FOR YOU TO EXPLORE

- Core: 1, 2
- Optional: none

MATERIALS

- CAS (recommended)
- graphing calculators
- Blackline Master 8.7

HOMEWORK

- Core: 3, 4, 5, 6
- Optional: 7, 8, 9, 10

Launch

Students can get started on the For You to Explore problems right away.

Explore

Have students work on the For You to Explore problems during class time. The goal is to have students experience some of the important concepts that they learn later in this investigation. Monitor students' success. Try to address general stumbling blocks as you detect them. Note the more difficult concepts so that you can give them greater attention later during the investigation.

You may want to use Blackline Master 8.7 on an overhead and fill it in as students supply the entries, or you may want to hand out copies for students to complete individually.

Wrap Up

If time allows, go over Problem 2.

Answers

For You to Explore

1. **a.** $\frac{1}{2}$

   b. See back of book.

   c. This provides an upper sum since the function $f(x) = x^{-2}$ is decreasing (as you move from left to right) on the interval $[1, 2]$ and it uses the left endpoint of each subdivision.

   d. $UF_n[1, 2](x^{-2}) = \frac{r}{2}$, where $r = \sqrt[n]{2}$

   e. $\frac{1}{2}$

   f. $LF_n[1, 2](x^{-2}) = \frac{1}{2r}$, where $r = \sqrt[n]{2}$

   g. $\frac{1}{2}$

   h. $\frac{1}{2}$

2. $S[1, 2](x^m) = \frac{1}{m+1}(2^{m+1} - 1)$ for m an integer, $m \neq -1$

Exercises

HOMEWORK
- Core: 3, 4, 5, 6
- Optional: 7, 8, 9, 10

Exercises Practicing Habits of Mind

On Your Own

3. a. Use Fermat's method to find $S[1, 2](x^{-3})$. Do not use the general formula you found in Problem 2.

b. Does your result in part (a) agree with what you get if you replace m with -3 in

$$\frac{1}{m+1}(2^{m+1} - 1)$$

4. Not everything that works for nonnegative exponents works for negative ones.

a. What is $S[0, 2](x^3)$?

b. Describe the difficulty in finding $S[0, 2](x^{-3})$.

5. Use Fermat's method to find $S[1, 2](x^{-4})$. Does it agree with what you get if you replace m with -4 in

$$\frac{1}{m+1}(2^{m+1} - 1)?$$

6. Use Fermat's method to find $S[1, 3](x^{-3})$.

Maintain Your Skills

7. Find $S[1, 100](x^{-2})$.

8. Find $S[1, 200](x^{-2})$.

9. Find a closed-form expression for $S[1, b](x^{-2})$.

10. a. Does the area under the graph of $y = x^{-2}$ on the interval $[1, b]$ get gradually closer to a particular number when b becomes larger and larger?

b. What happens to $S[1, b](x^{-3})$ as b becomes very large?

Answers

Exercises

3. $S[1, 2](x^{-3}) = \frac{3}{8}$

4. a. $S[0, 2](x^3) = 4$

b. There is a difficulty in computing $S[0, 2](x^{-3})$: computing $UF_n[0, 2](x^{-3})$ is impossible since one of its rectangles has an undefined height ($y = x^{-3}$ is undefined for $x = 0$).

5. $S[1, 2](x^{-4}) = \frac{7}{24}$; yes

6. $S[1, 3](x^{-3}) = \frac{4}{9}$

7. $S[1, 100](x^{-2}) = 0.99$

8. $S[1, 200](x^{-2}) = 0.995$

9. $S[1, b](x^{-2}) = 1 - \frac{1}{b}$

10. a. The area gets closer to 1.

b. Since $S[1, b](x^{-3}) = \frac{1}{2}\left(1 - \frac{1}{b^2}\right)$, $S[1, b](x^{-3})$ approaches $\frac{1}{2}$ as b gets very large.

8.8 The Area Under $y = \frac{1}{x}$

In the last lesson, you saw that the formula

$$S[1, 2](x^m) = \frac{1}{m+1}(2^{m+1} - 1)$$

holds for all integer exponents m, both positive and negative, with one notable exception, namely when $m = -1$. This lesson deals with that one exception.

In fact, the formula holds for all rational exponents, i.e., all curves of the form $y = x^{p/q}$ where p and q are integers and $q \neq 0$, so long as $\frac{p}{q} \neq -1$.

For You to Do

1. Approximate $S[1, 2](x^{-1})$ using Fermat's method. Use your calculator to obtain approximations for 20 (or 200) subdivisions.

For Discussion

2. Using the graph of $y = \frac{1}{x}$, explain why
$$S[1, 10]\left(\tfrac{1}{x}\right) = S[1, 2]\left(\tfrac{1}{x}\right) + S[2, 10]\left(\tfrac{1}{x}\right)$$
3. More generally, if $1 < a < b$, explain why
$$S[1, b]\left(\tfrac{1}{x}\right) = S[1, a]\left(\tfrac{1}{x}\right) + S[a, b]\left(\tfrac{1}{x}\right)$$

Using a calculator or computer, you can approximate $S[1, 2](x^{-1})$ to any degree of accuracy you like by taking more and more subdivisions. But it turns out that the actual value of the area is irrational, just like the area of the unit circle. No fraction will ever give the exact area.

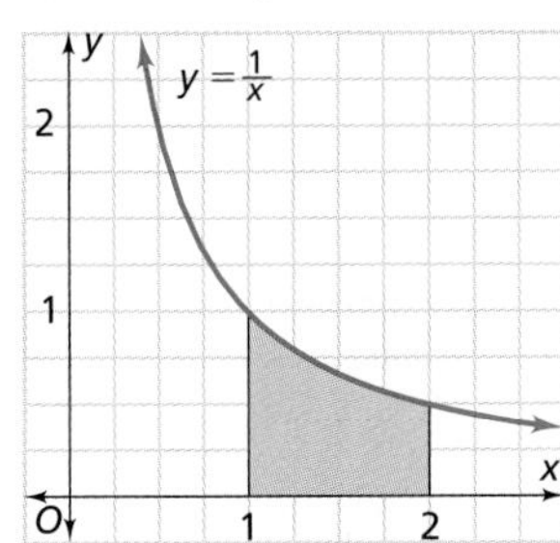

Not only is $S[1, 2](x^{-1})$ irrational, but so are $S[1, 3](x^{-1})$, $S[1, 4](x^{-1})$, and $S[1, a](x^{-1})$ where a is any integer greater than 1. In fact, the function defined for $a \geq 1$ by

$$a \mapsto S[1, a](x^{-1})$$

has no algebraic closed-form equivalent expression.

For You to Do

1. See back of book.

For Discussion

2. Line $x = 2$ divides the region under $y = \frac{1}{x}$ between 1 and 10 in two distinct parts, A and B. The area of A is $S[1, 2]\left(\frac{1}{x}\right)$ and the area of B is $S[2, 10]\left(\frac{1}{x}\right)$, so the area of the whole region between 1 and 10, $S[1, 10]\left(\frac{1}{x}\right)$, is the sum of the areas of A and B, which equals $S[1, 2]\left(\frac{1}{x}\right) + S[2, 10]\left(\frac{1}{x}\right)$.

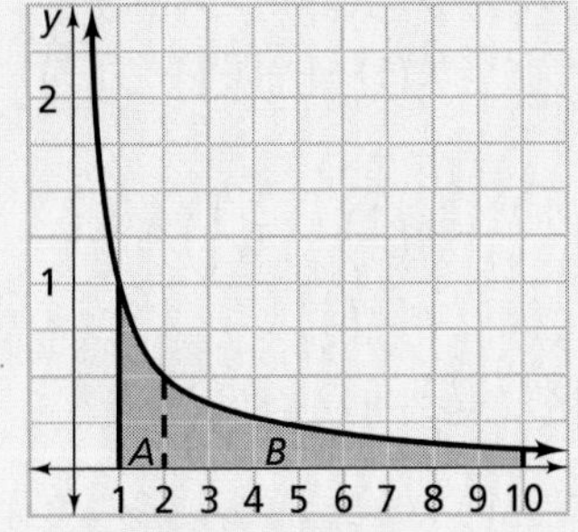

3. See back of book.

Lesson Overview

GOAL

- Develop formulas for calculating $S[1, a](x^m)$ where m is any integer.

This lesson introduces students to the case $m = -1$ through explicit numerical calculations. It is worth discussing the recurring theme in mathematics; you come upon an object that you cannot express in terms of objects you know. So you name it, add it to your toolkit, and start using it as if it had the same status as the other objects you know. And students learn in the next lesson that in fact this newly-named function is a familiar object after all.

Students also learn a nice and surprising fact about the geometry of the graph of $y = \frac{1}{x}$.

While the lesson looks technical, it should be routine for students who have been working on the exercises.

CHECK YOUR UNDERSTANDING
- Core: 1, 2, 3, 4
- Optional: 5, 6
- Extension: 7, 8, 9, 10

MATERIALS
- CAS (recommended)
- graphing calculators
- Blackline Master 8.8

HOMEWORK
- Core: 11, 12, 13, 15, 16
- Optional: 17
- Extension: 14

Launch

It is worth giving some care to a discussion of why the formula

$$S[1, 2](x^m) = \frac{1}{m+1}(2^{m+1} - 1)$$

holds for all integer values except $m = -1$, and then discussing why the case $m = -1$ fails. This is a great way to summarize what has been done so far.

Explore

For You to Do

PROBLEM 1 Students' answers will vary because they can approximate $S[1, 2](x^{-1})$ in different ways, such as by upper sum or lower sum.

PROBLEMS 2 AND 3 You may want to make copies of Blackline Master 8.8 for students to mark on as you take them through the discussion.

For Discussion

PROBLEM 4 Students' answers may vary depending on whether they use the lower sum or the upper sum, and the number of subdivisions they choose.

PROBLEM 6 Students may say that the two regions seem proportional in some way—over the interval [3, 6] the region under the function $y = \frac{1}{x}$ seems "one-third as high" and "three times as wide" as it is over the interval [1, 2].

For Discussion

4. Use your calculator or computer to make a table for the function $a \mapsto S[1, a](x^{-1})$ for integer values of a between 1 and 10. Of course, these will be approximate values.

5. Graph this function.

Although this function, $a \mapsto S[1, a](x^{-1})$, does not have a simple algebraic closed form, it is of central importance in mathematics. For now, call it $\mathcal{L}$.

In the early 17th century, monk Gregory of St. Vincent made a remarkable discovery about the function $\mathcal{L}$. His idea was to compare the area under the graph of $y = \frac{1}{x}$ between $x = a$ and $x = b$ to the area under the same curve between $x = ta$ and $x = tb$ for positive values of t.

To begin, compare the two areas below, $A_1 = S[1, 2]\left(\frac{1}{x}\right)$ and $A_2 = S[3, 6]\left(\frac{1}{x}\right)$.

So, $a = 1$, $b = 2$, and $t = 3$.

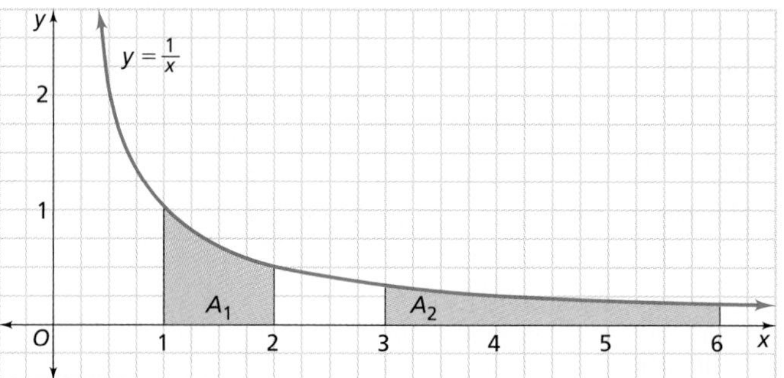

For Discussion

6. Which area do you think is greater?

One way to decide which is greater is to look at the upper and lower sums. Gregory looked at the Cavalieri sums rather than the Fermat sums. He took equal subdivisions along the x-axis.

Answers

For Discussion

4. See back of book.

5.

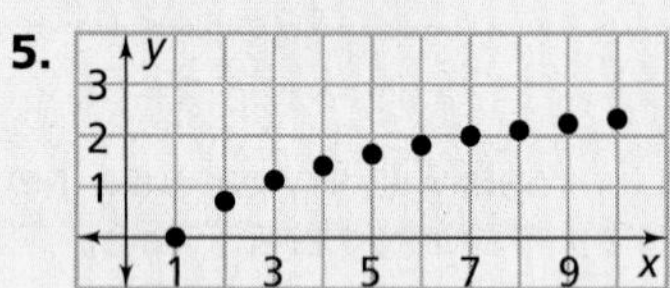

6. Check students' work.

7.
$$U_3[1, 2]\left(\tfrac{1}{x}\right) = \tfrac{1}{3} \cdot 1 + \tfrac{1}{3}\left(\tfrac{4}{3}\right)^{-1} + \tfrac{1}{3}\left(\tfrac{5}{3}\right)^{-1}$$
$$= \tfrac{1}{3}(1) + \tfrac{1}{3}\left(\tfrac{3}{4}\right) + \tfrac{1}{3}\left(\tfrac{3}{5}\right)$$
$$= \tfrac{1}{3} + \tfrac{1}{4} + \tfrac{1}{5}$$
$$U_3[3, 6]\left(\tfrac{1}{x}\right) = 1\left(\tfrac{1}{3}\right) + 1\left(\tfrac{1}{4}\right) + + 1\left(\tfrac{1}{5}\right)$$
$$= \tfrac{1}{3} + \tfrac{1}{4} + \tfrac{1}{5}$$

For Discussion

7. Show that

$$U_3[1, 2]\left(\tfrac{1}{x}\right) = U_3[3, 6]\left(\tfrac{1}{x}\right)$$

by matching each rectangle in $U_3[1, 2]\left(\frac{1}{x}\right)$ with a rectangle in $U_3[3, 6]\left(\frac{1}{x}\right)$ that has the same area.

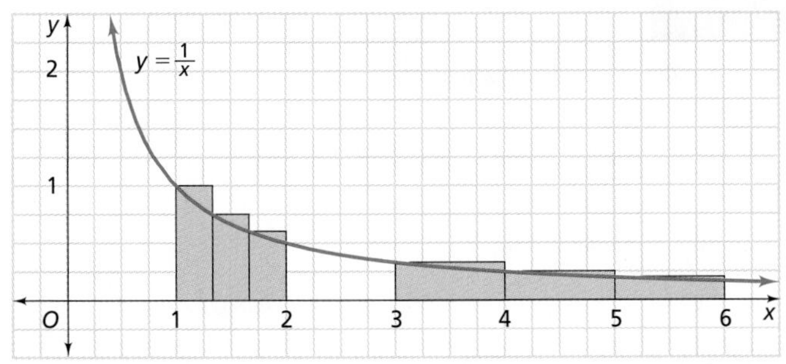

For You to Do

8. Show that

$$U_4[1, 2]\left(\tfrac{1}{x}\right) = U_4[3, 6]\left(\tfrac{1}{x}\right)$$

9. Show that

$$U_n[1, 2]\left(\tfrac{1}{x}\right) = U_n[3, 6]\left(\tfrac{1}{x}\right)$$

The upper sums are always equal. Similarly, the lower sums are always equal. It follows that

$$S[1, 2]\left(\tfrac{1}{x}\right) = S[3, 6]\left(\tfrac{1}{x}\right)$$

Check the equality of the lower sums for yourself.

Actually, Gregory proved a much more general statement.

Theorem 8.1 ***Gregory of St. Vincent's Theorem***

For any $t > 0$ and any real numbers a, b with $1 \le a < b$,

$$S[a, b]\left(\tfrac{1}{x}\right) = S[ta, tb]\left(\tfrac{1}{x}\right)$$

For Discussion

PROBLEM 7 There is another way to see why the upper sums are equal to each other. The left rectangle in $U_3[3, 6]\left(\frac{1}{x}\right)$ is three times as wide and one-third as tall as the left triangle in $U_3[1, 2]\left(\frac{1}{x}\right)$; that is why they have the same area. The other corresponding rectangles have the same areas, for the same reason.

Wrap Up

Exercises 8, 9, and 10 lead students through an explanation—gory details and all—of why Theorem 8.1 is true. If students are curious, use these exercises to frame a discussion. Alternatively, Exercises 4 and 7 provide a good preview for the next lesson.

Assessment Resources

Lesson Quiz 8.8

1. Show that
$$\mathcal{L}(20) = \mathcal{L}(4) + \mathcal{L}(5)$$

2. Find the approximate value of a in each of the following cases.
   a. $\mathcal{L}(a) = 7$ b. $\mathcal{L}(a) = 9$
   c. $\mathcal{L}(a) = 11$ d. $\mathcal{L}(a) = 13$

3. Suppose a and b are numbers such that $\mathcal{L}(a) = 4$ and $\mathcal{L}(b) = 7$. Find each of the following.
   a. $\mathcal{L}(ab)$ b. $\mathcal{L}(a^2)$
   c. $\mathcal{L}(b^5)$ d. $\mathcal{L}\left(\frac{b}{a}\right)$

For You to Do

8.
$$U_4[1, 2]\left(\tfrac{1}{x}\right) = \tfrac{1}{4}\cdot 1 + \tfrac{1}{4}\left(\tfrac{5}{4}\right)^{-1} + \tfrac{1}{4}\left(\tfrac{6}{4}\right)^{-1} + \tfrac{1}{4}\left(\tfrac{7}{4}\right)^{-1}$$
$$= \tfrac{1}{4} + \tfrac{1}{4}\left(\tfrac{4}{5}\right) + \tfrac{1}{4}\left(\tfrac{4}{6}\right) + \tfrac{1}{4}\left(\tfrac{4}{7}\right)$$
$$= \tfrac{1}{4} + \tfrac{1}{5} + \tfrac{1}{6} + \tfrac{1}{7}$$
$$U_4[3, 6]\left(\tfrac{1}{x}\right) = \tfrac{3}{4}\cdot\tfrac{1}{3} + \tfrac{3}{4}\left(\tfrac{15}{4}\right)^{-1} + \tfrac{3}{4}\left(\tfrac{18}{4}\right)^{-1} + \tfrac{3}{4}\left(\tfrac{21}{4}\right)^{-1}$$
$$= \tfrac{3}{4}\left(\tfrac{1}{3}\right) + \tfrac{3}{4}\left(\tfrac{4}{15}\right) + \tfrac{3}{4}\left(\tfrac{4}{18}\right) + \tfrac{3}{4}\left(\tfrac{4}{21}\right)$$
$$= \tfrac{1}{4} + \tfrac{1}{5} + \tfrac{1}{6} + \tfrac{1}{7}$$

Therefore,
$$U_4[1, 2]\left(\tfrac{1}{x}\right) = U_4[3, 6]\left(\tfrac{1}{x}\right).$$

9.
$$U_n[1, 2]\left(\tfrac{1}{x}\right) = \tfrac{1}{n}\cdot 1 + \tfrac{1}{n}\left(\tfrac{n+1}{n}\right)^{-1} + \cdots + \tfrac{1}{n}\left(\tfrac{2n-1}{n}\right)^{-1}$$
$$= \tfrac{1}{n} + \tfrac{1}{n}\left(\tfrac{n}{n+1}\right) + \cdots + \tfrac{1}{n}\left(\tfrac{n}{2n-1}\right)$$
$$= \tfrac{1}{n} + \tfrac{1}{n+1} + \cdots + \tfrac{1}{2n-1}$$
$$U_n[3, 6]\left(\tfrac{1}{x}\right) = \tfrac{3}{n}\cdot\tfrac{1}{3} + \tfrac{3}{n}\left(\tfrac{3n+3}{n}\right)^{-1} + \cdots + \tfrac{3}{n}\left(\tfrac{6n-3}{n}\right)^{-1}$$
$$= \tfrac{1}{n} + \tfrac{3}{n}\left(\tfrac{n}{3(n+1)}\right) + \cdots + \tfrac{3}{n}\left(\tfrac{n}{3(2n-1)}\right)$$
$$= \tfrac{1}{n} + \tfrac{1}{n+1} + \cdots + \tfrac{1}{2n-1}$$

Therefore,
$$U_n[1, 2]\left(\tfrac{1}{x}\right) = U_n[3, 6]\left(\tfrac{1}{x}\right)$$

Exercises

HOMEWORK

- Core: 11, 12, 13, 15, 16
- Optional: 17
- Extension: 14

Check Your Understanding

EXERCISE 7 may be a lot of work for students now—in fact, you may want to suggest that students just try one part. In the next lesson, Sasha and Derman hit on a way to make this estimation much easier.

EXERCISES 8–10 take the students through a proof of Theorem 8.1.

Exercises Practicing Habits of Mind

Check Your Understanding

1. Use your calculator to make a table for $\mathcal{L}(a)$ for values of a between 1 and 10, in increments of 0.5.
2. Suppose you allow a to take on real values between 1 and 10. Sketch the graph of $a \mapsto S[1, a](x^{-1})$ for $1 \leq a \leq 10$.
3. **Write About It** There must be a number a for which $\mathcal{L}(a) = 1$. Between what two integers is a? Explain.
4. Show that $\mathcal{L}(2^3) = 3\mathcal{L}(2)$.
5. Make a conjecture about $\mathcal{L}(r^m)$ based on Exercise 4. Are there any restrictions on r and m?
6. Prove that $\mathcal{L}(r^m) = m \cdot \mathcal{L}(r)$ if $r > 1$ and $m \geq 0$ is an integer.
7. **Take It Further** Find the approximate value of a in each of the following cases.
   a. $\mathcal{L}(a) = 1$ **b.** $\mathcal{L}(a) = 2$ **c.** $\mathcal{L}(a) = 3$
   d. $\mathcal{L}(a) = 4$ **e.** $\mathcal{L}(a) = 6$

You can use your calculator to check this numerically.

Exercises 8–10 will take you through a proof of Theorem 8.1.

8. **Take It Further** Suppose you are trying to compute

$$U_n[a, b]\left(\tfrac{1}{x}\right)$$

   a. Let Δ_1 denote the width of each rectangle. Express Δ_1 in terms of a, b, and n.
   b. Find
   - the height of the first rectangle
   - the height of the second rectangle
   - the height of the third rectangle
   - the height of the ith rectangle

   c. Find
   - the area of the first rectangle
   - the area of the second rectangle
   - the area of the third rectangle
   - the area of the ith rectangle

Answers

Exercises

1. See back of book.

2.

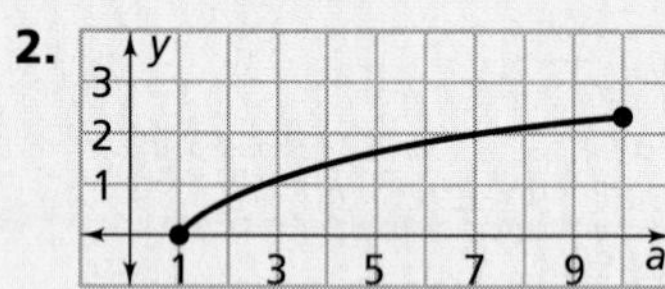

3. Using the previous graph and table, $\mathcal{L}(2) < 1$ and $\mathcal{L}(3) > 1$. Therefore, the number which $\mathcal{L}(x)$ is equal to 1 is between 2 and 3.

4. Using Theorem 8.1,

$$\begin{aligned}\mathcal{L}(2^3) &= S[1, 2^3]\left(\tfrac{1}{x}\right)\\ &= S[1, 2]\left(\tfrac{1}{x}\right) + S[2, 2^2]\left(\tfrac{1}{x}\right) + S[2^2, 2^3]\left(\tfrac{1}{x}\right)\\ &= S[1, 2]\left(\tfrac{1}{x}\right) + S[1, 2]\left(\tfrac{1}{x}\right) + S[1, 2]\left(\tfrac{1}{x}\right)\\ &= 3 \cdot S[1, 2]\left(\tfrac{1}{x}\right)\\ &= 3\mathcal{L}(2)\end{aligned}$$

5. $\mathcal{L}(r^m) = m\mathcal{L}(r);\ m \geq 0, r \geq 1$

6. See back of book.

7. a. ≈ 2.71828
b. ≈ 7.38906
c. ≈ 20.085
d. ≈ 54.5982
e. ≈ 403.429

8. a. $\Delta_1 = \dfrac{b - a}{n}$

b.
- $\dfrac{1}{a}$
- $\dfrac{n}{(n-1)a + b}$
- $\dfrac{n}{(n-2)a + 2b}$
- $\dfrac{n}{(n-i)a + ib}$

c.
- $\dfrac{b-a}{na}$
- $\dfrac{b-a}{(n-1)a + b}$
- $\dfrac{b-a}{(n-2)a + 2b}$
- $\dfrac{b-a}{(n-i)a + ib}$

9. **Take It Further**

Suppose you are trying to compute

$$U_n[ta, tb]\left(\frac{1}{x}\right)$$

a. Let Δ_2 denote the width of each rectangle. Express Δ_2 in terms of a, b, t, and n, How does Δ_2 relate to Δ_1 from Exercise 8?

Remember, $\Delta_2 = t\Delta_1$.

b. Find:

- the height of the first rectangle
- the height of the second rectangle
- the height of the third rectangle
- the height of the ith rectangle

c. Find

- the area of the first rectangle
- the area of the second rectangle
- the area of the third rectangle
- the area of the ith rectangle

d. Show that the area of each rectangle in $U_n[a, b]\left(\frac{1}{x}\right)$ is equal to the area of each rectangle in $U_n[ta, tb]\left(\frac{1}{x}\right)$.

e. Explain why $U_n[a, b]\left(\frac{1}{x}\right) = U_n[ta, tb]\left(\frac{1}{x}\right)$.

10. **Take It Further** Show that $S[a, b]\left(\frac{1}{x}\right) = S[ta, tb]\left(\frac{1}{x}\right)$.

On Your Own

11. Without using the results of Exercises 8 and 9, show that

$$U_3[1, 3]\left(\frac{1}{x}\right) = U_3[3, 9]\left(\frac{1}{x}\right)$$

by matching each rectangle in $U_3[1, 3]\left(\frac{1}{x}\right)$ with a rectangle in $U_3[3, 9]\left(\frac{1}{x}\right)$ that has the same area.

12. Without using the results of Exercises 8 and 9, show that

$$U_4[1, 5]\left(\frac{1}{x}\right) = U_4[3, 15]\left(\frac{1}{x}\right)$$

9. a. $\Delta_2 = \frac{tb - ta}{n}$; $\Delta_2 = t\Delta_1$

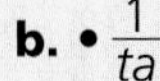

b.
- $\frac{1}{ta}$
- $\frac{n}{(n-1)ta + tb}$
- $\frac{n}{(n-2)ta + 2tb}$
- $\frac{n}{(n-i)ta + itb}$

c.
- $\frac{b-a}{na}$
- $\frac{b-a}{(n-1)a + b}$
- $\frac{b-a}{(n-2)a + 2b}$
- $\frac{b-a}{(n-i)a + ib}$

d. Each of the corresponding rectangles have equal area.

e. The two approximations consist of the same terms being added, $U_n[a, b]\left(\frac{1}{x}\right) = U_n[ta, tb]\left(\frac{1}{x}\right)$.

10. Since the two sums add exactly the same terms, they must be equal.

Since the actual areas are the values the upper sums approach as n gets larger, and the sums are the same, the areas must be the same.

11. $U_3[1, 3]\left(\frac{1}{x}\right) = \frac{2}{3} \cdot 1 + \frac{2}{3}\left(\frac{5}{3}\right)^{-1} + \frac{2}{3}\left(\frac{7}{3}\right)^{-1}$

$= \frac{2}{3} + \frac{2}{5} + \frac{2}{7}$

$U_3[3, 9]\left(\frac{1}{x}\right) = 2\left(\frac{1}{3}\right) + 2\left(\frac{1}{5}\right) + 2\left(\frac{1}{7}\right)$

$= \frac{2}{3} + \frac{2}{5} + \frac{2}{7}$

The left rectangle in $U_3[3, 9]\left(\frac{1}{x}\right)$ is three times as wide and one-third as tall as the left rectangle in $U_3[1, 3]\left(\frac{1}{x}\right)$, which is why they have the same area. The other corresponding rectangles also have the same areas, so the upper sums are equal to each other.

12. See back of book.

Additional Resources

PRINT RESOURCES
- Solution Manual
- Practice Workbook
- Assessment Resources
- Teaching Resources

TECHNOLOGY
- Interactive Textbook
- TeacherExpress CD-ROM
- ExamView CD-ROM
- PHSchool.com

Additional Practice

1. Show that

$$\mathcal{L}(15) = \mathcal{L}(3) + \mathcal{L}(5)$$

2. Find the approximate value of a in each of the following cases.
   a. $\mathcal{L}(a) = 5$ b. $\mathcal{L}(a) = 8$
   c. $\mathcal{L}(a) = 10$ d. $\mathcal{L}(a) = 12$

3. Suppose a and b are numbers such that $\mathcal{L}(a) = 6$ and $\mathcal{L}(b) = 5$. Find each of the following.
   a. $\mathcal{L}(ab)$ b. $\mathcal{L}(a^2)$
   c. $\mathcal{L}(b^6)$ d. $\mathcal{L}\left(\frac{b}{a}\right)$

4. Prove that $L_4[2, 6]\left(\frac{1}{x}\right) = L_4[4, 12]\left(\frac{1}{x}\right)$.

For Exercises 5 through 8, consider function h, with the following properties:

- The domain of h is $\mathbb{R}$.
- For all numbers x and y, $h(xy) = h(x) + h(y)$
- $h(5) = 1$
- h is increasing. That is, if $x < y$, then $h(x) < h(y)$ for all x and y.

5. Find each of the following.
   a. $h(5)$ b. $h(25)$ c. $h(125)$
   d. $h(5^4)$ e. $h(1)$

6. Find each of the following.
   a. $h\left(\frac{1}{5}\right)$ b. $h\left(\frac{1}{25}\right)$ c. $h\left(\frac{1}{125}\right)$

7. Suppose $h(4) \approx 0.86135$. Find approximations of each of the following.
   a. $h(16)$ b. $h(2)$ c. $h(20)$

8. Suppose $h(3) \approx 0.6826$. Explain why $h(\sqrt{3}) \approx 0.3413$.

Practice: For Lesson 8.8, assign Exercises 1–4.

13. What do the shaded regions suggest about the relative sizes of $\mathcal{L}(m_1)$ and $\mathcal{L}(m_2)$ when $1 \le m_1 < m_2$?

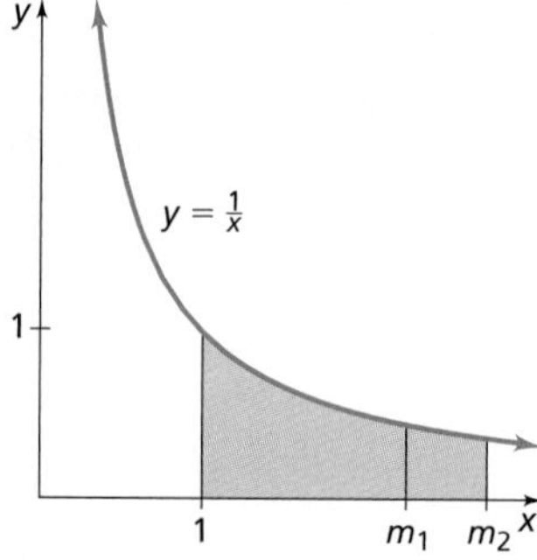

Go Online PHSchool.com

For additional practice, go to Web Code: bga-0808

14. Take It Further Suppose a and b are numbers such that $\mathcal{L}(a) = 7$ and $\mathcal{L}(b) = 9$. Find each of the following.

a. $\mathcal{L}(ab)$ b. $\mathcal{L}(a^2)$ c. $\mathcal{L}(a^{10})$ d. $\mathcal{L}\left(\frac{b}{a}\right)$

15. Why is $\mathcal{L}(1) = 0$?

16. Standardized Test Prep Which of the following is equal to $U_7[1, 3]\left(\frac{1}{x}\right)$?

A. $L_7[1, 3]\left(\frac{1}{x}\right)$ B. $U_7[2, 4]\left(\frac{1}{x}\right)$

C. $U_7[3, 6]\left(\frac{1}{x}\right)$ D. $U_7[4, 12]\left(\frac{1}{x}\right)$

Maintain Your Skills

17. a. Without using the results of Exercises 8 and 9, show that

$$U_n[1, 4]\left(\frac{1}{x}\right) = U_n[3, 12]\left(\frac{1}{x}\right)$$

b. Show that

$$U_6[1, 3]\left(\frac{1}{x}\right) = U_6[3, 9]\left(\frac{1}{x}\right)$$

c. Show that

$$U_n[1, 3]\left(\frac{1}{x}\right) = U_n[3, 9]\left(\frac{1}{x}\right)$$

Remember...

Theorem 8.1 is a theorem about $S[a, b]\left(\frac{1}{x}\right)$, and not about $U_n[a, b]\left(\frac{1}{x}\right)$.

Answers

13. If $1 < m_1 < m_2$, $S[1, m_1]\left(\frac{1}{x}\right) < S[1, m_2]\left(\frac{1}{x}\right)$ as shown in the picture (since the interval $[0, m_1]$ is contained within the interval $[0, m_2]$). But $S[1, m_1]\left(\frac{1}{x}\right) = \mathcal{L}(m_1)$ and $S[1, m_2]\left(\frac{1}{x}\right) = \mathcal{L}(m_2)$ therefore $\mathcal{L}(m_1) < \mathcal{L}(m_2)$.

14. a. 16 **b.** 14 **c.** 70 **d.** 2

15. Since there is no area under $y = \frac{1}{x}$ between 1 and 1, $S[1, 1]\left(\frac{1}{x}\right) = 0$, so $\mathcal{L}(1) = 0$.

16. D

17. See back of book.

8.9 Properties of the Function $\mathcal{L}$

The function $\mathcal{L}$ defined in Lesson 8.8 is really a familiar function in disguise. You will unmask the function in this lesson.

Minds in Action episode 30

Sasha and Derman are working on Problem 1 of the last lesson. They are approximating $S[1, 2](x^{-1})$ using Fermat's method.

Derman I found the Fermat Upper Sum by making another table.

Fermat Upper Sum for $y = x^{-1}$ on [1, 2]

	Base	Height	Area
1st rectangle	$r - 1$	1	$1(r - 1)$
2nd rectangle	$r^2 - r$	r^{-1}	$\frac{r^2 - r}{r} = r - 1$
3rd rectangle	$r^3 - r^2$	$(r^2)^{-1} = r^{-2}$	$r - 1$
4th rectangle	$r^4 - r^3$	$(r^3)^{-1} = r^{-3}$	$r - 1$
⋮	⋮	⋮	⋮
nth rectangle	$r^n - r^{n-1}$	$(r^{n-1})^{-1} = r^{-(n-1)}$	$r - 1$

Derman But how do I add up all those $(r - 1)$'s?

Sasha This is the easiest addition we've done so far! There are n of them, so we get $n(r - 1)$. And in this case, $r = \sqrt[n]{2}$, so the Fermat upper sum is $n(\sqrt[n]{2} - 1)$. So if we let $n = 200$, then we get an approximation of 0.6943497.

And it gets better. Look at our table—we could replace r^n with whatever we needed. The lower sum works pretty much the same way. We can approximate $\mathcal{L}(a)$ using $n(\sqrt[n]{a} - 1)$ as long as we make n big enough.

You will do this in the upcoming Check Your Understanding.

Derman Now, this is the kind of calculation I can get into!

Derman is excited because he and Sasha found a quick way of approximating $\mathcal{L}(a)$. $\mathcal{L}$ has lots of interesting properties, which you can derive using the definition $\mathcal{L}(a) = S[1, a]\left(\frac{1}{x}\right)$ and Theorem 8.1.

Lesson Overview

GOAL

- Investigate a mysteriously familiar function, $\mathcal{L}(a)$.

The title of this lesson, Properties of the Function $\mathcal{L}$, does not really do justice to the joy of realizing that $\mathcal{L}$ is really a logarithm function. Perhaps a better title is, "Surprise! It is a logarithm!" But that would give too much away. Sasha and Derman take real pleasure in unraveling the mysteries embedded in $\mathcal{L}$, and hopefully students take similar pleasure. The Check Your Understanding Exercises at the end of the lesson echo this sleuthing. Students get to play "function detective" again to figure out another function.

CHECK YOUR UNDERSTANDING
- Core: 2, 3, 4, 5
- Optional: 1

MATERIALS
- CAS (recommended)
- graphing calculators
- Blackline Master 8.9

HOMEWORK
- Core: 7, 8, 9, 10
- Optional: 6, 11

Launch

You might open this lesson by reviewing how to approximate $S[1, 2](x^{-1})$ using Fermat's method, just as Sasha and Derman do at the beginning of this lesson.

Explore

Minds in Action

You may wish to assign students Minds in Action roles and present the conversation to the class. This is more effective if you assign the roles one class day prior to the "performance." Urge the students to "get into" their parts by using their own words instead of memorizing lines.

Example

Problem Show that $\mathcal{L}(6) = \mathcal{L}(2 \cdot 3) = \mathcal{L}(2) + \mathcal{L}(3)$.

Solution

$$\begin{aligned}\mathcal{L}(6) &= S[1, 6]\left(\tfrac{1}{x}\right) \\ &= S[1, 2]\left(\tfrac{1}{x}\right) + S[2, 6]\left(\tfrac{1}{x}\right) \\ &= S[1, 2]\left(\tfrac{1}{x}\right) + S[1, 3]\left(\tfrac{1}{x}\right) \quad \text{by Theorem 8.1} \\ &= \mathcal{L}(2) + \mathcal{L}(3)\end{aligned}$$

There is nothing special about 2 and 3 (except that $6 = 2 \cdot 3$).

For You to Do

1. Show that $\mathcal{L}(12) = \mathcal{L}(3) + \mathcal{L}(4)$.
2. Show that $\mathcal{L}(rs) = \mathcal{L}(r) + \mathcal{L}(s)$, if r and s are greater than 1.

Minds in Action episode 31

Sasha and Derman are looking at properties of the function $\mathcal{L}$.

Sasha This function seems familiar. Look at its properties:

If $r > s \geq 1$ and m is a positive integer, then

$$\mathcal{L}(rs) = \mathcal{L}(r) + \mathcal{L}(s)$$

$$\mathcal{L}\left(\frac{r}{s}\right) = \mathcal{L}(r) - \mathcal{L}(s)$$

$$\mathcal{L}(r^m) = m\mathcal{L}(r)$$

$$\mathcal{L}(1) = 0$$

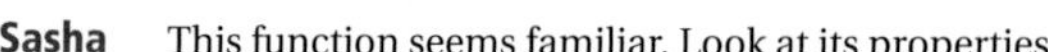

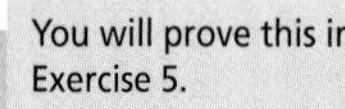

You will prove this in Exercise 5.

Derman It almost reminds me of exponential functions—or—

Sasha Logarithms! This function has exactly the same properties as a logarithmic function! Do you think this function is a logarithm?

Derman What would the base be?

Sasha Well, we could figure that out—we would just need to know what input a yields $\mathcal{L}(a) = 1$. We can use our approximation $\mathcal{L}(a) \approx n(\sqrt[n]{a} - 1)$ to get a pretty good estimate of a. Let's choose $n = 1{,}000{,}000$.

Answers

For You to Do

1. $$\begin{aligned}\mathcal{L}(12) &= S[1, 12]\left(\tfrac{1}{x}\right) \\ &= S[1, 3]\left(\tfrac{1}{x}\right) + S[3, 12]\left(\tfrac{1}{x}\right) \\ &= S[1, 3]\left(\tfrac{1}{x}\right) + S[1, 4]\left(\tfrac{1}{x}\right) \\ &= \mathcal{L}(3) + \mathcal{L}(4)\end{aligned}$$

2. $$\begin{aligned}\mathcal{L}(rs) &= S[1, rs]\left(\tfrac{1}{x}\right) \\ &= S[1, r]\left(\tfrac{1}{x}\right) + S[r, rs]\left(\tfrac{1}{x}\right) \\ &= S[1, r]\left(\tfrac{1}{x}\right) + S[1, s]\left(\tfrac{1}{x}\right) \\ &= \mathcal{L}(r) + \mathcal{L}(s)\end{aligned}$$

For You to Do

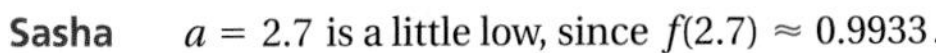

3. Use Sasha's approximation of $\mathcal{L}(a)$ to find a such that $\mathcal{L}(a) \approx 1$.

Minds in Action — episode 32

Sasha and Derman start looking for a value of a which makes $f(a) = 1{,}000{,}000\left(\sqrt[1{,}000{,}000]{a} - 1\right)$ approximately equal to 1.

Sasha $a = 2.7$ is a little low, since $f(2.7) \approx 0.9933$.

Derman And $a = 2.75$ is a little high, since $f(2.75) \approx 1.0116$.

Sasha Wait a second—it can't be—Derman, try e.

Derman $f(e) = 1$.

Sasha It's the natural logarithm! It must be the natural log! And in fact, look: If $n\left(a^{\frac{1}{n}} - 1\right) \approx 1$, then $a^{\frac{1}{n}} - 1 \approx \frac{1}{n}$, so $a^{\frac{1}{n}} \approx \frac{1}{n} + 1$ and $a \approx \left(1 + \frac{1}{n}\right)^n$. We are assuming n to be very large, so that's just the definition of e!

Sasha and Derman are pretty confident that $\mathcal{L}(x) = \log_e(x)$, but they need a proof. They know that $\mathcal{L}(e) = 1$. They can easily use that, together with the third and fourth items of Sasha's list of properties of $\mathcal{L}$, to prove the following theorem.

Theorem 8.2

If m is a nonnegative integer,

$$\mathcal{L}(e^m) = m$$

Theorem 8.2 covers only cases where the exponent m is a nonnegative integer. You can do better, with a little formal calculation.

Habits of Mind

Understand the process. This kind of reasoning is typical when one wants to extend the applicability of an equation from integers to rational numbers. After you study this kind of argument a few times, you can do it yourself.

For You to Do

3. Answers may vary. The answer should be approximately equal to $e \approx 2.71828$.

For You to Do

PROBLEM 3 Students may try something like this: Sasha's approximation:

$$\mathcal{L}(a) = n\left(\sqrt[n]{a} - 1\right)$$

Letting $n = 100$, find a so that $100\left(\sqrt[100]{a}\right) = 1$. If this equation holds, then $\sqrt[100]{a} = \frac{1}{100} + 1 = 1.01$, so $a = (1.01)^{100} \approx 2.7048$. For $n = 1000$, $a = (1.001)^{1000} \approx 2.7169$.

For Discussion

4. Suppose m is a positive integer. Prove that

$$\mathcal{L}\left(e^{\frac{1}{m}}\right) = \frac{1}{m}$$

by giving a reason for each step in this formal calculation:

$$1 = \mathcal{L}(e) = \mathcal{L}\left(e^{\frac{m}{m}}\right) \qquad m \text{ is a positive integer.}$$

$$= \mathcal{L}\left(\left(e^{\frac{1}{m}}\right)^m\right)$$

$$= m\,\mathcal{L}\left(e^{\frac{1}{m}}\right)$$

Divide both sides by m to conclude that

$$\frac{1}{m} = \mathcal{L}\left(e^{\frac{1}{m}}\right)$$

For You to Do

5. Use the same line of reasoning to prove that if $a \geq 1$,

$$\mathcal{L}\left(a^{\frac{1}{m}}\right) = \frac{1}{m}\mathcal{L}(a)$$

For Discussion

6. Prove that $\mathcal{L}\left(e^{\frac{q}{m}}\right) = \frac{q}{m}$ for any non-negative fraction $\frac{q}{m}$, by supplying the reasons.

$$\mathcal{L}\left(e^{\frac{q}{m}}\right) = \mathcal{L}\left((e^q)^{\frac{1}{m}}\right)$$

$$= \frac{1}{m}\mathcal{L}(e^q)$$

$$= \frac{1}{m}q\,\mathcal{L}(e)$$

$$= \frac{q}{m}$$

Since every real number can be approximated by fractions, the exponent rule extends even further, to real numbers. In calculus, you will prove the following result.

Theorem 8.3

If $r \geq 0$ is any real number, then

$$\mathcal{L}(e^r) = r$$

Answers

For Discussion

4. The first line is due to the properties $\mathcal{L}(e) = 1$ and $\frac{m}{m} = 1$.

   Line 2 is due to the property $a^{bc} = (a^b)^c$.

   Line 3 is due to the property $\mathcal{L}(x^m) = m\mathcal{L}(x)$ when m is a positive integer.

   The final equation follows by dividing both sides of the equation by m.

For You to Do

5. $\mathcal{L}(a) = \mathcal{L}\left(a^{\frac{m}{m}}\right) = \mathcal{L}\left(\left(a^{\frac{1}{m}}\right)^m\right) = m\mathcal{L}\left(a^{\frac{1}{m}}\right)$. Divide both sides by m to conclude: $\frac{1}{m}\mathcal{L}(a) = \mathcal{L}\left(a^{\frac{1}{m}}\right)$.

For Discussion

6. Line 1: multiplicative property of exponents

   Line 2: previous problem result

   Line 3: $\mathcal{L}(x^q) = q\mathcal{L}(x)$ since q is a positive integer

   Line 4: $\mathcal{L}(e) = 1$

Theorem 8.3 makes the connection between $\mathcal{L}$ and the natural logarithm. Suppose you want to find $\mathcal{L}(a)$. Find a real number r such that $e^r = a$—that is, $r = \ln a$. Then

Here $a \geq 1$ and $r \geq 0$.

$$\mathcal{L}(a) = \mathcal{L}(e^r) = r = \ln a$$

So, $\mathcal{L}(a) = \ln a$.

Theorem 8.4

If $a \geq 1$,

$$\mathcal{L}(a) = r \Leftrightarrow e^r = a$$

In other words, $\mathcal{L}$ is the natural logarithm

$$\mathcal{L}(a) = \ln a$$

Remember...

All this is still based on Sasha's convincing argument that $\mathcal{L}(e) = 1$.

Developing Habits of Mind

Think about it more than one way. You now have two ways to think about the natural logarithm function.

Method 1: The ln function is the logarithm to the base e—the inverse of the function $x \mapsto e^x$.

Method 2: The ln function is the function that gives the area under the graph of $y = \frac{1}{x}$ between $x = 1$ and $x = a$, where $a \geq 1$:

$$\ln a = S[1, a](x^{-1})$$

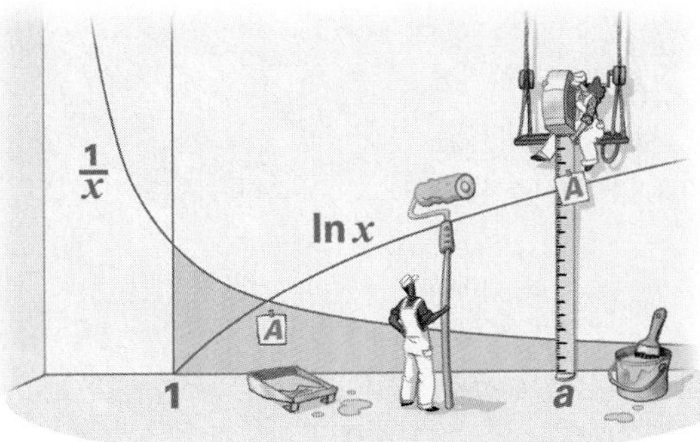

Wrap Up

If time allows, go over Exercises 2 through 5 in the Check Your Understanding section with students.

Assessment Resources

Lesson Quiz 8.9

For Exercises 1 and 2 consider a function, g, with the following properties:

- The domain of g is $\mathbb{R}$.
- For all numbers x and y, $g(xy) = g(x) + g(y)$
- $g(6) = 1$
- g is increasing. That is, if $x < y$, then $h(x) < h(y)$ for all x and y.

1. Find each of the following.

a. $g(6)$ **b.** $g(36)$

c. $g(216)$ **d.** $g(1)$

2. Suppose $g(9) \approx 1.22629$. Find approximations for each of the following.

a. $g(81)$ **b.** $g(3)$

c. $g\left(\frac{1}{3}\right)$ **d.** $g(54)$

Exercises

HOMEWORK
- Core: 7, 8, 9, 10
- Optional: 6, 11

Check Your Understanding

EXERCISE 1 You can give the students copies of Blackline Master 8.9 to use while working this exercise.

Exercises *Practicing Habits of Mind*

Check Your Understanding

1. In the Minds in Action episode that opens this lesson, Sasha says, "The lower sum works pretty much the same way." You will now see what she means.

a. Copy and complete the following table.

Fermat Lower Sum for $y = x^{-1}$ on [1, 2]			
	Base	Height	Area
1st rectangle	■	■	■
2nd rectangle	■	■	■
3rd rectangle	■	■	■
4th rectangle	■	■	■
⋮	⋮	⋮	⋮
*n*th rectangle	■	■	■

b. Add up the areas of the rectangles.

For Exercises 2 through 5, consider the function, g, with the following properties:

- The domain of g is $\mathbb{R}$.
- For all numbers x and y,

$$g(xy) = g(x) + g(y)$$

- $g(10) = 1$
- g is increasing. That is, if $x < y$, then $g(x) < g(y)$ for all x and y.

2. Find each of the following.

a. $g(10)$ **b.** $g(100)$ **c.** $g(10{,}000)$
d. $g(10^{100})$ **e.** $g(1)$

3. Find each of the following.

a. $g\left(\frac{1}{10}\right)$ **b.** $g\left(\frac{1}{100}\right)$ **c.** $g\left(\frac{1}{1000}\right)$ **d.** $g\left(\frac{1}{10^{100}}\right)$

4. Suppose $g(5) \approx 0.69897$. Find approximations of each of the following.

a. $g(25)$ **b.** $g(2)$ **c.** $g(50)$ **d.** $g(2^4 \cdot 5^7)$

Answers

Exercises

1. See back of book.

2. a. $g(10) = 1$ **b.** $g(100) = 2$
c. $g(10{,}000) = 4$ **d.** $g(10^{100}) = 100$
e. $g(1) = 0$

3. a. $g\left(\frac{1}{10}\right) = -1$ **b.** $g\left(\frac{1}{100}\right) = -2$
c. $g\left(\frac{1}{1000}\right) = -3$ **d.** $g\left(\frac{1}{10^{100}}\right) = -100$

4. a. $g(25) \approx 1.39794$
b. $g(2) \approx 0.30103$
c. $g(50) \approx 1.69897$
d. $g(2^4 \cdot 5^7) \approx 6.09691$

5. Note first that $0 = g(1) = g(y \cdot y^{-1}) = g(y) + g(y^{-1})$, so $g(y^{-1}) = -g(y)$. Therefore, if $n = -m$ is a negative integer (so m is positive),

$$g(y^n) = g(y^{-m}) = g((y^{-1})^m) = (g(y^{-1}))^m = (-g(y))^m = -mg(y) = ng(y).$$

a. $g\left(\frac{x}{y}\right) = g(x \cdot y^{-1}) = g(x) + g(y^{-1}) = g(x) - g(y)$

b. Since $g(5) = g((\sqrt{5})^2) = 2g(\sqrt{5})$, then $g(\sqrt{5}) = \frac{1}{2}g(5) = 0.349485$.

c. The function g satisfies all the properties of the common logarithm (log base 10) function, denoted by log or $\log_{10}$.

d.

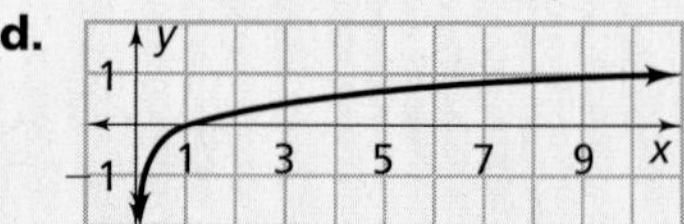

5. a. Show that, for all positive real numbers x and y, $g\left(\frac{x}{y}\right) = g(x) - g(y)$.

b. What is $g(\sqrt{5})$? Why?

c. The function g is actually a function you have seen before. Which one?

d. Sketch the graph of $y = g(x)$.

On Your Own

6. **Write About It** The definition of $\mathcal{L}$ is $\mathcal{L}(a) = S[1, a]\left(\frac{1}{x}\right)$.

This assumes that $a \geq 1$, and all theorems so far have retained that assumption.

But for $a \geq 1$, $\mathcal{L}(a) = \ln a$. Describe what it might mean to extend the definition of $\mathcal{L}(a)$ to $0 < a < 1$, so that for all positive a, $\mathcal{L}(a) = \ln a$.

For this definition to make sense, a must be greater than or equal to 1.

7. a. Show that $\mathcal{L}(4) = 2\mathcal{L}(2)$.

b. Show that $\mathcal{L}(8) = 3\mathcal{L}(2)$.

c. Show that $\mathcal{L}(16) = 4\mathcal{L}(2)$.

d. Show that $\mathcal{L}(2^n) = n\mathcal{L}(2)$.

e. Assuming only that $\mathcal{L}(rs) = \mathcal{L}(r) + \mathcal{L}(s)$, show that if $r > 1$ and m is a positive integer, then $\mathcal{L}(r^m) = m\mathcal{L}(r)$.

8. Assuming only that $\mathcal{L}(rs) = \mathcal{L}(r) + \mathcal{L}(s)$, show that if $r \geq s \geq 1$, then $\mathcal{L}\left(\frac{r}{s}\right) = \mathcal{L}(r) - \mathcal{L}(s)$.

9. Show that $\mathcal{L}(1) = 0$.

10. **Standardized Test Prep** Which of the following is a property of $\mathcal{L}(a)$?

a. For $a \geq 1$ and $b \geq 1$, $\mathcal{L}(a) + \mathcal{L}(b) = \mathcal{L}(a + b)$

b. For $a \geq 1$ and $b \geq 1$, $\mathcal{L}(a) + \mathcal{L}(b) = \mathcal{L}(ab)$

c. For $a \geq 1$ and $b \geq 1$, $\mathcal{L}(ab) \geq \mathcal{L}(a + b)$

d. For $a \geq 1$ and $b \geq 1$, $\mathcal{L}(a) \cdot (b) \geq \mathcal{L}(ab)$

For additional practice, go to Web Code: bga-0809

Maintain Your Skills

11. a. Find a such that $\mathcal{L}(a) = 2$.

b. Find a such that $\mathcal{L}(a) = 3$.

c. Find a such that $\mathcal{L}(a) = z$.

Additional Resources

PRINT RESOURCES
- Solution Manual
- Practice Workbook
- Assessment Resources
- Teaching Resources

TECHNOLOGY
- Interactive Textbook
- TeacherExpress CD-ROM
- ExamView CD-ROM
- PHSchool.com

Additional Practice

1. Show that
$$\mathcal{L}(15) = \mathcal{L}(3) + \mathcal{L}(5)$$

2. Find the approximate value of a in each of the following cases.
a. $\mathcal{L}(a) = 5$ b. $\mathcal{L}(a) = 8$
c. $\mathcal{L}(a) = 10$ d. $\mathcal{L}(a) = 12$

3. Suppose a and b are numbers such that $\mathcal{L}(a) = 6$ and $\mathcal{L}(b) = 5$. Find each of the following.
a. $\mathcal{L}(ab)$ b. $\mathcal{L}(a^2)$
c. $\mathcal{L}(b^6)$ d. $\mathcal{L}\left(\frac{b}{a}\right)$

4. Prove that $L_4[2, 6]\left(\frac{1}{x}\right) = L_4[4, 12]\left(\frac{1}{x}\right)$.

For Exercises 5 through 8, consider function h, with the following properties:

- The domain of h is $\mathbb{R}$.
- For all numbers x and y, $h(xy) = h(x) + h(y)$
- $h(5) = 1$
- h is increasing. That is, if $x < y$, then $h(x) < h(y)$ for all x and y.

5. Find each of the following.
a. $h(5)$ b. $h(25)$ c. $h(125)$
d. $h(5^4)$ e. $h(1)$

6. Find each of the following.
a. $h\left(\frac{1}{5}\right)$ b. $h\left(\frac{1}{25}\right)$ c. $h\left(\frac{1}{125}\right)$

7. Suppose $h(4) \approx 0.86135$. Find approximations of each of the following.
a. $h(16)$ b. $h(2)$ c. $h(20)$

8. Suppose $h(3) \approx 0.6826$. Explain why $h(\sqrt{3}) \approx 0.3413$.

Practice: For Lesson 8.9, assign Exercises 5–8.

6. You can define $\mathcal{L}(a)$ to be $-S[a, 1]\left(\frac{1}{x}\right)$, which equals $-S\left[1, \frac{1}{a}\right]\left(\frac{1}{x}\right)$ by Gregory's Theorem, which equals $-\mathcal{L}\left(\frac{1}{a}\right)$

7. a. $\mathcal{L}(4) = \mathcal{L}(2 \cdot 2) = \mathcal{L}(2) + \mathcal{L}(2) = 2\mathcal{L}(2)$

b. $\mathcal{L}(8) = \mathcal{L}(2 \cdot 2 \cdot 2) = \mathcal{L}(2) + \mathcal{L}(2) + \mathcal{L}(2) = 3\mathcal{L}(2)$

c. $\mathcal{L}(16) = \mathcal{L}(4 \cdot 4) = \mathcal{L}(4) + \mathcal{L}(4) = 2\mathcal{L}(2) + 2\mathcal{L}(2) = 4\mathcal{L}(2)$

d. $\mathcal{L}(2^n) = \mathcal{L}(2 \cdot 2 \cdot 2 \cdot \cdots \cdot 2)$, where a total of n 2's are multiplied. But this equals $\mathcal{L}(2) + \mathcal{L}(2) + \cdots + \mathcal{L}(2)$ where there are a total of n copies of $\mathcal{L}(2)$ being added. This equals $n\mathcal{L}(2)$. Note that you could also prove this by mathematical induction.

e. $\mathcal{L}(r^m) = \mathcal{L}(r \cdot r \cdot r \cdot \cdots \cdot r)$, where a total of m r's are multiplied. But this equals $\mathcal{L}(r) + \mathcal{L}(r) + \cdots + \mathcal{L}(r)$ where there are a total of m copies of $\mathcal{L}(r)$ being added. This equals $m\mathcal{L}(r)$. Note that you could also prove this by mathematical induction.

8. if $r \geq s \geq 1$, then
$\mathcal{L}(r) = \mathcal{L}\left(\frac{r}{s} \cdot s\right) = \mathcal{L}\left(\frac{r}{s}\right) + \mathcal{L}(s)$,
so $\mathcal{L}\left(\frac{r}{s}\right) = \mathcal{L}(r) - \mathcal{L}(s)$

9. By the previous problem,
$\mathcal{L}(1) = \mathcal{L}\left(\frac{r}{r}\right) = \mathcal{L}(r) - \mathcal{L}(r) = 0$.

10. B

11. Recall that $\mathcal{L}(e) = 1$.
a. $a = e^2$
b. $a = e^3$
c. $a = e^z$

Lesson Overview

GOAL

- Find the area under the graph of $y = e^x$ between $x = 0$ and $x = 1$.

This lesson provides a sketch of a proof of a special case of the theorem that states

$$S[a, b](e^x) = e^b - e^a$$

(The details of this proof need to wait for a full course in calculus.) This property (and the corresponding property for derivative) implies that the exponential function is *fixed* by the derivative, and this is behind much of the utility that this function enjoys.

This lesson frequently appeals to evidence in the absence of proof. Make sure students know the gaps in the arguments, and assure them that they will fill in all the gaps someday in a calculus course.

CHECK YOUR UNDERSTANDING

- Core: 1, 4, 6
- Optional: 2, 3, 5
- Extension: 7

MATERIALS

- CAS (recommended)
- graphing calculators

HOMEWORK

- Core: 11
- Optional: 8, 9, 10, 12

Launch

To launch this lesson, have students jump right into the first For Discussion.

Explore

For Discussion

PROBLEM 5 If students have trouble with this problem, suggest that they choose a specific value of n to calculate an approximation. The exact value is $e - 1$.

8.10 The Area Under $f(x) = e^x$

Take a closer look at the graph of the function $f(x) = e^x$.

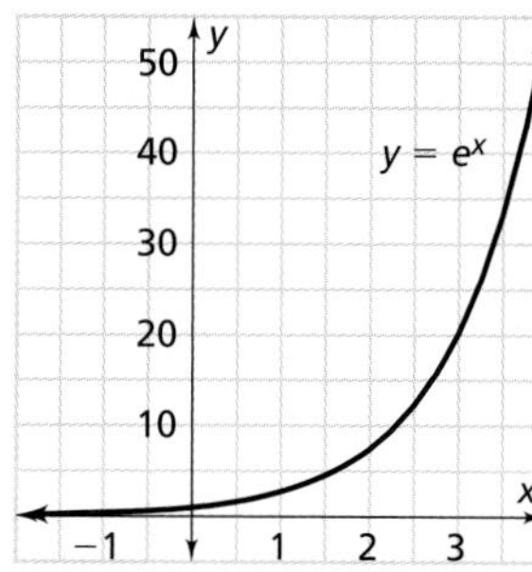

For Discussion

Analyze the graph of $f(x) = e^x$ by answering the following questions.

1. Does the graph cross the y-axis? If so, where? If not, why not?
2. Does the graph cross the x-axis? If so, where? If not, why not?
3. What happens as the x-values become larger and larger positive numbers?
4. What happens as the x-values become larger and larger negative numbers?

The focus of the chapter has been on finding the areas under curves. What is the area under the graph of $y = e^x$, from $x = a$ to $x = b$? To begin to answer this question, consider first the interval $[0, 1]$

For Discussion

5. Approximate the area under the graph of $y = e^x$ from 0 to 1, $S[0, 1](e^x)$.

If you tried to use the method of Fermat in Problem 5, you probably got stuck. Fermat designed his method to result in a sum of a geometric sequence. Since $f(x) = e^x$ is an exponential function, and not a power function like $f(x) = x^m$, the resulting sum is not that of a geometric sequence.

That is, in $f(x) = e^x$ the x is in the exponent, not used as the base.

Answers

For Discussion

1. Any positive number raised to the zero power will equal 1, so $e^0 = 1$, and therefore the function cross the y-axis at $y = 1$.
2. The function will never cross the x-axis, since no power of a nonzero number can ever equal 0.
3. As the x-values become larger and larger positive numbers, so do the function output values.
4. As the x-values become larger and larger negative numbers, the function outputs approach 0.
5. about 1.71828

Example

Problem Find the area under the curve $f(x) = e^x$ from $x = 0$ to $x = 1$.

Solution First, find the lower sum $L_n[0, 1](e^x)$ using Cavalieri's method.

	Base	Height	Area
1st rectangle	$\frac{1}{n}$	$e^0 = 1$	$\frac{1}{n} \cdot 1 = \frac{1}{n}$
2nd rectangle	$\frac{1}{n}$	$e^{\frac{1}{n}}$	$\frac{1}{n} \cdot e^{\frac{1}{n}} = \frac{e^{\frac{1}{n}}}{n}$
3rd rectangle	$\frac{1}{n}$	$e^{\frac{2}{n}}$	$\frac{1}{n} \cdot e^{\frac{2}{n}} = \frac{e^{\frac{2}{n}}}{n}$
4th rectangle	$\frac{1}{n}$	$e^{\frac{3}{n}}$	$\frac{1}{n} \cdot e^{\frac{3}{n}} = \frac{e^{\frac{3}{n}}}{n}$
⋮	⋮	⋮	⋮
nth rectangle	$\frac{1}{n}$	$e^{\frac{n-1}{n}}$	$\frac{1}{n} \cdot e^{\frac{n-1}{n}} = \frac{e^{\frac{n-1}{n}}}{n}$

Add the areas of all the rectangles.

$$\begin{aligned} L_n[0, 1](e^x) &= \frac{1}{n} + \frac{e^{\frac{1}{n}}}{n} + \frac{e^{\frac{2}{n}}}{n} + \frac{e^{\frac{3}{n}}}{n} + \frac{e^{\frac{4}{n}}}{n} + \cdots + \frac{e^{\frac{n-1}{n}}}{n} \\ &= \frac{1}{n}\left(1 + e^{\frac{1}{n}} + e^{\frac{2}{n}} + e^{\frac{3}{n}} + e^{\frac{4}{n}} + \cdots + e^{\frac{n-1}{n}}\right) \\ &= \frac{1}{n}\left(1 + e^{\frac{1}{n}} + \left(e^{\frac{1}{n}}\right)^2 + \left(e^{\frac{1}{n}}\right)^3 + \left(e^{\frac{1}{n}}\right)^4 + \cdots + \left(e^{\frac{1}{n}}\right)^{n-1}\right) \end{aligned}$$

Use the formula for simplifying a geometric series:

$$\begin{aligned} &\frac{1}{n}\left(1 + e^{\frac{1}{n}} + \left(e^{\frac{1}{n}}\right)^2 + \left(e^{\frac{1}{n}}\right)^3 + \left(e^{\frac{1}{n}}\right)^4 + \cdots + \left(e^{\frac{1}{n}}\right)^{n-1}\right) \\ &= \frac{1}{n}\left(\frac{\left(e^{\frac{1}{n}}\right)^n - 1}{e^{\frac{1}{n}} - 1}\right) \\ &= \frac{1}{n}\left(\frac{e - 1}{e^{\frac{1}{n}} - 1}\right) \\ &= \frac{e - 1}{n\left(e^{\frac{1}{n}} - 1\right)} \end{aligned}$$

Remember...

$1 + q + q^2 + \cdots + q^{n-1} = \frac{q^n - 1}{q - 1}$

Next, determine what happens to $\frac{e - 1}{n(e^{\frac{1}{n}} - 1)}$ as you increase the number of subdivisions, n. This is the same as calculating the value of

$$\lim_{n \to \infty} \frac{e - 1}{n\left(e^{\frac{1}{n}} - 1\right)}$$

Since $e - 1$ is a constant, you can move it out in front of the limit expression:

$$\lim_{n \to \infty} \frac{e - 1}{n\left(e^{\frac{1}{n}} - 1\right)} = (e - 1) \lim_{n \to \infty} \frac{1}{n\left(e^{\frac{1}{n}} - 1\right)}$$

Wrap Up

Make sure students understand the steps of the example. They will use the same process in Exercise 1 of the Check Your Understanding section.

Assessment Resources

Lesson Quiz 8.10

1. Use your knowledge of $S[0,1](e^x)$ to find each of the following.
   a. $S[0, 1](e^x) + 4$
   b. $S[0, 1](e^x + 4)$
   c. $S[-1, 0](e^{-x} + 4)$
   d. $S[1, e](\ln x + 4)$

2. Here is another *continued fraction*, similar to the one in the lesson.

$$1 + a_0 + \cfrac{1}{a_1 + \cfrac{1}{a_2 + \cfrac{2}{a_3 + \cfrac{3}{a_4 + \cfrac{4}{a_5 + \cdots}}}}}$$

   Find the value of the expression for each of the following sets of numbers. Round your answers to five decimal places.
   a. $[a_0; a_1, a_2] = [1; 1, 2]$
   b. $[a_0; a_1, a_2, a_3, a_4] = [1; 1, 2, 3, 4]$
   c. $[a_0; a_1, a_2, a_3, a_4, a_5, a_6] = [1; 1, 2, 3, 4, 5, 6]$

3. Do the values you found of the continued fraction in Exercise 2 seem to approach a number as the last term a_n increases? If so, what is it?

Rewrite $e^{\frac{1}{n}}$ as $\sqrt[n]{e}$. Then

$$\lim_{n\to\infty} \frac{1}{n\left(\sqrt[n]{e} - 1\right)} = \frac{1}{\lim_{n\to\infty}\left[n\left(\sqrt[n]{e} - 1\right)\right]} = \frac{1}{\mathcal{L}(e)} = \frac{1}{\ln e} = 1$$

So,

$$(e - 1)\lim_{n\to\infty} \frac{1}{n\left(e^{\frac{1}{n}} - 1\right)} = e - 1$$

This means that the lower sum $L_n[0, 1](e^x)$ approaches $e - 1$ as you increase the number of subdivisions. Now, all you have to do is check that the upper sum approaches the same value. You will do this in Exercise 1.

Developing Habits of Mind

Visualize. Often, when you cannot figure out the value of a limit, you can turn to the graph for a hint of how the expression behaves. Plot the n-values on the horizontal axis and the outputs of the expression on the vertical axis. If the expression approaches one number as n grows larger, that number is *probably* the value of the limit. This does not work every time. *Sometimes* the outputs of the n-values you are looking at seem to tend towards one number, but for much much larger n-values the expression behaves differently.

Look at the graph of the expression $\frac{1}{n\left(e^{\frac{1}{n}} - 1\right)}$.

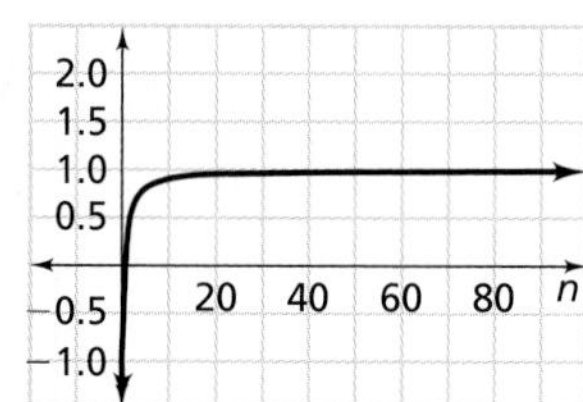

As n increases, the value of the expression becomes closer and closer to 1. This is evidence to support the conjecture that

$$\lim_{n\to\infty} \frac{1}{n\left(e^{\frac{1}{n}} - 1\right)} = 1$$

Exercises *Practicing Habits of Mind*

Check Your Understanding

1. **a.** Find the upper sum for the curve $f(x) = e^x$ from $x = 0$ to $x = 1$ with n subdivisions, $U_n[0, 1](e^x)$.

   b. Use the fact that $\lim_{n\to\infty} L_n[0, 1](e^x) = e - 1$ and the results from part (a) to find $S[0, 1](e^x)$.

2. Find $S[a, a + 1](e^x)$ where a is any real number.

3. **Write About It** Consider the function $f(x) = e^{ax} + b$ where a and b are constants. How do a and b affect the shape of the graph?

4. Use your knowledge of $S[0, 1](e^x)$ to find each of the following.

   a. $S[0, 1](e^x + 3)$ **b.** $S[-1, 0](e^{-x})$ **c.** $S[-1, 0](e^{-x} + 7)$

5. Find the area of the shaded region.

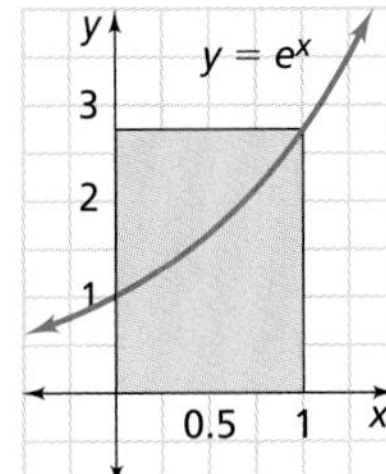

6. This is the graph of $y = \ln x$.

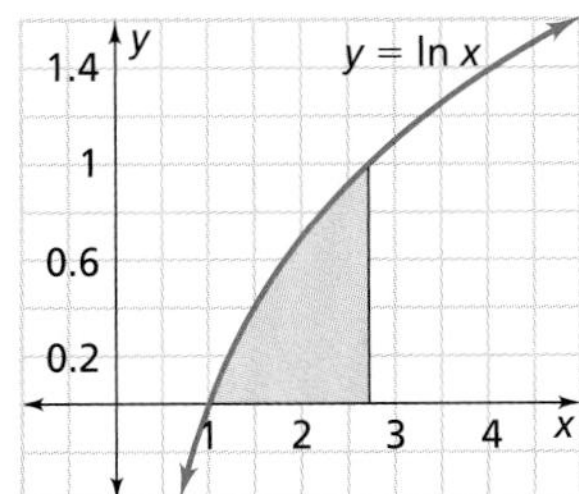

   a. Describe the relationship between the graphs of $y = \ln x$ and $y = e^x$.

   b. What is the area of the shaded region, $S[1, e](\ln x)$?

Exercises

HOMEWORK

- Core: 11
- Optional: 8, 9, 10, 12

Answers

Exercises

1. a. $U_n[0, 1](e^x) = \dfrac{e^{\frac{1}{n}} \cdot (e - 1)}{n(e^{\frac{1}{n}} - 1)}$

b. $S[0,1](e^x) = e-1$

2. $S[a, a + 1](e^x) = e^{a+1} - e^a$

3. Answers may vary. Sample:

- The constant a determines the direction and the rate at which the function increases or decreases. If a is positive, $f(x)$ grows when x grows, and the larger a is, the faster $f(x)$ grows. If a is changed to $-a$, the graph becomes reflected about the y-axis. So, if $a < 0$, $f(x)$ becomes smaller when x grows. If $a = 0$ the graph becomes a horizontal line of $y = 1 + b$.
- The value of b does not affect the shape of the graph, just how high or low on the coordinate plane it is located: $f(x) = e^{ax} + b$ is b higher than $g(x) = e^{ax}$.

4. a. $e + 2$

b. $e - 1$

c. $e + 6$

5. e

6. a. The graphs of $\ln(x)$ and e^x are reflections of each other about the line with equation $y = x$.

b. $S[1, e](\ln x)$ = (the area of the rectangle from the previous problem) *minus* $S[0, 1](e^x)$, which equals $e - (e - 1) = 1$.

Additional Resources

PRINT RESOURCES
- Solution Manual
- Practice Workbook
- Assessment Resources
- Teaching Resources

TECHNOLOGY
- Interactive Textbook
- TeacherExpress CD-ROM
- ExamView CD-ROM
- PHSchool.com

Additional Practice

1. Use your knowledge of $S[0, 1](e^x)$ to find each of the following.
   a. $S[0, 1](e^x + 5)$
   b. $S[0, 1](e^x + 8)$
   c. $S[-1, 0](e^{-x} + 1)$
   d. $S[-1, 0](e^{-x} + 3)$

2. Use your knowledge of the relationship between $f(x) = e^x$ and the natural logarithm function to find the area bounded by the y-axis and the graphs of $y = \ln x$, $y = 3$, and $y = 4$.

3. Copy and complete the following table using a calculator.

n	$\left(1 - \frac{1}{n}\right)^{-n}$
10	
100	
1000	
10,000	
100,000	

4. Do the values you found in the table in Exercise 3 seem to approach a particular number as n increases? If so, what is it?

5. Recall, from Chapter 3, that to find the slope of the line tangent to the graph of the function f at the point $(a, f(a))$, you find the slopes of a series of secant lines over progressively smaller intervals that have a as an endpoint. Find the slope of the line tangent to the graph of $y = e^x$ at $(1, e)$ by doing the following.
   a. Copy and complete the following table using a calculator.

t	$\frac{e^{1+t} - e}{t}$
0.1	
0.01	
0.001	
0.0001	
0.00001	

   b. Do the values you found in the table seem to approach a particular number as t decreases? If so, what is it?

Practice: For Lesson 8.10, assign Exercises 1–5.

7. **Take It Further** Use your knowledge of $S[a, a + 1](e^x)$ from Exercise 2 to find

$$S[a, b](e^x)$$

where a and b are natural numbers with $a \leq b$.

On Your Own

8. Copy and complete the following tables.

a.

n	$\left(\frac{2n+1}{2n-1}\right)^n$
10	■
100	■
1000	■
10,000	■

b.

n	$1 + \frac{1}{1!} + \frac{1}{2!} + \cdots + \frac{1}{n!}$
4	■
7	■
10	■
13	■

9. Let $[a_0; a_1, a_2, a_3, \ldots]$ represent the *continued fraction*

$$a_0 + \cfrac{1}{a_1 + \cfrac{1}{a_2 + \cfrac{1}{a_3 + \ldots}}}$$

Find the value of each expression.

a. $[a_0; a_1, a_2, a_3] = [2; 1, 2, 1]$

b. $[a_0; a_1, a_2, a_3, a_4, a_5, a_6] = [2; 1, 2, 1, 1, 4, 1]$

c. $[a_0; a_1, a_2, a_3, a_4, a_5, a_6, a_7, a_8, a_9] = [2; 1, 2, 1, 1, 4, 1, 1, 6, 1]$

When you get to the last term, simply stop.
$[2; 1, 2, 1] = 2 + \cfrac{1}{1 + \cfrac{1}{2 + \frac{1}{1}}}$

10. Do the values you found in Exercise 9 seem to approach a particular number as you add more terms a_n? If so, what is it?

11. **Standardized Test Prep** Which of the following is not a property of $S[r, s](e^x)$?
    A. If $a < b$ then $S[a, b](e^x) = e^b - e^a$
    B. If $a < b$ then $S[a, b](e^x) > 0$
    C. For all $a > 0$, $S[0, a](e^x) = e^a$
    D. If $a < b < c$, $S[a, b](e^x) + S[b, c](e^x) = S[a, c](e^x)$

Go Online PHSchool.com
For additional practice, go to Web Code: bga-0810

Maintain Your Skills

12. In each of the tables in Exercise 8, do the values seem to approach a particular number as n becomes larger and larger? If so, what is it?

Answers

7. $S[a, b](e^x) = e^b - e^a$

8. a.

n	$\left(\frac{2n+1}{2n-1}\right)^n$
10	≈2.72055141
100	≈2.71830448
1000	≈2.71828205
10,000	≈2.71828183

b.

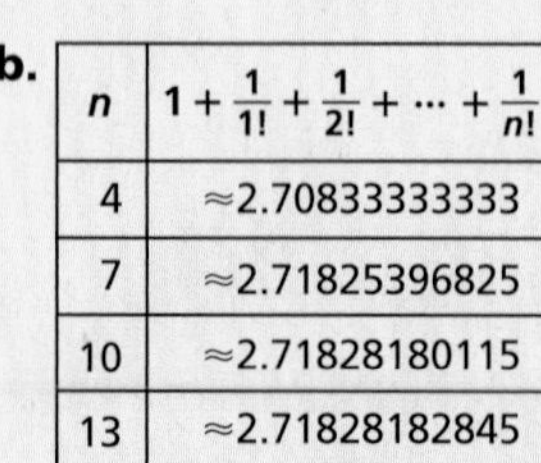

n	$1 + \frac{1}{1!} + \frac{1}{2!} + \cdots + \frac{1}{n!}$
4	≈2.70833333333
7	≈2.71825396825
10	≈2.71828180115
13	≈2.71828182845

9. a. 2.75

b. $\frac{106}{39} \approx 2.71794872$

c. $\frac{1457}{536} \approx 2.71828358$

10. Yes; e

11. C

12. Yes; n gets larger, both $\left(\frac{2n+1}{2n-1}\right)^n$ and $1 + \frac{1}{1!} + \frac{1}{2!} + \cdots + \frac{1}{n!}$ approach e.

In this investigation, you found that one formula describes the area under the graph of $y = x^m$ for all values of m other than -1. You learned that the area below $y = x^{-1}$, or $y = \frac{1}{x}$, is related to the natural logarithm. You also calculated the area below $y = e^x$. The following questions will help you summarize what you have learned.

1. What is the value of $S[1, e](\ln x)$?
2. What is the value of $S[-1, 0](e^{-x} + 7)$?
3. What is the value of $S[1, 2](x^{-2})$?
4. What is the value of $S[1, 2](x^{-1})$?
5. What is the value of $S[0, 1](e^x)$?

Radiocarbon dating involves using the natural logarithm function to solve an equation of the form $N = N_0 e^{-\lambda t}$.

Mathematical Reflections

EXERCISES 3–5 At the start of the investigation, you may have assigned these as Questions 1–3 for students to think and write about.

Mathematical Reflections

1. $S[1, e](\ln x) = 1$
2. $S[-1, 0](e^{-x} + 7) = e + 6$
3. $S[1, 2](x^{-2}) = \frac{1}{2}$
4. $S[1, 2](x^{-1}) = \ln(2)$
5. $S[0, 1](e^x) = e - 1$

Project

This project is about a sequence of polynomials called the *Chebyshev polynomials*, named after the Russian mathematician Pafnuty Lvovich Chebyshev (1821–1894). These polynomials have applications in many areas of mathematics and science. This project explores using the polynomials to produce *multiple angle formulas* for cosine. Other applications come up in differential equations, statistics, and number theory. One example of a mathematical application is in algebra; you can calculate the equation whose roots are the *n*th power of the roots of a given quadratic with Chebyshev polynomials (see A. Cuoco, "Raising the Roots," *Mathematics Magazine* 72:5, 1999). Benjamin Sinwell's article "The Chebyshev Polynomials, Patterns and Derivation" in Volume 98, No. 1 (August 2004) of the NCTM journal *Mathematics Teacher*, contains a nice investigation of the polynomials. Note that the project does not mention the name Chebyshev, because doing so might send students running to the web. That is fine, but it changes the nature of the project from mathematical research to library research. The decision—whether or not to let students know that this is an established theory—is up to you.

You can turn the students loose on the project as soon as you start Chapter 8. The project draws on may of the topics seen in this course, and they do not need the material from Chapter 8 until the very last exercise. Think about checking in once a week to see what students are doing and to advise them with any questions they have. Try not to make the connection to trigonometric identities before they get to Exercise 5. You might consider asking for first drafts or, if you have time, asking students to give preliminary reports in class. Many precalculus classes have juniors left after the seniors leave. This is a nice way to spend the "lame duck" time.

Project: Using Mathematical Habits

A Delightful Sequence of Polynomials

In Chapter 5, you investigated function definitions with a two term recurrence like the definition of the Fibonacci numbers:

$$f(n) = \begin{cases} 0 & \text{if } n = 0 \\ 1 & \text{if } n = 1 \\ f(n-1) + f(n-2) & \text{if } n > 1 \end{cases}$$

In Chapter 5, you found a closed-form definition $f(n) = \dfrac{\left(\frac{1+\sqrt{5}}{2}\right)^n - \left(\frac{1-\sqrt{5}}{2}\right)^n}{\sqrt{5}}$ for this function. You developed methods for finding closed-form definitions for any function defined by a two-term recurrence.

The outputs of the functions in Chapter 5 are numbers, real or complex. This project is about a sequence of polynomials that show up all over mathematics and science and are defined by a similar two-term recurrence:

$$t(n, x) = \begin{cases} 1 & \text{if } n = 0 \\ x & \text{if } n = 1 \\ 2x \cdot t(n-1, x) - t(n-2, x) & \text{if } n > 1 \end{cases}$$

Here is an example.

Problem Find the normal form for the first four polynomials you get from *t*.

Solution The definition gives the first two polynomials.

$$t(0, x) = 1 \text{ and } t(1, x) = x$$

Use the recurrence to find $t(2, x)$.

$$\begin{aligned} t(2, x) &= 2x \cdot t(1, x) - t(0, x) \\ &= 2x \cdot x - 1 \\ &= 2x^2 - 1 \end{aligned}$$

Now that you know $t(2, x)$, you can find $t(3, x)$.

$$\begin{aligned} t(3, x) &= 2x \cdot t(2, x) - t(1, x) \\ &= 2x(2x^2 - 1) - x \\ &= 4x^3 - 3x \end{aligned}$$

1. Model the definition of $t(n, x)$ in your FML.
2. Find the normal form for $t(n, x)$ for all *n* from 0 through 10. Make a table of your results.

Answers

Project

1. Answers may vary. Sample: (This program displays $t(n, x)$ for $n \geq 1$.)

```
Define poly(n) = Prgm
    3 → m
    1 → a
    x → b
    While m < n + 2
    {a, b} → j
    j[2] → a
    2 · x · j[2]
    −j[1] → b
    1 + m → m
    EndWhile
    Disp "polynomial is"
    Disp expand(b)
    EndPrgm
```

2. See back of book.

The variables n and x in the definition of t serve different purposes. The input n is a nonnegative integer—an index that tells you which polynomial you have. The input x, on the other hand, is the variable in the nth polynomial. If you were doing a strictly algebraic investigation of the function t, you would not need to include x in the definition. You could use the definition

$$s(n) = \begin{cases} 1 & \text{if } n = 0 \\ x & \text{if } n = 1 \\ 2x \cdot s(n-1) - s(n-2) & \text{if } n > 1 \end{cases}$$

If you did this, s would be a function that assigns nonnegative integers to polynomial expressions. But, in this project, you should think of $t(n, x)$ as a polynomial function of x, so that $t(3, 5)$ is a number—the third polynomial evaluated at 5. This allows you, for example, to graph the various polynomials.

Some people like to use subscripts for the index, so they write $t_n(x)$ or s_n. Making the index an input rather that a subscript helps you remember that sequences are just functions defined on non-negative integers, and it allows you to model the sequence in your CAS with exactly the same notation as you use when you write it on paper.

The project title claims that the sequence of polynomials is delightful. The rest of the project is a collection of exercises that will help you understand this claim.

3. a. Extend your table to include each polynomial $t(n, x)$ for n up through 18.

b. Find, describe, and explain several patterns in the coefficients or the terms of the polynomials.

4. Make your own polynomial function gallery for the $t(n, x)$.

a. Sketch the graphs of $t(n, x)$ for $0 \le n \le 10$. Draw each graph on a separate set of axes over $-1 \le x \le 1$.

b. Describe some interesting properties of your graphs. Explain the properties and why you find them interesting.

c. Overlay the graphs of $t(n, x)$ for $0 \le n \le 10$ on the same set of axes. Describe some interesting properties of the picture.

5. Solve each of the equations $t(n, x) = 0$ for $0 \le n \le 6$.

3–5. See back of book.

6. a. See back of book.

b. (1, 3) (1, 5) (1, 7) (1, 9) (1, 11) (1, 13) (1, 15) (1, 17) (2, 6) (2, 10) (2, 14) (2, 18) (3, 9) (3, 15) (4, 12) (5, 15) (6, 18)

c. If m and n are positive integers such that $t(m, x)$ is a factor of $t(n, x)$, then m is a factor of n.

EXERCISE 3 If students model t in their CAS, they can use a spreadsheet to extend the tables. On the handheld, these are hard to see, so if they are not using a computer, they may just as well generate each polynomial with the CAS and record the results by hand. You might demonstrate how this looks on a computer.

You can establish the patterns in the solution by induction, using the defining recurrence. These are only the beginning. Note the constant terms. For one teacher's analysis of some subtle properties of the coefficients, see Benjamin Sinwell's article "The Chebyshev Polynomials, Patterns and Derivation" in Volume 98, No. 1 (August 2004) of the NCTM journal *Mathematics Teacher*.

EXERCISE 4 You can explain many of the features students notice by the fact that $t(n, \cos\alpha) = \cos n\alpha$. You may want to revisit this exercise during the wrap up after students see the connection to multiple angle formulas.

EXERCISE 5 Behind the scenes, the zeros of $t(n, x)$ are zeros of $\cos nx$. You might want to bring this up during the wrap up.

EXERCISE 6 You can generate the table of factorizations with a CAS, but do not let the calculator have all the fun—many of these are doable by hand. The complete story is that $t(m, x)$ is a factor of $t(n, x)$ if and only if m is a factor of n *and* $\frac{m}{n}$ is odd. This is a consequence of the connection with trigonometry that Exercises 5 and 6 develop. Exercises 7 and 8 provide scaffolding to reach the result about odd $\frac{m}{n}$.

EXERCISE 11 The solution to each part uses the solution to the preceding part.

EXERCISE 13 The problem, phrased in terms of calculus, is to evaluate

$$\int_{-1}^{1} t(n, x)\, dx$$

In calculus, students might let $x = \cos u$ so that $dx = -\sin u du$. Adjusting limits, the integral becomes

$$\int_{0}^{\pi} \cos nu \sin u\, du$$

You can evaluate this integral via the techniques developed in first semester calculus.

Wrap Up

There is a great deal to wrap up. Now is the time to search the web for information about Chebyshev and his polynomials. Perhaps you could ask the class to read the Sinwell paper. You certainly want to discuss how the "trigonometric connection" explains some of the striking patterns in the polynomials and their graphs. Ask students to find some other applications of Chebyshev polynomials. And what about formulas for $\sin n\alpha$?

Here is an interesting connection from applied mathematics. Suppose you have a mystery function defined between -1 and 1 that comes from some experiment. It is not necessarily a polynomial, but it has a smooth graph. You want to approximate it with a polynomial of degree n using Lagrange interpolation, and you get to pick the $n + 1$ points on the graph to use. What points give the best interpolation (where "best" means that the absolute value of the integral of their difference is smallest). Most people think you should pick the evenly spaced ones. However, interpolating at the zeros of $t(n + 1, x)$ results in the best fit. This is delightful, indeed.

6. a. Write down the factorizations of each polynomial $t(n, x)$ over $\mathbb{Z}$ for $1 \le n \le 18$.

b. For what pairs (m, n) on your list is $t(m, x)$ a factor of $t(n, x)$?

c. Make a conjecture that describes the relation between m and n if $t(m, x)$ a factor of $t(n, x)$.

7. In Lesson 2.7, you learned that

$$\cos 2\alpha = 2\cos^2 \alpha - 1$$

for all real numbers α. So, if $h(x) = 2x^2 - 1$,

$$h(\cos\alpha) = \cos 2\alpha$$

a. Find a polynomial function g such that

$$g(\cos\alpha) = \cos 3\alpha$$

b. Find a polynomial function k such that

$$k(\cos\alpha) = \cos 4\alpha$$

8. Exercise 7 suggests that there might be a new sequence of polynomials $h(n, x)$ defined on nonnegative integers with the property that

$$h(n, \cos\alpha) = \cos n\alpha$$

Show that, in fact, the polynomials $t(n, x)$ do the job. That is, prove the following theorem.

Theorem 8.5

Suppose $t(n, x)$ is the sequence of polynomials defined by

$$t(n, x) = \begin{cases} 1 & \text{if } n = 0 \\ x & \text{if } n = 1 \\ 2x \cdot t(n-1, x) - t(n-2, x) & \text{if } n > 1 \end{cases}$$

Then, for all nonnegative integers n,

$$t(n, \cos\alpha) = \cos n\alpha$$

9. Each of the following functions has infinitely many zeros. Find formulas that describe the zeros of each.

a. $\alpha \mapsto \cos\alpha$ **b.** $\alpha \mapsto \cos 2\alpha$ **c.** $\alpha \mapsto \cos 3\alpha$

d. $\alpha \mapsto \cos 4\alpha$ **e.** $\alpha \mapsto \cos 5\alpha$

f. $\alpha \mapsto \cos k\alpha$ (in terms of k)

10. Revisit Exercise 6c and prove your conjecture.

11. Suppose $f(x) = 2x - \frac{1}{x}$. Write each expression as a quotient of two polynomials in normal form.

a. $f(x)$ **b.** $2x - \dfrac{1}{f(x)}$

c. $2x - \dfrac{1}{2x - \frac{1}{f(x)}}$ **d.** $2x - \dfrac{1}{2x - \frac{1}{2x - \frac{1}{f(x)}}}$

e. $2x - \dfrac{1}{2x - \frac{1}{2x - \frac{1}{2x - \frac{1}{f(x)}}}}$

12. a. Develop a conjecture about a pattern in the results of Exercise 11.

b. Prove your conjecture.

13. This chapter was about finding areas under curves.

a. Make a table for the area bounded by the graph of $y = t(n, x)$ between -1 and 1 for $0 \le n \le 10$.

b. Make some conjectures based on patterns you see in your table.

c. Prove as many of your conjectures as you can.

14. Use the methods of Chapter 5 to show that
$t(n, x) = \frac{1}{2}\left(\left(x + \sqrt{x^2 - 1}\right)^n + \left(x - \sqrt{x^2 - 1}\right)^n\right)$

Answers

7. a. $g(x) = 4x^3 - 3x$

b. $k(x) = 8x^4 - 8x^2 + 1$

8. See back of book.

9. a. $\frac{(2k - 1)\pi}{2}$, for all integers k

b. $\frac{(2k - 1)\pi}{4}$, for all integers k

c. $\frac{(2k - 1)\pi}{6}$, for all integers k

d. $\frac{(2k - 1)\pi}{8}$, for all integers k

e. $\frac{(2k - 1)\pi}{10}$, for all integers k

f. $\frac{(2k - 1)\pi}{2n}$, for all integers k

10. See back of book.

11. a. $\frac{2x^2 - 1}{x}$

b. $\frac{4x^3 - 3x}{2x^2 - 1}$

c. $\frac{8x^4 - 8x^2 + 1}{4x^3 - 3x}$

d–e. See back of book.

12–14. See back of book.

Review

Go Online PHSchool.com

For vocabulary review, go to Web Code: bgj-0851

In **Investigation 8A,** you learned how to

- estimate the areas of irregularly-shaped objects
- use a method for estimating the area under the graph of $y = x^2$ over intervals in the first quadrant
- find a surprising way to compute the area under the graph of $y = x^2$ exactly

The following questions will help you check your understanding.

1. In this exercise, you will estimate the area under $y = \sin x$ between 0 and π using the figure below.

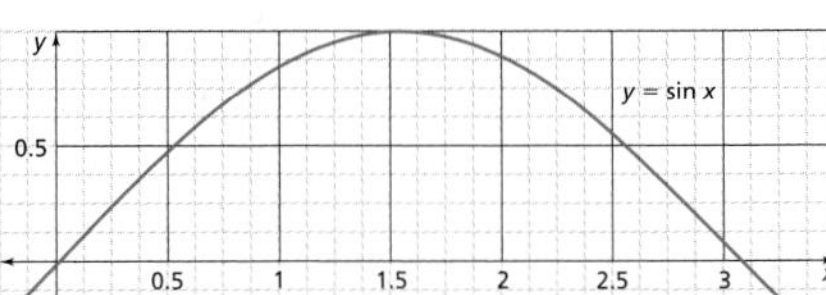

a. Using the $\frac{1}{2}$ unit grid, provide an upper bound for the area under the curve.

b. Using the $\frac{1}{2}$ unit grid, provide a lower bound for the area under the curve.

c. Using the $\frac{1}{8}$ unit grid (the smaller grid in the picture), provide an upper bound for the area under the curve.

d. Using the $\frac{1}{8}$ unit grid, provide a lower bound for the area under the curve.

e. Use the $\frac{1}{8}$ grid upper and lower estimates to find an even better estimate of the area under the curve. Explain your reasoning.

2. Compute $L_4[0, 1](x^2)$ and $U_4[0, 1](x^2)$, the lower and upper estimates of the area under the graph of $y = x^2$ between 0 and 1 with four subdivisions.

3. Compute $S[0, 1](x^2)$, the exact value of the area under the graph of $y = x^2$ between 0 and 1.

4. Compute the lower and upper estimates, $L_4\left[-\frac{\pi}{2}, 0\right](\cos x)$ and $U_4\left[-\frac{\pi}{2}, 0\right](\cos x)$, of the area under the graph of $y = \cos x$.

In **Investigation 8B,** you learned to

- compute the area under the graph of $y = x^3$ between 0 and 1
- use the closed form for $\sum_{k=1}^{n} k^m$ for various values of m to compute areas
- use Fermat's method to compute the area under the graph of $y = x^m$ between 1 and 2 for any positive integer m

The following questions will help you check your understanding.

5. Cavalieri showed that

$$\sum_{k=1}^{n} k^3 = \frac{n^2(n+1)^2}{4}$$

for all positive integers n. Use this result to confirm the following identities. (You might find at least one of them useful in the next exercise.)

a. $\sum_{k=1}^{n-1} k^3 = \frac{n^2(n-1)^2}{4}$ for all positive integers n.

b. $\sum_{k=1}^{n} (2k)^3 = \frac{8n^2(n+1)^2}{4}$ for all positive integers n.

c. $\sum_{k=1}^{n} (rk)^3 = \frac{r^3n^2(n+1)^2}{4}$ for all positive integers n and all real numbers r.

Review

1. a. 3

b. $\frac{3}{4}$

c. Answers may vary. Sample: $\frac{142}{64}$, or $\frac{71}{32}$

d. Answers may vary. Sample: $\frac{106}{64}$, or $\frac{53}{32}$

e. Answers may vary. Sample: 1.9375; The average is between the low estimate and the high estimate, so it should be closer to the actual area than either of them.

2. $L_4[0, 1](x^2) = \frac{7}{32}$, $U_4[0, 1](x^2) = \frac{15}{32}$

3. $S[0,1](x^2) = \frac{1}{3}$

4. $L_4\left[-\frac{\pi}{2}, 0\right](\cos x) \approx 0.790766$

$U_4\left[-\frac{\pi}{2}, 0\right](\cos x) \approx 1.183465$

5. See back of book.

Review continued

6. Compute the lower and upper sum estimates $L_n[0, 2](x^3)$ and $U_n[0, 2](x^3)$. Then investigate their behavior when n becomes larger and larger in order to compute the exact value of the area under the graph of $y = x^3$ between 0 and 2.

7. Use Fermat's Method to compute the area under the graph of $y = x^m$ between 1 and b where b is a positive number greater than 1.

In **Investigation 8C,** you learned to

- develop formulas for calculating $S[1, a](x^m)$ when m is a negative integer
- investigate a mysteriously familiar function $\mathcal{L}$.
- find the area under the graph of $y = e^x$

The following questions will help you check your understanding.

8. Determine the area under the graph of $y = \frac{1}{x^3}$ between 1 and 4.

9. Suppose f satisfies the property that $f(10) = 1$ and $f(xy) = f(x) + f(y)$ for all positive x and y. You proved some other properties in class and homework, but for now, just use the given information.

   a. Explain why the given information, along with the fact that $\frac{x}{y} \cdot y = x$, implies that $f(\frac{x}{y}) = f(x) - f(y)$ for all positive x and y.

   b. Explain why part (a), along with the given information, helps to show that $f(1) = 0$.

   You also showed that $f(x^m) = m \cdot f(x)$ for all x when m is a positive integer. You may use this fact, along with all the other properties discussed, to make the following computations.

   c. Compute $f(100{,}000{,}000)$.

   d. If $f(2) \approx 0.301$, approximate $f(5)$.

   e. If $f(2) \approx 0.301$, approximate $f(80)$.

   f. If $f(2) \approx 0.301$, approximate $f(\frac{1}{50})$.

10. Use the method of Archimedes to compute the area under the graph of $y = e^x$ between 0 and 1. You will need to use the fact that $\lim_{n\to\infty} n\left(e^{\frac{1}{n}} - 1\right) = 1$.

Answers

6. $L_n[0, 2](x^3) = 4 - \frac{8}{n} + \frac{4}{n^2}$ and
$U_n[0, 2](x^3) = 4 + \frac{8}{n} + \frac{4}{n^2}$ and
both sums approach 4 as $n \to \infty$.
So the exact area under $y = x^3$ between 0 and 2 is 4.

7. $\frac{b^{m+1} - 1}{m + 1}$

8. $\frac{15}{32}$

9. a. $f(x) = f\left(\frac{x}{y} \cdot y\right) = f\left(\frac{x}{y}\right) + f(y)$,
so $f\left(\frac{x}{y}\right) = f(x) - f(y)$

b. $f(1) = f\left(\frac{1}{1}\right)$, and by the result proved in part (a),
$f\left(\frac{1}{1}\right) = f(1) - f(1) = 0$.
Therefore, $f(1) = 0$.

c. 8

d. 0.699

e. 1.903

f. −1.699

10. $e - 1$

Chapter 8 Test

Go Online PHSchool.com

For a chapter test, go to Web Code: bga-0853

Multiple Choice

1. If T is an increasing function satisfying $T(xy) = T(x) + T(y)$, which of the following properties is also true?
   - A. $T(1) = 1$
   - B. $T(1) = -1$
   - C. $T(1) = 0$
   - D. $T(1)$ is undefined

2. Suppose T is the function defined in Exercise 1. Which of the following properties is also true?
   - A. $T(x^3) = (T(x))^3$ for all positive real numbers x.
   - B. $T(x^3) = x \cdot T(3)$ for all positive real numbers x.
   - C. $T(x^3) = 3T(x)$ for all positive real numbers x.
   - D. $T(x^3) = T(x) - T(3)$ for all positive real numbers x.

3. Which of the following statements is true about the area under $y = x^2$ between 0 and 1?
   - A. The area is equal to $\frac{1}{2}$.
   - B. The area is greater than $\frac{1}{2}$.
   - C. The area is less than $\frac{1}{2}$.
   - D. The area is infinite.

Open Response

4. Compute $LF_4[1, 3](x^2)$, the lower Fermat sum with 4 subdivisions, to approximate the area under $y = x^2$ between 1 and 3. Note that the points of the subdivisions are 1, r, r^2, r^3 and r^4.

5. Suppose L is an increasing function satisfying $L(1) = 0$, $L(10) = 1$, $L(4) \approx 0.602$, and $L(xy) = L(x) + L(y)$.
   - a. Approximate $L(40)$.
   - b. Approximate $L(2)$.
   - c. Approximate $L(5)$.
   - d. Explain how you know that $L(x^2) = 2L(x)$ for all $x > 0$.
   - e. Explain how you know that $L(\frac{1}{y}) = -L(y)$ for all $y > 0$.

6. The area under $y = 2x^2$ between -1 and 1 is equal to $\frac{4}{3}$. Explain how you can use this information to compute the area between the x-axis and the curve $y = 2x^2 - 2$ (region shaded in the figure below).

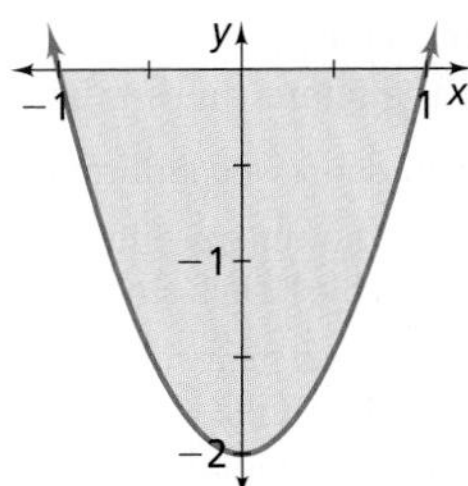

Challenge Problem

7. Use Fermat's method to compute $S[1, b](x^4)$, the area under $y = x^4$ between 1 and b, where $b > 1$.

Test

Assessment Resources

Chapter Test Form A page 1 of 2

Multiple Choice

1. If T is an increasing function satisfying $T(4) = 3$, $T(xy) = T(x) + T(y)$, which of the following properties is also true?
   A. $T(2) = \frac{3}{4}$ B. $T(2) = -1$ C. $T(2) = \frac{1}{2}$ D. $T(2) = \frac{3}{2}$

2. Suppose T is the function defined in Exercise 1. Which of the following properties is also true?
   - A. $T(x^2) = (T(x))^2$ for all positive real numbers x.
   - B. $T(x^2) = xT(2)$ for all positive real numbers x.
   - C. $T(x^2) = 2T(x)$ for all positive real numbers x.
   - D. $T(x^2) = T(x) + T(2)$ for all positive real numbers x.

3. The graph of $y = \sqrt{x}$ is given below. Which of the following statements is true about the area under the graph of $y = \sqrt{x}$ between 0 and 1?
   - A. The area is equal to $\frac{1}{2}$.
   - B. The area is greater than $\frac{1}{2}$.
   - C. The area is less than $\frac{1}{2}$.

Open Response

4. Compute $LF_4[1,4](x^3)$, the lower Fermat sum with 4 subdivisions to approximate the area under $y = x^3$ between 1 and 4. Note that the points of the subdivisions are 1, r, r^2, r^3, and r^4.

Also available: Form B

Test

1. C
2. C
3. C
4. $2\sqrt[4]{27} - 8\sqrt[4]{3} + 6\sqrt{3} + 2$, or about 6.423
5. a. $L(40) = L(4 \cdot 10) = L(4) + L(10) = 0.602 + 1 = 1.602$

   b. $0.602 = L(4) = L(2 \cdot 2) = L(2) + L(2) = 2L(2)$, so $L(2) = \frac{0.602}{2} = 0.301$

   c. $1 = L(10) = L(2) + L(5)$, so $L(5) = 1 - L(2) = 1 - 0.301 = 0.699$

   d. $L(x^2) = L(x \cdot x) = L(x) + L(x) = 2L(x)$

   e. $0 = L(1) = L\left(y \cdot \frac{1}{y}\right) = L(y) + L\left(\frac{1}{y}\right)$, so $L\left(\frac{1}{y}\right) = 0 - L(y) = -L(y)$.

6. If you translate the parabola and shaded region up 2 units, then the equation of the new parabola is $y = 2x^2$ and the shaded region is the part not below $y = 2x^2$ that is bounded by $y = 2x^2$, $y = 2$, the x-axis and the vertical lines $x = -1$ and $x = 1$. So the area of the shaded region is 4 − (area below $y = 2x^2$ from $x = -1$ to $x = 1$) $= 4 - \frac{4}{3} = \frac{8}{3}$.
7. $\frac{b^5 - 1}{5}$

Cumulative Review

Assessment Resources

Quarter Test page 1 of 3

Multiple Choice

1. A spinner has five equally-sized wedges containing the numbers 3, 5, 7, 8 and 12. You are to spin the spinner three times. What is the expected value for the sum of three spins?
   A. 7 **B.** 24 **C.** 21 **D.** 32

2. You play a game of chance that has a probability of winning $p = 0.2$. If you play the game 20 times, what is the probability that you win exactly three times? Round off your answer to two decimal places.
   A. 0.21 **B.** 0.35 **C.** 0.55 **D.** 0.80

3. A number cube has the numbers 4, 4, 6, 8, 10 and 12 on its faces. If you are to roll twice, what is the probability that the sum of the faces rolled is exactly 14?
   A. $\frac{1}{36}$ **B.** $\frac{1}{18}$ **C.** $\frac{1}{9}$ **D.** $\frac{1}{6}$

4. A bag contains 20 tickets numbered 1 through 20. You randomly select a ticket, then place it back in the bag and again select a ticket. Finally, you add the two numbers drawn. Find the mean and standard deviation for the sum of the two numbers. Round your answers to two decimal places.
   A. mean = 21; standard deviation = 66.5
   B. mean = 10.5; standard deviation = 33.25
   C. mean = 21; standard deviation = 8.15
   D. mean = 10.5; standard deviation ≈ 3.24

5. What is the value of $L_4[1, 3](x^3)$, the lower sum approximation of the area under $y = x^3$ between 1 and 3?
   A. 27 **B.** 20 **C.** 19.75 **D.** 14

6. Which of the following sums represents $U_4[0, 2](4 - x^2)$, the upper sum approximation of the area under $y = 4 - x^2$ between 0 and 2 using 4 subdivisions?
   A. $\left(\frac{1}{2}\right)\left(\frac{1}{2}\right)^2 + \left(\frac{1}{2}\right)(1)^2 + \left(\frac{1}{2}\right)\left(\frac{3}{2}\right)^2 + \left(\frac{1}{2}\right)(2)^2$
   B. $\left(\frac{1}{2}\right)(4 - 0^2) + \left(\frac{1}{2}\right)\left(4 - \left(\frac{1}{2}\right)^2\right) + \left(\frac{1}{2}\right)(4 - 1^2) + \left(\frac{1}{2}\right)\left(4 - \left(\frac{3}{2}\right)^2\right)$
   C. $\left(\frac{1}{2}\right)\left(4 - \left(\frac{1}{2}\right)^2\right) + \left(\frac{1}{2}\right)(4 - 1^2) + \left(4 - \left(\frac{3}{2}\right)^2\right) + \left(\frac{1}{2}\right)(4 - 2^2)$
   D. $\left(\frac{1}{4}\right)(4 - 0^2) + \left(\frac{1}{4}\right)\left(4 - \left(\frac{1}{2}\right)^2\right) + \left(\frac{1}{4}\right)(4 - 1^2) + \left(\frac{1}{4}\right)\left(4 - \left(\frac{3}{2}\right)^2\right)$

Also available: Form B

Cumulative Review

1. Find the value of the following expression.
$$\sqrt{2}\cos 45° \sin 45° + \tan\pi - \tan 30° \tan 60° + 3\cos\frac{\pi}{3}$$

2. Solve the equation $\tan^3 x - 3\tan x = 0$ on $0 \le x \le \pi$.

3. Find the simplified form of the expression
$$\sin\frac{3\pi}{7}\cos\frac{2\pi}{7} - \cos\frac{3\pi}{7}\sin\frac{2\pi}{7}$$

4. Simplify each of the following.
   a. $\left(\frac{\sqrt{2}}{2} - \frac{\sqrt{2}}{2}i\right)^4$ **b.** $\left(\frac{\sqrt{3}}{2} + \frac{1}{2}i\right)^6$

5. Find the slope and the equation of the line tangent to the graph of the function $f(x) = x^3 + 2x$ at the point $(1, 3)$.

6. Sketch the graph of $y = \frac{x + 3}{x^2 + x - 6}$. Identify all asymptotes and any holes in the graph.

7. Six students will perform in a student recital.
   a. Find how many different programs are possible if each student performs once.
   b. Find how many different programs are possible if the winner and runner-up of a soloist competition perform last and next to last and the other four students can perform in any order.

8. Simplify each of the following.
   a. $\frac{_{11}P_4}{4!}$ **b.** $\frac{1}{5}\binom{100}{98}$

9. A quadratic function q has a difference table that begins as follows.

Input, x	Output, $q(x)$	Δ	Δ^2
0	−1	−1	6
1	−2	5	6
2	3	11	6

Determine the value of $q(10)$.

10. Define f as
$$f(n) = \begin{cases} 2 & \text{if } n = 0 \\ 1 & \text{if } n = 1 \\ 2 \cdot f(n-1) - 3 \cdot f(n-2) & \text{if } n > 0 \end{cases}$$
Find $f(n)$ for $0 \le n \le 6$.

11. Consider the equation
$$25x^2 - 144y^2 - 3600 = 0$$
   a. Show that the graph of the equation is a hyperbola.
   b. Find the coordinates for the foci $(c, 0)$ and $(-c, 0)$.
   c. The graphs of the equations $y = \frac{b}{a}x$ and $y = -\frac{b}{a}x$ are the asymptotes of the hyperbola. Find the equations of the asymptotes for this hyperbola.
   d. Sketch the graph of the hyperbola and its asymptotes. Identify the foci and the intercepts.

12. A line has vector equation $X = P + tD$. What are the values of P and D if $t = 2$ and $X = (3, 5)$? If $t = 5$, $X = (9, -4)$?

13. A tetrahedron (a pyramid with four congruent triangular faces) has faces numbered 1 through 4. You roll it and record the number on the face not showing—the face on the bottom. You perform the experiment three times and find the sum of the three rolls.
   a. Find a polynomial that models the possible outcomes.
   b. Determine the possible sums.
   c. Determine the number of times each sum will occur.
   d. Find the sum or sums that will occur most often.

Answers

Cumulative Review

1. $\frac{\sqrt{2} + 1}{2}$

2. $0, \frac{\pi}{3}, \frac{2\pi}{3}, \pi$

3. $\sin\frac{\pi}{7}$

4. **a.** −1
   b. −1

5. $m = 5$; $y = 5x - 2$

6. horizontal asymptote: $y = 0$; vertical asymptote: $x = 2$; hole in the graph at $\left(-3, -\frac{1}{5}\right)$

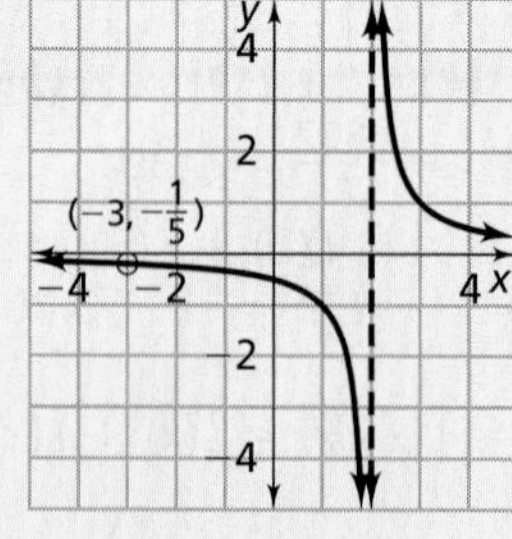

7. **a.** 720 **b.** 48

8. **a.** 330 **b.** 990

9. 259

10. 2, 1, −4, −11, −10, 13, 56

11. **a.** Transform the equation to the form $\frac{x^2}{12^2} - \frac{y^2}{5^2} = 1$, the standard-form equation of a hyperbola.
   b. (13, 0) and (−13, 0)
   c. $y = \frac{5}{12}x$ and $y = -\frac{5}{12}x$
   d.

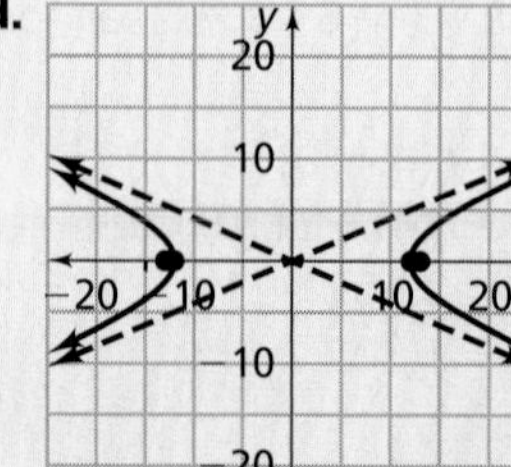

14. For the sum of the faces of the tetrahedrons in Exercise 13, calculate each of the following values.

   a. the mean

   b. the mean absolute deviation

   c. the variance

   d. the standard deviation

15. Find the expected value for the number of heads when you toss one coin five times.

16. a. Find the mean and standard deviation for the sum of the numbers showing on top of a number cube when you roll it 10 times.

   b. Using a calculator, find the value predicted by the normal distribution for the probability of a sum of 20.

   c. Using a calculator, find the value predicted by the normal distribution for the probability of a sum between 20 and 50.

17. The State Department of Agriculture has determined the size of pumpkins grown in their state is normally distributed. The mean diameter is 10.4 inches and the standard deviation is 1.3 inches.

   a. To qualify as "Grade A," a pumpkin must be within one standard deviation of the mean. Find how many pumpkins were rated Grade A if farmers harvested 2.5 million pumpkins.

   b. Give a range of diameters in which approximately 95% of all pumpkins should lie.

   c. "Mini" pumpkins are rated smaller than three standard deviations below the mean and are sold as novelties. Determine the maximum diameter for these pumpkins and the number of them in the 2.5 million pumpkin crop.

   d. Customers look for "monster" pumpkins, rated as two standard deviations or greater than the mean. Determine the minimum diameter to qualify as a "Monster" pumpkin.

18. a. Copy the graph below. Sketch the rectangles the areas of which make up $U_4[1, 3]\left(\frac{1}{x}\right)$.

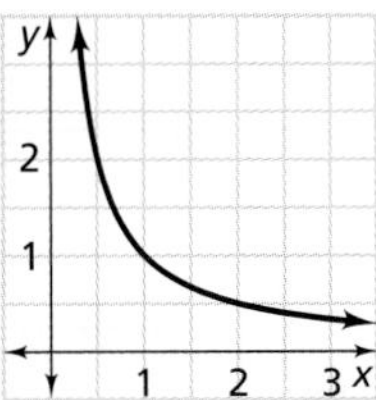

   b. Compute $U_4[1, 3]\left(\frac{1}{x}\right)$.

   c. On another copy of the same graph, sketch the rectangles the areas of which make up $L_4[1, 3]\left(\frac{1}{x}\right)$.

   d. Compute $L_4[1, 3]\left(\frac{1}{x}\right)$.

19. Consider the function $f(x) = \sqrt{x}$ on the interval $[0, 1]$.

   a. Compute $U_4[0, 1](\sqrt{x})$.

   b. Compute $L_4[0, 1](\sqrt{x})$.

   c. Compute the average of $U_4[0, 1](\sqrt{x})$ and $L_4[0, 1](\sqrt{x})$.

   d. Given that the area under the graph of $y = \sqrt{x}$ between 0 and 1 is $\frac{2}{3}$, find the percent error using the three approximations.

20. Use Fermat's method to compute $S[1, 3](x^4)$, the area under the curve $y = x^4$ between 1 and 3.

End-of-Year Test — page 1 of 4

Multiple Choice

1. Find the value of $a^2 \cos 0 + ab \sin^3 \frac{\pi}{2} - b^2 \sin \pi$, if a and b are real numbers.
   A. $ab + b^2$ B. $a^2 + ab$ C. ab D. $a^2 - b^2$

2. Solve the equation $3 \tan^2 x - 1 = 0$ for x in $0 \le x < \pi$.
   A. $\frac{\pi}{3}, \frac{2\pi}{3}$ B. $\frac{\pi}{6}$ C. $\frac{\pi}{6}, \frac{5\pi}{6}$ D. $\frac{\pi}{3}$

3. Determine which expression is identically equal to $\sec^2 x - \cos^2 x \cdot \sec^2 x$.
   A. $\tan^2 x$ B. $\cos^2 x$ C. $\sin^2 x$ D. $\sec^2 x$

4. If $z = \text{cis}\,\frac{2\pi}{6}$, find the value of $\sum_{k=1}^{5} z^k$.
   A. z^6 B. z C. $-z$ D. -1

5. Let $f(x) = 2x^2 - 3x + 8$, and expand f in powers of $x + 2$. Which of the following is a term in that expansion?
   A. $-11(x + 2)$ B. $5(x + 2)$ C. $7(x + 2)$ D. $-9(x + 2)$

6. Which of the following is *not* a property of the natural logarithm function?
   A. $\ln(MN) = \ln M + \ln N$ B. $\ln \frac{M}{N} = M - \ln N$
   C. $\ln M^p = p \ln M$ D. $\ln x = \frac{\log x}{\log e}$

7. How many different anagrams can be formed from the word DECK?
   A. 1 B. 4 C. 24 D. 256

8. What is the coefficient of a^3b^4 in the expansion of $(a + b)^7$?
   A. 35 B. 42 C. 64 D. 81

9. Define f recursively as

$$f(n) = \begin{cases} 7 & \text{if } n = 0 \\ f(n-1) - 12 & \text{if } n > 0 \end{cases}$$

   What is $f(5)$?
   A. -53 B. -41 C. 41 D. 53

Also available: Form B

12. $P = (-1, 11)$, $D = (2, -3)$

13. a. $(x + x^2 + x^3 + x^4)^3$

   b. 3 through 12

   c.

Sum	3	4	5	6	7	8	9	10	11	12
Number	1	3	6	10	12	12	10	6	3	1

   d. 7 and 8

14. a. 7.5 b. 1.59
   c. 3.75 d. 1.936

15. 2.5

16. a. 3.5, 2.917 b. 0.00156
   c. 0.9945

17. a. 1.7 million
   b. 7.8 in. to 13 in.
   c. 6.5 in.; 3750
   d. 13 in.

18. a.

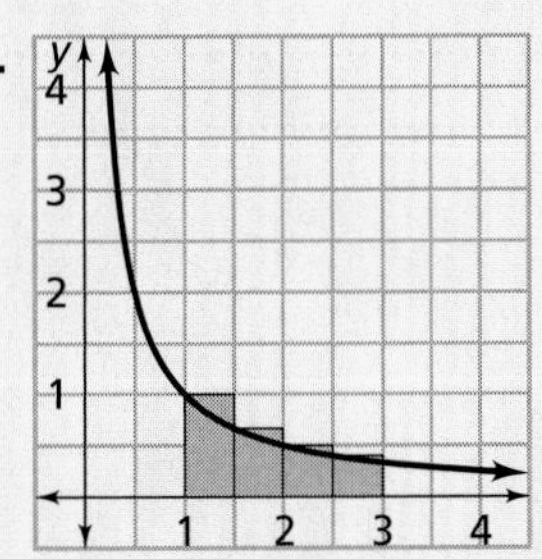

   b. $\frac{77}{60} = 1.28$

   c.

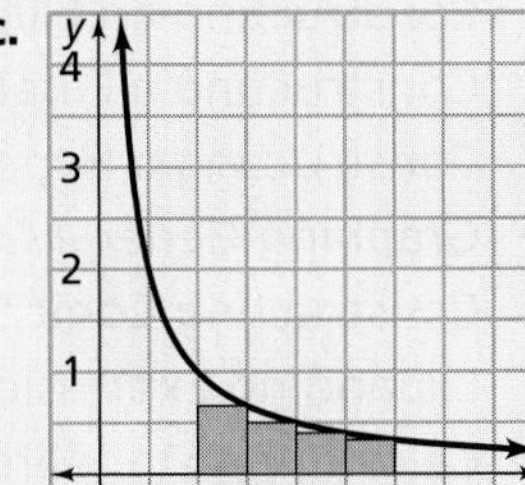

   d. $\frac{19}{20} = 0.95$

19. a. $\frac{1}{4}\left(\frac{3}{2} + \frac{\sqrt{2}}{2} + \frac{\sqrt{3}}{2}\right) \approx 0.7683$

   b. $\frac{1}{4}\left(\frac{1}{2} + \frac{\sqrt{2}}{2} + \frac{\sqrt{3}}{2}\right) \approx 0.5183$

   c. $\frac{1}{4}\left(1 + \frac{\sqrt{2}}{2} + \frac{\sqrt{3}}{2}\right) \approx 0.6433$

   d. $E_{U_4} \approx 0.15$ or 15%, $E_{L_4} \approx -0.22$ or -22%, $E_{avg} \approx -0.04$ or -4%

20. 48.4

TI-Nspire™ Technology Handbook

Recognizing how to use technology to support your mathematics is an important habit of mind. Although the use of technology in this course is independent of any particular hardware or software, this handbook gives examples of how you can apply the TI-Nspire™ handheld technology.

Handbook Contents

Comparing Angle Measure and Arc Length, Lesson 1.2

1. Put the handheld in degree mode. Choose **Circle** from the **Shapes** menu. Place the cursor at the origin. Press enter.

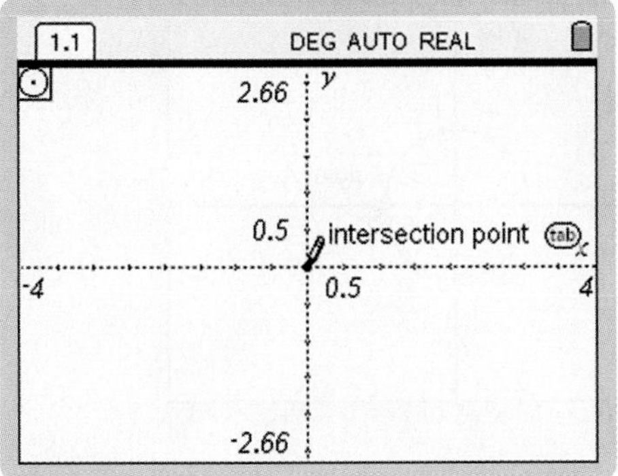

2. Place the cursor close the point (1, 0). The cursor will jump to the point (1, 0). Press enter. Press ⇧ A to label the point.

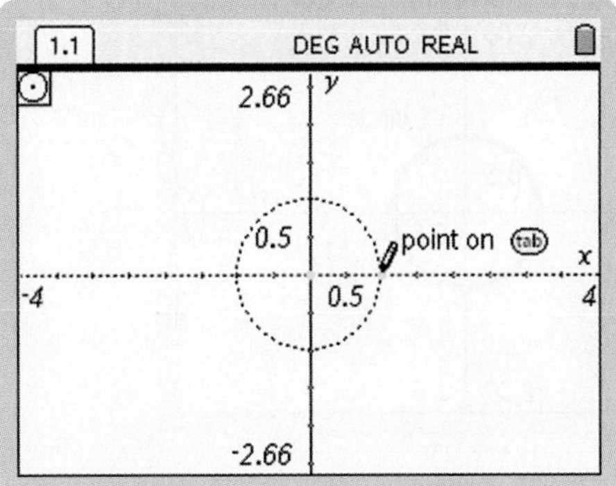

3. Choose **Segment** from the **Points & Lines** menu. Draw a segment on the screen. Press B ' to label the end point.

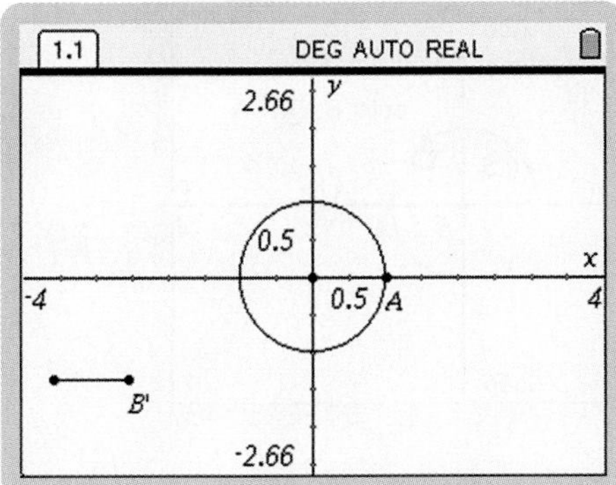

4. Choose **Length** from the **Measurement** menu. Place the cursor on the segment. Press enter.

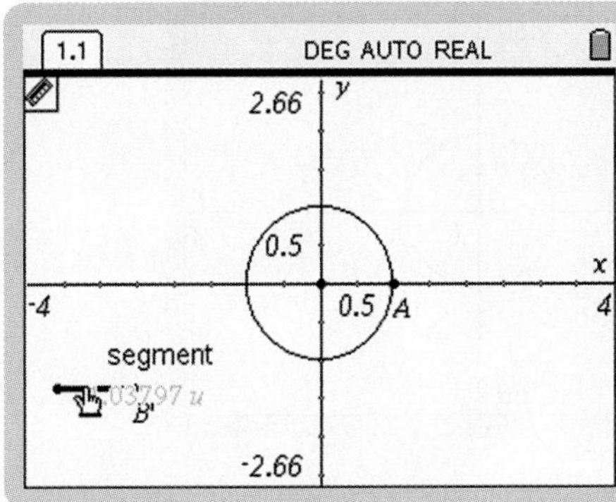

5. Move the cursor to drag the measurement to the desired location. Press enter to anchor it.

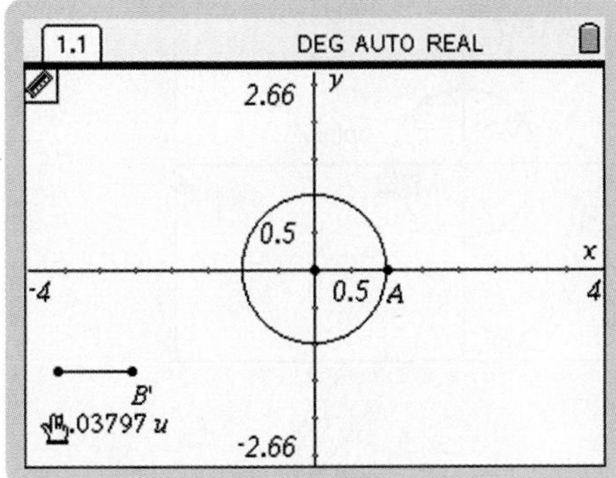

6. Choose **Measurement transfer** from the **Construction** menu. Place the cursor on the length of the segment. Press enter.

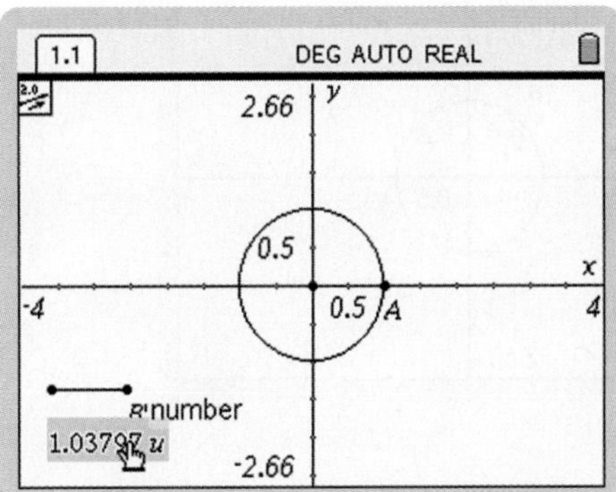

Comparing Angle Measure and Arc Length (continued)

7. Place the cursor on the circle. Press **enter**.

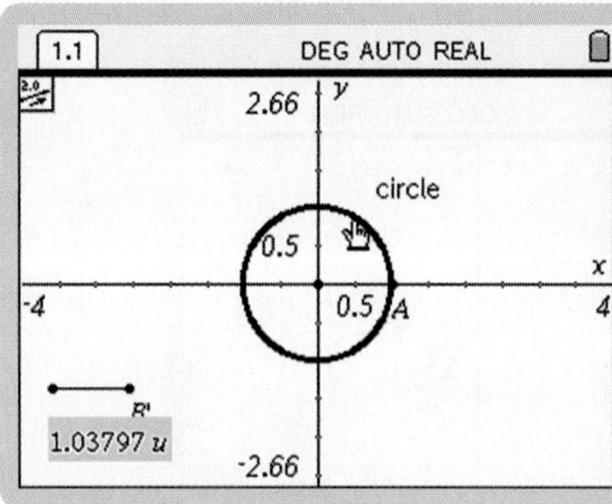

8. Place the cursor on point *A*. Press **enter**. The length of the arc from *A* to the new point that appears is equal to the length of the segment.

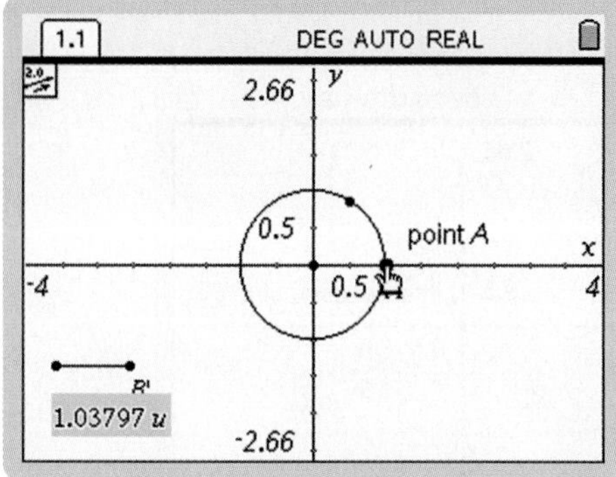

9. Use the **Text** tool from the **Actions** menu to label the new point.

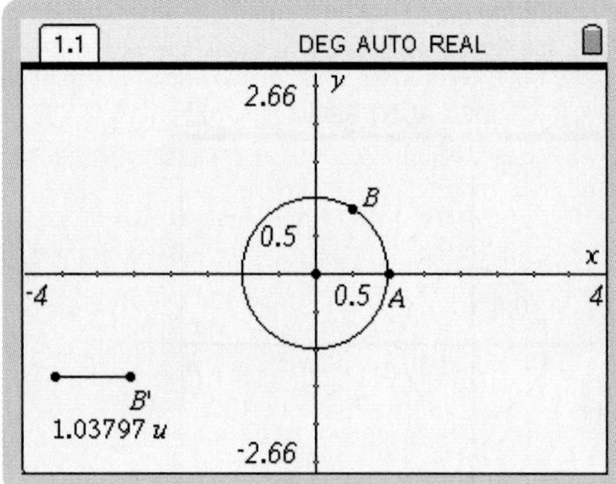

10. Choose **Coordinates and Equations** from the **Actions** menu. Place the cursor on point *B*. Press **enter**.

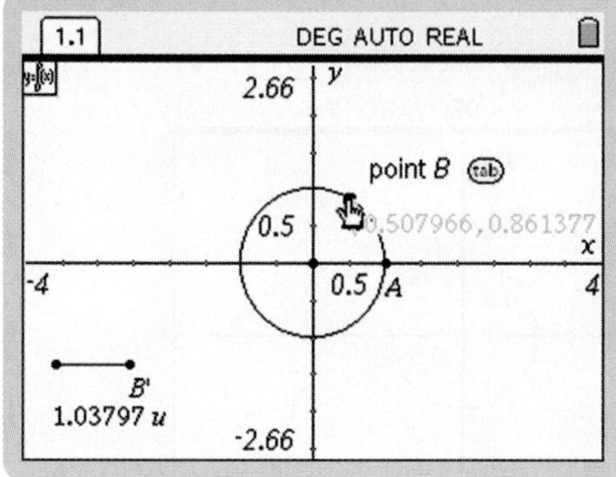

11. Move the cursor to drag the coordinates to the desired location. Press **enter** to anchor it.

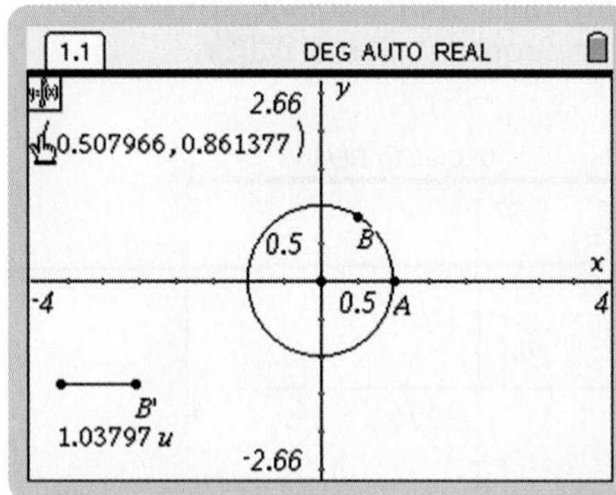

12. Choose **Angle** from the **Measurement** menu. Place the cursor on point *A*. Press **enter**.

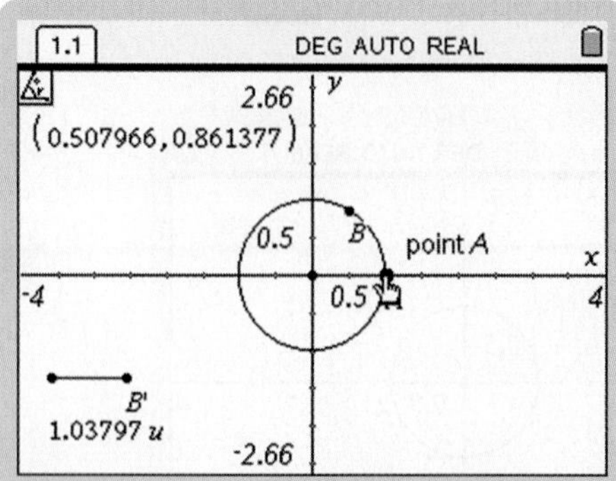

Comparing Angle Measure and Arc Length (continued)

13. Place the cursor on the origin. Press enter.

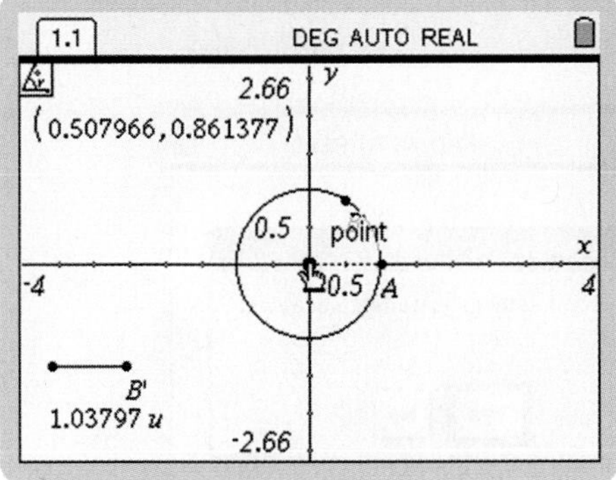

14. Place the cursor on point *B*. Press enter.

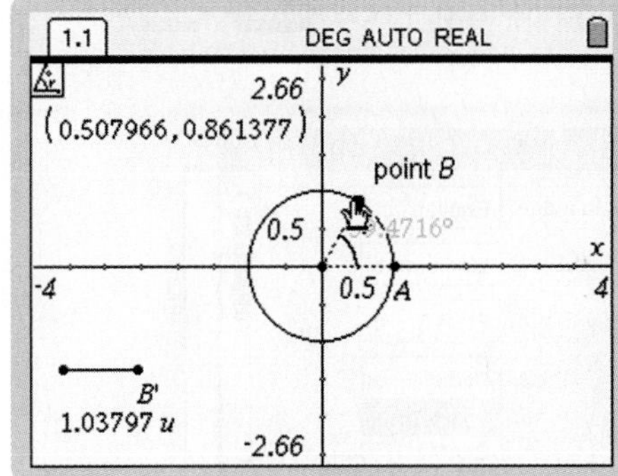

15. Move the cursor to drag the angle measurement to the desired location. Press enter to anchor it.

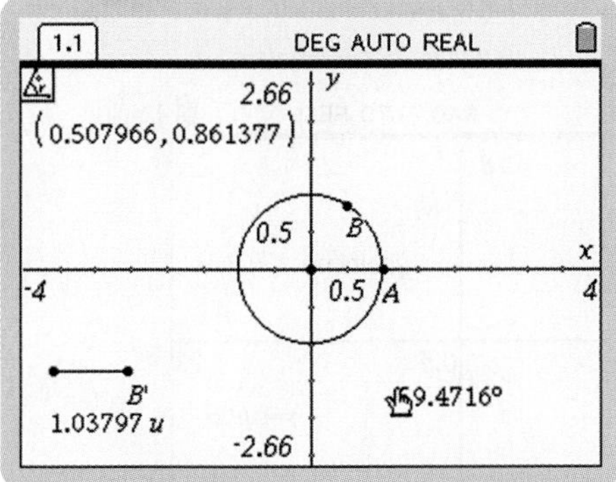

16. Move the cursor to point *B′*. Press ctrl to grab the point. Drag the point and observe the relationship between the length of the segment and the angle measurement.

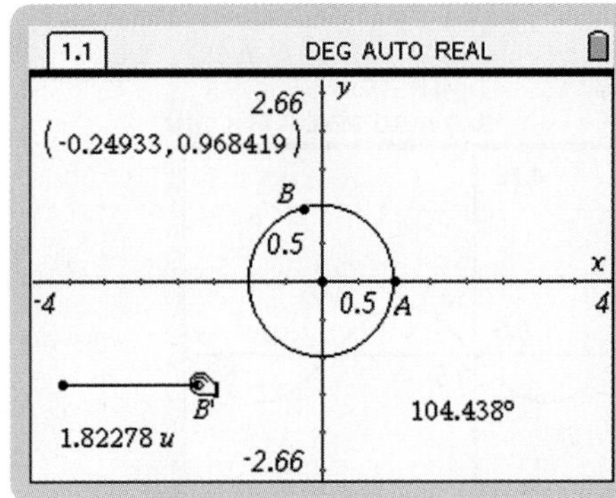

Putting the Handheld in Radian Mode, Lesson 1.2

1. Press . Choose **System Info.** Press enter.

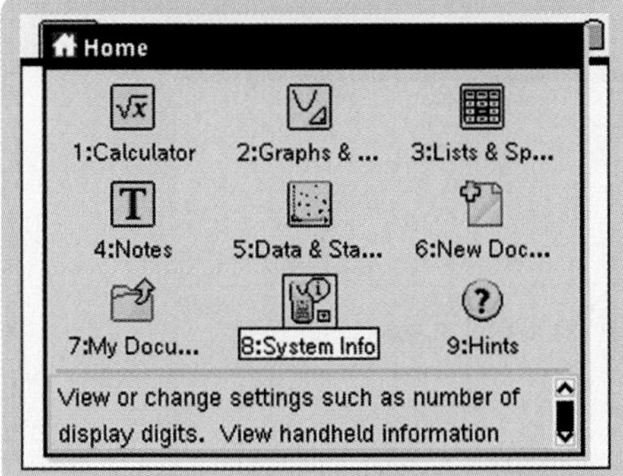

2. Choose **System Settings**. . . . Press enter.

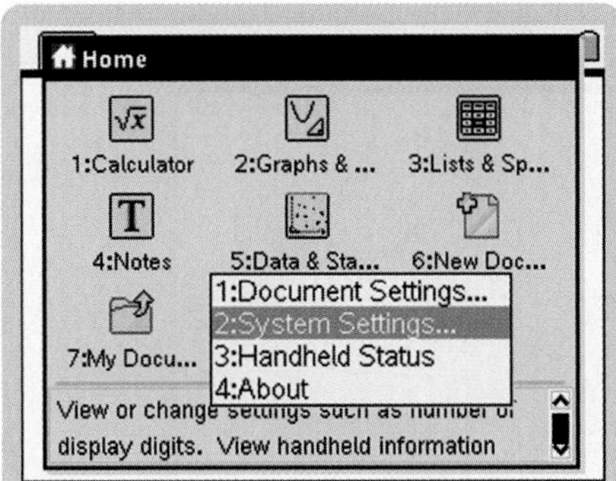

Putting the Handheld in Radian Mode (continued)

3. Press tab until you reach the **Angle** field. Press ▽ to open the menu. Press ▽ until **Radian** is highlighted. Press enter enter.

4. Press enter to confirm the change to Radian mode.

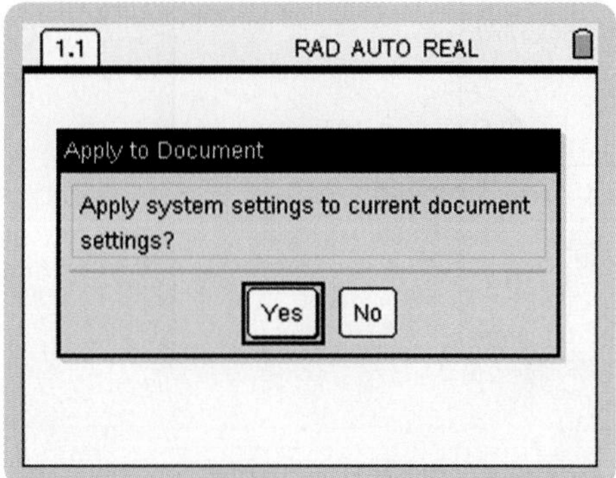

Measuring the Slope of a Line Secant to a Sine Curve, Lesson 1.5

1. Start with the graph of $y = \sin x$.

2. Choose **Point On** from the **Points & Lines** menu. Place the cursor on the curve. Press enter.

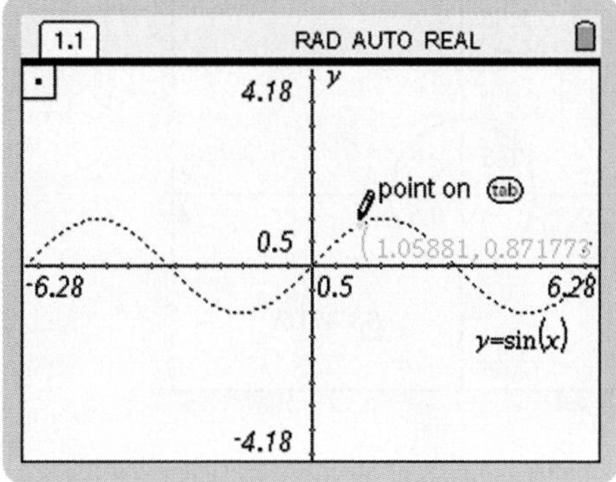

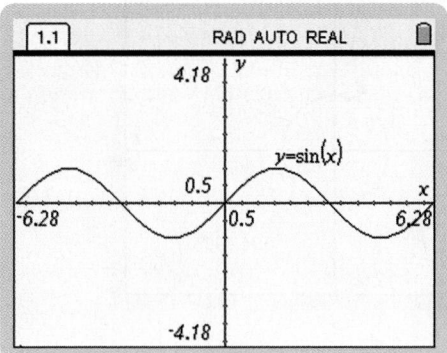

3. Press A to label the point.

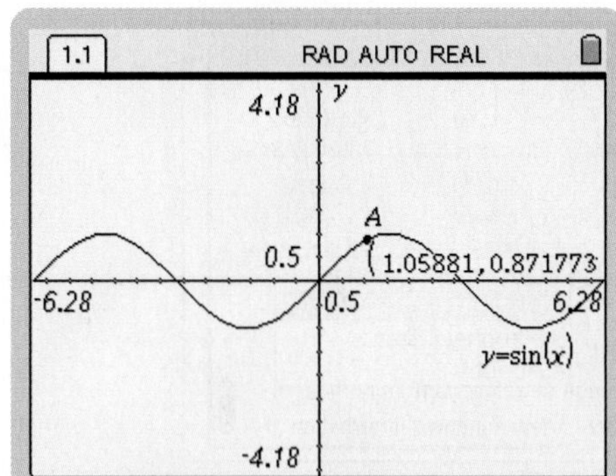

4. Place point *B* on the curve in the same way.

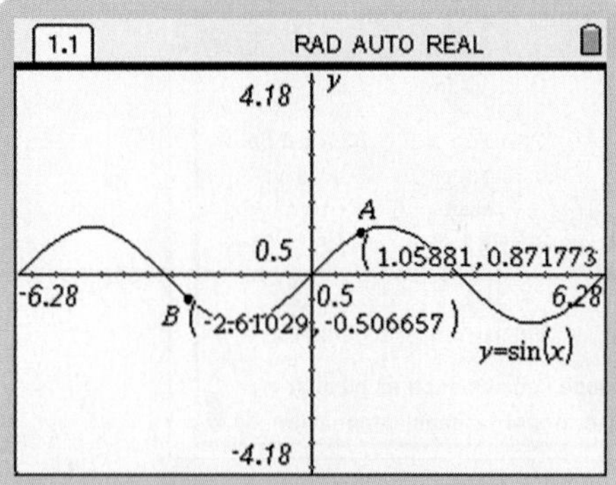

Measuring the Slope of a Line Secant to a Sine Curve (continued)

5. Choose **Line** from the **Points & Lines** menu. Place the cursor on point *B*. Press enter. Place the cursor on point *A*. Press enter.

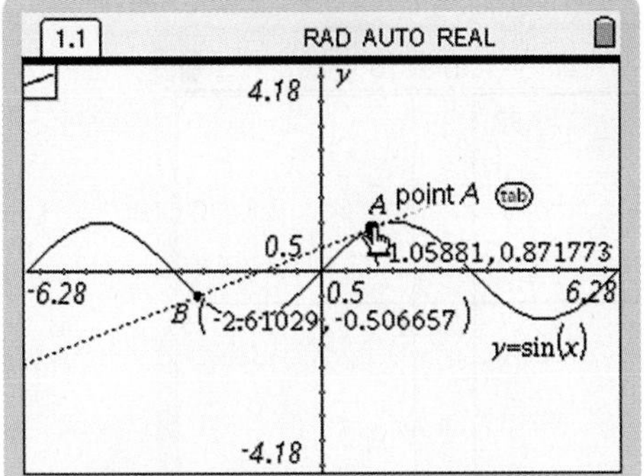

6. Choose **Slope** from the **Measurement** menu. Place the cursor on the line. Press enter.

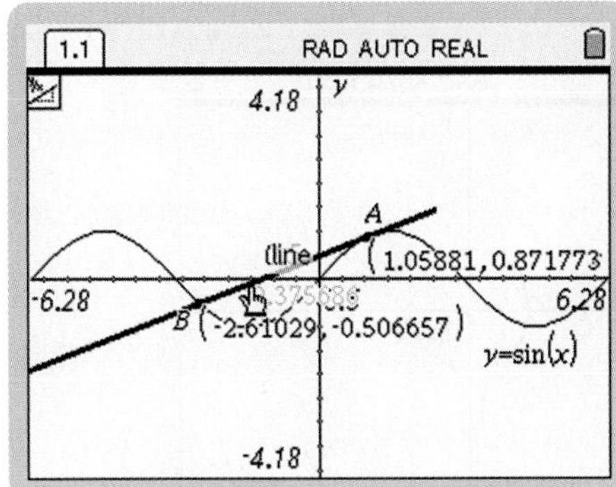

7. Move the cursor to drag the slope to the desired location. Press enter to anchor it.

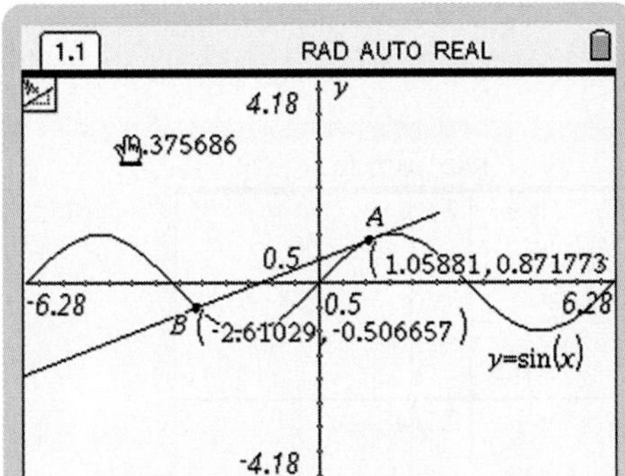

8. Place the cursor on point *B*. Press ctrl to grab it. Drag point *B* along the curve. Observe how the slope changes.

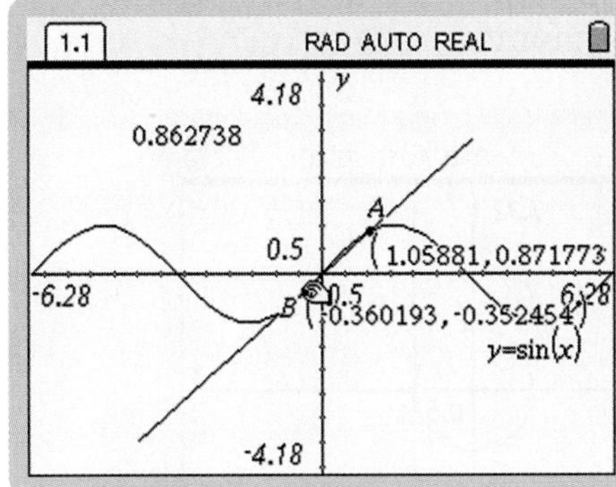

Modeling the Tangent Function, Lesson 1.7

1. Construct a circle with center at the origin that passes through the point *A*(1, 0).

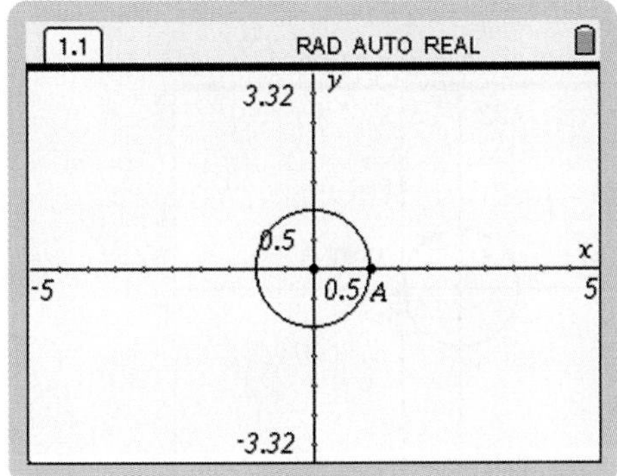

2. Choose **Perpendicular** from the **Construction** menu. Place the cursor on the *x*-axis. Press enter.

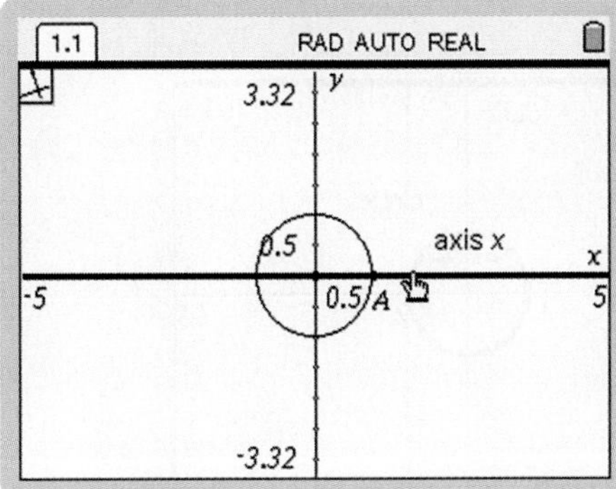

Modeling the Tangent Function (continued)

3. Place the cursor on point *A*. Press enter to set the line through *A* perpendicular to the *x*-axis.

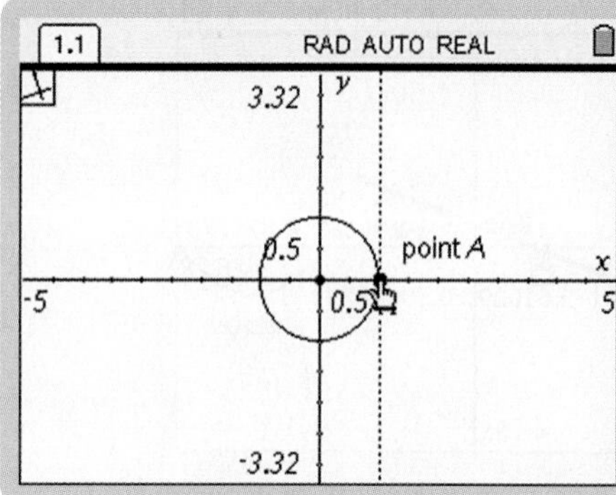

4. Choose **Segment** from the **Points & Lines** menu. Construct a segment in an open area of the screen. After setting the second endpoint, press B ' to label it.

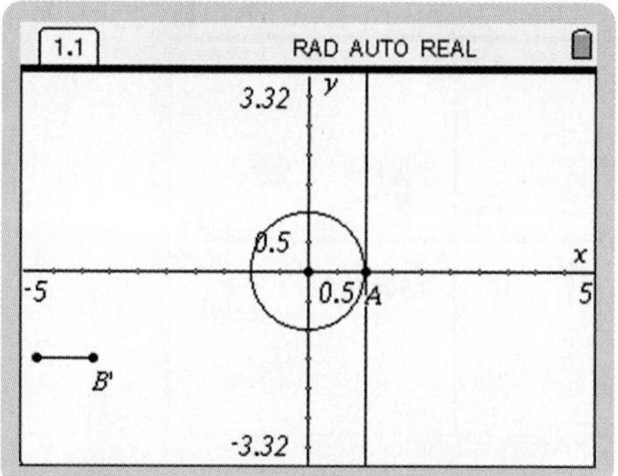

5. Choose **Length** from the **Measurement** menu. Place the cursor on the segment. Press enter to measure the length. Move the cursor to drag the measurement to the desired location. Press enter to anchor it.

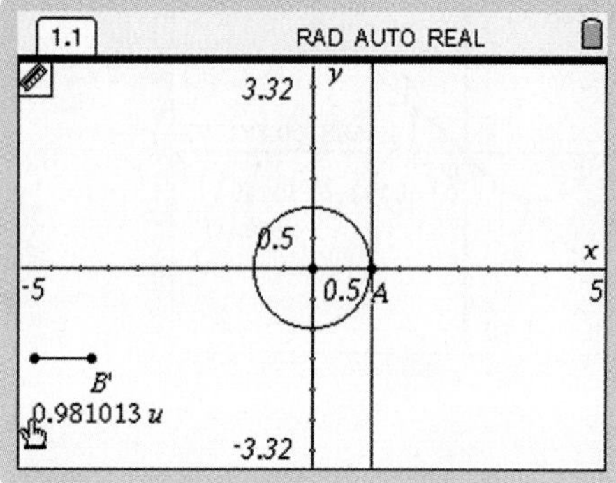

6. Choose **Measurement transfer** from the **Construction** menu. Place the cursor on the length of the segment. Press enter.

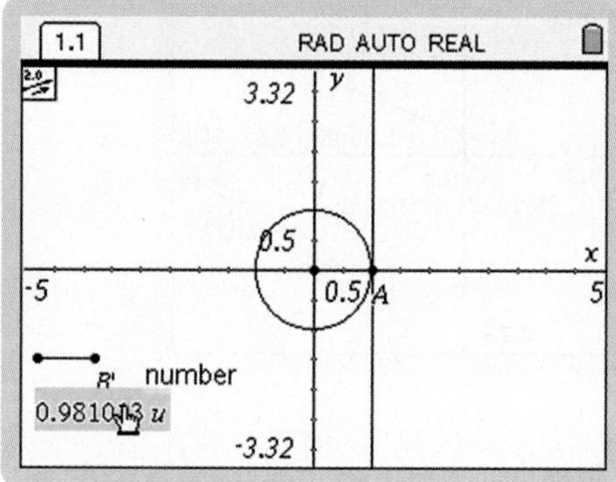

7. Place the cursor on the circle. Press enter.

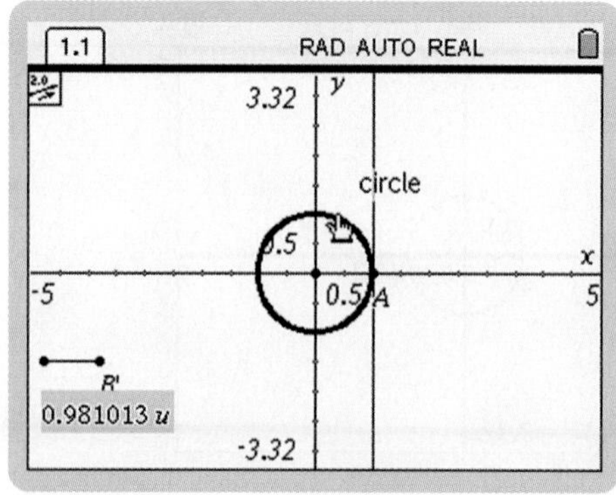

8. Place the cursor on point *A*. Press enter. The length of the arc from *A* to the new point that appears is equal to the length of the segment.

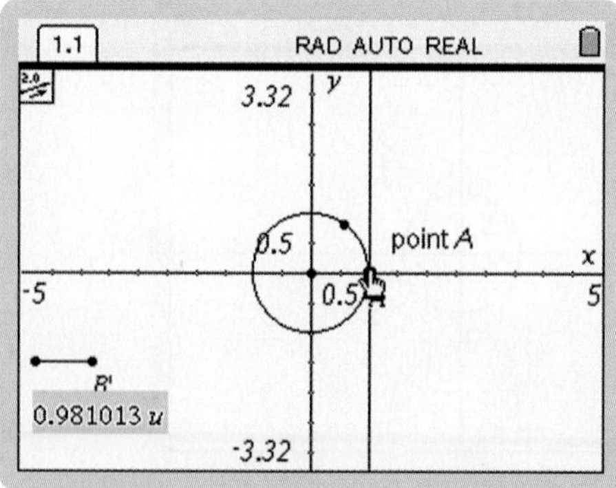

Modeling the Tangent Function (continued)

9. Use the **Text** tool in the **Actions** menu to label the new point.

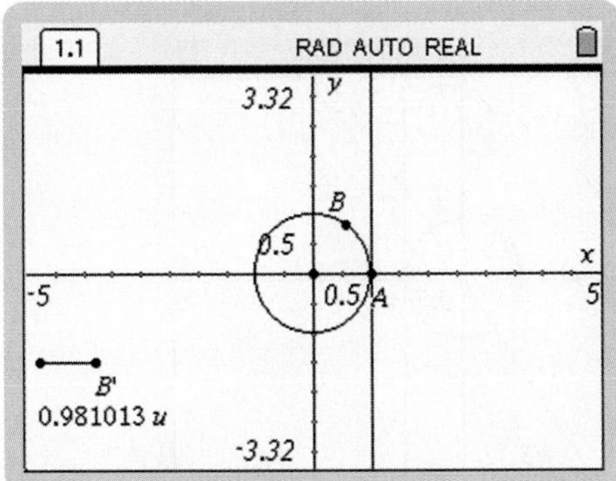

10. Choose **Line** from the **Points & Lines** menu. Place the cursor on the origin. Press enter. Place the cursor on the point *B*. Press enter.

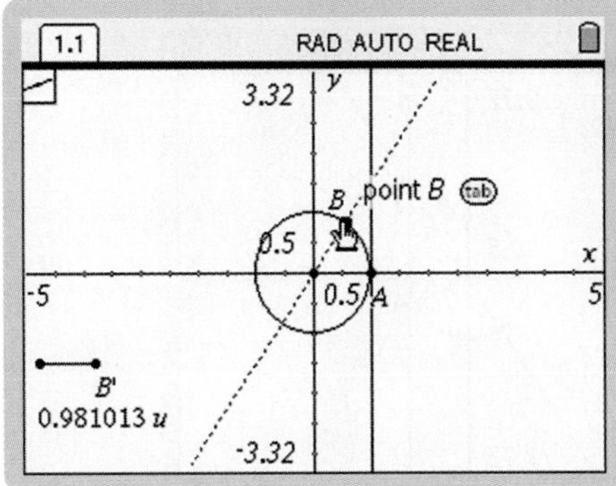

11. Choose **Intersection Point(s)** from the **Points & Lines** menu. Place the cursor on the line through the origin. Press enter.

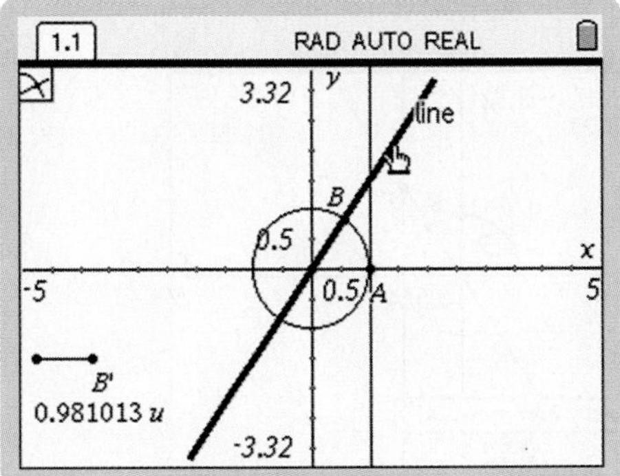

12. Place the cursor on the vertical line through the point *A*. Press enter to construct the intersection of the two lines.

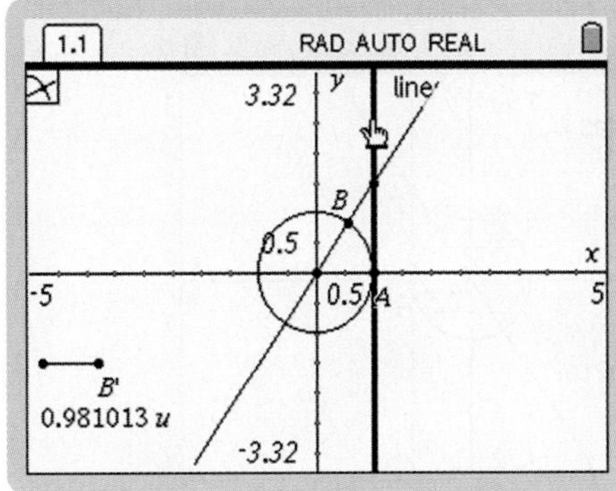

13. Use the **Text** tool in the **Actions** menu to label the new point.

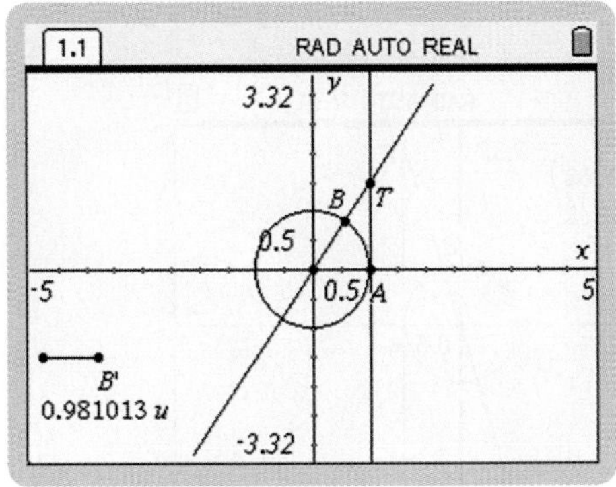

14. Choose **Coordinates and Equations** from the **Actions** menu. Place the cursor on point *T*. Press enter.

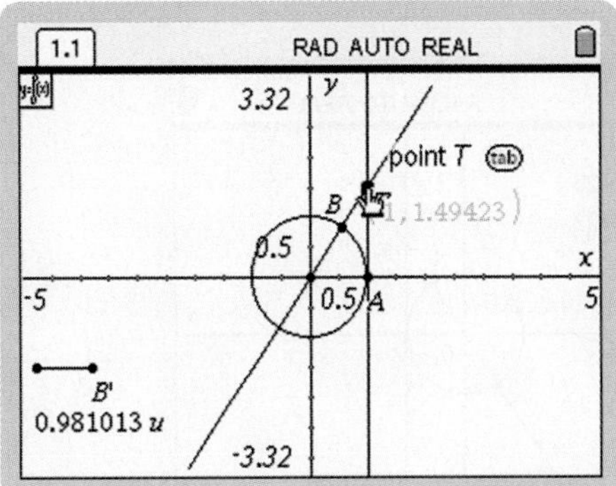

Modeling the Tangent Function (continued)

15. Move the cursor to drag the coordinates to the desired location. Press **enter** to anchor it.

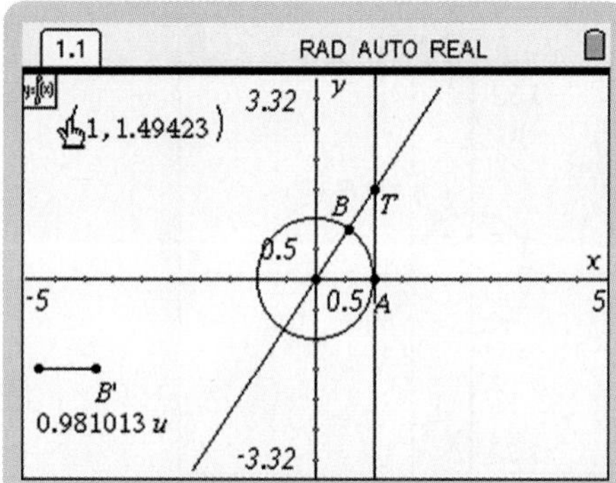

16. Choose **Text** from the **Actions** menu. Click on an empty area of the screen. Type **T** **A** **N** **(** **V**. Press **enter**.

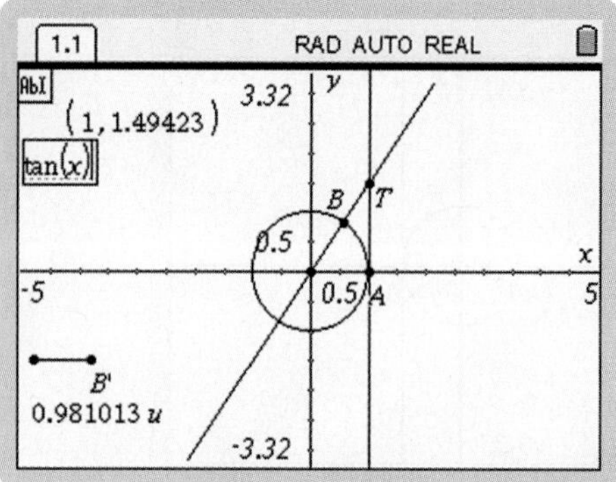

17. Choose **Calculate** from the **Actions** menu. Place the cursor on the text you wrote in step 16. Press **enter**.

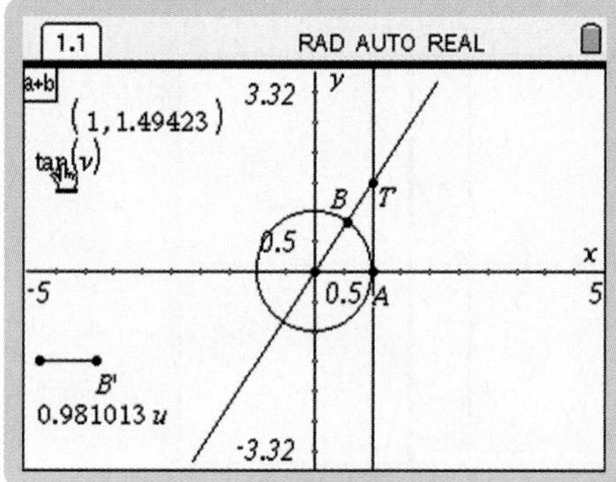

18. Place the cursor on the length of the segment. Press **enter**.

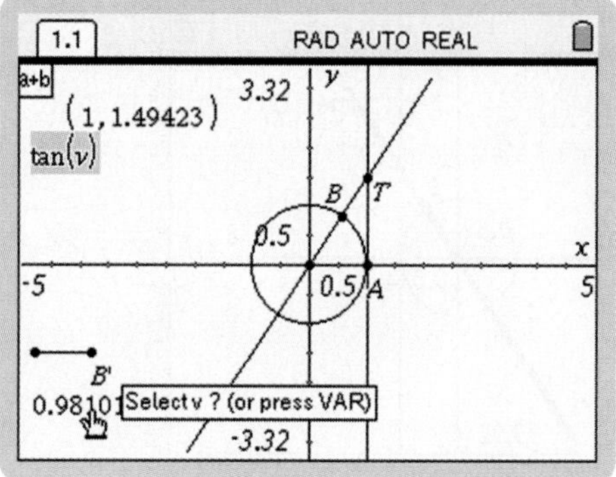

19. Move the cursor to drag the result of the calculation to the desired location. Press **enter** to anchor it.

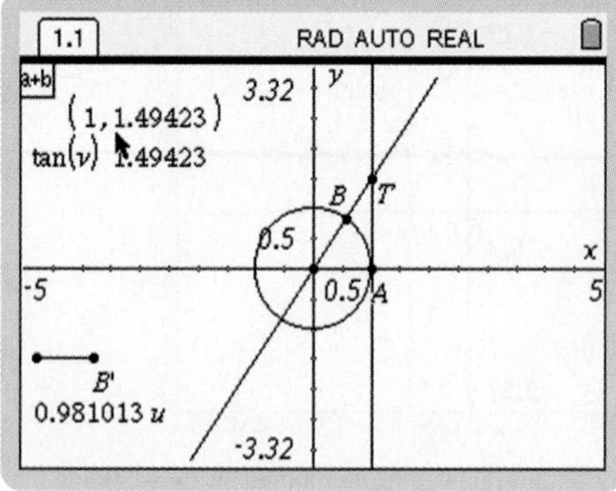

20. Place the cursor on the point B'. Press **ctrl** **grab** to grab it. Drag the point and observe the relationship between the coordinates of T, and the tangent of $m\widehat{AB}$.

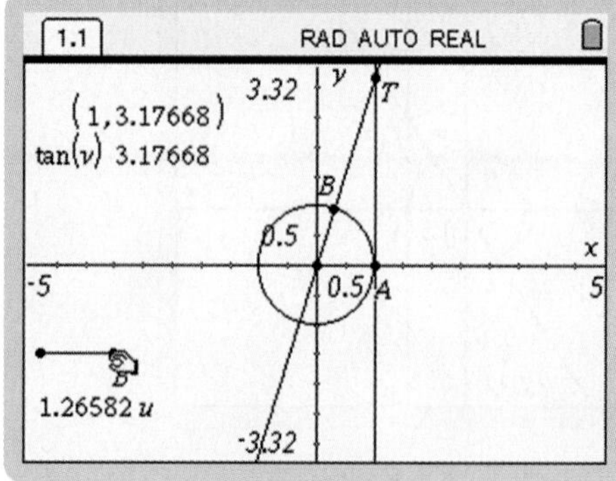

Graphing Composed Functions, Lesson 1.11

1. Choose **Define** from the **Actions** menu. Define g as a function of x.

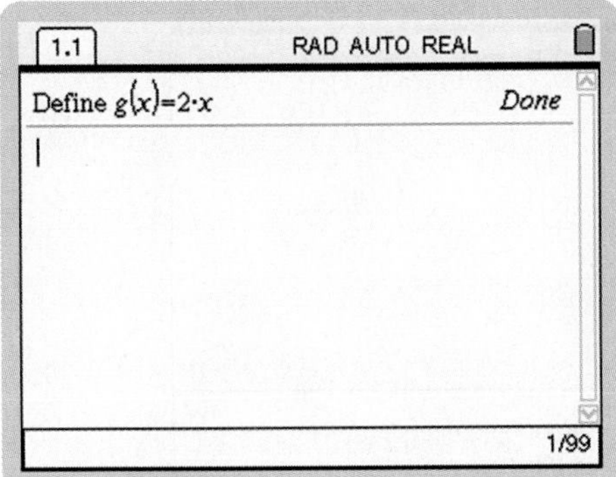

2. Press ctrl home. Choose the **Page Layout** menu. Choose **Layout 3** from the **Select Layout** submenu.

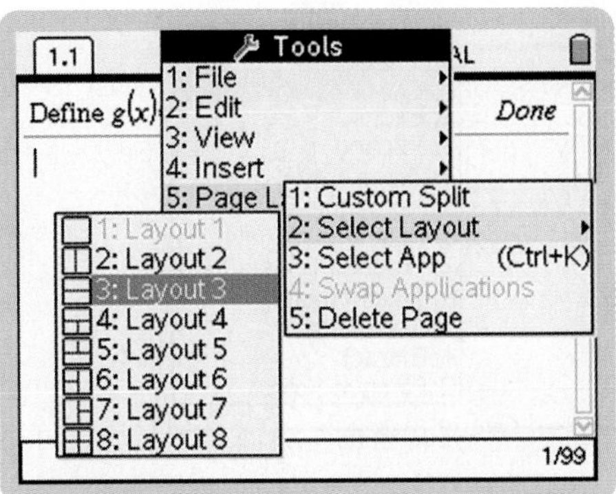

3. Press ctrl tab to highlight the new window pane.

4. Add the Graphs & Geometry application. Choose **Zoom – Trig** from the Window menu. Press ctrl G to hide the function entry line.

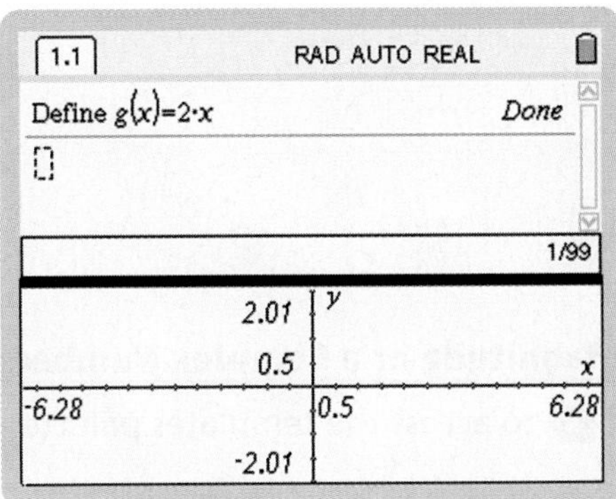

5. Use the **Text** tool in the **Actions** menu to write "$y = \sin(g(x))$" on the screen. Drag the text to the axes to graph the equation.

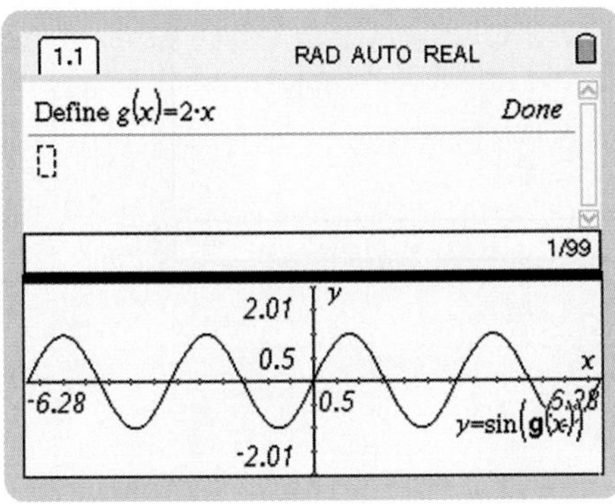

6. Press ctrl tab to switch back to the Calculator application. Redefine the function g. Observe the change in the graph of $y = \sin(g(x))$.

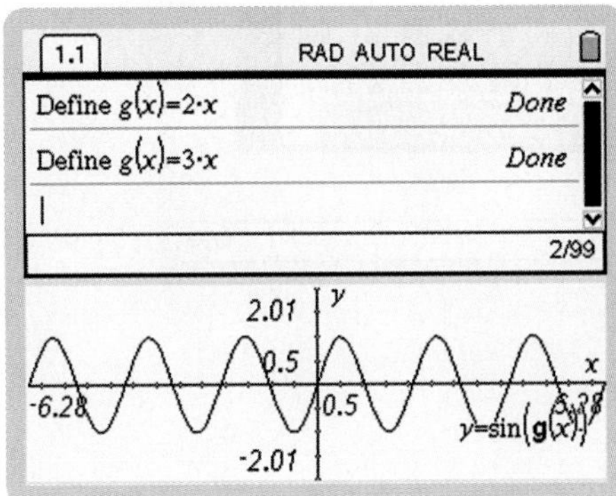

Solving Trigonometric Equations, Lesson 1.12

1. Choose **Solve** from the **Algebra** menu.

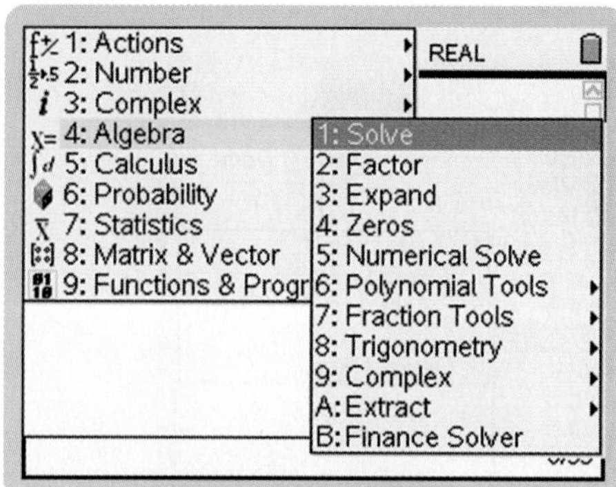

2. Type the equation, followed by a comma, then the variable. Press **enter**.

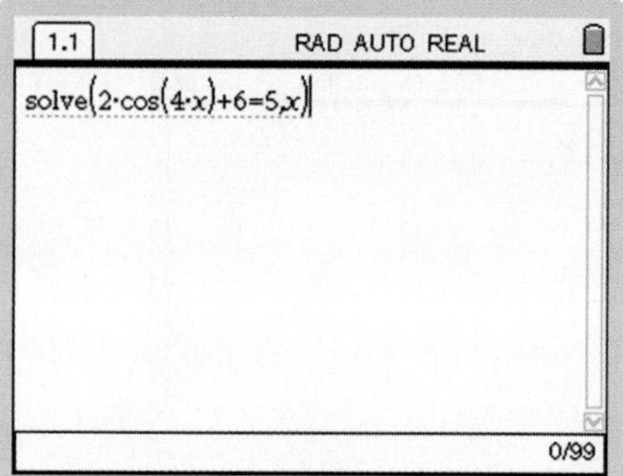

3. The general solution uses the variable ***n1***, which ranges over the integers. (You may also see ***n2***, ***n3***, ***n4***, and so on, as variables that range over the integers.)

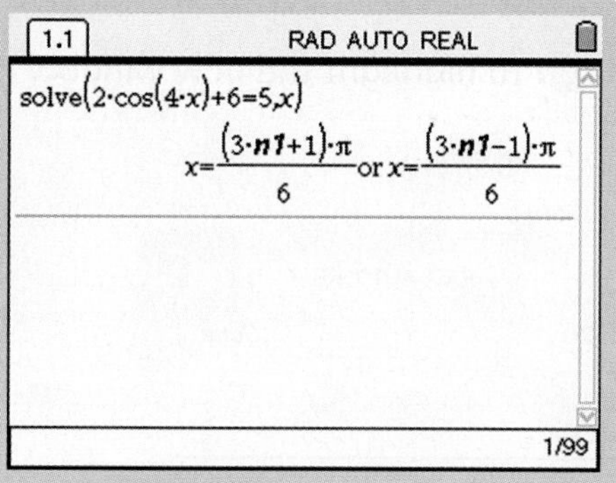

Finding the Magnitude of a Complex Number, Lesson 2.2

1. Press **ctrl** **×** to access the templates palette. Choose |□|.

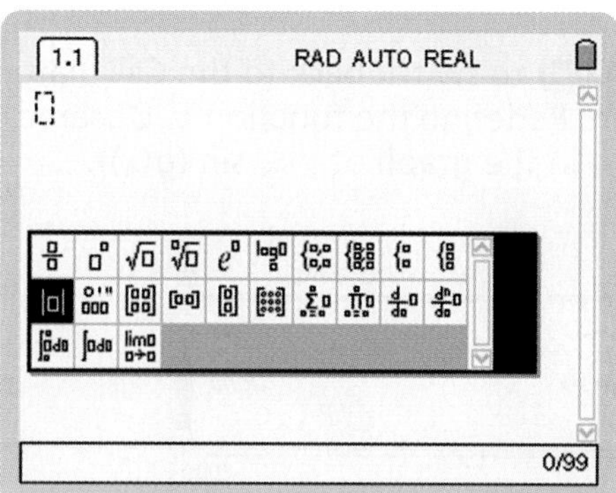

2. Type the complex number. Press **enter**.

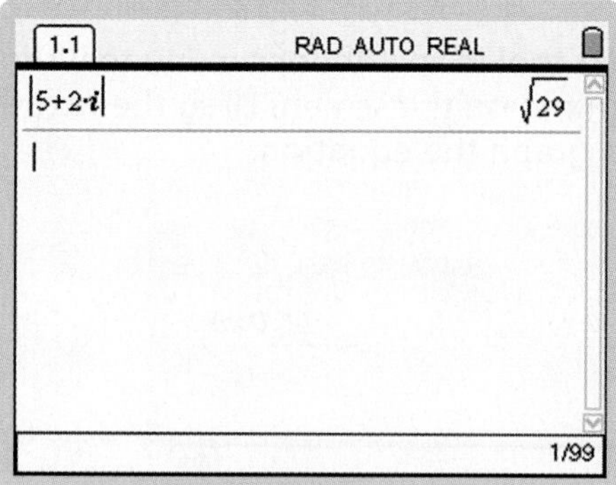

Finding Complex Solutions, Lesson 2.8

1. Type **C** **S** **O** **L** **V** **E** **(**. Then type the equation, followed by a comma, and the variable to solve for.

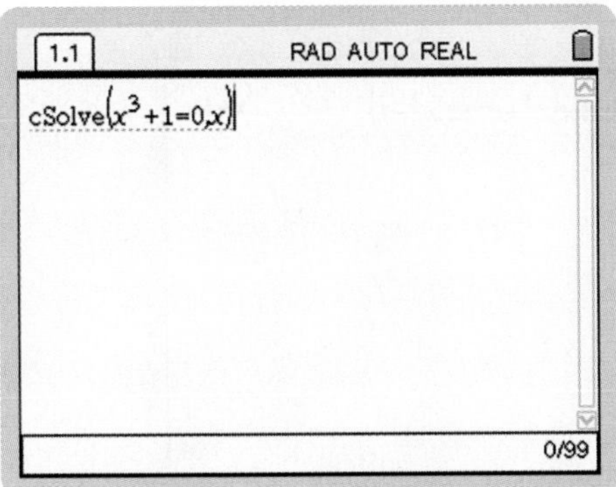

2. Press **enter**.

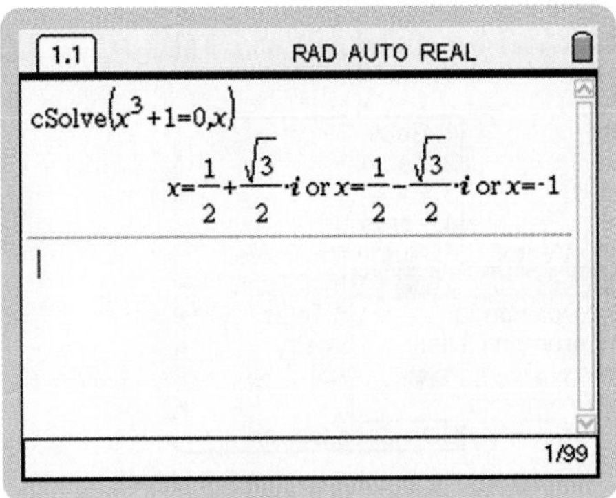

Modeling a Piecewise Defined Function, Lesson 2.11

1. Choose **Define** from the **Actions** menu. Type **P** **(** **N** **,** **X** **)** **=**. Press **ctrl** **×** to access the templates palette. Choose ⊞.

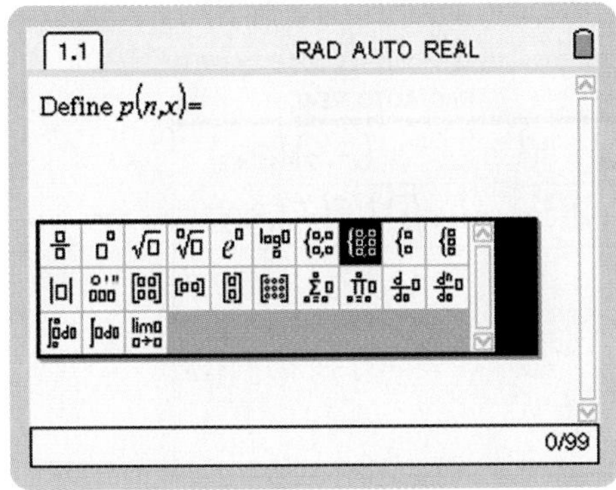

2. Select the correct number of function pieces, 3, in the dialog box. Press **enter**.

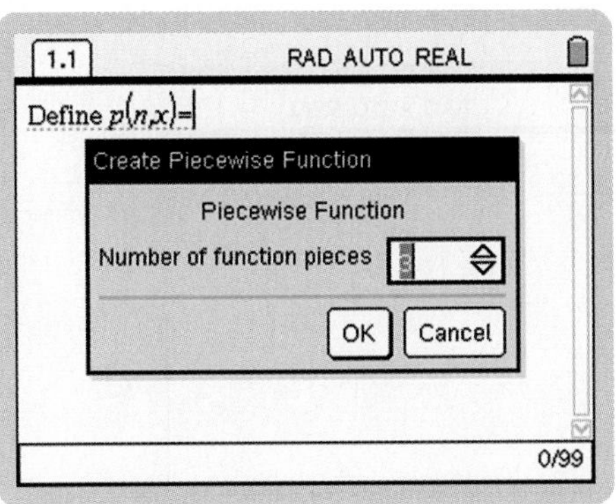

3. Press **tab** to move from box to box.

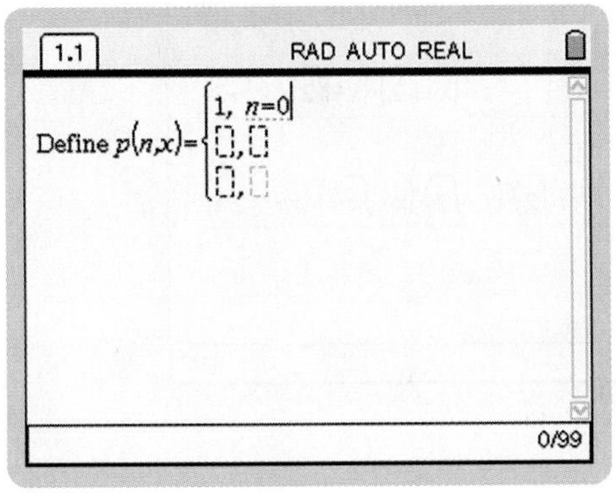

1.1 RAD AUTO REAL

Define $p(n,x)=\begin{cases}1, & n=0\\ \square, & \square\\ \square, & \square\end{cases}$

0/99

4. Complete the function definition. Press **enter**.

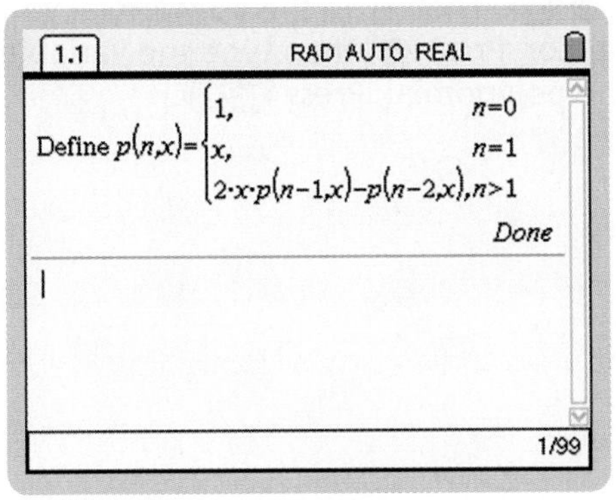

1.1 RAD AUTO REAL

Define $p(n,x)=\begin{cases}1, & n=0\\ x, & n=1\\ 2\cdot x\cdot p(n-1,x)-p(n-2,x), & n>1\end{cases}$

Done

1/99

Using the polyRemainder Function, Lesson 2.12

1. Choose the **Polynomial Tools** submenu from the **Algebra** menu. Choose **Remainder of Polynomial**.

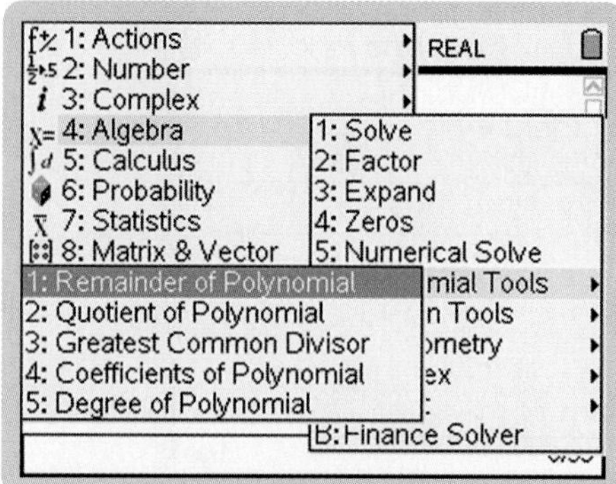

2. Enter two polynomials. The first is divided by the second. Press enter. The result is the remainder of the polynomial division.

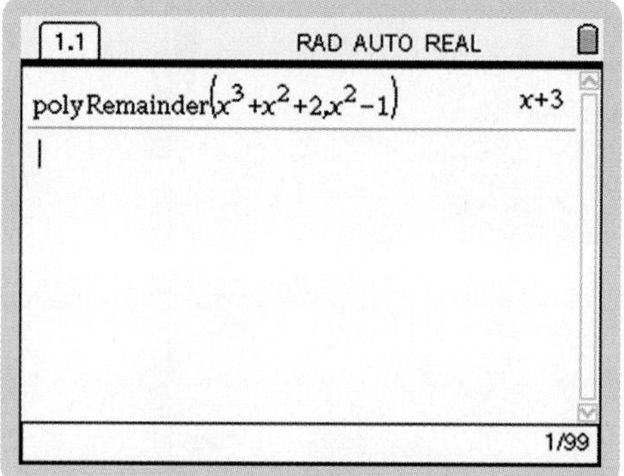

Factoring a Polynomial Over $\mathbb{Z}$, $\mathbb{R}$, and $\mathbb{C}$, Lesson 2.12

1. To factor a polynomial over $\mathbb{Z}$, press F A C T O R (, then type the polynomial you want to factor. Press enter.

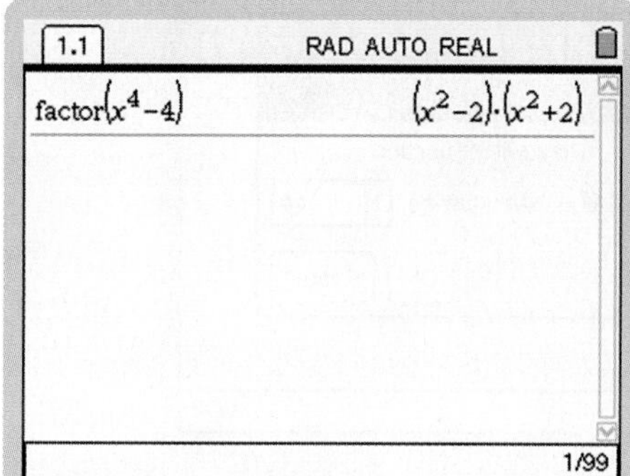

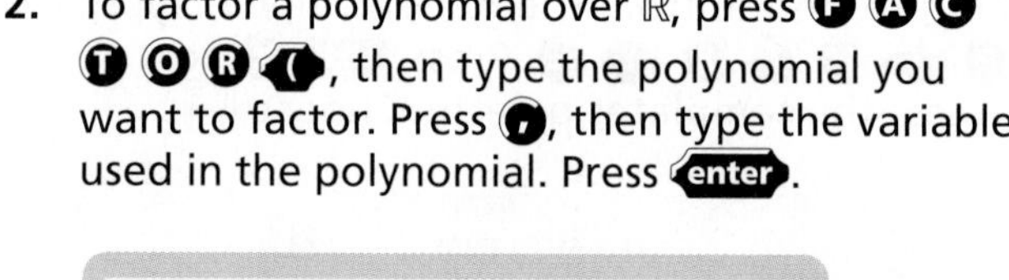

2. To factor a polynomial over $\mathbb{R}$, press F A C T O R (, then type the polynomial you want to factor. Press ,, then type the variable used in the polynomial. Press enter.

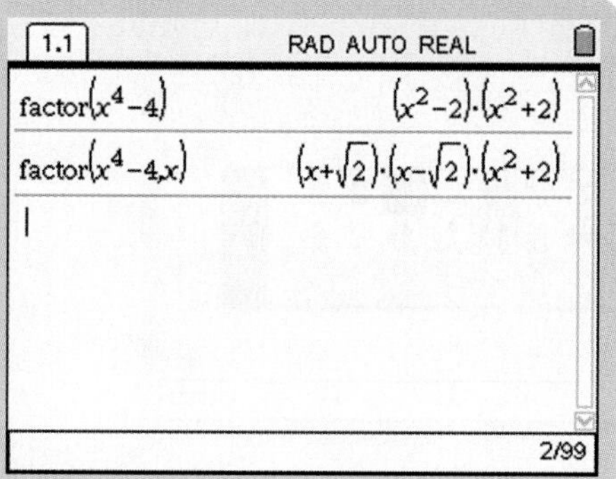

3. To factor a polynomial over $\mathbb{C}$, press C F A C T O R (. Then type the polynomial you want to factor. Press ,, then type the variable used in the polynomial. Press enter.

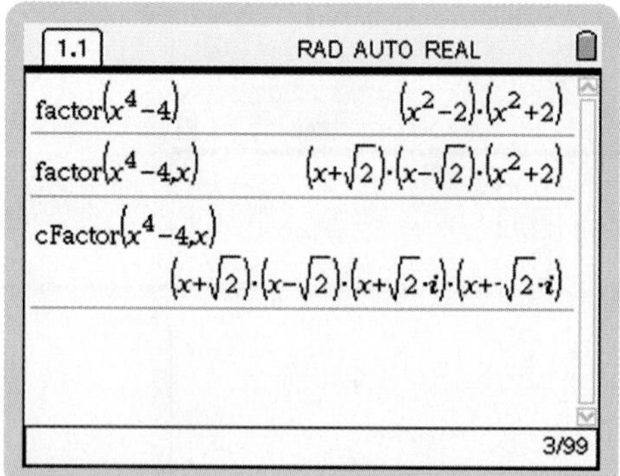

Finding the Equation of a Secant Line, Lesson 3.3

1. Graph the equation.

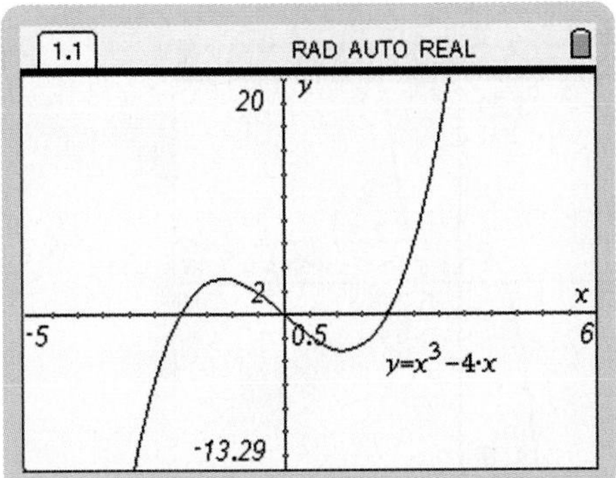

2. Follow steps 2–5 of *Finding the Slope of a Line Secant to a Sine Curve* to construct a secant line.

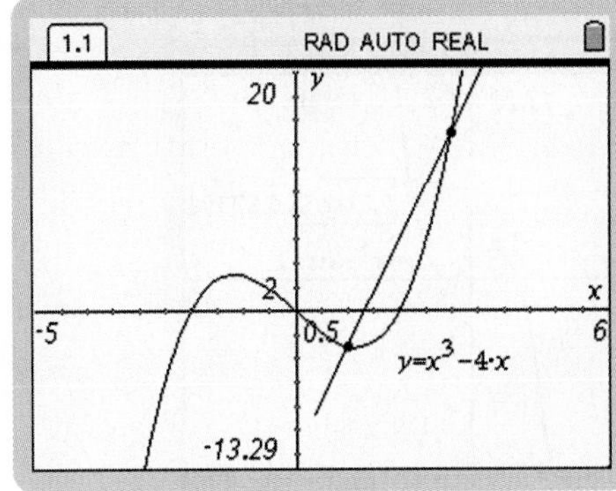

3. Choose **Coordinate and Equations** from the **Actions** menu. Place the cursor on the secant line. Press **enter**.

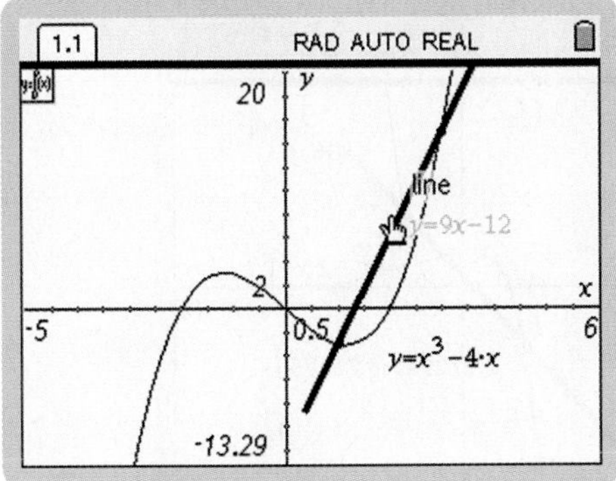

4. Move the cursor to drag the equation to the desired location. Press **enter** to anchor it.

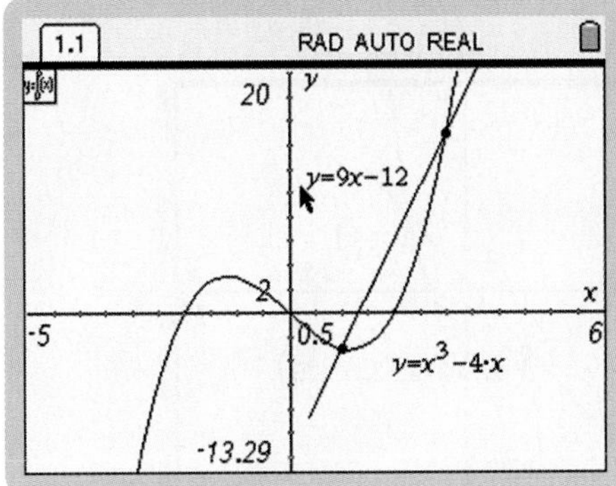

Finding the Slope of a Secant Line, Lesson 3.3

1. Graph the equation $y = x^3 - 2x + 1$.

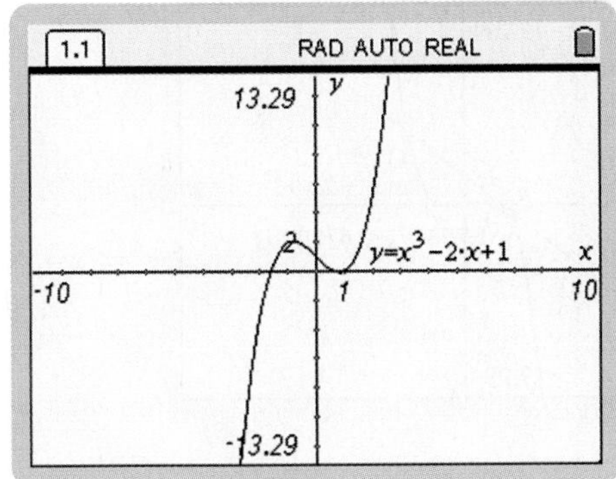

2. Choose **Point On** from the **Points & Lines** menu. Place the cursor on the curve. Press **enter**.

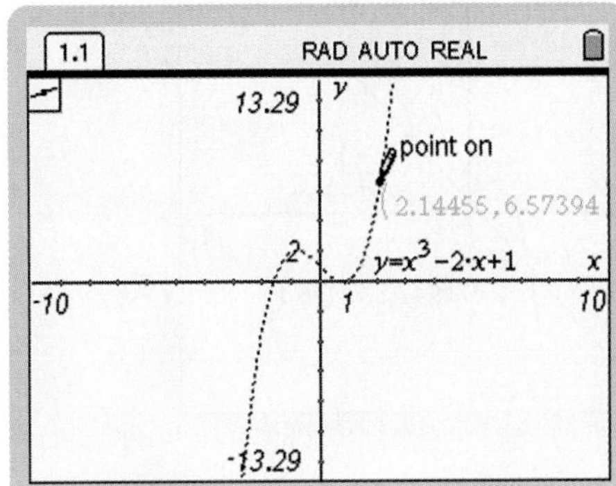

Finding the Slope of a Secant Line (continued)

3. Place the cursor on the x-coordinate of the new point. Press [click] [click].

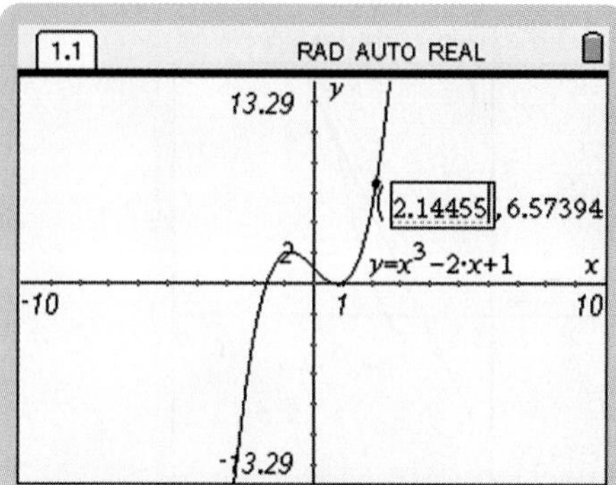

4. Press [ctrl] [del] to delete the x-coordinate. Press [2] to change the x-coordinate to 2. Press [enter]. The point jumps to (2, f(2)).

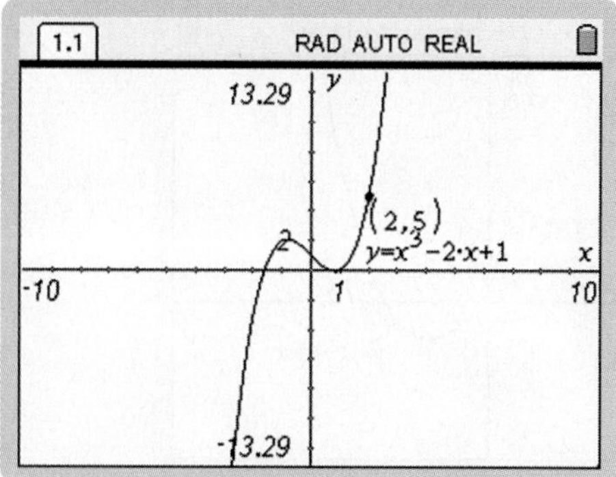

5. Construct a secant line through the point (2, 5). Label the other point the secant passes through B.

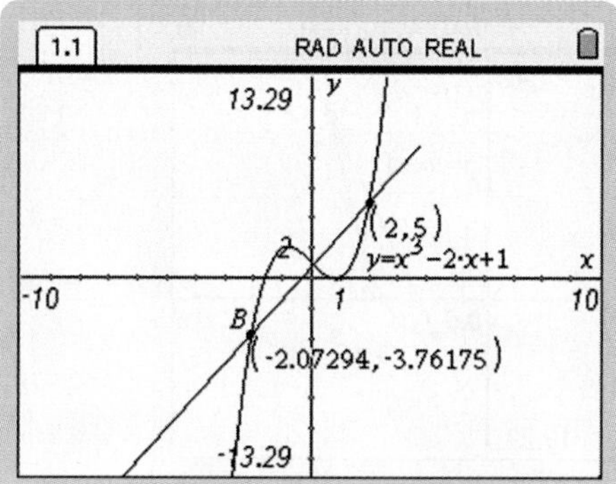

6. Choose **Slope** from the **Measurement** menu. Place the cursor on the secant line. Press [enter].

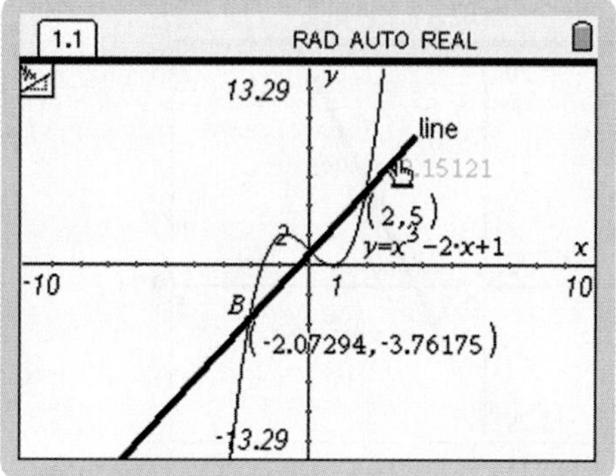

7. Move the cursor to drag the slope to the desired location. Press [enter] to anchor it.

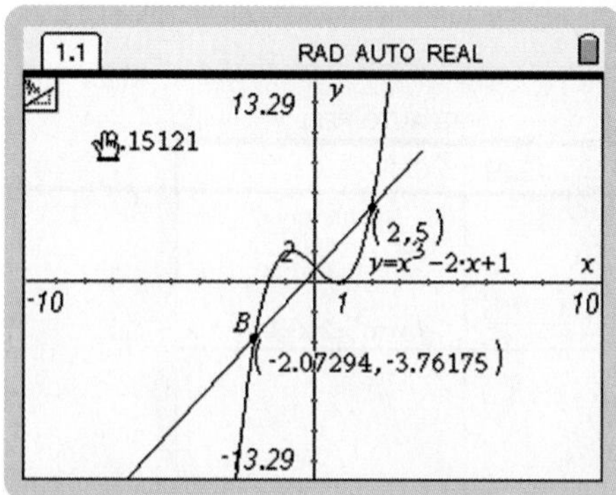

8. Place the cursor on point B. Press [ctrl] [click] to grab it. Drag point B and observe how the slope of the secant changes.

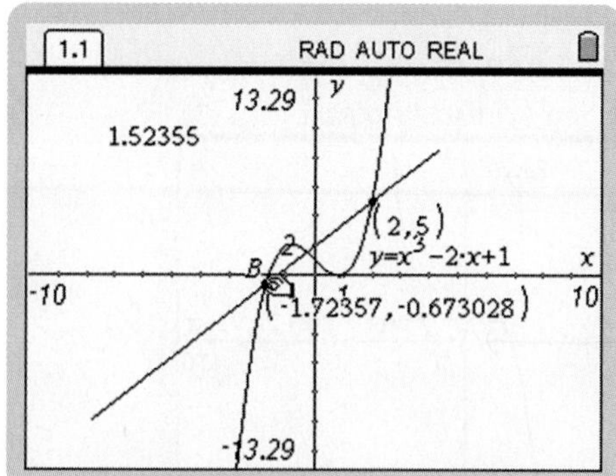

Finding a Taylor Expansion, Lesson 3.4

1. Press T A Y L O R (.

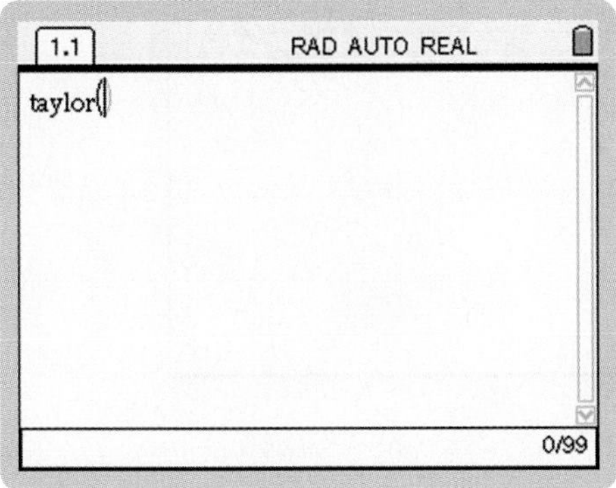

2. Enter the polynomial, the variable of the polynomial, the degree of the Taylor expansion, and the center of the expansion. Separate each with commas. Press enter.

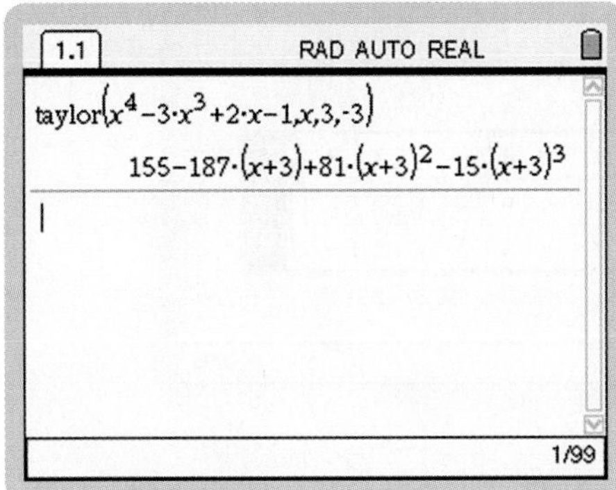

Constructing a Tangent Line, Lesson 3.5

1. Choose **Point On** from the **Points & Lines** menu. Place the cursor on the curve. Press enter.

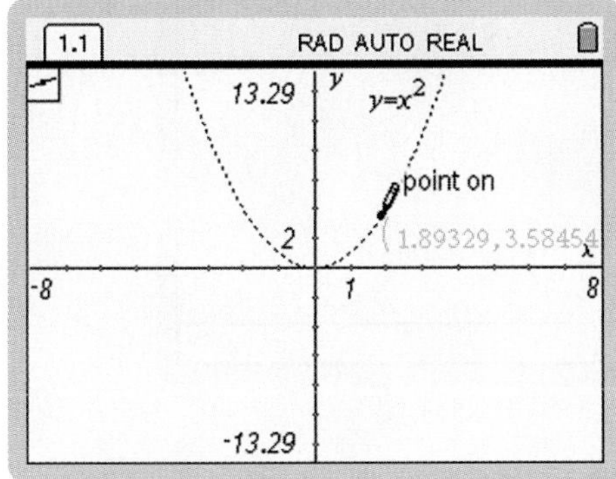

2. Choose **Tangent** from the **Points & Lines** menu. Place the cursor on the point. Press enter.

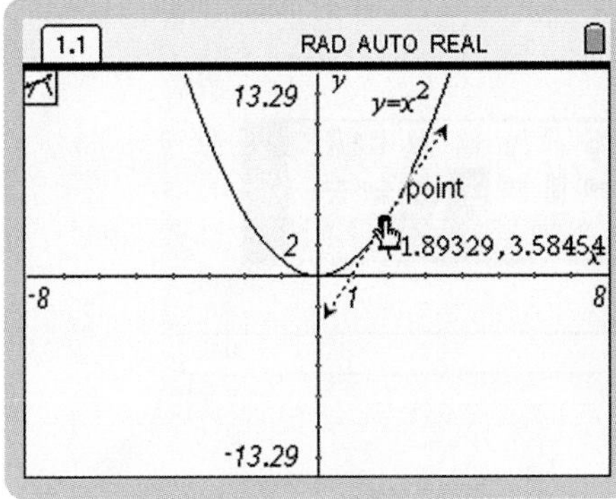

3. Place the cursor on the point. Press ctrl to grab it. Drag the point to the desired location. The line remains tangent to the curve at the point.

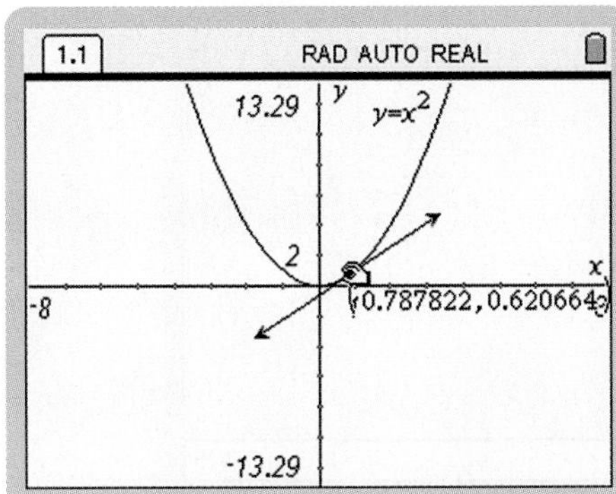

Using the number *e*, Lesson 3.11

1. Press ctrl ⊗ to access the templates palette. Choose *e*.

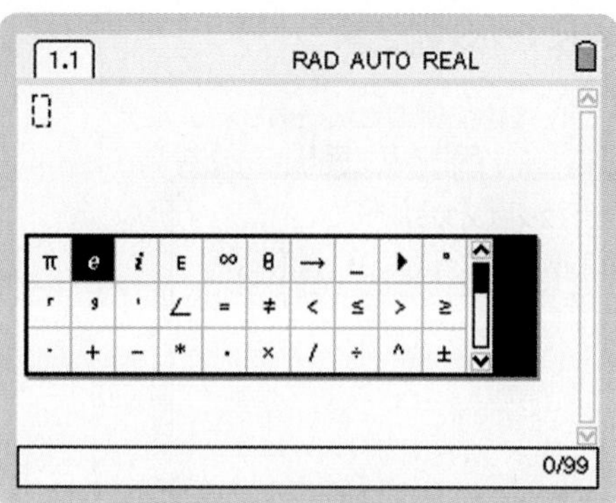

2. Press ctrl enter to find the approximate value of *e*.

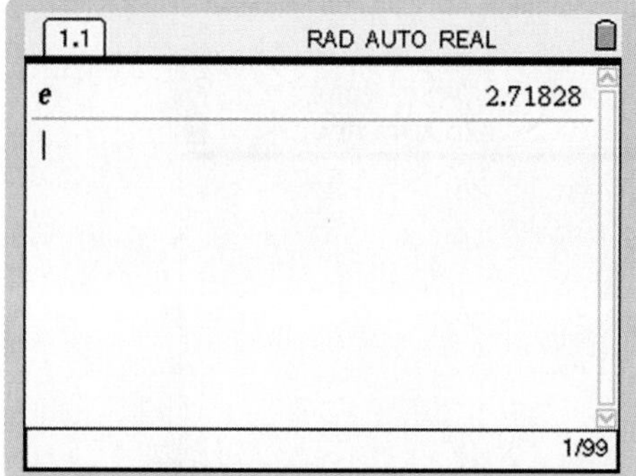

Evaluating an Infinite Sum, Lessons 3.11, 3.12

1. Press ctrl ⊗ to access the templates palette. Choose $\sum$.

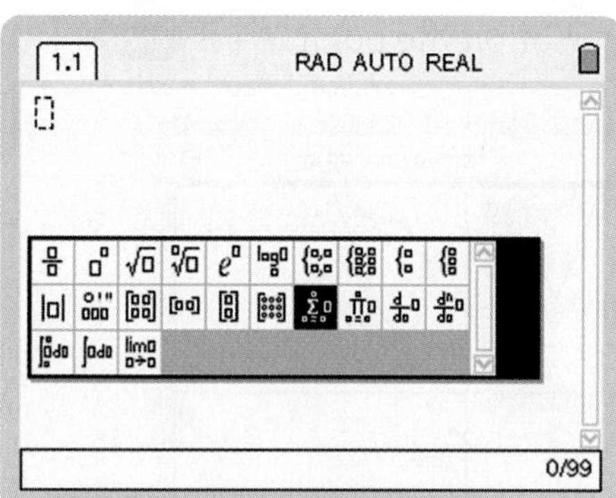

2. Press tab to move from box to box.

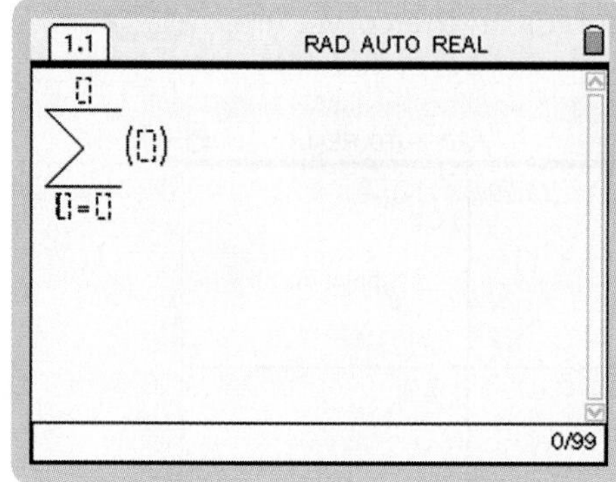

3. To enter ∞, press ctrl *i*.

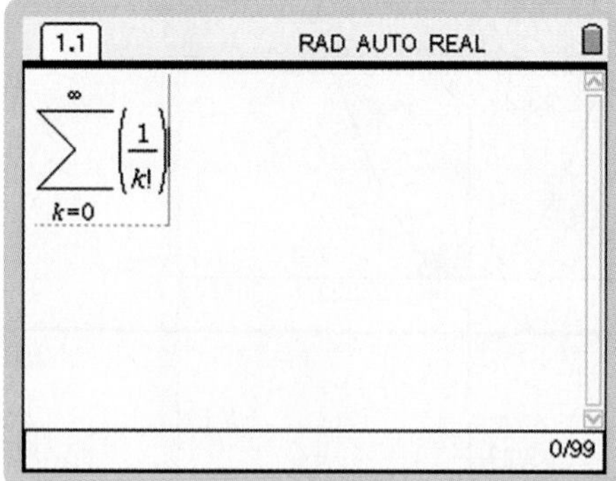

4. Press enter to evaluate the sum.

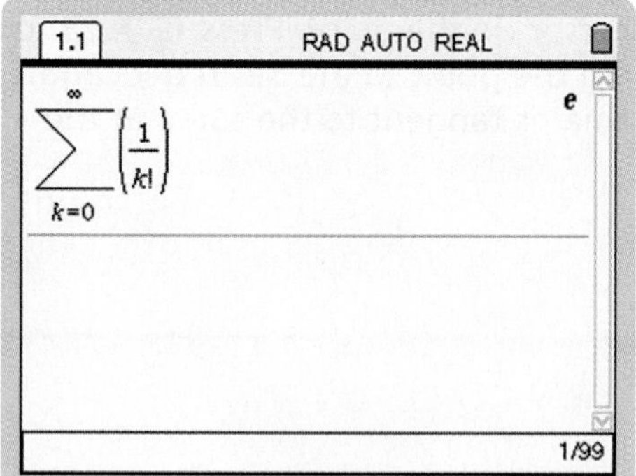

Evaluating a Limit, Lesson 3.11

1. Press ctrl ⊗ to access the templates palette. Choose $\lim_{\square\to\square}\square$.

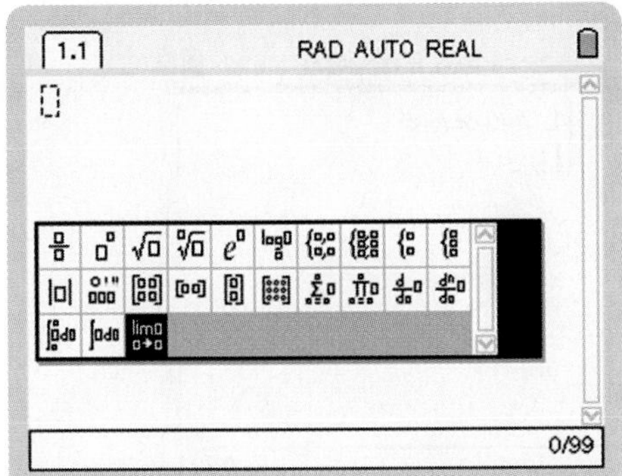

2. Press tab to move from box to box. To enter ∞ Press ctrl ⓘ.

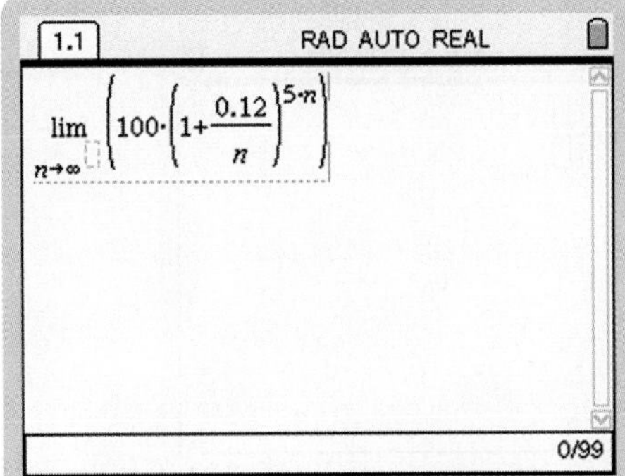

3. Press enter to evaluate the limit.

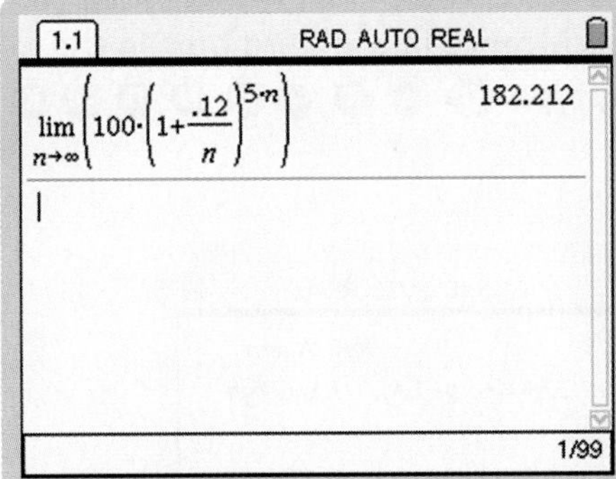

Modeling a Recursively Defined Function in Two Variables, Lesson 4.11

1. Choose **Define** from the **Actions** menu. Press C (N , K) =.

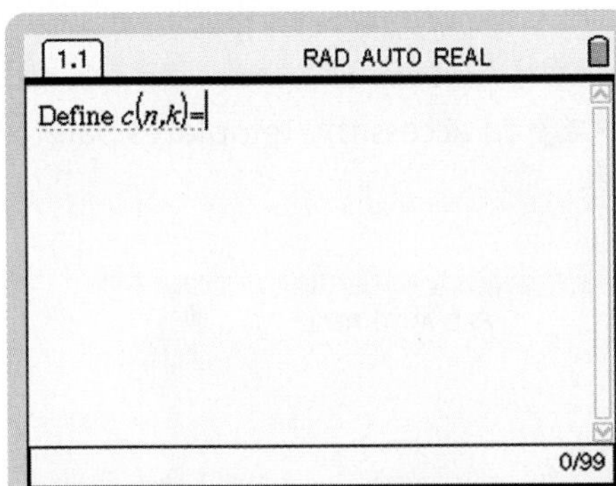

2. Press ctrl ⊗ to access the templates palette. Choose the piecewise template.

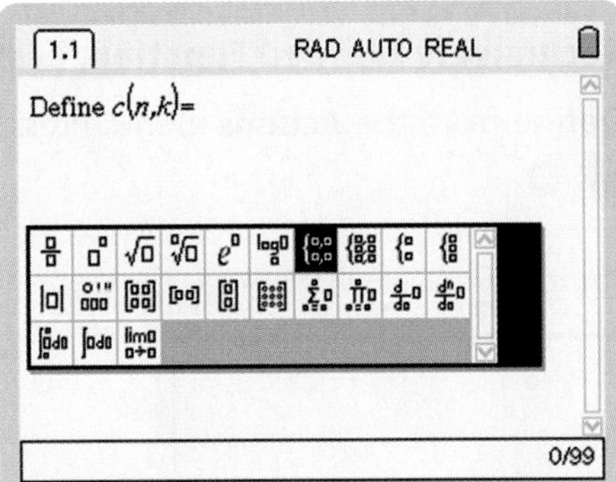

Modeling a Recursively Defined Function in Two Variables (continued)

3. Press **[tab]** to move from box to box.

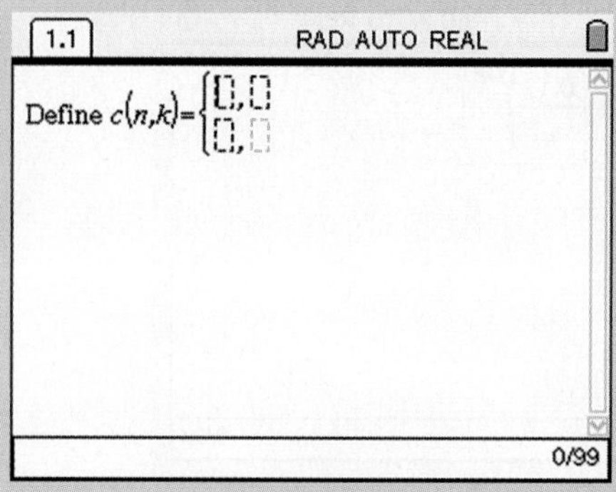

4. In the second box, type **[K] [=] [0] [space] [O] [R] [space] [K] [=] [N]**.

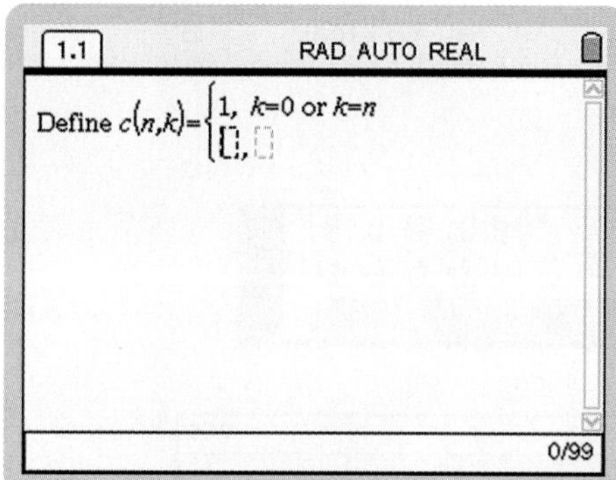

5. Enter the recurrence in the third box. In the fourth box, type **[0] [<] [K] [space] [A] [N] [D] [space] [K] [<] [N]**.

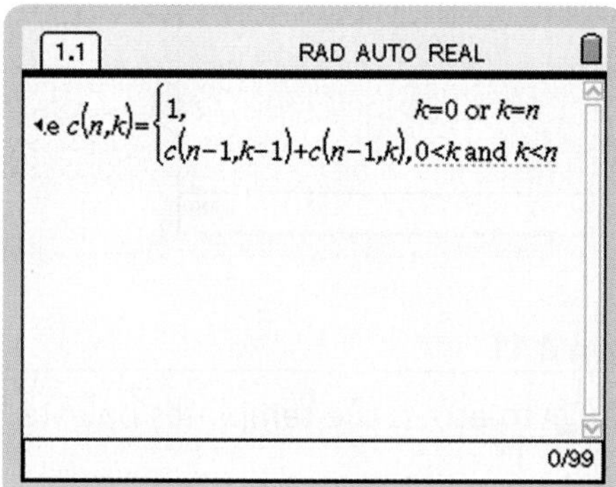

6. Press **[enter]** to complete the definition.

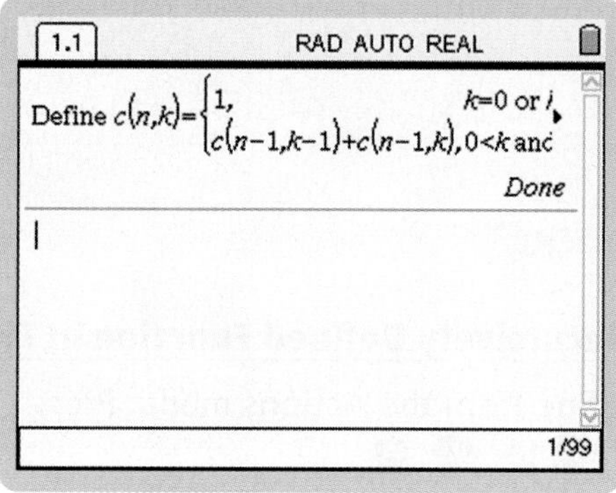

Modeling a Recursively Defined Function, Lesson 5.1

1. Choose **Define** from the **Actions** menu. Press **[C] [(] [N] [)] [=]**.

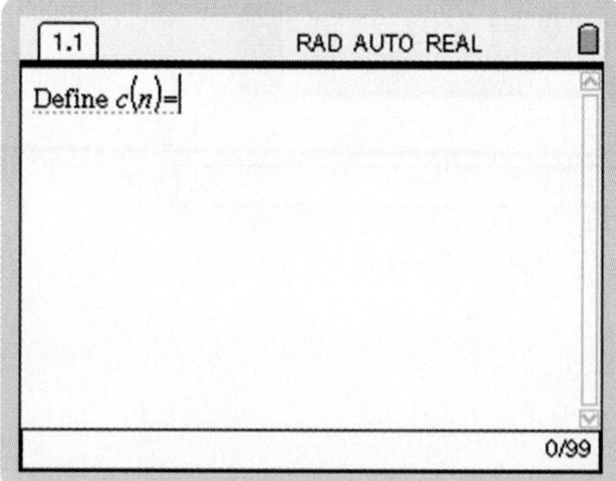

2. Press **[ctrl] [⊗]** to access the templates palette. Choose [piecewise template].

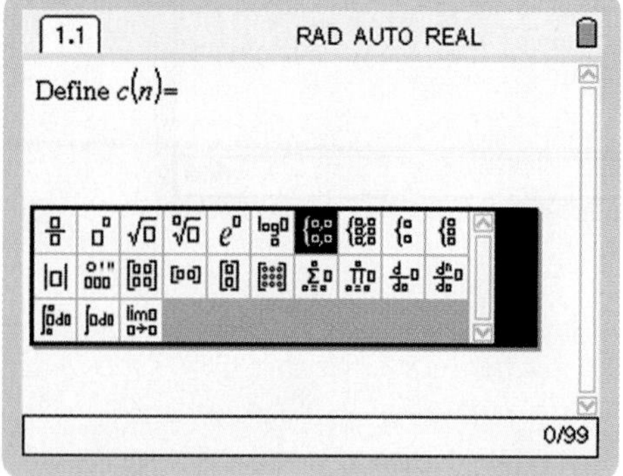

Modeling a Recursively Defined Function (continued)

3. Press tab to move from box to box.

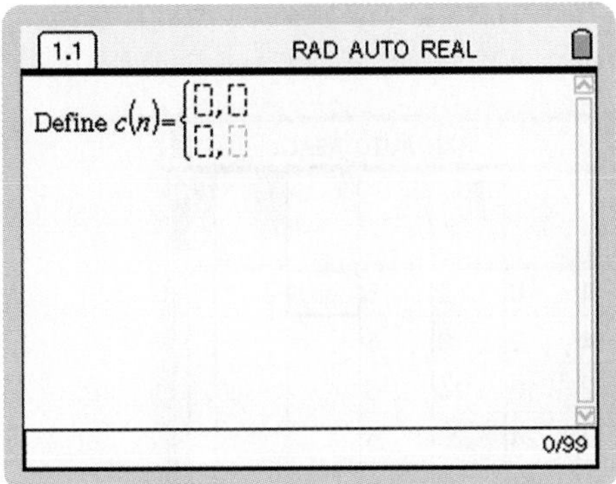

4. Press enter to complete the definition.

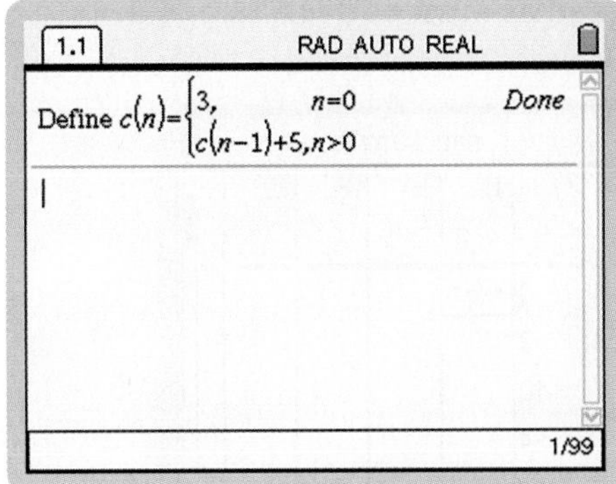

Making a Difference Table in a Spreadsheet, Lesson 5.7

1. Start with the input in column A of a spreadsheet, and the output in column B.

	A	B	C	D	E	F	G
1	0	-4					
2	1	-4					
3	2	-2					
4	3	8					
5	4	32					

C1

2. Navigate to cell C1. Type = B 2 − B 1. Press enter.

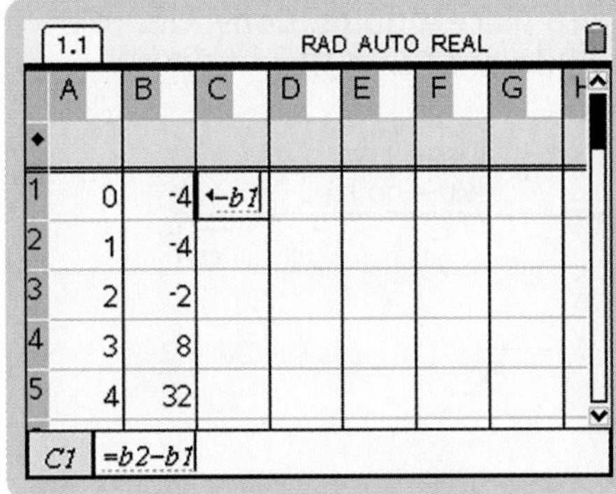

3. Navigate back to cell C1. Choose **Fill Down** from the **Data** menu.

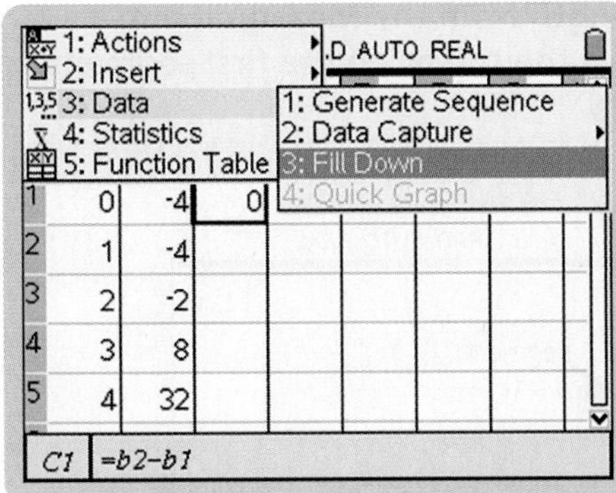

4. Press ▽ to outline the desired area to fill down. Press enter.

	A	B	C	D	E	F	G
8	7	248					
9	8	388					
10	9	572					
11	10	806					
12							

C1 =b2−b1

TI-Nspire Handbook

Making a Difference Table in a Spreadsheet (continued)

5. To make a column of second differences, navigate to cell D1. Type = c 2 − c 1. Then proceed as in steps 3–4.

1.1 RAD AUTO REAL

	A	B	C	D	E	F	G	H
◆								
1	0	-4	0	←c1				
2	1	-4	2					
3	2	-2	10					
4	3	8	24					
5	4	32	44					

D1 =c2–c1

6. Make additional difference columns in a similar way.

1.1 RAD AUTO REAL

	A	B	C	D	E	F	G	H
◆								
1	0	-4	0	2	6			
2	1	-4	2	8	6			
3	2	-2	10	14	6			
4	3	8	24	20	6			
5	4	32	44	26	6			

F1

Constructing an Ellipse, Lesson 6.6

1. Choose **Point** from the **Points & Lines** menu. Press enter to place a point. Construct two points. Label them *F1* and *F2*.

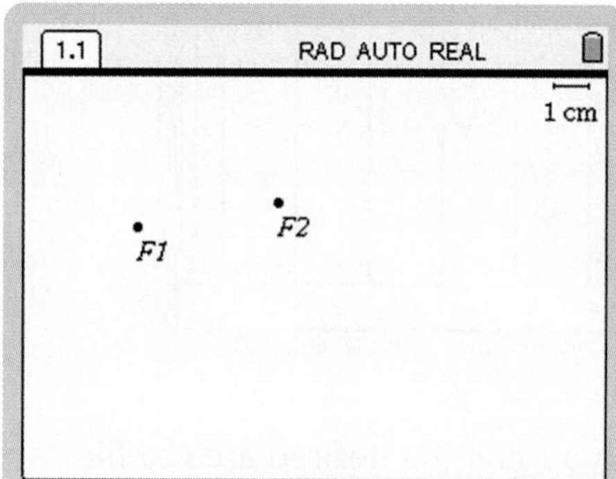

2. Choose **Segment** from the **Points & Lines** menu. Construct a segment with one endpoint at *F1*.

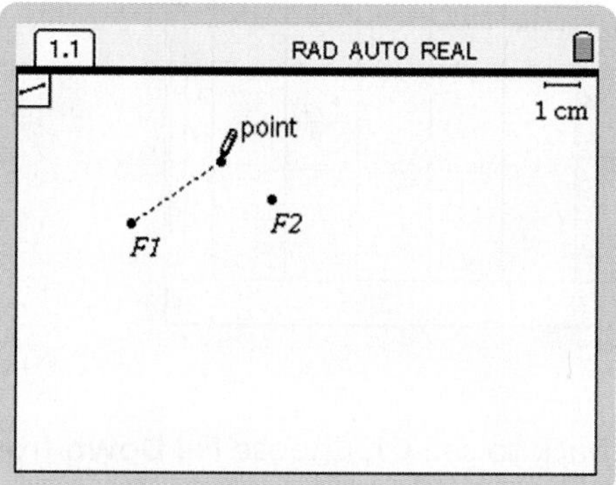

3. Construct a segment that shares an endpoint with the segment from step 2, and with the other endpoint at *F2*.

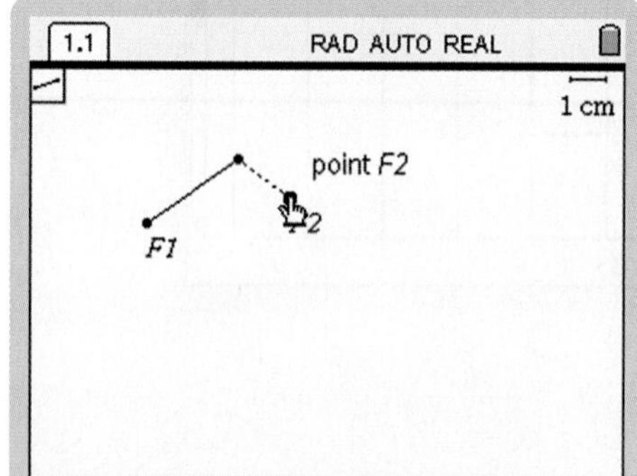

4. Choose **Length** from the **Measurement** menu. Place the cursor on the first segment. Press enter.

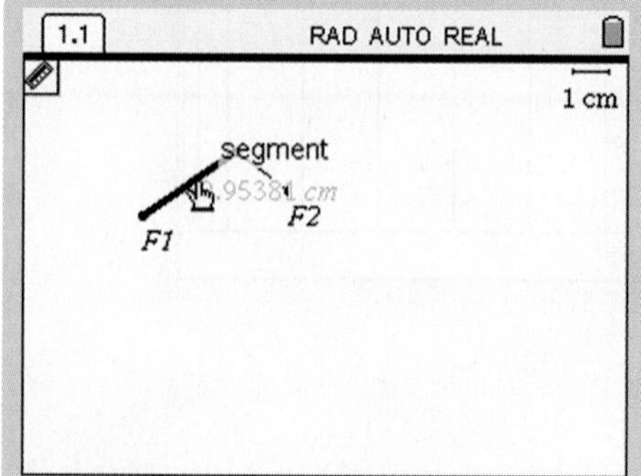

Constructing an Ellipse (continued)

5. Move the cursor to drag the length to the desired location. Press enter to anchor it.

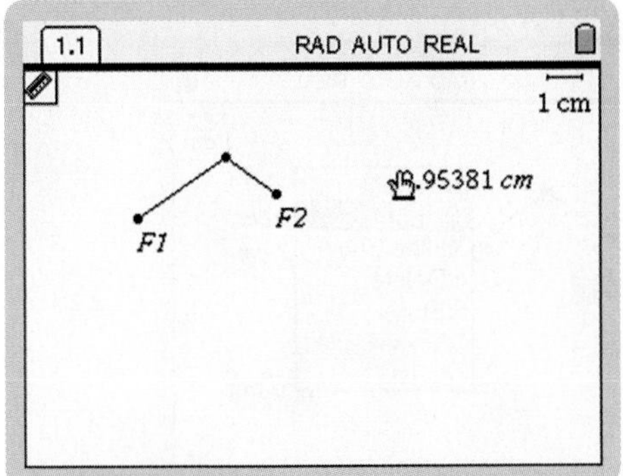

6. Measure the length of the other segment in a similar way.

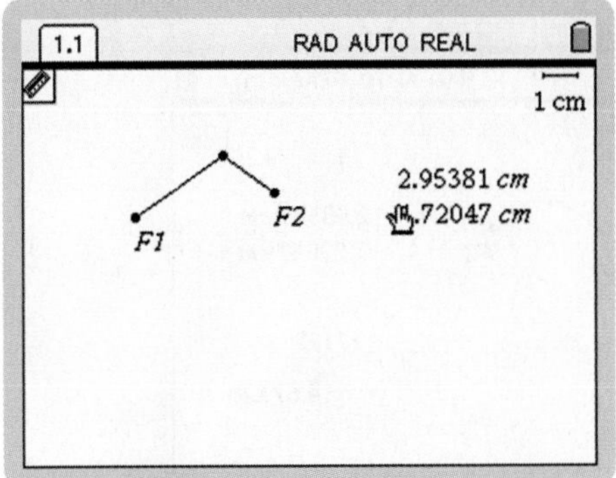

7. Choose **Text** from the **Actions** menu. Press enter on an open area of the screen. Press S 1 + S 2. Press enter.

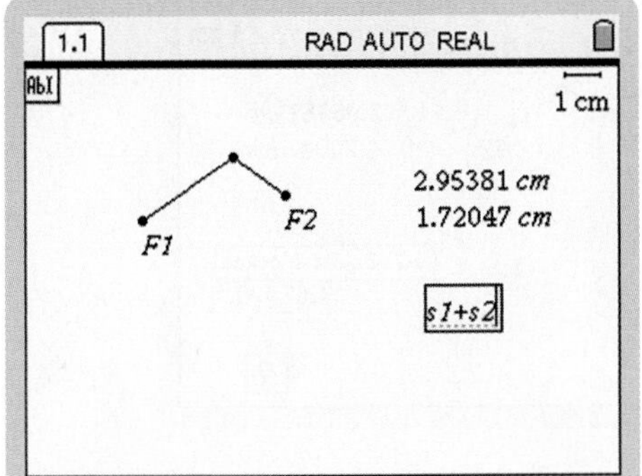

8. Choose **Calculate** from the **Actions** menu. Place the cursor on the expression *s*1 + *s*2. Press enter.

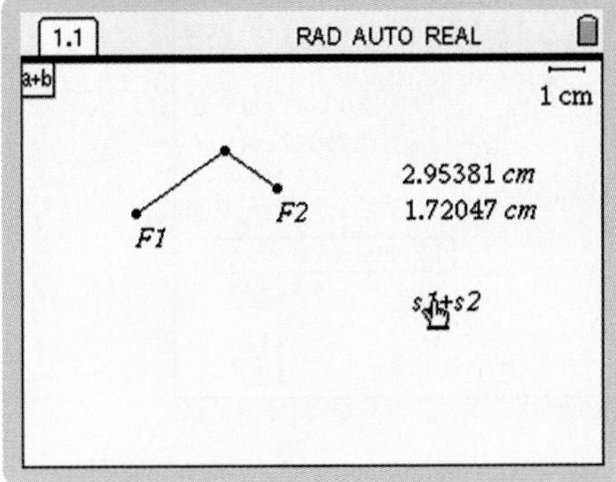

9. Place the cursor on the first segment length. Press enter.

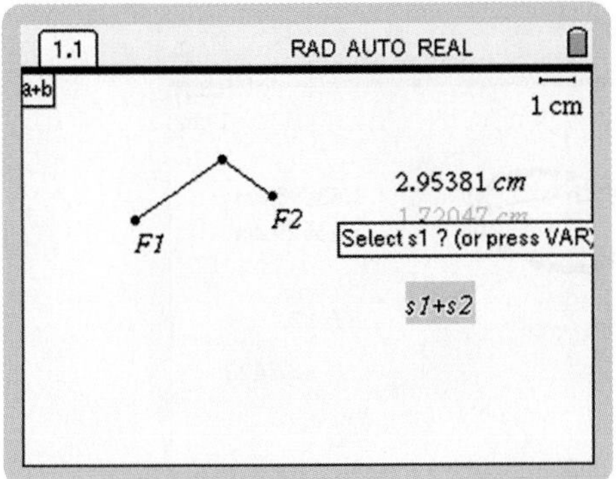

10. Place the cursor on the second segment length. Press enter.

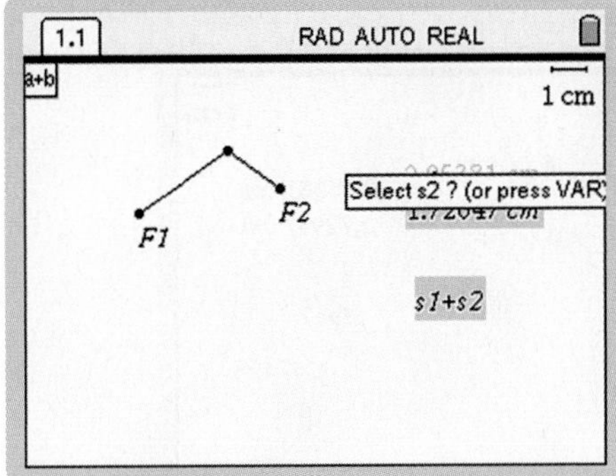

Constructing an Ellipse (continued)

11. Move the cursor to drag the result of the calculation to the desired location. Press enter to anchor it.

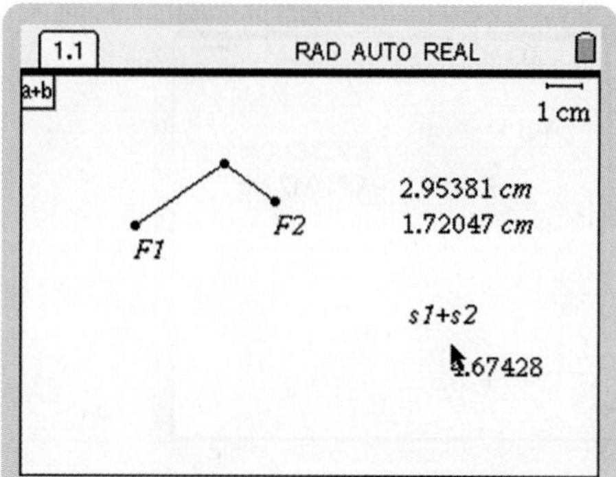

12. Place the cursor on the result of the calculation. Press ctrl menu. Choose **Attributes**.

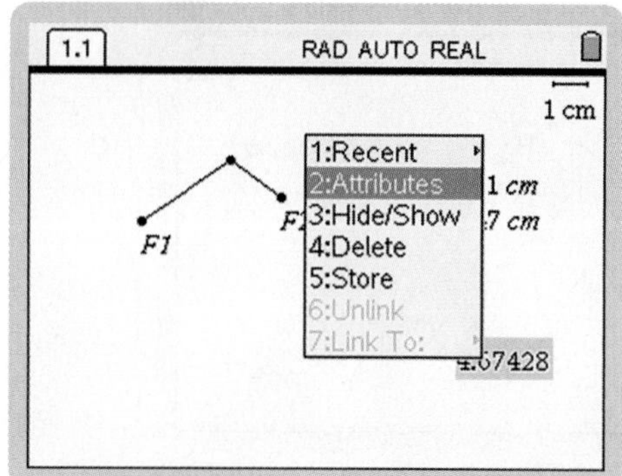

13. Press ▽ to select the Lock/Unlock attribute.

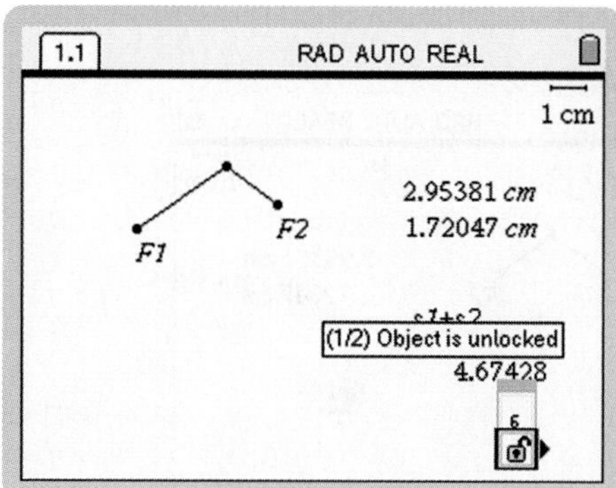

14. Press ▷ enter to lock the sum.

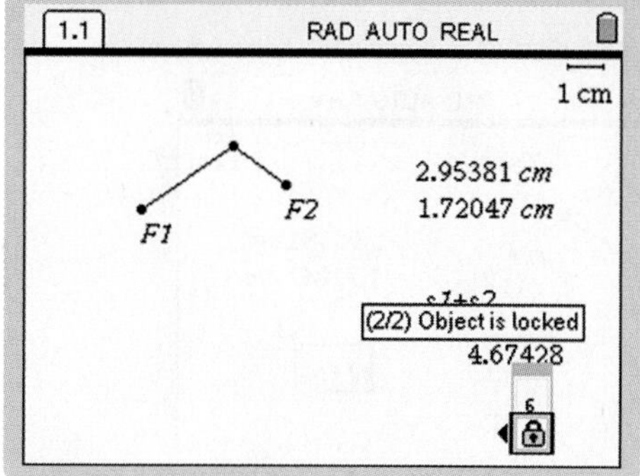

15. Choose **Geometry Trace** from the **Trace** menu. Place the cursor on the common endpoint of the two segments. Press enter. Press ctrl to grab the point.

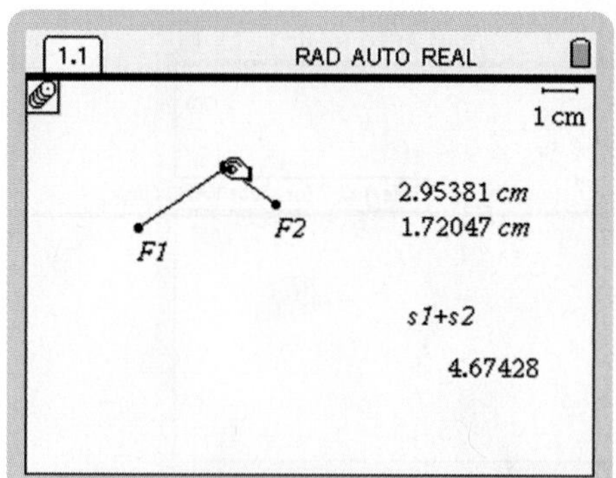

16. Drag the point. The sum of the lengths of the two segments remains constant. The point traces the path of an ellipse.

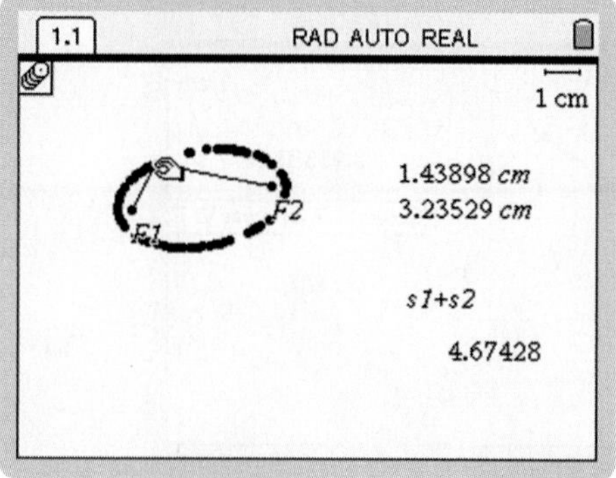

Constructing a Parabola, Lesson 6.6

1. Choose **Line** from the **Points & Lines** menu. Draw the directrix. Label the line *d*.

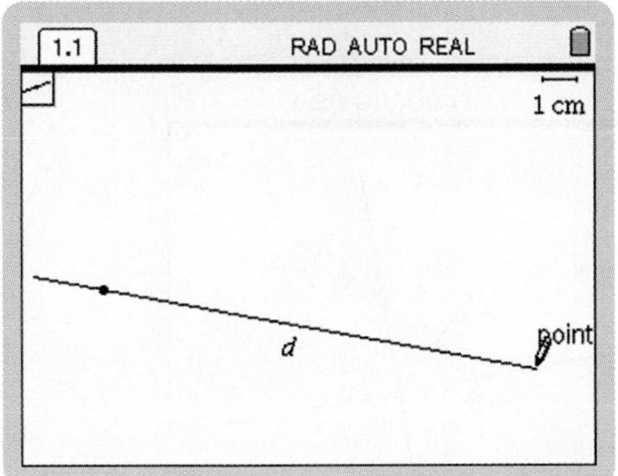

2. Choose **Point** from the **Points & Lines** menu. Place the focus on the screen. Label the point *F*.

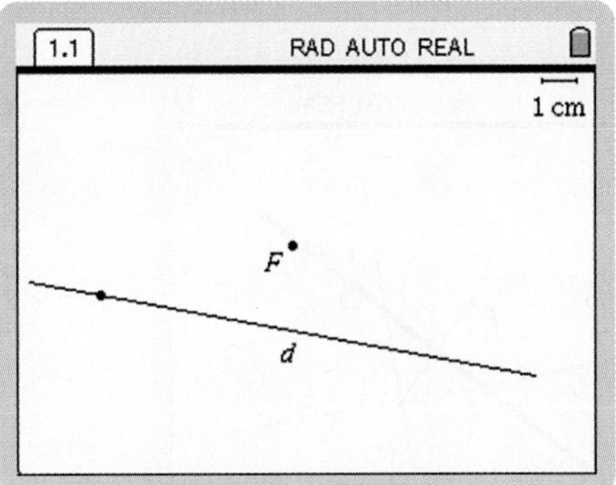

3. Choose **Segment** from the **Points & Lines** menu. Place the cursor on line *d*. Press **enter**. Place the cursor on point *F*. Press **enter**.

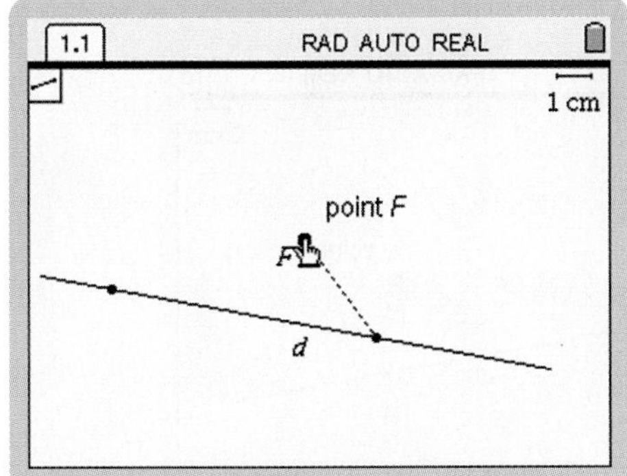

4. Choose **Perpendicular Bisector** from the **Construction** menu. Place the cursor on the segment. Press **enter**.

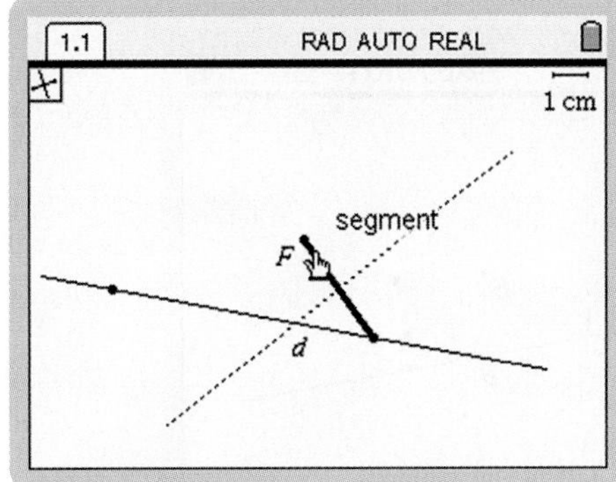

5. Choose **Perpendicular** from the **Construction** menu. Place the cursor on line *d*. Press **enter**. Place the cursor on the intersection of line *d* and the segment. Press **enter**.

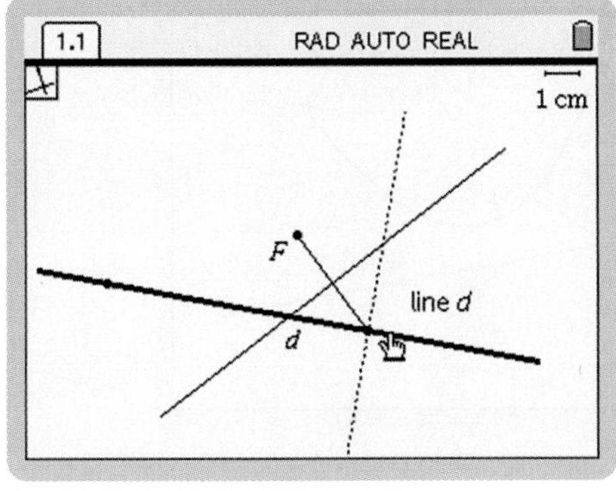

6. Choose **Intersection Point(s)** from the **Points & Lines** menu. Place the cursor on the perpendicular line you constructed in step 5. Press **enter**.

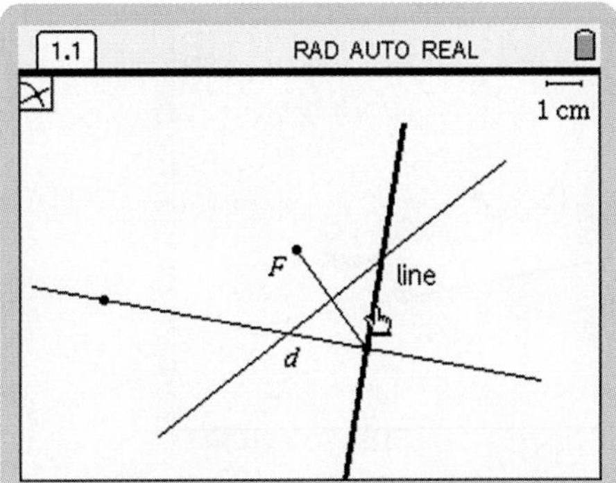

Constructing a Parabola (continued)

7. Place the cursor on the perpendicular bisector you constructed in step 4. Press enter.

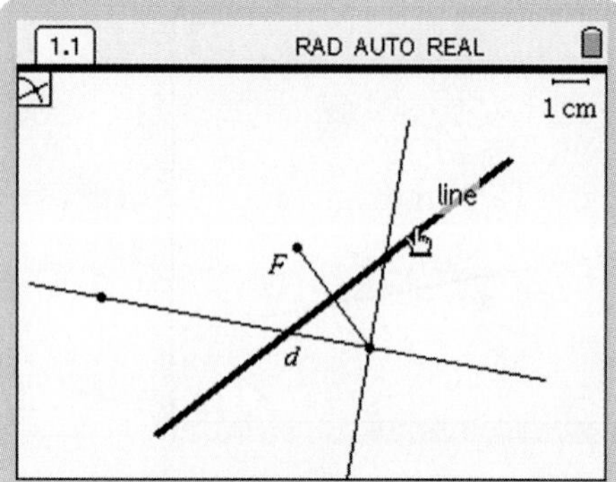

8. Choose **Hide/Show** from the **Actions** menu. Place the cursor on the perpendicular bisector from step 4. Press enter to hide the line.

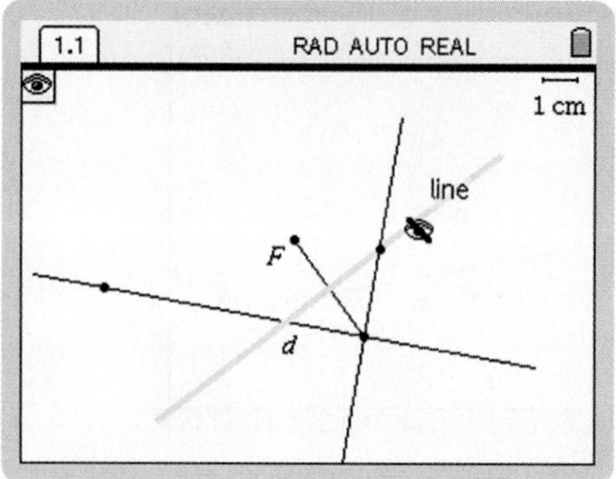

9. Hide the segment and the line perpendicular to the directrix in the same way.

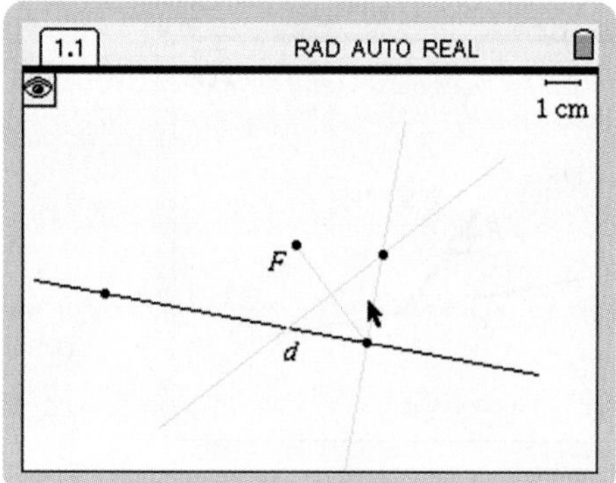

10. Choose **Locus** from the **Construction** menu. Place the cursor on the intersection point you constructed in step 7. Press enter.

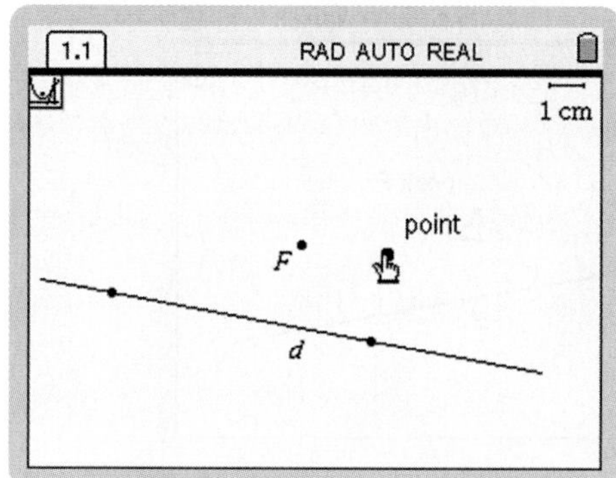

11. Place the cursor on the intersection of the directrix and the segment you constructed in step 3.

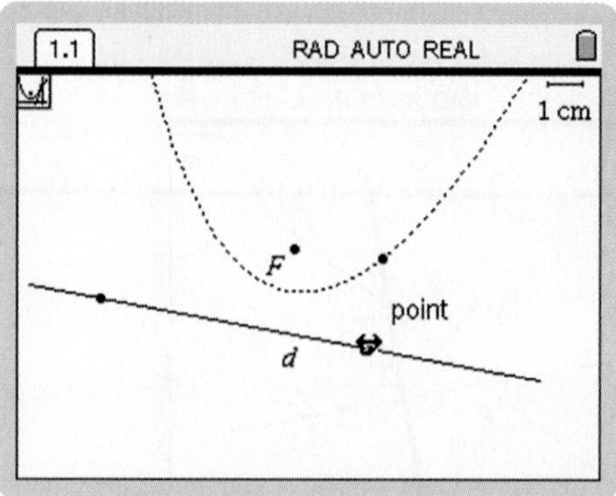

12. Press enter to construct the parabola.

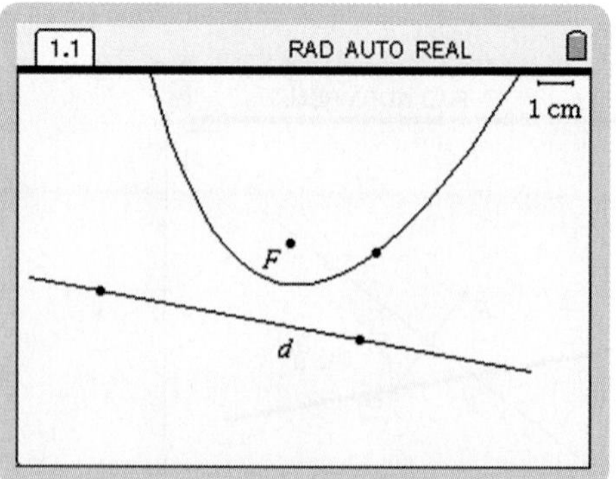

Constructing a Hyperbola, Lesson 6.6

1. Choose **Point** from the **Points & Lines** menu. Place two points on the screen. Label them *F1* and *F2*.

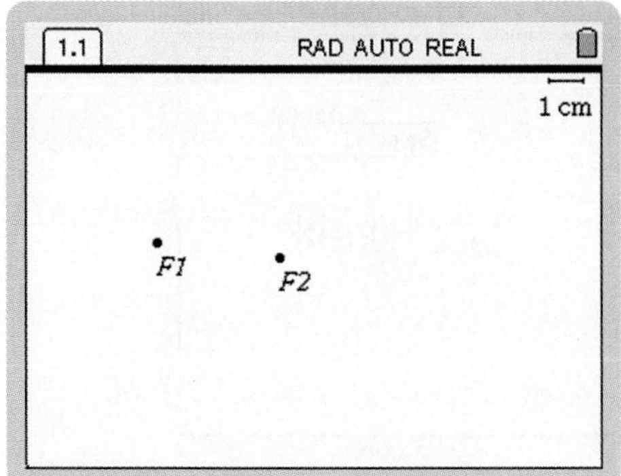

2. Choose **Segment** from the **Points & Lines** menu. Construct two segments with endpoints *F1* and *F2* that have a common endpoint.

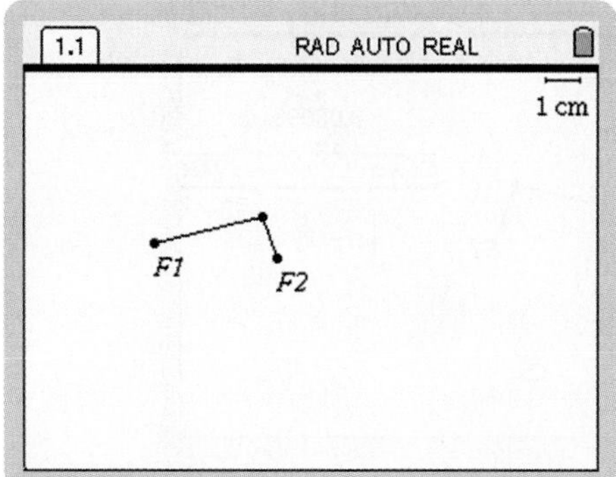

3. Choose **Length** from the **Measurement** menu. Place the cursor on the first segment. Press **enter**. Move the cursor to drag the length to the desired location. Press **enter** to anchor it.

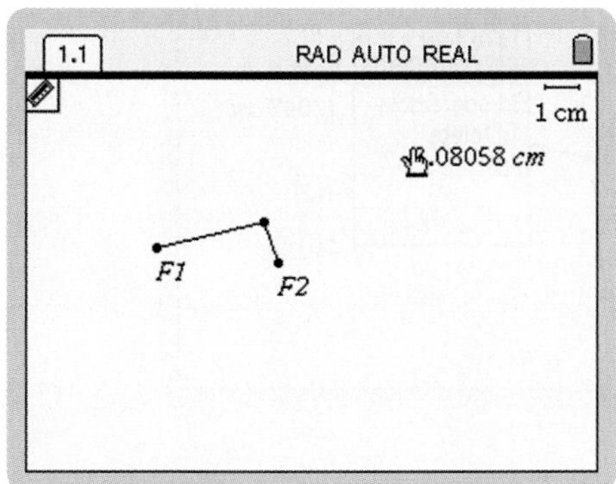

4. Find the length of the second segment in the same way.

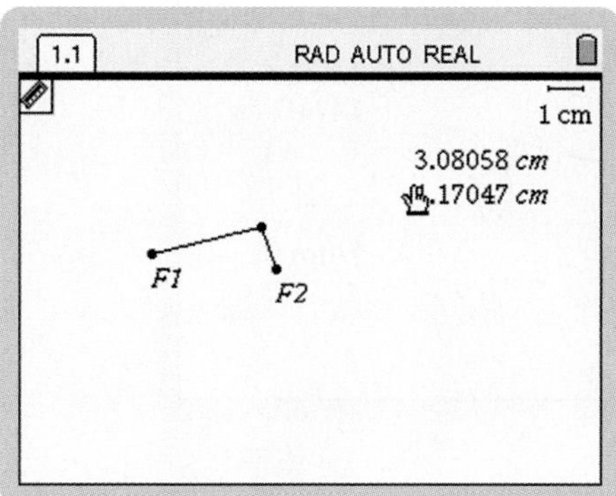

5. Choose **Text** from the **Actions** menu. Click on an open part of the screen. Type **A** **B** **S** **(** **S** **1** **−** **S** **2** **)**. Press **enter**.

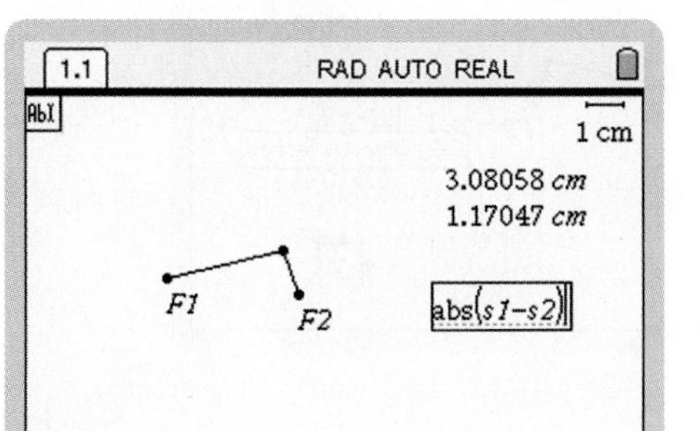

6. Choose **Calculate** from the **Actions** menu. Place the cursor on the text you wrote in step 5. Press **enter**.

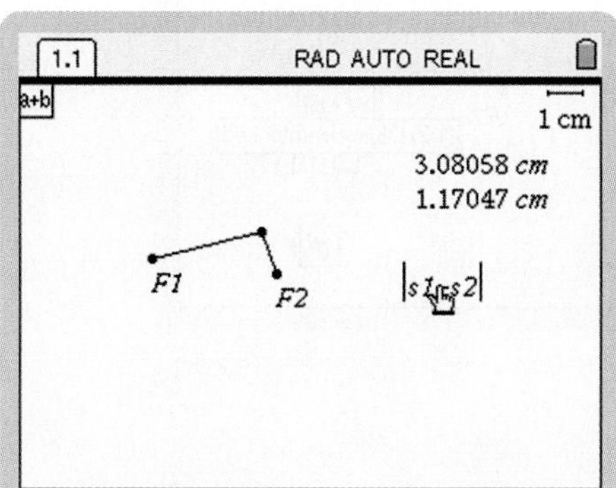

Constructing a Hyperbola (continued)

7. Place the cursor on the first length.
Press enter.

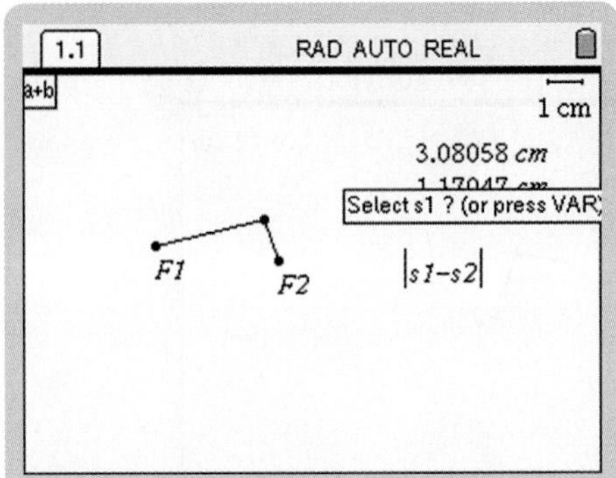

8. Place the cursor on the second length.
Press enter.

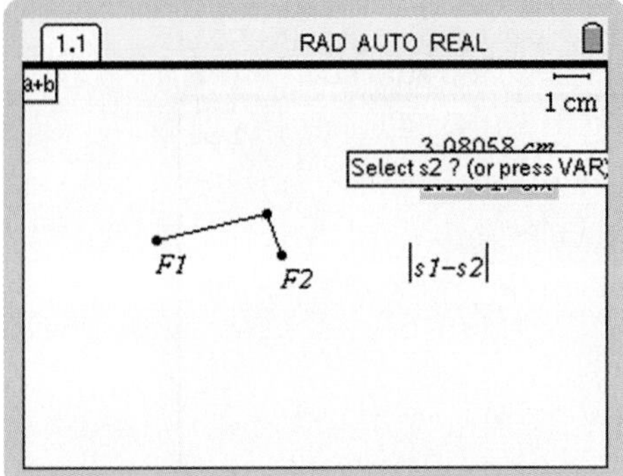

9. Move the cursor to drag the result of the calculation to the desired location.
Press enter to anchor it.

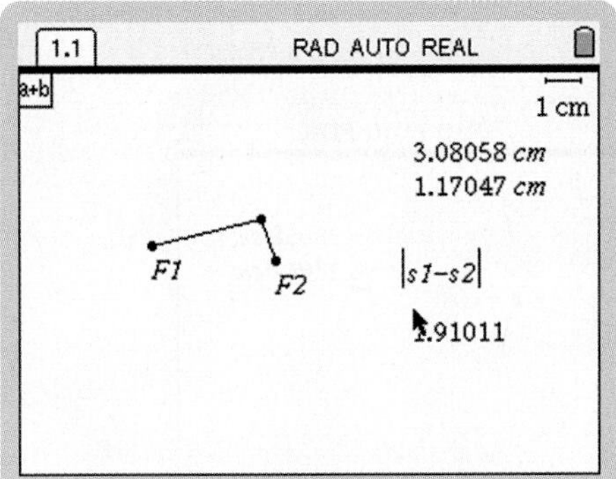

10. Place the cursor on the result of the calculation.
Press ctrl menu. Choose **Attributes**.

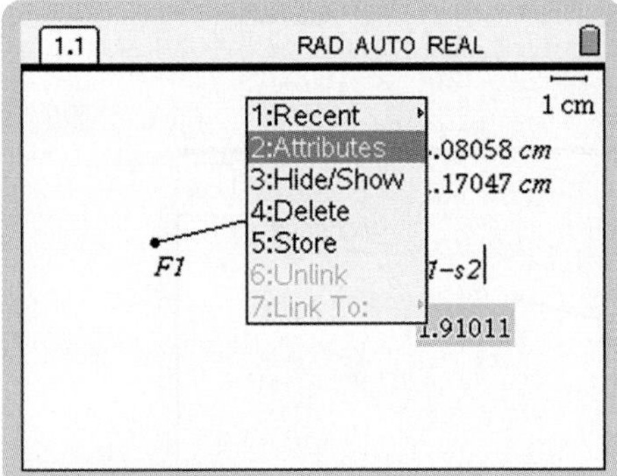

11. Press ▽ to select the Lock/Unlock attribute.

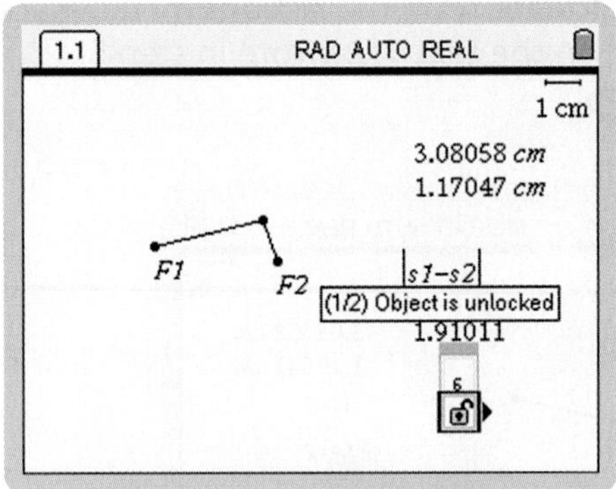

12. Press ▷ enter to lock the value of $|s1 - s2|$.

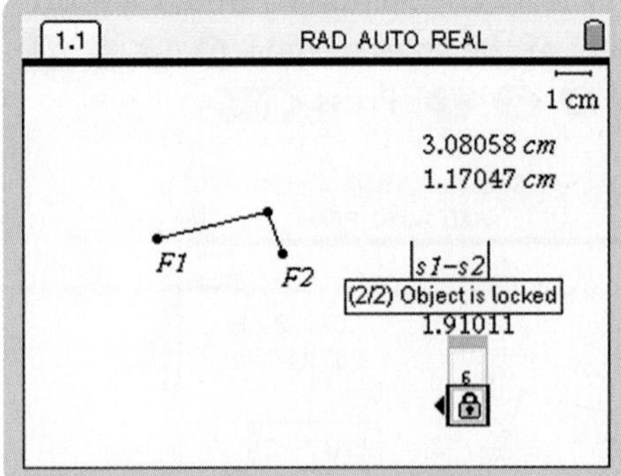

Constructing a Hyperbola (continued)

13. Choose **Geometry Trace** from the **Trace** menu. Place the cursor on the common endpoint of the two segments. Press enter. Press ctrl click to grab the point.

14. Drag the point. The absolute value of the difference of the lengths of the two segments remains constant. The point traces the path of an ellipse.

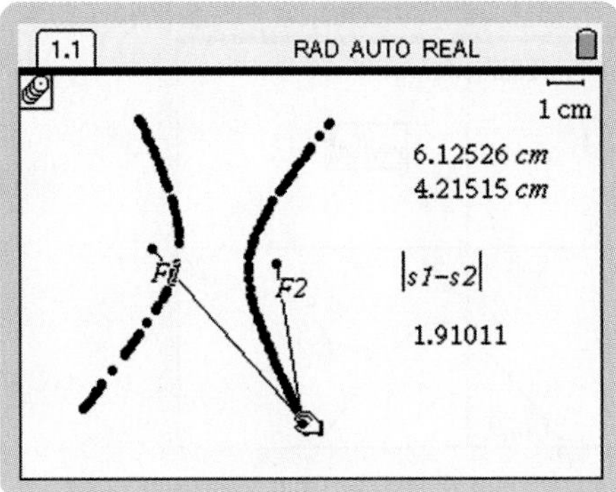

Graphing General Conic Sections, Chapter 6 Project

1. Choose **Solve** from the **Algebra** menu. Type the equation solve. Press ,, then type the variable to solve for. Press enter.

2. Define g and h using the two solutions you got in step 1.

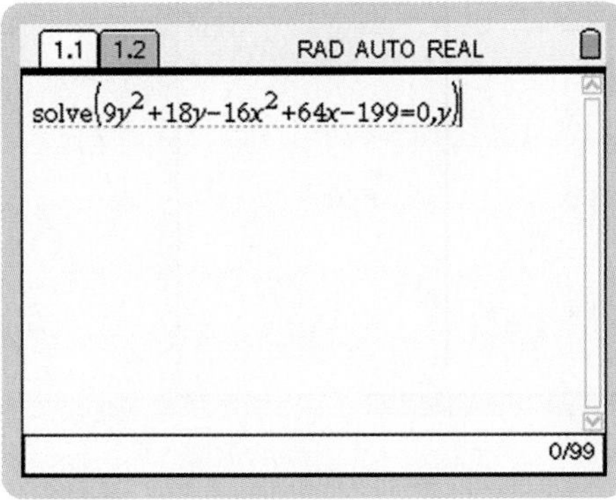

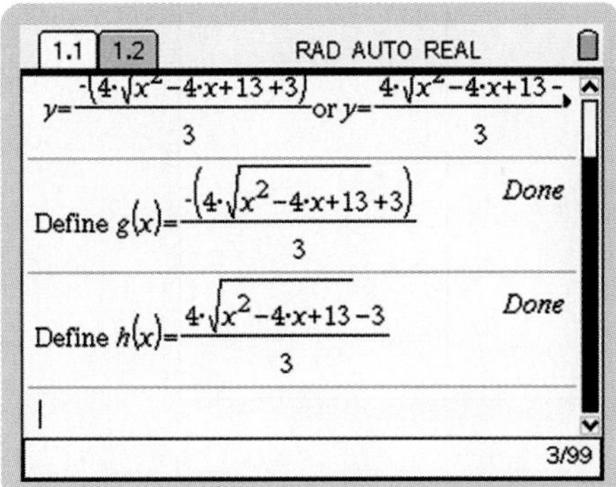

3. Navigate to the Graphs & Geometry application. Choose **Text** from the **Actions** menu. Click on an empty area of the screen. Press Y = G (X) enter.

4. Place the cursor on the equation $y = g(x)$. Press ctrl click to grab it. Drag it to an axis. Press enter to graph the equation.

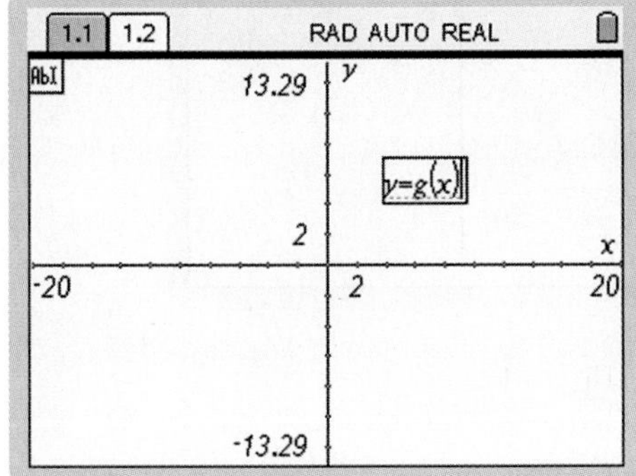

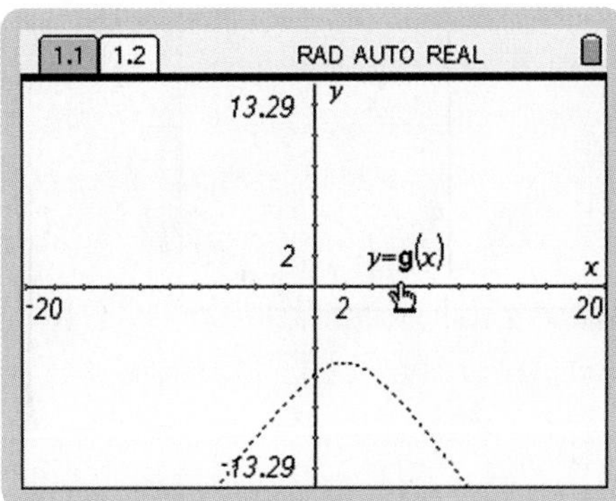

Graphing General Conic Sections (continued)

5. Choose **Text** from the **Actions** menu. Click on an empty area of the screen. Press Y = H (X) enter.

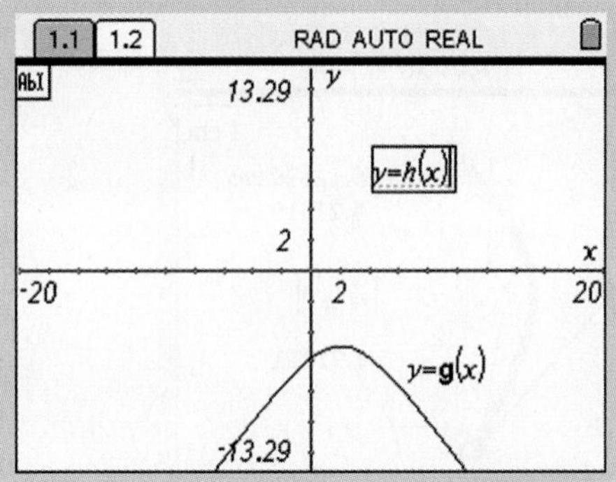

6. Place the cursor on the equation $y = h(x)$. Press ctrl to grab it. Drag it to an axis. Press enter to graph the equation.

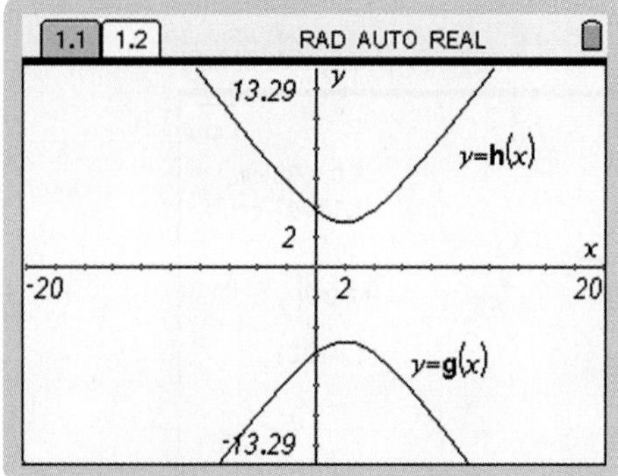

Constructing Conic Sections Using Eccentricity, Lesson 6.9

1. Draw the directrix and focus. Label them d and F respectively.

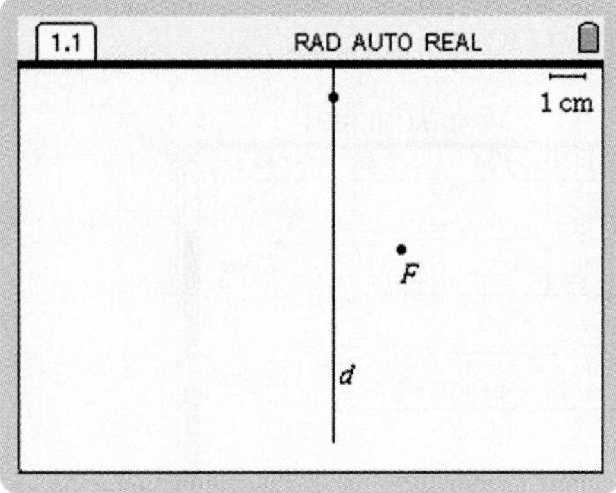

2. Draw two lines.

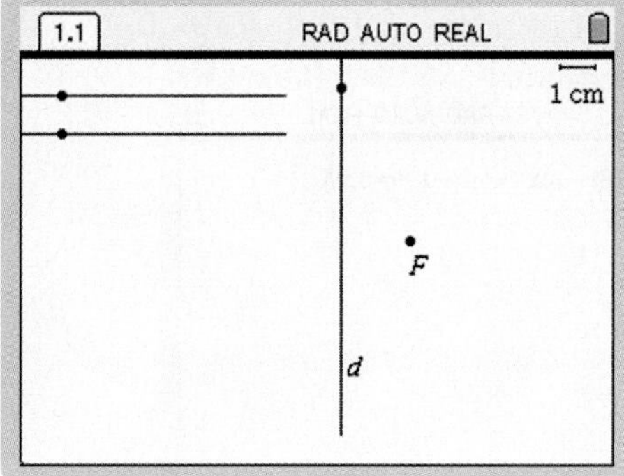

3. Construct a segment on each of the two lines you drew in step 2.

4. Use the **Hide/Show** tool to hide lines so that only the segments are visible.

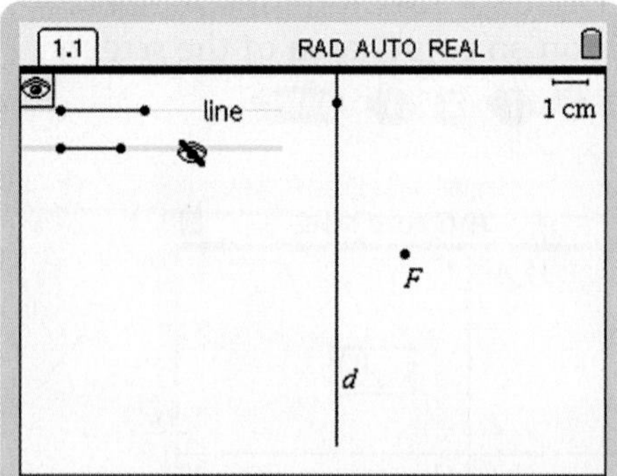

Constructing Conic Sections Using Eccentricity (continued)

5. Use the **Length** tool from the **Measurement** menu to measure the length of the bottom segment. Drag the length to an open area of the screen.

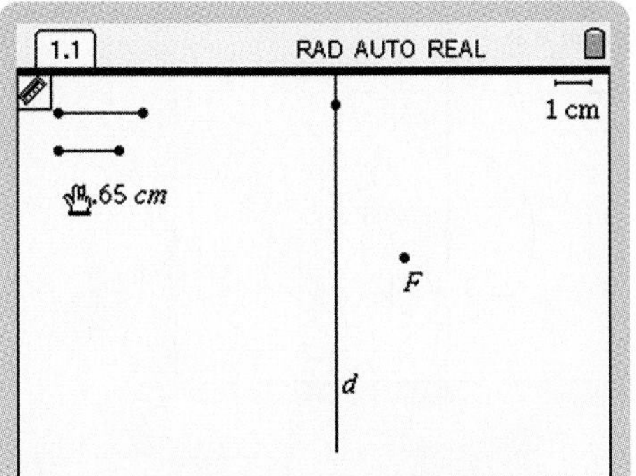

6. Double click on the length measurement. Move the cursor to the beginning of the text box. Press E = enter.

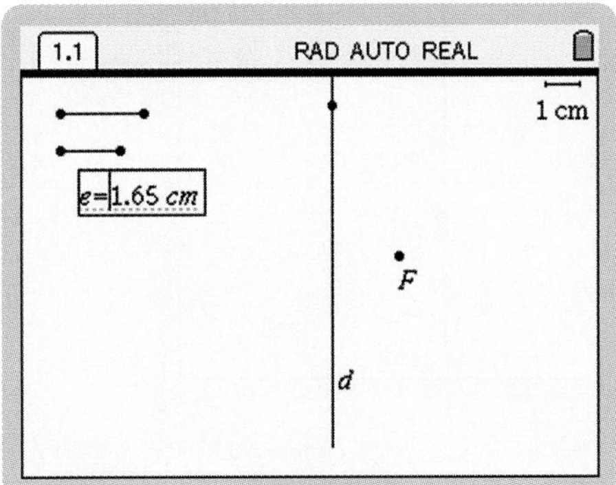

7. Choose **Dilate** from the **Transformation** menu. Place the cursor on the left endpoint of the top segment. Press enter.

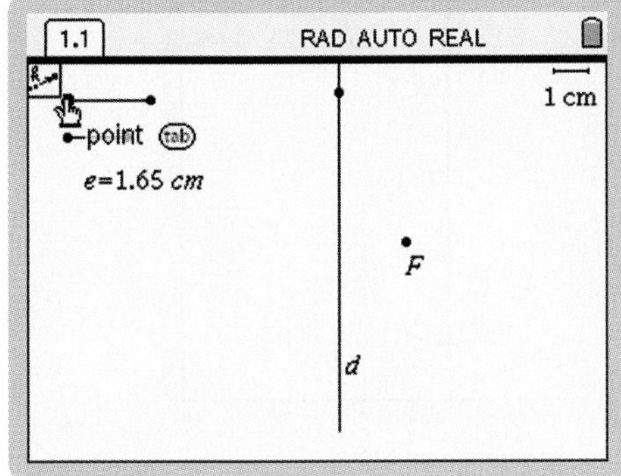

8. Place the cursor on the right endpoint of the top segment. Press enter.

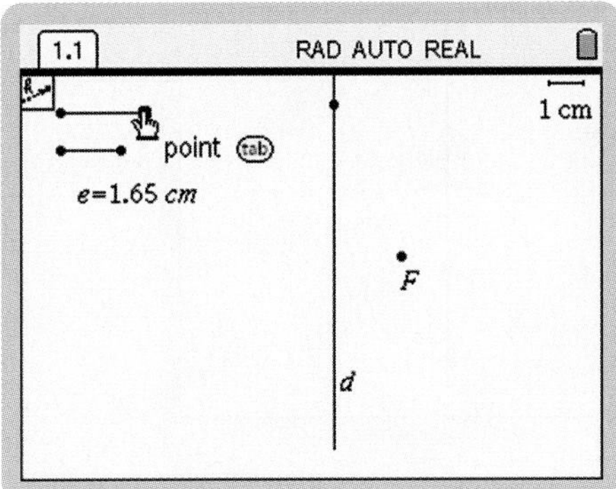

9. Place the cursor on the length measure. Press enter. A new point appears.

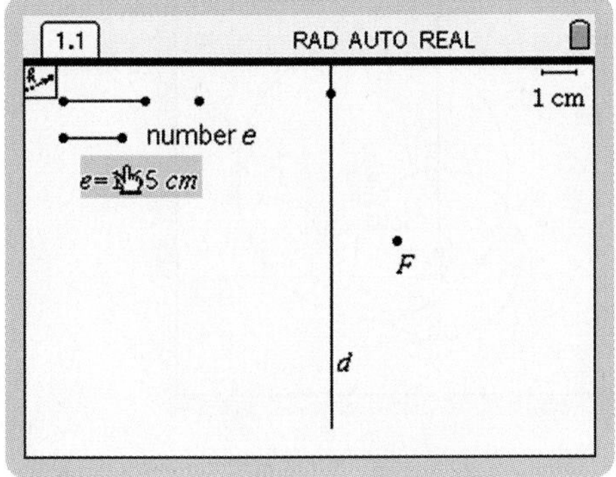

10. Choose **Compass** from the **Construction** menu. Place the cursor on the top segment. Press enter.

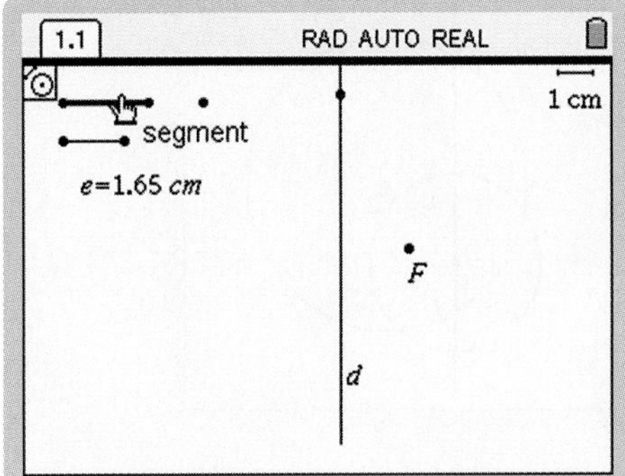

Constructing Conic Sections Using Eccentricity (continued)

11. Place the cursor on line *d*. Press enter.

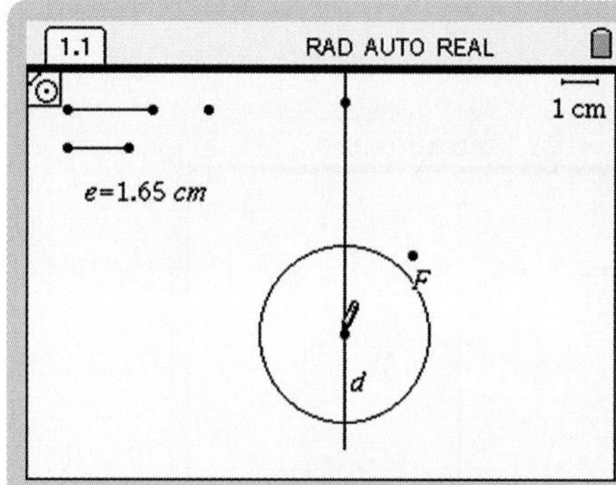

12. Use the **Hide/Show** tool to hide the top segment.

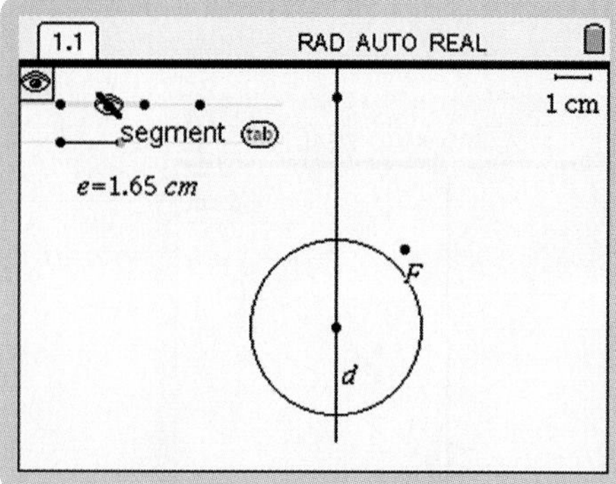

13. Construct a segment with one endpoint at the right endpoint of the segment you hid in step 12, and the other endpoint at the new point from step 9.

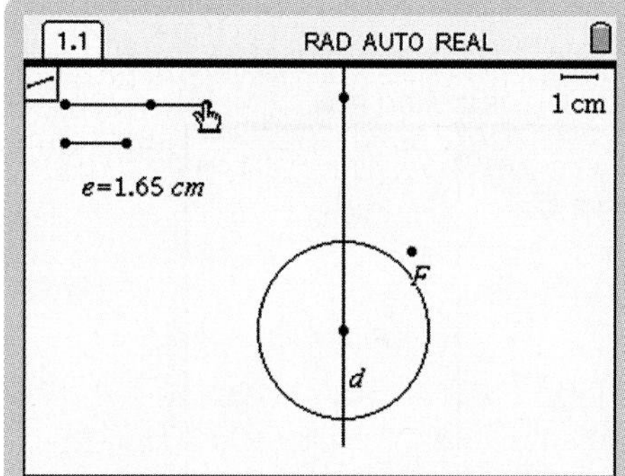

14. Choose **Compass** from the **Construction** menu. Place the cursor on the top segment. Press enter.

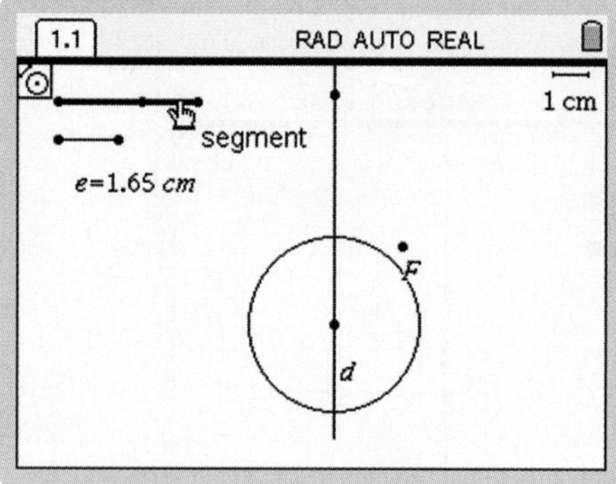

15. Place the cursor on the point *F*. Press enter.

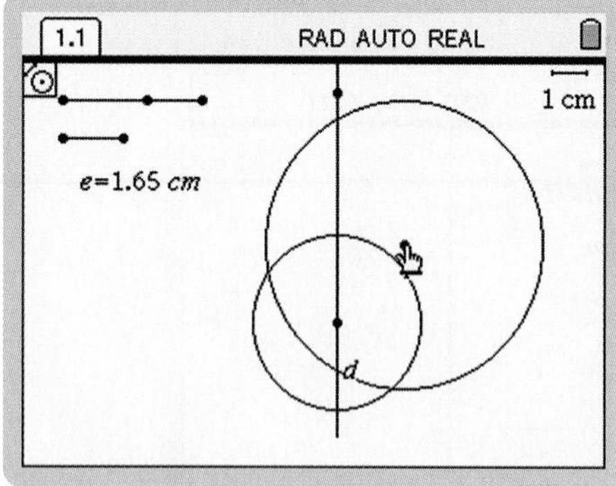

16. Choose **Perpendicular** from the **Construction** menu. Place the cursor on the center of the circle you constructed in step 11. Press enter.

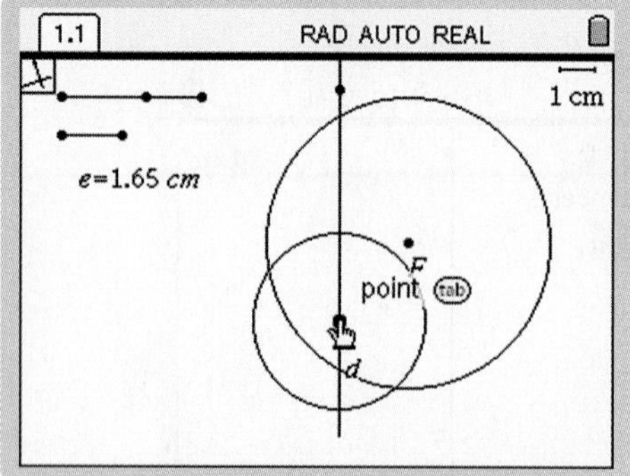

17. Place the cursor on the directrix. Press enter.

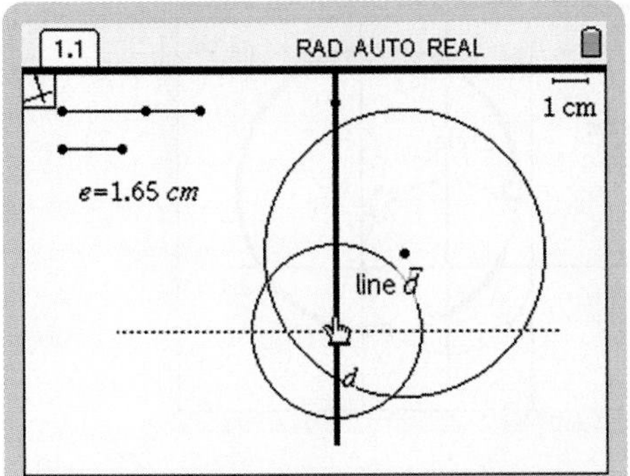

18. Choose **Intersection Point(s)** from the **Points & Lines** menu. Place the cursor on the line you constructed in step 17. Press enter.

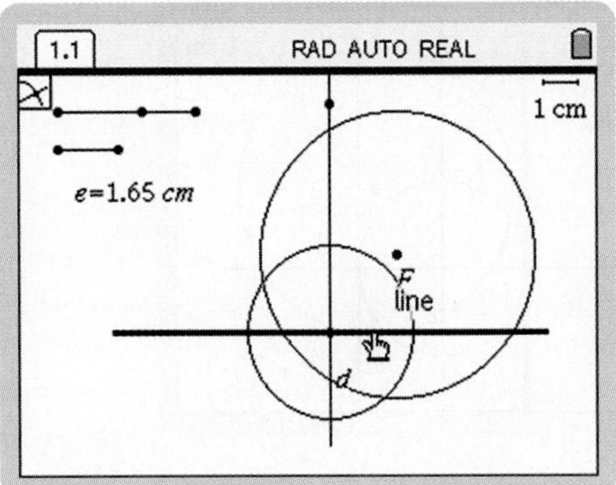

19. Place the cursor in the circle with center on the directrix. Press enter.

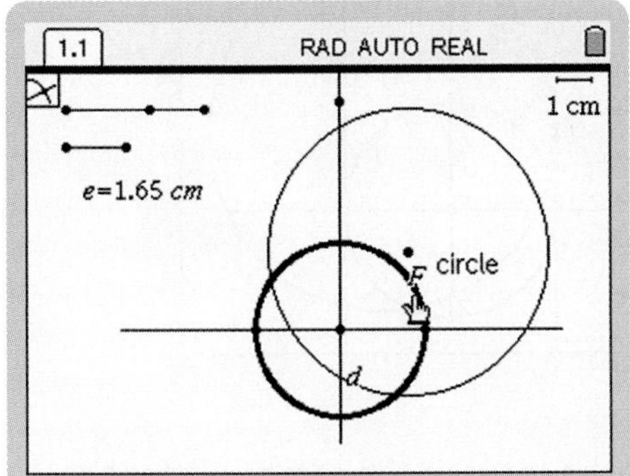

20. Construct lines through the resulting intersection points that are perpendicular to the line you constructed in step 17. Press enter.

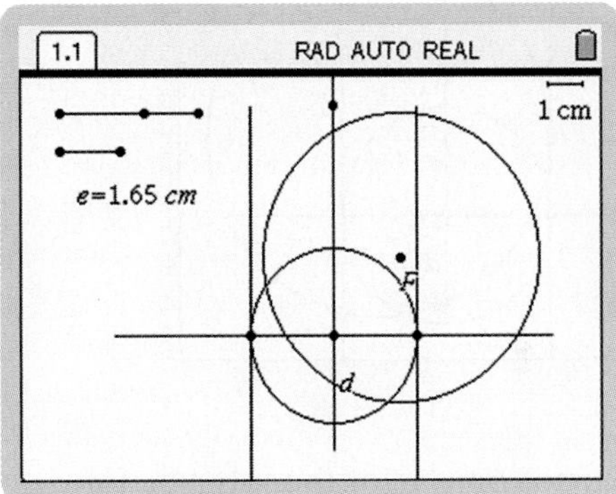

21. Choose **Intersection Point(s)** from the **Points & Lines** menu. Place the cursor on one of the lines you constructed in step 20. Press enter.

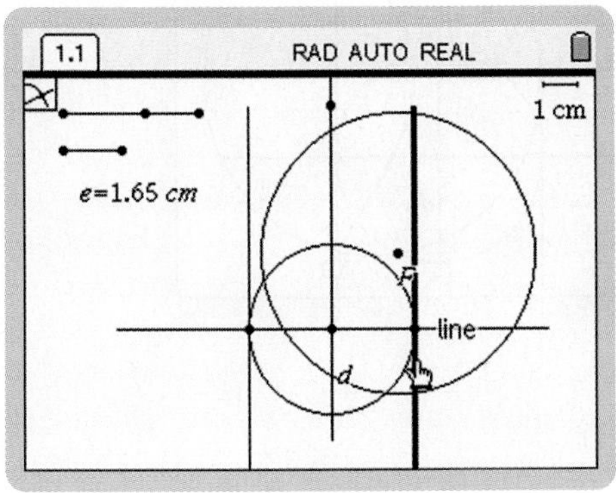

22. Place the cursor on the circle with center at *F*. Press enter.

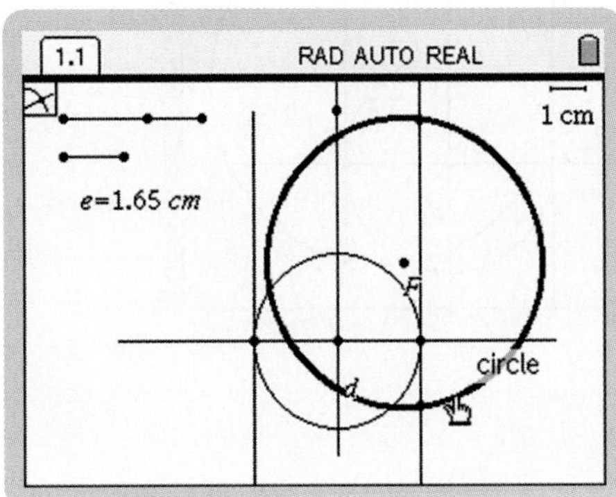

Constructing Conic Sections Using Eccentricity (continued)

23. Place the cursor on the other line you constructed in step 20. Press enter.

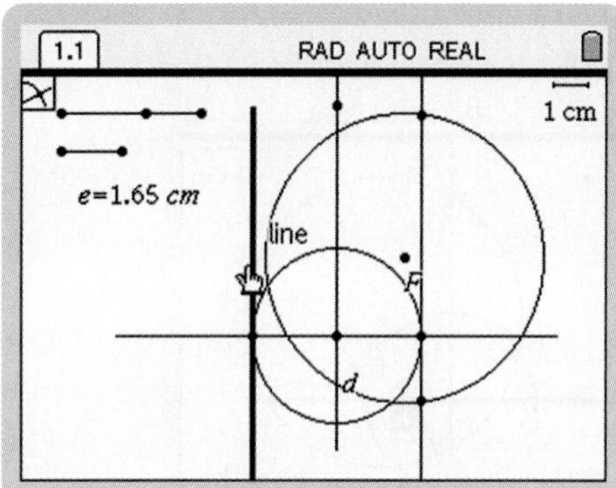

24. Place the cursor on the circle with center at *F*. Press enter.

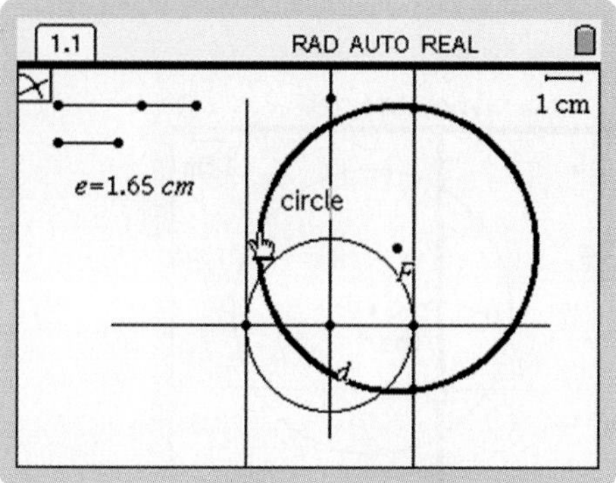

25. If there are no intersection points in step 24, drag the middle point in the top segment until intersection points appear.

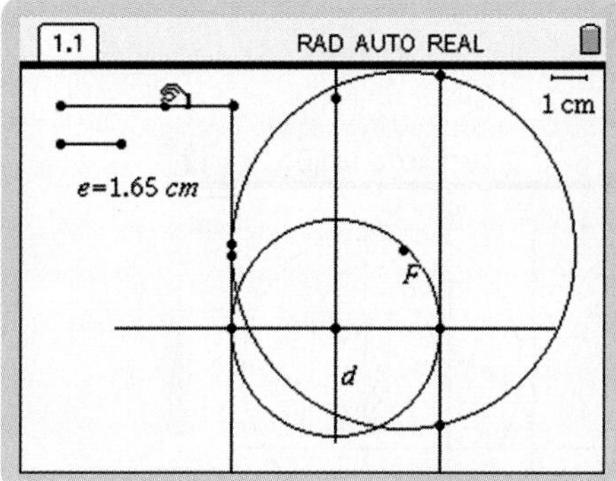

26. Choose **Locus** from the **Construction** menu. Place the cursor the middle point in the top segment. Press enter.

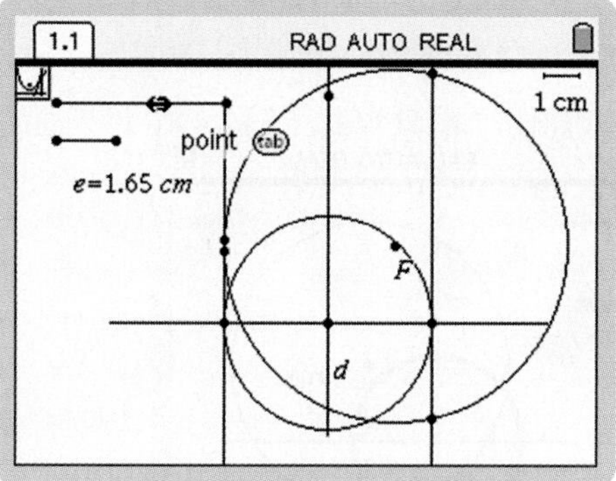

27. Place the cursor on one of the intersection points from step 22. Press enter.

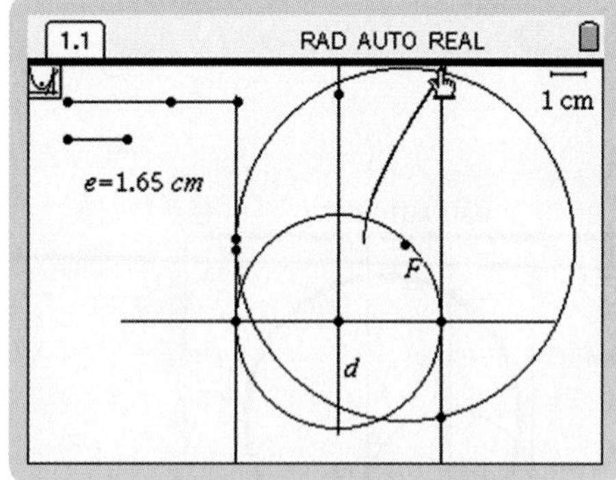

28. Construct the locus in the same way for the other intersection point.

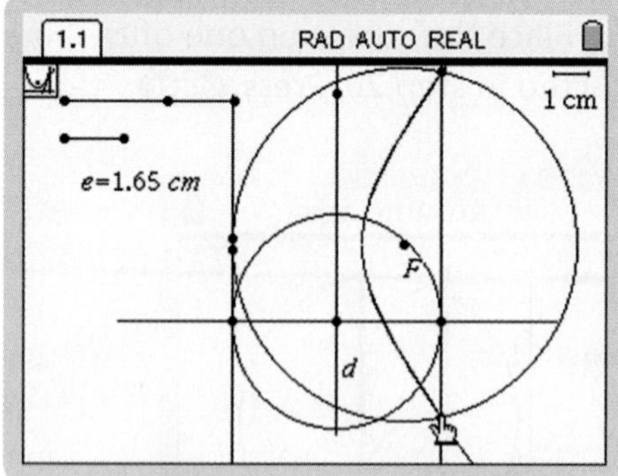

Constructing Conic Sections Using Eccentricity (continued)

29. Construct the loci in the same way for the other pair of intersection points.

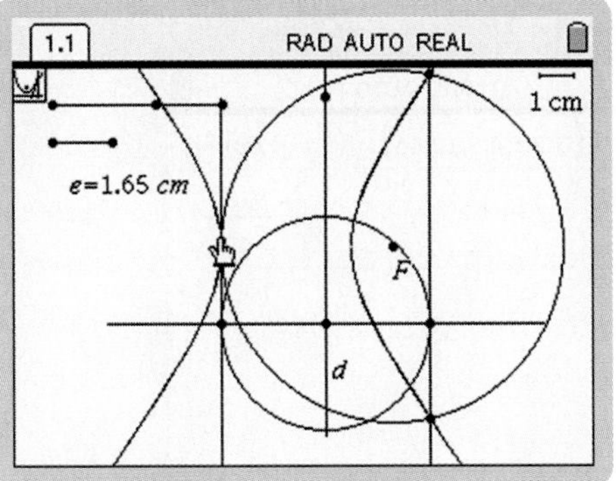

30. Use the **Hide/Show** tool from the **Actions** menu to hide the points and lines used in the construction.

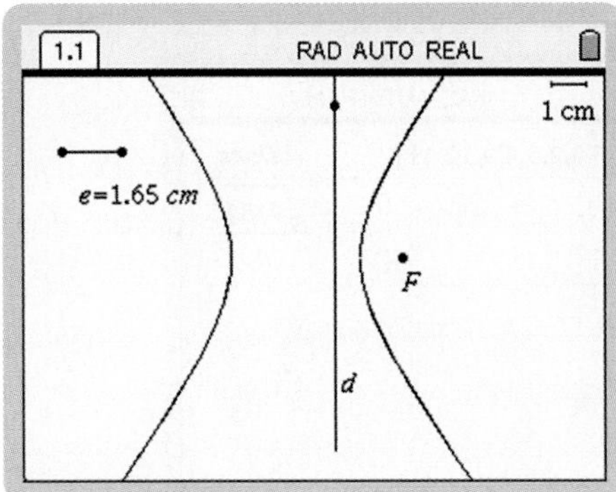

31. Drag one endpoint of the segment to change the value of e. When $e = 1$, the locus is a parabola.

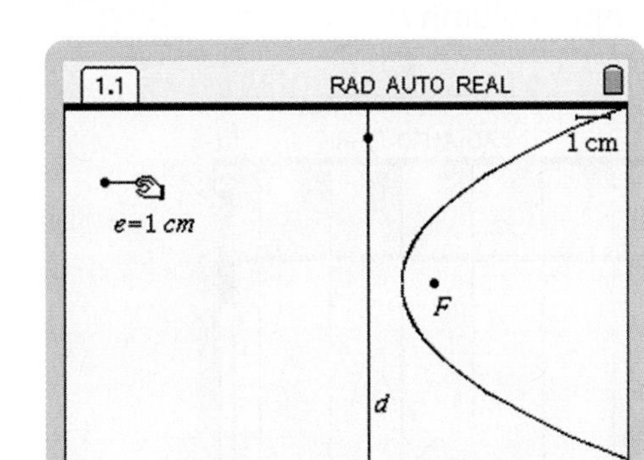

32. When $e < 1$, the locus is an ellipse.

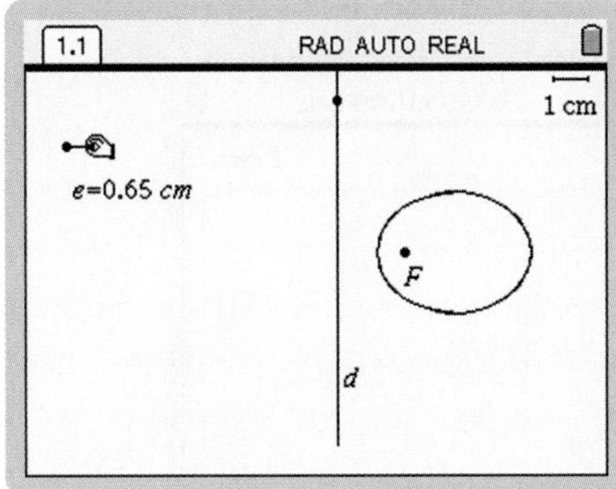

Expanding Expressions, Lessons 7.1, 7.3

1. Press E X P A N D (. Type an expression. Press enter.

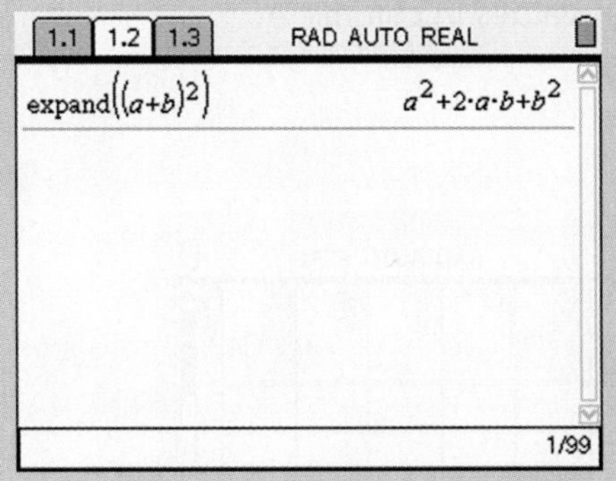

Calculating Standard Deviation and Variance, Lesson 7.7

1. Choose **List Math** from the **Statistics** menu. Choose **Population Standard Deviation**. Enter a list variable, or manually type a list in curly braces ({ and }) Press enter.

2. Choose **List Math** from the **Statistics** menu. Choose **Population Variance**. Enter a list variable, or manually type a list in curly braces ({ and }). Press enter.

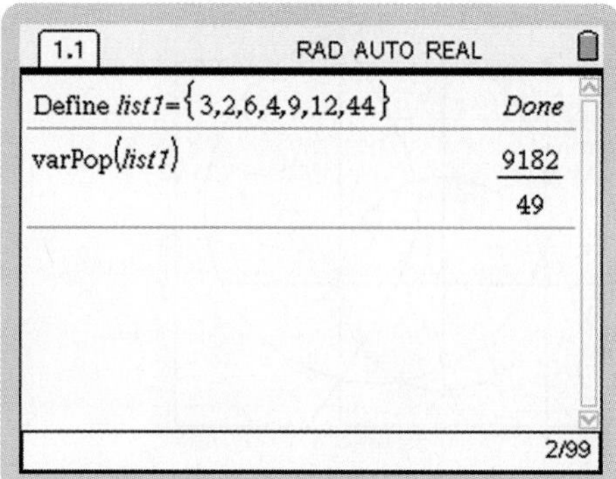

Making a Function Table, Lesson 7.10

1. Define a function *f*.

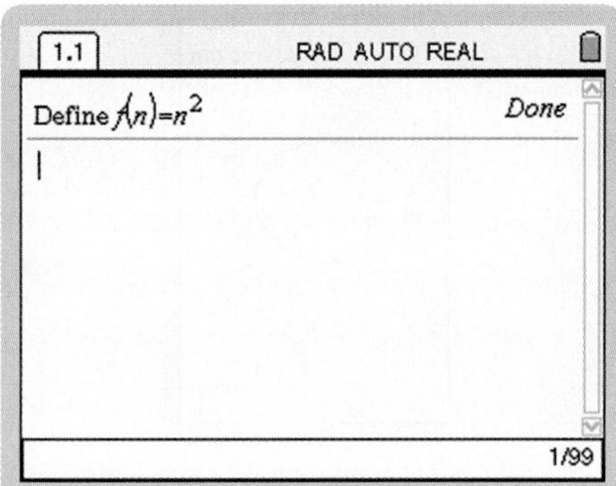

2. Navigate to the Lists & Spreadsheet application. Label the input column *n*.

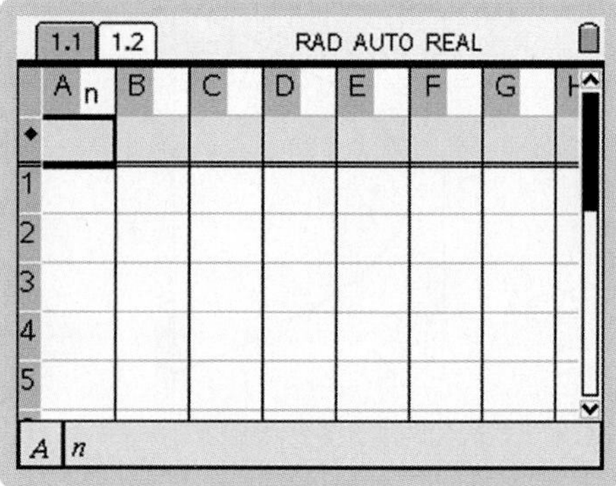

3. Enter input values in column A.

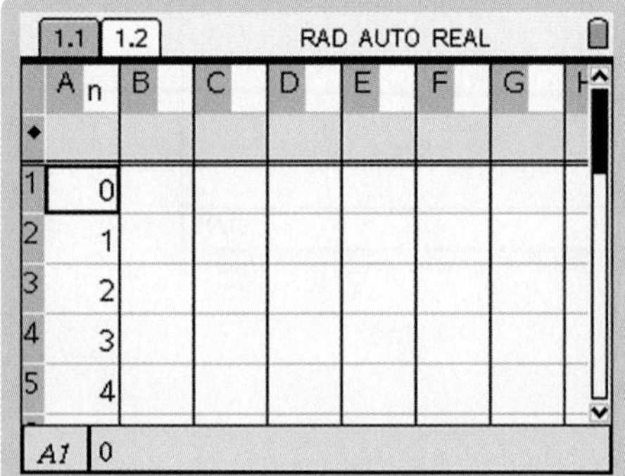

4. Navigate to the second row of the column header in column B. Press = F (' N ctrl (enter.

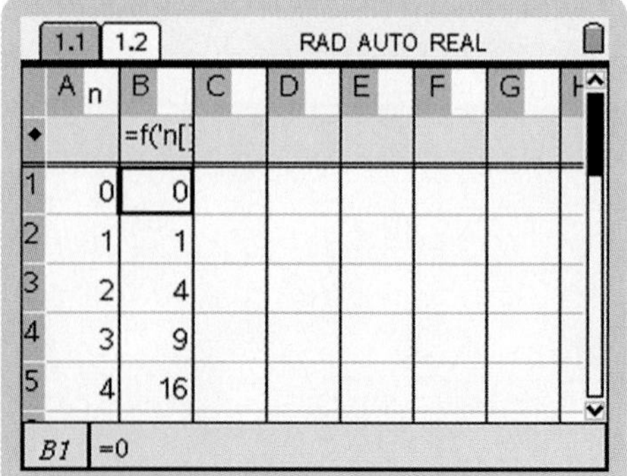

Making a Scatter Plot, Lesson 7.12

1. Column A consists of the value of *m* from 1 to 20. Column B consists of the probability of *m* successes in 20 trials, where each trial has a 0.5 probability of success.

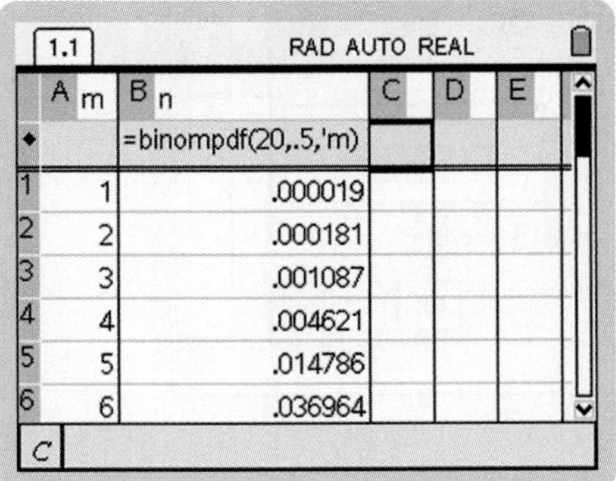

2. Navigate to the Data & Statistics application.

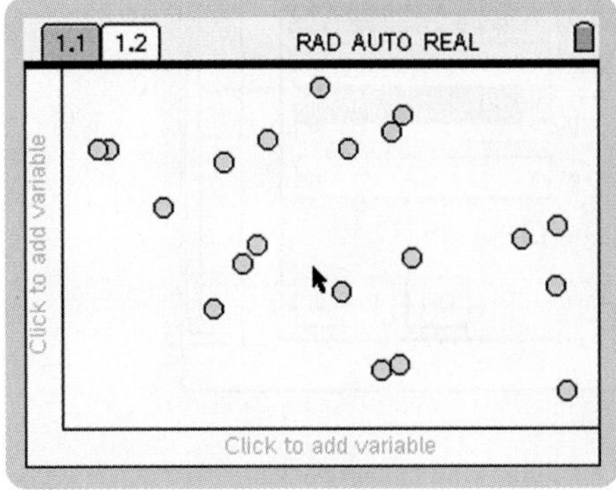

3. Click below the horizontal axis to add a variable. Choose the variable *m*.

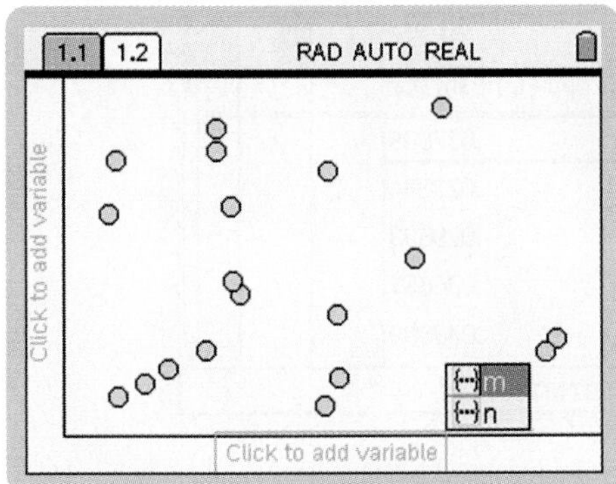

4. Click below the vertical axis to add a variable. Choose the variable *n*.

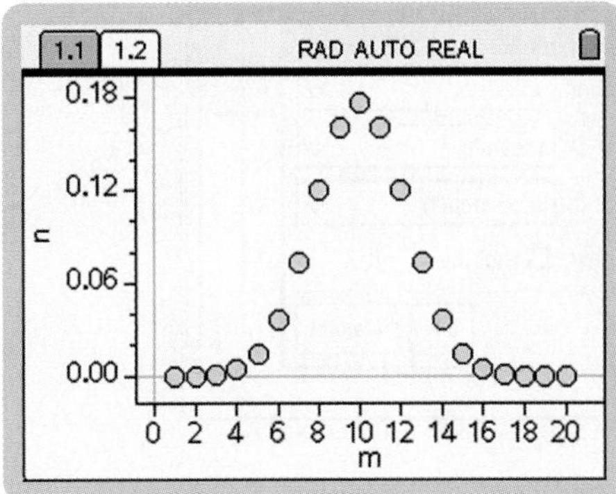

Defining a Normal Distribution, Lesson 7.12

1. Navigate to the second row of the column header in an empty column.

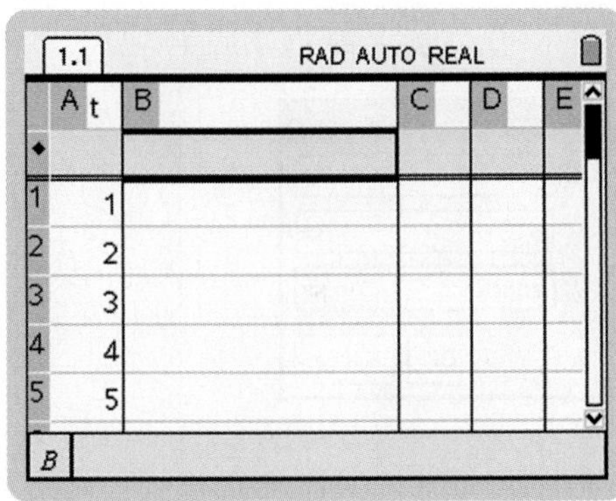

2. Press ⊜ Choose **Distributions** from the **Statistics** menu. Choose **Normal Pdf**.

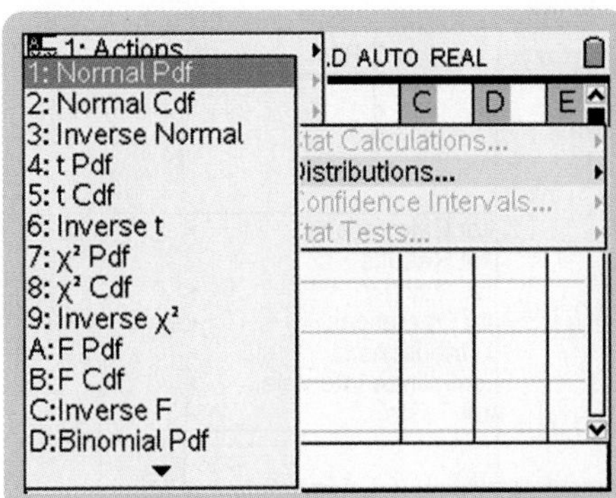

Defining a Normal Distribution (continued)

3. Choose 't from the drop down menu.

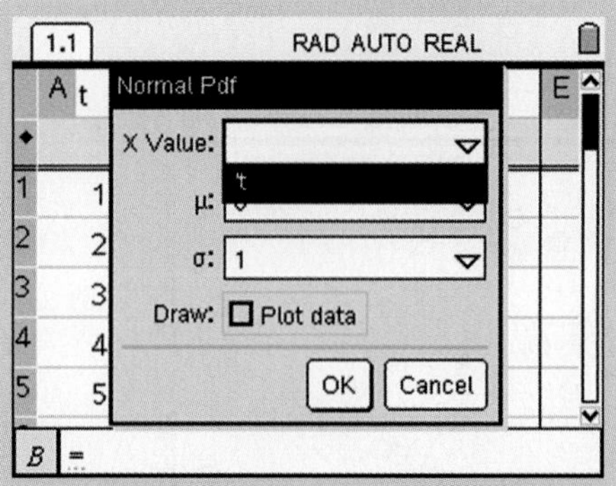

4. Press tab to move to the μ field. Type M E A N (' T). Press enter.

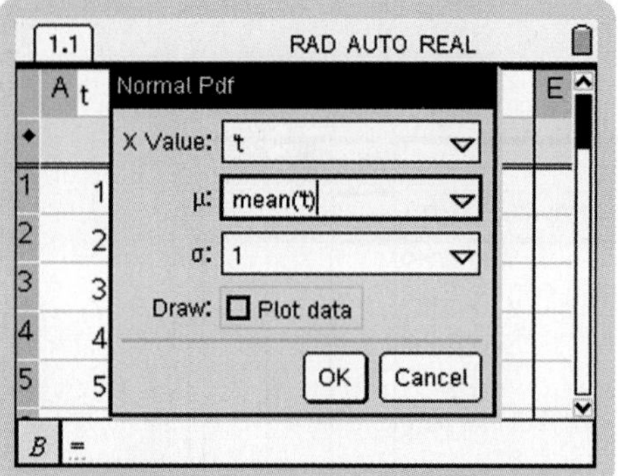

5. Press tab the σ field. Type S T D E V P O P (' T). Press enter enter.

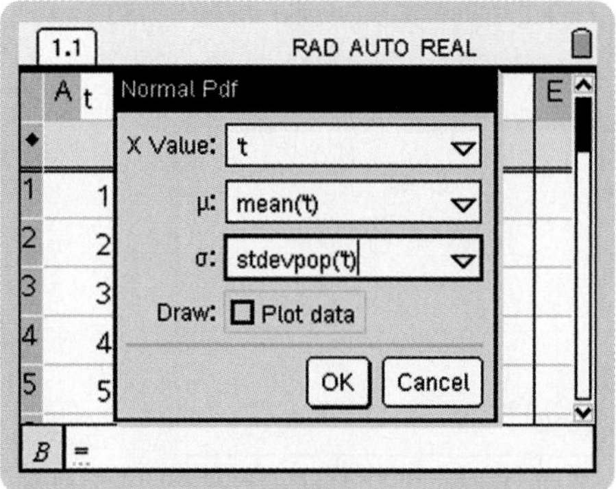

6. Press enter to populate the column.

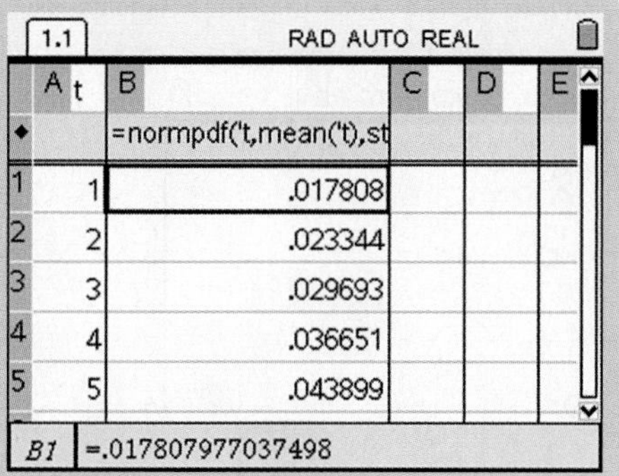

Using the normPdf command, Lesson 7.12

1. Choose **Distributions** from the **Statistics** menu. Choose **Normal Pdf**.

2. Press tab to move between the **X Value**, μ, and σ fields. Enter the appropriate values. Press enter enter.

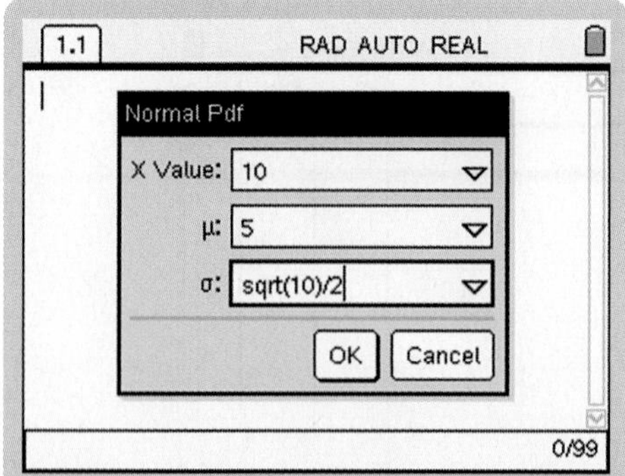

Using the normPdf command (continued)

3. Press enter.

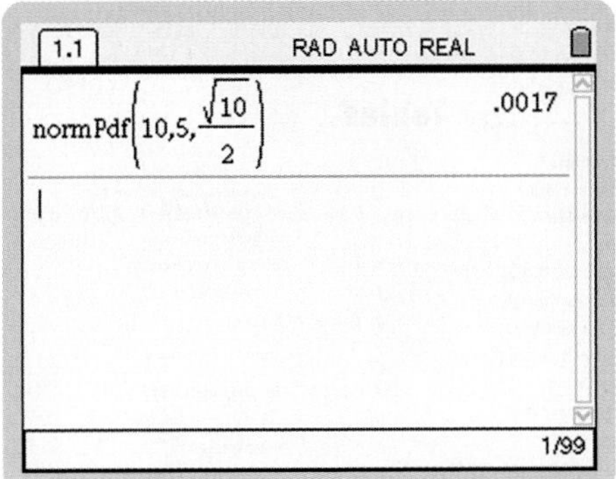

Using the normCdf Command, Lesson 7.13

1. Choose **Distributions** from the **Statistics** menu. Choose **Normal Cdf**.

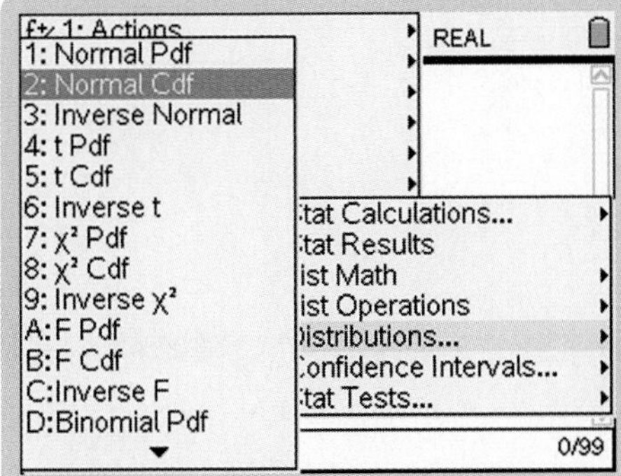

2. Press tab to move between the **Lower Bound**, **Upper Bound**, μ, and σ fields. Enter the appropriate values. Press enter enter.

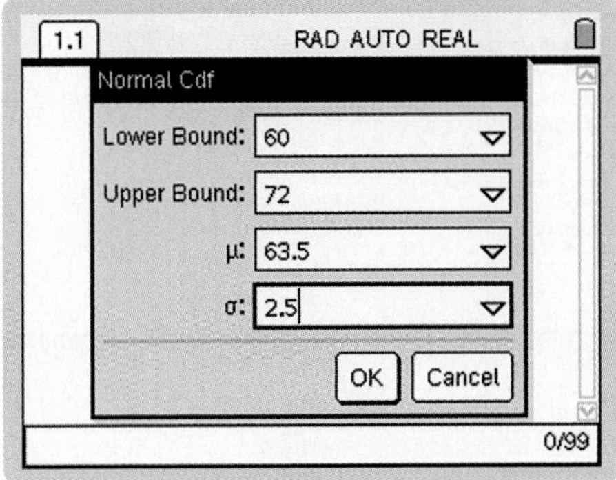

3. Press enter.

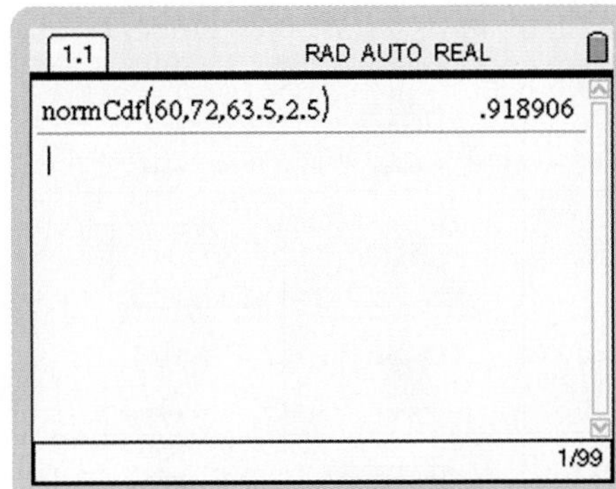

Tables

Table 1 Math Symbols

Symbol	Meaning
Δ	difference (delta)
$\Leftrightarrow$	if and only if
A	point A
A'	image of A, A prime
$\overrightarrow{AB}$	ray from A through B
$\overleftrightarrow{AB}$	line through A and B
$\overline{AB}$	segment from A to B
AB	length of $\overline{AB}$
$\overrightarrow{AB}$	vector from A to B
$\angle A$	angle A
$\angle ABC$	angle with sides $\overrightarrow{BA}$ and $\overrightarrow{BC}$
$m\angle A$	measure of angle A
$\triangle ABC$	triangle with vertices A, B, and C
$\Pi(P)$	power of a point P
$\Pi_S(P)$	signed power of a point P
π	pi, the ratio of the circumference of a circle to its diameter
ϕ	phi, the golden ratio
$\sin\theta$	sine of θ
$\cos\theta$	cosine of θ
$\tan\theta$	tangent of θ
$\sec\theta$	secant of θ
$\csc\theta$	cosecant of θ
$\cot\theta$	cotangent of θ
$\sin^{-1} x$	inverse sine of x
$\cos^{-1} x$	inverse cosine of x
$\tan^{-1} x$	inverse tangent of x
$\log_b x$	logarithm of x, base b
$\ln x$	natural logarithm of x
$n!$	n factorial
$\binom{n}{k}$	the nth row, kth column entry of Pascal's triangle
$_nP_k$	number of permutations of n objects, taken k at a time
$_nC_k$	number of combinations of n objects, taken k at a time
$\lvert A\rvert$	frequency of event A
$P(A)$	probability of event A
$f^{-1}(x)$	inverse function of f
$g \circ f(x)$	$g(f(x))$
$\sum_{k=1}^{n}$	summation notation
$f^{-1}(x)$	inverse function of f
$\mathbb{N}$	set of natural numbers
$\mathbb{Z}$	set of integers
$\mathbb{Q}$	set of rational numbers
$\mathbb{R}$	set of real numbers
$\mathbb{C}$	set of complex numbers
i	$\sqrt{-1}$
$x + yi$	complex number
$\overline{z}$	conjugate of a complex number
$\lvert z\rvert$	magnitude of a complex number
$\arg(z)$	argument of a complex number
$N(z)$	norm of a complex number
$\operatorname{cis}\theta$	complex number $\cos\theta + i\sin\theta$
$\overline{x}$	mean
σ	standard deviation
σ^2	variance
$N(\mu, \sigma)$	normal distribution
$\mathcal{R}_A$	linear fractional transformation
$\mathcal{A}_{(a,b)}$	affine transformation
T_a	translation map
$L_n[a, b](f(x))$	lower sum
$U_n[a, b](f(x))$	upper sum
$S[a, b](f(x))$	area under curve
$LF_n[a, b](f(x))$	Fermat lower sum
$UF_n[a, b](f(x))$	Fermat upper sum
$\mathcal{L}$	function $a \mapsto S[1, a](x^{-1})$

Table 2 Measures

	United States Customary	Metric
Length	12 inches (in.) = 1 foot (ft)	10 millimeters (mm) = 1 centimeter (cm)
	36 in. = 1 yard (yd)	100 cm = 1 meter (m)
	3 ft = 1 yard	1000 mm = 1 meter
	5280 ft = 1 mile (mi)	1000 m = 1 kilometer (km)
	1760 yd = 1 mile	
Area	144 square inches (in.^{2}) = 1 square foot (ft^2)	100 square millimeters (mm^2) = 1 square centimeter (cm^2)
	9 ft^2 = 1 square yard (yd^2)	10,000 cm^2 = 1 square meter (m^2)
	43,560 ft^2 = 1 acre (a)	10,000 m^2 = 1 hectare (ha)
	4840 yd^2 = 1 acre	
Volume	1728 cubic inches (in.^{3}) = 1 cubic foot (ft^3)	1000 cubic millimeters (mm^3) = 1 cubic centimeter (cm^3)
	27 ft^3 = 1 cubic yard (yd^3)	1,000,000 cm^3 = 1 cubic meter (m^3)
Liquid Capacity	8 fluid ounces (fl oz) = 1 cup (c)	1000 milliliters (mL) = 1 liter (L)
	2 c = 1 pint (pt)	1000 L = 1 kiloliter (kL)
	2 pt = 1 quart (qt)	
	4 qt = 1 gallon (gal)	
Weight and Mass	16 ounces (oz) = 1 pound (lb)	1000 milligrams (mg) = 1 gram (g)
	2000 pounds = 1 ton (t)	1000 g = 1 kilogram (kg)
		1000 kg = 1 metric ton
Temperature	32°F = freezing point of water	0°C = freezing point of water
	98.6°F = normal body temperature	37°C = normal body temperature
	212°F = boiling point of water	100°C = boiling point of water
Time	60 seconds (s) = 1 minute (min)	365 days = 1 year (yr)
	60 minutes = 1 hour (h)	52 weeks (approx.) = 1 year
	24 hours = 1 day (d)	12 months = 1 year
	7 days = 1 week (wk)	10 years = 1 decade
	4 weeks (approx.) = 1 month (mo)	100 years = 1 century

Table 3 Formulas From Geometry

You may need geometric formulas as you work through your precalculus book. Here are some perimeter, area, and volume formulas.	$P = 2\ell + 2w$ $A = \ell w$ **Rectangle**	$P = 4s$ $A = s^2$ **Square**
$C = 2\pi r$ or $C = \pi d$ $A = \pi r^2$ **Circle**	$A = \frac{1}{2}bh$ **Triangle**	$A = bh$ **Parallelogram**
$A = \frac{1}{2}(b_1 + b_2)h$ **Trapezoid**	$V = Bh$ $V = \ell wh$ **Rectangular Prism**	$V = \frac{1}{3}Bh$ **Pyramid**
$V = Bh$ $V = \pi r^2 h$ **Cylinder**	$V = \frac{1}{3}Bh$ $V = \frac{1}{3}\pi r^2 h$ **Cone**	$V = \frac{4}{3}\pi r^3$ **Sphere**

Properties and Theorems

Chapter 2

Theorem 2.1, p. 88

The absolute value of a complex number is equal to the square root of its norm.

$$|z| = \sqrt{N(z)}$$

Theorem 2.2 ***The Multiplication Law,*** **p. 100**

Given complex numbers $z = a \operatorname{cis} \alpha$ and $w = b \operatorname{cis} \beta$,

$$zw = (a \operatorname{cis} \alpha)(b \operatorname{cis} \beta) = ab \operatorname{cis}(\alpha + \beta)$$

In other words,
- $|zw| = |z| \cdot |w|$
- $\arg(zw) = \arg(z) + \arg(w)$

Theorem 2.3 ***The Angle-Sum Formulas,*** **p. 111**

The following two equations are true for all values of α and β.

$$\cos(\alpha + \beta) = \cos\alpha\cos\beta - \sin\alpha\sin\beta$$
$$\sin(\alpha + \beta) = \sin\alpha\cos\beta + \cos\alpha\sin\beta$$

Corollary 2.3.1 ***The Angle-Difference Formulas,*** **p. 112**

The following two equations are true for all values of α and β.

$$\cos(\alpha - \beta) = \cos\alpha\cos\beta + \sin\alpha\sin\beta$$
$$\sin(\alpha - \beta) = \sin\alpha\cos\beta - \cos\alpha\sin\beta$$

Corollary 2.3.2 ***The Double-Angle Formulas,*** **p. 112**

The following two equations are true for all values of θ.

$$\cos 2\theta = \cos^2\theta - \sin^2\theta$$
$$\sin 2\theta = 2\sin\theta\cos\theta$$

Theorem 2.4 ***DeMoivre's Theorem,*** **p. 128**

For all real θ, $(\operatorname{cis}\theta)^n = \operatorname{cis} n\theta$.

Corollary 2.4.1, p. 129

For all real θ, $(r \operatorname{cis}\theta)^n = r^n \operatorname{cis} n\theta$.

Theorem 2.5 ***The Factor Theorem,*** **p. 133**

Suppose $f(x)$ is a polynomial. Then $x - a$ is a factor of $f(x)$ if and only if the number a is a root of the equation $f(x) = 0$.

Theorem 2.6, p. 139

If n is a positive integer, the roots of the equation

$$x^n - 1 = 0$$

are

$$1, z, z^2, \ldots, z^{n-1}$$

where

$$z = \operatorname{cis}\frac{2\pi}{n}$$

If $n \geq 3$, these roots lie on the vertices a regular n-gon inscribed in the unit circle in the complex plane.

Theorem 2.7 ***Cardano's Formula,*** **p. 157**

The roots of $x^3 + px + q = 0$ are

$$\sqrt[3]{\frac{-q + \sqrt{\frac{27q^2 + 4p^3}{27}}}{2}} + \sqrt[3]{\frac{-q - \sqrt{\frac{27q^2 + 4p^3}{27}}}{2}}$$

Chapter 3

Theorem 3.1 ***The Change of Sign Theorem,*** **p. 173**

Suppose f is a polynomial function and there are two numbers a and b such that $f(a) < 0$ and $f(b) > 0$. Then, $f(c) = 0$ for some number c between a and b.

Theorem 3.2 ***The Intermediate Value Theorem for Polynomials,*** **p. 173**

Suppose f is a polynomial function and a and b are two numbers such that $f(a) < f(b)$. Then for any number c between $f(a)$ and $f(b)$ there is at least one number d between a and b such that $f(d) = c$.

Theorem 3.3 ***The Odd Degree Root Theorem,*** **p. 177**

A polynomial function of odd degree has at least one real root.

Theorem 3.4, p. 199

Let $f(x)$ be a polynomial and $a, b \in \mathbb{R}$. Write

$$f(x) = (x - a)(x - b)q(x) + r(x)$$

where $r(x)$ is a linear function. Then the graph of $y = r(x)$ is the secant to the graph of $y = f(x)$ through $(a, f(a))$ and $(b, f(b))$.

Theorem 3.5, p. 199

Let $f(x)$ be a polynomial and $a \in \mathbb{R}$. Write

$$f(x) = (x - a)^2 q(x) + r(x)$$

where $r(x)$ is a linear function. Then the graph of $y = r(x)$ is the tangent to the graph of $y = f(x)$ at $(a, f(a))$.

Theorem 3.6, p. 211

Let h be a rational function.
1. If h has an infinite discontinuity at $x = a$, then the graph of h has $x = a$ as a vertical asymptote.
2. If h has a removable discontinuity at $x = a$, then the graph of h has a hole at $x = a$.

Theorem 3.7, p. 212

Let $h(x) = \frac{f(x)}{g(x)}$ be a rational function with $\deg f = m$ and $\deg g = n$.
1. If $m < n$, then $\lim\limits_{x\to\infty} h(x) = 0$.
2. If $m = n$, then $\lim\limits_{x\to\infty} h(x)$ is the ratio of the leading coefficients of f and g.

Moreover, the graph of h has a horizontal asymptote with equation $y = L$ where $L = \lim\limits_{x\to\infty} h(x)$.

Theorem 3.8, p. 214

Let $h(x) = \frac{f(x)}{g(x)}$ be a rational function with $\deg f > \deg g$. Then

$$\lim_{x\to\infty} h(x) = \infty \text{ or } -\infty.$$

Moreover, if you write

$$\frac{f(x)}{g(x)} = q(x) + \frac{r(x)}{g(x)}$$

where q and r are polynomials with $\deg r < \deg g$, then the graph of q is a nonhorizontal asymptote of the graph of h.

Theorem 3.9, p. 222

Suppose that f is a rational function for which the denominator is not zero at $x = r$. Suppose also that you use the method of undetermined coefficients to write

$$f(x) = m + n(x - r) + p(x)(x - r)^2$$

finding first the number m and then the number n. Then p is a rational function that is defined at $x = r$.

Theorem 3.10, p. 228

Suppose A and B are 2×2 matrices with real coefficients. Then

$$\mathcal{R}_A \circ \mathcal{R}_B = \mathcal{R}_{AB}$$

Lemma 3.11, p. 248

Let $k \geq 0$ be an integer. Then

$$\lim_{n\to\infty} \frac{\binom{n}{k}}{n^k} = \frac{1}{k!}$$

Theorem 3.12, p. 249

$$\lim_{n\to\infty}(1 + \tfrac{1}{n})^n = 1 + \frac{1}{1!} + \frac{1}{2!} + \frac{1}{3!} + \cdots = \sum_{k=0}^{\infty} \frac{1}{k!}$$

Theorem 3.13, p. 260

The tangent to the graph of $y = \ln x$ at the point $(a, \ln a)$ has slope $\frac{1}{a}$.

Theorem 3.14, p. 261

The tangent to the graph of $y = e^x$ at the point (a, e^a) has slope e^a.

Chapter 4

Theorem 4.1, p. 287

It is possible to make m^n different strings of length n using m different symbols, if you can use a symbol more than once.

Theorem 4.2, p. 307

$${}_nC_k = \frac{{}_nP_k}{k!} = \frac{n!}{k!(n-k)!}$$

Theorem 4.3 ***The Pascal-Combinations Connection,*** **p. 309**

For any $n \geq 0$ and all k such that $0 \leq k \leq n$,

$$\binom{n}{k} = {}_nC_k$$

Theorem 4.4 ***The Binomial Theorem,*** **p. 328**

For any integers n and k with $0 \leq k \leq n$,

$$(a + b)^n = \binom{n}{0}a^n b^0 + \binom{n}{1}a^{n-1}b^1 + \binom{n}{2}a^{n-2}b^2 + \cdots$$
$$\cdots + \binom{n}{k}a^{n-k}b^k + \cdots + \binom{n}{n-1}a^1 b^{n-1} + \binom{n}{n}a^0 b^n$$

Chapter 5

Theorem 5.1, p. 367

Use straight lines extending infinitely in either direction to draw a map that divides the plane into any number of regions. Two colors are enough to color the map so that no two regions with a common border have the same color.

Theorem 5.2 ***Newton's Difference Formula,*** **p. 391**

Suppose you have a table with integer inputs from 0 to m:

Input	Output	Δ	Δ^2	Δ^3	...	Δ^m
0	a_0	a_1	a_2	a_3	...	a_m
1						
2						
3						
4						
5						
6						
⋮						
m						

A polynomial function that fits the table is

$$f(x) = \sum_{k=0}^{m} a_k \binom{x}{k}$$

Theorem 5.3 ***Closure of Solutions,*** **p. 423**

If two functions r and s satisfy the two-term recurrence

$$f(n) = Af(n-1) + Bf(n-2)$$

then so does any linear combination

$$t(n) = k \cdot r(n) + j \cdot s(n)$$

where k and j are real numbers.

Theorem 5.4 ***Closed-Form Equivalent for f(n) = Af(n − 1) + B,*** **p. 428**

Define f by

$$f(n) = \begin{cases} p & \text{if } n = 0 \\ Af(n-1) + B & \text{if } n > 0 \end{cases}$$

Then for nonnegative integer inputs, a closed-form equivalent for f is

$$f(n) = A^n \cdot p + B\left(\frac{A^n - 1}{A - 1}\right)$$

Theorem 5.5 ***Monthly Payments,*** **p. 431**

On a loan for C dollars taken out for n months with an APR of i percent compounded monthly, the monthly payment is m dollars where

$$m = \frac{q^n(q-1)}{q^n - 1}C$$

and $q = 1 + \frac{i}{1200}$.

Chapter 6

Theorem 6.1 ***Power of a Point Theorem,*** **p. 458**

Given a point P and a circle, take any line through P that intersects the circle in two points A and B. Then $PA \cdot PB$ is constant, no matter what line you choose through P. This constant is called the power of the point P. The power is a function of the point, so write the power of P as $\Pi(P)$.

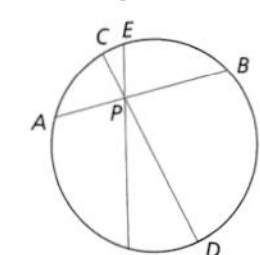

$$PA \cdot PB = PC \cdot PD = PE \cdot PF$$

Corollary 6.1.1, p. 458

Inside a circle, the power of a point d units away from the center of a circle with radius r is $r^2 - d^2$.

Corollary 6.1.2, p. 459

Outside a circle, the power of a point d units away from the center of a circle with radius r is $d^2 - r^2$.

Theorem 6.2, p. 460

The signed power of point $P(x, y)$ with respect to the circle with equation $x^2 + y^2 + Cx + Dy + E = 0$ is

$$\Pi_S(P) = x^2 + y^2 + Cx + Dy + E$$

Theorem 6.3, p. 476

An equation for the parabola with focus $(0, c)$ and directrix with equation $y = -c$ is

$$x^2 = 4cy$$

Theorem 6.4, p. 478

The ellipse with foci $(c, 0)$ and $(-c, 0)$ and string length $2a$ has equation

$$1 = \frac{x^2}{a^2} + \frac{y^2}{b^2}$$

where $b^2 = a^2 - c^2$.

Theorem 6.5, p. 480

The hyperbola with foci $(c, 0)$ and $(-c, 0)$ and constant difference $2a$ has equation

$$1 = \frac{x^2}{a^2} - \frac{y^2}{b^2}$$

where $b^2 = c^2 - a^2$.

Theorem 6.6, p. 488

The graph of

$$rx^2 + ty^2 + ux + vy + w = 0$$

is a (possibly degenerate) conic. In fact, the nature of the conic is determined by the sign of rt:

- If $rt > 0$, the graph is an ellipse.
- If $rt = 0$, the graph is a parabola.
- If $rt < 0$, the graph is a hyperbola.

Theorem 6.7, p. 494

Let F be a fixed point, d be a fixed line, and e be a positive real number. The set of points P such that $\frac{PF}{Pd} = e$ is a (possibly degenerate) conic. It is an ellipse if $e < 1$, a parabola if $e = 1$, and a hyperbola if $e > 1$.

Theorem 6.8, p. 519

In any triangle, the three medians are concurrent. Moreover, on each median the common point is $\frac{2}{3}$ the distance from the vertex to the opposite side.

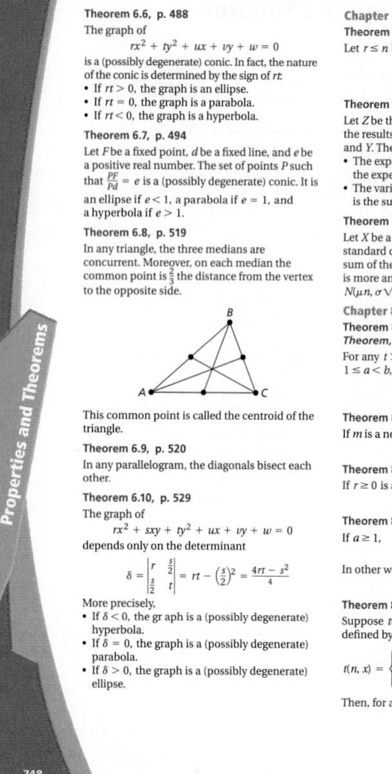

This common point is called the centroid of the triangle.

Theorem 6.9, p. 520

In any parallelogram, the diagonals bisect each other.

Theorem 6.10, p. 529

The graph of

$$rx^2 + sxy + ty^2 + ux + vy + w = 0$$

depends only on the determinant

$$\delta = \begin{vmatrix} r & \frac{s}{2} \\ \frac{s}{2} & t \end{vmatrix} = rt - \left(\frac{s}{2}\right)^2 = \frac{4rt - s^2}{4}$$

More precisely,

- If $\delta < 0$, the gr aph is a (possibly degenerate) hyperbola.
- If $\delta = 0$, the graph is a (possibly degenerate) parabola.
- If $\delta > 0$, the graph is a (possibly degenerate) ellipse.

Chapter 7

Theorem 7.1 *Vandermonde's Identity,* p. 564

Let $r \le n$ be nonnegative integers. Then

$$\binom{n}{r} = \sum_{k=0}^{r} \binom{n}{k} \cdot \binom{n-r}{r-k}$$

Theorem 7.2, p. 586

Let Z be the random variable defined by adding the results of independent random variables X and Y. Then

- The expected value, or mean, of Z is the sum of the expected values for X and Y, and
- The variance, or mean squared deviation, of Z is the sum of the variances X and Y.

Theorem 7.3 *Central Limit Theorem,* p. 612

Let X be a random variable with mean μ and standard deviation σ. The distribution for the sum of the outputs of X over n experiments is more and more closely approximated by $N(\mu n, \sigma\sqrt{n})$ as n grows larger.

Chapter 8

Theorem 8.1 *Gregory of St. Vincent's Theorem,* p. 679

For any $t > 0$ and any real numbers a, b with $1 \le a < b$,

$$S[a, b]\left(\tfrac{1}{x}\right) = S[ta, tab]\left(\tfrac{1}{x}\right)$$

Theorem 8.2, p. 685

If m is a nonnegative integer, then

$$\mathcal{L}(e^m) = m$$

Theorem 8.3, p. 687

If $r \ge 0$ is any real number, then

$$\mathcal{L}(e^r) = r$$

Theorem 8.4, p. 687

If $a \ge 1$,

$$\mathcal{L}(a) = r \Leftrightarrow e^r = a$$

In other words, $\mathcal{L}$ is the natural logarithm

$$\mathcal{L}(a) = \ln a$$

Theorem 8.5, p. 698

Suppose $t(n, x)$ is the sequence of polynomials defined by

$$t(n, x) = \begin{cases} 1 & \text{if } n = 0 \\ x & \text{if } n = 1 \\ 2x \cdot t(n-1, x) - t(n-2, x) & \text{if } n > 1 \end{cases}$$

Then, for all nonnegative integers n,

$$t(n, \cos\alpha) = \cos n\alpha$$

Glossary

A

affine combination (p. 518) A point C is an affine combination of points A and B if C is on the line determined by A and B. C can expressed as $C = (1 - k)A + B$ for some real number k.

affine transformation (p. 231) Let a and b be real numbers with $a \neq 0$. An affine transformation by (a, b) is a transformation $\mathcal{A}_{(a, b)}$ of $\mathbb{R}$ given by $\mathcal{A}_{(a, b)}(x) = ax + b$ for any real number x.

algebraic numbers (p. 146) Algebraic numbers are numbers that satisfy an equation with rational coefficients.

amplitude (p. 62) The amplitude of a sinusoidal function f is the distance from its average value to the maximum or minimum.

anagram (p. 300) An anagram is a rearrangement of the letters in a word or phrase.

apex (p. 468) The apex of an infinite double cone is the fixed point used to generate the cone.

arc (p. 7) An arc is a set of points of a circle that lie in the interior of a particular central angle.

argument (p. 89) The argument of a complex number z, written $\arg(z)$, is the angle measured in a counterclockwise direction from the positive real axis to the ray from the origin through z.

asymptote (p. 39) An asymptote is a line that the graph of a function approaches, but does not intersect.

average rate of change (p. 180) Let f be any function and let A and B be two points on the graph of $y = f(x)$. The average rate of change of $f(x)$ with respect to x between A and B is the slope $m(A, B)$.

axis (p. 468) The axis of an infinite double cone is the line through the apex perpendicular to the circle used to make the cone.

B

base case (p. 347) A base case a is place where a rule starts.

Bernoulli trial (p. 596) A Bernoulli trial is an experiment with two outcomes—typically called success and failure.

binomial coefficients (p. 382) The binomial coefficients are the coefficients of the binomial expansion $(x + y)^n$ where the coefficient of the $x^{n-k}y^k$ term is $\binom{n}{k}$.

C

central angle (p. 7) A central angle for a circle is an angle that has its vertex at the center of the circle.

centroid (p. 449) The centroid of a triangle is the intersection of its medians.

characteristic polynomial (p. 421) Suppose a function satisfies the recurrence $f(n) = Af(n - 1) + Bf(n - 2)$. The characteristic polynomial for this recurrence is $x^2 - Ax - B$.

closed-form definition (p. 346) A closed-form definition for a function f lets you find the $f(n)$ for any input n by direct calculation.

combination (p. 305) A combination of elements a set S is a subset of S. The number of combinations of n objects, taken k at a time, is ${}_nC_k = \frac{n!}{k!(n - k)!}$.

complementary (p. 52) Two angles are complementary if they add up to 90 degrees.

complex numbers (p. 145) The set of complex numbers $\mathbb{C}$ consists of all expressions in the form $a + bi$ where:

- a and b are real numbers
- $i^2 = -1$
- Addition and multiplication are carried out as if $a + bi$ were a polynomial in i, together with the new rule $i^2 = -1$.

concurrent (p. 519) A set of lines are concurrent if they share a common point.

confidence interval (p. 615) A confidence interval is the range of values about the mean for a given percentage.

conic sections (p. 468) Conic sections are curves that result from the intersection of infinite double cones and planes.

conjugate (p. 85) The conjugate of a complex number $z = x + yi$ is the complex number $x - yi$ and is denoted by $\overline{z}$.

continuous (p. 171) A function f is continuous at an input a if you can make $f(x)$ as close as you to $f(a)$ by making x as close as you want to a.

continuously compounded interest (p. 243) Continuously compounded interest is computed by taking the limit as the frequency of compounding increases.

convex combination (p. 518) A point C is a convex combination of points A and B if C is on the line segment between A and B. C can be expressed as $C = (1 - k)A + B$ for some real number k where $0 \leq k \leq 1$.

coordinatize (p. 450) Coordinatize a geometric shape by making a general version in the coordinate plane.

cumulative density function (p. 619) The cumulative density function (CDF) finds the amount of area under the normal curve between two values for a given mean and standard deviation.

cycle (p. 46) One cycle of the graph of a periodic function f results as the input x ranges over one fundamental period.

cyclotomic identity (p. 145) The identity $\zeta^{n-1} + \zeta^{n-2} + \cdots + \zeta^2 + \zeta + 1 = 0$ where ζ is a primitive nth root of unity is called a cyclotomic identity.

cyclotomy (p. 124) Cyclotomy ("circle division") is the connection between the roots of equations of the form $x^n - 1 = 0$, where n is a positive integer, and regular polygons.

D

Dandelin sphere (p. 472) A Dandelin sphere is a sphere inside a double cone that is tangent to both the cone and a plane slicing the cone.

decreasing (p. 26) A function f is decreasing on an interval if for any two values in the interval a and b, $a < b$, then $f(a) > f(b)$.

determinant (p. 227) Let $A = \begin{pmatrix} a & b \\ c & d \end{pmatrix}$ be a 2×2 matrix with real entries. The determinant of A is $\det A = ad - cb$.

deviation (p. 575) The deviation of an output value of a random variable is the difference between the output value and the mean of the random variable.

diagonal (p. 320) A diagonal of a polygon is a segment which connects two to the polygon's vertices but is not a polygon's side.

difference table (p. 374) A difference table is a table of the difference of outputs when the inputs are evenly spaced.

dilation (p. 507) A dilation is any geometric transformation that expands or contracts the plane (or space) using some particular point as the center.

direction of a vector (p. 506) The direction of a vector includes both slope of a vector and orientation.

directrix (p. 472) A parabola can be defined by the set of points equidistant from a fixed point and line. The directrix of the parabola is the fixed line.

distance formula (p. 444) The distance formula between points $A(x_1, y_1)$ and $B(x_2, y_2)$ is $d(A, B) = \sqrt{(x_2 - x_1)^2 + (y_2 - y_1)^2}$

double cone (p. 449) The graph of $z^2 = x^2 + y^2$ is called a double cone.

E

e (factorial definition) (p. 250) The factorial definition of e is given by

$$e = 1 + \frac{1}{1!} + \frac{1}{2!} + \frac{1}{3!} + \cdots = \sum_{k=0}^{\infty} \frac{1}{k!}$$

e (limit definition) (p. 243) The limit definition of e is given by

$$e = \lim_{n\to\infty}\left(1 + \frac{1}{n}\right)^n$$

The value of e is approximately 2.17828.

eccentricity (p. 495) The eccentricity is the ratio of the distance between the foci to the distance between the vertices.

ellipse (p. 469) An ellipse is the curve you get by slicing an infinite double cone with a plane that intersects only one branch of the cone in a closed curve.

equilibrium point (p. 429) An equilibrium point is a repeating value of an iteration. If $f(n) = f(n - 1) = C$, then C is an equilibrium point.

even function (p. 108) A function f is an even function if it satisfies $f(-x) = f(x)$ for all numbers x in its domain. If the point (x, y) is on the graph of f, the point $(-x, y)$ is also on the graph.

event (p. 542) An event is a subset of a sample space, a set of outcomes.

expected value (p. 558) The expected value of a random variable X is the sum when each value of X is multiplied by its probability. The typical notation is

$$E(X) = \sum_i x_i \cdot p_i$$

where the x_i are the values of the random variable, and the p_i are the probabilities of each value. An alternative notation is

$$E(X) = \sum_i s_i \cdot P(X = s_i)$$

where $P(X = s_i)$ is the probability that the random variable X takes on the value s_i.

experimental probability (p. 592) The experimental probability of an event is equal to the ratio between the number of times the event occurred and the total number of trials of the experiment.

F

factorial (p. 299) The factorial of a positive integer n is defined as the descending product $n \cdot (n - 1) \cdot (n - 2) \cdot \cdots \cdot 2 \cdot 1$, stopping at 1. Denote the factorial of n by $n!$ Using this definition, 0! is not defined. Define $0! = 1$.

Farey sequence of order *n* (p. 296) The Farey sequence of order n, denoted F_n, is the set of all fractions from 0 to 1, inclusive, with denominators less than or equal to n.

Fermat lower sum (p. 663) The Fermat lower sum $UF_n[a, b](f(x))$ is the lower approximation of the area under the graph of the function $f(x)$ from $x = a$ to $x = b$ when the number of Fermat subdivisions is n.

Fermat upper sum (p. 664) The Fermat upper sum $UF_n[a, b](f(x))$ is the upper approximation of the area under the graph of the function $f(x)$ from $x = a$ to $x = b$ when the number of Fermat subdivisions is n.

Fibonacci sequence (p. 353) The Fibonacci sequence is a sequence in which each term is the sum of the previous two terms and the first two terms of the sequence are 0 and 1:

$$F(n) = \begin{cases} 0 & \text{if } n = 0 \\ 1 & \text{if } n = 1 \\ F(n - 1) + F(n + 2) & \text{if } n > 1 \end{cases}$$

focus, foci (p. 470) The focus of a parabola is the fixed point in the locus definition of a parabola.

The foci of an ellipse are the two fixed points used in the locus definition of an ellipse.

The foci of a hyperbola are the two fixed points used in the locus definition of a hyperbola.

Focus is the singular of foci.

Four-Color Theorem (p. 367) The Four-Color Theorem says that if you have a map of countries which are all solid areas, without holes or separated colonies, then four colors suffice to color the map so that no two countries sharing a common border have the same color.

frequency (p. 549) Let A be an event. The frequency of the event $|A|$ is the number of outcomes in A.

functional equation (p. 412) A functional equation tells how various outputs of a function are related.

G

generator (p. 468) The generator of an infinite double cone is the rotating line through the apex used to make the cone.

golden ratio (p. 142) The golden ratio is the number $\phi = \frac{1 + \sqrt{5}}{2}$.

H

head of a vector (p. 503) The head of a vector $\overrightarrow{PQ}$ is at point Q.

histogram (p. 554) A histogram is a graphical representation that shows frequencies as bars.

hockey-stick property (p. 375) The hockey-stick property of difference tables is that any number in the table (other than inputs) is the sum of the top value in its column and all the numbers above it in the column immediately to its right.

hole (p. 211) A hole in a graph is a point at which a graph of a function is not connected but can be made connected by adding the point.

hyperbola (p. 469) A hyperbola is the curve you get by slicing an infinite double cone with a plane that intersects both branches of the cone.

I

identically equal (p. 107) Identically equal expressions are two expressions such that one expression can be transformed to the other using the basic rules of algebra and any other proven identities or theorems.

identity (p. 107) An identity is any equation that equates two identically equal expressions.

increasing (p. 26) A function f is increasing on an interval if for any two values in the interval a and b, $a < b$, then $f(a) < f(b)$.

independent (p. 544) Two events A and B are independent if the result from one event has no effect on the other. If A and B are independent, then $P(A \text{ and } B) = P(A) \cdot P(B)$.

infinite discontinuity (p. 211) Let $h(x) = \frac{f(x)}{g(x)}$ be a rational function such that

- $f(x) = (x - a)^m \cdot p(x)$
- $g(x) = (x - a)^n \cdot q(x)$

where $p(a), q(a) \neq 0$. h has an infinite discontinuity at $x = a$ if $n > m \geq 0$.

infinite double cone (p. 468) An infinite double cone is the surface made by rotating a line in space fixed at one point. The line is rotated by moving another point on the line along a circle.

instantaneous speed (p. 197) Let d be the distance function of time t. The instantaneous speed of d at $t = a$ is the slope of the tangent to the graph of $y = d(t)$ at the point $(a, d(a))$.

inverse function (p. 43) Suppose a function f is a one-to-one function with domain A and range B. The inverse function f^{-1} is a function with these properties.

- f^{-1} has domain B and range A
- $f(f^{-1}(x)) = x$

isomorphic (p. 281) If two problems have the same mathematical structure, then they are isomorphic.

isosceles trapezoid (p. 456) An isosceles trapezoid is a trapezoid with opposite nonparallel sides that are congruent.

isosceles triangle (p. 454) An isosceles triangle is a triangle with at least two sides congruent.

K

***k* of the way from *A* to *B* (p. 518)** For any points A and B and for any real number k, k of the way from A to B is the point $A + k(B - A) = (1 - k)A + kB$.

L

linear combination (p. 423) A linear combination of x and y is $ax + by$, where a and b are real numbers.

linear fractional transformation (p. 227) Let

$$A = \begin{pmatrix} a & b \\ c & d \end{pmatrix}$$

be a 2×2 matrix with real entries. The linear fractional transformation associated with A is the rational function

$$\mathcal{R}_A(x) = \frac{ax + b}{cx + d}$$

locus (p. 470) A locus is the set of all points that satisfy an equation.

M

machine formula (p. 578) The machine formula for computing the variance is the mean of the squares minus the square of the mean.

magnitude (p. 87) The modulus of a complex number z, denoted by $|z|$, is the distance between the complex number and 0 in the complex plane.

In some older texts, the magnitude of a complex number is called the modulus.

Mahler polynomials (p. 391) The Mahler polynomials are the polynomials that match the binomial coefficients. The first few Mahler polynomials are:

k	$\binom{x}{k}$ (Factored)	$\binom{x}{k}$ (Expanded)
0	1	1
1	x	x
2	$\frac{x(x-1)}{2!}$	$\frac{-x+x^2}{2}$
3	$\frac{x(x-1)(x-2)}{3!}$	$\frac{2x-3x^2+x^3}{6}$
4	$\frac{x(x-1)(x-2)(x-3)}{4!}$	$\frac{-6x+11x^2-6x^3+x^4}{24}$
5	$\frac{x(x-1)(x-2)(x-3)(x-4)}{5!}$	$\frac{24x-50x^2+35x^3-10x^4+x^5}{120}$

major axis (p. 477) The major axis of an ellipse is the longer of the two intersections of the ellipse with the axes of symmetry of the ellipse.

mathematical induction (p. 360) Mathematical induction is a method of proof used to show that a fact is true for set of integers (typically positive or nonnegative ones). A proof by mathematical induction involves two parts:

Step 1 Show that the fact is true fro the first few cases (often using tabulation by hand or by computer).

Step 2 Show that if the fact is true up to some integer $(n - 1)$, it must also be true for n.

maximum (p. 27) The maximum of a graph is the highest value achieved on the vertical axis.

mean absolute value deviation (p. 576) The mean absolute value deviation is calculated by first finding the absolute value of each deviation and then finding the mean of these numbers.

mean squared deviation (p. 576) The mean squared deviation is calculated by first finding the square of each deviation, and then finding the mean of these numbers.

median (p. 448) A median of a triangle is a segment connecting a vertex to the midpoint of the opposite side.

midline (p. 455) A midline is a segment that connects the midpoints of two sides of a triangle.

midline of a trapezoid (p. 456) The midline of a trapezoid is the segment connecting the midpoints of the two non-parallel sides.

Midline Theorem (p. 455) The Midline Theorem states that the segment joining the midpoints of two sides of a triangle is parallel to the third side and its measure is equal to half the measure of the third side.

midpoint formula (p. 444) The midpoint formula of the segment between points $A(x_1, y_1)$ and $B(x_2, y_2)$ is

$$M(A, B) = \left(\frac{x_1 + x_2}{2}, \frac{y_1 + y_2}{2}\right)$$

minimum (p. 27) The minimum of a graph is the lowest value achieved on the vertical axis.

minor axis (p. 477) The minor axis of an ellipse is the shorter of the two intersections of the ellipse with the axes of symmetry of the ellipse.

modulus (p. 87) *See* **magnitude.**

mutually exclusive (p. 544) Two events A and B are mutually exclusive if they do not share any outcomes in the same sample space: whenever $P(A \text{ and } B) = 0$. If A and B are mutually exclusive, then $P(A \text{ or } B) = P(A) + P(B)$.

N

natural logarithm function (p. 255) The natural logarithm function ln is the logarithm to the base e:

$$\ln x = \log_e x$$

norm (p. 88) The norm of a complex number z, written $N(z)$, is the product of the number and its conjugate, $z\bar{z}$.

normal distribution (p. 611) A normal distribution $N(\mu, \sigma)$ is a probability distribution determined by the values of the mean μ and standard deviation σ.

***n*th root of unity (p. 125)** An nth root of unity is each complex number that satisfies the equation $x^n - 1 = 0$.

O

odd function (p. 108) A function f is an odd function if it satisfies $f(-x) = -f(x)$ for all numbers x in its domain. If the point (x, y) is on the graph of f, the point $(-x, -y)$ is also on the graph.

one-to-one (p. 43) A function f is one-to-one if $f(a) = f(b)$ only when $a = b$.

outcome (p. 542) An outcome is an element of a sample space.

P

parabola (p. 469) A parabola is the curve you get by slicing an infinite double cone with a plane that is parallel to its generator.

parallelogram (p. 450) A parallelogram is a quadrilateral with two pairs of parallel sides.

parameter (p. 512) In the vector form $X = P + tD$, the variable t is called a parameter.

parametric equations (p. 512) Vector equations for lines are sometimes called parametric equations for lines.

period (p. 15) The period of a periodic function is the smallest value p such that, for all x, $f(x + p) = f(x)$.

periodic (p. 15) A nonconstant function f is periodic if there exits a real number $p > 0$ such that, for all x, $f(x + p) = f(x)$.

permutation (p. 298) A permutation is a one-to-one function from a set to itself. The number of permutations of n objects, taken k at a time, is ${}_nP_k = \frac{n!}{(n - k)!}$.

perpendicular (p. 444) Two lines in the plane are perpendicular if and only if the product of their slopes is -1, or if one line is vertical and the other is horizontal.

perpendicular bisector (p. 445) A perpendicular bisector is a line that is perpendicular to a line segment at the segment's midpoint.

phase shift (p. 64) The phase shift of a sinusoidal function

$$f(x) = A\sin(ax + b) + B \text{ or}$$
$$f(x) = A\cos(ax + b) + B$$

is the amount of horizontal translation required to obtain the graph of $y = f(x)$ from the graph of

$$y = A\sin ax \text{ or } y = A\cos ax$$

respectively.

point-tester (p. 444) A point-tester is an equation used to determine whether particular points are on a graph.

polar coordinates (p. 92) Polar coordinates (r, θ) denote a direction (an angle θ counterclockwise from the reference axis) and distance r.

polar form for complex numbers (p. 93) The polar form for complex numbers is written $r(\cos\theta + i\sin\theta)$, where r is a non-negative real number and θ is a measurement either in degrees or radians.

power functions (p. 174) Power functions are polynomial functions with only one term.

power of a point (p. 458) The power of a point P, d units from the center of a circle of radius r, with respect to the circle is given by $\Pi(P) = |d^2 - r^2|$.

primitive *n*th root of unity (p. 150) A primitive nth root of unity is a solution to $x^n - 1 = 0$ that is not a solution any equation $x^m - 1 = 0$ where $m < n$.

probability density function (p. 619) The probability density function (PDF) finds the height on a normal curve at a value for a given mean and standard deviation to approximate the height in the matching histogram.

probability distribution (p. 607) A probability distribution is a function that assigns a probability to each numeric output of a random variable.

probability histogram (p. 603) A probability histogram is a histogram where the heights (and areas) of the bars are probabilities instead of frequencies.

probability of an event (p. 542) The probability of an event A, denoted $P(A)$, is the number of outcomes in A, divided by the number of outcomes in the sample space S.

$$P(A) = \frac{\text{number of outcomes in } A}{\text{number of outcomes in } S} = \frac{|A|}{|S|}$$

Pythagorean identity (p. 20) $\cos^2 x + \sin^2 x = 1$

R

radian (p. 9) A radian is an arc of length 1 unit on the unit circle.

random variable (p. 555) A random variable is function whose inputs are outcomes, and whose outputs are numbers.

rational functions (p. 205) Rational functions are functions of the form $x \mapsto \frac{p(x)}{q(x)}$, where p and q are polynomial functions of x.

reciprocal functions (p. 206) Functions f and g are called reciprocal functions if they have the property that $g(x) = \frac{1}{f(x)}$ for any x in the domain of both functions.

rectangular coordinates (p. 92) Rectangular coordinates (x, y) denote distances along two axes that are perpendicular.

rectangular form for complex numbers (p. 93) The rectangular form for complex numbers is written $x + yi$, where x and y are real numbers.

recurrence (p. 412) A recurrence is a special kind of functional equation that tells how the output of function at integer n is related to the outputs at integers less than n.

recursive definition (p. 347) A recursive definition of a function f defines most of the outputs of f in terms of other outputs.

removable discontinuity (p. 211) Let $h(x) = \frac{f(x)}{g(x)}$ be a rational function such that

- $f(x) = (x - a)^m \cdot p(x)$
- $g(x) = (x - a)^n \cdot q(x)$

where $p(a), q(a) \neq 0$. h has a removable discontinuity at $x = a$ if $m \geq n > 0$.

rhombus (p. 453) A rhombus is a quadrilateral with four congruent sides.

root mean squared deviation (p. 576) The root mean squared deviation is calculated by finding the square root of the mean squared deviation.

roots of unity (p. 134) Roots of unity are solutions to $x^n = 1$.

S

sample space (p. 542) The sample space is a set.

scalar (p. 501) A scalar is a real number.

secant (p. 180) Let f be a function and suppose A and B are distinct points on the graph of $y = f(x)$. A line secant to the graph of $y = f(x)$ is the line passing through A and B.

signed power of a point (p. 459) The signed power of a point P, d units from the center of a circle of radius r, with respect to the circle is given by $\Pi_S(P) = d^2 - r^2$.

sinusoidal function (p. 60) A sinusoidal function is a function that's defined by a formula of the form

$$f(x) = A\sin(ax + b) + b \text{ or}$$
$$f(x) = A\cos(ax + b) + B$$

where A, B, a, or b are real numbers.

slope formula (p. 444) The slope formula between points $A(x_1, y_1)$ and $B(x_2, y_2)$ is

$$m(A, B) = \frac{y_2 - y_1}{x_2 - x_1}$$

slope of a vector (p. 505) The slope of a vector with displacement $D = (c, d)$ is $\frac{d}{c}$.

spread (p. 575) The spread of the output values of a random variable is the difference of the maximum output value and the minimum output value.

standard deviation (p. 577) The standard deviation σ for a data set $\{x_1, x_2, \ldots, x_n\}$ is given by

$$\sigma = \sqrt{\frac{\sum_i (x_i - \bar{x})^2}{n}}$$

where $\bar{x}$ is the mean of the data set.

The standard deviation is the common name for the root mean squared deviation.

structure-preserving map (p. 228) The map $A \mapsto \mathcal{R}_A$ is said to be structure-preserving because the product AB maps to the composition $\mathcal{R}_A \circ \mathcal{R}_{B'}$

subset (p. 283) A subset is any group of elements from a set.

T

tail of a vector (p. 503) The tail of a vector $\overrightarrow{PQ}$ is at point P.

tangent line (p. 198) Let f be a function and A is a point on the graph of $y = f(x)$. The tangent line to the graph of $y = f(x)$ at A is the line secant between A and itself.

Taylor expansion (p. 190) The Taylor expansion for a function f about c is the expression of $f(x)$ in terms of powers of $x - c$.

theoretical probability (p. 592) The theoretical probability of an event is equal to the ratio of the number of outcomes that meet the criteria for the event to the total number of possible outcomes.

translation (p. 231) A translation by a real number g is a transformation T_g of $\mathbb{R}$ given by $T_g(x) = x + g$ for any real number x.

trapezoid (p. 456) A trapezoid is a quadrilateral with one pair of parallel sides.

turning point (p. 27) A turning point for a function is an input x where the function changes from increasing to decreasing, or from decreasing to increasing. Sometimes the phrase turning point refers to the actual coordinates $(x, f(x))$ of the point where this change occurs.

two-term recurrence (p. 413) A two-term recurrence is a recurrence that depends on the two previous terms.

U

unit normal distribution (p. 617) The unit normal distribution is a normal distribution that has mean 0 and standard deviation 1. Here are it's equation and graph:

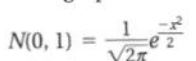

$$N(0, 1) = \frac{1}{\sqrt{2\pi}}e^{\frac{-x^2}{2}}$$

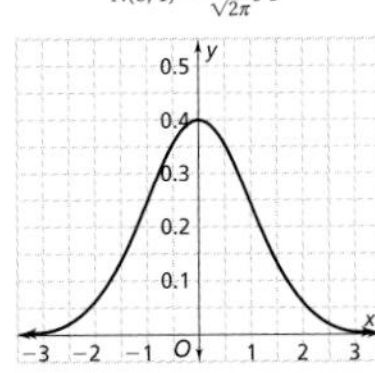

up-and-over property (p. 375) The up-and-over property of difference tables is that any number in the table (other than inputs) is the sum of two numbers—the number directly above it and the number directly to the right of the one above it.

V

variance (p. 577) The variance σ^2 for a data set $\{x_1, x_2, \ldots, x_n\}$ is given by

$$\sigma^2 = \frac{\sum_i (x_i - \bar{x})^2}{n}$$

where $\bar{x}$ is the mean of the data set.

The variance is the common name for the mean squared deviation.

vector (p. 503) A vector $\overrightarrow{PQ}$ is an arrow with tail at point P and head at point Q.

vector equation of a line (p. 511) Let P be a point, D be a vector, and k be a scalar. Then $X = P + kD$ is called the vector equation of a line. You may replace the scalar k by the letter t.

vertical displacement (p. 62) The vertical displacement of a sinusoidal function f is its average value. More precisely, it is the average of the maximum and the minimum values of f.

vertices (p. 477) The vertices of an ellipse are the endpoints of the major and minor axes of the ellipse.

Z

***z*-score (p. 598)** The z-score is the number of standard deviations away from the mean.

Selected Answers

Chapter 1

Lesson 1.1

On Your Own

11. b. Start with $\frac{3\pi}{2}$ and add 2π repeatedly.
14. The maximum and minimum values for the x-coordinates are 1 and -1, respectively, and likewise for the y-coordinates. For one trip around the circle, the maximum value of the x-coordinates occurs when the distance walked is 0 m and 2π m, and the minimum value occurs when the distance walked is π m. The maximum value of the y-coordinates occurs when the distance walked is $\frac{\pi}{2}$ m, and the minimum value occurs when the distance walked is $\frac{3\pi}{2}$ m.

Lesson 1.2

Check Your Understanding

1. a. $\cos\frac{2\pi}{3} = -\frac{1}{2}$, $\sin\frac{2\pi}{3} = \frac{\sqrt{3}}{2}$ **b.** $\cos\frac{4\pi}{3} = -\frac{1}{2}$, $\sin\frac{4\pi}{3} = -\frac{\sqrt{3}}{2}$ **c.** $\cos\frac{5\pi}{3} = \frac{1}{2}$, $\sin\frac{5\pi}{3} = -\frac{\sqrt{3}}{2}$ **d.** $\cos\frac{6\pi}{3} = 1$, $\sin\frac{6\pi}{3} = 0$ **2.** $\cos\frac{\pi}{4} = \sin\frac{\pi}{4} = \frac{\sqrt{2}}{2}$

3.

x	$\cos x$	$\sin x$
0	1	0
$\frac{\pi}{6}$	$\frac{\sqrt{3}}{2}$	$\frac{1}{2}$
$\frac{\pi}{4}$	$\frac{\sqrt{2}}{2}$	$\frac{\sqrt{2}}{2}$
$\frac{\pi}{3}$	$\frac{1}{2}$	$\frac{\sqrt{3}}{2}$
$\frac{\pi}{2}$	0	1
$\frac{2\pi}{3}$	$-\frac{1}{2}$	$\frac{\sqrt{3}}{2}$
$\frac{3\pi}{4}$	$-\frac{\sqrt{2}}{2}$	$\frac{\sqrt{2}}{2}$
$\frac{5\pi}{6}$	$-\frac{\sqrt{3}}{2}$	$\frac{1}{2}$
π	-1	0
$\frac{7\pi}{6}$	$-\frac{\sqrt{3}}{2}$	$-\frac{1}{2}$
$\frac{5\pi}{4}$	$-\frac{\sqrt{2}}{2}$	$-\frac{\sqrt{2}}{2}$
$\frac{4\pi}{3}$	$-\frac{1}{2}$	$-\frac{\sqrt{3}}{2}$
$\frac{3\pi}{2}$	0	-1
$\frac{5\pi}{3}$	$\frac{1}{2}$	$-\frac{\sqrt{3}}{2}$
$\frac{7\pi}{4}$	$\frac{\sqrt{2}}{2}$	$-\frac{\sqrt{2}}{2}$
$\frac{11\pi}{6}$	$\frac{\sqrt{3}}{2}$	$-\frac{1}{2}$
2π	1	0
$\frac{13\pi}{6}$	$\frac{\sqrt{3}}{2}$	$\frac{1}{2}$
$\frac{9\pi}{4}$	$\frac{\sqrt{2}}{2}$	$\frac{\sqrt{2}}{2}$
$\frac{7\pi}{3}$	$\frac{1}{2}$	$\frac{\sqrt{3}}{2}$

4. $\cos^2 x + \sin^2 x = 1$ **5. a.** Yes; the vertical line through $\left(\frac{4}{5}, 0\right)$ intersects the unit circle in two points. **b.** $\pm\frac{3}{5}$ **6.** B **7. a.** Yes; answers may vary. Sample: $\sin 33 \approx 0.999912$ **b.** No; if $\sin x = -1$, then x must be a number of the form $\frac{3\pi}{2} + n(2\pi)$, where n is an integer.

On Your Own

8. $\left(\frac{\sqrt{3}}{2}, \frac{1}{2}\right)$ **11. b.** negative **14.** -1

Lesson 1.3

Check Your Understanding

1. A **2. a.** 0.36; 0.64 **b.** ± 0.8
c.

3. The solutions are approximately 0.9 and 5.4.

4. a. $\cos\left(-\frac{\pi}{2}\right) = 0$, $\sin\left(-\frac{\pi}{2}\right) = -1$
b. $\cos\left(-\frac{\pi}{3}\right) = \frac{1}{2}$, $\sin\left(-\frac{\pi}{3}\right) = -\frac{\sqrt{3}}{2}$
5. a. They are equal. **b.** They are opposites.
6. a. not always **b.** always **c.** always **d.** not always

On Your Own

7.

8. Quadrant IV **12. b.** The period of the new graph will be half the period of the graph in part (a).

Lesson 1.4

Check Your Understanding

1. $\frac{7\pi}{6}$ and $\frac{11\pi}{6}$ **2.** all numbers of the forms $\frac{7\pi}{6} + 2\pi n$ and $\frac{11\pi}{6} + 2\pi n$, where n is an integer **3.** -0.7599
4. all measures of the forms $50° + 360°n$ and $130° + 360°n$, where n is an integer **5.** 0.79

6. a–e. Answers may vary. Samples are given.
a. $\sin x = 1$ **b.** $\sin x = \frac{1}{2}$ **c.** $\cos x = 2$ **d.** $\sin 2x = \frac{1}{2}$
e. $\sin 3x = \frac{1}{2}$ **7.** $\alpha = 0, \theta = \frac{\pi}{6}$ or $\alpha = 0, \theta = \frac{5\pi}{6}$

On Your Own

8. -1 and $\frac{3}{5}$ **10. b.** $\cos 160° = -\cos 20°$
14. a. $\theta \approx 56.3° + 360°n$ and $\theta \approx 123.7° + 360°n$, where n is an integer **15.** $\frac{\pi}{3}, \frac{\pi}{2}, \frac{3\pi}{2}, \frac{5\pi}{3}$

Lesson 1.5

Check Your Understanding

1. The slope is 0. **2.** The maximum slope is 1, and it occurs where $x = 2\pi n$ (n an integer). The minimum slope is -1, and it occurs where $x = (2n + 1)\pi$ (n an integer). You can estimate these maximum and minimum slopes by examining the graph of $y = \sin x$.
3. a. $y = x$ **b.** 1 **4. a.** The graph should look the same as the graph of $y = \cos x$. **b.** the cosine function
5. a.

b. The functions have the same value for each value of x since $\cos^4 x - \sin^4 x = (\cos^2 x + \sin^2 x)(\cos^2 x - \sin^2 x) = 1 \cdot (\cos^2 x - \sin^2 x) = \cos^2 x - \sin^2 x$.

On Your Own

6. c. The values of x where the maximum and minimum of $y = \sin x$ occur are, respectively, $\frac{\pi}{2}$ units greater than those for $y = \cos x$. **7. a.** in intervals of the form $\left[-\frac{\pi}{2} + 2\pi n, \frac{\pi}{2} + 2\pi n\right]$, where n is an integer **11.** The graph of $c(x)$ is the same as the graph of $y = 1$.

Lesson 1.6

On Your Own

7. a. 2 **8. b.** $\sec x$ is larger for $0 < x < \frac{\pi}{2}$. By definition, $\tan x = \frac{\sin x}{\cos x}$ and $\sec x = \frac{1}{\cos x}$. For $0 < x < \frac{\pi}{2}$, we have $\frac{\sin x}{\cos x} < \frac{1}{\cos x}$ since $\sin x < 1$. Therefore $\tan x < \sec x$.

Lesson 1.7

Check Your Understanding

1. a.

b.

c.

d.

e.

2. $\cos^2 x + \sin^2 x = 1$ for all values of x, so $\cos x = \pm\sqrt{1 - \sin^2 x}$. Since $0 < 0.38 < \frac{\pi}{2}$, $\cos 0.38 = \sqrt{1 - \sin^2 0.38}$. Therefore, use the calculator to evaluate $\frac{\sin 0.38}{\sqrt{1 - \sin^2 0.38}}$.

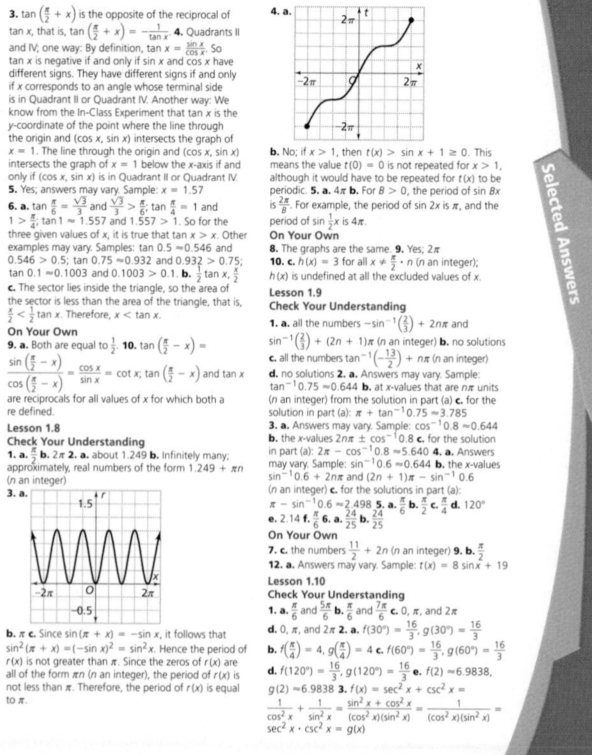

3. $\tan\left(\frac{\pi}{2} + x\right)$ is the opposite of the reciprocal of $\tan x$, that is, $\tan\left(\frac{\pi}{2} + x\right) = -\frac{1}{\tan x}$. **4.** Quadrants II and IV; one way: By definition, $\tan x = \frac{\sin x}{\cos x}$. So $\tan x$ is negative if and only if $\sin x$ and $\cos x$ have different signs. They have different signs if and only if x corresponds to an angle whose terminal side is in Quadrant II or Quadrant IV. Another way: We know from the In-Class Experiment that $\tan x$ is the y-coordinate of the point where the line through the origin and $(\cos x, \sin x)$ intersects the graph of $x = 1$. The line through the origin and $(\cos x, \sin x)$ intersects the graph of $x = 1$ below the x-axis if and only if $(\cos x, \sin x)$ is in Quadrant II or Quadrant IV.
5. Yes; answers may vary. Sample: $x = 1.57$
6. a. $\tan\frac{\pi}{6} = \frac{\sqrt{3}}{3}$ and $\frac{\sqrt{3}}{3} > \frac{\pi}{6}$; $\tan\frac{\pi}{4} = 1$ and $1 > \frac{\pi}{4}$; $\tan 1 \approx 1.557$ and $1.557 > 1$. So for the three given values of x, it is true that $\tan x > x$. Other examples may vary. Samples: $\tan 0.5 \approx 0.546$ and $0.546 > 0.5$; $\tan 0.75 \approx 0.932$ and $0.932 > 0.75$; $\tan 0.1 \approx 0.1003$ and $0.1003 > 0.1$. **b.** $\frac{1}{2}\tan x$, $\frac{x}{2}$
c. The sector lies inside the triangle, so the area of the sector is less than the area of the triangle, that is, $\frac{x}{2} < \frac{1}{2}\tan x$. Therefore, $x < \tan x$.

On Your Own

9. a. Both are equal to $\frac{1}{2}$. **10.** $\tan\left(\frac{\pi}{2} - x\right) = \frac{\sin\left(\frac{\pi}{2} - x\right)}{\cos\left(\frac{\pi}{2} - x\right)} = \frac{\cos x}{\sin x} = \cot x$; $\tan\left(\frac{\pi}{2} - x\right)$ and $\tan x$ are reciprocals for all values of x for which both a re defined.

Lesson 1.8

Check Your Understanding

1. a. $\frac{\pi}{2}$ **b.** 2π **2. a.** about 1.249 **b.** Infinitely many; approximately, real numbers of the form $1.249 + \pi n$ (n an integer)
3. a.

b. π **c.** Since $\sin(\pi + x) = -\sin x$, it follows that $\sin^2(\pi + x) = (-\sin x)^2 = \sin^2 x$. Hence the period of $r(x)$ is not greater than π. Since the zeros of $r(x)$ are all of the form πn (n an integer), the period of $r(x)$ is not less than π. Therefore, the period of $r(x)$ is equal to π.

4. a.

b. No; if $x > 1$, then $t(x) > \sin x + 1 \geq 0$. This means the value $t(0) = 0$ is not repeated for $x > 1$, although it would have to be repeated for $t(x)$ to be periodic. **5. a.** 4π **b.** For $B > 0$, the period of $\sin Bx$ is $\frac{2\pi}{B}$. For example, the period of $\sin 2x$ is π, and the period of $\sin\frac{1}{2}x$ is 4π.

On Your Own

8. The graphs are the same. **9.** Yes; 2π
10. c. $h(x) = 3$ for all $x \neq \frac{\pi}{2} \cdot n$ (n an integer); $h(x)$ is undefined at all the excluded values of x.

Lesson 1.9

Check Your Understanding

1. a. all the numbers $-\sin^{-1}\left(\frac{2}{3}\right) + 2n\pi$ and $\sin^{-1}\left(\frac{2}{3}\right) + (2n + 1)\pi$ (n an integer) **b.** no solutions
c. all the numbers $\tan^{-1}\left(-\frac{13}{2}\right) + n\pi$ (n an integer)
d. no solutions **2. a.** Answers may vary. Sample: $\tan^{-1} 0.75 \approx 0.644$ **b.** at x-values that are $n\pi$ units (n an integer) from the solution in part (a) **c.** for the solution in part (a): $\pi + \tan^{-1} 0.75 \approx 3.785$
3. a. Answers may vary. Sample: $\cos^{-1} 0.8 \approx 0.644$ **b.** the x-values $2n\pi \pm \cos^{-1} 0.8$ **c.** for the solution in part (a): $2\pi - \cos^{-1} 0.8 \approx 5.640$ **4. a.** Answers may vary. Sample: $\sin^{-1} 0.6 \approx 0.644$ **b.** the x-values $\sin^{-1} 0.6 + 2n\pi$ and $(2n + 1)\pi - \sin^{-1} 0.6$ (n an integer) **c.** for the solutions in part (a): $\pi - \sin^{-1} 0.6 \approx 2.498$ **5. a.** $\frac{\pi}{6}$ **b.** $\frac{\pi}{2}$ **c.** $\frac{\pi}{4}$ **d.** 120°
e. 2.14 **f.** $\frac{\pi}{6}$ **6. a.** $\frac{24}{25}$ **b.** $\frac{24}{25}$

On Your Own

7. c. the numbers $\frac{11}{2} + 2n$ (n an integer) **9. b.** $\frac{\pi}{2}$
12. a. Answers may vary. Sample: $t(x) = 8\sin x + 19$

Lesson 1.10

Check Your Understanding

1. a. $\frac{\pi}{6}$ and $\frac{5\pi}{6}$ **b.** $\frac{\pi}{6}$ and $\frac{7\pi}{6}$ **c.** 0, π, and 2π
d. 0, π, and 2π **2. a.** $f(30°) = \frac{16}{3}$, $g(30°) = \frac{16}{3}$
b. $f\left(\frac{\pi}{4}\right) = 4$, $g\left(\frac{\pi}{4}\right) = 4$ **c.** $f(60°) = \frac{16}{3}$, $g(60°) = \frac{16}{3}$
d. $f(120°) = \frac{16}{3}$, $g(120°) = \frac{16}{3}$ **e.** $f(2) \approx 6.9838$, $g(2) \approx 6.9838$ **3.** $f(x) = \sec^2 x + \csc^2 x = \frac{1}{\cos^2 x} + \frac{1}{\sin^2 x} = \frac{\sin^2 x + \cos^2 x}{(\cos^2 x)(\sin^2 x)} = \frac{1}{(\cos^2 x)(\sin^2 x)} = \sec^2 x \cdot \csc^2 x = g(x)$

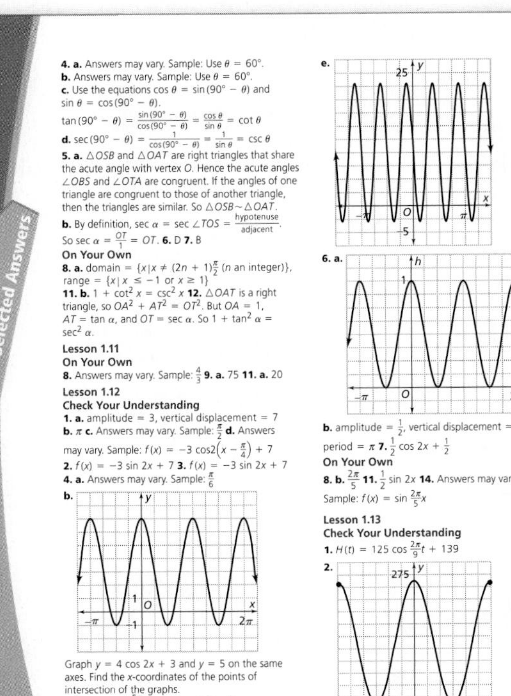

4. a. Answers may vary. Sample: Use $\theta = 60°$.
b. Answers may vary. Sample: Use $\theta = 60°$.
c. Use the equations $\cos\theta = \sin(90° - \theta)$ and $\sin\theta = \cos(90° - \theta)$.
$\tan(90° - \theta) = \frac{\sin(90° - \theta)}{\cos(90° - \theta)} = \frac{\cos\theta}{\sin\theta} = \cot\theta$
d. $\sec(90° - \theta) = \frac{1}{\cos(90° - \theta)} = \frac{1}{\sin\theta} = \csc\theta$
5. a. $\triangle OSB$ and $\triangle OAT$ are right triangles that share the acute angle with vertex O. Hence the acute angles $\angle OBS$ and $\angle OTA$ are congruent. If the angles of one triangle are congruent to those of another triangle, then the triangles are similar. So $\triangle OSB \sim \triangle OAT$.
b. By definition, $\sec\alpha = \sec\angle TOS = \frac{\text{hypotenuse}}{\text{adjacent}}$. So $\sec\alpha = \frac{OT}{1} = OT$. **6.** D **7.** B

On Your Own

8. a. domain $= \{x \mid x \neq (2n + 1)\frac{\pi}{2}$ (n an integer)$\}$, range $= \{x \mid x \leq -1$ or $x \geq 1\}$
11. b. $1 + \cot^2 x = \csc^2 x$ **12.** $\triangle OAT$ is a right triangle, so $OA^2 + AT^2 = OT^2$. But $OA = 1$, $AT = \tan\alpha$, and $OT = \sec\alpha$. So $1 + \tan^2\alpha = \sec^2\alpha$.

Lesson 1.11
On Your Own

8. Answers may vary. Sample: $\frac{4}{3}$ **9. a.** 75 **11. a.** 20

Lesson 1.12
Check Your Understanding

1. a. amplitude = 3, vertical displacement = 7
b. π **c.** Answers may vary. Sample: $\frac{\pi}{2}$ **d.** Answers may vary. Sample: $f(x) = -3\cos 2\left(x - \frac{\pi}{4}\right) + 7$
2. $f(x) = -3\sin 2x + 7$ **3.** $f(x) = -3\sin 2x + 7$
4. a. Answers may vary. Sample: $\frac{\pi}{6}$
b.

Graph $y = 4\cos 2x + 3$ and $y = 5$ on the same axes. Find the x-coordinates of the points of intersection of the graphs.
c. $\frac{\pi}{6} + n\pi$ and $\frac{5\pi}{6} + n\pi$ (n an integer)
5. a. $g(x) = 13\sin\left(4 \cdot \frac{\pi}{4} - \pi\right) + 10 = 13\sin 0 + 10 = 10$ **b.** amplitude = 13, vertical displacement = 10 **c.** maximum = 23, minimum = −3 **d.** $\frac{\pi}{2}$

e.

6. a.

b. amplitude $= \frac{1}{2}$, vertical displacement $= \frac{1}{2}$, period $= \pi$ **7.** $\frac{1}{2}\cos 2x + \frac{1}{2}$

On Your Own

8. b. $\frac{2\pi}{5}$ **11.** $\frac{1}{2}\sin 2x$ **14.** Answers may vary. Sample: $f(x) = \sin\frac{2\pi}{5}x$

Lesson 1.13
Check Your Understanding

1. $H(t) = 125\cos\frac{2\pi}{9}t + 139$
2.

3. a. 1 min 31 s **b.** about $7\frac{1}{2}$ min **c.** 7 min 29 s
4. a. 8:24 P.M., 8:48 A.M. (next day) **b.** 2:12 P.M.; 2:36 A.M. (next day)

c. The numbers along the horizontal axis represent minutes.

5. $H(t) = 3.5\cos\frac{2\pi}{12.4}(t - 8) + 5.5$
6.

7. a. about 4 ft; about 4.6 ft **b.** about 5.5 ft
c. Answers may vary. Sample: about 11:30 P.M.
d. Answers may vary. Sample: about 10:49 A.M.
8. a. about 3.77 ft/s **b.** about 2.57 mph
c. The first two times are $t = 15$ s and $t = 45$ s.

On Your Own

10. B **13.** the Ferris wheel with radius 36 ft
14. b. about 2.99 ft

Chapter 2

Lesson 2.1
On Your Own

8. c. $f(1 + i) = (1 + i - 1)^2 + 1 = i^2 + 1 = 0$
10. d. 25 **12. b.** amplitude = 1, period = π

Lesson 2.2
Check Your Understanding

1. a. $\sqrt{17}$ **b.** $\sqrt{5}$ **c.** $\sqrt{13}$ **d.** $\sqrt{61}$
2. a. 17 **b.** 5 **c.** 13 **d.** 61
Each product is the square of the corresponding answer in Exercise 1.

3. a.

$\arg(z) \approx 0.588$, $\arg(i \cdot z) \approx 2.159$
b.

$\arg(z) \approx 1.816$, $\arg(i \cdot z) \approx 3.387$
c.

$\arg(z) \approx 4.391$, $\arg(i \cdot z) \approx 5.961$
d.

$\arg(z) \approx 5.300$, $\arg(i \cdot z) \approx 0.588$
4. a. magnitude $= 2\sqrt{2}$, argument $= \frac{\pi}{4}$
b. magnitude $= 2\sqrt{2}$, argument $= \frac{7\pi}{4}$
c. magnitude $= 2\sqrt{2}$, argument $= \frac{3\pi}{4}$
d. magnitude $= 2\sqrt{2}$, argument $= \frac{5\pi}{4}$

5. a. $|iz| = |z|$, $\arg(iz) = \arg(z) + \frac{\pi}{2}$
b. $|i^2 z| = |z|$, $\arg(i^2 z) = \arg(z) + \pi$
c. $|(-i)z| = |z|$, $\arg((-i)z) = \arg(z) + \frac{3\pi}{2}$
d. $|2z| = 2|z|$, $\arg(2z) = \arg(z)$
e. $\left|\frac{1}{z}\right| = \frac{1}{|z|}$, $\arg\left(\frac{1}{z}\right) = 2\pi - \arg(z)$

On Your Own

6. $|3z| = 3|z|$ and $\arg(3z) = \arg(z)$
9. a. $(\cos^2 t - \sin^2 t) + (2\sin t\cos t)i$ **13. c.** 10

Lesson 2.3
Check Your Understanding

1. a. magnitude = 5, argument = 60°
b. magnitude $= \frac{1}{5}$, argument = 300°
2. a. magnitude = 25, argument = 120°
b. magnitude = 125, argument = 180°
c. magnitude = 1, argument = 0° (or 360°)
3. a.

b.

c. $-5\sqrt{3} - 5i$ **4. a.** $4\cos\frac{2\pi}{3} + 4i\sin\frac{2\pi}{3}$
b. $-2 + 2i\sqrt{3}$ **5. a.** Answers may vary. Samples: $a = 5$ cis 60° or $a = \frac{5}{2} + \frac{5\sqrt{3}}{2}i$, $b = 3$ cis 30° or $b = \frac{3\sqrt{3}}{2} + \frac{3}{2}i$ **b.** $15i$; magnitude = 15, argument = 90° **6. a.** Check students' work. The values of θ will vary, but for each value of θ that is selected, the number z should be on the ray that has endpoint O and makes an angle of measure θ with the positive x-axis, and z should be 3 units from O.
b. The circle with center O and radius 3; $|z| = 3$ since $z = 3$ cis θ. Since there are no restrictions on θ, all points 3 units from O are included.
7. a. $|\text{cis}\,\theta| = |\cos\theta + i\sin\theta| = \sqrt{\cos^2\theta + \sin^2\theta} = 1$ **b.** $|r\,\text{cis}\,\theta| = |r| \cdot |\text{cis}\,\theta| = |r| \cdot 1 = |r|$

On Your Own

8. b. magnitude = 10, argument = 330°
11. b. $(\cos\alpha\cos\beta - \sin\alpha\sin\beta) + (\cos\alpha\sin\beta + \sin\alpha\cos\beta)i$

Lesson 2.4
Check Your Understanding

1. a. $|z^2| = 9$, $\arg(z^2) = 240°$ **b.** Answers may vary. Sample: $z^3 = 3^3$ cis $3(120°) = 27(\cos 360° + i\sin 360°) = 27(1 + i \cdot 0) = 27$
2. To find $|z^2|$, square $|z|$; to find $\arg(z^2)$, multiply $\arg(z)$ by 2. To find $|z^3|$, cube $|z|$; to find $\arg(z^3)$, multiply $\arg(z)$ by 3. In general, if n is a nonnegative integer, to find $|z^n|$, raise $|z|$ to the nth power; to find $\arg(z^n)$, multiply $\arg(z)$ by n. **3. a.** false
b. true; $3^3 = 27$ and $3 \cdot 40° = 120°$ **c.** false
d. true; $3^3 = 27$ and $3 \cdot 160° = 480°$ and $480° - 360° = 120°$ **4.** Answers may vary. Sample: $|zw| \approx 13$, $\arg(zw) \approx 160°$ **5.** To find the magnitude of the product, multiply the magnitudes of the two numbers. To find the argument of the product, use the sum modulo 360° of the arguments of the numbers.
6. a.

Since $|i| = 1$, all the powers have magnitude 1. Multiplying a number by i rotates the number around O counterclockwise by 90°. Since 360° is evenly divisible by 90°, the set of powers consists of just 4 numbers.
b.

Since $|-i| = 1$, all the powers have magnitude 1. Because of the minus sign, multiplying by $-i$ rotates the other number not counterclockwise but clockwise

around O by 90°. Since 360° is evenly divisible by 90°, the set of powers consists of just 4 numbers.
c.

$|z| = \sqrt{2}$ and $\arg(z) = 45°$, so for each nonnegative integer n, you can obtain z^{n+1} if you rotate z^n counterclockwise 45° and then scale by $\sqrt{2}$.
d.

$|z| = \sqrt{2}$ and $\arg(z) = 315°$, so for each nonnegative integer n, you can obtain z^{n+1} if you rotate z^n clockwise 45° and then scale by $\sqrt{2}$.
e.

$|z| = \sqrt{5}$ and $\arg(z) \approx 26.6°$, so for each nonnegative integer n, you can obtain z^{n+1} if you rotate z^n counterclockwise by about 26.6° and then scale by $\sqrt{5}$.

f.

$|z| = \sqrt{5}$ and $\arg(z) \approx 333.4349°$, so for each nonnegative integer n, you can obtain z^{n+1} if you rotate z^n clockwise by about 26.6° and then scale by $\sqrt{5}$.

On Your Own

9. a. Answers may vary. Sample: $1 + i$ and $5 + 5i$
11. b. Quadrant I; $\arg(zw)$ is the sum of $\arg(z)$ and $\arg(w)$, or about 398°. Since 398° − 360° = 38°, the vector for zw will be in Quadrant I.
12. b. $\left|\frac{z}{w}\right| = \sqrt{2}$, $\arg\left(\frac{z}{w}\right) = \tan^{-1}\left(\frac{1}{7}\right) \approx 8.13°$

Lesson 2.5
On Your Own

11. D **15.** $\cot x$ **18.** $\frac{\pi}{6}, \frac{5\pi}{6}, \frac{7\pi}{6}, \frac{11\pi}{6}$

Lesson 2.6
Check Your Understanding

1. Answers may vary. Sample: $\cos 3x = \cos^3 x - 3\sin^2 x\cos x$, $\sin 3x = 3\sin x\cos^2 x - \sin^3 x$
2. a. Answers may vary. Sample: $\frac{\sqrt{2}}{2} + \frac{\sqrt{2}}{2}i$ and $\frac{\sqrt{3}}{2} + \frac{1}{2}i$ **b.** $\cos 75° = \frac{\sqrt{6} - \sqrt{2}}{4}$, $\sin 75° = \frac{\sqrt{6} + \sqrt{2}}{4}$ **c.** $\frac{1}{2}$ **3. a.** $\frac{16}{65} + \frac{63}{65}i$ **b.** $\frac{63}{65}$
4. a. $\cos(\alpha + \beta) + \cos(\alpha - \beta) = \cos\alpha\cos\beta - \sin\alpha\sin\beta + \cos\alpha\cos(-\beta) - \sin\alpha\sin(-\beta) = \cos\alpha\cos\beta - \sin\alpha\sin\beta + \cos\alpha\cos\beta + \sin\alpha\sin\beta = 2\cos\alpha\cos\beta$ **b.** $\sin(\alpha + \beta) + \sin(\alpha - \beta) = 2\sin\alpha\cos\beta$
5. Check students' work. **6.** $\tan(\alpha + \beta) = \frac{\tan\alpha + \tan\beta}{1 - \tan\alpha\tan\beta}$
7. $\cos(\alpha + \beta + \gamma) = \cos\alpha\cos\beta\cos\gamma - \cos\alpha\sin\beta\sin\gamma - \sin\alpha\cos\beta\sin\gamma - \sin\alpha\sin\beta\cos\gamma$
$\sin(\alpha + \beta + \gamma) = \cos\alpha\cos\beta\sin\gamma + \cos\alpha\sin\beta\cos\gamma + \sin\alpha\cos\beta\cos\gamma - \sin\alpha\sin\beta\cos\gamma$

On Your Own

8. c. $\cos\left(x + \frac{\pi}{4}\right) = \frac{\sqrt{2}}{2}\cos x - \frac{\sqrt{2}}{2}\sin x$,
$\sin\left(x + \frac{\pi}{4}\right) = \frac{\sqrt{2}}{2}\sin x + \frac{\sqrt{2}}{2}\cos x$
11. a. $\tan 2x = \frac{2\tan x}{1 - \tan^2 x}$
13. a. $\frac{6 - \sqrt{35}}{12} + \frac{2\sqrt{7} + 3\sqrt{5}}{12}i$

Lesson 2.7
Check Your Understanding

1. a.
$$\begin{aligned}\tan^2 x - \sin^2 x &= \frac{\sin^2 x}{\cos^2 x} - \sin^2 x\\ &= \left(\frac{1}{\cos^2 x} - 1\right)\sin^2 x\\ &= \left(\frac{1 - \cos^2 x}{\cos^2 x}\right)\sin^2 x\\ &= \frac{\sin^2 x}{\cos^2 x}\cdot\sin^2 x\\ &= \tan^2 x\sin^2 x\end{aligned}$$

b.
$$\begin{aligned}\frac{\cos x}{1 - \sin x} &= \frac{\cos x}{1 - \sin x}\cdot\frac{1 + \sin x}{1 + \sin x}\\ &= \frac{\cos x(1 + \sin x)}{1 - \sin^2 x}\\ &= \frac{\cos x(1 + \sin x)}{\cos^2 x}\\ &= \frac{1 + \sin x}{\cos x}\end{aligned}$$

c.
$$\begin{aligned}\cot^2 x - \cos^2 x &= \frac{\cos^2 x}{\sin^2 x} - \cos^2 x\\ &= \left(\frac{1}{\sin^2 x} - 1\right)\cos^2 x\\ &= \left(\frac{1 - \sin^2 x}{\sin^2 x}\right)\cos^2 x\\ &= \frac{\cos^2 x}{\sin^2 x}\cdot\cos^2 x\\ &= \cot^2 x\cos^2 x\end{aligned}$$

d.
$$\begin{aligned}\frac{\sin x}{1 - \cos x} &= \frac{\sin x}{1 - \cos x}\cdot\frac{1 + \cos x}{1 + \cos x}\\ &= \frac{\sin x(1 + \cos x)}{1 - \cos^2 x}\\ &= \frac{\sin x(1 + \cos x)}{\sin^2 x}\\ &= \frac{1 + \cos x}{\sin x}\end{aligned}$$

2. The second equation is an identity. $(\cos x + \sin x)^2 = \cos^2 x + 2\cos x\sin x + \sin^2 x = 2\cos x\sin x + 1 = \sin 2x + 1$
3. Since $\cos(\alpha + \beta) + \cos(\alpha - \beta) = 2\cos\alpha\cos\beta$ is an identity, $\cos 5x + \cos 3x = 2\cos 4x\cos x$. Hence $\cos 5x = 2\cos x\cos 4x - \cos 3x$.
4. This identity follows directly from the identity $\cos(\alpha + \beta) + \cos(\alpha - \beta) = 2\cos\alpha\cos\beta$ if you let $\alpha = (n + 1)x$ and $\beta = (n - 1)x$.

5. a.
$$\begin{aligned}&(\sec x\sin x)^2 - (\sec x + 1)(\sec x - 1)\\ &= \frac{\sin^2 x}{\cos^2 x} - \left(\sec^2 x - 1\right)\\ &= \tan^2 x - \tan^2 x\\ &= 0\end{aligned}$$
b. Since $(\sec x\sin x)^2 - (\sec x + 1)(\sec x - 1) = 0$ is an identity, you obtain an identity if you add $(\sec x + 1)(\sec x - 1)$ to both sides.

On Your Own

6. b. Use the formula in Exercise 4, and let $n = 2$ to get $\cos 3x = 2\cos x\cos 2x - \cos x$. On the right side of this equation, replace $\cos 2x$ with $2\cos^2 x - 1$ and simplify to get $\cos 3x = 4\cos^3 x - 3\cos x$.

9. a.
$$\begin{aligned}\frac{\sec x + 1}{\tan x} &= \frac{\sec x + 1}{\tan x}\cdot\frac{\sec x - 1}{\sec x - 1}\\ &= \frac{\sec^2 x - 1}{\tan x(\sec x - 1)}\\ &= \frac{\tan^2 x}{\tan x(\sec x - 1)}\\ &= \frac{\tan x}{\sec x - 1}\end{aligned}$$

Lesson 2.8
On Your Own

9. c. 288° **13.** $4 + i$ and $4 - i$; sum = 8, product = 17

Lesson 2.9
Check Your Understanding

1. a. $|z^2| = 9$, $\arg(z^2) = \frac{2\pi}{3}$
b. $|z^3| = 27$, $\arg(z^3) = \pi$
c. $|z^5| = 243$, $\arg(z^5) = \frac{5\pi}{3}$
d. $|10z| = 30$, $\arg(10z) = \frac{\pi}{3}$
e. $|z^0| = 1$, $\arg(z^0) = 0$
f. $|z^{-1}| = \frac{1}{3}$, $\arg(z^{-1}) = \frac{5\pi}{3}$
2. $\sqrt{3}\text{ cis }\frac{\pi}{6}$, $\sqrt{3}\text{ cis }\frac{7\pi}{6}$
3. a. $|z^3| = 64$, $\arg(z^3) = 0$
b. $|z^3| = 64$, $\arg(z^3) = 0°$
c. $|z^3| = 8$, $\arg(z^3) = \frac{\pi}{2}$
d. $|z^3| = 8$, $\arg(z^3) = \frac{\pi}{2}$
4. sum = 0, product = $8i$ **5. a.** a^2 is a solution of $x^{11} = 1$ if and only if $(a^2)^{11} = 1$. Since $(a^2)^{11} = (a^{11})^2 = 1^2 = 1$, a^2 is a solution.
b. The proof is the same as in part (a), but with 2 replaced by k.

On Your Own

6. The solutions are -2 and $\pm 4\sqrt{5}$; their sum is -2, and their product is 160. **11. b.** cis 0, cis $\frac{2\pi}{5}$, cis $\frac{4\pi}{5}$, cis $\frac{6\pi}{5}$, and cis $\frac{8\pi}{5}$ **14.** $\frac{\sqrt{2} + \sqrt{6}}{4}$

Lesson 2.10
Check Your Understanding

1. a. The solution in Quadrant I should be labeled ω, ω^6, the solution in Quadrant II should be labeled ω^2, the solution in Quadrant III should be labeled ω^3, ω^{13}, the solution in Quadrant IV should be labeled ω^4, and the solution on the positive part of the real axis should be labeled ω^5. **b.** 1 **2. a.** 0 **b.** 0 **c.** The sum in part (b) is the sum of the imaginary parts of the six roots of $x^6 = 1$, and this sum must be 0 since the sum of the roots is 0.

3.

4. a.

b. The plot in part (a) is part of the plot from Exercise 3, so this illustrates graphically that the solutions of $x^6 - 1 = 0$ are solutions of $x^{12} - 1 = 0$. Algebraically, the solutions of $x^6 - 1 = 0$ are the numbers cis$\frac{2\pi}{6}k$ where k goes from 0 to 5. The solutions of $x^{12} - 1 = 0$ are the numbers cis$\frac{2\pi}{6}n$ where n goes from 0 to 11. **c.** This result follows immediately from part (b). **5.** Every multiple of 5 greater than 5 will work. **6.** 6 **7.** Yes; $n = 36$
8. a. Answers may vary. Sample: i **b.** Answers may vary. Sample: cis$\left(\frac{4\pi}{9}\right)$ **c.** yes

On Your Own

10. a. -1 **12. b.** 0 **15. a.** Suppose $z = x + yi$ and that z is a root of unity. Then $\frac{1}{z} = \frac{1}{x + yi} = \frac{x - yi}{x^2 + y^2}$. But $x^2 + y^2 = 1$ since z is a root of unity. So $\frac{1}{z} = x - yi = \bar{z}$.

Lesson 2.11
Check Your Understanding

1. 18 **2. a.** z^{21} = cis 357° **b.** Yes; 360 times
c. all rational values of θ **3. a.** $z^4 = \left(\text{cis }\frac{2\pi}{5}\right)^4 = \text{cis }\frac{8\pi}{5} = \text{cis}\left(-\frac{2\pi}{5}\right)$ **b.** Use the result from part (a). $z + z^4 = \text{cis }\frac{2\pi}{5} + \text{cis}\left(-\frac{2\pi}{5}\right) = 2\cos\frac{2\pi}{5}$
4. a. $(x - 1)(x^4 + x^3 + x^2 + x + 1)$ **b.** z is a root of $(z - 1)(z^4 + z^3 + z^2 + z + 1) = 0$, and since $z \neq 1$, the value of $z^4 + z^3 + z^2 + z + 1$ must be 0. It follows that $z^4 + z^3 + z^2 + z = -1$.
5. a. From Exercise 3(b), we know that $z + z^4$ is positive, since $2\cos\frac{2\pi}{5}$ is positive. (We know this is so because $0 < \frac{2\pi}{5} < \frac{\pi}{2}$.) By Exercise 4(b), $z^2 + z^3 = -1 - (z + z^4)$, and subtracting a positive number from -1 results in a negative number.
b. This result follows immediately from Exercise 4(b). **c.** $z^3 + z^4 + z^6 + z^7$, or $z + z^2 + z^3 + z^4$ (since $z^6 = z$ and $z^7 = z^2$) **d.** $ab = -1$ follows directly from part (c) and Exercise 4(b).
6. $a = \frac{-1 + \sqrt{5}}{2}$, $b = -\frac{1 + \sqrt{5}}{2}$
7. a. Use the result from Exercise 6, the fact that $a = z + z^4$, and Exercise 3(b) to obtain $2\cos 72° = \frac{-1 + \sqrt{5}}{2}$. This last equation gives $\cos 72° = \frac{-1 + \sqrt{5}}{4}$.
b. $\sin 72° = \frac{\sqrt{10 + 2\sqrt{5}}}{4}$
c. $z^0 = 1$, $z = \frac{-1 + \sqrt{5}}{4} + \frac{\sqrt{10 + 2\sqrt{5}}}{4}i$,
$z^2 = -\frac{1 + \sqrt{5}}{4} + \frac{\sqrt{10 - 2\sqrt{5}}}{4}i$,
$z^3 = -\frac{1 + \sqrt{5}}{4} - \frac{\sqrt{10 - 2\sqrt{5}}}{4}i$,
$z^4 = \frac{-1 + \sqrt{5}}{4} - \frac{\sqrt{10 + 2\sqrt{5}}}{4}i$
8. $x^5 - 1 = (x - 1)(x^4 + x^3 + x^2 + x + 1)$, so the given factorization is correct if $x^4 + x^3 + x^2 + x + 1$ equals $(x^2 + \Phi x + 1)\left(x^2 - \frac{1}{\Phi}x + 1\right)$. Expand this last expression and collect like terms to obtain $x^4 + \left(\Phi - \frac{1}{\Phi}\right)x^3 + x^2 + \left(\Phi - \frac{1}{\Phi}\right)x + 1$. Use $\Phi = \frac{1 + \sqrt{5}}{2}$ to show that $\Phi - \frac{1}{\Phi} = 1$. It follows that $x^4 + x^3 + x^2 + x + 1 = (x^2 + \Phi x + 1)\left(x^2 - \frac{1}{\Phi}x + 1\right)$.

On Your Own

9. 30 sides **10.** Let $\overline{AM}$ be the altitude to the base $\overline{BC}$ of isosceles $\triangle ABC$. Right triangle trigonometry tells you that $\cos\angle B = \cos 72° = \frac{BM}{1} = BM$. Likewise, $CM = \cos 72°$. **14.** $-\frac{\sqrt{5} + 1}{4}$

Lesson 2.12
Check Your Understanding

1. a. 0 **b.** 7 **c.** 1 **2. a.** 0 **b.** 0 **c.** -1 **3.** $f(n) = 5$ if n is a multiple of 5, otherwise $f(n) = 0$ **4. a.** 0 **b.** 1 **c.** 5 **5.** 5 **6. a.** 0 **b.** 0 **7. a.** cis$\left(\frac{2\pi}{12}\cdot 1\right)$, cis$\left(\frac{2\pi}{12}\cdot 5\right)$, cis$\left(\frac{2\pi}{12}\cdot 7\right)$, cis$\left(\frac{2\pi}{12}\cdot 11\right)$ **b.** $x^{12} - 1 = (x - 1)\cdot(x + 1)(x^2 + 1)(x^2 + x + 1)(x^2 - x + 1)\cdot(x^4 - x^2 + 1)$
The table shows which powers of ζ make which factors equal to 0.

Factor	Powers of ζ
$x - 1$	ζ^0
$x + 1$	ζ^6
$x^2 + 1$	ζ^3, ζ^9
$x^2 + x + 1$	ζ^4, ζ^8
$x^2 - x + 1$	ζ^2, ζ^{10}
$x^4 - x^2 + 1$	$\zeta, \zeta^5, \zeta^7, \zeta^{11}$

On Your Own

9. -7 **11. c.** $(x - 1)(x - \zeta)(x - \zeta^2)(x - \zeta^3)\cdot(x - \zeta^4)$, where $\zeta = \text{cis }\frac{2\pi}{5} = \frac{-1 + \sqrt{5}}{4} + \frac{\sqrt{10 + 2\sqrt{5}}}{4}i$ **15. a.** If $\zeta = \text{cis }\frac{2\pi}{9}$, then the primitive 9th roots of unity are $\zeta, \zeta^2, \zeta^4, \zeta^5, \zeta^7$, and ζ^8.

Chapter 3
Lesson 3.1
On Your Own

8. Not possible. For the graph to meet the first and third conditions, it would have to change directions more than just twice, as described in the second condition.
9. Answers may vary. Sample: $f(x) = |x + 3| - 2$

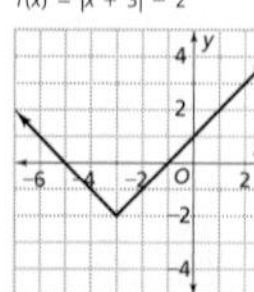

Lesson 3.2
Check Your Understanding

1. At birth, height in inches is larger; later in life, weight in pounds is larger. Since both change continuously, there must be at least one intersection.
2. a. $a(5) = 0$ **b.** $a(5.001)$ is a very small positive number. **c.** $a(0) = 30$ **d.** $a(0.001)$ is approximately 30. **e.** $a(1000)$ is a very large positive number.
f. $a(0.999)$ is a very small positive number.
g. $a(-1000)$ is a very large negative number.
3. a. Answers may vary. Sample: $g(x) = x^2 + 4x - 21$ **b.** Answers may vary. Sample: $h(x) = -\frac{2}{3}x^2 + \frac{4}{3}x + 10$ **c.** Answers may vary. Sample: $j(x) = -\frac{2}{3}x^2 + \frac{4}{3}x + 12$ **4. a.** x must be within 0.033 of 5. **b.** x must be within 0.0033 of 5. **c.** x must be within 0.00033 of 5. **d.** x must be within $0.00000033 = 3.3\cdot 10^{-7}$ of 5. **5.** The maximum number of intersections is 3 and the minimum number of intersections is 1. **6.** Consider fourth degree polynomials with a positive leading coefficient. Some possible shapes are:

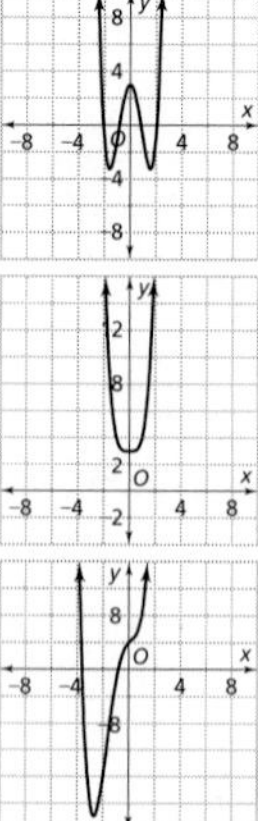

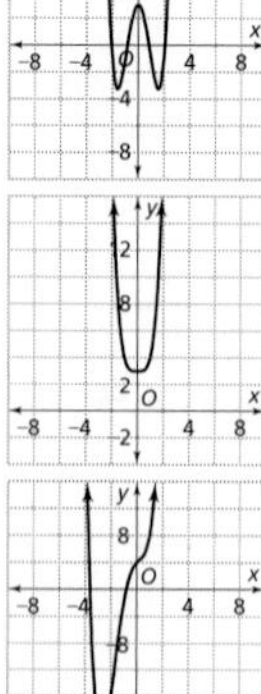

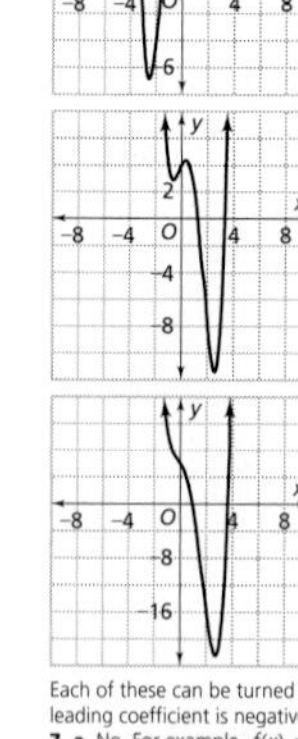

Each of these can be turned upside-down if the leading coefficient is negative.
7. a. No. For example, $f(x) = x^3$ has only one real zero. **b.** Yes. Since f has at least one real zero, $f\cdot g$ will have at least one real zero. **c.** Yes. Every zero of f is also a zero of f^2. Since f has at least one real zero, so does f^2. **d.** No. For example, $f(x) = x^3 + x^2$ and $g(x) = -x^3 + 4$ each have real zeros, but $k(x) = f(x) + g(x) = x^2 + 4$ does not. **e.** Yes. The composition of two cubic functions is a polynomial function of degree 9, and it must have at least one real zero.

On Your Own

9. a. $b(-5) = 0$ since one of the factors is zero. **b.** $b(-5.001)$ is a little bit less than 0. **c.** $b(0) = 30$ **d.** $b(0.001)$ is a little bit less than 30. **g.** $b(-1000)$ is a very large negative number. **11. a.** x must be within 0.059 of 5. **b.** x must be within 0.0059 of 5.

12. If the fourth degree polynomial rises, falls, rises, and falls and crosses the x-axis at $(-5,0)$, $(-1,0)$, and intersects it somewhere on the positive x-axis, it is of the form $f(x) = A(x + 5)(x + 1)(x - b)^2$ where $A < 0$ and $b > 0$. Choose some positive value for b, say $b = 1$. Then

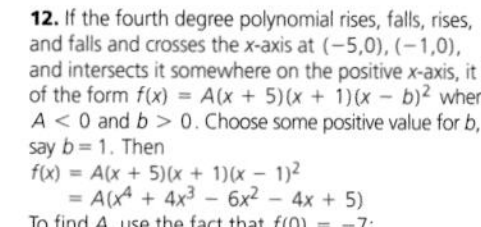

$$\begin{aligned}f(x) &= A(x + 5)(x + 1)(x - 1)^2\\ &= A(x^4 + 4x^3 - 6x^2 - 4x + 5)\end{aligned}$$
To find A, use the fact that $f(0) = -7$:
$f(0) = A(5) = -7 \Rightarrow A = -\frac{7}{5}$
A polynomial that satisfies the conditions is
$$\begin{aligned}f(x) &= -\frac{7}{5}(x^4 + 4x^3 - 6x^2 - 4x + 5)\\ &= -\frac{7}{5}x^4 - \frac{28}{5}x^3 + \frac{42}{5}x^2 + \frac{28}{5}x - 7\end{aligned}$$
14. a. $g(x)$ takes on large positive values.
b. $g(x)$ takes on large negative values.
18. Answers may vary. **a.** Yes; sample: $f(x) = x^4 + 1$. **b.** Yes; sample: $f(x) = x^3 + 8$. **c.** Yes; sample:
$$\begin{aligned}f(x) &= (x - 1)(x - 2)(x - 3)\\ &= x^3 - 6x^2 + 11x - 6\end{aligned}$$
19. Yes; sample: let $g(x) = x^3 - 4x + 1$. If $a = -3$, then $g(-3) = -14$ and if $b = 3$, $g(3) = 16$, but $g(x) = 0$ three times between $a = -3$ and $b = 3$. $g(x) = 0$ between $x = -3$ and $x = -2$, between $x = 0$ and $x = 1$ and between $x = 1$ and $x = 2$.

Lesson 3.3
Check Your Understanding

1. a. The average rate of change is 7.
b. The equation of the secant is $8x - y = -33$.
c. $m = a + b$
2. a. The equation of the secant is $\frac{y - 5}{x - 2} = 10.0601$ or $10.0601x - y = 15.1202$.
b. The equation of the secant is $\frac{y - 5}{x - 2} = b^2 + 2b + 2$ or $(b^2 + 2b + 2)x - y = 2b^2 + 4b - 1$.
c.

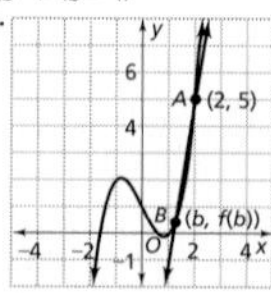

As b moves closer to 2, the slope gets closer to 10.

3. a. Answers may vary. Sample:

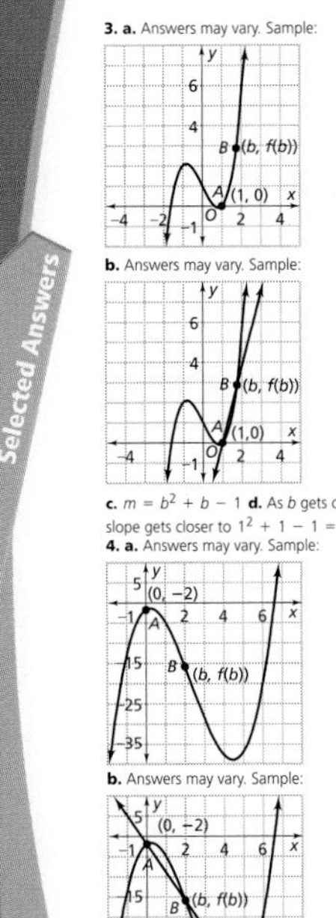

b. Answers may vary. Sample:

c. $m = b^2 + b - 1$ **d.** As b gets closer to 1, the slope gets closer to $1^2 + 1 - 1 = 1$.

4. a. Answers may vary. Sample:

b. Answers may vary. Sample:

c. $m = \frac{f(b) - (-2)}{b}$
$= \frac{b^3 - 7b^2 + 3b - 2 + 2}{b}$
$= \frac{(b)(b^2 - 7b + 3)}{b} = b^2 - 7b + 3$

d. As b gets closer to 0, the slope gets closer to $0^2 - 7(0) + 3 = 3$. **5.** $m = 3a + 3b + 5$
6. a. $(0, -10)$ **b.** $(0, 33)$ **c.** $(0, -ab)$ **7.** The slope is $a^2 + ab + b^2 = (a - b)^2 + 3ab = (a + b)^2 - ab$. Either the second or third expression must always be positive unless $a = b = 0$, which cannot happen since $a \neq b$. **8. a.** 9000 ft or approx. 1.7 mi **b.** 18,000 ft or approx. 3.4 mi **c.** 40,500 ft or approx. 7.7 mi **d.** $900t$ ft **9. a.** 0 ft; Pete has not caught John yet. **b.** 12,000 ft, or about $2\frac{1}{4}$ mi; Pete has not caught John yet. **c.** 42,000 ft, or about 8 mi; Pete has passed John. **d.** $1200(t - 10)$, where $t \geq 10$ **e.** Solve $900t = 1200(t - 10)$. **10. a.** Yakov **b.** 2 s **c.** 20 ft **d.** Yakov: 10 ft/s; Demitri: 5 ft/s **e.** $y = 10x$ **f.** $y = 5x + 10$ **g.** $10x = 5x + 10$

On Your Own

11. a.

d.

12. a.

b.

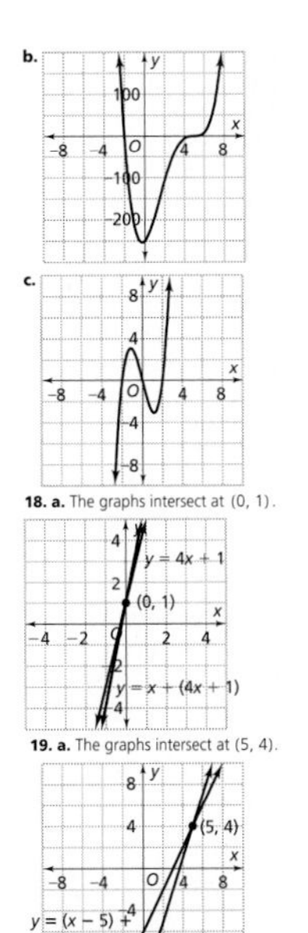

c.

18. a. The graphs intersect at (0, 1).

19. a. The graphs intersect at (5, 4).

Lesson 3.4
Check Your Understanding

1. a. The expansion is $2x^3 + 5x^2 + x - 1 = 101 + 85(x - 3) + 23(x - 3)^2 + 2(x - 3)^3$.
b. The expansion is $x^2 + 2x - 3 = 12 + 8(x - 3) + (x - 3)^2$.
c. The expansion is $2x^3 + 5x^2 + x - 1 = 113 + 93(x - 3) + 24(x - 3)^2 + 2(x - 3)^3$.
d. The expansion is $8x^3 + 20x^2 + 4x - 4 = 404 + 340(x - 3) + 92(x - 3)^2 + 8(x - 3)^3$.
e. The expansion is $8x^3 + 19x^2 + 2x - 1 = 392 + 332(x - 3) + 91(x - 3)^2 + 8(x - 3)^3$.
2. a. The expansion is $2x^3 + 5x^2 + x - 1 = 37 + 45(x - 2) + 17(x - 2)^2 + 2(x - 2)^3$.
b. The expansion is $x^2 + 2x - 3 = 5 + 6(x - 2) + (x - 2)^2$.
c. The expansion is $2x^3 + 6x^2 + 3x - 4 = 42 + 51(x - 2) + 18(x - 2)^2 + 2(x - 2)^3$.
d. The expansion is $6x^3 + 15x^2 + 3x - 3 = 111 + 135(x - 2) + 51(x - 2)^2 + 6(x - 2)^3$.
e. The expansion is $2x^5 + 9x^4 + 5x^3 - 14x^2 - 5x + 3 = 185 + 447(x - 2) + 392(x - 2)^2 + 157(x - 2)^3 + 29(x - 2)^4 + 2(x - 2)^5$.
3. $x^2 + 2x - 3 = a^2 + 2a - 3 + (2a + 2)(x - a) + (x - a)^2$
4. a. $27 + 27(x - 3) + 9(x - 3)^2 + (x - 3)^3$ **b.** $9 + 6(x - 3) + (x - 3)^2$ **c.** $3 + (x - 3)$ **d.** $1 + 0(x - 3)$ **5.** Yes, it works for $f(x) = 2x^3 + 5x^2 + x - 1$. It will work for any cubic.

On Your Own

6. a. $379 + 201(x - 5) + 35(x - 5)^2 + 2(x - 5)^3$ **b.** $32 + 12(x - 5) + (x - 5)^2$ **c.** $1073 + 579(x - 5) + 103(x - 5)^2 + 6(x - 5)^3$ **d.** $143{,}641 + 152{,}358(x - 5) + 66{,}931(x - 5)^2 + 15{,}586(x - 5)^3 + 2029(x - 5)^4 + 140(x - 5)^5 + 4(x - 5)^6$
7. The expansion is $rx^2 + sx + t = 9r + 3s + t + (6r + s)(x - 3) + r(x - 3)^2$. **8.** The expansion is $rx^2 + sx + t = a^2r + as + t + (2ar + s)(x - a) + r(x - a)^2$. **10. a.** 31 **b.** $-10x + 31$ **c.** $-4x^2 - 10x + 31$ **13. a.** $x^2 = 1 + 2(x - 1) + (x - 1)^2$ **b.** $x^3 = 1 + 3(x - 1) + (x + 2)(x - 1)^2$
f. $x^n = 1 + n(x - 1) + (x - 1)^2 \sum_{k=1}^{n-1} (k \cdot x^{n-k-1})$ for positive integer n.

Lesson 3.5
Check Your Understanding

1. $y = 10x - 25$ **2.** $y = 3x - 2$ **3.** $y = 2ax - a^2$
4.

x	$f(x)$	Slope of tangent at $(x, f(x))$
−1	2	−2
0	1	0
1	2	2
2	5	4
3	10	6
4	17	8
10	101	20
100	10,001	200

5.

x	$f(x)$	Slope of tangent at $(x, f(x))$
−1	0	−1
0	0	1
1	2	3
2	6	5
3	12	7
4	20	9
10	110	21
100	10,100	201

6. a. $y = 2(x - 1) + 1 = 2x - 1$
b. $y = 3(x - 1) + 1 = 3x - 2$
c. $y = 4(x - 1) + 1 = 4x - 3$
d. $y = 5(x - 1) + 1 = 5x - 4$
e. $y = 6(x - 1) + 1 = 6x - 5$
f. $y = (x - 1) + 1 = x$
7. Using the results of Exercise 6, the tangent will be $y = n(x - 1) + 1$.

On Your Own

8. The equation of the tangent is $y = 2x + 2$; the slope of the tangent line is 2.
10. a. $y = 2a(x - a) + a^2 = 2ax - a^2$
b. $y = 3a^2(x - a) + a^3 = 3a^2x - 2a^3$
c. $y = 4a^3(x - a) + a^4 = 4a^3x - 3a^4$
11. Use your solution to Exercise 10. The equation of the tangent will be $y = na^{n-1}(x - a) + a^n = na^{n-1}x - (n - 1)a^n$.

Lesson 3.6
On Your Own

9. $x = -\frac{1}{5}$ or $x = 2$ **10. a.** Answers may vary. Sample: $f(x) = \frac{x - 3}{x^2}$ **b.** Answers may vary. Sample: $f(x) = \frac{1}{x - 5}$ **c.** Answers may vary. Sample: $f(x) = \frac{x - 3}{x - 5}$ **d.** Answers may vary. Sample: $f(x) = \frac{x^2 - 5x + 1}{x - 5}$
12. a.

x	$k(x)$
0	2
1	3
2	4
3	not defined
4	6

b. $\frac{(x - 3)(x + 2)}{x - 3} = x + 2$ **c.** $k(x)$ is *not* the same function as $m(x) = x + 2$, because the domain of $m(x)$ is $\mathbb{R}$, while the domain of $k(x)$ is $\{x \mid x \neq 3\}$.

Lesson 3.7
Check Your Understanding

1. a. 0 **b.** ∞ **c.** 0 **d.** $-\infty$ **2. a.** $\frac{3}{5}$ **b.** $\frac{10}{3}$ **c.** $\frac{5}{2}$ **d.** −2 **e.** ∞ **f.** 0 **3. a.** $y = 1$ **b.** $x = -2$ **c.** $\left(4, \frac{5}{6}\right)$
4. Answers may vary. **a.** $f(x) = \frac{4x}{x - 5}$ **b.** $f(x) = \frac{x}{(x - 2)(x - 5)}$ **c.** $f(x) = \frac{x - 2}{(x - 2)(x + 3)}$ **d.** $f(x) = \frac{x(x - 2)}{x - 1}$ **5.** $K = \frac{1}{6}$ **6. a.** $f(10) = 10.1$ and $f(100) = 100.01$. **b.** The graph approaches the line $y = x$. **c.** $f(0.1) = 10.1$ and $f(0.01) = 100.01$. **d.** The graph of $f(x)$ as x approaches zero goes to ∞; the function has a vertical asymptote $x = 0$.
e.

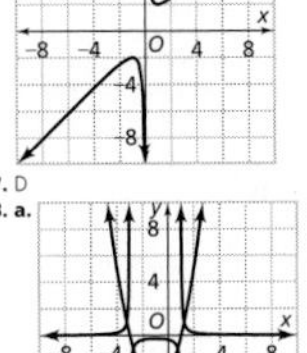

7. D
8. a.

b. $-1 + \sqrt{3}$; $-1 - \sqrt{3}$; $-1 + \sqrt{5}$; $-1 - \sqrt{5}$
9. a. $d(x) = 0.75$; $d(2x) = 0.5$; $d(3x) = 0.25$; $d(4x) = 0$
b.

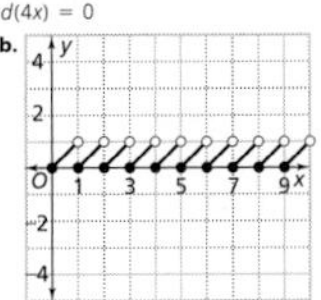

c.

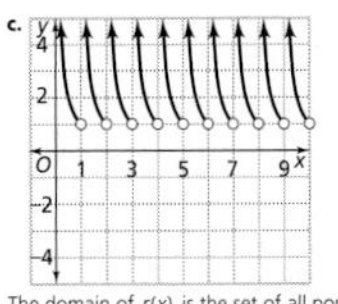

The domain of $r(x)$ is the set of all positive real numbers that are not integers. Its range is the positive real numbers.

On Your Own

10. a. $y = 2$ **b.** $x = -3$ **c.** $\left(2, \frac{3}{5}\right)$
11. a. $\{x \mid x \neq -2, 2\}$ **b.** $\{x \mid x \neq -2, 2\}$
12. a. $\frac{1}{2}$ **b.** $\frac{1}{2}$ **c.** 0 **d.** 0 **e.** ∞
15. a. $f(x) = \frac{x + 11}{(x + 11)(x + 3)}$ so for all $x \neq -11$ $f(x) = g(x)$. These two functions are not the same, however, because −11 does not belong to the domain of $f(x)$. **b.** The graphs look the same on the calculator because the hole is not visible, but if you look at the table you will see that the function is undefined at $x = -11$.

Lesson 3.8
Check Your Understanding

1. $y = -\frac{1}{2} + \frac{1}{4}(x - 2)$ **2.** Since $f(x) = \frac{1}{x}$ and $g(x) = -\frac{1}{x}$ are reflections of each other over the x-axis, their tangents at $x = 2$ will also be reflections of each other over the x-axis. **3.** The equation of the tangent at $(a, h(a))$ is $y = \frac{1}{a^2} + \frac{-2}{a^3}(x - a)$.
4.

x	Slope of tangent to f	Slope of tangent to h
$\frac{1}{10}$	−100	−2000
$\frac{1}{4}$	−16	−128
$\frac{1}{2}$	−4	−16
1	−1	−2
2	$-\frac{1}{4}$	$-\frac{1}{4}$
4	$-\frac{1}{16}$	$-\frac{1}{32}$
10	$-\frac{1}{100}$	$-\frac{1}{500}$

This makes sense because the slope of the tangent to the graph of f must be negative everywhere, but the slope of the tangent to the graph of h will be positive for negative x-values and negative for positive x-values.
5. $y = 2(x + 2) - 7$ **6.** $A = 6, B = -2$

7. a. The slope of the line tangent to f at $x = 4$ is $-\frac{3}{2}$.

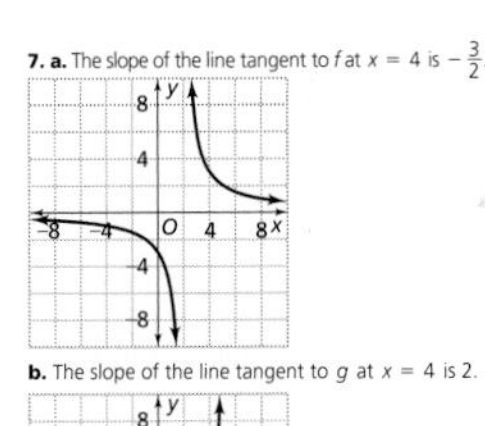

b. The slope of the line tangent to g at $x = 4$ is 2.

c. The slope of the line tangent to h at $x = 4$ is $\frac{1}{2}$.

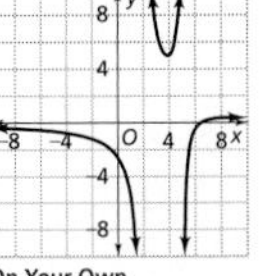

On Your Own

9. $y = 1 - \frac{3}{13}(x - 3)$
10.

x	Slope of tangent to f	Slope of tangent to g
−2	$-\frac{1}{4}$	$\frac{3}{4}$
−1	−1	0
$-\frac{1}{2}$	−4	−3
0	undefined	undefined
$\frac{1}{2}$	−4	−3
1	−1	0
2	$-\frac{1}{4}$	$\frac{3}{4}$
3	$-\frac{1}{9}$	$\frac{8}{9}$

11. a. The slope of the line tangent to $j(x)$ at $x = 2$ is $-\frac{4}{25}$. **b.** The slope of the line tangent to $j(x)$ at $x = -2$ is $\frac{4}{25}$. **c.** The answers to parts (a) and (b) are opposites, because $j(x)$ is symmetric across the y-axis.
12. $y = \frac{b}{d} + \frac{ad - bc}{d^2}x$

Lesson 3.9
Check Your Understanding
1. a. $x = -\frac{7}{2}$; $y = \frac{3}{2}$ **b.** $x = -\frac{5}{3}$; $y = \frac{5}{7}$
c.

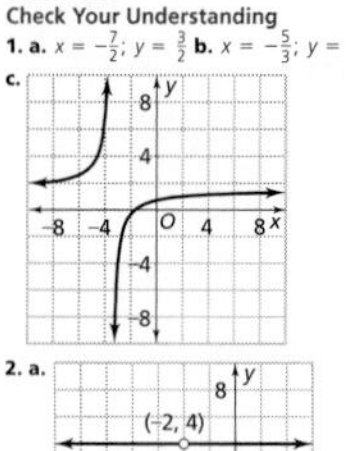

2. a.

b. $D = 8$ **c.** $\lim_{x\to\infty} b(x) = 4$
3. a. The graph has a vertical asymptote $x = -\frac{D}{C}$ if $AD \neq BC$; it has a hole if $AD = BC$.
b. $\lim_{x\to\infty} c(x) = \lim_{x\to\infty}\left(\frac{A}{C} + \frac{B - \frac{AD}{C}}{Cx + D}\right) = \frac{A}{C}$; The graph has a horizontal asymptote: $y = \frac{A}{C}$.
4. Answers may vary. Sample:
$A = \begin{pmatrix} 0 & 1 \\ 1 & 0 \end{pmatrix}$; $A = \begin{pmatrix} 0 & -1 \\ 1 & 0 \end{pmatrix}$; $A = \begin{pmatrix} 0 & 1 \\ 1 & -2 \end{pmatrix}$;
$A = \begin{pmatrix} 1 & 0 \\ 1 & -2 \end{pmatrix}$; $A = \begin{pmatrix} 1 & -1 \\ 1 & 3 \end{pmatrix}$; $A = \begin{pmatrix} 2 & 1 \\ 1 & 3 \end{pmatrix}$;
$A = \begin{pmatrix} 2 & 1 \\ 3 & -1 \end{pmatrix}$

5. a.

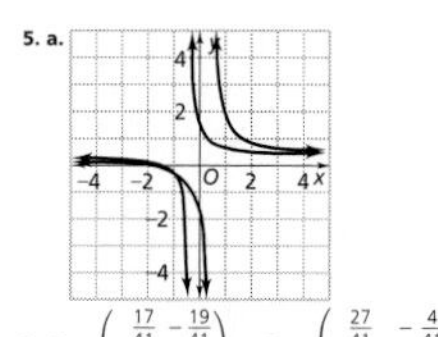

b. $C = \begin{pmatrix} \frac{17}{41} & -\frac{19}{41} \\ -\frac{2}{41} & \frac{36}{41} \end{pmatrix}$ **c.** $D = \begin{pmatrix} \frac{27}{41} & -\frac{4}{41} \\ -\frac{32}{41} & \frac{26}{41} \end{pmatrix}$
6. a.

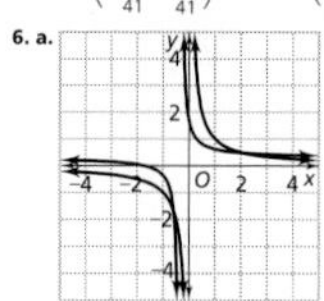

b. $T_g = T_{\frac{3}{10}}$ and $\mathcal{A}_{(e,f)} = \mathcal{A}_{\left(\frac{100}{41}, \frac{30}{41}\right)}$
c. Scale horizontally by a factor of $\frac{41}{100}$, then translate $\frac{3}{10}$ units left and $\frac{3}{10}$ units up.
7. There will be a fixed point if $(d - a)^2 + 4bc \geq 0$.
On Your Own
9. b. $T_g = T_{\frac{2}{3}}$ and $\mathcal{A}_{(e,f)} = \mathcal{A}_{(9,21)}$
c. Scale horizontally by a factor of $\frac{1}{9}$, then translate $\frac{7}{3}$ units left and $\frac{2}{3}$ units up.
10. $\frac{3}{2}$ **11.** $f(x)$ has no vertical asymptotes because its domain is $\mathbb{R}$. A necessary condition for $f(x)$ to have a vertical asymptote in $x = k$ is that $f(x) = k$ is not in the function's domain.

Lesson 3.10
On Your Own
8. a.

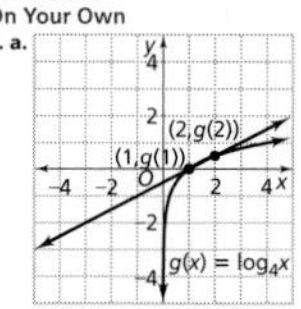

The slope of the secant is 0.5.

b. Since the slope is positive and a little more than 0.5, a good estimate might be 0.7.
9.

Base b	Slope of tangent to $f(x) = \log_b x$ at $x = 1$
2	1.443
3	0.910
4	0.721
5	0.621
8	0.481
10	0.434

Lesson 3.11
Check Your Understanding
1. a. \$400; \$800; $100(2)^t$ **b.** \$596.05; \$1455.19; $100(2.441406)^t$ **c.** \$2008.55 **2. a.** \$106.00; \$112.36; $100(1.06)^t$ **b.** \$106.09; \$112.55; $100(1.03)^{2n} = 100(1.0609)^n$ **c.** The 100 is the amount Jamie invested. The 1.005 is $1 + \frac{0.06}{12}$, 0.06 is the interest rate expressed as a decimal, 12 is the number of times it is compounded in a year (monthly). $36 = 12 \cdot 3$ is (number of times compounded in a year)(number of years).
3. $B = P\left(1 + \frac{0.05}{n}\right)^{nt}$ **4. a.** \$105.09 **b.** \$105.12 **c.** \$105.13 **d.** \$105.13 **5. a.** \$128.40 **b.** \$164.87 **c.** \$271.83 **d.** \$738.91 **6. a.** \$128.40 ≈ 47.237e **b.** \$164.87 ≈ 60.653e **c.** \$271.83 ≈ 100e **d.** \$738.91 ≈ 271.828e
7. a.
$$\frac{1}{K} = \frac{x}{n}$$
$$n \cdot \frac{1}{K} = n \cdot \frac{x}{n}$$
$$\frac{n}{K} = x$$
$$n = Kx$$
b. $\left(1 + \frac{x}{n}\right)^n = \left(1 + \frac{1}{K}\right)^{Kx}$
c. The two limits are the same because as $n \to \infty$, $K \to \infty$.
d.
$$\lim_{K\to\infty}\left(1 + \frac{1}{K}\right)^{Kx} = \lim_{K\to\infty}\left(\left(1 + \frac{1}{K}\right)^K\right)^x = \left(\lim_{K\to\infty}\left(1 + \frac{1}{K}\right)^K\right)^x = e^x$$
8.
$$\lim_{n\to\infty} P\left(1 + \frac{r}{n}\right)^{nt} = P\left(\lim_{n\to\infty}\left(1 + \frac{r}{n}\right)^n\right)^t = P(e^r)^t = Pe^{rt}$$
On Your Own
10. a. Her balance is \$2000; It is multiplied by a factor of 10. **b.** \$2718.28

11. a. $B(3) = \$1197.22$; $B(5) = \$1349.86$; $B(t) = 1000 \cdot e^{0.06 \cdot t}$ dollars **b.** It will take approximately 11.55 years for the balance to double. **c.** It will take approximately 23.1 years for the balance to become \$4000. **12.** The better investment is the account at 6% APR compounded annually.
14. $m = 0.055$
Lesson 3.12
Check Your Understanding
1. a. $1 + \frac{1}{1!} + \frac{1}{2!} + \frac{1}{3!} + \cdots + \frac{1}{13!} \approx 2.7182818285$; fourteen terms ($k = 13$).
b. $\left(1 + \frac{1}{10^7}\right)^{10^7} \approx 2.71828169255$; six
2. a. $q(0.05) = 1.05125$ and $e^{0.05} = 1.05127$; approximately −0.02% **b.** $q(0.5) = 1.625$ and $e^{0.05} = 1.64872$; approximately −1.44%
c. $q(-1) = 0.5$ and $e^{-1} = 0.36788$; approximately 35.91%
3. $x \approx 0.693$ **4. a.** (0.693, 2) **b.** (1.099, 3)
5. a. $\sum_{k=0}^{\infty} \frac{(-1)^k}{k!} \approx 0.36788$ **b.** The summation gives the same rule as e^x where $x = -1$. So it should equal e^{-1}, and it does.
6. a.

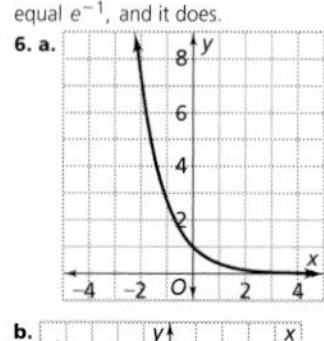

b.

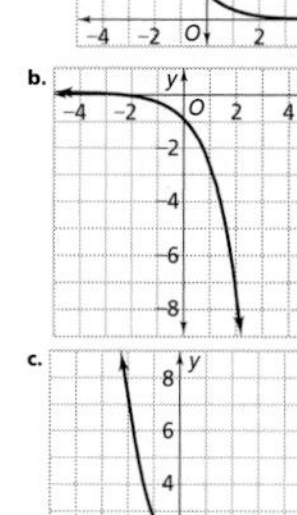

c.

On Your Own
8. a. $c(0.1) = 1.10516666667$ and $f(0.1) = 1.10517091808$; −0.00038%
b. $c(0.2) = 1.22133333333$ and $f(0.2) = 1.22140275816$; −0.00568%
$c(0.5) = 1.64583333333$ and $f(0.5) = 1.6487212707$; −0.17516%
$c(1) = 2.66666666667$ and $f(1) = 2.71828182846$; −1.89882%
$c(2) = 6.33333333$ and $f(2) = 7.38905609893$; −14.28765%
c. The graphs are very close together for small values of x. As x gets larger, the graphs are farther apart.
d. There are two solutions: $x = -0.00017$ and $x = -0.00015$.
9. e^2 **10. a.** $k \approx 1.09861$ **c.** $n \approx 2.70805$
e. no solution

Lesson 3.13
Check Your Understanding
1. 6.931 **2. a.** $p = 4$; $M = 3$ **b.** $\frac{1}{3}\ln 2$
c. $-2\ln 5$ **3. a.** 2 **b.** 10 **c.** −1 **d.** 5
4. a. $\ln 3$ **b.** $m = \ln 5$ **c.** $e^{x\ln 2} = e^{\ln 2^x} = 2^x$
5. $a^x = e^{\ln a^x} = e^{x\ln a} = e^{kx}$ where $k = \ln a$.
6. a. $x \approx 2.807$ **b.** $z \approx 2.990$ **c.** $x \approx -1.672$
d. $x = \frac{\ln c - \ln a}{\ln b - \ln d} = \frac{\ln\frac{c}{a}}{\ln\frac{b}{d}}$ **7. a.** $(3, \ln 3)$ **b.** $(\ln 3, 3)$
c. $(2, e^2)$ **d.** $(e^2, 2)$ **e.** $g = e^4$ **f.** $p = \ln 4$
On Your Own
8. a. 1.099 **e.** 0.511 **f.** undefined **9. a.** \$134.99; \$182.21; \$332.01 **d.** $t = \frac{\ln\frac{B}{100}}{0.06}$; 38.38 years
10. a. 34.7 years **b.** 23.1 years **f.** $\frac{\ln 2}{0.01p}$ years

Lesson 3.14
Check Your Understanding
1. a. The slope of the tangent at any point is equal to the y-value of that point. **b.** The slope of the tangent at any point is equal to the y-value of that point times 2. **c.** The slope of the tangent at any point is equal to the y-value of that point times 5. **d.** The slope of the tangent at any point is equal to the y-value of that point times $\ln 2$.
2. a. $\ln 2$ **b.** $\ln 16$ **c.** $\ln 5^5$

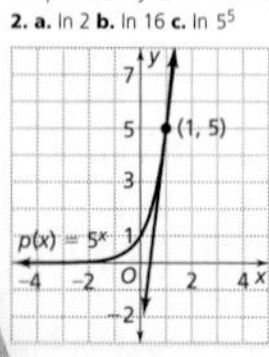

3. a. $5^0 \ln 5 = \ln 5$ **b.** $\ln 8 = \ln 2^3 = 3\ln 2$
c. Base e, because $e^0 \ln e = 1$. **d.** $b = 1$, but this is just a horizontal line: $y = 1^x \to y = 1$. **4. a.** This is the definition of logarithm. **b.** $2^y = x \Rightarrow \ln 2^y = \ln x \Rightarrow y\ln 2 = \ln x$ **c.** Divide both sides by $\ln 2$ to get $y = \frac{\ln x}{\ln 2}$. Since $\log_2 x = y$, $\log_2 x = y = \frac{\ln x}{\ln 2}$.
5. a. The slope is 3 times the reciprocal of the x-value.
b. The slope is the reciprocal of the x-value.
c. The slope is the reciprocal of the x-value times $\frac{1}{5}$.
d. The slope is the reciprocal of the x-value times $\frac{1}{\ln 2}$.
6. a. $\frac{1}{\ln 2} \approx 1.443$ **b.** $\frac{1}{4\ln 2} \approx 0.361$
c. $\frac{1}{5\ln 5} \approx 0.124$

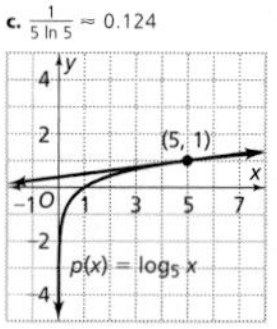

7. a. $\frac{1}{\ln 5} \approx 0.621$ **b.** The output for base 8 will be $\frac{1}{\ln 8} = \frac{1}{\ln 2^3} = \frac{1}{3\ln 2} = \frac{1}{3}\left(\frac{1}{\ln 2}\right)$ and $\frac{1}{\ln 2}$ is the output for base 2. **c.** The slope of the tangent will be 1 if $\frac{1}{\ln b} = 1 \Rightarrow \ln b = 1 \Rightarrow b = e$. **d.** The slope of the tangent will never be zero.
On Your Own
8. a. $(\ln 8, 8)$ **b.** The y-intercept is $-8\ln 8 + 8 \approx -8.636$, which is negative. **9.** $y = ex$; $(1, e)$
10. $slope = Abe^{bx} = b \cdot p(x)$ **11.** $slope = \frac{A}{x}$

Chapter 4
Lesson 4.2
Check Your Understanding
1. Not isomorphic; the area is found by using multiplication alone, but the perimeter is found using addition at least once. **2.** Isomorphic; both problems can be solved by using the same calculation of subtracting 45 and 99 from 230. **3.** Isomorphic; both problems can be solved by solving the same equation, $x + 2x = 18$. **4.** Isomorphic; both problems can be solved by using the same calculation of dividing 740 by 60 to find the smallest integer number. **5.** Answers may vary. Samples are given. **a.** The Red Sox scored nine runs and the Yankees scored seven runs in the same game. How many more runs did the Red Sox score? **b.** Three friends divide a dozen cookies equally among them. How many cookies does each friend get?

6. Answers will vary. Samples are given.
a. • Joe had \$40 at the beginning of the day. He spent \$3 on breakfast and \$7 on lunch. How much money does he have left for dinner?
• Paula had 40 baseball cards. She gave 3 to Jesse, and 7 to Kira. How many does she have left?
b. • If seven people go out to dinner and each contributes eight dollars toward the bill, what is the total contribution?
• Mr. Hill made cookies for the 8 students on the Math Team. He made enough so that each student could have exactly 7 cookies. How many cookies did he make?
7. The text explained how Problems 1 and 3 can be viewed as essentially the same.
In Problem 2, let 1 denote the color green and 2 denote the color red. Then let the ones digit denote the color of the circle, let the tens digit denote the color of the triangle, and finally let the hundreds digit denote the color of the square. In Problem 4, let 1 denote a head and 2 to denote a tail. Then let the hundreds digit denote the first toss, let the tens digit denote the second toss, and the ones digit denote the third toss.
On Your Own
9. 16 four-digit numbers **11.** Isomorphic; both problems can be solved by using the same calculation of multiplying 15 and 7. **12.** Isomorphic; both problems can be solved using the same calculation of taking the sum of the integers from 1 to 10.

Lesson 4.3
Check Your Understanding
1. a. $f(n) = \begin{cases} 2 & \text{if } n = 1 \\ f(n-1) \cdot 2 & \text{if } n > 1 \end{cases}$ **b.** $f(n) = 2^n$
2. 81 numbers **3. a.** 243 numbers **b.** 3^n numbers
4. m^n **5.** 24 ways **6.** 24 ways **7.** 362,880 batting orders. **8.** 120 ways **9.** $n!$ ways
On Your Own
10. 18 ways **13.** 1800 numbers. **16.** 17,576,000 license plates

Lesson 4.4
Check Your Understanding
1. 8 functions **2.** 780 words **3.** There are $k + k^2 + \cdots + k^n$ words (that is, n words if $k = 1$ and $\frac{k^{n+1} - k}{k - 1}$ words if $k > 1$)
4. $365^{25} \approx 1.14 \times 10^{64}$ **5.** 32,768 functions
On Your Own
6. a. 9 functions **7.** 6720 functions

Lesson 4.6
Check Your Understanding
1. Answers may vary. Sample: Since ${}_nP_k = \frac{n!}{(n-k)!}$ when $1 \leq k \leq n$, then ${}_nP_n = \frac{n!}{(n-n)!} = \frac{n!}{0!} = \frac{n!}{1} = n!$ **2.** 360 functions **3.** 360 functions

4. 7,880,400 **5. a.** 81 numbers **b.** 9 numbers.
c. Dull number; there are more dull numbers than funny numbers in the bag. **6.** dull number
7. funny number **8.** funny number **9. a.** 6 anagrams
b. 3 anagrams **c.** 1 anagram **10. a.** 24 anagrams
b. 12 anagrams **c.** 6 anagrams **d.** 4 anagrams
e. 1 anagrams **11. a.** 60 anagrams **b.** 1260 anagrams
c. 720 anagrams
On Your Own
15. $\frac{1}{12} \approx 8.3\%$ **16.** $\frac{11}{23} \approx 47.8\%$ **21.** 720 anagrams
22. 360 anagrams

Lesson 4.7
Check Your Understanding
1. 64,684,950 committees **2.** 64,684,950 groups
3. For each distinct committee of 4 people you choose, you leave behind a distinct *non-committee* of 196 people. So, there are the same number of committees of 4 people and committees of 196 people. **4. a.** ${}_7P_3 = \frac{7!}{4!}$ **b.** ${}_7C_3 = \frac{7!}{4! \cdot 3!}$
5. From the previous exercise, ${}_7C_3 = \frac{{}_7P_3}{3!} = \frac{{}_7P_3}{{}_3P_3}$. This makes sense, since every combination of 3 particular objects accounts for $3! = 6$ of the permutations of 3 of the 6 objects.
6. Use the formulas for ${}_nC_k$ and ${}_nP_k$:
$$\begin{aligned} {}_nC_k &= \frac{{}_nP_k}{k!} \\ &= \frac{n!}{(n-k)! \cdot k!} \\ &= \frac{n!}{(n-k)! \cdot [n-(n-k)]!} \\ &= \frac{{}_nP_{n-k}}{(n-k)!} \\ &= {}_nC_{n-k} \end{aligned}$$
7. Every combination of 3 objects from a set of 10 can be arranged in $3! = 6$ ways (that is, has $3! = 6$ permutations). So, ${}_{10}C_3 \cdot 6$ is the number of possible permutations of 3 objects chosen from a set of 10, or ${}_{10}P_3$. **8.** ${}_{10}P_3$ represents the number of subsets of 3 cards you can make from a set of 10 cards, and ${}_{10}C_7$ represents the number of subsets of 7 cards you can make from a set of 10 cards. But, every time you make a different subset of 3 cards, you leave behind a different group of seven cards—that is, there are as many subsets of 7 cards as there are of 3 cards: ${}_{10}C_3 = {}_{10}C_7$. The same argument would hold for any subset of k cards chosen from a set of n cards: ${}_nC_k = {}_nC_{(n-k)}$. **9.** Answers may vary. Sample: To find ${}_nP_k$, you count all of the different ways you can pick k objects from a set of n objects and line them up in a row. To find ${}_nC_k$, you count all of the different ways you can pick k objects from a set of n objects (without lining them up). So, to find permutations, you are finding all the combinations, and then also

rearranging them. Combinations do not count the rearrangements since "order doesn't matter" with combinations.

10. a. 6 choices **b.** 3 choices **c.** 3 choices

11. Suppose we have a group of 7 people, including a girl named Kira, and we want to choose a committee of 4 people from this group. There are ${}_7C_4$ ways to do this. Or, we can think of it in terms of the committees that contain and don't contain Kira

$${}_7C_4 = \text{number of possible committees Kira is on} + \text{number of committee Kira is not on.}$$

If Kira is on the committee, then there are 6 people left who can fill the remaining 3 spots on the committee. So, there are ${}_6C_3$ different committees that can be made with Kira. If Kira is not on the committee, the entire committee needs to be chosen from the other 6 people. So, there are ${}_6C_4$ 4-person committees that can be made without Kira. That is,

$${}_7C_4 = {}_6C_3 + {}_6C_4$$

12. a. ${}_{10}C_6 = {}_9C_6 + {}_9C_5$. **b.** Suppose we have a group of 10 people, including a person named Gill. We want to make a committee of 6 people from this group of 10. There are ${}_{10}C_6$ different committees we could make. However,

$${}_{10}C_6 = \text{number of possible committees Gill is on} + \text{number of committees Gill is not}$$

If Gill is on a committee, then there are 9 remaining people to fill the other 5 spots on the committee. So, there are ${}_9C_5$ different committees that can be made with Gill. If Gill is not on the committee, then the entire committee of 6 people needs to be chosen from the remaining 9 people. So, there are ${}_9C_6$ different committees that can be made without Gill. Thus:

$${}_{10}C_6 = {}_9C_6 + {}_9C_5$$

13. The proof follows the same logic as Exercises 11 and 12. Suppose we have a group of n people (including Jan and at least one other person) and we would like to make a committee of k people from this group. The committee will have someone on it, and it will not have everyone on it (so $0 < k < n$). There are ${}_nC_k$ different possible committees that can be made. Since the committees must, have someone on them ($k > 0$), some of these committees will contain Jan. Since the committees do not contain everyone ($k < n$), some of them will not contain Jan. If Jan is on a committee, then there are $n - 1$ people remaining to fill the $k - 1$ remaining spot (and since $0 \le k - 1 < n - 1$, it is possible to make a committee of $k - 1$ people from a group of $n - 1$ people, and if $k - 1 = 0$, then there's only 1 choice: NOBODY). So, there are ${}_{n-1}C_{k-1}$ different committees that contain Jan. If Jan is not on the committee, then the committee of k people must made from the remaining $n - 1$ people (and since $k \le n - 1$, it is possible to make a committee of k people from a group of $n - 1$ people). So, there are ${}_{n-1}C_k$ different committees that do not contain Jan. Thus,

$${}_nC_k = {}_{n-1}C_{k-1} + {}_{n-1}C_k.$$

14. a. ${}_nC_0 = {}_{n-1}C_0 = 1$ **b.** ${}_nC_n = {}_{n-1}C_{n-1} = 1$

15.

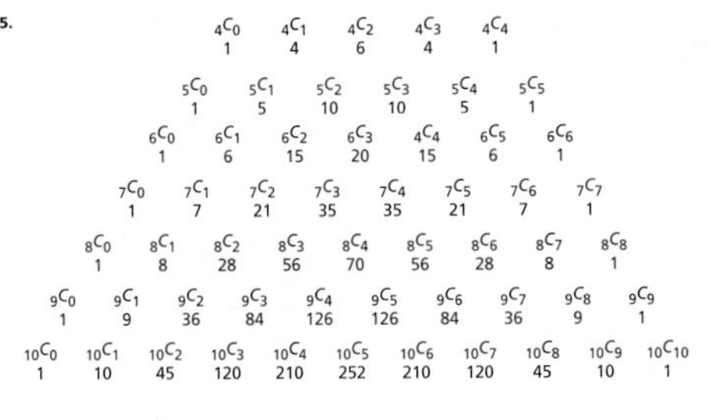

16. To see that ${}_nC_k = \binom{n}{k}$ we need to show that combinations satisfy the recursive definition of $\binom{n}{k}$:

$\binom{n}{0} = \binom{n}{n} = 1$ (far left and far right entries equal 1);

$\binom{n}{k} + \binom{n}{k+1} = \binom{n+1}{k+1}$ (sum of two entries is the entry is the entry below them)

That is, we need to show that

$${}_nC_0 = {}_nC_n = 1;$$
$${}_nC_k + {}_nC_{k+1} = {}_{n+1}C_{k+1}$$

But we've already shown these statements to be true, so the theorem is true.

17. Answers may vary. Sample: Let $\binom{5}{6} = 0$, because there are 0 ways to choose six objects from a set of five.
18. 252 combinations **19.** 1; 8; 28; 56; 70; 56; 28; 8; 1
20. The sum of all the entries in row n of Pascal's triangle is 2^n.

On Your Own

21. 210 assignments **28. a.** 5985 committees **b.** 1140 committees **c.** 4845 committees
31. b. $\binom{11}{4}$ or $\binom{11}{7}$; 330 groups **38.** 126 numbers

Lesson 4.8

Check Your Understanding

1. 720 ways **2.** 5040 ways **3.** 300 numbers
4. 756 committees **5.** 240 ways **6. a.** 362,880 ways **b.** 2880 ways **c.** 282,240 ways **d.** 2880 ways **e.** 326,880 ways

On Your Own

7. b. 237 ways **10.** 182 flights **12.** 16 ways

Lesson 4.9

On Your Own

11. b. 8 paths **13. b.** 12, 870 routes
15. 756,756 ways

Lesson 4.10

Check Your Understanding

1. a. $(x + y)^7 = x^7 + 7x^6y + 21x^5y^2 + 35x^4y^3 + 35x^3y^4 + 21x^2y^5 + 7xy^6 + y^7w$
b. $(x + 2y)^5 = x^5 + 10x^4y + 40x^3y^2 + 80x^2y^3 + 80xy^4 + 32y^5$
2. a. 792 **b.** the term containing a^7b^5 **c.** the term containing a^6b^6 **3. a.** $\binom{50}{13} = 354, 860, 518, 600$
b. $\binom{50}{1} = 50$ **c.** $\binom{50}{25} = 126, 410, 606, 437, 752$
4. All sums are equal to 0. **5.** Answers may vary. Sample: $32x^5 + 240x^4 + 720x^3 + 1080x^2 + 810x + 243$; factors as $(2x + 3)^5$

On Your Own

7. a. $\binom{n}{0}x^n - \binom{n}{1}x^{n-1} + \binom{n}{2}x^{n-2} + \cdots + (-1)^k\binom{n}{k}x^{n-k} + \cdots + (-1)^{n-1}\binom{n}{n-1}x + (-1)^n\binom{n}{n}$

Lesson 4.11

Check Your Understanding

1. Use mathematical induction. Since $2^0 = 1 = \binom{n}{0}$, the base case is confirmed. For good measure, notice that the sum of the entries in row 1 is $1 + 1 = 2 = 2^1$. For the induction step, suppose $m \ge 1$ and sum of the entries in row m of the triangle is 2^m. Then

$$\begin{aligned}
2^{m+1} = 2^m + 2^m &= \sum_{k=0}^{m}\binom{m}{k} + \sum_{k=0}^{m}\binom{m}{k}\\
&= \left[\binom{m}{0} + \binom{m}{1} + \cdots + \binom{m}{m}\right]\\
&\quad + \left[\binom{m}{0} + \binom{m}{1} + \cdots + \binom{m}{m}\right]\\
&= \binom{m}{0} + \left[\binom{m}{0} + \binom{m}{1}\right] + \left[\binom{m}{1}\right.\\
&\quad \left. + \binom{m}{2}\right] + \left[\binom{m}{2} + \binom{m}{3}\right]\\
&\quad + \cdots + \left[\binom{m}{m-2} + \binom{m}{m-1}\right]\\
&\quad + \left[\binom{m}{m-1} + \binom{m}{m}\right] + \binom{m}{m}\\
&= \binom{m}{0} + \binom{m+1}{1} + \binom{m+1}{2}\\
&\quad + \binom{m+1}{3} + \cdots + \binom{m+1}{m-1}\\
&\quad + \binom{m+1}{m} + \binom{m}{m}\\
&= \binom{m+1}{0} + \binom{m+1}{1}\\
&\quad + \cdots + \binom{m+1}{m} + \binom{m+1}{m+1}
\end{aligned}$$

The final sum is the sum of the entries in row $m + 1$ of Pascal's Triangle, so the conjecture is proved.
2. Entry k in row n of Pascal's Triangle, ${}_nC_k$, is the number of subsets of size k that can be made from a set with n elements. Therefore, the sum of these entries represents the number of all subsets (the subsets of each possible size from 0 to n), which we already know is 2^n. **3.** Since $\binom{n}{n}$ is the number of the subsets of the set $\{1, 2, 3, \ldots, n\}$ containing all n elements and there is only one such subset (the set itself). Therefore, $\binom{n}{n} = 1$. **4.** $\binom{n}{n} = \frac{n!}{n!0!} = \frac{n!}{n!} = 1$

5. We know that $\binom{n}{k} = {}_nC_k$ is the number of subsets of $\{1, 2, 3, \ldots, n\}$ that contain k elements. But for every k-element subset, there is a unique $n - k$ element subset consisting of the elements that are *not* included in the particular k-element subset. Also, for every $n - k$-element subset, there is a unique k-element subset (consisting of the remaining elements). But this means that ${}_nC_k = {}_nC_{n-k}$, so $\binom{n}{k} = \binom{n}{n-k}$.
6. First, notice that $(a + b)^n = (b + a)^n$. But, according to the Binomial Theorem,

$$(a + b)^n = \sum_{k=0}^{n}\binom{n}{n-k}a^{n-k}b^k \text{ and}$$
$$(b + n)^n = \sum_{k=0}^{n}\binom{n}{n-k}b^{n-k}a^k.$$

In the expansion of $(a + b)^n$, the coefficient of $a^{n-k}b^k$ is $\binom{n}{n-k}$, but in the expansion of $(b + a)^n$, the cofficient of $a^{n-k}b^k$ is $\binom{n}{k}$. Therefore, $\binom{n}{k} = \binom{n}{n-k}$.
7. $\binom{n}{1}$ is the number of 1-element subsets of a set with n elements. Since there are n 1-element subsets (containing each of the n elements individually), $\binom{n}{1} = n$. **8.** $\binom{n}{1}$ is the cofficient of ab^{n-1} in the expansion of $(a + b)^n$. Since there are n ways to choose an a from the n parentheses, $\binom{n}{1} = n$.

On Your Own

11. $\binom{n}{k} = \frac{n!}{k!(n-k)!} = \frac{n!}{(n-k)!k!} = \binom{n}{n-k}$

Chapter 5

Lesson 5.1

On Your Own

7. a. ℝ **b.** $\{x \mid x \ne 4\}$ **c.** $\{x \mid x > 0\}$ **d.** $\{1, 2, 3\}$
8. a. Answers may vary. Sample answer form: $h(x) = A$, $k(x) = A + (x - 1)(x - 2)(x - 3)(x - 4)(x - 5)$
b. Answers may vary. Sample answer form: $m(x) = A$, $n(x) = A + (x - 6)(x - 7)(x - 8)(x - 9)(x - 10)$
11. $269.74

Lesson 5.2

Check Your Understanding

1. $B(n) = \begin{cases} 0 & n = 0 \\ B(n-1) + 2n & n > 0 \end{cases}$

2. $G(n) = \begin{cases} -7 & n = 0 \\ G(n-1) + 3 & n > 0 \end{cases}$

3. $K(x) = \begin{cases} 1 & x = 0 \\ K(x-1) + 2x - 1 & x > 0 \end{cases}$

4. $\beta(n) = \begin{cases} 0 & n = 0 \\ \beta(n-1) + n & n > 0 \end{cases}$

5. $\varepsilon(n) = \begin{cases} 2 & n = 0 \\ \varepsilon(n-1) + 2^{n-1} & n > 0 \end{cases}$

6. $\kappa(n) = \begin{cases} 0 & n = 0 \\ \kappa(n-1) + 2n - 1 & n > 0 \end{cases}$

7. $\gamma(n) = \begin{cases} 0 & n = 0 \\ \gamma(n-1) + \frac{1}{2}n(n-1) & n > 0 \end{cases}$

8. No. In the base case, n is an integer. Therefore, $g(n)$ is only defined for integer n.

On Your Own

9. $B(n) = \begin{cases} 0 & n = 0 \\ 1.03 \cdot B(n-1) + 500 & n > 0 \end{cases}$

$B(5) = 2654.57$

10.

a	$h(a)$
0	3
1	11
2	19
3	27
4	35
5	43

$h(a) = 8a + 3$

11.

m	$f(m)$
0	0
1	2
2	6
3	12
4	20
5	30

$f(m) = m(m + 1)$

14. $T(n) = \begin{cases} 1 & n = 0 \\ T(n-1) \cdot 3 & n > 0 \end{cases}$

Lesson 5.3

Check Your Understanding

1. a. The balance at $n = 0$ is $2000 (initial balance), and in subsequent months the balance decreases by $50 (monthly payment) and increases by 1.5% of the previous balance (monthly interest).
b. $B(6) = 1875.41$; $B(12) = 1739.18$; $B(24) = 1427.33$

c. $B(n) = \begin{cases} 2000 & n = 0 \\ 1.015 \cdot B(n-1) - 50 & n > 0 \end{cases}$

$B(48) = 608.70$

2. $2^{25} - 1 = 33{,}554{,}431$

3. a.

n	$\frac{F(n+1)}{F(n)}$
1	1
2	2
3	1.5
4	$1.6\overline{6}$
5	1.6
6	1.625
7	1.6154 . . .
8	1.619 . . .
9	1.61764 . . .
10	1.61818 . . .

b. The ratios approach $\frac{1 + \sqrt{5}}{2} \approx 1.618034$.

4. a. $L(n) = \begin{cases} 2 & n = 0 \\ 1 & n = 1 \\ L(n-1) + L(n-2) & n > 1 \end{cases}$

b. $L(10) = 123$ **c.** The ratio approaches $\frac{1 + \sqrt{5}}{2} \approx 1.618034$, the golden ratio.

d.
$$\begin{aligned}
L(n) &= L(n-1) + L(n-2)\\
&= F(2) \cdot L(n-1) + F(1) \cdot L(n-2)\\
&= F(3) \cdot L(n-2) + F(2) \cdot L(n-3)\\
&= F(4) \cdot L(n-3) + F(3) \cdot L(n-4)\\
&\vdots\\
&= F(n) \cdot L(1) + F(n-1) \cdot L(0)\\
&= F(n) + 2F(n-1)\\
&= F(n+1) + F(n-1)
\end{aligned}$$

5. a.

n	$P(n)$
0	2
1	5
2	3
3	−2
4	−5
5	−3
6	2
7	5
8	3
9	−2
10	−5

b. $P(50) = 3$ **c.** No, because $P(1.5)$ and $P(0.5)$ are not defined. **d.** the set of nonnegative integers

6.

n	$g(n)$
0	0.4472
1	0.7236
2	1.1708
3	1.8944
4	3.0652
5	4.9597
6	8.0249
7	12.9846
8	21.0095
9	33.9941
10	55.0036

On Your Own

7. a. $712.58 **b.** $1178.52
8. a. $505.91 **b.** $1000.06

10. a.

n	$t(n)$
1	−1
2	1
3	−1
4	1
5	−1
6	1
7	−1
8	1
9	−1
10	1

b. $s(n) = (-1)^n$

11. a.

n	$t(n)$
1	−1
2	1
3	−1
4	1
5	−1
6	1
7	−1
8	1
9	−1
10	1

b. $t(n) = (-1)^n$

Lesson 5.4

Check Your Understanding

1.

a	$M(a)$
0	5
1	8
2	11
3	14
4	17
5	20

$m(a) = \begin{cases} 5 & a = 0 \\ m(a-1) + 3 & a > 0 \end{cases}$

$$\begin{aligned}
m(1001) &= m(1000) + 3\\
&= M(1000) + 3\\
&= (3 \cdot 1000 + 5) + 3\\
&= (3 \cdot 1000 + 3) + 5\\
&= 3 \cdot 1001 + 5\\
&= M(1001)
\end{aligned}$$

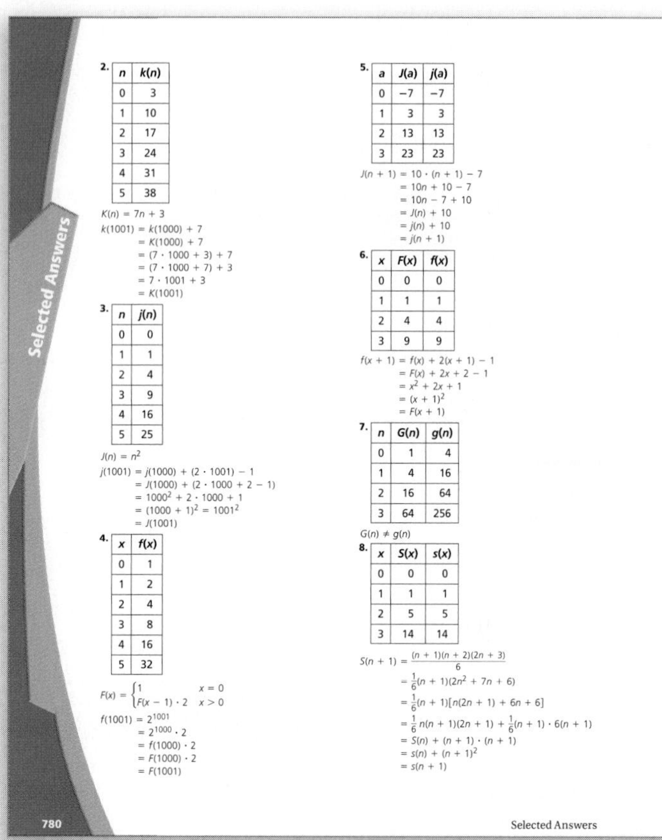

2.

n	$k(n)$
0	3
1	10
2	17
3	24
4	31
5	38

$K(n) = 7n + 3$

$$\begin{aligned} k(1001) &= k(1000) + 7 \\ &= K(1000) + 7 \\ &= (7 \cdot 1000 + 3) + 7 \\ &= (7 \cdot 1000 + 7) + 3 \\ &= 7 \cdot 1001 + 3 \\ &= K(1001) \end{aligned}$$

3.

n	$j(n)$
0	0
1	1
2	4
3	9
4	16
5	25

$J(n) = n^2$

$$\begin{aligned} j(1001) &= j(1000) + (2 \cdot 1001) - 1 \\ &= J(1000) + (2 \cdot 1000 + 2 - 1) \\ &= 1000^2 + 2 \cdot 1000 + 1 \\ &= (1000 + 1)^2 = 1001^2 \\ &= J(1001) \end{aligned}$$

4.

x	$f(x)$
0	1
1	2
2	4
3	8
4	16
5	32

$$F(x) = \begin{cases} 1 & x = 0 \\ F(x-1) \cdot 2 & x > 0 \end{cases}$$

$$\begin{aligned} f(1001) &= 2^{1001} \\ &= 2^{1000} \cdot 2 \\ &= f(1000) \cdot 2 \\ &= F(1000) \cdot 2 \\ &= F(1001) \end{aligned}$$

5.

a	$J(a)$	$j(a)$
0	−7	−7
1	3	3
2	13	13
3	23	23

$$\begin{aligned} J(n+1) &= 10 \cdot (n+1) - 7 \\ &= 10n + 10 - 7 \\ &= 10n - 7 + 10 \\ &= J(n) + 10 \\ &= j(n) + 10 \\ &= j(n+1) \end{aligned}$$

6.

x	$F(x)$	$f(x)$
0	0	0
1	1	1
2	4	4
3	9	9

$$\begin{aligned} f(x+1) &= f(x) + 2(x+1) - 1 \\ &= F(x) + 2x + 2 - 1 \\ &= x^2 + 2x + 1 \\ &= (x+1)^2 \\ &= F(x+1) \end{aligned}$$

7.

n	$G(n)$	$g(n)$
0	1	4
1	4	16
2	16	64
3	64	256

$G(n) \neq g(n)$

8.

x	$S(x)$	$s(x)$
0	0	0
1	1	1
2	5	5
3	14	14

$$\begin{aligned} S(n+1) &= \frac{(n+1)(n+2)(2n+3)}{6} \\ &= \frac{1}{6}(n+1)(2n^2 + 7n + 6) \\ &= \frac{1}{6}(n+1)[n(2n+1) + 6n + 6] \\ &= \frac{1}{6}n(n+1)(2n+1) + \frac{1}{6}(n+1) \cdot 6(n+1) \\ &= S(n) + (n+1) \cdot (n+1) \\ &= s(n) + (n+1)^2 \\ &= s(n+1) \end{aligned}$$

780 Selected Answers

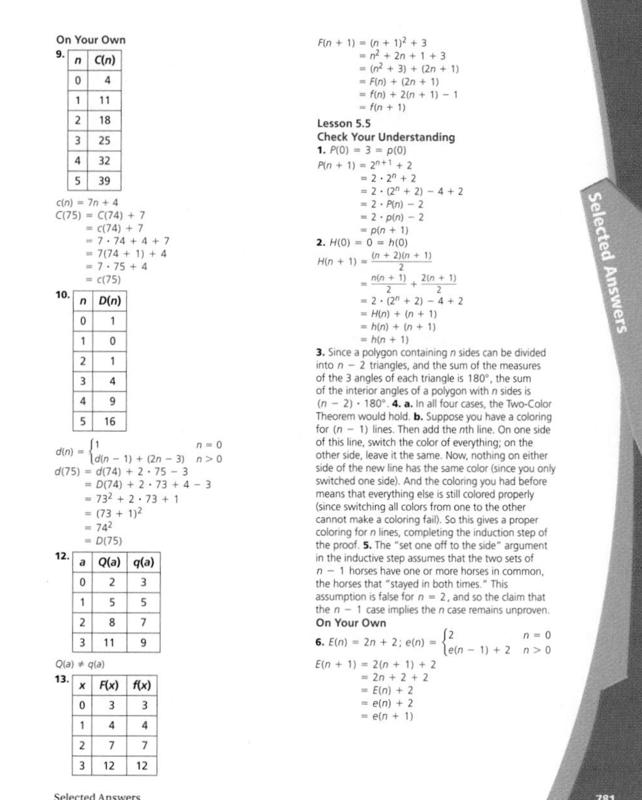

On Your Own

9.

n	$C(n)$
0	4
1	11
2	18
3	25
4	32
5	39

$c(n) = 7n + 4$

$$\begin{aligned} C(75) &= C(74) + 7 \\ &= c(74) + 7 \\ &= 7 \cdot 74 + 4 + 7 \\ &= 7(74 + 1) + 4 \\ &= 7 \cdot 75 + 4 \\ &= c(75) \end{aligned}$$

10.

n	$D(n)$
0	1
1	0
2	1
3	4
4	9
5	16

$$d(n) = \begin{cases} 1 & n = 0 \\ d(n-1) + (2n-3) & n > 0 \end{cases}$$

$$\begin{aligned} d(75) &= d(74) + 2 \cdot 75 - 3 \\ &= D(74) + 2 \cdot 73 + 4 - 3 \\ &= 73^2 + 2 \cdot 73 + 1 \\ &= (73 + 1)^2 \\ &= 74^2 \\ &= D(75) \end{aligned}$$

12.

a	$Q(a)$	$q(a)$
0	2	3
1	5	5
2	8	7
3	11	9

$Q(a) \neq q(a)$

13.

x	$F(x)$	$f(x)$
0	3	3
1	4	4
2	7	7
3	12	12

$$\begin{aligned} F(n+1) &= (n+1)^2 + 3 \\ &= n^2 + 2n + 1 + 3 \\ &= (n^2 + 3) + (2n + 1) \\ &= F(n) + (2n + 1) \\ &= f(n) + 2(n+1) - 1 \\ &= f(n+1) \end{aligned}$$

Lesson 5.5

Check Your Understanding

1. $P(0) = 3 = p(0)$

$$\begin{aligned} P(n+1) &= 2^{n+1} + 2 \\ &= 2 \cdot 2^n + 2 \\ &= 2 \cdot (2^n + 2) - 4 + 2 \\ &= 2 \cdot P(n) - 2 \\ &= 2 \cdot p(n) - 2 \\ &= p(n+1) \end{aligned}$$

2. $H(0) = 0 = h(0)$

$$\begin{aligned} H(n+1) &= \frac{(n+2)(n+1)}{2} \\ &= \frac{n(n+1)}{2} + \frac{2(n+1)}{2} \\ &= 2 \cdot (2^n + 2) - 4 + 2 \\ &= H(n) + (n+1) \\ &= h(n) + (n+1) \\ &= h(n+1) \end{aligned}$$

3. Since a polygon containing n sides can be divided into $n - 2$ triangles, and the sum of the measures of the 3 angles of each triangle is 180°, the sum of the interior angles of a polygon with n sides is $(n - 2) \cdot 180°$. **4. a.** In all four cases, the Two-Color Theorem would hold. **b.** Suppose you have a coloring for $(n - 1)$ lines. Then add the nth line. On one side of this line, switch the color of everything; on the other side, leave it the same. Now, nothing on either side of the new line has the same color (since you only switched one side). And the coloring you had before means that everything else is still colored properly (since switching all colors from one to the other cannot make a coloring fail). So this gives a proper coloring for n lines, completing the induction step of the proof. **5.** The "set one off to the side" argument in the inductive step assumes that the two sets of $n - 1$ horses have one or more horses in common, the horses that "stayed in both times." This assumption is false for $n = 2$, and so the claim that the $n - 1$ case implies the n case remains unproven.

On Your Own

6. $E(n) = 2n + 2$; $e(n) = \begin{cases} 2 & n = 0 \\ e(n-1) + 2 & n > 0 \end{cases}$

$$\begin{aligned} E(n+1) &= 2(n+1) + 2 \\ &= 2n + 2 + 2 \\ &= E(n) + 2 \\ &= e(n) + 2 \\ &= e(n+1) \end{aligned}$$

Selected Answers 781

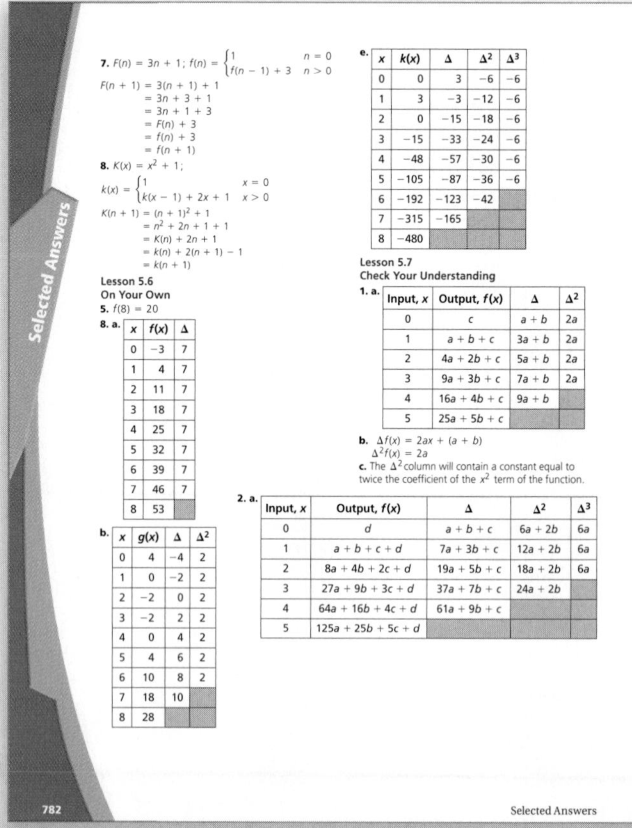

7. $F(n) = 3n + 1$; $f(n) = \begin{cases} 1 & n = 0 \\ f(n-1) + 3 & n > 0 \end{cases}$

$$\begin{aligned} F(n+1) &= 3(n+1) + 1 \\ &= 3n + 3 + 1 \\ &= 3n + 1 + 3 \\ &= F(n) + 3 \\ &= f(n) + 3 \\ &= f(n+1) \end{aligned}$$

8. $K(x) = x^2 + 1$;

$$k(x) = \begin{cases} 1 & x = 0 \\ k(x-1) + 2x + 1 & x > 0 \end{cases}$$

$$\begin{aligned} K(n+1) &= (n+1)^2 + 1 \\ &= n^2 + 2n + 1 + 1 \\ &= K(n) + 2n + 1 \\ &= k(n) + 2(n+1) - 1 \\ &= k(n+1) \end{aligned}$$

Lesson 5.6

On Your Own

5. $f(8) = 20$

8. a.

x	$f(x)$	Δ
0	−3	7
1	4	7
2	11	7
3	18	7
4	25	7
5	32	7
6	39	7
7	46	7
8	53	

b.

x	$g(x)$	Δ	Δ^2
0	4	−4	2
1	0	−2	2
2	−2	0	2
3	−2	2	2
4	0	4	2
5	4	6	2
6	10	8	2
7	18	10	
8	28		

e.

x	$k(x)$	Δ	Δ^2	Δ^3
0	0	3	−6	−6
1	3	−3	−12	−6
2	0	−15	−18	−6
3	−15	−33	−24	−6
4	−48	−57	−30	−6
5	−105	−87	−36	−6
6	−192	−123	−42	
7	−315	−165		
8	−480			

Lesson 5.7

Check Your Understanding

1. a.

Input, x	Output, $f(x)$	Δ	Δ^2
0	c	$a + b$	$2a$
1	$a + b + c$	$3a + b$	$2a$
2	$4a + 2b + c$	$5a + b$	$2a$
3	$9a + 3b + c$	$7a + b$	$2a$
4	$16a + 4b + c$	$9a + b$	
5	$25a + 5b + c$		

b. $\Delta f(x) = 2ax + (a + b)$
$\Delta^2 f(x) = 2a$
c. The Δ^2 column will contain a constant equal to twice the coefficient of the x^2 term of the function.

2. a.

Input, x	Output, $f(x)$	Δ	Δ^2	Δ^3
0	d	$a + b + c$	$6a + 2b$	$6a$
1	$a + b + c + d$	$7a + 3b + c$	$12a + 2b$	$6a$
2	$8a + 4b + 2c + d$	$19a + 5b + c$	$18a + 2b$	$6a$
3	$27a + 9b + 3c + d$	$37a + 7b + c$	$24a + 2b$	
4	$64a + 16b + 4c + d$	$61a + 9b + c$		
5	$125a + 25b + 5c + d$			

782 Selected Answers

b. $\Delta f(x) = 3ax^2 + (3a + 2b)x + (a + b + c)$
$\Delta^2 f(x) = 6ax + (6a + 2b)$
$\Delta^3 f(x) = 6a$
c. The Δ^3 column will contain a constant equal to 6 times the coefficient of the x^3 term.
3. a. degree 2 **b.** No; any function that equals zero at the x-values shown on the table could be added to a polynomial function that fits the table, and the resulting function would also fit the table.
4. a. $49 + 76$ **b.** $11 + 2 \cdot 38 + 38$
c. $-1 + 3 \cdot 12 + 3 \cdot 26 + 12$
d. $1 + 4 \cdot (-2) + 6 \cdot 14 + 4 \cdot 12 + 0$
5. Continue using the up-and-over property all the way up to the top row.

$$251 = 1 + 5(-2) + 10 \cdot 14 + 10 \cdot 12 + 5 \cdot 0 + 1 \cdot 0$$

6. $N(10) = 2051$; $N(10)$ could be written in terms of the numbers across the top row using the numbers in the tenth row of Pascal's triangle (i.e. $N(10) = a + 10b + 45c + 120d + 210e + 252f + 210g + 120h + 45i + 10j + k$).

On Your Own

9. a. $P(n) = -18$; $P(n + 1) = P(n) + \Delta$
b. $P(97) = -473$ **c.** $P(n) = -5n + 12$
10. This table could represent a third-order polynomial (cubic function) with leading coefficient equal to one-sixth of the Δ^3 term, or 2. **11. a.** The Δ and Δ^2 columns are not constant. **b.** 1

Lesson 5.8

Check Your Understanding

1. a.

Input, x	Output, $a(x)$	Δ	Δ^2
0	10	−2	6
1	8	4	6
2	12	10	6
3	22	16	6
4	38	22	6
5	60	28	
6	88		

b. $a(5) = 1 \cdot 10 + 5 \cdot (-2) + 10 \cdot 6 = 60$ **c.** 88
2. a. 2 **b.** $f(x) = \frac{1}{2}x(x - 1)$

c.

Input, x	Output, $f(x)$	Δ	Δ^2
0	0	0	1
1	0	1	1
2	1	2	1
3	3	3	1
4	6	4	1
5	10	5	
6	15		

3. $g(x) = \frac{x(x-1)(x-2)}{6}$

4. a. $\binom{8}{0} = 1$; $\binom{8}{1} = 8$; $\binom{8}{2} = 28$

b.

n	$T(n)$	Δ	Δ^2
0	a	b	c
1	$a + b$	$b + c$	c
2	$a + 2b + c$	$b + 2c$	c
3	$a + 3b + 3c$	$b + 3c$	c
4	$a + 4b + 6c$	$b + 4c$	c
5	$a + 5b + 10c$	$b + 5c$	c
6	$a + 6b + 15c$	$b + 6c$	c
7	$a + 7b + 21c$	$b + 7c$	c
8	$a + 8b + 28c$	$b + 8c$	c

5. a. 3

b.

x	$g(x)$	Δ	Δ^2	Δ^3	Δ^4
0	0	0	0	1	0
1	0	0	1	1	0
2	0	1	2	1	0
3	1	3	3	1	0
4	4	6	4	1	
5	10	10	5		
6	20	15			
7	35				

c. These numbers are along the third diagonal in Pascal's Triangle. **d.** These numbers are along the second diagonal in Pascal's Triangle.

Selected Answers 783

6. a.

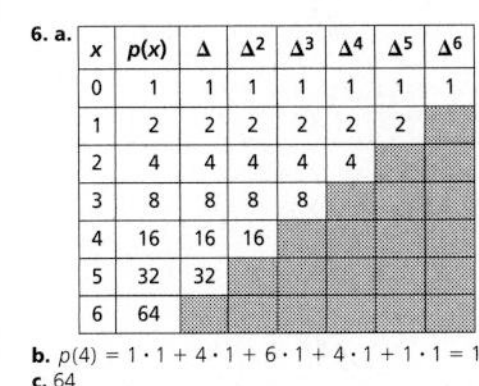

x	$p(x)$	Δ	Δ^2	Δ^3	Δ^4	Δ^5	Δ^6
0	1	1	1	1	1	1	1
1	2	2	2	2	2	2	
2	4	4	4	4	4		
3	8	8	8	8			
4	16	16	16				
5	32	32					
6	64						

b. $p(4) = 1 \cdot 1 + 4 \cdot 1 + 6 \cdot 1 + 4 \cdot 1 + 1 \cdot 1 = 16$
c. 64

On Your Own

7. a. $h(7) = 10$ **b.** $h(10) = 100$ **c.** $h(97) = 26{,}200$
9. a. $f(x) = -2x^2 - 6x + 5$
b. $f(x) = x^3 - 5x^2 - 4x + 5$
10. Answers may vary. Samples:

a.

Input	Output	Δ
0	0	12
1	12	−6
2	6	−20
3	−14	0
4	−14	12
5	−2	2
6	0	

b.

Input	Output	Δ
0	5	12
1	17	−6
2	11	−20
3	−9	0
4	−9	12
5	3	2
6	5	

Lesson 5.9

Check Your Understanding

1. $\binom{x}{4} = \frac{x(x-1)(x-2)(x-3)}{4!}$

$\binom{x}{5} = \frac{x(x-1)(x-2)(x-3)(x-4)}{5!}$

$\binom{x}{6} = \frac{x(x-1)(x-2)(x-3)(x-4)(x-5)}{6!}$

In general, the kth Mahler polynomial is

$\binom{x}{k} = \frac{x(x-1)(x-2)\cdots(x-k+1)}{k!}$

2. $f(n) = n^4 + 3n^2 - 5n + 6$ **3. a.** 0, 1, 2 **b.** 0, 2, 4 **c.** 0, 1, 6, 6 **d.** 0, 2, 12, 12 **e.** 0, 2, 8, 6
4. Method 1: Work backwards to build a difference table for all values of the function between 0 and 9, then use the top row to determine the function.

$$f(x) = 39 \cdot \binom{x}{0} - 16 \cdot \binom{x}{1} + 4 \cdot \binom{x}{2} = 2x^2 - 18x + 39$$

Method 2: Pretend the outputs start at 0 and find $g(x) = 2x^2 - 6x + 3$. Then replace x with $x - 3$ and expand to obtain $g(x - 3) = f(x) = 2x^2 - 18x + 39$.

5. a. If $f(x) = \binom{x}{3}$,

$$\begin{aligned}\Delta f(x) &= f(x+1) - f(x)\\ &= \binom{x+1}{3} - \binom{x}{3}\\ &= \frac{(x+1)x(x-1)}{6} - \frac{x(x-1)(x-2)}{6}\\ &= \frac{x(x-1)}{6}[(x+1) - (x-2)]\\ &= \frac{x(x-1)}{6} \cdot 3\\ &= \frac{x(x-1)}{2}\\ &= \binom{x}{2}\end{aligned}$$

b. If $f(x) = \binom{x}{k}$,

$$\begin{aligned}\Delta f(x) &= f(x+1) - f(x)\\ &= \binom{x+1}{k} - \binom{x}{k}\\ &= \frac{(x+1)x(x-1)\cdots(x-k+2)}{k!} - \frac{x(x-1)(x-2)\cdots(x-k+1)}{k!}\\ &= \frac{x(x-1)\cdots(x-k+2)}{k!} \cdot [(x+1) - (x-k+1)]\\ &= \frac{x(x-1)\cdots(x-k+2)}{k!} \cdot k\\ &= \frac{x(x-1)\cdots(x-k+2)}{(k-1)!}\\ &= \binom{x}{k-1}\end{aligned}$$

6. a.

x	$g(x)$	Δ	Δ^2	Δ^3
0	1	4	16	64
1	5	20	80	320
2	25	100	400	
3	125	500		
4	625			

$$g(3) = 1 \cdot \binom{3}{0} + 4 \cdot \binom{3}{1} + 16 \cdot \binom{3}{2} + 64 \cdot \binom{3}{3} = 125$$

b. You can generalize the argument in part (a) for $g(n)$ for any nonnegative integer n:

$$g(n) = \sum_{k=0}^{n} 4^k \binom{n}{k} = 5^n$$

c. Let $h(x) = (p + 1)^x$.

x	$h(x)$	Δ	Δ^2	Δ^3
0	1	p	p^2	p^2
1	p 1 1	$p(p$ 1 1)	$p^2(p$ 1 1)	$p^3(p$ 1 1)
2	$(p$ 1 1$)^2$	$p(p$ 1 1$)^2$	$p^2(p$ 1 1$)^2$	
3	$(p$ 1 1$)^3$	$p(p$ 1 1$)^3$		
4	$(p$ 1 1$)^4$			

The top row of the difference table contains powers of p; therefore by the same argument made for $g(n)$,

$$h(n) = \sum_{k=0}^{n} p^k \binom{n}{k} = (p + 1)^n$$

7. Incorrect; a periodic function such as $f(x) = 5 + \sin 2\pi x$ would have a difference table with $\Delta = 0$. If f is a polynomial function, then it must be constant.

On Your Own

8. $f(x) = 2x^3 + 5x^2 - x - 17$

9. $S(n) = \frac{n(n+1)(2n+1)}{6}$ **10.** $C(n) = \frac{n^2(n+1)^2}{4}$

Lesson 5.10

Check Your Understanding

1. a.

k	k^3	Δ	Δ^2	Δ^3
0	0	1	6	6
1	1	7	12	6
2	8	19	18	6
3	27	37	24	
4	64	61		
5	125			

b. $\frac{n^2(n-1)^2}{4}$ **2.** $n(n - 1)(2n - 1)$

3. a.

x	$f(x)$	Δ	Δ^2	Δ^3	Δ^4
0	0	1	14	36	24
1	1	15	50	60	24
2	16	65	110	84	
3	81	175	194		
4	256	369			
5	625				

b. $x^4 = 0 \cdot \binom{x}{0} + 1 \cdot \binom{x}{1} + 14 \cdot \binom{x}{2} + 36 \cdot \binom{x}{3} + 24 \cdot \binom{x}{4}$

Then $\sum_{k=0}^{n-1} k^4 = 0 \cdot \binom{n}{1} + 1 \cdot \binom{n}{2} + 14 \cdot \binom{n}{3} + 36 \cdot \binom{n}{4} + 24 \cdot \binom{n}{5}$

c. $\sum_{k=0}^{n-1} k^4 = \frac{n(n-1)}{2} + 14 \cdot \frac{n(n-1)(n-2)}{6} + 36 \cdot \frac{n(n-1)(n-2)(n-3)}{24} + 24 \cdot \frac{n(n-1)(n-2)(n-3)(n-4)}{120}$

4. a. Substitute $(n - 1)$for n and the formulas are the same. **b.** Write n^4 as $\frac{30n^4}{30}$ and factor both sides to demonstrate that these two expressions are equal. **5. a.** The volume is made up of five smaller shapes: $5 \times 5 \times 1$, $4 \times 4 \times 1$, $3 \times 3 \times 1$, $2 \times 2 \times 1$, and $1 \times 1 \times 1$.
$V = 1^2 + 2^2 + 3^2 + 4^2 + 5^2$
b. $5 \times 6 \times 11$ **c.** The dimensions of the box are n by $(n + 1)$ by $(2n + 1)$. Since six congruent shapes were used to build the box, the volume of each shape is $V = \frac{n(n+1)(2n+1)}{6}$, which also equals $1^2 + 2^2 + 3^2 + 4^2 + 5^2$.

6.

$f(x)$	1	x	x^2	x^3	x^4	x^5
$\binom{x}{0}$	1	-	-	-	-	-
$\binom{x}{1}$	0	1	-	-	-	-
$\binom{x}{2}$	0	$-\frac{1}{2}$	$\frac{1}{2}$	-	-	-
$\binom{x}{3}$	0	$\frac{1}{3}$	$-\frac{1}{2}$	$\frac{1}{6}$	-	-
$\binom{x}{4}$	0	$-\frac{1}{4}$	$\frac{11}{24}$	$-\frac{1}{4}$	$\frac{1}{24}$	-
$\binom{x}{5}$	0	$\frac{1}{5}$	$-\frac{5}{24}$	$-\frac{7}{24}$	$-\frac{1}{12}$	$\frac{1}{120}$

Patterns: Reciprocals of the factorial numbers appear along the diagonal; within each row, the terms always alternate signs; the x column contains reciprocals of all positive integers in an alternating positive/negative pattern. This matrix is the inverse of the matrix from Exercise 16 in Lesson 5.9.

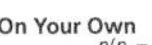

On Your Own

7. a. $3n$ **b.** $\frac{n(n-1)}{2}$ **c.** $\frac{5n(n-1)}{2}$
10. $f(n) = n^2 + 6n + 8$
11. $f(n) = A + Cn + B \cdot \frac{n(n-1)}{2}$

Lesson 5.11

On Your Own

6. a. The function defined matches the description in the problem.

b.

n	$r(n)$
0	$\frac{7}{2}$
1	$\frac{29}{7}$
2	$\frac{133}{29}$
3	$\frac{641}{133}$
4	$\frac{3157}{641}$
5	$\frac{15{,}689}{3157}$
6	$\frac{78{,}253}{15{,}689}$

c. Yes, it approaches 5. **d.** Except for $r(0) = 2$, $r(n) \to 5$ as n grows without bound. $r(0) = 2$ repeatedly returns 2. **8. a.** Check students' work.
b. The outputs appear to be approaching 2.
c. The long-term behavior of the outputs seems independent of the starting number. They always approach 2.

Lesson 5.12

Check Your Understanding

1. a. $f(6) = 300$; $f(4) = \frac{100}{3}$ **b.** $K = \frac{100}{243}$ or $\frac{100}{3^5}$
c. $f(n) = 100 \cdot 3^{n-5}$ **2. a.** $g(4) = 20.25$
b. $g(n) = 64 \cdot \left(\frac{3}{4}\right)^n$ **c.** 256 **d.** 256.0000
3. a. $h(n) = 4^n$; $j(n) = 6^n$
b.

$$\begin{aligned}10k(n-1) - 24k(n-2) &= 10(5 \cdot 4^{n-1} + 8 \cdot 6^{n-1}) - 24(5 \cdot 4^{n-2} + 8 \cdot 6^{n-2})\\ &= 50 \cdot 4^{n-1} + 80 \cdot 6^{n-1} - 120 \cdot 4^{n-2} - 192 \cdot 6^{n-2}\\ &= 50 \cdot 4^{n-1} + 80 \cdot 6^{n-1} - 30 \cdot 4 \cdot 4^{n-2} - 32 \cdot 6 \cdot 6^{n-2}\\ &= 50 \cdot 4^{n-1} + 80 \cdot 6^{n-1} - 30 \cdot 4^{n-1} - 32 \cdot 6^{n-1}\\ &= 20 \cdot 4^{n-1} + 48 \cdot 6^{n-1}\\ &= 5 \cdot 4 \cdot 4^{n-1} + 8 \cdot 6 \cdot 6^{n-1}\\ &= 5 \cdot 4^n + 8 \cdot 6^n\\ &= k(n)\end{aligned}$$

c. $r(n) = 5 \cdot 4^n - 2 \cdot 6^n$

4. a. $b = 0$ **b.** $f(1)$ is 32 away from b and $f(2)$ is 64 away from b. **5. a.** $b = -3$ **b.** $j(1)$ is 32 away from b and $j(2)$ is 64 away from b. **6. a.** 0 **b.** $g(0)$ is 64 away from the limit; $g(1)$ is 48 away from the limit; $g(2)$ is 36 away from the limit. **7. a.** $r(x) = 40$

b.

n	$r(n)$	Δ	÷
0	104	−16	0.75
1	88	−12	0.75
2	76	−9	0.75
3	67	−6.75	0.75
4	60.25	−5.0625	0.75
5	55.1875	−3.7969	0.75
6	51.3906	−2.8477	0.75
7	48.5430	−2.1357	
8	46.4072		

On Your Own

8. Expand the left side to $1 + r^2 + r^3 + \cdots + r^{n-1}$, then multiply by −1 to get $-1 - r^2 - r^3 - \ldots - r^{n-1}$. Adding together these terms leaves just $(1 - r^n)$ as the result of the expansion. **10. a.** $f(n) = 3 \cdot 4^n$
b. 4,194,303 **12. c.** yes **d.** no **e.** yes

Lesson 5.13

Check Your Understanding

1. a. 266 and 1282; $A = 2$, $B = 2$ **b.** −117 and −609; $A = 1$, $B = -1$ **c.** 149 and 673; $A = 3$, $B = 1$
d. 39 and 203; $A = -\frac{1}{3}$, $B = \frac{1}{3}$ **e.** −70 and −390; $A = \frac{5}{3}$, $B = -\frac{2}{3}$ **f.** $-70x + 39y$ and $-390x + 203y$; $A = \frac{5x - y}{3}$, $B = \frac{y - 2x}{3}$ **2. a.** 10 and 3

b.

$$\begin{aligned}&13 \cdot 10^{n-1} - 30 \cdot 10^{n-2}\\ &= 13 \cdot 10^{n-1} - 3 \cdot 10 \cdot 10^{n-2}\\ &= 13 \cdot 10^{n-1} - 3 \cdot 10^{n-1}\\ &= 10 \cdot 10^{n-1}\\ &= 10^n\end{aligned}$$

c.

$$\begin{aligned}&13 \cdot 3^{n-1} - 30 \cdot 3^{n-2}\\ &= 13 \cdot 3^{n-1} - 10 \cdot 3 \cdot 3^{n-2}\\ &= 13 \cdot 3^{n-1} - 10 \cdot 3^{n-1}\\ &= 3 \cdot 3^{n-1}\\ &= 3^n\end{aligned}$$

d.

$$\begin{aligned}&13(10^{n-1} + 3^{n-1}) - 30(10^{n-2} + 3^{n-2})\\ &= (13 \cdot 10^{n-1} - 30 \cdot 10^{n-2}) + (13 \cdot 3^{n-1} - 30 \cdot 3^{n-2})\end{aligned}$$

See proofs in parts (b) and (c) to complete the proof.
3. $t(n) = 3 \cdot 3^n + 2 \cdot 5^n$ **4.** $t(n) = 3^n + 7^n$
5. $h(n) = (1 + \sqrt{2})^n$; $j(n) = (1 - \sqrt{2})^n$
6. Answers may vary. Sample: Use the quadratic equation $x^2 = Ax + B$ to find the two roots that are used to determine the closed form. Either root of the equation $x^2 - Ax - B = 0$ can be the base.

7. $f(n) = \frac{\left(\frac{1+\sqrt{5}}{2}\right)^n - \left(\frac{1-\sqrt{5}}{2}\right)^n}{\sqrt{5}}$

On Your Own

8. a. $f(n) = 4^n + 5^n$ **b.** $f(n) = 10(4^n + 5^n)$
9. a. Answers may vary. Sample: One way would be to tabulate $f(n)$ and notice that a common ratio between terms emerges, suggesting that this ratio might fit the recurrence.

b.

$$\begin{aligned}&8 \cdot 6^{n-1} - 12 \cdot 6^{n-2}\\ &= 8 \cdot 6^{n-1} - 2 \cdot 6 \cdot 6^{n-2}\\ &= 8 \cdot 6^{n-1} - 2 \cdot 6^{n-1}\\ &= 6 \cdot 6^{n-1}\\ &= 6^n\end{aligned}$$

c. $f(n) = 6^n + 2^n$ **d.** $f(n) = 4 \cdot 6^n + 2^n$
10. $f(n) = \frac{7}{3} \cdot 4^n - \frac{1}{3} \cdot (-2)^n$
12. $L(n) = \left(\frac{1+\sqrt{5}}{2}\right)^n + \left(\frac{1-\sqrt{5}}{2}\right)^n$

Lesson 5.14

Check Your Understanding

1. $B(n) = 500\left(\frac{1.03^n - 1}{0.03}\right)$
2. $B(n) = D\left(\frac{(1+r)^n - 1}{r}\right)$

3. a.

Years n	Trees $T(n)$
0	25,000
1	23,000
2	21,400
3	20,120
4	19,096
5	18,277
6	17,621
7	17,097

b.

Number of Trees vs. Time
Trees $T(n)$
25,000
20,000
15,000
10,000
5,000
0
0 1 2 3 4 5 6 7
Year n

c. 15,000

d.

Years n	Trees $T(n)$	$T(n) - 15{,}000$	÷
0	25,000	10,000	0.8
1	23,000	8000	0.8
2	21,400	6400	0.8
3	20,120	5120	0.8
4	19,096	4096	0.8
5	18,277	3277	0.8
6	17,621	2621	0.8
7	17,097	2097	0.8

e. $T(n) = 15{,}000 + 10{,}000 \cdot 0.8^n$
4. $B = -13{,}000$ **5.** If x is an equilibrium point, then $f(n) = x$ for all n. Therefore:
$x = Ax + B$
$x - Ax = B$
$x(1 - A) = B$
$x = \frac{B}{1 - A}$
6. a. $\frac{P}{r}$ **b.** $B - \frac{P}{r}$ **c.** $f(1)$ is $(1 + r)\left(B - \frac{P}{r}\right)$ away from the equilibrium point.
$f(2)$ is $(1 + r)^2\left(B - \frac{P}{r}\right)$ away from the equilibrium point.
$f(n)$ is $(1 + r)^n\left(B - \frac{P}{r}\right)$ away from the equilibrium point.
d. $f(n) = \frac{P}{r} + (1 + r)^n\left(B - \frac{P}{r}\right)$
e. $P = \frac{Br(1+r)^n}{(1+r)^n - 1}$

On Your Own

7. a. \$1,355,121.84 **b.** \$803,195.64 **c.** \$493,537.82

8. a.

n	$f(n)$
0	P
1	$AP + B$
2	$A^2P + AB + B$
3	$A^3P + A^2B + AB + B$
4	$A^4P + A^3B + A^2B + AB + B$

b. $f(n) = A^nP + B\left(\frac{A^n - 1}{A - 1}\right)$
9. a. $f(36) = 1.005^{36} \cdot 12{,}000 - p\left(\frac{1.005^{36} - 1}{0.005}\right)$
b. \$365.06

Chapter 6

Lesson 6.1

On Your Own

8. $(\sqrt{13}, 2)$, $(\sqrt{13}, -2)$, $(-\sqrt{13}, 2)$, $(-\sqrt{13}, -2)$
11. d. $AX = \sqrt{2}$, $BX = 4\sqrt{2}$, $CX = 4$, $DX = 2$, therefore $AX \cdot BX = CX \cdot DX = 8$

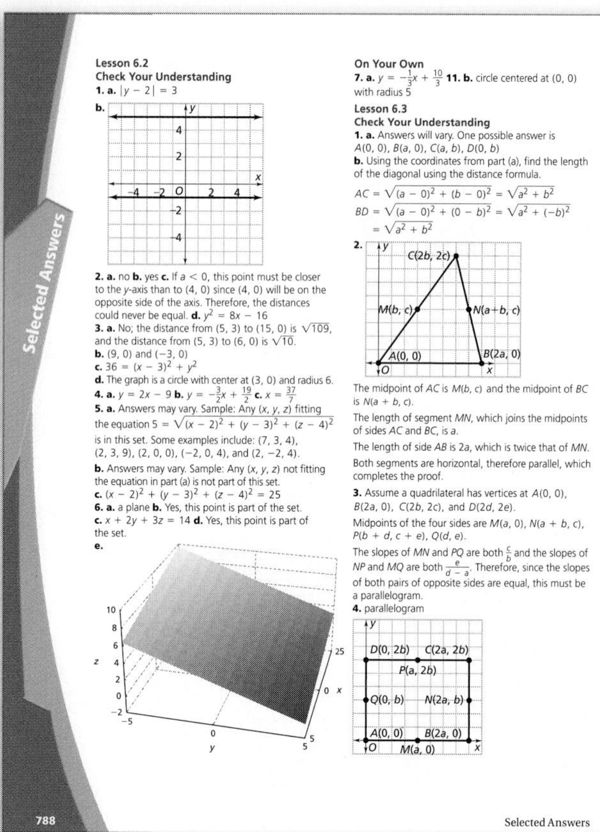

Lesson 6.2
Check Your Understanding

1. a. $|y - 2| = 3$

b.

2. a. no **b.** yes **c.** If $a < 0$, this point must be closer to the y-axis than to (4, 0) since (4, 0) will be on the opposite side of the axis. Therefore, the distances could never be equal. **d.** $y^2 = 8x - 16$

3. a. No; the distance from (5, 3) to (15, 0) is $\sqrt{109}$, and the distance from (5, 3) to (6, 0) is $\sqrt{10}$.
b. (9, 0) and (−3, 0)
c. $36 = (x - 3)^2 + y^2$
d. The graph is a circle with center at (3, 0) and radius 6.

4. a. $y = 2x - 9$ **b.** $y = -\frac{3}{2}x + \frac{19}{2}$ **c.** $x = \frac{37}{7}$

5. a. Answers may vary. Sample: Any (x, y, z) fitting the equation $5 = \sqrt{(x - 2)^2 + (y - 3)^2 + (z - 4)^2}$ is in this set. Some examples include: (7, 3, 4), (2, 3, 9), (2, 0, 0), (−2, 0, 4), and (2, −2, 4).
b. Answers may vary. Sample: Any (x, y, z) not fitting the equation in part (a) is not part of this set.
c. $(x - 2)^2 + (y - 3)^2 + (z - 4)^2 = 25$

6. a. a plane **b.** Yes, this point is part of the set.
c. $x + 2y + 3z = 14$ **d.** Yes, this point is part of the set.
e.

On Your Own

7. a. $y = -\frac{1}{3}x + \frac{10}{3}$ **11. b.** circle centered at (0, 0) with radius 5

Lesson 6.3
Check Your Understanding

1. a. Answers will vary. One possible answer is $A(0, 0)$, $B(a, 0)$, $C(a, b)$, $D(0, b)$
b. Using the coordinates from part (a), find the length of the diagonal using the distance formula.

$$AC = \sqrt{(a - 0)^2 + (b - 0)^2} = \sqrt{a^2 + b^2}$$
$$BD = \sqrt{(a - 0)^2 + (0 - b)^2} = \sqrt{a^2 + (-b)^2} = \sqrt{a^2 + b^2}$$

2. $C(2b, 2c)$, $M(b, c)$, $N(a + b, c)$, $A(0, 0)$, $B(2a, 0)$

The midpoint of AC is $M(b, c)$ and the midpoint of BC is $N(a + b, c)$.

The length of segment MN, which joins the midpoints of sides AC and BC, is a.

The length of side AB is $2a$, which is twice that of MN.

Both segments are horizontal, therefore parallel, which completes the proof.

3. Assume a quadrilateral has vertices at $A(0, 0)$, $B(2a, 0)$, $C(2b, 2c)$, and $D(2d, 2e)$.

Midpoints of the four sides are $M(a, 0)$, $N(a + b, c)$, $P(b + d, c + e)$, $Q(d, e)$.

The slopes of MN and PQ are both $\frac{c}{b}$ and the slopes of NP and MQ are both $\frac{e}{d - a}$. Therefore, since the slopes of both pairs of opposite sides are equal, this must be a parallelogram.

4. parallelogram

$D(0, 2b)$, $C(2a, 2b)$, $P(a, 2b)$, $Q(0, b)$, $N(2a, b)$, $A(0, 0)$, $B(2a, 0)$, $M(a, 0)$

Assume a quadrilateral has vertices at $A(0, 0)$, $B(2a, 0)$, $C(2a, 2b)$, $D(0, 2b)$.

Midpoints of the four sides are $M(a, 0)$, $N(2a, b)$, $P(a, 2b)$, $Q(0, b)$.

Similar to the previous problem, the slopes of MN and PQ are equal and the slopes of NP and MQ are equal. Therefore, since the slopes of both pairs of opposite sides are equal, this must be a parallelogram. Also, since $MN = NP$, $MNPQ$ is a rhombus.

5. Answers may vary. Sample: Joey assumes that the two lines of symmetry of the rhombus are perpendicular. He does this by placing them along the axes. It would be alright for Joey to place one line of symmetry on the axis, then prove the other must lie along the axis as well. But by building the rhombus in this way, Joey has assumed what he is trying to prove, which is invalid.

6. $S(b, c)$, $R(a + b, c)$, $P(0, 0)$, $Q(a, 0)$

Assume a parallelogram has vertices at $P(0, 0)$, $Q(a, 0)$, $R(a + b, c)$, $S(b, c)$.

The slope of diagonal PR is $\frac{c}{a + b}$, and the slope of diagonal SQ is $\frac{c}{b - a}$.

If these diagonals are perpendicular, then

$$\frac{c}{a + b} \cdot \frac{c}{b - a} = -1$$
$$\frac{c^2}{b^2 - a^2} = -1$$
$$c^2 = a^2 - b^2$$
$$c^2 + b^2 = a^2$$

To prove $PQRS$ is a rhombus, you must show that two consecutive sides are congruent. The length of PQ is a and the length of QR is $\sqrt{b^2 + c^2}$. If the diagonals are perpendicular, then $a^2 = b^2 + c^2$, so $PQ = QR$ and the parallelogram must be a rhombus.

On Your Own

8. Answers may vary. Sample: One way is to use $B(2b, 0)$ and $C(0, 2c)$. Midpoint of BC is $D(b, c)$.

$$AD = \sqrt{b^2 + c^2}$$
$$BD = \sqrt{(2b - b)^2 + (0 - c)^2} = \sqrt{b^2 + c^2}$$
$$CD = \sqrt{(0 - b)^2 + (2c - c)^2} = \sqrt{b^2 + c^2}$$

All three lengths are the same.

11. Answers may vary. Sample: Assume coordinates $A(0, 0)$, $B(2a, 0)$, $C(2b, 2c)$, $D(2d, 2c)$.

The length of AB is $2a$ and the length of CD is $2b - 2d$. The average of these lengths is $a + b - d$.

The midline's endpoints are $M(d, c)$ and $N(a + b, c)$. The distance between M and N is $a + b - d$.

Lesson 6.4
Check Your Understanding

1.

Consider point P outside the circle.

Pick $\overleftrightarrow{OP}$ where O is the center of the circle so that $OP = d$ and AB is a diameter.

$PA = d + r$ and $PB = d - r$, therefore the power of point P with respect to the circle is

$PA \cdot PB = (d + r)(d - r) = d^2 - r^2$

2. a. Center is (−3, 4)and radius is 7.
b.
c. The two x-intercepts are $(-3 + \sqrt{33}, 0)$ and $(-3 - \sqrt{33}, 0)$.

The two y-intercepts are $(0, 4 + 2\sqrt{10})$ and $(0, 4 - 2\sqrt{10})$.

3. a. 24 **b.** 24 **c.** (4, 4) and (−3, −3); $P = 24$

4. As the intersection points get closer together, the line through P comes closer and closer to being a tangent of the circle. If PA is the tangent to the circle, then $(PA)^2$ equals the power of point P. This means that if point P is d units away from the center of the circle, and $d > r$, the length of the tangent from P to the circle is $\sqrt{d^2 - r^2}$.

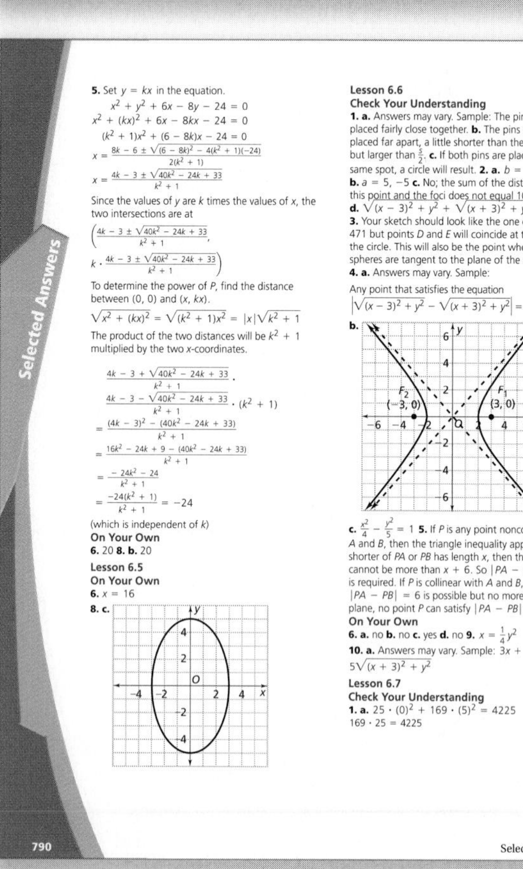

5. Set $y = kx$ in the equation.

$$x^2 + y^2 + 6x - 8y - 24 = 0$$
$$x^2 + (kx)^2 + 6x - 8kx - 24 = 0$$
$$(k^2 + 1)x^2 + (6 - 8k)x - 24 = 0$$
$$x = \frac{8k - 6 \pm \sqrt{(6 - 8k)^2 - 4(k^2 + 1)(-24)}}{2(k^2 + 1)}$$
$$x = \frac{4k - 3 \pm \sqrt{40k^2 - 24k + 33}}{k^2 + 1}$$

Since the values of y are k times the values of x, the two intersections are at

$$\left(\frac{4k - 3 \pm \sqrt{40k^2 - 24k + 33}}{k^2 + 1}, k \cdot \frac{4k - 3 \pm \sqrt{40k^2 - 24k + 33}}{k^2 + 1}\right)$$

To determine the power of P, find the distance between (0, 0) and (x, kx).

$$\sqrt{x^2 + (kx)^2} = \sqrt{(k^2 + 1)x^2} = |x|\sqrt{k^2 + 1}$$

The product of the two distances will be $k^2 + 1$ multiplied by the two x-coordinates.

$$\frac{4k - 3 + \sqrt{40k^2 - 24k + 33}}{k^2 + 1} \cdot \frac{4k - 3 - \sqrt{40k^2 - 24k + 33}}{k^2 + 1} \cdot (k^2 + 1)$$
$$= \frac{(4k - 3)^2 - (40k^2 - 24k + 33)}{k^2 + 1}$$
$$= \frac{16k^2 - 24k + 9 - (40k^2 - 24k + 33)}{k^2 + 1}$$
$$= \frac{-24k^2 - 24}{k^2 + 1}$$
$$= \frac{-24(k^2 + 1)}{k^2 + 1} = -24$$

(which is independent of k)

On Your Own

6. 20 **8. b.** 20

Lesson 6.5
On Your Own

6. $x = 16$

8. c.

Lesson 6.6
Check Your Understanding

1. a. Answers may vary. Sample: The pins should be placed fairly close together. **b.** The pins should be placed far apart, a little shorter than the string length s but larger than $\frac{s}{2}$. **c.** If both pins are placed in the same spot, a circle will result. **2. a.** $b = 4, -4$
b. $a = 5, -5$ **c.** No; the sum of the distances between this point and the foci does not equal 10.
d. $\sqrt{(x - 3)^2 + y^2} + \sqrt{(x + 3)^2 + y^2} = 10$

3. Your sketch should look like the one on page 471 but points D and E will coincide at the center of the circle. This will also be the point where the two spheres are tangent to the plane of the sliced circle.

4. a. Answers may vary. Sample:

Any point that satisfies the equation
$\left|\sqrt{(x - 3)^2 + y^2} - \sqrt{(x + 3)^2 + y^2}\right| = 4$.

b. F_2 (−3, 0), F_1 (3, 0)

c. $\frac{x^2}{4} - \frac{y^2}{5} = 1$ **5.** If P is any point noncollinear with A and B, then the triangle inequality applies: if the shorter of PA or PB has length x, then the longer cannot be more than $x + 6$. So $|PA - PB| < 6$ is required. If P is collinear with A and B, then $|PA - PB| = 6$ is possible but no more. In the entire plane, no point P can satisfy $|PA - PB| = 10$.

On Your Own

6. a. no **b.** no **c.** yes **d.** no **9.** $x = \frac{1}{4}y^2$
10. a. Answers may vary. Sample: $3x + 25 = 5\sqrt{(x + 3)^2 + y^2}$

Lesson 6.7
Check Your Understanding

1. a. $25 \cdot (0)^2 + 169 \cdot (5)^2 = 4225$
$169 \cdot 25 = 4225$

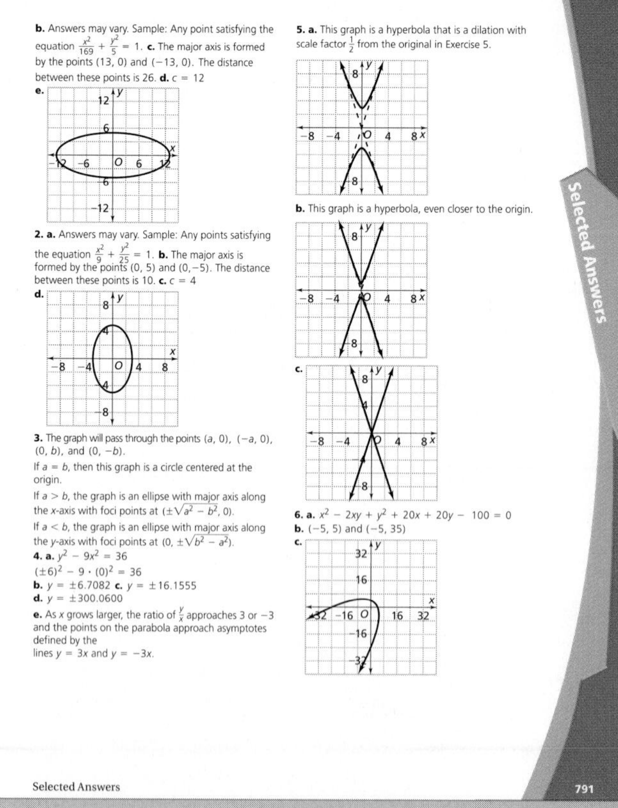

b. Answers may vary. Sample: Any point satisfying the equation $\frac{x^2}{169} + \frac{y^2}{5} = 1$. **c.** The major axis is formed by the points (13, 0) and (−13, 0). The distance between these points is 26. **d.** $c = 12$
e.

2. a. Answers may vary. Sample: Any points satisfying the equation $\frac{x^2}{9} + \frac{y^2}{25} = 1$. **b.** The major axis is formed by the points (0, 5) and (0,−5). The distance between these points is 10. **c.** $c = 4$
d.

3. The graph will pass through the points $(a, 0)$, $(-a, 0)$, $(0, b)$, and $(0, -b)$.

If $a = b$, then this graph is a circle centered at the origin.

If $a > b$, the graph is an ellipse with major axis along the x-axis with foci points at $(\pm\sqrt{a^2 - b^2}, 0)$.

If $a < b$, the graph is an ellipse with major axis along the y-axis with foci points at $(0, \pm\sqrt{b^2 - a^2})$.

4. a. $y^2 - 9x^2 = 36$
$(\pm 6)^2 - 9 \cdot (0)^2 = 36$
b. $y = \pm 6.7082$ **c.** $y = \pm 16.1555$
d. $y = \pm 300.0600$
e. As x grows larger, the ratio of $\frac{y}{x}$ approaches 3 or −3 and the points on the parabola approach asymptotes defined by the lines $y = 3x$ and $y = -3x$.

5. a. This graph is a hyperbola that is a dilation with scale factor $\frac{1}{2}$ from the original in Exercise 5.

b. This graph is a hyperbola, even closer to the origin.

c.

6. a. $x^2 - 2xy + y^2 + 20x + 20y - 100 = 0$
b. (−5, 5) and (−5, 35)
c.

On Your Own

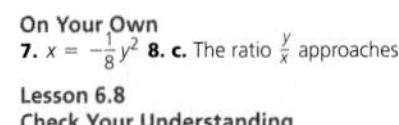

7. $x = -\frac{1}{8}y^2$ **8. c.** The ratio $\frac{y}{x}$ approaches $\frac{3}{4}$.

Lesson 6.8

Check Your Understanding

1. a. (3, 2)

b.

x	y
6	undefined
7	2
8	4.25
9	5.3541
11	7.1962
13	8.8739
23	16.6969
43	31.8496
103	76.9400
1003	751.9940

c. The graph becomes asymptotic to the line $y - 2 = \frac{3}{4}(x - 3)$.

2. a.

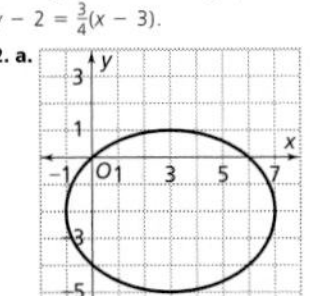

b. no

c.

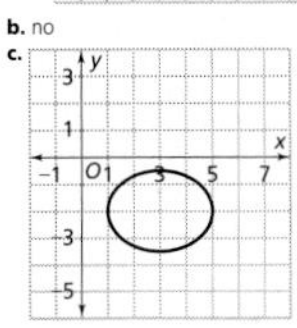

d. (graph: point (3, −2))

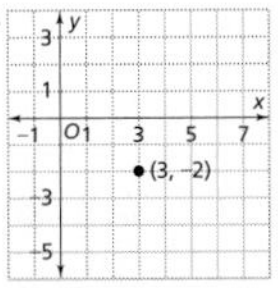

e. No graph, since the equation has no solution.

f. $N = 916$

3. a. Yes; hyperbola

b.

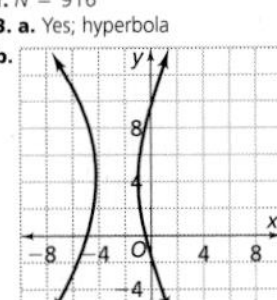

4. a. No; this equation is a single point

b.

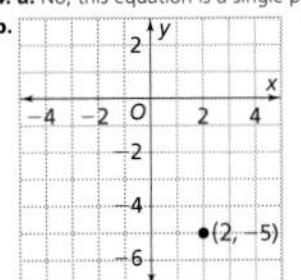

5. a. $(y - 2)^2 = 4(x + 3)^2 - 16$ **b.** The next step in solving this equation is to take a square root, which results in two answers (a positive and negative root).

c. $f_1(x) = 2 + \sqrt{4(x + 3)^2 - 16}$

$f_2(x) = 2 - \sqrt{4(x + 3)^2 - 16}$

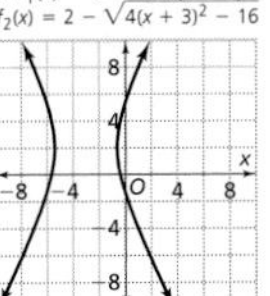

6.

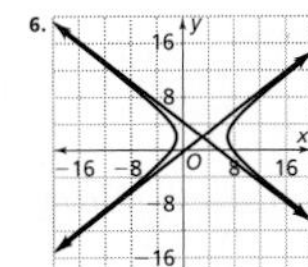

7. $y = \frac{1}{x}$

On Your Own

8. Answers may vary. Sample: The first equation is the sum of squares, and squares can never be negative. The second equation is the difference of squares, and that can be negative. **10. a.** $x \le -16$ or $x \ge -2$

11. (4, 10) and (4, 0)

Lesson 6.9

Check Your Understanding

1. a. $\frac{3}{5}$ **b.** $\frac{4}{5}$ **c.** $\frac{1}{5}$ **d.** $\frac{\sqrt{3}}{2}$ **2.** $\frac{(x - 8)^2}{16} + \frac{y^2}{12} = 1$

3. $\frac{(x - 8)^2}{16} + \frac{y^2}{12} = 1$; Center = (8, 0)

4. a. Center = (−6, 5); vertices = (−12, 5) and (0, 5); foci = (−15, 5) and (3, 5) **b.** $e = 1.5$

c.

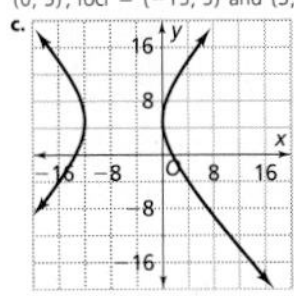

5. $e = 3$ **6. a.** If $e = 1$, the definition gives $PF = Pd$, which matches the locus definition of a parabola given in Lesson 6.6. **b.** Let $e < 1$ and use the distance formula to determine the equation of the ellipse.

$\sqrt{x^2 + (y - 1)^2} = e|y + 1|$

Solving this equation yields

$$\frac{x^2}{\frac{1 - e^2}{4e^2}} + \frac{\left(y - \frac{1 + e^2}{1 - e^2}\right)^2}{\frac{(1 - e^2)^2}{4e^2}} = 1$$

Based on this equation, $a = \frac{2e}{1 - e^2}$ and $b = \frac{2e}{\sqrt{1 - e^2}}$,

therefore $c = \frac{2e^2}{1 - e^2}$.

The eccentricity is given by $\frac{c}{a} = \frac{2e^2/(1 - e^2)}{2e/(1 - e^2)} = e$.

c. Using the same methods, find $a = \frac{2e}{e^2 - 1}$, $b = \frac{2e}{\sqrt{e^2 - 1}}$, $c = \frac{2e^2}{e^2 - 1}$ to show that $\frac{c}{a} = e$.

7.

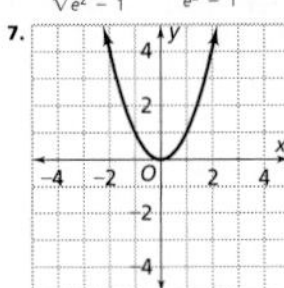

a. The graph looks very similar to $y = x^2$. **b.** Answers may vary. Sample: The ellipse must have a very high eccentricity and a vertex at (0, 0).

On Your Own

10. a. $e = 6$ **12.** (−5,7)

Lesson 6.10

On Your Own

6. c. $y = -\frac{1}{2}x + \frac{5}{2}$

8. a. The figure will be identical but all sides will be only half as long.

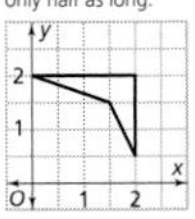

Lesson 6.11

Check Your Understanding

1. Assume point P has coordinates (x, y). Then point Q has coordinates $(x + c, y + d)$.

Assume point R has coordinates (m, n). Then point S has coordinates $(m + c, m + d)$.

a. The slope of $\overrightarrow{PQ}$ is $\frac{(y + d) - y}{(x + c) - x} = \frac{d}{c}$. Similarly, the slope of $\overrightarrow{RS}$ is $\frac{d}{c}$.

b. The length of $\overrightarrow{PQ}$ is $\sqrt{((x + c) - x)^2 + ((y + d) - y)^2} = \sqrt{c^2 + d^2}$. Similarly, the length of $\overrightarrow{RS}$ is $\sqrt{c^2 + d^2}$.

c. The displacement vector provides the direction. Since they have the same displacement, they must point in the same direction. **2.** If $\overrightarrow{PQ}$ has direction vector D, then $Q = P + kD$ for some positive scalar k. Similarly, $S = R + mD$ for some positive scalar m. The length of $\overrightarrow{PQ}$ is the length of kD, and the length of $\overrightarrow{RS}$ is the length of mD. But these are given to be equal; therefore $k = m$ as long as D is nonzero. Since $k = m$, then $Q - P = kD = mD = S - R$.

3. (6, 6) **4.** $A + U + V$

5.

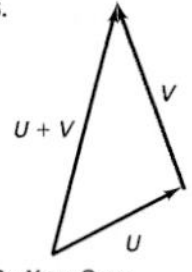

On Your Own

6. a. $(t_1 + a_1, t_2 + a_2)$ **e.** (1, 1, 1)

Lesson 6.12

Check Your Understanding

1. (4, 6): yes; (−5, −5): no; (13, 18): yes

2. $y = 2x - 2$ **3. a.** $\frac{4}{3}$ **b.** $\frac{3}{4}$ **c.** $\frac{4}{3}$ **d.** $\frac{4}{3}$

4. a–d. Answers may vary. Samples are given.

a. $X = (0, 1) + t(2, 3)$ **b.** $X = (5, 3) + t(1, 4)$

c. $X = (0, 3) + t(2, -3)$ **d.** $X = (-2, 3) + t(5, -2)$ or $X = (3, 1) + t(5, -2)$ are two equations.

5. $y = \frac{17}{3}$ **6.** no **7.** For the lines to be the same, it is necessary that D' be a scalar multiple of D (i.e., the lines are parallel). Once it is known that the lines are parallel, then check to see if P' is on the first line. If that turns out to be true, the lines are identical, since a line is uniquely determined by a point and a slope.

8. a.

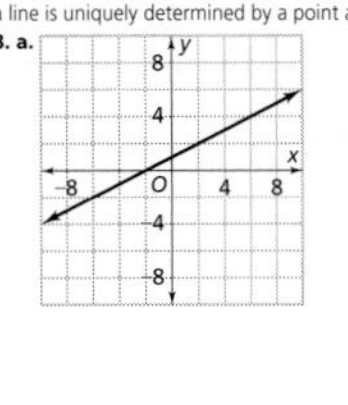

b. (graph)

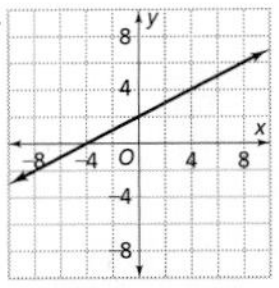

c. The direction vector is scaled, but the direction is not changed. Since the two lines have the same direction vector, they must be parallel.

On Your Own

9. Answers may vary. Sample: $X = (2, 3) + t(-3, 1)$

13. a. The paths intersect and these cars crash.

14. $z = 7$

Lesson 6.13

Check Your Understanding

1. a. $\overrightarrow{AB} = B - A = (3, 1) - (0, 0) = (3, 1)$. Similarly, $\overrightarrow{DC} = C - D = (4, 5) - (1, 4) = (3, 1)$. Therefore, sides AB and DC are parallel and equal in length, and $ABCD$ must be a parallelogram. **b.** (2, 2.5)

c. (2, 2.5)

2. Answers may vary. Sample: One way is to find the midpoints of two opposite sides, say AB and CD, draw the "midline" segment between them, and take the midpoint of that segment.

$$\frac{\frac{1}{2}(A + B) + \frac{1}{2}(C + D)}{2} = \frac{A + B + C + D}{4}$$

Another way is to draw both diagonals and mark the midpoints of each. Now take the midpoint of the segment between them.

$$\frac{\frac{1}{2}(A + C) + \frac{1}{2}(B + D)}{2} = \frac{A + B + C + D}{4}$$

3. a. They bisect each other. The midpoint of PR is

$$\frac{P + R}{2} = \frac{\frac{1}{2}(A + B) + \frac{1}{2}(C + D)}{2} = \frac{A + B + C + D}{4}$$

The midpoint of QS is also $\frac{A + B + C + D}{4}$. So the two lines intersect at their midpoints, bisecting each other. **b.** They are parallel and equal in length. Prove that $Q - P = R - S$ to show that these are equivalent vectors.

$Q - P = \frac{B + C}{2} - \frac{B + A}{2} = \frac{C - A}{2}$ and

$R - S = \frac{C + D}{2} - \frac{A + D}{2} = \frac{C - A}{2}$

The vectors are equivalent, so PQ and RS are equal in length and parallel.

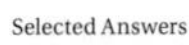

4. a.

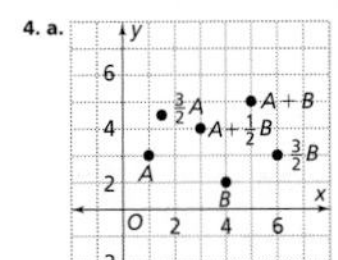

b. $\frac{1}{2}(A + (A + B)) = \frac{1}{2}((1, 3) + (5, 5)) = (3, 4) = (1, 3) + \frac{1}{2}(4, 2)$ **c.** The midpoint of the segment from A to $(A + B)$ is $\frac{A + (A + B)}{2} = A + \frac{1}{2}B$. **d.** For any points C, D, the trisection point of CD closer to C is $\frac{2}{3}C + \frac{1}{3}D$. Therefore, the trisection point closer to $\frac{3}{2}A$ of the segment from $\frac{3}{2}A$ to $\frac{3}{2}B$ is $\frac{2}{3}\left(\frac{3}{2}A\right) + \frac{1}{3}\left(\frac{3}{2}B\right) = A + \frac{1}{2}B$. **5. a.** 1 to 3 **b.** 1 to 3 **c.** The quarter point of PC, the quarter point of QB, and the midpoint of the median, are all $\frac{1}{2}A + \frac{1}{4}B + \frac{1}{4}C$. Therefore, they are all the same point. **d.** S bisects the median line.

6. The parallelogram can be fully labeled using the given information.

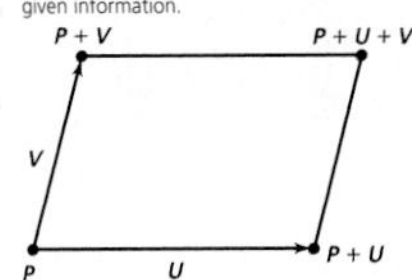

The midpoint of both diagonals is $P + \frac{1}{2}(U + V)$, so the diagonals bisect each other.

7. Two sides are parallel if the direction vector for one is a scalar multiple of the direction vector for the other. So the figure includes the givens. To show that opposite sides have equal length, you have to show that $k = j = 1$. By the parallelogram law,

$U + V = jV + kU$

$(1 - k)U = (j - 1)V$

But since U and V are not parallel, the only way two multiples of them could be equal is if the coefficients are 0. That is $(1 - k) = (j - 1) = 0$. Which implies $k = j = 1$ as desired.

On Your Own

8. $(1 - k)A + kB = A + d(B - A)$. If k varies through all nonnegative numbers, you get all points starting at A in the direction of B. You get beyond B when $k > 1$. **9. a.** Given point D is inside the triangle. Draw a line from vertex A through D to E on side BC. Since E is between B and C, E is a convex combination of B and C, and $E = (1 - k)B + kC$ for some k with $0 < k < 1$. Because D is some convex combination of A and E, then $D = (1 - j)A + jE$ for some j with $0 < j < 1$. By substitution, $D = (1 - j)A + j(1 - k)B + jkC$. These coefficients, $1 - j$, $j(1 - k)$, jk, are a, b, c. All of these must be positive, and

$(1 - j) + j(1 - k) + jk = 1 - j + j - jk + jk = 1$

Chapter 7

Lesson 7.1

On Your Own

7. b. $\frac{19}{25}$ **d.** $\frac{35}{49}$ **8. a.** 120

Lesson 7.2

Check Your Understanding

1. a. $\frac{1}{2}$ **b.** $\frac{1}{4}$ **c.** $\frac{1}{2}$ **d.** $\frac{1}{2}$ **e.** 0 **f.** $\frac{1}{36}$ **g.** $\frac{35}{36}$

2. The results are not equally likely because there are 5 ways to roll a sum of 8 on two dice out of 36 outcomes; $\frac{5}{36}$ **3.** 15; HHTTTT, HTHTTT, HTTHTT, HTTTHT, HTTTTH, THHTTT, THTHTT, THTTHT, THTTTH, TTHHTT, TTHTHT, TTHTTH, TTTHHT, TTTHTH, TTTTHH

4. $\binom{6}{2} = 15$; this represents 15 ways to pick two items from a group of six. **5.** 20; this is the coefficient of the t^3h^3 term; $(t + h)^6 = t^6 + 6t^5h + 15t^4h^2 + 20t^3h^3 + 15t^2h^4 + 6th^5 + t^6$ **6.** $\frac{21}{216}$

On Your Own

9. $\frac{84}{512}$ **10. a.** $\frac{1}{6}$ **11. a.** 36

Lesson 7.3

Check Your Understanding

1. a.

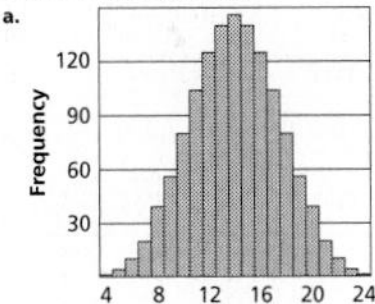

b. To roll a 5, the only possible roll is the four variations of 1-1-1-2. To roll a 23, the only possible roll is the four variations of 6-6-6-5. Also, the frequencies appear symmetric on either side of 14.

2. $\frac{1}{2}$ **3. a.** $x^2 + x^3 + x^4 + x^5 + x^6 + x^{10}$ **b.** 20; $\frac{95}{1296}$ **4. a.** Answers may vary. Sample: $2x^5$ represents the two faces with 5 on them, while the other exponents indicate single faces with 1 through 4 on them. **b.** 13; $\frac{164}{1296}$ **5. a.** $q(x) = 4x^{10} + 4x^9 + 5x^8 + 6x^7 + 7x^6 + 4x^5 + 3x^4 + 2x^3 + x^2$; this represents the frequencies of the sums when the 1-2-3-4-5-5 number cube is rolled twice. **b.** 36 **c.** 4 **d.** 4 **6. a.** $\frac{3}{50}$ or 0.06 **b.** $\frac{425}{1000}$ or 0.425 **c.** $\frac{7760}{10,000}$ or 0.776

On Your Own

7. a. $1 + x + 2x^2 + x^7$ **b.** $\frac{72}{625}$ **8. a.** 0.2; 0.2 **b.** $(0.2)^6 = 0.000064$

Lesson 7.4

Check Your Understanding

1. a. $\frac{1}{24}$ **b.** $\frac{3}{8}$ **2.** 1 **3.** \$5719.53 **4.** There is nothing wrong with Daisuke's calculation. His mistake was in the interpretation of his r esults. Expected value is not a probability and can be greater than 1. $\frac{12}{8}$ represents the number of heads expected when you toss 3 coins.
5. a. $(0.2r + 0.8w)^6 = 0.000064r^6 + 0.001536r^5w + 0.01536r^4w^2 + 0.08192r^3w^3 + 0.24576r^2w^4 + 0.39322rw^5 + 0.26214w^6$; each term is the probability of getting a specific number of questions correct. **b.** 1.2
6. a. $(x^1 + x^2 + x^3 + x^{10})^3 = x^{30} + 3x^{23} + 3x^{22} + 3x^{21} + 3x^{16} + 6x^{15} + 9x^{14} + 6x^{13} + 3x^{12} + x^9 + 3x^8 + 6x^7 + 7x^6 + 6x^5 + 3x^4 + x^3$
b. $\frac{27}{64}$ **7.** 16

On Your Own

8. b. \$14,925.80 **10. a.** 7 **b.** 10.5 **13.** 0

Lesson 7.5

Check Your Understanding

1.

Matches	Frequency
0 correct	2,118,760
1 correct	1,151,500
2 correct	196,000
3 correct	12,250
4 correct	250
5 correct	1

2. $\frac{5}{11}$ **3.** $\frac{44,800,030}{146,107,962} \approx 0.30662$
4. a. $\frac{1,000,000m + 28,800,030}{146,107,962} = 0.006844m + 0.197115$, where m is the number of millions
b. 0.88154 **c.** greater than \$117,308,932
5.

Ticket Type	Frequency	Payout
5 balls + bonus	1	Jackpot
5 balls + no bonus	45	\$250,000
4 balls + bonus	255	\$10,000
4 balls + no bonus	11,475	\$150
3 balls + bonus	12,750	\$150
3 balls + no bonus	573,750	\$7
2 balls + bonus	208,250	\$10
1 ball + bonus	1,249,500	\$3
Bonus only	2,349,060	\$2
Losing ticket	171,306,450	\$0
Total outcomes	**175,711,536**	

0.25029 **6.** \$10.64.

On Your Own

7. $\frac{6}{7}$ **8. a.** $\frac{1,110,353,500}{65,530,000} \approx 16.9468$ **b.** \$200,046,500
11. a. 720

Lesson 7.6

On Your Own

4. a. higher **d.** higher **e.** Bill should go higher for $n \leq 53$ and lower for $n \geq 54$.

Lesson 7.7

Check Your Understanding

1. a. 4.5 **b.** 1.5 **c.** 2.917 **d.** 1.708 **2. a.** 7 **b.** 3 **c.** 11.667 **d.** 3.4156 **3. a.** 3.3333 **b.** 1.3333 **c.** 2.2222 **d.** 1.4907 **4. a.** 3 **b.** 0 **c.** 0 **d.** 0 **5. a.** The mean increases by c, but the mean absolute deviation, variance, and standard deviation are unchanged. Answers may vary. Sample: Compare the data set 1, 2, 3, 4, 5, 6 with the data set from Exercise 1. The mean increased by 1, but the other values are the same.
b. The mean, mean absolute deviation, and standard deviation are multiplied by k, and the variance is multiplied by k^2. Answers may vary. Sample: Compare the data set 1, 2, 3, 4, 5, 6 with the data from Exercise 2. The mean, mean absolute deviation, and standard deviation were multiplied by 2. The variance was multiplied by 4. **6.** 3.96; 1.8018

7. Let the original data be $\{x_1, x_2, \ldots, x_n\}$ with mean $\bar{x}$. **a.** The new data is $\{(x_1 + c), (x_2 + c), \ldots, (x_n + c)\}$. The mean of the data $\frac{x_1 + c + x_2 + c + \ldots x_n + c}{n} = \frac{x_1 + x_2 + \ldots + x_n + n \cdot c}{n} = \frac{x_1 + x_2 + \ldots + x_n}{n} + c = \bar{x} + c$ Each deviation is $(x_i + c) - (\bar{x} + c)$; the value of c cancels. **b.** The new data is $\{kx_1, kx_2, \ldots, kx_n\}$. The mean of the data is $\frac{kx_1 + kx_2 + \ldots + kx_n}{n} = k \cdot \frac{x_1 + x_2 + \ldots + x_n}{n} = k\bar{x}$. Each deviation is $kx_i - k\bar{x} = k(x_i - \bar{x})$; each deviation is k times larger. The variance will be k^2 times larger since each deviation is the variance squared. **8.** 7; $\frac{35}{18}$; $\frac{35}{6}$; 2.415; the mean and variance are doubled and the standard deviation is $\sqrt{2}$ times as large. The mean absolute deviation is larger by factor of $\frac{35}{27}$ which doesn't seem to be part of the pattern.

On Your Own

9. a. $\frac{1}{2}$ **b.** $\frac{1}{2}$ and $-\frac{1}{2}$ **10. b.** 1, 0, 0, −1
12. b. $\frac{9}{2}$; 25

Lesson 7.8

Check Your Understanding

1. a.

Sum	Frequency
3	1
4	3
5	6
6	10
7	15
8	21
9	25
10	27
11	27
12	25
13	21
14	15
15	10
16	6
17	3
18	1

b. 10.5 **c.** $\frac{35}{4}$; $\frac{\sqrt{35}}{2}$ **d.** 3 times **e.** $\sqrt{3}$ times
2. a. 7; 25; 5 **b.** 16; 144; 12 **c.** 18; 256; 16

3. a.

+	1	7	13	25	34
2	3	9	15	27	36
12	13	19	25	37	46

b. 23; 169; 13
4. a.

Y	1	7	13	25	34
10	11	17	23	35	44
10	11	17	23	35	44
10	11	17	23	35	44
10	11	17	23	35	44
50	51	57	63	75	84

b. 34; 400; 20 **5.** 17 **6. a.** Spinner A: 5; Spinner B: 10.8; Spinner C: 12.8 **b.** 11.2 **c.** 16.32 **d.** Answers may vary. Sample: There is not an obvious pattern in the relationships of the mean absolute deviation of the combined spinners. **7.** Answers may vary. Sample: If the original standard deviations are a and b, and the new standard deviation is c. The numbers for the standard deviation are in the relationship, $a^2 + b^2 = c^2$.

On Your Own

8. a. $\frac{5}{2}$; $\frac{11}{12}$; $\frac{\sqrt{33}}{6}$ **12. b.** −6.25 cents; yes, the game will make money over time. **13. a.** 25; 5

Lesson 7.9

Check Your Understanding

1. $\frac{1}{5}$; 0.16; 0.4 **2. a.** $\frac{1}{25}$; $\frac{8}{25}$; $\frac{16}{25}$ **b.** 0.4; 0.32; $\sqrt{0.32} \approx 0.566$ **3.** 0.6; 0.48; $\sqrt{0.48} \approx 0.693$ **4.** 4; 3.2; $\sqrt{3.2} \approx 1.789$ **5. a.** $\frac{1}{4}$; $\frac{1}{2}$ **b.** $\frac{1}{2}$; $\sqrt{0.5} \approx 0.707$ **c.** 1; 1 **d.** $\frac{9}{4}$; $\frac{3}{2}$ **e.** 25; 5 **6. a.** 3 **b.** Answers may vary. Sample: Yes, it is unusual most results should be in the range 18 ± 3, between 15 and 21. Only 10 head is far outside this range. **c.** 0.003699 or 0.37% **7. a.** p; $p(1 - p)$; $\sqrt{p(1 - p)}$ **b.** np; $np(1 - p)$; $\sqrt{np(1 - p)}$

On Your Own

8. a. 781.25; 27.95 **c.** 3125; 55.90 **9. e.** $\frac{5n}{36}$; $\frac{\sqrt{5n}}{6}$

Lesson 7.10

Check Your Understanding

1. a. 0.0514 **2. a.** 0.0690 **3. a.** 40; 5.7735 **b.** Answers may vary. Sample: This is an unusual result. Most of the results should be from 40 ± 5.7735. This is roughly from 34 to 46. Getting only 20 sixes is far outside this range. **4. a.** Each question has $p = 0.2$ probability of getting a correct answer. They are independent of one another, so the probability of getting n consecutive questions right is 0.2^n.

b. 0.0115 or 1.15% **c.** 0.2054 or 20.54%
5. a. $f(n) = \binom{20}{n}(0.20)^n(0.8)^{(20-n)}$
b.

n	$f(n)$
0	0.0115
1	0.0576
2	0.1369
3	0.2054
4	0.2182
5	0.1746
6	0.1091
7	0.0545
8	0.0222
9	0.0074
10	0.0020

6. 0.2054; the coefficient is the probability of getting 3 correct and 17 wrong answers.
7.
$$\begin{aligned} p(1-p)^2 + p^2(1-p) &= p(1-p) \\ &= p(1 - 2p + p^2) + p^2 - p^3 \\ &= p - 2p^2 + p^3 + p^2 - p^3 \\ &= p - p^2 \\ &= p(1-p) \end{aligned}$$
8.

Number of Successes	Probability	Product
2	p^2	$2p^2$
1	$2p(1-p)$	$2p(1-p)$
0	$(1-p)^2$	0
Total		$2p$

Success	Deviation	Deviation²	Probability	Product
2	$2-2p$	$(2-2p)^2$	p^2	$(2-2p)^2 \cdot p^2$
1	$1-2p$	$(1-2p)^2$	$2p(1-p)$	$(1-2p)^2 \cdot 2p(1-p)$
0	$-2p$	$(-2p)^2$	$(1-p)^2$	$(-2p)^2 \cdot (1-p)^2$
Total				$2p(1-p)$

On Your Own

9. a. pq **b.** $(1 - p)(1 - q)$ **c.** $p + q - 2pq$
11. 14; $\frac{146}{1296} \approx 0.1127 \approx 11.27\%$

Lesson 7.11

On Your Own

5. a. $\frac{13}{162} \approx 0.0802$ **b.** 1 **9. a.** 0.2475 **c.** 0.0782

Lesson 7.12

Check Your Understanding

2. a. 0.2066; **b.** 0.2051 **c.** 0.73% **3. a.** 50; 5 **b.** 0.2995 **c.** 0.0301 **d.** 0.41% **4. a.** 1800; 900 **b.** mean doubles to 3600; standard deviation is multiplied by $\sqrt{2}$ to 42.43 **c.** 3558 to 3642
5. a.

b.

c.

d.

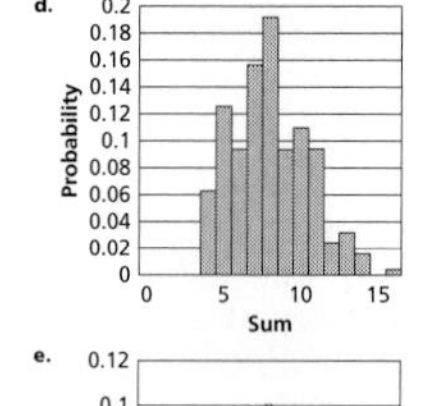

e.

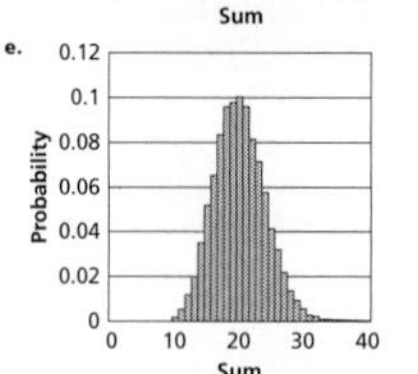

6. a. 100; 17.68 **b.** 82 to 118 **7. a.** 45 to 55 heads
b. $\sum_{k=45}^{55}\binom{100}{k} \cdot 0.5^k \cdot 0.5^{100-k} \approx 0.7287$

On Your Own

8. a. 1740 to 1860 heads **9. a.** 18; 3.55 **b.** 0.183 to 0.417 **12. c.** 0.040029 **d.** 0.040915

Lesson 7.13

Check Your Understanding

1. a. 68% **b.** 95% **c.** 2.5% **2. a.** 68% **b.** 60 to 78 inches **3. a.** 1250; 25 **b.** 16% **4. a.** 0.42074 **b.** 0.344578 **c.** 0.274253 **d.** 0.158655 **e.** 0.022750 **f.** 0.000032 **g.** 0 **5.** using the binomial theorem: 0.00013475, using the normal CDF: 0.00026605
6. a. .675 **b.** 1 **c.** 1.65 **d.** 2.58

On Your Own

7. a. 84% **b.** 10.6% **8.** 0.21% **12.** 52.2%

Chapter 8

Lesson 8.1

On Your Own

11. $3ab$ **13.** A regular polygon with n sides can be divided into n congruent triangles with base $\frac{P}{n}$ and height a. Each triangle has area $\frac{Pa}{2n}$, so the polygon has area $\frac{1}{2}Pa$.

Lesson 8.2

Check Your Understanding

1. The area should not change significantly, but tracing between the fingers will increase the perimeter. **2.** One idea: use string to carefully match the perimeter of the hand, then measure the length of string needed.
3. Answers will vary. **4.** Answers will vary.
5.

a. $A_{lower} = 0$; $A_{upper} = 4$ in.; $A_{average} = 2$ in. **b.** ≈36% **c.** $A_{lower} = 1$ in.; $A_{upper} = 4$ in.; $A_{average} = \frac{5}{2}$ in. **d.** ≈20% **e.** A grid with squares of side 0.001 in. would be fine enough.

On Your Own

7. a. A dart is most likely to land in the "You win" region because this region takes up more than half of the board. **b.** The probability is equal to the "You win" area $\left(\frac{1}{4}\pi\right)$ divided by the area of the dartboard (1), which equals $\frac{1}{4}\pi \approx 79\%$.

Lesson 8.3

Check Your Understanding

1. Answers may vary. However, the following are essential to any algorithm.
- Divide the interval [0, 1] into the given number of equal pieces.
- For the lower sum: on each piece, build a rectangle with that base and height equal to the value of the function for the left-hand endpoint.
- For the upper sum: on each piece, build a rectangle with that base and height equal to the value of the function for the right-hand endpoint.
- To compute either sum, add up the areas of all respective rectangles.

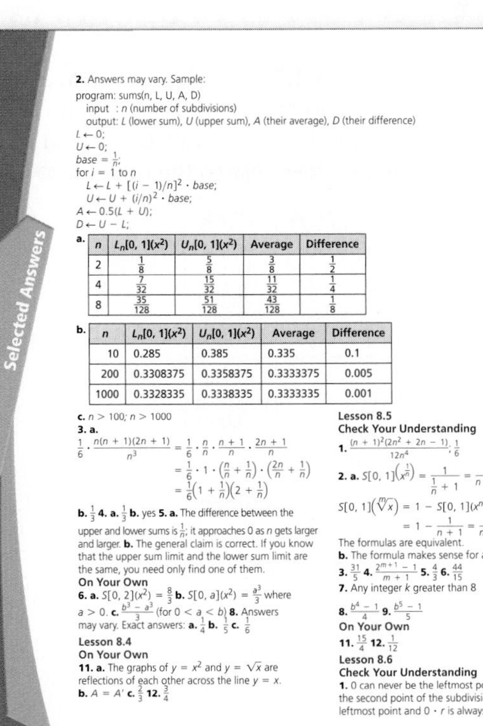

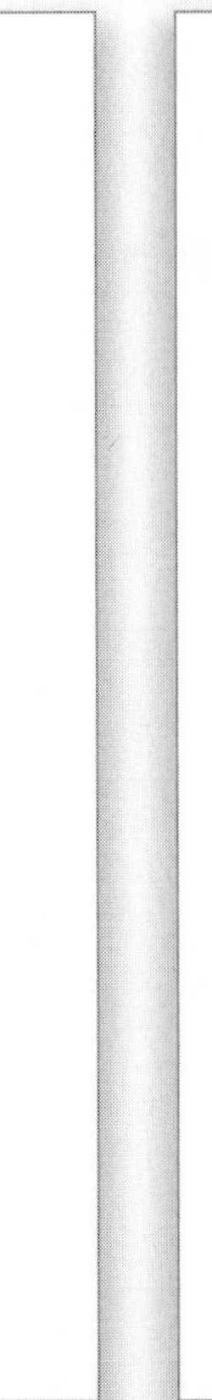

2. Answers may vary. Sample:

```
program: sums(n, L, U, A, D)
  input  : n (number of subdivisions)
  output: L (lower sum), U (upper sum), A (their average), D (their difference)
L ← 0;
U ← 0;
base = 1/n;
for i = 1 to n
  L ← L + [(i − 1)/n]^2 · base;
  U ← U + (i/n)^2 · base;
A ← 0.5(L + U);
D ← U − L;
```

a.

n	$L_n[0, 1](x^2)$	$U_n[0, 1](x^2)$	Average	Difference
2	$\frac{1}{8}$	$\frac{5}{8}$	$\frac{3}{8}$	$\frac{1}{2}$
4	$\frac{7}{32}$	$\frac{15}{32}$	$\frac{11}{32}$	$\frac{1}{4}$
8	$\frac{35}{128}$	$\frac{51}{128}$	$\frac{43}{128}$	$\frac{1}{8}$

b.

n	$L_n[0, 1](x^2)$	$U_n[0, 1](x^2)$	Average	Difference
10	0.285	0.385	0.335	0.1
200	0.3308375	0.3358375	0.3333375	0.005
1000	0.3328335	0.3338335	0.3333335	0.001

c. $n > 100$; $n > 1000$

3. a.

$$\frac{1}{6}\cdot\frac{n(n+1)(2n+1)}{n^3} = \frac{1}{6}\cdot\frac{n}{n}\cdot\frac{n+1}{n}\cdot\frac{2n+1}{n} = \frac{1}{6}\cdot 1\cdot\left(\frac{n}{n}+\frac{1}{n}\right)\cdot\left(\frac{2n}{n}+\frac{1}{n}\right) = \frac{1}{6}\left(1+\frac{1}{n}\right)\left(2+\frac{1}{n}\right)$$

b. $\frac{1}{3}$ **4. a.** $\frac{1}{3}$ **b.** yes **5. a.** The difference between the upper and lower sums is $\frac{1}{n}$; it approaches 0 as n gets larger and larger. **b.** The general claim is correct. If you know that the upper sum limit and the lower sum limit are the same, you need only find one of them.

On Your Own

6. a. $S[0, 2](x^2) = \frac{8}{3}$ **b.** $S[0, a](x^2) = \frac{a^3}{3}$ where $a > 0$. **c.** $\frac{b^3 - a^3}{3}$ (for $0 < a < b$) **8.** Answers may vary. Exact answers: **a.** $\frac{1}{4}$ **b.** $\frac{1}{5}$ **c.** $\frac{1}{6}$

Lesson 8.4

On Your Own

11. a. The graphs of $y = x^2$ and $y = \sqrt{x}$ are reflections of each other across the line $y = x$.
b. $A = A'$ **c.** $\frac{2}{3}$ **12.** $\frac{3}{4}$

Lesson 8.5

Check Your Understanding

1. $\frac{(n+1)^2(2n^2+2n-1)}{12n^4}$; $\frac{1}{6}$

2. a. $S[0, 1]\left(x^{\frac{1}{n}}\right) = \frac{1}{\frac{1}{n}+1} = \frac{n}{n+1}$;

$$S[0, 1]\left(\sqrt[m]{x}\right) = 1 - S[0, 1](x^n) = 1 - \frac{1}{n+1} = \frac{n}{n+1}$$

The formulas are equivalent.
b. The formula makes sense for all n except $n = -1$.
3. $\frac{31}{5}$ **4.** $\frac{2^{m+1}-1}{m+1}$ **5.** $\frac{4}{3}$ **6.** $\frac{44}{15}$
7. Any integer k greater than 8
8. $\frac{b^4-1}{4}$ **9.** $\frac{b^5-1}{5}$

On Your Own

11. $\frac{15}{4}$ **12.** $\frac{1}{12}$

Lesson 8.6

Check Your Understanding

1. 0 can never be the leftmost point of the interval, since the second point of the subdivision must be r times the leftmost point and $0 \cdot r$ is always 0 no matter what r is.

2. a. $1, r = \sqrt[n]{2}, r^2, \ldots, r^{n-2}, r^{n-1}, r^n = 2$

b.

	Base	Height	Area
1st rectangle	$r - 1$	1	$1(r-1)$
2nd rectangle	$r^2 - r = r(r-1)$	r^m	$r^{m+1}(r-1)$
3rd rectangle	$r^3 - r^2 = r^2(r-1)$	$(r^2)^m = r^{2m}$	$r^{2(m+1)}(r-1)$
4th rectangle	$r^4 - r^3 = r^3(r-1)$	$(r^3)^m = r^{3m}$	$r^{3(m+1)}(r-1)$
⋮	⋮	⋮	⋮
nth rectangle	$r^n - r^{n-1} = r^{n-1}(r-1)$	$(r^{n-1})^m = r^{(n-1)m}$	$r^{(n-1)(m+1)}(r-1)$

c. $LF_n[1, 2](x^m) = (1 + r^{m+1} + (r^{m+1})^2 + (r^{m+1})^3 + \cdots + (r^{m+1})^{(n-1)})(r-1)$
d. $LF_n[1, 2](x^m) = \frac{2^{m+1}-1}{\sum_{i=0}^{m} r^i}$ **e.** It approaches $\frac{2^{m+1}-1}{m+1}$.

3.

	Base	Height	Area
1st rectangle	$r - 1$	r^m	$r^m(r-1)$
2nd rectangle	$r^2 - r = r(r-1)$	$(r^2)^m = r^{2m}$	$r^{2m+1}(r-1)$
3rd rectangle	$r^3 - r^2 = r^2(r-1)$	$(r^3)^m = r^{3m}$	$r^{3m+2}(r-1)$
4th rectangle	$r^4 - r^3 = r^3(r-1)$	$(r^4)^m = r^{4m}$	$r^{4m+3}(r-1)$
⋮	⋮	⋮	⋮
nth rectangle	$r^n - r^{n-1} = r^{n-1}(r-1)$	$(r^n)^m = r^{nm}$	$r^{nm+(n-1)}(r-1)$

$$UF_n[1, 2](x^m) = \frac{2^{m+1}-1}{\sum_{i=0}^{m} r^i}\cdot r^m$$

4. Since the actual area, $S[1, 2](x^m)$, lies between $LF_n[1, 2](x^m)$ and $UF_n[1, 2](x^m)$ for each n and both the lower and upper sums approach $\frac{2^{m+1}-1}{m+1}$ as n gets larger, $S[1, 2](x^m) = \frac{2^{m+1}-1}{m+1}$.
5. a. $LF_n[3, 6](x^m) = \frac{6^{m+1} - 3^{m+1}}{1 + r + \cdots + r^m}$ **b.** It approaches $\frac{1}{m+1}\cdot(6^{m+1} - 3^{m+1})$.
6. a. $LF_n[2, 3](x^m) = \frac{3^{m+1} - 2^{m+1}}{1 + r + r^2 + r^3 + \cdots + r^m}$
b. It approaches $\frac{1}{m+1}\cdot(3^{m+1} - 2^{m+1})$.
7. a. $LF_n[2, 6](x^m) = \frac{6^{m+1} - 2^{m+1}}{1 + r + r^2 + r^3 + \cdots + r^m}$
b. It approaches $\frac{1}{m+1}\cdot(6^{m+1} - 2^{m+1})$.
8. When $0 < a < b < hc$, this is true because of the additive property of area. Suppose A is the region under $y = x^m$ between a and b, B is the region under $y = x^m$ between b and c, and C is the region under $y = x^m$ between a and c. Then since the union of A and B is C and since A and B have no overlap, the area of C is the sum of the areas of A and B. That is, $S[a, c](x^m) = S[a, b](x^m) + S[b, c](x^m)$.

On Your Own

9. a. $LF_3[1, 2](x^5) = (r-1)(1 + r^6 + (r^6)^2)$
b. $LF_5[1, 2](x^5) = (r-1)(1 + r^6 + (r^6)^2 + (r^6)^3 + (r^6)^4)$
11. a. $LF_5[1, 2](x^2) = (r-1)(1 + r^3 + (r^3)^2 + (r^3)^3 + (r^3)^4)$ **b.** $LF_5[1, 2](x^2) = \frac{r^{15}-1}{r^2+r+1}$
c. $r = \sqrt[5]{2} \approx 1.1487$; $LF_5[1, 2](x^2) = \frac{7}{(\sqrt[5]{2})^2 + \sqrt[5]{2} + 1} \approx 2.0183$
12. $r = \sqrt{2} \approx 1.0718$; $LF_{10}[1, 2](x^2) \approx 2.1736$
13. a. $LF_3[1, 2](x^4) = (r-1)(1 + r^5 + (r^5)^2)$
b. $LF_4[1, 2](x^4) = (r-1)(1 + r^5 + (r^5)^2 + (r^5)^3)$
14. $\frac{31}{5}$ **18. a.** $LF_n[5, 10](x^m) = \frac{10^{m+1} - 5^{m+1}}{\sum_{i=0}^{m} r^i}$
b. It approaches $(10^{m+1} - 5^{m+1})\cdot\frac{1}{m+1}$

Lesson 8.7

On Your Own

3. a. $\frac{3}{8}$ **b.** yes **4. a.** 4 **b.** Computing $UF_n[0, 2](x^{-3})$ is impossible, since one of its rectangles has an undefined height ($y = x^{-3}$ is undefined for $x = 0$).

Lesson 8.8

Check Your Understanding

1. Answers will vary but should be close to the values in the table.

a	$\mathcal{L}(a)$
1	0
1.5	0.405465108108
2	0.69314718056
2.5	0.916290731874
3	1.09861228867
3.5	1.2527629685
4	1.38629436112
4.5	1.50407739678
5	1.60943791243
5.5	1.70474809224
6	1.79175946923
6.5	1.8718021769
7	1.94591014906
7.5	2.01490302054
8	2.07944154168
8.5	2.1400661635
9	2.19722457734
9.5	2.25129179861
10	2.30258509299

2.

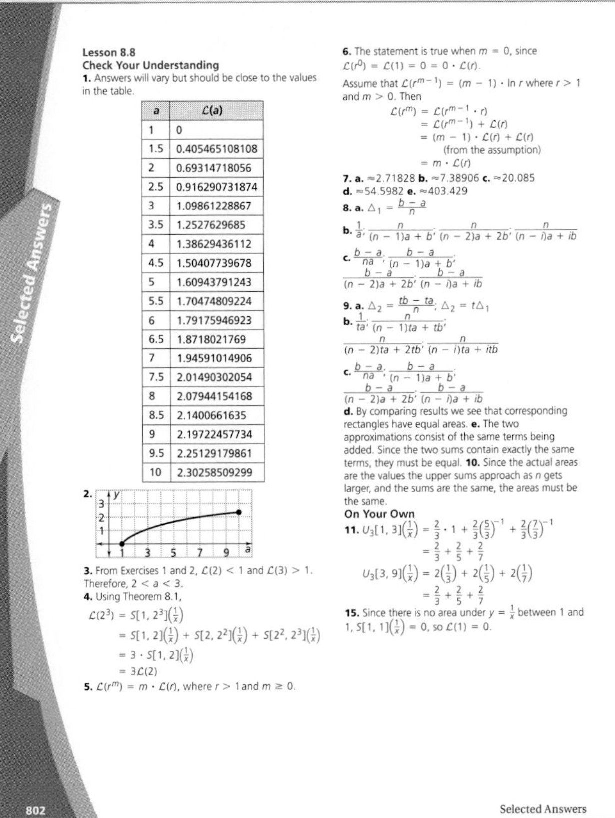

3. From Exercises 1 and 2, $\mathcal{L}(2) < 1$ and $\mathcal{L}(3) > 1$. Therefore, $2 < a < 3$.
4. Using Theorem 8.1,

$$\mathcal{L}(2^3) = S[1, 2^3]\left(\tfrac{1}{x}\right) = S[1, 2]\left(\tfrac{1}{x}\right) + S[2, 2^2]\left(\tfrac{1}{x}\right) + S[2^2, 2^3]\left(\tfrac{1}{x}\right) = 3\cdot S[1, 2]\left(\tfrac{1}{x}\right) = 3\mathcal{L}(2)$$

5. $\mathcal{L}(r^m) = m\cdot\mathcal{L}(r)$, where $r > 1$ and $m \geq 0$.

6. The statement is true when $m = 0$, since $\mathcal{L}(r^0) = \mathcal{L}(1) = 0 = 0\cdot\mathcal{L}(r)$.
Assume that $\mathcal{L}(r^{m-1}) = (m-1)\cdot\ln r$ where $r > 1$ and $m > 0$. Then

$$\mathcal{L}(r^m) = \mathcal{L}(r^{m-1}\cdot r) = \mathcal{L}(r^{m-1}) + \mathcal{L}(r) = (m-1)\cdot\mathcal{L}(r) + \mathcal{L}(r) \text{ (from the assumption)} = m\cdot\mathcal{L}(r)$$

7. a. ≈ 2.71828 **b.** ≈ 7.38906 **c.** ≈ 20.085
d. ≈ 54.5982 **e.** ≈ 403.429
8. a. $\triangle_1 = \frac{b-a}{n}$
b. $\frac{1}{a}$; $\frac{n}{(n-1)a+b}$; $\frac{n}{(n-2)a+2b}$; $\frac{n}{(n-i)a+ib}$
c. $\frac{b-a}{na}$; $\frac{b-a}{(n-1)a+b}$; $\frac{b-a}{(n-2)a+2b}$; $\frac{b-a}{(n-i)a+ib}$
9. a. $\triangle_2 = \frac{tb-ta}{n}$; $\triangle_2 = t\triangle_1$
b. $\frac{1}{ta}$; $\frac{n}{(n-1)ta+tb}$; $\frac{n}{(n-2)ta+2tb}$; $\frac{n}{(n-i)ta+itb}$
c. $\frac{b-a}{na}$; $\frac{b-a}{(n-1)a+b}$; $\frac{b-a}{(n-2)a+2b}$; $\frac{b-a}{(n-i)a+ib}$
d. By comparing results we see that corresponding rectangles have equal areas. **e.** The two approximations consist of the same terms being added. Since the two sums contain exactly the same terms, they must be equal. **10.** Since the actual areas are the values the upper sums approach as n gets larger, and the sums are the same, the areas must be the same.

On Your Own

11.

$$U_3[1, 3]\left(\tfrac{1}{x}\right) = \tfrac{2}{3}\cdot 1 + \tfrac{2}{3}\left(\tfrac{5}{3}\right)^{-1} + \tfrac{2}{3}\left(\tfrac{7}{3}\right)^{-1} = \tfrac{2}{3} + \tfrac{2}{5} + \tfrac{2}{7}$$

$$U_3[3, 9]\left(\tfrac{1}{x}\right) = 2\left(\tfrac{1}{3}\right) + 2\left(\tfrac{1}{5}\right) + 2\left(\tfrac{1}{7}\right) = \tfrac{2}{3} + \tfrac{2}{5} + \tfrac{2}{7}$$

15. Since there is no area under $y = \frac{1}{x}$ between 1 and 1, $S[1, 1]\left(\frac{1}{x}\right) = 0$, so $\mathcal{L}(1) = 0$.

Lesson 8.9

Check Your Understanding

1. a.

Fermat Lower Sum for $y = x^{-1}$ on [1, 2]			
	Base	Height	Area
1st rectangle	$r - 1$	$\frac{1}{r}$	$(r-1)\frac{1}{r}$
2nd rectangle	$r^2 - r = r(r-1)$	$\frac{1}{r^2}$	$(r-1)\frac{1}{r}$
3rd rectangle	$r^3 - r^2 = r^2(r-1)$	$\frac{1}{r^3}$	$(r-1)\frac{1}{r}$
4th rectangle	$r^4 - r^3 = r^3(r-1)$	$\frac{1}{r^4}$	$(r-1)\frac{1}{r}$
⋮	⋮	⋮	⋮
nth rectangle	$r^n - r^{n-1} = r^{n-1}(r-1)$	$\frac{1}{r^n}$	$(r-1)\frac{1}{r}$

b. The sum of the rectangles is $n\left(\sqrt[n]{2} - 1\right)2^{-\frac{1}{2}}$
2. a. 1 **b.** 2 **c.** 4 **d.** 100 **e.** 0 **3. a.** −1 **b.** −2 **c.** −3
d. −100 **4. a.** ≈ 1.39794 **b.** ≈ 0.30103
c. ≈ 1.69897 **d.** ≈ 6.09691 **5. a.** Note first that $0 = g(1) = g(y\cdot y^{-1}) = g(y) + g(y^{-1})$, so $g(y^{-1}) = -g(y)$. Then $g\left(\frac{x}{y}\right) = g(x\cdot y^{-1}) = g(x) + g(y^{-1}) = g(x) - g(y)$.
b. Since $g(5) = g((\sqrt{5})^2) = 2g(\sqrt{5})$, we know $g(\sqrt{5}) = \frac{1}{2}g(5) = 0.349485$. **c.** The function g satisfies all the properties of the common logarithm (log base 10) function, denoted by log or $\log_{10}$.
d.

The graph of $y = g(x)$.

On Your Own

7. a. $\mathcal{L}(4) = \mathcal{L}(2\cdot 2) = \mathcal{L}(2) + \mathcal{L}(2) = 2\mathcal{L}(2)$
9. From Exercise 8, $\mathcal{L}(1) = \mathcal{L}\left(\frac{r}{r}\right) = \mathcal{L}(r) - \mathcal{L}(r) = 0$.

Lesson 8.10

Check Your Understanding

1. a. $\frac{e^{1/n}\cdot(e-1)}{n(e^{1/n}-1)}$ **b.** $e - 1$ **2.** $e^{a+1} - e^a$

3. Answers may vary but should contain the following ideas:
- The constant a determines the direction and the rate at which the function increases or decreases: if a is positive, $f(x)$ grows when x grows, and the bigger a is the faster $f(x)$ grows; if a is changed to $-a$, the graph becomes reflected about the y-axis. So, if $a < 0$, $f(x)$ becomes smaller when x grows. If $a = 0$, the graph becomes a horizontal line, the graph of $y = 1 + b$.
- The value of b does not affect the shape of the graph, just how high or low on the coordinate plane it is located: $f(x) = e^{ax} + b$ is b higher than $g(x) = e^{ax}$ if $b > 0$, and lower than $g(x) = e^{ax}$ if $b < 0$. **4. a.** $e + 2$ **b.** $e - 1$ **c.** $e + 6$ **5.** e

6. a. The graphs of $\ln x$ and e^x are reflections of each other about the line with equation $y = x$. **b.** 1
7. $e^b - e^a$

On Your Own

8. a.

n	$\left(\frac{2n+1}{2n-1}\right)^n$
10	≈2.72055141
100	≈2.71830448
1000	≈2.71828205
10,000	≈2.71828183

b.

n	$1 + \frac{1}{1!} + \frac{1}{2!} + \cdots + \frac{1}{n!}$
4	≈2.70833333333
7	≈2.71825396825
10	≈2.71828180115
13	≈2.71828182845

9. a. $\frac{11}{4} = 2.75$ **b.** $\frac{106}{39} \approx 2.71794872$
c. $\frac{1457}{536} \approx 2.71828358$

Additional Answers

Chapter 1

Lesson 1.1 pp. 5–6

For You to Explore

2.

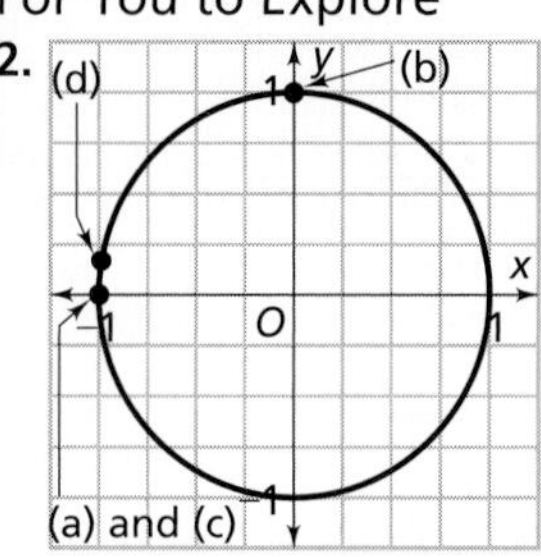

3b. y, 1, x, −1, O, 1, −1

Exercises **12a.**

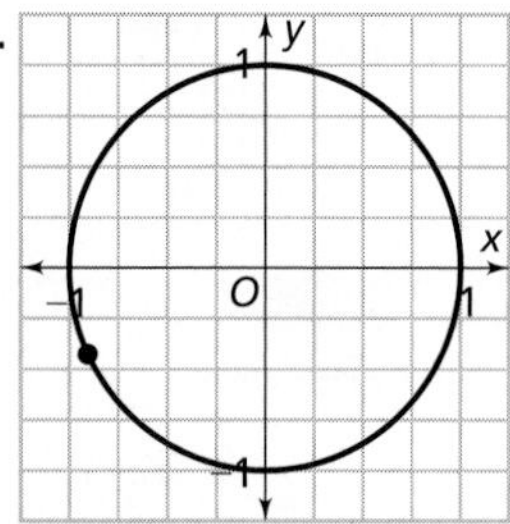

15.

Distance	Coordinates
0	(1, 0)
$\frac{\pi}{4}$	$\left(\frac{\sqrt{2}}{2}, \frac{\sqrt{2}}{2}\right)$
$\frac{\pi}{2}$	**(0, 1)**
$\frac{3\pi}{4}$	$\left(-\frac{\sqrt{2}}{2}, \frac{\sqrt{2}}{2}\right)$
π	(−1, 0)
$\frac{5\pi}{4}$	$\left(-\frac{\sqrt{2}}{2}, -\frac{\sqrt{2}}{2}\right)$
$\frac{3\pi}{2}$	**(0, −1)**
$\frac{7\pi}{4}$	$\left(\frac{\sqrt{2}}{2}, -\frac{\sqrt{2}}{2}\right)$
2π	**(1, 0)**
$\frac{9\pi}{4}$	$\left(\frac{\sqrt{2}}{2}, \frac{\sqrt{2}}{2}\right)$
$\frac{5\pi}{2}$	**(0, 1)**

Lesson 1.2 pp. 7–12

Exercises **3.**

x	cos x	sin x
0	**1**	**0**
$\frac{\pi}{6}$	$\frac{\sqrt{3}}{2}$	$\frac{1}{2}$
$\frac{\pi}{4}$	$\frac{\sqrt{2}}{2}$	$\frac{\sqrt{2}}{2}$
$\frac{\pi}{3}$	$\frac{1}{2}$	$\frac{\sqrt{3}}{2}$
$\frac{\pi}{2}$	**0**	**1**
$\frac{2\pi}{3}$	$-\frac{1}{2}$	$\frac{\sqrt{3}}{2}$
$\frac{3\pi}{4}$	$-\frac{\sqrt{2}}{2}$	$\frac{\sqrt{2}}{2}$
$\frac{5\pi}{6}$	$-\frac{\sqrt{3}}{2}$	$\frac{1}{2}$
π	**−1**	**0**
$\frac{7\pi}{6}$	$-\frac{\sqrt{3}}{2}$	$-\frac{1}{2}$
$\frac{5\pi}{4}$	$-\frac{\sqrt{2}}{2}$	$-\frac{\sqrt{2}}{2}$
$\frac{4\pi}{3}$	$-\frac{1}{2}$	$-\frac{\sqrt{3}}{2}$
$\frac{3\pi}{2}$	0	−1
$\frac{5\pi}{3}$	$\frac{1}{2}$	$-\frac{\sqrt{3}}{2}$
$\frac{7\pi}{4}$	$\frac{\sqrt{2}}{2}$	$-\frac{\sqrt{2}}{2}$
$\frac{11\pi}{6}$	$\frac{\sqrt{3}}{2}$	$-\frac{1}{2}$
2π	**1**	**0**
$\frac{13\pi}{6}$	$\frac{\sqrt{3}}{2}$	$\frac{1}{2}$
$\frac{9\pi}{4}$	$\frac{\sqrt{2}}{2}$	$\frac{\sqrt{2}}{2}$
$\frac{7\pi}{3}$	$\frac{1}{2}$	$\frac{\sqrt{3}}{2}$

Lesson 1.5 pp. 24–27

For You to Do **1.** Values for the secant slopes may vary but should be reasonably close to the values below.

x	sin x	Slope
0	0	1.000
$\frac{\pi}{6}$	$\frac{1}{2}$	0.866
$\frac{\pi}{4}$	$\frac{\sqrt{2}}{2}$	0.707
$\frac{\pi}{3}$	$\frac{\sqrt{3}}{2}$	0.500
$\frac{\pi}{2}$	1	0.000
$\frac{2\pi}{3}$	$\frac{\sqrt{3}}{2}$	−0.500
$\frac{3\pi}{4}$	$\frac{\sqrt{2}}{2}$	−0.707
$\frac{5\pi}{6}$	$\frac{1}{2}$	−0.866
π	0	−1.000
$\frac{7\pi}{6}$	$-\frac{1}{2}$	−0.866
$\frac{5\pi}{4}$	$-\frac{\sqrt{2}}{2}$	−0.707
$\frac{4\pi}{3}$	$-\frac{\sqrt{3}}{2}$	−0.500
$\frac{3\pi}{2}$	−1	0.000
$\frac{5\pi}{3}$	$-\frac{\sqrt{3}}{2}$	0.500
$\frac{7\pi}{4}$	$-\frac{\sqrt{2}}{2}$	0.707
$\frac{11\pi}{6}$	$-\frac{1}{2}$	0.866
2π	0	1.000

Exercises 9.

x	$\cos x$	Slope
0	1	0
$\frac{\pi}{6}$	$\frac{\sqrt{3}}{2}$	−0.500
$\frac{\pi}{4}$	$\frac{\sqrt{2}}{2}$	−0.707
$\frac{\pi}{3}$	$\frac{1}{2}$	−0.866
$\frac{\pi}{2}$	0	−1
$\frac{2\pi}{3}$	$-\frac{1}{2}$	−0.866
$\frac{3\pi}{4}$	$-\frac{\sqrt{2}}{2}$	−0.707
$\frac{5\pi}{6}$	$-\frac{\sqrt{3}}{2}$	−0.500
π	−1	0
$\frac{7\pi}{6}$	$-\frac{\sqrt{3}}{2}$	0.500
$\frac{5\pi}{4}$	$-\frac{\sqrt{2}}{2}$	0.707
$\frac{4\pi}{3}$	$-\frac{1}{2}$	0.866
$\frac{3\pi}{2}$	0	1
$\frac{5\pi}{3}$	$\frac{1}{2}$	0.866
$\frac{7\pi}{4}$	$\frac{\sqrt{2}}{2}$	0.707
$\frac{11\pi}{6}$	$\frac{\sqrt{3}}{2}$	0.500
2π	1	0

When $\cos x$ has its maximum or minimum value, the slope is 0. The maximum value of the slope is 1 and occurs when $x = \frac{3\pi}{2}$, and the minimum value of the slope is -1 and occurs when $x = \frac{\pi}{2}$. The graph of $r(x)$ looks the same as the graph of $y = -\sin x$.

14b. maximum = 12, minimum = 2

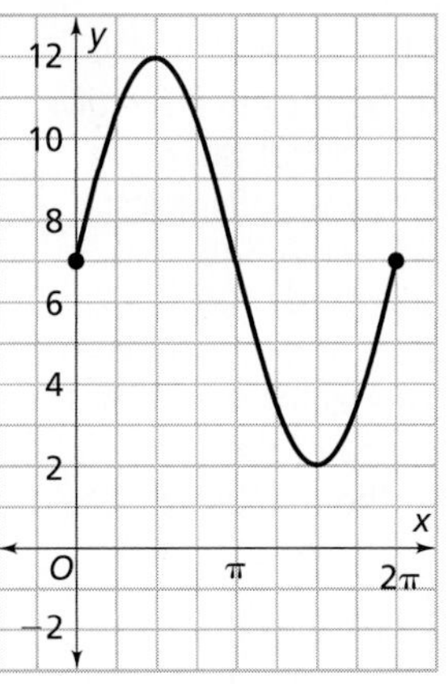

c. maximum = −2, minimum = −12

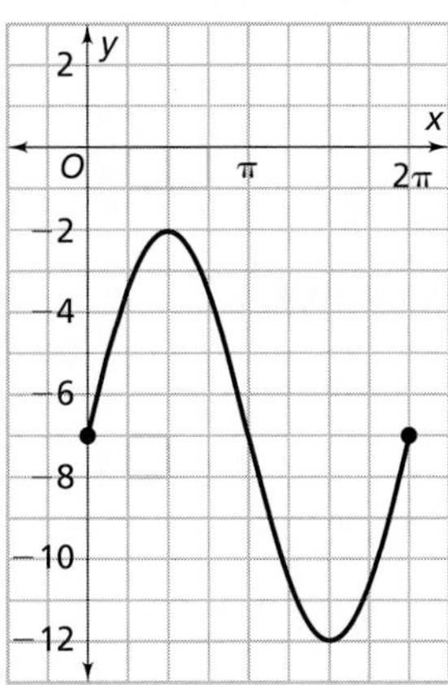

d. maximum = 15, minimum = −5

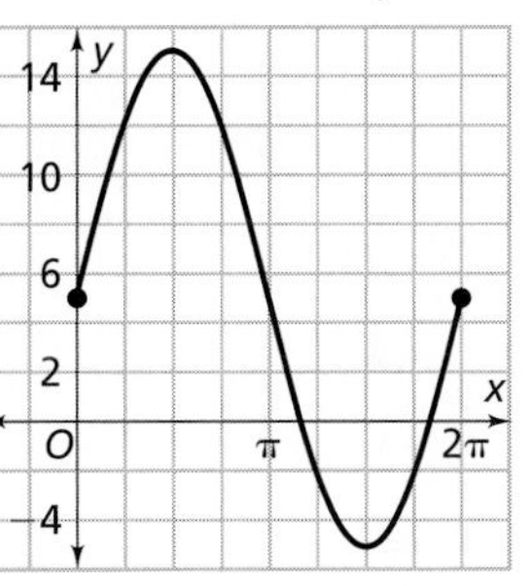

Mathematical Reflections p. 28

4.

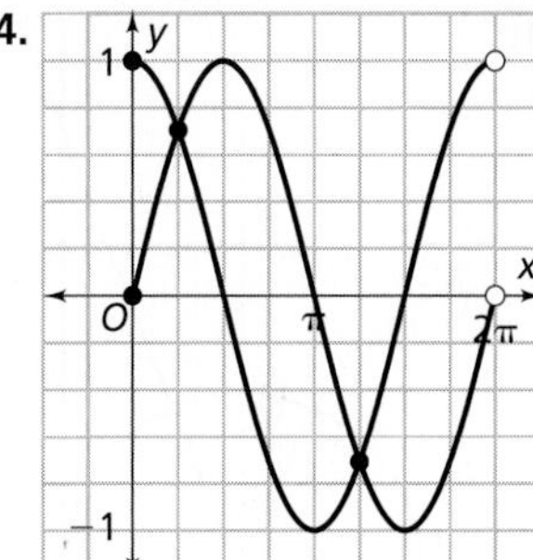

Lesson 1.6 pp. 31–32

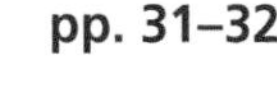

For You to Explore

2.

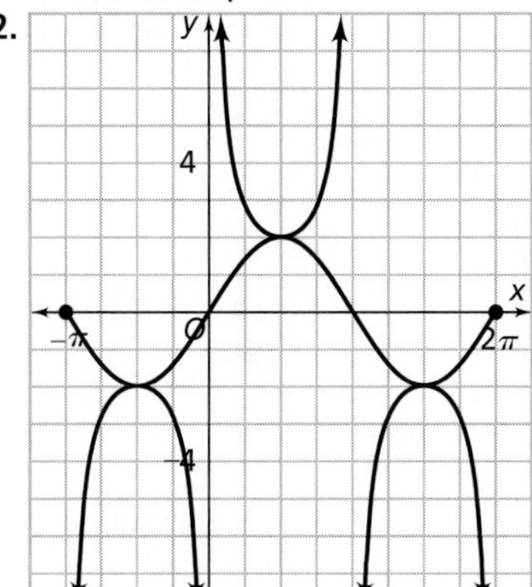

4a.

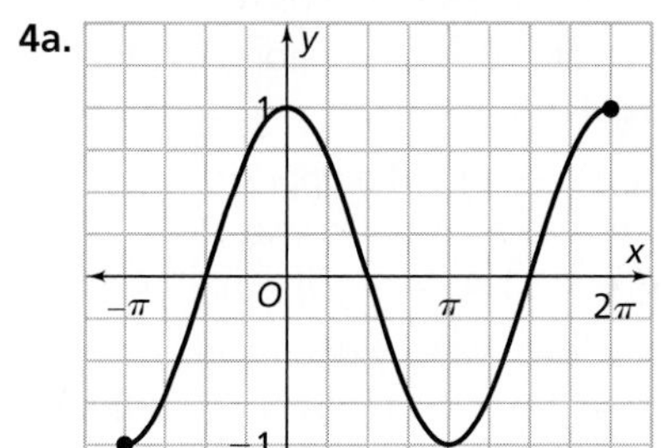

5. See Figure 1.

Figure 1

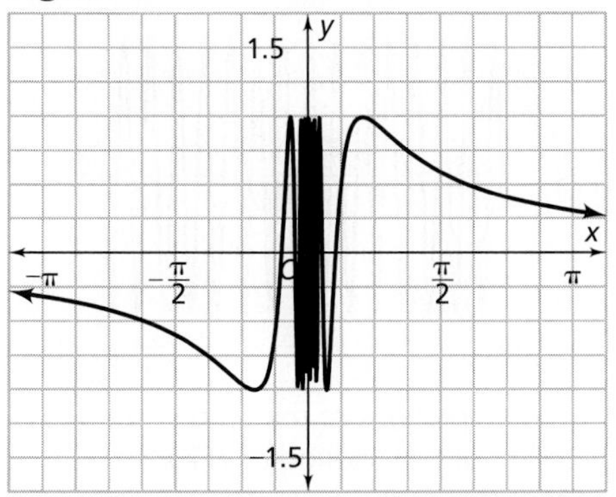

Outside the interval $\left[-\frac{1}{\pi}, \frac{1}{\pi}\right]$, the graph approaches the x-axis asymptotically from below as x decreases more and more, and it approaches the x-axis asymptotically from above as x increases more and more. In the interval $\left[-\frac{1}{\pi}, \frac{1}{\pi}\right]$, the graph oscillates between the lines $y = -1$ and $y = 1$ more and more rapidly as x gets closer and closer to 0. The function is undefined for $x = 0$.

Lesson 1.7 pp. 33–37

Exercises **1d.**

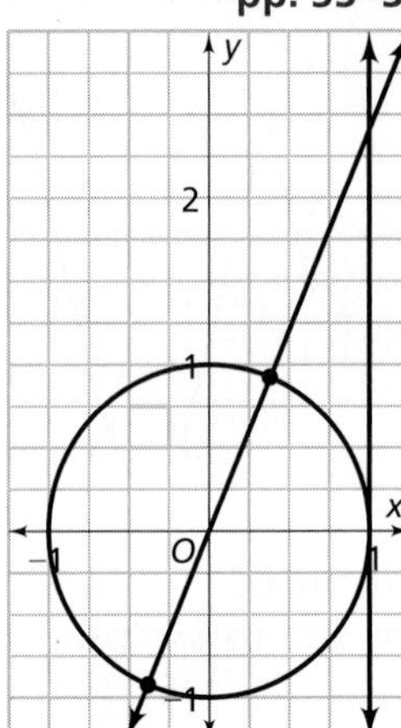

e.

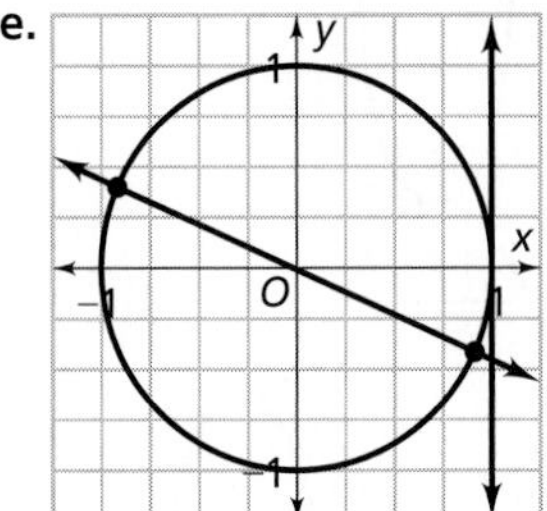

2. $\cos^2 x + \sin^2 x = 1$ for all values of x, so $\cos x = \pm\sqrt{1 - \sin^2 x}$. Since $0 < 0.38 < \frac{\pi}{2}$, $\cos 0.38 = \sqrt{1 - \sin^2 0.38}$. Therefore, use the calculator to evaluate $\frac{\sin 0.38}{\sqrt{1 - \sin^2 0.38}}$. **3.** $\tan\left(\frac{\pi}{2} + x\right)$ is the opposite of the reciprocal of $\tan x$, that is, $\tan\left(\frac{\pi}{2} + x\right) = -\frac{1}{\tan x}$. **4.** Quadrants II and IV; one way: by definition, $\tan x = \frac{\sin x}{\cos x}$. So $\tan x$ is negative if and only if $\sin x$ and $\cos x$ have different signs. They have different signs if and only if x corresponds to an angle whose terminal side is in Quadrant II or Quadrant IV; another way: from the In-Class Experiment, $\tan x$ is the y-coordinate of the point where the line through the origin and $(\cos x, \sin x)$ intersects the graph of $x = 1$. The line through the origin and $(\cos x, \sin x)$ intersects the graph of $x = 1$ below the x-axis if and only if $(\cos x, \sin x)$ is in Quadrant II or Quadrant IV.
5. Yes; answers may vary. Sample: $x = 1.57$

6a. $\tan\frac{\pi}{6} = \frac{\sqrt{3}}{3}$ and $\frac{\sqrt{3}}{3} > \frac{\pi}{6}$; $\tan\frac{\pi}{4} = 1$ and $1 > \frac{\pi}{4}$; $\tan 1 \approx 1.557$ and $1.557 > 1$. So for the three given values of x, it is true that $\tan x > x$. Other examples may vary. Samples:
$\tan 0.5 \approx 0.546$ and $0.546 > 0.5$;
$\tan 0.75 \approx 0.932$ and $0.932 > 0.75$;
$\tan 0.1 \approx 0.1003$ and $0.1003 > 0.1$.
b. $\frac{1}{2}\tan x$, $\frac{x}{2}$ **c.** The sector lies inside the triangle, so the area of the sector is less than the area of the triangle, that is, $\frac{x}{2} < \frac{1}{2}\tan x$. Therefore, $x < \tan x$.

7.

x	$\tan x$
0	0
$\frac{\pi}{6}$	$\frac{\sqrt{3}}{3}$
$\frac{\pi}{4}$	1
$\frac{\pi}{3}$	$\sqrt{3}$
$\frac{\pi}{2}$	undefined
$\frac{2\pi}{3}$	$-\sqrt{3}$
$\frac{3\pi}{4}$	-1
$\frac{5\pi}{6}$	$-\frac{\sqrt{3}}{3}$
π	0
$\frac{7\pi}{6}$	$\frac{\sqrt{3}}{3}$
$\frac{5\pi}{4}$	1
$\frac{4\pi}{3}$	$\sqrt{3}$
$\frac{3\pi}{2}$	undefined
$\frac{5\pi}{3}$	$-\sqrt{3}$
$\frac{7\pi}{4}$	-1
$\frac{11\pi}{6}$	$-\frac{\sqrt{3}}{3}$
2π	0
$\frac{13\pi}{6}$	$\frac{\sqrt{3}}{3}$
$\frac{9\pi}{4}$	1

Lesson 1.11 pp. 57–59

For You to Explore

1a.

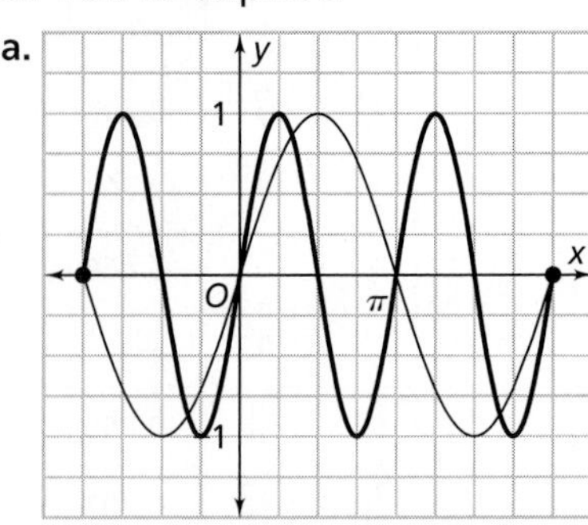

The amplitudes of the graphs are the same, but the period of $f(2x)$ is $\frac{1}{2}$ the period of $f(x)$.

b.

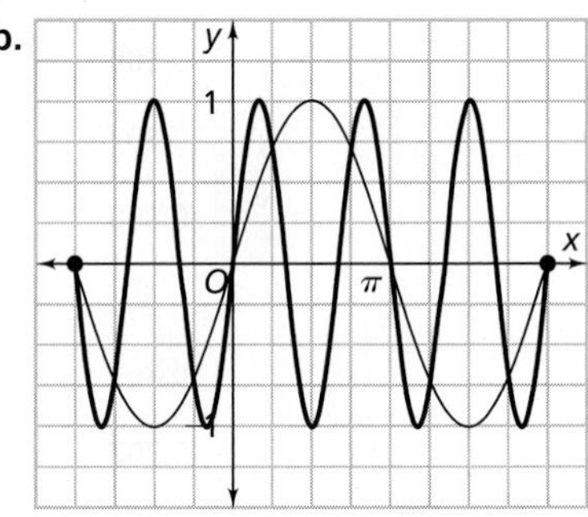

The amplitudes of the graphs are the same, but the period of $f(3x)$ is $\frac{1}{3}$ the period of $f(x)$.

c.

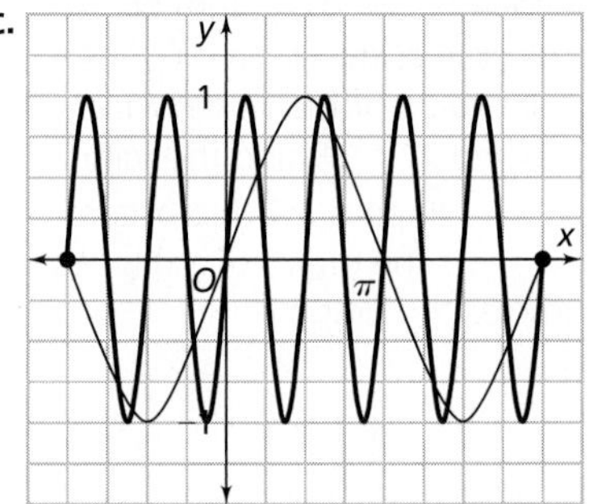

The amplitudes of the graphs are the same, but the period of $f(4x)$ is $\frac{1}{4}$ the period of $f(x)$.

d.

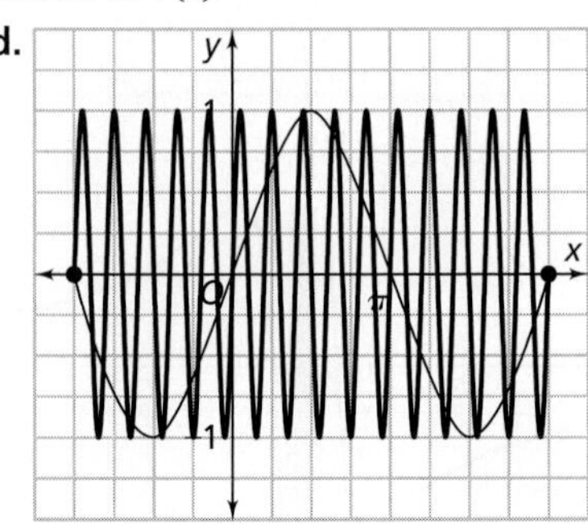

The amplitudes of the graphs are the same, but the period of $f(10x)$ is $\frac{1}{10}$ the period of $f(x)$.

2a.

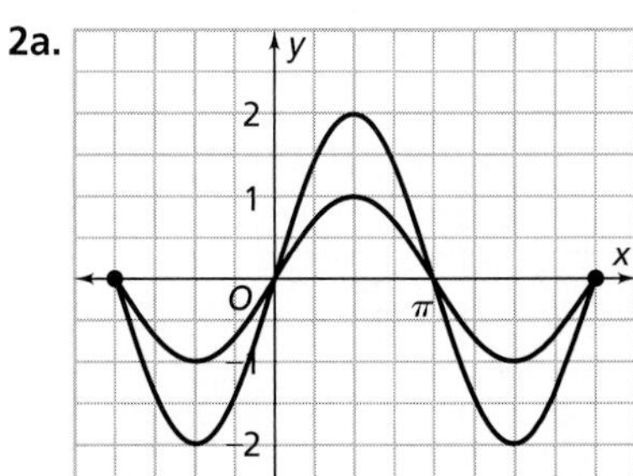

The periods of the graphs are the same, but the amplitude of $2\,f(x)$ is 2 times the amplitude of $f(x)$.

b.

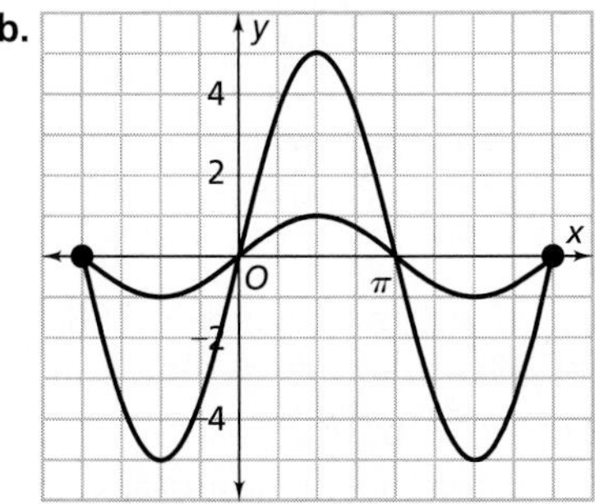

The periods of the graphs are the same, but the amplitude of $5\,f(x)$ is 5 times the amplitude of $f(x)$.

c.

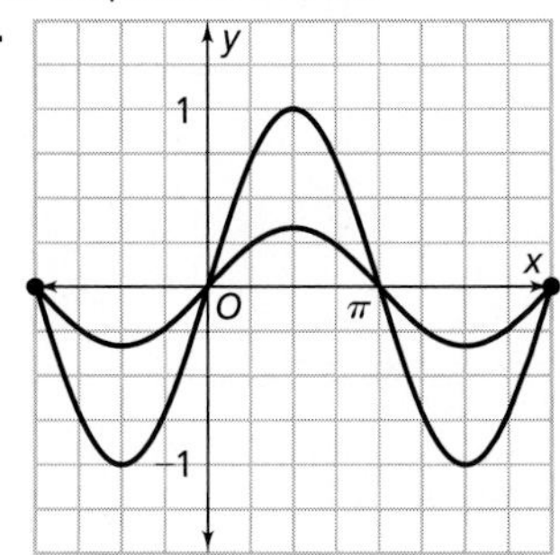

The periods of the graphs are the same, but the amplitude of $\frac{1}{3}\,f(x)$ is $\frac{1}{3}$ the amplitude of $f(x)$.

d.

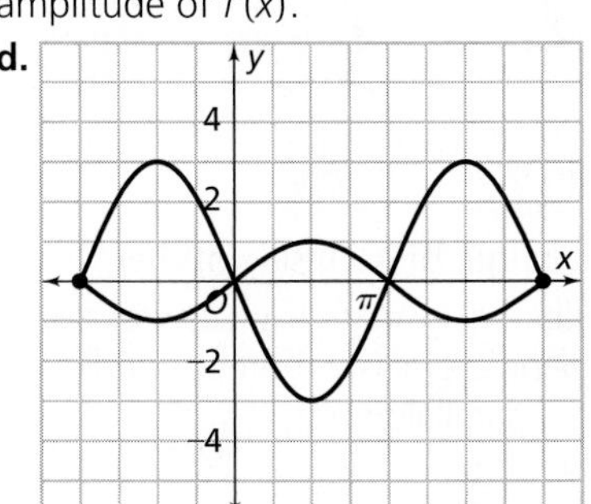

The periods of the graphs are the same, but the amplitude of $-3\,f(x)$ is 3 times the amplitude of $f(x)$. Also, note that you can obtain the graph of $-3\,f(x)$ by stretching the graph of $f(x)$ vertically by a factor of 3 and then reflecting the resulting graph across the x-axis.

3a.

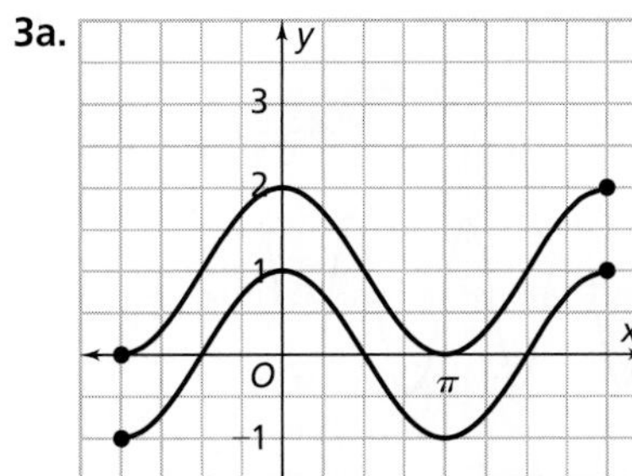

The amplitudes of the graphs are the same. The graph of $g(x) + 1$ is the graph of $g(x)$ translated up 1 unit.

b.

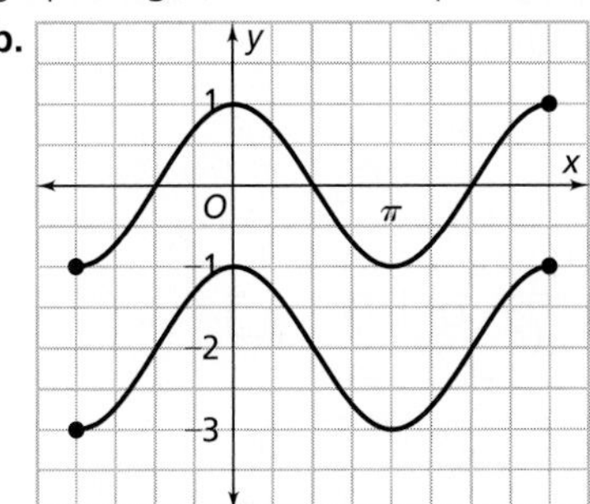

The amplitudes of the graphs are the same. The graph of $g(x) - 2$ is the graph of $g(x)$ translated down 2 units.

c.

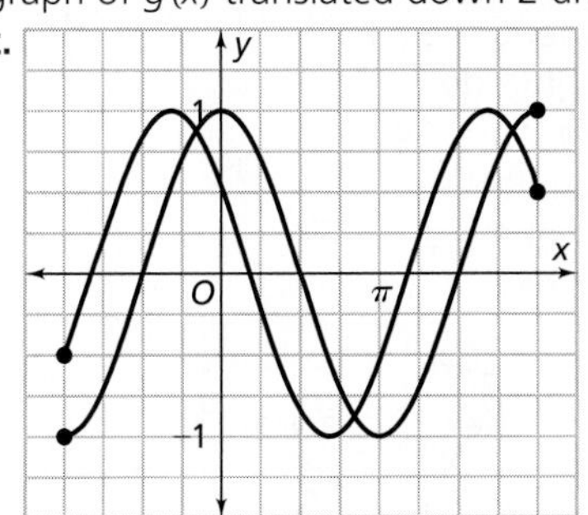

The amplitudes of the graphs are the same. The graph of $g(x + 1)$ is the graph of $g(x)$ translated left 1 unit.

d.

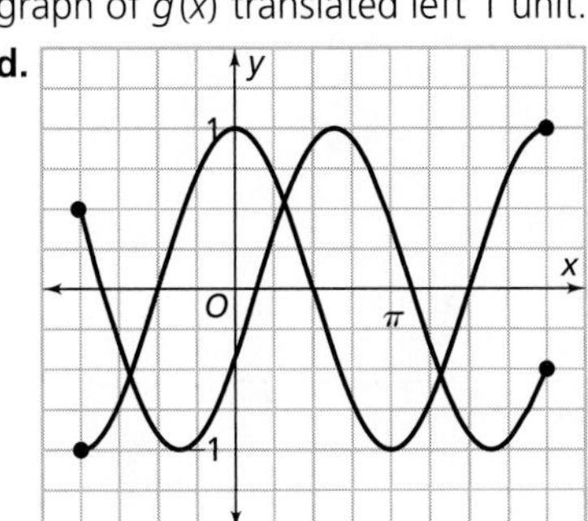

The amplitudes of the graphs are the same. The graph of $g(x - 2)$ is the graph of $g(x)$ translated right 2 units.

4a.

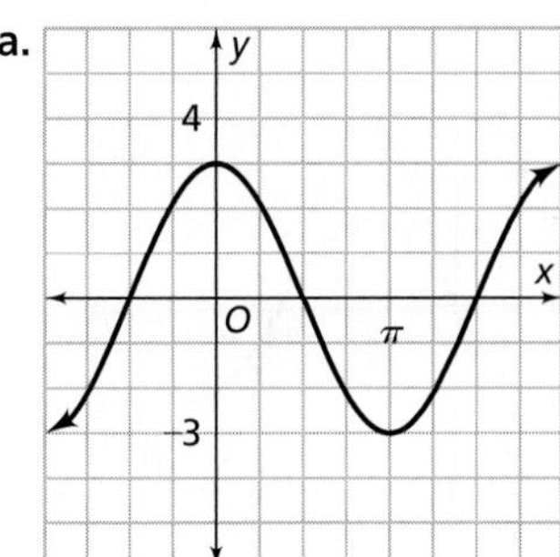

b.

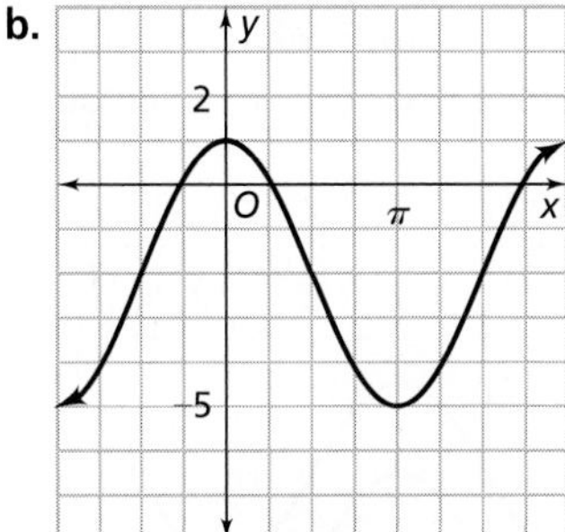

c.

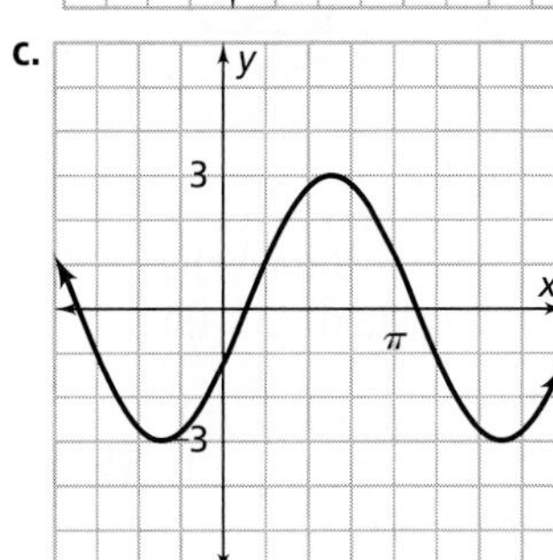

d.

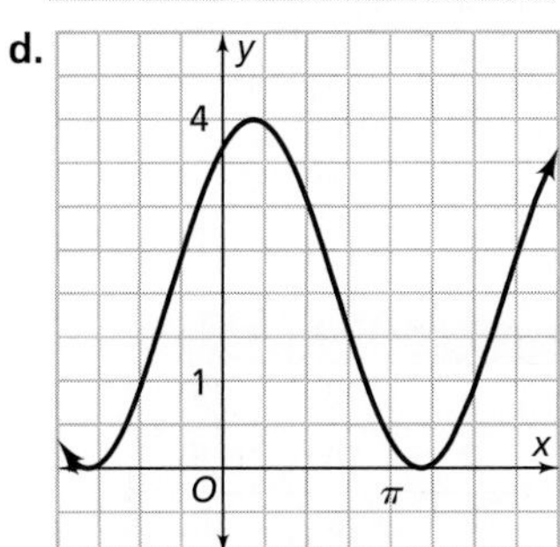

Mathematical Reflections p. 77

5a.

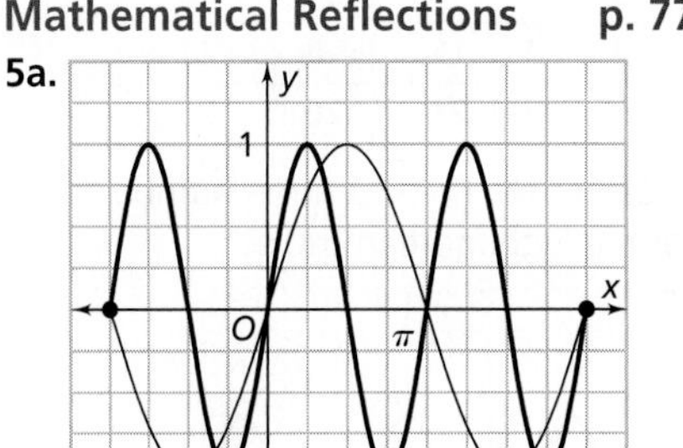

The graph of this function is the graph of $f(x)$ shrunk horizontally by a factor of $\frac{1}{2}$.

Additional Answers

b.

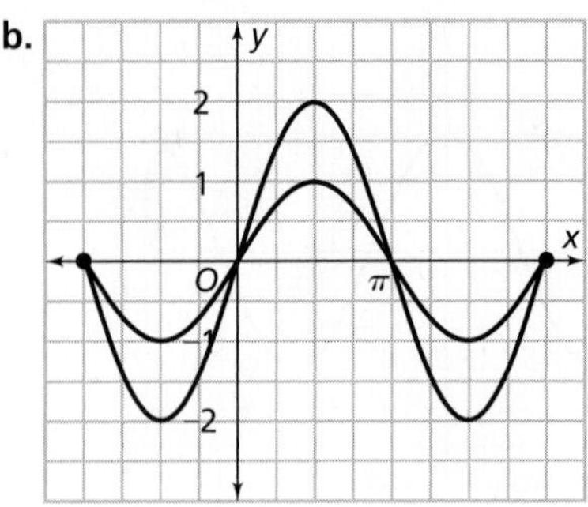

The graph of this function is the graph of $f(x)$ stretched vertically by a factor of 2.

c.

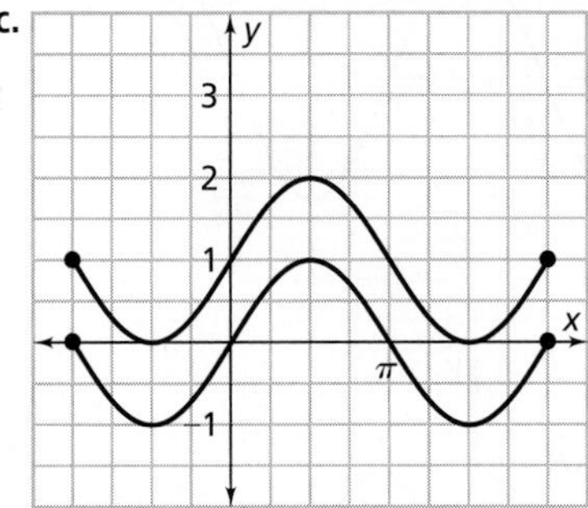

The graph of this function is the graph of $f(x)$ translated up 1 unit.

Chapter 2

Lesson 2.1 pp. 85–86

For You to Explore

7. $(x^2 - y^2)^2 + (2xy)^2$
$= (x^4 - 2x^2y^2 + y^4) + 4x^2y^2$
$= x^4 + 2x^2y^2 + y^4$
$= (x^2 + y^2)^2$

Exercises **11a.** 5, 12, 13

b.

x	y	$x^2 - y^2$	$2xy$	$x^2 + y^2$
3	2	5	12	13
2	1	3	4	5
3	1	8	6	10
4	3	7	24	25
4	1	15	8	17
5	2	21	20	29

In each row, the last three numbers form a Pythagorean triple.

12a.

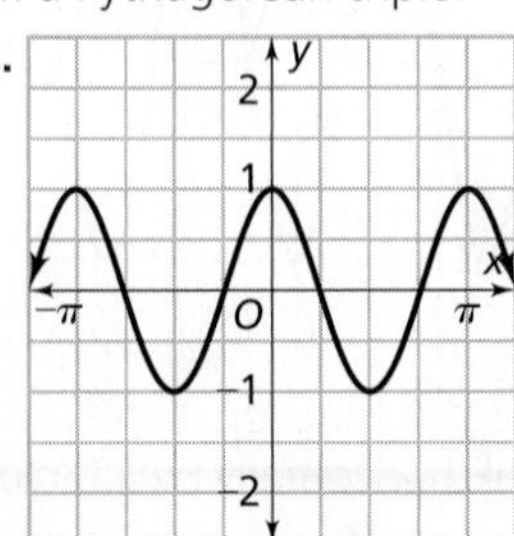

b. amplitude = 1, period = π
c. The graph is the same as in part (a).
d. The graphs are the same.

13a. $x^3 - 3xy^2$

b.

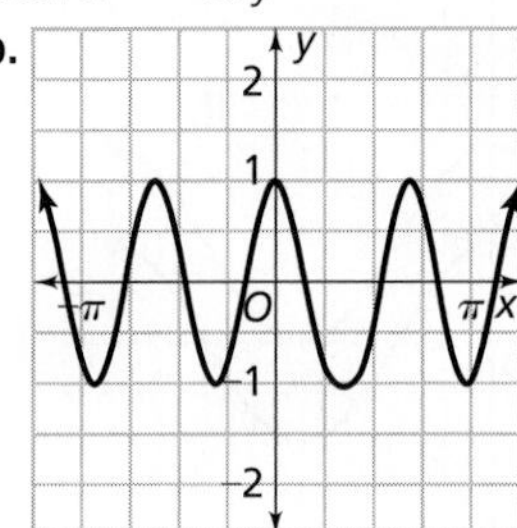

c. The graph is the same as in part (b).
d. The graphs are the same.

Lesson 2.2 pp. 87–91

For You to Do

6.

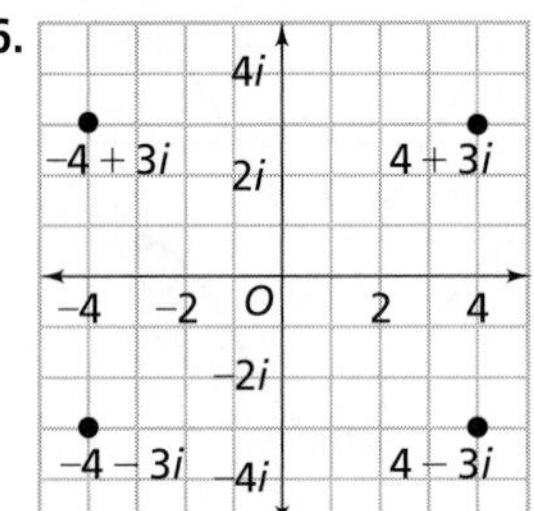

a. magnitude = 5, argument ≈ 36.87°
b. magnitude = 5, argument ≈ 323.13°
c. magnitude = 5, argument ≈ 143.13°
d. magnitude = 5, argument ≈ 216.87°

Exercises

3a.

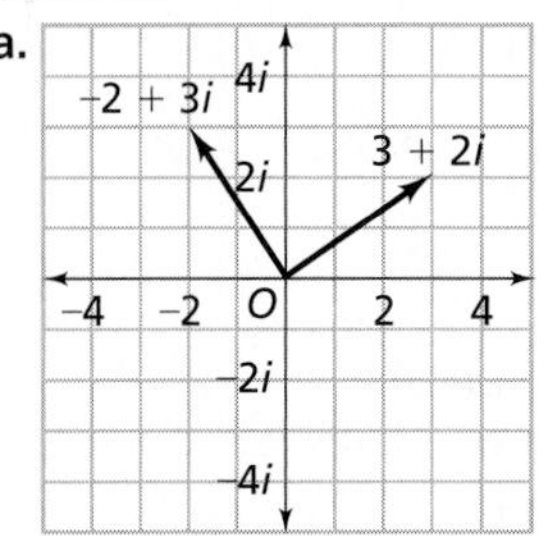

$\arg(z) \approx 0.588$, $\arg(i \cdot z) \approx 2.159$

b.

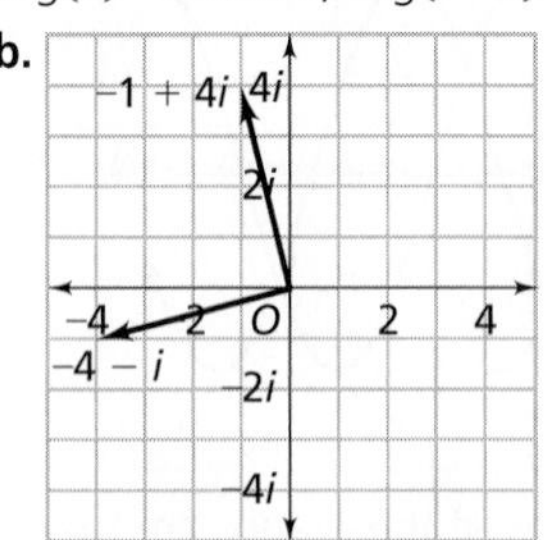

$\arg(z) \approx 1.816$, $\arg(i \cdot z) \approx 3.387$

c.

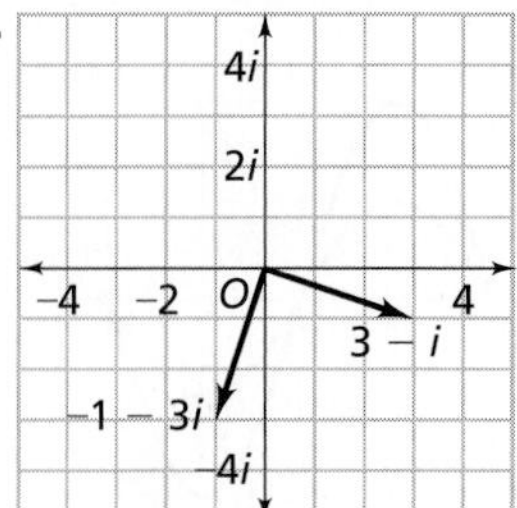

$\arg(z) \approx 4.391$, $\arg(i \cdot z) \approx 5.961$

d.

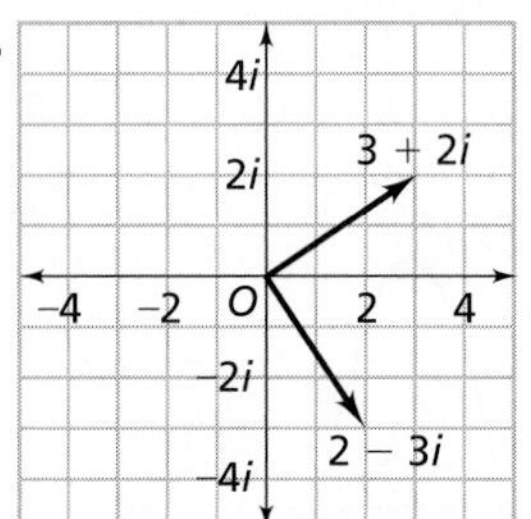

$\arg(z) \approx 5.300$, $\arg(i \cdot z) \approx 0.588$

5a. $|iz| = |z|$, $\arg(iz) = \arg(z) + \frac{\pi}{2}$ or $\arg(z) - \frac{3\pi}{2}$ **b.** $|i^2z| = |z|$, $\arg(i^2z) = \arg(z) + \pi$ or $\arg(z) - \pi$
c. $|(-i)z| = |z|$, $\arg((-i)z) = \arg(z) + \frac{3\pi}{2}$ or $\arg(z) - \frac{\pi}{2}$
d. $|2z| = 2|z|$, $\arg(2z) = \arg(z)$
e. $\left|\frac{1}{z}\right| = \frac{1}{|z|}$, $\arg\left(\frac{1}{z}\right) = 2\pi - \arg(z)$

8a. Answers may vary. Sample:

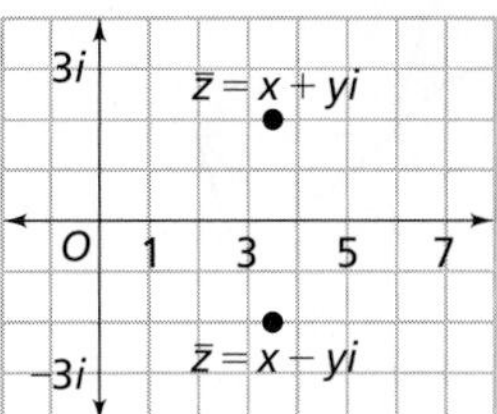

b.

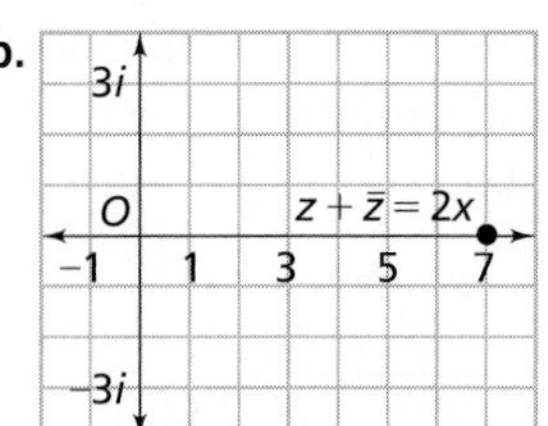

c. The length of each side of the quadrilateral is $\sqrt{x^2 + y^2}$. Therefore, the quadrilateral is a rhombus and hence a parallelogram.

11. ± 2, $\pm 2i$

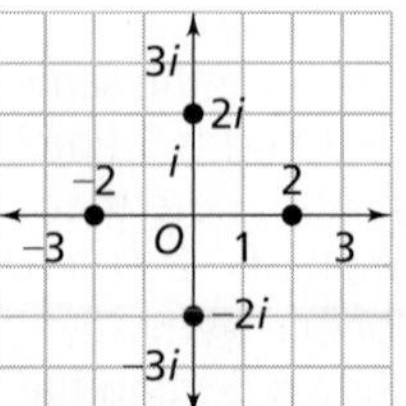

14a. For 1 and -1, both magnitudes are 1. The directions are 0 and π, respectively. **b.** For 1, $-\frac{1}{2} + \frac{\sqrt{3}}{2}i$, and $-\frac{1}{2} - \frac{\sqrt{3}}{2}i$, the magnitudes are 1. The directions are 0, $\frac{2\pi}{3}$, and $\frac{4\pi}{3}$, respectively. **c.** For 1, -1, i, and $-i$, the magnitudes are 1. The directions are 0, π, $\frac{\pi}{2}$, and $\frac{3\pi}{2}$, respectively.
15. If you expand $(ac - bd)^2 + (bc + ad)^2$ and collect like terms, you get $a^2c^2 + b^2d^2 + b^2c^2 + a^2d^2$. You get the same result if you expand $(a^2 + b^2)(c^2 + d^2)$. Therefore, the given equation is an identity.

17.

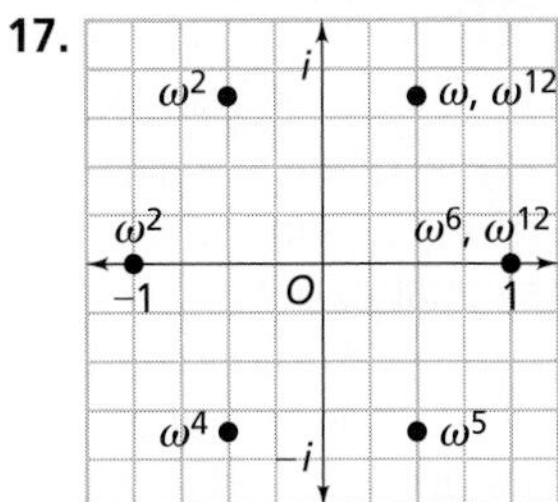

Lesson 2.3 pp. 92–96

Exercises **13c.** $|z| = \sqrt{x^2 + y^2}$ and $|w| = \sqrt{c^2 + d^2}$, so $|z| \cdot |w| = \sqrt{(x^2 + y^2)(c^2 + d^2)} = \sqrt{c^2x^2 + d^2x^2 + c^2y^2 + d^2y^2}$. Since $zw = (cx - dy) + (dx + cy)i$, $|zw| = \sqrt{(cx - dy)^2 + (dx + cy)^2}$. Expand and collect terms under the radical sign, and you get $\sqrt{c^2x^2 + d^2x^2 + c^2y^2 + d^2y^2}$. So $|z| \cdot |w| = |zw|$. **15a.** $|w| = 2$, $\arg(w) = \frac{\pi}{3}$ (or 60°); $|zw| = 4$, $\arg(zw) = \frac{\pi}{2}$ (or 90°) **b.** $|w| = 5$, $\arg(w) = \frac{\pi}{2}$ (or 90°); $|zw| = 10$, $\arg(zw) = \frac{2\pi}{3}$ (or 120°) **c.** $|w| = 10$, $\arg(w) = 0$ (or 0°); $|zw| = 20$, $\arg(zw) = \frac{\pi}{6}$ (or 30°) **d.** $|w| = \sqrt{2}$, $\arg(w) = \frac{\pi}{4}$ (or 45°); $|zw| = 2\sqrt{2}$, $\arg(zw) = \frac{5\pi}{12}$ (or 75°) **e.** $|w| = \sqrt{5}$, $\arg(w) \approx 2.678$ (or $\approx 153.435°$); $|zw| = 2\sqrt{5}$, $\arg(zw) \approx 3.202$ (or $\approx 183.435°$)

Lesson 2.4 pp. 97–104

Exercises

6a.

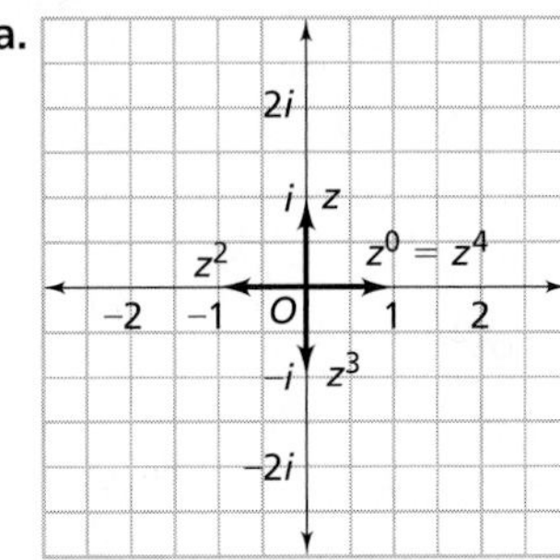

Since $|i| = 1$, all the powers have magnitude 1. Multiplying a number by i rotates the number around O counterclockwise by 90°. Since 360° is evenly divisible by 90°, the set of powers consists of just 4 numbers.

b.

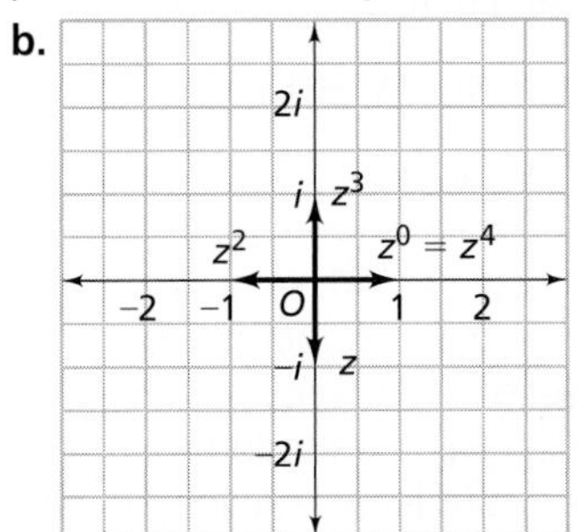

Since $|-i| = 1$, all the powers have magnitude 1. Because of the minus sign, multiplying by $-i$ rotates the other number not counterclockwise but clockwise around O by 90°. Since 360° is evenly divisible by 90°, the set of powers consists of just 4 numbers.

c.

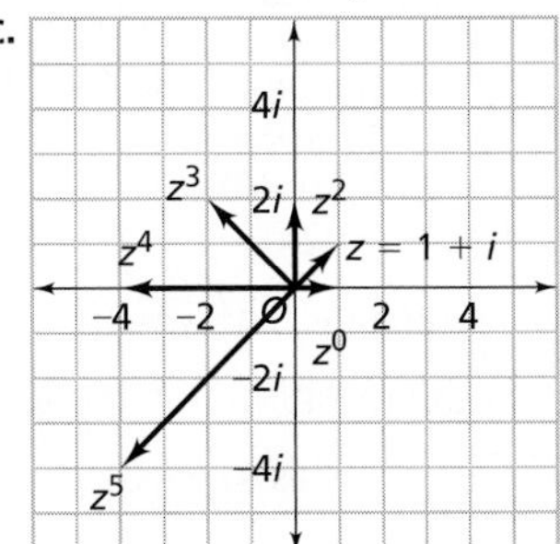

$|z| = \sqrt{2}$ and $\arg(z) = 45°$, so for each nonnegative integer n, you can obtain z^{n+1} if you rotate z^n counterclockwise 45° and then scale by $\sqrt{2}$.

d.

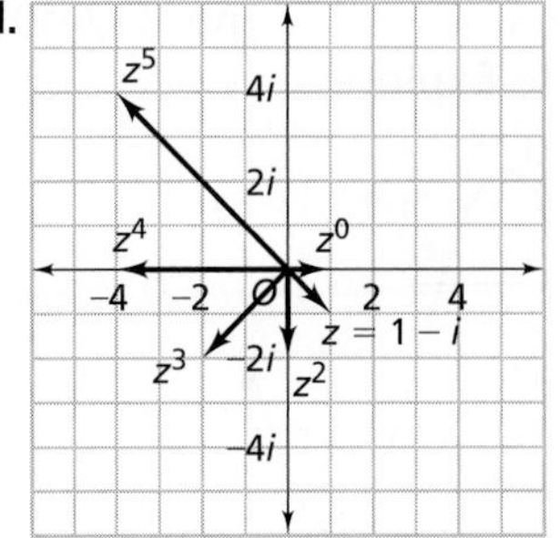

$|z| = \sqrt{2}$ and $\arg(z) = 315°$, so for each nonnegative integer n, you can obtain z^{n+1} if you rotate z^n clockwise 45° and then scale by $\sqrt{2}$.

e.

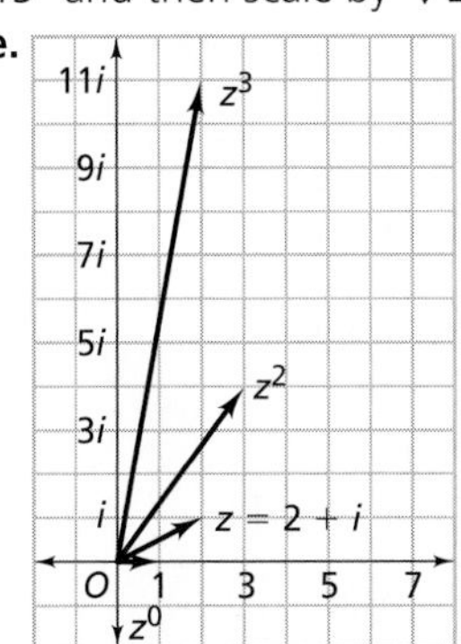

$|z| = \sqrt{5}$ and $\arg(z) \approx 26.6°$, so for each nonnegative integer n, you can obtain z^{n+1} if you rotate z^n counterclockwise by about 26.6° and then scale by $\sqrt{5}$.

f.

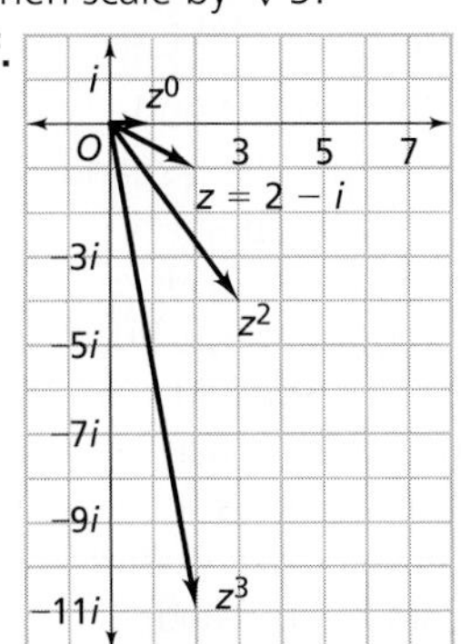

$|z| = \sqrt{5}$ and $\arg(z) \approx 333.4349°$, so for each nonnegative integer n, you can obtain z^{n+1} if you rotate z^n clockwise by about 26.6° and then scale by $\sqrt{5}$.
13e. The graph should be the circle with radius 1 centered at the origin (the unit circle). **f.** The graph should show points for the numbers $0 + 0i$ and $1 + 0i$. **g.** The graph should be the circle with radius 1 centered at the origin (the unit circle) plus the origin.
16a. 0 **b.** 1 **c.** $\frac{1}{2} + \frac{\sqrt{3}}{2}i$ **d.** 0 **e.** 1 **f.** $\frac{1}{2} + \frac{\sqrt{3}}{2}i$

Additional Answers

Lesson 2.5 **pp. 107–109**

For You to Explore

4.

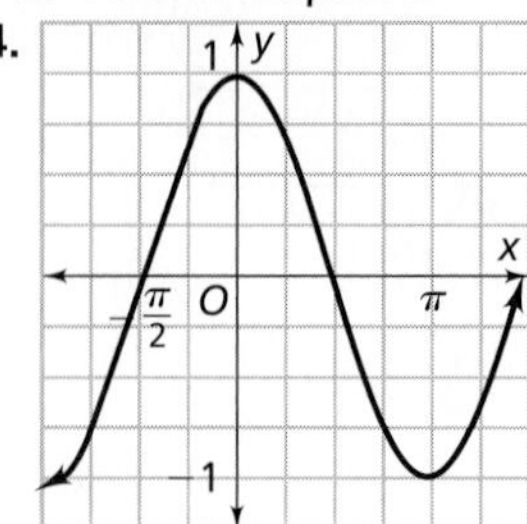

The graph is identical to $y = \cos x$.

Lesson 2.6 **pp. 110–115**

Exercises

9e. $\tan\left(x + \frac{\pi}{2}\right) = \dfrac{\sin\left(x + \frac{\pi}{2}\right)}{\cos\left(x + \frac{\pi}{2}\right)}$

$= \dfrac{\sin x \cos \frac{\pi}{2} + \cos x \sin \frac{\pi}{2}}{\text{s} \atop \cos x \cos \frac{\pi}{2} - \text{ in } x \sin \frac{\pi}{2}}$

$= \dfrac{\cos x}{-\sin x} = -\dfrac{1}{\tan x}$

f. $\tan\left(x + \frac{\pi}{4}\right) = \dfrac{\sin\left(x + \frac{\pi}{4}\right)}{\cos\left(x + \frac{\pi}{4}\right)} =$

$\dfrac{\sin x \cos \frac{\pi}{4} + \cos x \sin \frac{\pi}{4}}{\cos x \cos \frac{\pi}{4} - \sin x \sin \frac{\pi}{4}}$, and since $\cos \frac{\pi}{4}$ and $\sin \frac{\pi}{4}$ are both equal to $\frac{\sqrt{2}}{2}$, this last fraction can be simplified to $\frac{\sin x + \cos x}{\cos x - \sin x}$, or $\frac{\cos x + \sin x}{\cos x - \sin x}$. **14.** Since $\cos(-B) = \cos B$ and $\sin(-B) = -\sin B$, you can expand the given expression to obtain $(\cos A \cos B + \sin A \sin B) +$ $(\sin A \cos B - \cos A \sin B)i$. But the given expression is also equal to $(\text{cis } A)(\text{cis } (-B))$, which equals $\text{cis } (A - B)$, or $\cos(A - B) +$ $i \sin(A - B)$. Hence $\cos(A - B) =$ $\cos A \cos B + \sin A \sin B$ and $\sin(A - B) = \sin A \cos B -$ $\cos A \sin B$. **15.** In $\sin(A + B) \sin(A - B)$, replace $\sin(A + B)$ with $\sin A \cos B +$ $\cos A \sin B$ and $\sin(A - B)$ with $\sin A \cos B - \cos A \sin B$. Expand the resulting expression to obtain $\sin^2 A \cos^2 B - \cos^2 A \sin^2 B$. In this last expression, replace $\cos^2 B$ with $1 - \sin^2 B$ and $\cos^2 A$ with $1 - \sin^2 A$. Expand and simplify to obtain $\sin^2 A - \sin^2 B$.

Lesson 2.7 **pp. 116–121**

Exercises

1c. $\cot^2 x - \cos^2 x = \dfrac{\cos^2 x}{\sin^2 x} - \cos^2 x$

$= \left(\dfrac{1}{\sin^2 x} - 1\right)\cos^2 x$

$= \left(\dfrac{1 - \sin^2 x}{\sin^2 x}\right)\cos^2 x$

$= \dfrac{\cos^2 x}{\sin^2 x} \cdot \cos^2 x$

$= \cot^2 x \cos^2 x$

d. $\dfrac{\sin x}{1 - \cos x} = \dfrac{\sin x}{1 - \cos x} \cdot \dfrac{1 + \cos x}{1 + \cos x}$

$= \dfrac{\sin x(1 + \cos x)}{1 - \cos^2 x}$

$= \dfrac{\sin x(1 + \cos x)}{\sin^2 x}$

$= \dfrac{1 + \cos x}{\sin x}$

5a. $(\sec x \sin x)^2 -$ $(\sec x + 1)(\sec x - 1)$

$= \dfrac{\sin^2 x}{\cos^2 x} - \left(\sec^2 x - 1\right)$

$= \tan^2 x - \tan^2 x = 0$

b. Since $(\sec x \sin x)^2 -$ $(\sec x + 1)(\sec x - 1) = 0$ is an identity, you obtain an identity if you add $(\sec x + 1)(\sec x - 1)$ to both sides. **6a.** Use the formula in Exercise 4, and let $n = 1$ to get $\cos 2x = 2 \cos x \cos x - \cos 0 =$ $2 \cos^2 x - 1$. **b.** Use the formula in Exercise 4, and let $n = 2$to get $\cos 3x = 2 \cos x \cos 2x - \cos x$. On the right side of this equation, replace $\cos 2x$ with $2 \cos^2 x - 1$ and simplify to get $\cos 3x = 4 \cos^3 x - 3 \cos x$.

10a. $\dfrac{2 \tan x}{1 + \tan^2 x} = \dfrac{2 \tan x}{\sec^2 x}$

$= 2 \cdot \dfrac{\sin x}{\cos x} \cdot \dfrac{\cos^2 x}{1}$

$= 2 \sin x \cos x$

$= \sin 2x$

b. In $\frac{1 - \tan^2 x}{1 + \tan^2 x}$, replace $\tan^2 x$ with $\frac{\sin^2 x}{\cos^2 x}$. Simplify the resulting fraction to obtain $\frac{\cos^2 x - \sin^2 x}{\cos^2 x + \sin^2 x}$. This expression equals $\frac{\cos^2 x - \sin^2 x}{1}$, or $\cos 2x$.

11b. The given equation is an identity if and only if $\dfrac{1 + \cos x}{\sin x} - \dfrac{1 + \cos x + \sin x}{1 - \cos x + \sin x} = 0$ is an identity. Subtract the fractions on the left side to get

$\dfrac{(1 + \cos x)(1 - \cos x + \sin x) - \sin x(1 + \cos x + \sin x)}{\sin x(1 - \cos x + \sin x)} = 0.$

When you expand and collect terms in the numerator, you get $\dfrac{1 - \cos^2 x - \sin^2 x}{\sin x(1 - \cos x + \sin x)} = 0$. Since the numerator in this last equation is equal to 0, the original equation is an identity.

Mathematical Reflections **p. 122**

7. $\text{cis } 2x = \text{cis } x \text{ cis } x$, so $\cos 2x + i \sin 2x = (\cos x + i \sin x)^2 =$ $(\cos^2 x - \sin^2 x) + (2 \sin x \cos x)i$. Set the real parts equal and the imaginary parts equal to get $\cos 2x = \cos^2 x - \sin^2 x$ and $\sin 2x = 2 \sin x \cos x$. **8.** Identities that have already been proved provide substitutions that you can use to prove other identities.

Mid-Chapter Test **p. 123**

6a.

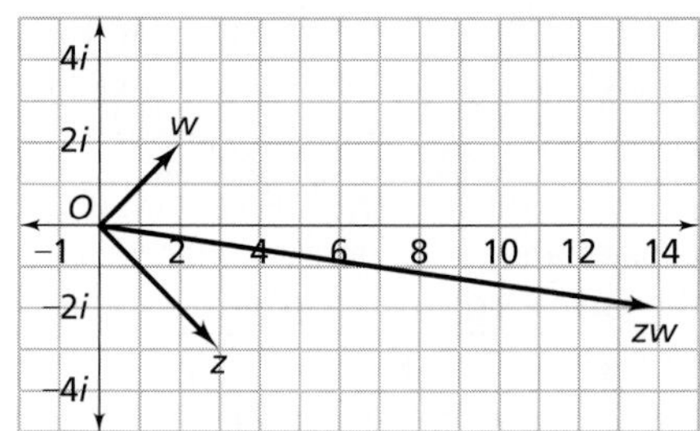

b.

	$a + bi$	Magnitude	Direction (radians)
z	$3 - 4i$	5	≈5.356
w	$2 + 2i$	$2\sqrt{2}$	≈0.786
zw	$14 - 2i$	$10\sqrt{2}$	≈6.141

Lesson 2.8 **pp. 125–127**

For You to Explore

3b.

c.

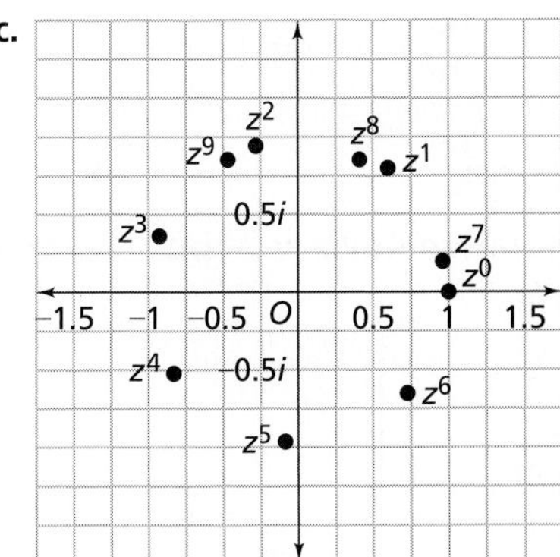

d.

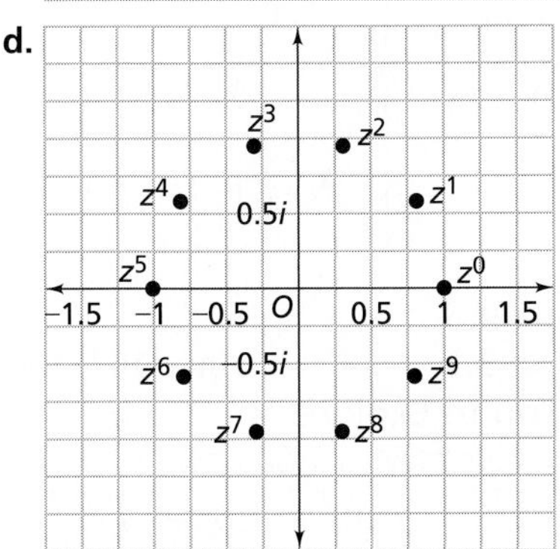

e.

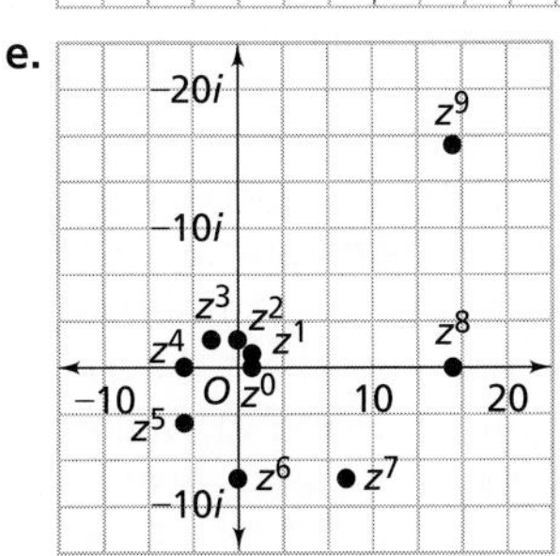

f.

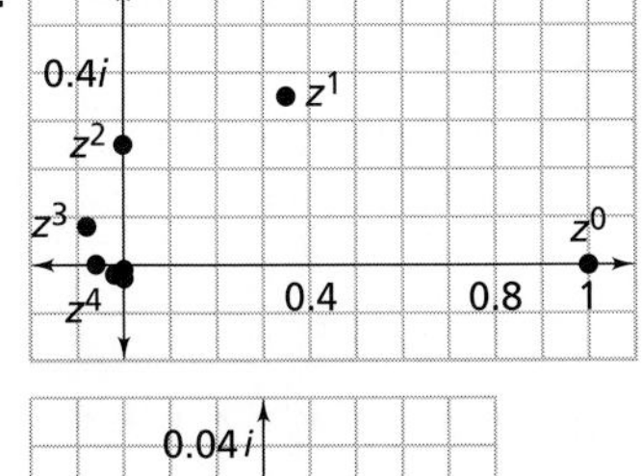

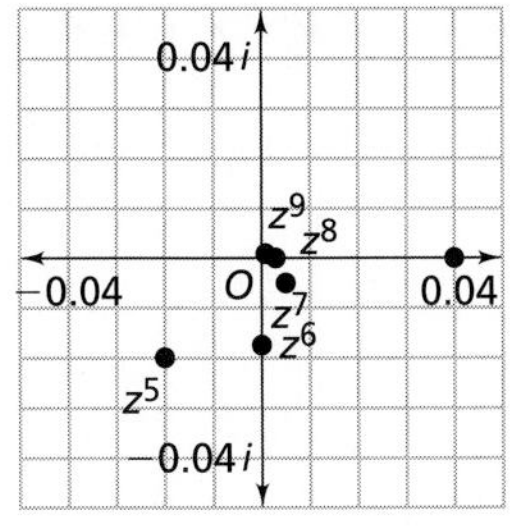

Lesson 2.9 **pp. 128–131**

Exercises **8.** $\cos 5x = \cos^5 x - 10\cos^3 x \sin^2 x + 5\cos x \sin^4 x$

12a.

Lesson 2.10 **pp. 132–138**

Exercises **17a.** If a is an nth root of unity, then $a = \text{cis}\,\frac{2\pi k}{n}$ for some integer k such that $0 \leq k \leq n - 1$. The roots of $x^2 - a = 0$ are $\text{cis}\,\frac{\pi k}{n}$ and $-\text{cis}\,\frac{\pi k}{n}$. If k is even, then $k = 2h$ for some h such that $0 \leq h \leq n - 1$. Therefore both $\text{cis}\,\frac{\pi k}{n}$ and $-\text{cis}\,\frac{\pi k}{n}$ $\left(\text{that is, cis}\,\frac{2\pi h}{n} \text{ and } -\text{cis}\,\frac{2\pi h}{n}\right)$ are nth roots of unity. (This is true regardless of the value of n, even or odd.)

Now suppose k is odd. The root $-\text{cis}\,\frac{\pi k}{n}$ of $x^2 - a = 0$ can be rewritten in a different form.

$$-\text{cis}\,\frac{\pi k}{n} = -\cos\frac{\pi k}{n} - i\sin\frac{\pi k}{n}$$

$$= \cos\left(\pi + \frac{\pi k}{n}\right) + i\sin\left(\pi + \frac{\pi k}{n}\right)$$

$$= \cos\frac{\pi(n+k)}{n} + i\sin\frac{\pi(n+k)}{n}$$

If n is odd, then $\cos\frac{\pi(n+k)}{n} + i\sin\frac{\pi(n+k)}{n}$ is an nth root of unity. In all cases, therefore, $\text{cis}\,\frac{\pi k}{n}$ or $-\text{cis}\,\frac{\pi k}{n}$ will be an nth root of unity.

18a.

Equation	# New Roots
$x-1=0$	1
$x^2-1=0$	1
$x^3-1=0$	2
$x^4-1=0$	2
$x^5-1=0$	4
$x^6-1=0$	2
$x^7-1=0$	6
$x^8-1=0$	4
$x^9-1=0$	6
$x^{10}-1=0$	4

Lesson 2.11 **pp. 139–144**

Exercises **7a.** Use the result from Exercise 6, the fact that $a = z + z^4$, and Exercise 3(b) to obtain $2\cos 72° = \frac{-1+\sqrt{5}}{2}$. This last equation gives $\cos 72° = \frac{-1+\sqrt{5}}{4}$.

b. $\sin 72° = \frac{\sqrt{10+2\sqrt{5}}}{4}$

c. $z^0 = 1$, $z = \frac{-1+\sqrt{5}}{4} + \frac{\sqrt{10+2\sqrt{5}}}{4}i$, $z^2 = -\frac{1+\sqrt{5}}{4} + \frac{\sqrt{10-2\sqrt{5}}}{4}i$, $z^3 = -\frac{1+\sqrt{5}}{4} - \frac{\sqrt{10-2\sqrt{5}}}{4}i$, $z^4 = \frac{-1+\sqrt{5}}{4} - \frac{\sqrt{10+2\sqrt{5}}}{4}i$

Lesson 2.12 **pp. 145–153**

Exercises **15b.** The factorization of $x^9 - 1$ over $\mathbb{Z}$ is $(x-1)(x^2+x+1)(x^6+x^3+1)$. The regular polygon with vertices at the roots of $x^9 - 1 = 0$ has vertices at ζ^k for $k = 0$ to 8. The table shows which powers of ζ make which factors equal to 0.

Factor	Powers of ζ
$x-1$	ζ^0
x^2+x+1	ζ^3, ζ^6
x^6+x^3+1	$\zeta, \zeta^2, \zeta^4, \zeta^5, \zeta^7, \zeta^8$

21a. $P_0 + P_1 + 1 = 0$, so $P_0 + P_1 = -1$. If you multiply P_0 by P_1, you obtain $\zeta^{30} + \zeta^{29} + \zeta^{28} + 3\zeta^{27} + 2\zeta^{26} + 2\zeta^{25} + \zeta^{24} + 3\zeta^{23} + 3\zeta^{22} + 3\zeta^{21} + 4\zeta^{20} + 4\zeta^{19} + 4\zeta^{18} + 4\zeta^{16} + 4\zeta^{15} + 4\zeta^{14} + 3\zeta^{13} + 3\zeta^{12} + 3\zeta^{11} + \zeta^{10} + 2\zeta^9 + 2\zeta^8 + 3\zeta^7 + \zeta^6 + \zeta^5 + \zeta^4$. Replace powers with exponents greater than 17 with their equivalents to obtain $\sum_{k=1}^{16} 4\zeta^k = 4\sum_{k=1}^{16}\zeta^k = 4(-1) = -4$. So $P_0P_1 = -4$.

Solve the system consisting of the equations $P_0 + P_1 = -1$ and $P_0P_1 = -4$ in the usual way. One solution is $P_0 = \frac{-1-\sqrt{17}}{2}$ and $P_1 = \frac{-1+\sqrt{17}}{2}$. The other solution is $P_0 = \frac{-1+\sqrt{17}}{2}$ and $P_1 = \frac{-1-\sqrt{17}}{2}$. In the present situation, the original definitions of P_0 and P_1 imply that $P_0 > P_1$. (You can verify this by using a calculator.) So you can eliminate the first solution and conclude that $P_0 = \frac{-1+\sqrt{17}}{2}$ and $P_1 = \frac{-1-\sqrt{17}}{2}$.

22a–b. See Figure 2.

Project **p. 155–158**

8. In what follows, let

$$r = \sqrt[3]{\frac{-q + \sqrt{\frac{27q^2 + 4p^3}{27}}}{2}} \text{ and}$$

$$s = \sqrt[3]{\frac{-q - \sqrt{\frac{27q^2 + 4p^3}{27}}}{2}}.$$

a. The discriminant D is $q^2 - 4(1)\left(-\frac{p^3}{27}\right)$, or $q^2 + \frac{4p^3}{27}$. So if $D = 0$, it follows that $27D = 27q^2 + 4p^3$.

b. If $27q^2 + 4p^3 > 0$, then both r and s are real, and one root of $x^2 + px + q = 0$ is the real number $r + s$. The other two roots are $\left(\frac{-1 + i\sqrt{3}}{2}\right)r + \left(\frac{-1 - i\sqrt{3}}{2}\right)s$ and $\left(\frac{-1 - i\sqrt{3}}{2}\right)r + \left(\frac{-1 + i\sqrt{3}}{2}\right)s$, and both are clearly imaginary.

c. If $27q^2 + 4p^3 = 0$, then $r + s$ becomes $2\sqrt[3]{\frac{-q}{2}}$, which is a real root of the cubic equation. Note that in this case $r = s$. The other two roots become $-r$ and $-s$ which are real and equal. Hence there are two distinct real roots, and one of them has multiplicity 2.

d. If $27q^2 + 4p^3 < 0$, then

$$r^3 = \frac{-q + i\sqrt{\frac{27q^2 + 4p^3}{-27}}}{2} \text{ and}$$

$$s^3 = \frac{-q - i\sqrt{\frac{27q^2 + 4p^3}{-27}}}{2} \text{ Also}$$

$p < 0$. r^3 and s^3 are imaginary conjugates and $|r^3| = |s^3| = \sqrt{\frac{-p^3}{27}}$, and if the argument of r^3 is θ, then $r^3 = \sqrt{\frac{-p^3}{27}} \operatorname{cis} \theta$ and $s^3 = \sqrt{\frac{-p^3}{27}} \operatorname{cis}(-\theta)$. Apply Theorem 2.10 and conclude that

$$r + s = \sqrt[3]{\sqrt{\frac{-p^3}{27}} \operatorname{cis} \theta} + \sqrt[3]{\sqrt{\frac{-p^3}{27}} \operatorname{cis}(-\theta)} = \sqrt{\frac{-p}{3}} \operatorname{cis} \frac{\theta}{3} + \sqrt{\frac{-p}{3}} \operatorname{cis} \frac{-\theta}{3} = 2\sqrt{\frac{-p}{3}} \cos \frac{\theta}{3}.$$

Since $p < 0$, $2\sqrt{\frac{-p}{3}} \cos \frac{\theta}{3}$ is a real root of $x^2 + px + q = 0$.

Let $\omega = \frac{-1 + \sqrt{3}}{2}$. Then $\omega = 1 \operatorname{cis} \frac{2\pi}{3}$ and $\omega^2 = 1 \operatorname{cis} \frac{-2\pi}{3}$. Therefore, the other two roots of $x^2 + px + q = 0$ are

$$\omega\left(\sqrt{\frac{-p}{3}} \operatorname{cis} \frac{\theta}{3}\right) + \omega^2\left(\sqrt{\frac{-p}{3}} \operatorname{cis} \frac{-\theta}{3}\right) = 2\sqrt{\frac{-p}{3}} \cos \frac{\theta + 2\pi}{3}$$

and

$$\omega^2\left(\sqrt{\frac{-p}{3}} \operatorname{cis} \frac{\theta}{3}\right) + \omega\left(\sqrt{\frac{-p}{3}} \operatorname{cis} \frac{-\theta}{3}\right) = 2\sqrt{\frac{-p}{3}} \cos \frac{\theta - 2\pi}{3}.$$

These two roots are real. All of the roots are distinct.

Review **pp. 159–160**

5a. $\operatorname{cis}\left(x + \frac{3\pi}{4}\right) = (\operatorname{cis} x)\left(\operatorname{cis} \frac{3\pi}{4}\right) = (\cos x + i \sin x)\left(\cos \frac{3\pi}{4} + i \sin \frac{3\pi}{4}\right) = \left(-\frac{\sqrt{2}}{2} \cos x - \frac{\sqrt{2}}{2} \sin x\right) + i\left(\frac{\sqrt{2}}{2} \cos x - \frac{\sqrt{2}}{2} \sin x\right)$

$\cos\left(x + \frac{3\pi}{4}\right)$ is the real part of the number in the last line above. So $\cos\left(x + \frac{3\pi}{4}\right) = -\frac{\sqrt{2}}{2} \cos x - \frac{\sqrt{2}}{2} \sin x$.

Cumulative Review **pp. 162–163**

20.

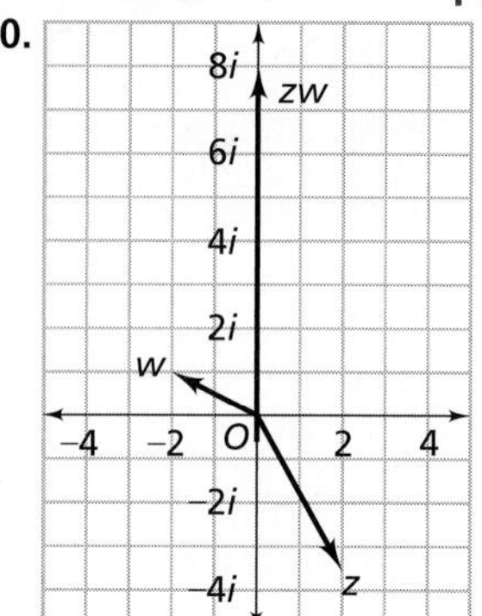

Chapter 3

Lesson 3.1 **pp. 167–169**

For You to Explore

2. Answers may vary. Sample:

$f(x) = \frac{7}{10}(x + 5)(x + 1)(x - 2)$

Expand on your CAS to get

$\frac{7}{10}x^3 + \frac{14}{5}x^2 - \frac{49}{10}x - 7$.

Suppose you choose (2, 0) to be the third point where the graph crosses the x-axis. A function $f(x)$ that satisfies all the given conditions will have the form $f(x) = a(x + 5)(x + 1)(x - 2)$ where a is positive. Since the graph crosses $(0, -7)$, it follows that $f(0) = -7$, so $-7 = a(0 + 5)(0 + 1)(0 - 2)$, and therefore $a = \frac{7}{10}$.

Figure 2

22a. $r_0 + r_4 = Q_0$ follows at once from the definitions of r_0, r_4, and Q_0;
$r_0 r_4 = \zeta^{29} + \zeta^{20} + \zeta^{14} + \zeta^5 = \zeta^{12} + \zeta^3 + \zeta^{14} + \zeta^5 = Q_1$.
Using the known values for Q_0 and Q_1, solve the system of equations in the exercise. Then use the fact that $r_0 > r_4$ to obtain r_0 and r_4.

$$r_4 = \frac{-\left(\sqrt{-2\left(8\sqrt{2(\sqrt{17} + 17)} - (\sqrt{17} - 1)\sqrt{-2(\sqrt{17} - 17)} - 2(3\sqrt{17} + 17)\right)} - \sqrt{-2(\sqrt{17} - 17)} - \sqrt{17} + 1\right)}{8},$$

$$r_0 = \frac{\sqrt{-2\left(8\sqrt{2(\sqrt{17} + 17)} - (\sqrt{17} - 1)\sqrt{-2(\sqrt{17} - 17)} - 2(3\sqrt{17} + 17)\right)} + \sqrt{-2(\sqrt{17} - 17)} + \sqrt{17} - 1}{8}$$

b. $$\frac{\sqrt{-2\left(8\sqrt{2(\sqrt{17} + 17)} - (\sqrt{17} - 1)\sqrt{-2(\sqrt{17} - 17)} - 2(3\sqrt{17} + 17)\right)} + \sqrt{-2(\sqrt{17} - 17)} + \sqrt{17} - 1}{16}$$

Exercises

4f.

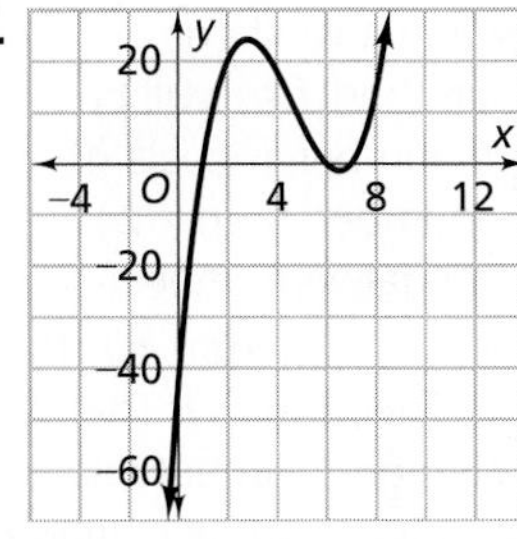

5a.

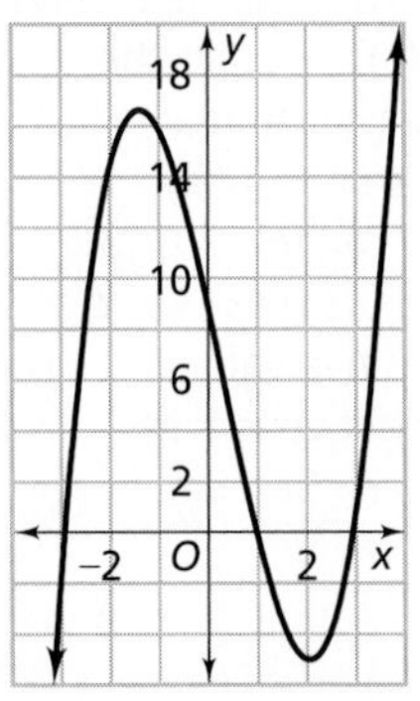

b.

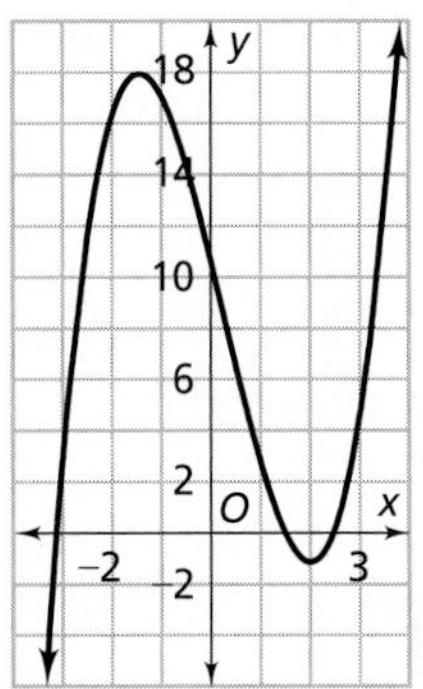

c.

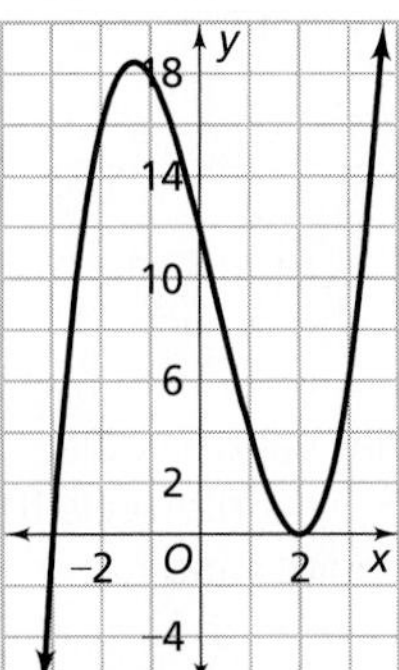

d.

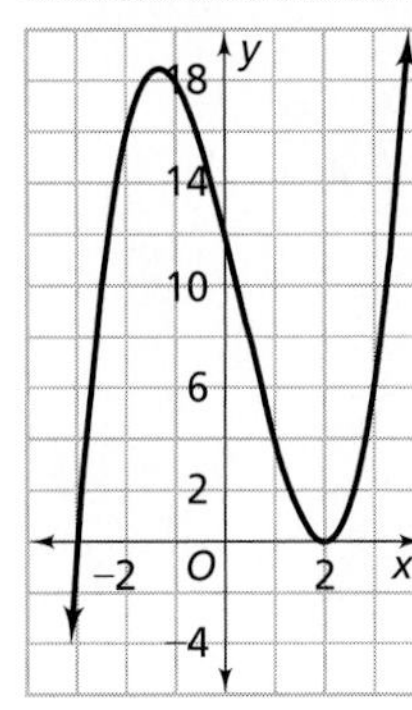

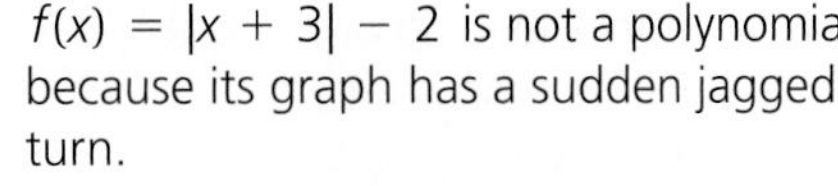

9. Answers may vary. Sample: $f(x) = |x + 3| - 2$ is not a polynomial because its graph has a sudden jagged turn.

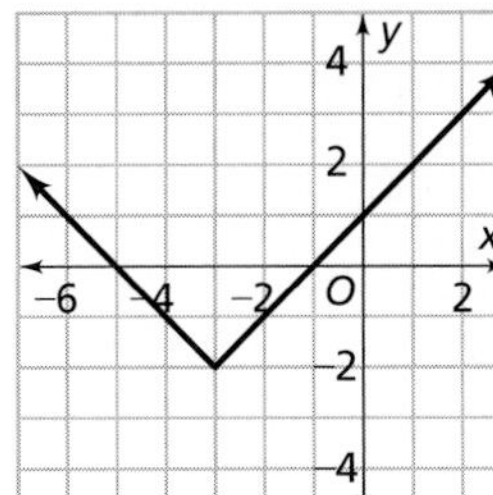

11a.

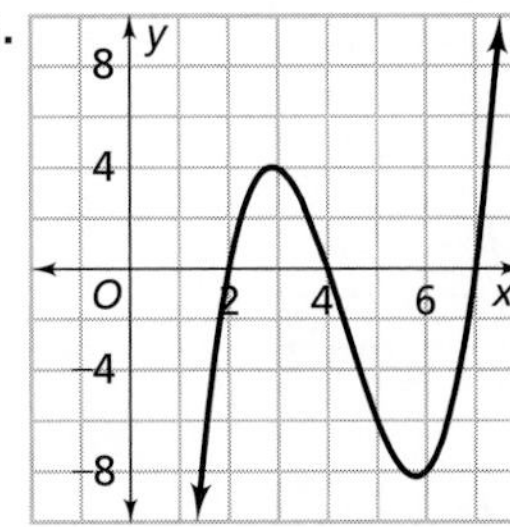

b.

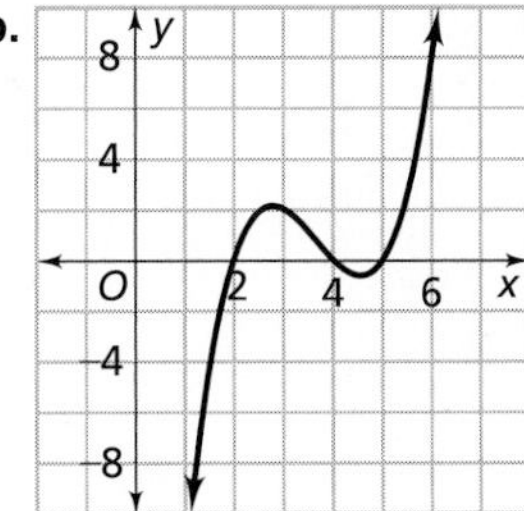

c.

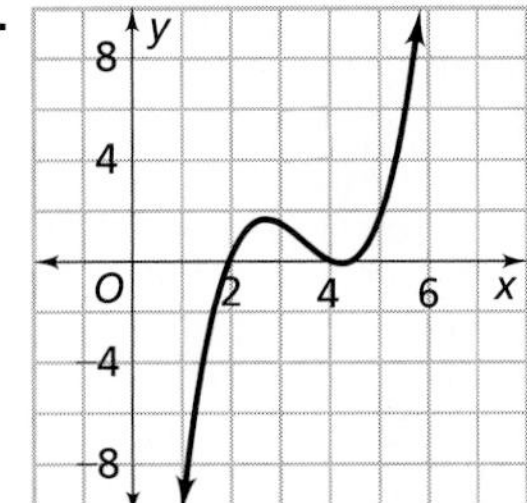

d.

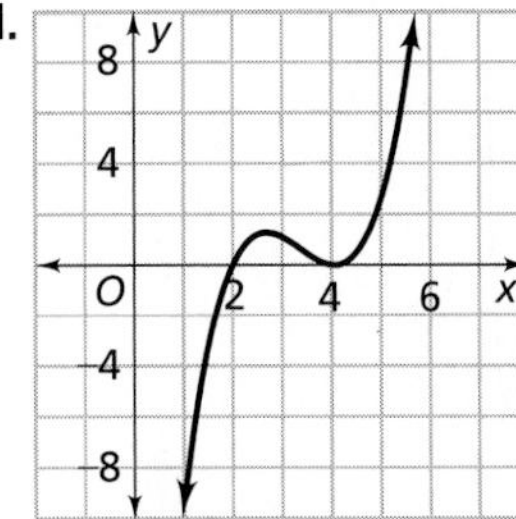

e.

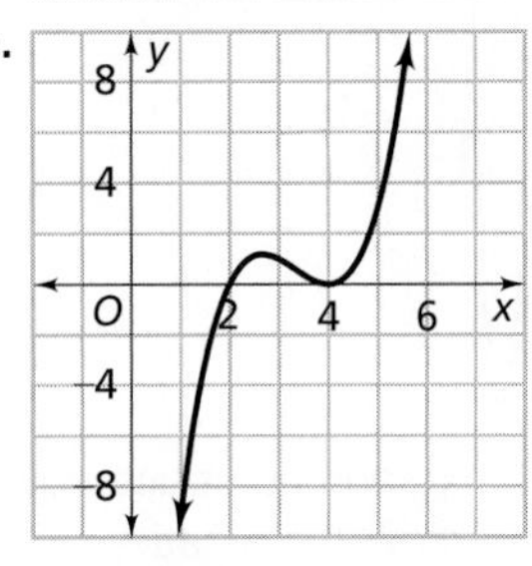

13a.

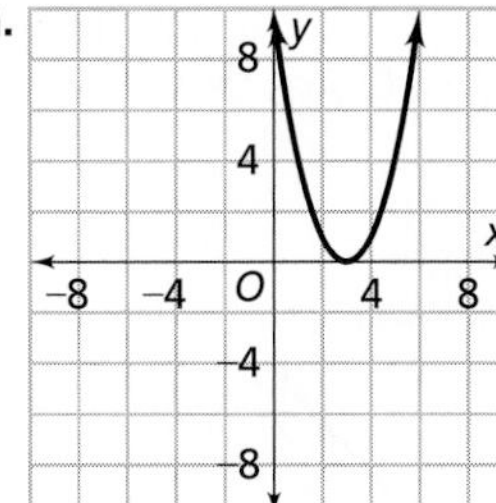

b.

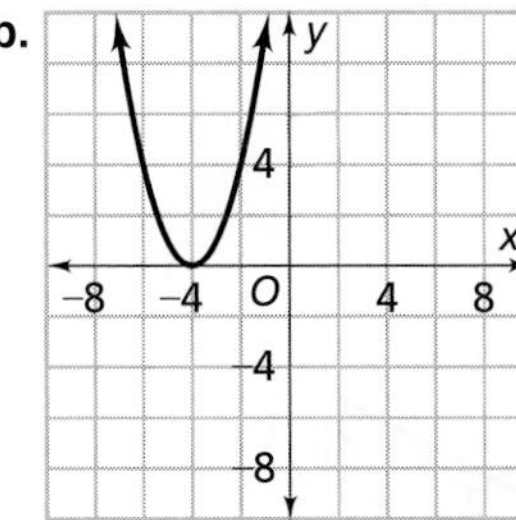

c.

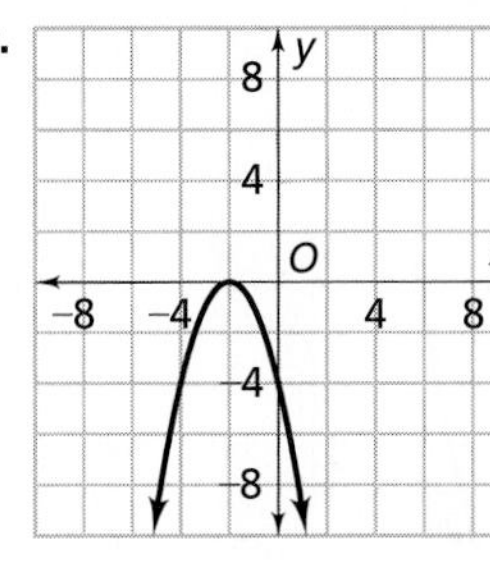

d.

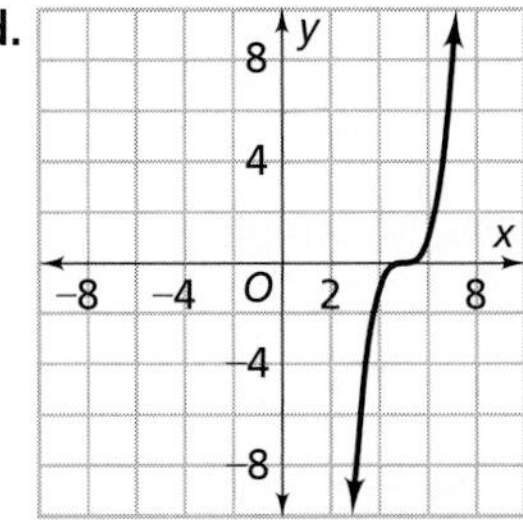

e.

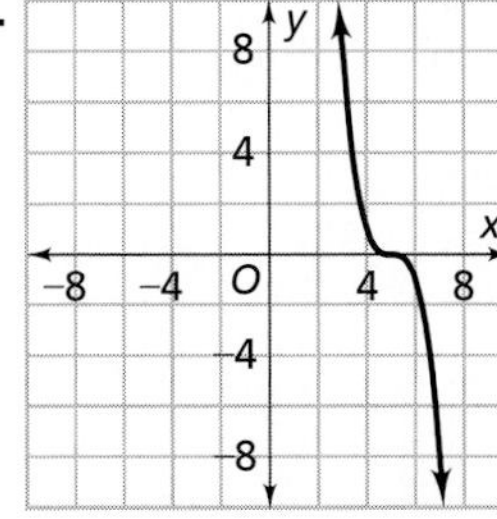

f.

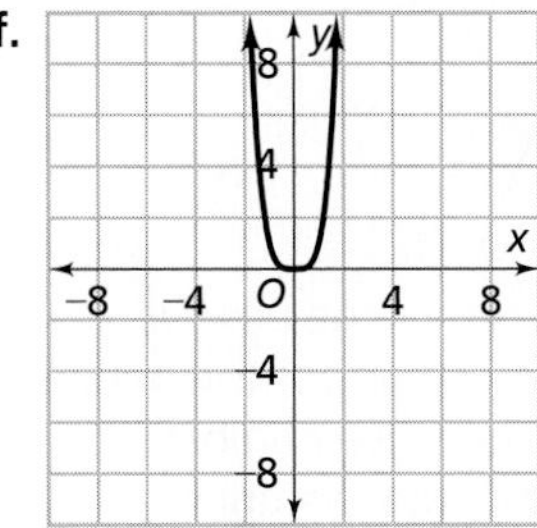

Lesson 3.2 **pp. 170–179**

For You to Do **6.** Answers may vary. Sample:

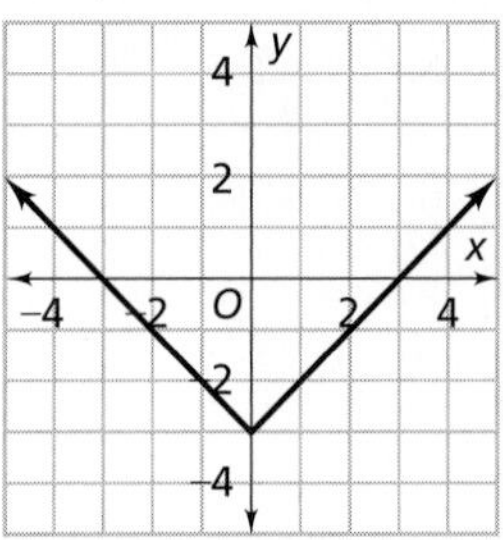

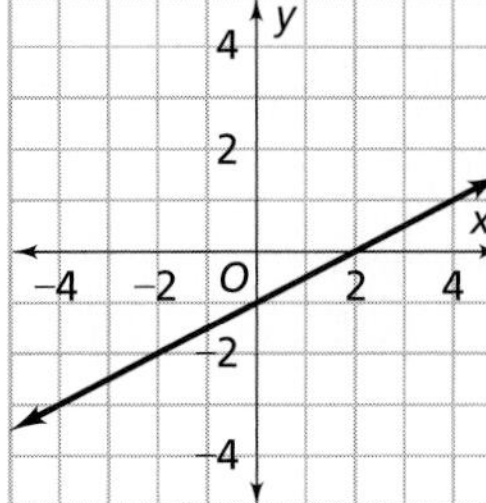

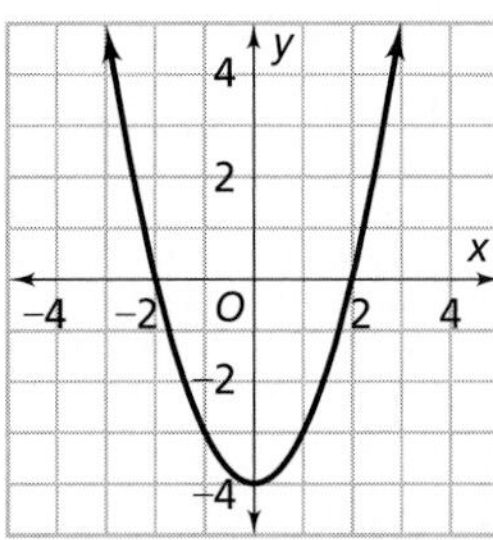

7. Answers may vary. Sample:

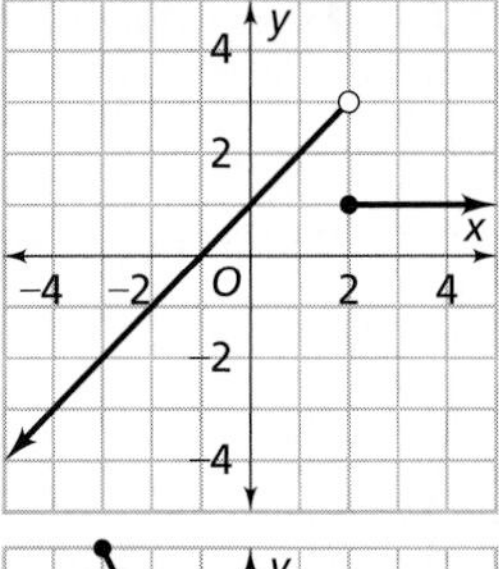

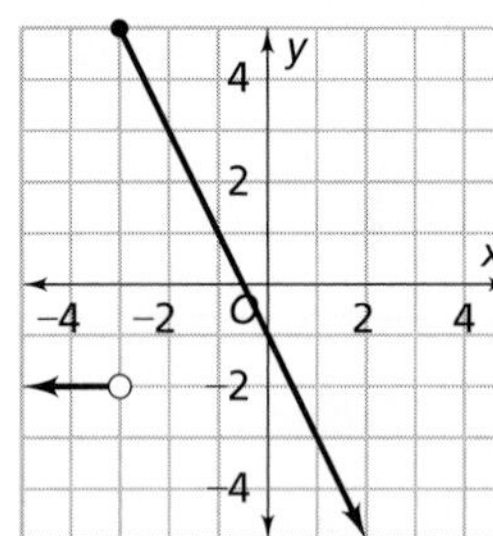

Exercises **2e.** very large positive number **f.** a very small positive number **g.** a very large negative number **3a.** Answers may vary. Sample: $g(x) = x^2 + 4x - 21$ **b.** Answers may vary. Sample: $h(x) = -\frac{2}{3}x^2 + \frac{4}{3}x + 10$ **c.** Answers may vary. Sample: $j(x) = -\frac{2}{3}x^2 + \frac{4}{3}x + 12$

6. Consider fourth degree polynomials with a positive leading coefficient. Some possible shapes are:

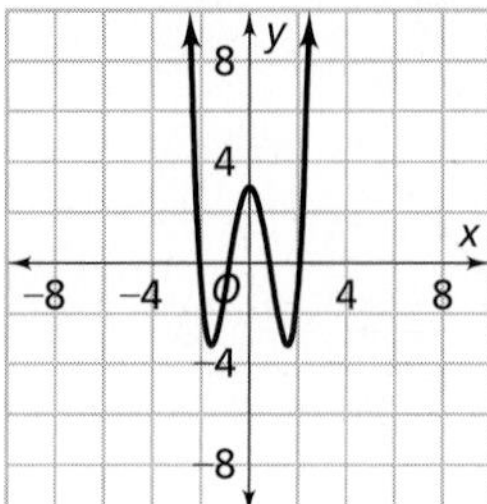

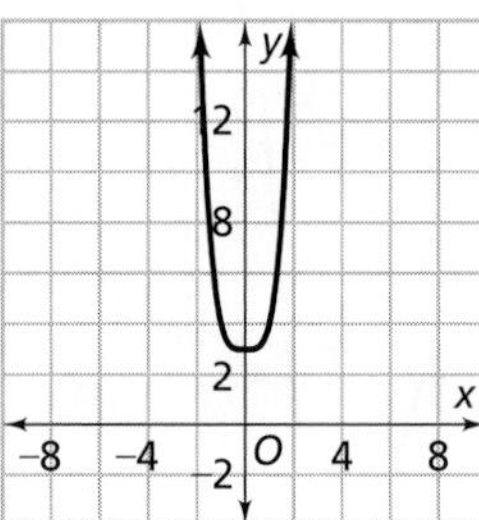

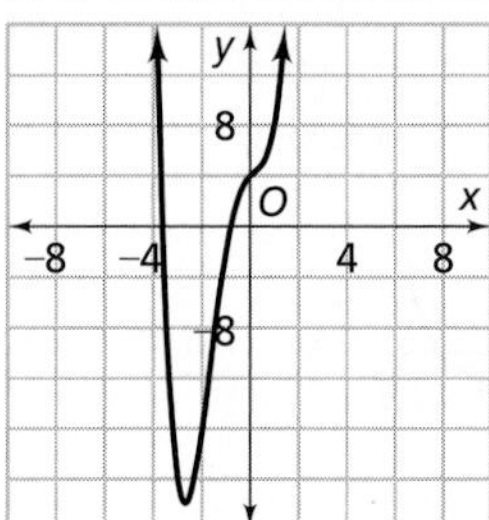

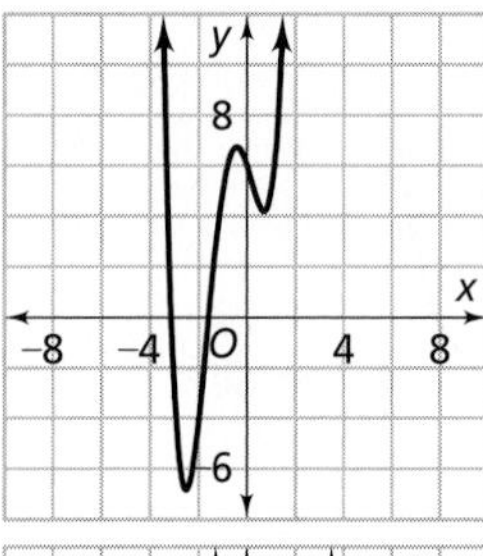

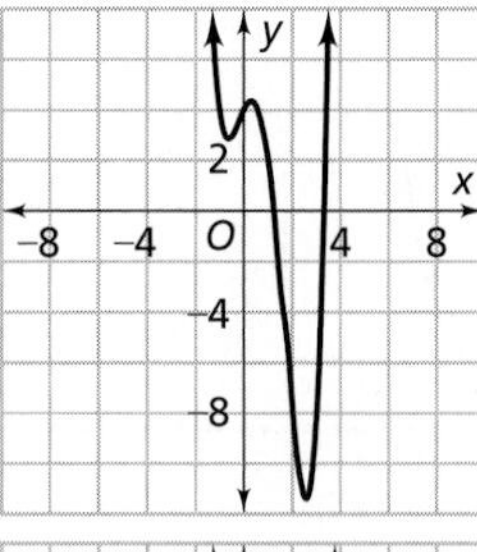

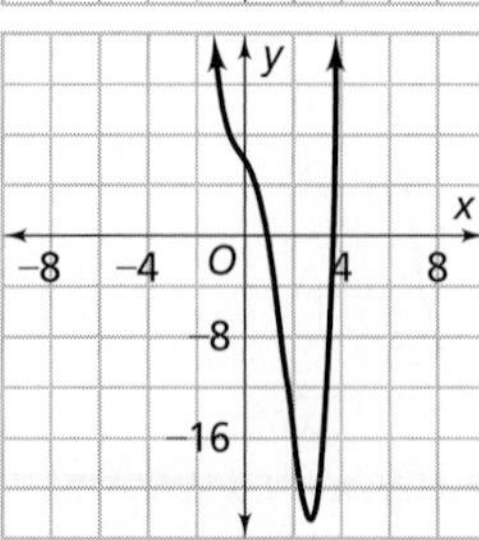

Each of these can be turned upside-down if the leading coefficient is negative.

10. If f is a polynomial function of odd degree and a is a large positive number, then $f(a)$ will be a large positive number. If b is a large negative number, then $f(b)$ will be a large negative number ($\text{negative}^{\text{odd power}} = \text{negative}$). The Change of Sign Theorem says that if a polynomial changes sign between a and b, there must be some c between a and b where $f(c) = 0$. So the function has at least one real root. **13a.** The maximum is 4, and the minimum is 0. **b.** Yes, 1 or 3 intersections are possible. **14a.** $g(x)$ takes on large positive values. **b.** $g(x)$ takes on large negative values. **c.** Answers may vary. Sample:

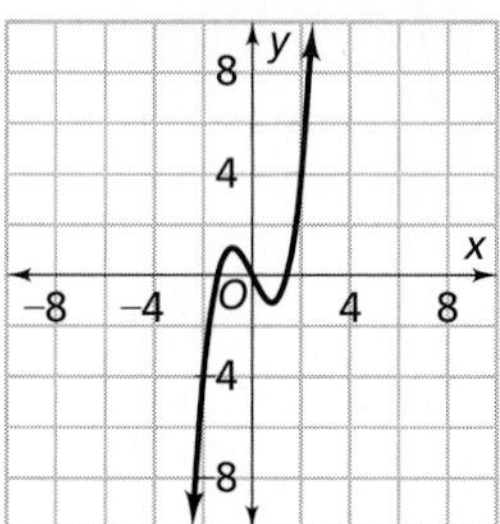

16a. The maximum is 4 and the minimum is 0; Answers may vary. Sample:

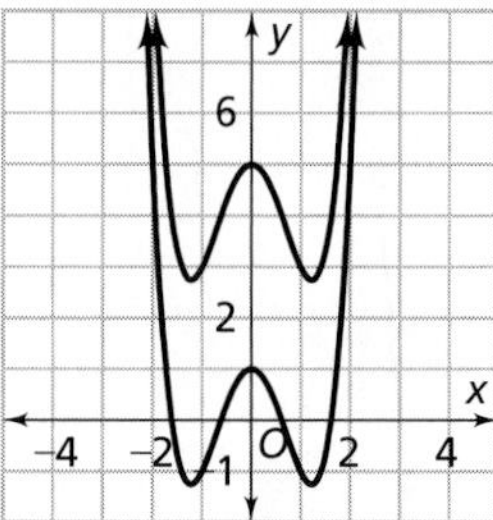

b. Yes; Answers may vary. Sample: $h(x) = x^4 - 3x^2 - 4$ intersects the x-axis in exactly 2 points and has exactly 2 real roots, $x = \pm 2$.

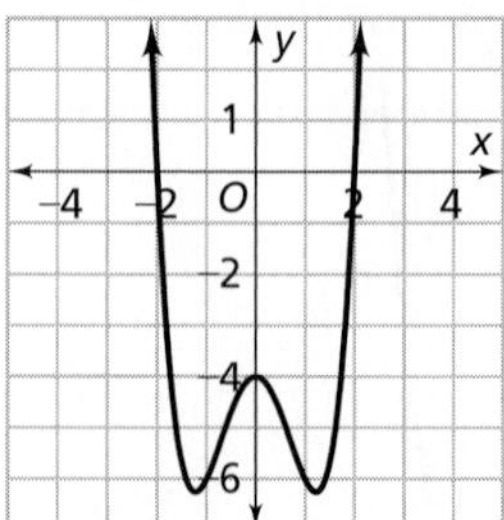

Lesson 3.3 pp. 180–188

Exercises **2c.**

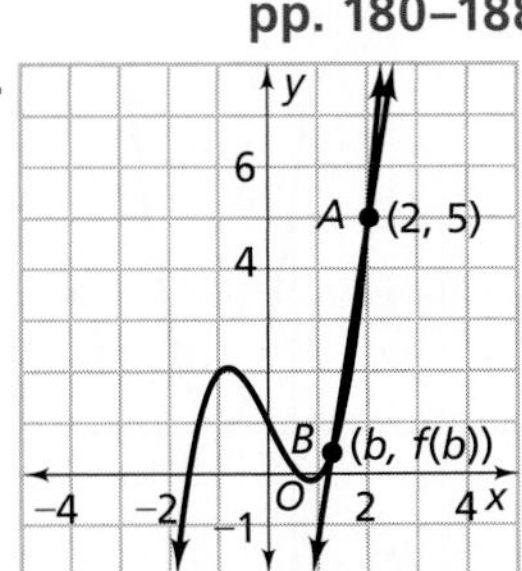

As b moves closer to 2, the slope gets closer to 10.

3a. Answers may vary. Sample:

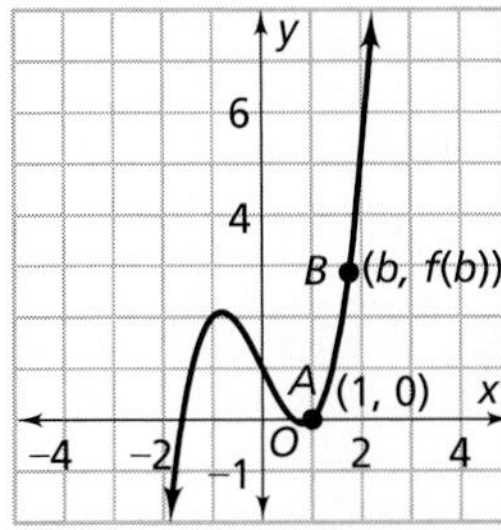

b. Answers may vary. Sample:

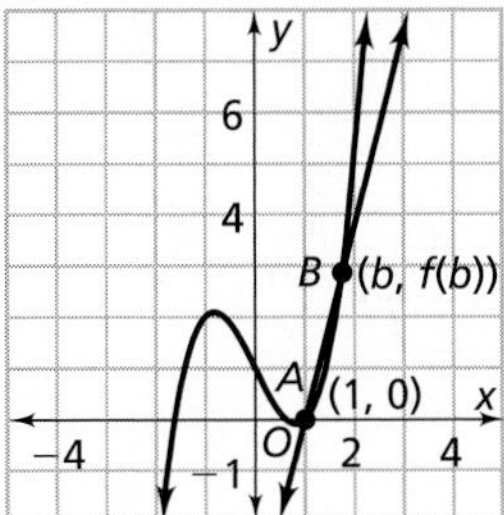

4a. Answers may vary. Sample:

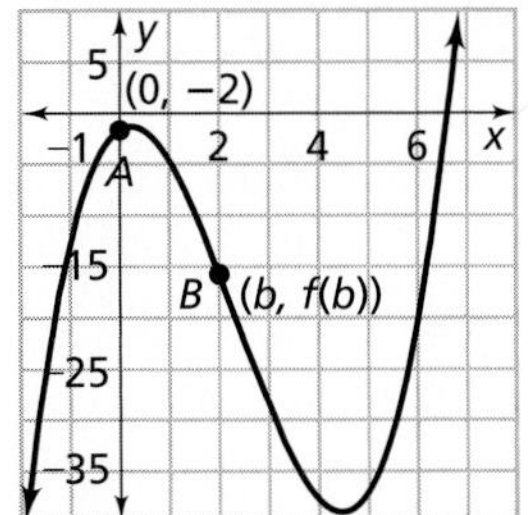

b. Answers may vary. Sample:

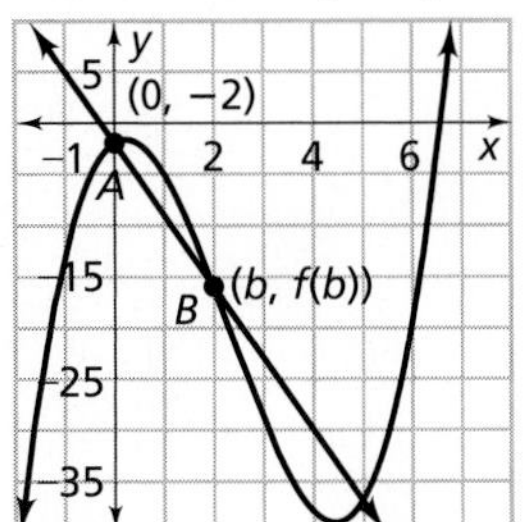

c. $m = b^2 - 7b + 3$ **d.** As b gets closer to 0, the slope gets closer to $0^2 - 7(0) + 3 = 3$.

11c.

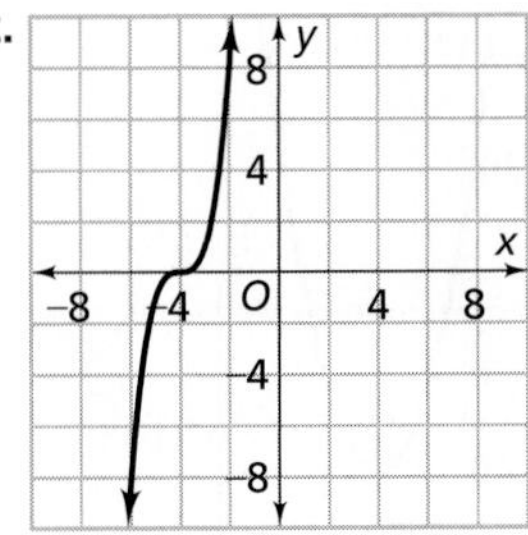

d.

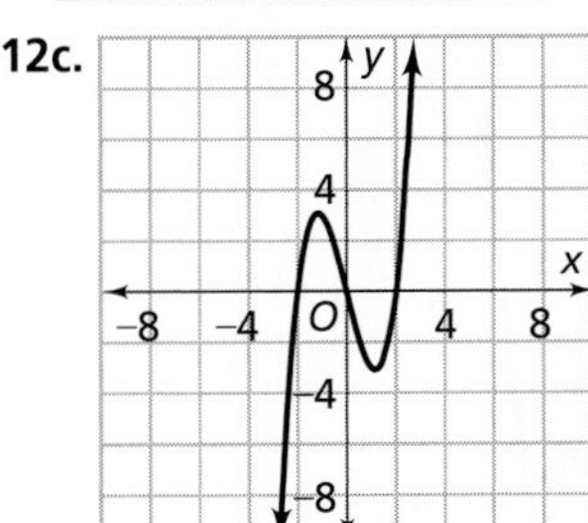

12c.

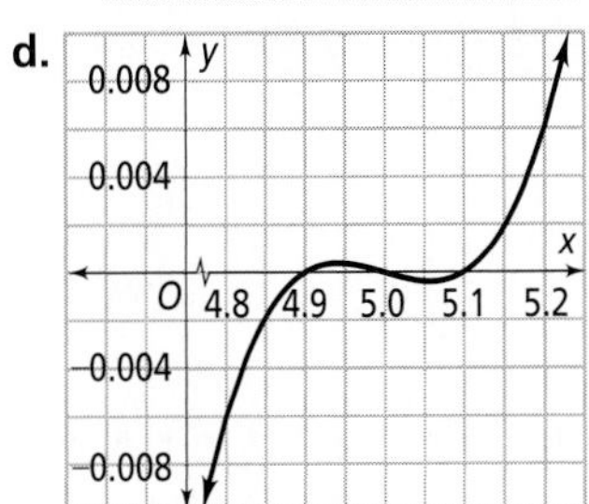

d.

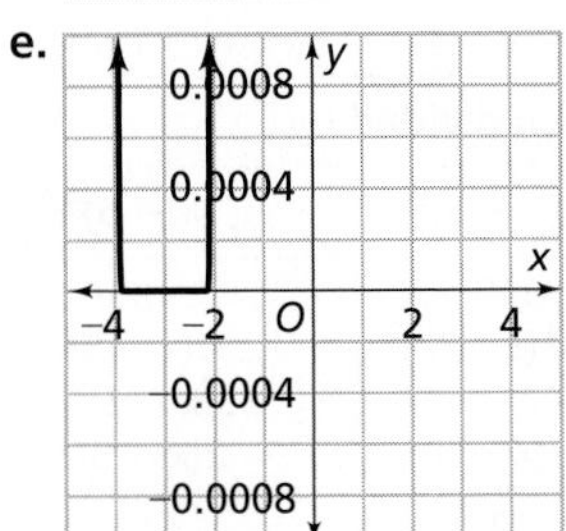

e.

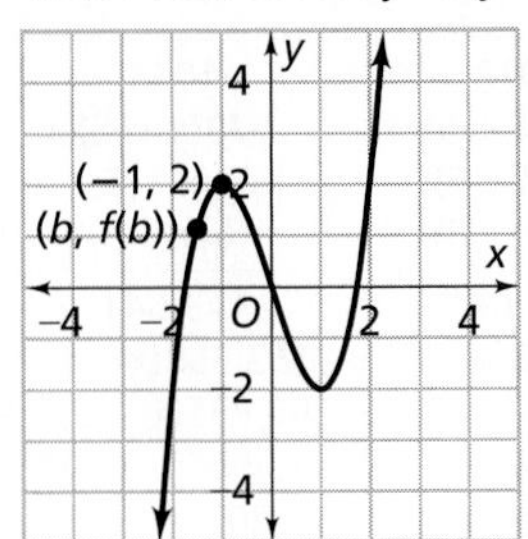

15a. Answers may vary. Sample:

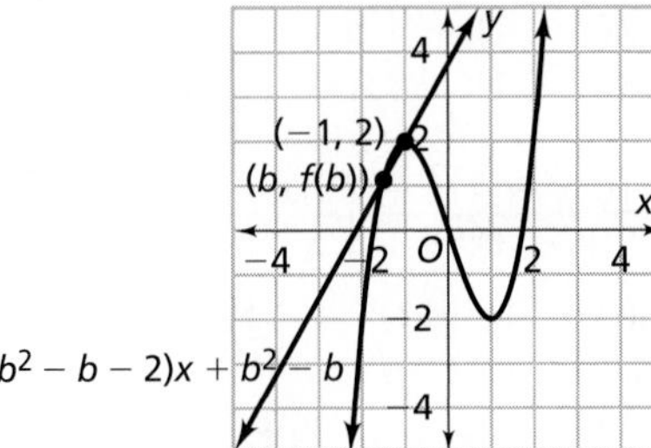

b. Answers may vary. Sample:

18a.

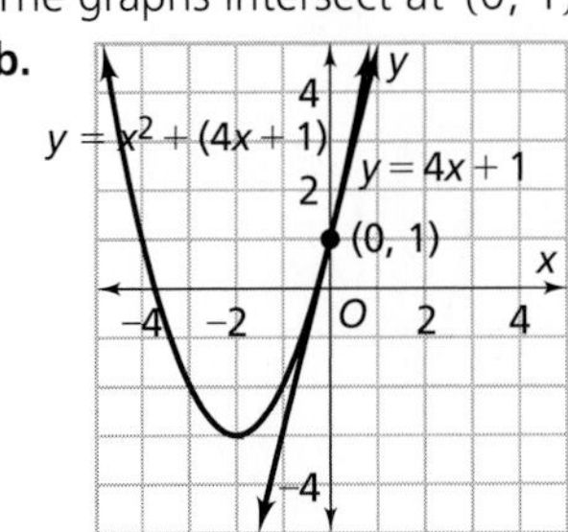

The graphs intersect at (0, 1).

b.

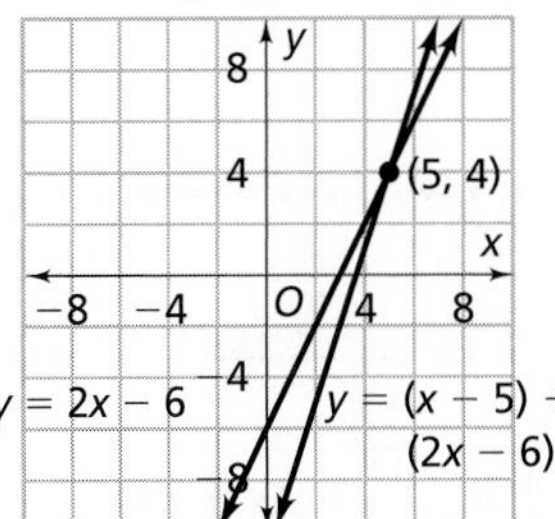

The graphs intersect at (0, 1).

19a. The graphs intersect at (5, 4).

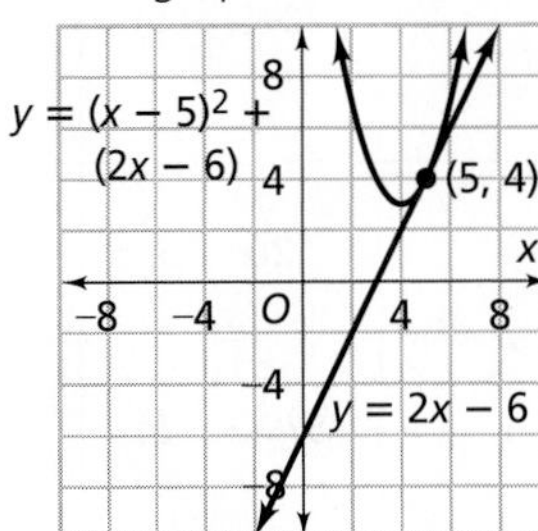

b. The graphs intersect at (5, 4).

Lesson 3.4 pp. 189–196

Exercises **6d.** $143{,}641 + 152{,}358(x - 5) + 66{,}931(x - 5)^2 + 15{,}586(x - 5)^3 + 2029(x - 5)^4 + 140(x - 5)^5 + 4(x - 5)^6$

Additional Answers

12. See Figure 3. **14a.** $(x - 1)^2 + 2(x - 1) + 1$ **b.** $(x - 1)^3 + 3(x - 1)^2 + 3(x - 1) + 1$ **c.** $(x - 1)^5 + 5(x - 1)^4 + 10(x - 1)^3 + 10(x - 1)^2 + 5(x - 1) + 1$ **d.** $x^n = ((x - 1) + 1)^n = \sum_{k=0}^{n} \binom{n}{k}(x - 1)^{n-k}$

15a.

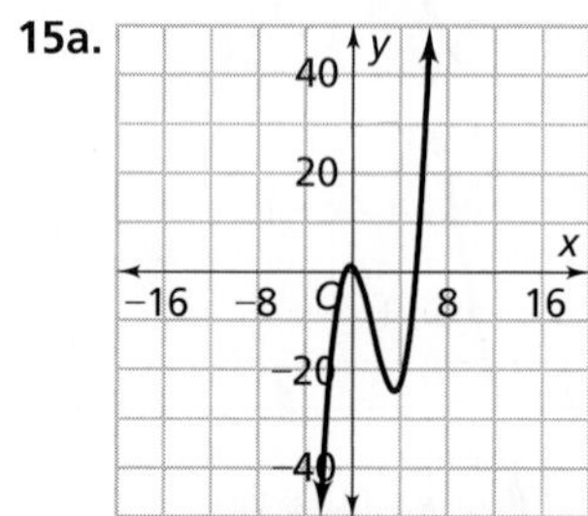

b.

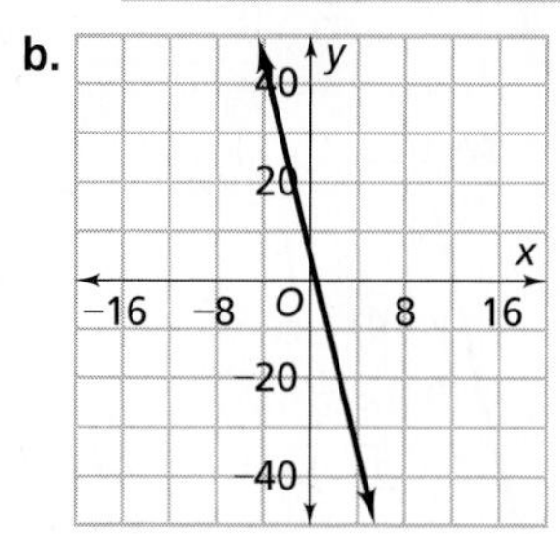

c.

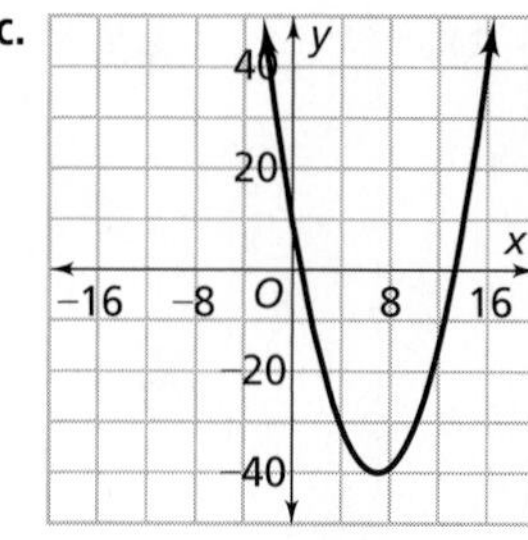

d.

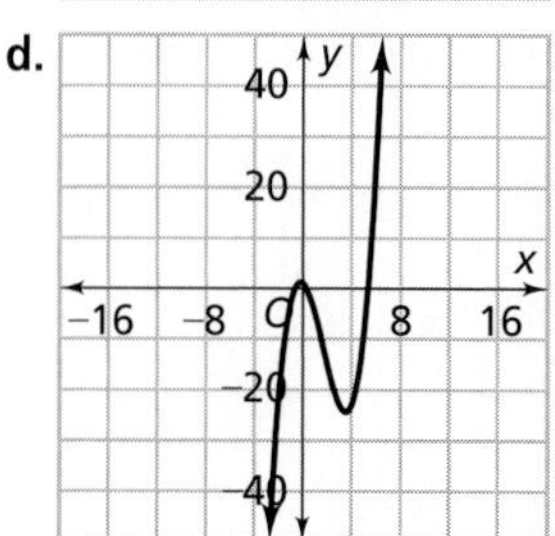

17a. $22(x - 3) + 18$

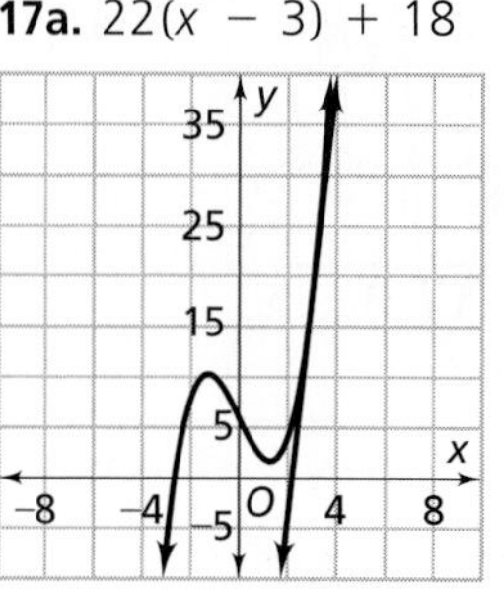

b. -4

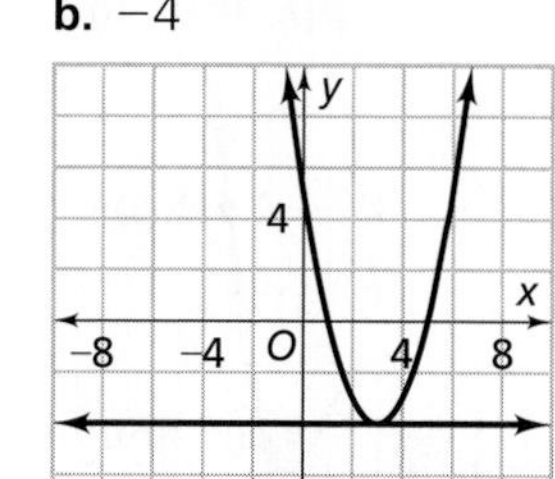

c. $27(x - 3) + 27$

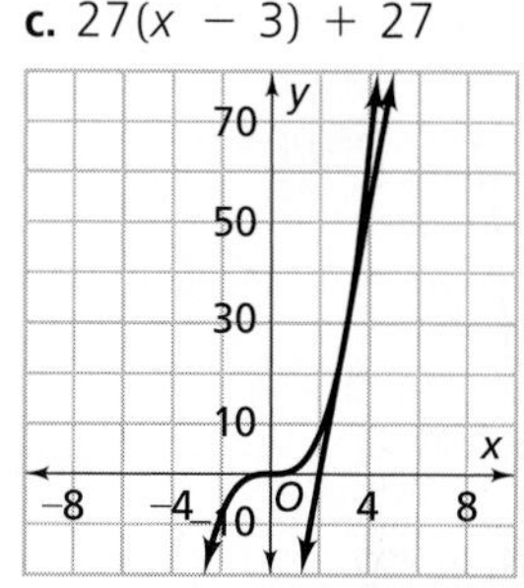

d. $43(x - 3) + 49$

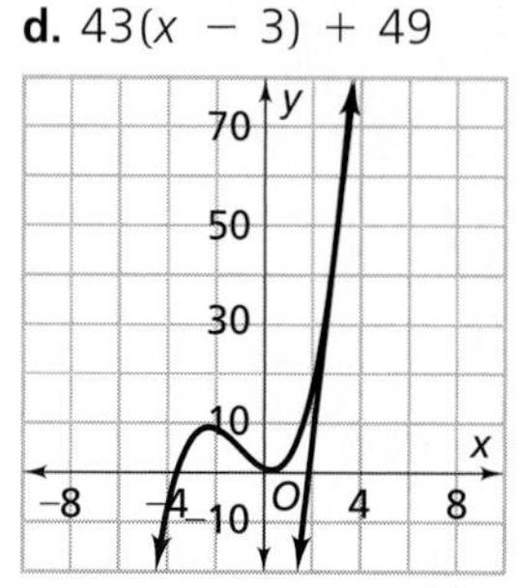

Figure 3

	remainder when divided by...					
	$x - 5$	**$(x - 5)^2$**	**$(x - 5)^3$**	**$(x - 5)^4$**	**$(x - 5)^5$**	**$(x - 5)^6$**
$f(x)$	379	$379 + 201(x - 5)$	$379 + 201(x - 5) + 35(x - 5)^2$	$379 + 201(x - 5) + 35(x - 5)^2 + 2(x - 5)^3$	$379 + 201(x - 5) + 35(x - 5)^2 + 2(x - 5)^3$	$379 + 201(x - 5) + 35(x - 5)^2 + 2(x - 5)^3$
$g(x)$	32	$32 + 12(x - 5)$	$32 + 12(x - 5) + (x - 5)^2$	$32 + 12(x - 5) + (x - 5)^2$	$32 + 12(x - 5) + (x - 5)^2$	$32 + 12(x - 5) + (x - 5)^2$
$3f(x) - 2g(x)$	1073	$1073 + 579(x - 5)$	$1073 + 579(x - 5) + 103(x - 5)^2$	$1073 + 579(x - 5) + 103(x - 5)^2 + 6(x - 5)^3$	$1073 + 579(x - 5) + 103(x - 5)^2 + 6(x - 5)^3$	$1073 + 579(x - 5) + 103(x - 5)^2 + 6(x - 5)^3$
$f(x) \cdot f(x)$	143,641	143,641 + 152,358$(x - 5)$	143,641 + 152,358$(x - 5)$ + 66,931$(x - 5)^2$	143,641 + 152,358$(x - 5)$ + 66,931$(x - 5)^2$ + 15,586$(x - 5)^3$	143,641 + 152,358$(x - 5)$ + 66,931$(x - 5)^2$ + 15,586$(x - 5)^3$ + 2029$(x - 5)^4$	143,641 + 152,358$(x - 5)$ + 66,931$(x - 5)^2$ + 15,586$(x - 5)^3$ + 2029$(x - 5)^4$ + 140$(x - 5)^5$

e. $12(x - 3) + 8$

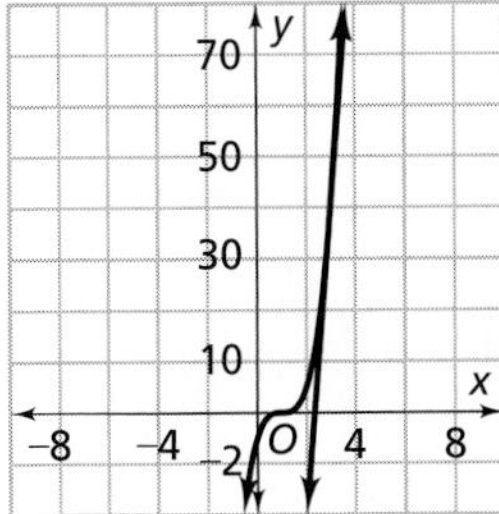

f. 0

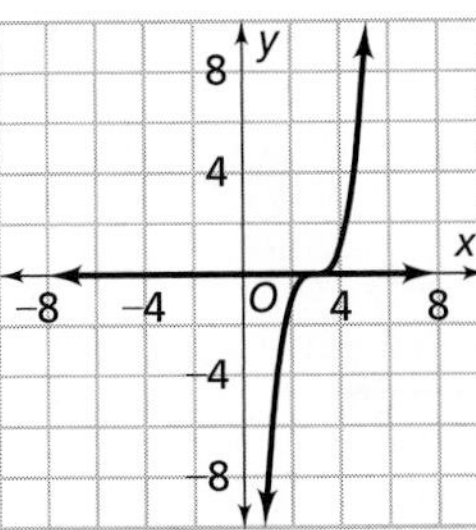

Lesson 3.5 **pp. 197–202**

For You to Do **6.** See Figure 4.
Exercises **4.** See Figure 5.
5. See Figure 6. **9.** See Figure 7.

Mathematical Reflections p. 203

1a. Expression 2 shows the x-intercepts: $(-1, 0)$, $(3, 0)$, and $(4, 0)$, and allows you to find the y-intercept $(0, 12)$. You can also use the signs of the factors to determine the sign of the function.

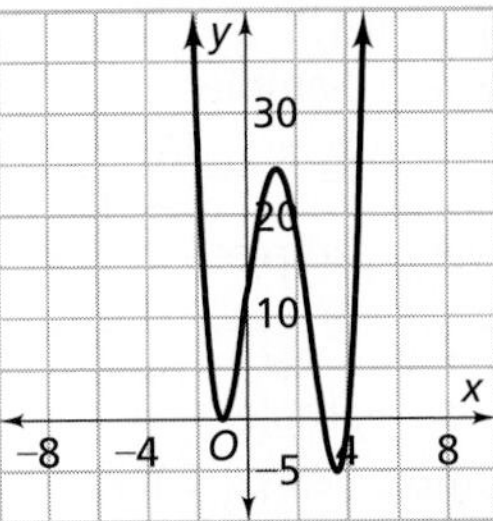

b. Read off the last two terms in Expression 3 to find the equation of the tangent, which is $y = 4(x - 1) + 24 = 4x + 20$. **2.** Answers may vary. Samples: **a.** There is no graph of a third-degree polynomial without an x-intercept, by the Odd Degree Theorem. Non-real roots come in conjugate pairs, so there could be a pair of non-real roots, but the third factor necessitated by the odd degree of the polynomial guarantees that there is at least one real root for any third degree polynomial equation.

b.

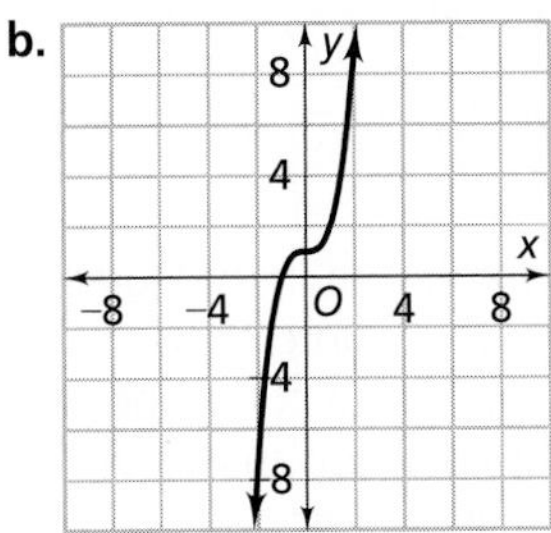

c.

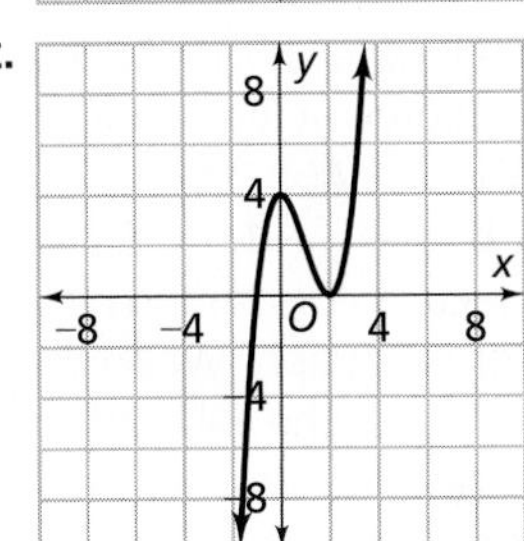

Figure 4

x	$y = x^2$	Slope of the tangent at (x, x^2)
−1	1	−2
0	0	0
1	1	2
2	4	4
3	9	6
4	16	8
10	100	20
100	10,000	200

Figure 5

x	$f(x)$	Slope of tangent at $(x, f(x))$
−1	2	−2
0	1	0
1	2	2
2	5	4
3	10	6
4	17	8
10	101	20
100	10,001	200

Figure 6

x	$f(x)$	Slope of the tangent at $(x, f(x))$
−1	0	−1
0	0	1
1	2	3
2	6	5
3	12	7
4	20	9
10	110	21
100	10,100	201

Figure 7

x	$f(x)$	Slope of the tangent at $(x, f(x))$
−1	−1	3
0	0	0
1	1	3
2	8	12
3	27	27
4	64	48
10	1000	300
100	1,000,000	30,000

d.

e. There is no graph of a third-degree polynomial with four x-intercepts, because each x-intercept corresponds to a factor of the polynomial by the Factor Theorem. If a graph has four x-intercepts, it has at least four factors, and must have degree at least four.
3a. $f(x) = (x + 4)^3 - 4(x + 4)^2 - 11(x + 4) - 6$ **b.** $y = -11x - 50$
4. Each of the factors corresponds to an x-intercept of the graph. When that factor is equal to zero, the value of the function is also zero. It's also fairly easy to substitute $x = 0$ into the factored form of a polynomial to find the y-intercept. You can also use the signs of the factors to determine the sign of the function at any value of x.

Lesson 3.6 **pp. 205–208**

For You to Explore

2.

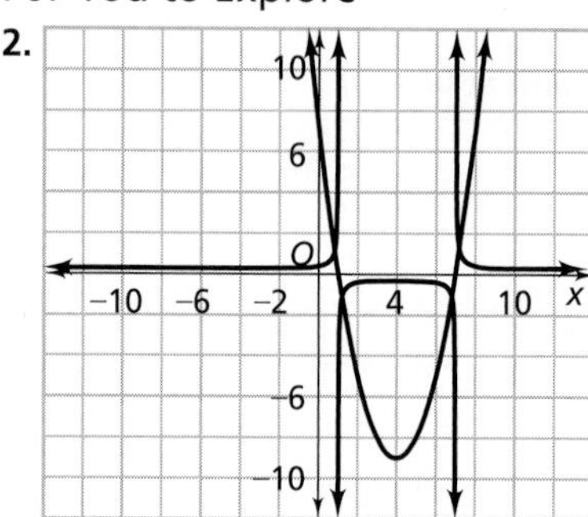

3b.

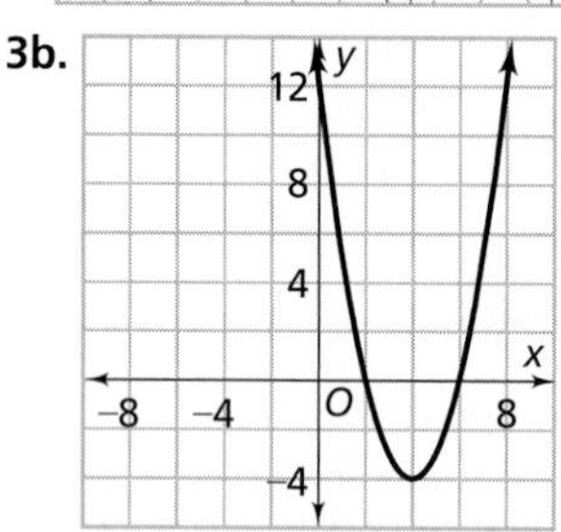

c.

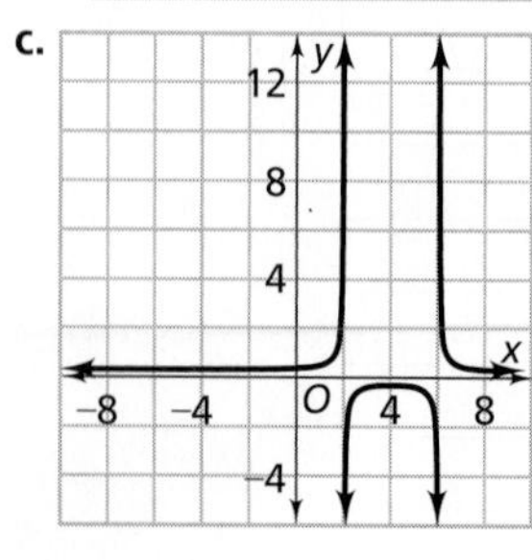

4b. Near $x = 3$, $f(x)$ has a vertical asymptote. As x approaches 3 from the left, $f(x)$ approaches $-\infty$. As x approaches 3 from the right, $f(x)$ approaches ∞. However, $g(x)$ does not have an asymptote at $x = 3$. Instead it has a hole at $\left(3, \frac{1}{6}\right)$.
5a. Answers may vary. Sample: $f(x) = \dfrac{(x - 3)(x - 5)}{x - 1} = \dfrac{x^2 - 8x + 15}{x - 1}$
b. Answers may vary. Sample: $f(x) = \dfrac{2}{(x - 3)(x - 5)} = \dfrac{2}{x^2 - 8x + 15}$
c. Answers may vary. Sample: $f(x) = \dfrac{1}{x - 2}$ **d.** Answers may vary. Sample: $f(x) = \dfrac{3x^2}{x^2 + 2x + 1}$
6b. $f(x) = \dfrac{3x}{x - 2}$

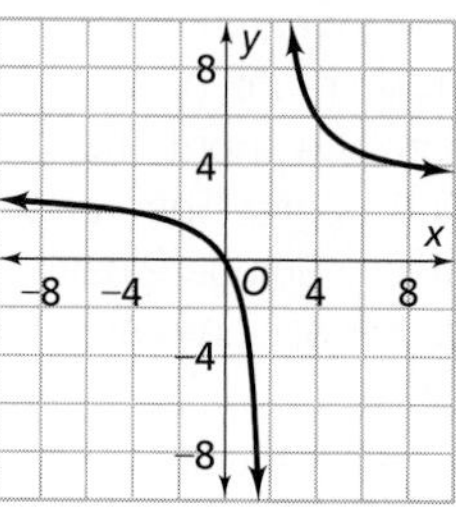

c. $f(x) = \dfrac{1}{x^2 - 1}$

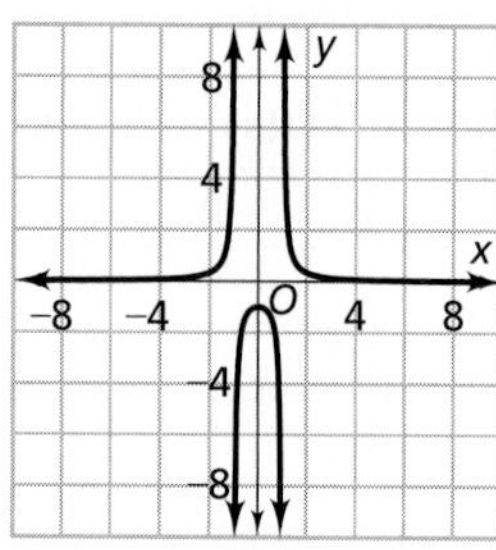

d. $f(x) = \dfrac{-1}{x^2 - 1}$

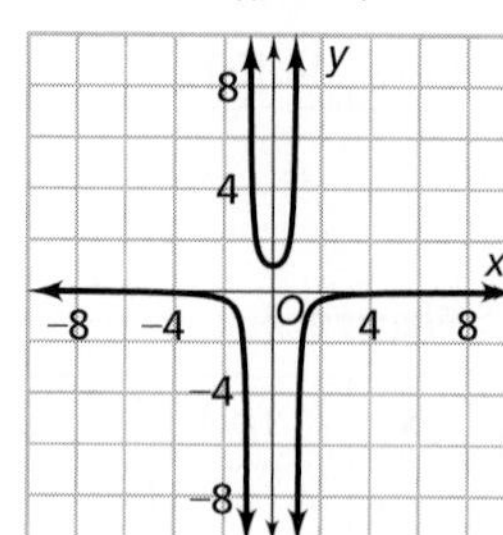

e. $f(x) = \dfrac{x - 2}{x^2 - 4}$

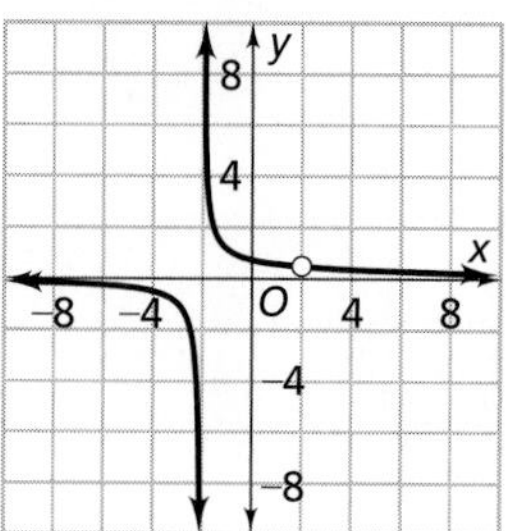

f. $f(x) = \dfrac{1}{x^3}$

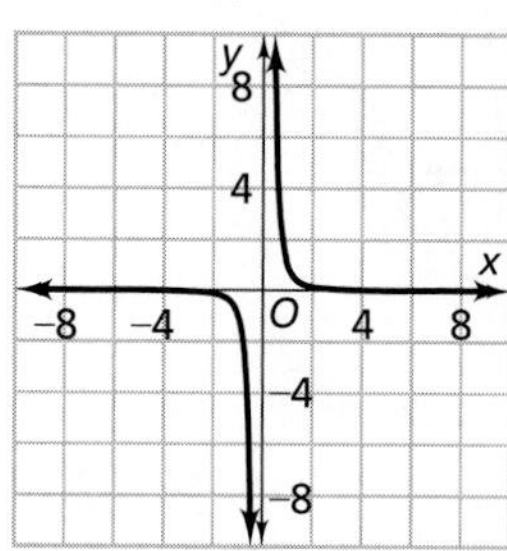

g. $f(x) = \dfrac{x^2 - 1}{x^3 - 1}$

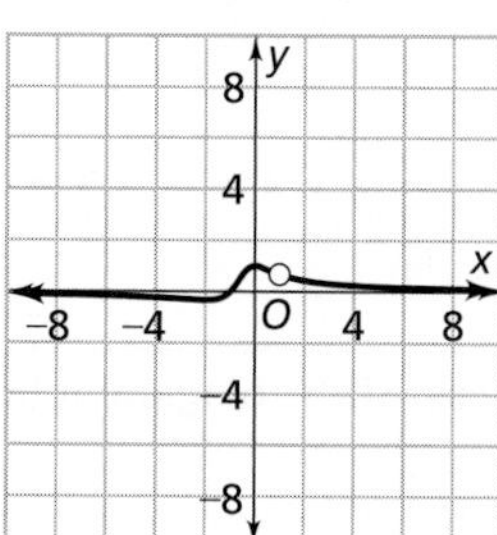

h. $f(x) = \dfrac{3}{x^4 - 1}$

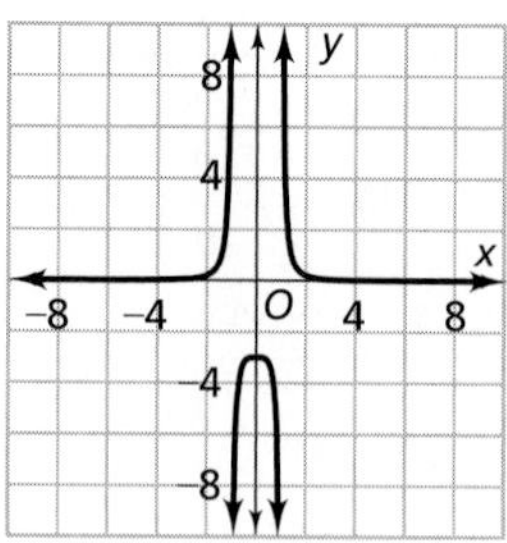

i. $f(x) = \dfrac{x^2}{x^4 - 1}$

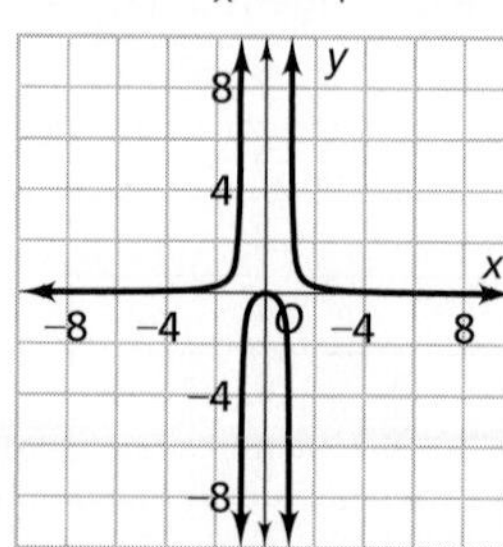

j. $f(x) = \dfrac{x^2 - 9}{x - 2}$

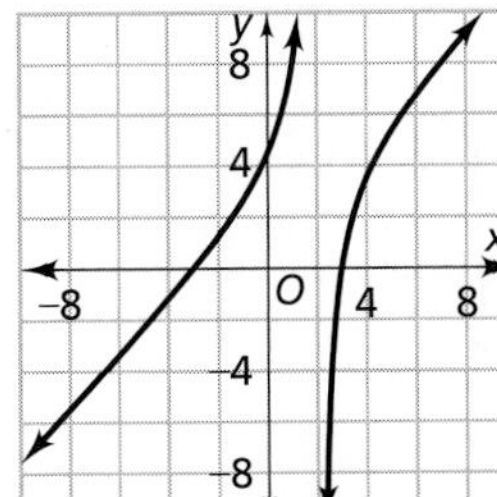

7a. You can see that when $x > 0$, $h(x) = 1$; when $x < 0$, $h(x) = -1$. 0 is not in the domain because the function here is undefined. **b.** As x approaches 0 coming from the negative numbers, the limit is -1, but if x approaches 0 from the positive numbers the limit is 1.

8a. $j(100) \approx 100$ and $j(0.01) \approx 100$
b. $x = 1$ **c.** For any value of x we have:

$$(x - 1)^2 \geq 0$$
$$x^2 - 2x + 1 \geq 0$$
$$x^2 + 1 \geq 2x$$

For $x > 0$, you can divide both sides by x, and the inequality stays the same way.

$$\frac{x^2 + 1}{x} \geq \frac{2x}{x}$$
$$j(x) = x + \frac{1}{x} \geq 2$$

Exercises

11.

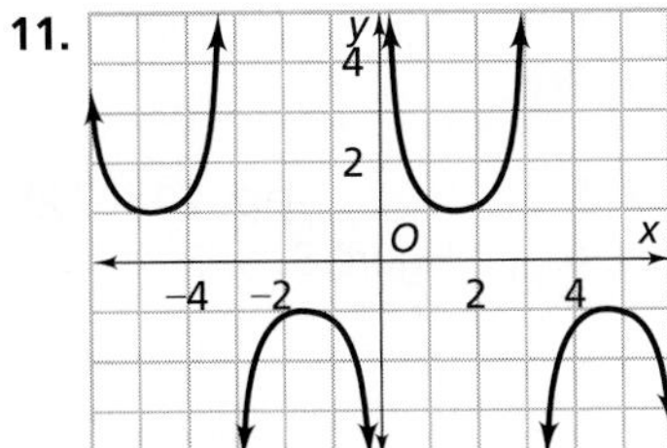

12a.

x	$k(x)$
0	2
1	3
2	4
3	not defined
4	6

15a.

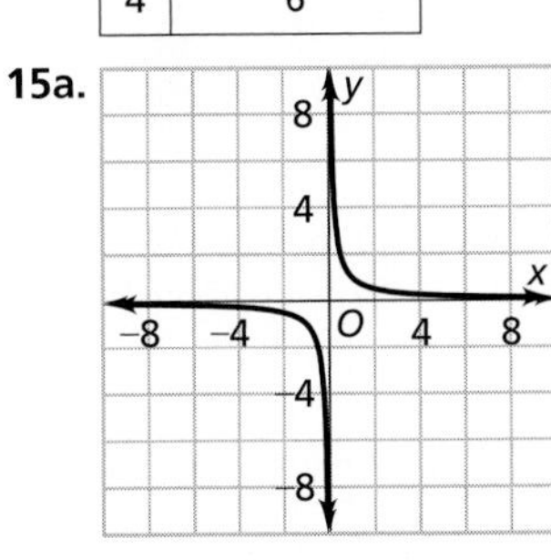

b.

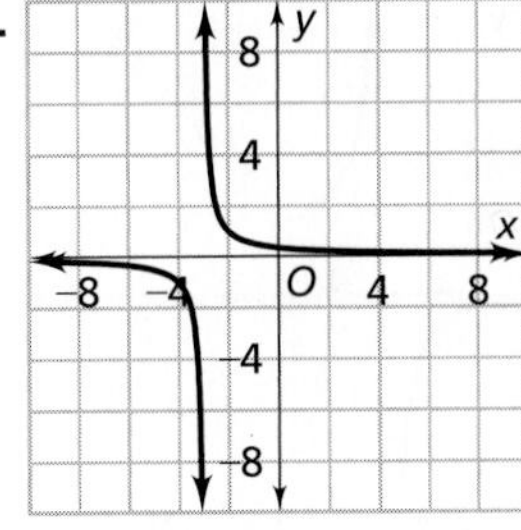

c.

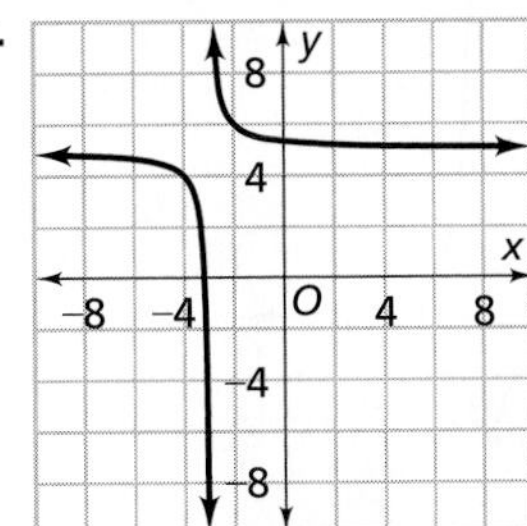

d.

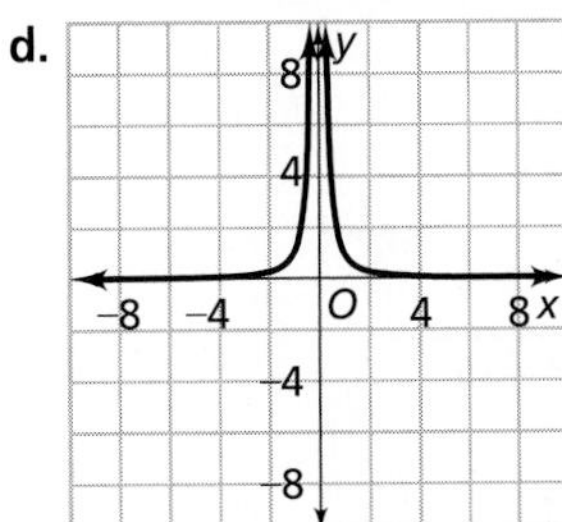

e.

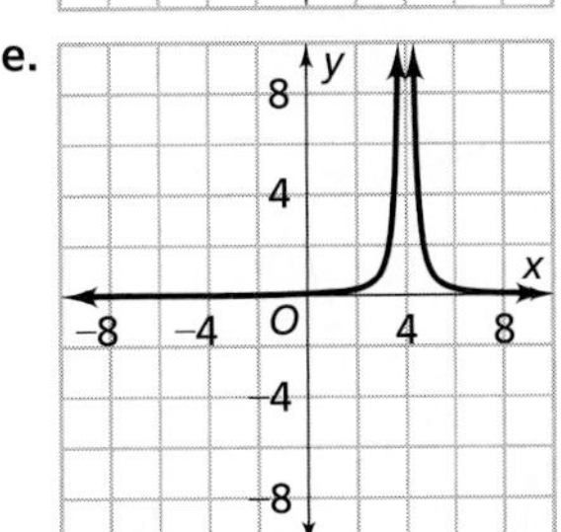

f.

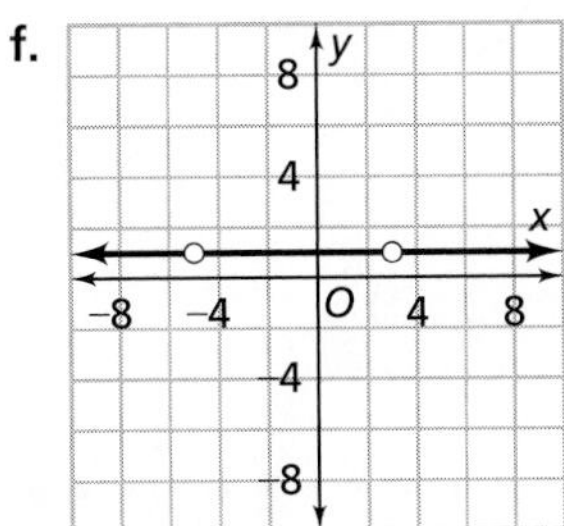

16a.

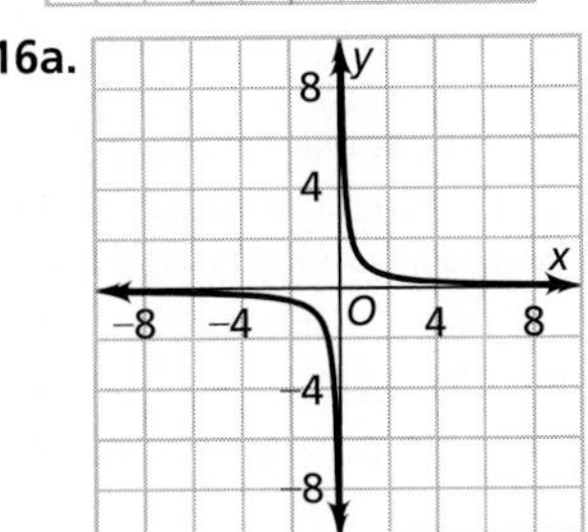

b.

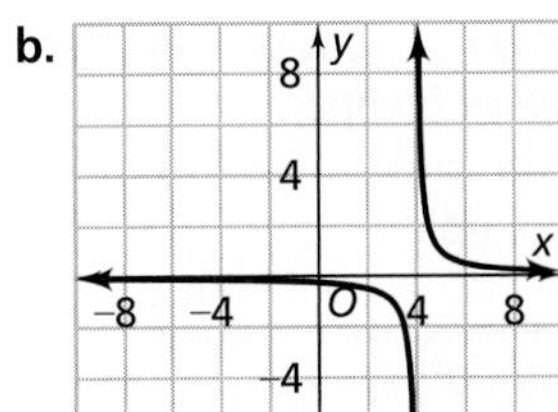

c.

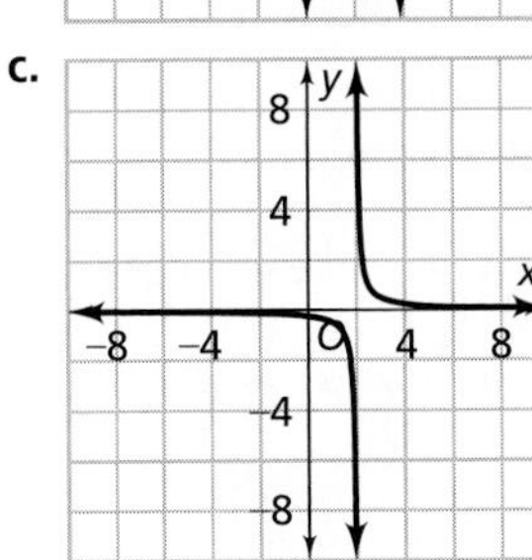

d.

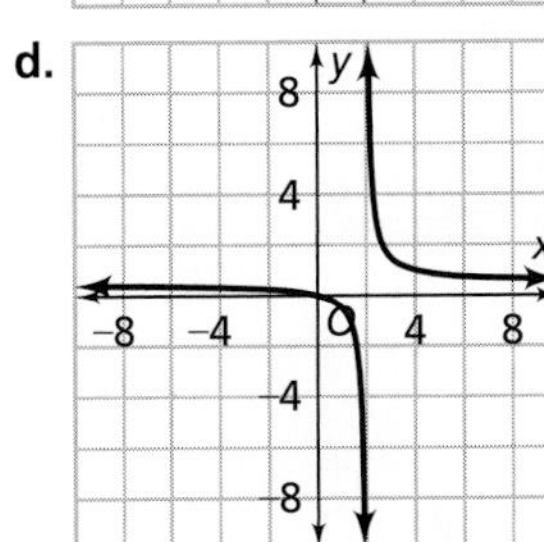

e.

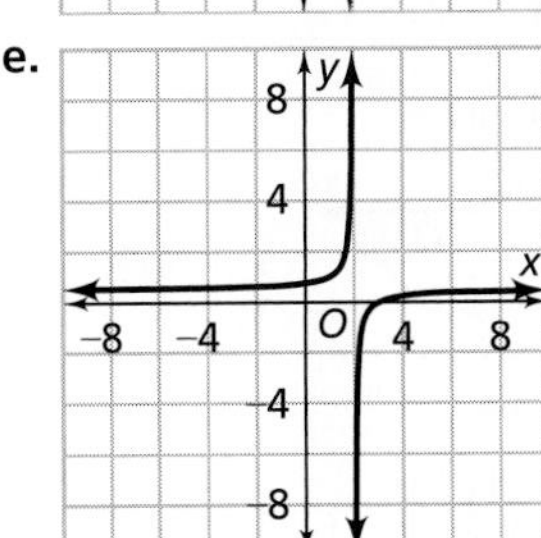

f.

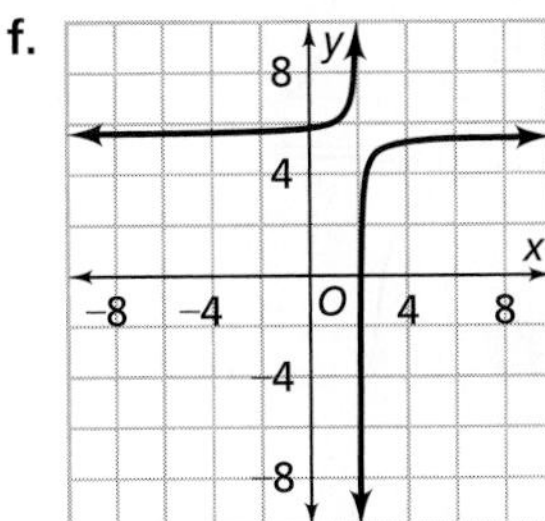

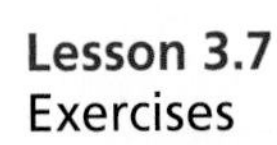

Lesson 3.7 **pp. 209–217**

Exercises

13a.

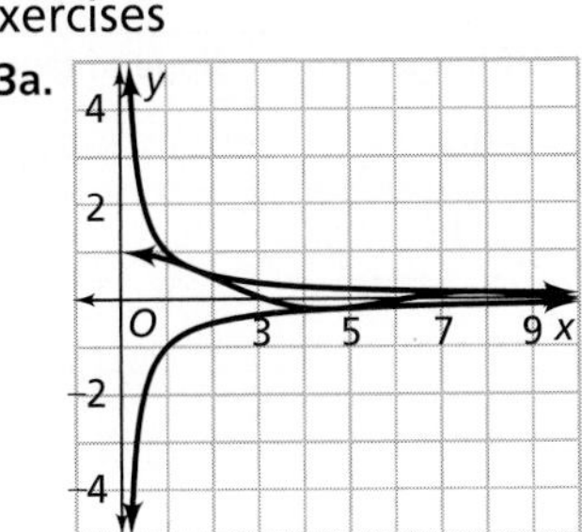

14. Answers may vary, but should include the idea of comparing the degree of the numerator and denominator. Samples:

- The function $f(x) = \frac{x}{x^2 - 2}$ has a horizontal asymptote at 0.
- The function $f(x) = \frac{cx}{x - 2}$ has a horizontal asymptote at $y = c$.
- The function $f(x) = \frac{x^2}{x - 2}$ has no horizontal asymptote.

16a. $\frac{1}{x + 2} - \frac{1}{x + 3} = \frac{x + 3 - (x + 2)}{(x + 2)(x + 3)}$

$= \frac{1}{(x + 2)(x + 3)} = \frac{1}{x^2 + 5x + 6}$

$= \frac{1}{(x + 2)(x + 3)}$

b.

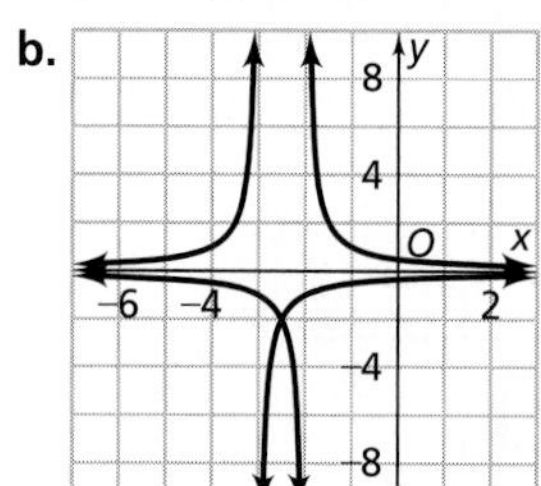

c.

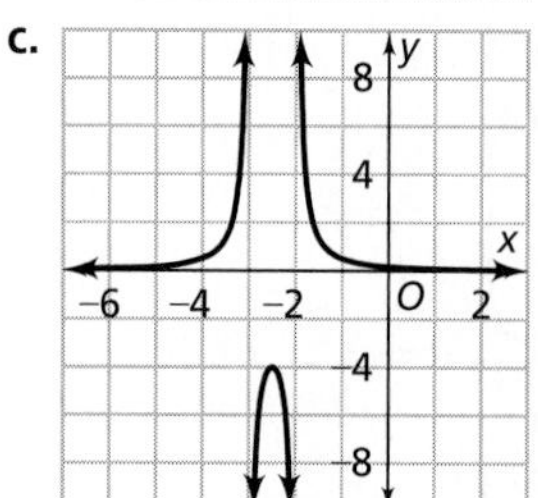

17b.

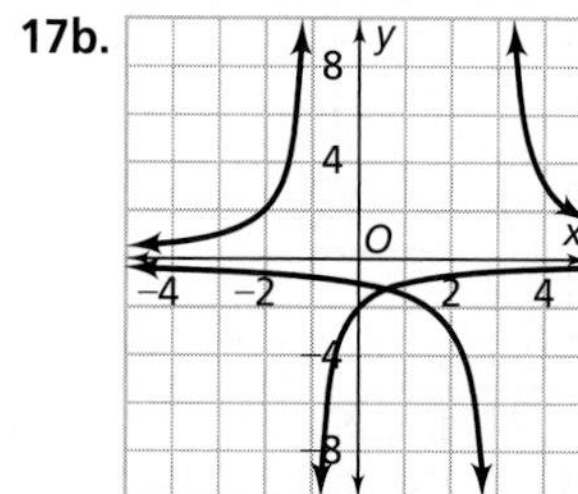

c.

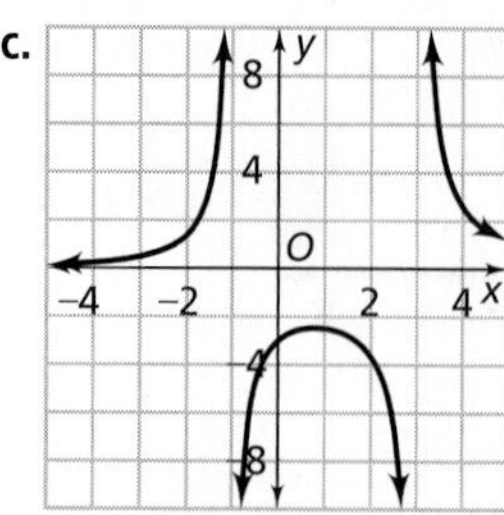

19a.

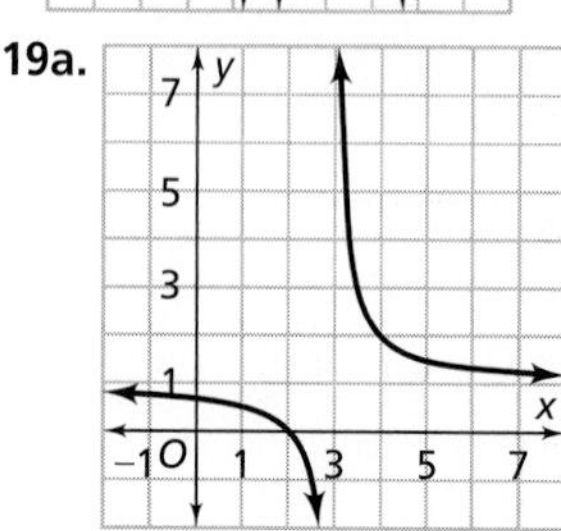

b.

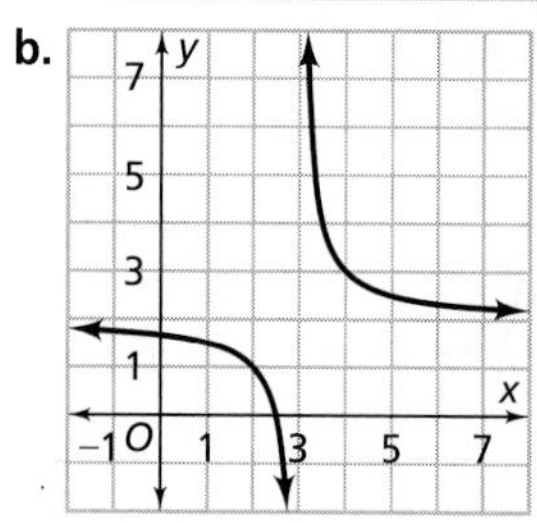

c.

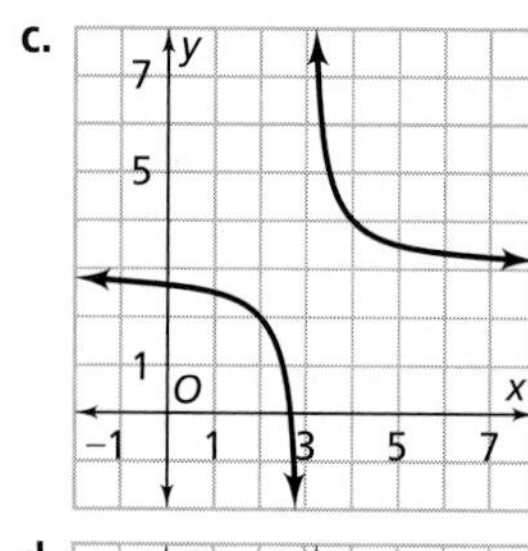

d.

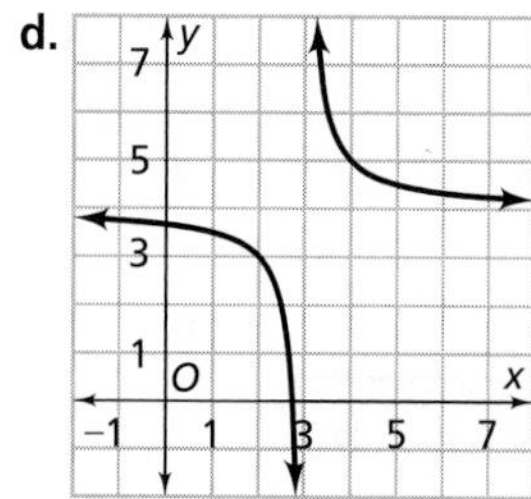

22b.

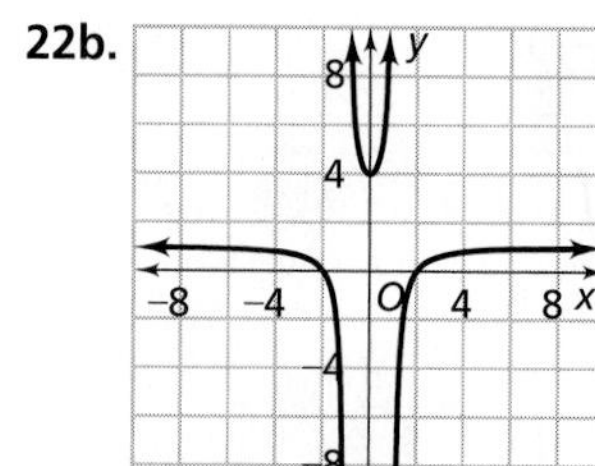

c.

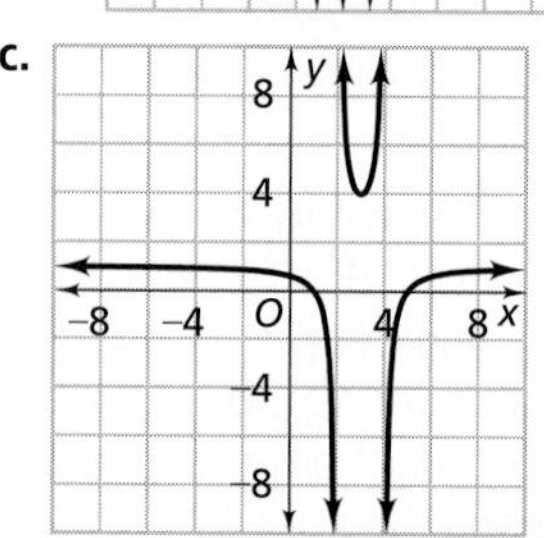

d.

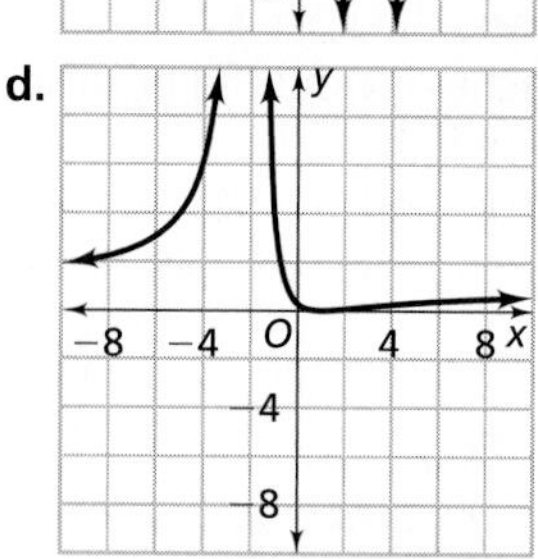

e.

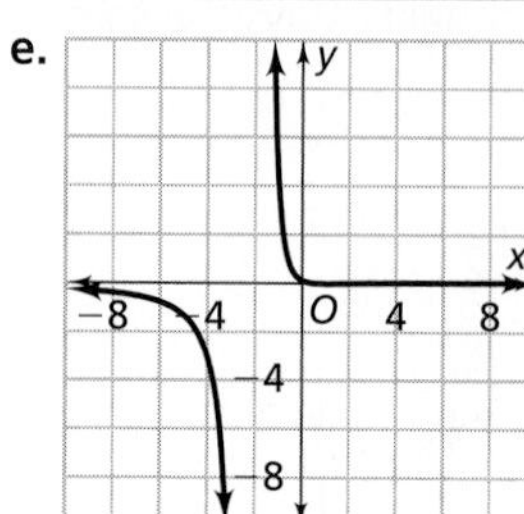

Lesson 3.8 **pp. 218–225**

Exercises **4.** See Figure 8.

Figure 8

x	Slope of tangent to f	Slope of tangent to h
$\frac{1}{10}$	-100	-2000
$\frac{1}{4}$	-16	-128
$\frac{1}{2}$	-4	-16
1	-1	-2
2	$-\frac{1}{4}$	$-\frac{1}{4}$
4	$-\frac{1}{16}$	$-\frac{1}{32}$
10	$-\frac{1}{100}$	$-\frac{1}{500}$

This makes sense because the slope of the tangent to the graph of f must be negative everywhere, but the slope of the tangent to the graph of h will be positive for negative values of x and negative for positive values of x.

7b. 2;

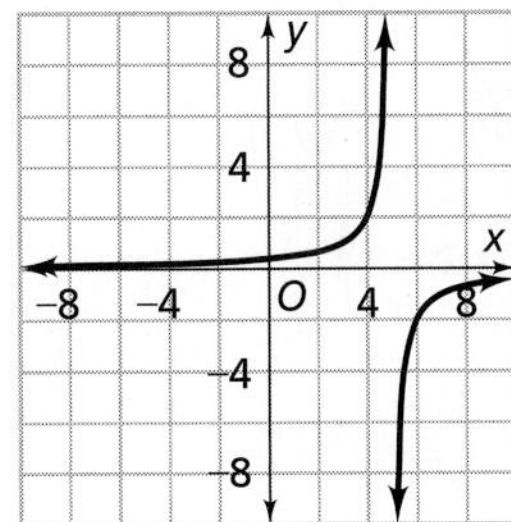

c. $\frac{1}{2}$;

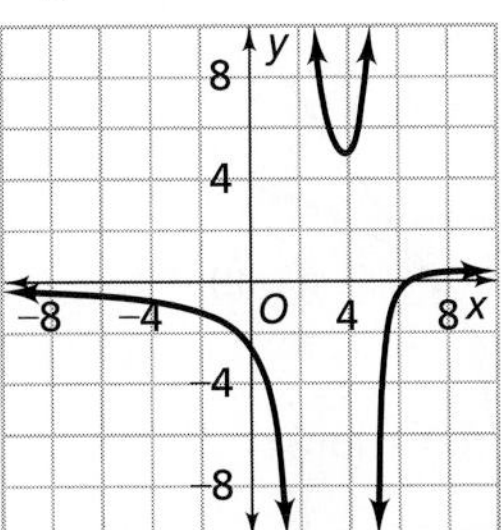

10. See Figure 9.

15a–d.

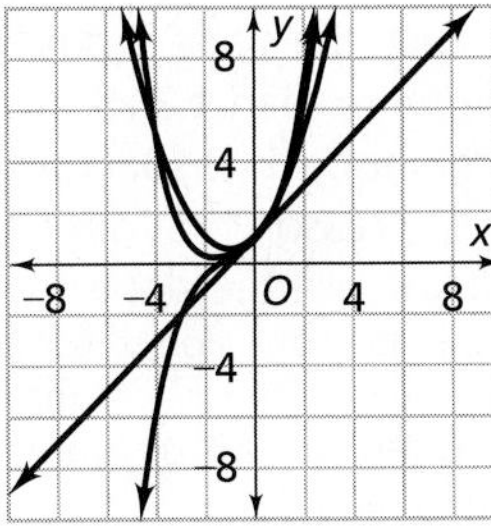

Lesson 3.9 **pp. 226–235**

Exercises

8a.

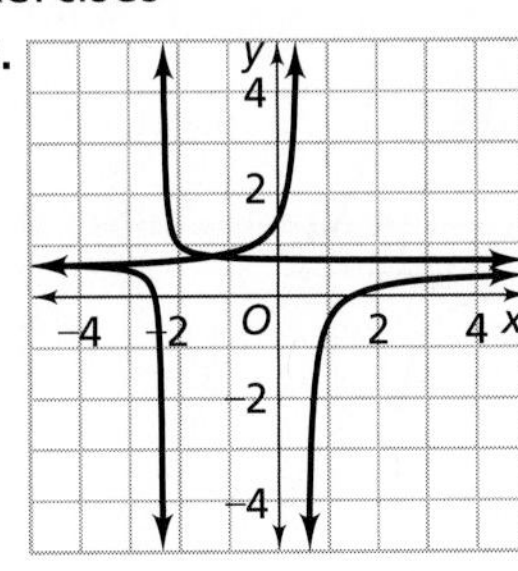

b. $C = \begin{pmatrix} 6 & 11 \\ -2 & -5 \end{pmatrix}$

c. $D = \begin{pmatrix} -23 & 16 \\ -34 & 24 \end{pmatrix}$

9a.

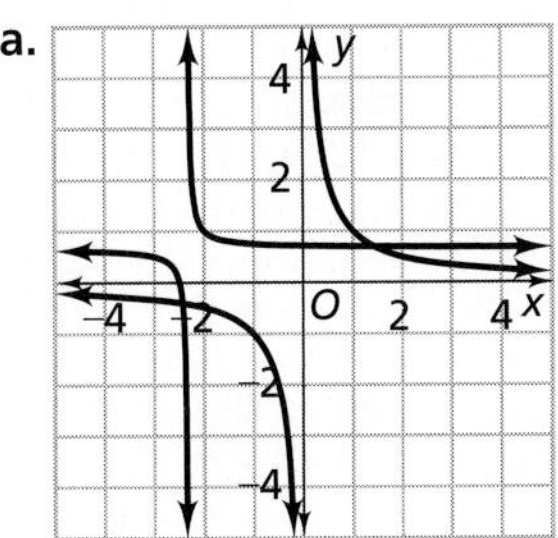

b. $T_g = T_{\frac{2}{3}}$ and $\mathcal{A}_{(e,\,f)} = \mathcal{A}_{(9,\,21)}$

c. Scale horizontally by a factor of $\frac{1}{9}$, then translate $\frac{7}{3}$ units left and $\frac{2}{3}$ units up.

11. $f(x)$ has no vertical asymptotes because its denominator is never 0. This is because $x^2 + 1 = 0$ has no real solution.

12.

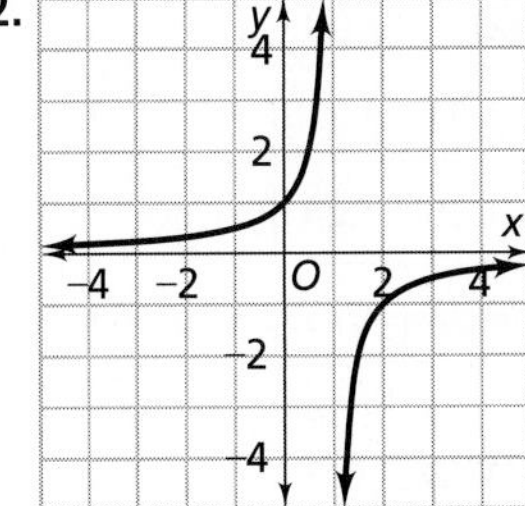

13a.

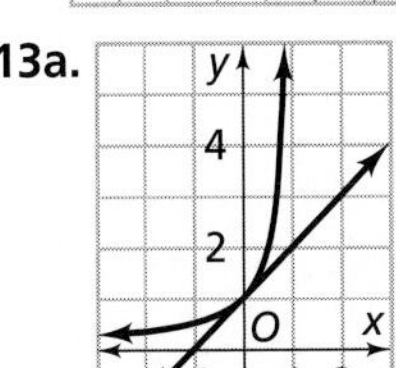

b.

x	$f(x)$	$g(x)$
0.1	$\frac{10}{9} \approx 1.1$	1.1
0.2	$\frac{5}{4} = 1.25$	1.2
0.5	2	1.5
0.8	5	1.8

c.

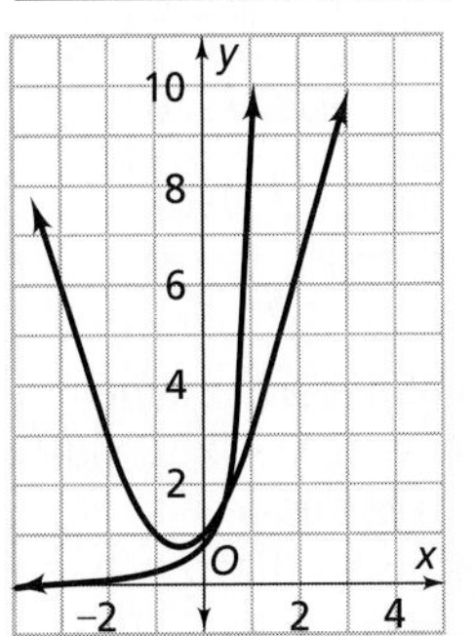

Figure 9

x	Slope of tangent to f	Slope of tangent to g
-2	$-\frac{1}{4}$	$\frac{3}{4}$
-1	-1	0
$-\frac{1}{2}$	-4	-3
0	undefined	undefined
$\frac{1}{2}$	-4	-3
1	-1	0
2	$-\frac{1}{4}$	$\frac{3}{4}$
3	$-\frac{1}{9}$	$\frac{8}{9}$

d.

x	$f(x)$	$h(x)$
0.1	$\frac{10}{9} \approx 1.11$	1.11
0.2	$\frac{5}{4} = 1.25$	1.24
0.5	2	1.75
0.8	5	2.44

e.

f.

x	$f(x)$	$j(x)$
0.1	$\frac{10}{9} \approx 1.11$	1.11111
0.2	$\frac{5}{4} = 1.25$	1.24992
0.5	2	1.96875
0.8	5	3.68928
1.1	−10	7.71561

14a. $\sqrt{A}$ **b.** $(x - \sqrt{A})^2 \geq 0$, which after expansion and rearrangement leads to $x^2 + A \geq (2\sqrt{A})x$. Divide both sides by x to obtain $x + \frac{A}{x} \geq 2\sqrt{A}$, which says that $2\sqrt{A}$ is the minimum value of $x + \frac{A}{x}$. This minimum value is the output when $x = \sqrt{A}$.

Mathematical Reflections p. 236

1. Answers may vary. Samples:

a. $f(x) = \frac{x^2 - 3x}{x - 3}$

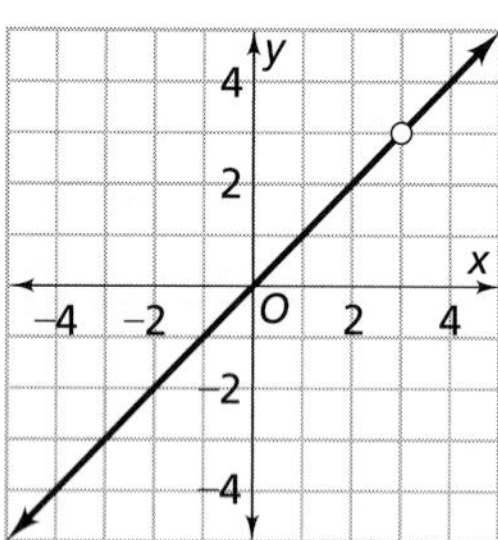

b. $f(x) = \frac{1}{x - 3}$

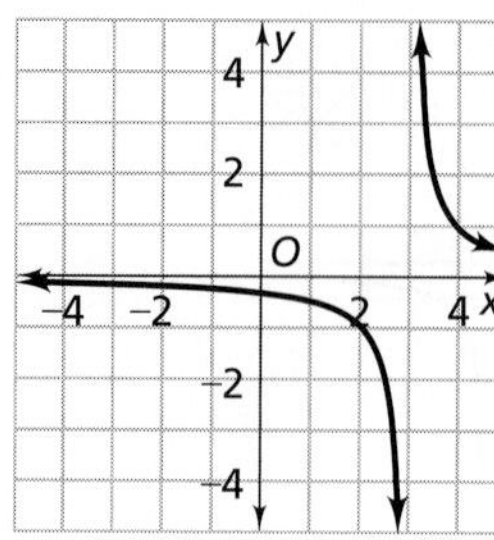

2. Answers may vary. Samples:

a. $f(x) = \frac{1}{x}$

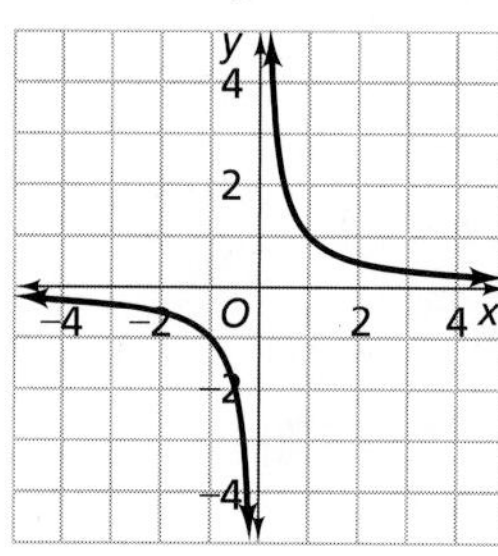

b. $f(x) = \frac{2x}{x - 3}$

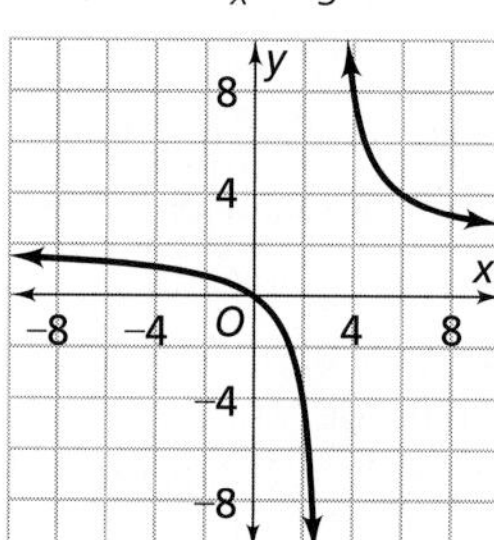

3c.

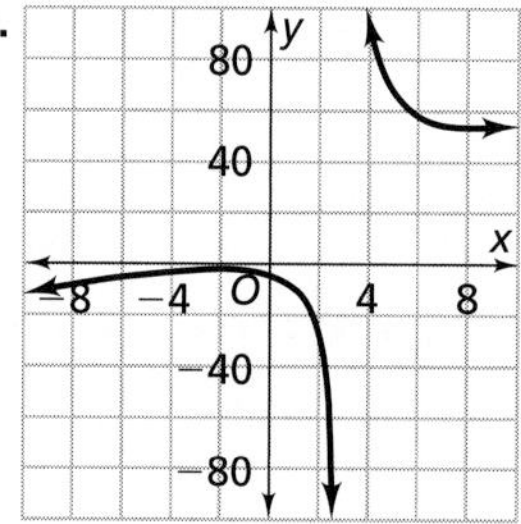

Lesson 3.10 pp. 239–241

For You to Explore

3a.

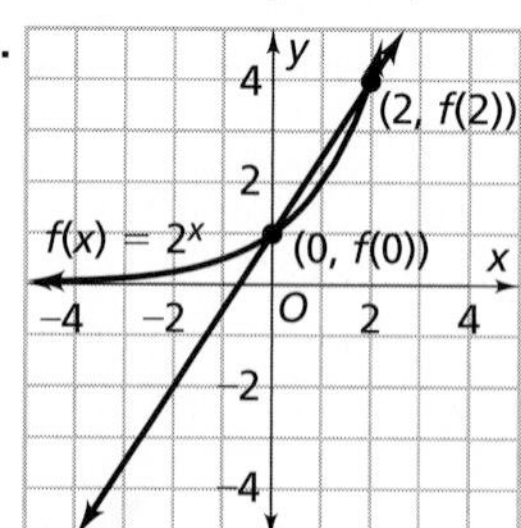

The slope of the secant is $\frac{3}{2}$.

b.

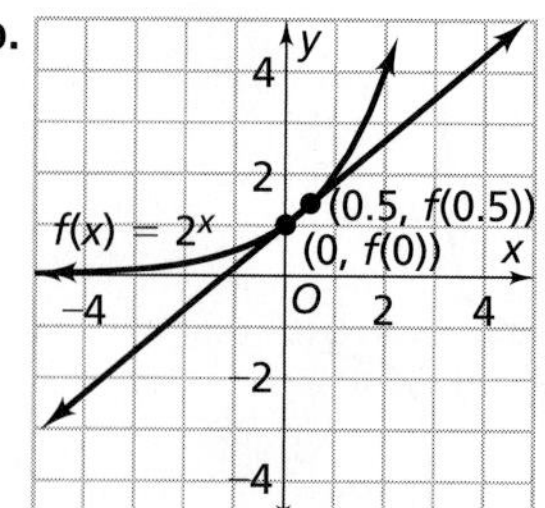

The slope of the secant is $2\sqrt{2} - 2 \approx 0.828$.

Exercises

7b.

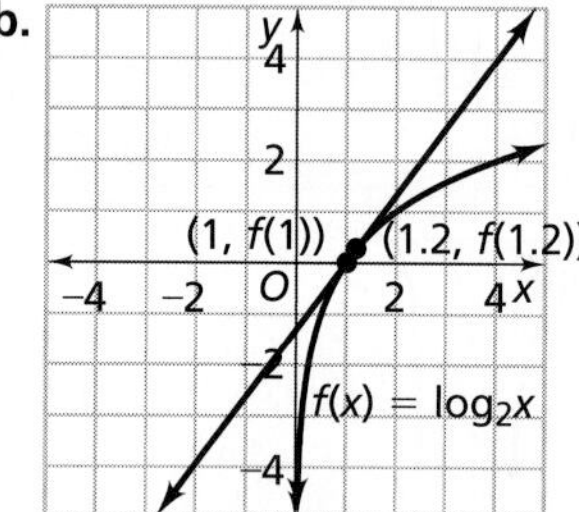

The slope of the secant is approximately 1.315. **c.** Since the slope is positive and a little more than 1.315, a good estimate might be 1.4. **10.** From the table you can reason that b is between 2 and 3. If you use the slope formula: $\frac{\log_b 1.0001 - \log_b 0}{01.0001 - 1} = \frac{\log_b 0.0001 - 0}{0.0001}$ and try different values of b, a good estimate is $b = 2.72$.

11a. $1 + x + \frac{x^2}{4}$ **b.** $1 + x + \frac{x^2}{3} + \frac{x^3}{27}$

c. $1 + x + \frac{3x^2}{8} + \frac{x^3}{16} + \frac{x^4}{256}$

12a. $f(1, 1) = 2$, $f(1, 2) = 2.25$, $f(1, 3) = 2.37037$, $f(1, 4) = 2.441406$, $f(1, 10) = 2.593742$, $f(1, 100) = 2.704874$, $f(1, 10{,}000) = 2.718146$

b. $f(2, 1) = 3$, $f(2, 2) = 4$, $f(2, 3) = 4.629630$, $f(2, 4) = 5.0625$, $f(2, 10) = 6.191736$, $f(2, 100) = 7.244646$, $f(2, 10{,}000) = 7.387579$

c. $f(0.05, 1) = 1.05$, $f(0.05, 4) = 1.05095$, $f(0.05, 12) = 1.05116$, $f(0.05, 365) = 1.05127$, $f(0.05, 10{,}000) = 1.051271$

Lesson 3.11 pp. 242–247

Exercises **13.**

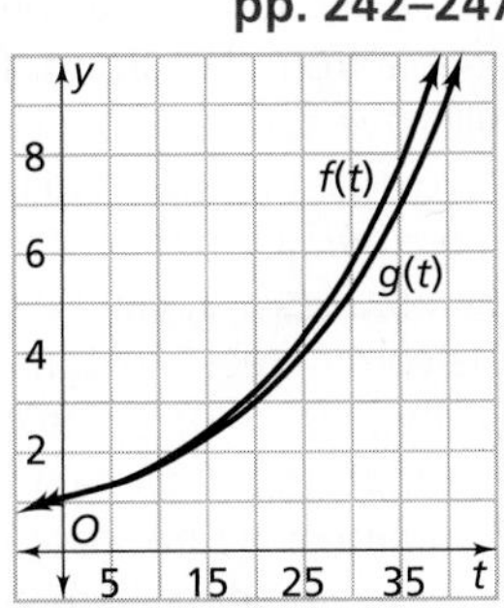

17c. $1 + x + \frac{9x^2}{20} + \frac{3x^3}{25}$

d. $1 + x + \frac{(n-1)x^2}{2!n} + \frac{(n-1)(n-2)x^3}{3!n^2}$

18a. 1 **b.** $\frac{1}{2}$ **c.** $\frac{1}{3!} = \frac{1}{6}$ **d.** $\frac{1}{4!} = \frac{1}{24}$
e. $\frac{1}{5!} = \frac{1}{120}$

Lesson 3.12 pp. 248–253

Exercises **6a.**

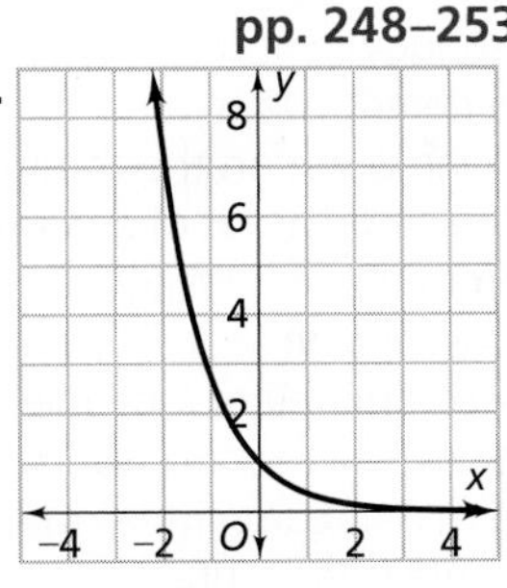

b.

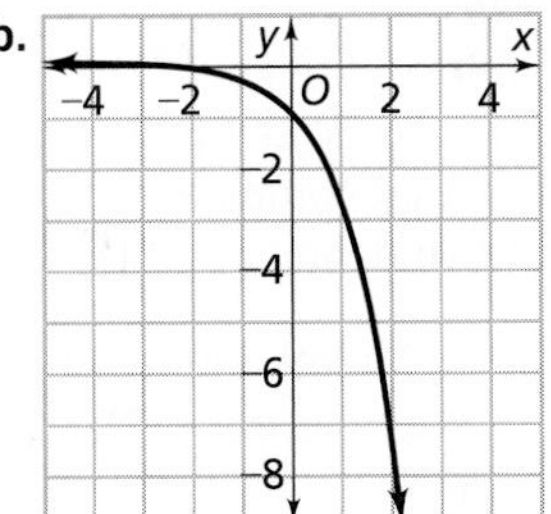

c.

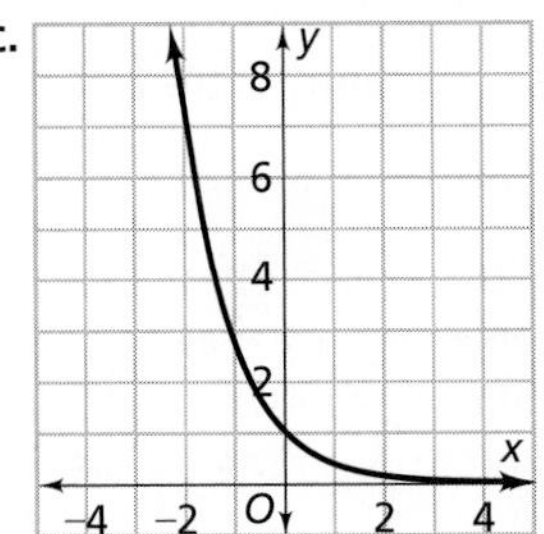

8b. $c(0.2) = 1.22133333333$, $f(0.2) = 1.22140275816$, -0.00568%; $c(0.5) = 1.64583333333$, $f(0.5) = 1.6487212707$, -0.17516%; $c(1) = 2.666666666667$, $f(1) = 2.71828182846$, -1.89882%; $c(2) = 6.33333333$, $f(2) = 7.38905609893$; -14.28765%

11.

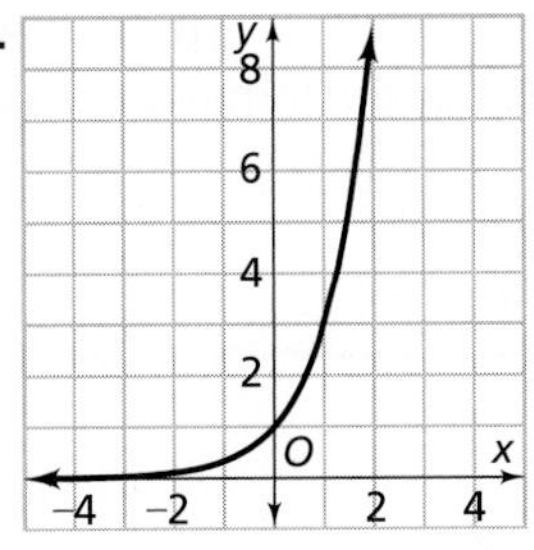

12a. Sketch of a proof: Rewrite $1 - \frac{1}{n}$ to $\frac{n-1}{n}$ to $\frac{1}{\frac{n}{n-1}}$ then make the substitution $k = n - 1$. Then it is $\frac{1}{\left(1 + \frac{1}{k}\right)^{k+1}}$ but the limit makes $k + 1$ and k the same, and you are done.

b. Sketch of proof: Substitute $\frac{x}{n} = \frac{1}{-K} \Rightarrow n = -Kx$ where $K > 0$. Show that $\left(\lim_{K\to\infty}\left(1 - \frac{1}{K}\right)^K\right)^{-x} = (e^{-1})^{-x}$.

Lesson 3.13 pp. 254–259

In-Class Experiment

1.

x	ln x
0	undefined
1	0
2	0.69315
3	1.09861
4	1.38629
5	1.60944
6	1.79176
7	1.94591
8	2.07944
9	2.19722
10	2.30259

Lesson 3.14 pp. 260–265

Exercises **2c.** ln 5^5

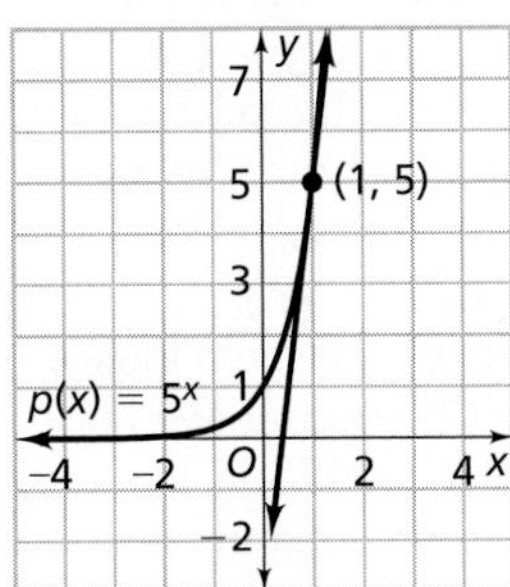

Mathematical Reflections p. 266

6. The more frequently you compound the interest, the greater your yield, but there is an upper bound. As the number of times you compound the interest increases, the limit is *continuous compounding,* so that the total amount b that an investment of P dollars at interest rate r over a period of t years is worth is $b = Pe^{rt}$.

Project pp. 267–269

6a. $A + B = 2$
$-5A - 2B = -13$

b. $A = 3, B = -1$

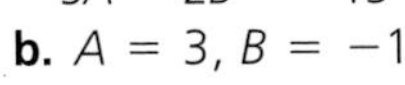

c.

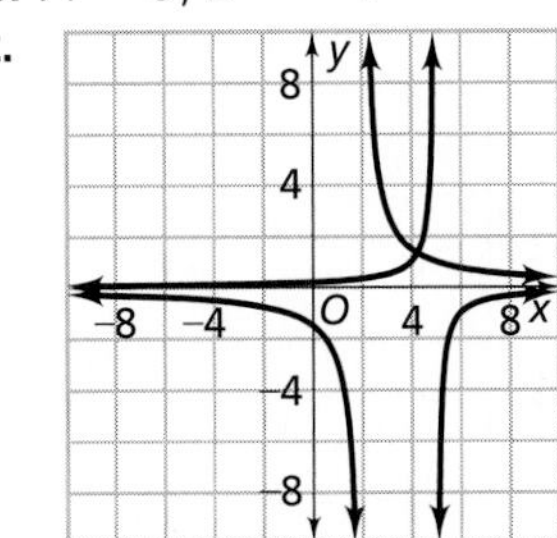

d.

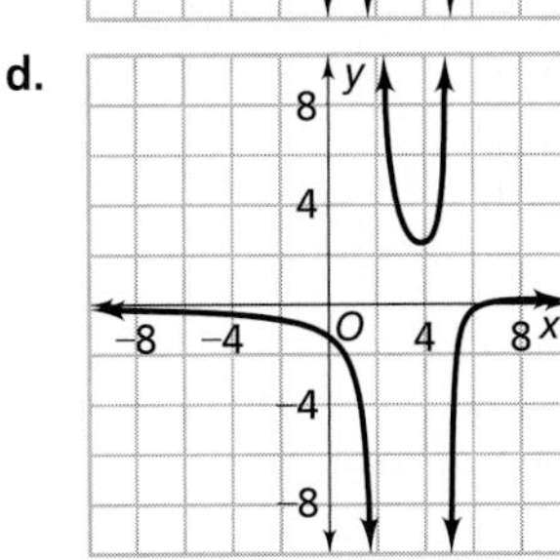

7a. $A = -\frac{19}{3}, B = \frac{31}{3}$

b.

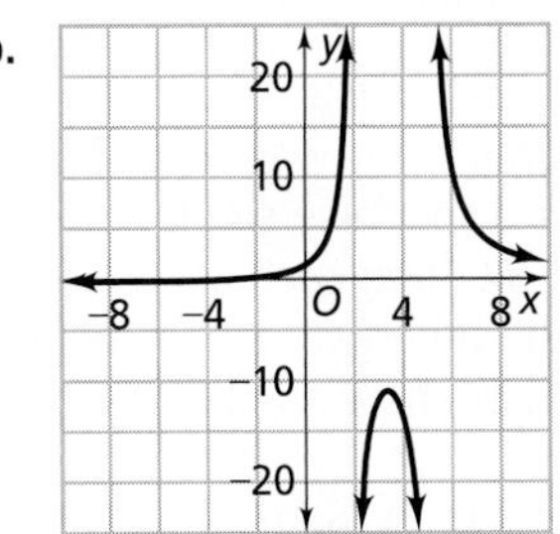

8a. $A = 6, B = 0$

b.

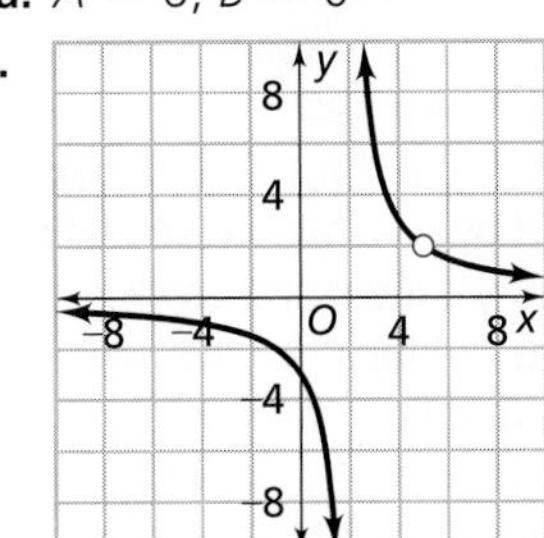

The graph is just like that of $y = \frac{6}{x - 2}$, except for a hole at (5, 2).

12a. The quotient is $x + 3$ and the remainder is $2x - 13$.

b. 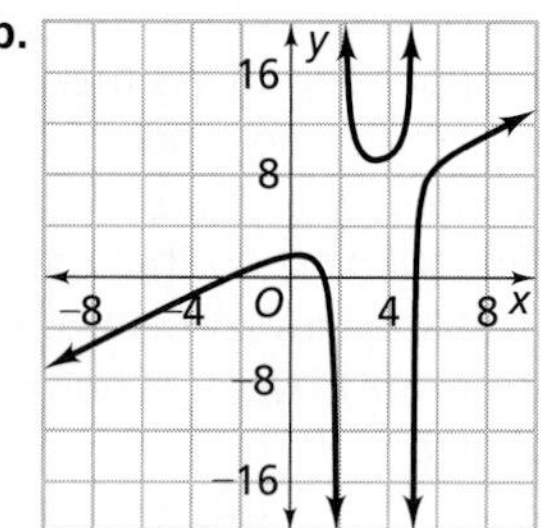

c. $A = 1, B = 3, C = 3, D = 1$

13c.

n	$p(n)$
0	0
1	1
2	1
3	2
4	3
5	5
6	8
7	13
8	21
9	34
10	55

Chapter 4

Lesson 4.2 pp. 279–284

Exercises 14a. Answers may vary. Sample:

- If 27 people are evenly separated into groups of 9, how many groups will there be?
- Derman's baseball team has 9 players on it. They wanted to buy their coach a special jersey. If the jersey cost \$27 and each of the players contributed an equal amount to its purchase, how much did each player pay?

b. Answers may vary. Sample:

- Sarah volunteered for community service for three weeks in a row. The first week she worked 6 hours, and she increased the number of hours she worked by one each week. How many hours total did she work?
- Sasha has 6 goldfish, Tony, has 7 goldfish, and Derman has 8 goldfish. How many goldfish do they have together?

Lesson 4.7 pp. 304–315

Exercises 6. Use the formulas for ${}_nC_k$ and ${}_nP_k$:

$$\begin{aligned} {}_nC_k &= \frac{{}_nP_k}{k!} \\ &= \frac{n!}{(n-k)! \cdot k!} \\ &= \frac{n!}{(n-k)! \cdot [n-(n-k)]!} \\ &= \frac{{}_nP_{n-k}}{(n-k)!} \\ &= {}_nC_{n-k} \end{aligned}$$

9. Answers may vary. Sample: to find ${}_nP_k$, you count all of the different ways you can pick k objects from a set of n objects and line them up in a row. To find ${}_nC_k$, you count all of the different ways you can pick k objects from a set of n objects (without lining them up). So, to find permutations, you are finding all the combinations, and then also rearranging them. Combinations do not count the rearrangements since order does not matter with combinations. **11.** Answers may vary. Sample: suppose we have a group of 7 people, including a girl named Kira, and we want to choose a committee of 4 people from this group. There are ${}_7C_4$ ways to do this. Or, we can think of it in terms of the committees that contain and do not contain Kira:

${}_7C_4$ = number of possible committees Kira is on + of committee Kira is not on

If Kira is on the committee, then there are 6 people left who can fill the remaining 3 spots on the committee. So, there are ${}_6C_3$ different committees that can be made with Kira. If Kira is not on the committee, the entire committee needs to be chosen from the other 6 people. So, there are ${}_6C_4$ four-person committees that can be made without Kira. That is,

$${}_7C_4 = {}_6C_3 + {}_6C_4$$

13. The proof follows the same logic as Exercises 11 and 12. Suppose we have a group of n people (including Jan and at least one other person) and we would like to make a committee of k people from this group. The committee will have someone on it, and it will not have everyone on it (so $0 < k < n$). There are ${}_nC_k$ different possible committees that can be made. Since the committees must, have someone on them ($k > 0$), some of these committees will contain Jan. Since the committees do not contain everyone ($k < n$), some of them will not contain Jan. If Jan is on a committee, then there are $n - 1$ people remaining to fill the $k - 1$ remaining spot (and since $0 \leq k - 1 < n - 1$, it is possible to make a committee of $k - 1$ people from a group of $n - 1$ people, and if $k - 1 = 0$, then there's only 1 choice: nobody). So, there are ${}_{n-1}C_{k-1}$ different committees that contain Jan. If Jan is not on the committee, then the committees of k people must made from the remaining $n - 1$ people (and since $k \leq n - 1$, it is possible to make a committee of k people from a group of $n - 1$ people). So, there are ${}_{n-1}C_k$ different committees that do not contain Jan. Thus,

$${}_nC_k = {}_{n-1}C_{k-1} + {}_{n-1}C_k.$$

15. See Figure 10. **16.** To see that ${}_nC_k = \binom{n}{k}$, show that combinations satisfy the recursive definition of $\binom{n}{k}$:

$\binom{n}{0} = \binom{n}{n} = 1$ (far left and far right entries equal 1)

$\binom{n}{k} + \binom{n}{k+1} = \binom{n+1}{k+1}$ (sum of two entries is the entry is the entry below them)

That is, show that

$${}_nC_0 = {}_nC_n = 1$$
$${}_nC_k + {}_nC_{k+1} = {}_{n+1}C_{k+1}$$

But you have already shown these statements to be true, so the theorem is true.

Lesson 4.9 pp. 325–327

For You to Explore 3. Answers may vary, but should include 10 entries from the following diagram. See Figure 11.

Review p. 336

1. Answers may vary. Sample:

- Ian collects old records. He has 28 records in his collection. For his birthday, 2 of his friends each gave him 3 more records. How many records are in his collection now?
- During the first three quarters of its last game, the River High football team scored 28 points. But in the final quarter, they added 2 field goals at 3 points for each field goal. What was the final point total for River High?

Cumulative Review pp. 338–339

10a.

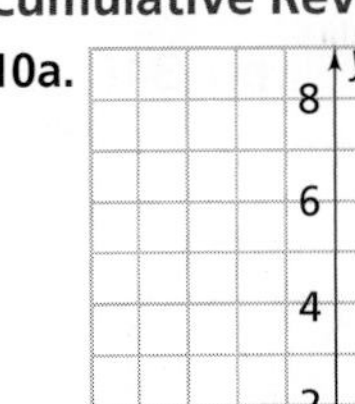

Figure 10

$_4C_0$ $_4C_1$ $_4C_2$ $_4C_3$ $_4C_4$
1 4 6 4 1

$_5C_0$ $_5C_1$ $_5C_2$ $_5C_3$ $_5C_4$ $_5C_5$
1 5 10 10 5 1

$_6C_0$ $_6C_1$ $_6C_2$ $_6C_3$ $_6C_4$ $_6C_5$ $_6C_6$
1 6 15 20 15 6 1

$_7C_0$ $_7C_1$ $_7C_2$ $_7C_3$ $_7C_4$ $_7C_5$ $_7C_6$ $_7C_7$
1 7 21 35 35 21 7 1

$_8C_0$ $_8C_1$ $_8C_2$ $_8C_3$ $_8C_4$ $_8C_5$ $_8C_6$ $_8C_7$ $_8C_8$
1 8 28 56 70 56 28 8 1

$_9C_0$ $_9C_1$ $_9C_2$ $_9C_3$ $_9C_4$ $_9C_5$ $_9C_6$ $_9C_7$ $_9C_8$ $_9C_9$
1 9 36 84 126 126 84 36 9 1

$_{10}C_0$ $_{10}C_1$ $_{10}C_2$ $_{10}C_3$ $_{10}C_4$ $_{10}C_5$ $_{10}C_6$ $_{10}C_7$ $_{10}C_8$ $_{10}C_9$ $_{10}C_{10}$
1 10 45 120 210 252 210 120 45 10 1

Figure 11

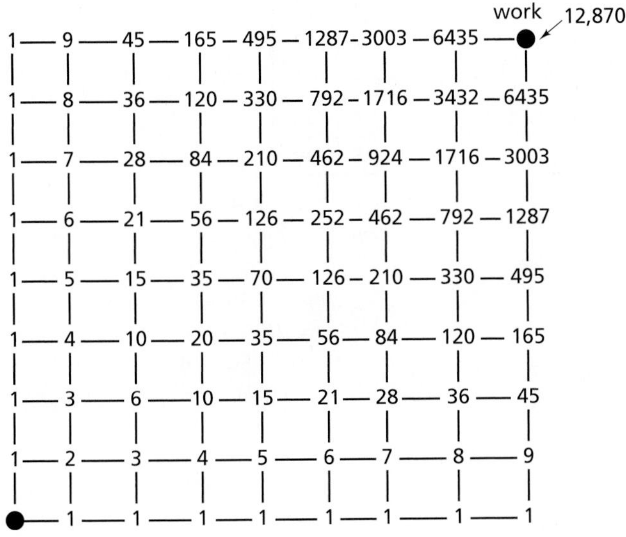

Chapter 5

Lesson 5.2 pp. 346–351

Exercises

10.

a	$h(a)$
0	3
1	11
2	19
3	27
4	35
5	43

$h(a) = 8a + 3$

11.

m	$f(m)$
0	0
1	2
2	6
3	12
4	20
5	30

$f(m) = m(m + 1)$

12.

m	$c(m)$
0	3
1	4
2	6
3	9
4	13
5	18

$c(m) = \frac{1}{2}m(m + 1) + 3$

13.

t	$j(t)$
0	−1
1	1
2	5
3	11
4	19
5	29

$j(t) = t(t + 1) - 1$

19a.

n	$T(n)$
0	0
1	1
2	5
3	14
4	30
5	55
6	91

Lesson 5.3 pp. 352–356

Exercises

3a.

n	$\frac{F(n+1)}{F(n)}$
1	1
2	2
3	1.5
4	$1.\overline{6}$
5	1.6
6	1.625
7	1.6154 . . .
8	1.619 . . .
9	1.61764 . . .
10	1.61818 . . .

5a.

n	$P(n)$
0	2
1	5
2	3
3	−2
4	−5
5	−3
6	2
7	5
8	3
9	−2
10	−5

Lesson 5.4 pp. 357–362

Exercises

2.

n	$k(n)$
0	3
1	10
2	17
3	24
4	31
5	38

$K(n) = 7n + 3$

$$\begin{aligned} k(1001) &= k(1000) + 7 \\ &= K(1000) + 7 \\ &= (7 \cdot 1000 + 3) + 7 \\ &= (7 \cdot 1000 + 7) + 3 \\ &= 7 \cdot 1001 + 3 \\ &= K(1001) \end{aligned}$$

3.

n	$j(n)$
0	0
1	1
2	4
3	9
4	16
5	25

$J(n) = n^2$

$$\begin{aligned} j(1001) &= j(1000) + (2 \cdot 1001) - 1 \\ &= J(1000) + (2 \cdot 1000 + 2 - 1) \\ &= 1000^2 + 2 \cdot 1000 + 1 \\ &= (1000 + 1)^2 = 1001^2 \\ &= J(1001) \end{aligned}$$

4.

x	$f(x)$
0	1
1	2
2	4
3	8
4	16
5	32

$$F(x) = \begin{cases} 1 & x = 0 \\ F(x - 1) \cdot 2 & x > 0 \end{cases}$$

$$\begin{aligned} f(1001) &= 2^{1001} \\ &= 2^{1000} \cdot 2 \\ &= f(1000) \cdot 2 \\ &= F(1000) \cdot 2 \\ &= F(1001) \end{aligned}$$

9.

n	$C(n)$
0	4
1	11
2	18
3	25
4	32
5	39

$c(n) = 7n + 4$

$$\begin{aligned} C(56) &= C(55) + 7 \\ &= c(55) + 7 \\ &= 7 \cdot 55 + 4 + 7 \\ &= 7(55 + 1) + 4 \\ &= 7 \cdot 56 + 4 \\ &= c(56) \end{aligned}$$

10.

n	$D(n)$
0	1
1	0
2	1
3	4
4	9
5	16

$$d(n) = \begin{cases} 1 & n = 0 \\ d(n-1) + (2n-3) & n > 0 \end{cases}$$

$$\begin{aligned} d(56) &= d(55) + 2 \cdot 56 - 3 \\ &= D(55) + 2 \cdot 54 + 4 - 3 \\ &= 54^2 + 2 \cdot 54 + 1 \\ &= (54+1)^2 \\ &= 55^2 \\ &= D(56) \end{aligned}$$

11.

n	$E(n)$
0	0
1	4
2	12
3	24
4	40
5	60

$e(n) = 2n(n+1)$

$$\begin{aligned} E(56) &= E(55) + 4 \cdot 56 \\ &= e(55) + 4 \cdot 56 \\ &= 2 \cdot 55 \cdot 56 + 4 \cdot 56 \\ &= 2 \cdot (55 + 2) \cdot 56 \\ &= 2 \cdot 56 \cdot 57 \\ &= e(56) \end{aligned}$$

12.

a	$Q(a)$	$q(a)$
0	2	3
1	5	5
2	8	7
3	11	9

$Q(a) \neq q(a)$

13.

x	$F(x)$	$f(x)$
0	3	3
1	4	4
2	7	7
3	12	12

$$\begin{aligned} F(n+1) &= (n+1)^2 + 3 \\ &= n^2 + 2n + 1 + 3 \\ &= (n^2 + 3) + (2n + 1) \\ &= F(n) + (2n + 1) \\ &= f(n) + 2(n+1) - 1 \\ &= f(n+1) \end{aligned}$$

14.

n	$Z(n)$	$z(n)$
0	2	2
1	6	6
2	18	18
3	54	54

$$\begin{aligned} Z(n+1) &= 2 \cdot 3^{n+1} \\ &= 3 \cdot (2 \cdot 3^n) \\ &= 3 \cdot Z(n) \\ &= 3 \cdot z(n) \\ &= z(n+1) \end{aligned}$$

15.

x	$C(x)$	$c(x)$
0	0	0
1	1	1
2	9	9
3	36	36

$$\begin{aligned} C(n+1) &= \left(\frac{(n+1)(n+2)}{2}\right)^2 \\ &= \left(\frac{n^2 + 3n + 2}{2}\right)^2 \\ &= \left(\frac{n^2 + n}{2} + \frac{2n + 2}{2}\right)^2 \\ &= \left(\frac{n(n+1)}{2} + (n+1)\right)^2 \\ &= \left(\frac{n(n+1)}{2}\right)^2 + 2 \cdot \frac{n(n+1)}{2} \cdot \\ &\quad (n+1) + (n+1)^2 \\ &= C(n) + n(n+1)^2 + (n+1)^2 \\ &= c(n) + (n+1) \cdot (n+1)^2 \\ &= c(n) + (n+1)^3 \\ &= c(n+1) \end{aligned}$$

Lesson 5.5 pp. 363–368

Exercises **8.** $K(x) = x^2 + 1$;

$$k(x) = \begin{cases} 1 & x = 0 \\ k(x-1) + 2x + 1 & x > 0 \end{cases}$$

$$\begin{aligned} K(n+1) &= (n+1)^2 + 1 \\ &= n^2 + 2n + 1 + 1 \\ &= K(n) + 2n + 1 \\ &= k(n) + 2(n+1) - 1 \\ &= k(n+1) \end{aligned}$$

9. $P(n) = 3^n$;

$$P(n) = \begin{cases} 1 & n = 0 \\ P(n-1) \cdot 3 & n > 0 \end{cases}$$

$$\begin{aligned} P(m+1) &= 3^{m+1} \\ &= 3^m \cdot 3 \\ &= P(m) \cdot 3 \\ &= p(m) \cdot 3 \\ &= p(m+1) \end{aligned}$$

10. $W(a) = \left(\frac{1}{2}\right)^a$;

$$w(a) = \begin{cases} 1 & a = 0 \\ w(a-1) \cdot \frac{1}{2} & a > 0 \end{cases}$$

$$\begin{aligned} W(n+1) &= \left(\frac{1}{2}\right)^{n+1} \\ &= \left(\frac{1}{2}\right)^n \cdot \frac{1}{2} \\ &= W(n) \cdot \frac{1}{2} \\ &= w(n) \cdot \frac{1}{2} \\ &= w(n+1) \end{aligned}$$

11. $\varepsilon(t) = 2^t + 1$;

$$\eta(n) = \begin{cases} 2 & t = 0 \\ \eta(t-1) + 2^{t-1} & t > 0 \end{cases}$$

$$\begin{aligned} \varepsilon(n+1) &= 2^{n+1} + 1 \\ &= 2^n \cdot 2 + 1 \\ &= 2^n + 2^n + 1 \\ &= 2^n + 1 + 2^n \\ &= \varepsilon(n) + 2^n \\ &= \eta(n) + 2^n \\ &= \eta(n+1) \end{aligned}$$

13a. Let $f(n) = \sum_{k=0}^{n-1} k$ and

$$F(n) = \frac{n(n-1)}{2}.$$

$$\begin{aligned} f(0) &= 0 = F(0) \\ f(m+1) &= f(m) + m \\ &= F(m) + m \\ &= \frac{m(m-1)}{2} + m \\ &= \frac{m(m+1)}{2} \\ &= F(m+1) \end{aligned}$$

b. Let $g(n) = \sum_{k=0}^{n-1} \frac{k(k-1)}{2}$ and

$$G(n) = \frac{n(n-1)(n-2)}{6}.$$

$$\begin{aligned} g(0) &= 0 = G(0) \\ g(m+1) &= g(m) + \frac{m(m-1)}{2} \\ &= G(m) + \frac{m(m-1)}{2} \\ &= \frac{m(m-1)(m-2)}{6} + \frac{m(m-1)}{2} \\ &= \frac{1}{6} m(m-1)[(m-2) + 3] \\ &= \frac{1}{6}(m+1)m(m-1) \\ &= G(m+1) \end{aligned}$$

c. Let $h(n) = \sum_{k=0}^{n-1} \frac{k(k-1)(k-2)}{6}$ and

$$H(n) = \frac{n(n-1)(n-2)(n-3)}{4!}.$$

$$h(0) = 0 = H(0)$$

$$\begin{aligned} h(m+1) &= h(m) + \frac{m(m-1)(m-2)}{6} \\ &= H(m) + \frac{m(m-1)(m-2)}{6} \\ &= \frac{m(m-1)(m-2)(m-3)}{24} + \frac{m(m-1)(m-2)}{6} \\ &= \frac{1}{24}m(m-1)(m-2)[(m-3)+4] \\ &= \frac{1}{24}(m+1)m(m-1)(m-2) \\ &= H(m+1) \end{aligned}$$

Mathematical Reflections p. 369

4. Combine like terms to get

$$f(n) = \begin{cases} 3 & n = 0 \\ 0.8f(n-1) + 5 & n > 0 \end{cases}$$

and solve for $f(36)$.

5. $g(n) = \begin{cases} 10 & \text{if } n = 0 \\ g(n-1) + 2n - 1 & \text{if } n > 0 \end{cases}$

7. Establish one or more base cases, and then use an induction proof to show that if the functions agree up to $n - 1$, they must agree at n. **8.** The ratio of consecutive Fibonacci numbers approaches $\phi = \frac{1+\sqrt{5}}{2} \approx 1.618$.

Lesson 5.6 pp. 371–373

Exercises 6a.

x	P(x)	Δ	Δ²	Δ³
0	0	0	0	1
1	0	0	1	1
2	0	1	2	1
3	1	3	3	1
4	4	6	4	1
5	10	10	5	1
6	20	15	6	
7	35	21		
8	56			

8c.

x	h(x)	Δ	Δ²
0	40	−40	20
1	0	−20	20
2	−20	0	20
3	−20	20	20
4	0	40	20
5	40	60	20
6	100	80	20
7	180	100	
8	280		

d.

x	j(x)	Δ	Δ²
0	0	3	−2
1	3	1	−2
2	4	−1	−2
3	3	−3	−2
4	0	−5	−2
5	−5	−7	−2
6	−12	−9	−2
7	−21	−11	
8	−32		

e.

x	k(x)	Δ	Δ²	Δ³
0	0	3	−6	−6
1	3	−3	−12	−6
2	0	−15	−18	−6
3	−15	−33	−24	−6
4	−48	−57	−30	−6
5	−105	−87	−36	−6
6	−192	−123	−42	
7	−315	−165		
8	−480			

f.

x	m(x)	Δ	Δ²	Δ³
0	0	−15	30	30
1	−15	15	60	30
2	0	75	90	30
3	75	165	120	30
4	240	285	150	30
5	525	435	180	30
6	960	615	210	30
7	1575	825		
8	2400			

9a.

x	N(x)	Δ	Δ²	Δ³
0	1	−2	14	12
1	−1	12	26	12
2	11	38	38	12
3	49	76	50	12
4	125	126	62	12
5	251	188	74	
6	439	262		
7	701			

Lesson 5.8 pp. 381–387

Exercises 10b. Answers may vary. Sample:

Input	Output	Δ
0	5	12
1	17	−6
2	11	−20
3	−9	0
4	−9	12
5	3	2
6	5	

Lesson 5.9 pp. 388–396

Exercises 6b. You can generalize the argument in part (a) for $g(n)$ for any non-negative integer n:

$$g(n) = \sum_{k=0}^{n} 4^k \binom{n}{k} = 5^n$$

c. See Figure 12.

Figure 12

6c. Let $h(x) = (p+1)^x$.

x	h(x)	Δ	Δ²	Δ³
0	1	p	p^2	p^2
1	$p+1$	$p(p+1)$	$p^2(p+1)$	$p^3(p+1)$
2	$(p+1)^2$	$p(p+1)^2$	$p^2(p+1)^2$	
3	$(p+1)^3$	$p(p+1)^3$		
4	$(p+1)^4$			

The top row of the difference table contains powers of p, therefore by the same argument made for $g(n)$,

$$h(n) = \sum_{k=0}^{n} p^k \binom{n}{k} = (p+1)^n$$

13b.

n	$D(n)$	Δ	Δ^2	Δ^3	Δ^4
0	1	−1	1	−1	1
1	0	0	0	0	0
2	0	0	0	0	0
3	0	0	0	0	0
4	0	0	0	0	0
5	0	0	0	0	0

The top row alternates between 1 and −1.

16. See Figure 13.

Lesson 5.10 pp. 397–405

Exercises

3a.

x	$f(x)$	Δ	Δ^2	Δ^3	Δ^4
0	0	1	14	36	24
1	1	15	50	60	24
2	16	65	110	84	
3	81	175	194		
4	256	369			
5	625				

8.

n	$A(n)$	$B(n)$
0	0	0
1	0	0
2	1	1
3	3	9
4	6	36
5	10	100
6	15	225
7	21	441
8	28	784
9	36	1296
10	45	2025

9b.

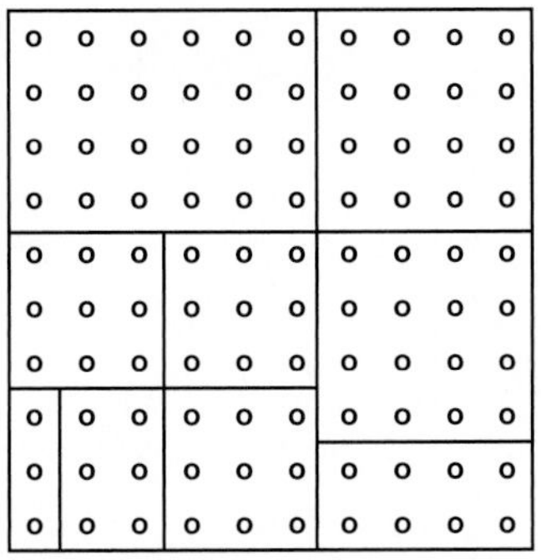

c. See Figure 14.

d. Let n be odd. The previous square will be $\frac{n(n-1)}{2}$ on a side if the pattern works to this point. Then you can add $\frac{n-1}{2}$ squares to each edge, a total of $n - 1$ squares. One more square fits in the corner to complete the pattern, and the new large square has side: $\frac{n(n-1)}{2} + n = \frac{n(n+1)}{2}$.

Lesson 5.11 pp. 409–411

For You to Explore

1a.

n	$f(n)$
0	1
1	3
2	4
3	7
4	11
5	18
6	29
7	47
8	76

b.

n	$f(n)$
0	5
1	15
2	20
3	35
4	55
5	90
6	145
7	235
8	380

The results are all 5 times as large as those in part (a).

Figure 13

$f(x)$	$\binom{x}{0}=1$	$\binom{x}{1}=x$	$\binom{x}{2}=\frac{x(x-1)}{2!}$	$\binom{x}{3}=\frac{x(x-1)(x-2)}{3!}$	$\binom{x}{4}$	$\binom{x}{5}$
0	1	-	-	-	-	-
x	0	1	-	-	-	-
x^2	0	1	2	-	-	-
x^3	0	1	6	6	-	-
x^4	0	1	14	36	24	-
x^5	0	1	30	150	240	120

Patterns: Factorial numbers appear down the diagonal of the table, the $\binom{x}{1}$ column is always 1, the numbers in each column are multiples of the column number.

Figure 14

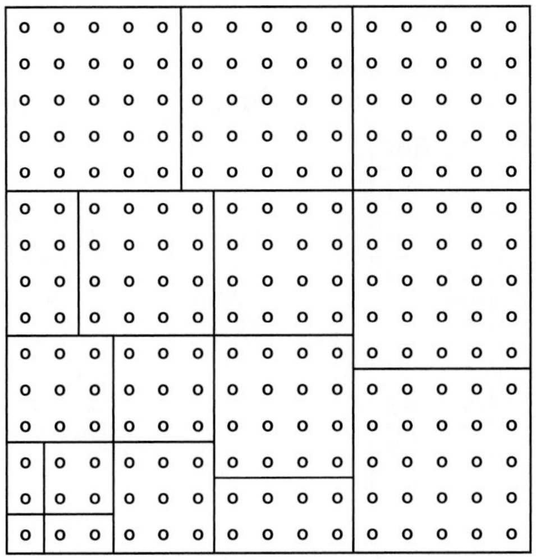

c.

n	$f(n)$
0	2
1	−2
2	0
3	−2
4	−2
5	−4
6	−6
7	−10
8	−16

d.

n	$f(n)$
0	7
1	13
2	20
3	33
4	53
5	86
6	139
7	225
8	364

The results are the sum of the results from parts (b) and (c).

e.

n	$f(n)$
0	3
1	17
2	20
3	37
4	57
5	94
6	151
7	245
8	396

The results are the differences of the results from parts (b) and (c).

2a.

n	$f(n)$
0	1
1	3
2	9
3	27
4	81
5	243
6	729
7	2187
8	6561

$f(n) = 3^n$

b.

n	$f(n)$
0	5
1	15
2	45
3	135
4	405
5	1215
6	3645
7	10,935
8	32,805

Each result is five times as large as the one in part (a).
$f(n) = 5 \cdot 3^n$

c.

n	$f(n)$
0	2
1	−2
2	2
3	−2
4	2
5	−2
6	2
7	−2
8	2

$f(n) = 2 \cdot (-1)^n$

d.

n	$f(n)$
0	7
1	13
2	47
3	133
4	407
5	1213
6	3647
7	10,933
8	32,807

The results are the sum of the results from parts (b) and (c).
$f(n) = 5 \cdot 3^n + 2 \cdot (-1)^n$

e.

n	$f(n)$
0	3
1	17
2	43
3	137
4	403
5	1217
6	3643
7	10,937
8	32,803

The results are the differences of the results from parts (b) and (c).
$f(n) = 5 \cdot 3^n - 2 \cdot (-1)^n$

4b.

n	$f(n)$
0	1
1	2
2	$\frac{3}{2}$
3	$\frac{5}{3}$
4	$\frac{8}{5}$
5	$\frac{13}{8}$
6	$\frac{21}{13}$
7	$\frac{34}{21}$
8	$\frac{55}{34}$
9	$\frac{89}{55}$
10	$\frac{144}{89}$

Exercises **6b.**

n	$r(n)$
0	$\frac{7}{2}$
1	$\frac{29}{7}$
2	$\frac{133}{29}$
3	$\frac{641}{133}$
4	$\frac{3157}{641}$
5	$\frac{15{,}689}{3157}$
6	$\frac{78{,}253}{15{,}689}$

Lesson 5.12 **pp. 412–418**
Exercises

15d.

n	$t(n)$
0	2
1	−7
2	25
3	−91
4	337
5	−1267
6	4825
7	−18,571

The ratio of consecutive terms is approaching −4.
$f(n) = (-4)^n + (-3)^n$

e.

n	$t(n)$
0	2
1	7
2	25
3	91
4	337
5	1267
6	4825
7	18,571

The ratio of consecutive terms is approaching 4.
$f(n) = 4^n + 3^n$

f.

n	$t(n)$
0	2
1	6
2	116
3	936
4	10,256
5	98,976
6	1,004,096
7	9,983,616

The ratio of consecutive terms is approaching 10.
$f(n) = 10^n + (-4)^n$

Lesson 5.14 **pp. 427–432**
Exercises **3b.** See Figure 15.
c. 15,000 **d.** See Figure 16.
e. $T(n) = 15,000 + 10,000 \cdot 0.8^n$

Mathematical Reflections **p. 433**
1b. See Figure 17.

Figure 15

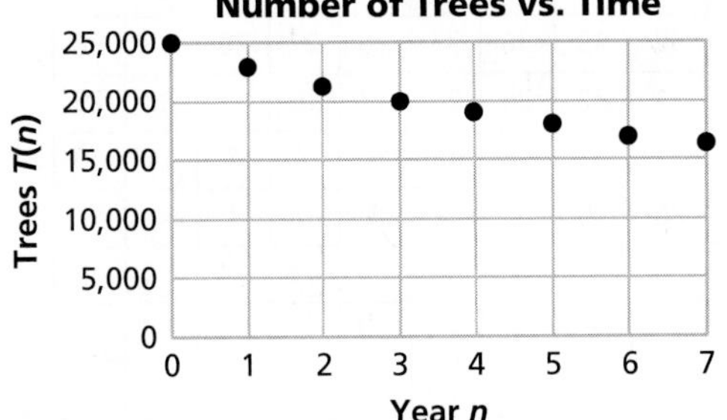

Figure 16

Years n	Trees $T(n)$	$T(n)-15,000$	÷
0	25,000	10,000	0.8
1	23,000	8000	0.8
2	21,400	6400	0.8
3	20,120	5120	0.8
4	19,096	4096	0.8
5	18,277	3277	0.8
6	17,621	2621	0.8
7	17,097	2097	0.8

Figure 17

n	$f(n)$
0	0
1	50
2	90
3	122
4	147.6
5	168.1
6	184.5
7	197.6
8	208.1
9	216.4
10	223.2

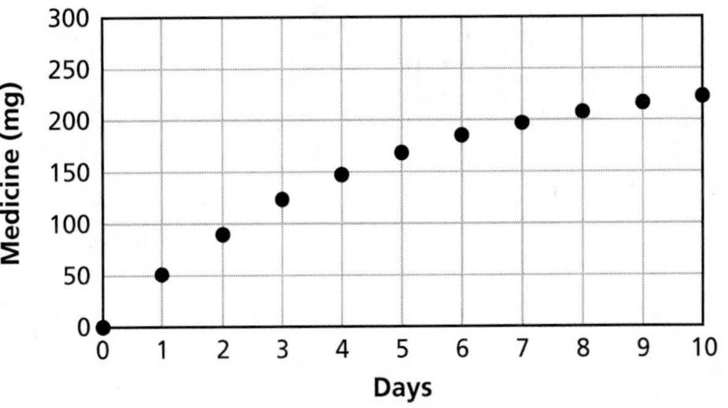

Chapter 6

Lesson 6.1 pp. 441–443

For You to Explore

2.

3.

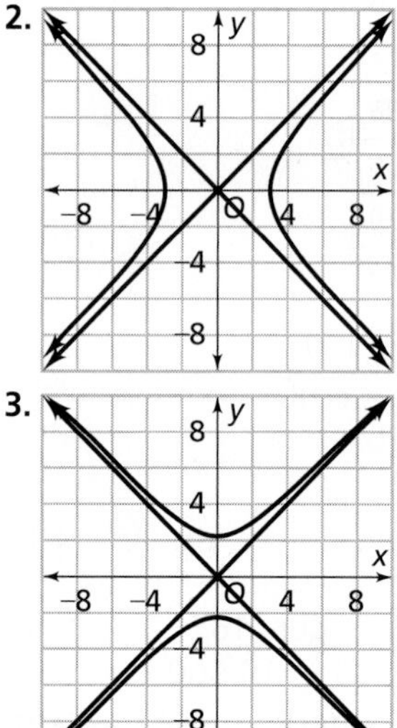

5.

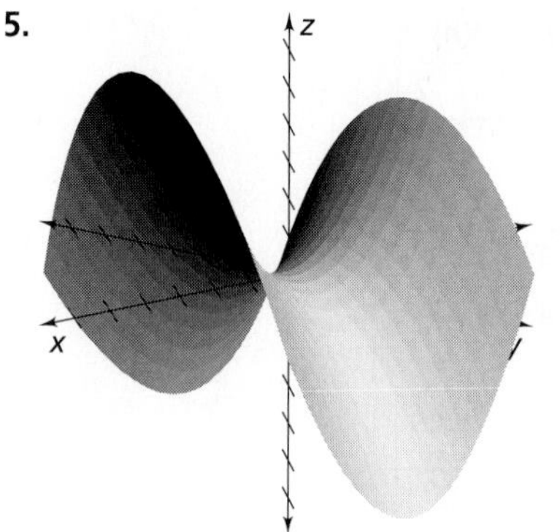

Exercises **6.** See Figure 18.

7.

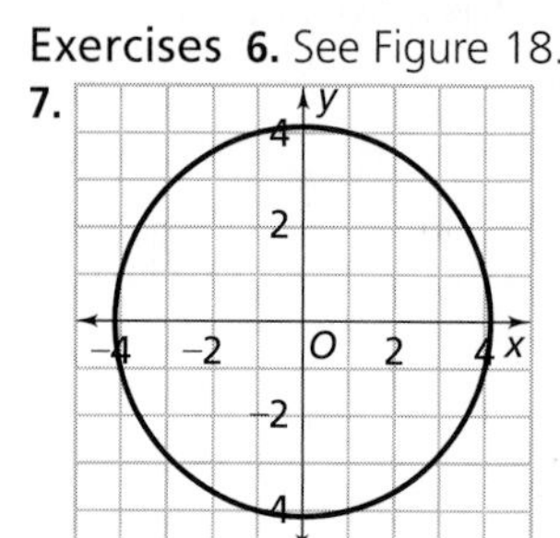

9.

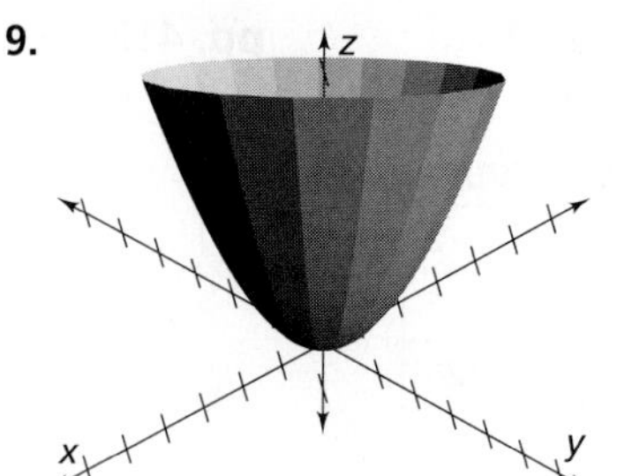

Lesson 6.2 pp. 444–449

Exercises **6e.** See Figure 19.

9. See Figure 20.

11f.

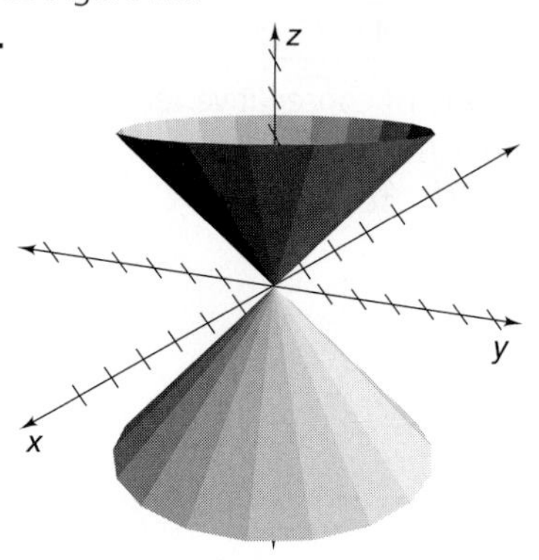

Figure 18

	−5	−4	−3	−2	−1	0	1	2	3	4	5
5	50	41	34	29	26	25	26	29	34	41	50
4	41	32	25	20	17	16	17	20	25	32	41
3	34	25	18	13	10	9	10	13	18	25	34
2	29	20	13	8	5	4	5	8	13	20	29
1	26	17	10	5	2	1	2	5	10	17	26
0	25	16	9	4	1	0	1	4	9	16	25
−1	26	17	10	5	2	1	2	5	10	17	26
−2	29	20	13	8	5	4	5	8	13	20	29
−3	34	25	18	13	10	9	10	13	18	25	34
−4	41	32	25	20	17	16	17	20	25	32	41
−5	50	41	34	29	26	25	26	29	34	41	50

Figure 19

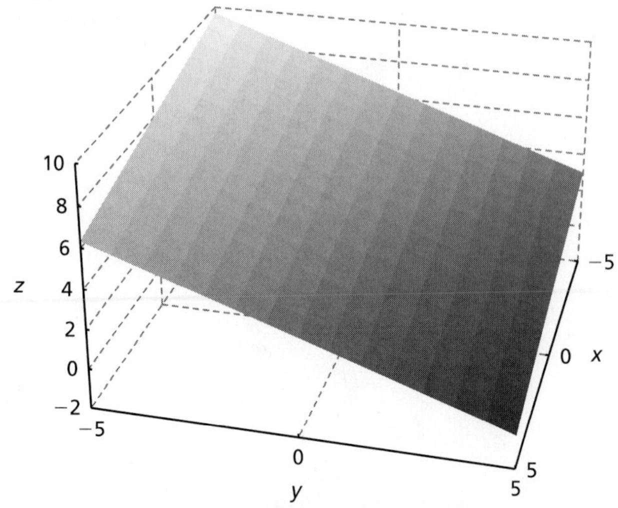

Figure 20

	−5	−4	−3	−2	−1	0	1	2	3	4	5
5	76	63	52	43	36	31	28	27	28	31	36
4	65	52	41	32	25	20	17	16	17	20	25
3	56	43	32	23	16	11	8	7	8	11	16
2	49	36	25	16	9	4	1	0	1	4	9
1	44	31	20	11	4	−1	−4	−5	−4	−1	4
0	41	28	17	8	1	−4	−7	−8	−7	−4	1
−1	40	27	16	7	0	−5	−8	−9	−8	−5	0
−2	41	28	17	8	1	−4	−7	−8	−7	−4	1
−3	44	31	20	11	4	−1	−4	−5	−4	−1	4
−4	49	36	25	16	9	4	1	0	1	4	9
−5	56	43	32	23	16	11	8	7	8	11	16

Lesson 6.3 pp. 450–456

Exercises

6.

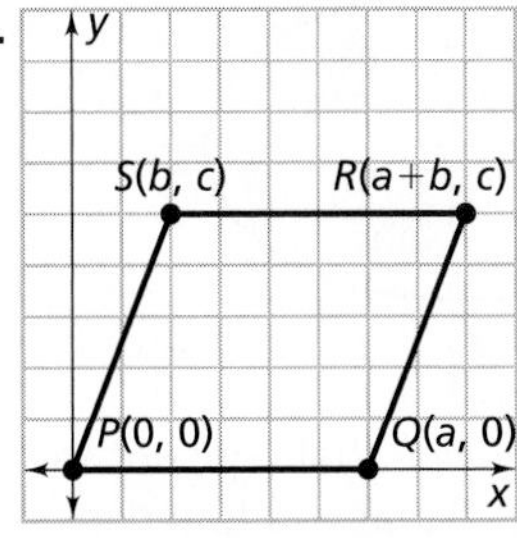

Assume a parallelogram with vertices at $P(0, 0)$, $Q(a, 0)$, $R(a + b, c)$, $S(b, c)$.

The slope of diagonal PR is $\frac{c}{a + b}$, and the slope of diagonal SQ is $\frac{c}{b - a}$.

If these diagonals are perpendicular, then:

$$\frac{c}{a + b} \cdot \frac{c}{b - a} = -1$$

$$\frac{c^2}{b^2 - a^2} = -1$$

$$c^2 = a^2 - b^2$$

$$c^2 + b^2 = a^2$$

To prove $PQRS$ is a rhombus, you must show that two consecutive sides are congruent. The length of PQ is a and the length of QR is $\sqrt{b^2 + c^2}$. If the diagonals are perpendicular, then $a^2 = b^2 + c^2$, so $PQ = QR$ and the parallelogram must be a rhombus.

9a. Answers may vary. Sample: $A(a, 0)$, $B(-a, 0)$, $C(0, a\sqrt{3})$.

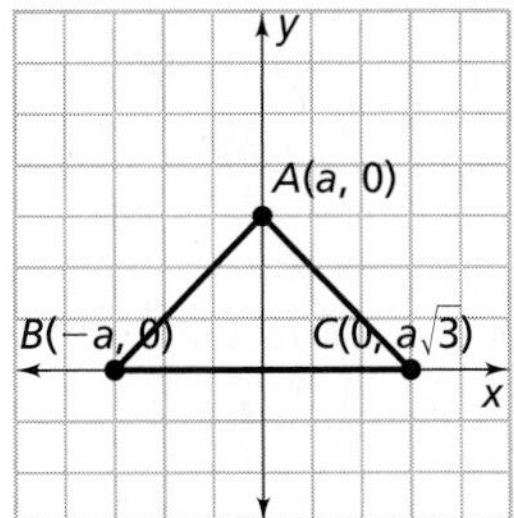

b. Using the result of part (a), the y-axis is the perpendicular bisector of AB and also passes through point C, therefore it is a median. If you choose different coordinates, the same proof can be used to show that all three perpendicular bisectors are medians.

10a. Answers may vary. Sample: $A(a, 0)$, $B(b, c)$, $C(-b, c)$, $D(-a, 0)$.

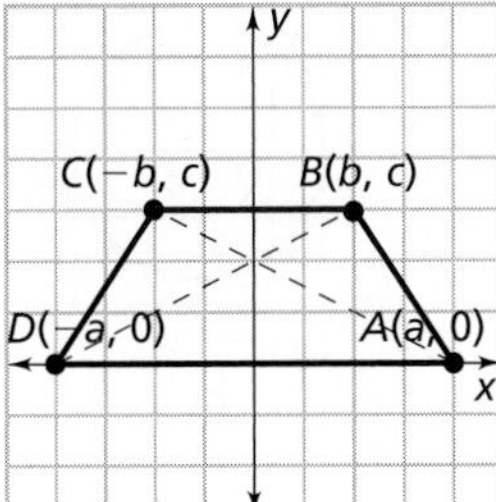

b. The length of diagonal AC is $\sqrt{(a + b)^2 + (0 - c)^2} = \sqrt{(a + b)^2 + c^2}$.

The length of diagonal BD is $\sqrt{(b + a)^2 + (c - 0)^2} = \sqrt{(a + b)^2 + c^2}$.

Therefore these two diagonals are equal in length.

The midpoint of diagonal AC is $\left(\frac{a - b}{2}, \frac{c}{2}\right)$.

The midpoint of diagonal BD is $\left(\frac{b - a}{2}, \frac{c}{2}\right)$.

Therefore, the midpoints are not equal (the lines do not bisect each other) unless $a = b$. Since this is a trapezoid, not a rectangle, then a cannot equal b.

11. Answers may vary. Sample: Assume coordinates $A(0, 0)$, $B(2a, 0)$, $C(2b, 2c)$, $D(2d, 2c)$.

The length of AB is $2a$ and the length of CD is $2b - 2d$. The average of these lengths is $a + b - d$.

The midline's endpoints are $M(d, c)$ and $N(a + b, c)$. The distance between M and N is $a + b - d$.

12. Answers may vary. Sample:

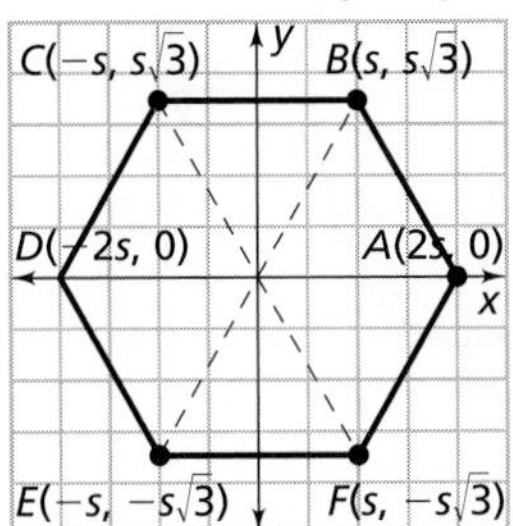

$A(2s, 0)$, $B(s, s\sqrt{3})$, $C(-s, s\sqrt{3})$, $D(-2s, 0)$, $E(-s, -s\sqrt{3})$, $F(s, -s\sqrt{3})$

Lesson 6.4 pp. 457–462

Exercises **9.** Answers may vary. Samples:

1) The signed power is given by $d^2 - r^2$. However, for the center of a circle, $d = 0$. Therefore the signed power is equal to $-r^2$.

2) Any chord through the center of a circle is a diameter with two pieces equal to r. The unsigned power is r^2, but inside the circle the sign is negative, therefore the signed power is equal to $-r^2$.

3) The power for any point with respect to a circle centered at (h, k) with radius r is given by $(x - h)^2 + (y - k)^2 - r^2$, so for the center (h, k) the first terms are zero, leaving $-r^2$ as the power.

11. Equation of circle = $x^2 + y^2 + Cx + Dy + E = 0$

The center of this circle is $\left(-\frac{C}{2}, -\frac{D}{2}\right)$ and the radius is $\frac{\sqrt{C^2 + D^2 - 4E}}{2}$.

The power is defined by $d^2 - r^2$ where d^2 is the distance from (x, y) to the center.

$$d^2 = \left(x + \frac{C}{2}\right)^2 + \left(y + \frac{D}{2}\right)^2$$

$$r^2 = \frac{C^2 + D^2 - 4E}{4}$$

$$d^2 - r^2 = \left(x^2 + Cx + \frac{C^2}{4}\right) + \left(y^2 + Dy + \frac{D^2}{4}\right) - \frac{C^2 + D^2 - 4E}{4}$$

$$= x^2 + y^2 + Cx + Dy + E$$

Mathematical Reflections p. 463

4. Let the four vertices of the parallelogram be $(0, 0)$, $(a, 0)$, (b, c), and $(a + b, c)$.

The lengths of the horizontal sides are a and the lengths of the other two sides are $\sqrt{b^2 + c^2}$. Therefore the sum of the squares of the lengths of the four sides is:

$$a^2 + a^2 + b^2 + b^2 + c^2 + c^2$$

$$= 2a^2 + 2b^2 + 2c^2$$

The length of the diagonal starting at the origin is $\sqrt{(a + b)^2 + c^2}$ and the length of the other diagonal is $\sqrt{(b - a)^2 + c^2}$. Therefore the sum of the squares of the lengths of the diagonals is:

$$(b - a)^2 + c^2 + (a + b)^2 + c^2 =$$
$$b^2 - 2ab + a^2 + c^2 + a^2 +$$
$$2ab + b^2 + c^2 = 2a^2 + 2b^2 + 2c^2$$

Additional Answers

8. Answers may vary. Samples: One way is to complete the square on x and y to get an equation in the form $(x - h)^2 + (y - k)^2 = r^2$. The center of this circle is (h, k) and the radius is r. A second way is to look at the coefficients in the normal form equation $x^2 + y^2 + Cx + Dy + E = 0$ where the center of the circle is $\left(-\frac{C}{2}, -\frac{D}{2}\right)$. To find the radius, plug the coordinates of the center into the normal form of the equation.

Lesson 6.5 **pp. 465–467**

For You to Explore

4a.

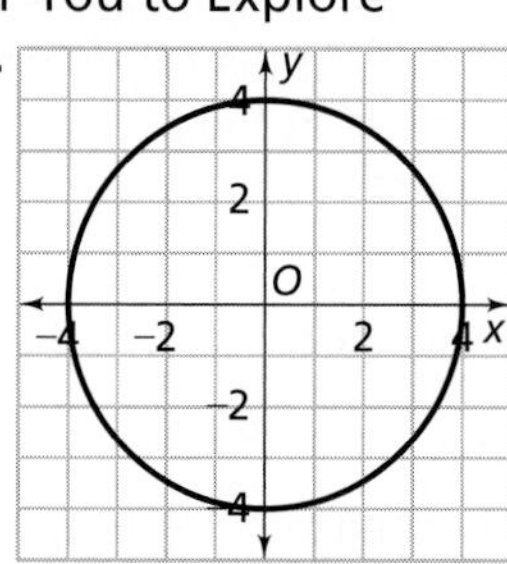

b.

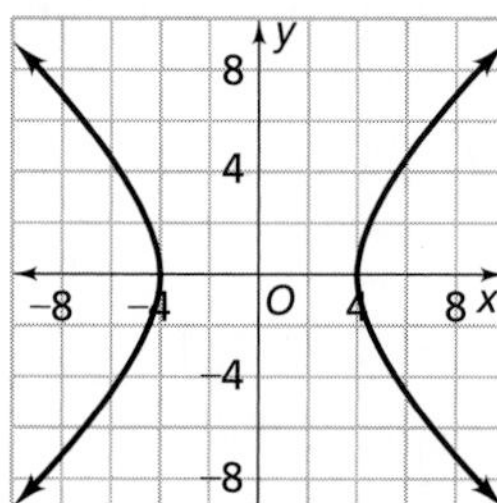

c.

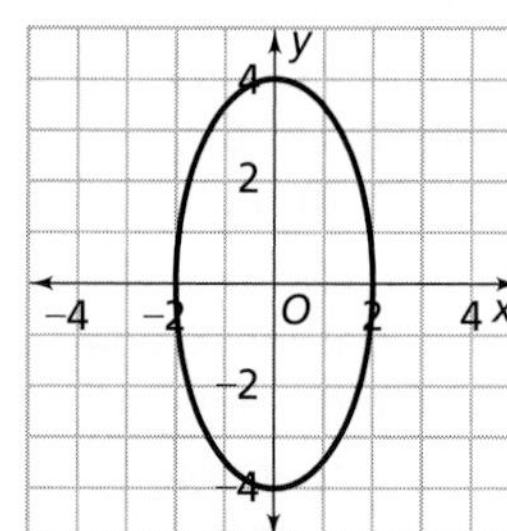

d.

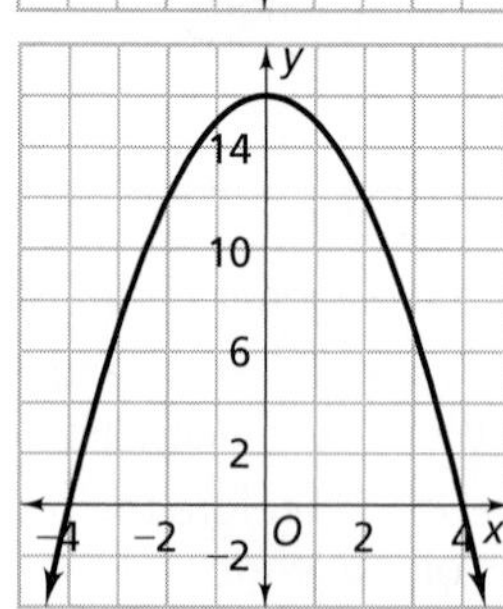

Exercises 7b.

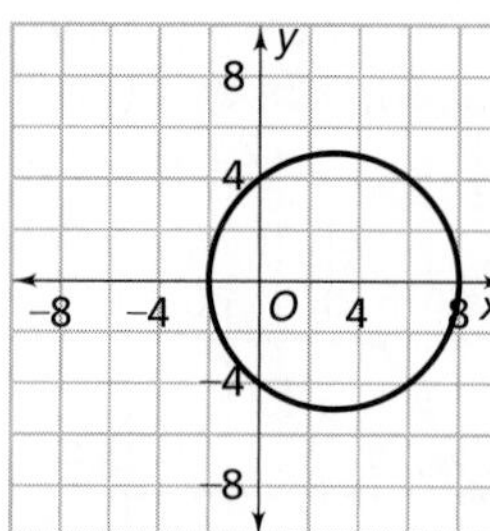

c.

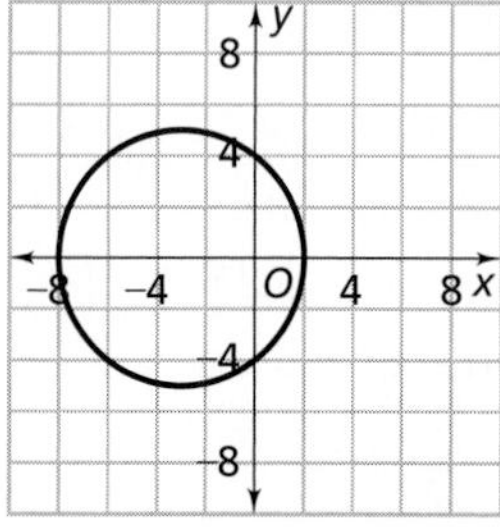

d.

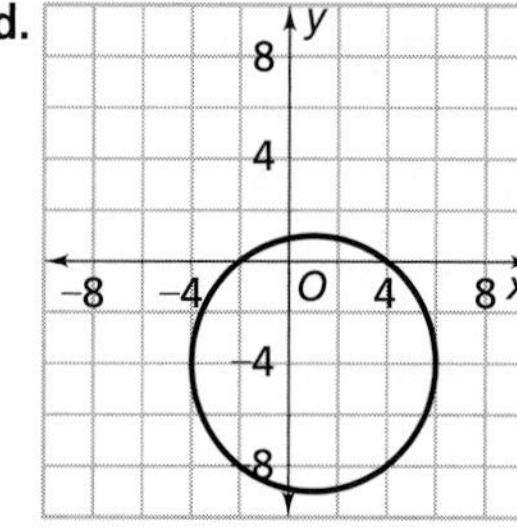

e. Same graph as part (a).

8b.

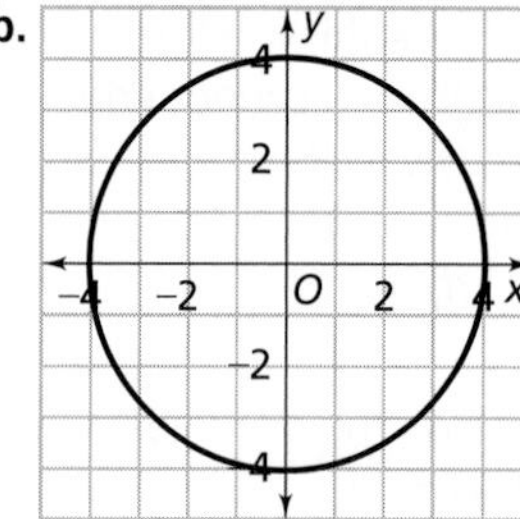

c.

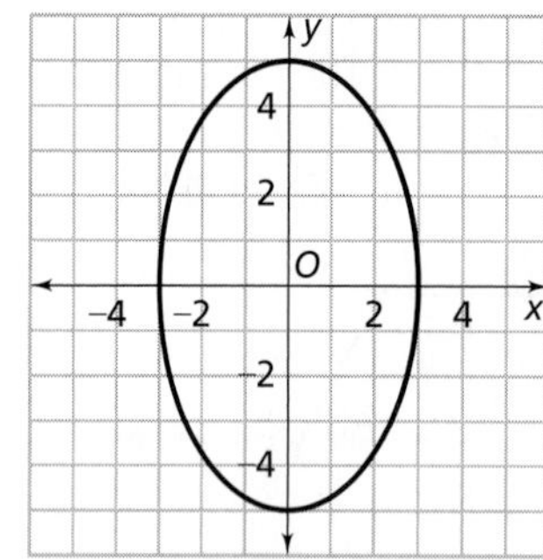

d.

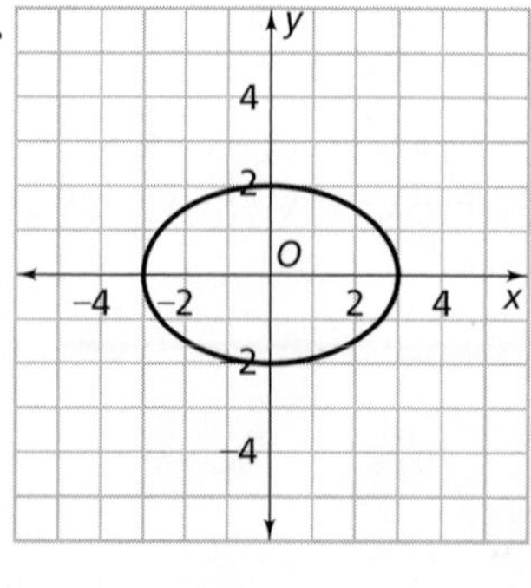

e.

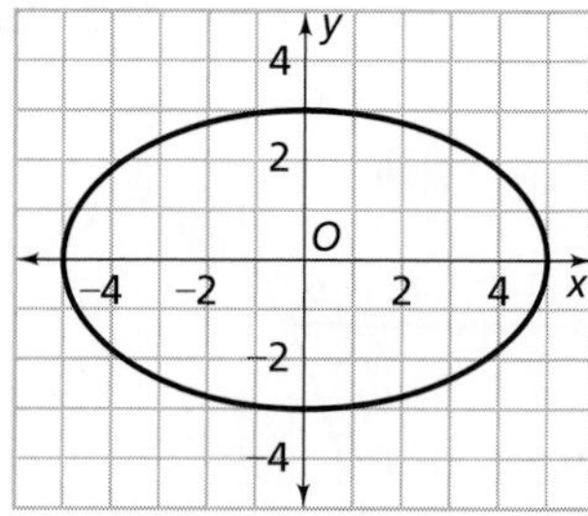

9c. The contour line that contains the optimum point P that you found in part (a) is an ellipse with foci Y and T that is tangent to the river's edge. It must touch the river's edge at some point, or you could not fill the bucket. If it touches the river's edge at more than one point, then you have not found the best point. All points between the two intersections of the ellipse and the river's edge have a smaller total path length, and are better choices.

Lesson 6.6 **pp. 468–474**

Exercises 3. Your sketch should look like the one on page 471 but points D and E will coincide at the center of the circle. This will also be the point where the two spheres are tangent to the plane of the sliced circle. **4a.** Answers may vary. Any point that satisfies the equation $\left|\sqrt{(x - 3)^2 + y^2} - \sqrt{(x + 3)^2 + y^2}\right| = 4$.

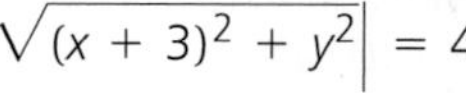

b.

c. $\frac{x^2}{4} - \frac{y^2}{5} = 1$ **5.** If P is any point non-collinear with A and B, then the triangle inequality applies: if the shorter of PA or PB has length x, then the longer cannot be more than $x + 6$. So $|PA - PB| < 6$ is required. If P is collinear with A and B, then $|PA - PB| = 6$ is possible but $|PA - PB|$ cannot be greater than 6. In the entire plane, no point P can satisfy $|PA - PB| = 10$.

11a. $\dfrac{x^2}{\left(\frac{s}{2}\right)^2} + \dfrac{y^2}{\frac{(s^2 - 36)}{4}} = 1$ **b.** Answers may vary. Accept any point satisfying the equation $\dfrac{x^2}{100} + \dfrac{y^2}{91} = 1$.

c.

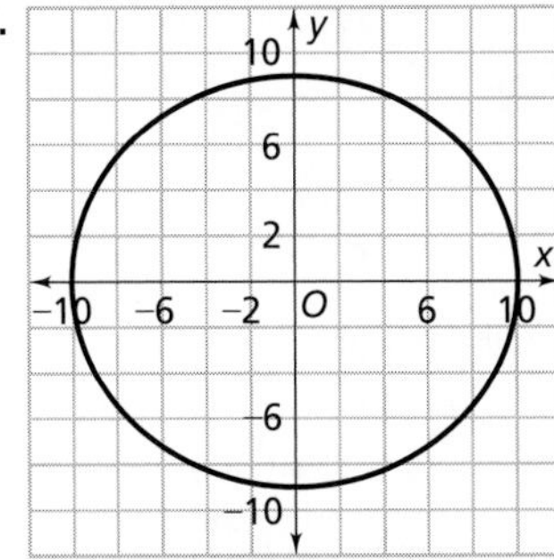

d.

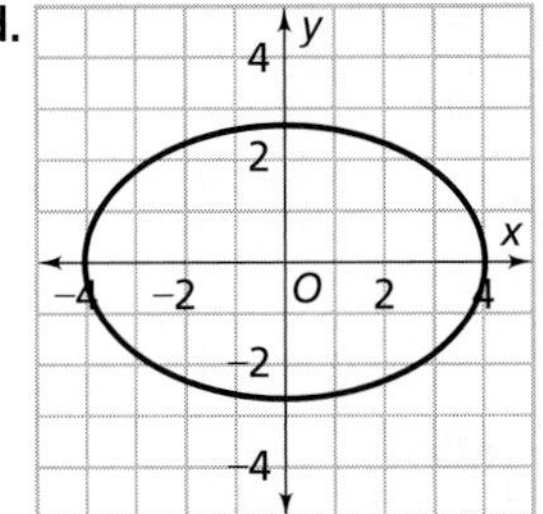

e. undefined **12.** B

13a.

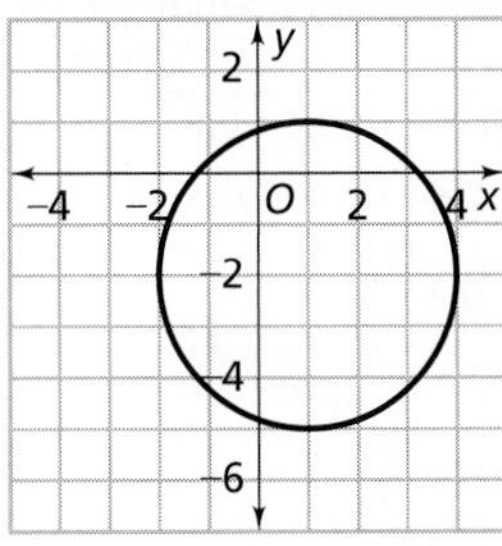

b.

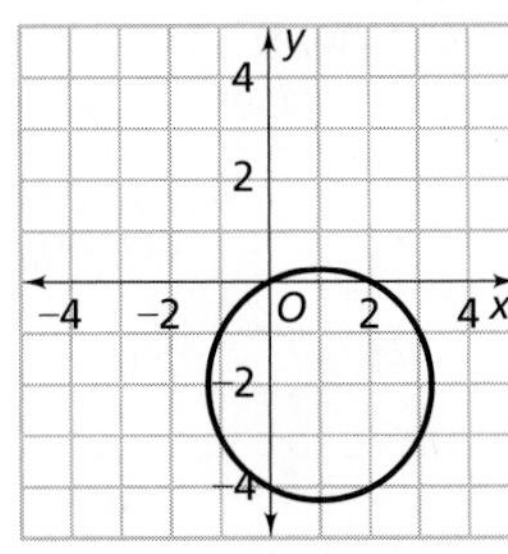

c.

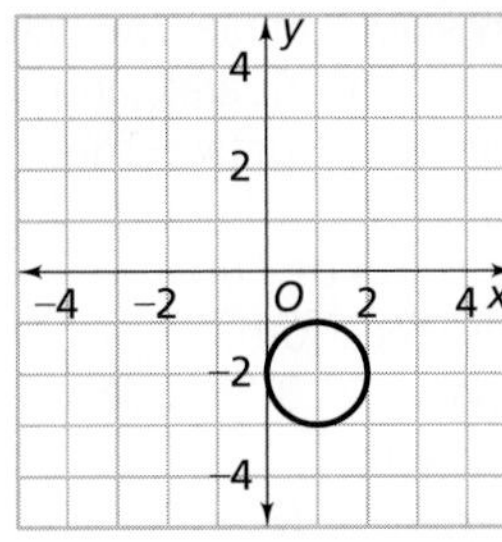

d.

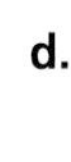

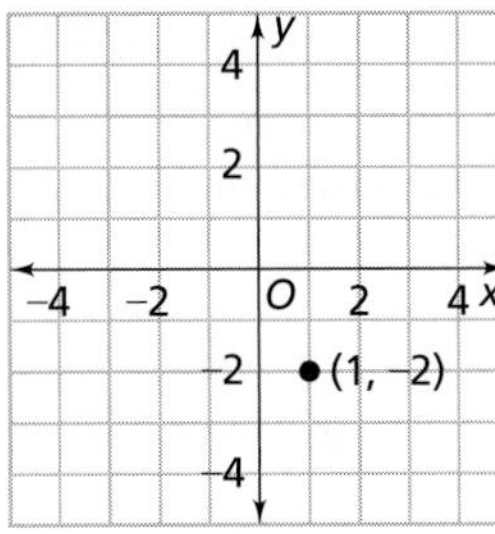

e. undefined

Lesson 6.7 pp. 475–483

Exercises 5a. This graph is a hyperbola that is a dilation with scale factor $\frac{1}{2}$ from the original in Exercise 4.

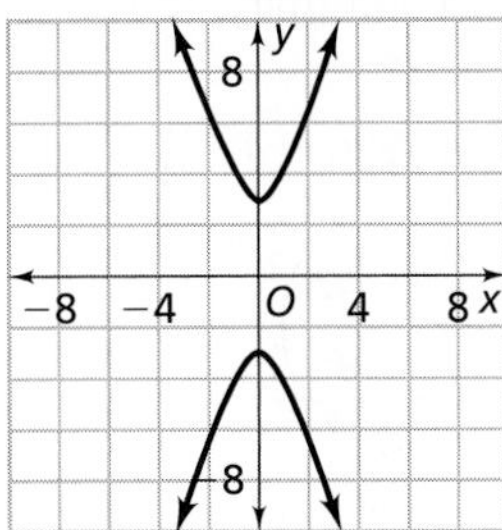

b. This graph is a hyperbola, even closer to the origin.

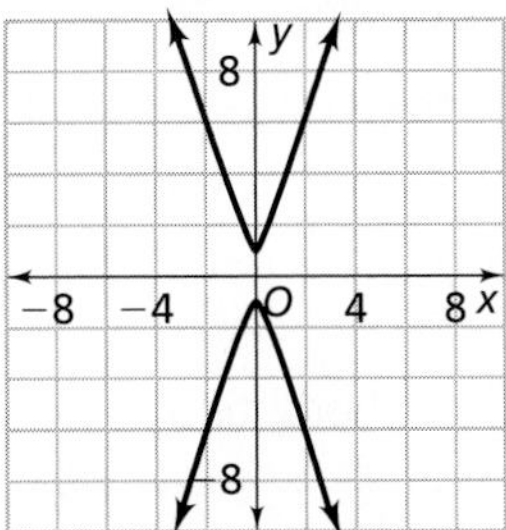

c.

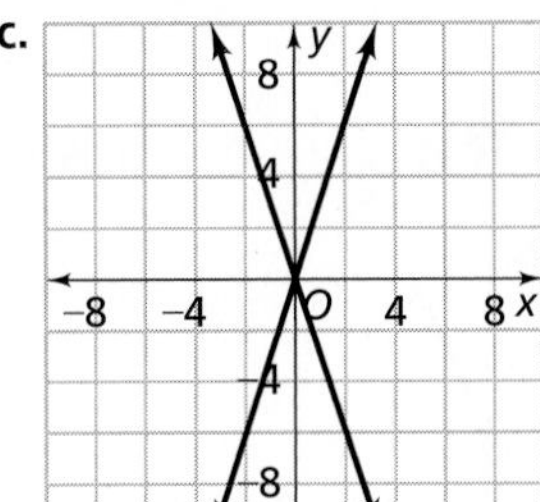

6c.

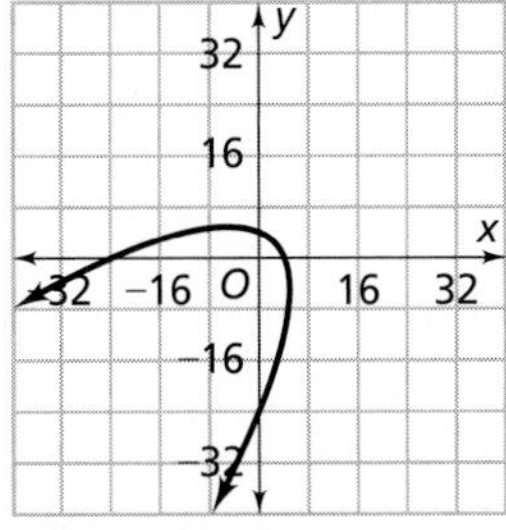

8b.

x	y
3	undefined
4	0
5	2.2500
6	3.3541
8	5.1962
10	6.8739
20	14.6969
40	29.8496
100	74.9400
1000	749.9940

10c.

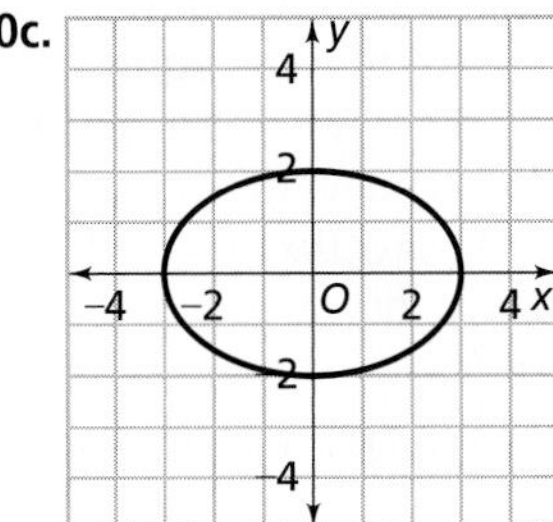

11c. $(1 + 5\sqrt{2}, 1 - 5\sqrt{2})$ and $(1 - 5\sqrt{2}, 1 + 5\sqrt{2})$

d. $51x^2 + 98xy + 51y^2 - 200x - 200y = 0$

e.

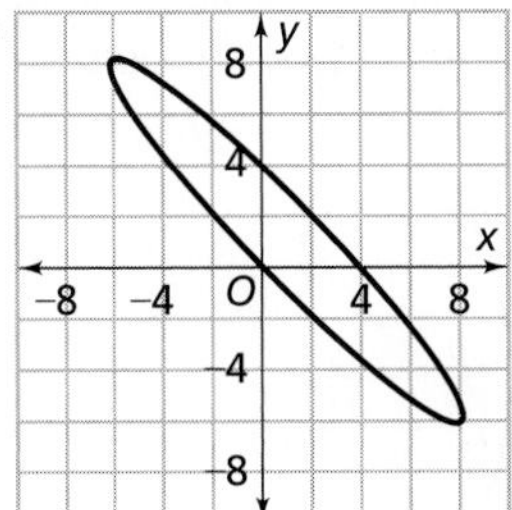

Additional Answers

12. Starting with the right branch of the hyperbola:

$\sqrt{(x + c)^2 + y^2} - \sqrt{(x - c)^2 + y^2} = 2a$

$\sqrt{(x + c)^2 + y^2} = 2a + \sqrt{(x - c)^2 + y^2}$

$(x + c)^2 + y^2 = 4a^2 + 4a\sqrt{(x - c)^2 + y^2} + (x - c)^2 + y^2$

$x^2 + 2cx + c^2 + y^2 = 4a^2 + 4a\sqrt{x^2 - 2cx + c^2 + y^2} + x^2 - 2cx + c^2 + y^2$

$4cx - 4a^2 = 4a\sqrt{x^2 - 2cx + c^2 + y^2}$

$cx - a^2 = a\sqrt{x^2 - 2cx + c^2 + y^2}$

$c^2x^2 - a^4 = a^2x^2 - 2a^2cx + a^2c^2 + a^2y^2$

$(c^2 - a^2)x^2 - (a^2)y^2 = a^2(c^2 - a^2)$

Let $b^2 = c^2 - a^2$:

$b^2x^2 - a^2y^2 = a^2b^2$ or $\frac{x^2}{a^2} - \frac{y^2}{b^2} = 1$

Repeat with the left branch of the hyperbola to prove that the equation works for the entire hyperbola. **13.** D

14a. Focus: $(0, 1)$; directrix: $y = -1$

b. Focus: $(1, 0)$; directrix: $x = -1$

c. Focus: $(0, -1)$; directrix: $y = 1$

d. Focus: $(-1, 0)$; directrix: $x = 1$

e. Focus: $\left(0, \frac{1}{8}\right)$; directrix: $y = -\frac{1}{8}$

f. Focus: $\left(\frac{1}{8}, 0\right)$; directrix: $x = -\frac{1}{8}$

Lesson 6.8 pp. 484–491

Exercises 5a. $(y - 2)^2 = 4(x + 3)^2 - 16$ **b.** The next step in solving this equation is to take a square root, which results in two answers (a positive and negative root).

c.

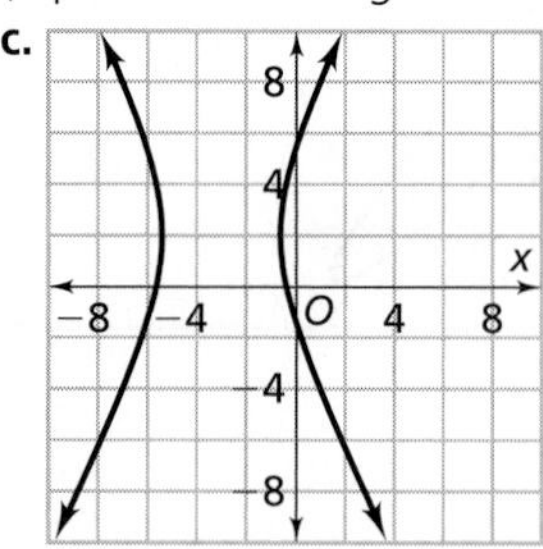

6.

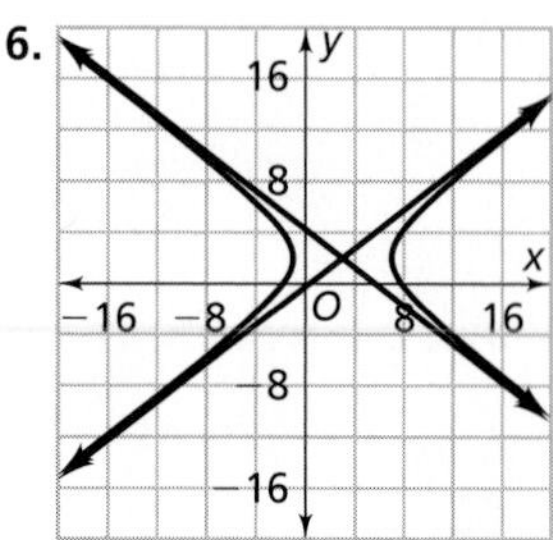

8. Answers may vary. Sample: the first equation is the sum of squares, and squares can never be negative. The second equation is the difference of squares, and that can be negative.

14. Using the distance formula, the distance from $(x - 3, y - 4)$ to $(0, 12)$ is equal to the distance from (x, y) to $(3, 16)$:

$\sqrt{(x - 3 - 0)^2 + (y - 4 - 12)^2} = \sqrt{(x - 3)^2 + (y - 16)^2}$

This can be repeated to demonstrate the same case for the other points.

16c. $(2 \pm 2\sqrt{3}, -1)$
d. $(2 \pm \sqrt{7}, -1)$ **e.** $(2, -1)$
f. Not possible, since the major axis is vertical.

Lesson 6.9 pp. 492–497

Exercises 6a. If $e = 1$, the definition gives $PF = Pd$, which matches the locus definition of a parabola given in Lesson 6.6. **b.** Let $e < 1$, use the distance formula to determine the equation of the ellipse.

$\sqrt{x^2 + (y - 1)^2} = e|y + 1|$

Solving this equation yields:

$$\frac{x^2}{\frac{1 - e^2}{4e^2}} + \frac{\left(y - \frac{1 + e^2}{1 - e^2}\right)^2}{\frac{\left(1 - e^2\right)^2}{4e^2}} = 1$$

Based on this equation, $a = \frac{2e}{1 - e^2}$ and $b = \frac{2e}{\sqrt{1 - e^2}}$, therefore $c = \frac{2e^2}{1 - e^2}$

The eccentricity is given by

$$\frac{c}{a} = \frac{\frac{2e^2}{(1 - e^2)}}{\frac{2e}{(1 - e^2)}} = e$$

c. Using the same methods, find $a = \frac{2e}{e^2 - 1}$, $b = \frac{2e}{\sqrt{e^2 - 1}}$, $c = \frac{2e^2}{e^2 - 1}$ to show that $\frac{c}{a} = e$.

Mid-Chapter Test p. 499

11c.

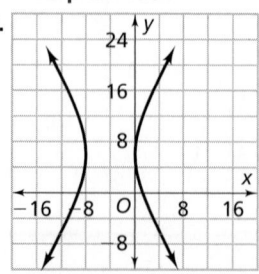

Lesson 6.10 pp. 501–502

For You to Explore

2b.

c.

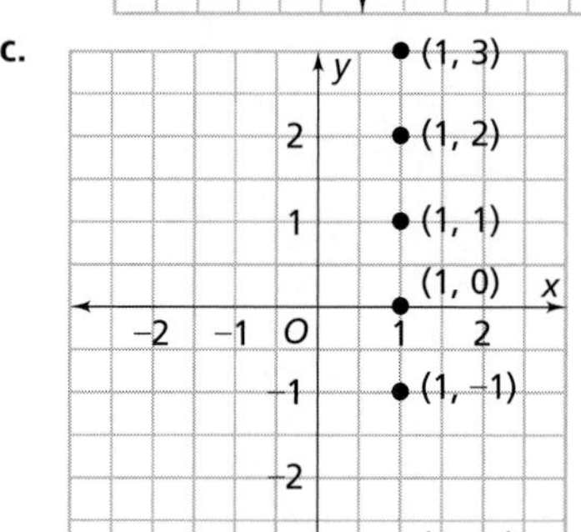

d.

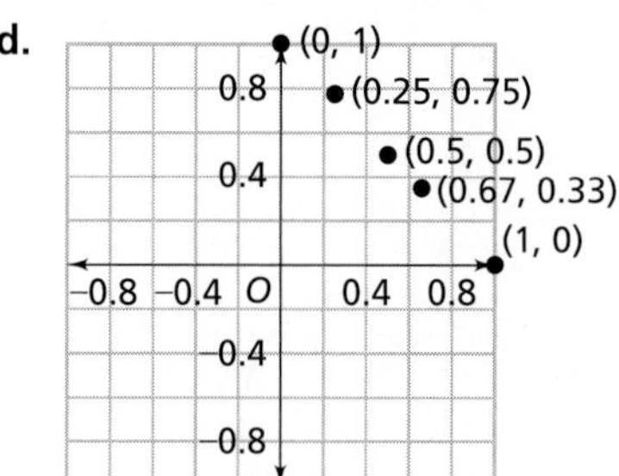

e.

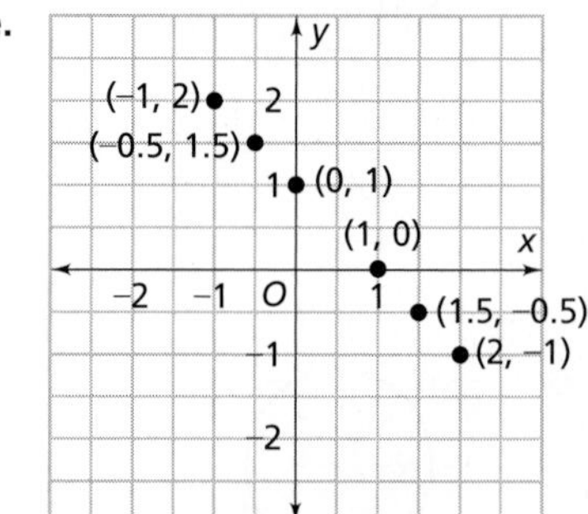

f.

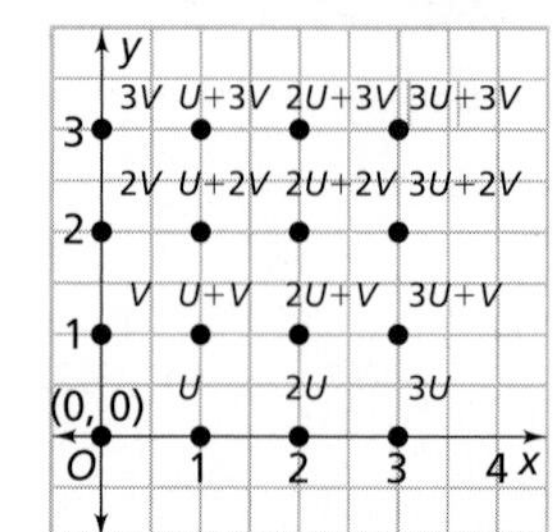

g. Any point (p, q) can be written as $(p, q) = p(1, 0) + q(0, 1)$.

3a.

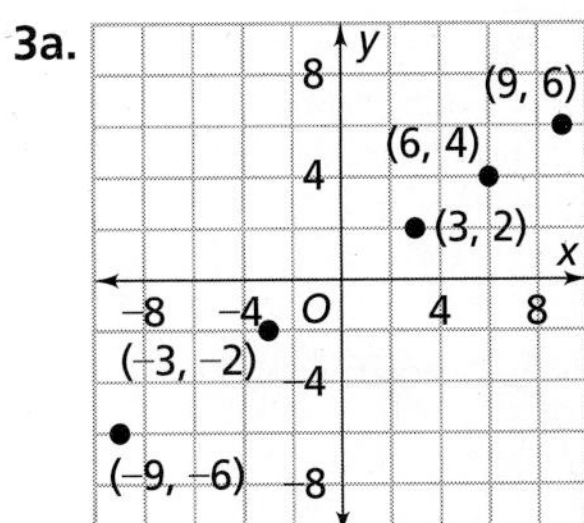

b.

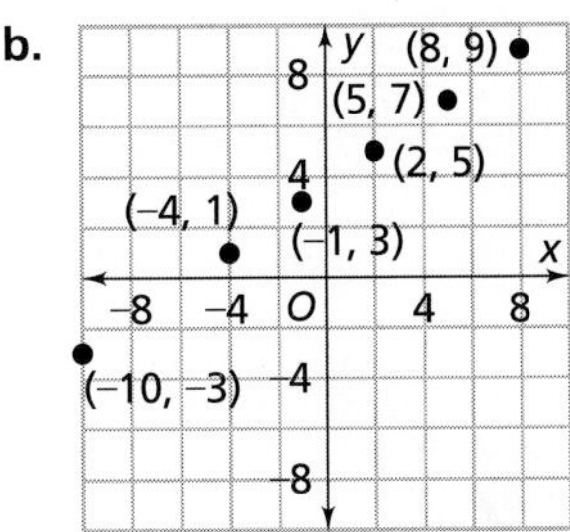

c.

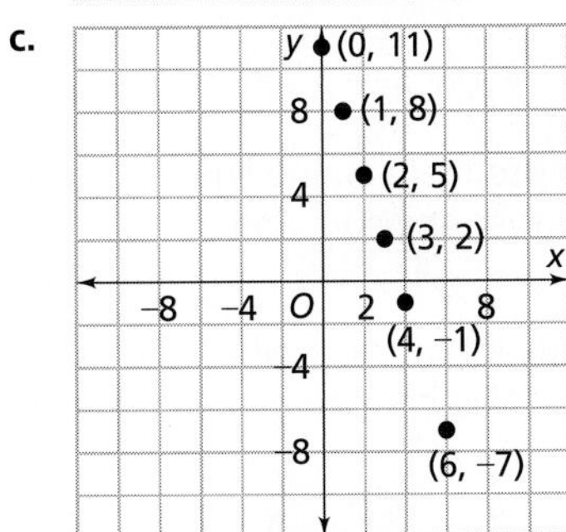

d.

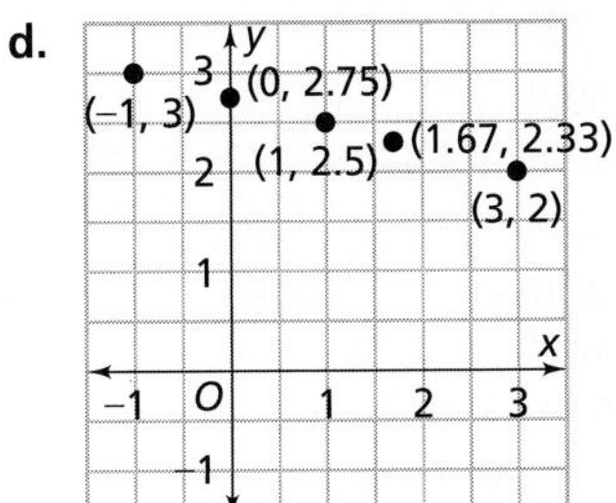

e.

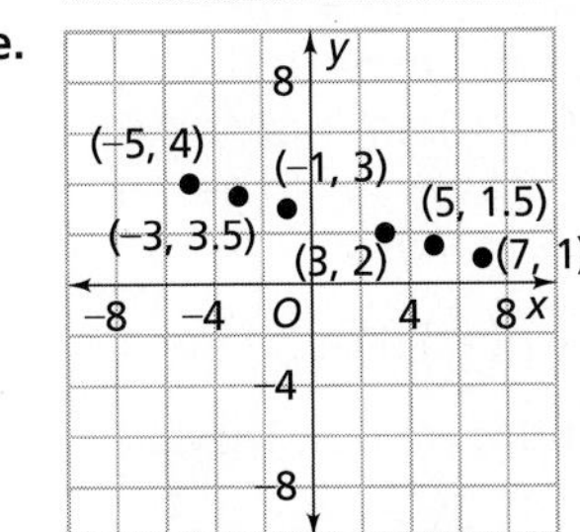

In each part, the points are collinear. In (d) all the points are on the line segment between *U* and *V*. In (e) they are on the line determined by *U* and *V* but outside the segment between them.

4.

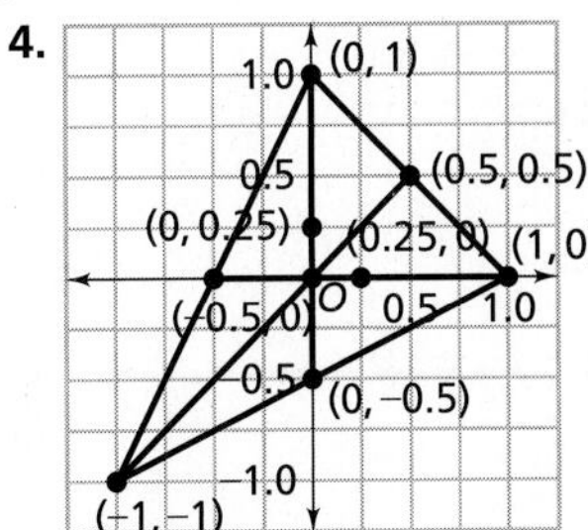

Exercises 8a. The figure is identical but all sides are only one half as long.

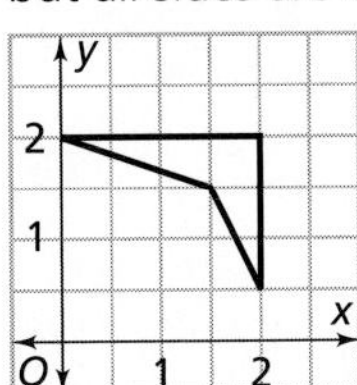

b.

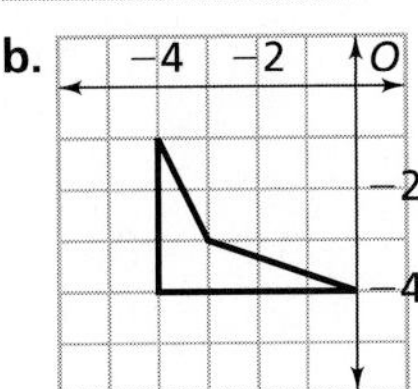

c. The figure will be the same as the figure in part (a) since doubling those dimensions will produce the original figure. **9a.** $\begin{pmatrix} 15 \\ 21 \end{pmatrix}$ **b.** $\begin{pmatrix} -10 \\ -14 \end{pmatrix}$ **c.** $\begin{pmatrix} 20 \\ -90 \end{pmatrix}$ **d.** $\begin{pmatrix} 13 \\ -6 \end{pmatrix}$ **e.** Each term is multiplied by *a*.

Lesson 6.11 **pp. 503–508**

Exercises 1a. The slope of $\overrightarrow{PQ}$ is $\frac{(y + d) - y}{(x + c) - x} = \frac{d}{c}$. Similarly, the slope of $\overrightarrow{RS}$ is $\frac{d}{c}$. **b.** The length of $\overrightarrow{PQ}$ is $\sqrt{((x + c) - x)^2 + ((y + d) - y)^2}$ $= \sqrt{c^2 + d^2}$.
Similarly, the length of $\overrightarrow{RS}$ is $\sqrt{c^2 + d^2}$. **c.** The displacement vector provides the direction. Since they have the same displacement, they must point in the same direction. **2.** If $\overrightarrow{PQ}$ has direction vector D, then $Q = P + kD$ for some positive scalar k. Similarly, $S = R + mD$ for some positive scalar m. The length of $\overrightarrow{PQ}$ is the length of kD, and the length of $\overrightarrow{RS}$ is the length of mD. But these are given to be equal; therefore $k = m$ as long as D is nonzero. Since $k = m$, then $Q - P = kD = mD = S - R$.

8b.

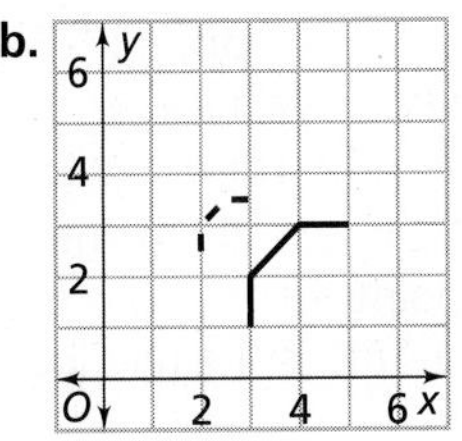

c.

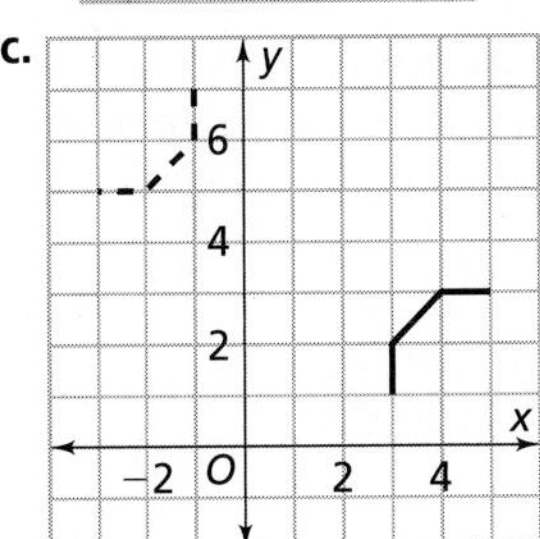

Lesson 6.12 **pp. 509–516**

Exercises

13a. The paths intersect and these cars crash. **b.** The paths do not intersect, and thus do not crash. **c.** The paths do not intersect, and thus do not crash. **d.** The paths intersect, but the cars do not crash. **16.** The first equation and the third equation are the same. The second equation cannot be the same because it has a different slope. The first and third have the same slope and share the point (10, 17) when $t = 3$ and $s = 0$. **20a.** These lines have the same slope and both share the points (1, 0) and (0, 1).

b.

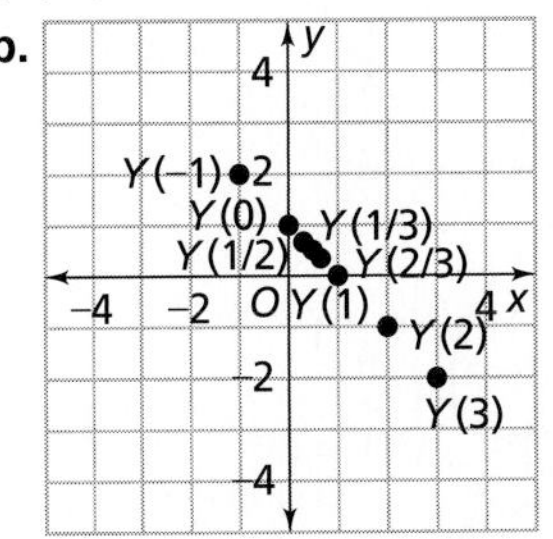

21. All points are located on the line through *P* and *Q*. **a.** midpoint of the segment from *P* to *Q* **b.** the trisection closer to *Q* of the segment from *P* to *Q* **c.** the trisection closer to *P* of the segment from *P* to *Q* **d.** one-fifth of the way from *P* to *Q* **e.** on the opposite side of *P* that is as far from it as *Q* **f.** the point on the opposite side of *P* that is twice as far from it as *Q*

Lesson 6.13 **pp. 517–524**

Exercises 11. ΔPQR is similar to ΔABC by a factor of 2. For instance, $\overrightarrow{RP} = 2\overrightarrow{AC}$. Furthermore, the points A, B, C are the midpoints of the sides of ΔPQR. That is, ΔABC is the midpoint triangle of ΔPQR.

To show this, first note that P is an affine combination of A and $\frac{1}{2}(B + C)$ with $k = 2$. Similar statements hold for Q, R. Therefore:

$$\begin{aligned} P &= -A + 2\left(\frac{B + C}{2}\right) \\ &= -A + B + C \\ Q &= A - B + C \\ R &= A + B - C \end{aligned}$$

Therefore $P - R = 2C - 2A = 2(C - A) = 2\overrightarrow{AC}$, as claimed, and similar methods can be used for the other sides.

Project **pp. 526–529**

3. $x^2 + xy + y^2 = 1$

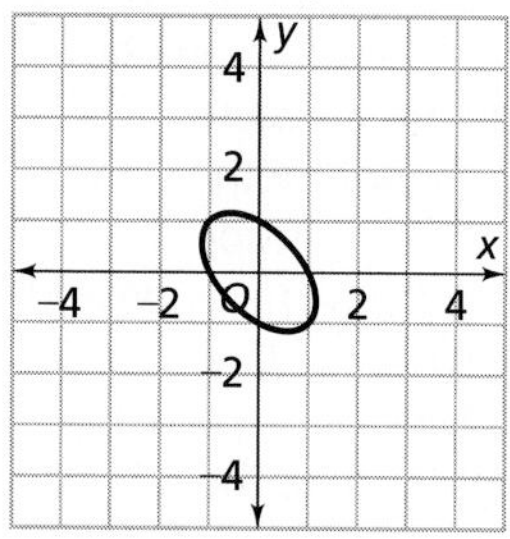

4. $x^2 + xy + y^2 = 4$

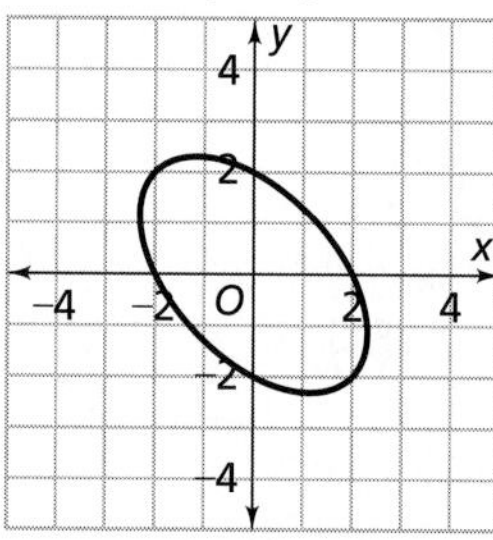

5. $41x^2 - 24xy + 34y^2 = 51$

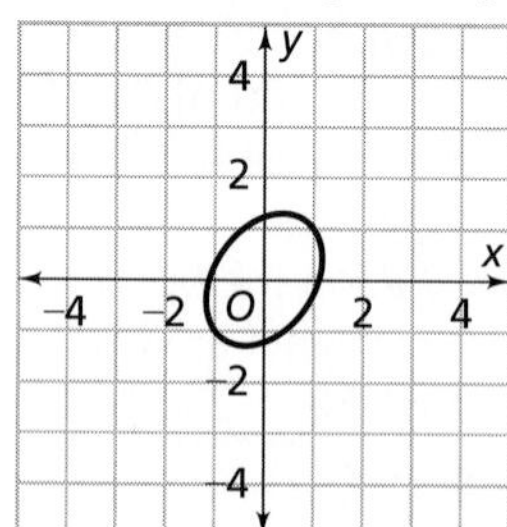

6. $41x^2 - 24xy + 34y^2 = 90$

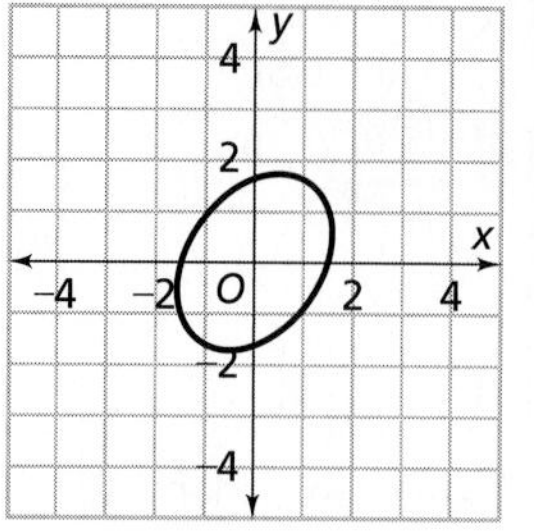

7. $5x^2 + 15xy + 2y^2 = 8$

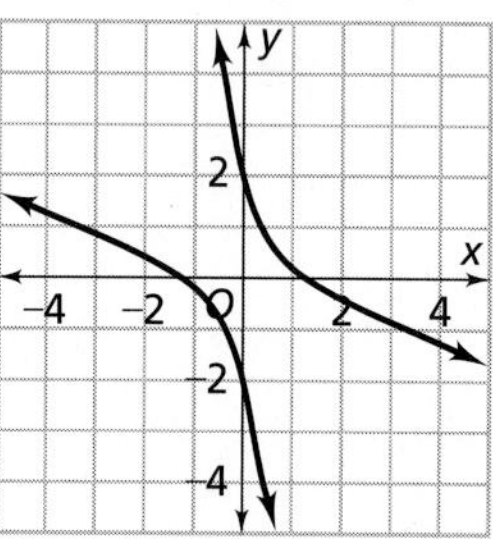

8. $5x^2 - 10xy + 5y^2 - 10y = 8$

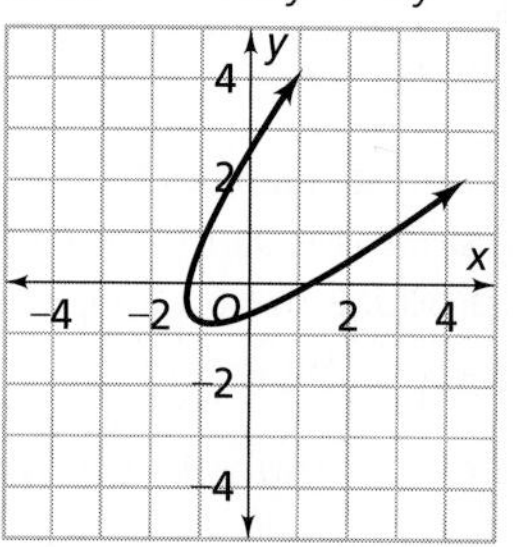

9. $9x^2 + 24xy + 16y^2 = 49$

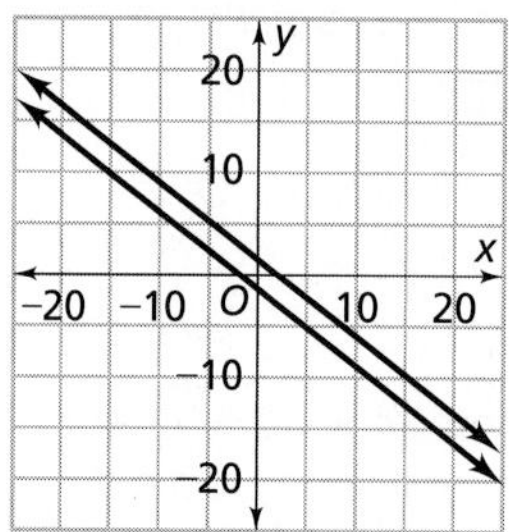

10. $xy = 1$

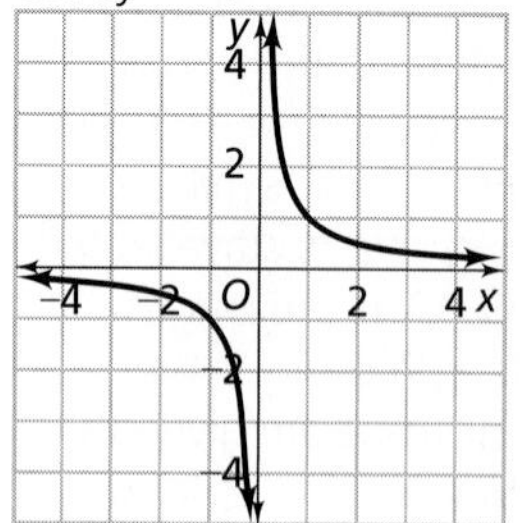

11. $xy = -1$

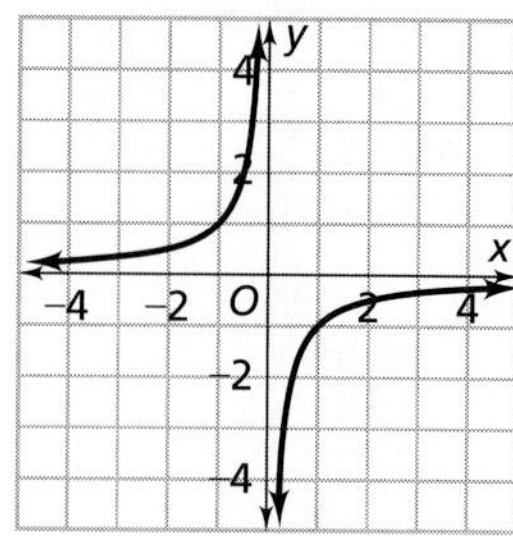

12. $13x^2 + 10xy + 13y^2 = 47$

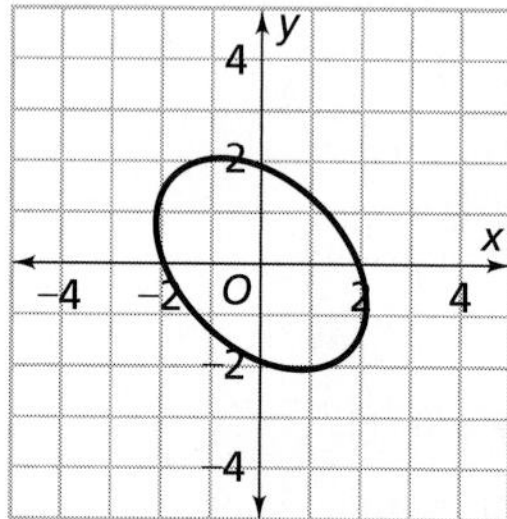

20. Suppose there are no linear terms. You are given the equation

$$rx^2 + sxy + ty^2 = -w \qquad (*)$$

and you want to know what its graph looks like. You hope to find an angle θ so that, if

$$\begin{aligned} \cos\theta\, x' + \sin\theta\, y' &= x \\ -\sin\theta\, y' + \cos\theta\, y' &= y \end{aligned} \qquad (**)$$

Just to remove clutter, let $m = \cos\theta$ and $n = \sin\theta$. Substitute (**) in (*):

$r(mx' + ny')^2 +$
$s(mx' + ny')(-nx' + my') +$
$t(-nx' + my')^2 = -w$

Using a CAS to expand the left side, the coefficient of $x'y'$ is

$-sm^2 + 2(r - t)mn + sn^2$

So, you want this to be 0. That is,

$-sm^2 + 2(r - t)mn + sn^2 = 0$

Divide both sides by m^2 to get an equation in $\frac{n}{m} = \tan\theta$.

$$-s + 2(r - t)\left(\frac{n}{m}\right) + t\left(\frac{n}{m}\right)^2 = 0$$

The roots of this are real. They are

$$\tan\theta = \frac{t - r + \sqrt{(t - r)^2 + s^2}}{s}$$

or

$$\tan\theta = \frac{t - r - \sqrt{(t - r)^2 + s^2}}{s}$$

Hence you can write the original equation

$$(x \quad y)\begin{pmatrix} r & \frac{s}{2} \\ \frac{s}{2} & t \end{pmatrix}\begin{pmatrix} x \\ y \end{pmatrix} = -w \text{ as}$$

$$\begin{pmatrix} x' & y' \end{pmatrix}\begin{pmatrix} r & \frac{s}{2} \\ \frac{s}{2} & t \end{pmatrix}(R_\theta)^{-1}\begin{pmatrix} x' \\ y' \end{pmatrix} = -w$$

and you know that the left-hand side has no cross term. Hence the equation becomes $r'(x')^2 + s'(y')^2 = -w$ whose graph is determined by the sign of $r's'$. But, as in the example,

$$R_\theta\begin{pmatrix} r & \frac{s}{2} \\ \frac{s}{2} & t \end{pmatrix}(R_\theta)^{-1} = \begin{pmatrix} r' & 0 \\ 0 & s' \end{pmatrix}$$

So both sides have the same determinant and trace. In particular

$$r's' = \det\left(R_\theta\begin{pmatrix} r & \frac{s}{2} \\ \frac{s}{2} & t \end{pmatrix}(R_\theta)^{-1}\right) =$$

$$\det\begin{pmatrix} r & \frac{s}{2} \\ \frac{s}{2} & t \end{pmatrix} = rt - \left(\frac{s}{2}\right)^2$$

And the theorem follows.

If there are linear terms, you can translate by completing the square to remove them. There is one case (where either r or s is 0) that you have to handle separately.

Chapter 7

Lesson 7.1 pp. 539–540

Exercises **7a.**

	1	2	3	4	5
1	(1,1)	(1,2)	(1,3)	(1,4)	(1,5)
2	(2,1)	(2,2)	(2,3)	(2,4)	(2,5)
3	(3,1)	(3,2)	(3,3)	(3,4)	(3,5)
4	(4,1)	(4,2)	(4,3)	(4,4)	(4,5)
5	(5,1)	(5,2)	(5,3)	(5,4)	(5,5)

b. $\frac{19}{25}$ **c.** $\frac{23}{36}$ **d.** $\frac{35}{49}$ **8a.** 120 **b.** Answers may vary. Sample: 5.145%. **9a.** 40 **b.** Answers may vary. Sample: 6.895%.

Lesson 7.2 pp. 541–547

Exercises **12a.** 45 **b.** $\frac{28}{45}$

c.

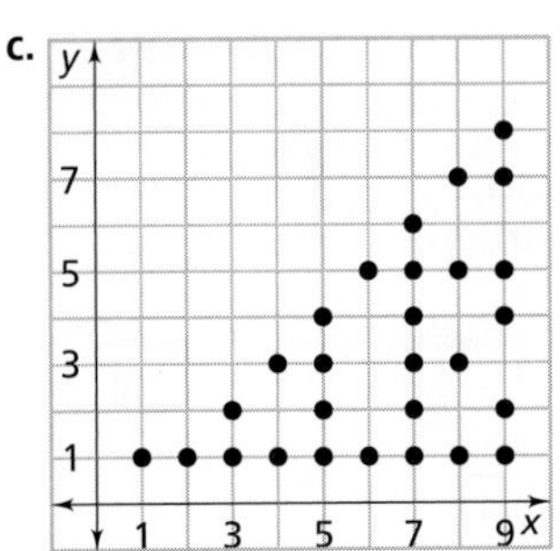

13a. $\frac{144}{1024}$ or $\frac{9}{64}$ **b.** $\frac{1020}{1024}$ or $\frac{255}{256}$ **14.** A

15.

n	Number of elements F_n
1	2
2	3
3	5
4	7
5	11
6	13
7	19
8	23
9	29
10	33

Answers may vary. Sample: The number of elements is always odd.

Lesson 7.3 pp. 548–553

Exercises

1a.

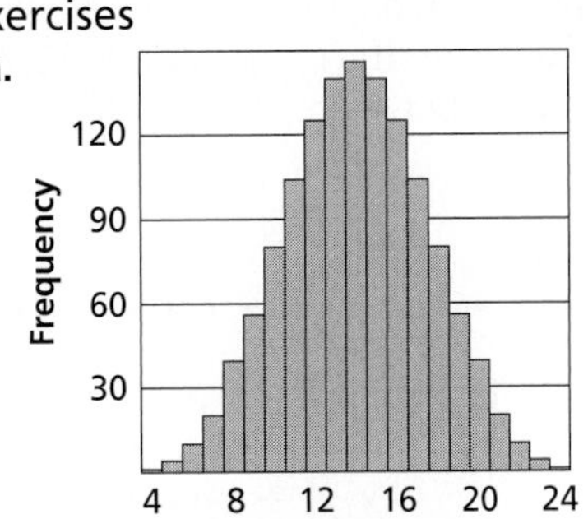

5a. $q(x) = 4x^{10} + 4x^9 + 5x^8 + 6x^7 + 7x^6 + 4x^5 + 3x^4 + 2x^3 + x^2$; this represents the frequencies of the sums when the 1-2-3-4-5-5 number cube is rolled twice. **b.** 36 **c.** 4 **d.** 4 **6a.** 0.06 **b.** $\frac{425}{1000}$ or 0.425 **c.** $\frac{7760}{10{,}000}$ or 0.776

11.

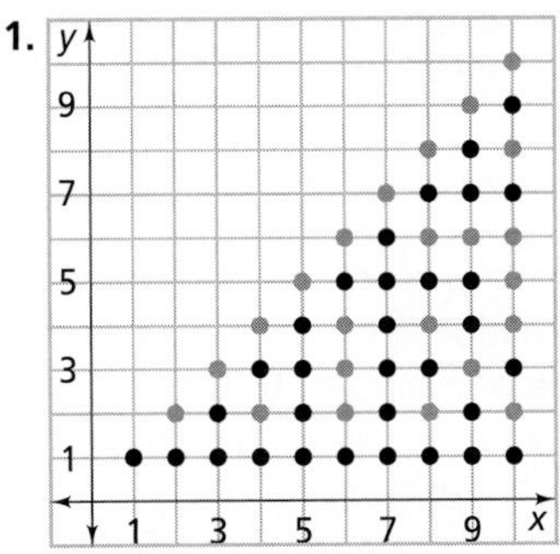

15.

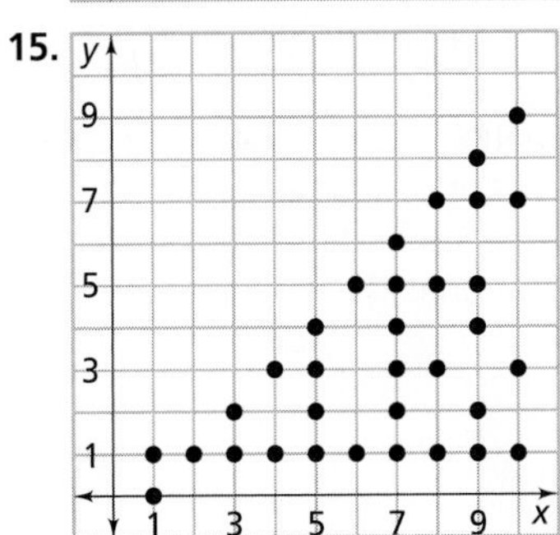

The points plotted are the same as the ones plotted in Exercise 11 that have no common factor greater than 1.

Lesson 7.4 pp. 554–561

Exercises **5a.** $(0.2r + 0.8w)^6 = 0.000064r^6 + 0.001536r^5w + 0.01536r^4w^2 + 0.08192r^3w^3 + 0.24576r^2w^4 + 0.39322rw^5 + 0.26214w^6$; each term is the probability of getting a specific number of questions correct. **17.** See Figure 21.

Figure 21

n	Number of Elements in F_n	Relatively Prime Pairs
1	2	1
2	3	2
3	5	4
4	7	6
5	11	10
6	13	12
7	19	18
8	23	22
9	29	28
10	33	32

Lesson 7.5 pp. 562–569

Exercises 5. See Figure 22.

Lesson 7.7 pp. 575–581

Exercises 7. Let the original data be $\{x_1, x_2, \ldots, x_n\}$ with mean $\bar{x}$. **a.** The new data is $\{(x_1 + c), (x_2 + c), \ldots, (x_n + c)\}$. The mean of the data is

$$\frac{x_1 + c + x_2 + c + \ldots x_n + c}{n}$$
$$= \frac{x_1 + x_2 + \ldots + x_n + n \cdot c}{n}$$
$$= \frac{x_1 + x_2 + \ldots + x_n}{n} + c = \bar{x} + c$$

Each deviation is $(x_i + c) - (\bar{x} + c)$; the value of c cancels. **b.** The new data is $\{kx_1, kx_2, \ldots, kx_n\}$. The mean of the data is $\frac{kx_1 + kx_2 + \ldots + kx_n}{n}$

$$= k \cdot \frac{x_1 + x_2 + \ldots + x_n}{n} = k\bar{x}.$$

Each deviation is $kx_i - k\bar{x} = k(x_i - \bar{x})$; each deviation is k times larger. The variance will be k^2 times larger since each deviation is the variance squared.

Lesson 7.8 pp. 582–590

Exercises 1a. The polynomial is $(x + x^2 + x^3 + x^4 + x^5 + x^6)^3$.

Sum	Frequency
3	1
4	3
5	6
6	10
7	15
8	21
9	25
10	27
11	27
12	25
13	21
14	15
15	10
16	6
17	3
18	1

14. See Figure 23.

Lesson 7.9 pp. 591–595

Exercises 12a. 550; 28.72281
b. Answers may vary. Sample: Yes, this is unusually high; most of the time the sum will be in the range 550 ± 28.7, or roughly between 521 and 579. A sum of 600 is above this range, so this is an unusual result, but not unbelievable. **13.** Answers may vary. Sample: The mean for 100 spins on the Wheel of Fish would be 400 fish. The variance is 1250, and the standard deviation is about 35.4. Most of the results will be between 365 and 435. 500 fish is more than 3 standard deviations from the mean. So the manager can be assured that it is very unlikely, though possible, to give away more than 500 fish. **14.** D **15a.** 0.4019 **b.** 0.4019 **c.** 0.1608 **d.** 0.0354

16. $\binom{5}{0}\left(\frac{1s}{6}\right)^5\left(\frac{5n}{6}\right)^0 + \binom{5}{1}\left(\frac{1s}{6}\right)^4\left(\frac{5n}{6}\right)^1 + \binom{5}{2}\left(\frac{1s}{6}\right)^3\left(\frac{5n}{6}\right)^2 + \binom{5}{3}\left(\frac{1s}{6}\right)^2\left(\frac{5n}{6}\right)^3 + \binom{5}{4}\left(\frac{1s}{6}\right)^1\left(\frac{5n}{6}\right)^4 + \binom{5}{5}\left(\frac{1s}{6}\right)^0\left(\frac{5n}{6}\right)^5$

Here s stands for rolling a six, and n stands for rolling a non-six. The expansion gives the probability for each category. The coefficient for the s^5 is the probability of rolling five sixes. The coefficient of the s^2n^3 term is the probability of rolling exactly 2 sixes.

Lesson 7.10 pp. 596–600

Exercises 7. $p(1 - p)^2 + p^2(1 - p)$
$= p(1 - 2p + p^2) + p^2 - p^3$
$= p - 2p^2 + p^3 + p^2 - p^3$
$= p - p^2$
$= p(1 - p)$

Figure 22

Ticket Type	Frequency	Payout
5 balls + bonus	1	Jackpot
5 balls + no bonus	45	$250,000
4 balls + bonus	255	$10,000
4 balls + no bonus	11,475	$150
3 balls + bonus	12,750	$150
3 balls + no bonus	573,750	$7
2 balls + bonus	208,250	$10
1 ball + bonus	1,249,500	$3
Bonus only	2,349,060	$2
Losing ticket	171,306,450	$0
Total outcomes	**175,711,536**	

0.25029; the expected return for a $1 ticket is 25 cents.

Figure 23

14. There are mn total terms.

$$\overline{xy} = \frac{(x_1y_1 + x_2y_1 + \ldots + x_ny_1) + (x_1y_2 + x_2y_2 + \ldots + x_ny_2) + (\ldots) + (x_1y_m + x_2y_m + \ldots + x_ny_m)}{mn}$$
$$= \frac{y_1(x_1 + x_2 + \ldots + x_n) + y_2(x_1 + x_2 + \ldots + x_n) + y_m(x_1 + x_2 + \ldots + x_n)}{mn}$$
$$= \frac{(x_1 + x_2 + \ldots + x_n)(y_1 + y_2 + \ldots + y_m)}{mn}$$
$$= \frac{(x_1 + x_2 + \ldots + x_n)}{n} \cdot \frac{(y_1 + y_2 + \ldots + y_m)}{m}$$
$$= \bar{x} \cdot \bar{y}$$

8. See Figure 24.

Lesson 7.11 pp. 603–606

Exercises **10.**

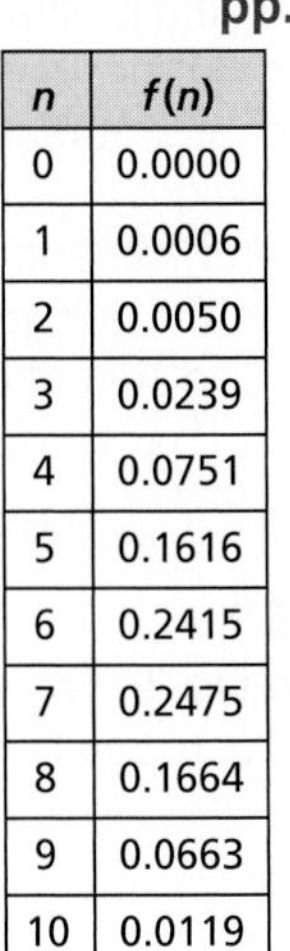

n	$f(n)$
0	0.0000
1	0.0006
2	0.0050
3	0.0239
4	0.0751
5	0.1616
6	0.2415
7	0.2475
8	0.1664
9	0.0663
10	0.0119

Lesson 7.12 pp. 607–616

Exercises **5c.**

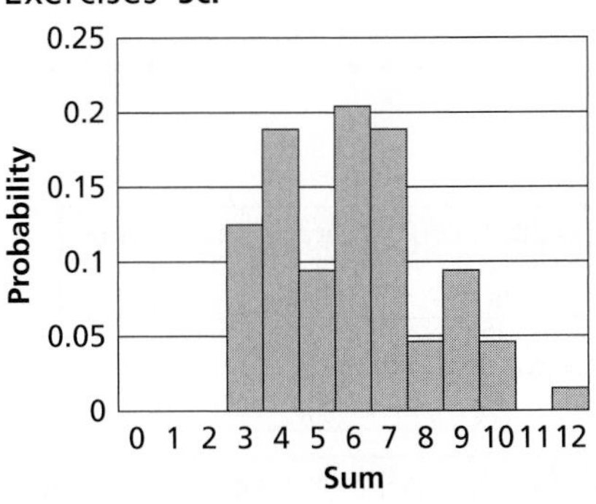

15a. Sum of Two Rolls

b.

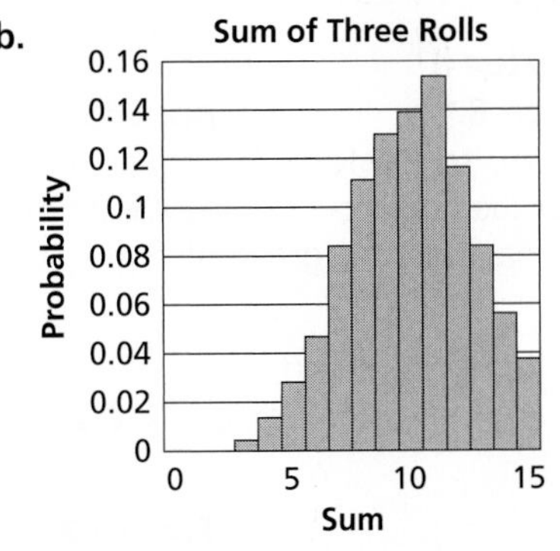

c.

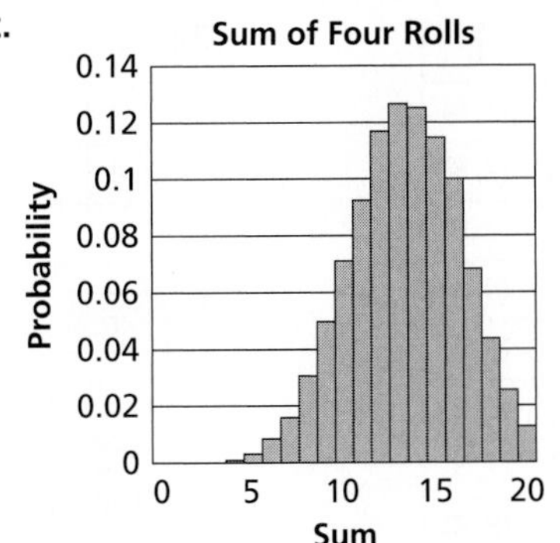

Lesson 7.13 pp. 617–622

Exercises **11.** Answers may vary. Sample: Consider a Bernoulli experiment with probability of success p and n trials. The mean is np and the standard deviation is $\sqrt{np(1-p)}$. The 95% confidence interval is two standard deviations on either side of the mean, so its range is $np \pm 2\sqrt{np(1-p)}$. The proportion of observed successes is found by dividing by n, so it is $p \pm 2\frac{\sqrt{np(1-p)}}{n}$. Now consider $4n$ trials. The 95% confidence interval changes to $4np \pm 2\sqrt{4np(1-p)}$ or $4np \pm 4\sqrt{np(1-p)}$. The width of the confidence interval has doubled. But the proportion of observed successes is now found by dividing by $4n$. It is $p \pm \frac{4\sqrt{np(1-p)}}{4n}$ which is equivalent to $p \pm \frac{\sqrt{np(1-p)}}{n}$. The width of the interval has been cut exactly in half.

14b.

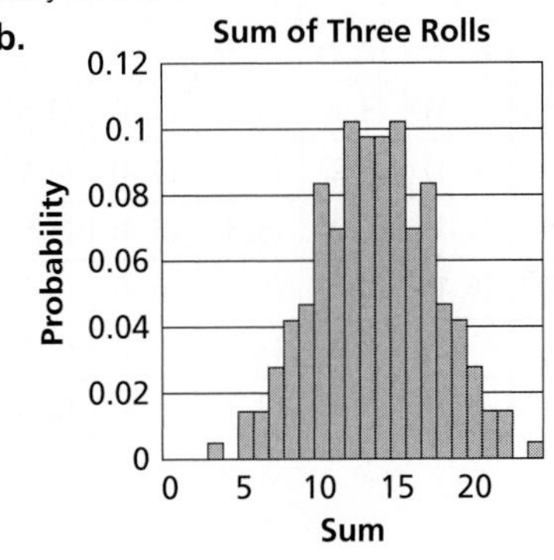

Figure 24

Number of Successes	Probability	Product
2	p^2	$2p^2$
1	$2p(1-p)$	$2p(1-p)$
0	$(1-p)^2$	0
Total		$2p$

Success	Deviation	Deviation^2	Probability	Product
2	$2-2p$	$(2-2p)^2$	p^2	$(2-2p)^2 \cdot p^2$
1	$1-2p$	$(1-2p)^2$	$2p(1-p)$	$(1-2p)^2 \cdot 2p(1-p)$
0	$-2p$	$(-2p)^2$	$(1-p)^2$	$(-2p)^2 \cdot (1-p)^2$
Total				$2p(1-p)$

c.

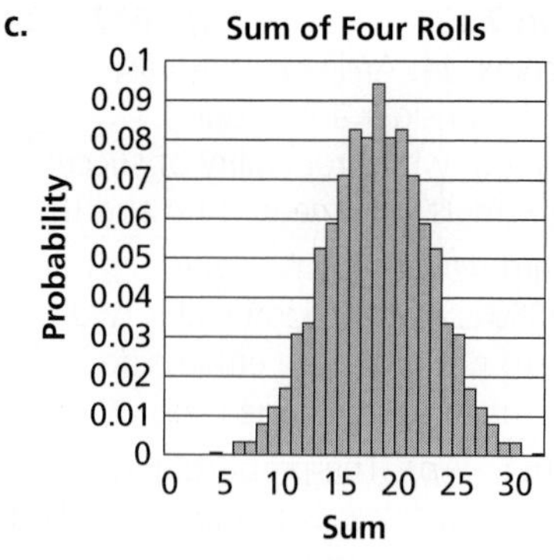

Mathematical Reflections p. 623
5. Todd will make at least 110 of 164 free throws about 22% of the time. **6.** About 56.54% of the women's heights will be in this range. **7.** Let X be a random variable with mean μ and standard deviation σ. The distribution for the sum of the outputs of X over n experiments is more and more closely approximated by $N\left(\mu n, \sigma\sqrt{n}\right)$ as n grows larger. **8.** Answers may vary. Sample: Repeated events make many different probability histograms all behave similarly, and the normal distribution models them, the Central Limit Theorem drives this. **9.** about 20.05%

Review pp. 626–627
1a. See Figure 25.

Chapter 8

Lesson 8.1 pp. 633–636
For You to Explore 10. The area under the graph of $f(x) = kx$ is k times the area under the graph of $f(x) = x$.

Exercises 11. $3ab$, $\frac{5}{2}ab$ **12.** As the previous problem illustrates, a regular polygon with n sides can be divided up into n congruent triangles with base $\frac{P}{n}$ and height a (where P is the polygon's perimeter and a is the distance from the polygon's center to each edge). The area of each triangle is $\frac{1}{2} \cdot \frac{P}{n} \cdot a = \frac{P}{2n}a$, so the area of the polygon is $n \cdot \frac{P}{2n}a = \frac{1}{2}Pa$.

Lesson 8.3 pp. 642–650
For You to Do 9. See Figure 26.
Exercises 2a–b. See Figure 27.

Figure 25

	1	2	3	4	5	6	7	8
1	(1, 1)	(1, 2)	(1, 3)	(1, 4)	(1, 5)	(1, 6)	(1, 7)	(1, 8)
2	(2, 1)	(2, 2)	(2, 3)	(2, 4)	(2, 5)	(2, 6)	(2, 7)	(2, 8)
3	(3, 1)	(3, 2)	(3, 3)	(3, 4)	(3, 5)	(3, 6)	(3, 7)	(3, 8)
4	(4, 1)	(4, 2)	(4, 3)	(4, 4)	(4, 5)	(4, 6)	(4, 7)	(4, 8)
5	(5, 1)	(5, 2)	(5, 3)	(5, 4)	(5, 5)	(5, 6)	(5, 7)	(5, 8)
6	(6, 1)	(6, 2)	(6, 3)	(6, 4)	(6, 5)	(6, 6)	(6, 7)	(6, 8)
7	(7, 1)	(7, 2)	(7, 3)	(7, 4)	(7, 5)	(7, 6)	(7, 7)	(7, 8)
8	(8, 1)	(8, 2)	(8, 3)	(8, 4)	(8, 5)	(8, 6)	(8, 7)	(8, 8)

Figure 26

Upper sums for different number of subdivisions		
Number of subdivisions n	**Upper sum $U_n[0, 1](x^2)$**	**Approximate value**
6	$\frac{1}{6^3}(1^2 + 2^2 + 3^2 + 4^2 + 5^2 + 6^2)$	0.4212963
7	$\frac{1}{7^3}(1^2 + 2^2 + 3^2 + 4^2 + 5^2 + 6^2 + 7^2)$	0.4081633
8	$\frac{1}{8^3}(1^2 + 2^2 + 3^2 + 4^2 + 5^2 + 6^2 + 7^2 + 8^2)$	0.3984375
9	$\frac{1}{9^3}(1^2 + 2^2 + 3^2 + 4^2 + 5^2 + 6^2 + 7^2 + 8^2 + 9^2)$	0.3909465
⋮	⋮	
15	$\frac{1}{15^3}\sum_{i=1}^{15} i^2$	0.3674074
⋮	⋮	
n	$\frac{1}{n^3}\sum_{i=1}^{n} i^2$	

Figure 27

2a.

n	$L_n[0, 1](x^2)$	$U_n[0, 1](x^2)$	Average	Difference
2	$\frac{1}{8}$	$\frac{5}{8}$	$\frac{3}{8}$	$\frac{1}{2}$
4	$\frac{7}{32}$	$\frac{15}{32}$	$\frac{11}{32}$	$\frac{1}{4}$
8	$\frac{35}{128}$	$\frac{51}{128}$	$\frac{43}{128}$	$\frac{1}{8}$

b.

n	$L_n[0, 1](x^2)$	$U_n[0, 1](x^2)$	Average	Difference
10	0.285	0.385	0.335	0.1
200	0.3308375	0.3358375	0.3333375	0.005
1000	0.3328335	0.3338335	0.3333335	0.001

Additional Answers

Lesson 8.4 **pp. 653–656**

For You to Explore **2.** Answers may vary. Samples:

n	$L_n[0, 1]\,(x^3)$	$U_n[0, 1]\,(x^3)$
2	$\frac{1}{16}$	$\frac{9}{16}$
3	$\frac{1}{9}$	$\frac{4}{9}$
4	0.14	0.39
5	0.16	0.36
6	0.174	0.34
7	0.1837	0.327

Beginning with $n = 7$ the values of the upper sum $U_n[0, 1](x^3)$ are smaller than the actual area $S[0, 1](x^2)$, confirming that the area $S[0, 1](x^3)$ is smaller than the area $S[0, 1](x^2)$.

5. See Figure 28.

Lesson 8.6 **pp. 663–670**

Exercises **2b.** See Figure 29.

c. $LF_n[1, 2](x^m) = (1 + r^{m+1} + (r^{m+1})^2 + (r^{m+1})^3 + \cdots + (r^{m+1})^{(n-1)})(r - 1)$

3. See Figure 30.

Figure 28

Number of subdivisions n	Upper Sum Approximation for Different Numbers of Subdivisions, $U_n[0,1](x^3)$
4	0.390625
5	0.36
6	$\frac{1}{6^4} \cdot (1^3 + 2^3 + 3^3 + 4^3 + 5^3 + 6^3) \approx 0.34028$
7	$\frac{1}{7^4} \cdot (1^3 + 2^3 + 3^3 + 4^3 + 5^3 + 6^3 + 7^3) \approx 0.32653$
⋮	⋮
15	$\frac{1}{15^4} \cdot \sum_{i=1}^{15} i^3 \approx 0.28444$
n	$\frac{1}{n^4} \cdot \sum_{i=1}^{n} i^3$

Figure 29

Fermat Lower Sum for $y = x^m$: $LF_n[1, 2](x^m)$

	base	height	area
1st rectangle	$r - 1$	1	$1(r - 1)$
2nd rectangle	$r^2 - r = r(r - 1)$	r^m	$r^{m+1}(r - 1)$
3rd rectangle	$r^3 - r^2 = r^2(r - 1)$	$(r^2)^m = r^{2m}$	$r^{2(m+1)}(r - 1)$
4th rectangle	$r^4 - r^3 = r^3(r - 1)$	$(r^3)^m = r^{3m}$	$r^{3(m+1)}(r - 1)$
⋮	⋮	⋮	⋮
nth rectangle	$r^n - r^{n-1} = r^{n-1}(r - 1)$	$(r^{n-1})^m = r^{(n-1)m}$	$r^{(n-1)(m+1)}(r - 1)$

Figure 30

Fermat Upper Sum for $y = x^m$: $UF_n[1, 2](x^m)$

	base	height	area
1st rectangle	$r - 1$	r^m	$r^m(r - 1)$
2nd rectangle	$r^2 - r = r(r - 1)$	$(r^2)^m = r^{2m}$	$r^{2m+1}(r - 1)$
3rd rectangle	$r^3 - r^2 = r^2(r - 1)$	$(r^3)^m = r^{3m}$	$r^{3m+2}(r - 1)$
4th rectangle	$r^4 - r^3 = r^3(r - 1)$	$(r^4)^m = r^{4m}$	$r^{4m+3}(r - 1)$
⋮	⋮	⋮	⋮
nth rectangle	$r^n - r^{n-1} = r^{n-1}(r - 1)$	$(r^n)^m = r^{nm}$	$r^{nm+(n-1)}(r - 1)$

$$UF_n[1, 2](x^m) = \frac{2^{m+1} - 1}{\sum_{i=0}^{m} r^i} \cdot r^m$$

Additional Answers

Lesson 8.7 pp. 675–676

For You to Explore **1b.** See Figure 31.

Lesson 8.8 pp. 677–682

For You to Do **1.** Answers may vary. Sample:

n	$n(\sqrt[n]{2} - 1)$
20	≈ 0.7052985
200	≈ 0.6943497
1,000,000	≈ 0.6931474

For Discussion **3.** If, $b > 1$, and a number a such that $1 < a < b$, the shape under $y = \frac{1}{x}$ between 1 and b will be broken in two parts by the line $x = a$, so the area will be the sum of the areas of the two parts. **4.** Answers may vary. Sample: using the upper sum,

$$UF_n[1, a](x^{-1}) = n\left(\sqrt[n]{a} - 1\right)$$

with $n = 1{,}000{,}000$ subdivisions to approximate $S[1, a](x^{-1})$,

a	$1{,}000{,}000(\sqrt[1{,}000{,}000]{a} - 1)$
1	0
2	≈ 0.6931474
3	≈ 1.0986129
4	≈ 1.3862953
5	≈ 1.6094392
6	≈ 1.7917611
7	≈ 1.945912
8	≈ 2.0794437
9	≈ 2.197227
10	≈ 2.3025877

Exercises **1.** Answers will vary, but should be close to the values in the table.

a	$\mathcal{L}(a)$
1	0
1.5	0.405465108108
2	0.69314718056
2.5	0.916290731874
3	1.09861228867
3.5	1.2527629685
4	1.38629436112
4.5	1.50407739678
5	1.60943791243
5.5	1.70474809224
6	1.79175946923
6.5	1.8718021769
7	1.94591014906
7.5	2.01490302054
8	2.07944154168
8.5	2.1400661635
9	2.19722457734
9.5	2.25129179861
10	2.30258509299

6. Answers may vary. Sample: This statement is true when $m = 0$, since $\mathcal{L}(r^0) = \mathcal{L}(1) = 0 = 0 \cdot \mathcal{L}(r)$. Assume that $\mathcal{L}(r^{m-1}) = (m - 1)\,\mathcal{L}(r)$ where $r > 1$ and $m > 0$, then

$$\begin{aligned}
&\mathcal{L}(r^m)\\
&= S[1, r^m](x^{-1})\\
&= S[1, r](x^{-1}) + S[r, r^m](x^{-1})\\
&= S[1, r](x^{-1}) + S[1, \tfrac{r^m}{r}](x^{-1})\\
&= S[1, r](x^{-1}) + S[1, r^{m-1}](x^{-1})\\
&= \mathcal{L}(r) + \mathcal{L}(r^{m-1})\\
&= \mathcal{L}(r) + (m-1)\mathcal{L}(r)\\
&= m\mathcal{L}(r)
\end{aligned}$$

12. $U_4[1, 5]\left(\frac{1}{x}\right)$

$$= 1(1)^{-1} + 1(2)^{-1} + 1(3)^{-1} + 1(4)^{-1}$$
$$= 1 + \tfrac{1}{2} + \tfrac{1}{3} + \tfrac{1}{4}$$

$U_4[3, 15]\left(\frac{1}{x}\right)$

$$= 3(3)^{-1} + 3(6)^{-1} + 3(9)^{-1} + 3(12)^{-1}$$
$$= 1 + \tfrac{1}{2} + \tfrac{1}{3} + \tfrac{1}{4}$$

17. width of rectangle $\Delta = \frac{b-a}{n}$; area of ith rectangle $= \frac{b-a}{n} \cdot \frac{1}{a + \frac{i(b-a)}{n}} = \frac{b-a}{(n-i)a + ib}$

a. $U_n[1, 4]\left(\frac{1}{x}\right)$: area of ith rectangle

$$= \frac{b-a}{(n-i)a + ib} = \frac{4-1}{(n-i)\cdot 1 + i \cdot 4} = \frac{3}{n+3i}$$

$U_n[3, 12]\left(\frac{1}{x}\right)$: area of ith rectangle

$$= \frac{b-a}{(n-i)a + ib} = \frac{12-3}{(n-i)\cdot 3 + i \cdot 12} = \frac{9}{3n+9i} = \frac{9}{3(n+3i)} = \frac{3}{n+3i}$$

Since the area of each corresponding rectangle is the same, $U_n[1, 4]\left(\frac{1}{x}\right) = U_n[3, 12]\left(\frac{1}{x}\right)$.

b. $U_6[1, 3]\left(\frac{1}{x}\right)$: area of ith rectangle

$$= \frac{b-a}{(n-i)a + ib} = \frac{3-1}{(6-i)\cdot 1 + i \cdot 3} = \frac{2}{6+2i} = \frac{1}{3+i}$$

$U_6[3, 9]\left(\frac{1}{x}\right)$: area of ith rectangle

$$= \frac{b-a}{(n-i)a + ib} = \frac{9-3}{(6-i)\cdot 3 + i \cdot 9} = \frac{6}{18+6i} = \frac{1}{3+i}$$

Since the area of each corresponding rectangle is the same, $U_6[1, 3]\left(\frac{1}{x}\right) = U_6[3, 9]\left(\frac{1}{x}\right)$

Figure 31 Fermat Upper Sum for $y = x^{-2}$, $UF_n[1, 2](x^{-2})$

	base	height	area
1st rectangle	$r - 1$	1	$1(r-1)$
2nd rectangle	$r^2 - r = r(r-1)$	r^{-2}	$r^{-1}(r-1)$
3rd rectangle	$r^3 - r^2 = r^2(r-1)$	r^{-4}	$r^{-2}(r-1)$
4th rectangle	$r^4 - r^3 = r^3(r-1)$	r^{-6}	$r^{-3}(r-1)$
⋮	⋮	⋮	⋮
nth rectangle	$r^n - r^{n-1} = r^{n-1}(r-1)$	$r^{-2(n-1)}$	$r^{-(n-1)}(r-1)$

c. $U_n[1, 3](\frac{1}{x})$: area of rectangle

$= \frac{b - a}{(n - i)a + ib} = \frac{3 - 1}{(n - i) \cdot 1 + i \cdot 3}$

$= \frac{2}{n + 2i}$

$U_n[3, 9](\frac{1}{x})$: area of rectangle

$= \frac{b - a}{(n - i)a + ib} = \frac{9 - 3}{(n - i) \cdot 3 + i \cdot 9}$

$= \frac{6}{3n + 6i} = \frac{2}{n + 2i}$

Since the area of each corresponding rectangle is the same, $U_n[1, 3]\left(\frac{1}{x}\right) = U_n[3, 9]\left(\frac{1}{x}\right)$

Lesson 8.9 **pp. 683–689**

Exercises

1a. See Figure 32.

b. The sum of the rectangles is $n(r - 1)r^{-1} = n\left(\sqrt[n]{2} - 1\right)2^{-\frac{1}{n}}$ since $r = \sqrt[n]{2}$.

Project **pp. 696–698**

2–3a. See Figure 33. **b.** Answer may vary. Sample: The degree of $t(n, x)$ is n. The leading coefficient of $t(n, x)$ is 2^{n-1}. The polynomial function $t(n, x)$ is an odd function when n is odd and an even function when n is even.

Figure 32 Fermat Lower Sum for $y = x^{-1}$ on [1, 2]

	base	height	area
1st rectangle	$r - 1$	$\frac{1}{r}$	$(r - 1)\frac{1}{r}$
2nd rectangle	$r^2 - r = r(r - 1)$	$\frac{1}{r^2}$	$(r - 1)\frac{1}{r}$
3rd rectangle	$r^3 - r^2 = r^2(r - 1)$	$\frac{1}{r^3}$	$(r - 1)\frac{1}{r}$
4th rectangle	$r^4 - r^3 = r^3(r - 1)$	$\frac{1}{r^4}$	$(r - 1)\frac{1}{r}$
⋮	⋮	⋮	⋮
nth rectangle	$r^n - r^{n-1} = r^{n-1}(r - 1)$	$\frac{1}{r^n}$	$(r - 1)\frac{1}{r}$

Figure 33

n	$t(n, x)$
0	1
1	x
2	$2x^2 - 1$
3	$4x^3 - 3x$
4	$8x^4 - 8x^2 + 1$
5	$16x^5 - 20x^3 + 5x$
6	$32x^6 - 48x^4 + 18x^2 - 1$
7	$64x^7 - 112x^5 + 56x^3 - 7x$
8	$128x^8 - 256x^6 + 160x^4 - 32x^2 + 1$
9	$256x^9 - 576x^7 + 432x^5 - 120x^3 + 9x$
10	$512x^{10} - 1280x^8 + 1120x^6 - 400x^4 + 50x^2 - 1$
11	$1024x^{11} - 2816x^9 + 2816x^7 - 1232x^5 + 220x^3 - 11x$
12	$2048x^{12} - 6144x^{10} + 6912x^8 - 3584x^6 + 840x^4 - 72x^2 + 1$
13	$4096x^{13} - 13{,}312x^{11} + 16{,}640x^9 - 9984x^7 + 2912x^5 - 364x^3 + 13x$
14	$8192x^{14} - 28{,}672x^{12} + 39{,}424x^{10} - 26{,}880x^8 + 9408x^6 - 1568x^4 + 98x^2 - 1$
15	$16{,}384x^{15} - 61{,}440x^{13} + 92{,}160x^{11} - 70{,}400x^9 + 28{,}800x^7 - 6048x^5 + 560x^3 - 15x$
16	$32{,}768x^{16} - 131{,}072x^{14} + 212{,}992x^{12} - 180{,}224x^{10} + 84{,}480x^8 - 21{,}504x^6 + 2688x^4 - 128x^2 + 1$
17	$65{,}536x^{17} - 278{,}528x^{15} + 487{,}424x^{13} - 452{,}608x^{11} + 239{,}360x^9 - 71{,}808x^7 + 11{,}424x^5 - 816x^3 + 17x$
18	$131{,}072x^{18} - 589{,}824x^{16} + 1{,}105{,}920x^{14} - 1{,}118{,}208x^{12} + 658{,}944x^{10} - 228{,}096x^8 + 44{,}352x^6 - 4320x^4 + 162x^2 - 1$

4a.

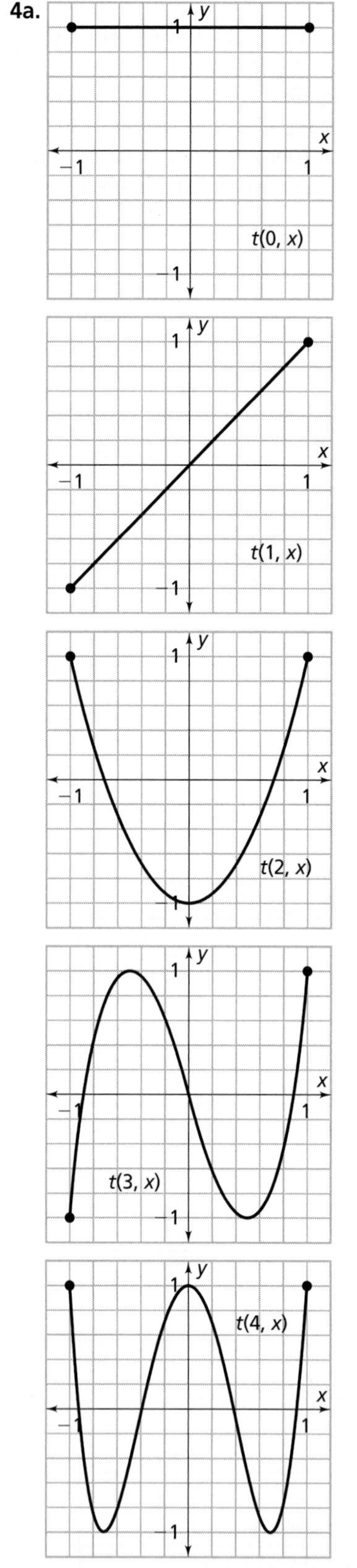

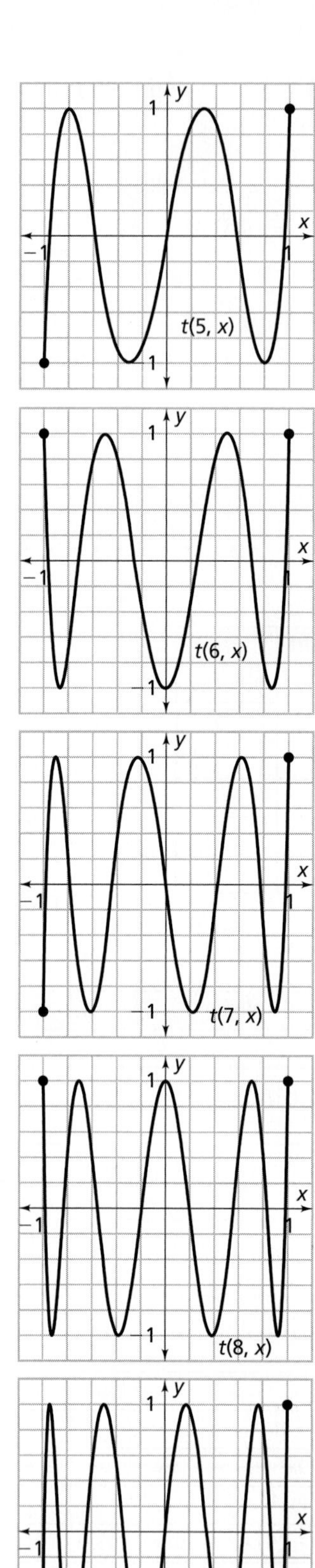

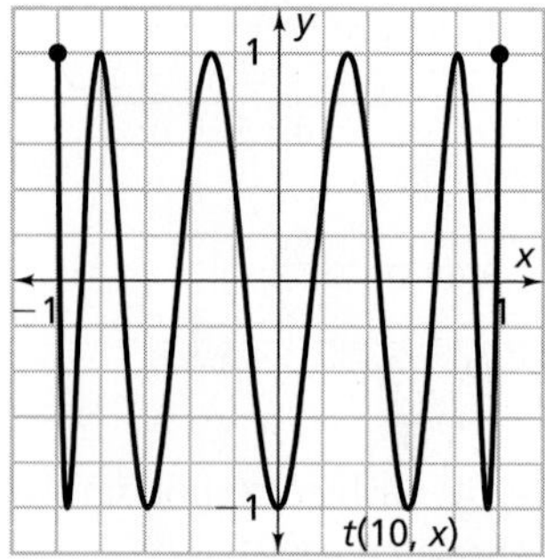

b. Answers may vary. Sample: When n is even, the graph is symmetric about the y-axis, when n is odd, the graph is symmetric with respect to the origin; several of the graphs have x-intercepts in common.

c.

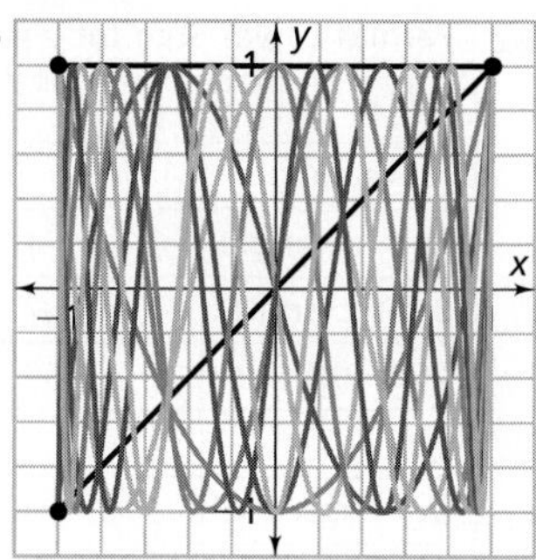

Answers may vary. Sample: There seem to be a few points that several of the graphs have in common. (These are in addition to shared x-intercepts.) **5.** See Figure 34. **6a.** See Figure 35. **8.** It is easy to show that $\cos(n + 1)\alpha = 2 \cos \alpha \cos n\alpha - \cos(n - 1)\alpha$. This implies that $n \mapsto \cos n\alpha$ satisfies the same recurrence as $t(n, x)$. It also satisfies the same base cases. So:

$$t(n, x) = \begin{cases} 1 & \text{if } n = 0 \\ x & \text{if } n = 1 \\ 2xt(n - 1, x) & \text{if } n > 1 \\ -t(n - 2, x) & \end{cases}$$

and

$$\cos n\alpha = \begin{cases} 1 & \text{if } n = 0 \\ \cos \alpha & \text{if } n = 1 \\ 2 \cos \alpha \cos(n - 1)\alpha & \text{if } n > 1 \\ -\cos(n - 2)\alpha & \end{cases}$$

It follows by induction that $t(n, \cos \alpha) = \cos n\alpha$ for all nonnegative integers n.

10. By the factor theorem, $t(m, x)$ will be a factor of $t(n, x)$ if and only if the zeros of $t(m, x)$ are among the zeros of $t(n, x)$. So, the question comes down to finding when every number of the form $\frac{(2j - 1)\pi}{2m}$ is also of the form $\frac{(2k - 1)\pi}{2n}$.

In particular, consider when $\frac{\pi}{2m}$ is also of the form $\frac{(2k - 1)\pi}{2n}$ for some j.

If $\frac{\pi}{2m} = \frac{(2k - 1)\pi}{2n}$, then $n = (2k - 1)m$, so n is an odd multiple of m. And, conversely, if n is an odd multiple of m, say $n = (2k - 1)m$, then

$$\frac{(2j - 1)\pi}{2m} = \frac{(2j - 1)\pi}{2 \cdot \frac{n}{2k - 1}} = \frac{(2j - 1)(2k - 1) \cdot \pi}{2n} = \frac{\text{odd} \cdot \pi}{2n}$$

So every zero of $t(m, x)$is a zero of $t(n, x)$

11d. $\frac{16x^5 - 20x^3 + 5x}{8x^4 - 8x^2 + 1}$

e. $\frac{32x^6 - 48x^4 + 18x^2 - 1}{16x^5 - 20x^3 + 5x}$

12a. Answers may vary. Sample: The continued fraction with n levels simplifies to $\frac{t(n + 1, x)}{t(n, x)}$. **b.** This follows by induction and from the recurrence $t(n + 1, x) = 2xt(n, x) - t(n - 1, x)$, since you can divide both sides by $t(n, x)$ to obtain the following:

$$\frac{t(n + 1, x)}{t(n, x)} = 2x - \frac{t(n - 1, x)}{t(n, x)} = 2x - \frac{1}{\frac{t(n, x)}{t(n - 1, x)}}$$

Figure 34

n	$t(n, x)$	Roots of $t(n, x) = 0$
0	1	none
1	x	0
2	$2x^2 - 1$	$\pm\frac{\sqrt{2}}{2}$
3	$4x^3 - 3x$	$0, \pm\frac{\sqrt{3}}{2}$
4	$8x^4 - 8x^2 + 1$	$\pm\frac{\sqrt{2+\sqrt{2}}}{2}, \pm\frac{\sqrt{2-\sqrt{2}}}{2}$
5	$16x^5 - 20x^3 + 5x$	$0, \pm\frac{\sqrt{10 - 2\sqrt{5}}}{4}, \pm\frac{\sqrt{10 + 2\sqrt{5}}}{4}$
6	$32x^6 - 48x^4 + 18x^2 - 1$	$\pm\frac{\sqrt{2}}{2}, \pm\frac{\sqrt{2+\sqrt{3}}}{2}, \pm\frac{\sqrt{2-\sqrt{3}}}{2}$

Figure 35

n	Factorization of $t(n, x)$
1	x
2	$2x^a - 1 + 2x^3$
3	$x(4x^2 - 3)$
4	$8x^4 - 8x^2 + 1$
5	$x(16x^4 - 20x^2 + 5)$
6	$(2x^2 - 1)(16x^4 - 16x^2 + 1)$
7	$x(64x^6 - 112x^4 + 56x^2 - 7)$
8	$128x^8 - 256x^6 + 160x^4 - 32x^2 + 1$
9	$x(-4x^2 + 3)(-64x^6 + 96x^4 - 36x^2 + 3)$
10	$(2x^2 - 1)(256x^8 - 512x^6 - 304x^4 - 48x^2 + 1)$
11	$x(1024x^{10} - 2816x^8 + 2816x^6 - 1232x^4 + 220x^2 - 11)$
12	$(8x^4 - 8x^2 + 1)(256x^8 - 512x^6 + 320x^4 - 64x^2 + 1)$
13	$x(4096x^{12} - 13{,}312x^{10} + 16{,}640x^8 - 9984x^6 + 2912x^4 - 364x^2 + 13)$
14	$(2x^2 - 1)(4096x^{12} - 12{,}288x^{10} + 13{,}568x^8 - 6656x^6 + 1376x^4 - 96x^2 + 1)$
15	$x(4x^2 + 3)(-16x^4 + 20x^2 - 5)(256x^8 - 448x^6 + 224x^4 - 32x^2 + 1)$
16	$32{,}768x^{16} - 131{,}072x^{14} + 212{,}992x^{12} - 180{,}224x^{10} + 84{,}480x^8 - 21{,}504x^6 + 2688x^4 - 128x^2 + 1$
17	$x(65{,}536x^{16} - 278{,}528x^{14} + 487{,}424x^{12} - 452{,}608x^{10} + 239{,}360x^8 - 71{,}808x^6 + 11{,}424x^4 - 816x^2 + 17)$
18	$(2x^2 - 1)(16x^4 - 16x^2 + 1)(4096x^{12} - 12{,}288x^{10} + 13{,}824x^8 - 7168x^6 + 1680x^4 - 144x^2 + 1)$

13a.

n	Area
0	2
1	0
2	$-\frac{2}{3}$
3	0
4	$-\frac{2}{15}$
5	0
6	$-\frac{2}{35}$
7	0
8	$-\frac{2}{63}$
9	0
10	$-\frac{2}{99}$

b. It seems that for odd n, the value is 0. For even n, it seems that the value is $-\frac{2}{n^2 - 1}$. **c.** It is easy to prove the conjecture for odd n. The function is odd, so the negative area to the left of the y-axis cancels the positive area to the right of the x-axis.

14. Suppose that $t(n, x) = (A(x))^n$ for some $A(x)$. Then from $t(n, x) = 2xt(n - 1, x) + t(n - 2, x)$ you get $(A(x))^n = 2x(A(x))^{n-1} - (A(x))^{n-2}$ Divide both sides by $(A(x))^{n-2}$ and re-arrange to find that $(A(x))^2 - 2x(A(x)) + 1 = 0$

This is a quadratic equation in $A(x)$ with coefficients that are polynomials in x. Use the quadratic formula to find that $A(x) = x \pm \sqrt{x^2 - 1}$. By the methods of Chapter 5, the general solution is of the form $r(x)\left(x + \sqrt{x^2 - 1}\right) + s(x)\left(x - \sqrt{x^2 - 1}\right)$. Now use the base cases to find that $r(x)$ and $s(x)$ are both equal to $\frac{1}{2}$.

Review pp. 699–700

5a.
$$\sum_{k=1}^{n-1} k^3 = \sum_{k=1}^{n} k^3 - n^3 = \frac{n^2(n+1)^2}{4} - n^3 = \frac{n^2(n^2 + 2n + 1)}{4} - n^3 = \frac{n^4 + 2n^3 + n^2 - 4n^3}{4} = \frac{n^4 - 2n^3 + n^2}{4} = \frac{n^2(n^2 - 2n + 1)}{4} = \frac{n^2(n-1)^2}{4}$$

b.
$$\sum_{k=1}^{n} (2k)^3 = \sum_{k=1}^{n} 8k^3 = 8 \cdot \sum_{k=1}^{n} k^3 = 8 \cdot \frac{n^2(n+1)^2}{4} = \frac{8n^2(n+1)^2}{4}$$

c.
$$\sum_{k=1}^{n} (rk)^3 = \sum_{k=1}^{n} r^3k^3 = r^3 \cdot \sum_{k=1}^{n} k^3 = r^3 \cdot \frac{n^2(n+1)^2}{4} = \frac{r^3n^2(n+1)^2}{4}$$

Index

Teacher Edition entries appear in blue type.

K

L

M

N

O

P

Q

R

S

T

U

V

W

Z

Acknowledgments

Staff Credits

The Pearson people on the CME Project team—representing design, editorial, editorial services, digital product development, publishing services, and technical operations—are listed below. Bold type denotes the core team members.

Ernest Albanese, Scott Andrews, Carolyn Artin, Michael Avidon, Margaret Banker, Suzanne Biron, Beth Blumberg, Stacie Cartwright, Carolyn Chappo, Casey Clark, Bob Craton, Sheila DeFazio, Patty Fagan, **Frederick Fellows**, **Patti Fromkin**, Paul J. Gagnon, Cynthia Harvey, Gillian Kahn, Jonathan Kier, Jennifer King, Elizabeth Krieble, Sara Levendusky, Lisa Lin, Clay Martin, **Carolyn McGuire**, Rich McMahon, Eve Melnechuk, Cynthia Metallides, **Hope Morley**, Christine Nevola, Jen Paley, Mairead Reddin, Marcy Rose, Rashid Ross, Carol Roy, Jewel Simmons, Ted Smykal, Kara Stokes, Richard Sullivan, Tiffany Taylor-Sullivan, Catherine Terwilliger, Mark Tricca, Lauren Van Wart, Paula Vergith, **Joe Will**, **Kristin Winters**, Allison Wyss

Additional Credits

Gina Choe, Lillian Pelaggi, Deborah Savona

Cover Design and Illustration
9 Surf Studios

Cover Photography
Peter Sterling/Getty Images, Inc.

Interior Design
Pronk&Associates

Illustration
Rich McMahon, Ted Smykal

Photography
Unless otherwise indicated, all photos are the property of Pearson Education, Inc.

Table of Contents: vi, Jim Richardson/CORBIS; **viii,** All Canada Photos/Alamy; **xi,** Roger Ressmeyer/CORBIS; **xiii,** Philip Gould/CORBIS

Chapter 1: Pages 2–3, Paul Chesley/Getty Images; **4,** Gilbert Iundt; Jean-Yves Ruszniewski/TempSport/Corbis; **13,** Arnulf Husmo/Getty Images; **23,** Jim Richardson/CORBIS; **28,** Patrik Giardino/CORBIS; **30,** 123luftbild/Peter Arnold, Inc.; **43,** Image Source Pink/Alamy; **49,** Lori Lee Miller/Alamy; **56,** Jeffrey Greenberg/Photo Researchers, Inc.; **59,** Siephoto/Masterfile; **73,** Bettmann/CORBIS; **77,** Ray Coleman/Photo Researchers, Inc.; **79,** Gerald Hoberman/drr.net

Chapter 2: Pages 82–83, CORBIS; **84,** Gregory Sams/Photo Researchers, Inc.; **92,** Image Farm Inc./Alamy; **105,** GIPhotostock/Photo Researchers, Inc.; **106,** Perry Mastrovito/Corbis; **118,** Grant Faint/Getty Images; **122,** Eddie Gerald/Alamy; **124,** Iain Masterson/Alamy; **131,** The Granger Collection, New York; **140,** The Granger Collection, New York; **144,** FoodCollection/SuperStock; **154,** travelstock44/Alamy

Chapter 3: Pages 164–165, Last Resort/Digital Vision/Getty Images; **166,** Peter Arnold, Inc./Alamy; **186,** Jim Craigmyle/CORBIS; **204,** Jim Sugar/CORBIS; **219,** All Canada Photos/Alamy; **227,** Funk Zone Studios/Getty Images; **230,** Funk Zone Studios/Getty Images; **238,** Michael Maslan Historic Photographs/CORBIS; **238,** Gérard Boutin/zefa/Corbis; **263,** Russell Illig/age footstock; **265,** The Granger Collection, New York

Chapter 4: Pages 274–275, Troy GB images/Alamy; **276,** FogStock/Alamy; **293,** Daikusan/Getty Images; **294,** Richard T. Nowitz/CORBIS; **300,** Photothèque R. Magritte-ADAGP/Art Resource, NY; **314,** Will Hart/Photo Edit, Inc.; **322,** Margot Granitsas/The Image Works; **335,** Alan Sirulnikoff/Getty Images

Chapter 5: Pages 340–341, Ben Welsh/age footstock; **342,** Scott Halleran/Getty Images; **370,** SSPL/The Image Works; **396,** Chris Potter/Alamy; **406,** Chris Howes/Wild Places Photography/Alamy; **408,** Joe Sohm/drr.net; **432,** Flint/Corbis

Chapter 6: Pages 438–439, Louie Psihoyos/Getty Images; **440,** Dennis Hallinan/Alamy; **454,** Roger Ressmeyer/CORBIS; **460,** Jack Hollingsworth/Getty Images; **464,** Jim West/Alamy; **466,** William Manning/Alamy; **488,** Martin Dohrn/Photo Researchers, Inc.; **500,** Roger Bamber/Alamy; **516,** Frank Krahmer/Getty Images; **520,** Bora/Alamy

Chapter 7: Pages 536–537, Paolo Curto/Getty Images; **538–539,** Gallo Images-Anthony/age footstock; **541,** John Gillmoure/CORBIS; **570,** Kevin Schafer/Getty Images; **572,** Court Mast/Getty Images; **579,** James W. Porter/CORBIS; **582,** UPI Photo/Brian Kersey/drr.net; **602,** Paul Katz/photolibrary.com; **612,** University Library, UGent

Chapter 8: Pages 630–631, John Pack/Stock Illustration Source/Getty Images; **632,** NASA/Corbis; **649,** The Bridgeman Art Library/Getty Images; **651,** SSPL/The Image Works; **652,** Philip Gould/CORBIS; **671,** 2008 photolibrary.com; **674,** Tim Wright/CORBIS; **695,** James King-Holmes/Photo Researchers, Inc.

Editorial Development
LaurelTech

Note: Every effort has been made to locate the copyright owner of material reprinted in this book. Omissions brought to our attention will be corrected in subsequent editions.